RHS Plant Finder 2013

Devised by Chris Philip
and Realised by Tony Lord

Editor-in-Chief
Janet Cubey

RHS Editors
James Armitage Dawn Edwards
Neil Lancaster Christopher Whitehouse

Compiler
Judith Merrick

Published by
The Royal Horticultural Society
80 Vincent Square
London SW1P 2PE

First edition April 1987
Twenty-seventh edition April 2013

British Library Cataloguing Publication Data.
A Catalogue record for this book is available from the British Library.

ISBN 978-1-907057-40-3

Compiled by
The Royal Horticultural Society
80 Vincent Square,
London SW1P 2PE
Registered charity no: 222879/SC038262

www.rhs.org.uk

Illustrations by Sarah Young
Maps by Alan Cooper

Produced for The Royal Horticultural Society by **Peter Cooling**

Printed and bound by CPI Group (UK) Ltd, Croydon, CR0 4YY

The Compiler and the Editors of the *RHS Plant Finder* have taken every care, in the time available, to check all the information supplied to them by the nurseries concerned. Nevertheless, in a work of this kind, containing as it does hundreds of thousands of separate computer encodings, errors and omissions will, inevitably, occur. Neither the RHS, the Publisher nor the Editors can accept responsibility for any consequences that may arise from such errors.

If you find mistakes we hope that you will let us know so that the matter can be corrected in the next edition.

Front cover photograph: *Iris* 'Early Light' (Clive Nichols)
Back cover from top to bottom: *Dahlia* 'Freya's Paso Doble' (RHS/Leigh Hunt), *Aquilegia longissima* (RHS/Carol Sheppard), *Viburnum opulus* 'Aureum' (RHS/Graham Titchmarsh), *Rosa* Graham Thomas = 'Ausmas' (RHS/Carol Sheppard), *Daphne odora* 'Mae-jima' (RHS/Sara Draycott), *Heuchera* 'Tiramisu' (Martin Mulchinock)

www.rhs.org.uk

Contents

INTRODUCTION

The *RHS Plant Finder* exists to put enthusiastic gardeners in touch with suppliers of plants. The book is divided into two related sections – **PLANTS** and **NURSERIES**. **PLANTS** includes an A–Z Plant Directory of about 70,000 plant names, against which are listed a series of nursery codes. These codes point the reader to the full nursery details contained in the **NURSERIES** section towards the back of the book.

The *RHS Plant Finder* is comprehensively updated every year and provides the plant lover with the richest source of suppliers known to us.

As you will see from the entries in the **NURSERY DETAILS BY CODE** many nurseries do not now publish a printed catalogue but produce an online version only. This is a growing trend, fuelled by the cost of printing a full catalogue.

It is important to remember when ordering that many of the nurseries listed in the book are small, family-run, businesses that propagate their own material. They cannot therefore guarantee to hold large stocks of the plants they list. Some will, however, propagate to order.

NEW IN THIS EDITION

We have decided to abandon the double year in the title in favour of a single year for this edition and henceforward. The double year has caused confusion both for nurseries and the general public so, although the data will still be current from April to April, we hope that by using a single year for each edition we will eliminate such misunderstandings.

The 2013 edition of the book reflects the decisions made by the RHS Advisory Committee on Nomenclature and Taxonomy (now renamed the Nomenclature and Taxonomy Advisory Group) during 2012. A major change has been the revision of the genus *Citrus*, with previous segregates (including *Fortunella* & *Poncirus*) all now sunk into *Citrus*. The Nomenclature Notes section (see p.24) now gives a quick overview of this and other changes made during the past year.

The principal change reflected in this edition is the revision of the RHS Hardiness Ratings. This year's essay by Dr John David, RHS Acting Head of Science, discusses the reasoning behind the introduction of the new system.

Allied to this, are the results of the Award of Garden Merit (AGM) Review which takes place every ten years. Those plants which have kept or been newly awarded AGM status, are listed in this edition (where offered by participating nurseries).

AVAILABLE FROM THE COMPILER

APPLICATION FOR ENTRY

Nurseries appearing in the *RHS Plant Finder* for the first time this year are printed in bold type in the *Nursery Index by Name* starting on p.927.

If you wish your nursery to be considered for inclusion in the next edition of the *RHS Plant Finder* (2014), contact the Compiler at the address below. Entries to the book are free.

PLANTS LAST LISTED IN EARLIER EDITIONS

Plants cease to be listed for a variety of reasons. For more information turn to *How to Use the Plant Directory* on p.18. A listing of around 60,000 plants listed in earlier editions, but for which we currently have no known supplier, is available online at www.rhs.org.uk/rhsplantfinder/documents.asp.

LISTS OF NURSERIES FOR PLANTS WITH MORE THAN 30 SUPPLIERS

To prevent the book from becoming too big, we do not print the nursery codes where more than 30 nurseries offer the same plant. The plant is then listed as being "Widely available". This is detailed more fully in *How to Use the Plant Directory* on p.18.

If any readers have difficulty in finding such a plant, we will be pleased to send a full list of all the nurseries that we have on file as stockists. All such enquiries must include the full name of the plant being sought, as shown in the *RHS Plant Finder*, together with an A5 size SAE.

The above may be obtained from:
The Compiler, *RHS Plant Finder*, RHS Garden Wisley, Woking, Surrey GU23 6QB
Email: plantfinder@rhs.org.uk
This information is also available online.

THE RHS PLANT FINDER ONLINE

The *RHS Plant Finder* is available on the Internet. Visit the Royal Horticultural Society's website **www.rhs.org.uk** and search the *RHS Plant Finder Online*.

ACKNOWLEDGEMENTS

This edition was compiled by Judith Merrick with help from Gill Skilton, June Skinner and Deborah Chubb. Richard Sanford managed the revision of the AGM and hardiness ratings data. Rupert Wilson and Julia Barclay administered the RHS Horticultural Database, using the BG-Base™ Collection Management Software.

RHS botanists, James Armitage, Dawn Edwards, Neil Lancaster and Christopher Whitehouse undertook the task of editing the new plant names for this edition of the book.

We also acknowledge the contributions of the following colleagues: Simon Maughan, Rae Spencer Jones, Diana Levy and Louise Bowering of RHS Media; John David and Sharon McDonald of RHS Science and Jim Gardiner, RHS Director of Horticulture. We are indebted to Kerry Walter of BG Base (UK) Ltd, Max Phillips of Strange Software Ltd and Alan Cooper, without their professional assistance we would be unable to produce the book. Finally, we thank Peter Cooling, of Peter Cooling Publishing, not only for his skill in turning our mass of raw data into a publishable format, but also for his forbearance.

Our colleagues on the RHS Nomenclature and Taxonomy Advisory Group, along with the RHS International Cultivar Registrars, have all provided valuable guidance and information. Many nurseries have supplied helpful information on plants, which has proved useful in verifying some of the more obscure names, and have suggested corrections to existing entries. Some of these remain to be checked and will be entered in the next edition, although those that contravene the Codes of Nomenclature may have to be rejected. We appreciate your patience while these checks are made. We are also grateful to all our regular correspondents and to the many readers who have made comments and suggestions.

Clematis	D. Donald, Int. Cultivar Registrar, RHS
Chrysanthemum	J. Barker (2007–08, 2013)
Conifers	S. McDonald, Int. Cultivar Registrar, RHS
Dahlia	R. Hedge, (Hon. Asst. Cultivar Registrar), S. McDonald, Int. Cultivar Registrar, RHS Wisley
Dianthus	Dr A.C. Leslie, Int. Cultivar Registrar, RHS
Heathers	Dr E.C. Nelson, Int. Cultivar Registrar
Ilex	S. Andrews (2006)
Iris	J. Hewitt (2005, 2007–08)
Lilium	D. Donald, Int. Cultivar Registrar, RHS
Meconopsis	Dr E. Stevens (2003, 2005 & 2007)
Narcissus	S. McDonald, Int. Cultivar Registrar, RHS
Nerine	Dr J.C. David (2009)
Rhododendron	Dr A.C. Leslie, Int. Cultivar Registrar, RHS
Sorbus	Dr H. McAllister
Thymus	M. Easter (2003–11)
Viburnum	C. Sanders

Janet Cubey
RHS Chief of Horticultural Informatics
February 2013

CONSERVATION AND THE ENVIRONMENT

Invasive Plants

As the *RHS Plant Finder* demonstrates, gardens in Britain have been greatly enriched by the diversity of plants introduced to cultivation from abroad. While the vast majority of those introduced have enhanced our gardens, a few have proved to be highly invasive and to threaten native habitats. Once such plants are established it is very difficult, costly and potentially damaging to native ecosystems to eradicate or control the invasive "alien" species. Gardeners can help by choosing not to buy or distribute non-native invasive plants and by taking steps to prevent them escaping into the wild and by disposing of them in a responsible way.

Ten of the most serious invasive non-native species are no longer listed in the *RHS Plant Finder*. Any cultivars or varieties of them that are listed are believed to be less invasive than the species themselves. These 10 plants are:

**Azolla filiculoides* – fairy fern
**Crassula helmsii* – New Zealand pygmy weed
Elodea nuttalli – Nuttall's waterweed
Fallopia japonica – Japanese knotweed
Heracleum mantegazzianum – giant hogweed
**Hydrocotyle ranunculoides* – floating pennywort
Impatiens glandulifera – Himalayan balsam
Lagarosiphon major – curly waterweed
**Ludwigia grandiflora* – water primrose
**Myriophyllum aquaticum* – parrot's feather

From April 2014 the five aquatic species indicated by * above will be banned from sale. After that point anyone trading in these species will be liable to a £5000 fine or a six months prison sentence.

Further species are considered to present a threat to UK habitats and gardeners are encouraged to grow alternative plants. Guidance on this can be found in three booklets:

Gardening without harmful invasive plants
Landscaping without harmful invasive plants
Keeping ponds and aquaria without harmful invasive plants

These are available on the Plantlife website (www.plantlife.org.uk) or by post from Plantlife. For further information on non-native invasive species see the GB non-native species secretariat website (www.nonnativespecies.org)

Bringing plants back from abroad

Travelling can be a great source of inspiration for gardeners and often provides an opportunity to encounter new and interesting plants. Anyone wishing to bring plants back into Britain from overseas must realise, however, that this is a complex matter. Various regulations are in force that apply to amateur gardeners as well as to commercial nurseries. The penalties for breaking these can be serious.

Some of the most important regulatory instruments are listed below.

Plant Health regulations are in place to control the spread of pests and diseases. Plants are divided into the categories of prohibited, controlled and unrestricted, but there are also limits that vary according to the part of the world you are travelling from. For full details contact the Food and Environment Research Agency, (www.fera.defra.gov.uk/plants/plant Health/index.cfm).

The Convention on International Trade in Endangered Species (CITES) affects the transport of animal and plant material across international boundaries. Its aim is to prevent exploitative trade and thereby to prevent harm and the ultimate extinction of wild populations. A tighter regime on trade in species of wild fauna and flora exists in the EU that requires export permits for any plants listed in Appendices A, B & C and import permits for Appendices A & B. There is a further Appendix D for non-CITES listed species that the EU consider to be endangered. A broad range of plants is covered in these Appendices, including *Cactaceae* and *Orchidaceae* and, although species are mentioned in the convention title, the restrictions cover all cultivars and hybrids of listed species too, except for specific exclusions, where there are annotations in the Appendices. Details of the plants listed in the Appendices can be found on the website of the UK's CITES Management Authority, Animal Health, (www.defra.gov.uk/animalhealth/cites/legislation.html).

The Convention on Biological Diversity (CBD or the "Rio Convention") recognises the property rights of individual countries in relation to their own biodiversity. It exists to enable access to that biodiversity, but equally to ensure the sharing of any benefit derived from it. In principle it is possible to collect plant material from other countries that have asserted their rights under the CBD, by ensuring that you have obtained documentary evidence of prior informed consent on the basis of mutually agreed terms for any uses that the material will be put to in the future. In practice the legal requirements for collecting plant material varies from country to country and it is advisable to contact the National Focal Point for further information. These details and other information on the

Convention can be found on the CBD website (www.cbd.int).

European Habitats Directive. The full implementation of this Directive into UK law in 2007 extended protection to all of the European Protected Species (EPS) listed in the Appendices of that Directive (these are Appendices II(b) and IV(b) for plants) whether they are native to the UK or not. This requires a licence for material of any of these species collected in the wild after 1994. These are issued by Natural England (for England), the Countryside Council for Wales (in Wales) and Scottish Natural Heritage (for Scotland), (www.jncc.gov.uk/page-1374).

Contact addresses:

Plantlife
14 Rollestone Street
Salisbury
Wiltshire
SP1 1DX
Tel: (01722) 342730

Wildlife Licensing and Registration Service (WRLS)
Animal Health
1/17 Temple Quay House
2 The Square
Temple Quay
Bristol
BS1 6EB
Tel: 0117 372 8774

Plant Health
Room 10GA01
The Food and Environment Research Agency
Sand Hutton
York
YO41 1LZ
Tel: (01904) 465625

Joint Nature Conservation Committee
Monkstone House
City Road
Peterborough
PE1 1JY
Tel: (01733) 562626

Department for Environment, Food & Rural Affairs (Defra)
Nobel House
17 Smith Square
London
SW1P 3JR
Email for general biodiversity queries:
biodiversity@defra.gsi.gov.uk

A NEW SYSTEM OF PLANT HARDINESS RATINGS FOR THE BRITISH ISLES

Almost by definition, users of the ***RHS Plant Finder*** are likely to be seekers out of new and unusual plants and inevitably one of the prime considerations when deciding to buy an unfamiliar plant is its likelihood of survival in the purchaser's garden. The complex factors that contribute to a plant's survival are generally, but perhaps misleadingly, referred to as "hardiness". Misleading, because in most people's minds, at least in the UK and similar temperate climates, this means the ability of a plant to survive our winter; or even the early or late frosts that signal the beginning or the end of our summer. Misleading also, as nurseryman Bob Brown of Cotswold Garden Flowers has deftly explained, because a plant's survival and success depends upon many other factors: climatic, edaphic, cultural and genetic. (Brown, 2000; Gardiner, 2013).

Against such an unpromising background, it is perhaps not surprising that in the UK attempts to devise a system to codify plant hardiness have been limited and rather basic, such as the one developed by the RHS in the 1960s, with a simple scale of H1 to H4, where H1 signified plants suitable only for greenhouses and H4 for bone-hardy plants. In continental climates, where there is a clearer transition between winter and spring, there is much greater scope for a system based on minimum winter temperatures. Indeed, it was at the Arnold Arboretum, Harvard, (Massachusetts) in the continental climate of North Eastern USA, where the zone system was first developed and which, since the 1940s, has been expanded and refined by the United States Department of Agriculture (USDA). In its most recent edition (USDA, 2012) it now extends from Z1 (Arctic) to Z13 (more or less tropical), with an 'a' and a 'b' for each zone, defined by steps of 5°F (2·8°C). It is this system, with its beguiling simplicity and its appeal to the more competitive plantsmen, which has taken root in the minds of gardeners and nurserymen alike. So much so, that it has become widely followed outside the US, even in the UK, where its drawbacks are frequently evident.

It is interesting to note that the USDA system does not find much favour on the US Pacific coast. Here another system has been developed which is regularly updated in the *Sunset Western Garden Book* (Brenzel, 2012). Although it uses zones, mapped out in considerable detail, and the zone definitions contain an element of winter temperatures, that is not the sole criterion. The descriptions of the 24 zones for mainland United States also note summer temperatures, growing season and even give a nod to native vegetation. Suffice it to say, the "Sunset" zones bear little similarity to the USDA map. Other systems have been devised in other countries (Brady, 2008) but generally what they gain in accuracy and objectivity they lose in practicality for the general gardener.

While the simple system originally devised by the RHS had some benefits, the increasing sophistication of gardeners and the wider array of plants being introduced, as well as the obvious difference that what might be regarded as H4 in southern England may well be considered to be H3 or H2 in colder regions, has led to a widespread view that it was time to overhaul the system.

Therefore in 2011 the RHS assembled a group of leading horticultural authorities to advise it on a new hardiness rating system. The approach they have recommended, although anchored to a scale of minimum winter temperatures, takes into account differences in plant performance due to different locations and ways of growing the plants. For this reason the RHS H1 is for greenhouse cultivation (see Table p.9) and in the new ratings distinguishes the different levels of cultivation under glass. The new RHS ratings have the advantage of being founded on a measurable and objective scale (avoiding the subjectivity of the old system) while being given some flexibility derived from the description.

There is no direct correspondence between the "old" and the "new" ratings. All plants that have been granted the RHS Award of Garden Merit (AGM) have been reassessed for hardiness as part of the 2012 AGM Review. These changes are reflected in this edition (2013) of the ***RHS Plant Finder***.

Dr John David
RHS Acting Head of Science

References

Brenzel, K.N. (Ed.) (2012). Sunset *Western Garden Book* (9th Ed). Sunset Publishing Corporation: Menlo Park, California.

Brady, M. (2008). Hardiness zone maps of the northern hemisphere. *The Plantsman*, n.s. 7: 170-176.

Brown, R. (2000). Hardiness in Plants: A Nurseryman's Perspective. *Hortus* 54: 31-40.

Gardiner, J. (2013). New RHS hardiness ratings. *The Garden* 138(2): 68-69.

USDA (2012). Plant Hardiness Zone Map. http://plant hardiness.ars.usda.gov/PHZMWeb/ (Accessed 12 Feb. 2013)

RHS PLANT HARDINESS RATINGS TABLE

Rating[1]	Temperature range[2] (°C)	Category	Definition	USDA zones
H1a	>15	Heated greenhouse – tropical	Under glass all year	13
H1b	10 to 15	Heated greenhouse – subtropical	Can be grown outside in the summer	12
H1c	5 to 10	Heated greenhouse – warm temperate	Can be grown outside in the summer. (Most bedding plants, tomatoes and cucumbers.)	11
H2	1 to 5	Tender – Cool or frost-free greenhouse	Tolerant of low temperatures, but not surviving being frozen. Except in frost-free inner-city areas or coastal extremities requires glasshouse conditions. (Most succulents, many subtropical plants, annual bedding plants, many spring-sown vegetables.)	10b
H3	-5 to 1	Half hardy – unheated greenhouse/mild winter	Hardy in coastal and relatively mild parts of the UK except in severe winters and at risk from sudden (early) frosts. May be hardy elsewhere with wall shelter or good microclimate. Likely to be damaged or killed in cold winters, particularly with no snow cover or if pot grown. Can often survive with some artificial protection in winter. (Many Mediterranean-climate plants, spring sown vegetables for later harvesting).	9b/10a
H4	-10 to -5	Hardy – average winter	Hardy through most of the UK apart from inland valleys, at altitude and central/northerly locations. May suffer foliage damage and stem dieback in harsh winters in cold gardens. Some normally hardy plants may not survive long wet winters in heavy or poorly drained soil. Plants in pots are more vulnerable to harsh winters, particularly evergreens and many bulbs. (Many herbaceous and woody plants, winter brassicas, leeks.)	8b/9a
H5	-15 to -10	Hardy – cold winter	Hardy in most places throughout the UK even in severe winters. May not withstand open/exposed sites or central/northern locations. Many evergreens will suffer foliage damage, and plants in pots will be at increased risk. (Many herbaceous and woody plants, some brassicas, leeks.)	7b/8a
H6	-20 to -15	Hardy – very cold winter	Hardy in all of UK and northern Europe. Many plants grown in containers will be damaged unless given protection. (Herbaceous and woody plants from continental climates.)	6b/7a
H7	<-20	Very hardy	Hardy in the severest European continental climates including exposed upland locations in the UK. (Herbaceous and woody plants from continental climates.)	1–6a

1 New hardiness ratings supersede the previous RHS hardiness ratings (H1-H4) which are not the direct equivalents of the new ratings.

2 The temperature ranges are intended to be absolute minimum winter temperatures (°C), not the long-term average annual extreme minimum temperature used for the USDA zones.

RHS Plant Trials Bulletins

The Trials Bulletins give the results and findings of RHS Trials. The detailed descriptions and images of the plants that were given the Award of Garden Merit are included, as well as updates on nomenclature, cultivation details and a table comparing the different characteristics of the entries in the trial.

Begonia Rex Cultorum Group
Canna
Clematis alpina and *C. macropetala*
Dahlia
Daisies (yellow perennial)
Delphinium
Fuchsia, hardy
Geranium, hardy (Stage 1)
Geranium, hardy (Stage 2)
Geranium, hardy (Stage 3)
Hyacinthaceae (little blue bulbs)
Hydrangea paniculata
Iris, bearded
Lavandula, hardy
Miscanthus
Peppers, chilli
Peppers, sweet
Potatoes, salad
Potentilla, shrubby
Rhododendron yakushimanum and hybrids
Runner Beans
Saxifraga, silver
Sedum, herbaceous

If you would like a copy of any of these, please contact:
The Trials Office, RHS Garden Wisley, Woking, Surrey GU23 6QB. Please enclose an A4 SAE and a cheque for £2.00 per copy (as a donation towards costs) made out to the Royal Horticultural Society.

In addition to the above there are four bulletins that are only available on the RHS Website: *Caryopteris*, *Perovskia*, *Pittosporum* and *Spiraea japonica*.
To view and download any of these RHS Plant Trials Bulletins online, please visit:
www.rhs.org.uk/trials

EXTENDED GLOSSARY

This glossary combines some of the helpful introductory sections from older editions in an alphabetical listing. A fuller, more discursive account of plant names, *Guide to Plant Names*, and a detailed guide to the typography of plant names, *Recommended Style for Printing Plant Names*, are both available as RHS Advisory Leaflets. To request a copy of either please send an A4 sae to The Compiler at the contact address given on page 5.

ADVISORY COMMITTEE ON NOMENCLATURE AND TAXONOMY

See under the new name of **Nomenclature and Taxonomy Advisory Group**

AUTHORITIES

In order that plant names can be used with precision throughout the scientific world, the name of the person who coined the name of a plant species (its author, or authority) is added to the plant name. Usually this information is of little consequence to gardeners, except in cases where the same name has been given to two different plants or a name is commonly misapplied. Although only one usage is correct, both may be encountered in books, so indicating the author is the only way to be certain about which plant is being referred to. This can happen equally with cultivars. Authors' names, where it is appropriate to cite them, appear in a smaller typeface after the species or cultivar name to which they refer and are abbreviated following Brummitt and Powell's *Authors of Plant Names*.

🏆 AWARD OF GARDEN MERIT

The Award of Garden Merit (AGM) is intended as a practical guide for the gardener and is therefore awarded only after a period of assessment by the RHS Standing and Joint Committees. The AGM is awarded only to plants that are:

- excellent for ordinary use in appropriate conditions
- available
- of good constitution
- essentially stable in form and colour
- reasonably resistant to pests and diseases

The AGM symbol is cited in conjunction with the **hardiness** rating. A full list of AGM plants may be found on the RHS website at www.rhs.org.uk/agmplants.

The AGM plant list has, to date, been re-examined every 10 years. The latest review was carried out during 2012 and published in February 2013.

BOTANICAL NAMES

The aim of the botanical naming system is to provide each different plant with a single, unique, universal name. The basic unit of plant classification is the species. Species that share a number of significant characteristics are grouped together to form a genus (plural **genera**). The name of a species is made up of two elements; the name of the genus followed by the specific epithet, for example, *Narcissus romieuxii*.

Variation within a species can be recognised by division into subspecies (usually abbreviated to subsp.), varietas (or variety abbreviated to var.) and forma (or form abbreviated to f.). Whilst it is unusual for a plant to have all of these, it is possible, as in this example, *Narcissus romieuxii* subsp. *albidus* var. *zaianicus* f. *lutescens*.

The botanical elements are always given in italics, with only the genus taking an initial capital letter. The rank indications are never in italics. In instances where the rank is not known it is necessary to form an invalid construction by quoting a second epithet without a rank. This is an unsatisfactory situation, but requires considerable research to resolve.

In some genera, such as *Hosta*, we list the cultivar names alphabetically with the species or **hybrid** to which they are attributed afterwards in parentheses. For example, *Hosta* 'Reversed' (*sieboldiana*). In other situations where the aim is not to create a list alphabetically by cultivar name we would recommend styling this as *Hosta sieboldiana* 'Reversed'.

CLASSIFICATION OF GENERA

Genera that include a large number of species or with many cultivars are often subdivided into informal horticultural classifications or more formal Cultivar Groups, each based on a particular characteristic or combination of characteristics. Colour of flower or fruit and shape of flower are common examples and, with fruit, whether a cultivar is grown for culinary or dessert purposes. How such groups are named differs from genus to genus.

To help users of the *RHS Plant Finder* find the plants they want, the classifications used within cultivated genera are listed using codes and plants are marked with the appropriate code in brackets after its name in the Plant Directory. To find the explanation of each code, simply look it up under the genus concerned in the **Classification of Genera** starting on p.25. The codes relating to edible fruits are also listed here, but these apply across several genera.

Collectors' References

Abbreviations (usually with numbers) following a plant name refer to the collector(s) of the plant. These abbreviations are expanded, with a collector's name or expedition title, in the section **Collectors' References** starting on p.20.

A collector's reference may indicate a new, as yet unnamed range of variation within a species. The inclusion of collectors' references in the *RHS Plant Finder* supports the book's role in sourcing unusual plants.

The Convention on Biological Diversity calls for conservation of biodiversity, its sustainable use and the fair and equitable sharing of any derived benefits. Since its adoption in 1993, collectors are required to have prior informed consent from the country of origin for the acquisition and commercialisation of collected material.

Common Names

In a work such as this, it is necessary to refer to plants by their botanical names for the sake of universal comprehension and clarity. However, at the same time we recognise that with fruit and vegetables most people are more familiar with their common names than their botanical ones. Cross-references are therefore given from common to botanical names for fruit, vegetables and the commoner culinary herbs throughout the Plant Directory.

Cultivar

Literally meaning cultivated variety, cultivar names are given to denote variation within species and that generated by hybridisation, in cultivation. To make them easily distinguishable from botanical names, they are not printed in italics and are enclosed in single quotation marks. Cultivar names coined since 1959 should follow the rules of the International Code of Nomenclature for Cultivated Plants (**ICNCP**).

Descriptive Terms

Terms that appear after the main part of the plant name are shown in a smaller font to distinguish them. These descriptive elements give extra information about the plant and may include the **collector's reference**, **authority**, or what colour it is. For example, *Clematis henryi* B&SWJ 3402, *Penstemon* 'Sour Grapes' M. Fish, *Lobelia tupa* dark orange-flowered.

Families

Genera are grouped into larger groups of related plants called families. Most family names, with the exception of eight familiar names, end with the same group of letters, *-aceae*. While it is still acceptable to use these eight exceptions, the modern trend adopted in the *RHS Plant Finder* is to use alternative names with *–aceae* endings. The families concerned are *Compositae* (*Asteraceae*), *Cruciferae* (*Brassicaceae*), *Gramineae* (*Poaceae*), *Guttiferae* (*Clusiaceae*), *Labiatae* (*Lamiaceae*), *Leguminosae* (split here into *Caesalpiniaceae*, *Mimosaceae* and *Papilionaceae*), *Palmae* (*Arecaceae*) and *Umbelliferae* (*Apiaceae*).

Apart from these exceptions we now follow (from 2010) *Mabberley's Plant Book* (3rd edition).

Genus (plural – genera)

Genera used in the *RHS Plant Finder* are almost always those given in Brummitt's *Vascular Plant Families and Genera.* For spellings and genders of generic names, Greuter's *Names in Current Use for Extant Plant Genera* has also been consulted. See **Botanical Names**.

Grex

Within orchids, hybrids of the same parentage, regardless of how alike they are, are given a grex name. Individuals can be selected, given cultivar names and propagated vegetatively. For example, *Pleione* Versailles gx 'Bucklebury', where Versailles is the grex name and 'Bucklebury' is a selected **cultivar**.

Group

This is a collective name for a group of cultivars within a genus with similar characteristics. The word Group is always included and, where cited with a cultivar name, it is enclosed in brackets, for example, *Actaea simplex* (Atropurpurea Group) 'Brunette', where 'Brunette' is a distinct cultivar in a group of purple-leaved cultivars.

Another example of a Group is *Rhododendron polycladum* Scintillans Group. In this case *Rhododendron scintillans* was a species that is now botanically 'sunk' within *R. polycladum*, but it is still recognised horticulturally as a Group.

Group names are also used for swarms of hybrids with the same parentage, for example, *Rhododendron* Polar Bear Group. These were formerly treated as

grex names, a term now used only for orchids. A single clone from the Group may be given the same cultivar name, for example, *Rhododendron* 'Polar Bear'.

HARDINESS

Hardiness ratings are shown for **Award of Garden Merit** plants. To assist gardeners to determine more clearly which plants are hardy in their local area, the RHS has introduced a new, enhanced, hardiness rating scheme in 2013, to coincide with the publication of the new **Award of Garden Merit** plant list. The categories now used are as follows: Temperature ranges given are intended to be absolute minimum winter temperatures (°C).

H1a = Heated greenhouse – tropical >15
H1b = Heated greenhouse – subtropical 10 to 15
H1c = Heated greenhouse – warm temperate 5 to 10
H2 = Tender – cool or frost-free greenhouse 1 to 5
H3 = Half-hardy – unheated greenhouse/mild winter 5 to 1
H4 = Hardy – average winter -10 to -5
H5 = Hardy – cold winter -15 to -10
H6 = Hardy – very cold winter -20 to -15
H7 = Very hardy <-20

Further definition of these categories can be found on the RHS website and in the Feb 2013 edition of *The Garden*. (See also essay on p.8.)

HYBRIDS

Some species, when grown together, in the wild or in cultivation, are found to interbreed and form hybrids. In some instances a hybrid name is coined, for example hybrids between *Primula hirsuta* and *P. minima* are given the name *Primula* × *forsteri*, the multiplication sign indicating hybrid origin. Hybrid formulae that quote the parentage of the hybrid are used where a unique name has not been coined, for example *Rhododendron calophytum* × *R. praevernum*. In hybrid formulae you will find parents in alphabetical order, with the male (m) and female (f) parent indicated where known. Hybrids between different genera are also possible, for example × *Mahoberberis* is the name given to hybrids between *Mahonia* and *Berberis*.

There are also a few special-case hybrids called graft hybrids, where the tissues of two plants are physically rather than genetically mixed. These are indicated by an addition rather than a multiplication sign, so *Laburnum* + *Cytisus* becomes + *Laburnocytisus*.

ICNCP

The ICNCP is the International Code of Nomenclature for Cultivated Plants. First published in 1959, the most recent (8th) edition was published in 2009.

Cultivar names that do not conform to this Code, and for which there is no valid alternative, are flagged I (for invalid). This code states that the minimum requirement is for a cultivar name to be given in conjunction with the name of the genus. However, in the *RHS Plant Finder* we choose to give as full a name as possible to give the gardener and botanist more information about the plant, following the Recommendation in the Code.

NOMENCLATURE AND TAXONOMY ADVISORY GROUP

This Group advises the RHS on individual problems of nomenclature regarding plants in cultivation and, in particular, use of names in the *RHS Horticultural Database*, reflected in the annual publication of the *RHS Plant Finder*.

The aim is always to make the plant names in the *RHS Plant Finder* as consistent, reliable and stable as possible and acceptable to gardeners and botanists alike, not only in the British Isles but around the world. Recent proposals to change or correct names are examined with the aim of creating a balance between the stability of well-known names and botanical and taxonomic correctness. In some cases the conflicting views on the names of some groups of plants will not easily be resolved. The Group's policy is then to wait and review the situation once a more obvious consensus is reached, rather than rush to rename plants only to have to change them again when opinions have shifted.

In 2013 the Group is chaired by Dr Alan Leslie (RHS) and includes: Dr Crinan Alexander, Susyn Andrews, Chris Brickell, Dr James Compton, Mike Grant, Dr John Grimshaw, Dr Stephen Jury, Dr Tony Lord, Prof David Mabberley, Dr Charles Nelson, Chris Sanders, with Dr Janet Cubey, Dr John David and Julian Shaw (attending RHS staff), and Dr Christopher Whitehouse (RHS) as Secretary.

NOTES ON NOMENCLATURE AND IDENTIFICATION

The **Notes on Nomenclature and Identification**, p.24, give further information for names that are complex or may be confusing. See also **Nomenclature and Taxonomy Advisory Group**.

PLANT BREEDERS' RIGHTS

Plants covered by an *active* grant of Plant Breeders' Rights (PBR) are indicated throughout the Plant Directory. Grants indicated are those awarded by both UK and EU Plant Variety Rights offices. Because grants can both come into force and lapse at any time, this book can only aim to represent the situation at one point in time, but it is hoped that this will act as a useful guide to growers and gardeners. UK and EU grants represent the published position as of the end of December 2012. We do not give any indication where PBR grants may be pending.

To obtain PBR protection, a new plant must be registered and pass tests for distinctness, uniformity and stability under an approved name. This approved name, under the rules of the **ICNCP**, established by a legal process, has to be regarded as the cultivar name. Increasingly however, these approved names are a code or "nonsense" name and are therefore often unpronounceable and meaningless, so the plants are given other names designed to attract sales when they are released. These secondary names are often referred to as selling names but are officially termed **trade designations**.

For further information on UK PBR contact:
Plant Variety Rights Office,
Food and Environment Research Agency,
Whitehouse Lane,
Huntingdon Road,
Cambridge CB3 0LF
Tel: (01223) 342350
Website: www.fera.defra.gov.uk/plants/plantVarieties/

For details of plants covered by EU Community Rights contact:
Community Plant Variety Office (CPVO),
3 Boulevard Maréchal Foch, BP 10121,
FR-49101 Angers Cedex 02, France
Tel: 00 33 (02) 41 25 64 00
Fax: 00 33 (02) 41 25 64 10
Website: www.cpvo.europa.eu

The *RHS Plant Finder* takes no responsibility for ensuring that nurseries selling plants with PBR are licensed to do so.

Reverse Synonyms

It is likely that users of this book will come across names in certain genera that they did not expect to find. This may be because species have been transferred from another genus (or **genera**). A list of **Reverse Synonyms** is available online at www.rhs.org.uk/rhsplantfinder/documents.asp. Alternatively, a copy can be requested by sending a sae (1 × 2nd class letter stamp) to The Compiler at the address given on page 5.

Selling Names

See **Trade Designations**

Series

With seed-raised plants and some popular vegetatively-propagated plants, especially bedding plants and pot plants such as *Petunia* or *Verbena*, Series have become increasingly popular. A Series contains a number of similar cultivars, but differs from a **Group** in that it is a marketing device, with cultivars added to create a range of flower colours in plants of similar habit. Individual colour elements within a Series may be represented by slightly different cultivars over the years.

The word Series is always included and, where cited with a cultivar name it is enclosed in brackets, for example *Aquilegia* 'Robin' (Songbird Series). The Series name usually follows the rest of the plant name, but sometimes in this book we list it before the cultivar name in order to group members of a Series together when they occur next to one another on the page.

Species

See under **Botanical Names**

Subspecies

See under **Botanical Names**

Synonyms

Although the ideal is for each species or cultivar to have only one name, anyone dealing with plants soon comes across a situation where one plant has received two or more names, or two plants have received the same name. In each case, only one name and application, for reasons of precision and stability, can be regarded as correct. Additional names are known as synonyms. Further information on synonyms and why plants change names is available in *Guide to Plant Names*. See the introduction to this glossary for details of how to request a copy.

See also **Reverse Synonyms**.

Trade Designations

A **trade designation** is the name used to market a plant when the cultivar name is considered unsuitable for selling purposes. It is styled in a different typeface and without single quotation marks.

In the case of **Plant Breeders' Rights** it is a legal requirement for the cultivar name to appear with the trade designation on a label at the point of sale. Most plants are sold under only one trade designation, but some, especially roses, are sold under a number of names, particularly when cultivars are introduced from other countries. Usually, the correct cultivar name is the only way to ensure that the same plant is not bought unwittingly under two or more different trade designations. The *RHS Plant Finder* follows the recommendations of the **ICNCP** when dealing with trade designations and PBR. These are always to quote the cultivar name and trade designation together and to style the trade designation in a different typeface, without single quotation marks, for example *Choisya* × *dewitteana* Goldfingers = 'Limo'PBR. Here Goldfingers is the trade designation and 'Limo' is the cultivar name that has been granted **Plant Breeders' Rights**. This may also be styled in other ways, such as *Choisya* × *dewitteana* GOLDFINGERS ('Limo')PBR.

TRANSLATIONS

When a cultivar name is translated from the language of first publication, the translation is regarded as a **trade designation** and styled accordingly. We endeavour to recognise the original cultivar name in every case and to give an English translation where it is in general use.

VARIEGATED PLANTS

Following a suggestion from the Variegated Plant Group of the Hardy Plant Society, a (v) is cited after those plants which are "variegated". The dividing line between variegation and less distinct colour marking is necessarily arbitrary and plants with light veins, pale, silver or dark zones, or leaves flushed in paler colours, are not shown as being variegated unless there is an absolutely sharp distinction between paler and darker zones.

For further details of the Variegated Plant Group, please write to:

Brian Dockerill
19 Westfield Road
Glyncoch
Pontypridd
Mid-Glamorgan
CF37 3AG

VARIETY

See under **Botanical Names** and **Cultivar**

HORTAX
The Horticultural Taxonomy Group

If you have an interest in the names of garden plants and wish to learn more or would like to make a comment about the International Code of Nomenclature for Cultivated Plants (ICNCP) visit the HORTAX website: www.hortax.org.uk

SYMBOLS AND ABBREVIATIONS

SYMBOLS APPEARING TO THE LEFT OF THE NAME

- `*` Name not validated. Not listed in the appropriate International Registration Authority checklist nor in works cited in the Bibliography. For fuller discussion see p.11
- I Invalid name. See *International Code of Botanical Nomenclature 2006* and *International Code of Nomenclature for Cultivated Plants 2009*. For fuller discussion see p.11
- § Plant listed elsewhere in the Plant Directory under a synonym
- × Hybrid genus
- \+ Graft hybrid genus

SYMBOLS APPEARING TO THE RIGHT OF THE NAME

- ✿ Plant Heritage (NCCPG) National Plant Collection® exists for all or part of this genus. Provisional Collections appear in brackets. Full details of the Plant Heritage Collections are found in the *2011 National Plant Collections® Directory* available from: www.plantheritage.com or Plant Heritage, 12 Home Farm, Loseley Park, Guildford, Surrey GU3 1HS
- ♀H4 The Royal Horticultural Society's Award of Garden Merit, see p.11
- (d) double-flowered
- (F) Fruit
- (f) female
- (m) male
- (v) variegated plant, see p.15
- PBR Plant Breeders Rights see p.13
- **new** New plant entry in this edition

For abbreviations relating to individual genera see **Classification of Genera** p.25

For **Collectors' References** see p.20

For symbols used in the **Nurseries** section see p.833

SYMBOLS AND ABBREVIATIONS USED AS PART OF THE NAME

- × hybrid species
- aff. affinis (akin to)
- agg. aggregate, a single name used to cover a group of very similar plants, regarded by some as separate species
- ambig. ambiguous, a name used by two authors for different plants and where it is unclear which is being offered
- cf. compare to
- cl. clone
- f. forma (botanical form)
- gx grex
- sensu lato in the broadest sense
- sp. species
- subsp. subspecies
- subvar. subvarietas (botanical subvariety)
- var. varietas (botanical variety)

It is not within the remit of this book to check that nurseries are applying the right names to the right plants or to ensure nurseries selling plants with Plant Breeders' Rights are licensed to do so.

Please, never use an out of date edition

PLANTS

WHATEVER PLANT YOU ARE LOOKING FOR, MAYBE AN OLD FAVOURITE OR A MORE UNUSUAL CULTIVAR, SEARCH HERE FOR A LIST OF THE SUPPLIERS THAT ARE CLOSEST TO YOU.

How to Use the Plant Directory

Nursery Codes

Look up the plant you require in the alphabetical Plant Directory. Against each plant you will find one or more four-letter codes, for example WCru, each code represents one nursery offering that plant. The first letter of each code indicates the main area of the country in which the nursery is situated. For this geographical key, refer to the **Nursery Codes and Symbols** on p.832.

Turn to the **Nursery Details by Code** starting on p.836 where, in alphabetical order of codes, you will find details of each nursery which offers the plant in question. If you wish to visit any nursery, you may find its location on one of the maps (following p.933). Please note, however, that not all nurseries, especially mail order only nurseries, choose to be shown on the maps. For a fuller explanation of how to use the nursery listings please turn to p.833. **Always check that the nursery you select has the plant in stock before you set out.**

Plants with more than 30 Suppliers

In some cases, against the plant name you will see the term 'Widely available' instead of a nursery code. If we were to include every plant listed by all nurseries, the *RHS Plant Finder* would become unmanageably bulky. We therefore ask nurseries to restrict their entries to those plants that are not already well represented. As a result, if more than 30 nurseries offer any plant the Directory gives no nursery codes and the plant is listed instead as being 'Widely available'.

You should have little difficulty in locating these in local nurseries or garden centres. However, if you are unable to find such plants, we will be pleased to send a full list of all the nurseries that we have on file as stockists. To obtain a list, please see the Introduction on p.4 or go to www.rhs.org.uk/rhsplantfinder/.

Finding Fruit, Vegetables and Herbs

You will need to search for these by their botanical names. Common names are cross-referenced to their botanical names in the Plant Directory.

If you have Difficulty Finding your Plant

If you cannot immediately find the plant you seek, look through the various species of the genus. You may be using an incomplete name. The problem is most likely to arise in very large genera such as *Phlox* where there are a number of possible species, each with a large number of cultivars. A search through the whole genus may well bring success. Please note that, for space reasons, the following are not listed in the Plant Directory: annuals, orchids, except hardy terrestrial orchids; cacti, except hardy cacti.

Cross-references

It may be that the plant name you seek is a synonym. Our intention is to list nursery codes only against the correct botanical name. Where you find a synonym you will be cross-referred to the correct name. Occasionally you may find that the correct botanical name to which you have been referred is not listed. This is because it was last listed in an earlier edition as explained below.

Plants Last Listed in Earlier Editions

It may be that the plant you are seeking has no known suppliers and is thus not listed.

The loss of a plant name from the Directory may arise for a number of reasons – the supplier may have gone out of business, or may not have responded to our latest questionnaire and has therefore been removed from the book. Such plants may well be still available but we have no current knowledge of their whereabouts. Alternatively, some plants may have been misnamed by nurseries in previous editions, but are now appearing under their correct name.

To obtain a listing of plants last listed in earlier editions please see the Introduction on p.4 or go to our website where it is available as a pdf.

Please, never use an out of date edition

USING THE PLANT DIRECTORY

The main purpose of the Plant Directory is to help the reader correctly identify the plant they seek and find its stockist. Each nursery has a unique identification code which appears to the right of the plant name. Turn to Nursery Details by Code on p.836 for the address, opening times and other details of the nursery. The first letter of each nursery code denotes its geographical region. Turn to the map on p.933 to find your region code and then identify the nurseries in your area.

Another purpose of the Directory is to provide more information about the plant through the symbols and other information. For example, if it has an alternative names, is new to this edition or has received the RHS Award of Garden Merit.

Euonymus (*Celastraceae*)

	Name	Nursery codes
	B&L 12543	EPla EWes
	B&SWJ 4457	WPGP
	CC 4522	CPLG
	alatus 🏆H4	Widely available
	- B&SWJ 8794	WCru
	- var. ***apterus***	EPfP
	- Chicago Fire	see *E. alatus* 'Timber Creek'
	- 'Ciliodentatus'	see *E. alatus* 'Compactus'
§	- 'Compactus' 🏆H4	Widely available
§	- 'Fire Ball'	EPfP
	- Little Moses = 'Odom'	MBlu
*	- 'Macrophyllus'	EPfP
	- 'Rudy Haag'	CPMA EPfP
	- 'Select'	see *E. alatus* 'Fire Ball'
	- 'Silver Cloud' **new**	EPfP
§	- 'Timber Creek'	CPMA EPfP MBlu MBri NLar
	americanus	EPfP GIBF MBlu NLar
	- 'Evergreen' **new**	EPfP
	- narrow-leaved	EPfP NLar
	atropurpureus	EPfP
	'Benkomoki' **new**	MGos
	bungeanus	CMCN EPfP EPla NLar
	- 'Dart's Pride'	CPMA EPfP NLar
	- 'Fireflame'	EPfP NLar
*	- var. ***mongolicus***	EPfP
	- 'Pendulus'	EPfP MBlu SIFN
	- var. ***semipersistens***	CPMA EPla
	carnosus	EPfP NLar
	'Copper Wire'	EMil SPoG
	cornutus var. ***quinquecornutus***	CPMA EPfP LPan MBlu NBhm NLar SIFN SPoG WPGP WPat
	'Den Haag'	EPfP MBri
	echinatus	EPfP EPla
	- BL&M 306	SLon
	europaeus	Widely available
	- f. ***albus***	CPMA CTho EPfP LTwo NLar
	- 'Atropurpureus'	CMCN CTho EPfP MBlu MBri NLar SIFN
	- 'Atrorubens'	CPMA
	- 'Aucubifolius' (v)	EPfP
*	- 'Aureus'	CNat
	- 'Brilliant' **new**	EPfP
*	- f. ***bulgaricus***	EPfP
	- 'Chrysophyllus'	EPfP MBlu NLar
	- 'Howard'	EPfP
	- var. ***intermedius***	ENot EPfP MAsh MBlu NLar
	- 'Miss Pinkie'	CEnd CMCN
	- 'Pumilis' **new**	EPfP
	- 'Red Cascade' 🏆H4	Widely available
	- 'Scarlet Wonder'	CPMA EPfP MBri NLar
	- 'Thornhayes'	CTho EPfP
I	- 'Variegatus' **new**	EPfP
	farreri	see *E. nanus*
	fimbriatus	EPfP
	fortunei Blondy = 'Interbolwi'[PBR] (v)	Widely available

ABBREVIATIONS
To save space a dash indicates that the previous heading is repeated. If written out in full the name would be Euonymus alatus *'Fire Ball'.*

NEW
Plant new to this edition.

DESCRIPTIVE TERM
See p.12.

SYMBOLS TO THE LEFT OF THE NAME
Provides information about the name of the plant. See p.16 for the key.

SYMBOLS TO THE RIGHT OF THE NAME
Tells you more about the plant itself, e.g. (v) *indicates that the plant is variegated,* (F) *= fruit. See p.16 for the key.*

SELLING NAMES
See p.14.

🏆H4
This plant has received the RHS Award of Garden Merit. See p.11.

CROSS-REFERENCES
Directs you to the correct name of the plant and the nursery codes. See p.18.

NURSERY CODE
A unique code identifying each nursery. Turn to p.836 for details of the nurseries.

WIDELY AVAILABLE
Indicates that more than 30 Plant Finder nurseries supply the plant, and it may be available locally. See p.18.

PBR
Plant Breeders' Rights. See p.13.

SUPPLEMENTARY KEYS TO THE DIRECTORY

COLLECTORS' REFERENCES

Abbreviations following a plant name, refer to the collector(s) of the plant. These abbreviations are expanded below, with a collector's name or expedition title. For a fuller explanation, see p.12.

A&JW Watson, A. & J.
A&L Ala, A. & Lancaster, Roy
AB&S Archibald, James; Blanchard, John W. & Salmon, M.
AC Clark, Alan J.
AC&H Apold, J.; Cox, Peter & Hutchison, Peter
AC&W Albury; Cheese, M. & Watson, J.M.
ACE AGS Expedition to China (1994)
ACL Leslie, Alan C.
AER Robinson, Allan
AGS/ES AGS Expedition to Sikkim (1983)
AGSJ AGS Expedition to Japan (1988)
AH Hoog, A.
AIM Avent, Tony Mexico (1994)
Airth Airth, Murray
Akagi Akagi Botanical Garden
AL&JS Sharman, Joseph L. & Leslie, Alan C.
APA Cox, K.; Hootman, S.; Hudson, T.; et al, Expedition to Arunchal Pradesh (2005)
ARG Argent, G.C.G.
ARGS Alaska Rock Garden Society trip to China
ARJA Ruksans, J. & Siesums, A.
B Blanchard, John
B&F MA Brown, Robert & Fisher, Rif & Middle Atlas (2007)
B L. Beer, Len
B&L Brickell, Christopher D. & Leslie, Alan C.
B&M & BM Brickell, Christopher D. & Mathew, Brian
B&S Bird P. & Salmon M.
B&SWJ Wynn-Jones, Bleddyn & Susan
B&V Burras, K. & Vosa, C.G.
BB Bartholomew, B.
BC Chudziak, W.
BC&W Beckett; Cheese, M. & Watson, J.M.
Beavis Beavis, Derek S.
Berry Berry, P.
Berry & Brako Berry, P. & Brako, Lois
BKBlount Blount, B.K.
BL&M University of Bangor Expedition to NE Nepal
BM Mathew, Brian F.
BM&W Binns, David L.; Mason, M. & Wright, A.
BOA Boardman, P.
Breedlove Breedlove, D.
BR Rushbrooke, Ben
BS Smith, Basil
BSBE Bowles Scholarship Botanical Expedition (1963)
BSSS Crûg Expedition, Jordan (1991)
Bu Bubert, S.
Burtt Burtt, Brian L.
BWJ Wynn-Jones, Bleddyn
C Cole, Desmond T.
C&C Cox, P.A. & Cox, K.N.E.
C&Cu Cox, K.N.E. & Cubey, J.
C&H Cox, Peter & Hutchison, Peter
C&K Chamberlain & Knott
C&R Christian & Roderick
C&S Clark, Alan & Sinclair, Ian W.J.
C&V K.N.E. Cox & Vergera, S.
C&W Cheese, M. & Watson, J.M.
CC Chadwell, Christopher
CC&H Chamberlain, David F.; Cox, Peter & Hutchison, P.
CC&McK Chadwell, Christopher & McKelvie, A.
CC&MR Chadwell, Christopher & Ramsay
CCH&H Chamberlain, D.F.; Cox, P.; Hutchison, P. & Hootman, S.
CCH&H Chamberlain, Cox, Hootman & Hutchison
CD&R Compton, J.; D'Arcy, J. & Rix, E.M.
CDB Brickell, Christopher D.
CDC Coode, Mark J.E.; Dockrill, Alexander
CDC&C Compton; D'Arcy; Christopher & Coke
CDPR Compton; D'Arcy; Pope & Rix
CE&H Christian, P.J.; Elliott & Hoog
CEE Chengdu Edinburgh Expedition China (1991)
CGG Glendoick Gardens Expedition to Guizou (2009)
CGV Vosa, Canio

CGW Grey-Wilson, Christopher
CH Christian, P. & Hoog, A.
CH&M Cox, P.; Hutchison, P. & Maxwell-MacDonald, D.
CHP&W Kashmir Botanical Expedition
CL Lovell, Chris
CLD Chungtien, Lijiang & Dali Exped. China (1990)
CM&W Cheese M.; Mitchel J. & Watson, J.
CN&W Clark; Neilson & Wilson
CNDS Nelson, C. & Sayers D.
Cooper Cooper, R.E.
Cox Cox, Peter A.
CPC Cobblewood Plant Collection
CPN Compton, James
CS Stapleton, Christopher
CSE Cyclamen Society Expedition (1990)
CT Teune, Carla
CWJ Colley, Finlay; Wynn-Jones, Bleddyn, Taiwan (2007)
Dahl Dahl, Sally
DBG Denver Botanic Garden, Colorado
DC Cheshire, David
DF Fox, D.
DG Green, D.
DHTU Hinkley, D., Turkey (2000)
DJH Hinkley, Dan
DJHC Hinkley D., China
DJHS Hinkley, D., Sichuan
DJHV Hinkley, D., Vietnam
DM Millais, David
Doleshy Doleshy, F.L.
DS&T Drake, Sharman J. & Thompson
DWD Rose, D.
DZ Zummell, D.
ECN Nelson, E. Charles
EDHCH Hammond, Eric D.
EGM Millais, T.
EKB Balls, Edward K.
EM East Malling Research Station
EMAK Edinburgh Makalu Expedition (1991)
EMR Rix, E.Martyn
EN Needham, Edward F.
ENF Fuller, E. Nigel
ETE Edinburgh Taiwan Expedition (1993)
ETOT Kirkham, T.S.; Flanagan, Mark
F Forrest, G.
F&M Fernandez & Mendoza, Mexico
F&W Watson, J. & Flores, A.
Farrer Farrer, Reginald
FK Kinmonth, Fergus W.
FMB Bailey, F.M.
G Gardner, Martin F.
G&K Gardner, Martin F. & Knees, Sabina G.
G&P Gardner, Martin F. & Page, Christopher N.
GDJ Dumont, Gerard
GG Gusman, G.
GS Sherriff, George
Green Green, D.
Guitt Guittoneau, G.G.
Guiz Guizhou Expedition (1985)
GWJ Goddard, Sally; Wynne-Jones, Bleddyn & Susan
G-W&P Grey-Wilson, Christopher & Phillips
H Huggins, Paul
H&B Hilliard, Olive M. & Burtt, Brian L.
H&D Howick, C. & Darby
H&M Howick, Charles & McNamara, William A.
H&W Hedge, Ian C. & Wendelbo, Per W.
Harry Smith Smith, K.A.Harry
Hartside Hartside Nursery
HCM Heronswood Expedition to Chile (1998)
HECC Hutchison; Evans; Cox, P.; Cox, K.
HEHEHE Zetterlund, H. et al, Gothenburg Botanic Gardens Expedition to northern China
Hird Hird
HH&K Hannay, S & S & Kingsbury, N.
HLMS Springate, L.S.
HM&S Halliwell, B.; Mason, D. & Smallcombe
HOA Hoog, Anton
HRS Hers, J.
Hummel Hummel, D.
HW&E Wendelbo, Per; Hedge, I. & Ekberg, L.
HWEL Hirst, J.Michael; Webster, D.
HWJ Crûg Heronswood Joint Expedition
HWJCM Crûg Heronswood Expedition
HWJK Crûg Heronswood Expedition, East Nepal (2002)
HZ Zetterlund, Henrik
ICE Instituto de Investigaciónes Ecológicas Chiloé & RBGE
IDS International Dendrological Society
ISI Int. Succulent Introductions
J&JA Archibald, James & Jennifer
J. Jurasek Jurasek, J.
JCA Archibald, James
JE Jack Elliott
JJ Jackson, J.
JJ&JH Halda, J. & Halda, J.
JJH Halda, Joseph J.
JLS Sharman, J.L.
JM-MK Mahr, J.; Kammerlander, M.
JMT Mann Taylor, J.
JN Nielson, Jens
JR Russell, J.
JRM Marr, John
JW Watson, J.M.
K Kirkpatrick, George
K&LG Gillanders, Kenneth & Gillanders, L.
K&Mc Kirkpatrick, George & McBeath, Ronald J.D.
K&P Josef Kopec & Milan Prasil
K&T Kurashige, Y. & Tsukie, S.
KC Cox, Kenneth

KEKE	Kew/Edinburgh Kanchenjunga Expedition (1989)
KGB	Kunming/Gothenburg Botanical Expedition (1993)
KM	Marsh, K.
KR	Rushforth, K.D.
KRW	Wooster, K.R. (distributed after his death by Kath Dryden)
KW	Kingdon-Ward, F.
KWJ	Crûg-World of Ferns Joint Expedition, Vietnam (2007)
L	Lancaster, C. Roy
L&S	Ludlow, Francis & Sherriff, George
LA	Long Ashton Research Station clonal selection scheme
LB	Bird P.; Salmon, M.
LEG	Lesotho Edinburgh/Gothenburg Expedition (1997)
Lismore	Lismore Nursery, Breeder's Number
LM&S	Leslie, Mattern & Sharman
LP	Palmer, W.J.L.
LS&E	Ludlow, Frank; Sherriff, George & Elliott, E. E.
LS&H	Ludlow, Frank; Sherriff, George & Hicks, J. H.
LS&T	Ludlow, Frank; Sherriff, George & Taylor, George
M&PS	Mike & Polly Stone
M&T	Mathew & Tomlinson
Mac&W	McPhail & Watson
McB	McBeath, R.J.D.
McLaren	McLaren, H.D.
MDM	Myers, Michael D.
MECC	Scottish Rock Garden Club, Nepal (1997)
MESE	Alpine Garden Society Expedition, Greece (1999)
MF	Foster, Maurice
MH	Heasman, Matthew T.
MK	Kammerlander, Michael
MP	Pavelka, Mojmir
MPF	Frankis, M.P.
MS	Salmon, M.
MS&CL	Salmon, M. & Lovell, C.
MSF	Fillan, M.S.
NAPE	Hootman, S.; et al, Expedition to Naglaland and Arunachal Pradesh (2003)
NICE	North India Expedition (1997)
NJM	Macer, N.J.
NN	Nielsen & Nielsen (2009)
NNS	Ratko, Ron
NS	Turland, Nick
NVD	Expedition to Vietnam
NVFDE	Northern Vietnam First Darwin Expedition
Og	Ogisu, Mikinori
ORO	Oron, Peri
OS	Sonderhousen, O.
P. Bon	Bonavia, P.
P&C	Paterson, David S. & Clarke, Sidney
P&W	Polastri & Watson, J. M.
PAB	Barney, P.A.
PB	Bird, Peter
PC&H	Pattison, G.; Catt, P. & Hickson, M.
PD	Davis, Peter H.
PDM	Purdom, William
PF	Furse, Paul
PJC	Christian, Paul J.
PJC&AH	P.J. Christian & A. Hogg
PNMK	Nicholls, P.; Kammerlander, M.
Polunin	Polunin, Oleg
Pras	Prasil, M.
PS&W	Polunin, Oleg; Sykes, William & Williams, John
PW	Wharton, Peter
R	Rock, J.F.C.
RB	Brown, R.
RBS	Brown, Ray, Sakharin Island
RCB AM	Brown, Robert, Expedition to Armenia
RCB/Arg	Brown, Robert, Argentina, (2002)
RCB E	Brown, Robert, Expedition to Spain (Andalucia)
RCB/Eq	Brown, Robert, Ecuador, (1988)
RCB RA	Brown, Robert
RCB RL	Brown, Robert, Expedition to Lebanon
RCB/TQ	Brown, Robert, Turkey (2001)
RE	Evans, Ron
RH	Hancock, R.
RKMP	Ruksans, J.; Krumins, A.; Kitts, M.; Paivel, A.
RM	Ruksans, J. & Kitts, M.
RMRP	Rocky Mountain Rare Plants, Denver, Colorado
RS	Suckow, Reinhart
RSC	Richard Somer Cocks
RV	Richard Valder
RWJ	Crûg Farm-Rickards Ferns Expedition to Taiwan (2003)
S&B	Blanchard, J.W. & Salmon, M.
S&F	Salmon, M. & Fillan, M.
S&L	Sinclair, Ian W.J. & Long, David G.
S&SH	Sheilah & Spencer Hannay
Sandham	Sandham, John
SB&L	Salmon, Bird & Lovell
SBEC	Sino-British Expedition to Cangshan
SBEL	Sino-British Lijiang Expedition
SBQE	Sino-British Expedition to Quinghai
Sch	Schilling, Anthony D.
SD	Sashal Dayal
SDR	Rankin, Stella & David
SEH	Hootman, Steve
SEP	Swedish Expedition to Pakistan
SF	Forde, P.
SG	Salmon, M. & Guy, P.
SH	Hannay, Spencer

Sich	Simmons, Erskine, Howick & Mcnamara
SJ	Johansson, Stellan
SLIZE	Swedish-Latvian-Iranian Zagros Expedition to Iran (May 1988)
SOJA	Kew/Quarryhill Expedition to Southern Japan
SS&W	Stainton, J.D. Adam; Sykes, William & Williams, John
SSNY	Sino-Scottish Expedition to NW Yunnan (1992)
T	Taylor, Nigel P.
T&K	Taylor, Nigel P. & Knees, Sabina
TH	Hudson, T.
TS&BC	Smythe, T. & Cherry, B.
TSS	Spring Smyth, T.L.M.
TW	Tony Weston
USDAPI	US Department of Agriculture Plant Index Number
USDAPQ	US Dept. of Agriculture Plant Quarantine Number
USNA	United States National Arboretum
VHH	Vernon H. Heywood
VV	Victor, David
W	Wilson, Ernest H.
W&B	Watkins, D. & Brown, R., Bulgaria (2012)
WM	McLewin, William
Woods	Woods, Patrick J.B.
Wr	Wraight, David & Anke
WWJ	Wharton, Peter; Wynn-Jones, Bleddyn & Susan
Yu	Yu, Tse-tsun

NOMENCLATURAL NOTES

This year we have decided to overhaul the Nomenclatural Notes section and so each year we will now use these pages to highlight new name changes, following the work of the RHS Advisory Committee for Nomenclature and Taxonomy. This Committee has had a name change at the start of 2013 and will be known as the **Nomenclature and Taxonomy Advisory Group** (NATAG) from here onwards.

If you have any suggestions for other name changes that you would like to be considered for adoption within the ***RHS Plant Finder***, then please write, stating your reasons in full, to:

The Chairman
Nomenclature and Taxonomy Advisory Group
Royal Horticultural Society
RHS Garden, Wisley
Woking
Surrey
GU23 6QB

The following changes have been made to the names used in the RHS Horticultural Database and reflected in the ***RHS Plant Finder*** based upon decisions of the RHS Advisory Committee for Nomenclature and Taxonomy during 2012.

- *Agapanthus* Ardernei hybrid should be styled as a cultivar epithet and is not the same as 'Ardernei'
- *Caloscordum* sunk into *Allium*
- Large flowered variants of *Caltha palustris* that have previously wrongly been called *C. polypetala* are attributed to *C. palustris* var. *major*.
- New treatment of *Citrus*, previous segregates (including *Fortunella*, *Poncirus*, and their bigeneric hybrids) all sunk into *Citrus*. This follows the classification of David Mabberley and both he and James Wearn have provided help to enable this significant change to be made.
- *Clematis campaniflora* is accepted as a distinct species rather than a subspecies of *C. viticella*.
- The name *Crocus* × *cultorum* has never been validly published, therefore the cultivars previously attributed to that cross are now just listed under the genus without a hybrid epithet.
- Accept 'Alba' as a distinct clone under *Fuchsia magellanica* var. *molinae*

Nothofagus alpina is now considered to be the correct name for the species previously regarded as *N. nervosa*. The hybrid between *N. alpina* and *N. obliqua* is therefore correctly named as *N.* × *dodecaphelps*.

- Use *Ocimum* × *africanum* in place of *O.* × *citriodorum*
- *Pennisetum setaceum* 'Rubrum' now classified as the hybrid *P.* × *advena* 'Rubrum'
- A number of changes to *Prunus* have been made and we will follow the *Manual of Japanese Flowering Cherries* (1982) in most cases:
    - *P. cerasifera* 'Ruby' is a mirabelle plum.
    - *P. incisa* f. *yamadei* – it was suggested to follow MJFC and use *yamadei*.
    - 'Kulilensis Ruby' is just an orthographic variant of *P. nipponica* var. *kurilensis* 'Ruby'.
    - 'Brilliant' should be 'Brillant' as it was raised in Germany.
    - 'Branklyn' and 'Dorothy Clive' should both be cultivars not forms.
    - 'Mahogany Lustre' is thought to be a seedling of *P.* × *schmidtii* not assigned to *P. serrula*. It should be listed without any specific epithet.
    - 'Takasago' would have been imported pre-1865, although this was a vernacular name but it could be used as a cultivar name. The attribution to *P.* × *sieboldii* was inappropriate and not needed for this complex hybrid.
    - The following cherry names are trade names as they were deliberate substitutions:
        - § BLUSHING BRIDE see 'Shogetsu'
        - § CANDY FLOSS see 'Matsumae-beni-murasaki'
        - § PINK PARASOL see 'Matsumae-hanagasa'
    - Changed rank of *Synthyris missurica* var. *stellata* to subspecies
    - *Tasmannia* recognised as a separate genus from *Drimys*.

This is not an exhaustive list of the changes made to the RHS Horticultural Database; many more changes are made during the year by the botanical team at the RHS. This list is to highlight the key changes of the Nomenclature and Taxonomy Advisory Group.

CLASSIFICATION OF GENERA

Genera including a large number of species, or with many cultivars, are often subdivided into informal horticultural classifications, or formal cultivar groups in the case of *Clematis* and *Tulipa*. The breeding of new cultivars is sometimes limited to hybrids between closely-related species, thus for *Saxifraga* and *Primula*, the cultivars are allocated to the sections given in the infrageneric treatments cited. Please turn to p.11 for a fuller explanation.

ACTINIDIA

(s-p) Self-pollinating

BEGONIA

(C) Cane-like
(R) Rex Cultorum
(S) Semperflorens Cultorum
(T) × *tuberhybrida* (Tuberous)

CHRYSANTHEMUM

(By the National Chrysanthemum Society)
(1) Indoor Large (Exhibition)
(2) Indoor Medium (Exhibition)
(3a) Indoor Incurved: Large-flowered
(3b) Indoor Incurved: Medium-flowered
(3c) Indoor Incurved: Small-flowered
(4a) Indoor Reflexed: Large-flowered
(4b) Indoor Reflexed: Medium-flowered
(4c) Indoor Reflexed: Small-flowered
(5a) Indoor Intermediate: Large-flowered
(5b) Indoor Intermediate: Medium-flowered
(5c) Indoor Intermediate: Small-flowered
(6a) Indoor Anemone: Large-flowered
(6b) Indoor Anemone: Medium-flowered
(6c) Indoor Anemone: Small-flowered
(7a) Indoor Single: Large-flowered
(7b) Indoor Single: Medium-flowered
(7c) Indoor Single: Small-flowered
(8a) Indoor True Pompon
(8b) Indoor Semi-pompon
(9a) Indoor Spray: Anemone
(9b) Indoor Spray: Pompon
(9c) Indoor Spray: Reflexed
(9d) Indoor Spray: Single
(9e) Indoor Spray: Intermediate
(9f) Indoor Spray: Spider, Quill, Spoon or Any Other Type
(10a) Indoor, Spider
(10b) Indoor, Quill
(10c) Indoor, Spoon
(11) Any Other Indoor Type
(12a) Indoor, Charm
(12b) Indoor, Cascade
(13a) October-flowering Incurved: Large-flowered
(13b) October-flowering Incurved: Medium-flowered
(13c) October-flowering Incurved: Small-flowered
(14a) October-flowering Reflexed: Large-flowered
(14b) October-flowering Reflexed: Medium-flowered
(14c) October-flowering Reflexed: Small-flowered
(15a) October-flowering Intermediate: Large-flowered
(15b) October-flowering Intermediate: Medium-flowered
(15c) October-flowered Intermediate: Small-flowered
(16) October-flowering Large
(17a) October-flowering Single: Large-flowered
(17b) October-flowering Single: Medium-flowered
(17c) October-flowering Single: Small-flowered
(18a) October-flowering Pompon: True Pompon
(18b) October-flowering Pompon: Semi-pompon
(19a) October-flowering Spray: Anemone
(19b) October-flowering Spray: Pompon
(19c) October-flowering Spray: Reflexed
(19d) October-flowering Spray: Single
(19e) October-flowering Spray: Intermediate
(19f) October-flowering Spray: Spider, Quill, Spoon or Any Other Type
(20) Any Other October-flowering Type
(21a) Korean: Anemone
(21b) Korean: Pompon
(21c) Korean: Reflexed
(21d) Korean: Single
(21e) Korean: Intermediate
(21f) Korean: Spider, Quill, Spoon, or any other type
(22a) Charm: Anemone
(22b) Charm: Pompon
(22c) Charm: Reflexed
(22d) Charm: Single
(22e) Charm: Intermediate
(22f) Charm: Spider, Quill, Spoon or Any Other Type
(23a) Early-flowering Outdoor Incurved: Large-flowered

(23b) Early-flowering Outdoor Incurved: Medium-flowered
(23c) Early-flowering Outdoor Incurved: Small-flowered
(24a) Early-flowering Outdoor Reflexed: Large-flowered
(24b) Early-flowering Outdoor Reflexed: Medium-flowered
(24c) Early-flowering Outdoor Reflexed: Small-flowered
(25a) Early-flowering Outdoor Intermediate: Large-flowered
(25b) Early-flowering Outdoor Intermediate: Medium-flowered
(25c) Early-flowering Outdoor Intermediate: Small-flowered
(26a) Early-flowering Outdoor Anemone: Large-flowered
(26b) Early-flowering Outdoor Anemone: Medium-flowered
(27a) Early-flowering Outdoor Single: Large-flowered
(27b) Early-flowering Outdoor Single:Medium-flowered
(28a) Early-flowering Outdoor Pompon: True Pompon
(28b) Early-flowering Outdoor Pompon: Semi-pompon
(29a) Early-flowering Outdoor Spray: Anemone
(29b) Early-flowering Outdoor Spray: Pompon
(29c) Early-flowering Outdoor Spray: Reflexed
(29d) Early-flowering Outdoor Spray: Single
(29e) Early-flowering Outdoor Spray: Intermediate
(29f) Early-flowering Outdoor Spray: Spider, Quill, Spoon or Any Other Type
(29Rub) Early-flowering Outdoor Spray: Rubellum
(30) Any Other Early-flowering Outdoor Type

Clematis

(Cultivar Groups as per Matthews, V. (2002) *The International Clematis Register & Checklist 2002*, RHS, London.)

(A) Atragene Group
(Ar) Armandii Group
(C) Cirrhosa Group
(EL) Early Large-flowered Group
(F) Flammula Group
(Fo) Forsteri Group
(H) Heracleifolia Group
(I) Integrifolia Group
(LL) Late Large-flowered Group
(M) Montana Group
(T) Texensis Group
(Ta) Tangutica Group
(V) Viorna Group
(Vb) Vitalba Group
(Vt) Viticella Group

Dahlia

(Classification according to The International Dahlia Register (1969), 20th Supp. (2009) formed through consultation with national dahlia societies.)(Sin)

1 Single
(Anem) 2 Anemone-flowered
(Col) 3 Collerette
(WL) 4 Waterlily (unassigned)
(LWL) 4B Waterlily, Large
(MWL) 4C Waterlily, Medium
(SWL) 4D Waterlily, Small
(MinWL) 4E Waterlily, Miniature
(D) 5 Decorative (unassigned)
(GD) 5A Decorative, Giant
(LD) 5B Decorative, Large
(MD) 5C Decorative, Medium
(SD) 5D Decorative, Small
(MinD) 5E Decorative, Miniature
(SBa) 6D Small Ball
(MinBa) 6E Miniature Ball
(Pom) 7 Pompon
(C) 8 Cactus (unassigned)
(GC) 8A Cactus, Giant
(LC) 8B Cactus, Large
(MC) 8C Cactus, Medium
(SC) 8D Cactus, Small
(MinC) 8E Cactus, Miniature
(S-c) 9 Semi-cactus (unassigned)
(GS-c) 9A Semi-cactus, Giant
(LS-c) 9B Semi-cactus, Large
(MS-c) 9C Semi-cactus, Medium
(SS-c) 9D Semi-cactus, Small
(MinS-c) 9E Semi-cactus, Miniature
(Misc) 10 Miscellaneous
(Fim) 11 Fimbriated
(SinO) 12 Single Orchid (Star)
(DblO) 13 Double Orchid
(P) 14 Peony-flowered
(B) Botanical
(DwB) Dwarf Bedding
(Lil) Lilliput (in combination)

Dianthus

(By the RHS)

(b) Carnation, border
(M) Carnation, Malmaison
(pf) Carnation, perpetual-flowering
(p) Pink
(p,a) Pink, annual

Fruit

(B) Black (*Vitis*), Blackberry (*Rubus*), Blackcurrant (*Ribes*)
(Ball) Ballerina (*Malus*)
(C) Culinary (*Malus, Prunus, Pyrus, Ribes*)

(Cider) Cider (*Malus*)
(D) Dessert (*Malus, Prunus, Pyrus, Ribes*)
(F) Fruit
(G) Glasshouse (*Vitis*)
(O) Outdoor (*Vitis*)
(P) Pinkcurrant (*Ribes*)
(Perry) Perry (*Pyrus*)
(R) Red (*Vitis*), Redcurrant (*Ribes*)
(S) Seedless (*Citrus, Vitis*)
(W) White (*Vitis*), Whitecurrant (*Ribes*)

Fuchsia

(E) Encliandra
(T) Variants and hybrids of *F. triphylla*

Gladiolus

(B) Butterfly
(E) Exotic
(G) Giant
(L) Large
(M) Medium
(Min) Miniature
(N) Nanus
(P) Primulinus
(S) Small
(Tub) Tubergenii

Hepatica nobilis

(Adapted from the International Hepatica Society classification for *Hepatica nobilis*)
(1) Hyoujun (normal)
(2) (degenerated anther)
(3) Otome (degenerated stamen)
(4) Henka (petal deformity)
(5/d) Herashibe (semi-double, primitive)
(5A/d) Choji (semi-double, primitive)
(6/d) Nidan (semi-double, advanced)
(7/d) Sandan (double, primitive)
(8/d) Karako (double, advanced)
(9/d) Sene-e (double, completed)

Hydrangea macrophylla

(H) Hortensia
(L) Lacecap

Iris

(Adapted from the American Iris Society Classification)
(AB) Arilbred
(BB) Border Bearded
(Cal-Sib) Series *Californicae* × Series *Sibiricae*
(CH) Californian Hybrid
(DB) Dwarf Bearded (not assigned)
(Dut) Dutch
(IB) Intermediate Bearded
(J) Juno (subgenus *Scorpiris*)
(La) Louisiana Hybrid
(MDB) Miniature Dwarf Bearded
(MTB) Miniature Tall Bearded
(Rc) Regeliocyclus (Section *Regelia* × Section *Oncocyclus*)
(SDB) Standard Dwarf Bearded
(Sib) Siberian
(Sino-Sib) Series *Sibiricae*, chromosome number 2n=40
(SpH) Species Hybrid
(Spuria) Spuria
(TB) Tall Bearded

Lilium

(Classification according to *The International Lily Register* (ed. 4, 2007))
(I) Asiatic hybrids derived from *L. amabile, L. bulbiferum, L. callosum, L. cernuum, L. concolor, L. dauricum, L. davidii, L.* × *hollandicum, L. lancifolium, L. lankongense, L. leichtlinii, L.* × *maculatum* and *L. pumilum, L.* × *scottiae, L. wardii* and *L. wilsonii.*
(II) Martagon hybrids derived from *L. dalhansonii, L. hansonii, L. martagon, L. medeoloides and L. tsingtauense*
(III) Euro-Caucasian hybrids derived from *L. candidum, L. chalcedonicum, L. kesselringianum, L. monadelphum, L. pomponium, L. pyrenaicum* and *L.* × *testaceum.*
(IV) American hybrids derived from *L. bolanderi, L.* × *burbankii, L. canadense, L. columbianum, L. grayi, L. humboldtii, L. kelleyanum, L. kelloggii, L. maritimum, L. michauxii, L. michiganense, L. occidentale, L.* × *pardaboldtii, L. pardalinum, L. parryi, L. parvum, L. philadelphicum, L. pitkinense, L. superbum, L. vollmeri, L. washingtonianum* and *L. wigginsii.*
(V) Longiflorum lilies derived from *L. formosanum, L. longiflorum, L. philippinense and L. wallichianum.*
(VI) Trumpet and Aurelian hybrids derived from *L.* × *aurelianense, L. brownii, L.* × *centigale, L. henryi, L.* × *imperiale, L.* × *kewense, L. leucantheum, L. regale, L. rosthornii, L. sargentiae, L. sulphureum* and *L. sulphurgale* (but excluding hybrids of *L. henryi* with all species listed in Division VII).
(VII) Oriental hybrids derived from *L. auratum, L. japonicum, L. nobilissimum, L.* × *parkmanii, L rubellum* and *L. speciosum* (but excl. all hybrids of these with *L. henryi*).
(VIII) Other hybrids not covered by any of the previous divisions (I-VII)
(IX) Species and cultivars of species

a/ upward-facing flowers
b/ outward-facing flowers
c/ downward-facing flowers
/a trumpet-shaped flowers
/b bowl-shaped flowers
/c flat flowers (or with only tepal tips recurved)
/d recurved flowers

MALUS SEE FRUIT

NARCISSUS

(By the RHS, revised 1998)

(1) Trumpet
(2) Large-cupped
(3) Small-cupped
(4) Double
(5) Triandrus
(6) Cyclamineus
(7) Jonquilla and Apodanthus
(8) Tazetta
(9) Poeticus
(10) Bulbocodium
(11a) Split-corona: Collar
(11b) Split-corona: Papillon
(12) Miscellaneous
(13) Species

NYMPHAEA

(H) Hardy
(D) Day-blooming
(N) Night-blooming
(T) Tropical

PAPAVER

(Not a horticultural classification, used to save space in this publication)

(SPS) Super Poppy Series

PAEONIA

(S) Shrubby

PELARGONIUM

(A) Angel
(C) Coloured Foliage (in combination)
(Ca) Cactus (in combination)
(d) Double (in combination)
(Dec) Decorative
(Dw) Dwarf
(DwI) Dwarf Ivy-leaved
(Fr) Frutetorum
(I) Ivy-leaved
(Min) Miniature
(MinI) Miniature Ivy-leaved
(R) Regal
(Sc) Scented-leaved
(St) Stellar (in combination)
(T) Tulip (in combination)
(U) Unique
(Z) Zonal

PRIMULA

(Classification by Section as per Richards. J. (2002) *Primula* (2nd edition). Batsford, London)

(Ag) *Auganthus*
(Al) *Aleuritia*
(Am) *Amethystinae*
(Ar) *Armerina*
(Au) *Auricula*
  (A) Alpine Auricula
  (B) Border Auricula
  (S) Show Auricula
  (St) Striped Auricula
(Bu) *Bullatae*
(Ca) *Capitatae*
(Cf) *Cordifoliae*
(Ch) *Chartaceae*
(Co) *Cortusoides*
(Cr) *Carolinella*
(Cu) *Cuneifoliae*
(Cy) *Crystallophlomis*
(Da) *Davidii*
(De) *Denticulatae*
(Dr) *Dryadifoliae*
(F) *Fedtschenkoanae*
(G) *Glabrae*
(Ma) *Malvaceae*
(Mi) *Minutissimae*
(Mo) *Monocarpicae*
(Mu) *Muscarioides*
(Ob) *Obconicolisteri*
(Or) *Oreophlomis*
(Pa) *Parryi*
(Pe) *Petiolares*
(Pf) *Proliferae*
(Pi) *Pinnatae*
(Pr) *Primula*
  (Poly) Polyanthus
  (Prim) Primrose
(Pu) *Pulchellae*
(Py) *Pycnoloba*
(R) *Reinii*
(Si) *Sikkimenses*
(So) *Soldanelloides*
(Sp) *Sphondylia*
(Sr) *Sredinskya*
(Su) *Suffrutescentes*
(Y) *Yunnannenses*

PRUNUS SEE FRUIT

PYRUS SEE FRUIT

RHODODENDRON

(A) Azalea (deciduous, species or unclassified hybrid)

(Ad) Azaleodendron
(EA) Evergreen azalea
(G) Ghent azalea (deciduous)
(K) Knap Hill or Exbury azalea (deciduous)
(M) Mollis azalea (deciduous)
(O) Occidentalis azalea (deciduous)
(R) Rustica azalea (deciduous)
(V) Vireya rhododendron
(Vs) Viscosa azalea (deciduous)

RIBES *SEE* FRUIT

ROSA

(A) Alba
(Bb) Bourbon
(Bs) Boursault
(Ce) Centifolia
(Ch) China
(Cl) Climbing (in combination)
(D) Damask
(DPo) Damask Portland
(F) Floribunda or Cluster-flowered
(G) Gallica
(Ga) Garnette
(GC) Ground Cover
(HM) Hybrid Musk
(HP) Hybrid Perpetual
(HT) Hybrid Tea or Large-flowered
(Min) Miniature
(Mo) Moss (in combination)
(N) Noisette
(Patio) Patio, Miniature Floribunda or Dwarf Cluster-flowered
(Poly) Polyantha
(Ra) Rambler
(RH) Rubiginosa hybrid (Hybrid Sweet Briar)
(Ru) Rugosa
(S) Shrub
(SpH) Spinosissima Hybrid
(T) Tea

RUBUS *SEE* FRUIT

SAXIFRAGA

(Classification by Section from Gornall, R.J. (1987). *Botanical Journal of the Linnean Society,* 95(4): 273-292)

(1) *Ciliatae*
(2) *Cymbalaria*
(3) *Merkianae*
(4) *Micranthes*
(5) *Irregulares*
(6) *Heterisia*
(7) *Porphyrion*
(8) *Ligulatae*
(9) *Xanthizoon*
(10) *Trachyphyllum*
(11) *Gymnopera*
(12) *Cotylea*
(13) *Odontophyllae*
(14) *Mesogyne*
(15) *Saxifraga*

TULIPA

(Classification by Cultivar Group from *Classified List and International Register of Tulip Names* by Koninklijke Algemeene Vereniging voor Bloembollencultuur 1996)

(1) Single Early Group
(2) Double Early Group
(3) Triumph Group
(4) Darwin Hybrid Group
(5) Single Late Group (including Darwin Group and Cottage Group)
(6) Lily-flowered Group
(7) Fringed Group
(8) Viridiflora Group
(9) Rembrandt Group
(10) Parrot Group
(11) Double Late Group
(12) Kaufmanniana Group
(13) Fosteriana Group
(14) Greigii Group
(15) Miscellaneous

VERBENA

(G) Species and hybrids considered by some botanists to belong to the separate genus *Glandularia.*

VIOLA

(C) Cornuta Hybrid
(dVt) Double Violet
(ExVa) Exhibition Viola
(FP) Fancy Pansy
(PVt) Parma Violet
(SP) Show Pansy
(T) Tricolor
(Va) Viola
(Vt) Violet
(Vtta) Violetta

VITIS *SEE* FRUIT

The Plant Directory

A

Abelia ✿ (*Caprifoliaceae*)

	Auderose = 'Minaud'PBR	EPla ETwe LAst
	biflora	LRHS
	'Canyon Creek' ♀H5 **new**	LAst
	chinensis misapplied	see *A.* × *grandiflora*
§	***chinensis*** R.Br.	CBcs CExl CMCN CMac ELan EPfP ETwe EWTr LRHS MAsh MMuc SEND SHil SKHP SPer SPoG SRms WFar WGrn WPat
	'Edward Goucher' ♀H5	CBcs CDoC CDul CMac COtt CWSG EAEE ELan EPfP LBMP LRHS MAsh MBri MGos MRav MSwo SEND SGbt SGol SPer SPlb SWvt WFar WPat WSHC
	engleriana	CExl EPfP EPla LRHS MAsh MBlu NLar NSoo SEND SLon SSpi
	floribunda ♀H5	CBcs CDul CExl CHel CMac CSam CSde ECre ELan ELon EPfP LRHS MAsh MRav NLar NSoo SBrt SEND SGbt SGol SKHP SPer SPoG SRms SSpi WPat
§	× ***grandiflora***	Widely available
	- 'Aurea'	see *A.* × *grandiflora* 'Gold Spot'
	- 'Brockhill Allgold'	EPfP
	- 'Compacta'	LRHS WFar
	- Confetti = 'Conti'PBR (v)	CBcs CDoC CMac CSBt ELan EPfP LAst LRHS MAsh MGos MRav NLar SCob SGol SLim SPer SPoG SWvt WFar
§	- 'Francis Mason' (v)	Widely available
§	- 'Gold Spot' (v)	EPfP LRHS MGos MWat NLar SPer WPat
	- 'Gold Strike'	see *A.* × *grandiflora* 'Gold Spot'
	- Golden Panache = 'Minpan'	MRav
	- 'Goldsport'	see *A.* × *grandiflora* 'Gold Spot'
	- 'Hopleys'PBR (v) ♀H5	CBcs CDoC CMac CSBt CTri ELan EPfP LRHS MAsh MBri MGos MRav NLar SCob SEND SLon SPoG SRms SWvt WGrn WHar
	- 'Kaleidoscope'PBR (v)	Widely available
	- Lucky Lots = 'Wevo2' (v) **new**	SCob
	- 'Panache' (v)	CDoC LLHF WCot
	- 'Prostrate White'	CMac EBee ECrN LRHS NLar
	- 'Semperflorens'	LRHS
	- 'Sherwoodii'	CDoC EBee ECrN EPfP LRHS MAsh MBri MGos SLim WPat WRHF
	- 'Sunrise' (v)	EPfP NLar SLim
	- Sunshine Daydream = 'Abelops'PBR (v)	CEnd LLHF MPkF SCob
	- 'Variegata'	see *A.* × *grandiflora* 'Francis Mason'
§	'Lynn' **new**	MPkF SCob
	mosanensis	CAbP CMCN ELan EPfP LLHF LRHS MBlu MBri MGil NLar SLon SPoG SSpi WSHC
	Petite Garden = 'Minedward'PBR	CDoC LLHF LRHS MBri
	Pinky Bells	see *A.* 'Lynn'
	rupestris misapplied	see *A.* × *grandiflora*
	rupestris Lindl.	see *A. chinensis* R.Br.
	schumannii	CAbP CBcs CDul CExl CMHG CMac COtt CSBt CTri ECrN ELan EPfP LRHS MAsh MBri MGos MMuc MRav NLar SGbt SHil SKHP SLim SLon SPer SWvt WGrn WPat
	triflora	CAbP CExl ECre NLar NSoo SBrt SEND SKHP WFar WSHC

Abeliophyllum (*Oleaceae*)

distichum	CBcs CDoC CEnd ECrN ELan ELon EPfP IDee LBMP LRHS MAsh MBlu MGos NSoo SGol SPer SSpi SWvt WCFE WSHC
- Roseum Group	CBcs CDoC CExl CJun ELan ELon EPfP LRHS MAsh MGos MMuc MRav SKHP SLon SPer SPoG

Abelmoschus (*Malvaceae*)

esculentus	SVic

Abies (*Pinaceae*)

alba	CAco CDul NWea
- 'Bystricka'	MAsh NLar
- 'Compacta'	CKen
- 'Green Spiral'	NLar
- 'King's Dwarf'	CKen
- 'Microphylla'	CKen
- 'Münsterland'	CKen NLar
- 'Nana' misapplied	see *Picea glauca* 'Nana'
- 'Nana' ambig.	CKen
- 'Pendula'	CKen
- 'Pyramidalis'	NLar
amabilis 'Spreading Star'	SLim
arizonica	see *A. lasiocarpa* var. *arizonica*
balsamea	CDul GKin
- 'Cook's Blue'	CKen
- Hudsonia Group	CDoC CKen CMac EHul LRHS NWad SLim WIce
- 'Jamie'	CKen MAsh NLar
- 'Le Feber'	CKen
- 'Nana'	CKen EHul LRHS MAsh MJak NPCo NWad
- var. ***phanerolepis*** 'Bear Swamp'	CKen NHol
- 'Piccolo'	CDoC CKen LRHS NLar
- 'Prostrata'	MBri
- 'Renswoude'	CKen
- 'Tyler Blue'	CKen NLar
- 'Verkade's Prostrate'	CKen

*	***borisii-regis*** 'Pendula'	CKen
	brachyphylla dwarf	see *A. homolepis* 'Prostrata'
	cephalonica	CDul CKen CMCN NWea
	- 'Greg's Broom'	CKen
§	- 'Meyer's Dwarf'	CMac LRHS NLar NPCo SBod SLim
	- 'Nana'	see *A. cephalonica* 'Meyer's Dwarf'
	cilicica 'Spring Grove'	CKen
	colimensis NJM 09.074	WPGP
	concolor	CBcs CDul CTho CUse LRHS MJak MMuc NWea SEND WMou
	- 'Archer's Dwarf'	CKen NLar NPCo SLim
	- 'Aurea'	NLar NPCo
	- 'Birthday Broom'	CKen
	- 'Blue Sapphire'	CKen
§	- 'Compacta' ♀H7	CDoC CKen LRHS MBri MGos NHol NLar NPCo NWea SLim
	- 'Fagerhult'	CKen
	- 'Gable's Weeping'	CKen
	- 'Glauca'	see *A. concolor* Violacea Group
	- 'Glauca Compacta'	see *A. concolor* 'Compacta'
	- 'Hillier Broom'	see *A. concolor* 'Hillier's Dwarf'
§	- 'Hillier's Dwarf'	CKen
	- 'Husky Pup'	CKen
	- (Lowiana Group) 'Creamy'	CKen NLar NPCo
	- 'Masonic Broom'	CKen
	- 'Mike Stearn'	CKen
	- 'Mora'	CKen
	- 'Ostrov nad Ohri'	CKen
	- 'Piggelmee'	CKen MAsh
	- 'Pygmy'	CKen
	- 'Scooter'	CKen NLar
	- 'Sherwood's Blue'	NPCo
§	- Violacea Group	CKen MAsh MGos SLim
	- - prostrate	EUJe LRHS NHol NLar
	- 'Wattez Prostrate'	LRHS
	- 'Wattezii'	CKen
	- 'Wintergold'	CKen MGos NHol NLar NPCo SLim
	delavayi	CDul EPfP NWea
	- var. ***delavayi***	CExl
	- - Fabri Group	see *A. fabri*
I	- 'Nana'	CKen
§	***fabri***	CKen
	fargesii	CKen
	forrestii	CKen
	fraseri	CDul CTho NWea WMou
	- 'Blue Bonnet'	CKen NLar
	- 'Raul's Dwarf'	CKen
	grandis	CBcs CDul CJun ELan EPfP MMuc NWea
	- 'Compacta'	CKen
	- 'Van Dedem's Dwarf'	CKen NLar SLim
	homolepis	CKen
§	- 'Prostrata'	CKen
	koreana ♀H7	CAco CBcs CDoC CDul CJun CKen CMac CTho EHul ELan EPfP GKin LAst LRHS MAsh MBlu MGos MJak MMuc NHol NPCo NWea SBod SGol SLim SPoG SWvt WHar WMou
	- 'Alpin Star'	CKen MAsh NLar
	- 'Blaue Zwo'	CKen
	- 'Blauer Eskimo' ♀H7	CKen MAsh SLim
	- 'Blauer Pfiff'	CKen
	- 'Blinsham Gold'	CKen
	- 'Blue Emperor'	MBlu
	- 'Blue Magic'	CKen NLar
	- 'Bonsai Blue'	IVic
I	- 'Brevifolia'	NLar
	- 'Brilliant'	CKen NLar
	- 'Cis' ♀H7	CDoC CKen LRHS NHol NLar NWad SLim WGor
	- 'Crystal Globe'	CKen
	- 'Dark Hill'	NLar
	- 'Doni-tajuso'	CKen
	- 'Eisregen'	CKen
	- 'Festival'	NHol NLar NPCo
	- 'Fliegender Untertasse'	IVic
	- 'Frosty'	SLim
	- 'Gait'	CKen NLar
	- 'Golden Glow'	NLar SLim
	- 'Goldener Traum'	CKen NLar
	- 'Green Carpet'	CKen LRHS SLim
	- 'Horstmann'	CKen NPCo
	- 'Ice Breaker' ♀H7	MAsh SLim
	- 'Inverleith'	CKen
	- 'Kleiner Prinz'	NLar
	- 'Kohout'	CKen
	- 'Kohout's Icebreaker' PBR	CKen
	- 'Kristallkugel'	MAsh NLar NPCo
	- 'Lippetal'	CKen
	- 'Luminetta'	CKen LRHS NHol
	- 'Nadelkissen'	CKen NHol
	- 'Nisbet'	LRHS NHol NPCo SCoo
	- 'Oberon'	CDoC CKen MAsh MBri NHol NWad
	- 'Piccolo'	CKen
	- 'Pinocchio'	CDoC CKen NHol NWad
	- 'Ry'	NLar
	- 'Schneestern'	NLar
	- 'Sherwood Compact'	CKen
	- 'Shorty'	CKen NLar
	- 'Silberkugel'	CKen CMen MAsh NLar NWad SLim
	- 'Silberlocke' ♀H7	CDoC CDul CKen EBee GKin LRHS MAsh MBlu MBri MGos NLar SCoo SLim
	- 'Silbermavers'	CKen
	- 'Silberperl'	CKen CMen LRHS MBri NLar
	- 'Silberzwerg'	NLar
	- 'Silver Show'	CDoC CDul CKen NHol NLar SLim
	- 'Threave'	CKen NHol NLar
	- 'Tundra'	NLar NPCo
	- 'Verdener Dom'	NLar
	- 'Wellenseind'	CKen
	lasiocarpa 'Alpine Beauty'	CKen NLar
§	- var. ***arizonica***	CDul
	- - 'Compacta' Hornibr. ♀H7	CDoC CKen CMac MBri MGos NHol NLar NPCo SLim
	- - 'Kenwith Blue'	CKen NPCo SLim
	- 'Chikov' **new**	CKen
	- 'Compacta' Beissn.	LRHS MAsh SBod
	- 'Day Creek'	CKen NLar
	- 'Duflon'	CKen MAsh
	- 'Elaine'	CKen
	- 'Green Globe'	CKen LRHS NLar
	- 'Joe's Alpine'	CKen
	- 'Kyle's Alpine'	CKen
	- 'Logan Pass'	CKen
	- 'Lopalpun' **new**	CKen
	- 'Mulligan's Dwarf'	CKen
	- 'Prickly Pete'	CKen NLar
I	- 'Prostrata'	CMac
	- 'Stevens Blue'	CKen MAsh NLar
	- 'Toenisvorst'	CKen
	- 'Utah'	CKen
I	***magnifica*** 'Nana'	CKen

	– witches' broom	CKen
	nebrodensis	CKen
	– 'Sicilian Gold' **new**	NLar
	nobilis	see *A. procera*
	nordmanniana	CAco CCVT CDul CJun CMac CTho EHul ELan EPfP EWTr LBuc MJak MMuc NEgg NWea SEND SPoG WHar WMou
	– 'Arne's Dwarf'	CKen
	– 'Barabits' Compact'	MBri NLar
	– 'Barabits' Spreader'	CKen
	– 'Dahlheim'	MAsh
	– subsp. ***equi-trojani***	CDul NWea
	– – 'Archer'	CKen NPCo
	– – 'Franke' **new**	NLar
	– 'Golden Spreader' ♀H7	CDoC CKen CMac EPla LRHS MAsh MBlu MBri MGos NLar NPCo SCoo SLim SPoG WThu
	– 'Hasselt'	CKen
	– 'Jakobsen'	CKen
I	– 'Reflexa'	NPCo
	– 'Silberspitze'	CKen
	numidica	CKen
	– 'Glauca'	CKen
	– 'Lawrenceville'	NPCo
	pindrow	NWea
	pinsapo	CDul
	– 'Atlas'	MAsh
	– 'Aurea' ♀H5	CKen LRHS MPkF NHol SLim
I	– 'Aurea Nana'	CKen
	– 'Fastigiata'	MPkF NLar SGol
	– 'Glauca' ♀H5	CAco CDoC CDul CKen CTho ELan LRHS MBlu NLar SLim
	– 'Hamondii'	CKen
I	– 'Horstmann'	CKen NHol NPCo SLim
	– 'Kelleriis'	EUJe
	– 'Pendula'	CKen
	– 'Quicksilver'	CKen
	– 'San Pedro'	CKen
§	***procera***	CBcs CDul CUse EWTr MJak NWea
	– 'Bizarro'	NLar
	– 'Blaue Hexe'	CKen IVic LRHS MAsh SLim
	– 'Delbar Cascade'	CKen
	– Glauca Group	CAco CDoC CDul CTho ECrN EPfP GKin LRHS MAsh MBlu MBri NHol NLar SLim
	– – 'Glauca Prostrata'	EUJe GKin SLim
	– 'La Graciosa'	NLar
	– 'Noble's Dwarf'	SLim
	– 'Obrighofen'	NLar
	– 'Prostrata'	MAsh NLar
	– 'Rat Tail' **new**	NLar
	– 'Sherwoodii'	CKen SLim
	Rosemoor hybrid	CKen
	sachalinensis	CKen
	sibirica	EPfP
	spectabilis	EPfP
	veitchii	CAco CTho NPCo
	– 'Heddergott'	CKen NHol NPCo SLim
	– 'Heine'	CKen NLar
	– 'Kramer'	CKen
I	– 'Pendula'	CKen IVic
	– 'Rumburk'	CKen MAsh SLim
	– var. ***sikokiana*** **new**	NLar
	– 'Syców'	CKen
	vejarii	SLim

Abromeitiella see *Deuterocohnia*

Abrotanella (*Asteraceae*)

sp.	ECho

Abutilon ✿ (*Malvaceae*)

'Amiti'	GFai
'Apricot Belle'	SMDP
'Ashford Red'	CBcs CCCN ELan LRHS SKHP SMDP WCot WKif
'Boule de Neige'	SMrm
'Canary Bird' ♀H1b	CBcs CCCN CHEx CHll CSde SMDP WKif
'Cannington Carol' (v) ♀H1b	CCCN CHll ELan LLHF SEND SLim WCot
'Cannington Peter' (v) ♀H1b	CCCN
'Cannington Sonia' (v)	SMDP
'Cloth of Gold'	CMac
'Cynthia Pike' (v)	LRHS
'Flamenco'	CCCN CWGN
'Heather Bennington'	SMDP
'Henry Makepeace'	SMDP
'Hinton Seedling'	CCCN CRHN
× ***hybridum*** hort. apricot-flowered	CHEx
– red-flowered	CHEx
indicum	WCot
'Ines'	SChF WPGP
'Jacqueline Morris'	LRHS SMrm
'John Thompson'	CCCN CHel CWGN WCot
'Kentish Belle' ♀H3	Widely available
'Linda Vista Peach' ♀H1b	SMDP
'Louis Marignac'	GFai
'Marion' ♀H1b	CRHN LRHS SMDP SMrm
'Master Michael'	CMac SEND
megapotamicum ♀H3	Widely available
– 'Variegatum' (v) ♀H3	CBcs CCCN CHel CMac ELan EPfP LRHS MGos MSCN NEgg SEND SEle SKHP SLim SLon SPer SPoG SWvt WCot WGrn XLum
– 'Wisley Red'	CBcs CRHN CSPN LRHS SKHP SMDP
× ***milleri*** hort. ♀H3	CCCN CMac CRHN WCot
– 'Variegatum' (v)	CCCN CHEx CHel CMac LRHS SEND WCot
'Nabob' ♀H1b	CBcs CCCN CDoC CExl CHel CRHN CSde EUJe LSou MOWG SMDP SMrm SPoG
'Old Rose Belle'	GFai
'Orange Hot Lava'	CExl WPGP
'Orange Vein'	SMDP
'Patrick Synge'	CCCN CHGN CHll CMHG EBtc MOWG SPhx WPGP
pictum 'Thompsonii' (v) ♀H1b	CCCN CHEx
'Pink Lady'	CCCN
'Red Bells'	GFai
'Red Hot Lava' **new**	SChF
'Russels Dwarf'	CCCN
'Savitzii' (v) ♀H1b	MSCN
'Silver Belle'	CCCN
'Simcox White'	CCCN
'Souvenir de Bonn' (v) ♀H1b	CBcs CCCN CHll LSou SMDP SMrm
× ***suntense***	CBcs CCCN CMHG CSBt EBee ELan EPfP EUJe EWld LRHS MSCN NPer SChF SEND SMDP
– 'Jermyns' ♀H4	CAbP CExl ELan EPfP GCra LRHS MBri MGos SCoo SKHP SPoG SWvt

– 'Violetta'	EBee
'Tango'	CCCN CWGN EUJe SEND
variegated, salmon-flowered (v)	LAst
'Victory'	CCCN CWGN SKHP
vitifolium	CBcs CCCN CDTJ EPfP IDee NEgg SPad SPer SPtp WBor WKif
– 'Album'	CBcs CCCN CDul CExl CHll ELan GCal SEND SPer SSpi
– 'Tennant's White' ♀H4	CAbP CCCN CExl EPfP GGal LRHS MBri SKHP
– 'Veronica Tennant' ♀H4	CExl EPfP WGwG
'Waltz'	CCCN CWGN EUJe LLHF SEND
'Westfield Bronze' (v)	CRHN SMDP

Acacia (*Mimosaceae*)

acinacea	SPlb
adunca	SPlb
angustissima	SPlb
armata	see *A. paradoxa*
axillaris	SPlb
baileyana ♀H2	CBcs CCCN CEnd CMac CSBt CTsd EHoe ELan EPfP EUJe EWTr LRHS MGos MWat SBig SCoo SEND SPer SPlb SWvt WFar WPat
– var. ***aurea***	SPlb
– 'Purpurea' ♀H3	Widely available
– 'Songlines'	LRHS MBri MGos SHil
boormanii	EBee SPlb WPGP
caven ♀H2 NJM 08.0021	WPGP
covenyi	SMad WPGP
cultriformis	CCCN CTsd ESwi SEND
dealbata ♀H2	Widely available
– 'Argentea'	LRHS MGos
– 'Gaulois Astier'	CSBt LRHS MBri MGos SHil SWvt
– subsp. ***subalpina***	WPGP
drummondii new	COtt
'Exeter Hybrid'	CSBt
fimbriata	CRHN
floribunda 'Lisette'	LRHS MGos SHil
gregorii	SPlb
julibrissin	see *Albizia julibrissin*
karroo	CArn CDTJ SPlb
longifolia	CBcs CCCN CDTJ IDee LRHS
– subsp. ***sophorae***	CCCN
macradenia	SPlb
mearnsii	CCCN EBee
melanoxylon	CBcs CDTJ CTsd ESwi MTPN SEND SPlb
nanodealbata	SPad
§ ***paradoxa*** ♀H2	NSoo
pataczekii	CSBt EPfP WPGP
pendula	SPlb
podalyriifolia	CCCN SPlb
pravissima ♀H3	CAbb CBcs CChe CDoC CDul CExl CHEx CHel CHll CMac CTri CTsd EBee ELan EPfP EUJe LPal LRHS MGil MOWG NSoo SArc SEND SLim SPlb SPoG SWvt WBor WPGP WSHC
– 'Bushwalk Baby'	MOWG
retinodes ♀H2	CBcs CCCN CDTJ CDoC CTsd EPfP IDee LRHS MTPN SEND SPad SWvt
riceana	CCCN CTsd SVen
rubida	CTsd SPlb
sentis	see *A. victoriae*
spectabilis	CCCN SPlb
suaveolens	SPlb
verticillata	CBcs CCCN CDTJ CHGN CHll CSde CTsd EPfP MOWG MTPN
– riverine form	CExl EPfP LRHS
§ ***victoriae***	SPlb

Acaena (*Rosaceae*)

adscendens misapplied	see *A. affinis*, *A. saccaticupula* 'Blue Haze'
adscendens ambig. 'Glauca'	EHoe NBir
§ ***affinis***	ECou MCot SDix
anserinifolia misapplied	see *A. novae-zelandiae*
buchananii	CTri EBee ECho ECou EHoe EPPr GAbr GBin GEdr MBrN MMuc NLar SCob SRms
caerulea hort.	see *A. caesiiglauca*
§ ***caesiiglauca***	CTri GAbr GQue MLHP
eupatoria	EBee
inermis	SPlb
– 'Purpurea'	CSam EBee ECha ECou EHoe EWes GAbr GBin GEdr GQue NDov NHol NLar NRya NWad SPlb WMoo XLum
magellanica	GCal GKev
microphylla ♀H5	CSam CTri ECou GBin MBel MBrN NLar SPlb SRms WMoo
– Copper Carpet	see *A. microphylla* 'Kupferteppich'
– 'Glauca'	see *A. caesiiglauca*
§ – 'Kupferteppich'	CSam ECho ECtt EHoe ELan EPPr GAbr GBin GCal GCrg GKev GQue MBri MRav NBir NBro NChi NLar SCob SRms WMoo WPat XLum
minor var. ***antarctica***	GBin
§ ***novae-zelandiae***	CTri EBee ECou SDix WMoo XLum
'Pewter'	see *A. saccaticupula* 'Blue Haze'
'Purple Carpet'	see *A. microphylla* 'Kupferteppich'
'Purple Haze'	CSpe SCob
§ ***saccaticupula*** 'Blue Haze'	EBee ECha ECho ECou EDAr EHoe LRHS MBrN MRav SPer SPlb SRms WMoo
tesca	GBin

Acalypha (*Euphorbiaceae*)

'Mini Red'	LAst
pendula	see *A. reptans*
§ ***reptans***	CCCN

Acanthocalyx see *Morina*

Acantholimon (*Plumbaginaceae*)

acerosum	XSen
androsaceum	see *A. ulicinum*
araxanum new	GKev
armenum	XSen
– var. ***balansae*** new	LLHF
glumaceum	LLHF
trojanum	XSen
§ ***ulicinum***	XEll XSen

Acanthopanax see *Eleutherococcus*

ricinifolius	see *Kalopanax septemlobus*

Acanthus ✿ (*Acanthaceae*)

arboreus	XLum
balcanicus misapplied	see *A. hungaricus*
'Candelabra'	MAvo
caroli-alexandri	see *A. spinosus* L.
dioscoridis	GCal SMHy WHil

	– var. ***perringii***	CCon CDes EBee ECha GBin MNrw NLar WCot WFar XLum
	eminens	WCot
	hirsutus	CMea EPri IFoB WCot WHil
	– subsp. ***syriacus***	GCal SMrm
	'Hollande du Nort'	GBin XLum
§	***hungaricus***	CHid CMHG CMac EAEE EBee ELan GBin LRHS MBel MMuc MRav NLar SCob SDix SPer SWat WCot WFar WHil WMnd WWEG XLum XSen
	– AL&JS 90097YU	WHil
	– MESE 561	EPPr
	longifolius Host	see *A. hungaricus*
	mollis	Widely available
	– 'Fielding Gold'	see *A. mollis* 'Hollard's Gold'
	– free-flowering	ESwi GCal MAvo WHil XLum
§	– 'Hollard's Gold'	Widely available
	– 'Jefalba'	see *A. mollis* (Latifolius Group) 'Rue Ledan'
	– Latifolius Group	MRav SRms WHil WHoo
§	– – 'Rue Ledan'	EBee ECtt EPPr EShb GBin LRHS MAvo NGdn SMHy SPhx WCot WWEG XLum
	– 'Long Spike'	GCal WHil
	– 'Niger'	WHil
	– 'Tasmanian Angel' (v)	CBct CWGN ECtt IBoy MHol SCob WCot XLum
	'Morning's Candle'	CBct EBee ECtt MBri NGdn NLar SGol WFar WHil XLum
	sennii	CAby CCse CDes IMou SMad SPhx WSHC XLum
	spinosus misapplied	see *A. spinosus* Spinosissimus Group
§	***spinosus*** L.	Widely available
	– Ferguson's form	WCot WHil XLum
	– 'Lady Moore' (v)	WHil XLum
	– 'Royal Haughty'	MAvo WFar XLum
§	– Spinosissimus Group	CBct CCon CMHG CTsd ECha ELan GBin GCal GCra IBoy LEdu MAvo MRav SMrm SWat WCot WFar WHil WMnd
	'Summer Beauty'	ECtt EWes GBin MAvo MRav WCot WFar WHil WHoo WWEG XLum
	'Whitewater' (v)	CBct CWGN EBee ECtt GEdr LRHS MAvo MHol MSCN NLar NSti NWad SBig SCob SPoG WCot

Acca (*Myrtaceae*)

sellowiana (F)	CAgr CBcs CDTJ CDul CExl CHel CHll CMac COtt CTsd ELan EPfP EShb ETwe LAst LRHS LSou MGos NPla SCob SEle SLim SPer SPlb SPoG SVic SWvt WSHC XSen
– 'Apollo' (F)	IDee LRHS
– 'Mammoth' (F)	CBcs CCCN
– 'Triumph' (F)	CBcs CCCN
– 'Unique' (F)	EUJe
– 'Variegata' (F/v)	CCCN

Acer ✿ (*Sapindaceae*)

	amoenum B&SWJ 10916	WCru
	– B&SWJ 10977 **new**	WCru
	– 'Firecracker' PBR	see *A. palmatum* var. *dissectum* 'Firecracker'
	buergerianum	CAco CBcs CDul CJun CMCN CMen MPkF NLar SGol WMou
	– var. ***formosanum*** CWJ 12477	WCru
	– B&SWJ 12676 from South Korea **new**	WCru
	– 'Himcode'	NLar
	– 'Mino-yatsubusa'	MPkF
	– 'Miyasama-yatsubusa'	MPkF
	– 'Naruto'	CMCN MPkF
	campbellii	MBlu
	– subsp. ***campbellii*** GWJ 9360	WCru
	– 'Exuberance'	CJun
	campestre ♀H6	Widely available
	– 'Autumn Red'	NPCo
	– 'Carnival' (v) ♀H6	CCVT CEnd EBee ECrN ELon EPla MAsh MBlu MPkF NLar NPCo SCob SGol SPer SPoG SWvt WHar WPat
	– 'Eco Sentry' PBR	EBee
	– 'Elsrijk'	CCVT CLnd SCoo SGol
	– 'Evelyn'	see *A. campestre* 'Queen Elizabeth'
	– 'Evenley Red'	CDul MBlu WPGP
	– 'Pendulum'	CEnd
	– 'Postelense'	EBee EPla MBlu
	– 'Pulverulentum' (v)	NPCo
§	– 'Queen Elizabeth'	MGos SGol
	– 'Red Shine'	SGol WMou
	– 'Royal Ruby'	MGos
*	– 'Ruby Glow' ♀H6	CEnd ECrN
	– 'Schwerinii'	CDul
I	– 'Silver Celebration' (v)	CJun
	– 'William Caldwell'	CAco CEnd CTho EBee ECrN MBlu MBri
	capillipes	CBcs CDul CMCN CTho ECrN ELan EPla GKin LRHS MGos MJak MMuc NSoo NWea SCob SPlb WHCr WHar WPGP
	– 'Antoine'	MBri
	– 'Candy Stripe'	see *A.* × *conspicuum* 'Candy Stripe'
	– 'Honey Dew'	CJun SSta
	aff. ***capillipes***	LAst MWat
	cappadocicum	CCVT CDul CEnd CLnd CMCN ECrN MMuc MSnd NWea WMou
	– 'Aureum' ♀H6	CAco CBcs CDoC CDul CEnd CLnd CMCN CTho EBee ECrN ELan EPfP EPla GBin GKin IArd LRHS MAsh MBlu MBri MGos MRav NLar SCob SGol SPer SWvt WFar WHar
	– var. ***mono***	see *A. pictum*
	– 'Rubrum' ♀H6	CBcs CDul CMCN COtt EBee ECrN EPfP EPla GBin GKin IDee LRHS MBlu MGos MMuc MRav SCob SEND SGol SPer WFar WHar WHer
	– var. ***tricaudatum***	CExl
	cappadocicum × (× ***conspicuum*** 'Phoenix') **new**	CAco
	carpinifolium	CDul IArd MBlu MPkF NLar WPGP
	– B&SWJ 10955	WCru
	– B&SWJ 11124	WCru
§	***caudatifolium***	WPat
	– CWJ 12403	WCru
	– RWJ 9843	WCru
§	***caudatum*** GWJ 9279	WCru
	– GWJ 9317	WCru
	– HWJK 2240	WCru
	– HWJK 2338	WCru
	– subsp. ***ukurunduense***	MPkF
	– – B&SWJ 8658	WCru

circinatum	CBcs CCVT CDoC CDul CJun CLnd CMCN ECrN EPla IVic MBlu MMuc MSnd NLar SEND SPlb WMou
- B&SWJ 9565	WCru
- 'Burgundy Jewel'	CJun
- 'Little Gem'	CJun
- 'Monroe'	CJun SGol
- 'Pacific Fire'	CJun
- 'Sunglow'	CJun
circinatum* × *palmatum	SBig
cissifolium	CMCN EPfP EPla IArd NLar
- B&SWJ 10801	WCru
§ × ***conspicuum*** 'Candy Stripe'	CJun NLar WPGP
- 'Elephant's Ear'	CJun NLar
- 'Mozart'	CJun MBlu MBri MPkF NLar SSta
- 'Phoenix'	CEnd CJun CMCN CRos CTho EPfP GKin IVic LRHS MBlu NLar SSta WCot WHar WPGP WPat
- 'Silver Ghost'	MPkF
§ - 'Silver Vein'	CDoC CEnd CJun CMCN EPfP NLar SSta SWvt WPGP
crataegifolium	SSta
- B&SWJ 11036	WCru
- B&SWJ 11355	WCru
- 'Ittai-san-nishiki'	SSta
- 'Meuri-keade-no-fuiri' (v)	MPkF
- 'Meuri-no-ōfu' (v)	MPkF SSta
- 'Veitchii' (v)	CJun EBee EPfP MBlu MPkF NLar SBig SSpi SSta
creticum misapplied	see *A. sempervirens*
dasycarpum	see *A. saccharinum*
davidii	CBcs CDoC CDul CExl CLnd CMCN CPne CTsd ECrN MBlu MGos MMuc MRav SCob SGol SLim SPer SSta WPat
- AC 1471	MSnd
§ - 'Canton'	CJun SSta
- 'Cantonspark'	see *A. davidii* 'Canton'
- 'Cascade'	CJun MBlu SSta
- 'Ernest Wilson'	CBcs NLar SSta
- 'George Forrest' 🏆H5	CAco CDoC CDul CExl CJun CLnd CMCN CMac CTho EBee ECrN ELan EPfP GBin LAst LRHS MMuc NLar NWea SCob SEND SPer SPoG SSta WHar WMou
- 'Hagelunie'	SBir SSta
- 'Hansu-suru' (v)	SSta
- 'Karmen'	CBcs CDul CJun EPfP SSta WPGP
- 'Madeline Spitta'	CMCN MBri
- 'Purple Bark'	CExl CJun SBir SSta
- 'Rosalie'	CBcs CJun EPfP MBlu MBri NLar SBir SSta WHor
- 'Sekka'	SSta
- 'Serpentine'	CBcs CDoC CJun CMCN CNWT ELan EPfP EPla GBin IDee MBlu MBri NEgg NLar SSta
- 'Silver Vein'	see *A.* × *conspicuum* 'Silver Vein'
discolor	CMCN
elegantulum	CExl CJun GBin IDee WPGP
erianthum	CMCN
erythranthum B&SWJ 11733	WCru
- DJHV 06147	WCru
fabri	CDul CExl
- WWJ 11614	WCru
flabellatum	CJun CMCN WPat
- var. ***yunnanense***	MMuc MSnd

forrestii	CExl
- BWJ 7515	WCru
- 'Alice'	CEnd CJun SSta
- 'Inoense' **new**	SSta
- 'Sirene'	CJun SSta
- 'Sparkling'	CJun NLar
× ***freemanii***	CMCN
- 'Armstrong'	CCVT SGol
- Autumn Blaze = 'Jeffersred' 🏆H6	CBcs CCVT CDoC CLnd CMCN COtt EPfP IArd LRHS MBlu MGos MMuc NLar SBir SCoo SGol SPer SPoG WHar WMou
- Autumn Fantasy = 'Dtr 102'	LRHS
- Celebration = 'Celzam'	CCVT MGos
- 'Indian Summer'	see *A.* × *freemanii* 'Morgan'
§ - 'Morgan'	CJun NLar
fulvescens	see *A. longipes*
ginnala	see *A. tataricum* subsp. *ginnala*
globosum	see *A. platanoides* 'Globosum'
grandidentatum	see *A. saccharum* subsp. *grandidentatum*
griseum 🏆H5	Widely available
grosseri	CDul CMCN CTri SGol
- var. ***hersii***	CBcs CDoC CDul CMac EBee ELan EPfP EPla GBin LRHS MBri MMuc MRav NLar NWea SChF SCob SLim SPer SPoG SSta SWvt WHar
- 'Leiden'	EPfP
heldreichii	CMCN
henryi	CBcs CDul EPfP NEgg NLar
heptaphlebium B&SWJ 11695	WCru
- B&SWJ 11713	WCru
- DJHV 06063	WCru
- FMWJ 13369 **new**	WCru
hyrcanum	LRHS
japonicum	CMCN MMuc SEWo
- B&SWJ 8417	WCru
§ - 'Aconitifolium' 🏆H6	Widely available
- 'Aki-hi'	NLar
- 'Ao-jutan'	CJun
- 'Attaryi'	CMen MPkF NLar NPCo WPat
- 'Aureum'	see *A. shirasawanum* 'Aureum'
- 'Emmit's Pumpkins'	CJun
- 'Ezo-no-momiji'	see *A. shirasawanum* 'Ezo-no-momiji'
- 'Fairy Lights'	NLar
- 'Filicifolium'	see *A. japonicum* 'Aconitifolium'
- 'Green Cascade' 🏆H6	CAco CEnd CJun CMCN CMac CMen IVic LRHS MGos MPkF NLar NPCo SBig SGol WPat
- 'King's Copse'	CJun LRHS
- 'Laciniatum'	see *A. japonicum* 'Aconitifolium'
- f. ***microphyllum***	see *A. shirasawanum* 'Microphyllum'
- 'Ogurayama'	see *A. shirasawanum* 'Ogurayama'
- 'Ō-isami'	EPfP MPkF SBig
- 'Ō-taki'	CJun
- 'Vitifolium' 🏆H6	CAco CDoC CEnd CJun CMCN CMac CSBt ELan EPfP GBin LRHS MBlu MBri MGos MPkF NEgg NLar NPCo SBig SGol SPer SSta WCFE WPGP
kawakamii	see *A. caudatifolium*
laevigatum B&SWJ 11684	WCru
- FMWJ 13378 **new**	WCru
- NJM 10.049 **new**	WPGP

§	- var. ***reticulatum*** B&SWJ 11698	WCru
	laurinum NJM 10.048 **new**	WPGP
	- NJM 10.087 **new**	WPGP
	- NJM 10.111 **new**	WPGP
	- NJM 10.112 **new**	WPGP
	laxiflorum	SSta
§	***longipes***	CMCN
	macrophyllum	CDul CMCN EPfP IDee MBlu
	mandshuricum	CDul MBlu
§	***maximowiczianum***	CBcs CMCN CTho ELan MMuc MPkF SGol SSta
	maximowiczii	MPkF WHCr
	micranthum ♀H6	CDul CMCN EBee EPfP GKin MBlu NLar SSpi WHar WPGP
	miyabei	MPkF
	mono	see *A. pictum*
	monspessulanum	CDul CMCN MMuc SEND
	morifolium B&SWJ 11473	WCru
	morrisonense Hayata	see *A. caudatifolium*
	negundo	CAco CDul CMCN CTho ECrN NWea SCob SWvt
	- 'Auratum'	CMCN SGol
	- 'Aureomarginatum' (v)	ECrN SGol
	- 'Aureovariegatum' (v)	CBcs
§	- 'Elegans' (v)	CDul CEnd CMCN SCoo WHar
	- 'Elegantissimum'	see *A. negundo* 'Elegans'
	- 'Flamingo' (v)	CAco CBcs CCVT CDoC CDul CEnd CMac CWSG ECrN ELan ELon EPfP LRHS MAsh NLar NWea SCob SGol SHil SPer SPoG SWvt WFar WHar
	- 'Kelly's Gold'	CAco CBcs CTho NLar NWea SCob SGol WHar
	- 'Sensation'	NLar
	- 'Variegatum' (v)	CBcs ECrN SGol
	- var. ***violaceum*** ♀H6	CEnd CMCN SVen
	- 'Winter Lightning' ♀H6	CTho NLar
	nikoense misapplied	see *A. maximowiczianum*
	'Norwegian Sunset'	CCVT
	oblongum	CMCN
	- KWJ 12232	WCru
	- WWJ 11851	WCru
	oliverianum	CExl
	- subsp. ***formosanum*** CWJ 12437	WCru
	opalus	CMCN SEND
	orientale misapplied	see *A. sempervirens*
	orizabense	EBee
	Pacific Sunset = 'Warrenred'	NLar
	palmatum	CBcs CCVT CDul CMCN CMHG CMen CSBt CTri CUse EPfP EPla EWTr GKin MBlu MGos NEgg NWea SArc SCob SEWo SGol SPlb SWvt WFar WHar WPat
	- 'Akane'	CMen
§	- 'Aka-shigitatsu-sawa'	CBcs CJun CMCN CMen LRHS MGos MJak MPkF NLar SGol
	- 'Akegarasu'	CMen NLar
	- 'Akita-yatsubusa'	MPkF
	- 'Alpenweiss'	CJun
	- 'Amagi-shigure'	CJun MPkF
	- 'Amber Ghost'	CJun
	- 'Aoba-jo'	CJun CMen MPkF NPCo
	- 'Ao-kanzashi' (v)	MPkF NLar
	- 'Ao-seigen'	CJun
	- 'Aoshime-no-uchi'	see *A. palmatum* 'Shinobuga-oka'

	- 'Aoyagi'	CDul CEnd CJun CMCN CMen LRHS MGos MPkF NLar NPCo SBod SSta WPat
	- 'Aoyagi-gawa' **new**	CJun
§	- 'Arakawa'	CEnd CMCN CMac CMen MPkF NPCo
	- 'Arakawa-ukon'	CJun NLar
	- 'Aratama'	CJun CMen LRHS MJak MPkF
	- 'Ariadne' (v) ♀H6	CEnd CJun LRHS MBri MGos MPkF NLar SBig SCoo SPoG WMou WPat
	- 'Ariake-nomura'	CMen MPkF
	- 'Asahi-zuru' (v)	CBcs CJun CMCN CMen CRos LRHS MBri MGos MPkF NLar SBod SHil SPer
	- 'Ashurst Wood'	SBig
	- 'Atrolineare'	CMen MPkF NLar NPCo
	- 'Atropurpureum'	Widely available
	- 'Atropurpureum Novum'	MPkF NLar SGol
	- 'Attraction'	CMCN CMen
	- 'Aureum'	CAco CMCN CMen ELan EPfP EPla IBoy LMil LRHS MAsh MBlu MGos MPkF NLar NPCo SPoG SSpi WCFE
	- Autumn Glory Group	CAco CEnd CJun CMac CMen SBod WPat
	- 'Autumn Red'	CMen NPCo
*	- 'Autumn Showers'	CEnd CJun
	- 'Azuma-murasaki'	CJun CMen MPkF NLar NPCo
	- 'Beni-chidori'	CMen
	- 'Beni-gasa'	CJun MPkF WPat
	- 'Beni-hime'	MBri MPkF WPat
	- 'Beni-hoshi'	MPkF
	- 'Beni-kagami'	CEnd CJun CMCN MPkF NLar SGol
	- 'Beni-kawa'	CJun CMen MPkF NPCo SBig SGol WPat
	- 'Beni-komachi'	CAco CBcs CEnd CJun CMCN CMen EBee LRHS MBri MGos MPkF NLar NSoo SBod SHil SSta
	- 'Beni-maiko' ♀H6	CEnd CJun CMCN CMen CRos EPfP LRHS MBri MGos MJak MPkF NLar NSoo SBig SCoo SHil SWvt WPat
	- 'Beni-musume'	MPkF
	- 'Beni-otake'	CAco CBcs CJun CMen ELan EPfP EUJe IVic LMil LRHS MBri MGos MPkF NLar NPCo SBig SCob
	- 'Beni-otome'	MPkF
	- 'Beni-schichi-henge' (v)	CBcs CEnd CJun CMCN CMen CRos CWGN GKin LBMP LMil LRHS MAsh MBri MGos MJak MPkF NHol NLar NPCo SBig SBod SCoo SGol SHil SSta WPat
	- 'Beni-shidare'	see *A. palmatum* var. *dissectum* 'Toyama-nishiki'
	- 'Beni-shi-en'	CJun MPkF NLar WPat
	- 'Beni-shigitatsu-sawa'	see *A. palmatum* 'Aka-shigitatsu-sawa'
	- 'Beni-tsukasa' (v) ♀H6	CEnd CJun CMen EPfP LRHS MAsh MPkF NLar SBod SChF SSpi SSta
	- 'Beni-tsuru'	MPkF
	- 'Beni-ubi-gohon'	CJun MJak MPkF NLar
	- 'Beni-zuru'	WPat
	- 'Berry Broom'	MPkF NLar
	- 'Berry Dwarf'	CJun MPkF
	- 'Bi Hō'	CJun IVic NLar SGol
	- 'Bloodgood' ♀H6	Widely available
	- 'Bloodgood' seedling **new**	CAco
	- 'Bonfire' misapplied	see *A. palmatum* 'Seigai'
	- 'Bonfire' ambig.	CJun
	- 'Bonnie Bergman'	CJun
	- 'Boskoop Glory'	GKin

	Name	Suppliers
	- 'Brandt's Dwarf'	NLar WPat
	- 'Burgundy Lace' ♀H6	CAco CBcs CDoC CEnd CJun CMCN CMen ELan EPfP EUJe GKin LMil LRHS MAsh MBri MGos MJak MPkF NPCo SBig SBod SCoo SGol SPer SPoG SSta WPat
	- 'Butterfly' (v)	CBcs CDoC CEnd CJun CMCN CMac CMen CWGN CWSG EBee ELan IVic LAst LMil LRHS MAsh MBlu MGos MPkF NLar NPCo NPri SBod SCob SCoo SGol SLim SPoG SWvt WFar
	- 'Calico'	CJun
	- 'Caperci Dwarf'	MPkF
	- 'Carlis Corner'	CJun MPkF
	- 'Carminium'	see *A. palmatum* 'Corallinum'
	- 'Chikuma-no'	CMen MPkF NLar
	- 'Chirimen-nishiki' (v)	MPkF
	- 'Chishio Improved'	CAco CEnd CJun CMCN CMac CMen CTho EPfP LRHS MAsh MGos MPkF NHol NLar SBig SWvt
	- 'Chitose-yama' ♀H6	CDul CEnd CJun CMCN CMen EPfP GBin GKin LRHS MAsh MBri MGos MPkF NLar NPCo SBod SGol SLim SSta WPat
§	- 'Chiyo-hime'	CAco ELan EPfP NLar NSoo
	- 'Collingwood Ingram'	SGol
	- 'Coonara Pygmy'	CAco CJun CMCN CMac CMen GKin LRHS MGos MPkF SBod SCoo
	- 'Coral Pink'	CJun CMen MPkF SGol SSta
§	- 'Corallinum' ♀H6	CAco CEnd CJun CMCN CMen LRHS MPkF NLar NPCo WCFE WPat
	- var. ***coreanum*** B&SWJ 8606	WCru
	- - 'Korean Gem'	CJun CMen MPkF NPCo
	- 'Crimson Prince'	CJun MPkF SCoo
	- 'Crippsii'	CMac CMen EUJe GBin LRHS MGos MPkF SBod SCoo SGol
	- 'Deshōjō'	CMCN CMen COtt CWSG MBlu MGos MPkF NLar SCoo SGol
	- 'Diana'	CJun CMen MPkF NLar SGol
	- 'Diane Verkade'	MPkF
	- var. ***dissectum***	Widely available
	- - 'Ao-shidare'	CJun
	- - 'Autumn Fire'	CJun
	- - 'Baby Lace'	CWGN IVic
	- - 'Balcombe Green'	SBig
	- - 'Baldsmith'	CJun CLnd EUJe LBuc LMil LRHS MGos MPkF NLar SBod WPat
	- - 'Barrie Bergman'	CJun WPat
	- - 'Beni-fushigi'	MPkF
	- - 'Beni-shidare Tricolor' (v)	see *A. palmatum* var. *dissectum* 'Toyama-nishiki'
	- - 'Beni-shidare Variegated' (v)	see *A. palmatum* var. *dissectum* 'Toyama-nishiki'
	- - 'Berrima Bridge'	CJun
	- - 'Bewley's Red'	CJun
	- - 'Brocade'	CJun IVic MPkF WPat
	- - 'Bronzewing'	CJun
	- - 'Chantilly Lace'	CJun IBoy MPkF
	- - 'Crimson Princess'	CBcs LMil LRHS MBri MJak MPkF
	- - 'Crimson Queen' ♀H6	Widely available
	- - Dissectum Atropurpureum Group	CBcs CJun CMac CRos CTri ELan EPfP LRHS MAsh MGos NWea SBig SCob SCoo SLim SReu SSta SWvt WFar
	- - 'Dissectum Flavescens'	CEnd CJun CMac CMen LMil MBlu MPkF NPCo SBod
§	- - 'Dissectum Nigrum'	CAco CJun CMac CMen LRHS MAsh MPkF NLar NPCo WPat
	- - 'Dissectum Palmatifidum'	CDoC CMen EUJe LRHS MPkF NPCo SCoo SGol SPer
	- - 'Dissectum Rubrifolium'	MPkF
§	- - 'Dissectum Variegatum' (v)	CJun MPkF NPCo
	- - Dissectum Viride Group	CBcs CJun CMCN CMac CMen CRos CSBt ELan EPfP LAst LMil LRHS MAsh MBlu MGos MSwo NEgg NPCo NWea SBod SLim SPer SSta SWvt WCFE
	- - 'Ellen'	CJun MPkF NLar WPat
	- - 'Emerald Lace' ♀H6	CJun CRos GKin LBuc LMil LRHS MBri MGos MPkF NLar NSoo SBod SHil SSta WCFE WPat
	- - 'Felice'	CJun MPkF WPat
	- - 'Filigree' (v)	CAco CJun CMCN CMen EPfP LRHS MAsh MGos MPkF NLar NPCo SBig SBod SSta WCFE WPat
§	- - 'Firecracker' PBR	LRHS MPkF NLar
	- - 'Garnet' ♀H6	Widely available
	- - 'Goshiki-shidare' (v)	see *A. palmatum* var. *dissectum* 'Toyama-nishiki'
	- - 'Green Globe'	CJun LRHS
	- - 'Green Hornet'	CJun
	- - 'Green Lace'	CMen MPkF
	- - 'Green Mist'	CJun LRHS WPat
	- - 'Hanzel'	WPat
	- - 'Inaba-shidare' ♀H6	CAco CBcs CDoC CDul CEnd CJun CMCN CMen CSam ELan EPfP GBin IVic LMil LRHS MAsh MGos MJak MPkF MRav NLar NPCo SBod SCob SGol SPer SPoG SWvt WCFE WPat
I	- - 'Kawaii'	CJun
	- - 'Kiri-nishiki'	CJun CMen LRHS MPkF NLar NPCo
	- - 'Lace Lady'	LRHS
*	- - 'Lionheart'	CAco CJun CMen CWGN LRHS MGos MPkF NLar NPCo SBod SCoo
	- - 'Nomura-nishiki' (v)	CMen
	- - 'Octopus'	CJun NLar
	- - 'Orangeola' ♀H6	CJun CMen COtt CSBt EUJe IBoy IVic LRHS MAsh MGos MJak MPkF NHol NLar NPCo SBig SBod SCob SCoo SGol SPoG SSta WPat
	- - 'Ornatum' ♀H6	CAco CMCN CMen EPfP GBin MGos MPkF MRav NEgg NLar NPCo NPri SBod SCob SCoo WCFE
	- - 'Otto's Dissectum'	CJun
	- - 'Pendulum Julian'	CMCN LRHS MPkF
	- - 'Pink Ballerina' (v)	CJun NLar
	- - 'Pink Filigree'	CJun CMen EPfP LRHS MPkF NLar
	- - 'Raraflora'	CJun
	- - 'Red Autumn Lace'	CJun WPat
	- - 'Red Dragon'	CAco CDoC CJun CMen CWGN EUJe LMil LRHS MAsh MPkF NLar NPCo SBig SBod WPat
	- - 'Red Feather'	CJun
	- - 'Red Filigree Lace'	CEnd CJun CMCN CMen CWGN LRHS MGos MPkF NPCo SBig WPat
	- - 'Red Select'	MPkF
	- - 'Seiryū' ♀H6	Widely available
§	- - 'Shōjō-shidare'	CEnd CJun CMen LRHS MPkF NLar
	- - 'Shu-shidare'	CJun
	- - 'Spring Delight'	CJun MPkF NLar
	- - 'Suisei' (v)	MPkF
	- - 'Sunset'	CJun MPkF
	- - 'Tamukeyama'	CAco CJun CMCN CMen ELan EUJe LMil LRHS MBri MGos MJak MPkF

NLar NPCo SBod SCob SCoo SGol SLau WHor WPat
§ - - 'Toyama-nishiki' (v) CEnd CJun CMCN CMen CWGN MPkF NLar NPCo SBod
- - 'Waterfall' CJun CMCN
- - 'Watnong' CJun EUJe LRHS MPkF WPat
- - 'Zaaling' CAco CMen CTho NPCo
- 'Donzuru-bo' CJun
- 'Dormansland' SBig
- 'Dragon's Fire' CJun
- 'Earthfire' MJak MPkF WPat
I - 'Ebbingei' CMac
- 'Eddisbury' ♀H6 CEnd CJun CMen CSBt EPfP GBin MBlu MPkF NLar SSta WPGP WPat
- 'Edna Bergman' CJun
- 'Effegi' see *A. palmatum* 'Fireglow'
- 'Eimini' MPkF
§ - 'Elegans' ♀H6 CMen EPfP LRHS MPkF NLar NPCo
- 'Elizabeth' CJun
- 'Emma' **new** ETwe
- Emperor 1 see *A. palmatum* 'Wolff'
- 'Englishtown' MPkF NLar WPat
- 'Enkan' CEnd CJun CMen COtt CWGN EBee LRHS MBri MGos MPkF NLar NPri SBod SGol WPat
- 'Eono-momiji' CMen
- 'Ever Red' see *A. palmatum* var. *dissectum* 'Dissectum Nigrum'
- 'Fairy Hair' CJun
- 'Fall's Fire' CJun NLar
- 'Fascination' CJun
- 'Fior d'Arancio' CJun IVic MPkF NLar WPat
- 'Fireball' CJun
§ - 'Fireglow' CAco CBcs CDoC CEnd CJun CMCN CMen CSBt GBin LMil LPal LRHS MBri MGos MJak MPkF NEgg NLar NPCo SBod SCob SCoo SGol SPer WCFE WPat
- 'First Ghost' (v) CJun
- 'Frederici Guglielmi' see *A. palmatum* var. *dissectum* 'Dissectum Variegatum'
- 'Fujian Red' **new** LRHS SBod
- 'Garyū' MPkF
- 'Geisha' MPkF
- 'Geisha Gone Wild' (v) CJun MPkF
- 'Gentaku' CJun
- 'Germaine's Gyration' CJun
- 'Gibbsii' CMen
I - 'Globosum' IBoy MPkF
- 'Glowing Embers' CJun MPkF WPat
- 'Golden Pond' CJun
- 'Goshiki-kotohime' (v) CJun CMCN NLar SBod
- 'Goten-nomura' NLar
- 'Grace' CJun
- 'Grandma Ghost' CJun
- 'Green Flag' CJun
- 'Green Star' WPat
- 'Green Trompenburg' CJun CMen GBin MPkF NEgg NLar NPCo
- 'Groundcover' MPkF
§ - 'Hagoromo' CAco CMac CMen MPkF NPCo SCoo
- 'Hana-matoi'[PBR] (v) CMCN
- 'Hanami-nishiki' CMen MPkF WPat
- 'Haru-iro' CJun
- 'Harusame' (v) MPkF NLar WPat
- 'Hazeroino' (v) CMen MPkF
- 'Heartbeat' CJun LRHS MPkF WPat
- 'Heffner's Red' CJun MPkF
- 'Helena' see *A. shirasawanum* 'Helena'
- var. ***heptalobum*** CMCN
- 'Heptalobum Elegans Purpureum' see *A. palmatum* 'Hessei'
- 'Herbstfeuer' CJun MPkF
§ - 'Hessei' CEnd CMen MPkF NLar
- 'Higa-sayama' (v) CAco CBcs CEnd CJun CMCN CMen CWGN IVic MGos MPkF NLar SBod SGol WPat
- 'Hino-tori-nishiki' CMen NLar SGol
- 'Hiryu' WPat
- 'Hōgyoku' CJun CMCN CMen LRHS MPkF
- 'Hondoshi' NLar
- 'Hōno-o' MPkF
- 'Hoshi-kuzu' MPkF
- 'Hupp's Dwarf' CJun MPkF
- 'Hupp's Red Willow' NLar
- 'Ibo-nishiki' CMen MPkF NPCo
- 'Ichigyōji' CEnd CJun CMen IVic MAsh NLar NPCo SBig SChF WPGP WPat
- 'Ightham Gold' SSta
- 'Iijima-sunago' CMen MPkF
- 'Inazuma' CAco CBcs CDoC CJun CMCN CMen LMil LRHS MGos MPkF NLar SBod SCoo SGol SLau WPat
- 'Irish Lace' CJun
- 'Isobel' **new** SBod
- 'Iso-chidori' MPkF
- 'Issai-nishiki' CMen MPkF
* - 'Issai-nishiki-kawazu' MPkF
- 'Jane' CJun MPkF
- 'Japanese Sunrise' CJun
- 'Jerre Schwartz' CRos EBee EPfP LRHS MGos MPkF NLar SHil WPat
- 'Jirō-shidare' CJun EPfP MPkF NLar SBig
- 'JJ' CJun
- 'Julia D.' CJun
- 'Kaba' CMen IVic MPkF
- 'Kagero' (v) MPkF
§ - 'Kagiri-nishiki' (v) CAco CBcs CJun CMCN CMac CMen CWGN IVic MPkF NEgg NLar
- 'Kamagata' CAco CBcs CEnd CJun CMCN CMen GKin IVic LRHS MAsh MGos MPkF NLar NPCo SCoo WPat
- 'Kandy Kitchen' CJun CMen
- 'Karaori-nishiki' (v) CMen MPkF NLar SPer
- 'Karasu-gawa' (v) CJun CMen CWGN MPkF
- 'Kasagiyama' CEnd CJun CMen LRHS MPkF NLar SBod
- 'Kasen-nishiki' CMen MPkF
- 'Kashima' CAco CEnd CJun CMCN CMen LRHS MPkF NLar NPCo WPat
- 'Kashima-yatsubusa' MPkF
- 'Katja' CJun CMen MPkF
- 'Katsura' ♀H6 Widely available
- 'Katsura-nishiki' MPkF NPCo
- 'Kawahara Rose' MPkF
- 'Ki-hachijō' CJun CMCN CMen MPkF NLar WPat
- 'Killarney' CJun
- 'Kingsville Variegated' (v) MPkF
- 'Kinky Krinkle' CJun
- 'Kinran' CAco CMen LRHS MPkF NPCo
- 'Kinshii' ♀H6 CEnd CJun CMCN CMen EPfP GBin IVic LRHS MPkF NLar NPCo WPat
- 'Kiyohime' ♀H6 CAco CDoC CMCN CMen MPkF NPCo WPat

- 'Koba-shōjō' MPkF
- 'Kogane-nishiki' CMen NLar SGol
- 'Kogane-sakae' CJun MPkF
- 'Kokobunji-nishiki' (v) MPkF
- 'Komache-hime' CJun CMen MPkF WPat
- 'Komon-nishiki' (v) CJun CMen MPkF
- 'Koriba' CJun MPkF NLar
- 'Koshibori-nishiki' MPkF NPCo
§ - 'Koshimino' CJun
- 'Kotohime' CJun CMCN CMen CRos GKin IVic MGos MPkF NLar SBig SCoo SHil SPoG
- 'Koto-ito-komachi' CJun CMen LRHS MPkF NPCo
- 'Koto-maru' MPkF NLar SGol
- 'Koto-no-ito' CMCN EBee LMil LRHS MBlu MGos MPkF NLar SBod SGol WPat
- 'Koya-san' CMen MPkF NLar
- 'Kurabu-yama' CMen MPkF
- 'Kuro-hime' WPat
- 'Kurui-jishi' LRHS MPkF
- 'Kyōryū' MPkF
- 'Kyra' CMen MPkF
- 'Leather Leaf' MPkF
§ - 'Linearilobum' CAco CBcs CDoC CMen EPfP GBin IVic LMil LRHS MGos MPkF NLar SBod SCoo SLau
- 'Little Princess' see *A. palmatum* 'Chiyo-hime'
- 'Lozita' NLar WPat
- 'Lutescens' CMen MPkF NPCo
- 'Lydia' MPkF
- 'Maiko' CMen MPkF
- 'Mama' CMen
- 'Mapi-no-machi-hime' CEnd CJun CMCN CMen ELan LBMP LRHS MAsh MGos MPkF NHol WPat
- 'Marakumo' MPkF
- 'Marasaki-yama' MPkF
- 'Mardi Gras' CJun
- 'Margaret' MPkF WPat
- 'Margaret Bee' CJun NLar
- 'Marjan' CJun MPkF
- 'Marlo'PBR LRHS MAsh MGos MRav NLar NPri NSoo SHil
- 'Masamurasaki' CMen MPkF
- 'Masukagami' (v) CEnd CJun MPkF NLar
- 'Matsu-ga-e' (v) CMen MPkF
- 'Matsukaze' CJun CMCN CMen
- var. ***matsumurae*** B&SWJ 11100 WCru
- - B&SWJ 11195 **new** WCru
- 'Matsuyoi' CJun MPkF NLar
- 'Meihō-nishiki' CJun
- 'Melanie' CJun SBig
- 'Meoto' CJun
- 'Midori-no-teiboku' CJun MPkF
- 'Mikawa-yatsubusa' CAco CMCN CMac CMen EUJe IVic LRHS MGos MPkF NLar NPCo SBod SGol WPat
- 'Mikazuki' (v) CJun
- 'Mimaye' CJun
- 'Mini Mondo' MPkF
- 'Mirte' CJun CMen MPkF NLar SBig SBod SGol
- 'Mizuho-beni' CJun CMen NLar
- 'Mizu-kuguri' MPkF NLar
- 'Momoiro-koya-san' CJun MPkF NLar SBod SGol WPat
- 'Mon Papa' CJun CMen NLar
- 'Monzukushi' CJun MPkF
- 'Moonfire' CBcs CJun CMCN ELan EPfP LRHS MAsh MGos MPkF SGol WPat
* - 'Muncaster' SBig
- 'Murasaki-hime' MPkF
- 'Murasaki-kiyohime' CAco CEnd CJun CMCN CMen LRHS MPkF WPat
- 'Mure-hibari' CJun CMen MPkF
- 'Murogawa' CJun CMen
- 'Musashino' CJun SGol
- 'Nakata' NLar
- 'Nanase-gawa' MPkF
- 'Nicholsonii' CMen IVic MPkF NLar NPCo WPat
- 'Nigrum' CMCN CTri WPat
- 'Nishiki-gasane' (v) CMen MPkF
§ - 'Nishiki-gawa' CEnd CJun CMen LRHS MPkF NPCo
- 'Nishiki-momiji' CMen
- 'Nishiki-yamato' NLar
- 'Nomura' CJun CMen
- 'Nomurishidare' misapplied see *A. palmatum* var. *dissectum* 'Shōjō-shidare'
- 'Nomurishidare' Wada SSpi
- 'Nuresagi' CEnd CJun MPkF WPat
- 'Ōgi-nagashi' (v) MPkF NLar
- 'Ōgi-no-sen' MPkF
- 'Ōgon-sarasa' CJun MPkF
- 'Ojishi' CMen MPkF
- 'Ō-kagami' CAco CBcs CDoC CEnd CJun CMac CMen CSBt EPfP LRHS MAsh MGos MPkF NLar SBod SCoo WCFE WPat
- 'Okina' NLar
- 'Okukuji-nishiki' CJun
- 'Okushimo' CEnd CJun CMCN CMen IVic LRHS MPkF NLar NPCo SSta WPat
- 'Omato' CJun MAsh MPkF SBig
- 'Omure yama' CAco CDoC CEnd CJun CMCN CMen EPfP LMil LRHS MGos MPkF NLar NPCo SBod SCob SCoo SGol SPer SSta
- 'Orange Dream' ♀H6 Widely available
- 'Oranges and Lemons' CJun SGol
- 'Oregon Sunset' CJun MPkF NLar WPat
- 'Oridono-nishiki' (v) CBcs CDoC CEnd CJun CMCN CMac CMen CWGN ELan EPfP LRHS MAsh MBlu MGos MPkF NEgg NLar SBod SLim SPoG SSta
- 'Oriental Mystery' CJun
- 'Ōsakazuki' ♀H6 Widely available
- 'Ōshio-beni' CJun CMen NPCo
- 'Ōshū-shidare' CJun CMen IBoy MPkF
- 'Oto-hime' CJun CMen LRHS MPkF
- 'Otome-zakura' CJun CMen LRHS MPkF SBod
- 'Peaches and Cream' (v) CBcs CJun CMen MPkF NLar SBod SGol SPer SSta
- 'Peve Chameleon' MPkF
- 'Peve Dave' MPkF NLar
- 'Peve Multicolor' CJun MPkF NLar
- 'Peve Ollie'PBR GKin MPkF
- 'Peve Stanley' MPkF NLar
- 'Phoenix' CJun EBee EPla LRHS MAsh MBri MGos MPkF NLar NPri NSoo SBod SHil
- 'Pine Bark Maple' see *A. palmatum* 'Nishiki-gawa'
- 'Pink Passion' (v) **new** NLar
- 'Pixie' CJun CMen EUJe IVic LRHS MGos MPkF NLar SBod SCob WPat
- 'Princetown Gold' NLar
- 'Pung-kil' IVic MPkF

	– 'Purple Ghost'	CJun NLar
	– 'Red Baron'	CJun IBoy WPat
	– 'Red Blush'	CJun
	– 'Red Cloud'	CJun MPkF
	– 'Red Elf'	MPkF
	– 'Red Emperor'	ELan EUJe IBoy LMil LRHS MBri MPkF NLar SCob SPer WPat
	– 'Red Flame'	NLar
	– 'Red Flash'	CJun CMen MPkF
	– 'Red Jonas'	MPkF
	– 'Red Pygmy' 🏆H6	Widely available
	– 'Red Spider'	CJun
	– 'Red Wood'	CDoC CJun SGol SLau
	– 'Redwine'[PBR]	CRos EPfP GBin LRHS MPkF SHil
	– 'Renjaku-maru'	MPkF
	– 'Reticulatum'	see *A. palmatum* 'Shigi-tatsu-sawa'
	– 'Ribesifolium'	see *A. palmatum* 'Shishi-gashira'
	– 'Rising Sun'	CJun NLar
	– 'Rokugatsu-en-nishiki'	WPat
	– 'Roseomarginatum'	see *A. palmatum* 'Kagiri-nishiki'
	– 'Rough Bark Maple'	see *A. palmatum* 'Arakawa'
	– 'Rubrum'	CMen
I	– 'Rubrum Kaiser'	CJun
	– 'Ruby Ridge'	CJun
	– 'Ruby Star'	CJun MPkF
	– 'Rufescens'	MPkF WPat
	– 'Ryokū-ryū'	CMen MPkF
	– 'Ryusen'	CJun NLar
	– 'Ryuzu'	CJun MPkF
	– 'Sagara-nishiki' (v)	CAco CEnd CJun CMen LRHS MPkF NPCo
	– 'Sai-ho'	MPkF
	– 'Saint Jean'	MPkF
	– 'Samidare'	CJun MPkF NLar
	– 'Sandra'	CMen MPkF
	– 'Sango-kaku' 🏆H6	Widely available
	– 'Saoshika'	CJun CMen MPkF NLar
	– 'Sa-otome'	CMen MPkF
	– 'Satsuki-beni'	CJun CMen MPkF NPCo SBod
	– 'Sazanami'	CEnd CJun CMen MPkF NLar NPCo WPat
	– 'Scolopendriifolium'	see *A. palmatum* 'Linearilobum'
§	– 'Seigai'	CJun MPkF
	– 'Seigen'	CAco CEnd CJun CMCN CMen LRHS MPkF
	– 'Seiun-kaku'	CJun CMen MPkF NLar WPat
	– 'Sekimori'	CJun NLar SBig
	– 'Sekka-yatsubusa'	CMCN CMen MPkF NLar
	– 'Semi-no-hane'	CJun NLar
	– 'Senkaki'	see *A. palmatum* 'Sango-kaku'
	– 'Septemlobum Elegans'	see *A. palmatum* 'Elegans'
	– 'Septemlobum Purpureum'	see *A. palmatum* 'Hessei'
	– 'Sessilifolium' dwarf	see *A. palmatum* 'Hagoromo'
	– 'Sessilifolium' tall	see *A. palmatum* 'Koshimino'
	– 'Shaina'	CBcs CDoC CEnd CJun CMen COtt CRos CSBt CWGN EPfP IVic LRHS MBlu MBri MGos MPkF NLar NSoo SCoo SGol SHil SLim WMou
	– 'Sharon'	WPat
	– 'Sharp's Pygmy'	CJun CMen MPkF SBod SGol WPat
	– 'Sherwood Flame'	CDoC CJun CMen LRHS MAsh MBlu MGos MPkF NLar NPCo SCoo SGol
	– 'Shichigosan'	CMen
	– 'Shichihenge'	NLar
	– 'Shidava Gold'	CJun LRHS MPkF WPat
	– 'Shi-en'	MPkF
	– 'Shigarami'	CJun CMen MPkF
§	– 'Shigi-tatsu-sawa' (v)	CEnd CJun CMCN CMac CMen LRHS MGos MPkF NLar NPCo SBig
	– 'Shigure-bato'	CJun MPkF
	– 'Shigurezome'	MPkF NLar
	– 'Shikageori-nishiki'	CJun CMen MPkF
	– 'Shime-no-uchi'	CJun MPkF SBig
	– 'Shimofuri-nishiki'	MPkF
	– 'Shin-chishio'	CJun
	– 'Shindeshōjō' 🏆H6	Widely available
	– 'Shin-nyo' **new**	MBlu
§	– 'Shinobuga-oka'	CBcs CJun CMCN CMen EUJe MPkF SGol SLau
	– 'Shinonome'	CJun CMen MPkF NLar
	– 'Shirazz' (v)	CDoC CWGN IBoy LMil LRHS MBri MGos MPkF NLar SBod SCob SPer SPoG
§	– 'Shishi-gashira' 🏆H6	CAco CDoC CJun CMCN CMac CMen EBee EUJe GKin IArd IVic LRHS MBlu MBri MGos MPkF NLar NPCo SBod SCoo SGol SPoG WPat
	– 'Shishio'	CBcs CMCN CMen LMil LRHS MPkF SBig SBod SSpi WPat
	– 'Shishio-hime'	MPkF
	– 'Shishi-yatsubusa'	CJun MPkF
	– 'Shōjō'	CJun CMCN NLar
	– 'Shōjō-no-mai'	CJun
	– 'Shōjō-nomura'	CEnd CMen MPkF NLar WPat
	– 'Sister Ghost'	CJun
	– 'Skeeter's Broom'	CAco CJun CMen ELan EPfP EUJe GBin IArd IBoy LBuc LMil LRHS MBri MGos MPkF NLar NPCo SBig SBod SCoo WPat
*	– 'Sode-nishiki'	CJun MPkF NLar
	– 'Starfish'[PBR]	MPkF
	– 'Stella Rossa'	CEnd CJun LRHS MPkF NLar
	– 'Sumi-nagashi'	CAco CBcs CDoC CMen ETwe GBin LMil LRHS MGos MJak MPkF NLar NPCo SBod SCoo SGol SLau WPat
I	– 'Summer Gold'	CJun COtt MPkF NLar SWvt
	– 'Sunshine'	MPkF SBod
	– 'Susan'	MPkF
	– 'Taiyō-nishiki'	CJun MPkF
	– 'Takao'	CMen
	– 'Tama-hime'	CJun CMen LRHS MPkF NLar NPCo WPat
	– 'Tana'	CJun CMCN CMen EPfP MPkF NLar WPat
	– 'Tarō-yama'	CJun MPkF WPat
	– 'Tatsuta'	CMen MPkF
	– 'Taylor'[PBR] (v)	CEnd COtt CRos CWGN EPfP IVic LRHS MAsh MGos MPkF NLar NPri NSoo SCoo SHil SPoG
	– 'Tennyo-no-hoshi'	CMen MPkF NLar NPCo
	– 'Tiger Rose'	CJun
	– 'Tiny Tim'	CJun MPkF
	– 'Tobiosho'	CJun
	– 'Tōhoku Shichi-henge'	COtt
	– 'Trompenburg' 🏆H6	Widely available
	– 'Tsuchigumo'	CJun CMen MPkF NLar
	– 'Tsukasa Silhouette'	CJun
	– 'Tsukuma-no'	MPkF
	– 'Tsukushigata'	MPkF SGol WPat
	– 'Tsuma-gaki'	CDoC CJun CMCN CMen EPfP LRHS MBri MGos MPkF NLar NPCo WPat
	– 'Tsuri-nishiki'	CJun CMen MPkF
	– 'Twombly's Red Sentinel'	CJun MBlu MPkF
	– 'Ueno-homare'	CMen EUJe MPkF

- 'Ueno-yama'	CBcs CJun EUJe MPkF NLar SGol SPer WPat
- 'Uki-gumo' (v)	CBcs CEnd CJun CLnd CMCN CMac CMen ELan GKin LMil LRHS MGos NHol NLar SBig SBod SCoo SPer SPoG SSta
- 'Ukon'	CJun CMen LMil LRHS MJak MPkF NPCo SCoo
- 'Umegae'	CJun
- 'Uncle Ghost'	CJun
- 'Usu-midori'	CJun
- 'Utsu-semi'	CJun MPkF
- 'Van der Akker'	CJun
- 'Versicolor' (v)	CJun CMCN MPkF
- 'Vic Pink'	CJun
- 'Victoria'	SGol
- 'Villa Taranto' ♀H6	CDoC CEnd CJun CMCN CMen EPfP EUJe IVic LMil LRHS MBri MGos MPkF NLar NPCo SBod SCoo SGol WPGP WPat
- 'Volubile'	CMCN CMen MPkF NPCo WPat
- 'Wabito'	CJun CMen MPkF
- 'Waka-midori'	CMen
- 'Waka-momiji' (v)	CJun
- 'Wakehurst Pink' (v)	CMCN MPkF WPat
- 'Wendy'	CJun CMen IVic MPkF NLar SGol WPat
- 'Westonbirt Orange' **new**	MBri
- 'Westonbirt Red' **new**	MBri
- 'Wetumpka Red'	CJun
- 'Whitney Red'	CMen
- 'Wildgoose'	MPkF
- 'Will's Devine'	CJun
- 'Wilson's Pink Dwarf'	CEnd CJun CMen COtt GKin IVic LRHS MBri MGos MPkF NLar NPCo NSoo SBod SChF SCoo SPoG WPat
- 'Winter Flame'	CJun GBin LMil MPkF NHol WPat
§ - 'Wolff'	MPkF
- 'Wolff's Broom'	MPkF WPat
- 'Wou-nishiki'	CMCN CMen MPkF NPCo
- 'Yana-gawa'	CMen
- 'Yasemin'	CJun CMen CWGN IVic MPkF NLar NPCo SBig
- 'Yatsubusa'	MPkF
- 'Yezo-nishiki' (v)	CMen LRHS MBlu MPkF NLar
- 'Yūba-e'	MPkF NLar WPat
- 'Yūgure'	IVic MPkF
- 'Yuri-hime'	MPkF
papilio	see *A. caudatum*
pauciflorum 'Blaze Away'	CJun LRHS MAsh
pectinatum GWJ 9354	WCru
- subsp. ***pectinatum*** B&SWJ 8270	WCru
- - HWJ 569	WCru
- - HWJ 944	WCru
pensylvanicum	CAco CBcs CDul CMCN CTho ELan EPfP MGos MMuc MRav NEgg NWea SCob SEND SPer SSpi SSta WPat
- 'Erythrocladum'	CEnd CJun CMCN EPfP MAsh MBri MGos NHol NLar SLim WPGP
pentaphyllum	SBig
§ ***pictum***	CMCN
- subsp. ***okamotoanum***	CMCN
- - B&SWJ 12623	WCru
- subsp. ***pictum*** f. ***ambiguum*** B&SWJ 8806	WCru
- 'Shufu-nishiki'	CMCN
- 'Usugomo'	WPat
aff. ***pictum*** MCN0931	CMCN
- MCN0951	CMCN
platanoides	CAco CBcs CCVT CDoC CDul CLnd CMCN CSBt CTri ECrN ELan EPfP MGos MMuc MSwo NWea SEND SEWo SGol SPer WHar WMou
- 'Cleveland'	CBcs
- 'Columnare'	CLnd CMCN SCoo
- 'Crimson King' ♀H6	Widely available
- 'Crimson Sentry'	CCVT CDoC CDul CEnd CLnd CTri EBee ECrN ELan EPfP EPla IArd IVic LAst MAsh MGos MRav SGol SWvt WHar
- 'Deborah'	CAco CBcs CDul CLnd CTho EWTr SGol
- 'Dissectum'	CAco WPat
- 'Drummondii' (v)	Widely available
- 'Emerald Queen'	CDul ECrN
- 'Faassen's Black'	CDul CJun
§ - 'Globosum'	CLnd CMCN ECrN NLar SWvt
- 'Goldsworth Purple'	CLnd
- 'Laciniatum'	CMCN GBin WPat
- 'Marit'	WPat
- 'Olmsted'	CLnd
- Princeton Gold = 'Prigo'PBR ♀H6	CAco CBcs CDoC EBee ECrN ELan EMil EPla GQue LBuc LRHS MAsh MBri MGos NWea SCoo SEWo SGol SLim SPer SPoG WHar
- 'Reitenbachii'	CDul
- 'Royal Red'	CDul MRav NLar SCoo SEWo
- 'Schwedleri' ♀H6	CMCN SGol
- 'Stollii'	WPat
- subsp. ***turkestanicum***	CMCN SSta
pseudoplatanus	CAco CBcs CCVT CDul CLnd CMCN CSBt CTri ECrN ELan LBuc MGos NWea SGol SPer WHar WMou
§ - 'Atropurpureum'	CDul ECrN NWea SEWo WHar
- 'Brilliantissimum' ♀H6	Widely available
- 'Corstorphinense'	CDul
- f. ***erythrocarpum*** 'Erythrocarpum'	CMac
- 'Gadsby'	CDul EBee
- 'Negenia'	CDul
- 'Prinz Handjéry'	CBcs CDul CEnd CMCN CTri MGos NHol NLar NWea SGol SPer WHar
- 'Spaethii' misapplied	see *A. pseudoplatanus* 'Atropurpureum'
- f. ***variegatum*** 'Esk Sunset' (v)	CLnd EBee ELan EPla MGos MPkF NLar SMad SPoG WHar
- - 'Leopoldii' ambig. (v)	CBcs CCVT CDul CMCN ECrN ELan SPer SWvt
- - 'Simon-Louis Frères' (v)	CBcs CCVT CDul CLnd CMCN ECrN LAst MAsh MGos NLar SBod SCrf SGol SWvt WHar
- 'Worley'	CBcs CDul CLnd CMCN CMac COtt ECrN MRav NWea SGol SLim SPer
pseudosieboldianum	CMCN IArd MBlu MPkF
- B&SWJ 8468	WCru
- B&SWJ 8746	WCru
- B&SWJ 8769	WCru
- var. ***microsieboldianum*** B&SWJ 8766	WCru
- subsp. ***takesimense*** B&SWJ 8500	WCru
- - B&SWJ 8540	WCru

	Name	Suppliers
	pubipalmatum	LRHS
	pycnanthum	EPfP
	'Red Flamingo' (v)	CJun CRos CWSG EPla LRHS MBlu MBri MGos MPkF NLar SGol SMad SPoG
	reticulatum	see *A. laevigatum* var. *reticulatum*
	rubescens CWJ 12438	WCru
	rubrum	CAco CAgr CBcs CDul CLnd CMCN CSBt CTho CTri CUse EBee ECrN ELan EPfP EWTr MGos MMuc NEgg NWea SCoo SEWo SGol WCFE WHar WMoo WMou
	- Autumn Flame	see *A. rubrum* 'Pete's Red'
	- 'Autumn Flame'	CLnd
	- 'Autumn Spire'	CJun
	- 'Brandywine'	CAco CDul CJun COtt CTho EBee EPfP LRHS MAsh MBlu MBri NLar NWea SBir SCoo SPoG WHar
	- 'Candy Ice' (v)	CJun
	- 'Embers'	CJun NLar
	- Fairview Flame	see *A. rubrum* 'Pete's Fairview'
	- Fireball = 'Firzam'	CJun
	- 'Firedance'	CJun
	- 'Joseph'	NLar
	- 'New World'	SCoo
	- 'Northwind'	CJun
	- 'Northwood'	CJun
	- 'October Glory' ♀H6	Widely available
§	- 'Pete's Fairview'	CLnd MMuc SEND SPer
§	- 'Pete's Red'	MPkF
	- 'Red King'	CJun
	- Red Sunset = 'Franksred' ♀H6	CAco CCVT CEnd CJun CLnd CMCN CTho EBee ELan EPfP NLar SBir SCoo SGol SLim SPer
	- 'Scanlon'	CAco CBcs CDul CEnd CJun CMCN CTho ELan EPfP LAst SLim SPer
	- 'Schlesingeri'	CEnd CJun CLnd CMac EPfP
I	- 'Sekka' **new**	MBlu
	- 'Somerset'	CAco CDul CJun CTho CTri EBee SCoo WHar
	- Summer Red = 'Hosr'	CLnd EBee LRHS SCoo
	- 'Sun Valley'	CJun EBee MAsh NWea SCoo WHar
	- 'Tilford'	CJun SCoo SSta
§	***rufinerve***	CAco CBcs CCVT CDoC CDul CLnd CMCN CTho CTri EBee ELan EPfP EPla MBri MMuc NEgg NLar NWea SCoo SGol SPer SSta SWvt WHar
	- B&SWJ 10845	GKin WCru
	- B&SWJ 10924	WCru
	- B&SWJ 10959	WCru
	- B&SWJ 11571	WCru
	- 'Albolimbatum' (v)	CEnd CJun CMCN EBee MBri SBig SSta
	- 'Erythrocladum'	CJun MBlu SKHP
	- 'Ko-fuji-nishiki'	SSta
I	- 'Sunshine' **new**	SSta
	- 'Winter Gold'	CJun EPfP NLar SSta
	- 'Yellow Ribbon' **new**	WHor
§	***saccharinum***	CAco CBcs CCVT CDul CLnd CMCN COtt CTri ECrN ELan EPfP MGos MMuc MSnd NLar NWea SCoo SGol SPer WHar
	- 'Born's Gracious'	CJun
	- 'Fastigiatum'	see *A. saccharinum* 'Pyramidale'
	- f. ***laciniatum***	EBee MBlu MMuc SGol SPer
	- - 'Laciniatum Wieri'	CDul CMCN NLar SGol
	- 'Lutescens'	CDul
§	- 'Pyramidale'	CLnd ECrN NWea SPer
	saccharum	CAco CAgr CBcs CDul CMCN CTho ECrN EPfP MBlu NEgg
	- 'Brocade'	CJun
	- 'Fiddlers Creek'	CJun
§	- subsp. ***grandidentatum***	EPfP
§	***sempervirens***	EPfP LEdu MPkF SChF
	'Sensu'	CJun
	'Serendipity' **new**	SSta
	serrulatum CWJ 12437	WCru
	shirasawanum	CMCN
§	- 'Aureum' ♀H6	Widely available
	- 'Autumn Moon'	CAco CBcs CJun CMCN CMen CWGN EPfP LRHS MBri MPkF NLar NPCo NPri SCob SCoo SGol SLim SPer SPoG WPat
§	- 'Ezo-no-momiji'	CJun CMen MPkF NPCo
	- 'Gloria'	MPkF SGol
§	- 'Helena'	MPkF WPat
	- 'Jordan'PBR	CDul CEnd COtt CRos CWGN LRHS MBri MGos MPkF SHil SPoG
	- 'Lovett'	CJun
§	- 'Microphyllum'	MPkF
	- 'Mr Sun'	CJun
§	- 'Ogurayama'	CAco CJun CMen NPCo
	- 'Palmatifolium'	CJun LRHS
	- 'Red Dawn'	CJun
	- 'Susanne'	CJun CMen MPkF SGol
	- var. ***tenuifolium*** B&SWJ 11073	WCru
	sieboldianum ♀H6	CAco CDul CMen CTho CTri ECrN MAsh MBlu MMuc SGol WHCr WHar WMou WPGP WPat
	- B&SWJ 10849	WCru
	- B&SWJ 11049	WCru
	- B&SWJ 11090	WCru
	- 'Sode-no-uchi'	CJun CMen MPkF NPCo
	- var. ***tsushimense*** B&SWJ 10962	WCru
	sikkimense B&SWJ 11689	WCru
	- B&SWJ 11703	WCru
	- DJHV 06152	WCru
	- WWJ 11601	WCru
	- WWJ 11613	WCru
	- WWJ 11853	WCru
	'Silver Cardinal' (v)	CBcs CEnd CJun CMCN EPfP MBlu MGos MPkF NLar SSta WHar
	'Silver Vein'	see *A.* × *conspicuum* 'Silver Vein'
	sinense	CMCN
	spicatum	EPfP NLar
§	***stachyophyllum***	GQui
	- BWJ 8101	WCru
§	***sterculiaceum***	EPla
	- subsp. ***franchetii***	NLar
	tataricum	CMCN ECrN
§	- subsp. ***ginnala***	CAco CBcs CDul CLnd CMCN CNWT CTri MBlu MGos NLar NWea SGol
	- - 'Flame'	CDul CJun EBee ECrN ELan EPfP EPla MGos MMuc MSnd NLar NWea
	- - 'Red Wing'	CJun
	tegmentosum ♀H5	CDul CJun CMCN EBee EPfP MBlu NLar SSta WHor
	- subsp. ***glaucorufinerve***	see *A. rufinerve*
	tetramerum	see *A. stachyophyllum*
	tonkinense subsp. ***liquidambarifolium*** DJHV 06173	WCru

	trautvetteri	CMCN
	triflorum ♀H6	CBcs CCVT CDul CJun CMCN EPfP MBlu MBri NLar SSpi
	truncatum	MPkF
	- B&SWJ 8914	WCru
	- 'Akikaze-nishiki' (v)	CJun MPkF
	tschonoskii	MPkF
	subsp. ***koreanum***	
	'Valley Phantom' **new**	SSta
	velutinum	CMCN
	villosum	see *A. sterculiaceum*
	'Viper'	CDul GQue MBri
	'White Tigress'	CAco CBcs CDoC CJun CTho EPfP GQue LRHS MBri SPoG SSta WHar WPGP WPat
	× ***zoeschense***	CMCN MPkF
	- 'Annae'	SGol

Aceriphyllum see *Mukdenia*

× *Achicodonia* (*Gesneriaceae*)

	'Dark Velvet'	WDib

Achillea (*Asteraceae*)

	ageratifolia ♀H5	CMea ECha ECho ECtt EDAr GJos NGdn SRms XLum
§	***ageratum***	CArn CBod CPrp CUse ECho ELau ENfk GPoy LEdu MHer MNHC SIde SRms WFar WGwG WHer WJek XLum
	'Alabaster'	LRHS NDov SPhx
	Anthea = 'Anblo'[PBR]	CKno CPrp CWCL EBee ECtt IBoy LBMP LRHS MAsh MCot MRav MSpe NLar NPri SHar SRGP SRms SWvt WCAu
§	'Apfelblüte' (Galaxy Series)	CAby CWCL EBee ECha ECtt ELan EPfP EWTr GKin LRHS MBel MMuc MRav MSpe NDov NGdn NHol NSbr NSti SCob SEND SPer SRms WGwG WMnd WPtf WWEG
	Appleblossom	see *A.* 'Apfelblüte'
	'Apricot Beauty'	ECtt GQue
	'Apricot Delight' (Tutti Frutti Series)	MNrw NCGa
	argentea misapplied	see *A. clavennae*, *A. umbellata*
	argentea Lamarck	see *Tanacetum argenteum*
I	***argentifolia*** hort.	WKif
	aurea	see *A. chrysocoma*
	'Bahama'	GBin GQue NBro
	'Belle Epoque'	WBrk WWEG
	biebersteinii	XLum
	'Breckland Bouquet'	EWes
	'Breckland Cream' **new**	EBee
	'Breckland Ruby'	EWes
	'Carmina Burana'	CMea
	cartilaginea	see *A. salicifolia*
	'Christine's Pink'	MSpe MTis
§	***chrysocoma***	ECho MWat WMoo
	- 'Grandiflora'	ECha LPla MMuc NGdn WBrk WWEG
§	***clavennae***	GKev MWat SBch SRms WAbe WIce XSen
	clypeolata Sibth. & Sm.	EBee EPPr LRHS NLar SPlb SRms XLum
	coarctata	NBir XSen
	Colorado Group	CBod CNec LRHS
	'Coronation Gold' ♀H7	CDoC CPrp CWCL EBee ECtt ELan EPfP GBuc IBoy LAst LRHS MNFA MRav MWat NChi NDov SCob SPer SWvt WCAu WCot WWEG XLum
	'Credo' ♀H7	CAby CPrp ECha ECtt EPPr EPfP EWTr EWoo GBin IBoy LPla LRHS MBel MNFA MRav MSpe NGdn NHol NLar NSti SMad SMrm SPer SWat WBrk WCAu WMnd WWEG
	crithmifolia	XLum
	decolorans	see *A. ageratum*
	Desert Eve Series **new**	NPri
	- 'Desert Eve Deep Rose' **new**	EBee
	- 'Desert Eve Light Yellow' **new**	LRHS
	- Desert Eve Red = 'Desred' **new**	LRHS
	- Desert Eve Yellow = 'Desyel' **new**	EBee
	'Emily May' **new**	WCot
	erba-rotta subsp. ***moschata***	NBro
§	'Fanal'	Widely available
	'Faust'	ELon MNrw SMrm
	'Federsee'	MArl
	'Feuerland'	CMac CSam EBee ECha ECtt ELon EPPr EPfP GBin GKin GQue LRHS MRav MSpe NBir NDov NGdn NSti SMrm SPer SPoG WFar WWEG
	filipendulina	WHrl
	- 'Cloth of Gold' ♀H7	Widely available
	- 'Gold Plate' ♀H7	Widely available
	- 'Parker's Variety' ♀H7	EBee GQue NBre WFar WMoo XLum
	'Fleur van Zonneveld'	MSpe NDov
	Flowers of Sulphur	see *A.* 'Schwefelblüte'
	(Forncett Series) 'Forncett Beauty'	SWvt
	- 'Forncett Candy'	WWEG
	- 'Forncett Citrus'	EPPr MAvo
	- 'Forncett Fletton'	CAby CCon CWCL ECtt ELon EPPr EPfP GBin GKin MAsh MBel MNFA MNrw MRav MSpe NGdn NHol WCAu WWEG
	- 'Forncett Ivory'	EBee EPPr
	fraasii	XSen
	'Gloria Jean'	SHar SPhx
	'Gold and Grey'	SMrm WWEG
	grandifolia misapplied	see *Tanacetum macrophyllum* (Waldst. & Kit.) Sch.Bip.
§	***grandifolia*** Friv.	CSam LPla MHin MRav NBro SPhx WBor WFar WHer WMnd WMoo WOld WOut
	'Great Expectations'	see *A.* 'Hoffnung'
	'Heidi' ♀H7	MRav WWEG
	'Heinrich Vogeler'	EBee
	'Hella Glashoff' ♀H7	CWCL EBee ELon GBin LRHS NDov
§	'Hoffnung'	CWCL MSpe WWEG
	× ***huteri***	ECho ECtt EDAr GCrg MMuc MRav NGdn SBch SEND SIgm SRms
	'Inca Gold'	CWCL ECGP ECha ECtt EPPr EPla EShb GBuc GQue LRHS MCot MRav MSpe NCGa NHol NSti WCFE WFar WGwG WHoo WWEG
	'Jacqueline'	EWll MTis
	× ***kellereri***	XSen
	'King Alfred'	CMea
	× ***kolbiana***	MWat SRms
§	'Lachsschönheit' (Galaxy Series) ♀H7	CAby CKno CSpe CWCL EBee ECha ECtt ELan EPfP GMaP IBoy

	LAst LRHS MBNS MCot MRav NBir NDov NHol NLar NOrc NSti SCob SPer WBrk WHoo WMnd WWEG
× ***lewisii*** 'King Edward' ♀H5	ECho EDAr EPfP GMaP NBir SRms WAbe WFar WIce
ligustica	WCot
'Lucky Break' ♀H7	SDix WCot
macrophylla	MBNS NBre
'Marie Ann'	CWCL ECtt GQue NLar SPhx SRGP
'Marmalade'	MRav SMrm WWEG
'Martina' ♀H7	CAby CDoC ECtt EPPr EWoo GBin GBuc GKin GQue LAst LBMP LRHS MAsh MBNS MBel MCot MRav NDov NGdn NHol NOrc SRGP WCAu WCot WHea WWEG
'McVities'	CWCL ECtt EPPr MSpe MTis WMnd WWEG
millefolium	CArn CHab CWld ELau ENfk GPoy MNHC NMir SRms WHer WJek WOut WSFF XLum
- 'Bloodstone'	ECtt EWes MRav
- 'Carla Hussey'	WFar
- 'Cassis'	CSpe GQue LRHS MCot NGBl NLar SPtp WBor WBrk WMoo WOut
§ - 'Cerise Queen'	Widely available
- 'Chamois'	MNrw
- 'Cherry King'	NBir
- 'Christel'	EWes GBin
- 'Circus'	XLum
- 'Dark Lilac Beauty'	CWCL
- 'Kelwayi'	WPtf
- Kirschkönigin	see *A. millefolium* 'Cerise Queen'
- 'Lansdorferglut' ♀H7	EBee EPPr LPla LRHS MTis NDov SPhx WWEG
- 'Laura'	CSam CWGN EBee LSou MAsh MBri MNrw NCGa WBrk
- 'Lavender Beauty'	see *A. millefolium* 'Lilac Beauty'
§ - 'Lilac Beauty'	ECha ELon EPPr EPfP GBin GBuc GMaP IBoy IPot LRHS MBri MGos MHol MMuc MRav NBir NDov NEgg NLar SCob SHil SRms WCAu WFar WWEG XLum
* - 'Lilac Queen'	MArl
- 'Little Suzie'	CWGN MAsh MBri
- 'Old Brocade'	EShb WWEG
- Pastel Shades	IFoB WFar
- 'Peggy Sue'	CWGN ECtt WFar
- 'Pomegranate' (Tutti Frutti Series)	CMos CWCL CWGN MNrw MTis NCGa NLar SHar XLum
- 'Pretty Woman'	CSam CWGN MBri
- 'Raspberry Ripple'	GBin
- 'Red Beauty'	CWCL ELan EPfP GBin MBNS MSpe SRms WWEG XLum
- 'Red Salmon'	EWes
- 'Red Velvet'	Widely available
- 'Rose Madder'	Widely available
- 'Salmon Pink'	IBoy
- 'Salmon Queen'	NHol WFar
- 'Sammetriese'	ELon MNrw SMad SPhx WWEG
- 'Schneetaler'	GBin
- 'Serenade'	EBee ECtt MAsh MSpe
- 'Sue's Pink'	CSam
- (Summer Fruits Series) 'Summer Fruits Carmine' **new**	MPro
- - 'Summer Fruits Lemon' **new**	MPro
- - 'Summer Fruits Salmon' **new**	MPro
- 'Summertime'	WFar
- 'White Queen'	EBee
- 'Wonderful Wampee'	EBee MNrw NLar WCot
'Mondpagode' ♀H7	ECGP EPPr EWTr LPla LRHS MAvo MBNS MCot MNFA MRav NCGa NGdn NHol SMHy SPhx WGwG WHoo WKif WWEG
* 'Moonbeam'	GKin SEND
'Moonshine' ♀H7	Widely available
'Moonwalker'	CAbP EPfP SPav WCot XLum
nana	WFar
nobilis subsp. ***neilreichii***	CSpe ECGP EHoe EPla EWTr GQue IBoy IKil LAst MMuc MNrw NSti SPer SWvt WCot WGwG WPtf WWEG
'Paprika' (Galaxy Series)	Widely available
'Peardrop'	NBre
'Petra'	MNrw MTis XLum
pindicola subsp. ***integrifolia***	EWes
pink-flowered from Santa Cruz Island	CKno CWCL
'Pink Grapefruit' (Tutti Frutti Series)	MNrw MTis NCGa NLar WCAu
'Pretty Belinda'	CUse EBee ECtt EPfP IPot LAst LPla LRHS LSou MBel MBri MCot MSpe NLar NPri NSti SKHP SPoG SRms WCAu WFar WWEG
'Prospero'	WCot WWEG
ptarmica	CArn CBod CBre ELau MHer NMir SRms WWtn XLum
* - 'Ballerina'	MBNS MWhi NBre NDov NGdn NLar
- Innocence	see *A. ptarmica* 'Unschuld'
- 'Major'	WCot
- 'Nana Compacta'	CSpe ECha EPPr GBin IBoy LRHS NBir SPlb WCFE WFar WWEG
- 'Noblessa' **new**	GCal
- 'Perry's White' (d)	CBcs CBre ECha MNrw SRGP WCot
- 'Stephanie Cohen'	see *A. sibirica* 'Stephanie Cohen'
- The Pearl Group seed-raised (d)	CTri ELan MMuc SGbt SPlb SWat WFar WMoo
- - 'Boule de Neige' (clonal) (d)	GKin IBoy MRav MSpe NPer NSti SPer XLum
- - 'The Pearl' (clonal) (d)	CBod CMac CSBt CWCL EBee ECha EPfP GJos IBoy IFoB LPot LRHS LSun MBel MHol MLHP MRav MWat NBid NBir NBro NLar SRms WBor WCot WFar WHer WJek
§ - 'Unschuld'	NBir
pyrenaica	XLum
'Ruby Wine'	WFar
'Safran'	LRHS XLum
§ ***salicifolia***	WFar
- 'Silver Spray'	GQue NLar SPav WOut
'Sally'	EPPr MSpe
Salmon Beauty	see *A.* 'Lachsschönheit'
'Sandra Wagg' **new**	ECtt
'Sandstone'	see *A.* 'Wesersandstein'
'Saucy Seduction' (Tutti Frutti Series)	CWCL ELon NLar
§ 'Schwefelblüte'	MRav NBir SMrm
'Schwellenburg'	EBee NBre WCot
sibirica	CHid EBee LEdu LRHS MMuc
subsp. ***camschatica*** 'Love Parade'	MNrw NLar SGbt SPer SPtp WWEG XLum

§ – 'Stephanie Cohen' CPrp GBee GBin WFar WWEG
'Stephanie' ECtt EPPr EWes MSpe
Summer Berries Group CBod LRHS
Summer Pastels Group EPfP IBoy LRHS MGos NLar NOrc SPoG SRms WFar WWtn XLum
– 'Peachy Seduction'PBR **new** MTis
– 'Strawberry Seduction' **new** MTis
'Summerwine' ♀H7 Widely available
'Sunbeam' SHar
'Sunny Seduction' ELon MTis
I 'Taygetea' ECtt ELan EPPr EPfP LPal MBNS SCob SDix SPer SRkn WCAu WCot WSHC WWEG XLum
'Terracotta' Widely available
'The Beacon' see *A.* 'Fanal'
'Tissington Flame' MAvo MTis
'Tissington Old Rose' MNrw MTis
tomentosa ♀H5 CTri ECha ECho ECtt
§ – 'Aurea' ECho NBro
– 'Goldie' EDAr LRHS
– 'Maynard's Gold' see *A. tomentosa* 'Aurea'
'Tri-colour' NGdn
§ ***umbellata*** WAbe XSen
'W.B. Childs' ELan MCot MNrw MRav NDov SHar
'Walther Funcke' Widely available
§ 'Wesersandstein' CWCL ECtt EPPr GBin GMaP LRHS MNrw NBir SCob SGbt WWEG
'Wilczekii' SRms
'Yellowstone' EWes

× *Achimenantha* (*Gesneriaceae*)

'Aries' EABi WDib
'Cool Inferno' **new** WDib
'Himalayan Sunrise' LAma WDib
'Inferno' ♀H1c EABi WDib
'Pisces' WDib
'Texas Blue Bayou' WDib
'Texas Spotted Leopard' EABi
'Tyche' EABi

Achimenes (*Gesneriaceae*)

'Addano' WDib
'Ambroise Verschaffelt' ♀H1c EABi LAma WDib
'Ami Van Houtte' WDib
'Apricot Glow' EABi WDib
'Aquamarine' WDib
'Ballerina' WDib
'Blue David' EABi
'Blue Sparkles' EABi SDeJ
'Boy David' EABi
'Caligula' EABi WDib
'Cameo Rose' WDib
'Camille Brozzoni' EABi
'Cascade Fairy Pink' WDib
'Cascade Fashionable Pink' WDib
'Cascade Rose Red' WDib
'Cascade Violet Night' WDib
'Cattleya' LAma
cettoana **new** WDib
'Charity' WDib
'Charm' LAma SDeJ WDib
'Cherry Blossom' EABi
'Claret' EABi WDib
'Clouded Yellow' EABi
'Coral Cameo Mix' EABi
'Côte d'Ivoire' EABi
'Crackerjack' WDib
'Crummock Water' EABi WDib
'Derwentwater' EABi
'Donna' EABi
'Dot' EABi
'Double Picotee Rose' (d) **new** WDib
'Double Pink Rose' (d) WDib
'English Waltz' EABi
erecta EABi WDib
'Erlkönig' WDib
'Escheriana' LAma
'Extravaganza' WDib
'Flamenco' WDib
'Flaming Embers' EABi
'Glory' EABi WDib
grandiflora 'Robert Dressler' EABi
'Grape Wine' EABi
'Hard to Get' EABi
'Harry Williams' EABi LAma WDib
'Hilda Michelssen' ♀H1c EABi WDib
'Himalayan Angel' EABi LAma
'Himalayan Double' **new** LAma
'Himalayan Mandarin' **new** EABi LAma
'Himalayan Sunset' **new** EABi
'Jay Dee Coral' WDib
'Jay Dee Large White' WDib
'Jay Dee Pink' WDib
'Jay Dee Purple' WDib
'Jennifer Goode' EABi WDib
'Johanna Michelssen' WDib
'Jubilee Gem' EABi
'Just Divine' EABi WDib
'Kim Blue' WDib
'Lady in Black' **new** WDib
'Light Lilac' WDib
'Little Beauty' WDib
longiflora 'Major' WDib
'Maxima' LAma
'Menuett' WDib
mexicana LAma SDeJ
misera WDib
'Opal' WDib
'Orange Delight' EABi WDib
'Orange Queen' EABi
'Palette Salmon' (Palette Series) EABi
'Pally' WDib
'Patens Major' EABi WDib
'Peach Blossom' LAma SDeJ WDib
'Peach Glow' EABi WDib
'Pearly Queen' EABi
pedunculata WDib
'Petite Fadette' EABi
'Pink Beauty' EABi
'Pink Rose' (d) EABi
'Platinum' EABi
'Primadonna' SDeJ WDib
'Pulcherrima' SDeJ
'Purple King' WDib
'Purple Queen' WDib
'Purple Triumph' WDib
'Queen of Queens' WDib
'Rainbow' EABi WDib
'Rainbow Warrior' **new** WDib
'Red Elfe' EABi

'Red Giant'	EABi
'Red Hilda Michelssen'	WDib
'Rhino'	EABi
'Rosa Charm'	EABi
'Rose Dream'	EABi
'Santa Claus' **new**	WDib
'Schneewittchen' **new**	WDib
'Serge Saliba'	EABi WDib
'Show-off'	WDib
skinneri **new**	WDib
'Snow Princess'	SDeJ
'Stan's Delight' (d) ♀H1c	EABi WDib
'Sterntaler'	WDib
'Summer Sunset'	EABi
'Sweet & Sour'	EABi WDib
'Tango'	WDib
'Tarantella'	EABi WDib
'Teresa'	EABi
(Tetra Series) 'Tetra Himalayan Purple'	LAma WDib
- 'Tetra Verschaffelt'	EABi
- 'Tetra Wine Red Charm'	EABi
'Tiger Eye'	WDib
'Valse Bleu' **new**	WDib
'Vie-en-Rose'	EABi
'Violacea Semiplena' (d)	WDib
'Vivid'	EABi LAma WDib
'Weinrot Elfe'	WDib
'Wetterlow's Triumph'	EABi WDib
'Yellow Beauty'	WDib

Achlys (*Berberidaceae*)

japonica	WCru
triphylla	IMou WCru

Achnatherum see *Stipa*

Achyranthes (*Amaranthaceae*)

bidentata	CArn
- var. ***longifolia*** PAB 8037 **new**	LEdu

Acidanthera see *Gladiolus*

Acinos (*Lamiaceae*)

§ ***alpinus***	EBee EDAr EWTr GJos LLHF SBch SPhx WAbe WJek XLum
§ ***corsicus***	WHoo WKif

Aciphylla (*Apiaceae*)

aurea	GBin GCal GKev SPlb
colensoi	CMen
congesta	CMen EPot
crosby-smithii	EPot GLin
dieffenbachii	EUJe
glaucescens	EUJe GKev SPlb
hectorii	CMen
kirkii	CMen
'Lomond'	EBee
montana	CMen EPot GLin
pinnatifida	CMen
simplex	CMen
spedenii	CMen

Acis (*Amaryllidaceae*)

§ ***autumnalis*** ♀H5	CAby CAvo CBro CDes CElw CTal CTca CTri ECha ECho EPot EWes GKev LEdu LRHS NBir SBch SRms SRot WAbe WHea WHil WHoo WOld WPGP WSHC
- var. ***oporantha***	EPri
- var. ***oporantha*** from Morocco	ECho
- var. ***pulchella***	ECho NRog
- 'September Snow'	ELan GKev NRog
ionica **new**	NMin
nicaeensis	CDes CTal ECho GCal GKev LLHF LRHS NWad WAbe WCot WThu
§ ***rosea***	CTal ECho NRog WAbe
§ ***tingitana***	CBro ECho
§ ***trichophylla***	ECho
- f. ***purpurascens***	CDes ECho MPie WCot
§ ***valentina***	ECho NRog SRot WCot

Acmella (*Asteraceae*)

§ ***oleracea***	CArn CUse

Acmena (*Myrtaceae*)

smithii	ECou

Acnistus (*Solanaceae*)

australis	see *Iochroma australe*

Aconitum (*Ranunculaceae*)

CNDS 036 from Burma	WCru
alboviolaceum	EPla
var. ***alboviolaceum*** f. ***albiflorum***	
- - - B&SWJ 4105	WCru
- - - B&SWJ 8444	WCru
- var. ***purpurascens*** B&SWJ 8477	WCru
altissimum	see *A. lycoctonum* subsp. *vulparia*
anglicum	see *A. napellus* subsp. *napellus* Anglicum Group
* ***angulosum*** **new**	EWld
§ ***anthora***	CArn EPfP IKil MHol NLar
arcuatum	see *A. fischeri* var. *arcuatum*
austroyunnanense	CMea EWld WHal WSHC
- BWJ 7902	WCru
autumnale misapplied	see *A. carmichaelii* Wilsonii Group
autumnale Rchb.	see *A. fischeri* Rchb.
× ***bicolor***	see *A.* × *cammarum* 'Bicolor'
'Blue Lagoon'PBR	CWGN EBee IPot
'Blue Opal'	CDes EBee ECtt EWes
'Blue Sceptre'	GBin NLar
'Bressingham Spire' ♀H7	ECtt ELan ELon EPfP GBuc GCra GKin GMaP IBoy IKil LAst LPla LRHS MAvo MCot NCGa NDov NGdn NLar NOrc NPer NPri SPer SRms WCAu WFar WMnd
bulbilliferum HWJK 2120	WCru WSHC
§ × ***cammarum*** 'Bicolor' ♀H7	Widely available
- 'Eleanora'	CCon ECtt EPPr EPfP EWes GBuc GCra GMaP LRHS LSou NLar SPer SRms WCot
- 'Grandiflorum Album'	CAby LPla MNrw NDov
- 'Pink Sensation'PBR	CAby GQue LLHF NDov NLar
§ ***carmichaelii***	CArn CHel CMea CSam ELan EPfP GBin GBuc GCra GKin IFoB IFro LAst LRHS LSou MMuc MNrw NBro NEgg NGdn NOrc NPCo NSoo SGol SMrm SRms WCot WFar WHoo
- Arendsii Group	ECtt GKev LAst SPhx SRot WCAu
- - 'Arendsii' ♀H7	Widely available

- - 'Cloudy'[PBR] NLar
- 'Moody Blues' EBee
- 'Redleaf'[PBR] see *A. carmichaelii* 'Royal Flush'
- 'River Avon' WCot
- 'River Dee' WCot
- 'River Devon' WCot
- 'River Finn' WCot
- 'River Lugg' WCot
- 'River Medway' WCot
- 'River Nene' WCot
- 'River Ouse' WCot
- 'River Spey' WCot
- 'River Tees' WCot
- 'River Teifi' WCot
- 'River Trent' WCot
- 'River Welland' WCot

§ - 'Royal Flush'[PBR] CAby CMea CWGN EBee ECtt EPfP GBin IBoy LBMP MBNS MNrw NLar NPCo SPer WCot
- var. ***truppelianum*** WCot
- - HWJ 732 EBee WCot WCru

§ - Wilsonii Group EBee ECGP EWoo GMaP LPla LRHS MCot MRav MWat MWhi NCGa NDov NEgg WHoo XLum
- - 'Barker's Variety' CKno ELon GBuc GCal GQue LRHS NGdn NLar NSti SRms WCot
- - 'Kelmscott' ♀H7 ECtt EWes MCot MRav SDix SMHy WFar
- - 'Spätlese' CAbP CSam CWGN EBee ECtt ELon GCal LBMP LEdu LRHS LSou LSun MCot MHol NBir NDov NGdn NLar SGbt SMHy SMrm WCot

§ ***chasmanthum*** LRHS
- GWJ 9393 new WCru

chiisanense B&SWJ 4446 WCru
cilicicum see *Eranthis hyemalis* Cilicica Group
'Cloudy' EBee ECtt LEdu NGdn SPer WCot
compactum see *A. napellus* subsp. *vulgare*
confertiflorum see *A. anthora*
delphiniifolium CExl
elliotii EBee
elwesii EBee
episcopale CTal WCot WCru
aff. ***episcopale*** CLD 1426 GBuc WFar
excelsum see *A. lycoctonum* subsp. *lycoctonum*
ferox EBee ELon EWes LLHF
- HWJK 2217 WCru
- GWJ 9333 from Sikkim new WCru

fischeri misapplied see *A. carmichaelii*

§ ***fischeri*** Rchb. CBod EBee MSCN NCGa NLar WCot
- B&SWJ 8809 WCru

§ - var. ***arcuatum*** B&SWJ 774 WCru

formosanum B&SWJ 3057 WCru
fukutomei B&SWJ 337 MRav WCru
gammiei GWJ 9418 WCru
gmelinii see *A. lycoctonum* subsp. *lycoctonum*
grossedentatum LPla NLar

§ ***hemsleyanum*** CAby CExl CHVG CMea CRHN CTal CWGN ECtt EWTr EWld GCra NBid SGSe WCru
- dark blue-flowered MLHP
- 'Red Wine' EWld WCot

hyemale see *Eranthis hyemalis*
'Ivorine' CSam CTri EBee ECha ELan ELon EPfP EPla GBuc GCra GMaP IBoy LAst LEdu LRHS MAsh MCot MHol MNrw NGdn NLar NPri SBod SCob SPer WFar WPnP
jaluense B&SWJ 8741 WCru
japonicum EBee GCal NLar WCot
- var. ***hakonense*** CExl
- var. ***montanum*** B&SWJ 5507 WCru

§ - subsp. ***napiforme*** EWes WCot
- - B&SWJ 943 EBee ELon WCru

§ - subsp. ***subcuneatum*** B&SWJ 6228 WCru

krylovii WCot
kusnezoffii WCot
laciniatum GWJ 9254 WCru
- GWJ 9324 WCru

lamarckii see *A. lycoctonum* subsp. *neapolitanum*
lasianthum see *A. lycoctonum* subsp. *vulparia*
leucostomum new GCal
loczyanum B&SWJ 11529 WCru WSHC
longecassidatum B&SWJ 4277 WCru
- B&SWJ 8486 WCru

lycoctonum CTal NLar NOrc
- 'Darkeyes' CAbP WCot WFar

§ - subsp. ***lycoctonum*** CCon SRms WCot

§ - subsp. ***moldavicum*** WCot

§ - subsp. ***neapolitanum*** EBee ECtt GCal GMaP IMou MMuc NLar
- 'Russian Yellow' GCal

§ - subsp. ***vulparia*** CArn CCon CMac EBee GPoy MNrw MRav NEgg NGdn WCot

mairei see *A. vilmorinianum*
moldavicum see *A. lycoctonum* subsp. *moldavicum*
nagarum WCot
- KR 7589 CDes WPGP

napellus CArn CBod CHel CMHG CSpe ECtt EPfP GAbr GKev GPoy LAst LEdu LRHS MBel MCot MMuc MNHC MWat SRms SWat WBor WFar WHar WHoo WShi XLum
- 'Bergfürst' CAby CMea EBee LPla MNFA NDov
- 'Blue Valley' COtt EBee ELan EPfP EWes WHil
- 'Gletschereis' EBee LRHS
- subsp. ***napellus*** SRms

§ - - Anglicum Group MCot WCot
- 'Rubellum' ELan GQue IBoy IMou MCot MMuc NBir NBro NLar NPri SPoG WMnd
- 'Schneewittchen' CSpe EBee EWes GQue
- 'Sphere's Variety' EBee

§ - subsp. ***vulgare*** CTal
- - 'Albidum' CBod CCon CMea ELan ELon EPfP EWTr EWoo GAbr GMaP LAst LEdu LRHS MBel MPro NBid NHol NLar NPri SGol SPer SPoG WBor
- - 'Carneum' GCra NChi WHer WKif

napiforme see *A. japonicum* subsp. *napiforme*
nasutum new WCot
neapolitanum see *A. lycoctonum* subsp. *neapolitanum*
'Newry Blue' EBee GBuc IGor IMou LRHS MNFA MRav NBir NLar NWad SRms
orientale misapplied see *A. lycoctonum* subsp. *vulparia*
orientale ambig. NEoE

paniculatum misapplied	see *A. variegatum* subsp. *paniculatum*
piepunense	EBee GKev
proliferum	WCot
- B&SWJ 4107	WCru
pseudohuiliense	CExl
pseudolaeve B&SWJ 8663	WCru
- var. ***erectum*** B&SWJ 8466	WCru
pubiceps white-flowered	GCal
pyramidale	see *A. napellus* subsp. *vulgare*
pyrenaicum misapplied	see *A. lycoctonum* subsp. *neapolitanum*
ranunculifolius	see *A. lycoctonum* subsp. *neapolitanum*
sachalinense	WCot
- subsp. ***yezoense***	GCal NLar WCot
senanense var. ***incisum*** B&SWJ 11032	WCru
- subsp. ***paludicola*** B&SWJ 10866 new	WCru
seoulense B&SWJ 694	WCru
- B&SWJ 864	WCru
- BWJ 4107	IMou
septentrionale	see *A. lycoctonum* subsp. *lycoctonum*
'Shirui Blue' new	LEdu
'Spark's Variety' 🏆H7	Widely available
spicatum GWJ 9394	WCru
'Stainless Steel' 🏆H7	Widely available
subcuneatum	see *A. japonicum* subsp. *subcuneatum*
× ***tubergenii***	see *Eranthis hyemalis* Tubergenii Group
uchiyamae B&SWJ 1005	WCru
- B&SWJ 1216	ELon EPPr WCru
- B&SWJ 4446	NLar
variegatum	EBee GCal
§ - subsp. ***paniculatum***	MLHP WCot
§ ***vilmorinianum*** BWJ 8055	WCru
violaceum var. ***robustum***	see *A. chasmanthum*
volubile misapplied	see *A. hemsleyanum*
volubile Pall.	CCon
vulparia	see *A. lycoctonum* subsp. *vulparia*
yamazakii	EBee WCru
zigzag var. ***ryohakuense*** B&SWJ 8906	WCru

Aconogonon see *Persicaria*

Acorus ✿ (*Acoraceae*)

calamus	CArn CBAq CBen CKno CWat EHon ELau GPoy MNHC MSKA MWts NPer SWat WHer WMAq
- subsp. ***angustatus***	GPoy
- 'Argenteostriatus' (v)	CBAq CBen CRow CWat ECha EHon MCot MMuc MWts NOrc SCob SGSe SRms SWat WMAq WWEG
* ***christophii***	ELon EPPr EWes
gramineus	ELau GPoy MSKA NPer SWat WHer
- 'Golden Delight'	SCob SGSe
- 'Golden Edge' (v)	ELon EWes MBri
- 'Hakuro-nishiki' (v)	EHoe EPPr GBin LRHS MGos MMoz NBid NWad SCob SGSe SRms SWvt WMoo XLum
- 'Kinchinjunga' (v)	IFro
- 'Licorice'	EPPr GBin GCal SPoG WGrn
- 'Masamune' (v)	EWes GBin GCal
- 'Minimus Aureus'	CBre GCal
- 'Oborozuki' misapplied	see *A. gramineus* 'Ōgon'
- 'Oborozuki' (v)	EHoe
§ - 'Ōgon' (v)	Widely available
- var. ***pusillus***	EPla NBro WWEG
- 'Variegatus' (v)	Widely available
- 'Yodo-no-yuki' (v)	EBee
'Intermedius'	NPer

Acradenia (*Rutaceae*)

frankliniae	CBcs CMHG CMac CTsd EBee EPfP MBlu SEND SKHP SPlb WHor WPGP

Actaea (*Ranunculaceae*)

alba misapplied	see *A. pachypoda*, *A. rubra* f. *neglecta*
arizonica	CTal EBee GCal LPla LRHS NLar SPhx WCru
asiatica	CDes
- B&SWJ 616	WCru
- B&SWJ 6351 from Japan	WCru
- B&SWJ 8694 from Korea	WCru
- BWJ 8174 from China	WCru
biternata B&SWJ 8917	WCru
- B&SWJ 11190	WCru
'Chocoholic'	CLAP EBee ECtt ELan GBBs GBin IKil IPot MAvo MCot
§ ***cimicifuga***	CLAP ECha GCal GPoy
§ ***cordifolia***	EBee GBin GMaP LRHS NGdn NLar SHar SWvt WBor
- variegated (v)	EBee
dahurica	CArn GBin GQue SWat WCot
- B&SWJ 8426	WCru
- B&SWJ 8573	WCru
- tall	GBin NBid
aff. ***dahurica*** new	CArn
elata	IMou WCot
erythrocarpa	see *A. rubra*
frigida B&SWJ 2966	WCru
heracleifolia B&SWJ 8843	WCot WCru
§ ***japonica***	GCal NLar SHar
- B&SWJ 5828	WCru
- B&SWJ 11136	WCru
- B&SWJ 11526 new	WCru
- from Cheju Do	IMou LEdu
- var. ***acutiloba*** B&SWJ 6257	WCru
- compact	GBin
- - B&SWJ 8758A	WCot WCru
mairei	GCal IMou LRHS
- BWJ 7635	WCru
- BWJ 7939	WCru
§ ***matsumurae***	CExl
- B&SWJ 11187	WCru
- B&SWJ 11528	WCru
- 'Elstead Variety' 🏆H7	CExl GCal MRav
- 'White Pearl'	Widely available
§ ***pachypoda***	CBro CExl CTal EBee EPfP GBin GCal GLog GPoy IGor NBid NLar WCru
- 'Misty Blue'	CBct CWGN EBee ECtt ESwi GEdr IPot LBMP LSou MBel MHol NLar NMyG SHar SMad SPoG WCot
- f. ***rubrocarpa***	GCal
§ ***podocarpa***	EBee SPlb SRms WCru
racemosa 🏆H7	CArn CBod CMac EBee ELan EPfP GBin GCal GPoy LRHS NBid NGdn NLar NSti SPer SWvt WFar

§ **rubra** CBro EBee ECha ELan GCal MCot MMHG MNrw NBid NLar SMad WCru
- B&SWJ 9555 WCru
- **alba** see *A. pachypoda*, *A. rubra* f. *neglecta*
§ - f. **neglecta** GCal GQue MBel SKHP WCot WCru
simplex EBee GCra NEgg SWat WCot
- B&SWJ 8653 WCru
- B&SWJ 8664 WCru
- B&SWJ 10957 WCru
- B&SWJ 11133 WCru
§ - Atropurpurea Group Widely available
- - 'Bernard Mitchell' CCon
- - 'Black Negligee' Widely available
- - 'Braunlaub' new GKin
- - 'Brunette' ♀H7 Widely available
- - 'Carbonella' ECtt GBin MAsh SMDP
- - 'Hillside Black Beauty' CLAP GBin GEdr GKin GMaP LRHS MNrw NBir WCot
- - 'James Compton' ♀H7 CExl CLAP CPar ECha ECtt EHoe EPfP GCal GKin GMaP IBoy IKil IPot LRHS MAsh MAvo MBNS MCot NBid NBir NDov NGdn NLar NOrc SWvt WCAu WCFE WFar WMoo
- - 'Mountain Wave' ECtt WCot WPGP
- 'Cally Dappled' (v) new MAvo
- 'Pink Spike' Widely available
§ - 'Prichard's Giant' CLAP EBee GBin GCal MRav MSpe NLar WFar
- **ramosa** see *A. simplex* 'Prichard's Giant'
- 'Silver Axe' GCal NGdn
- variegated (v) CDes WCot
spicata EPPr GBin GCra GPoy NLar WCru
- from England WCru
taiwanensis B&SWJ 3413 WCru
- RWJ 9996 WCru
yesoensis B&SWJ 6355 WCru
- B&SWJ 10860 WCru
yunnanensis GCal

Actinella see *Tetraneuris*

Actinidia (*Actinidiaceae*)

BWJ 8161 from China WCru
arguta CPne
- (f/F) CAgr NLar
- B&SWJ 4455 from Jejudo, South Korea WCru
- B&SWJ 4823 from Japan WCru
- B&SWJ 8529 from Ulleungdo, South Korea WCru
- 'Ambrosia' (f/F) new MCoo
- 'Ambrosia Grande' new NLar
- 'Ananasnaya' (f/F) CAgr
- 'Bayern' (F) CAgr
- 'Geneva 2' (f/F) CAgr
- 'Honigbeere' new NLar
- 'Issai' (s-p/F) CAgr CBcs CCCN EPfP EPom LRHS MGos NLar SVic WCot
- 'Jumbo' (f/F) CAgr SVic
- 'Ken's Red' (F) CAgr SVic
- 'Kiwai Vert' (f/F) CAgr
- LL#1 (m) CAgr
- LL#2 (f/F) CAgr
- LL#3 (m) CAgr
- 'Meader' (m) CAgr
- 'MSU' (F) CAgr
- 'Purpurna Sadowa' (f/F) NLar
- 'Shoko' (f) WCru
- 'Unchae' (m) WCru
- 'Weiki' (m) CAgr LRHS MCoo SVic
chinensis misapplied see *A. deliciosa*
chinensis Planch. WCru
var. **setosa** B&SWJ 3563 new
§ **deliciosa** MRav WSHC
- 'Atlas' (m) CAgr NLar SDea
- 'Hayward' (f/F) CAgr CBcs CCCN CDul CHEx CHel CMac EPfP NLar SCob SDea SEND SWvt WFar
- 'Jenny' (s-p/F) CAgr CEnd CHEx CMac CSut CTri CUse EPfP EPom LAst LBuc LRHS MBri MGos SCob SDea SPer SPoG SPre SVic WFar
- Solissimo = 'Renact' new LRHS
- 'Solo' (s-p/F) CBcs CCCN CDoC CMac CSBt ECrN EPfP LRHS MCoo NLar NPri SEND SLim SPer SWvt WPGP
- 'Tomuri' (m) CBcs CCCN CHEx CMac COtt EBee EPfP NLar SWvt
hypoleuca B&SWJ 5942 WCru
kolomikta ♀H5 Widely available
- (m) MBlu NPla
- B&SWJ 4243 WCru
- 'Doctor Szymanowski' new WPGP
- 'Tomoko' (f/F) WCru
- 'Yazuaki' (m) WCru
melanandra SPlb WPGP
petelotii FMWJ 13137 new WCru
- HWJ 628 WCru
pilosula misapplied see *A. tetramera* var. *maloides*
pilosula (Finet & Gagnep.) Stapf ex Hand.-Mazz. GGal LRHS SHil SRms
polygama GCal
- B&SWJ 5444 WCru
- B&SWJ 8525 from Korea WCru
- B&SWJ 8923 from Japan WCru
- B&SWJ 12564 from Korea new WCru
rufa B&SWJ 3525 WCru
aff. **strigosa** HWJK 2367 WCru
tetramera B&SWJ 3564 WCru
§ - var. **maloides** ♀H5 CBcs CDoC CExl CSPN CWGN EBee EUJe EWTr GCal GGal MGil MGos NLar SBrt SCoo SKHP WBor WCru WPGP WSHC

Adansonia (*Malvaceae*)

grandidieri SPlb
madagascariensis SPlb
rubrostipa SPlb
za SPlb

Adelocaryum see *Lindelofia*

Adenanthos (*Proteaceae*)

sericeus SPlb SVen

Adenium (*Apocynaceae*)

obesum ♀H1a LToo
- subsp. **boehmianum** LToo
- subsp. **swazicum** LToo

Adenocarpus (*Papilionaceae*)

	decorticans	SPlb SVen

Adenophora (*Campanulaceae*)

	sp.	MHol
	'Afterglow'	see *Campanula rapunculoides* 'Afterglow'
	asiatica	see *Hanabusaya asiatica*
	aurita	WCot
	bulleyana	CCon CHVG ELan GCra GJos LRHS MNHC NBid NGdn NLar SGSe SPav SPlb WCot
	capillaris subsp. ***leptosepala***	EWld
	- - BWJ 7986	WCru
	coelestis	CExl NBid
	- B&SWJ 7998	WCru
	confusa	WHer WSHC
	grandiflora B&SWJ 8555	WCru
	khasiana	CExl LLHF NLar XLum
	lamarkii B&SWJ 8738	WCru
	latifolia misapplied	see *A. pereskiifolia*
	latifolia ambig. white-flowered	MMuc
	liliifolia	ELan EPfP GAbr GCal GKev LRHS MMuc NLar NPer WFar XLum
	maximowicziana B&SWJ 11008	WCru
	morrisonensis RWJ 10008	WCru
§	***nikoensis***	NBid
§	***pereskiifolia***	EWes SGSe SHar SPlb WCot
	polyantha	GAbr GKev NLar SRms
	polymorpha	see *A. nikoensis*
	potaninii	CCon EBee ELan MMuc SEND WHal
	- lilac-flowered	WFar
	- pale-flowered	MMuc WHal
	remotiflora B&SWJ 8741	WCru
	- B&SWJ 11016	WCru
	takedae B&SWJ 11424	WCru
	- var. ***howozana***	MLHP
	taquetii	CPBP
	tashiroi	CPrp XLum
	triphylla	SGSe
	- B&SWJ 8608	WCru
	- B&SWJ 10916	WCru
	- var. ***hakusanensis***	LLHF
	- var. ***japonica*** B&SWJ 10933	WCru
	uehatae	GEdr
	- B&SWJ 126	SKHP WCru

Adesmia (*Papilionaceae*)

	longipes	SPlb

Adiantum ✿ (*Pteridaceae*)

	sp.	CMac
	aethiopicum	XBlo
§	***aleuticum*** ♕H6	CLAP LPal MMoz NBro NLar SPlb WFib WPGP
	- 'Imbricatum'	CBty CElw CLAP ECha ELon GEdr IKil ISha IVic LPal LRHS MGos NBid NLar NMyG SDix SRms WCot WFib XLum
§	- 'Japonicum'	CDes NBir WPGP
	- 'Miss Sharples'	CBod CBty CDTJ CLAP ECha ELon GEdr LRHS MGos NBid NLar NMyG SRms WPGP
§	- 'Subpumilum' ♕H5	CLAP NBid WFib
	- 'Tasselatum' **new**	WCot
	andicola B&SWJ 10448 **new**	WCru
	bonatianum	CExl
	capillus-veneris	CBty ISha SGSe WFib
	- 'Mairisii'	see *A.* × *mairisii*
	chilense	EFtx
	cuneatum	see *A. raddianum*
	hispidulum	CBty CCCN ISha LRHS NLos
	- 'Bronze Venus'	CCCN LRHS SRms
§	× ***mairisii*** ♕H5	CBty EFtx ISha LRHS NLos
	pedatum misapplied	see *A. aleuticum*
	pedatum ambig.	CBty ISha
	pedatum L.	CBcs CHEx CLAP ECha EFer ELan ELon EPfP EShb GMaP LAst LPot LRHS MBri SWat WPGP
	- Asiatic form	see *A. aleuticum* 'Japonicum'
	- 'Japonicum'	see *A. aleuticum* 'Japonicum'
	- 'Roseum'	see *A. aleuticum* 'Japonicum'
	- var. ***subpumilum***	see *A. aleuticum* 'Subpumilum'
	peruvianum	WCot
	poiretii **new**	WCot
§	***raddianum*** ♕H1c	EFtx
	- 'Fragrans'	see *A. raddianum* 'Fragrantissimum'
§	- 'Fragrantissimum'	EShb
	- 'Gracilis'	see *A. raddianum* 'Gracillimum'
§	- 'Gracillimum'	EFtx
	- 'Kensington Gem' ♕H1c	EFtx
	- 'Lady Geneva' **new**	WCot
	- 'Micropinnulum'	EFtx
	venustum ♕H7	CBty CExl CFil CHEx CHVG CLAP EFer EFtx EPot EWTr ISha IVic MCot MWat NCGa SChr SKHP SPlb SRms SWat WCot WFib WHal WPGP

Adina (*Rubiaceae*)

	rubella	ETwe NLar

Adlumia (*Papaveraceae*)

	fungosa	CArn CSpe LRHS

Adonis (*Ranunculaceae*)

	amurensis misapplied	see *A.* 'Fukujukai', *A. multiflora*
	amurensis ambig.	CMea EBee ECGP GEdr LEdu LLHF WCot
	- 'Pleniflora'	see *A. multiflora* 'Sandanzaki'
	brevistyla	GBuc GEdr WAbe
	'Chichibu-beni'	GEdr
§	'Fukujukai'	ECha
§	***multiflora***	ECho SRot
	- 'Beni-nadeshiko' **new**	GEdr
	- 'Hakuju'	GEdr
	- 'Hanazono' (d)	GEdr
§	- 'Sandanzaki' (d)	EBee GEdr IGor
	ramosa	GEdr
	vernalis	EBee GPoy NLar WCot

Adoxa (*Adoxaceae*)

	moschatellina	CDes CSpe EBee ECho LEdu NMir NRya WHer WSFF WShi

Aechmea (*Bromeliaceae*)

	sp.	XBlo
	'Blue Rain'[PBR]	LAir
	blumenavii **new**	LAir
	bracteata **new**	LAir

	calyculata **new**	LAir
	caudata	LAir NLos
	- short **new**	LAir
	- var. ***variegata***	CHEx NLos
	chlorophylla **new**	LAir
	cylindrata 'Bicolor' **new**	LAir
	'Echidna' **new**	LAir SPlb
	fasciata ♀H1a	LAir XBlo
	- 'Primera'PBR	LAir
	'Flamingo' **new**	LAir
	gamosepala	NLos
	- var. ***nivea***	LAir
	nudicaulis ♀H1a **new**	NLos
	- var. ***capitata*** **new**	NLos
I	- - f. ***albomarginata*** **new**	NLos
	- 'La Tigra' **new**	LAir
	- 'Parati' **new**	LAir
	- var. ***plurifolia*** **new**	LAir
	ramosa	XBlo
	recurvata	LAir NLos
	- 'Artichoke' **new**	LAir
	- var. ***benrathii***	LAir
	- 'Paraguay' **new**	NLos
	- var. ***recurvata*** **new**	LAir NLos
	'Suenos' **new**	LAir
	victoriana	XBlo
	- var. ***discolor*** **new**	NLos
	wittmackiana 'Warren Loose' **new**	LAir

Aegle (*Rutaceae*)

sepiaria	see *Citrus trifoliata*

Aegopodium (*Apiaceae*)

podagraria 'Dangerous' (v)	CHid
- gold-margined (v)	EPPr WWEG
- 'Variegatum' (v)	CBod EBee ECha EHoe EPPr EPla EShb GMaP LRHS LSou MAsh MBel MRav MWhi NBid NPri NSti SEND SPer SPoG WCFE WCot WHil WMoo WSHC WWEG XLum

Aeonium (*Crassulaceae*)

	sp.	CArn
	arboreum	CDTJ CHEx CHel EShb GCal SEND SMrm WCot
	- 'Atropurpureum'	CAbb CCCN CDTJ CHEx CRos CSde CSuc EShb NPer SEND SPer WCot
	- var. ***holochrysum***	CSuc
I	- 'Magnificum'	EShb ESwi GBin SArc
	- 'Variegatum' (v)	CSuc NPer
	balsamiferum	CCCN CDTJ CHEx CHel CSuc IDee SChr
	'Black Cap'	CCCN
	'Black Magic'	CSuc
	'Blushing Beauty' ♀H1c	CSuc EShb
	'Bronze Medal'	CSuc
	canariense	CCCN CDTJ CHEx CSuc SVen
	- var. ***palmense***	SVen
	castello-paivae	EShb SChr
	ciliatum	CSuc SPlb
	'Copper Kettle'	CSuc
	'Cornish Tribute' **new**	CTre
	'Cristata Sunburst'	CDTJ WCot
	cuneatum	CSde SEND
	'Cyclops'	CSuc
	davidbramwellii	CSuc
*	***decorum*** 'Variegatum' (v)	WCot
	'Dinner Plate'	CDTJ CHEx MHin
	'Dinner Plate' × ***haworthii***	CHEx
	× ***domesticum***	see *Aichryson* × *aizoides* var. *domesticum*
*	***escobarii***	CSuc
	'Garnet'	CSuc
	glandulosum	CSuc SVen
	glutinosum	CSuc
	goochiae	CSuc SBch
	gorgonium	CSuc
	haworthii ♀H1c	CDTJ CHEx SBHP SEND SVen
	- 'Variegatum' (v) ♀H1c	CDTJ CSuc CTre EShb SChr SVen
	hierrense	CSuc CTre SPlb WCot
	holochrysum Webb & Berth.	CAbb
	'Lemon-Lime' (v)	CSuc WCot
	leucoblepharum	CSuc
	lindleyi	CSuc SChr
	'Logan Rock' **new**	CTre
	× ***mascaense***	CSuc
*	***multiflorum*** 'Variegatum' (v)	CDTJ
	nobile	CBrP CSuc
	percarneum	EShb
	'Plum Purdy'	CSuc
I	'Pygmaeum'	CSuc
	sedifolium	CSuc CTre
	simsii	CSuc
	simsii × 'Zwartkop'	CCCN CSuc CTre
	spathulatum	CSuc
	'Sunburst' (v) ♀H1c	CSuc CTre WCot
	'Suncup'	CSuc
	tabuliforme ♀H1c	CCCN CDTJ CSpe CSuc CTre SMad SPlb WCot
	- 'Cristatum'	WCot
	undulatum	SPlb
	urbicum	CHEx EShb
	valverdense	CSuc
	'Velour'	CSuc
	'Voodoo'	CSuc ESwi EUJe WCot
	'Zwartkin'	CSuc
	'Zwartkop' ♀H1c	CAbb CBcs CCCN CHEx CHVG CHel CHll CSpe CTre ECtt EShb EUJe EWll GBin LSou MCot MSCN NPer NPla SArc SChr SEND SEle SMad SMrm SPlb SRot SWvt WCot WWFP

Aeschynanthus ✿ (*Gesneriaceae*)

	'Big Apple'	WDib
	Black Pagoda Group	WDib
	buxifolius KR 7798	WAbe WCot
	'Fire Wheel'	WDib
	hildebrandii	WDib
	'Hot Flash'	WDib
	'Little Tiger'	WDib
	longicalyx	WDib
§	***longicaulis*** ♀H1c	WDib
	marmoratus	see *A. longicaulis*
	radicans ♀H1c	WDib
	'Scooby Doo'	WDib
	speciosus ♀H1c	WDib

Aesculus ✿ (*Sapindaceae*)

arguta	see *A. glabra* var. *arguta*

	× ***arnoldiana***	CDul CMCN NLar
	assamica NJM 10.030	WPGP
	– WWJ 11886	WCru
	'Autumn Splendor'	EPfP
§	× ***bushii***	CDul CMCN NLar
	californica	CBcs CDul CHel CMCN CMac EPfP ERod SKHP WPGP
	× ***carnea***	CDul SGol WHar
	– 'Aureomarginata' (v)	ERod LLHF WHar
	– 'Briotii'	CAco CBcs CCVT CDoC CDul CEnd CHel CLnd CMac CSBt CTho EBee ECrN ELan EPfP EPla LAst LBuc MGos MMuc NLar NWea SCob SCoo SEND SEWo SPer WFar WHar
	– 'Plantierensis'	CDul
*	– 'Variegata' (v)	CDul CMCN
	chinensis	CBcs CMCN
	flava ♀H5	CAco CDul CLnd CMCN CTho ELan EPfP EWTr MBri MMuc SEND
	– f. ***vestita***	CDul MBlu MBri NLar
	georgiana	see *A. sylvatica*
	glabra	CDul CMCN CTho
§	– var. ***arguta***	CMCN NLar WPat
	– 'Autumn Blaze'	EPfP
	– 'October Red'	EPfP MBri
	glaucescens	see *A.* × *neglecta*
	hippocastanum	CAco CBcs CCVT CDul CLnd CMac CSBt CTho CTri EBee ECrN ELan EPfP EPla LAst LBuc MGos MMuc MSwo NLar NWea SCob SEND SEWo SGol SPer WFar WHar
	– 'Aureomarginata' (v)	CMac
§	– 'Baumannii' (d)	CDoC CDul CLnd CMCN ECrN ELan EPfP EPla ERod MGos MSwo NWea SCob SPer
	– 'Digitata'	CDul CMCN WPat
	– 'Flore Pleno'	see *A. hippocastanum* 'Baumannii'
	– 'Gimborn's Pride' **new**	NLar
	– 'Hampton Court Gold'	CDul CMCN CMac EPla
	– f. ***laciniata***	CDul CMCN ERod IArd NLar SMad WCot WPat
	– 'Monstrosa'	WPat
	– 'Wisselink'	CDul CMCN ECrN WCot WPat
	indica	CDul CHEx CLnd CMCN ECrN ELan EPfP EPla EWTr LEdu SEND SGol
	– 'Sydney Pearce' ♀H5	CBcs CDul CEnd CJun CMCN EPfP EPla ERod MBlu MBri NLar SBrt SLim WPat
	× ***marylandica***	CDul WPat
	× ***mississippiensis***	see *A.* × *bushii*
	× ***mutabilis*** 'Harbisonii'	WPat
	– 'Induta'	CDul CLnd CMCN EPfP GBin IArd MBri SKHP
§	– 'Penduliflora'	CDul
§	× ***neglecta***	CMCN NLar
	– 'Autumn Fire'	CLnd EBee EPfP GBin LRHS MBri SLim SPoG WPat
	– 'Erythroblastos' ♀H5	CBcs CDul CEnd CJun CMCN EPfP ERod EUJe MAsh MBlu MBri MRav SCoo SMad SPer SPoG WCot WPat
	parviflora ♀H5	CBcs CDul CMCN CMac CTri EBee ELan EPfP EPla EWTr GKin IDee MBlu MGos MMuc MPkF MRav NEgg NLar SEND SGol SMad SPer SWvt WHar
§	***pavia***	CBcs CDul CMCN EPfP
	– 'Atrosanguinea'	CEnd CLnd CMCN EPfP ERod MBri SKHP
I	– 'Biltmore Buckeye'	MPkF
	– var. ***discolor*** 'Koehnei'	CMCN EPfP MBri NLar SPoG
	– 'Penduliflora'	see *A.* × ***mutabilis*** 'Penduliflora'
	– 'Purple Spring'	WPat
	– 'Rosea Nana'	CMCN WPat
	splendens	see *A. pavia*
§	***sylvatica***	CMCN
	turbinata	CBcs CDul
	wilsonii	CBcs CExl

Aethionema (*Brassicaceae*)

	armenum	ECho
	capitatum	CPBP ECho SIgm
	glaucinum	ECho
§	***grandiflorum*** ♀H5	ECho ELan GJos NBro SRms XLum XSen
	– Pulchellum Group ♀H5	GJos GKev
	iberideum	MWat SRms
*	***kotschyi*** hort.	EDAr WAbe
	oppositifolium	LLHF MWat
	pulchellum	see *A. grandiflorum*
	schistosum	LLHF
	'Warley Rose' ♀H5	ECho ELan EPot GCrg LRHS MAsh MSCN NBir NSla SBch SRms WIce WThu XSen
	'Warley Ruber'	CMea ECho WAbe

Aethusa (*Apiaceae*)

cynapium	CSpe

Aextoxicon (*Aextoxicaceae*)

punctatum	CBcs

Afrocarpus (*Podocarpaceae*)

falcatus	ECou

Afrocrocus (*Iridaceae*)

unifolius from Roggeveld	ECho

Agapanthus ✿ (*Agapanthaceae*)

	sp.	WHil
	'Adonis'	IBlr
	'African Moon'	CPen CPne CPrp
	'African Skies'	CPne CPrp IBal LRHS NHoy SEND SFai
	africanus misapplied	CElw CExl CHel CTsd CWCL EBee ELan EPfP EPot EUJe GBBs GKev ITim LPal LRHS MJak MWat SArc SChr SCob SPer SRot SVic WBor WWEG XLum
	– 'Albus' misapplied	CBcs CDoC CExl CHel CWCL EBee ELan EPfP EPot GKev LPal LRHS LSun MGos NSoo SCob SDeJ SEND SGol SPer SRms WBor WWEG XLum
	'Aimee'	CBro
	'Alan Street' **new**	CAvo
	'Albus' ambig.	GKev GMaP MHer MWat
I	'Albus Nanus'	IBal
I	'Albus Roseus'	SFai
	'Alice Gloucester'	CPrp
	'Amsterdam'	CPen EBee IMou NHoy
	'Angela'	CPen CPrp IBal MAvo NHoy
	'Aphrodite'	IBlr
	'Aquamarine'	CAvo EPri LLWG LPla NHoy
	'Arctic Star'	CCCN CExl CKno CPen CPne CPou CPrp CTca CWCL EBee ELon EWoo

		IBal LRHS LSou NHoy NLar NPri SDys SFai
	'Ardernei Hybrid'	CAvo CExl ECha ECtt EWes GAbr GCal IBal IBlr LSou SMrm WCot WGwG WPGP WWEG
§	'Argenteus Vittatus' (v) ♀H2	CPen NHoy
	'Arosa'	IMou
	'Atlas'	IBlr
	'Aureovittatus' (v)	IBal NHoy
	'Baby Blue'	see *A.* 'Blue Baby' Rom.
	'Baby Pete'PBR	CPen NHoy
	Back in Black = 'B in B'PBR	CBro CCCN CExl COtt CWCL ELan EPfP EWes IBal MBNS MBri MRav NBid NHoy SCob SHyH SMrm SPer WCot WFar
	'Ballerina'	CPne IBal
	'Ballyrogan'	IBlr
	'Bangor Blue'	IBlr
	'Barnfield Blue'	CPne CPrp IBal NHoy SFai
	'Barnsley'	NHoy
	'Basutoland'	LRHS
	'Becky' **new**	CPne
	'Beeches Dwarf'	NHoy
	'Beloved'	NHoy
	'Ben Hope'	CBro IBlr NHoy WCot
	'Beth Chatto'	see *A. campanulatus* 'Albovittatus'
	'Bethlehem Star'	CPne
	'Bicton Bell'	IBlr
	'Bicton Bride' **new**	CPne
	'Big Blue'	CCCN CHel CMac CPrp CWCL EBee GKev LSou SEND SRkn
	'Black Beauty'	IBal LRHS
	'Black Buddhist'	CBod CCCN CHel COtt CPen CWCL EBee ECtt EPri GBuc IBal LRHS MGos MWat NGdn NHoy NPri SFai SGol SPer
	'Black Magic'	CPne IBal NHoy SFai
	'Black Pantha'PBR	Widely available
§	'Blauwe Valk' **new**	EPfP
§	'Blue Baby' Rom.	CCCN CChe CPen ELan ELon IBlr LRHS NHoy XTur
	Blue Bird	see *A.* 'Blauwe Valk'
	'Blue Bird'	CRos LRHS MBri SHil
	'Blue Brush'	CAbb CSBt EPfP IBal LRHS NHoy SCoo SEND
	'Blue Cascade'	IBlr
	'Blue Companion'	CPrp IBlr NHoy WMnd
	'Blue Diamond' ambig.	CMac NHoy
	'Blue Dot'	CPrp ECtt EPfP LLHF LRHS LSou NGdn SDys
	'Blue Dragon'	NHoy
	'Blue Formality'	IBal IBlr
	'Blue Giant'	CBro CCCN CChe CHel CKno CPrp EBee IBlr LRHS MGos MNFA NHoy SCob SWat WPGP WWEG
	'Blue Globe'	CHid EBee EPri GMaP LRHS
	'Blue Heaven'PBR	CPne CWGN EWoo IBal LSun MBri NHoy SCob
	'Blue Horizons' (v)	CCCN NHoy
	'Blue Ice'	CPen CPne CPou CPrp EBee IBal NHoy
	'Blue Imp'	CBro IBlr
	'Blue Jay'	CPen
	'Blue Magic' **new**	EBee IBal NHoy
	'Blue Moon'	CAbP CAvo CBro CHel CPen CPrp CUse EBee ECha ECtt EWoo IBal IBlr LLWG LRHS LSun MAvo MCot MHol NHoy NLar SHyH SMrm SPer WCot
	'Blue Prince'	CPen EBee LRHS NHoy
	'Blue Rinse'	CAvo
	'Blue Skies' ambig.	NCGa NHoy
I	'Blue Skies' Dunlop	IBlr
	'Blue Sparkler'	CPne
	'Blue Spear'	CPen
	'Blue Triumphator'	CTca EPfP EWll GBin GKev GMaP LRHS MHer MNHC NHoy SCob WWEG
	'Blue Umbrella'	COtt NHoy SRkn
	'Blue Velvet'	CPne LSun
	'Blue Yonder' **new**	NHoy
	blue-flowered	WCFE
	Bluestorm = 'Atiblu'PBR	EPfP IBal LBuc LRHS MBri NHoy SArc SCob
	'Bluety'PBR	CPen NHoy
	'Bray Valley'	CPne
	'Bressingham Blue'	CBro CPne CPrp CTri EWes GCal IBal IBlr LRHS MRav NHoy SFai SMHy SWat
	'Bressingham Bounty'	IBal LRHS
	'Bressingham White'	LRHS MRav NCGa NHoy SWat
	'Bridal Bouquet'	EBee GBin IBal NHoy SFai
	'Brilliant Blue' **new**	NHoy
	'Bristol'	IBal
	'Buckingham Palace'	CBro CDes CPne EBee EWes GAbr IBlr MAvo NChi NHoy WPGP
	'Cally Blue'	GAbr GCal IBal NHoy
	'Cally Longstem'	EBee EPri GCal
	'Cally Pale Blue'	IBal
	campanulatus	CMac CPrp ELan EPfP EWTr GKin IBal IBlr IGor LRHS MCot MMuc MRav NEgg NHoy SEND SWat WFar WPGP
	- var. ***albidus***	CHel ECha ELan EPfP EShb GKin IBlr LRHS MMuc NBid NGdn NHoy NSoo SEND SPer WGwG WHoo WPGP
§	- 'Albovittatus' (v)	ECho IBal LSou NHoy
	- bright blue-flowered	GCal IBal
	- 'Cobalt Blue'	GBin GKin LPal LRHS LSou MAvo MMuc MNrw NGdn NHoy
	- dark blue-flowered	MMuc
	- dwarf blue-flowered	NPCo
	- 'Oxford Blue'	IBal IBlr NHoy
	- subsp. ***patens*** ♀H4	EPfP IBal LRHS MRav SWat WPGP
	- - deep blue-flowered	CCon IBlr LRHS NHoy WWEG
	- 'Profusion'	CBro CPne CPrp ECha EPri IBal IBlr LRHS NHoy
	- variegated (v)	EBee ECha NPer
	- 'Wedgwood Blue'	EBee IBal IBlr LRHS NHoy
	- 'Wendy'	CPne IBal IBlr LRHS NHoy
	- 'White Hope'	IBal IBlr
	'Carefree'	CPne IBal
	'Castle of Mey'	CAvo CBod CBro CExl CFil CPrp EBee GAbr IBlr LPla LRHS LSou NHoy SFai WPGP
§	***caulescens*** ♀H2	CPne IBal IBlr LRHS SMHy WPGP
	- subsp. ***angustifolius***	CCon CHid ELon IBal IBlr LPla MHol SMad SPer WCot WPGP
	- subsp. ***caulescens***	IBlr SWat
	'Cedric Morris'	CPen IBlr NHoy
	'Celebration'	CPne
	'Chandra'	CAvo IBlr
	'Charlotte'PBR	CMac CPen EBee EPfP LRHS NHoy SPoG
	'Cherry Holley'	ELon
	'Chika's Blue'	MAvo

	'Clarence House'	CBro CPen CPrp
	'Cloudy Days'	CPne
	coddii	CExl EPri EWes IBlr MHer SMrm WCot
	'Colin Edward'	NHoy
	'Columba'	CPen EBee ELon IBal LAma NBid NHoy
	comptonii	see *A. praecox* subsp. *minimus*
	'Congratulations'	NHoy
	'Cool Blue'	MAvo
	'Corina'	EBee
	'Crystal Drop'	CExl CPen CPne CPou CPrp EPri IBal LRHS NHoy SFai SWat WPGP
	'Dainty Lady'	NHoy
	Danube	see *A.* 'Donau'
	'Dart Valley' **new**	CPne
	'Dartmoor'	CPne
	'Delft'	CPrp EBee IBal IBlr LRHS
	'Delft Blue' **new**	IBal
	'Density'	IBlr
	'Devon Dawn'	IMou
	'Dnjepr'	CBro EBee
	'Dokter Brouwer'	CKno GKev IBoy IKil LRHS MCot NHoy SHyH
§	'Donau'	CBro CPen EBee EPri EWoo GKev IBal NBir NHoy NOrc NSoo SGol SWat WCot
	Double Diamond = 'Rfdd'	CPen CPne CWCL EBee EPri EWTr EWes IBal LRHS LSou NHoy SCob SFai SPoG
	'Dream'	NHoy
	dyeri	see *A. inapertus* subsp. *intermedius*
	'Early Blue'	EBee EWoo NHoy
	'Ed Carman' (v)	LSou
	'Eggesford Sky'	CPne CPrp NHoy SFai
	'Elaine Anne'	NHoy
	'Elisabeth'	NHoy
	'Elizabeth Salisbury'	CPne
	'Enigma'	Widely available
	'Enigma Variations' **new**	EBee
	'Essence of Summer'	WCot
	'Ethel's Joy'	CPen
	'Eve'	IBlr
	'Evening Eclipse' **new**	IBal
	'Evening Star'	CPne
	'Exmoor'	CPne
	'Findlay's Blue'	SMHy
	'Finnline' (v)	CPen CPne SRms
	'Flore Pleno' (d)	Widely available
	'Forget-me-not'	NHoy
	'Gayle's Lilac'	CBcs CCCN CElw CExl COtt CPen CPrp ECtt ELan ELon EPfP EWTr GKin LRHS LSou MRav NGdn NHoy SEND SMrm WGwG WWEG XTur
	'Gem'	CPne ELon
	'Getty White'	EWTr LRHS
	'Glacier' **new**	NHoy
	'Glacier Stream'	CBro CPen EPri GBuc IKil NHoy XTur
	'Glen Avon'	CAbb CCCN CCon CExl COtt CPen CPrp EBee EPfP GBin IBal LRHS MWat NHoy NLar SCoo SEND SFai SLon
	'Gold Strike'PBR	NHoy SFai
	'Golden Drops' (v) **new**	NHoy
	'Golden Rule' (v)	EHoe GBuc IBal IBlr
	'Goliath'	CPne

	'Hanneke'	CPen CPne
	'Happy Birthday'	NHoy
	Headbourne hybrid 152 **new**	EPla
§	Headbourne hybrids	Widely available
	Headbourne hybrids dark blue-flowered	GBuc LRHS NPCo
	Headbourne hybrids dwarf	GBuc
	'Headbourne White'	CAvo EPri
	'Heather Gail'	NHoy
	'Heavenly Blue'	CCCN CPne
	'Helen'	IBlr
	'Holbeach'	CPen
	'Holbrook'	CSam
	'Holly Ann'	NHoy
	'Hoyland'	NHoy
	'Hoyland Blue' **new**	NHoy
	'Hoyland Brilliant White' **new**	NHoy
	'Hoyland Chelsea Blue' **new**	NHoy
	'Hyacinth'	NHoy
	'Ice Blue Star'	CBro
	'Ice Lolly'	CBro CPen IKil
	inapertus	CAvo CBro CFil CPrp CSpe CTre EWes GGal LPla SMHy SWat WCot WPGP
	- dwarf	IBlr
	- subsp. ***hollandii***	EBee GCal IBal IBlr NHoy SWat
	- - 'Zealot'	IBlr
	- 'Ice Cascade'	CCCN CPen EBee IBal LRHS NHoy SWat
	- 'Icicle'	GCal
	- subsp. ***inapertus***	IBlr SWat
I	- - 'Albus'	CDes IBlr
	- - 'Cyan'	IBlr
	- - 'White'	CPrp IBal
§	- subsp. ***intermedius***	CPrp EPfP GKev IBlr NHoy SWat
	- - 'Long Tom'	CExl CPne EPri LRHS WPGP
	- - white-flowered	CPen CPou
	- large	IBal
	- 'Little Black Number'	CPen
	- 'Margaret'	CCCN MBri
	- 'Midnight Cascade'	CCCN CExl CPar CPen EBee ECtt ELan IBal IPot LRHS MBri MCot NBid NHoy SCob SFai SRms SWat
I	- 'Nigrescens'	CPen IPot WCot
	- subsp. ***parviflorus***	IBlr
	- subsp. ***pendulus***	CCon IBlr LRHS WPGP
	- - 'Black Magic' **new**	NHoy
	- - 'Graskop'	Widely available
	- - 'Violet Dusk'	IBlr
	- 'Sapphire Cascade'	CPen IBal LRHS NHoy SWat
	'Indigo Dreams'	CPne CPrp NHoy SFai
	'Inkspots'	CCCN CMac CPen CRos CSpe CWCL EPfP GBin IBal LRHS LSou LSqu SFai SPoG
	'Innocence'	IBlr
	'Intermedius' Leichtlin	CWCL IBal
I	'Intermedius' van Tubergen	EBee NBid
	'Isis'	CAvo CBro CCon CPrp CSam CSde CTri ECha GBuc IBal IBlr LRHS NHoy
	'Jacaranda'	EBee IBal LRHS NHoy NPri SFai SPer
	'Jack's Blue'	Widely available
	'Jersey Giant'	NHoy
	'Jodie'	CPne ELon
	'Johanna'	CPen
	Johannesberg hybrids	ECha EPfP

'Jolanda' CPrp ELon IBal LAma
'Kingston Blue' IBal IBlr IGor NBid NHoy WWEG
'Kobold' CBro NHoy WFar
'Lady Edith' IBlr
§ 'Lady Grey' IBlr
'Lady Moore' IBlr IGor SMHy
'Lapis' CHel CHid CPne CPrp EBee IBal NHoy SFai SHyH
'Latent Blue' IBlr
'Lavender Girl' **new** ECha
'Lavender Haze' CCCN CPen CPne EPfP IBal LRHS MWat NHoy NPri SFai
'Leicester' CPen
'Liam's Lilac' CAvo CCCN CExl CKno CPar CPen CPne CPou CPrp ELon EWoo IBal LRHS MWat NHoy NLar NPri SFai WCot
'Lilac Flash' CPen
'Lilac Time' CExl CPne CPrp IBlr WCot
'Lilliput' CBcs CBro CCCN CMac CMea CPrp CSpe ECha ECtt ELan EPfP EPla EShb GBuc GKev GMaP IBal LLWG LRHS MRav NGdn SBod SPer SRms WFar WMnd
'Little Beauty' NHoy
'Little White' CPen
'Littlecourt' CBro
'Loch Hope' ♀H6 CAvo CBro CDoC CPne CSam ECtt ELon EPfP EWoo GCal IBal LRHS MAvo MHol MRav NHoy SPer WCot WHoo
'Loch Inch' **new** EBee
'Loma' **new** CPne
'Luly' CPen CPne CPrp CRos EPfP LRHS MGos NHoy SHil SWat
'Luna' CPne EBee NHoy
'Lydenburg' CPen CPne EPri IBal IBlr NHoy
'Lyn Valley' CPrp NHoy SFai
'Mabel Grey' see *A.* 'Lady Grey'
'Magnifico' IBlr
'Marchants Cobalt Cracker' SMHy
'Marcus' CPne IBal
'Margaret' IBal LRHS NHoy
'Mariètte' CPen EBee
'Marnie' **new** CPne
'Martine' CPen EBee
'Maureen' CPne NHoy SFai
'May Snow' (v) WCot
'Megan's Mauve' CAvo CKno CPne CPou CPrp EBee ELon EPri IBal LRHS LSou NPri NSti SFai SHyH WCot
'Meibont' (v) IBal WCot
'Mercury' IBlr
'Metalica' NHoy
Midknight Blue = 'Monmid' NHoy WSHC XTur
'Midnight' CPen EWes
'Midnight Blue' ambig. CAby CPen ELan IBal IGor MGos
'Midnight Blue' P. Wood GCal IBlr LRHS
'Midnight Dream' CPen EBee ECtt IBal MBri NHoy SFai STPC
§ 'Midnight Star' Widely available
'Miniature Blue' SWat
'Misty Dawn' (v) CHel CUse EBee ECtt IBal MHol NHoy SFai SHyH WCot
mixed seedlings IBal NHoy NOrc
mixed white-flowered WCFE
'Mole Valley' **new** CPne
'Molly Howick' LRHS
'Mood Indigo' CPne NHoy SFai
'Moonlight Star' **new** NHoy
'Moonshine' CPen
I 'Mooreanus' misapplied EBee EPfP IBal IGor NBid
'Mount Stewart' IBal IBlr
'My Love' NHoy
'Nana Blue' **new** SHyH
'Navy Blue' see *A.* 'Midnight Star'
'Newa' EBee
'Nikki' CMea CPne
'Norman Hadden' IBlr
'Northern Light' CPen LLHF
'Northern Star'PBR Widely available
mutans see *A. caulescens*
'Nyx' IBlr
'Oslo' NHoy
'Oxbridge' IBlr
'Pacific Blue' EBee IBal NHoy SHyH
Palmer's hybrids see *A.* Headbourne hybrids
'Paris' CPen
'Patent Blue' CPrp IBal IBlr
'Patriot' EPfP LRHS
'Pauline' NHoy
'Penelope Palmer' CPrp IBlr
'Peter Franklin' CPne NHoy SFai
'Peter Pan' ambig. Widely available
'Peter Pan' Giridlion LLWG
'Phantom' CAbb CDes CPne CPrp GCal IBal IBlr IMou NHoy SFai SPer WPGP
Pine Cottage hybrids CPne
'Pinocchio' CPen IMou NHoy SDeJ
'Plas Merdyn Blue' IBlr
'Plas Merdyn White' IBal IBlr NHoy
'Podge Mill' CAvo IBlr SMHy
'Polar Ice' CCon CPen CPne EBee ELon EPri EWoo IBal IBlr IBoy LAma LRHS NHoy WCAu XTur
'Polar White' NHoy
'Porcelain' IBal IBlr
praecox ♀H2 CPrp EShb IBal IBlr NHoy
- 'Albiflorus' ♀H2 CBcs CBro CPou CPrp CTri EPri IBal LRHS NEgg NHoy SEND
- 'Floribundus' SWat
- 'Maximus Albus' CPne CPou IBal IBlr
§ - subsp. ***minimus*** CElw CPou IBal IBlr NHoy SEND SWat
- - 'Adelaide' CPrp
- - blue-flowered SWat
- - white-flowered SWat
- 'Neptune' IBlr
§ - subsp. ***orientalis*** CBro CCCN CSut IBlr SWat
- - 'Cape Blue' CPrp
- - 'Mount Thomas' CPrp
- - 'Silver Star' (v) CPen NHoy
- subsp. ***praecox*** IBlr
- - azure-flowered CPrp SWat
- - 'Variegatus' see *A.* 'Argenteus Vittatus'
- 'Saturn' IBlr
- Slieve Donard form IBlr
- 'Uranus' IBlr
- 'Venus' IBlr
- 'Vittatus' (v) NHoy
'Premier' CPrp IBal IBlr LRHS NHoy
'Princess Margaret' IBal
§ 'Purple Cloud' Widely available
'Purple Delight' CPne CPrp IBal
'Purple Emperor' **new** CPne NHoy
'Purple Fountain' **new** CPne NHoy SFai

'Purple Haze' CBod CPen
'Purple Ripple' **new** CPne
'Purple Star' CCCN CKno
'Queen Anne' NHoy
'Queen Mother' CHid LRHS
Queen Mum = 'Pmn06'PBR CAby CCCN CDoC CExl CHVG CHel CMea CPen CPne CPrp CRos ECtt ELon EPfP EPla EPri GBin IBal LRHS MAvo MBri MGos NHoy SFai SHil SHyH SMrm STPC XTur
'Quink Drops' SMHy
'Radiant Star' IBal LRHS NHoy
'Regal Beauty' CPen CPne CPrp CSBt EBee EShb EWoo IBal LRHS NBid NHoy NLar SFai
'Remembrance' NHoy
'Rhapsody in Blue' CPne
'Rhone' CBro IBlr
'Rosewarne' CBcs CBod CCCN CExl GBin IBal IBlr NHoy NLar
'Rotterdam' CPen NHoy
'Royal Blue' CBro GMaP IBal LPla NHoy
'Ruan Vean' **new** CPrp
'Sally Anne' CPne
'San Gabriel' (v) CPne
'Sandringham' CDes CPen CPne EBee EWes IBlr LSou NHoy SEND SFai WPGP
'Sapphire' IBlr
'Sarah'PBR CCCN CPen CPne IBal LSou NHoy SEND SFai SHyH
'Sea Coral' CCCN CCon CMac CPrp EBee EPri LRHS NHoy
'Sea Foam' CMac CPen CPne NLar
'Sea Mist' CCCN CPne EBee
'Sea Spray' CCCN EBee EPri IBal NHoy
'Selma Bock' CPen CPne
'Senna'PBR CCCN CExl IBal LSou NHoy
'Septemberhemel' CPen
'Silver Anniversary' NHoy
'Silver Baby' CKno COtt CPen CPne CPrp ELon EPfP EPri IBal LRHS NHoy SRms
'Silver Jubilee' CPne
'Silver Lining' ECtt IBal LRHS NHoy
'Silver Mist' CPen CPne IBlr SWat
Silver Moon = 'Notfred'PBR (v) CAbb CCCN CPen EBee ELan EPfP EWes EWoo IBal LBMP LRHS LSou MAsh MBri MGos NHoy NPri NSti SCob SFai SPoG WCot
'Silver Sceptre' IBlr
'Silver Stream' NHoy
'Sky' CAbb CAvo CPne CSBt EPfP EPri EWoo IBal IBlr LRHS LSou MWat NBid NPri SFai SKHP SPoG SRkn SRms SWat
'Sky Pendulous' CBcs
'Sky Rocket' CPne IBal IBlr
'Sky Star' IBal
'Slieve Donard' IBlr
'Snow Cloud' CAbb CBro CExl CPen CRos CSBt EBee EPfP IBal LRHS MWat NHoy NLar SEND SFai SLon
'Snow Pixie' CBro CSpe EBee IBal LSou NHoy SFai SHyH
'Snow Princess' CHel CPen ELon EPfP IBal
'Snow Shadows' CBro
'Snowball' CBcs CDoC CExl CHel CPen LRHS LSou NHoy NLos SGSe WWEG
'Snowdrops' CCCN EBee ELan SGSe SKHP
'Snowstorm'PBR EBee EPfP IBal LBuc MBri
'Sofie'PBR CPen MBri NHoy SFai STPC
'Sophie' XTur
'Southern Cross' IBal LRHS SFai
'Southern Star' IBal
'Spokes' IBlr
'Star Quality' IBal LBuc LRHS SFai
'Starburst' IBlr
'Stardust' IBal LBuc LRHS
'Stargazer' EBee LBuc LRHS
'Stars and Stripes' IBal IPot LRHS NPri SFai
'Stéphanie Charm' CPen
'Storm Cloud' Reads see *A.* 'Purple Cloud'
'Storm Cloud' (d) CBro CCon
'Streamline' CBcs CBro CDoC CElw CHel CKno CMea COtt CTca EBee ECtt ELon EPfP EShb GAbr GKin GMaP IBal LAst LRHS LSou MGos MRav NHoy SDys SEND SFai WWEG
'Summer Clouds' ELan NHoy
'Summer Days' **new** CPne CPrp IBal NHoy SFai
'Summer Skies' CPne IBal NHoy
'Sunfield' CKno CPrp EPfP IBal LAma LRHS NHoy NLar NPer
'Super Star' CBro
I 'Supreme' IBlr
'Sylvia'PBR NHoy
'Sylvine' CPen CPne
'Tall Boy' CPne IBal IBlr
'Tarka' CExl CPen CPne CPrp CWCL ELon EWoo IBal LRHS LSou NHoy NLar SDys SFai SHil
'Taw Valley' CAbb CHVG CKno COtt CPen CPne CPrp EBee ELon EWoo IBal LRHS NHoy SFai SHil SHyH SLon SMad SPoG WPGP
'Thumbelina' CBro CKno CMac CPne CUse CWCL EBee IBal LRHS LSou NHoy NLar SFai XLum
'Timaru' Widely available
'Tinkerbell' (v) CBcs CBro CCCN COtt CPne CPrp EBee EHoe ELan EPfP EPri EShb IBal LEdu LRHS LSou MGos MRav NPer SGSe SPoG SRms SWvt
'Tiny Tim' CSpe
'Titan' IBlr
'Titch' **new** CPne
'Tom Thumb' CAvo CExl CHel ECtt EPfP GBin IBal LBMP LRHS LSou NHoy NPri SFai SRkn SRot
'Torbay' CElw CHel CPrp EAEE ECtt ELon EPfP EShb EWTr GAbr GCal GKin IBal LLWG LRHS MNrw NCGa NEgg NHol SEND WHoo WWEG
'Tornado' CPen EBee ECGP ECtt ELon IBal LPla LRHS MNrw NHoy SEND SFai STPC WCot
'Tranquil' NHoy
Tresco hybrid CHEx
'Tresco Select' NHoy
'Triangle' CPen
'Tsolo' **new** CPne
'Twilight' IBlr
'Twilight Zone' **new** IBal
umbellatus L'Hérit. see *A. africanus*
umbellatus Redouté see *A. praecox* subsp. *orientalis*
'Underway' EWes GCal GKev IBlr LPla
'Vallée Blanche' **new** XTur

'Vallée Bleue' XTur
'Vallée de la Belle' **new** XTur
'Vallée de la Loire' XTur
'Vallée de la Sarthe' XTur
'Vallée de l'Authion' XTur
'Vallée du Cap' XTur
'Vallée du Lathan' **new** XTur
'Velvet Night' CPen
'Wavy Navy' CPen
'Wedding Day' NHoy SFai
'Wembworthy' CPne CPrp NHoy SFai
'White Avon' CPen CPne
'White Baby' XTur
'White Dragon' NHoy
'White Dwarf' see *A.* white-flowered, dwarf
'White Heaven'PBR CAby CDoC CHVG CHel CPen CPrp CSpe EBee ECtt ELon EWoo GAbr IBal LPla LRHS LSou LSun MAvo MCot MHol NHoy SCob SEND SFai SHyH SMrm SWat WCot WWEG
'White Ice' CBcs CPen
'White Orb' NHoy
'White Smile' EPri MBri
'White Starlet' NHoy
'White Superior' CPen EBee EPfP GMaP LAst
'White Umbrella' LRHS NHoy
white-flowered CHEx
§ white-flowered, dwarf CBro CKno CPen EBee ECha ECtt EPfP EShb EWTr GBuc IBal LRHS MWat NBir NGdn NHol SEND
'Whitestorm' NHoy SCob
'Whitney'PBR CPen IBlr
'Windlebrooke' CCCN EAJP EPri LPla
'Windsor Castle' CPen CPrp IBal IBlr
'Windsor Grey' Widely available
'Winsome' IBlr
'Wolga' CBro EBee
'Wolkberg' Kirstenbosch IBlr
'Yves Klein' IBlr
'Zachary' CPen CPne CPou CPrp ELon LRHS
'Zebra' NHoy

Agapetes (*Ericaceae*)

'Ludgvan Cross' ♀H2 CCCN CTsd EBee SEle
serpens ♀H2 CCCN CHEx CHll SLon
- 'Scarlet Elf' CCCN LRHS
smithiana var. ***major*** GGGa

Agastache (*Lamiaceae*)

'After Eight' EBee IBoy LRHS NCGa NDov
anethiodora see *A. foeniculum* (Pursh) Kuntze
anisata see *A. foeniculum* (Pursh) Kuntze
aurantiaca SPhx
- 'Apricot Sprite' EPfP LRHS MHer MPro MSCN NGdn NSoo SRkn SRms WHar
- 'Lilac Sprite' LRHS
- 'Peach Margarita' (Cocktail Series) MPro
'Blackadder' Widely available
'Blue Boa' CWGN ECtt MNHC NCGa
'Blue Delight' SBch
'Blue Fortune' ♀H6 CBcs ECha LPla LRHS MAvo MBri MCot MRav NDov NLar NSoo SCob SMad SPer SPhx SWvt WWEG
'Bolero' CSpe LRHS MAvo
§ ***cana*** SPhx
- 'Heatwave'PBR LRHS MAvo NDov WCot
- 'Purple Pygmy' EPfP SRot
'Cotton Candy'PBR IBoy
'Firebird' EAEE EBee ECtt ELan GKin LSou NSoo SPer SWat SWvt
foeniculum misapplied see *A. rugosa*
§ ***foeniculum*** (Pursh) Kuntze CArn CMea EBee ELan ENfk GMaP GPoy MCot MHer MNHC SPav SPhx SRms WHea WJek WWEG XLum
- 'Alabaster' CBcs EBee NLar
- 'Alba' NBre SHDw SPav
'Globetrotter' SPhx WSHC
'Kolibri' ECtt NDov
'Linda' CSpe NDov WCot
§ ***mexicana*** SPav
- 'Red Fortune'PBR CAbP CBct CMea CWGN CWld EAEE ECtt EPla LRHS MCot MHol MPie MSCN NEgg NLar NSti SCob SEND SMad SPad SPoG WCot WRHF
- 'Rosea' see *A. cana*
- 'Sangria' LRHS MAvo MCot NGdn SPad SPhx SRms
nepetoides EPPr NDov SPav
'Painted Lady' CSpe ECtt WHea
pallidiflora MRav
var. ***neomexicana*** 'Lavender Haze'
'Pink Beauty' GBBs MAvo NLar
'Pink Panther' WSHC
'Pink Pop' EPfP SPad
'Purple Flame' **new** EAEE
'Purple Haze' LRHS NDov WWEG
'Raspberry Summer'PBR CWGN ECtt EPla LRHS LSou MNHC NCGa NDov NLar SCob WAul
'Rose Mint' CSpe
§ ***rugosa*** CAby CArn CBod CUse ECha ELau GPoy LEdu MNHC SPav SPhx SPlb SRms SWat WHea WJek WMoo
- B&SWJ 4187 from Korea WCru
- f. ***albiflora*** NBre
- - 'Alabaster' MAvo NDov
- - 'Liquorice White' EBee ELan EPfP MBel NLar SMrm SPlb WGwG
- 'Golden Jubilee' CAby CBod CSpe EAEE EBee ECha ECtt ELan EPla IBoy LRHS MAvo MHer MNHC MSpe NLar NOrc NSti NWad SCob SPoG SRms SWvt WJek WMoo WWEG XLum
- Heronswood strain CSpe
- 'Honey Bee Blue' NWad
- 'Korean Zest' WCru
- 'Liquorice Blue' CKno CTsd ELan EPfP LPot MBel MSpe MWat NEgg NGBl NGdn NOrc NWad SPer SPoG SWvt WHea WMoo WWEG
rupestris CSpe EWTr SPhx XLum
- 'Apache Sunset' SPlb
'Serpentine' CSpe ECtt NDov SPhx WWEG
'Summer Fiesta'PBR ECtt IBoy LSou MBri MNrw NCGa NDov
'Summer Glow'PBR CKno CMos CWGN ECtt GBin IPot LLHF LSou MBel MNrw NCGa NDov SCob SDys SPoG WHlf
'Summer Love'PBR CSpe ECtt LSou MNrw NCGa NDov NLar
'Summer Sky'PBR ECtt LRHS NCGa NDov
'Summer Sunset' CMea CWGN EAEE EPla LSou NCGa SCob SPoG

'Tangerine Dreams'	ECtt EPfP MAvo NCGa NEgg SBch SCoo WHil
'Tango'	LRHS SGbt SMrm
'Tutti-frutti'	ECtt
urticifolia	CSpe WHea
- 'Alba'	CSpe

Agathaea see *Felicia*

Agathis (*Araucariaceae*)

australis	CBrP CDoC

Agathosma (*Rutaceae*)

ovata	CCCN

Agave ✿ (*Asparagaceae*)

sp.	WCot
albomarginata	CDTJ
americana ♀H2	CAbb CBcs CBen CDoC CHEx CHel EPfP EShb EUJe LPal LRHS LSun NLos SArc SCob SEND SMad SPlb SPre SVen SWvt
- 'Marginata' (v) ♀H2	CBrP CDTJ CFil CHll NSbr SEND SVen WCot WSFF
- 'Mediopicta' misapplied	see *A. americana* 'Mediopicta Alba'
- 'Mediopicta' (v) ♀H2	CDTJ CFil CHEx SArc SBig
§ - 'Mediopicta Alba' (v) ♀H2	CBrP CDTJ CFil CJun CTre ESwi SEND WCot
- 'Mediopicta Aurea' (v)	CFil WCot
- var. ***oaxacensis***	WPGP
- subsp. ***protamericana***	CDTJ
- subsp. ***protamericana*** × ***scabra*** F&M 310	WPGP
- 'Striata' (v)	EShb WCot
- 'Variegata' (v) ♀H2	CAbb CBcs CBen CDoC CFil CHEx CSde EPfP EShb EUJe EWes LPal LRHS LSun MGos MRav NPer NPla NSoo SArc SChr SCob SMad SPlb SWvt WCot
angustifolia	see *A. vivipara* var. *vivipara*
- var. ***marginata*** hort.	SBig WCot
applanata	CFil CJun WPGP
asperrima	CDTJ CHel
§ - subsp. ***maderensis***	SPlb
atrovirens	WCot
- var. ***mirabilis***	CDTJ CFil
- - F&M 245	WPGP
attenuata	CAbb CBrP CDTJ SBig SPlb WCot WPGP
'Bloodspot'	WCot
boldinghiana	WCot
bovicornuta	WCot
bracteosa	CCCN CDTJ WCot
celsii	see *A. mitis* var. *mitis*
cerulata subsp. ***nelsonii***	CDTJ
chrysantha	CCCN CDTJ CTre EBee WCot WGrn
- 'Black Canyon'	WCot
colimana	see *A. ortgiesiana*
colorata	CCCN CDTJ CJun WCot
'Cornelius'	WCot
cupreata	CDTJ
de-meesteriana	MHin
deserti	CDTJ CDoC CHel CJun CTre LRHS WCot
- var. ***simplex*** new	WCot
difformis	CDTJ
- NJM 05.034	WPGP
durangensis	SPlb
elongata	see *A. vivipara* var. *vivipara*
ensifera	CJun
felgeri	CDTJ
ferdinandi-regis	see *A. victoriae-reginae*
ferox	see *A. salmiana* var. *ferox*
filifera ♀H2	CCCN CDTJ CHEx CJun CTre SChr SPlb
flexispina	SPlb
garciae-mendozae	CDTJ
geminiflora	CCCN CDTJ CFil CHel CJun CTre EShb
gentryi	CDTJ CFil LPal SPlb
- F&M 213A	WPGP
ghiesbreghtii	CTre
gigantea	see *Furcraea foetida*
× ***gracilipes***	WPGP
guadalajarana	CDTJ
guttata	WCot
havardiana	CFil WCot XSen
- DJH 1326	WCot
horrida	CDTJ CFil CJun SBig
- subsp. ***horrida***	SPlb
- 'Perotensis'	EShb
hurteri	CDTJ
impressa	WCot
kerchovei	WCot
lechuguilla	CDTJ SChr WCot XSen
lophantha	see *A. univittata*
- var. ***caerulescens***	see *A. univittata*
'Macha Mocha'	WCot
macroacantha ♀H1c	CDTJ
maculosa	WCot
marmorata	CJun WCot
maximilliana	SPlb
mckelveyana	WCot
§ ***mitis*** var. ***mitis***	CDTJ CDoC SPlb
- var. ***mitis*** × ***variegata***	WCot
montana	CDTJ CFil EUJe LPal NLos SChr SMad SPlb WCot
- F&M 221	WPGP
- F&M 289	WPGP
neomexicana	CCCN CDTJ CFil EBee SPlb XSen
- S&B 948	WCot
nizandensis	CHEx
§ ***obscura***	CDTJ WCot
oroensis	WCot
§ ***ortgiesiana***	WCot
ovatifolia	CDTJ CFil CJun SKHP SPlb
- NJM 09.002	WPGP
palmeri	CCCN CFil EBee WCot
panamana	see *A. vivipara* var. *vivipara*
parrasana ♀H2	CDTJ WPGP
parryi ♀H2	CDTJ CDoC CHel CTre GKev LPal SPlb WCot WPGP XSen
- var. ***couesii***	SKHP XSen
- 'Cream Spike' (v)	CFil ESwi WCot WGrn
- var. ***huachucensis***	CDTJ WCot
- 'Ohi-kissho-ten-nishiki' (v)	WCot
- subsp. ***parryi***	CDTJ WCot WPGP
- var. ***truncata*** variegated (v)	WCot
parviflora ♀H2	WCot
polyacantha var. ***xalapensis***	see *A. obscura*
potatorum 'Gary Fisher'	WCot
salmiana	CDTJ CFil SBig SPlb
- F&M 290	WPGP

- subsp. ***crassispina*** SPlb
§ - var. ***ferox*** CDTJ CDoC CHel CTre SArc SBig SPlb
scabra CCCN CDoC CHel EBee WCot
- subsp. ***maderensis*** see *A. asperrima* subsp. *maderensis*
schidigera LPal WCot
- 'Shira-ito-no-ohi' (v) WCot
schottii CDTJ WCot
'Sharkskin Shoes' WCot
shrevei subsp. ***magna*** SPlb
sileri WCot
stictata WCot
striata subsp. ***falcata*** WCot
* - ***rubra*** CDTJ SPlb
stricta ♀H2 CCCN CDTJ WCot
- 'Nana' CDTJ
aff. ***stricta*** **new** WCot
tequilana variegated (v) WCot
toumeyana ♀H2 CAbb CTre WCot
- var. ***bella*** CDTJ XSen
triangularis CDTJ
undulata WCot
- 'Chocolate Chips' WCot
§ ***univittata*** CDTJ CJun LPal WCot
- 'Quadricolor' (v) CDTJ NLos SMad SPlb WCot
utahensis ♀H3 SEND SPlb WCot XSen
- var. ***eborispina*** WCot XSen
- subsp. ***kaibabensis*** WCot XSen
variegata WCot
- B&SWJ 10234 WCru
§ ***victoriae-reginae*** ♀H2 CCCN CDTJ CJun CTre LPal SChr
- dwarf WCot
virginica WCot
§ ***vivipara*** var. ***vivipara*** WCot
wocomahi WCot
xylonacantha SChr SPlb WCot

Ageratina (*Asteraceae*)

§ ***altissima*** CHid CMac MCot
- 'Braunlaub' CBod CPrp ECtt MMuc NBir NLar SEND SHar SWat WMnd WPtf WWtn
- 'Chocolate' Widely available
§ ***aromatica*** MRav NBro SHar SWat
§ ***ligustrina*** CExl CHel CMHG CRHN CSde CTri EBee ECha EHoe ELan EWTr EWoo GCal LRHS MBlu NCGa SBrt SDix SEND SLim SPer SPhx SPoG SRkn SRms WPGP WPat WSFF WSHC

Ageratum (*Asteraceae*)

'Blue Champion' LAst NPri
corymbosum CHll CSpe
houstonianum 'Blue Danube' CWCL
- 'High Tide Blue' NPri

Agonis (*Myrtaceae*)

flexuosa CCCN

Agrimonia (*Rosaceae*)

eupatoria CArn CBod CHab CWld ENfk GPoy MHer MNHC NMir SWat WHer WHfH
* - var. ***alba*** NLar
grandiflora EBee
odorata misapplied see *A. procera*
odorata (L.) Mill. see *A. repens*
pilosa CArn EBee
§ ***procera*** EBee
§ ***repens*** WMoo

Agropyron (*Poaceae*)

glaucum see *Elymus hispidus*
magellanicum see *Elymus magellanicus*
pubiflorum see *Elymus magellanicus*

Agrostemma (*Caryophyllaceae*)

coronaria see *Lychnis coronaria*
githago CHab CWld MNHC
- 'Ocean Pearl' CSpe MCot SPhx

Agrostis (*Poaceae*)

calamagrostis see *Stipa calamagrostis*
§ ***canina*** 'Silver Needles' (v) NBir WWEG
capillaris CHab
§ ***montevidensis*** NWsh SMad
nebulosa CKno SPhx
- 'Fibre Optics' see *Panicum* 'Fibre Optics'
stolonifera 'Julia Ann' (v) WCot

Aichryson (*Crassulaceae*)

§ × ***aizoides*** var. ***domesticum*** CSuc
- var. ***domesticum*** 'Variegatum' (v) ♀H1c EBak WCot
villosum CFil

Ailanthus (*Simaroubaceae*)

§ ***altissima*** CAco CBcs CCVT CDul CExl CMac EBee EPfP EUJe IDee LEdu NWea SEND SPer SPlb SWvt
- var. ***tanakae*** CWJ 12452 WCru
- - RWJ 9906 WCru
glandulosa see *A. altissima*

Ainsliaea (*Asteraceae*)

acerifolia B&SWJ 4795 WCru
- var. ***subapoda*** B&SWJ 11537 WCru
apiculata B&SWJ 11397 WCru
- var. ***acerifolia*** B&SWJ 6059 WCru
chapaensis B&SWJ 11720 WCru
- B&SWJ 11732 **new** WCru
latifolia FMWJ 13426 **new** WCru
nervosa B&SWJ 11344 WCru
petelotii FMWJ 13427 **new** WCru
tonkinensis B&SWJ 11819 WCru
uniflora GEdr
- B&SWJ 11336 WCru

Ajania (*Asteraceae*)

§ ***pacifica*** EBee
- 'Silver Edge' XLum

Ajuga (*Lamiaceae*)

ciliata var. ***villosior*** CCon
genevensis LRHS SPhx
incisa EBee EWld GBin GCal SIgm
- 'Bikun' (v) CDes EBee SRGP WCot WSHC
- 'Blue Enigma' CExl CLAP EWes IMou NLar
'Little Court Pink' see *A. reptans* 'Purple Torch'
metallica hort. see *A. pyramidalis*

'Pink Lightning' (v) new ECtt
'Pink Spires' NCot WFar
§ ***pyramidalis*** CArn
- 'Metallica Crispa' CBct CBre EBee ECho ELan EPri EWes GKin NBir NEoE NHol NLar SRms SWvt WFar
reptans CArn CHab CTri ECtt ENfk GKev GPoy LRHS MBel MCot MHer MNHC NMir WJek WOut XLum
- f. ***albiflora*** CRow WHfH
- - 'Alba' CArn CBre ECtt ELon MRav NBro SRms WMoo
- 'Arctic Fox' (v) ECho LSou MRav MSCN SWvt
- 'Argentea' see *A. reptans* 'Variegata'
§ - 'Atropurpurea' ECha ECho ELan EPfP LRHS MGos MLHP MSpe NWad SEND SGol SPer SPlb SRms SWvt WBrk WJek WWEG XLum
- Black Scallop = 'Binblasca'[PBR] Widely available
- 'Braunherz' CBct CTri ECho ECtt EHoe ELan EPfP EShb GAbr GMaP IGor LRHS MAsh MBri MHer MWat NBir NLar SCob SGol SPer SWvt WFar WHar WHil WHoo WMoo
- 'Burgundy Glow' (v) CBcs CBct CBod CWCL ECha ECho EHoe ELan EPfP GMaP IFro LAst LBuc LRHS MAsh MGos MHer MJak SCob SGol SPad SPer SPlb SPoG SRms SWvt WMoo
§ - 'Catlin's Giant' ♀H7 Widely available
- 'Choc Ice' new EPPr
- 'Chocolate Chip' see *A. reptans* 'Valfredda'
- 'Delight' (v) ECho EPot
- 'Dixie Chip' EPfP NLar
- 'Evening Glow' WMoo
- 'Flisteridge' CNat
- 'Golden Beauty' ECtt WOut
- 'Golden Glow' (v) LRHS
- 'Grey Lady' GBuc
- 'Harlequin' (v) SWvt
- 'John Pierpoint' SHar
- 'Jumbo' see *A. reptans* 'Jungle Beauty'
§ - 'Jungle Beauty' EAEE EPfP MRav XLum
- 'Macrophylla' see *A. reptans* 'Catlin's Giant'
- 'Mahogany' new CBod
§ - 'Multicolor' (v) CBcs CBct ECho ELan LRHS MRav SPlb SPoG SRms SWvt WMoo
- 'Palisander' ECtt
- 'Party Colours' CLAP
- 'Pink Elf' CMHG ECho GCra MRav NBro SWat WFar WWEG
- 'Pink Surprise' EHoe EPri MHer MLHP NRya
- 'Purple Brocade' EHoe
§ - 'Purple Torch' NBir NLar SRms
- 'Purpurea' see *A. reptans* 'Atropurpurea'
- 'Rainbow' see *A. reptans* 'Multicolor'
- 'Rosea' EAEE EBee ELon WMoo XLum
- 'Rowden Royal Purple' CRow EBee
- 'Toffee Chip'[PBR] (v) LSou SGol
- 'Tricolor' see *A. reptans* 'Multicolor'
§ - 'Valfredda' CBod ECho ECtt EPfP GKev LRHS NLar SRms WBrk WCot WGwG WMoo
§ - 'Variegata' (v) CBct ECho ECtt EPfP MHol SEND SPer SPoG SRms SWat WFar
Sugar Plum = 'Binsugplu'[PBR] ELon

Akebia ✿ (*Lardizabalaceae*)

sp. GGal
longeracemosa CRHN SBrt SChF
- B&SWJ 3606 CExl LEdu WCot WCru WPGP
× ***pentaphylla*** CRHN ELan EPfP EWTr LRHS MAsh MRav NLar SPer
- B&SWJ 2829 WCru
quinata Widely available
- B&SWJ 4425 WCru
- 'Alba' CBcs CHll CMen CSPN CWGN NLar SMDP WPat
- 'Amethyst' EBee EMil SKHP
- 'Amethyst Glow' EPfP LRHS NLar SPer SPoG
- cream-flowered CHel CRHN EBee EPfP EWld LRHS MRav SKHP SPer SPoG SRms SSta SWvt WCru WPGP
- 'Shirobana' MBlu
- variegated (v) CBcs LLHF SMad WPat
- 'White Chocolate' ♀H5 ESwi NLar WCru WSHC
trifoliata CBcs CRHN ELan EPfP EWld LRHS SEND SLim SLon WOld
- B&SWJ 2829 WCru
- B&SWJ 5063 WCru

Alangium (*Cornaceae*)

platanifolium CAbP CBcs CExl EBee SBrt WPGP
- var. ***macrophyllum*** EPfP ETwe SEND SPoG WBor
- var. ***platanifolium*** NLar

Albizia (*Mimosaceae*)

chinensis EPfP LRHS
distachya see *Paraserianthes lophantha*
§ ***julibrissin*** CAco CArn CDTJ EBee EPfP EPla NEgg NLos
- 'Ernest Wilson' ETwe EWld MTPN WGrn
- 'Evy's Purple' SGol
- Ombrella = 'Boubri'[PBR] ELan EPfP LRHS MBri WHar WPGP
- f. ***rosea*** ♀H2 CArn CBcs CDul CExl CHEx CLnd CMCN CSpe CWGN EBee ELan ELon EPfP EUJe LRHS MGos NSoo SArc SEND SHil SLim SPad SPlb SPoG SPtp SSpi WPGP WSHC
- 'Rouge d'Été' MPkF
I - 'Rouge Selection' EMil EPfP LRHS
- 'Summer Chocolate'[PBR] ♀H2 CBcs CDul CWGN EBee ELan EPfP LRHS LSqu MPkF NPri SCoo SHil SPer SPoG WHar WPGP
kalkora SPlb
lophantha see *Paraserianthes lophantha*

Albuca ✿ (*Asparagaceae*)

JCA 15856 CTca
from Lesotho GCal
§ ***abyssinica*** EBee GKev
acuminata new CDes
angolensis CPou
aurea CTca
bainesii see *A. abyssinica*
* ***batliana*** ECho
batteniana CCon ECho
canadensis (L.) F.M. Leight CPou WCot WHil
cooperi ECho
'Dirk Wallace' CExl
fastigiata ECho
fragrans EBee
glauca EBee ECho

humilis	CExl ECho EPot LLHF NRya WAbe WHil
longifolia	ECho
namaquensis	WHil
nelsonii	CAvo CDes CPne CPrp CTca EBee ECho GKev LAma WCot WHil
setosa	CDes CTca EBee ECho
shawii	CBod CCon CDes CMos CPne CPou CTca EAJP EBee ECho EPla EPot EPri GKev GKin LAst MHer NCGa SPoG WAbe WGwG WHil
trichophylla	WHil

× *Alcalthaea* (*Malvaceae*)

suffrutescens 'Parkallee' (d)	CAbP CDes CSpe EBee ECha ECtt ELon LPla LRHS LSun MAvo MNrw NGdn NLar SEND SPad SPhx WBrk WCot WWFP XLum
- 'Parkfrieden' (d)	CDes CSpe ECtt ELon MAvo MNrw SPhx XLum
- 'Parkrondell' (d)	CDes ECha ECtt ELon LPla MAvo MNrw SHar WCot XLum
- 'Poetry' **new**	ECtt
- white-flowered	IFro

Alcea (*Malvaceae*)

'Apple Blossom' (d)	EPfP SMrm
'Arabian Nights'	SPav
'Blackcurrant Whirl'	SPav
ficifolia	NChi SPav WMoo
'Happy Lights'	ELon SMrm
'Las Vegas' **new**	LSun NCGa SMrm
'Peaches 'n' Dreams'	EPfP NGBl
§ ***rosea***	SVic
- 'Blacknight' (Spotlight Series)	SMrm
- Chater's Double Group (d)	ECtt EPfP IBoy MBri MHol MPro SPoG SRms WHar WRHF
- - chamois (d)	EPfP
- - chestnut brown-flowered (d)	EPfP
- - golden-yellow flowered (d) **new**	SMrm
- - maroon-flowered (d)	CBod EPfP LAst NPri SPoG
- - pink-flowered (d)	CBod ELan EPfP NSoo
- - red-flowered (d)	CBod ELan EPfP MPro SPoG
- - rose pink-flowered (d) **new**	NPri
- - salmon pink-flowered (d)	CBod ELan EPfP
- - scarlet-flowered (d)	EPfP NPri NSoo SPoG
- - violet-flowered (d)	CBod EPfP NPri
- - white-flowered (d)	CBod ELan EPfP NPri NSoo SMrm SPoG
- - yellow-flowered (d)	CBod EPfP NPri NSoo SPoG SRms
- - apricot-flowered (d) **new**	MPro NPri
- 'Crème de Cassis'	ELan EPfP LRHS NGBl SPav
- double apricot-flowered (d)	EBee
- double yellow-flowered (d)	EBee
- (Halo Series) 'Halo Apricot' **new**	CBod LRHS
- - 'Halo Blush' **new**	LRHS
- - 'Halo Cerise' **new**	LRHS
- - 'Halo Cream' **new**	LRHS
- - 'Halo Red' **new**	EBee LRHS
- 'Mars Magic' (Spotlight Series)	CBod EPfP MNHC MWat SMrm
- 'Nigra'	CSpe ECtt ELan EPfP IBoy LAst LPal LRHS MHer MNHC MPro MSpe MWat NGBl NGdn NPri SBod SPer SPhx SRms WCAu WHar WWEG XEll
- 'Polarstar' (Spotlight Series)	MNHC
- single pink-flowered	EWoo
- Spring Celebrities Group (d)	CWCL
- Summer Carnival Group	SMrm SRms
- 'Sunshine' (Spotlight Series)	CHVG EPfP MWat
- 'The Watchman'	NSoo
§ ***rugosa***	MSpe SHar SPav XSen

Alchemilla ✿ (*Rosaceae*)

sp.	CUse
abyssinica	EBee
alpina misapplied	see *A. conjuncta*, *A. plicatula*
alpina ambig.	MCot
alpina L.	CMea EBee ECho EHoe ELan EPfP EWTr GKev GPoy LEdu LRHS MMuc MRav MWat NChi SBch SEND SRms SWat WMoo
§ ***conjuncta***	CArn CMac CPrp CSam EBee ECha ELan EPfP EShb GAbr GMaP MHer MLHP MNFA MRav NBid NChi NRya SPer SPlb SRms WJek WKif
ellenbeckii	ECho EPfP GAbr IMou WPGP WWFP
epipsila	EBee ELan EShb GCal LRHS LSun NLar SPhx
erythropoda ♀H5	Widely available
- Turkish form **new**	ECha
faeroensis	WMoo WPtf XLum
- var. ***pumila***	EBee GEdr WAbe
glaucescens	CNat
hoppeana misapplied	see *A. plicatula*
hoppeana (Reichenb.) Dalla Torre	EBee
iniquiformis	EBee WPGP
lapeyrousei	EBee NChi
mollis ♀H7	Widely available
- 'Robustica'	MMuc SEND SPlb SWat WFar WMoo WPnP
- 'Thriller'	CBod EPfP LRHS WFar
'Mr Poland's Variety'	see *A. venosa*
pedata	CHid NChi
peristerica	EBee
§ ***plicatula***	NLar
saxatilis	MWhi NLar
sericata 'Gold Strike'	IMou LBMP MWhi SHar SMad WHil
straminea	MRav
valdehirsuta	EBee
§ ***venosa***	EBee SMHy
vetteri	EBee LRHS WHrl
vulgaris misapplied	see *A. xanthochlora*
§ ***xanthochlora***	CArn GPoy NLar SRms WFar WHer

Aldrovanda (*Droseraceae*)

vesiculosa	EFEx

alecost see *Tanacetum balsamita*

Alectorurus (*Liliaceae*)

yedoensis var. ***platypetalus***	EBee GEdr GKev

Alectryon (*Sapindaceae*)

excelsus	CBcs ECou

Aletris (*Melanthiaceae*)

farinosa	CArn

Aliciella (*Polemoniaceae*)

subnuda new	CPBP

Alisma (*Alismataceae*)

lanceolatum	MSKA
plantago-aquatica	CBAq CBen CHab CRow CSpe EHon MSKA MWts NPer SWat WMAq WWtn XBlo
- var. ***parviflorum***	CBAq MSKA MWts SPlb SWat

Alkanna (*Boraginaceae*)

matthioli	CArn

Allamanda (*Apocynaceae*)

cathartica	CCCN

Alliaria (*Brassicaceae*)

petiolata	CArn GPoy NMir WHer WOut WSFF

Allium (*Alliaceae*)

sp.	GEdr
RCB UA 5	WCot
SSSE 250	GEdr
§ ***acuminatum***	ECho GBin NBir NRog
I - 'Album'	ECho LRHS
acutiflorum	LAma NRog
aflatunense misapplied	see *A. hollandicum*
aflatunense ambig.	ECho LRHS SCob SDeJ SEND WWEG
I - 'Alba'	ECho
akaka	NRog
'Akbulak'	EBee ECho LAma
albopilosum	see *A. cristophii*
alexeianum new	NRog
altaicum	ECho
altissimum	LAma NRog
- 'Goliath'	CTca GKev NRog WCot
amabile	see *A. mairei* var. *amabile*
'Ambassador'	CBro CMea CTca ERCP LAma LRHS MAvo MNrw NRog SPhx WCot
amethystinum 'Red Mohican' new	ERCP
ampeloprasum	CPrp EBee ECha ECho LAma NRog SPlb WHer WShi
- var. ***babingtonii***	CAgr CArn CTca GPoy LEdu NRog WHer WShi
§ - 'Elephant'	LEdu
amphibolum	EBee ECho EPot LAma NRog
amplectens	ECho LAma LLHF NRog
- 'Graceful Beauty'	ERCP NRog SCob SDeJ WCot XEll
anceps	NRog
§ ***angulosum***	CAvo CTca ECho EWld GKev LAma LEdu LPla NRog SMrm WCot
aschersonianum	ERCP SDeJ
atropurpureum	CBod EBee ECha ELan EPfP ERCP LAma LRHS MCot MWat NRog SDeJ SPer SPhx
atroviolaceum	WCot
azureum	see *A. caeruleum*
backhousianum	LAma NRog
balansae	ECho
barszczewskii	NRog
'Beau Regard' ♀H7	CTca CWCL EBee ELan ERCP LAma LRHS NLar NRog
beesianum misapplied	see *A. cyaneum*
beesianum W.W. Sm. ♀H5	CDes CPom NBir NRya
- 'Album'	ECho
bisceptrum new	NRog
blandum	see *A. carolinianum*
bodeanum	see *A. cristophii*
'Bolero'	CAvo EBee LRHS NRog
bulgaricum	see *Nectaroscordum siculum* subsp. *bulgaricum*
§ ***caeruleum*** ♀H5	CAby CArn CAvo CBro CSpe CTca CTri EAJP EBee ECho ECtt EPfP EPot ERCP LAma LPot LRHS MBri MGos MNrw NBir NLar NRog NRya SCob SDeJ SPer SPhx
- ***azureum***	see *A. caeruleum*
caesium ♀H5	CAvo ECho ERCP NRog
caespitosum	ECho
callimischon subsp. ***callimischon***	ECho EPot NRog
- subsp. ***haemostictum***	CDes ECho NRog WCot
'Cameleon' new	ECho ERCP LAma LRHS NRog
campanulatum	NRog
canadense	CArn
§ ***carinatum***	ECho GKev MBel
§ - subsp. ***pulchellum*** ♀H5	CBro EBee ECha ECho EPot GKev LAma LLWP LRHS LSun MHer MMuc MNFA MNrw MWat NDov NRog SEND SPhx WThu
- - f. ***album*** ♀H5	CBro EBee ECha ECho GKev LEdu LLWP LSun MNrw MWat NDov NRog SBch SMrm SPhx WPtf
§ ***carolinianum***	ECho LAma NRog
cepa	CBod SVic
- Aggregatum Group	ELau GPoy
- - 'Golden Gourmet' ♀H3	SVic
- - 'Matador' ♀H3	SVic
- - 'Pikant'	SVic
- 'Kew White'	WCot
- 'Perutile'	CArn CHby GPoy LEdu MHer SHDw
- Proliferum Group	CAgr CArn CHby CPrp EOHP GAbr GPoy LEdu MHer MNHC SIde WGwG WHer WJek XLum
- 'Red Brunswick'	SVic
- var. ***viviparum***	ECho LAma NRog
- 'White Lisbon' ♀H4	SVic
cernuum	CAby CAvo CBod CBro CMea CTca EBee ECha ECho EPfP EPot ERCP GBin GKev LAma LEdu LRHS MBel MCot MLHP MNrw MSpe NRog SDeJ SKHP SPhx SRms
§ - 'Hidcote' ♀H5	CSam WKif
- 'Major'	see *A. cernuum* 'Hidcote'
- var. ***obtusum***	ECho
- pink-flowered	NBir
- 'White Dwarf'	EBee ECho NRog SBch
chinense	GPoy LEdu
cirrhosum	see *A. carinatum* subsp. *pulchellum*
colchicifolium	NRog
cowanii	see *A. neapolitanum* Cowanii Group
crenulatum	CPom LAma NRog
crispum	NRog
§ ***cristophii*** ♀H7	Widely available
cupanii	ECho
cupuliferum	NRog
curtum RCB RL 13	WCot
§ ***cyaneum*** ♀H5	CPBP CPom ECho GEdr LAma LBee LRHS MHer NRog NRya WCot

- ACE 1363 new	EPot
cyathophorum	ECho
§ - var. ***farreri***	CArn CAvo CBre CBro CPom ECho EPot LEdu LLWP LRHS MLHP MNrw MRav NChi NRya WCot WPtf WThu
darwasicum RM 8274	ECho WCot
decipiens	ECho LAma NRog
diabaloense	NRog
dichlamydeum	NRog
douglasii new	NRog
§ ***drummondii***	LRHS
'Early Emperor'	CWCL EBee EPfP ERCP LAma LRHS NRog SCob
elatum	see *A. macleanii*
elburzense new	NRog
'Emir'	NRog
ericetorum	CPom NRog WCot
falcifolium	CTal ECho EPot LAma LLHF NMin NRog WCot
farreri	see *A. cyathophorum* var. *farreri*
fasciculatum	LAma
fimbriatum	ECho NRog
- var. ***purdyi***	NRog
'Firmament'	CAvo CBro ECha ERCP LAma LRHS NRog SDeJ SPhx WCot
fistulosum	CArn CHby ECho ELau ENfk GBin GKev GPoy LAma LEdu MHer MMuc MNHC NPri SEND SIde SRms SVic WCot WGwG WJek XLum
- 'Red Welsh'	SRms WJek
flavum ♀H4	CArn CBro CTca ECGP ECha ECho EPot ERCP GKev LAma LRHS NSla SDeJ SMad WGwG WThu WWEG
§ - 'Blue Leaf'	ECho LEdu NBir SMrm
- subsp. ***flavum***	EBee ECho NRog
- - var. ***minus***	ECho MMuc NRog SEND
- 'Glaucum'	see *A. flavum* 'Blue Leaf'
- var. ***nanum***	ECho EPot NRog
- subsp. ***tauricum***	CSpe ECho NRog SPhx WCot
'Forelock'	CAvo CTca EBee ERCP LAma MNrw NRog SCob WCot XEll
forrestii	ECho GKev WCot
geyeri	EBee ECho GBin WCot
giganteum	CAvo CBcs CBod CTca CWCL EBee ECtt ELan EPfP ERCP GKev GPoy IBoy LAma LRHS MAvo MBri MWat NLar NOrc NRog SCob SDeJ SPer SPoG SRms SWat SWvt
'Gladiator' ♀H7	CAvo CCon CTca CWCL EBee ECtt EPfP ERCP GMaP LAma LRHS LSun NOrc NRog SDeJ SPad
glaucum	see *A. senescens* subsp. *glaucum*
'Globemaster' ♀H7	CAby CAvo CBro CMea CTca CWCL EBee ECtt ELan EPfP EPot ERCP LAma LEdu LRHS MAvo MBri MMHG MNrw NLar SCob SDeJ SPer SPhx WCot
'Globus'	CTca EBee LAma NRog
goodingii	ECho
guttatum	ECho NRog
subsp. ***dalmaticum***	
- - HOA 9114	ECho
- subsp. ***sardoum***	NRog
- - CH 859	ECho
gypsaceum	NRog
haemanthoides	WCot
haematochiton	ECho NRog
'Hair'	see *A. vineale* 'Hair'
heldreichii	EBee ECho NRog
* ***hirtifolium*** var. ***album***	EBee ECho LAma NRog
'His Excellency'	CCon EBee ERCP LAma LRHS NRog SCob
§ ***hollandicum*** ♀H7	CAvo CBro CTca ECGP ECha ECtt EPfP GKev LAma NOrc NRog SPer SPlb WFar
- 'Purple Sensation' ♀H7	Widely available
- 'Purple Surprise' ♀H7	NBir WCot
hookeri ACE 2430	EPot LEdu WCot
- var. ***muliense***	GEdr LEdu
- 'Zorami'	LEdu
howellii var. ***clokeyi***	NRog
humile	ECho GEdr
hyalinum	NRog
- pink-flowered	EBee
inconspicuum	LAma NRog
§ ***insubricum*** ♀H5	CDes GEdr MNrw NBir NRog WAbe WPtf
'Jackpot'	ERCP LAma NRog
jajlae	see *A. rotundum* subsp. *jajlae*
jesdianum 'Michael Hoog'	see *A. rosenorum* 'Michael H. Hoog'
- 'Purple King'	ERCP LRHS MNrw NRog
- 'White Empress' PBR	CAvo EBee NRog SPhx
kansuense	see *A. sikkimense*
karataviense ♀H5	CAby CAvo CTca EBee ECha ELan EPot GAbr GKev LAma LRHS LSun MBri MCot NBir NLar NRog SCob SDeJ SWvt WHoo WRHF
- subsp. ***henrikii***	NRog
- 'Ivory Queen'	CAby CAvo CBro CTca EBee ECha EPfP ERCP GKev LAma LRHS NLar NRog SCob SDeJ SPlb WWFP
kharputense	NRog
komarovianum	see *A. thunbergii*
komarovii	LAma NRog
lacunosum new	NRog
- var. ***lacunosum***	NRog
ledebourianum	ECho LAma NRog
lemmonii new	NRog
lenkoranicum	CAvo CPom ECho GKev LAma NRog WCot
libani	XLum
litvinovii	LAma NRog
loratum	LAma NRog
'Lucy Ball'	EPfP ERCP LAma LRHS NBir NLar NRog SDeJ
§ ***lusitanicum***	CBro CTca ECha ECho ECtt ERCP GKev NBre NDov NRog SDix SMHy WCot
§ ***macleanii***	EBee ECho EPfP LAma LRHS NRog
macranthum	CPom EBee ECho EPot GBin GEdr GKev LAma NRog
macrochaetum	ECho
macropetalum	ECho
mairei	ECho LAma LLWP LRHS MMuc NRya
§ - var. ***amabile***	ECho GEdr NRya NSla WThu
- - pink-flowered	ECho
- - red-flowered	ECho
maximowiczii	ECho
- white-flowered	ECho LAma
'Mercurius' PBR	EBee ERCP LAma MNrw NRog SPhx WCot
meteoricum	CDes NRog WCot
'Miami'	ERCP NRog

	Name	Suppliers
	'Millennium'	WCot
	moly	CArn CWCL EBee ECho GKev LAma MBri MMuc MRav MWat NRog NRya SBod SCob SDeJ SEND SRms WCot XLum
	- 'Jeannine' 𝕐H5	CBro CTca EBee ECho EPot GAbr GBin LAma LRHS NRog WShi
	'Mont Blanc'	EBee ELan ERCP GBin GQue LAma LRHS MNrw NLar NRog SCob
	multibulbosum	see *A. nigrum*
	murrayanum misapplied	see *A. unifolium*
	murrayanum Regel	see *A. acuminatum*
	myrianthum	NRog
	- KMT-19-04 **new**	EBee
	narcissiflorum misapplied	see *A. insubricum*
§	***narcissiflorum*** Vill.	CPom CSpe EBee ECho MNrw
	neapolitanum	ECGP ECho EPot LAma LRHS MBri MCot NRog SBod SEND SPer SRms WGwG
§	- Cowanii Group	ECGP ECho LRHS NRog SDeJ WCot
	- 'Grandiflorum'	ECho GKev
§	***neriniflorum***	CDes WAbe
	nevii	NRog
	nevskianum	ECho LAma NRog SKHP
§	***nigrum***	CAvo CBro ECGP EPfP EPot ERCP LAma LRHS MCot NBir NRog SDeJ SPhx WCot WRHF
	nutans	CPrp GKev LAma LEdu MHer MNHC NRog SHDw WHal WHil WJek
	nuttallii	see *A. drummondii*
§	***obliquum***	CAvo CBro CPom ECha ECho ERCP LRHS NRog SPhx WCot
	ochotense	WCot
	odorum L.	see *A. ramosum* L.
	oleraceum	WHer
	olympicum	CDes NRog
§	***oreophilum***	CSam ECha ECho GKev LAma LRHS MLHP NRog SMrm SPer SRms WCot
	- 'Agalik'	ECho
	- 'Agalik Giant'	NRog
	- 'Samur'	WCot
	- 'Zwanenburg' 𝕐H5	ECho EPot
	orientale	NRog
	oschaninii	LAma NRog
	ostrowskianum	see *A. oreophilum*
	ovalifolium var. ***leuconeurum***	GEdr WCot
	pallasii	NRog
	pallens	CBre ECho NBir
§	***paniculatum***	NRog
*	- var. ***minor***	LAma NRog
	paradoxum	ECho LEdu NBir
	- var. ***normale***	CBro CDes CPom ECho EPot ERCP EWld NBir NRog WCot
	parciflorum **new**	NRog
	parvum **new**	NRog
	pedemontanum	see *A. narcissiflorum* Vill.
	pendulinum	NRog
	'Pinball Wizard'	CBro CTca CWCL ERCP LAma LRHS NRog
	'Pink Jewel'	ERCP NRog WCot
	platycaule	ECho LAma NRog SKHP WCot
	plummerae	EBee ECho GKev NRog SKHP
	plurifoliatum	ECho LAma
	polyphyllum	see *A. carolinianum*
	porrum 'Musselburgh'	NPri SVic
	protensum	NRog
	przewalskianum	LAma LEdu NRog
	pskemense	LAma NRog WCot
	pulchellum	see *A. carinatum* subsp. *pulchellum*
	'Purple Rain'	CBro ELan ERCP LAma NRog
	pyrenaicum misapplied	see *A. angulosum*
	pyrenaicum Costa & Vayr.	SEND
	ramosum Jacq.	see *A. obliquum*
§	***ramosum*** L.	ECho GKev LAma LEdu NRog
	'Rien Poortvliet'	LAma
	roborowskianum **new**	GKev WCot
	robustum	NRog
	rosenbachianum misapplied	see *A. stipitatum*
	rosenbachianum Regel	CBro LRHS
	- 'Akbulak'	LRHS
	- 'Album'	EPfP ERCP LAma NRog WCot
	- 'Michael Hoog'	see *A. rosenorum* 'Michael H. Hoog'
	- 'Shing'	IBal
§	***rosenorum*** 'Michael H. Hoog'	ECho EPot NRog
	roseum	ECho EPfP EPot GKev LAma LRHS NRog SDeJ
§	***rotundum*** subsp. ***jajlae***	ECho NRog WCot
	'Round and Purple'	ERCP LAma LEdu LRHS NRog
	sarawschanicum	NRog
	sativum	CArn ECho ENfk MHer NPri SIde SPoG SRms
	- 'Albanian Late'	LEdu
	- 'Elephant'	see *A. ampeloprasum* 'Elephant'
	- var. ***ophioscorodon***	ECho GPoy LAma SPlb
	saxatile	ECho GKev NRog
	schmitzii	CPom ECho
	schoenoprasum	Widely available
	- f. ***albiflorum***	CArn CPbn CPrp ECha ECho LEdu MHer NBir NCGa SIde WHer
	- 'Black Isle Blush'	CDes CPbn CTca EBee GPoy LEdu LPla MHer SMHy WPGP
	- 'Corsican White'	LEdu
	- fine-leaved	ELau NDov
	- 'Forescate'	CPrp CTca ECha EPla LAma LEdu LRHS MRav NBir SIde WAul WHoo XLum
	- medium-leaved	ELau NPri
	- 'Netherbyres Dwarf'	CArn
	- 'Pink Perfection'	GPoy LEdu LPla MHer NDov SMHy
	- 'Polyphant'	CBre
	- 'Shining Silver'	LEdu
	- var. ***sibiricum***	SDix WShi
	- 'Silver Chimes'	CDes EBee MRav
	- thick-leaved	ELau
	- 'Wallington White'	LEdu
	- 'Wilau'	ELau
	schubertii 𝕐H4	CAvo CBod CBro CHVG CSpe CTca CWCL ECtt ELan EPfP EPot ERCP GKev LAma LRHS MBri MNrw NDov NRog SCob SDeJ SPer SPhx WCot WWFP
	scorodoprasum	ECho SIde
	- 'Art'	EBee ERCP GKev NRog
	- subsp. ***jajlae***	see *A. rotundum* subsp. *jajlae*
	- 'Passion'	ERCP GKev NRog
	- subsp. ***scorodoprasum***	EBee ECho NRog
	senescens	CArn CBro CTca CTri ECGP EDAr EPot GJos IMou LAma LEdu LRHS MRav SBch SEND SMrm SRms XLum XSen

§ - subsp. ***glaucum*** CArn CAvo CMea CPBP CPrp CSpe CTal EAEE EBee ECha ECho EPla LAst LEdu LRHS MMuc MNFA NDov NGdn NLar NRog NRya SBod SEND SWat WCot XSen
- subsp. ***senescens*** ECho GKev LEdu NRog
sessiliflorum ECho
sewerzowii NRog
shelkovnikovii WCot
sibthorpianum see *A. paniculatum*
siculum see *Nectaroscordum siculum*
§ ***sikkimense*** CBod CCon CPom EBee ECho EWTr GBin GEdr LEdu LRHS MHer MMuc NSla SEND SMHy WCot
'Silver Spring' EPot ERCP MNrw NRog SDeJ WCot
sphaerocephalon Widely available
- subsp. ***arvense*** new NRog
'Spider' CAvo CBro CWCL ERCP NRog SPhx
splendens ECho
I - var. ***kurilense*** GEdr
stamineum new WCot
stellatum LRHS NRog WGwG
stellerianum WThu
var. ***kurilense***
§ ***stipitatum*** ERCP LAma NRog SPhx WCot
- 'Album' CBro NRog
- 'Mars' EBee EPfP ERCP LAma LRHS NRog
- 'Mount Everest' CAvo CBro CCon CHid CTca EPfP EPot ERCP GBin GKev GMaP LAma LRHS MWat NRog SDeJ SPer SPhx WCot WShi
- 'Violet Beauty' CCse CWCL LAma LRHS WCot
- 'White Giant' CTca CWCL EBee ERCP LRHS NRog
stracheyi WCot
'Stratos' EBee ERCP LAma
subhirsutum NRog XLum
subvillosum NRog
'Summer Beauty' see *A. lusitanicum*
'Summer Drummer' CTca EBee ERCP LEdu LRHS NRog SDeJ SPhx
suworowii new NRog
'Sweet Discovery' LAma NRog
taquetii see *A. thunbergii*
tauricola NRog
texanum LAma NRog
§ ***thunbergii*** ♀H5 EBee ECho LAma MHer NBir NRog NRya SPhx WAbe WWEG
- PAB 3821 LEdu
- 'Album' ECho WAbe
- 'Ozawa' CDes EBee ECho SRms WAbe WCot WOld
tibeticum see *A. sikkimense*
tolmiei NRog
var. ***platyphyllum*** new
- var. ***tolmiei*** new NRog
* ***tournefortii*** ECho
triquetrum ECho EDAr ELan ELau EPot LAma LEdu NBir SEND WCot WHer WMoo XLum
tschimganicum LAma NRog SKHP
tuberosum Widely available
- B&SWJ 8881 WCru
- purple/mauve-flowered CHby ECho ELau
tuncelianum new LEdu
umbilicatum NRog
§ ***unifolium*** ♀H4 CAvo CPom EBee ECho EPfP EPot ERCP GBin GKev LAma MHer MRav NBir NRog NSbr SDeJ SEND SMrm
ursinum CArn CHab CHby CWld ECho EOHP GPoy LAma LEdu MHer MMuc NRog WJek WSFF WShi
validum NNS 06-41 WCot
victorialis ECho
- 'Cantabria' CDes EBee GKev NRog WCot
vineale CArn NMir WHer
- PAB 2763 LEdu
- 'Dready' ECho GKev NRog
§ - 'Hair' CAby CTca EBee EPfP ERCP GKev LAma MCot NBir NRog SCob
violaceum see *A. carinatum*
virgunculae CDes CMea
wallichii EWes GKev GMaP GQue LEdu LLHF MBNS NBir NChi SKHP WCot XLum
- CLD 1500 new CDes
- PAB 2976 LEdu
- dark-flowered CPom WCot
woronowii NRog
zaprjagajevii WCot
zebdanense EBee ECho LAma NRog

almond see *Prunus dulcis*

Alnus ✿ (*Betulaceae*)

cordata ♀H5 CBcs CCVT CDoC CDul CLnd CMCN CMac CSBt CSto CTho CTri EBee ECrN ELan EPfP EWTr LBuc MGos NEgg NLar NWea SCob SEND SEWo SGol SPer SPlb WMou WOut
cremastogyne EBtc
fauriei from Niigata, Japan CSto
firma CSto
glutinosa CAco CBcs CCVT CDoC CDul CHab CLnd CMac CSBt CSto CTho CTri EBee ECrN EPfP LBuc MGos MJak NHed NWea SCob SEWo SGol SPer WHar WMou WSFF
- 'Aurea' CDul CEnd CTho MBlu MGos
- var. ***barbata*** CSto
- 'Imperialis' ♀H6 CAco CCVT CDoC CDul CEnd CLnd CTho EBee ECrN ELan EPfP EPla EWTr GBin IDee MBlu MBri MMuc MPkF NBro NLar NWea SCob SEND SEWo SGol SKHP SPer WHar
- 'Laciniata' CAco CCVT CDoC CDul CMac CTho ECrN MGos NLar WMou
- 'Pyramidalis' CDul
hirsuta CSto NWea
incana CAco CBcs CCVT CDoC CDul CLnd CMCN CTho ECrN LBuc MGos NLar NWea SCob SGol SPer WHar WMou
- 'Aurea' ♀H6 CAco CBcs CCVT CDul CEnd CLnd CMac CTho EBee ECrN ELan EPfP EPla IArd MBlu MGos MRav NBro NEgg NLar NWea SEWo SGol SPer SPoG WFar WHar
- 'Laciniata' CTho ELan MGos NLar SCoo WFar WMou
- 'Pendula' CAco CTho
maximowiczii CSto
- from Ulleungdo WCru

oregana see *A. rubra*
pendula B&SWJ 10895 WCru
rhombifolia EBtc
§ ***rubra*** CAco CCVT CDoC CDul CMCN CTho ELan MCoo NWea WMou
- f. ***pinnatisecta*** CAco CMCN CTho
sieboldiana WCru
× ***spaethii*** MBlu MMuc
subcordata CSto
viridis CAco CAgr CSto EBtc MCoo NWea
- subsp. ***sinuata*** CAgr CSto NWea

Alocasia (*Araceae*)

× ***amazonica*** ♀H1a XBlo
'Calidora' CDTJ MHin NSoo SPlb
cucullata XBlo
gageana CDTJ
macrorrhiza CCon CDTJ NLos SBig SPlb
- 'Variegata' (v) ♀H1a EUJe
'Mayan Mask' EUJe
odora CAbb CDTJ SPlb XBlo
plumbea XBlo

Aloe ✿ (*Asphodelaceae*)

aculeata CAbb
africana CAbb
arborescens CAbb CDTJ CDoC CHEx CTre EShb EUJe SEND SPlb
aristata ♀H3 CHEx EUJe SArc SChr SEND SPlb WPGP XLum
- 'Green Pearl'PBR SMad
barbadensis see *A. vera*
barberae CCCN CTre
betsileensis LToo
boylei CTre
brevifolia ♀H2 CAbb CTre EShb SArc
broomii CAbb CCCN CDoC CTre EPfP LToo SPlb
camperi 'Maculata' SEND
castanea CAbb
ciliaris CHll EShb
comptonii CAbb
cooperi CCCN CDTJ CDoC
descoingsii ♀H1b LToo
descoingsii* × *haworthioides CSuc
dichotoma CAbb CSuc CTre SPlb
dinteri CSuc
distans MHin
ecklonis CCCN CSuc SPlb
elegans LToo
excelsa CSuc
ferox CAbb CBod CCCN CDTJ CDoC CSuc CTre SBig
fosteri CDTJ CSuc
gerstneri CSuc
greatheadii CSuc
- var. ***davyana*** SChr
humilis CSuc SChr SEND
juvenna SRms
kedongensis SEND
krapohliana CAbb
lineata CAbb
littoralis CAbb
lutescens CAbb
maculata CDTJ CDoC CSuc
marlothii CAbb CCCN CSuc SPlb
melanacantha CAbb
microstigma CCCN CDoC
mitriformis EPfP SEND
mutabilis CHEx SChr SEND
peglerae SRms
petricola CAbb
plicatilis ♀H2 CCCN CDTJ CSuc EShb
pluridens CAbb
polyphylla ♀H3 CAbb CSuc CTre WCot WPGP
pratensis CCCN CDTJ
rauhii ♀H1b CTre
reitzii CAbb CTre SPlb
rivae CSuc
rugosifolia CSuc
sheilae CSuc
sinkatana CSuc
'Snowflake' CSuc
somaliensis ♀H1b SMad
speciosa CAbb
spectabilis CSuc
spicata CAbb
× ***spinosissima*** CDoC SChr
striata CAbb CCCN CSuc CTre EShb LToo SPlb
striatula ♀H3 CAbb CBrP CDTJ CDoC CHEx CSam CSde CSuc CTca CTre EUJe IBlr LEdu SArc SBHP SBig SChr SEND SKHP SMad SPlb SVen WCot WPGP
succotrina CAbb
suprafoliata CAbb
tenuior CSuc
thraskii CAbb CSuc
tomentosa LToo
vanbalenii CSuc
variegata (v) ♀H1b EShb MHin
§ ***vera*** ♀H1b CArn CCCN CDoC CHby CSpe CUse EOHP GPoy MHer MNHC NPer NPla NPri SBch SChr SEND SIde SMad SPlb SPre SVic WJek
wickensii LToo
yavellana SPlb

Aloe × *Haworthia* see × *Alworthia*

Aloinopsis (*Aizoaceae*)

spathulata new CPBP

Alonsoa (*Scrophulariaceae*)

'Bright Spark' CSpe
incisifolia CCCN CSpe
meridionalis CBod CCCN CDes
- 'Rebel' ECtt MSCN SRkn WBor
* - 'Salmon Beauty' LRHS
'Pink Beauty' CSpe
'Scarlet Lucky Lips' (v) ECtt LSou
warscewiczii CCCN
- 'Peachy-keen' CSpe

Alopecurus (*Poaceae*)

borealis subsp. ***glaucus*** EPPr LPot
pratensis CHab NOrc
- 'Aureovariegatus' (v) EHoe EPPr EPla GMaP NBid SPer SRms XLum
- 'Aureus' NBro SPlb WWEG
- 'No Overtaking' (v) EPPr

Alophia (*Iridaceae*)

lahue see *Herbertia lahue*

Aloysia (*Verbenaceae*)

	chamaedryfolia	EPfP LRHS
	citriodora	see *A. citrodora*
§	***citrodora*** ♀H3	Widely available
	gratissima	WJek
	triphylla	see *A. citrodora*

Alpinia (*Zingiberaceae*)

	formosana	LEdu
	galanga	CArn
	japonica	CExl LEdu
	- B&SWJ 8889	WCru
	- PAB 6441 **new**	LEdu
	nutans misapplied	see *A. zerumbet*
	speciosa	see *A. zerumbet*
§	***zerumbet*** B&SWJ 11512	WCru
	- 'Variegata' (v)	EBee EUJe MPkF NLos XBlo

Alsobia see *Episcia*

Alstroemeria ✿ (*Alstroemeriaceae*)

	'Adonis'PBR	EWoo LRHS SPer
	'Aimi'	CCon ELan MNrw SPer SWvt
	'Alexis'PBR	LRHS
	'Aliénor' (Midi Series)	XTur
	'Andigné' (Garden Series) **new**	XTur
	'Angelina'	LRHS SWvt
	'Anne' (Midi Series)	XTur
	'Antoine' (Maxi Series)	XTur
	'Apollo' ♀H4	CBcs CTsd ELan EWoo LRHS MBNS MNrw NBre SWvt
	'Arthur' (Maxi Series)	XTur
	'Athena'	LRHS
	'Aubance' (Garden Series)	XTur
	aurantiaca	see *A. aurea*
§	***aurea***	MRav SRms XLum
	- 'Apricot'	GCal
	- 'Dover Orange'	IGor
	- 'Lutea'	NLar SDeJ SPlb
	- 'Orange King'	CTsd ELan EPfP NLar SDeJ
	'Authion' (Garden Series)	XTur
	'Avanti'	LRHS
	'Avrillé' (Garden Series) **new**	XTur
	'Baracé' (Garden Series)	XTur
	'Baugé' (Garden Series)	XTur
	'Béatrice' (Midi Series)	XTur
	'Blushing Bride'	CCon MBNS SWvt
	'Bolero'	LRHS
	'Bonanza'	LRHS SLon SPer
	brasiliensis	CCon CTsd GCal WCot WSHC XLum
	- 'Cally Star' (v)	GCal NLar
	'Brezé' (Garden Series) **new**	XTur
	'Briançon' (Garden Series)	XTur
	'Cahors' (Planet Series) ♀H4	LRHS
	'Camille' (Mini Series)	XTur
	'Candé' (Garden Series) **new**	XTur
	'Candy Floss'	EPfP
	'Caroline' (Midi Series)	XTur
	'Charles' (Maxi Series)	XTur
	'Charm'	LRHS SPer
	'Chartrené' (Garden Series)	XTur
	'Chi Chi'	WCot
	'Chinon' (Garden Series)	XTur
§	'Christina'PBR	CBod LRHS MBNS SLon SWvt
	'Christine' (Midi Series)	XTur
	'Coronet' ♀H4	MBNS
	'Dandy Candy'	EBee LRHS MCot MHol MPie NGdn NLar WBrk WCot
	'Davina'PBR **new**	NLar
	'Dayspring Delight' (v)	GCal
§	Diana, Princess of Wales = 'Stablaco'	LRHS
	'Diane' (Midi Series)	XTur
	diluta subsp. ***chrysantha*** F&W 8700	WCot
	Doctor Salter's hybrids	SRms
	'Dorotheé' (Midi Series)	XTur
	'Douceur d'Automne'	LRHS
	Duchesses d'Anjou Series	see cultivars in Midi Series
	Ducs d'Anjou Series	see cultivars in Maxi Series
	'Elvira'	LRHS MNrw SPer
	'Evening Song'	LRHS MBNS MNrw SLon SWvt
	'Flaming Star'	CBcs
	'Fougeré' (Garden Series)	WHlf XTur
	'Frances' (v)	CAvo CBro
	'François' (Maxi Series) **new**	XTur
	'Freedom'	CDoC CWGN ECtt ELon EWoo LSou MAvo MBNS MHol NEgg NLar NSti SHar SMad SPoG WCot WOut
	'Friendship' ♀H5	CBcs CCon CTsd ELan EWoo LRHS NBre SPlb SWvt
	'Gaspard' (Mini Series)	XTur
	'Gloria'	CCon MBNS SWvt
	'Glory of the Andes' (v)	CWGN NLar
	'Golden Delight'	ELan LRHS MNrw
I	'Hatch Hybrid'	GCal
	'Hawera'	GCal
	'Héloïse' (Mini Series)	XTur
	'Henri' (Maxi Series)	XTur
	hookeri	ECho
	- subsp. ***cummingiana***	WCot
	Inca Adore = 'Koadore'	CExl SLon
	Inca Avanti = 'Koncavanti'PBR	LBuc
	Inca Azure = 'Konazur'PBR	CDoC MHol
	Inca Coral = 'Konocoral'	IBoy
	Inca Devotion = 'Konevotio'PBR	EBee NLar NMir
	Inca Exotica = 'Koexotica'	EBee MGos NMir SLon SPoG
	Inca Glow = 'Koglow'PBR	CExl CWGN EBee ELon LAst LSou MGos MHol NLar NPri SDeJ SLon
	Inca Husky = 'Konhusky' **new**	SCob
	Inca Ice = 'Koice'	CWGN MGos NLar SPoG
	Inca Joli = 'Koncajoli'PBR	LBuc
	Inca Lake = 'Koncalake'	EBee LBuc SCob
	Inca Pulse = 'Konpulse'PBR	CWGN EBee ELon GBin LRHS LSou MHol NLar SDeJ SLon SPoG
	Inca Smile = 'Koncasmile' **new**	SCob
	Inca Tropic = 'Kotrop'	CExl EBee MGos
	Inca Vito = 'Koncavito' **new**	SCob
	Inca Yuko = 'Koncayuko'PBR	CWGN LAst LBuc LRHS LSou NPri SLon SPoG
	Indian Summer = 'Tesronto'	CWGN LRHS NPri
	Inticancha Creamy Dark Pink = 'Tescreda'	SDeJ
	Inticancha Dark Purple = 'Tesdarklin'PBR	IBoy LSou WFar
	Inticancha Machu = 'Tesmach'	WFar
	Inticancha Maya = 'Tesmaya'	CWGN ECtt WFar

Inticancha Navayo = 'Tesnava'	ECtt WFar
Inticancha Purple = 'Tespurplin'PBR	CWGN ECtt WFar
Inticancha Red = 'Tesrobin'PBR	CWGN EBee ECtt WFar
Inticancha Sunlight = 'Tessunlight'PBR	LSou
Inticancha White Pink Blush = 'Tesblushin'PBR	WFar
isabellana **new**	WCot
'Isabelle' (Midi Series)	XTur
'Jacques' (Maxi Series) **new**	XTur
'Jalesne' (Garden Series)	XTur
Jardin Series	see cultivars in Garden Series
'Layon' (Garden Series)	XTur
ligtu hybrids	CAvo CBcs CCon ECha EPfP MNrw NLar NPer SDeJ SPer SRms SWvt WBrk WHoo XLum
- var. ***ligtu***	SMHy
'Liré' (Garden Series)	XTur
'Little Eleanor'	CCon LRHS
'Little Miss Christina'PBR	see *A.* 'Christina'
'Little Miss Davina'	CBod LRHS MBri
'Little Miss Isabel'	LRHS
'Little Miss Lucy'	CBod LRHS
'Little Miss Natalie'PBR	see *A.* 'Natalie'
'Little Miss Roselind'	see *A.* 'Roselind'
'Little Miss Sophie'PBR	see *A.* 'Sophie'
'Little Miss Tara'PBR	see *A.* 'Tara'
'Little Miss Veronica'	MBNS
'Louis' (Maxi Series)	XTur
'Louise' (Midi Series)	XTur
'Lucinda'	CBcs CCon SWvt
magnifica subsp. ***maxima***	WCot
'Marcé' (Garden Series) **new**	XTur
'Margot' (Mini Series)	XTur
'Marguerite' (Midi Series)	XTur
'Marie' (Midi Series)	XTur
'Marina'	MBNS
'Marissa'	GMaP
'Mars'	LRHS
'Mathilde' (Midi Series)	NLar XTur
'Mauve Majesty'	CBod CDoC ELon IBoy LRHS LSou MAvo MHol NLar NPri SMad SPoG WBrk WCot
'Mazé' (Garden Series)	XTur
'Montsoreau' (Garden Series)	WHlf XTur
'Moulin Rouge'	ELan LRHS MBNS SLon
§ 'Natalie'PBR	CBod LRHS MBri
'Neptune'	LRHS
'Nicolas' (Maxi Series)	XTur
'Océane' (Mini Series) **new**	XTur
'Orange Gem' ♀H4	MBNS
'Orange Glory' ♀H4	ELon EWoo GMaP IBoy MBNS SWvt
'Orange Supreme'	CBcs LRHS
'Oriana' ♀H4	EWoo SWvt
patagonica	ECho WAbe
'Pauline' (Mini Series)	XTur
pelegrina	ECho
'Philippe' (Maxi Series)	XTur
philippii	WCot
'Phoenix' (v) ♀H4	LRHS SLon SWvt
'Pink Perfection'	NLar
Pitchounes Series	see cultivars in Mini Series
'Polka'	EWoo MBNS
presliana F&W 10753 **new**	WCot
- RB 94103	WCot
Princess Amina = 'Zapriamin' **new**	LBuc
Princess Angela = 'Staprilan'	ELan MBNS NLar
Princess Anouska = 'Zaprinous'PBR	ELan LRHS NLar SLon SPer
Princess Camilla = 'Stapricamil'PBR	CBcs COtt LBuc LRHS SLon SPer SPoG
Princess Daniela = 'Стapridani'PBR	SCoo SPoG
Princess Diana	see *A.* Diana, Princess of Wales = 'Stablaco'
Princess Eliane = 'Zaprielia'PBR	LRHS
Princess Ella = 'Staprirange'	NLar
Princess Fabiana = 'Zaprifabi'PBR	COtt ELan LRHS NLar SPoG
Princess Felicia = 'Zapricia'PBR	CBcs COtt ELan LRHS SPer
Princess Isabella = 'Zapribel'PBR	COtt LRHS NLar
Princess Ivana = 'Staprivane'PBR	ELan LRHS NLar SPoG
Princess Juliana = 'Staterpa'	SPoG
Princess Julieta = 'Zaprijul'PBR	IBoy NLar SPoG
Princess Letizia = 'Zaprilet'PBR	LRHS
Princess Leyla = 'Stapriley'PBR	CBcs COtt LRHS MBNS SLon SPer SPoG
Princess Lilian = 'Zaprilian'PBR	LRHS
Princess Louise = 'Zaprilou'PBR	EBee LRHS
Princess Margaret	LRHS NLar
Princess Marilene = 'Staprilene'PBR	COtt MBNS
Princess Mary = 'Zaprimary'PBR	NLar
Princess Mathilde = 'Zaprimat'PBR	LRHS
Princess Monica = 'Staprimon'PBR	MBNS SPoG
Princess Oxana = 'Staprioxa'PBR	NLar
Princess Paola = 'Stapripal'PBR	LBuc LRHS MBNS SCoo
Princess Ragna	see *A.* Princess Stephanie
Princess Sara = 'Staprisara'PBR	COtt LRHS SPoG
Princess Sarah = 'Stalicamp'	MBNS
Princess Sissi = 'Staprisis'	SPoG
§ Princess Sophia = 'Stajello'	SPoG
§ Princess Stephanie = 'Stapirag'	NLar
Princess Susana = 'Staprisusa'	LRHS NLar SCoo SPoG
Princess Theresa = 'Zapriteres'PBR	COtt EPfP NLar
Princess Zavina = 'Staprivina'PBR	CBcs ELan LBuc LRHS MBNS NLar SPer
§ ***psittacina***	CAvo CBro CHll CMea CSam ECha ELan EPfP GBin GBuc GCal GCra

	MCot MHer SGSe SRms WSHC XLum
- 'Mona Lisa'	CBod EWll GBuc LSou XLum
- 'Royal Star' (v)	CBod CBro CExl CWCL EAEE ELan ELon EPfP EPla GBuc LRHS MAvo SHar SPoG SRms WCot WHoo WSHC WWEG XLum
pulchella Sims	see *A. psittacina*
'Purple Rain'	ELan LRHS MNrw SLon SWvt
'Querré' (Garden Series)	XTur
'Red Beauty' (v)	see *A.* 'Spitfire'
'Red Beauty'	CCon ELan GMaP LRHS MBNS SPer SWvt
'Red Elf' ♀H4	IBoy MBNS SWvt
'René' (Maxi Series)	XTur
'Rhubarb and Custard'	EPfP
Rock 'n' Roll = 'Alsdun01' (v)	LBuc NSoo
§ 'Roselind'	CCon ELan LRHS MBNS MBri SWvt
'Rosie' (Mini Series)	XTur
'Saturne'	EPfP LRHS
'Segré' (Garden Series) **new**	XTur
'Selina'	EWoo LRHS MBNS MNrw NBre
'Serenade'	CBcs ELan LRHS
'Serrant' (Garden Series)	XTur
'Sirius' (Planet Series) ♀H4	LRHS
§ 'Sophie'PBR	ELan LRHS MBNS SLon SWvt
§ 'Spitfire' (v) ♀H4	EPfP IBoy LRHS SLon SWvt WCot
'Spring Delight' (v)	WCot
'Strawberry Lace'	EBee EPfP
'Sunstar'	GMaP
'Sweet Laura'PBR	CBod CDoC ECtt ELon EWoo LLHF LRHS MAvo MBri MHol MPie NEgg NGdn NLar NPri NSti SHar SPoG WCot
'Tanya'	EWoo LRHS MNrw
§ 'Tara'PBR	CBod LRHS MBNS MBri NLar SPlb SWvt
'Tessa' ♀H4	LRHS MBNS NBre SLon
'Thorigné' (Garden Series)	WHlf XTur
'Tiercé' (Garden Series)	XTur
'Turkish Delight'	EPfP
'Uranus'	LRHS
'Ventura'	LRHS
'Venus' (Planet Series) **new**	LRHS
'William' (Maxi Series)	XTur
'Yellow Friendship' ♀H4	MBNS MNrw NLar SWvt
Yellow King	see *A.* Princess Sophia
'Yellow Queen'	IBoy
'Zoé' (Mini Series)	XTur

Althaea (*Malvaceae*)

armeniaca	GCal LPla NLar WCot WOut
cannabina	CArn CFis CSpe ELan GCal GQui LPla MBel MHer MNrw NGBl SGSe SHar SPhx WBor WCot WHal WHil WOld WSHC
officinalis	CArn CBod CHab CUse ELan ENfk GPoy MHer MNHC NLar SIde SRms WHer WHfH WJek WOut XLum
- ***alba***	LSou NLar
§ - 'Romney Marsh'	GCal MRav SEND WKif
rosea	see *Alcea rosea*
rugosostellulata	see *Alcea rugosa*

Altingia (*Hamamelidaceae*)

poilanei B&SWJ 11756	WCru

× *Alworthia* (*Asphodelaceae*)

'Black Gem'	EBee EPfP EShb MHer

Alyogyne (*Malvaceae*)

'Attraction'	ECou
hakeifolia	ECou
- 'Elle Maree'	CSpe ECou MOWG
- 'Melissa Anne'	ECou MOWG
§ ***huegelii***	CBod CCCN CSpe ECou SEle SRkn SRms
- 'Lavender Lass'	ECou
- 'Santa Cruz'	CCCN CHll CSpe EShb ETwe MOWG SEND SLon WPGP
- 'White Delight'	ECou
'Joy'	ECou
Magic Moments = 'Hutwow'	CSpe CWGN LAst LBuc NSoo SLon
'Shepherds Delight'	ECou

Alyssoides (*Brassicaceae*)

utriculata	WHil

Alyssum (*Brassicaceae*)

argenteum	ECho
bornmuelleri **new**	LLHF
caespitosum	WAbe
montanum	ECha ECho MWat SPlb SRms
§ - 'Berggold'	EPfP MMuc XLum
- 'Luna'	WHil
- Mountain Gold	see *A. montanum* 'Berggold'
oxycarpum	EPot WAbe
saxatile	see *Aurinia saxatilis*
spinosum	EPot
- 'Roseum' ♀H5	CMea CTri ECha ELan EPot GCrg MLHP MSCN MWat NSla SBch WAbe
* - 'Roseum Variegatum' (v)	EPot
stribrnyi	LLHF
tortuosum	SEND WAbe
wulfenianum	EDAr GAbr IFoB LLHF WIce XLum

Amaranthus (*Amaranthaceae*)

'Autumn Palette'	CSpe
caudatus 'Viridis' **new**	SPhx
hypochondriacus 'Pygmy Torch'	CSpe
tricolor	SRms

× *Amarcrinum* (*Amaryllidaceae*)

'Dorothy Hannibal'	WCot
memoria-corsii	CPrp ECho
- 'Howardii'	CCon CDes ECho EShb LEdu NRog SDeJ WCot

× *Amarine* (*Amaryllidaceae*)

'Fletcheri'	WCot
tubergenii 'Zwanenburg'	LAma WCot

× *Amarygia* (*Amaryllidaceae*)

§ ***bidwillii*** 'Alba'	CAvo CBro CPrp ECho NRog WCot
- 'Rosea'	NRog WCot
parkeri	ECho

Amaryllis (*Amaryllidaceae*)

§ ***belladonna*** ♀H3	CAby CBcs CBro CHEx CPne CPrp CTal CTca CTsd EBee ECho EPfP ERCP EShb LAma NRog SDeJ SEND WCot

- 'Johannesburg' WCot
- 'Kimberley' CPne
- 'Parkeri Alba' see × *Amarygia bidwillii* 'Alba'
- 'Purpurea' WCot
- white-flowered CDes ECho SDeJ WCot

Ambrosina (*Araceae*)

bassii new WCot
- from Tunisia ECho

Amelanchier (*Rosaceae*)

alnifolia CSpe CTho EBtc
- var. **cusickii** new SSta
- 'Forestburg' NLar
- 'Obelisk'PBR CDoC CDul ELan EPfP EPla GKin GQue LAst LBuc LLHF LRHS MAsh MBri MCoo MGos MJak NCGa NLar SCoo SPer SPoG WHar WPat
- pink-fruited NLar

§ - var. **pumila** MMHG
- var. **semi-integrifolia** NLar
- 'Smokey' CDul SSta

§ **arborea** CTho
- Tradition new NLar

'Autumn Glory' NLar
bartramiana CTho SSta
- 'Eskimo' NLar

canadensis K. Koch see *A. lamarckii*
canadensis Sieb. & Zucc. see *A. arborea*
canadensis ambig. CDul EPla IBoy NLar NPri SCob SEWo SPoG WFar WHar
canadensis (L.) Medik. CAco CAgr CDoC CJun CLnd CMac CSBt CSam CTho CTri CWSG EBee ECrN ELan EPfP LEdu LRHS MGos MRav MSwo NCGa NWea SPer WMoo WPat

§ - 'Glenn Form' CEnd EBee LRHS MAsh MGos NLar SGol SLim SPoG WHar
- 'Prince William' CAgr MCoo SSta
- Rainbow Pillar see *A. canadensis* 'Glenn Form'
- 'Tailored' new SSta

confusa Schmeil & Fitschen. see *A. lamarckii*
confusa N. Hyl. SSta
× **grandiflora** new SCob
- 'Autumn Brilliance' CEnd CJun NHol SGol
- 'Ballerina' Widely available
- 'Cole's Select' LRHS SKHP SSta
- 'Forest Prince' NLar SSta
- 'Princess Diana' ♀H6 NLar SCoo
- 'Robin Hill' ♀H6 CBcs CCVT CDul CLnd CMac COtt EBee ECrN ELan EMil EPfP EPla LAst LBuc MBlu MGos MRav NLar NWea SCob SCoo SEWo SGol WFar WHar
- 'Rubescens' CEnd CJun EBee EPla NLar SLon

'La Paloma' ♀H6 EPfP LRHS MAsh MBri MGos SCoo SLim WHar
laevis CBcs CDul CTri EPfP NLar
- 'Cumulus' NLar
- 'Prince Charles' NLar SSta
- 'R.J. Hilton' ♀H6 MAsh MBri NLar SCoo SSta WHar
- 'Snow Cloud' CDoC SSta
- 'Snowflakes' CEnd CJun LRHS MAsh MGos MWat NLar SEWo SLim SPer WHar

§ **lamarckii** ♀H6 Widely available
- 'Grandette' new SSta

nantucketensis new SSta
ovalis misapplied see *A. spicata* (Lam.) K. Koch
ovalis Medik. SPlb
- 'Edelweiss' CJun IArd MRav NEgg NLar SCoo

pumila see *A. alnifolia* var. *pumila*
rotundifolia ambig. CNWT MCoo
sanguinea 'Chimney Rock' NLar
sinica NLar
§ **spicata** (Lam.) K. Koch MCoo SSta
stolonifera CTri

× *Amelasorbus* (*Rosaceae*)

raciborskiana MBlu

Amicia (*Papilionaceae*)

zygomeris CAbb CBcs CCse CHEx CHGN CHll CPom CSpe EWes EWll GCal MCot SDix SEle SMad SMrm SPoG WCot WPGP
- 'John's Big Splash' (v) WCot

Ammi (*Apiaceae*)

majus CArn CBod CSpe LEdu LRHS MNHC SDix SPhx WCot WHfH WJek
visnaga CArn CBre CHby CSam CSpe ELau MNHC SPhx WHal WJek

Ammobium (*Asteraceae*)

calyceroides ECou

Ammocharis (*Amaryllidaceae*)

coranica ECho WCot

Ammophila (*Poaceae*)

arenaria CKno EBee IMou SMea XLum
breviligulata IMou XLum

Amomyrtus (*Myrtaceae*)

§ **luma** CAgr CBcs CDoC CDul CHEx CTri CTsd EBee ELan GGal GQui IDee WJek

Amorpha (*Papilionaceae*)

canescens EBee EWTr LRHS MNrw SPhx SPlb
fruticosa CAco CBcs EBtc EWTr MBlu NLar SEND SPlb
herbacea NLar
nana XLum
paniculata NLar

Amorphophallus ✿ (*Araceae*)

albus CDTJ EBee LEdu WCot
bulbifer CDTJ ESwi LAma LRHS SBig SDeJ SPlb WCot XLum
dunnii CDTJ LEdu
henryi WCot
kerrii CExl WCot
kiusianus B&SWJ 4845 WCru
konjac CDTJ CDes CExl CFil CHEx CSpe CTal EUJe LEdu SChF SPlb WPGP XLum
nepalensis WCot
ongsakulii new WCot
rivieri EBee GCal LEdu LRHS SDeJ WCot
stipitatus LEdu WCot
yuloensis new WCot

Ampelocalamus (*Poaceae*)

§ **mocrophyllum** ERod
scandens WPGP

Ampelocissus (*Vitaceae*)

sikkimensis HWJK 2066 — WCru

Ampelodesmos (*Poaceae*)

mauritanica — CHid CKno CSam EBee ECha EHoe EShb EWes IDee LPla MAvo SEND SMHy SMad SPlb WCot WWEG XLum

Ampelopsis (*Vitaceae*)

aconitifolia — NLar
- 'Chinese Lace' — CHel EBee EUJe EWTr LRHS MRav NLar

arborea — WCru
brevipedunculata — ELan MMHG SCoo SKHP SLim SPer WHar
- 'Citrulloides' — WCru
- var. **maximowiczii** 'Elegans' (v) — CBcs CHEx CHel CMac EBee ELan EPfP EShb LAst LRHS MGos MMuc MRav NBro SPer SPoG SWvt WCot WPat WSHC

delavayana — MMuc
henryana — see *Parthenocissus henryana*
megalophylla — ELan EShb GCal NLar SKHP SPer
sempervirens hort. ex Veitch — see *Cissus striata*
tricuspidata 'Veitchii' — see *Parthenocissus tricuspidata* 'Veitchii'

Amphicome see *Incarvillea*

Amsonia (*Apocynaceae*)

'Blue Ice' — EBee IPot WCot
ciliata — ELan GKev IKil LEdu LRHS NLar SHar SKHP XLum
- 'Spring Sky' — EBee

'Ernst Pagels' — SPhx
hubrichtii — CAby CCon CCse CHid CSpe EBee ECha ELon EPPr LEdu LPla LRHS LSun MNHC SMad SMrm SPad SPhx SWvt WHoo WPtf WSHC WWEG
illustris — CAbP CSpe EPPr GCal LEdu LPla LRHS NLar SHar SMHy SPhx WHil WHoo WSHC WWEG
jonesii — SBrt SMHy
§ **orientalis** — CCon CHll CMea CTri ECha GCal LEdu LRHS MCot MLHP MRav NCGa NDov NLar SMHy SPhx SPoG SVen SWvt WBor WCot WFar WPtf XEll
- 'Cally Dark Stem' **new** — GCal

tabernaemontana — Widely available
- 'Montana' — SPer SWvt
- var. **salicifolia** — CAby CSpe EBee EWll IMou IPot LEdu LRHS WCAu
- 'Stella Azul' — IPot

Amygdalus see *Prunus*

Amyris (*Rutaceae*)

madrensis — CFil

Anacamptis (*Orchidaceae*)

pyramidalis — EFEx WHer

Anacyclus (*Asteraceae*)

pyrethrum — GPoy
- var. **depressus** ♀[H4] — CTri ECho ELan EPfP GMaP MAsh MHol MMuc SEND SPlb SRot WCFE XLum
- - 'Garden Gnome' — CTri ECho SRms
- - 'Silberkissen' — CMea EDAr NSla

Anagallis (*Primulaceae*)

monellii Blue Compact = 'Wesanacomp' — LSou
- subsp. **linifolia** 'Blue Light' — CSpe
- 'Skylover' — CCCN LAst

tenella — LLWG MWts
- 'Studland' — EPot MHer WAbe

Ananas (*Bromeliaceae*)

comosus (F) — CCCN SPre
- 'Champaca' (F) — CCCN SPre

Anaphalioides (*Asteraceae*)

§ **bellidioides** — CTri

Anaphalis (*Asteraceae*)

alpicola — EPot
margaritacea — CBcs ECha ECtt GMaP NBid SRms WFar WHar WMoo WPtf
§ - 'Neuschnee' — CTri GJos NBre NLar WWEG XLum
- New Snow — see *A. margaritacea* 'Neuschnee'
- var. **yedoensis** — CTri MLHP MWat NBre SDix SPer

§ **nepalensis** var. **monocephala** — EBee NBre NSti
nubigena — see *A. nepalensis* var. *monocephala*
transnokoensis — EBee EWes
§ **trinervis** — CExl GCra LSun XLum
triplinervis ♀[H7] — CBod CHel EHoe ELan ELon EPfP EWTr EWoo GAbr GMaP IBoy IFoB LPal LRHS MCot MLHP MMuc MRav NBid NLar NPri NSti SPer WCAu WFar WHoo WMoo WWEG
- CC 1620 — EPPr NBir
§ - 'Sommerschnee' ♀[H7] — CMac EAJP ECha ECtt EHoe EPfP IBoy LBMP LPot LRHS MCot MHol MRav NEgg NLar NWad SEND SPer WMnd WPtf WWtn
- Summer Snow — see *A. triplinervis* 'Sommerschnee'

Anchusa (*Boraginaceae*)

sp. — CHab MPro
§ **azurea** — NLar
- 'Dropmore' — CTri EBee EPfP LRHS MRav NEgg NLar NOrc SCob SRms WHar WWEG
- 'Feltham Pride' — EBee ELan EPfP SRms SWvt WHoo SRms
- 'Little John' — SRms
- 'Loddon Royalist' — Widely available
- 'Opal' — IGor MAsh

'Cambridge Angel' **new** — GKev
capensis 'Blue Angel' — CWCL MNHC SWvt
cespitosa Lam. — ECho ELan EWes LLHF WAbe
italica — see *A. azurea*
laxiflora — see *Borago pygmaea*
myosotidiflora — see *Brunnera macrophylla*
officinalis — CArn MNHC
sempervirens — see *Pentaglottis sempervirens*

Ancylostemon (*Gesneriaceae*)

convexus B&SWJ 6624 — WCot WCru
- B&SWJ 7182 **new** — WCru

Andrachne (*Phyllanthaceae*)

colchica	EWTr WCot

Androcymbium (*Colchicaceae*)

cuspidatum 'Karoopoort'	ECho
dregei 'Loeriesfontein'	ECho
eucomoides 'Varsputs'	ECho
gramineum	ECho

Andromeda (*Ericaceae*)

glaucophylla f. ***latifolia***	IVic
polifolia	ECho WFar
- 'Alba'	EBee ECho LRHS MAsh SPer SPlb SWvt WFar
- 'Blue Ice'	EBee ELan IDee LRHS MAsh NHar NLar SLim SPer SPoG SSpi WAbe WFar WPat
- 'Blue Lagoon' new	NLar
- 'Compacta' ΨH5	CDoC CMac ECho GEdr MAsh NLar NWad SRms SWvt WFar WGwG
- 'Compacta Alba' ΨH5	ECho
- 'Grandiflora'	ECho GKev
- 'Kirigamine'	LRHS MAsh NHar
- 'Macrophylla' ΨH5	ECho GEdr NHar WPat WThu
- 'Nana'	EPfP LRHS
- 'Nikko'	CMac
- 'Shibutsu'	NHar

Andropogon (*Poaceae*)

gerardii	CAby CKno EBee EHoe EPPr LRHS MWhi NWsh SGSe SPhx WWEG XLum
scoparius	see *Schizachyrium scoparium*

Androsace (*Primulaceae*)

adenocephala	GKev WAbe
alashanica new	WAbe
alpina	WAbe
* ***bayanharshanensis***	WAbe
bisulca var. ***aurata***	EPot GKev
- 'Brahmaputrae'	CPBP GKev
brachystegia	EPot GKev
bulleyana	GKev
carnea	ECho GKev IFoB
- SDR 6357	GKev
- subsp. ***brigantiaca***	GKev NSla WAbe WHoo
- var. ***halleri***	see *A. carnea* subsp. *rosea*
- subsp. ***laggeri*** ΨH5	ECho LLHF NSla WAbe
- - 'Andorra'	NHar
§ - subsp. ***rosea*** ΨH5	ECho GKev IFoB ITim NHar WAbe
carnea × ***pyrenaica***	ECho LLHF
chaixii	IFoB
chamaejasme	ECho
- subsp. ***carinata***	GKev
ciliata	WAbe
cylindrica	CPBP ECho ITim LRHS WAbe
cylindrica × ***hirtella***	ECho LRHS WAbe
cylindrica × ***pyrenaica*** new	CPBP
delavayi	WAbe
- ACE 1786	WAbe
elatior	WAbe
flavescens new	CPBP GKev WAbe
geraniifolia	ECha GKev SRms WAbe
globifera	WAbe
halleri	see *A. carnea* subsp. *rosea*
hedraeantha	WAbe
himalaica	CPBP EPot WAbe
hirtella	IFoB ITim LLHF WAbe
idahoensis	WAbe
idahoensis × ***laevigata***	WAbe
jacquemontii	see *A. villosa* var. *jacquemontii*
kosopoljanskii	EPot
lactea	WAbe
laevigata	CPBP EPot ITim WAbe
- 'Gothenburg'	WAbe
- 'Saddle Mount'	WAbe
lanuginosa ΨH5	CBod CMea CSpe CTal ECho ECtt EDAr EHoe EPot GBin GEdr GKev MWat NHar NHol SBch SRms SRot WAbe WIce WOld
- 'Wisley Variety'	SIgm
lehmanniana	WAbe
- 'Gotëborg Yellow'	WAbe
lehmannii	GKev
limprichtii	see *A. sarmentosa* var. *watkinsii*
mariae	GKev WAbe
- var. ***tibetica*** new	EPot
× ***marpensis***	EPot WAbe WHal
microphylla	see *A. mucronifolia* G.Watt
'Millstream'	IFoB
minor	EPot GKev WAbe
§ ***mollis*** Kunth.	CPBP
montana	WAbe
mucronifolia misapplied	see *A. sempervivoides*
§ ***mucronifolia*** G.Watt	WAbe
mucronifolia G.Watt × ***sempervivoides***	CTal NHar SIgm WAbe
muscoidea	WAbe
- SEP 132	CPBP
- 'Breviscapa'	EPot
- 'Dolpo Lilac' new	WAbe
- Schacht's form	EPot WAbe
nivalis Chumstick form	LLHF
ochotensis	WAbe
primuloides	see *A. studiosorum*
pubescens	ECho ITim LLHF LRHS
pyrenaica	ECho ITim LLHF LRHS WAbe
rigida	EPot LLHF WAbe
robusta	EPot
- subsp. ***purpurea***	CPBP WAbe
- - 'Dolpo Dwarf'	WAbe
rotundifolia	GEdr
sarmentosa misapplied	see *A. studiosorum*
sarmentosa ambig.	GKev XLum
sarmentosa Wall.	SRms WHoo
- from Namche, Nepal	WAbe
- Galmont's form	see *A. studiosorum* 'Salmon's Variety'
- 'Sherriffii'	ECho EPot SIgm SRms WIce
§ - var. ***watkinsii***	CTal EPot GKev
- var. ***yunnanensis*** misapplied	see *A. studiosorum*
- var. ***yunnanensis*** Knuth	see *A. mollis* Kunth.
selago	WAbe
- 'Red Eye'	WAbe
§ ***sempervivoides*** ΨH5	ECho EDAr EPot GBin GCrg GJos GKev GMaP LRHS NHar NHol NSla SBch SIgm SPlb SRms WAbe WIce
- CC 4631	GKev
- 'Greystone'	EPot
- 'Susan Joan'	EPot GEdr GKev WAbe
spinulifera	GKev
squarrosula new	GKev
stenophylla new	MAsh

strigillosa	GKev WAbe
§ ***studiosorum*** 🏆H5	CPBP EPot GAbr GCrg GEdr GKev IFoB NSla WAbe
- 'Chumbyi'	EPot GEdr LLHF SHar SIgm SRms WIce WPat WThu
- 'Doksa'	CPBP CTal EPot GEdr IFoB SHar WAbe WIce
§ - 'Salmon's Variety'	CMea CTri SBch SIgm WAbe
tangulashanensis	CPBP LLHF WAbe
tapete ACE 1725	WAbe
vandellii	EPot GKev WAbe
villosa	IFoB WAbe
§ - var. ***jacquemontii***	CTal NHar SHar
- - lilac-flowered	EPot WAbe
- - pink-flowered	EPot SIgm WAbe
- subsp. ***taurica***	WAbe
vitaliana	see *Vitaliana primuliflora*
wardii	WAbe
watkinsii	see *A. sarmentosa* var. *watkinsii*
yargongensis	WAbe
zambalensis	WAbe
- pink-flowered **new**	GKev

Andryala (*Asteraceae*)

lanata	see *Hieracium lanatum*

Anemanthele (*Poaceae*)

§ ***lessoniana*** 🏆H4	Widely available
- 'Autumn Tints'	EHoe
- 'Gold Hue'	EHoe
- 'Sirocco' **new**	CBod

Anemarrhena (*Asparagaceae*)

asphodeloides	CArn WCot

Anemia (*Schizaeaceae*)

tomentosa **new**	ISha

Anemone ✿ (*Ranunculaceae*)

Chen Yi T49	WCot
aconitifolia Michx.	see *A. narcissiflora*
altaica	NLar SRms
amurensis	CExl
apennina 🏆H4	CAvo ECGP ECho GEdr WShi
- var. ***albiflora***	ECho EPPr EPot
- double-flowered (d)	ECho EPPr MAvo WCru
- 'Petrovac'	EBee ECho LEdu LLHF WCot
baicalensis	WOut WSHC
baldensis	ECho GBuc GEdr GKev ITim SRms
barbulata	CExl EBee EWes GBuc GEdr GKev NLar
biflora	ECho
blanda 🏆H4	ECho LAma LBMP LRHS MAsh MAvo MBri MLHP MNHC MWat NChi NLar SCob SEND WBor WFar WHar WOut WShi
I - 'Alba'	LRHS NChi
- blue-flowered	CAvo CBro CHVG CMea CTri ECho ELan EPfP EPot ERCP GAbr GKev GMaP IGor LEdu LRHS MBri SDeJ SPer SPhx SPoG SRms WCot WHoo
- 'Charmer'	EPot SDeJ
- 'Ingramii'	WCot
- var. ***rosea***	ECho ELan EPfP GKev LAma LRHS SBch SDeJ SPer SPoG
- - 'Pink Star'	CAvo ERCP GKev LAma NBir
- - 'Radar' 🏆H4	CAvo ECho EPot ERCP LAma MNrw NBir SDeJ WAbe
- 'Violet Star'	GKev SDeJ WCot
- 'White Splendour' 🏆H4	CAvo CBro CHVG CMea CTri ECho ELan EPfP EPot ERCP GAbr GKev IFro LAma LRHS NBir NLar SDeJ SMrm SPer SPhx SPoG SRms WWFP
- white-flowered	LRHS
'Bowles's Mauve' **new**	GEdr
caerulea	LEdu
canadensis	CSpe ECGP ELon EPPr GBuc GEdr NLar WCot
caroliniana	ECho GKev
caucasica	ECho
chapaensis HWJ 631	WCru
coronaria	SCob SVic
- De Caen Group	CHid EPfP GKev LAma LRHS SCob SPoG
- - 'Bicolor'	CHid GKev LAma SDeJ
- - blue-flowered **new**	LRHS
§ - - 'Die Braut'	ERCP GKev LAma NBir SDeJ
- - 'His Excellency'	see *A. coronaria* (De Caen Group) 'Hollandia'
§ - - 'Hollandia'	GKev LAma LPot SDeJ WHil
- - 'Mister Fokker'	CTca ERCP GKev LAma LPot SBod SDeJ
- - pink-flowered **new**	LRHS
- - red-flowered **new**	LRHS
- - The Bride	see *A. coronaria* (De Caen Group) 'Die Braut'
- - 'The Governor'	CTca GKev SDeJ
- (Harmony Series) 'Harmony Orchid'	LRHS
- - 'Harmony Pearl'	LRHS
- - 'Harmony Scarlet'	LRHS
- Saint Bridgid Group (d)	EPfP GKev LAma LRHS
- - 'Lord Lieutenant' (d)	CMea EPfP ERCP GKev NBir SBod SDeJ
- - 'Mount Everest' (d)	ERCP GKev NBir SDeJ
- - 'Saint Bridgid' (d)	CHid
- - 'The Admiral' (d)	EPfP GKev NBir SDeJ
- 'Sylphide' (Mona Lisa Series)	ERCP GKev LAma LPot NBir SDeJ
crinita	NLar
cylindrica	NLar XEll
dahurica	CHid
'Danish White'	MNrw
decapetala	GBuc LLHF MHer
demissa	GKev LLHF WCot WSHC
- SDR 3307	EBee
- var. ***major***	EBee
drummondii	GKev
eranthioides	EBee
fanninii	GCal
fasciculata	see *A. narcissiflora*
flaccida	CBro CLAP ECho EPPr GBin GEdr LRHS MAvo MMHG MNFA MNrw WCru WHal WSHC
globosa	see *A. multifida* Poir.
'Guernica'	ECho EWes
'Hatakeyama Double' (d)	GCal WSHC
'Hatakeyama Single'	CDes
hepatica L.	see *Hepatica nobilis*
§ ***hortensis***	CDes EBee ECho
§ ***hupehensis***	CExl EBee GMaP NOrc
- BWJ 8190	WCru
- f. ***alba***	CExl CLAP CSpe IFro WPGP
§ - 'Bowles's Pink' 🏆H7	CElw CExl ECho MBri WPGP
- 'Crispa'	see *A.* × *hybrida* 'Lady Gilmour' Wolley-Dod

- 'Eugenie' ECtt EPla GBuc NBir NDov
- 'Hadspen Abundance' ♀H7 CExl CMHG CMac ECha ECtt EPfP EWoo GAbr GCal GKin GMaP IVic LBMP LRHS MAsh MAvo MBNS MBri MCot MWat NBir NChi SGol SPer SPhx SWat SWvt WFar WWEG XLum
- var. ***hupehensis*** WFar
§ - var. ***japonica*** CPou SRms XLum
- - B&SWJ 4886 WCru
- - PAB 8884 new LEdu
- - 'Bodnant Burgundy' CDes LRHS WPGP
§ - - 'Bressingham Glow' CExl CMHG CMac CSam ECtt ELan EPfP EPla EPot GKin LRHS LSou MPro NBir NOrc SPer WBrk WFar WWEG
§ - - 'Pamina' ♀H7 Widely available
- - 'Pink Saucer' CNec
- - Prince Henry see *A. hupehensis* var. *japonica* 'Prinz Heinrich'
§ - - 'Prinz Heinrich' Widely available
§ - - 'Rotkäppchen' CBct CHVG ECtt EPla GBin GKin GQue IVic LRHS LSou LSun MCot MHol MSCN NGdn NHol NLar NSbr NSti SWvt WCAu WCot WSHC
- - 'Splendens' CHel CMHG EPfP GBBs LAst LRHS MBri MCot MMuc NGdn NLar SCob SHil SPer SRms SWvt WHal WWEG XLum
- 'Little Princess'PBR ECtt MNrw
- 'Ouvertüre' ECtt GBuc GQue WPGP
- 'Praecox' CHel CMea CNec EPfP EPla LRHS LSou MBNS MPro NBir NCGa NSti SHil SWvt WHil WMnd WWEG
- 'September Charm' see *A.* × *hybrida* 'September Charm'
- 'Superba' GBin WKif
§ × ***hybrida*** ECho NChi NEgg WHar WMoo
- 'Alba' misapplied (UK) see *A.* × *hybrida* 'Honorine Jobert'
- 'Alba Dura' see *A. tomentosa* 'Albadura'
- 'Albert Schweitzer' see *A.* × *hybrida* 'Elegans'
- 'Andrea Atkinson' Widely available
- 'Bowles's Pink' see *A. hupehensis* 'Bowles's Pink'
- 'Bressingham Glow' see *A. hupehensis* var. *japonica* 'Bressingham Glow'
- 'Coupe d'Argent' IKil
§ - 'Elegans' ♀H7 CSam ECtt GMaP LRHS MAsh MMuc NBir SEND SWat SWvt WFar
§ - 'Géante des Blanches' SMrm
§ - 'Honorine Jobert' ♀H7 Widely available
- 'Josephine' new WFar
§ - 'Königin Charlotte' ♀H7 Widely available
- 'Lady Gilmour' misapplied see *A.* × *hybrida* 'Montrose'
- 'Lady Gilmour' ambig. CHel EPla GAbr GMaP MBel MPie SMrm WHoo XLum
§ - 'Lady Gilmour' Wolley-Dod CSam ECtt EPfP GCra LEdu LRHS MRav NBir NChi WCot WCru WWEG XLum
- 'Loreley' EPfP GBuc NLar SWvt WWEG
- 'Luise Uhink' CPou
- 'Märchenfee' EBee MNrw
- 'Margarete' misapplied see *A.* × *hybrida* 'Montrose'
- 'Margarete' Kayser & Seibert CExl CPar ECtt ELan EPfP LRHS MBri MGos NDov NGdn WCot WCru
- 'Max Vogel' see *A.* × *hybrida* 'Elegans'
- 'Monterosa' see *A.* × *hybrida* 'Montrose'
§ - 'Montrose' CPou EBee ECha EWes GCal GMaP LRHS LSou MBri NBir NLar SBod SRms SWat
- 'Pamina' see *A. hupehensis* var. *japonica* 'Pamina'
- (Pretty Lady Series) 'Pretty Lady Diana' LBuc LRHS LSou NPri SLon SWvt
- - 'Pretty Lady Emily'PBR LBuc LRHS LSou MBri NPri SHar SLon SWvt
- - 'Pretty Lady Julia' LBuc LRHS NPri SHar SLon
- - 'Pretty Lady Susan' LBuc LRHS LSou NPri SHar SLon SWvt WHil
- Prince Henry see *A. hupehensis* var. *japonica* 'Prinz Heinrich'
- 'Profusion' CTri EBee LBuc LRHS WHal
- Queen Charlotte see *A.* × *hybrida* 'Königin Charlotte'
- 'Richard Ahrens' CBod ECtt EPfP EPla EWoo GBuc GCal GMaP LAst LRHS MGos MLHP MSCN NEgg NGdn NLar NOrc SPad SWat SWvt WCru WMnd WWEG
§ - 'Robustissima' COtt EBee EPfP EPla GMaP LLWP LRHS MCot MGos MNrw NBir NGdn NLar NSoo NSti SEND SPer SWat SWvt WMnd WMoo WWEG
- 'Rosenschale' LRHS MNrw WCru
- 'Rotkäppchen' see *A. hupehensis* var. *japonica* 'Rotkäppchen'
§ - 'September Charm' ♀H7 Widely available
- 'Serenade' CHel CSam ECtt EPfP GBBs LRHS MAsh MBri MRav MTis NBir NLar SMrm SPoG SRkn WCAu WMoo XLum
- Tourbillon see *A.* × *hybrida* 'Whirlwind'
§ - 'Whirlwind' Widely available
- 'White Queen' see *A.* × *hybrida* 'Géante des Blanches'
- Wirbelwind see *A.* × *hybrida* 'Whirlwind'
japonica see *A.* × *hybrida*, *A. hupehensis*, *A. hupehensis* var. *japonica*
- 'Crustata' CMac
keiskeana GEdr WCru
§ × ***lesseri*** CBro CCon CSpe ECha ECho ELan GKev SPhx SRms
leveillei CAby CElw CLAP CSpe CWCL EPPr GBuc GEdr GKev IPot LPla LRHS LSou MMuc NBir NGdn NLar NSti SPhx SWvt WAbe WCru WKif WPtf
- BWJ 7919 WCru
§ × ***lipsiensis*** CAvo CBro CDes ECho EPPr EPfP EPot GAbr GBBs GBin GMaP IFro MAvo MMoz MNrw NLar LRHS SBch SMrm WCru WFar WHal WPGP WSHC
- 'Pallida' ♀H5 CSam CSpe ECho ELon GBuc GEdr GKev LEdu LLWP MAvo MNFA NHar NLar SKHP WCot WShi XEll
- 'Schwefelfeuer' MAvo
- 'Vindobonensis' GEdr WCot
lithophila LLHF
magellanica hort. ex Wehrh. see *A. multifida* Poir.
matsudae B&SWJ 1452 WCru
multifida misapplied, red-flowered see *A.* × *lesseri*
§ ***multifida*** Poir. ECha ECho EPfP EPla GJos LRHS NBir NSti SRms WFar WHoo
- Annabella Series GKev
- - 'Annabella Deep Rose' WHrl
- - 'Annabella White' new GJos
- var. ***globosa*** GKev
- 'Major' CCon CMea CSpe EPfP SPhx WIce

	– 'Rubra'	EAEE EPfP EPla GBin GEdr GKev LSou NBir NEgg NLar SPoG WHar WHoo
	– white-flowered	WBor
	– yellow-flowered	CBro LPot NSum
§	***narcissiflora***	CSpe EBee ECho GKev MMHG NBir NChi SBrt WPtf
	nemorosa ♀H5	Widely available
	– 'Alba' **new**	WFar
	– 'Alba Plena' (d)	CSam ECha ECho EPPr GBuc MAvo NGdn NLar WFar WSHC
	– 'Allenii' ♀H5	CBro ECho ELon EPPr EPot GBin GBuc GMaP ITim LRHS MAvo MMoz MNFA MRav NRya WShi
	– 'Amy Doncaster'	CLAP ECho
	– 'Atley'	EBee GEdr MAvo
	– 'Atrocaerulea'	CLAP GBuc IBlr MAvo NLar
	– 'Ballyrogan Blue'	MNrw
	– 'Behemoth Blue' **new**	MAvo
	– 'Bill Baker's Pink'	CDes CLAP LEdu
	– 'Blue Beauty'	CLAP EBee ELon GBuc GMaP IBlr MAvo MNrw NSla SBch
	– 'Blue Bonnet'	ECho GBuc MAvo MNrw
	– 'Blue Eyes' (d)	CDes CElw CLAP EBee GBuc GEdr GMaP IBlr LEdu MAvo MMoz NBir NSla WCot WSHC
	– 'Blush' **new**	LEdu
	– 'Bowles's Purple'	EBee ECho ELon GBBs GBuc GEdr GMaP IBlr LRHS MNrw NBid NHar NRya SBch SKHP WBor WCot WFar
	– 'Bracteata'	CBro ECho GBuc GEdr MMHG MMoz
	– 'Bracteata Pleniflora' (d)	CLAP ECho ELon EPot GBuc GMaP IBlr MAvo MNrw NBir SBch WCot WHal
	– 'Buckland'	CLAP EBee EPfP IBlr MAvo SKHP
	– 'Caerulea'	EPot ITim
	– 'Cedric's Pink'	CLAP EPPr IBlr LLHF MAvo MNrw WFar
	– 'Celestial'	EBee ECho ELan EPPr GBuc MAvo
	– 'Dee Day'	CLAP EBee GBuc LEdu MAvo MNrw NHar
	– 'Dell Garden'	EPPr
	– 'Evelyn Meadows' ♀H5	CLAP
	– 'Flore Pleno' (d)	CDes ECho GAbr IFro MMoz NBir WBor WFar
	– 'Frühlingsfee'	MAvo NLar
	– 'Gerda Ramusen'	CDes CLAP ECho ELan ELon EWes GBuc LEdu LLHF
I	– 'Gigantea Rubra'	WCot
	– 'Good Blue'	MAvo
	– 'Green Dream'	MAvo
	– 'Green Fingers'	CLAP ECho EPPr GBuc GMaP MAvo MMHG MNrw WCot WSHC
	– 'Hakumane Senjuizaki'	WCot
	– 'Hannah Gubbay'	CLAP IBlr
	– 'Hilda'	CBct EBee ECho GBuc GEdr MNrw NBir NHar NRya
	– 'Ice and Fire'	LEdu
	– 'Jack Brownless'	LEdu
	– 'Kentish Pink'	GBBs GBin GMaP
	– 'Knightshayes Vestal' (d)	CExl CLAP MRav WCot
	– 'Kyffhäuser Rote'	WCot
	– 'Lady Doneraile'	CDes CLAP EPot GBuc NBir WFar
	– 'Latvian Pink'	ECho EPot GEdr LEdu MAvo
	– 'Leeds' Variety'	CLAP EPot GAbr GBin GBuc GMaP ITim LEdu MAvo MNrw NSla
	– 'Lionel Bacon'	LEdu MAvo

	– 'Lismore Blue'	ECho EPPr EPot
	– 'Lucia'	EPot GEdr
	– 'Lychette'	ECho EPPr EPot GAbr GBuc GEdr IBlr ITim MAvo MNrw
	– 'March Blue'	EPfP
	– 'Marie Rose'	EPot
	– 'Mart's Blue'	EBee EPfP GBuc MAvo WCot
	– 'Miss Eunice'	CDes CLAP
	– 'Monstrosa'	ECho EPot GBuc MAvo
	– 'New Pink'	CLAP IBlr
	– 'Noémie' **new**	XEll
	– 'Parlez Vous'	CExl ECho EPPr GEdr LEdu MAvo MNrw WPnP XEll
	– 'Pat's Pink'	WShi
	– 'Pentre Pink'	EPot IBlr MNrw
	– 'Picos Pink'	GBuc
	– 'Pink Carpet'	GEdr
	– pink-flowered	CLAP ECho MMuc
	– 'Ploeger's Plena' (d)	EBee
	– 'Polar Star'	CLAP
	– 'Robinsoniana' ♀H6	Widely available
	– 'Rosea'	CLAP ECho LEdu NLar SMrm
	– 'Royal Blue'	CBct CBro CHel CLAP ECho ELon EPPr EPot GAbr GBin GEdr GKev GMaP LAma LEdu MAvo NLar SMrm WCot WPnP
	– 'Rubra'	MNrw
	– 'Salt and Pepper'	MAvo
	– 'Slack Top Pink'	MAvo
	– 'Stammheim' (d)	CLAP EPPr
	– 'Super Allenii'	GBuc MAvo
	– 'Tilo' **new**	MAvo
	– 'Tinney's Blush'	CLAP
	– 'Tomas'	CLAP EBee ECho ELon EPot GBuc GEdr MAvo NHar NRya
	– 'Vestal' (d) ♀H5	Widely available
	– 'Virescens' ♀H5	CLAP CWCL ECho ELon EPPr EPot GAbr GBuc GEdr GKev GMaP MAvo MMoz NBir NHar WPtf WShi
	– 'Viridiflora'	CExl CLAP ECho EPfP GBuc MNrw NBir NSti WCot WSHC
	– 'Westwell Pink'	CLAP ECho EPPr LLHF MNrw WBor WCot WShi
	– white-flowered	LRHS
	– 'Wilks' Giant'	MAvo
	– 'Wilks' White'	ELon EPPr GEdr
	– 'Wisley Pink'	MAvo
	– 'Wyatt's Pink'	CLAP ELon EPot LEdu NCGa
	– 'Yerda Ramusem'	ECho EPPr GBuc MAvo
	nemorosa* × *ranunculoides	see *A.* × *lipsiensis*
	obtusiloba	CLAP GBuc GEdr NSla SRms WAbe
	– 'Alba'	WAbe
	– blue-flowered	WAbe
	– 'Large Blue' **new**	GEdr
	– 'Pradesh' **new**	GEdr
I	– 'Sulphurea'	EPot GEdr
	– yellow-flowered	WAbe
	palmata	EWes LEdu SGSe SMad WCot
	parviflora	GKev
	patens	see *Pulsatilla patens*
	pavonina	CMea CSpe ECha IBoy LRHS NBir SLon SMHy SPoG WAbe WCot
	– lilac-flowered	NBir
	– pink-flowered	NBir
	polyanthes	EBee GEdr LRHS
	prattii	CExl CLAP EPPr GEdr LEdu WHal
	pseudoaltaica	GEdr LEdu WCru

Name	Suppliers
– blue-flowered	GEdr
– 'Yuki-no-sei' (d)	GEdr
pulsatilla	see *Pulsatilla vulgaris*
quinquefolia	WCot
raddeana	ECho
* – f. ***rosea***	GEdr
ranunculoides ♀H5	Widely available
– 'Bill Baker'	LEdu
– 'Frank Waley'	WCot
– 'Fuchsis Traum'	CDes WCot
– 'Grandiflora'	MAvo
* – ***laciniata***	CLAP GBuc WCot
– 'Pleniflora' (d) ♀H5	CLAP ECha ECho EPPr EPot GBBs GBuc LRHS MAvo NLar WFar
– subsp. ***ranunculoides***	ECho GKev
– 'Semi-Plena'	ECho GEdr LEdu
– subsp. ***wockeana***	CDes CSam EBee ECho GBuc LEdu MAvo
reflexa	EBee GKev LLHF
riparia	see *A. virginiana* var. *alba*
rivularis	Widely available
– BWJ 7611	WCru
– CC 4588	CExl
– PAB 2477	LEdu
– 'Glacier'	MAvo MBel NLar
rupicola	NBir
× ***seemannii***	see *A.* × *lipsiensis*
stellata Lam.	see *A. hortensis*
stolonifera double-flowered (d)	EBee WCot WSHC
sulphurea misapplied	see *Pulsatilla alpina* subsp. *apiifolia*
sumatrana B&SWJ 11265	WCru
sylvestris	Widely available
– 'Elise Fellmann' (d)	CSpe EBee GBin GBuc WHal WHil
– 'Macrantha'	EPfP NGdn WCot
tetrasepala	WCot
§ ***tomentosa***	EPla LRHS SDix SRms SWat
§ – 'Albadura'	EBee
– 'Robustissima'	see *A.* × *hybrida* 'Robustissima'
trifolia L.	EPPr GBuc NBid NLar SRms WCot WFar
– pink-flowered	WFar
trullifolia	CDes GBee GBin GCal GCra WAbe
udensis **new**	GKev
vernalis	see *Pulsatilla vernalis*
virginiana	EBee GCal LEdu LPla MNrw NBid WHrl WWEG
§ – var. ***alba***	NLar
vitifolia misapplied	see *A. tomentosa*
'Wild Swan'	CMea CSpe CWCL CWGN ECtt EPfP EWoo IBoy LBMP LBuc LRHS LSou LSun MPnt NSti SHar SPer SPoG STPC SWvt WNPC

Anemonella (*Ranunculaceae*)

Name	Suppliers
thalictroides	CCon CElw CLAP CWCL ECho EFEx ELon EPot GAbr GBuc GEdr GKev ITim LAma MAvo MMoz NHar NLar NRya WAbe WFar WPnP XLum
– 'Alba Plena' (d)	ECho GBuc MAvo
– 'Amelia'	CLAP EPPr GBuc GEdr IGor NHar
– 'Babe'	WCot
– 'Betty Blake' (d)	ECho EPot GEdr GKev MMHG NRya WCot
– 'Cameo'	ECho EFEx EPPr EPot GEdr GKev MAvo NHar NRya WCot
– 'Dark Pink' **new**	CWCL
– 'Diamante'	WCot
– 'Double Green' (d)	EFEx
– 'Flore Pleno' (d)	GBuc
– 'Full Double White' (d)	ECho EFEx GKev
– 'Green Hurricane' (d)	ECho EFEx GEdr GKev NLar WCot
– large white-flowered	CDes
– f. ***rosea***	CAby CElw ECho ELan GBuc GKev LLHF NLar WAbe
– – 'Oscar Schoaf' (d)	ECho GBuc GEdr GKev ITim WAbe
– – semi-double pink-flowered (d)	CElw MAvo NLar
– semi-double white-flowered (d)	CElw EPPr WAbe
– 'Tairin'	GEdr
– white-flowered	GKev

Anemonopsis (*Ranunculaceae*)

Name	Suppliers
macrophylla	CExl CPBP CPom CSpe CTal EBee ECho EWes GCal GEdr MNrw MRav NLar SBch SMad SPhx SRms WCru WFar WPGP WSHC
– 'White Swan'	GBin GEdr WCru WSHC

Anemopsis (*Saururaceae*)

Name	Suppliers
sp.	CArn
californica	EBee EWay GBin GEdr IFoB LLWG MSKA MWts NLar SBrt WCot WPGP

Anethum (*Apiaceae*)

Name	Suppliers
graveolens	CArn ENfk GPoy MHer MNHC NPri SIde SRms SVic
– 'Dukat'	CUse ELau

angelica see *Angelica archangelica*

Angelica (*Apiaceae*)

Name	Suppliers
sp.	CHab
acutiloba	WFar
– var. ***iwatensis*** B&SWJ 11197	WCru
anomala B&SWJ 10886	WCru
archangelica	Widely available
– 'Corinne Tremaine' (v)	WHer
atropurpurea	CBod ECtt EPfP GCal GKev GMaP GQue LRHS MHer MNrw MRav NCGa SWat SWvt WFar
cartilaginomarginata B&SWJ 12663 **new**	WCru
dahurica	EWTr WOut
– B&SWJ 8603	WCru
decursiva	CArn
– B&SWJ 5746	WCru
edulis	SPhx
– B&SWJ 10968	LEdu WCru
gigas	Widely available
– B&SWJ 4170	WCru
hispanica	see *A. pachycarpa*
japonica B&SWJ 11480	WCru
montana	see *A. sylvestris*
morii RWJ 9802	WCru
§ ***pachycarpa***	CArn CSpe ELan EPri GBin GMaP LRHS MHer MRav MSpe NBir NLar SMrm WJek WWEG
pubescens	NDov
– B&SWJ 5593	WCru
– B&SWJ 11129	WCru

- var. ***matsumurae*** B&SWJ 6387 WCru
sachalinensis CSpe
sinensis CArn GPoy LEdu
'Summer Delight' see *Ligusticum scoticum*
§ ***sylvestris*** CArn CHab LLWG WOut
- 'Ebony' CAby CBod CBre CSpe CUse ECtt GAbr GBin LEdu LRHS MAsh MAvo MHer MTis NCGa NLar SHil SMDP SMrm SPad WCot
* - 'Purpurea' CSpe EWes GQue WPGP
- 'Vicar's Mead' CDes EBee LEdu LPla LRHS MBel NBir NChi NLar NSti SHar SPhx SWvt
taiwaniana CArn CBre CDTJ CSam ELan ESwi IMou NLar
ursina IMou

Angelonia (*Plantaginaceae*)

angustifolia Angelface Blue Improved ='Anbluim'PBR (Angelface Series) NPri

Anigozanthos (*Haemodoraceae*)

'Bush Ranger' (Bush Gems Series) CCCN
flavidus SPlb
- 'Ember' CCCN
- 'Illusion' CCCN
- 'Opal' CCCN
- 'Pearl' CCCN
- red-flowered SPlb
- 'Splendour' CCCN
- 'Yellow Gem' CCCN
manglesii ♀H1c SPlb SVen

Anisacanthus (*Acanthaceae*)

quadrifidus var. ***wrightii*** WCot

anise see *Pimpinella anisum*

Anisodontea (*Malvaceae*)

bryoniifolia new SVen
§ ***capensis*** CCCN CHGN CHll CTre ELan EPri GBee LAst MCot MOWG SChF SLim SMrm SPlb SRkn SRms SVen SWvt
- 'Tara's Pink' CSpe
'Crystal Rose' LRHS SHil XLum
'Donatella' SLim
'El Royo' CSpe CWGN ECtt LSou MAvo MHol MPie SDys SPad WCot XLum
'Elegant Lady' CSpe GFai
huegelii see *Alyogyne huegelii*
× ***hypomadara*** misapplied see *A. capensis*
julii SPlb SVen
'Large Magenta' LSou SWvt
scabrosa CChe GFai
- 'Miss Pinky'PBR new LRHS

Anisodus (*Solanaceae*)

carnioliciodes BWJ 7501 WCru
§ ***luridus*** EWld GCal

Anisotome (*Apiaceae*)

imbricata var. ***imbricata*** new WAbe

Annona (*Annonaceae*)

cherimola (F) CCCN XBlo

Anoiganthus see *Cyrtanthus*

Anomalesia see *Gladiolus*

Anomatheca (*Iridaceae*)

cruenta see *Freesia laxa*

Anopterus (*Escalloniaceae*)

glandulosus CFil WSHC

Anredera (*Basellaceae*)

§ ***cordifolia*** CRHN ECho EShb GKev LEdu

Antennaria (*Asteraceae*)

aprica see *A. parvifolia*
dioica CArn CTri ECtt EDAr GAbr GBin GJos GPoy MJak NSla SPlb SRms XLum
- 'Alba' EHoe
- 'Alex Duguid' EPot GEdr NWad SBrt
- 'Aprica' see *A. parvifolia*
- 'Minima' ECho EPot GCrg ITim MWat NBro NHar NSla WAbe
- red-flowered ECho
- var. ***rosea*** see *A. rosea*
- 'Rotes Wunder' CMea ECha EPot SBch WAbe
* - 'Rubra' ECha ECho ECtt EDAr GCrg MHer MMuc WIce WRHF XLum
'Joy' WAbe WHal
macrophylla hort. see *A. microphylla*
§ ***microphylla*** SRms
§ ***parvifolia*** CTri ECho SRms SRot
- var. ***rosea*** see *A. microphylla*
plantaginifolia EBee
§ ***rosea*** ♀H5 ECho GMaP MAsh NSla SPlb SRms WHal WHoo WIce

Antenoron see *Persicaria*

Anthemis ✿ (*Asteraceae*)

from Turkey ECtt EWes LLWP
arvensis CHab
§ 'Beauty of Grallagh' GBuc GCal SDix
'Cally Cream' GCal NCGa SMHy SPhx
'Cally White' GBin GCal WHil WWFP
carpatica NBro
- 'Karpatenschnee' LRHS SRms WWEG
cretica subsp. ***pontica*** NLar
'Daisy Bee' MAvo
frutescens Voss see *Argyranthemum frutescens*
'Grallagh Gold' misapplied, orange-yellow see *A.* 'Beauty of Grallagh'
'Grallagh Gold' ECtt EWes MWat NPer
§ ***marschalliana*** CFis CMea ECha ECho ECtt EDAr LRHS SMrm SPlb WCot
- subsp. ***pectinata*** GCrg NSla
nobilis see *Chamaemelum nobile*
punctata subsp. ***cupaniana*** ♀H4 Widely available
- - 'Nana' NPer SHar
rudolphiana see *A. marschalliana*
sancti-johannis CBod CMHG EAEE EPfP LRHS NPer NWad SPer SRms WMoo
Susanna Mitchell ='Blomit' EBee ECtt ELon GMaP LRHS MAvo MNrw MWat NBir NDov NWad

		SMrm SRGP SWvt WMnd WSHC WWEG XLum
	'Tetworth'	CPrp ECha ECtt ELan EPfP SMad WWEG
	tinctoria	CArn CBod CHby CMac EBee ENfk GPoy MHer NPer SRms SWvt WHfH WJek WSFF XLum
	- 'Alba'	EBee EWTr LRHS NLar NWad WFar WWEG XLum
	- 'Charme'PBR	CBod EPfP LAst LRHS MHol NLar NPCo SPoG SWvt WMnd
	- 'Compacta'	EWes GCal MNrw XLum
	- 'E.C. Buxton'	Widely available
	- 'Eva'	NDov WWEG
I	- 'Golden Rays'	SDix WWEG
	- 'Hall Farm Frilly'	ECtt ELon
	- 'Kelwayi'	CSBt CTri EPfP LRHS NBro NLar NPer SPer SRms SWat WMoo WWEG XLum
	- 'Lemon Ice'	EBee
	- 'Lemon Maid'	CCon ECtt ELon GBin LRHS SMrm
	- 'Sauce Hollandaise'	Widely available
	- 'Waddow Gold'	NWad
	- 'Wargrave Variety'	CElw CMac CPrp CSam CWCL ECha ECtt ELan EPfP EPla LBMP LRHS MAvo MNFA NBir NBro NChi NGdn NWad SDix SPhx SWvt WCAu WFar WMnd
	'Tinpenny Sparkle'	CAbP CBod CSam EBee ECtt EWll GAbr GMaP MAvo MHol MPie NLar NSti WAul WCot WFar WHoo WMnd WRHF WWEG
	triumfettii	NPer WCot
	tuberculata	NChi SBch
	zyghia	EBee

Anthericum (*Asparagaceae*)

	algeriense	see *A. liliago*
*	***bovei***	CBro
§	***liliago***	CSpe ECho ELan EWld GCal GKev GMaP IFoB LRHS LSun MCot MRav NCGa NLar WAul WPtf WWEG XEll
	- 'Major' ♀H5	CAvo CBro CDes EBee ECGP ECha ECho MLHP WPGP
	plumosum	see *Trichopetalum plumosum*
	ramosum	CDes CSpe ECha ECho EPot EPri EWes GCal GKev LRHS MBrN NBid NBir NCGa NLar SMrm SPhx WCot WPGP

Antholyza (*Iridaceae*)

coccinea	see *Crocosmia paniculata*
× ***crocosmioides***	see *Crocosmia* × *crocosmioides*
paniculata	see *Crocosmia paniculata*

Anthoxanthum (*Poaceae*)

odoratum	CHab ELau GPoy XLum

Anthriscus (*Apiaceae*)

cerefolium	CArn CHby ELau ENfk GPoy MHer MNHC SRms WJek
sylvestris	CArn CHab NMir SPhx WFar WOut WSFF
- 'Going for Gold' **new**	CNat
- 'Kabir'	LEdu
- 'Ravenswing'	Widely available
- 'Shateley Pink' **new**	LEdu

Anthurium (*Araceae*)

andraeanum 'Glowing Pink'	XBlo
- 'Red Heart'	XBlo
- 'Tivolo'	XBlo
'Aztec'	XBlo
Baleno = 'Anthauf4'PBR	XBlo
'Caribo'	XBlo
crenatum	XBlo
'Crimson'	XBlo
'Jungle Bush' **new**	LPal
'Magenta'	XBlo
'Mikra'	XBlo
'Octavia'	XBlo
Pico Bello = 'Anthcupcup'PBR	XBlo
Pink Champion = 'Antinkeles'PBR	XBlo
'Porcelaine White'	XBlo
Red Champion = 'Anthbnena'PBR	XBlo
'Vitara'	XBlo
White Champion = 'Anthefaqyr'PBR	XBlo

Anthyllis (*Papilionaceae*)

	hermanniae 'Compacta'	see *A. hermanniae* 'Minor'
§	- 'Minor'	WAbe
	montana	XSen
	- subsp. ***atropurpurea***	ECho LRHS
	- 'Rubra' ♀H5	ECho EDAr LLHF MNHC NSla
	- 'Rubra Compacta'	WAbe
	vulneraria	CHab NMir NRya SPhx WSFF
	- var. ***coccinea***	CPom EAJP ELan GAbr GBin MBel NSla SEND SGSe SPhx WCFE WHal WIce
	- dark red-flowered	CSpe

Antirrhinum (*Plantaginaceae*)

asarina	see *Asarina procumbens*
barrelieri	SEND
braun-blanquetii	GCra GLog SEND SPhx WCot WHil
'Eternal'	LRHS
hispanicum 'Avalanche'	ECtt
- subsp. ***hispanicum*** 'Roseum'	CMea LPot
majus 'Black Prince'	CSpe ECtt SPhx
- 'Cheerio' (mixed)	CWCL
- 'June Blake' (v)	WCot
- Liberty Classic Series	NPri
- - 'Liberty Classic Scarlet'	NPri
- - 'Liberty Classic Yellow'	NPri
- 'Night and Day'	CSpe WMoo
molle	CSpe GKev MCot MMuc NPer SChF WAbe
- pink-flowered	MCot SRms WAbe
- white-flowered	GKev WAbe
sempervirens	MHer WAbe XLum
siculum	WCot WHil

añu see *Tropaeolum tuberosum*

Aphelandra (*Acanthaceae*)

squarrosa 'Citrina'	XBlo

Aphyllanthes (*Asparagaceae*)

monspeliensis	SBrt XLum

Apios (*Papilionaceae*)

§ ***americana***	CAgr CCon CPom ECho EWes GBin LEdu NBir WCot WCru WSHC
tuberosa	see *A. americana*

Apium (*Apiaceae*)

graveolens	CArn CHab ELau ENfk GPoy MHer MNHC SIde SRms SVic WJek
- var. ***rapaceum*** 'Prinz' ♀H4	SVic
- (Secalinum Group) 'Par-cel'	MHer SRms

Apium × *Petroselinum* (*Apiaceae*)

hybrid, misapplied	see *A. graveolens* Secalinum Group

Apocynum (*Apocynaceae*)

cannabinum	CArn GPoy

Aponogeton (*Aponogetonaceae*)

desertorum	EWay LLWG
distachyos	CBAq CBen CRow CWat EHon EWay MSKA MWts NPer SCoo SVic SWat WMAq XLum

apple see *Malus domestica*

apricot see *Prunus armeniaca*

Aptenia (*Aizoaceae*)

cordifolia	CCCN NPer SChr SPlb SVen
- 'Variegata' (v)	CCCN

Aquilegia ✿ (*Ranunculaceae*)

sp.	SVic
akitensis misapplied	see *A. flabellata* var. *pumila*
'Alaska' (State Series) ♀H5	LRHS MBri SHil SMrm
* ***alba variegata*** (v)	ECho
alpina	CBod CMea CPrp EBee ECho EPfP LPal MAsh MNHC NGdn SCob SPer SRms WMoo XLum
amaliae	see *A. ottonis* subsp. *amaliae*
'Apple Blossom'	NBir
aragonensis	see *A. pyrenaica*
§ ***atrata***	CCon CLAP CPou ECho
aurea misapplied	see *A. vulgaris* golden-leaved
aurea Janka	GKev LLHF
barnebyi	CWCL
bertolonii ♀H5	CMea ECho EPot GKev LRHS NRya SRms WHoo WTou
- 'Blue Berry'	WThu
Biedermeier Group	EAJP ECho EPfP LRHS NGdn NNor NOrc SPoG SRot WFar WTou
'Blue Star' (Star Series)	EAEE ELan EPfP EPla GBin LRHS NEgg NPCo SPtp WGwG WTou
'Bluebird' (Songbird Series) ♀H4	LBuc LRHS NBir NPer NPri WFar
brevistyla	NNor
'Fruit and Nut Chocolate'	CAby CDes CHel EBee EUJe IKil MBNS MHol MPie WCot WFar
buergeriana	SPhx
- 'Calimero'	CHel CTsd MBNS MPro NLar SPtp
- var. ***oxysepala***	see *A. oxysepala*
'Bunting' (Songbird Series) ♀H4	MHer NPri SGbt
canadensis ♀H3	CLAP CSpe ECho EHoe ELan EPla GCrg GKev NBir NBro SRms WFar WTou XLum
- 'Corbett'	NLar
- 'Little Lanterns'	ECho EPPr NLar SGSe WHil WIce
- 'Nana'	WThu
'Cardinal' (Songbird Series)	LBuc LRHS
cazorlensis	see *A. pyrenaica* subsp. *cazorlensis*
chaplinei	GBin GKev NBir SBch
chrysantha	ECho EWld GBin GJos SGSe SIgm SRms SWvt WHil WKif WTou
- 'Denver Gold'	EShb MWhi SMrm
- 'Yellow Queen'	CExl CWCL EPPr EPfP EWoo GBin GMaP LPal LRHS MWat NCGa NGdn NPri SCob SGbt SPad SWvt WCFE WHil XLum
clematiflora	see *A. vulgaris* var. *stellata*
Clementine Series	EPfP
coerulea ♀H5	GJos GKev NNor SRms
- var. ***coerulea***	GKev
- var. ***ochroleuca***	CWCL
'Colorado' (State Series)	LRHS MBri SHil
'Crimson Star'	ELan EPfP GJos LRHS MPro SPer SPoG WMoo WTou
dichroa	EBee WPGP
discolor	GKev LLHF WThu
'Double Rubies' (d)	ELan MMuc SMrm WMoo WTou
'Dove' (Songbird Series) ♀H5	EWll LBuc LRHS MHer NPri SGbt SPer
I 'Dragonfly'	CBcs ELan EPfP LRHS MBel MJak NGdn SPer SPoG WTou
'Dragon's Breath' (mixed)	WTou
ecalcarata	see *Semiaquilegia ecalcarata*
einseleana	ECho LLHF
'Elegance'	WTou
'Elegant Moonstone'	WTou
'Elegant Opal'	WTou
'Elegant Ruby'	WTou
* 'Firecracker'	GJos
flabellata ♀H5	GCra
- f. ***alba***	CTri ECho ELan
- - 'White Jewel' (Jewel Series)	GKev
- 'Blackcurrant Ice'	EPfP LRHS
- 'Blue Angel'	LSun
- Cameo Series	GJos GMaP WFar
- - 'Cameo Blue and White'	NCGa SRms SRot WFar
- - 'Cameo Pink and White'	MHer NCGa
- - 'Cameo Rose and White'	SRms
- - 'Cameo Rose'	WFar
- - 'Cameo White'	SRot WFar
- 'Georgia' (State Series) ♀H5	LRHS MBri SMrm
- Jewel Series	ECho
- 'Ministar'	ECho EDAr GCrg WFar WHil XLum
- 'Nana Alba'	see *A. flabellata* var. *pumila* f. *alba*
§ - var. ***pumila*** ♀H5	CCon CWCL ECha ECho EDAr EWTr GEdr GKev LRHS LSun NGdn WTou
§ - - f. ***alba*** ♀H5	ECha ECho EDAr LRHS LSun SRms
- - 'Atlantis'	EPPr GBBs LRHS NPri
- - 'Flore Pleno' (d)	ECho
I - - f. ***kurilensis*** 'Rosea'	CCon EDAr GKev WAbe
- 'Vermont' (State Series)	MBri SMrm
'Flamboyant'	WTou
'Florida' (State Series) ♀H5	LRHS MBri SHil
formosa	CMea ECho NChi SMHy WKif WTou
- var. ***truncata***	SIgm
§ ***fragrans***	CCon CLAP CTsd ELan GEdr GJos GKev MMoz SGbt SMrm SPad WTou
glandulosa	LLHF
glauca	see *A. fragrans*

'Golden Guiness' WPnP
'Goldfinch' (Songbird Series) LBuc LRHS MHer NBir SGbt SMrm SPer WFar
'Heavenly Blue' EShb LRHS SPhx WTou
'Hensol Harebell' SHar SRms
'Iceberg' (*fragrans* hybrid) WTou
japonica see *A. flabellata* var. *pumila*
jonesii GKev SPlb
jonesii × ***saximontana*** GKev
'Kansas' (State Series) MBri
'Koralle' CBod WTou
'Kristall' SGbt SPhx XLum
laramiensis CPBP
'Leprechaun Gold' (v) EPfP LAst NGdn
'Lime Sorbet' LRHS SBod SRms
longissima CWld GKev MHer SGSe SHar WFar WHil WHoo
long-spurred hybrids **new** WTou
– white WTou
'Louisiana' (State Series) ♀H5 LRHS MBri SCob SHil SMrm
'Magpie' see *A. vulgaris* 'William Guiness'
'Maxi' CBod WTou
McKana Group Widely available
'Milk and Honey' NLar
'Montana' (State Series) MBri
Mrs Scott-Elliot hybrids CSBt EPfP LAst
Music Series SRms
'Nightingale' (Songbird Series) NPri SGbt
nigricans see *A. atrata*
nivalis LLHF
olympica EWes WTou
'Oranges and Lemons' SGSe WFar WTou
'Oregon' (State Series) **new** MBri
(Origami Series) 'Origami Red and White' ♀H5 NPri
– 'Origami Rose and White' ♀H5 NPri
– 'Origami Yellow' ♀H5 NPri
§ ***ottonis*** subsp. ***amaliae*** CPBP LLHF SIgm WAbe
§ ***oxysepala*** CExl CHel GCal WFar
– B&SWJ 4775 WCru
parviflora GKev
Perfumed Garden Group CPla CWld WFar
'Petticoats' SBod
'Purple Emperor'PBR EPfP
§ ***pyrenaica*** GKev
§ – subsp. ***cazorlensis*** ECho
'Red Hobbit' CBct CSpe EAEE EBee ELan EPfP EPla IBoy LRHS MBel MHer MHol NEgg NGdn SHil SPtp WBor WFar WGwG WHoo
'Red Star' (Star Series) CHel EAEE EPfP EPla LRHS NEgg WHil WTou
'Rhubarb and Custard' **new** MPro
'Robin' (Songbird Series) MHer SGbt SPer
rockii CCon CLAP EWes GCal GKev
– B&SWJ 7965 WCru
'Roman Bronze' see *Aquilegia* × *Semiaquilegia* 'Roman Bronze'
'Rose Queen' EPfP NNor SPtp WFar WHoo WTou
saximontana GEdr GKev NSla
§ 'Schneekönigin' CWCL GMaP LRHS WCFE
scopulorum GKev LLHF SIgm WAbe
Shooting Stars (mixed) WTou
sibirica CCon GKev LLHF
'Silver Queen' EBee ELan EWoo
'Simone's White' EBee
skinneri CExl CSpe ELan GEdr GLog WMnd
– 'Tequila Sunrise' CBod CSpe CWCL ELan GBin MHer NNor SMrm SPad SPtp
Snow Queen see *A.* 'Schneekönigin'
'Spitfire' LBuc LRHS NCGa NPri
(Spring Magic Series) Spring Magic Blue and White LRHS SCob WTou
– Spring Magic Navy and White LRHS
– Spring Magic Rose and Ivory LRHS WTou
– Spring Magic White LRHS SCob WTou
– Spring Magic Yellow WTou
State Series WWEG
stellata see *A. vulgaris* var. *stellata*
'Sunburst Ruby' CPla CWCL WMoo
'Sunshine' **new** EBee MPro WRHF
'Sweet Rainbows' (d) CPla
'Touchwood Black & Bruises' mixed doubles (d) **new** WTou
'Touchwood Crinoline Ladies' mixed doubles (d) **new** WTou
'Touchwood Harmony' mixed **new** WTou
'Touchwood Night Lights' mixed doubles (d) **new** WTou
'Touchwood Sunrise Surprises' mixed doubles (d) **new** WTou
triternata NNor
'Virginia' (State Series) LRHS MBri SHil
viridiflora CLAP EBee ELan EPfP GCal MBel WAbe WCot WHil WKif WMnd WTou
– 'Chocolate Soldier' CSpe CWCL
'Volcano!' (mixed) WTou
vulgaris CArn CHab CMHG CWCL CWld EPfP EWoo GAbr GKev GPoy LLWP MHer MMuc MNHC NBro NGdn NMir SEND SPlb WMoo WShi
– 'Adelaide Addison' ECha WHoo
– var. ***alba*** CMea EPfP EWoo LRHS SCob WTou
– 'Aureovariegata' see *A. vulgaris* Vervaeneana Group
– 'Blackbird' (Songbird Series) (d) CWCL
– 'Burnished Rose' CPla WTou
– ***clematiflora*** see *A. vulgaris* var. *stellata*
– (Clementine Series) 'Clementine Blue' (d) EPfP WCot WTou
– – 'Clementine Dark Purple' (d) EPfP LRHS SPoG
– – 'Clementine Red' (d) EPfP SPoG
– – 'Clementine Salmon Rose' (d) EPfP LRHS SPoG
– – 'Clementine White' (d) EPfP LRHS MWat SPoG
– 'Crystal Star' LRHS
– var. ***flore-pleno*** (d) LLWP WFar WTou
– – bicolour (d) WTou
– – black-flowered (d) WCot WTou
– – blue-flowered (d) WTou
– – 'Dorothy Rose' (Dorothy Series) (d) EWTr SPad SPtp
– – 'Double Pleat' (d) EPfP
– – 'Double Pleat' blue/white-flowered (d) CPrp
– – 'Double Pleat' pink/white-flowered (d) CPrp CWCL

	- - 'Jane Hollow' (d)	CPou
	- - pale blue-flowered (d)	WCot WTou
	- - pink-flowered (d)	WTou
	- - purple-flowered (d)	WTou
	- - red-flowered (d)	WTou
	- - 'Strawberry Ice Cream' (d)	NBro NNor WTou
*	- - 'White Bonnet' (d)	CWCL
	- - white-flowered (d)	WTou
§	- golden-leaved	ECho WTou
	- Grandmother's Garden Group	CBod
	- 'Heidi'	MMuc
	- 'Mellow Yellow'	CPla CTsd EHoe ELon LBuc LRHS SDix SGSe WMoo
	- 'Miss Coventry'	SMHy
	- Munstead White	see *A. vulgaris* 'Nivea'
§	- 'Nivea' ♀H7	CPou CSpe EBee ECha ELan EPfP EWoo NChi SPoG
	- 'Pink Spurless'	see *A. vulgaris* var. *stellata* pink-flowered
	- 'Pom Pom Crimson' (Pom Pom Series)	NBro WCot
	- scented	WTou
§	- var. ***stellata***	ELan GAbr GKev MWhi NBir NBro NNor WFar WHea WMoo WTou
	- - Barlow Series (d)	CHVG WFar WTou WWEG
	- - - 'Black Barlow' (d)	Widely available
	- - black-flowered	WTou
	- - 'Blue Barlow' (Barlow Series) (d)	CAby CSpe EBee ECtt EPfP EPla GMaP GQue LRHS MWat SCob SHil SPer SPhx SWvt WCot WMnd WTou WWEG XLum
	- - 'Blue Fountain'	WTou
	- - blue-flowered	NBir WTou
	- - 'Bordeaux Barlow' (Barlow Series) (d)	LRHS WTou
	- - 'Christa Barlow' (Barlow Series) (d)	EBee EPfP LRHS MBel NGdn NLar WTou
	- - double-flowered (d)	WTou
	- - 'Firewheel'	WMoo WTou
	- - 'Greenapples' (d)	CAbP CBre CHVG CHel CNor CWCL EBee ELan EPfP EWoo GBin GKev GQue LBMP LPla LRHS MCot MMuc MPie MWat SCob SMrm WCot WHoo WTou WWFP
	- - 'Nora Barlow' (Barlow Series) (d)	Widely available
§	- - pink-flowered	WTou
	- - red-flowered	WTou
	- - 'Rose Barlow' (Barlow Series) (d)	EPfP GBin LRHS WMnd WTou
	- - 'Royal Purple' (d)	NBro NNor WMoo
	- - 'Ruby Port' (d)	Widely available
	- - 'Ruby Port' crimped (d)	WPnP
	- - 'Touchwood Dreamtime'	WTou
	- - 'White Barlow' (Barlow Series) (d)	CAby EPfP IBoy LRHS SHil SPer SWvt WTou
	- - white-flowered	CSpe GCra NBir NBro WTou
	- variegated foliage	see *A. vulgaris* Vervaeneana Group
§	- Vervaeneana Group (v)	CMHG CWCL ELan EPfP LRHS NBir NPer SGSe SPlb SPoG SRms SWat WBor WFar WHoo WMoo WTou
	- - 'Lime Frost' (v)	WTou
	- - 'Woodside Blue' (v)	NWad WTou
	- - 'Woodside White' (v)	NBir WBrk WTou
§	- 'William Guiness'	Widely available
	- 'William Guiness Doubles' (d)	WMoo WTou
	- 'Winky Wooh' (Winky Series)	GBBs GBin WBor
	'White Star' (Star Series)	CHel CPrp EBee ELan EPfP EPla LAst LRHS NEgg SPer WTou WWEG
	white-flowered	WTou
	Winky Series	ELan GJos NCGa NNor SWvt WFar WTou
	- 'Winky Blue-White'	GBin LRHS NPri SMrm WCFE WTou
	- 'Winky Double Red-White' (d)	LRHS
	- 'Winky Purple-White'	LRHS NPri SMrm
	- 'Winky Red-White'	LRHS NPri SWvt WTou
	- 'Winky Rose-Rose'	LRHS SMrm
	yabeana	GEdr GKev WMoo
	'Yellow Star' (Star Series) ♀H4	CHel EPfP EPla MLHP SPer WGwG WRHF

Aquilegia × *Semiaquilegia* (*Ranunculaceae*)

	hybrid **new**	NPCo
	- blue-flowered	NGdn
§	'Roman Bronze'	CBod CPla WMoo

Arabis (*Brassicaceae*)

	albida	see *A. alpina* subsp. *caucasica*
	allionii **new**	GKev
	alpina	MAsh SPlb
§	- subsp. ***caucasica***	ECho GKev
	- - 'Corfe Castle'	ECtt
	- - 'Douler Angevine' (v)	CBod CMea ECtt ELon GCrg MAvo MHol NPri SPoG SRms WIce
	- - 'Flore Pleno' (d) ♀H5	CElw CHid CSpe CTri CWCL ECho ECtt ELan EWld GAbr GJos GMaP SBch SIgm SRms WHoo
	- - 'Pinkie'	ECho LPal
	- - 'Pixie Cream'	ECtt EDAr LBMP MMuc NGdn
	- - 'Rosea'	GJos LRHS NBir SRms
§	- - 'Schneehaube' ♀H6	CTri ECho ECtt EPfP GMaP LRHS MJak NBir NGdn SPoG SRms
	- - Snowcap	see *A. alpina* subsp. *caucasica* 'Schneehaube'
	- - 'Variegata' (v)	ECho ELan GMaP LAst NPri SPoG SRms
	androsacea	SRms
	× ***arendsii*** 'Compinkie'	GJos LBMP SPlb SRms
	blepharophylla	EPfP WSHC
§	- 'Frühlingszauber' ♀H5	CTri EAJP ELan EPfP GJos NBir NGdn NPri SEND SPoG SRms WRHF
	- 'Rose Delight'	LRHS
	- 'Rote Sensation'	ELan NGdn
	- Spring Charm	see *A. blepharophylla* 'Frühlingszauber'
	bryoides	LLHF
	carduchorum	XLum
	caucasica	see *A. alpina* subsp. *caucasica*
	collina	GJos
	ferdinandi-coburgi	ECho MWat NHol
	- 'Aureovariegata' (v)	CMea CTri ECho ECtt ELan SWvt
	- 'Old Gold'	CTal ECho EHoe EPfP LPot MAsh MHer NHol NRya SPoG SRms SRot SWvt WCFE
	- 'Variegata'	see *A. procurrens* 'Variegata'
	procurrens	WCot
	- 'Glacier' **new**	GJos
§	- 'Variegata' (v) ♀H5	CTal CTri ECho ECtt EHoe ELan EPfP EWes GKev MBrN MHer MJak MSCN SPlb SRms SRot
	purpurea	MMuc WMoo

Snow Cap — see *A. alpina* subsp. *caucasica* 'Schneehaube'
× ***wilczekii*** — EPot

Arachniodes (*Dryopteridaceae*)

davalliaeformis — CBty EFtx ISha LRHS
miqueliana — ISha
simplicior (v) — CBty CCCN EFtx ISha NLos WCot
standishii — CBty EFtx ISha LEdu LRHS NLos WCot

Araiostegia (*Davalliaceae*)

faberiana — CExl
hymenophylloides — SKHP
parvipinnata — see *A. perdurans*
§ ***perdurans*** — CFil WPGP
- B&SWJ 1608 — WCru
pulchra HWJ 1007 — WCru

Aralia ✿ (*Araliaceae*)

apioides — IMou
- EDHCH 9720 — WCru
armata B&SWJ 6916 **new** — WCru
- RWJ 10060 — WCru
bipinnata Blanco — WPGP
- RWJ 10101 — WCru
cachemirica — CDTJ CLAP GCal MBrN NBid NLar SDix SMad SPlb WCru WHal WMoo
californica — EBee GCal GPoy IGor LEdu NLar SKHP WCru
castanopsidicola CWJ 12411 — WCru
chapaensis B&SWJ 11812 — WCru
- HWJ 1013 **new** — WCru
chinensis misapplied — see *A. elata*
chinensis L. BWJ 8102 — WCru
continentalis — CLAP NLar WHoo
- B&SWJ 8437 **new** — WCru
- B&SWJ 8524 — WCru
cordata Thunb. — GCal LEdu WFar
- B&SWJ 5511 — CDes
- B&SWJ 5596 — WCru
- var. ***sachalinensis*** — NLar
- - B&SWJ 4773 **new** — WCru
- 'Sun King' — CAby CBod EBee ECtt EPfP ESwi EUJe IBoy LLWG LRHS LSun MBel MNrw MPie MSCN NLar NSti SCob SPoG SWvt WCot WFar
decaisneana B&SWJ 6794 **new** — WCru
- RWJ 9910 — WCru
echinocaulis **new** — SBrt
- PAB 9052 **new** — LEdu
§ ***elata*** — CAco CBcs CCVT CDoC CDul CExl CHel CHll CMac CTsd EBee ELan EPfP IDee LPal LRHS MBlu MGos MMuc SArc SCob SGol SLim SPer SPoG SWvt WFar
- B&SWJ 5480 — WCru
- 'Albomarginata' — see *A. elata* 'Variegata'
- 'Aureo-marginata' (v) — CMac
- 'Aureovariegata' (v) 🏆H5 — CBcs ELan EWes NLar SCob
- 'Golden Umbrella' (v) — EUJe NLar
- 'Silver Umbrella' (v) — EUJe
§ - 'Variegata' (v) 🏆H5 — CBcs ELan EPfP MGos NLar SCob SWvt
foliolosa B&SWJ 8360 — WCru
kansuensis BWJ 7650 — WCru
- CD&R 2289 — CDes WCru
leschenaultii B&SWJ 9515 — WCru
- B&SWJ 11789 — WCru
papyrifera — see *Tetrapanax papyrifer*
racemosa — CArn ETwe EUJe GPoy GQue LEdu LPla NLar SRms
- B&SWJ 9570 — WCru
searelliana B&SWJ 11736 — WCru
sieboldii de Vriese — see *Fatsia japonica*
spinosa L. — CAco CArn EBtc GQue LEdu MBlu NChi NEgg SPlb
subcordata HWJK 2385 — WCru
verticillata B&SWJ 11797 — WCru
vietnamensis B&SWJ 12349E — WCru

Araucaria (*Araucariaceae*)

angustifolia — WPGP
angustifolia × ***araucana*** — CFil SMad
§ ***araucana*** — Widely available
cunninghamii — ECou
excelsa misapplied — see *A. heterophylla*
§ ***heterophylla*** 🏆H2 — CCCN CDoC LPal SArc SEND
imbricata — see *A. araucana*

Araujia (*Apocynaceae*)

sericifera — CHll CMac CRHN CSde CSpe ECre SVen WCot WSHC

Arbutus ✿ (*Ericaceae*)

× ***andrachnoides*** 🏆H4 — CAbP CDul CHGN CJun CTho ELan EPfP GGal LRHS MAsh MRav SArc SMad SPer SPoG WPGP WPat
menziesii — CBcs CDoC CMCN EPfP IFro LRHS MBlu MGos MMuc NSoo WFar
× ***reyorum*** 'Marina' — CAbP CDoC CJun EBee ELan EPfP IVic LRHS MAsh MBlu SEND SMad SPer SPoG SSpi WPGP WPat
unedo — Widely available
- 'Atlantic' 🏆H5 — CCCN CJun EPfP LRHS MAsh MBri MGos SBig SGbt SGol SHil SWvt WPGP WPat
- 'Compacta' — CBcs CCCN CDoC EUJe IArd LRHS MAsh MGos NLar SLon SPoG SWvt
- 'Elfin King' — ELan EPfP LRHS MAsh NLar SLon SWvt
- 'Quercifolia' — CAbP CHll CJun ELan LLHF MAsh NLar WPat
- Roselily = 'Minlily' PBR — SBig
- f. ***rubra*** 🏆H5 — Widely available
xalapensis — CFil SPlb

Archontophoenix (*Arecaceae*)

alexandrae — LPal
cunninghamiana — CBrP XBlo

Arctanthemum (*Asteraceae*)

§ ***arcticum*** — ECha MMuc NLar XLum
- 'Polarstern' — EBee
- 'Roseum' — EBee

Arcterica see *Pieris*

Arctium (*Asteraceae*)

lappa — CArn GPoy SIde SRms SVic WHer WSFF
minus — NMir

Arctostaphylos (*Ericaceae*)

uva-ursi	GBin GPoy NLar SPlb
- 'Massachusetts'	NLar
- 'Snowcap'	MAsh
- 'Vancouver Jade'	CDoC GKin LRHS MAsh SCoo SLon SPer SPoG SRms SWvt

Arctotheca (*Asteraceae*)

calendula	CDes EBee WPGP

Arctotis (*Asteraceae*)

Hannah = 'Archnah'PBR	CAby CSpe ECtt MBNS WHil
Hayley = 'Archley'PBR	CCCN ECtt MBNS SMrm
'Heidi'	LAst MBNS WHil
'Holly'	LAst MBNS SMrm
'Hope'	MBNS
× ***hybrida*** hort. 'Apricot'	CCCN ECtt LAst SVen
- 'Flame' ♀H2	CAby CCCN ECtt LAst MBNS SCoo SMrm SRms SVen
- 'Red Devil'	CCCN EWoo LAst LSou MBNS SCoo SMrm SVen
- 'Wine'	CCCN LAst LSou MBNS SCoo SRkn
venusta	SMrm

Ardisia (*Primulaceae*)

japonica B&SWJ 1032	WCru
- 'Houkan' (v) **new**	WPGP
- var. ***minor*** B&SWJ 1841	WCru
- - B&SWJ 3809	WCru

Areca (*Arecaceae*)

triandra	XBlo

Arecastrum see *Syagrus*

Arenaria (*Caryophyllaceae*)

§ ***alfacariensis***	NLar WAbe
balearica	CWCL ECho EDAr EWes GCrg LLWG MAsh NRya NSla SPlb SRms
capillaris	CTri
grandiflora	XLum
kansuensis	NLar
ledebouriana	EDAr MWat NLar
montana ♀H5	CMea CTal ECha ECho ECtt EDAr EPfP EWTr EWoo GMaP ITim LRHS MGos MLHP MMuc NPri SPhx SPlb SRms SRot WAbe WIce WWFP
- 'Avalanche'	ECtt
- 'Blizzard'	EPfP
pseudacantholimon	LLHF
pulvinata	see *A. alfacariensis*
purpurascens	ECho EPot EWes GKev LLHF NLar SRms SRot WAbe
* ***scopolina*** **new**	GKev
tetraquetra	SIgm
- subsp. ***amabilis***	EPot
verna	see *Minuartia verna*

Arenga (*Arecaceae*)

engleri	LPal
micrantha	WCot

Argania (*Sapotaceae*)

spinosa	CFil WPGP

Argemone (*Papaveraceae*)

grandiflora	CSpe SBch
mexicana	ELan IMou

Argyranthemum ✿ (*Asteraceae*)

'Beth'	GBee
Butterfly = 'Ulyssis' ♀H2	LAst
canariense hort.	see *A. frutescens* subsp. *canariae*
Cherry Harmony = 'Supa532' (Daisy Crazy Series) (d)	MCot
Cherry Love = 'Supacher'PBR (Daisy Crazy Series) (d) ♀H2	CCCN
'Citronelle'	CBcs
'Cornish Gold' ♀H2	CBcs CCCN ECtt EShb
'Dana'	LAst
'Donington Hero' ♀H2	MHom
double pink-flowered (d)	SVen
'Flamingo'	see *Rhodanthemum gayanum*
§ ***foeniculaceum*** misapplied	CTri ELan
foeniculaceum misapplied pink-flowered	see *A.* 'Petite Pink'
§ ***foeniculaceum*** (Willd.) Webb & Sch.Bip.	MCot
- 'Royal Haze' ♀H2	CCCN CHll NPer
§ ***frutescens***	CHEx SEND WKif
§ - subsp. ***canariae*** ♀H2	CCCN
'Gill's Pink'	MHom WPnn
gracile	CHll
- 'Chelsea Girl' ♀H2	CCCN CHEx MCot MHom SPhx WKif
Gypsy Rose = 'M9/18d'	CCCN
'Jamaica Primrose' ♀H2	CSpe CTri ECtt SDix
'Jamaica Snowstorm'	see *A.* 'Snow Storm'
(LaRita Series) LaRita Banana Split = 'Kleaf10067' **new**	LRHS
- LaRita Red ♀H2	LAst
'Levada Cream' ♀H2	MHom WCot
Madeira Crested Merlot = 'Bonmadmerlo'PBR (Madeira Series) (d)	SVen
§ ***maderense*** ♀H2	CHll GCal
'Mary Wootton' (d)	ECtt MHom
mawii	see *Rhodanthemum gayanum*
Meteor Red = 'Supa742' (Daisy Crazy Series)	CBcs CHel CWGN MBNS MCot
§ 'Mrs F. Sander' (d)	MHom
ochroleucum	see *A. maderense*
Pacific Gold = 'Pacargone'PBR (d)	CBcs CWGN
§ 'Petite Pink' ♀H2	CCCN ECtt
Ping-Pong = 'Innping'PBR (d)	CCCN
'Pink Australian' (d)	MHom
'Pink Delight'	see *A.* 'Petite Pink'
Pomponette Pink = 'Supa392'PBR (d)	CBcs
'Powder Puff' (d)	ECtt
'Shirley's Yellow'	MHom
'Silver Queen'	see *A. foeniculaceum* misapplied
§ 'Snow Storm' ♀H2	MHom
'Snowflake' misapplied	see *A.* 'Mrs F. Sander'
Sole Mio = 'Supa3047' (d)	CWCL
'Starlight' ♀H2	MCot MHom
'Sugar and Ice' (d)	CCCN
'Sugar Baby' (d)	CCCN
'Summer Cloud'	MCot
'Summer Melody' (d)	CBcs CCCN

'Summer Pink'	CCCN
'Summer Stars' (Daisy Crazy Series) (d) ♀^{H2}	MHom
Summersong Blush Pink (Daisy Crazy Series) (d)	MCot
'Vancouver' (d) ♀^{H2}	CCCN CWCL ECtt SBHP
* 'Vera'	CCCN
'White Spider'	CCCN ELan

Argyrocytisus (*Papilionaceae*)

battandieri	Widely available
- 'Yellow Tail' ♀^{H4}	CEnd ELan EMil EPfP LRHS MBri MGos SHil SKHP SPoG SSta WHar

Arisaema ✿ (*Araceae*)

CC 4904	CExl
CC 5511	CExl
album	XLum
amurense	CElw CFil CLAP EBee ECho GBuc GCal GKev LAma MMoz SGSe
§ - subsp. ***robustum***	ECho GKev
asperatum	LAma
auriculatum	GKev LAma
biauriculatum	see *A. wattii*
brachyspathum	see *A. heterophyllum*
brevipes	CExl
candidissimum ♀^{H4}	CBro CCon CElw CFil CHel CLAP CPne CWCL ECha ELon EPfP EPot GBuc GCra GEdr LAma MRav NHar NLar NSla SDeJ SKHP WBor WHal WPGP WSHC
- red-flowered new	LAma
- white-flowered	CFil GEdr GKev LAma
- yellow-flowered	LAma
ciliatum	GBuc GEdr GKev LAma MAvo MMoz NHar NLar SRot
- var. ***liubaense***	CAby CFwr CWCL EPfP EPot EWld GBuc GKev MMoz WCot
- - CT 369	CDes CExl CLAP EPfP SDys SKHP WPGP WSHC
- - GG 97091	WCot
- variegated (v)	WCot
concinnum	CCon EWld GBin GEdr GKev LAma LPal WPnP XLum
consanguineum	CAby CBcs CBro CExl CFwr CHEx CLAP EBee EPfP GBin GCal GEdr GKev LAma MAvo MMoz NHar NLar SMrm WCot WPGP WPnP XLum
- B&SWJ 071	WCru
- CLD 1519	ECho GBuc
- subsp. ***kelung-insulare*** B&SWJ 256	WCru
- variegated (v)	WCot
costatum	CCCN CFil CHEx EBee ECho EPfP EPot GAbr GBin GEdr GKev LAma LPal MMoz SChF WCot WPGP XLum
dilatatum	GKev LAma
dracontium	EPot GKev LAma XLum
du-bois-reymondiae	LAma
ehimense	LAma
elephas	GKev LAma
engleri	GKev LAma
erubescens	GBin LAma
exappendiculatum	CAby CExl CFil CHel EBee GKev LAma MMoz
fargesii	CExl CFil CHel ECho GEdr GKev LAma MMoz SChF SKHP XLum
flavum	CDes CFil CWCL ECho EPfP EPot EWld GBuc GCal GKev LAma MMoz NHar SGSe SPlb
- CC 6303	EBee ITim
- subsp. ***abbreviatum***	GBin GBuc
- - CC 6300	ITim
formosanum B&SWJ 280	WCru
§ ***franchetianum***	CExl EBee GKev LAma
galeatum	EPot GBin GKev LAma WCot XLum
grapsospadix B&SWJ 7000	WCru
§ ***griffithii***	CBro CHel ECho GBin GBuc GEdr GKev LAma MMoz NBid NLar NSoo SDeJ XLum
- 'Numbuq'	GCra
- var. ***pradhanii***	GBin GEdr GKev LAma XLum
handelii	LAma
helleborifolium	see *A. tortuosum*
§ ***heterophyllum***	GKev LAma
inkiangense	LAma
intermedium	GBin GKev LAma MMoz MNrw XLum
iyoanum subsp. ***nakaianum***	LAma
jacquemontii	CAby CFil CLAP EBee ECho EWld GCra GEdr GKev GLog LAma NLar XLum
- CC 5184	ITim
japonicum Blume	see *A. serratum* var. *mayebarae*
japonicum Komarov	see *A. serratum*
jinshajiangense	CExl LAma
kishidae	GEdr GKev LAma
kiushianum	EFEx GKev LAma MMoz NLar WCot
leschenaultii	GKev
lichiangense	EBee GKev LAma
lingyunense	LAma
§ ***lobatum***	CExl LAma
maximowiczii	GEdr GKev LAma
meleagris	LAma
§ ***nepenthoides***	CFil ECho EPot GBin GEdr GKev LAma MMoz NLar NSoo WPnP XLum
ochraceum	see *A. nepenthoides*
onoticum	see *A. lobatum*
petelotii B&SWJ 9706	WCru
polyphyllum B&SWJ 3904	WCru
propinquum	EBee ECho GBin GKev LAma NLar XLum
purpureogaleatum	see *A. franchetianum*
rhizomatum	LAma
rhombiforme	LAma
ringens misapplied	see *A. amurense* subsp. ***robustum***
ringens ambig.	GEdr GKev SKHP
ringens (Thunberg) Schott	CDes EFEx LAma LEdu
- f. ***praecox*** B&SWJ 1515	WCru
- f. ***sieboldii*** B&SWJ 551	WCru
aff. ***ringens***	CHel
robustum	see *A. amurense* subsp. ***robustum***
saxatile	GKev LAma
sazensoo	GEdr GKev LAma
§ ***serratum***	ECho GKev LAma MMoz MNrw
§ - var. ***mayebarae***	GEdr GKev LAma
- var. ***serratum*** new	LAma
sikokianum	CBro EBee ECho EFEx EPot GEdr GKev LAma NLar SKHP WPnP
- variegated (v)	GEdr WCot
speciosum	CExl CFil CHEx EBee ECho EWld GBin GEdr LAma LPal MMoz NSoo SDeJ SPlb WCot WPnP XLum

*	- var. ***magnificum***	CBcs GBin GEdr GKev LAma NLar WPnP XLum
	- var. ***mirabile***	EBee GKev LAma XLum
	taiwanense	CAby CLAP GEdr SKHP WCot
	- B&SWJ 269	WCru
	- var. ***brevipedunculatum*** B&SWJ 1859	WCru
	- f. ***cinereum*** B&SWJ 3602 new	CDes
	- - B&SWJ 19121	WCru
	tashiroi	GKev LAma
	ternatipartitum	GKev LAma
	thunbergii	EFEx GEdr LAma
	- subsp. ***autumnale*** B&SWJ 1425	WCru
	- subsp. ***urashima***	EBee EFEx GKev LAma
§	***tortuosum***	CDes CExl CFil CPne ECha ECho EWld GBin GBuc GKev LAma LEdu MNrw NLar NSoo SChF WPGP WPnP XLum
	- 'Black Rod'	CFil
	- var. ***helleborifolium***	NBid XLum
	tosaense	GKev LAma
	triphyllum	CElw CExl CHel CLAP EBee EPot GKev GPoy LAma MMoz NLar SPlb WPnP WShi
	- subsp. ***triphyllum*** var. ***atrorubens***	CLAP
§	***utile***	EBee ECho EPot GBin GEdr GKev LAma XLum
	verrucosum	see *A. griffithii*
	- var. ***utile***	see *A. utile*
§	***wattii***	LAma
	yamatense	GKev
	- subsp. ***sugimotoi***	LAma
	yunnanense	CLAP LAma

Arisarum (*Araceae*)

	proboscideum	Widely available
	vulgare	ECho EPot

Aristea (*Iridaceae*)

	sp.	GGal
	africana 'Worcester'	ECho
§	***capitata***	CHel CHll CPrp CSpe IDee
	- pink-flowered	CHel CPrp CTre EPri
	ecklonii	CExl CHEx CPou CPrp CTca CTsd EBee EPri EShb MHer MSCN
	- GWJ 9469	WCru
	ensifolia	ELan
	grandis	CCon
	spiralis 'Paarl'	ECho
	thyrsiflora	see *A. capitata*
	woodii 'Clarens'	ECho

Aristolochia (*Aristolochiaceae*)

	sp.	CAco
	baetica	CExl
	californica	LEdu SKHP
	chilensis	CCCN SPlb
	clematitis	CArn ECho GPoy LEdu LPla WCot
	cucurbitifolia B&SWJ 7043	WCru
	delavayi	CHEx SVen
	durior	see *A. macrophylla*
	gigantea ♀H1b	CCCN CHll
	grandiflora	CCCN
	griffithii B&SWJ 2118	WCru
	heterophylla	see *A. kaempferi* f. *heterophylla*
	kaempferi	CCCN
	- B&SWJ 293	WCru
§	- f. ***heterophylla*** B&SWJ 3109	WCru
	× ***kewensis***	CCCN
	liukiuensis B&SWJ 4960	WCru
§	***macrophylla***	CArn CBcs CCCN CMac EPfP MRav SLim
	manshuriensis B&SWJ 12557	WCru
	moupinensis BWJ 8181	WCru
	onoei B&SWJ 4960	WCru
	rotunda	CArn SKHP
	sempervirens	CMac LEdu SBrt SGSe SKHP WCru WSHC
	sipho	see *A. macrophylla*
	tomentosa	SKHP

Aristotelia (*Elaeocarpaceae*)

§	***chilensis***	IVic LEdu
	- 'Variegata' (v)	CCCN CMCN CMac EBee GQui SBod SPlb
	fruticosa (f)	ECou
	- (m)	ECou
	- black-fruited (f)	ECou
	- white-fruited (f)	ECou
	macqui	see *A. chilensis*
	peduncularis	CExl
	serrata	ECou SVen
	- (f)	ECou
	- (m)	ECou

Armeria (*Plumbaginaceae*)

§	***alliacea*** (Cav.) Hoffmanns. & Link	ECha
	- f. ***leucantha***	SRms WMoo
	'Bloodgood'	ECho ECtt
	'Brutus'	CDes MAvo
	caespitosa	see *A. juniperifolia*
	- 'Bevan's Variety'	see *A. juniperifolia* 'Bevan's Variety'
	Joystick Series	MMuc
	- 'Joystick Lilac Shades'	EBee ELan EPfP LRHS
	- 'Joystick Red'	ELan EPfP EShb LRHS WHil WWFP
	- 'Joystick White'	ELan EPfP LRHS WHil
§	***juniperifolia*** ♀H5	CMea ECho ELan EPfP EPot GCrg GMaP LRHS MHer NSla SBch SPoG SRms WIce XLum
	- 'Alba'	CMea ECho ELan EPfP EPot GCrg GMaP LBMP MHer MMuc SBch SPoG SRms SRot WAbe WHoo WThu
	- 'Beechwood'	GCrg
§	- 'Bevan's Variety' ♀H5	ECha ECho ECtt ELan EPfP EPot GEdr GMaP LEdu MMuc NLar NRya SPoG SRms SRot WAbe WHoo
	- dark-flowered	WAbe
	- rose-flowered	ITim
	juniperifolia × ***maritima***	ECho SBch
§	***maritima***	CArn CHab CNec ECho EPfP GJos LAst LPot LRHS MBel MSCN NEgg SWvt WCFE WHfH WMoo
	- 'Alba'	CBcs CNec CTri CUse ECha ECho ELan EPfP GJos GMaP LEdu LSun MCot MMuc NRya SEND SPlb SPoG WCFE WMoo
	- 'Armada Rose'	LRHS
	- 'Bloodstone'	CTri ECho ECtt ELan MWat

	- 'Corsica'	CTri ECha MMuc NBir
	- Düsseldorf Pride	see *A. maritima* 'Düsseldorfer Stolz'
§	- 'Düsseldorfer Stolz'	CElw CNec CWld ECha ECho ECtt EDAr ELan EPfP GCrg GKev GMaP LRHS MCot MLHP SPoG SWvt WIce XLum
	- 'Laucheana'	WHoo WMoo
	- 'Ministicks Rose' new	LRHS
	- 'Ministicks White' new	LRHS
	- 'Morning Star Deep Rose' new	LSun
	- 'Morning Star White' new	LSun
	- 'Nifty Thrifty' (v)	CTri ECho ECtt EHoe EWes MHer SPoG SRms SRot
*	- 'Pink Lusitanica'	LBMP NLar
I	- 'Rubrifolia'	Widely available
I	- 'Rubrifolia Compacta'	GCrg WAbe
	- 'Ruby Glow'	CTri SBch
	- 'Schöne von Fellbach'	XLum
	- 'Splendens'	CBcs CTri ECho EDAr EPfP GMaP LAst LRHS LSun MCot MGos MHer MJak MMuc NMir NRya SBch SEND SPhx SPoG WMoo XLum
	- 'Splendens Alba'	XLum
	- 'Varretu'	GCrg
	- 'Vindictive' ♀H5	CMea CTri EPfP
	plantaginea misapplied	see *A. alliacea* (Cav.) Hoffmanns. & Link
	pseudarmeria	ECho ELan EPfP LPot XLum
	- (Ballerina Series) 'Ballerina' new	LEdu
	- - 'Ballerina Red' new	LRHS SHil SRms
	- - 'Ballerina White' new	LRHS SHil
	- hybrids	CTri ELan
	pungens	GKev
	splendens new	MJak
	- 'Perfecta' new	LRHS
	'Vesuvius'	WCot XLum
	vulgaris	see *A. maritima*
	welwitschii	IFoB SRms

Armoracia (*Brassicaceae*)

§	***rusticana***	CArn CBod CHby CTri CUse ELau ENfk GAbr GPoy MHer MMuc MNHC NPer NPri SIde SPoG SRms SVic WHer WJek
	- 'Variegata' (v)	EBee GCal IFoB LEdu MAvo NSti SMad SRms WHer WJek WMoo

Arnica (*Asteraceae*)

	sp.	CUse
	angustifolia	SRms
	subsp. ***alpina***	
	- subsp. ***iljinii***	NBir
	chamissonis Schmidt	see *A. sachalinensis*
	chamissonis Less.	CBod CHby EBee ENfk MNHC NLar WJek XLum
	montana	CArn GPoy MHer MNHC SRms SWat WHfH
§	***sachalinensis*** RBS 0206	EPPr

Arnoglossum (*Asteraceae*)

§	***plantagineum***	SPhx

Aronia ✿ (*Rosaceae*)

	arbutifolia	CAco CBcs CDul CTri CUse EPfP IDee MBlu SGol SLon SPlb
	- 'Erecta'	CDul CHel CTho EBee ELan EPfP ETwe EWTr GBin LRHS MBlu MMuc NLar SPoG SRms SWvt WCFE
	melanocarpa	CDul CMCN CPom CSpe CTsd ELan EPfP EWTr GKin LEdu LRHS MAsh WGrn
	- 'Autumn Magic'	CBcs CDoC CJun CTho EBee ELan EPfP GBin LAst LRHS LSou MAsh MMuc NEgg NLar SLon
	- var. ***grandifolia***	CJun
	- 'Hugin'	CAgr CJun LEdu MCoo NLar
	× ***prunifolia***	CAco CDoC ETwe GAbr LEdu WGrn
	- 'Aron' (F)	CJun
	- 'Brilliant'	CBcs CDoC CDul CTri EPfP GBin LRHS MBri NEgg NLar SGol SPer WHar
	- 'Karhumäki' (F)	NLar
	- 'Nero' (F)	CAgr CBcs GBin GGGa LEdu LRHS MBri MCoo NLar
	- 'Serina' (F)	CJun NLar
	- 'Viking' (F)	CAgr CDul CJun CTho ECrN EPfP EPom EWTr GBin GGGa LBuc LEdu LRHS MBlu MBri NBro NLar SGol

Arrhenatherum (*Poaceae*)

	elatius	CHab
	- var. ***bulbosum*** 'Variegatum' (v)	EBee EHoe ELan EPPr GBin GKev GMaP LBMP MMoz MMuc MWhi NBid NOak NOrc NWad SEND WMoo WWEG

Artemisia ✿ (*Asteraceae*)

	RBS 0207	CExl
	from Taiwan	WHer
§	***abrotanum***	Widely available
*	- 'Variegata' (v)	ELan
	absinthium	CArn CBod CEls CHab CUse ELan ENfk GPoy MHer MNHC NLar NSti SIde SRms SVic WHer WJek XLum XSen
	- 'Lambrook Giant'	CEls
	- 'Lambrook Mist'	CEls CFis CMac ECtt ELan EPfP EPla EWoo GCal GQue LRHS MRav SMrm SWat WMnd WWEG XLum
	- 'Lambrook Silver'	CArn CEls CExl CSam EBee ECha ELan EPfP EWoo GCal GMaP LPot LRHS MHer MMuc MRav NBro SCob SEND SLim SPer SWat SWvt WMnd WWEG
	- 'Silver Ghost'	CEls
	afra	CArn CEls XSen
§	***alba***	CEls GPoy MHer SRms WJek XSen
§	- 'Canescens' ♀H4	CEls CSam CTri EBee ECha ECtt ELan EPfP GMaP LAst LBMP LRHS MAsh MHer MRav SDix SEND SMrm WCFE WCot WMnd WWEG XSen
	annua	CArn CEls
	anomala	CArn CEls
	arborescens ♀H3	CArn CEls CUse SDix SPer WKif
	- 'Brass Band'	see *A.* 'Powis Castle'
	- 'Faith Raven' ♀H3	CEls GBin MBNS NLar
	- 'Porquerolles'	CEls
	argentea L'Hér.	CEls
	argyi	CEls
§	***armeniaca***	CEls ECho WHer XSen
	assoana	see *A. caucasica*

	atrata	CEls
	barrelieri	CEls
	caerulescens subsp. ***gallica***	CEls
	californica	CEls
	- 'Canyon Gray'	CEls
	campestris	XLum XSen
	- subsp. ***borealis***	CEls
	- subsp. ***campestris***	CEls
	- subsp. ***maritima***	CEls
	- - from Wales	CEls
	camphorata	see *A. alba*
	cana	CEls
	canariensis	see *A. thuscula*
	canescens misapplied	see *A. alba* 'Canescens'
	canescens Willd.	see *A. armeniaca*
	capillaris	CEls XLum
§	***caucasica*** ♀H4	CEls ECho EPot EWes MHer SChF SPhx SRms SRot
	chamaemelifolia	CBod CEls MHer SRms WJek XSen
	cretacea	see *A. nutans*
	discolor Dougl. ex Besser	see *A. michauxiana*
	douglasiana	CEls
	- 'Valerie Finnis'	see *A. ludoviciana* 'Valerie Finnis'
	dracunculus	ECha MNHC MRav SPlb SRms WBrk WHfH
	- French	CArn CBod CEls CHby CTsd CUse ELau ENfk GPoy LEdu MHer NPri SEND SIde WGwG WJek XLum
	- Russian	CEls CUse ENfk SVic
	- 'Thüringen'	IMou
	ferganensis	CEls
	filifolia	CEls
	fragrans Willd.	CEls
	frigida ♀H5	CEls XSen
	genipi	CEls
	glacialis	CEls
	gmelinii	CEls
	gnaphalodes	see *A. ludoviciana*
	gorgonum	CEls SEND
	'Hausserman'	XLum
	herba-alba	CEls XSen
	indica var. ***momiyamae*** new	CEls
	japonica	CEls
	kawakamii B&SWJ 088	WCru
	kitadakensis	CEls
	- 'Guizhou'	see *A. lactiflora* Guizhou Group
	laciniata	CEls
	lactiflora ♀H7	CEls CPrp EBee ECha ECtt ELan GBee GMaP MRav NGdn NOrc SDix SPer SRms WHfH WMoo XLum
	- NJM 11.010 new	WPGP
	- 'Elfenbein'	EPPr GCal IMou LPla MRav SMHy
§	- Guizhou Group	Widely available
	- - 'Dark Delight'	CEls CMos EBee ECtt EWes
	- 'Jim Russell'	CDes CEls CElw EBee ECtt EWes MAvo SPhx WWFP
	- 'Laigong' new	LEdu
	- ***purpurea***	see *A. lactiflora* Guizhou Group
	- 'Weisses Wunder'	EBee
	lanata Willd.	see *A. caucasica*
	lanata Lam.	XSen
	laxa	see *A. umbelliformis*
	'Little Mice'	CEls WWEG
§	***ludoviciana***	CEls ELan GBee IFoB MCot NLar NOrc NPer SRms WCFE WFar XLum

	- var. ***latifolia***	see *A. ludoviciana* subsp. *ludoviciana* var. *latiloba*
	- subsp. ***ludoviciana*** var. ***incompta***	CEls
	- - var. ***latiloba***	CEls EHoe NBro SWvt WCot WHoo
	- subsp. ***mexicana*** var. ***albula***	CEls SMrm
	- 'Silver Queen'	Widely available
	- 'Valerie Finnis' ♀H7	Widely available
	maritima	CArn MHer
	- var. ***maritima***	CEls
	mauiensis	CEls
§	***michauxiana***	CEls EBee
	molinieri	CEls XSen
	mutellina	see *A. umbelliformis*
	niitakayamensis	CEls
	nitida	CEls
§	***nutans***	CEls MCot MRav
	palmeri hort.	see *A. ludoviciana*
	aff. ***parviflora*** CLD 1531	CEls
	pedemontana	see *A. caucasica*
	pontica	CArn CEls EBee ECha EHoe ELan GMaP GPoy LEdu LRHS MAvo MBNS MHer MNHC MRav NBro NLar NSti SRms WCAu WFar WHfH WHoo WJek WWEG XSen
§	'Powis Castle' ♀H3	Widely available
	princeps	CArn CEls GPoy LEdu SIde
	procera Willd.	see *A. abrotanum*
	purshiana	see *A. ludoviciana*
	pycnocephala	CEls
	- 'David's Choice'	CEls
	ramosa	CEls
	'Rosenschleier'	EWes GCal LPla MAvo SHar WPGP WWEG WWtn
	schmidtiana ♀H5	CEls CFis ECha MWat SRms WKif
	- 'Nana' ♀H5	Widely available
	- 'Nana Attraction'	LRHS NLar SPad SRot
	selengensis	CEls
	splendens misapplied	see *A. alba* 'Canescens'
	splendens Willd.	SPhx
	- var. ***brachyphylla***	MAsh
	stelleriana	CEls CPrp CTri ECha EDAr GBee GKev IFoB MAvo MHer NBro NLar SPer SRms
	- RBS 0207	CEls NLar
	- 'Boughton Silver'	CEls EBee ECtt EHoe ELan EPfP EPla GMaP IKil LRHS MAsh MRav NLar NSti SMrm SPer SRms SWvt WWEG
	- 'Mori'	see *A. stelleriana* 'Boughton Silver'
	- 'Nana'	CEls SWvt
	- 'Prostrata'	see *A. stelleriana* 'Boughton Silver'
	- 'Silver Brocade'	see *A. stelleriana* 'Boughton Silver'
	taurica	CEls
§	***thuscula***	CEls
	tridentata	CArn WHer
§	***umbelliformis***	CEls
	vallesiaca	CEls
	verlotiorum	CEls
	vulgaris L.	CArn CBod CEls ELau GPoy MHer MNHC WHer
	- 'Cragg-Barber Eye' (v)	EBee
	- Oriental Limelight = 'Janlim' (v)	CEls EBee ECtt EHoe EPPr EPfP GAbr MJak MNHC MWhi NBir NEgg NLar SWvt
	- 'Variegata' (v)	CEls EBee EPfP NBir SEND WMoo XLum

× ***wurzellii***	CEls

Arthropodium (*Asparagaceae*)

candidum	ECGP ECho ECou EHoe MPie
- 'Capri'	LPot
- 'Maculatum'	ECho LEdu MPie SBrt SGSe SPlb
- ***purpureum***	ECho IKil
cirratum	CHel CSpe ECho IKil MHer MPie
- 'Matapouri Bay'	CAbb CBcs CHEx EBee ECre
milleflorum	SBrt
minus	CExl ECou

artichoke, globe see *Cynara cardunculus* Scolymus Group

artichoke, Jerusalem see *Helianthus tuberosus*

Arum (*Araceae*)

byzantinum	ECho
'Chameleon'	CDes EPPr NBir SEND SKHP SMad SPer WCot WWEG
§ ***concinnatum***	CTal ECho SChr SKHP
- 'Mount Ida'	ECho SKHP
cornutum	see *Sauromatum venosum*
creticum	CBro CCon CFil CMea CPne CSpe ECho GCal MNrw SKHP WBor WThu
- 'Karpathos'	CExl CTal GKev MMoz SKHP WCot
- 'Marmaris White'	CDes
- yellow-spotted	NBir
creticum × ***italicum***	EBee
cyrenaicum	CFil CPom ECho LEdu
- from Crete	ECho
dioscoridis	CPom ECho GCra GKev MMoz NMin
- JCA 195.197	WCot
- var. ***cyprium***	EBee ECho
§ - var. ***dioscoridis***	GKev
- var. ***liepoldtii***	see *A. dioscoridis* var. *dioscoridis*
- var. ***smithii***	see *A. dioscoridis* var. *dioscoridis*
dracunculus	see *Dracunculus vulgaris*
elongatum	CPom
hygrophilum	WCot
italicum	CArn CLAP CTri ECho GKev IBoy LAma LPal LSun NLar SDeJ SWat WCot WShi
- subsp. ***albispathum***	MMoz
- 'Black Spot'	EPPr
- 'Edward Dougal'	WCot
- 'Green Marble'	SEND WFar WWEG
- subsp. ***italicum***	ECho EPla GKev WBrk
- - 'Cyclops'	WWEG
§ - - 'Marmoratum' ♀H6	Widely available
- - 'Sparkler'	WCot
- - 'Spotted Jack'	MAvo WCot WWEG
- - 'Tiny'	CCon CDes CExl GCal SMHy SWvt WRHF WWEG
§ - - 'White Winter'	CDes CElw MAvo WBrk WCot WWEG
- 'Nancy Lindsay'	MMoz
- subsp. ***neglectum***	SChr
- - 'Miss Janay Hall' (v)	MMoz WCot
- 'Pictum'	see *A. italicum* subsp. *italicum* 'Marmoratum'
- 'Tresahor Beauty'	MAvo
italicum × ***maculatum***	WHer
jacquemontii	ECho
korolkowii	WCot
maculatum	CArn EPla EPot GKev GPoy LAma MHer MRav NLar WHer WShi
- 'Painted Lady' (v)	WCot
- 'Pleddel'	MRav
- Tar Spot Group	SEND
nickelii	see *A. concinnatum*
§ ***nigrum***	CPom ECho EWes LLHF WCot
orientale	EPot
palaestinum	CDes
petteri misapplied	see *A. nigrum*
pictum	CDes CExl CLAP CMac CTal ECho EWes LEdu LLHF
- 'Taff's Form'	see *A. italicum* subsp. *italicum* 'White Winter'
purpureospathum	CFil CPom EBee ECho EPPr WCot WPGP

Aruncus ✿ (*Rosaceae*)

aethusifolius ♀H7	Widely available
- 'Little Gem'	ECho WCru
asiaticus B&SWJ 8624	WCru
'Bastei' **new**	IMou
dioicus	Widely available
§ - (m) ♀H7	CBen CBod CDoC CMac CRow EHoe ELan IBoy MBNS MRav MWts NBro NSti SMad SPer SRms SWat WMoo
- var. ***acuminatus***	EBee
- Child of Two Worlds	see *A. dioicus* 'Zweiweltenkind'
- 'Glasnevin'	CUse ECtt GBee MRav NHol WFar
- var. ***kamtschaticus***	EWes NLar WHrl
- - RBS 0208	NGdn
- 'Kneiffii'	Widely available
§ - 'Zweiweltenkind'	GCal IPot NLar SMad WCot XLum
'Guinea Fowl'	CBod ELon GQue LEdu MAvo NGdn NLar NSti SMrm
'Horatio'	CBod CSam EBee ELan GBin IMou IPot LEdu LPla LRHS MHol MMuc MPie NDov NLar SMHy SMad SPhx WCot WRHF
'Johannifest'	CDes IMou IPot WCot
'Misty Lace'	GBin NCGa NGdn NLar SMrm
'Netzwerk' **new**	IMou
'Noble Spirit'	MBel NGdn NLar SGSe SWat
'Perlehuhn'	CDes EBee IMou
plumosus	see *A. dioicus*
sinensis	GAbr NBre
sylvestris	see *A. dioicus*
- 'Sommeranfang'	IMou
'Woldemar Meier'	EBee GBin IMou WCot

Arundinaria (*Poaceae*)

amabilis	see *Pseudosasa amabilis* (McClure) Keng f.
anceps	see *Yushania anceps*
auricoma	see *Pleioblastus viridistriatus*
disticha	see *Pleioblastus pygmaeus* 'Distichus'
falconeri	see *Himalayacalamus falconeri*
fargesii	see *Bashania fargesii*
fastuosa	see *Semiarundinaria fastuosa*
fortunei	see *Pleioblastus variegatus*
§ ***gigantea***	CDTJ MWht
- subsp. ***tecta***	CBcs
hindsii	see *Pleioblastus hindsii*
hookeriana misapplied	see *Himalayacalamus falconeri* 'Damarapa'
hookeriana Munro	see *Himalayacalamus hookerianus*

humilis see *Pleioblastus humilis*
japonica see *Pseudosasa japonica*
jaunsarensis see *Yushania anceps*
maling see *Yushania maling*
marmorea see *Chimonobambusa marmorea*
murielae see *Fargesia murielae*
nitida see *Fargesia nitida*
oedogonata see *Clavinodum oedogonatum*
palmata see *Sasa palmata*
pumila see *Pleioblastus argenteostriatus* f. *pumilus*
pygmaea see *Pleioblastus pygmaeus*
quadrangularis see *Chimonobambusa quadrangularis*
simonii see *Pleioblastus simonii*
spathiflora see *Thamnocalamus spathiflorus*
tessellata see *Thamnocalamus tessellatus*
vagans see *Sasaella ramosa*
variegata see *Pleioblastus variegatus*
veitchii see *Sasa veitchii*
viridistriata see *Pleioblastus viridistriatus*
'Wang Tsai' see *Bambusa multiplex* 'Floribunda'

Arundo (*Poaceae*)

donax CAbb CHEx CKno CPla ELan EPPr EPla EUJe EWes GCra GGal GMaP IDee LRHS MAvo MBlu MBrN MNrw MRav NSoo SArc SDix SEND SMad SPlb SPoG WHal WWEG
- 'Golden Chain' (v) CKno EPPr EWes LRHS SMad
- 'Macrophylla' CExl CFil CHGN CKno LEdu WPGP
- 'Variegata' see *A. donax* var. *versicolor*
§ - var. ***versicolor*** (v) CAbb CBcs CBod CHEx CKno CPrp ELan ELon EPPr EPla EUJe EWes GCal LEdu LLWG LRHS MAvo MBel MMoz MRav NLos SEND SMad SPlb SPoG WCot WWEG XLum
I - - 'Aureovariegata' (v) CDTJ
formosana CKno EPPr
- 'Golden Showers' ESwi EUJe NLos SEND

Asarina (*Plantaginaceae*)

barclayana see *Maurandya barclayana*
erubescens see *Lophospermum erubescens*
lophantha see *Lophospermum scandens*
lophospermum see *Lophospermum scandens*
§ ***procumbens*** CHel CTri CWld ECho GKev IBoy NBir NRya SPhx SRms WBrk WKif
- 'Alba' IFro

Asarum (*Aristolochiaceae*)

albomaculatum ECho
- B&SWJ 1726 WCru
arifolium EBee EPPr
campaniflorum ECho WCru
canadense CArn EBee ECho EWld GBBs GEdr GKev GPoy LEdu MMoz NLar WCru WWEG
cardiophyllum B&SWJ 11742 WCru
caudatum CDes CHEx CLAP ECha ECho EPfP GEdr LEdu NBro NLar SRms WCot WCru
- deciduous WCru
- white-flowered SKHP WCru
caudigerum B&SWJ 1517 WCru
- HWJ 641 from Vietnam WCru
caulescens ECho EPPr LAma WCru
- B&SWJ 5886 WCru
delavayi ECho GKev LAma LEdu NLar WCot WCru
epigynum 'Silver Web' WCru
europaeum ♀H6 Widely available
- PAB 4377 LEdu
fauriei WCru
forbesii ECho
hartwegii CLAP IMou WThu
* ***henryi*** **new** WThu
himalaicum GWJ 9341 WCru
hypogynum B&SWJ 3628 WCru
infrapurpureum B&SWJ 1994 WCru
- 'Taroko Web' WCru
kumageanum WCot
lemmonii LEdu
leptophyllum B&SWJ 1983 WCru
longirhizomatosum GEdr WCru
macranthum B&SWJ 1691 WCru
maculatum B&SWJ 1114 WCru
magnificum LAma WCru
maximum CCon CLAP ECho GKev LAma WCru
- 'Green Panda' **new** NLos
- 'Panda' **new** GEdr
- 'Silver Panda' CDes CExl ECtt ESwi EUJe GEdr SKHP
nipponicum B&SWJ 2839 WCru
petelotii HWJ 1043 WCru
pulchellum WCot WCru
sieboldii GPoy WCru
splendens CBct CBro CElw CHid ECho ELan EPfP GBin GKev LAma LEdu LPal MHol MPie MRav NLar NLos NSti SGSe SKHP SMad SPlb WCot WCru WFar XLum
taipingshanianum B&SWJ 1688 WCot WCru
- 'Elfin Yellow' WCru
wulingense CExl CTal WCru

Asclepias ✿ (*Apocynaceae*)

'Cinderella' GKev SGol
curassavica CCCN EShb LLWG SRkn XLum
- 'Red Butterfly' SLon
exaltata SBrt
§ ***fascicularis*** SBrt
fasciculata see *A. fascicularis*
fruticosa see *Gomphocarpus fruticosus*
hallii **new** SIgm
incarnata ELan IFoB LRHS MRav MWhi SBrt SPlb WOld XLum
- 'Alba' CPom
- 'Ice Ballet' CAbP CBod ELan GKev IFoB LLWG LRHS NLar SGSe SPer SPoG
* - 'Iceberg' SGol
- 'Soulmate' CBod EBee ELan EPfP LPot NOrc SGSe SPer WHil WKif
latifolia **new** SIgm
physocarpa see *Gomphocarpus physocarpus*
purpurascens CArn CPom EBee SBrt
rubra SBrt
speciosa MMuc NBre SBrt WPGP
sullivantii SBrt
syriaca CArn EBee MBel MMuc SGSe XLum

tuberosa	CArn CBcs CBod ECtt EPla GKev GPoy LAst MHer MNHC NOrc SCob SGSe SMad WGwG XLum
- Gay Butterflies Group	SMrm
- 'Hello Yellow'	CBod SGSe
verticillata	SBrt
viridis new	SBrt

Asimina (*Annonaceae*)

triloba (F)	CBcs MBlu NLar SGol SPlb
- 'Davis' (F)	CAgr
- 'Nc-1' (F)	CAgr
- 'Pennsylvania Golden' (F)	CAgr
- 'Prolific' (F)	CAgr
- 'Sunflowers'	CCCN

Asparagus (*Asparagaceae*)

RCB AM 23	WCot
asparagoides ♀H1c	EShb
densiflorus 'Mazeppa'	EShb
- 'Myersii' ♀H1c	EShb SEND
- Sprengeri Group ♀H1c	MMuc NGBl SEND
falcatus	SEND
filicinus	XBlo
- var. ***giraldii***	WCot
hardy, from Malawi	SKHP
aff. ***meiocladoss*** B&SWJ 8309	WCot WCru
officinalis 'Ariane'	WHar
- 'Backlim' ♀H4	ECrN EMil EPom
- 'Connover's Colossal' ♀H4	CHid CSBt MMuc MNHC SEND SVic WHar
- 'Crimson Pacific'	SVic
- 'Dariana' ♀H4	EMil SDea
- 'Gijnlim' ♀H4	ECrN EMil EPom MMuc SDea
- 'Guelph Millennium' ♀H5	EPom
- 'Jersey Knight'	SVic
- 'Mondeo' new	EPom
- 'Pacific 2000'	EPfP EPom
- 'Pacific Purple'	EPfP EPom
- 'Stewart's Purple' ♀H4	EPom WHar
pseudoscaber 'Spitzenschleier'	EBee EShb SDix WCot
retrofractus	WCot
scandens	EShb WCot
schoberioides	LEdu
- B&SWJ 8814	WCru
verticillatus	SGSe
virgatus	EShb SPlb WPGP

Asperula (*Rubiaceae*)

§ ***arcadiensis*** ♀H3	ECho WAbe WThu
aristata subsp. ***scabra***	CSpe ECha LPla WCot
- subsp. ***thessala***	see *A. sintenisii*
boissieri	ECho EPot WThu
cynanchica new	MMuc
daphneola	ECho EPot EWes WAbe
gussonei	ECho SIgm WAbe
lilaciflora	ECho
- var. ***caespitosa***	see *A. lilaciflora* subsp. *lilaciflora*
§ - subsp. ***lilaciflora***	ECho
nitida	ECho
- subsp. ***puberula***	see *A. sintenisii*
odorata	see *Galium odoratum*
§ ***sintenisii***	CMea ECho WAbe WHoo WThu
suberosa misapplied	see *A. arcadiensis*
taurina subsp. ***caucasica***	NLar WBor
tinctoria	CArn GPoy MHer SRms

Asphodeline (*Asphodelaceae*)

§ ***brevicaulis***	XSen
liburnica	CBro CSam ECha ELan EPri GAbr IMou SPhx WCot XSen
§ ***lutea***	Widely available
§ - 'Gelbkerze'	EBee EPfP LRHS
- Yellow Candle	see *A. lutea* 'Gelbkerze'
taurica	ECho EPot MBNS SMHy WCot XSen

Asphodelus (*Asphodelaceae*)

acaulis	CTal ECho LLHF WCot XLum
§ ***aestivus***	EBee EWes GCal MBel WCot
- Cally Spear strain	GCal
albus	CArn CAvo CBro CSpe ECha EPPr GJos IFoB MLHP NBid SPlb SRms WWEG XLum
brevicaulis	see *Asphodeline brevicaulis*
cerasiferus	see *A. ramosus*
fistulosus	GJos LEdu
lusitanicus	see *A. ramosus*
luteus	see *Asphodeline lutea*
microcarpus	see *A. aestivus*
§ ***ramosus***	CPar CTal ECho GCal MCot WCot

Aspidistra (*Asparagaceae*)

B&SWJ 6645 from Thailand new	WCru
Chen Yi 135	WCot
attenuata	IBlr IMou
- B&SWJ 377	WCru
aff. ***attenuata*** B&SWJ 2001 new	WCru
caespitosa 'Jade Ribbons'	see *A. hainanensis* 'Jade Ribbons'
'China Star'	CHEx ESwi WCot
daibuensis	IBlr
- B&SWJ 312b	ESwi WCru
- 'Totally Dotty' (v)	WCru
aff. ***daibuensis*** 'Tidy Trim'	WCru
elatior ♀H2	CBct CHEx CTsd EBak EShb ESwi IBlr LEdu MMuc MRav NPla SEND SMad WCot WWFP
- 'Akebono' (v)	WCot
- 'Asahi' (v)	IBlr WCot
- 'Hoshi-zora' (v)	IBlr WCot
- 'Lennon's Song' (v)	WCot
§ - 'Milky Way' misapplied	WCot
- 'Milky Way' (v)	EShb ESwi IBlr MMoz SEND
- 'Okame' (v)	WCot
- 'Variegata' (v) ♀H2	CHEx IBlr IFoB IFro NBir SEND
- 'Variegata Exotica' (v)	XBlo
§ ***hainanensis*** 'Jade Ribbons'	IBlr WCot
leshanensis (v)	IBlr
linearifolia 'Leopard'	ESwi IBlr WCot
lurida	EShb
- 'Ginga' (v)	see *A. elatior* 'Milky Way'
- 'Ginga Giant' (v)	WCot
- 'Irish Mist' (v)	IBlr
minutiflora	WCot
mushaensis B&SWJ 1953	WCru
aff. ***mushaensis*** 'Spotty Dotty' (v)	ESwi WCru
omeiensis	WCot
saxicola 'Uan Fat Lady'	see *A. zongbayi* 'Uan Fat Lady'
sutepensis B&SWJ 5216	WCru
tonkinensis new	WCru

	typica 'China Sun'	WCot
	zongbayi	WCot
§	- 'Uan Fat Lady'	ESwi WCot WCru

Asplenium ✿ (*Aspleniaceae*)

	antiquum	CBty
	- 'Osaka'	CBty
	bulbiferum misapplied	see *A.* × *lucrosum*
	bulbiferum ambig. × ***oblongifolium***	GBin
	bulbiferum Forst.f.	CBcs ESwi GBin
§	***ceterach***	WHer XLum
	daucifolium	NWad
	difforme × ***dimorphum***	CBty
	× ***ebenoides*** ♀H4	CBty
§	× ***lucrosum*** ♀H1c	CBty CKel ESwi LPal
	'Maori Princess'	GBin WFib
	nidus ♀H1b	XBlo
	oblongifolium	GBin
§	***scolopendrium*** ♀H6	Widely available
	- 'Angustatum' ♀H6	CBod CBty CLAP CWCL ELon EPPr EPfP EPla ERod EShb GBin GEdr LPal LRHS MBri MGos MMoz NEgg NLar NWad SCob SEND SGSe SPoG SRms WMoo WPnP
	- Crispum Group ♀H6	CLAP EFer ELan MWat NBid SRms SRot WFar WFib WPGP
	- - 'Crispum Bolton's Nobile'	WFib
	- - 'Golden Queen'	CLAP
	- Crispum Cristatum Group	CBod CLAP CTal MBri MMuc MWat SCob SEND WGrf
	- - 'Crispum Cristatum Bolton' **new**	WCot
	- Crispum Fimbriatum Group	CLAP
	- Cristatum Group	CBty CLAP CWCL EBee ECtt ELan ELon EPfP LAst LRHS MGos MMoz MRav NLar SPad SPer SPoG SRms SRot SWat WFib WMoo WPnP
	- Fimbriatum Group	CLAP LRHS
	- 'Furcatum'	CBty CDTJ CLAP EBee ELan MMuc NLar SEND
	- 'Kaye's Lacerated' ♀H5	CLAP EFer WFib
	- Laceratum Group	CLAP
	- Marginatum Group	EFer
	- 'Muricatum'	CLAP ELan GBin MRav NBid WFib
	- 'Ramocristatum'	CLAP
	- Ramomarginatum Group	CLAP ELan
	- 'Sagittatoprojectum Sclater'	WFib
	- Undulatum Group	CBty CDTJ CLAP EAEE EBee ECha EFtx EPfP EPla EUJe GEdr LPal LRHS MMoz MMuc MWat NBir NEgg NLar SBod SRms WGrf WPnP XLum
	- Undulatum Cristatum Group	CLAP
	trichomanes ♀H6	Widely available
	- Cristatum Group	SRms
	- Incisum Group ♀H6	EBee EFer NOrc SRms WAbe
	- 'Ramocristatum'	WAbe

Astartea (*Myrtaceae*)

fascicularis	ECou

Astelia (*Asteliaceae*)

	alpina	IBlr
	banksii	CBcs CBod CHEx CSpe EBee IBal LRHS MBri MGos SCoo SHil SLim WCot
§	***chathamica*** ♀H3	Widely available
	- 'Silver Spear'	see *A. chathamica*
	chathamica × ***fragrans***	ECou
	cunninghamii	see *A. solandri*
	fragrans	CBcs CCon ECou GCal GKev IBlr LEdu
	graminea	GCal
	grandis	CBcs IBlr LEdu
	nervosa	ECou IBlr LEdu SArc
	- 'Alpine Ruby'	IBlr
	- 'Bronze Giant'	IBlr
	- 'Silver Sabre'	IBlr
	- 'Westland'	CBcs CDoC CHel CKno COtt CTsd GCal IBlr LEdu LRHS MBri MGos NLos NSoo SCob SEND SHil SLim SPad SPoG SWvt WCot
	nivicola 'Golden Gem'	IBlr
	- 'Red Gem'	GCal LEdu
	petriei	IBlr
	'Red Devil'	CBcs CDoC CSpe ECou EPfP GBin IBoy LRHS MGos MHol SHil WCot WHer
	'Silver Mound'	EPfP SCob
	'Silver Shadow'	CDoC CUse LRHS MBri SHil WCot
§	***solandri***	ECou IBlr
	trinervia	GCal

Aster ✿ (*Asteraceae*)

	acris	see *A. sedifolius*
	ageratoides	CPou WOld
	- 'Ashvi'	WCot WOld
	- 'Asran'	CHVG EBee ECtt EHoe EPPr EWes GCal LSou MAvo MMuc MPie SEND WBrk WCot WOld WWEG XLum
	- 'Ezo Murasaki'	NDov WCot
	- 'Harry Smith'	NDov WWEG
	- 'Little Theo'	EBee
	- 'Stardust'	WOld
	- 'Starshine' PBR	ECtt EPPr IBoy LRHS MPie SHil WCot
	alpigenus	WHil
	- var. ***alpigenus***	LLHF
	- var. ***haydenii***	LLHF
	alpinus ♀H5	EBee ECho EPfP GJos LPot MAsh NRya SRms XSen
	- var. ***albus***	EDAr EPfP NBro NLar WCot
	- Dark Beauty	see *A. alpinus* 'Dunkle Schöne'
§	- 'Dunkle Schöne'	EAJP EDAr LRHS SRms
	- 'Goliath'	EPfP NBro NLar SPlb
	- 'Happy End'	CNec LRHS NLar SRms XLum
	- 'Pinkie'	EBee EDAr EPfP NLar
	- 'Trimix'	ECho NBir SRms
	- 'White Beauty'	SRms
	amelloides	see *Felicia amelloides*
	amellus	CArn WMoo
	- 'Blue King'	ECtt GBuc NWsh SWvt
	- 'Brilliant'	CBod ECha ECtt EPPr EPla GBuc LAst LSou MAvo MBNS MMuc MNFA MRav MWat SEND SMrm SPer SRGP WGwG WHoo WOld
	- 'Butzemann'	WCot
	- 'Doktor Otto Petschek'	ELon WCot
	- 'Forncett Flourish'	WCot WOld
	- 'Framfieldii' ♀H7	MNFA NDov SMHy WCot WOld WWEG

- 'Gründer'	IMou MAvo WOld
- 'Jacqueline Genebrier' ♀H7	ELon GBuc NDov WOld
- 'King George' ♀H7	Widely available
- 'Kobold'	WOld
- 'Lac de Genève'	WCot
- 'Lady Hindlip'	CSam IMou WCot
- 'Louise'	MBrN SBch
- 'Mira'	MNrw
- 'Moerheim Gem'	IMou WOld
- 'Mrs Ralph Woods'	WOld
- 'Nocturne'	IKil WCot WOld
- 'Peach Blossom'	WOld
- Pink Zenith	see *A. amellus* 'Rosa Erfüllung'
§ - 'Rosa Erfüllung'	CBod CMac EAJP EBee ECtt ELan ELon EPPr EPfP EPla GBin GBuc GMaP IVic LAst LRHS LSou MNrw MRav NWsh SCob SPhx SRGP SWvt WCAu WMnd WOld
- 'Rotfeuer'	ELon GQue
- 'Rudolph Goethe'	CNec EBee ECtt ELan EMil EPPr EPfP GBee IKil LAst LPot LRHS MWat SRGP WMoo WOld WWEG
- 'Silbersee'	CSam IMou
- 'Sonia'	EBee ECtt GBuc LRHS MNFA SWvt WOld
- 'Sonora'	LPla MNrw SPhx SRGP WKif WOld WWEG
- 'Sternkugel'	WOld
- 'Ultramarine'	WOld
- 'Vanity'	WOld
§ - 'Veilchenkönigin' ♀H7	Widely available
- Violet Queen	see *A. amellus* 'Veilchenkönigin'
- 'Weltfriede'	WOld
× ***amethystinus***	MNrw
- 'Freiburg' **new**	MNrw
'Anita Pfeiffer'	LRHS
'Anja's Choice'	EBee WOld
asperulus misapplied	see *A. peduncularis*
'Blue Butterfly' **new**	SPhx
'Blütenregen'	WCot
capensis 'Variegatus'	see *Felicia amelloides* variegated
§ ***carolinianus***	XEll
'Cassandra'	NCGa
'Cheavers'	LRHS
'Chilly Fingers' **new**	MAvo
ciliolatus	EBee
'Climax' misapplied	see *A. laevis* 'Arcturus', *A. laevis* 'Calliope'
'Climax' ambig.	CElw EBee ELan GCal GQue MMuc MRav NBid SEND SMrm XLum
'Climax' Vicary Gibbs	MNrw WOld
coelestis	see *Felicia amelloides*
coloradoensis	LLHF NSla
'Connecticut Snow Flurry'	see *A. ericoides* f. *prostratus* 'Snow Flurry'
'Coombe Fishacre' ♀H7	CBod EBee ELan ELon GBuc GCal LEdu LPla LRHS MNFA MNrw NCGa NDov NLar SPhx SWvt WCot WHoo WOld
cordifolius	EWoo SPhx
- from Piney Fork **new**	EPPr
- 'Aldebaran'	NDov WOld
- 'Chieftain' ♀H7	MNrw SPhx WOld
- 'Elegans'	CSam EBee SDix WMnd WOld
- 'Ideal'	NLar XLum
- 'Silver Spray'	CKno ECtt ELon GMaP GQue MHom MWat SRGP WOld XLum

- 'Sweet Lavender' ♀H7	EBee LRHS WOld WWEG
- 'White Chief'	WOld
corymbosus	see *A. divaricatus*
'Cotswold Gem'	WCot WOld
diffusus	see *A. lateriflorus*
diplostephioides	EPPr EPfP GBin GBuc IKil MBNS MMHG NLar SGSe SPlb WOld
§ ***divaricatus***	Widely available
§ - 'Eastern Star'	NCGa WCot WOld
- Raiche form	see *A. divaricatus* 'Eastern Star'
- 'Tradescant'	IMou MNrw
'Duchess' (mixed)	CWCL
dumosus	CExl
- 'Biteliness'	NLar WOld
- Sapphire = 'Kiesapphire'[PBR]	CHel CPrp ELon EWTr EWoo LRHS MBri MHol NEgg SRGP SRkn SWvt
'Dwarf Barbados'	EPfP LRHS
'Early Blue'	IBoy
ericoides	CKno NBre NOrc WOld WWEG
- 'Blue Star' ♀H6	CSam LRHS NLar WMnd WOld WWEG
- 'Blue Wonder'	XLum
- 'Brimstone' ♀H6	MRav WOld
- 'Cinderella'	CPrp EBee LRHS NSti WOld WWEG
- 'Constance'	WOld
- 'Deep Danziger' **new**	SPhx
- 'Erlkönig'	CBod EBee EPri EShb GCal GQue LAst NGdn NLar SDix SPer SWat SWvt WCot WMnd WOld XLum
- 'Esther'	CPrp ECha ELan SMrm WOld
- 'First Snow'	WCot
- 'Golden Spray' ♀H6	EBee ELon EPfP EWes GMaP GQue NLar NSoo WMnd WOld
- 'Herbstmyrte'	CSam LRHS
- 'Hon. Edith Gibbs'	WOld
- 'Monte Cassino'	see *A. pilosus* var. *pringlei* 'Monte Cassino'
- 'Pink Cloud' ♀H6	CBod CHVG CPrp ECtt EPfP EPla EPri EShb GBuc GCal LAst LEdu LRHS MNFA MSpe NCGa NOrc NWad SPer SRGP SWat WMnd WOld WWEG
- f. ***prostratus***	CBod EPot GBuc GQue MRav XSen
§ - - 'Snow Flurry' ♀H6	CAby CMea ECha ECtt ELon GBuc IMou LEdu LPla MAvo MNrw MWat NLar SBch SWvt WCot WHoo WMnd WOld WOut XLum
- 'Rosy Veil'	MHom NBir NGdn NLar WOld
- 'Schneegitter'	LRHS WCot XSen
- 'Sulphurea'	MWat
- 'Vimmer's Delight'	WCot
- 'White Heather'	ECtt NLar WMnd WOld WWEG
- 'Yvette Richardson'	CSam MHom SMHy WOld WWEG
falcatus	WCot
- var. ***commutatus***	WCot WOld
'Fanny's Fall'	see *A. oblongifolius* 'Fanny's'
foliaceus from Montana	EPPr
- var. ***parryi***	EBee
× ***frikartii***	CMac ELan EPfP EPla MRav SMrm SWvt
- 'Eiger'	WOld
- 'Flora's Delight'	ECtt EPla GCal LRHS MNrw MRav NLar SPer WCAu WOld WWEG
- 'Jungfrau'	CWGN EBee EPPr GBuc GMaP GQue IKil LRHS MRav NLar SPhx WOld WWEG
- 'Mönch' ♀H7	Widely available
- Wonder of Stafa	see *A.* × *frikartii* 'Wunder von Stäfa'

§	- 'Wunder von Stäfa' ♀H7	CBod CDes CEnd CExl CKno EAEE EBee ECtt ELan ELon EPfP EPla GBuc GMaP LRHS LSou MBNS MCot MHol MWat MWhi NBir NLar SWvt WCot WMnd WOld WWEG XLum
	furcatus	XLum
	glehnii 'Aglenii'	SMad
	'Glow in the Dark'	CDes MAvo MSpe NLar WBrk WCot WOld
	greatae	EBee
	'Herfstweelde'	CPrp EBee SMad SPhx WOld
§	× ***herveyi***	Widely available
	himalaicus	GKev NSla
	'Hon. Vicary Gibbs' (*ericoides* hybrid)	WOld WOut
	hybridus luteus	see *Solidago* × *luteus*
	'Ivy House'	ECtt
*	***kotarimus*** **new**	XLum
	'Kylie'	CAby CHVG CPrp ECtt LEdu MAvo MHom MNrw NCGa SPhx SRGP WBor WBrk WHil WOld
	laevis	LEdu NLar SPhx
§	- 'Arcturus'	CCon CElw MAvo MBel MHom MNrw NBir NCGa NSti SDix WCot WMnd WOld WWEG XLum
	- 'Blauhügel'	LPla NDov
§	- 'Calliope'	CElw CKno CMea CSam EBee ECtt GCal GMaP MHom MMuc MNFA MNrw MSpe MWat NBid NLar NWsh SEND SMad SMrm SPhx SWvt WHoo WKif WMnd WOld WWEG WWtn XLum
	- 'Cally Compact'	GQue NLar WOld
	- var. ***geyeri***	MNrw WOut
	- 'Nightshade'	MAvo MNrw WBrk WOld
	- 'Vesta'	WOld
	- white-flowered	WOld
	lanceolatus Willd.	EPPr NCGa
	- 'Edwin Beckett'	CBre MHom MNrw SWvt WOld
§	***lateriflorus***	SWvt WOld
	- 'Bleke Bet'	WCot WOld
	- 'Buck's Fizz'	ELan NDov NLar WOld WWEG
	- 'Chloe'	CSam NCGa SPhx
	- 'Datschi'	XLum
	- var. ***horizontalis*** ♀H7	Widely available
	- 'Jan'	WOld
	- 'Lady in Black'	Widely available
	- 'Lovely'	CSam SRGP WCot
	- 'Prince'	Widely available
	laterifolius 'Snow Flurry'	see *A. ericoides* f. *prostratus* 'Snow Flurry'
	'Les Moutiers'	MHom MNrw SPhx WBrk WOld
§	***linosyris***	EWes GBin MAvo NLar SPer SPhx WHer WOld XLum
	- 'Gold Dust'	GBin
	- 'Goldilocks'	see *A. linosyris*
	'Little Carlow' (*cordifolius* hybrid) ♀H7	Widely available
	'Little Dorrit' (*cordifolius* hybrid)	ECtt NWsh
	maackii	WCot
	macrophyllus	ELan GBee LRHS MSpe NLar WFar WOld WWtn
	- 'Albus'	EPPr WFar WOld
	- 'Twilight'	see *A.* × *herveyi*
	mongolicus	see *Kalimeris mongolica*
	'Mrs Dean'	ECtt
	natalensis	see *Felicia rosulata*
	(Newstars Series) 'Newstars Fantasy'	WCot
	- 'Newstars Glory'	ECtt WCot
	'Nicholas'	WCot WOld
	'Noreen'	MAvo WOld
	novae-angliae	CArn WOld
	- 'Alex Deamon'	ELon MAvo WBrk WOld
	- 'Anabelle de Chazal'	ECtt ELon MAvo WBrk WOld
	- 'Andenken an Alma Pötschke'	Widely available
	- 'Andenken an Paul Gerber'	ECtt ELon MAvo MHom MNrw WOld
	- 'Augusta'	ELon MAvo SPhx WBrk WOld
	- Autumn Snow	see *A. novae-angliae* 'Herbstschnee'
	- 'Barr's Blue'	CMac EBee ECtt ELon EPfP GCra MAvo MHom MMuc MTis MWat NLar NWsh SEND SPer SRms WBrk WCAu WFar WMoo WOld
	- 'Barr's Pink'	CBre CMac EBee ECtt ELon EPfP MAvo MCot MHom MLHP MMuc MPie MTis MWat NLar SEND WBrk WFar WOld WSFF
*	- 'Barr's Purple'	ECtt WBrk WCFE WFar WOld
	- 'Barr's Violet'	CHVG CPrp ECtt MAvo MHom NSti SRms WCot WFar WHal WHoo WHrl WMoo WOld WWEG
	- 'Bishop Colenso'	CAby EPPr
	- 'Brockamin'	MAvo MNrw WBrk
	- 'Brockamin Margaret'	WOld
	- 'Brunswick' **new**	WOld
	- 'Christopher Harbutt'	LEdu SRGP WBrk
	- 'Colwall Century'	MAvo WBrk WOld
	- 'Colwall Constellation'	MAvo WBrk WOld
	- 'Colwall Galaxy'	MAvo WBrk WHrl WOld
	- 'Colwall Orbit'	ECtt ELon WOld
	- 'Connie'	MNrw MSpe
	- 'Crimson Beauty'	ELon MAvo MHer MHom MNrw MWat WBrk WOld WWEG
	- 'Dapper Tapper'	ECtt MAvo WCot WOld
	- 'Evensong'	ECtt MAvo WBrk WOld
	- 'Festival'	WBrk
	- 'Foxy Emily'	ECtt MAvo WBrk WOld
	- 'Harrington's Pink' ♀H7	Widely available
	- 'Helen Picton'	CSam ECtt ELon MAvo MBrN MHer MHom MPie MWat NWsh WBrk WHoo WOld WWEG
§	- 'Herbstschnee'	Widely available
	- 'James' **new**	MAvo
	- 'James Ritchie'	CSam ELon LLHF MAvo WHoo WOld
	- 'John Davies'	MAvo MNrw SBch WHil WOld
	- 'Jon Baker'	MAvo WBrk
	- 'Kate Deamon'	WOld
	- 'Lachsglut'	ELon MAvo NLar WBrk WCot WOld
	- 'Ladies Day'	WOld
	- 'Little Bella'	WOld
	- 'Lou Williams'	CAby ECtt ELon LPla MAvo MNrw MWat WBrk WHil WOld WWEG
I	- 'Lucida'	MAvo SPhx WHal WOld WWEG
	- 'Lucinda'	ECtt
	- 'Lye End Beauty'	CKno ECtt ELon LLWP MAvo MHom MNFA MNrw MWat SBch WBrk WCot WHoo WMoo WOld
	- 'Mabelle'	NDov
	- 'Marina Wolkonsky'	CAby ECtt ELon EWes MAvo MNrw MTis MWat NLar SPhx WBrk WCot WKif WOld WWEG

- 'Millennium Star' ECtt ELon MAvo WOld
- 'Miss K.E. Mash' CPrp ECtt MAvo MHom NLar SRGP WBrk WOld WWEG
- 'Mrs S.T. Wright' CAby CPrp CTri ECtt EWes LEdu MAvo MBrN MHom MNFA MNrw SRGP WFar WOld WWEG
- 'Mrs S.T. Wright' short **new** MAvo
- 'Mrs S.W. Stern' WBrk WOld
- 'Naomi' MAvo WBrk WOld
- 'Pink Parfait' CSam ECtt IKil MAvo NGdn SRms WBrk WCot WOld
- 'Pink Victor' CTri MAvo SRms WMoo
- 'Pride of Rougham' EWes LLWP MAvo WBrk
- 'Primrose Upward' CAby MAvo MNrw NDov NWsh WCot WOld
- 'Purple Cloud' CSam ELon MAvo MHer MHom MWat NGdn WBrk WHal WOld WWEG

I - 'Purple Dome' Widely available
- 'Quinton Menzies' CSam ELon MAvo WBrk WOld WWEG
- 'Red Cloud' ELon MAvo MHer SMrm WBrk WOld
- 'Rosa Sieger' ♀H7 CAby CBre CPrp CSam ECtt ELon GMaP GQue LEdu MAvo MHom MNrw NGdn NLar SPhx WBor WBrk WHil WHoo WOld WWEG XLum
- 'Rose Williams' MAvo SBch WHil WOld
- 'Röter Stern' ECtt MAvo MPie WBrk WOld
- 'Rougham Pink' MAvo WBrk
- 'Rougham Purple' EWes
- 'Rougham Violet' WBrk
- 'Rubinschatz' ELon MAvo MHom MWat NWsh SRms WOld XLum
- 'Rudelsburg' EBee ECtt MAvo WBrk
- 'Saint Michael's' MAvo WOld
- 'Sayer's Croft' ECtt ELon MAvo MHom MWat WCot WHil WHoo WOld WOut
- September Ruby see *A. novae-angliae* 'Septemberrubin'

§ - 'Septemberrubin' CAby CMea EBee ECtt ELon EPfP EWTr IFoB LEdu LPla LSou MAvo MBel MMuc MNFA MRav NSti NWsh SEND SPhx SRGP WOld XLum
- 'Treasure' CBre ECtt ELon EWes LRHS MAvo NBre SMrm SPhx SRGP WBrk WMoo WOld
- 'Vibrant Dome'[PBR] MTis NLar
- 'Violet Dusk' WBrk
- 'Violet Haze' CMea ELon WBrk
- 'Violetta' ECtt ELon GMaP LSou MAvo MHom MNFA MNrw SCob SPhx WHil WHoo WKif WOld
- 'W. Bowman' ECtt MNrw WBrk WOld
- 'Wow' ELon SMrm WHil

'Novemberlaan' MSpe

novi-belgii WHer
- 'Ada Ballard' CFis CMac CWld EBee LRHS NEgg SMrm SRGP WMoo WOld WWEG
- 'Albanian' WOld
- 'Alderman Vokes' WOld
- 'Algar's Pride' ECtt WOld WWEG
- 'Alice Haslam' CMac CWld EBee ECtt ELan LRHS MJak NLar NOrc SRGP SRms WOld WWEG
- 'Angela Peel' EBee LRHS
- 'Anita Ballard' WOld
- 'Anita Webb' NBir WOld
- 'Anneke' NLar NSoo SRGP WOld
- 'Apollo' LRHS MWat NLar WOld
- 'Apple Blossom' WOld
- 'Audrey' CMac ECtt GMaP LPot LRHS MBNS NGdn NOrc SRGP SRms WOld
- 'Autumn Beauty' WOld
- 'Autumn Days' WOld
- 'Autumn Glory' WOld
- 'Autumn Rose' WOld
- 'Baby Climax' WOld
- 'Bahamas' (Island Series) CBod CNec EPfP LBMP LRHS NLar NPri NWsh SRms SWvt WCot
- 'Barbados' (Island Series) CBod EPfP LRHS NLar NPri SWvt WCot
- 'Beauty of Colwall' WOld
- 'Beechwood Challenger' MPie WBrk WOld
- 'Beechwood Charm' WOld
- 'Beechwood Rival' CTri WOld XEll
- 'Blandie' CTri SRGP WOld
- 'Blauglut' WOld
- 'Blue Baby' CMac
- 'Blue Bouquet' CTri SRms WOld
- 'Blue Boy' WOld WWEG
- 'Blue Danube' WOld
- 'Blue Eyes' WOld
- 'Blue Gown' CCse GCal GQue WOld WOut
- 'Blue Lagoon' CFis CMea ELan MMuc SRGP WBrk WOld

I - 'Blue Moon' Old Court Nurseries **new** WOld
- 'Blue Patrol' WOld
- 'Blue Radiance' WOld
- 'Blue Spire' WOld
- 'Blue Whirl' WOld
- 'Boningale Blue' WOld
- 'Boningale White' NDov WHil WOld
- 'Bridesmaid' WOld
- 'Bridgette' WOld
- 'Bright Eyes' SRGP WOld
- 'Brightest and Best' WOld
- 'Brigitte' NLar
- 'Cameo' WOld
- 'Cantab' WOld
- 'Carlingcott' WOld
- 'Carnival' CMac EBee ECtt IVic LRHS MMHG NOrc SRGP WOld
- 'Cecily' WOld WWEG
- 'Charles Wilson' CFis WOld
- 'Chatterbox' EBee ELan EPfP LPot LRHS MRav MWat NEgg NLar SRms WHar WOld
- 'Chelwood' WOld
- 'Chequers' CElw EBee MBNS MHer NEgg SRGP WOld
- 'Christina' see *A. novi-belgii* 'Kristina'
- 'Christine Soanes' WOld
- 'Cliff Lewis' WOld
- 'Climax Albus' see *A.* 'White Climax'
- 'Cloudy Blue' WOld
- 'Colonel F.R. Durham' WOld
- 'Coombe Gladys' WOld
- 'Coombe Margaret' WOld
- 'Coombe Radiance' WOld
- 'Coombe Ronald' MWat WOld
- 'Coombe Rosemary' ECtt NLar WBor WOld
- 'Coombe Violet' MWat WOld
- 'Countess of Dudley' CFis WOld

- 'Court Herald'	WOld
- 'Crimson Brocade'	CCon ECtt ELan EPfP LRHS MBri NLar NSoo SHil SPoG SRGP SRms SWvt
- 'Dandy'	CMac ELan EPfP LRHS NBir NGdn SRGP WOld
- 'Daniela'	SRms WBrk WOld
- 'Daphne Anne'	WOld
- 'Dauerblau'	WOld
- 'Davey's True Blue'	CTri WOld XLum
- 'David Murray'	WOld
- 'Dazzler'	ECtt WOld WWEG
- 'Destiny'	WOld
- 'Diana'	MAvo NWsh
- 'Diana Watts'	WOld
- 'Dietgard'	ELon MWat WOld WWEG
- 'Dolly'	CElw NBir SRms WOld WWEG
- 'Dora Chiswell'	WOld
- 'Dusky Maid'	ELon WOld
- 'Dwarf Ibiza'	LRHS
- 'Elizabeth'	CElw
- 'Elizabeth Hutton'	WOld
- 'Elsie Dale'	WOld
- 'Elta'	WOld
- 'Erica'	CElw MWat WOld
- 'Ernest Ballard'	WOld
- 'Eva'	ELon SRms WOld
- 'Eventide'	CElw CTri WOld
- 'Fair Lady'	MWat WOld
- 'Faith'	WOld
- 'Farncombe Lilac'	NCot
- 'Farncombe Wine Red'	NCot
- 'Fellowship' 🏆H6	CBod CDes CHVG ECtt ELon IKil LEdu MAvo MBri MMuc MNrw MWat NCGa SHar SRGP SRms SWvt WBrk WCot WOld WWEG
- 'Flamingo'	EBee LRHS WOld
- 'Freda Ballard'	CFis ECtt GMaP LRHS MWat SRGP WOld WWEG
- 'Freya'	CElw WOld WSHC
- 'Fuldatal'	WOld
- 'Gayborder Blue'	WOld
- 'Gayborder Royal'	CCon WOld
- 'Goliath'	WOld
- 'Grey Lady'	WOld WWEG
- 'Guardsman'	WOld
- 'Gulliver'	WOld WWEG
- 'Gurney Slade'	WOld
- 'Guy Ballard'	WOld
- 'Harrison's Blue'	MWat WOld
- 'Heinz Richard'	CFis ECha LRHS MHer MMuc NBir NGdn SRGP SRms WOld WWEG
- 'Helen'	ELon WOld
- 'Helen Ballard'	NBid SRms WOld
- 'Herbstgruss vom Bresserhof'	NBre NLar WOld
- 'Herbstpurzel'	WOld
- 'Hilda Ballard'	WOld
- 'Ibiza'	WCot
- 'Ilse Brensell'	WOld WWEG
- 'Irene'	WOld
- 'Janet Watts'	WOld
- 'Jean'	ELon MWat SRms WOld
- 'Jean Gyte'	WOld
- 'Jeanette'	SRms WOld
- 'Jenny'	Widely available
- 'Jollity'	WOld
- 'Jugendstil'	XLum

- 'Julia'	WOld
- 'Kassel'	SRms WOld
- 'King of the Belgians'	WOld
§ - 'Kristina'	EBee ECha EPPr ITim LRHS MMuc MNrw MRav NBir WOld WWEG
- 'Lady Frances'	EBee SRms WOld
- 'Lady in Blue'	CSBt ECtt ELan EPPr EPfP EPla LAst LEdu LRHS MBNS MGos MLHP MWat NEgg NGdn NSoo NWad SBod SGbt SHil SPer SPoG SRGP SRms SWat SWvt WCAu WHar WOld WWEG
- 'Lassie'	MWat WOld
- 'Lavender Dream'	WOld
- 'Lawrence Chiswell'	WOld
- 'Lederstrumpf'	NDov
- 'Lisa Dawn'	ECtt WOld
- 'Little Boy Blue'	SRms WOld XLum
- 'Little Man in Blue'	WOld WWEG
- 'Little Pink Beauty'	CNec ECtt ELan EPfP EWTr IBoy ITim LAst LRHS MBNS MJak NGdn NHol NWad SPer SRGP SRms WHar WOld WWEG
- 'Little Pink Lady'	SRms WOld
- 'Little Pink Pyramid'	SRms WOld WWEG
- 'Little Red Boy'	WOld
- 'Little Treasure'	WOld
- 'Madge Cato'	SRms WOld
- 'Mammoth'	WOld
- 'Margery Bennett'	WOld
- 'Marie Ann Neil'	SRms WOld
- 'Marie Ballard'	CMac CSBt GMaP LEdu LRHS MBri MHer MRav MWat MWhi NCGa NGdn NHol NLar NOrc NPer NSoo SGol SMrm SPer SRGP SRms SWat SWvt WCAu WOld WWEG XLum
- 'Marie's Pretty Please'	WOld
- 'Marjorie'	SRGP WOld XLum
- 'Mary Deane'	WOld
- 'Mauve Magic'	MWat SRms WOld WWEG
- 'Melbourne Belle'	WOld
- 'Melbourne Magnet'	WOld
- 'Midget'	WOld
- 'Mistress Quickly'	ECtt WOld WWEG
- 'Mittelmeer'	LRHS NDov WOld XLum
- 'Mount Everest'	NCGa NSoo WOld WWEG
- 'Mrs Leo Hunter'	WOld
- 'Neron'	IMou MNrw MPie NDov
- 'Nesthäkchen'	WOld
- 'Newton's Pink'	WOld
- 'Niobe'	WOld
- 'Norman's Jubilee'	EBee EPfP LRHS MHer NBir WOld WWEG
- 'Nursteed Charm'	WOld
- 'Oktoberschneekuppel'	WOld
- 'Pamela'	WOld
- 'Patricia Ballard'	CBcs CBod CCon CMac CSBt EBee GCra GMaP LRHS MHer MWat MWhi NBir NLar NPer NSoo NWad SGol SPer SRGP WOld WWEG
- 'Peace'	WOld
- 'Percy Thrower'	ECtt WOld
- 'Peter Chiswell'	SRms WOld
- 'Peter Harrison'	GMaP NBir WMnd WOld XLum
- 'Peter Pan'	NLar
- 'Petunia' **new**	CBod
- 'Pink Lace'	MBNS WOld
- 'Plenty'	WOld

– 'Porzellan'	CElw CFis EBee ECtt MAvo MBNS MNrw NGdn NLar SRGP WCot WHal WOld
– 'Pride of Colwall'	SRms WBrk WOld
– 'Priory Blush'	CElw WOld
– 'Professor Anton Kippenberg'	CFis EPfP GMaP LRHS MNrw MRav NLar SPer SRGP SRms SWvt WMnd WOld WWEG XLum
– 'Prosperity'	WOld
– 'Purple Dome'	CBod CFis CNec ECha ELan LEdu MHer MWat SCob SHar SRkn WOld WOut
– 'Ralph Picton'	WOld
– 'Rector'	see *A. novi-belgii* 'The Rector'
– 'Red Robin'	MSpe MWat
– 'Red Sunset'	SRms WOld
– 'Rembrandt'	ECtt NGdn SRGP
– 'Remembrance'	MWat SRms WOld WWEG
– 'Reverend Vincent Dale'	WOld
– 'Richness'	WOld
– 'Rose Bonnet'	CSBt LRHS SPlb WOld
– 'Roseanne'	WOld
– 'Rosebud' ambig.	WWEG
– 'Rosebud' Ballard	WOld
– 'Rosenquartz'	NLar
– 'Rosenwichtel'	NLar WHil WOld WWEG
– 'Royal Ruby'	CBod CFis EBee ECtt LRHS NLar WOld WWEG
– 'Royal Velvet'	WOld
– 'Rozika'	WOld
– 'Rufus'	WOld
– 'Sailor Boy'	NCGa
– 'Saint Egwyn'	WOld
– 'Sam Banham'	MNrw WOld
– 'Samoa' (Island Series)	CBod CNec CTsd EPfP EUJe LRHS LSou NLar NPri SRms WCot
– 'Sandford White Swan'	GBuc MHom WOld WWEG
– 'Sarah Ballard'	LRHS NLar SHil SRGP WBrk WOld
§ – 'Schneekissen'	CBod ECtt ELan EPfP GMaP LRHS MBNS MBri MHer MJak NSoo NWsh SPer SRGP SRms SWvt WHar WOld WWEG XLum
– 'Schneezicklein'	GBin
– 'Schöne von Dietlikon'	CKno MWat WOld XLum
– 'Schoolgirl'	WOld WWEG
– 'Sheena'	WOld
– 'Silberblaukissen'	WOld
§ – 'Silberteppich'	EBee
– Silver Carpet	see *A. novi-belgii* 'Silberteppich'
– Snow Cushion	see *A. novi-belgii* 'Schneekissen'
– 'Snowsprite'	CSBt ELan MWat NLar NOrc SGbt SGol SRGP SRms SWat WOld
– 'Sonata'	GMaP WOld
– 'Sophia'	MWat WOld
– 'Starlight'	ECtt IBoy NLar NSoo WRHF
– 'Steinebrück'	WOld
– 'Sterling Silver'	WOld
– 'Sun Queen'	WOld
– 'Sunset'	WOld
– 'Susan'	WOld
– 'Sweet Briar'	CElw WOld
– 'Tapestry'	WOld
– 'Terry's Pride'	SRGP WOld WWEG
– 'The Archbishop'	ECtt WOld XEll
– 'The Bishop'	WOld
– 'The Cardinal'	WOld
– 'The Dean'	WOld
§ – 'The Rector'	WOld
– 'The Sexton'	WOld
– 'Thundercloud'	MWat WOld
– 'Timsbury'	CElw SRms WOld WWEG
– 'Tovarich'	WOld
– 'Trudi Ann'	NBir WOld
– 'Twinkle'	WOld
– 'Victor'	WOld
– 'Vignem'	NSti
– 'Violet Lady'	WOld
– 'Waterperry'	MWat WBrk WOld
– 'White Ladies'	CBcs ECtt GCra GMaP LRHS MMuc MWat NLar NOrc SHil SPer SRGP XLum
– 'White Swan'	ECtt
– 'White Wings'	MWat WOld
– 'Winston S. Churchill'	CTri ELan EPfP GMaP IKil LEdu LRHS MHer MWat SPer SPlb SPoG SRGP WOld
oblongifolius	NWsh WOld XSen
§ – 'Fanny's'	CBod CPrp ECtt EPla GCal GQue MNFA NWad SPoG SRGP WCAu WOld
– 'October Skies'	EBee EWes MNrw
'Ochtendgloren' (*pringlei* hybrid) ♀H4	CDes CPrp CSam EBee ECtt EPPr EWes GBuc MHom MNrw MSpe NCGa NDov NLar SMrm WHal WOld WWEG
Octoberlight	see *A.* 'Oktoberlicht'
§ 'Oktoberlicht'	EBee LRHS MNrw NCGa WOld
oolentangiensis	NLar WOld
'Orchidee'	EBee EPri EWTr EWes MAvo
'Orpheus'	ECGP MNrw WBrk
pappei	see *Felicia amoena*
'Pearl Star'	WOld
§ ***peduncularis***	CUse EBee EPPr IMou LPla MAvo MHol NDov SGSe WOld WWEG
petiolatus	see *Felicia petiolata*
'Photograph' ♀H7	CHVG CSam EBee ECtt ELon EWes LEdu LRHS MAvo MHom SMrm WOld
§ ***pilosus*** var. ***demotus*** ♀H7	ECha EWes MRav NWad WOld
§ – var. ***pringlei*** 'Monte Cassino'	CSBt EAEE EPfP GQue LPot LRHS MBNS MRav MWat SMrm SPer SPhx SRGP SRms WOld WWEG XLum
– – 'October Glory'	CCse
– – 'Phoebe'	WOld
'Pink Star'	EBee ECtt ELon GMaP LEdu MNFA MRav MWat NDov NSti SBch SPhx WHoo WOld XLum
'Pinwheel' **new**	WCot
'Pixie Dark Eye' (*ericoides* hybrid)	CDes EBee ECtt SMHy WCot
'Pixie Red Eye' (*ericoides* hybrid)	WCot
'Prairie Lavender'	WOld
'Prairie Pink'	WOld
'Prairie Purple'	WCot WOld
'Prairie Violet'	WOld
'Primrose Path'	EBee LEdu MNrw NCGa WBrk WCot WOld
ptarmicoides	see *Solidago ptarmicoides*
puniceus	NLar XLum
pyrenaeus 'Lutetia'	CKno CPrp ECha EPla GBuc GCal GMaP MAvo MHom MNFA MNrw MWat NCGa NLar SPoG SPtp SRGP WKif WOld WWEG XLum
radula	CSam EPPr EWes IMou LPla MAvo MNrw NLar WOld WSHC

- 'August Sky' WCot
'Ringdove' (*ericoides* hybrid) ♀H6 CKno CPrp MAvo MHom MNFA NCGa NSti SRGP SWvt WCot WOld
'Rosa Star' WOld
'Rose Queen' MAvo
rotundifolius 'Variegatus' see *Felicia amelloides* variegated
sagittifolius Wed. XLum
× ***salignus*** WOld
- Scottish form WOld
§ ***scaber*** NWsh WCot
scandens see *A. carolinianus*
schreberi CCon EPPr EWes LEdu MAvo MSpe NCGa NWsh WBor WCot WOld WWtn
'Sea Spray' WCot
§ ***sedifolius*** ECtt ELan ELon EPla GAbr GQue LEdu MAvo MWat NBid NSti SDix SEND WCot WMnd WOld
- RCBAM 5 WCot
- 'Nanus' CExl ELan GCal MHom MNFA MRav NBir NLar NWsh SPer WCot WHil WMnd WOld XLum XSen
- 'Roseus' IMou
§ ***sibiricus*** NLar WOld
'Snow Flurry' see *A. ericoides* f. *prostratus* 'Snow Flurry'
'Soft Lass' WCot
souliei GKev NSla
spathulifolius WCot XLum
spectabilis EBee GCal IMou LRHS WOld
'Star of Chesters' MAvo WOld
stracheyi ITim
subcaeruleus see *A. tongolensis*
'Sunhelene' CDes EBee ECtt WCot
Sunplum = 'Danasplum'PBR LEdu
tataricus LPla
- 'Jindai' EBee
thomsonii WCot WOld
- 'Nanus' CAby GBee GMaP LRHS MCot MRav SPhx WCot WOld WSHC
Tonga = 'Dasfour' EPfP EWTr LRHS MHol NBir NLar NPri NWsh SRms SWvt WCot
§ ***tongolensis*** GKev
- 'Berggarten' LRHS MPie WOld
- 'Dunkleviolette' SRms
- 'Napsbury' LRHS WOld
- 'Wartburgstern' CCon EPfP LRHS MMuc SEND SGbt WWEG XLum
tradescantii misapplied see *A. pilosus* var. *demotus*
tradescantii L. ELan MBNS MRav NSti SMad WBrk WCot WOld
'Treffpunkt' IMou
trinervius var. ***harae*** WOld
tripolium WHer
'Triumph' WCot
turbinellus misapplied ♀H6 CAby CKno EPfP EWes GGal IKil LPla LRHS MMuc NGdn NWsh SMHy SPhx SRkn SWvt WWEG
turbinellus Lindl. CSam EBee EPfP EWTr GBee MWat NCGa NLar NSbr WCot WOld
- 'El Fin' **new** MNrw
- hybrid WOld
umbellatus CBre CKno ECha EPPr GQue MMuc NBir NDov NLar WCot WOld
'Vasterival' IMou MAvo MPie MSpe NCGa NDov SMHy WOut WWEG XLum
vimineus Lam. see *A. lateriflorus*
- 'Ptarmicoides' see *Solidago ptarmicoides*
§ 'White Climax' CSam MHom WBrk WCot
'Wood's Blue' LRHS
'Wood's Pink' LRHS WHil
'Wood's Purple' EBee LRHS WHil
'Yvonne' CBre

Asteranthera (*Gesneriaceae*)

ovata CExl CFil EPfP GGGa LRHS LSou SLon SPoG WAbe WPGP WSHC

Asteriscus (*Asteraceae*)

'Gold Coin' see *Pallenis maritima*
maritimus see *Pallenis maritima*
sericeus CSpe

Asteromoea (*Asteraceae*)

mongolica see *Kalimeris mongolica*

Asteropyrum (*Ranunculaceae*)

cavaleriei GEdr

Asterotrichion (*Malvaceae*)

discolor ECou SPlb SVen

Astilbe ✿ (*Saxifragaceae*)

CC 5201 CExl
'Alive and Kicking' MBri SCob
'Amerika' (× *arendsii*) CMHG CSBt SRms
'Amethyst' (× *arendsii*) CMHG CMac ELon EPfP LRHS MRav NBir NHol NSoo SPer WFar WMoo WWEG
'Angel Wings' (× *arendsii*) NEoE
'Anita Pfeifer' (× *arendsii*) CMHG ELon GBin IBoy NLar XLum
'Aphrodite' (*simplicifolia* hybrid) CBcs GCal MLHP
× ***arendsii*** EPfP IFoB NBre WHar WMoo XLum
'Astary White' (× *arendsii*) (Astary Series) LRHS
astilboides CMHG SWvt
'Atrorosea' (*simplicifolia* hybrid) SRms
'Avalanche' CAby GBin NHol SPad WMnd WWEG
§ 'Beauty of Ernst' (× *arendsii*) CBod EBee ELon EPfP LRHS LSou MAsh MBri MSCN SLon SRms WMoo
§ 'Beauty of Lisse' (× *arendsii*) ELon LSou MSCN WHil WOut
Bella Group (× *arendsii*) WMnd
'Bergkristall' (× *arendsii*) CMHG
'Betsy Cuperus' (*thunbergii* hybrid) CMHG EBee GBin NBre WCAu
'Bonn' (*japonica* hybrid) CWCL CWat MMuc NLar NSbr SCoo SRms
'Boogie Woogie'PBR (× *arendsii*) MAsh
§ 'Brautschleier' (× *arendsii*) ♀H7 CExl CMHG CMac CPrp CTri ECtt EPfP GBin GCra GKev LRHS NGdn NLar NPCo NSbr WPnP XLum
'Bremen' (*japonica* hybrid) CMHG GBin
'Bressingham Beauty' (× *arendsii*) Widely available
Bridal Veil (× *arendsii*) see *A.* 'Brautschleier'
§ 'Bronce Elegans' (*simplicifolia* hybrid) ♀H7 CCon CMHG CPrp ECha ELon EPfP GBin GBuc GMaP NEoE NHol NLar WMoo WOut WWEG
'Bronze Sprite' (*simplicifolia* hybrid) WFar
'Bronzelaub' (× *arendsii*) CMHG
* ***bumalda*** 'Bronze Pygmy' MMoz NHol

	Name	Suppliers
	'Bumalda' (× *arendsii*)	CCon CSBt CWCL ELon GBin GMaP IBoy LRHS MAsh NChi NEoE NGdn SPlb WGwG WMoo WWtn
	'Burgunderrot' (× *arendsii*)	EBee MBri MNrw NLar SMrm
	'Carminea'	CMHG
	'Carnea' (*simplicifolia* hybrid)	CMHG
	'Catherine Deneuve'	see *A.* 'Federsee'
	'Cattleya Dunkel' (× *arendsii*)	CMHG
	'Cattleya' (× *arendsii*)	CMHG CSam GBin GBuc LRHS NLar NSoo WMoo
	'Ceres' (× *arendsii*)	CMHG
	'Cherry Ripe'	see *A.* 'Feuer'
	chinensis	CMHG ECho LRHS WSHC
	- B&SWJ 8178	WCru
	- from Russia	GCal
	- 'Brokat'	GBin
	- 'Christian'	GBin
	- var. ***davidii***	CMHG EPla
	- - B&SWJ 8583	WCru
	- - B&SWJ 8645	WCru
	- 'Diamonds and Pearls'PBR	CWGN ECtt LSou MBri SCob WFar WHil
	- 'Finale'	ELon NEoE NHol SPer WFar WOut
	- 'Frankentroll'	CMHG
	- 'Intermezzo'	GBin GCal GMaP NEoE NLar
	- 'Little Vision in Pink'PBR	MBri MSCN WFar
	- 'Love and Pride'	LSou MBri
	- 'Milk and Honey'PBR	CWGN ECtt ELon EWTr LSou MBNS NSoo SGol WFar
§	- var. ***pumila*** 🏆H5	Widely available
	- - 'Serenade'	CMac NGdn
	- 'Purple Glory'	CMHG EWll IKil
	- 'Spätsommer'	CMHG
	- var. ***taquetii***	CMac ELan EPfP LRHS NSti SRms
	- - Purple Lance	see *A. chinensis* var. *taquetii* 'Purpurlanze'
§	- - 'Purpurlanze'	Widely available
§	- - 'Superba' 🏆H7	CMHG CMac CRow CTri ECha GBin IBoy LRHS MLHP NBro NWad SDix SMad SPer SRms WMoo
	- 'Troll'	GBin
	- 'Veronika Klose'	CMHG GBin NEoE NLar WWEG
	- 'Vision in Pink'PBR	CWCL ELan EPfP EWll LSou LSun MBNS MHol MNrw WFar WHil
	- 'Vision in Red'PBR	CWCL CWat ECtt ELan EPfP EWll IBoy LRHS LSou MBNS MBri MHol MNrw NLar NPCo NSoo SGbt SPoG WCAu WFar WMoo
	- 'Vision in White'	MBri NEoE NSoo SPoG WFar
	- 'Visions'	CMHG CMac CWCL EPfP IBoy LRHS LSou MBNS MBri NBro NEoE NGdn
	Cologne	see *A.* 'Köln'
	Color Flash	see *A.* 'Beauty of Ernst'
	Color Flash Lime	see *A.* 'Beauty of Lisse'
	'Country and Western'PBR (× *arendsii*)	LSou SCob
	'Crimson Feather'	see *A.* 'Gloria Purpurea'
	× ***crispa***	ECho
	- 'Gnom'	NHar
	- 'Lilliput'	ECtt GBee NBir NEoE NHar NLar NRya
§	- 'Perkeo' 🏆H5	CBcs CCon EBee ECho ECtt ELan EPfP GMaP LRHS NBir NEoE NHar NLar NMyG SRms WCot WMoo WWEG
	- 'Peter Pan'	see *A.* × *crispa* 'Perkeo'
	- 'Red Rog'	NEoE
	- 'Snow Queen'	NBir NEoE NHar
	'Darwin's Dream'	IBoy MNrw NEoE NLar
	'Darwin's Favourite' (× *arendsii*)	CWCL
	'Delft Lace'	EBee LBuc LRHS MAsh WMoo
	'Deutschland' (*japonica* hybrid)	Widely available
§	'Diamant' (× *arendsii*)	CHel CMHG MMuc MNrw NBir NGdn NHol SEND WFar
	Diamond	see *A.* 'Diamant'
	'Drayton Glory' (× *arendsii*)	see *A.* × *rosea* 'Peach Blossom'
	'Drum and Bass'PBR	IBoy LSou NLar NSoo
	'Dunkelachs' (*simplicifolia* hybrid)	EBee MSCN
	'Dusseldorf' (*japonica* hybrid)	CMHG CSam CWCL
	'Eden's Odysseus'	GBin IBoy NHol
	'Eden's Twinkle'	EBee
	'Elegans' (*simplicifolia* hybrid)	CMHG CMac
	'Elisabeth' (× *arendsii*) **new**	NBir
	Elizabeth Bloom = 'Eliblo'PBR (× *arendsii*)	CAby CHVG ELon EPla GAbr LLWG LRHS MHol MRav NDov NEgg NGdn NHol SGol
	'Elizabeth' (*japonica* hybrid)	CMHG
	'Ellie' (× *arendsii*)	CBod CMHG CMac CWCL GBin GQue LSou MAsh MBNS MBri MSCN NGdn NHol NLar SMrm WFar
	'Else Schluck' (× *arendsii*)	ECha
	'Erica' (× *arendsii*)	CAby CExl CMHG CTri NEoE NLar SPad WMoo WWEG
	'Etna' (*japonica* hybrid)	CBcs CMHG CSam ECtt IBoy MMuc NEgg NGdn NHol NLar NSir SGSe SMrm SRms WFar WHar WPnP
	'Europa' (*japonica* hybrid)	CMHG CMac ECtt GBin LRHS MGos NGdn NLar SPoG WHar WMoo
	'Fanal' (× *arendsii*) 🏆H7	Widely available
	'Fata Morgana' (× *arendsii* hybrid)	CMHG
§	'Federsee' (× *arendsii*)	CBcs CHVG CMHG CWCL EBee ECha ECtt ELan LRHS MBNS NBro NEoE NGdn WFar WWtn XLum
§	'Feuer' (× *arendsii*)	CMHG CMac ECtt ELan GBin GBuc LRHS NEgg NEoE NGdn NHol NLar NOrc SMrm WBor WGwG WMoo
	Fire	see *A.* 'Feuer'
	'Fireberry'PBR (Short 'n' Sweet Series)	EBee LSou NLar
	'Flamingo'PBR (× *arendsii*)	ECtt GBin MBNS NSoo
§	***formosa*** B&SWJ 10946	WCru
	'Gertrud Brix' (× *arendsii*)	CBcs CWat MMuc NBir NGdn SEND XLum
§	***glaberrima***	NBid
§	- var. ***saxatilis*** 🏆H5	EPfP GBin GEdr IFro NHar NSla WAbe WHal WThu
	- ***saxosa***	see *A. glaberrima* var. *saxatilis*
§	'Gloria Purpurea' (× *arendsii*)	CMHG ELon NSbr WMoo
	'Gloria' (× *arendsii*)	CMHG CMac CTri ECtt MRav
	Glow	see *A.* 'Glut'
§	'Glut' (× *arendsii*)	CCon CMHG CWCL EBee ECtt EWTr LRHS MMuc NGdn NHol SRms WFar
	'Granat' (× *arendsii*)	CAby CMHG CMac EAEE GBuc NBir NDov NEgg NGdn NHol NLar WMoo

*	Grande Group (× *arendsii*)	NBre
	grandis	CMHG GBee WHer
	- BWJ 8076A **new**	NLar
	'Grete Püngel' (× *arendsii*)	ECha GBin WWEG
	'Harmony' (× *arendsii*)	CMHG
	'Heart and Soul'[PBR]	CWGN EPfP LSou MBri
	'Hennie Graafland' (*simplicifolia* hybrid)	CBcs CMHG COtt CWCL GBin LSou NLar SHar WFar
	'Henry Noblett'	GBin
	'Holden Clough' (*japonica* hybrid)	NHol NWad
	Hyacinth	see *A.* 'Hyazinth'
§	'Hyazinth' (× *arendsii*)	CExl CMHG CPrp EBee GMaP LLWG LRHS LSou NBir NHol WFar
	'Icecream' (× *arendsii*) **new**	CBod MAsh
	'Inshriach Pink' (*simplicifolia* hybrid)	CBcs CMHG ECtt EHoe ELan LRHS NBir NHar NHol NLar SBch WHal WOut
	'Irrlicht' (× *arendsii*)	CBod CMHG CMac EBee ELan EPfP EShb EWTr GBin GBuc IBoy LRHS NWad SBod SGSe SMrm SRms SWat WPnP
	'Isa Hall'	CMHG NEoE
	japonica	CExl
*	- 'Pumila'	NBir NGdn
	- var. ***terrestris***	see *A. glaberrima*
	'Jo Ophorst' (*davidii* hybrid)	CMHG EBee ECtt GBuc LRHS NGdn NLar
	'Jump and Jive'[PBR]	LSou NSoo WFar
	'Juno'	XLum
	'Koblenz' (*japonica* hybrid)	CMHG CWCL
§	'Köln' (*japonica* hybrid)	CMHG CWat ELon GBin LRHS
	koreana	WCot
	- B&SWJ 8611	WCru
	- B&SWJ 8680	WCru
	'Kriemhilde'	CMHG MSCN
	'Kvële' (× *arendsii*)	CMHG WMoo
§	'Lachskönigin' (× *arendsii*)	CMHG
	'Lilli Goos' (× *arendsii*)	CMHG GBin GCal
	'Lollipop'	ECtt MBNS NEoE SRms
	longicarpa B&SWJ 6711	WCru
	macroflora	GCal
	'Magenta'	CMHG
	'Maggie Daley'	IBoy NBro NEoE WMoo
	'Mainz' (*japonica* hybrid)	CHVG CMHG ECtt
	'Mars' (× *arendsii*)	CMHG
	microphylla	CMHG
	- B&SWJ 11085	WCru
	- pink-flowered	CMHG
	'Midnight Arrow' (*davidii* hybrid)	CMHG
	'Moerheim Glory' (× *arendsii*)	GBin IBoy NBre NGdn NLar
	'Moerheimii' (*thunbergii* hybrid)	CMHG
	'Mont Blanc' (× *arendsii*)	CMHG
	'Montgomery' (*japonica* hybrid)	CMHG CWCL EBee ELon EShb GAbr GBin IKil LBMP LRHS MAsh MBNS MBri MNrw NBro NEgg NGdn NHol NLar
	'Nemo' **new**	CBod MAsh
	'New Wave'	MAsh
	'Nikki'	NEoE NLar
§	***okuyamae*** B&SWJ 10975	WCru
	'Opal'	CMHG
	Ostrich Plume	see *A.* 'Straussenfeder'
	'Paul Gaärder' (× *arendsii*)	CMHG
	'Peaches and Cream'	MMHG NBro NLar
	'Peter Barrow' (*glaberrima* hybrid)	GBin SRms
	'Pink Lightning'[PBR] (*simplicifolia* hybrid)	CWCL ECtt GAbr MBNS MBri NLar NOrc SMrm SPoG WFar
	Pink Pearl (× *arendsii*)	see *A.* 'Rosa Perle'
	'Poschka'	CCon NEoE
	'Professor van der Wielen' (*thunbergii* hybrid)	CCon CMHG EBee ECha GQue LRHS NHol NLar SPer SRms WWEG
	pumila	see *A. chinensis* var. *pumila*
	'Purple Rain'[PBR] (× *arendsii*)	CBod NSoo
	'Radius'	COtt MSCN NGdn NLar WHil WPnP
	'Red Baron'	CAby SPad
	Red Light	see *A.* 'Rotlicht'
	'Red Sentinel' (*japonica* hybrid)	CBcs CCon CHel COtt CWCL CWat EBee ELon EPfP EWoo GBin GMaP IBoy LRHS LSou LSun MAsh MBri MWat NBro NCGa NEoE NGdn NHol NLar NPCo SGSe WHil WOut
	'Red Thunder' **new**	EBee
	'Rheinland' (*japonica* hybrid) ♀H7	CBcs CMHG CWCL ELon GBin LRHS MBel MMuc NGdn NLar SCob SHil SRot WHoo WMnd WPnP
	'Rhythm and Blues'[PBR]	ECtt NLar
	rivularis	CMHG EBee SDix WCot
	- CC 5201	GKev
	- CC 6857 **new**	GKev
	- GWJ 9366	WCru
I	- 'Grandiflora'	GBin
§	- var. ***myriantha***	NBre
	- - BWJ 8076a	WCru
	- - SICH 757	CExl
	'Robinson's Pink'	NGdn
	'Rock and Roll'[PBR]	CBod MSCN WHil
§	'Rosa Perle' (× *arendsii*)	CHVG CMHG CSam NHol
§	× ***rosea*** 'Peach Blossom'	CBcs CMHG CPrp ELon GCra IBoy LRHS NBir NEoE NGdn SGbt SPoG SWvt WHoo WMnd WMoo WOut
	'Rosea' (*simplicifolia* hybrid)	NHol
	'Rot Straussenfeder' (× *arendsii*)	CBod GBin
§	'Rotlicht' (× *arendsii*)	CMHG CMac GBin LRHS NEoE NGdn NHol NLar WWFP
	'Salland'	EBee LRHS
	Salmon Queen	see *A.* 'Lachskönigin'
	'Salmonea' (*simplicifolia* hybrid)	CMHG
	'Saxosa'	see *A. glaberrima* var. *saxatilis*
	'Sheila Haxton' (*chinensis*)	LRHS NHar
	Showstar Group (× *arendsii*)	WHil WWtn
	simplicifolia ♀H5	LLWG SKHP WFar
	- 'Alba'	CMHG
	- Bronze Elegance	see *A.* 'Bronce Elegans'
	- 'Darwin's Snow Sprite'	CMac GBin MWts NHol NLar WFar
	- 'Jacqueline'	LSou MAsh NHol
*	- 'Nana Alba'	NEoE
	- 'Praecox Alba'	GBin WWEG
	- 'Rose of Cimarron'	NEoE
	- 'White Sensation'[PBR]	EBee GQue LRHS NLar
	'Snowdrift' (× *arendsii*)	CHid CMHG CWat GMaP IKil LBMP LLWG LRHS MBNS MBel MMuc MWat NBir NEoE NOrc SPer SWat WWEG
	'Solferino' (× *arendsii*)	CMHG
	'Spartan' (× *arendsii*)	see *A.* 'Rotlicht'
	'Spinell' (× *arendsii*)	CWCL GBuc NBre WMoo WPnP WWEG

	'Sprite' (*simplicifolia* hybrid) 🏆[H7]	Widely available
	'Stand and Deliver'[PBR]	ECtt
§	'Straussenfeder' (*thunbergii* hybrid) 🏆[H7]	CBod CMHG CMac CMos CTri EBee ECtt EPfP EPla GBin GMaP LBMP LRHS NBid NBir NBro NGdn NHol NLar NOrc SPer SPoG WCAu WMoo WWEG
	'Sugar Plum' (*simplicifolia* hybrid)	NGdn
	'Sugarberry'[PBR] (Short 'n' Sweet Series)	NLar
	'Superba'	see *A. chinensis* var. *taquetii* 'Superba'
	thunbergii	CExl
	- var. ***congesta*** B&SWJ 10961	WCru
	- var. ***formosa***	see *A. formosa*
	- var. ***hachijoensis***	EBee
	- - B&SWJ 5622	WCru
	- var. ***okuyamae***	see *A. okuyamae*
	- var. ***sikokumontanum*** B&SWJ 11164	WCru
	- var. ***terrestris*** B&SWJ 6125	WCru
	'To Have and To Hold'	LSou
	'Venus' (× *arendsii*)	ECtt GMaP LRHS MBNS MCot MMuc NGdn NHol NOrc SEND SPer SWat WFar WMoo
	'Vesuvius' (*japonica* hybrid)	CBcs NBro NLar
	virescens	see *A. rivularis* var. *myriantha*
	'Walküre' (× *arendsii*)	CMHG
	'Walter Bitner'	GBin LLWG LRHS MAsh MBNS NBre NHol SRGP
	'Washington' (*japonica* hybrid)	LAst LRHS NBre NGdn WPnP
§	'Weisse Gloria' (× *arendsii*)	CAby CHVG CMHG CMac CPrp ECha GBin GBuc LLWG LRHS NBro NDov NEgg NEoE NHol NOrc SCoo SHil SMrm WBor WCAu WMoo
	'White Diamond' (× *arendsii*) **new**	WFar
	White Gloria	see *A.* 'Weisse Gloria'
	'White Wings'[PBR] (*simplicifolia* hybrid)	NLar
	'William Reeves' (× *arendsii*)	CMHG NHol
	'Willie Buchanan' (*simplicifolia* hybrid)	CAby CBcs CBod CHid CMHG CPrp EHoe GAbr GBin GCrg GKev GMaP LBMP LRHS MWat NCGa NEgg NGdn NHar NHol SRms WAbe WCFE WFar WGwG WMoo WWEG
	Younique Carmine = 'Verscarmine'[PBR]	LSou MAsh MBri NPri
	Younique Cerise = 'Verscerise'[PBR] **new**	MAsh
	Younique Lilac = 'Verslilac'[PBR]	MAsh
	Younique Pink = 'Verspink'[PBR]	MAsh WHil
	Younique Red = 'Versred' **new**	MAsh
	Younique Silvery Pink = 'Versilverypink'[PBR]	LAst MAsh MBri NPri WFar
	Younique White = 'Verswhite'[PBR]	MAsh MBri NPri
	'Zuster Theresa' (× *arendsii*)	CHel CMHG CMos EBee ELon IBoy LRHS MBNS MNrw NBro

Astilboides (*Saxifragaceae*)

§	***tabularis***	Widely available

Astragalus (*Papilionaceae*)

angustifolius	XSen
canadensis	GJos LRHS
centralpinus	GJos
glycyphyllos	CArn GJos SPhx
looseri	WCot
lusitanicus	WCot
membranaceus	CArn

Astrantia ✿ (*Apiaceae*)

	'Atomic Sunburst'	GQue
	bavarica	GCal GKev MFie MSpe
	'Berendien Stam'	ECGP MAvo MFie
	'Bloody Mary'	CWCL EBee ELan GBuc MFie NGdn NLar
	'Buckland'	Widely available
	'Burgundy Manor'	SHar
	'Bury Court'	NDov
	carniolica	NEgg
	- ***major***	see *A. major*
	- 'Rubra'	CBcs EWoo GMaP MFie
	- 'Variegata'	see *A. major* 'Sunningdale Variegated'
	'Clear Pink'	NDov
	'Dark Shiny Eyes'	CExl CLAP ECtt GBin IBoy LLHF LPal LRHS MBNS MWat NGdn NLar NSti SPoG SWvt
	'Good Pink' **new**	LRHS
	'Hadspen Blood'	Widely available
	'Helen'	NLar
	helleborifolia	see *A. maxima*
	'Larch Cottage Clear Pink'	NLar
	'Larch Cottage Magic'	MAvo
	'Madeleine'	see *A. major* 'Madeleine van Bennekom'
§	***major***	Widely available
	- 'Abbey Road'[PBR]	CExl CKno CLAP CWCL ECtt EWoo GBin IBoy IKil LBMP LSou MFie NLar SCob SPoG SRkn SRms
I	- 'Alba'	CBcs CMHG CWCL EBee GKev IKil LPal LRHS MCot MFie MRav MSpe NBir NGdn NPer NPri SPer WMnd WMoo
	- 'Berdien' **new**	EBee
	- 'Best Pink' **new**	MAvo
	- subsp. ***biebersteinii***	LRHS MFie NBir
	- 'Bo-Ann'	CWCL IBoy MFie NLar WFar
	- 'Can Candy' **new**	MAvo
	- 'Celtic Star'	CSpe MFie SWvt
	- 'Claret'	Widely available
	- Cliff's form	MFie
	- 'Cottage Herbery'	MAvo
	- 'Dark Desire' **new**	NDov
	- 'Elaine's Pink' **new**	WHoo
	- 'Elmblut'	IMou MFie
	- 'Florence'[PBR]	CBct CNor CWGN ECtt EPfP GBin LRHS MBri MTis NCGa NDov NLar SMrm SPoG SWvt
	- 'Gill Richardson'	Widely available
	- 'Greenfingers'	EWes
	- 'Gwaun Valley'	WFar
	- subsp. ***involucrata***	LRHS MFie SWat
	- - 'Avondale' **new**	MAvo
	- - 'Barrister'	CSam GBuc MAvo MFie NLar

	- - 'Canneman'	EBee EWes LPla MFie NLar SMrm WCot
	- - 'Huntsman' new	MAvo
	- - 'Jumble Hole'	NDov
	- - 'Margery Fish'	see *A. major* subsp. *involucrata* 'Shaggy'
	- - 'Moira Reid'	CExl CLAP CSam ECtt ELan EPla GCal GMaP MAvo MCot MFie MNFA MRav
	- - 'Orlando'	CLAP MFie
§	- - 'Shaggy' ♀H7	Widely available
	- - 'Snape Cottage'	CDes
	- 'Jade Lady'	WFar
	- 'Jitse'	MAvo
	- 'Lars'	CExl CWCL ECtt ELan ELon EWoo GBin GCra IFoB LRHS MFie MHol MNrw MPro MWhi NBid NGdn NLar NSoo SPer SPoG SRms SRot SWvt WCAu
	- 'Lola'	CBcs EBee GBuc IBoy NLar
§	- 'Madeleine van Bennekom'	CLAP CNor EBee ECha GBin NCGa STPC
	- 'Penny's Pink'	CWCL EBee ELan EWoo MAvo MFie SHar WCot
	- 'Percy Picton'	MAvo
	- 'Pink Crush'	EBee LRHS
	- 'Pink Pride'	CWCL LSou MHol SHar WCAu
	- 'Pink Sensation'	EBee
	- 'Pink Surprise'	MAvo
	- 'Primadonna'	EPri GMaP MFie MHol NLar SPlb WMnd
	- 'Princesse Sturdza'	CWCL EBee LSou MBri
	- 'Reverse Sunningdale Variegated' (v)	LSou MFie
	- 'Rosa Lee'	CWCL MFie
	- var. ***rosea***	CBod CWCL EPfP GKev LRHS MFie MLHP MRav MSpe MWat MWhi NGdn SPer WCAu WFar WMoo
	- - George's form	CBct CKno CLAP CWCL ECtt MFie NCGa
	- 'Rosensinfonie'	CWCL EBee GMaP MFie NBro
§	- 'Rubra'	CBod CNec CSBt CSpe CWCL ELan EPfP GKin IBoy LAst LRHS MFie MGos MHol MPro MSpe NBir NChi NPer SCob SPad SPer SRms SWat WBor WCAu WCru WHal WHar WMoo
	- 'Ruby Cloud'	CHVG CHel CHid CWCL ECtt ELon EPri GBuc LBMP MFie MNrw NBro NGdn NSti SBod SGSe SMrm SRot WBor WMnd
	- 'Ruby Giant'	GKin
	- 'Ruby Glow'	MFie
	- 'Ruby Wedding'	Widely available
	- 'Silver Glow'	EBee ECtt
	- 'Star of Beauty' PBR	CLAP CMos CWCL ECtt ELan GBin IBoy LLWG LRHS LSou MBri MFie NCGa NGdn NLar NSti SCob SMrm SRms SRot SWvt WHlf
	- 'Star of Billion' PBR	CLAP CMos EBee ECtt ELan GBin IBoy LLWG LRHS LSun MBri MHol MTis NDov SCob SGol SWvt WCot WHlf
	- 'Star of Fire' PBR	EBee LLWG LRHS LSou MBel SCob SMrm SRot WFar
	- 'Star of Royals' PBR	CLAP ECtt GBin IPot LSou MBri SMrm WFar
	- 'Star of Summer'	CBod EBee LSou MSCN

	- 'Starburst'	EBee MFie
	- 'Stardust' new	EBee
	- 'Sue Barnes' (v)	GCal MFie
§	- 'Sunningdale Variegated' (v) ♀H7	Widely available
	- 'Titoki Point'	MFie WCot
	- 'Venice' PBR	CBct CLAP CMos CWCL CWGN ECtt GBuc IBoy IPot LRHS LSou LSun MAvo MNrw MSCN MTis MWhi NLar NSti SMrm SRms STPC SWvt WCAu
§	***maxima*** ♀H6	Widely available
	- 'Mark Fenwick'	MFie NBir
*	- ***rosea***	ECtt GQue MNrw MWhi NBir NGdn
	minor	EBee WCru
	'Moulin Rouge' PBR	Widely available
	'Old Warwickshire Pink' new	MAvo
	'Queen's Children'	GBuc SGol
	'Rainbow'	MFie NLar
	'Roma' PBR ♀H7	Widely available
	rubra	see *A. major* 'Rubra'
	'Ruby Star' PBR	CHel CLAP CMil EBee ECGP ECtt ELon GAbr GMaP IBoy IPot LRHS LSun MFie MHol MTis MWhi NDov NLar NSti SMrm SPer SWvt WBor WCot WHoo WMnd
	'Sheila's Red'	EAEE LRHS MBNS NDov
	'Snow Star' PBR	CWCL EBee EPfP EWoo GBin IKil LRHS MBNS MBri MFie NCGa NLar SHil SPoG
	'Star of Heaven'	NLar
	'Star of Passion' new	NLar
	'Star of Treasure' new	NLar WHlf
	'Stonehouse Perpetual'	CElw
	'Superstar' PBR	CAvo CBod CHel CMea CMil CUse EBee ECGP ECtt ELon EPfP GBin IBoy IPot LLWG LRHS MAvo MBNS MBel MHol MTis NDov NLar NPCo NSti SMrm SPer SWvt WCot WHoo
	'Warren Hills'	CLAP EBee GMaP MFie NLar
	'Washfield'	CWCL MTis NDov

Astrodaucus (*Apiaceae*)

orientalis	LEdu SPhx

Astrophytum (*Cactaceae*)

myriostigma ♀H2 new	SRms

Asyneuma (*Campanulaceae*)

canescens	LRHS LSou
limonifolium	ITim WAbe
- var. ***alpinum*** new	LLHF
pulvinatum	CPBP EPot WAbe

Asystasia (*Acanthaceae*)

bella	see *Mackaya bella*

Athamanta (*Apiaceae*)

cretensis	CArn
turbith	CSpe LEdu MNrw SBrt WPtf
vestina	SBrt SPhx

Athanasia (*Asteraceae*)

§	***parviflora***	SPlb SVen
	pinnata	SVen

Atherosperma (*Atherospermataceae*)

moschatum	CBcs CDoC CFil CHll SKHP

Athrotaxis (*Cupressaceae*)

cupressoides	CDoC CDul CKen WThu
laxifolia	CDoC CKen WThu
selaginoides	CDoC IGor

Athyrium ✿ (*Woodsiaceae*)

'Branford Beauty'	CCCN CLAP ISha LPal NLar WPGP
'Branford Rambler'	CLAP ISha
filix-femina ♀H7	Widely available
§ - subsp. ***angustum*** ♀H7	CBty CLAP ELan GBin LRHS MMoz MRav NGdn WMoo
- - f. ***rubellum*** 'Lady in Red' ♀H7	CBod CCCN CDes CKel CLAP CWCL EBee EFtx ESwi ISha LEdu LLWG LPal LRHS MBri MGos NLar SCob SPoG WMoo
- 'Congestum Minus' **new**	EFtx
- 'Corymbiferum'	SRms
- 'Crispum Grandiceps Kaye'	NGdn SRms
- Cristatum Group	CLAP EFer EFtx ELan MMoz NGdn SWat WFib
- - 'Angustato-cruciatum' **new**	ELan
- 'Dre's Dagger'	SPoG WFar
- 'Fieldii'	CLAP SRms
- 'Frizelliae' ♀H7	Widely available
- 'Frizelliae Capitatum'	CLAP WFib WPGP
- 'Frizelliae Cristatum'	EFtx SRms
- 'Grandiceps'	CLAP SRms
- 'Kaloxthrix Ruboid' **new**	EFtx
- 'Lady Victoria'	CLAP
- 'Lady-in-Lace' ♀H7	CLAP ITim LLHF LLWG MHol NMyG SMDP SMad WCot
- 'Minutissimum'	CBty CDes CLAP EBee ECha ELan ISha MMoz WCot
* - 'Nudicaule'	SRms
- Plumosum Group	CLAP MRav WFib XLum
- 'Plumosum Axminster'	CLAP EFer NLar WFar
- 'Plumosum Divaricatum'	SRms
- 'Plumosum Druery'	CLAP
- Red Stem	see *A. filix-femina* 'Rotstiel'
§ - 'Rotstiel'	CDTJ CLAP EBee LPal MMoz WMoo WPnP
- 'Setigerum Cristatum'	WFar
- 'Vernoniae' ♀H7	CBty CLAP ELan GAbr MMoz MRav NLar SGSe WGrf
- 'Vernoniae Cristatum'	CLAP WFib
- 'Victoriae'	CBty CCCN CDTJ CDes CWCL EFer ELan GMaP ISha LRHS NBid NGdn NLar NMyG SBod SGSe WMoo WWEG XLum
- 'Victoriae' seedling	MBri
- aff. 'Victoriae' **new**	CKel CTal
- Victoriae Group	see *A. filix-femina* subsp. *angustum*
'Ghost' ♀H6	CBty CCCN CDes CLAP EFtx ISha LRHS LSou MAvo MGos MPie MSCN NLar NSti WCot WFar WPat
goeringianum 'Pictum'	see *A. niponicum* var. *pictum*
niponicum	NMyG WHal
- f. ***metallicum***	see *A. niponicum* var. *pictum*
§ - var. ***pictum*** ♀H5	Widely available
- - 'Apple Court'	CBty CCCN EFtx ISha LRHS NLar
- - 'Burgundy Lace'	CBty CLAP EFtx LPal MCot MPnt NLar SMDP SMrm SPoG WCot WPat
* - - 'Cristatoflabellatum'	CDes CLAP EBee LRHS
- - 'Pewter Lace'	CBty MAvo NLar SMDP
- - 'Red Beauty'	CBcs CBty CDTJ CLAP ECha ELan EPfP GBin LRHS MMuc NLar SBod SEND SGol SHil SPoG SRkn WCot WMoo WPat WPnP
- - 'Regal Red'	CBty ISha LRHS NLos
- - 'Silver Falls' ♀H5	CBty CLAP EShb GEdr NMyG SMDP SMad SPoG WCot WPGP
- - 'Soul Mate'	CLAP
- - 'Ursula's Red'	CBcs CBty CLAP EFtx EShb LLWG LPal LRHS LSou MNrw MSCN NBid NBir NLar SMrm SPoG WCot WFar WPGP
- - 'Wildwood Twist'	CLAP NMyG WCot
'Ocean's Fury'	CAby CLAP EFtx GBin
okuboana	ISha
otophorum ♀H4	ISha MRav NBid SRms WPGP
- var. ***okanum*** ♀H5	Widely available
vidalii	CLAP EBee ISha LLWG LRHS LSou MMoz NLar NMyG WCot WFib XLum

Atractylodes (*Asteraceae*)

japonica	EFEx GEdr
macrocephala	CArn EFEx

Atragene see *Clematis*

Atriplex (*Amaranthaceae*)

canescens	NLar
cinerea	ECou
halimus	CArn CBcs CSde ECha ECre EHoe ELau EPPr MRav NLar SDix SLon SPer SPlb WCot
hortensis	ENfk
- var. ***rubra***	CArn CSpe ELan LSou MHer MNHC SHDw SIde SMrm SRms WJek

Atropa (*Solanaceae*)

acuminata	CArn
bella-donna	CArn GPoy SEND
mandragora	see *Mandragora officinarum*

Aubrieta (*Brassicaceae*)

sp.	MLHP MMuc
'Alba'	see *A.* 'Fiona'
albomarginata	see *A.* 'Argenteovariegata'
'Alix Brett'	CMea
'Ann Kendall'	ECtt
§ 'Argenteovariegata' (v) ♀H5	ECho ELan LRHS MJak
§ 'Aureovariegata' (v) ♀H5	CMea ECho ELan NPer XLum
(Axcent Series) 'Axcent Antique Magenta'	LRHS
- 'Axcent Antique Rose'	LRHS
- 'Axcent Blue with Eye'	LBuc LRHS
- 'Axcent Dark Red'	LRHS
- 'Axcent Deep Purple'	LBuc LRHS
- 'Axcent Lilac'	LRHS
- 'Axcent Violet with Eye'	LRHS
bicolour	CMea
Blaue Schönheit	see *A.* 'Blue Beauty'
'Blaumeise'	GCrg LRHS
§ 'Blue Beauty'	CBod CMea ECtt EPfP GBin MHol NLar WHoo
'Blue Whale'	CBod ECtt ELon GAbr SRms SRot SWvt
§ 'Bob Saunders' (d)	CFis CMea
'Bressingham Pink' (d) ♀H5	CMea ECtt ELan EPfP SPoG SRms

'Bressingham Red'	CUse ECtt ELan EPfP GCrg SPoG SRms
'Bubble Purple'	EPfP
canescens	CPBP XSen
- subsp. ***cilicica***	CTal
Cascade Series	CWCL GJos SPoG
- 'Blue Cascade'	MBNS SPlb SPoG SRms
- 'Lilac Cascade'	SPoG
- 'Purple Cascade'	CTri LBMP MAsh MBNS MJak SPlb SPoG SRms WRHF
- 'Red Cascade' ♀H5	CTri ECtt LBMP MBNS MJak SPlb SPoG
deltoidea	SVic XSen
- Variegata Group (v)	ECtt MHol NPri
- - 'Nana Variegata' (v)	CMea EPot
'Doctor Mules' ♀H5	ECtt SRms
'Doctor Mules Variegata' (v)	ECho ECtt EHoe ELan ELon EPfP LAst MAsh MHer NLar NWad SPoG SWvt WHoo
double pink-flowered (d)	CBod EPfP MHol
'Downers Variegata' (v)	ECtt EPot LSun NWad
'Elsa Lancaster'	NSla
§ 'Fiona'	ECtt EWoo MMuc
glabrescens	CMea CPBP WAbe
'Gloria'	CBod CMea ECtt EPot GAbr MHol NLar NSla SRot WBor WHoo WIce
'Gloriosa'	MAsh
'Golden Emperor'	MHer
'Golden King'	see *A.* 'Aureovariegata'
gracilis	CTal
- 'Kitte Rose'	ECtt LBuc LRHS
'Greencourt Purple' ♀H5	CFis ECho ELan MHer MWat
'Hamburger Stadtpark'	CWCL ECtt ELan EPfP EWoo GCrg SRot
'Kitte'	ECtt ELan EPfP GBin GCrg LRHS MHer NLar SPoG SRms
'Kitte Blue'	LBuc LRHS NPri WIce
'Kitte Purple'	CUse ELan
'Leichtlinii'	XLum
'Lime Variegated' (v) **new**	WIce
macedonica	EPot
pinardii	GKev XSen
'Pink Beauty'	ECtt WIce
'Purple Charm'	SRms
'Red Carpet'	ECtt ELan EPot MAsh MHer SRms
'Rose Queen'	CMea
Royal Series	MLHP
- 'Royal Blue'	EPfP MJak NEgg NLar SRms SRot WMoo XLum
- 'Royal Red'	EPfP SRms WMoo
- 'Royal Violet'	EPfP WMoo XLum
'Schofield's Double'	see *A.* 'Bob Saunders'
'Shobden' (v) **new**	WIce
'Silberrand'	ECha NSla
'Somerfield Silver'	ELan EPfP
'Somerford Lime' (v)	ECtt ELan EPfP LSou MHol SRms
'Swan Red' (v)	CBod ECtt EHoe ELon EPot LAst MAvo MHer MHol NEgg NLar NSla SRot WIce
thessala	CMea CPBP CTal
'Triumphante'	ECtt
'Valerie' (v)	ECtt EPot
'Westacre Gold'	ECtt
'Whitewell Gem'	WMoo XLum

Aucuba ✿ (*Garryaceae*)

chlorascens B&SWJ 11815 **new**	WCru
himalaica var. ***dolichophylla***	CFil
- - Og 95038 **new**	WCru
japonica	CAco CCVT CDul SCob SEWo WCru WFar
- 'Angelon'	CRos LRHS
- var. ***borealis*** (f) CWJ 12898 **new**	WCru
- 'Crassifolia' (m)	EBtc GBin SArc
- 'Crotonifolia' (f/v) ♀H5	Widely available
- 'Crotonifolia' (m/v)	CMac MAsh SGol SRms
- 'Dentata'	CHEx WCru
- 'February Star' (f/v)	SDix
- 'Gold Splash' (v)	WFar
- 'Golden King' (m/v) ♀H5	CDoC CMac ELan ELon EPfP LRHS MAsh MGos NLar NSoo SCob SGol SLim SPoG WFar
- 'Golden Spangles' (f/v)	CBcs CDoC EBee IVic LRHS NLar SWvt
- 'Goldstrike' (v)	LRHS MAsh SMad
- 'Hillieri' (f)	EBtc
- f. ***longifolia***	CMac NLar SArc SDix WCru
- - 'Longifolia' (f) **new**	MGos
- - 'Salicifolia' (f) ♀H5	ESwi MRav NLar SCob WCru
- 'Maculata' misapplied	see *A. japonica* 'Variegata'
- 'Marmorata'	CRos LRHS MBri MGos SHil
- 'Mr Goldstrike' (m/v)	EPfP LRHS
- Pepper Pot = 'Shilpot' (m/v) ♀H5	CHEx EPfP LRHS MAsh SLon SPoG WFar
- 'Pepperspot'PBR (m/v) **new**	CDoC WMoo
- 'Picturata' (m/v)	CDul CMac CSBt ELan ELon LRHS MAsh MGos NLar SEND SHil SPer WFar
- 'Rozannie' (f/m) ♀H5	CBcs CDoC CDul CEnd CMac CRos CSBt EAEE EBee ECrN ELan ELon EPfP IVic LRHS LSou MAsh MBlu MGos MRav NEgg NLar SCob SHil SLim SPer SPoG SWvt WFar WMoo
- 'Sulphurea Marginata' (f/v)	CBcs CMac COtt CTri EBee EPla ESwi LRHS NLar SPer WFar
§ - 'Variegata' (f/v)	Widely available
- - white-flowered, male (m/v) **new**	SGbt
omeiensis	CExl CFil
- B&SWJ 2864	WCru
- BWJ 8048	WCru
- L 614	CFil WPGP

Aulax (*Proteaceae*)

cancellata	SPlb

Aurinia (*Brassicaceae*)

§ ***saxatilis*** ♀H5	ECho EPfP MMuc NPri SPlb
- 'Argentea'	ECho
- 'Citrina' ♀H5	ECha ECtt MWat SRms
- 'Compacta'	CTri ECtt GJos WIce
- 'Dudley Nevill Variegated' (v)	ECha ECho ECtt ELon EWes GCrg MHer
- Gold Ball	see *A. saxatilis* 'Goldkugel'
- 'Gold Dust'	ECho NRya SRms
- 'Golden Queen'	CNor MHer
§ - 'Goldkugel'	ECho EPfP NPri SPoG WBor
- 'Variegata' (v)	NPri SPoG
sinuata 'Pebbles'	GJos

Austrocedrus (*Cupressaceae*)

§ ***chilensis***	CKen CMen IGor SBig SLim

Avena (*Poaceae*)

candida	see *Helictotrichon sempervirens*

Avenula see *Helictotrichon*

Averrhoa (*Oxalidaceae*)

carambola (F)	CCCN

avocado see *Persea americana*

Azalea see *Rhododendron*

Azara ✿ (*Salicaceae*)

sp.	NEgg
alpina	MGil
dentata	CBcs CHll CMac GGal WFar
- 'Variegata'	see *A. integrifolia* 'Variegata'
* ***integerrima***	GQui
integrifolia	CCCN MGil
- 'Uarie'	CCCN
§ - 'Variegata' (v)	LRHS
lanceolata	CBcs CDul CExl CPne CTri GBin GGal IDee LEdu WGrn
microphylla ♀H4	CBcs CDul CExl CHel CMac CTri EBee ELon EPfP EUJe GGal IVic LRHS MAsh MGil MGos MMuc NSoo SArc SEND SLim SPer SPlb SSpi WFar WPGP
* - 'Albovariegata' (v)	CTri
- 'Gold Edge' (v)	EPfP LRHS WFar
- 'Variegata' (v)	CBcs CDoC CExl CMac EBee EHoe EPfP GQui LBMP LRHS MAsh MGil MMuc MRav NLar SEND SLon SSpi WFar WPat
* ***patagonica***	MBlu
petiolaris	CTri LEdu MGil
serrata ♀H4	CBcs CDul CEnd CHel CTsd EPfP EShb EUJe GBin LRHS MGil MSCN NCGa NLar SDix SEND SGol SPer SRms SVen WBor WFar WHar WKif
- 'Maurice Mason'	EBee
uruguayensis	CCCN CExl EBtc GBin

Azorella (*Apiaceae*)

filamentosa	WAbe
glebaria misapplied	see *A. trifurcata*
glebaria A. Gray	see *Bolax gummifer*
gummifer	see *Bolax gummifer*
lycopodioides	WAbe
patagonica	WAbe
§ ***trifurcata***	CPar CSpe CTri ECho GAbr GCrg MMuc NBir SPlb WAbe
- 'Nana'	ECho GEdr MWat WThu XLum

Azorina (*Campanulaceae*)

§ ***vidalii***	SPlb

B

Babiana (*Iridaceae*)

angustifolia	ECho
'Blue Gem'	ECho
fragrans 'Porterville'	ECho
- 'Rawsonville'	ECho
patersoniae	SPlb
pygmaea	WCot
sambucina	NRog
stricta ♀H2	CCCN ECho SDeJ WHil
- Kew hybrids **new**	GKev
- 'Purple Star'	CExl ECho GKev NRog
- 'Tubergen's Blue'	ECho
tubulosa	NRog
villosa	ECho WCot
- 'Tulbagh'	ECho
* ***volubile*** **new**	NRog
'Zwanenburg's Glory'	CPrp ECho GKev WHil

Baccharis (*Asteraceae*)

halimifolia	CBcs ETwe GLin SEND
- 'Baccador'PBR **new**	SPoG
patagonica	LRHS MMuc SArc SEND SPhx SVen

Backhousia (*Myrtaceae*)

citriodora	CArn MHer

Bacopa (*Plantaginaceae*)

sp.	SWvt
'Snowflake'	see *Sutera cordata* 'Snowflake'

Baeckea (*Myrtaceae*)

gunniana	CExl
linifolia	SPlb
virgata	ECou SPlb

Baeometra (*Colchicaceae*)

uniflora 'Malmesbury'	ECho

Baimashania (*Brassicaceae*)

pulvinata **new**	WAbe

Balbisia (*Ledocarpaceae*)

peduncularis	CCCN

Baldellia (*Alismataceae*)

sp.	CBAq
ranunculoides	CRow EWay WMAq
- f. ***repens***	LLWG

Ballota (*Lamiaceae*)

sp.	COtt
acetabulosa	CArn CMHG ECha EWes WCot XSen
'All Hallow's Green'	see *Marrubium bourgaei* var. *bourgaei* 'All Hallows Green'
hirsuta	XSen
nigra	CArn GPoy MHer NMir SRms WHfH
§ - 'Archer's Variegated' (v)	MAvo
- 'Variegata'	see *B. nigra* 'Archer's Variegated'
pseudodictamnus ♀H4	CArn CBcs EBee ECha EHoe ELan EPfP ETwe EWoo GMaP LEdu LRHS MBel MCot MRav NPer NSti SCob SDix SEND SGSe SLon SPer WSHC XLum XSen
- B&M 8119	WCot
- from Crete	ECha
rupestris 'Frogswell Carolyn' (v)	IFro XSen

Balsamita see *Tanacetum*

Balsamorhiza (*Asteraceae*)

sagittata	ECho

Bambusa (*Poaceae*)

	glaucescens	see *B. multiplex*
§	***multiplex***	XBlo
	- 'Alphonso-Karrii'	ERod SBig
	- 'Elegans'	see *B. multiplex* 'Floribunda'
	- 'Fernleaf'	see *B. multiplex* 'Floribunda'
§	- 'Floribunda'	EShb XBlo
	- 'Golden Goddess'	XBlo
	- 'Silverstripe'	see *B. multiplex* 'Variegata'
§	- 'Variegata' (v)	XBlo
	- 'Wang Tsai'	see *B. multiplex* 'Floribunda'
	pubescens	see *Dendrocalamus strictus*
	ventricosa	SBig XBlo
	vulgaris	XBlo
	- 'Vittata'	ERod XBlo

banana see *Ensete*, *Musa*

Banksia (*Proteaceae*)

	aemula	MOWG
	canei	SPlb
	ericifolia	CDTJ CTre
	- var. ***ericifolia***	CCCN
	- var. ***macrantha***	SPlb
	grandis	CCCN CTre
	integrifolia	CCCN CDTJ CTre SPlb
	marginata	SPlb
	media	SPlb
	oblongifolia	SPlb
	paludosa	SPlb
	robur	CCCN SPlb
	serrata	SPlb
	speciosa	SPlb
	spinulosa	CTre
	- var. ***collina***	SPlb
	- var. ***spinulosa***	CBcs CCCN
	violacea	SPlb

Baptisia (*Papilionaceae*)

§	***alba***	EBee GBBs GBin MNrw
§	- var. ***macrophylla***	EWes LPla LRHS SDix SPhx
	australis ♀H7	Widely available
	- 'Caspian Blue'	CExl CWCL LEdu WSHC
	- 'Exaltata' ♀H7	WCot
	- var. ***minor***	SPhx WSHC
	- 'Nelson's Navy'	SMHy
	× ***bicolor*** 'Starlite' (Prairieblues Series)	CMos SKHP SMDP SPoG
§	***bracteata*** var. ***leucophaea***	LEdu LRHS LSou SPhx
	'Carolina Moonlight'	EWes IPot SKHP SMDP SPoG
	lactea	see *B. alba* var. *macrophylla*
	leucantha	see *B. alba* var. *macrophylla*
	megacarpa	SKHP
	pendula	see *B. alba*
	perfoliata new	EBee
	'Purple Smoke'	CAbP CAby CDes CExl CSpe ECtt EPPr GBuc LEdu LRHS MAvo MHol MNrw NSti SMHy SPad SPhx WAul WCAu WCot WPtf WRHF
	sphaerocarpa	EBee SPhx WCot
	tinctoria	CArn SPhx
	× ***variicolor*** 'Twilite' (Prairieblues Series)	CMos EBee EPfP EWes SKHP SMDP SPoG WNPC

Barbarea (*Brassicaceae*)

	praecox	see *B. verna*
	rupicola 'Sunnyola'	MMuc
§	***verna***	GPoy MHer SVic
	vulgaris 'Variegata' (v)	NBro WHer WMoo

Barleria (*Acanthaceae*)

	micans	CCCN
	repens	MOWG
	suberecta	see *Dicliptera sericea*

Barosma see *Agathosma*

Bartlettina (*Asteraceae*)

§	***sordida***	CCCN EUJe

Basella (*Basellaceae*)

	rubra	SHDw SPre

Bashania (*Poaceae*)

	KR 7613 new	MWht
§	***fargesii***	EPla ERod MMuc MRav MWht SEND
I	***qingchengshanensis***	EPla ERod MWht

basil see *Ocimum basilicum*

Bassia (*Amaranthaceae*)

	scoparia f. ***trichophylla***	CUse

Bauera (*Cunoniaceae*)

	rubioides	CTsd MOWG

Bauhinia (*Caesalpiniaceae*)

	alba hort.	see *B. variegata*
	galpinii	MOWG SPlb
*	***lutea***	CCCN
	natalensis	SPlb
	purpurea L.	CAco CCCN SPlb
	scandens	MOWG
	tomentosa	CCCN
§	***variegata***	CAco
	'White Lady'	CCCN
	yunnanensis	SBrt

Baumea see *Machaerina*

bay see *Laurus nobilis*

Beaucarnea (*Dracaenaceae*)

	recurvata ♀H1c	LPal SPlb

Beaufortia (*Myrtaceae*)

	elegans	SVen
	schaueri new	SVen
	sparsa	CTsd MOWG SVen
	squarrosa	SPlb

Beauverdia see *Leucocoryne*

Beckmannia (*Poaceae*)

	eruciformis	XLum

Bedfordia (*Asteraceae*)

	linearis	SPlb SVen

Beesia (*Ranunculaceae*)

	calthifolia	CBct CCon CDTJ CHid CMHG CPom CSpe CTal EBee EPfP GBBs IGor IMou LLHF MBel WCru WPGP
	- DJHC 98447	CDes CExl

	Name	Suppliers
	deltophylla	EWld WCot

Begonia ✿ (*Begoniaceae*)

	Name	Suppliers
	B&SWJ 2692 from Sikkim, India	WCot
	B&SWJ 10279	CHEx
	Chen Yi 5	WCot
	Chen Yi 7	WCot
	DJHC 580	WCot
	'Abel Carrière' (R)	WDib
	aconitifolia (C)	EShb
	albopicta (C)	EBak
	- 'Rosea' (C)	MOWG WDib
	'Albuquerque Midnight Sky' (R)	SBrm
	'Amazon Delta' (R)	SBrm
§	***annulata*** ♀H1b	ESwi WCru
	HWJK 2424	
	'Arctic Breeze'PBR (R)	SBrm
	'Argentea' (R)	EBak
	'Argenteo-guttata'	EShb
	'Axel Lange' (R)	SBrm
	'Aya' (C)	WDib
	'Baronessa'	SBrm
	'Beatrice Haddrell'	WDib
	(Belleconia Series)	ESwi
	Belleconia Apricot Blush = 'Innbellab'	
	- Belleconia Rose = 'Innbellro'PBR	ESwi
	- Belleconia Soft Orange = 'Imbellpea'	ESwi LAst
	'Benitochiba' (R) ♀H1b	CExl CHll CLAP ESwi EUJe LLWG LRHS LSou MAvo MHol NLar SGSe WCot WDib WGrn
	'Bethlehem Star'	WDib
§	'Bettina Rothschild' (R)	SBrm WDib
	'Blackberry Swirl' (R)	WDib
	'Blue Sky Pink' (Blue Sky Series)	LAst
	'Bokit'	WDib
	'Bokit' × ***imperialis***	WDib
	boliviensis (T)	CDoC ESwi GCal
	- 'Firecracker'	WDib
	Bonfire = 'Nzcone'PBR ♀H1b	EPfP LBuc SPoG
	'Bouton de Rose' (T)	SDeJ
	'Brown Twist'	WDib
	'Burgundy Velvet'	WDib
	'Burle Marx' ♀H1b	SDix WDib
	'Candy Floss'	WCru
	'Captain Nemo' (R)	SBrm
	carolineifolia ♀H1b	WDib
	'Casey Corwin' (R)	SBrm WDib
	cathayana **new**	GCal
	'Cathedral'	WDib
I	***chapaensis*** HWJ 642	WCru
	Cherry Bon Bon **new**	LBuc
	'China Curl' (R) ♀H1b	WDib
	chitoensis B&SWJ 1954	WCru
	chloroneura	WDib
	'Cleopatra' ♀H1b	WDib
	coccinea (C)	WDib
	'Connee Boswell' ♀H1b	CHll WDib
§	***corallina*** (C)	EBak
	cucullata (S)	SKHP
	- var. ***arenosicola*** (S)	CFil CSpe ECtt ESwi SEND SKHP WCot
	'Curly Fireflush' (R) ♀H1b	MSCN SBrm WDib
	'David Blais' (R) ♀H1b	WDib
	'Dawnal Meyer' (C)	WDib
I	'De Elegans'	WDib
	Devil Series (S)	NPri
	- 'Devil Red' (S)	LAst
	- 'Devil Rose' (S)	LAst
	- 'Devil White' (S)	LAst
	Devotion = 'Yadev'PBR (Million Kisses Series) ♀H1b	WGor
	'Dewdrop' (R) ♀H1b	WDib
	'Dibleys Pink Showers'PBR ♀H1b	WDib
	discolor	see *B. grandis* subsp. *evansiana*
	'Don Miller' (C)	WDib
	Dragon Wing Red = 'Bepared'PBR	EShb
	'Elda Haring' (R)	SBrm
	Elegance = 'Yagance'PBR (Million Kisses Series) ♀H1b	LSou WGor
	emeiensis	CSpe SGSe SKHP
	'Emerald Beauty' (R) ♀H1b	SBrm
	'Emerald Giant' (R)	WDib
	'Escargot' (R) ♀H1b	WDib
	'Etna' (R)	SBrm
	Fimbriata Group (T)	SDeJ
	'Fire Flush'	see *B.* 'Bettina Rothschild'
	'Fireworks' (R) ♀H1b	WDib
	'Flo'Belle Moseley' (C)	WDib
§	***foliosa*** var. ***miniata*** ♀H1b	CDoC CHll CSpe EBak MArl SDix WCot WDib
	- - pink-flowered	MOWG
	- - 'Rosea'	CDoC
	fuchsioides	see *B. foliosa* var. *miniata*
	'Glowing Embers'	LBuc SPoG
	gracilis (T) F&M 266	CFil
	- F&M 337	CFil
	grandis (T)	CPne XLum
§	- subsp. ***evansiana***	CAby CCon CHEx CHll CSpe CTal CTsd ELon EShb EUJe GCal LEdu LPla SBch SDix SEND SGSe SKHP SPlb WCot WCru WMoo
	- - B&SWJ 11188	WCru
	-.- var. ***alba*** hort. ♀H5	CAby CCon CDoC CFil CLAP CSpe CTal EPPr EShb ESwi EWld EWll GCal LEdu LPla LRHS NLos SBch SGSe SKHP SPoG SSpi WCot WMoo WPGP XLum
	- subsp. ***evansiana*** 'Claret Jug'	CDoC CExl CFil EBee ECtt ESwi WCot WGrn WPGP WWEG
	- - pink-flowered **new**	NLos
	- - 'Pink Parasol'	CLAP ESwi SMad WCru
	- - 'Simsii'	EBee
	- - 'Sublime'	LEdu WPGP
	- 'Sapporo'	CFil EBee EPPr ESwi GCal WCru
§	- subsp. ***sinensis*** (T)	EBee SGSe
I	- - 'Red Undies'	CLAP ESwi WCru
	aff. ***grandis*** subsp. ***sinensis*** (T)	SKHP
	- - BWJ 8133	WCru
	'Green Gold' (R) ♀H1b	SBrm WDib
	griffithii	see *B. annulata*
	'Gryphon'	EShb
	haageana hort. ex W. Watson	see *B. scharffii*
	hatacoa silver-leaved	EShb WDib
	Heaven Series (S)	LAst NPri
	'Helen Teupel' (R)	WDib
	'Hilo Holiday' (R) ♀H1b	WDib

Name	Suppliers
Honeymoon = 'Yamoon' (Million Kisses Series)	LAst
'Houston Fiesta' (R)	SBrm
(Illumination Series)	SCoo
'Illumination Apricot' (T/d)	
- 'Illumination Rose' (T/d)	SCoo
- 'Illumination Salmon Pink' (T/d)	SCoo
- 'Illumination White' (T/d)	SCoo
* ***illustris***	ECtt
'Inca Fire' PBR (R)	SBrm
'Indian Summer' PBR (R)	SBrm
× ***intermedia*** 'Bertinii' (T)	SDeJ
'Ironstone' (R) ♀H1b	SBrm
'La Paloma' (C)	WDib
Large-flowered Double Group (T/d)	SDeJ
'Lime Swirl'	WDib
'Limeade' ♀H1b	WDib
listada ♀H1b	WDib
'Little Brother Montgomery' ♀H1b	EShb SDix WDib
'Lois Burks' (C)	WDib
'Looking Glass' (C)	WDib
'Lucerna' (C)	EBak NLos
'Lucky Colours' (R)	SBrm
luxurians ♀H1b	CDoC CHEx CHll CSpe ESwi EUJe MNrw MPie SMad SPlb WCot WPGP
macduffieana	see *B. corallina*
maculata 'Wightii' (C)	CSpe WDib
'Magma' (R)	SBrm
'Maori Haze' PBR (R)	SBrm
Marginata Group (T)	SDeJ
'Marmaduke' ♀H1b	WCot WDib
'Marmorata' (T)	SDeJ
'Martin Johnson' (R) ♀H1b	WDib
masoniana ♀H1b	GCal WDib WSFF
'Merry Christmas' (R)	WDib
'Metallic Mist' PBR	CSpe ESwi LSou WGrn
'Midnight Magic' (R) ♀H1b	WDib
'Mikado' (R) ♀H1b	SBrm
Million Kisses Series	LBuc
'Mishmi Silver'	GCal WPGP
'Mr Kartuz' (R)	SBrm
'Munchkin' ♀H1b	WDib
'My Best Friend'	WDib
'Namur' (R) ♀H1b	WDib
Nonstop Series (T/d)	LAst SDeJ
'Organdy' (mixed)	LAst
'Pachea' (R)	SBrm
palmata	CDTJ CExl CHEx GCal SKHP
panchtharensis	CFil
- B&SWJ 2692 **new**	WCru
Passion = 'Yabos' (Million Kisses Series)	LSou
'Peardrop' PBR	SPoG
pedatifida	CCon SKHP
- DJHC 98473	WCru
Pendula Group (T)	SDeJ
'Picotee' (T)	CSut SDeJ
'Pink Champagne' (R) ♀H1b	WDib
I 'Pink Lady'	WCru
'Pink Pop' (R)	SBrm
'Pollux' ♀H1b	WDib
'Princess of Hanover' (R) ♀H1b	WDib
putii B&SWJ 7245	WCru
'Queen Olympus'	WDib
'Raspberry Swirl' (R)	WDib
ravenii (T)	CHEx SKHP
- B&SWJ 1954	GCal
'Razzmatazz' (R)	WDib
'Red Dragon' (R)	WDib
'Red Kiss' (R)	SBrm
'Red Robin' (R) ♀H1b	SBrm WDib
'Red Undies' (*grandis*)	see *B. grandis* subsp. *sinensis* 'Red Undies'
'Regal Minuet' (R) ♀H1b	SBrm WDib
rex (R)	SBrm
'Richard Galle'	LAst
'Ricinifolia'	GCal
'Rocheart' (R) ♀H1b	SBrm WDib
'Sal's Comet' (R) ♀H1b	WDib
'Sal's Moondust'	WDib
'Savannah Pink Parfait' (R)	SBrm
§ ***scharffii***	EBak EUJe SDix
'Scherzo'	WDib
serratipetala ♀H1b	EBak WDib
'Shamus'	WDib
* ***shepherdii***	WDib
sikkimensis	GCal
silletensis	GCal
subsp. ***mengyangensis***	
'Silver Cloud' (R) ♀H1b	WDib
'Silver Jewell' ♀H1b	WDib
'Silver Lace'	WDib
'Silver Splendor'	CLAP CSpe ECtt ESwi IBoy WCot WPGP
'Silver Spray' (R)	SBrm
sinensis	see *B. grandis* subsp. *sinensis*
sizemoreae	WDib
'Snow Storm'	WDib
* 'Snowcap' (C) ♀H1b	WDib
solananthera A. DC. ♀H1b	WDib
'Solid Silver' (R)	WDib
soli-mutata	WDib
sonderiana (T)	GCal
'Stained Glass'	WDib
(Summerwings Series)	ESwi
Summerwings Orange = 'Innbolora' PBR	
- Summerwings White = 'Innbolwhi' PBR	ESwi SMrm
sutherlandii (T) ♀H2	CCCN CDoC CExl CFil CPom EABi EBak EShb EWld LRHS NPer SAdn SBch SDix WCot WDib WPGP
- 'Papaya' (T)	CSpe
'Switzerland' (T)	SDeJ
taliensis	SKHP
- EDHCH 042	WCot WCru
- 'White-boned Demon'	SKHP
'Texastar'	WDib
'Thrush' (R)	SBrm
'Thurstonii' ♀H1b	EShb
'Tiger Paws' ♀H1b	EShb
'Tim Anderson' (R)	SBrm
* ***tripartita*** (T)	WDib
'Tuscan Bonfire' (R) **new**	SBrm
'Two Face'	WDib
'Tye Dye'	GCal WPGP
venosa	CDoC
'Vesuvius' (R)	WDib
'Vista' (R)	SBrm
'Wavy Green'	GCal WPGP
'Wild Swan'	WCru

Belamcanda see *Iris*

chinensis — see *Iris domestica*

Bellevalia (*Asparagaceae*)

atroviolacea — ECho
brevipedicellata — ECho
'Cream Pearl' — ECho WCot
desertorum JCA 0.227.690 — WCot
dubia — CDes CPom EBee ECho GCal WCot
forniculata — WCot
hyacinthoides — ECho WCot
mauretanica — ECho
§ ***paradoxa*** — CAby CHid EBee ECho ERCP MNrw SDeJ WCot
- white-flowered — ECho
pycnantha misapplied — see *B. paradoxa*
pycnantha ambig. — EPfP EWTr
- 'Green Pearl' — ECho SDeJ
romana — CPom EBee ECho ERCP GKev SDeJ WCot
sessiliflora — ECho
tabriziana — CDes ECho WCot
trifoliata — ECho
webbiana — ECho

Bellis (*Asteraceae*)

§ ***caerulescens*** — GAbr WWFP
perennis — CArn
- 'Alice' — GAbr WCot
- 'Big Bob' (d) **new** — WCot
- 'Dresden China' — EWes
- 'Galaxy White' (Galaxy Series) — EPfP
- Hen and Chickens — see *B. perennis* 'Prolifera' single-flowered
- 'Low and Behold' **new** — CNat
- old strain — WCot
§ - 'Prolifera' single-flowered — GAbr WCot
- 'Rusher Rose' — EPfP
- 'Single Blue' — see *B. caerulescens*
- 'The Pearl' — GAbr WCot
rotundifolia 'Caerulescens' — see *B. caerulescens*
sylvestris — CArn WCot

Belloa (*Asteraceae*)

chilensis — SPlb

Beloperone see *Justicia*

guttata — see *Justicia brandegeeana*

Bensoniella (*Saxifragaceae*)

oregona — CExl

Benthamiella (*Solanaceae*)

nordenskjoldii — WAbe
patagonica — WAbe
- F&W 9345 — ITim WAbe
- white-flowered — WAbe
- yellow-flowered — WAbe

Berberidopsis (*Berberidopsidaceae*)

corallina — CBcs CDoC CHel CMac CTri CWSG ELan EPfP GGal IArd IDee IVic LBMP LRHS MGos MOWG NLar SLim SPer SPoG SWvt WHar WSHC

Berberis ✿ (*Berberidaceae*)

CC 4730 — CExl
aggregata — MJak MMuc NBir SEND SPer SRms
amurensis — WPat
- var. ***latifolia*** B&SWJ 8539 — WCru
aquifolium — see *Mahonia aquifolium*
- 'Fascicularis' — see *Mahonia* × *wagneri* 'Pinnacle'
aristata ambig. — CArn
asiatica — CExl GPoy
'Baby Bear' — CJun
bealei — see *Mahonia japonica* Bealei Group
'Boughton Red' — WHor
× ***bristolensis*** — SRms
buxifolia 'Nana' misapplied — see *B. microphylla* 'Pygmaea'
calliantha — WFar
candidula C.K. Schneid. — CDul EBee EPfP LRHS MSwo NLar SLon SPer
- 'Jytte' — see *B.* 'Jytte'
× ***carminea*** 'Pirate King' — CHel CSBt EBee EPfP LRHS MAsh SPoG SWvt
darwinii 🏆H5 — Widely available
I - 'Compacta' — CChe CDoC CMac CRos ELan EPfP LAst LBuc LRHS MAsh NEgg NLar NSoo SHil SLim SPoG WCot
deinacantha AC 1010 — MSnd
dictyophylla — EBee ELan EPfP LRHS MGos MMuc NLar SKHP SLon SPer SPoG SSpi WSHC
dulcis 'Nana' — see *B. microphylla* 'Pygmaea'
dumicola — MSnd
empetrifolia — LEdu
× ***frikartii*** 'Amstelveen' 🏆H5 — CCVT CDoC ECrN ELan EPfP LAst LRHS MBNS MMuc MRav NLar SCob SEND WMoo
- 'Telstar' — EBtc EWTr MRav NEoE NLar SCob WMoo
gagnepainii misapplied — see *B. gagnepainii* var. *lanceifolia*
gagnepainii C.K. Schneid. — CDul CMac
§ - var. ***lanceifolia*** — CTri EBee EPla MGos MMuc NWea SEND SGol WHar
- - 'Fernspray' — EPfP EPla MRav SRms
- 'Purpurea' — see *B.* × *interposita* 'Wallich's Purple'
'Georgei' 🏆H5 — EPfP GQui LRHS WPat
'Goldilocks' — CJun EBee EPfP MBlu MMuc
goudotii B&SWJ 10769 — WCru
haematocarpa **new** — SIgm
heterophylla — GKev
× ***hybridogagnepainii*** 'Chenault' — ELan
- 'Robin Hood' — NEgg
hypokerina — CMac
insignis — GCal IDee
- subsp. ***insignis*** var. ***insignis*** — ELon LLHF WPat
- - B&SWJ 2432 — WCru
§ × ***interposita*** 'Wallich's Purple' — CCVT EPfP MRav MSwo SPer WMoo
jamesiana — LLHF MSnd WCot WPat
julianae — CAco CBcs CDul CMac ELan EPfP MGos MJak MMuc MSwo NEgg NHed NWea SEND SGol SPer SRms SWvt WFar WHar WSHC
§ 'Jytte' — EBee
koreana — EPfP NLar
- 'Rubin' — CAgr

Plant	Suppliers
'Little Favourite'	see *B. thunbergii* f. *atropurpurea* 'Atropurpurea Nana'
× ***lologensis*** 'Apricot Queen' 🏆H5	CBcs CMac EBee EPfP GBin LRHS MAsh MGos NLar SPer SPoG WPat
- 'Mystery Fire'	COtt ETwe IArd MAsh MBri MGos MJak NEgg NLar SGol SWvt WHar WMoo
- 'Stapehill'	CMac ELan EPfP LRHS MAsh
× ***media*** 'Dual Jewel'	NLar
- Park Jewel	see *B.* × *media* 'Parkjuweel'
§ - 'Parkjuweel'	CBcs CMac IArd MRav SRms WFar WMoo
- 'Red Jewel' 🏆H5	CDoC CMac ECrN EMil EPfP LRHS MAsh MBri MGos MMuc MRav NEgg SCob SEND SPer SPoG WCFE WFar WMoo
× ***mentorensis*** **new**	WCFE
microphylla	EPfP WCFE WFar
§ - 'Pygmaea'	CBcs CSBt EBee ELan EMil EPfP LRHS MAsh MGos MMuc MRav SCob SLim SPer
mitifolia	NLar
montana	WPGP WPat
morrisonensis	GBin
× ***ottawensis*** 'Auricoma'	SGol SWvt
- f. ***purpurea***	CCVT CMac LRHS WHar
§ - - 'Silver Miles' (v)	EHoe MRav NLar WFar WHar WPat
§ - - 'Superba'	Widely available
§ ***panlanensis***	LEdu
- 'Cally Rose'	GCal
poiretii	CExl
polyantha var. ***polyantha***	CTri
'Red Tears'	MMHG MRav NLar SPer WFar WMoo WPat
× ***rubrostilla*** 'Cherry Ripe'	CMac
- 'Wisley'	LRHS
sanguinea misapplied	see *B. panlanensis*
sieboldii	ELon LLHF MAsh MRav WCFE WPat
§ ***soulieana***	EPfP LRHS NWea
stenophylla Hance	see *B. soulieana*
× ***stenophylla*** Lindl. 🏆H5	CCVT CDoC CDul CSBt CTri EBee EPfP LBuc MBri MMuc MRav NWea SEND SGol SPer WFar WHar WMoo
- 'Autumnalis'	NEgg
- 'Claret Cascade'	MRav NLar SPer
- 'Compacta' **new**	WFar
- 'Corallina Compacta' 🏆H5	CHel CMac CMea ECho ELan EPfP EPot LRHS MAsh MHer SCob SIgm SPoG SRms WPat WThu
- 'Crawley Gem'	GBin NLar
- 'Etna'	ELan LRHS MAsh SCoo SPoG
- 'Irwinii'	CMac LRHS
- 'Nana'	LRHS SRms
- 'Pink Pearl' (v)	CMHG
subacuminata FMWJ 13290 **new**	WCru
- NJM 09.165	WPGP
taliensis	CExl
temolaica 🏆H5	CJun EBtc EPfP EWes MAsh MGos MSnd NLar NWea SMad SSta WCFE WPGP WPat
thunbergii	CBcs CDoC CDul CMac CNec EPfP LBuc NHed NLar NWea SCob SPer SWvt WFar WMou
- f. ***atropurpurea***	CAco CBcs CCVT CMac CRos CSBt CTri EAEE EBee ELan EPfP LBuc MGos MRav MSwo NEgg NLar NWea SCob SGol SPer SPlb SRms WHar WMoo WMou
- - 'Admiration'PBR 🏆H7	CBcs CDoC CSBt EBee ELan ELon EPfP EPla LBMP LBuc LLHF LRHS LSou LSqu MAsh MBri MGos MJak MMHG NEgg NHol NLar SCoo SLim SLon SPer SPoG SWvt WPat
§ - - 'Atropurpurea Nana' 🏆H7	Widely available
- - 'Bagatelle'	CDoC ELan EPfP EPot IArd IVic LAst LRHS MAsh MBri MGos MRav NLar SCob SLim SPer SPoG SWvt WCFE WHar WMoo WPat
- - 'Concorde' 🏆H7	EPfP LRHS
- - 'Dart's Red Lady' 🏆H7	CExl CRos CSBt EHoe ELan EPfP LRHS MAsh NLar SCob SLim SPer SPoG SWvt WFar WPat
- - 'Golden Ring' (v) 🏆H7	CAco CBcs CChe CDoC CDul CMac EHoe ELan EPfP LBMP LRHS MAsh MGos MRav NEgg SGbt SPer SPoG SWvt WFar WMoo WPat
- - 'Harlequin' (v) 🏆H7	CBcs CChe CDoC COtt CRos ELan EPfP LRHS MAsh MBri MGos NEgg NLar SEle SGol SHil SPer SPoG SRms SWvt WFar WHar WPat
- - 'Helmond Pillar'	Widely available
- - 'Pink Queen' (v)	CDul COtt EAEE ELan EPfP EWTr LRHS MAsh NLar WFar WPat
- - 'Red Chief'	CBcs CMac COtt CRos EHoe ELan EPfP LRHS MAsh MGos MJak MSwo NEgg SCob SGol SHil SLim SLon SPer SPoG SRms SWvt WFar WHar WMoo WPat
- - 'Red Pillar'	CChe CDoC CMac CRos EHoe ELan EPfP IVic LAst LRHS MAsh MBri MGos MWat NEgg SHil SWvt WPat
- - 'Red Rocket'	EBee ELan EPfP LRHS MPkF NEgg NLar SCob SCoo SPer WMoo
- - 'Rose Glow' (v) 🏆H7	Widely available
- - 'Rosy Rocket'PBR (v)	CWGN EBee ECrN ELan EPfP LRHS MAsh MRav NHol SPer
- 'Atropurpurea Superba'	see *B.* × *ottawensis* f. *purpurea* 'Superba'
- 'Aurea'	CBcs CDoC CDul CMac EHoe ELan EPfP EPot LBMP LRHS MBlu MGos MRav MWat NLar SCob SLim SPlb SRms SSpi SWvt WMoo
- Bonanza Gold = 'Bogozam'PBR	CBcs CDoC CMac EBee ELan EPfP LRHS MAsh MRav NLar SCob SIgm SLim SPer WPat
- 'Carpetbagger'	WHar
- 'Crimson Pygmy'	see *B. thunbergii* f. *atropurpurea* 'Atropurpurea Nana'
- 'Diabolic'	CRos LBuc LRHS MAsh MGos NHol SPer SPoG WGrn
- 'Erecta'	CMac EPfP MRav SPer WCFE
- 'Fireball'PBR 🏆H7	EPfP EPla LRHS
- 'Golden Rocket'PBR	CRos ELan EPfP EPla LLHF LRHS MAsh MGos MJak MPkF MRav MWat NEgg SCoo SPer SPoG WFar
- 'Golden Torch'	CNec CRos CSBt EBee ELan EPfP EPla LRHS MAsh MBri MRav NEgg NHol SHil SLim SWvt WPat
- 'Green Carpet'	CDul CMac LRHS MBlu NLar SGol SPoG WFar
- 'Green Mantle'	see *B. thunbergii* 'Kelleriis'
- 'Green Marble'	see *B. thunbergii* 'Kelleriis'
- 'Green Ornament'	NHol

§ - 'Kelleriis' (v) LRHS MRav NLar SLon
- 'Kobold' CMac EPfP LRHS MAsh MGos NEgg NLar SCob SLim SPer SPoG WMoo
- 'Maria'PBR ♀H7 CWGN EBee ELon GBin LLHF LRHS LSou MBri MGos MJak MPkF NLar NPri NSoo SCob SHil SPoG WGrn WHar WMoo
- 'Minor' new SRms
- 'Orange Rocket'PBR CBod CRos ELan EPfP EPla LRHS MAsh MPkF MRav MWat NEgg NHol SCoo SEle SHil SPer SPoG WFar WPat
- 'Pink Attraction' (v) NLar
- 'Pow-wow' CDoC COtt EBee ELan LRHS MAsh MGos NLar SCoo SEle SLim SPoG SWvt WPat
- 'Redtorch'PBR MMHG
- 'Silver Mile' see *B. ottawensis* f. *purpurea* 'Silver Miles'
- 'Somerset' CMac
- 'Starburst'PBR (v) CBcs CDoC CDul COtt CRos CSBt EPfP LRHS MAsh MBri MGos MPkF MWat NEgg NHol NPri SCoo SHil SLim SLon SPoG SRms SWvt
- 'Tiny Gold'PBR ELan EPla GBin LAst LBuc LRHS LSou MAsh MGos NLar SLim SLon SWvt WFar
* - 'Tricolor' (v) CMac MRav WFar WPat
trigona 'Orange King' CBcs CMac COtt CTri ELan EPfP LRHS MAsh MGos NEgg NLar SPer SPoG WHar WPat
valdiviana ♀H4 CBcs CExl CHel CJun CMHG EBee EPfP IArd IDee SKHP SMad SSpi WPGP WPat
verruculosa ♀H5 CBcs CDul EPfP EWTr LRHS MGos NLar NWea SCob SPer SRms SWvt WFar
- 'Hard's Rob' NLar
aff. ***verticillata*** B&SWJ 10672 WCru
virescens B&SWJ 2646D WCru
vulgaris CArn CNat GPoy MCoo NWea
- 'Wiltshire Wonder' (v) CNat
wilsoniae CBcs CDul CMac CTri ECre ELan EPfP MMuc NLar NWea SCob SEND SPer SRms WFar
- blue-leaved MAsh WFar
- var. ***guhtzunica*** EWes
xanthoclada NJM 11.007 new WPGP

Berchemia (*Rhamnaceae*)

racemosa NLar WSHC

bergamot see *Citrus* × *limon* Bergamot Group

Bergenia ✿ (*Saxifragaceae*)

'Abendglocken' CMac ECGP ECha ECtt EPfP GQue NSti WCot
§ 'Abendglut' Widely available
'Admiral' CBct ECha MLHP MNFA WCot
afghanica XLum
* ***agavifolia*** CBct XLum
'Andrea' WCot
'Angel Kiss' (Dragonfly Series) new WCot
'Apple Blossom' new EPfP LRHS
'Apple Court White' CBct
'Autumn Magic' CBct ELon EPfP GQue LAst LRHS LSou NPri
'Baby Doll' Widely available
'Bach' CBct CHel CUse EBee ECtt EPfP GEdr GQue LRHS LSou LSun MCot MNFA NLar NPCo NSti NWad SCob WCAu WCot WHil
§ 'Ballawley' clonal ECha GCal IBlr IGor IMou LRHS MLHP MRav NEgg WCot WMnd WWEG XLum
- seed-raised see *B.* Ballawley hybrids
'Ballawley Guardsman' CBct
§ Ballawley hybrids CMac SDix
'Bartók' CBct CDes CLAP CUse ECtt ESwi GQue IKil LPla NLar WCot WRHF
beesiana see *B. purpurascens*
'Beethoven' CBct ECha EPla GCra IGor MRav NBir WCot WPGP
Bell Tower see *B.* 'Glockenturm'
'Biedermeier' ♀H7 ECha
'Bizet' CBct XLum
'Borodin' CBct
'Brahms' CBct WCot
'Bressingham Beauty' CHel
'Bressingham Bountiful' CBct
'Bressingham Ruby'PBR CBct CBod CLAP EBee ECha ECtt ELon IPot LBMP LPal LRHS MBel MGos MHol MRav NBir NEgg SCob SGol SWvt WCot WHil WPGP
'Bressingham Salmon' CBct EBee ECtt ELan ELon GMaP MRav NLar SRms WCot WMnd
'Bressingham White' ♀H6 Widely available
'Britten' ♀H7 CBct IMou WCot
ciliata CBct CHEx CLAP CMac CTal CTca ECha EPri EShb EUJe GCra GEdr LEdu LRHS MLHP MRav NHol NLar SDix SGSe SPer WKif WPGP WSHC XLum
- 'Dumbo' new GBin
- f. ***ligulata*** see *B. pacumbis*
- 'Patricia Furness' CLAP
- 'Wilton' CBct CDes CLAP CTal MAvo WCot WSHC WWEG
ciliata × ***crassifolia*** see *B.* × *schmidtii*
'Claire Maxine' ♀H7 CBct CLAP CUse EBee ECtt GBin GCal LPla MPie NLar NWad SHar WCAu WCot
cordifolia Widely available
- 'Flore Pleno' CBct
- 'Jelle' CBct EBee WCAu
- 'Lunar Glow' CBct EBee ECha ECtt ELon EPfP ESwi EUJe LSou MBri MGos NCGa NLar NPri SPoG SRms WHil
- 'Purpurea' CBcs CDoC CMac CWCL EAEE EBee ECha ECrN ELan EPfP LBuc LRHS MLHP MRav NBir SCob SMrm SPer SRms SWvt XLum
- 'Rosa Schwester' CBct ECha
- 'Rosa Zeiten' ♀H7 CBct GBin IMou
- 'Rose' LRHS
- 'Tubby Andrews' (v) CBct CMac EBee EShb LEdu LRHS MAvo MBel MBrN NEgg NEoE NLar SRms WHrl WWEG
- 'Vinterglöd' EAEE EBee ELan ELon EPfP GMaP GQue IFoB LAst LRHS LSun MWat NGdn NLar SWvt WPnP XLum
crassifolia EPla GKev SRms WWEG XLum
- DF 90028 CBct GBin

- 'Autumn Red' CBct ECha WWEG
- 'Orbicularis' see *B.* × *schmidtii*
I - var. ***pacifica*** XLum
- - 'Cally Gem' EBee GCal
* ***cyanea*** CLAP WCot
'David' CBct ECha EWes WWEG
'Delbees' see *B.* 'Ballawley' clonal
'Doppelgänger' EBee
'Dragonfly Angel Kiss' **new** GBin
'Dragonfly Sakura' **new** GBin
'Eden's Dark Margin' CBct CBod CDoC CUse ECtt ELon GBin GEdr GQue IKil LRHS LSou MBri MNrw NEoE NLar NMyG SPoG WCot WHil WHoo
'Eden's Magic Giant' ♀H7 CAbP CBct CCon CUse ECGP ECtt ELon GBin IKil LPla LRHS MBNS MNrw MPie NLar NPCo SPoG SRms WCot
emeiensis CBct CDes CLAP CTal GCal IGor IMou LEdu SDix WCot WPGP
- hybrid MWat
'Eric Smith' ♀H7 CBct ECha GCal GCra MBri MNFA WMnd
'Eroica' ♀H7 CAby CBct CSpe CWld EBee ECha ECtt ELan ELon EPfP EWoo GBin IBoy LRHS LSou MBri MMuc MRav NLar NSti SCob SEND SPer SWvt WHoo WMnd WPtf
'Evening Glow' see *B.* 'Abendglut'
§ 'Glockenturm' CBct NEgg
'Goldfisch' EBee GBin
'Harzkristall' CBct CDoC GBin LRHS SPoG STPC SWvt
'Hellen Dillon' see *B. purpurascens* 'Irish Crimson'
'Ice Queen' CBct CMil CUse GBin LLHF WCot
'Jo Watanabe' CBct EPla MRav
'Kashmir' XLum
'Lambrook' see *B.* 'Margery Fish'
§ 'Margery Fish' CBct CFis ECha SPer
milesii see *B. stracheyi*
§ 'Morgenröte' ♀H6 CBcs CBct CBod CMac ECha ELon EPfP GMaP LRHS MGos MNFA MRav NHol NLar NSti SCob SRms SWvt WCFE WCot WWEG
'Morning Light' ECtt ELon NEoE
Morning Red see *B.* 'Morgenröte'
'Mrs Crawford' ECha
'Oeschberg' CBct GBin GCal
'Opal' CBct EBee GBin
'Overture' Widely available
§ ***pacumbis*** CHEx CLAP EBee GBin GCal NBid NSti
- B&SWJ 2693 WCru
- CC 1793 SBch WCot
- CC 3616 CBct CDes WCot WPGP
'Perfect' WMnd
'Pink Dragonfly' CMac ECtt ELon EPfP GBin LRHS NLar SWvt WCAu WCot
'Pink Frostwork' ECtt WCot
'Pink Ice' CBct CDes
'Pinneberg' CBct GBin
'Pugsley's Pink' ♀H7 CBct
§ ***purpurascens*** ♀H5 CMac EBee EPfP GMaP IGor LBMP SPer WWEG
- SDR 4548 GKev
- var. ***delavayi*** ♀H5 EBee LRHS NLar SRms
§ - 'Irish Crimson' ♀H7 CBct CDes ECha WCot
aff. ***purpurascens*** NGdn
- ACE 2175 WCot
'Purpurglocken' EBee ECtt GCal WCAu
'Red Beauty' EHoe EPfP IBoy LRHS MSnd
'Red Rush' EBee
'Rietheim' CBct EBee GBin
'Rosi Klose' CBct CLAP EBee ECha ECtt EHoe ELon EWes EWll GBin GCra LRHS MNFA MRav NGdn WCot WGwG WWEG
'Rosi Ruffles' EBee MBNS
'Rotblum' CBct CNec ECtt EHoe ELon EPfP GMaP LEdu MSCN NBir NGdn NOrc SCob SHar WCAu WHar WWEG
§ × ***schmidtii*** CBct CMac GBin MRav NBir NLar WCot WWEG
'Schneekissen' CBct CBod CMac CUse ECGP ECtt EPri LBMP MCot MRav WCAu
§ 'Schneekoenigin' CBct ECha GBin GCal MRav SWvt
§ 'Silberlicht' ♀H6 Widely available
Silverlight see *B.* 'Silberlicht'
'Simply Sweet' WCot
Snow Queen see *B.* 'Schneekoenigin'
§ ***stracheyi*** CBct CCon CExl ECha GBin GCal MLHP NBid NLar SDix WCot WFar WWEG
- CC 4609 EBee
- Alba Group ECha GCal SMHy WPGP WWEG
'Sunningdale' ♀H7 CBcs CBct CBod CMac ECha ELan EPfP GCra GMaP LRHS MRav NBir NGdn SPer SWvt WCAu WMnd WWEG
tianquanensis EBee
'Tim' EBee
'Walter Kienli' EBee GBin
Winter Fairy Tales see *B.* 'Wintermärchen'
§ 'Wintermärchen' ♀H7 CBct CBod CChe ECha ECtt ELan ELon EPfP EPla EShb GBin GCra LAst LRHS MLHP MMuc MRav NEoE NHol SEND SWvt WCAu WCot WWEG

Bergeranthus (*Aizoaceae*)

multiceps SChr

Berkheya (*Asteraceae*)

macrocephala SPlb
multijuga CSpe EWld LRHS SBHP
- 'Golden Spike' CBod MPro
purpurea CAby CBcs CSpe EAJP ELon EPfP EWTr IBoy LEdu LRHS MHol MMuc MNrw MPie MSpe SMrm SPlb WCot WHer WKif WMnd WSHC
- 'Silver Spike' CBod EAEE EPfP GBin LBMP MPro NGdn
- 'Zulu Warrior' CMac NGBl SBHP SRkn

Berlandiera (*Asteraceae*)

lyrata CArn MSCN

Berula (*Apiaceae*)

erecta NPer

Berzelia (*Bruniaceae*)

galpinii SPlb

Beschorneria (*Asparagaceae*)

albiflora CFil CSpe EBee WCot

calcicola WCot
'Red Bells' **new** WCot
rigida WCot
septentrionalis CAbP CAby CCon CDTJ CDoC CFil CHEx CSpe ESwi IBoy LRHS LSou LSun MBNS MHol NLos SEND SPad WCot WGrn
– variegated (v) **new** WCot
septentrionalis* × *yuccoides CFil CHll WPGP
tubiflora CDTJ CFil CHEx
wrightii CFil WCot
yuccoides 🏆H3 CAbb CBcs CExl CFil CHEx CPne ESwi IDee LEdu SArc SEND SPlb
– subsp. ***dekosteriana*** CFil
– 'Quicksilver' CBcs CCCN CDoC CEnd CExl CKno CSBt ELan EPfP EUJe IVic LRHS MBri NSoo SLim SSpi WGrn WPGP

Bessera (*Asparagaceae*)

elegans CAby CAvo CCon EBee ECho EPot GKev LAma MHer SDeJ

Beta (*Amaranthaceae*)

vulgaris SHDw SVic WHer
– 'Bull's Blood' CSpe WJek
– subsp. ***cicla*** SVic
var. ***flavescens*** Bright Lights 🏆H3
– – – 'Rhubarb Chard' 🏆H3 WJek
– subsp. ***maritima*** CAgr

Betonica see *Stachys*

Betula ✿ (*Betulaceae*)

alba L. see *B. pendula*, *B. pubescens*
albosinensis misapplied see *B. utilis*
albosinensis Burkill CLnd CMCN EBee EPfP
– W 4106 CSto
– from Gansu, China CSto
– 'Bowling Green' CExl CJun MBlu WPGP
§ – 'China Rose' 🏆H6 WPGP
– 'China Ruby' K. Ashburner see *B. albosinensis* 'China Rose'
– 'China Ruby' ambig. CDul CJun EBee EPfP SSpi
– 'China Ruby' B. Humphrey 🏆H6 WHCr
– 'Chinese Garden' CJun WPGP
– clone F see *B. albosinensis* 'Ness'
– 'Fascination' CCVT CMCN EBee IDee MBlu MGos NLar SKHP WHar WMou
– hybrid **new** CDul
– 'K. Ashburner' CJun CTho
§ – 'Ness' CJun CTho
– 'Pink Champagne' CJun CSto EPfP WPGP
– 'Red Panda' 🏆H6 CJun EBee GQue LRHS MBri NLar WHCr WPGP
– 'Rhinegold' MBlu
– 'Sable' SLim
– var. ***septentrionalis*** CBcs CCVT CDoC CDul CEnd CTho EBee ECrN ELon EPfP EPla EWTr GBin LAst LRHS MBlu MGos MRav MSwo NWea SCob SCoo SGol SLim SPer WMou WPGP
– – PDM 752 **new** WPGP
– – 'Kansu' CEnd CJun CLnd CTsd EBee LRHS MBri NLar NWea SBig SCoo WHCr WHar
– – 'Purdom' CJun CLnd SBig
§ ***alleghaniensis*** CCVT CDul CMCN CSto EPfP GBin MMuc NLar NWea SGol WCru
apoiensis 'Mount Apoi' CJun CLnd SBig
chichibuensis CJun MMHG MSnd WHer
chinensis CMCN
'Conyngham' CJun CTho MBlu SLau
cordifolia see *B. papyrifera* var. *cordifolia*
costata misapplied see *B. ermanii* 'Grayswood Hill'
costata ambig. CMCN ECrN SGol
costata Trautv. CTho EBee MSwo
* – 'Fincham Cream' CJun SBig
'Crimson Frost' EBee
dahurica Pall. CSto
– 'Maurice Foster' CDoC CJun CSto CTho WPGP
– 'Stone Farm' CJun
delavayi EBee
divaricata CJun
ermanii CBcs CCVT CDoC CDul CLnd CMCN CMac CSBt CTri ECrN ELan EPla EWTr GBin LAst MBlu MGos MMuc MRav NLar NWea SCob SGol WMou
– B&SWJ 10852 from Aomori, Japan **new** WCru
– from Hokkaido, Japan CSto
– from South Korea B&SWJ 8801 WCru WPat
– – B&SWJ 12600 **new** WCru
– 'Blush' CJun MBlu SBig SCoo
– var. ***ermanii*** MWat
– – MSF 825 EBee
– – MSF 865 WPGP
§ – 'Grayswood Hill' 🏆H6 CDul CEnd CHel CJun CLnd CMCN CMHG CSBt CTho CTri EBee EPfP MBlu MGos SCoo SLim SWvt WPGP
– 'Hakkoda Orange' CJun CTho SCoo WHar WPGP
– 'Holland' IArd IDee NLar
– 'Mount Zao' CJun CSto IVic WPGP
* – 'Pendula' CJun EBee GBin LLHF MBlu NWea SBig SBir SCoo
– 'Polar Bear' CJun CLnd EBee EPfP GBin MAsh MBlu MBri NLar SCoo SMad SSta WHCr WPGP
– 'Zao Purple' CDul
'Fetisowii' CDul CEnd CJun EBtc LRHS MBlu NLar SBig WHar
globispica CJun
'Hergest' 🏆H6 CDoC CJun EBee ECrN EPfP LRHS MAsh MBri MGos SCoo SLau WHCr WHar
insignis CSto
– B&SWJ 11751 WCru
'Inverleith' see *B. utilis* var. *jacquemontii* 'Inverleith'
jacquemontii see *B. utilis* var. *jacquemontii*
lenta CDul CMCN CSto EPfP IArd MBlu MMuc NWea
luminifera CJun EBee EBtc NLar
lutea see *B. alleghaniensis*
maximowicziana CDul CLnd CMCN CSto EPfP IDee NLar SGol
medwediewii CDul CJun CMCN CSto EBee EPfP EPla NLar NWea
– 'Gold Bark' 🏆H7 CJun CMCN EPfP MBlu
michauxii NLar WCru
nana CAco CDul GQue MGos MRav NHar NWea
– 'Glengarry' EPot GBin GCrg GEdr NLar

	nigra	CAco CBcs CCVT CDoC CDul CEnd CLnd CMCN CNWT CTho CTri EBee EPla EWTr MAsh MBri NLar SCob SEWo SGol WMou
	- 'Black Star'	EBee LRHS
§	- 'Cully'	CDoC CDul CLnd CTho ECrN EPla MGos MRav NWea SBig SCoo SGol WHCr
	- Dura-Heat = 'Bnmtf'	MGos NLar
	- Heritage	see *B. nigra* 'Cully'
	- 'Little King'	CJun MGos MPkF
	- 'Peter Collinson'	CJun
	- 'Shiloh Splash' **new**	SReu SSta
	- 'Summer Cascade'	CDoC EBee EPla LRHS MAsh SLon WHCr
	- Tecumseh Compact = 'Studetec'	MPkF SGol
	- Wakehurst form	EPfP SPer SPoG WPGP
	papyrifera	CAco CCVT CDul CLnd CMCN CMac CSBt CSto CTri ECrN ELan EPfP EWTr LBuc MBlu MGos MMuc MSwo NWea SCob SEND SGol SPer WHar
	- 'Belle Vue'	CSto EBee
§	- var. ***cordifolia***	CSto
	- - 'Clarenville'	CJun CSto EBee
	- var. ***papyrifera***	CSto
	- 'Saint George'	CJun CSto CTho EBee MBri WHCr
	- 'Vancouver'	CJun CTho MBlu
§	***pendula***	Widely available
	- 'Bangor'	CJun SSta
	- 'Black Prince' **new**	WHCr
	- f. ***crispa***	see *B. pendula* 'Laciniata'
	- 'Dalecarlica' misapplied	see *B. pendula* 'Laciniata'
	- 'Dalecarlica' ambig.	CBcs CCVT CSBt ECrN LRHS MRav SCrf SWvt WHCr
	- 'Dark Prince'	CJun
	- 'Fastigiata'	CCVT CDul CJun CLnd CSBt CTho EBee ECrN ELan EPla MGos MJak NWea SCoo SGol SPer SPoG
*	- 'Golden Beauty'	CDoC CDul CJun CMac EBee ECrN LAst MAsh MGos NLar SCoo SGol SLim SPer SSpi WHar
	- 'Golden Cloud'	GKin MJak
	- hybrid **new**	COtt
§	- 'Laciniata' ♀H7	CDul CLnd CMCN CMac CTho EBee ELan EPfP EPla EWTr IDee MAsh MBlu MGos MSwo NWea SCob SCoo SGol SPer WCFE WHar WMou
	- 'Long Trunk'	CDul EBee LAst LLHF MBlu SGol SLim WHar
	- 'Purpurea'	CCVT CDul CMCN CSBt EBee ECrN ELan ELon EPla EWTr GKin LAst MGos MSwo NLar NWea SCoo SGol SPer WFar
	- 'Silver Grace'	CJun ECrN SKHP
	- 'Tristis' ♀H7	Widely available
	- 'Youngii'	Widely available
	- 'Zwitsers Glorie'	CDul CJun NLar SKHP
§	***pendulata*** 'Spider Alley'PBR	GBin NLar
	platyphylla misapplied	see *B. platyphylla* subsp. *mandshurica*
	platyphylla Sukaczev Dakota Pinnacle = 'Fargo'	EBee NLar SCoo WHar
§	- subsp. ***mandshurica***	CSto MMuc MSnd
	- - 'Whitespire Senior'	CDul
	- subsp. ***platyphylla***	MSnd
	populifolia	CSto
	potaninii	MSnd
§	***pubescens***	CAco CCVT CDul CHab CSto CTri EBee ECrN EPla GQue MMuc NWea SCob SEND WMou
	- var. ***pubescens***	CSto
	raddeana	EBtc
	'Royal Frost'	CDul CJun EBee GQue IArd IDee MAsh MBlu NLar SLim SPoG WHar
	'Silver Trestles'PBR	see *B. pendulata* 'Spider Alley'
	szechuanica 'Liuba White'	CJun CTho
	- 'Moonlight'	SLau
§	***utilis***	CDul CMCN CSBt CSto ECrN NWea SEND SSta
	- BL&M 100 from central Nepal	CSto
	- GWJ 9259	WCru
	- H&M 1480 from Sichuan, China	CSto
	- HWJK 2250	WCru
	- HWJK 2345	WCru
	- S&L from Nepal	CDul
	- Sch 2168	EBee
	- SICH 667 from Sichuan, China	CSto
	- Yu 10163 from Yunnan, China	CSto
	- from eastern Nepal	CSto
	- 'Bhutan Sienna'	CJun CSto
	- 'Buddha'	WPGP
	- 'China Bronze'	WPGP
	- 'Darkness'	SLon WHCr WPGP
	- 'Fascination' ♀H6	CDul CJun CLnd EBee IArd MBri MGos NWea SCob SCoo SLim SSpi SSta WHCr
*	- 'Fastigiata'	CJun SBig SSta
	- 'Forrest's Blush' ♀H6	CDul CJun CSto EBee MBri SBig WHar WPGP
§	- var. ***jacquemontii***	Widely available
	- - Polunin	WPGP
	- - 'Doorenbos' ♀H6	Widely available
	- - 'Grayswood Ghost' ♀H6	CDoC CDul CEnd CJun CLnd CMCN CMHG CSto CTho CTri EBee ELan EPfP EPla MBlu MBri NLar SBig SBir SLau SLim SSta WHCr WHar WPGP
§	- - 'Inverleith'	CDul CJun CLnd EBee GBin GQue SBig SBir SCoo SLim WPGP
	- - 'Jermyns' ♀H6	CDul CEnd CHel CJun CLnd CMHG CTri EBee EPfP IVic LRHS MBlu MBri SCoo SLau SLim SPer SSta SWvt WHCr WHar WPGP
	- - 'McBeath'	SLau
	- - 'Silver Shadow' ♀H6	CDul CEnd CJun CLnd CTho EBee EPfP LRHS MAsh MBlu NLar NWea SBig SBir SCoo SKHP SLau SLim SPer SPoG SSta WHCr
	- - 'Trinity College'	CDul CJun CTri EBee LRHS MBri SBig SSpi WHCr WHar
	- 'Knightshayes'	CTho
	- 'Moonbeam'	CDul CJun CSBt EBee GQue LRHS MAsh MBri NWea SBig SCoo SPoG WHCr WHar
	- 'Mount Luoji'	CJun CSto WPGP
	- 'Nepalese Orange'	CJun CSto WPGP
	- var. ***occidentalis*** 'Kyelang'	CJun CTho IVic

- 'Park Wood' ♀H6 CJun CSto WPGP
- 'Polar Bear' LRHS
- var. ***prattii*** CJun CTho
- 'Ramdana River' CDoC CJun CMHG WPGP
- 'Schilling' CJun
- 'Sichuan Red' CSto
- 'Wakehurst Place Chocolate' ♀H6 CDul CJun CSBt CTho EBee GBin MBlu MBri NWea SBig SCoo SLim SSta WHCr WHar

cf. ***utilis*** CTri SGol
verrucosa see *B. pendula*

Biarum (*Araceae*)

S&L 604 WCot
SB&L 597 WCot
bovei ECho
carratracense from Spain WCot
davisii ECho EPot LAma WCot
dispar SB&L 294 WCot
- SB&L 564 WCot

ditschianum from Turkey WCot
marmarisense ECho NRog WCot
tenuifolium ECho WCot
- LB 295 WCot
- PB 357 WCot
- S&L 174 WCot
- subsp. ***abbreviatum*** MS 974 WCot
- - from Greece ECho
- subsp. ***arundanum*** WCot
- subsp. ***galianii*** PB 435 WCot
- subsp. ***idomenaeum*** MS 738 WCot
- subsp. ***zelebori*** ECho WCot
- - CRL 502 WCot
- - LB 300 WCot
- - PB 224 WCot
- - PB 334 WCot

Bidens (*Asteraceae*)

atrosanguinea see *Cosmos atrosanguineus*
§ ***aurea*** EAJP ECtt EPPr EWes LAst LEdu MNrw MSpe NPer NPri SMrm WBor WOld XLum
- 'Cream Streaked Yellow' GQue
- cream-flowered MNrw
- 'Golden Drop' LSou
- 'Hannay's Lemon Drop' CAby CDes CKno EAJP EBee ECtt ELon EPfP LPla LPot LSou MNrw MSpe SGbt SPoG SRms WBor WPGP

* - 'Lemon Queen' SMad
- 'Rising Sun' EWes
- white-flowered GCal

ferulifolia NPer
- Peter's Gold Rush ='Topteppich'PBR LSou
- Yellow Charm ='Danyel9' LSou

heterophylla Ortega see *B. aurea*
heterophylla misapplied CAby ECtt MCot MRav MWat WFar WHal WMoo XLum
- CD&R 1515 LPla

humilis see *B. triplinervia* var. *macrantha*
integrifolia SMad
'Pirate's Treasure' ECtt
§ ***triplinervia*** var. ***macrantha*** ELon

Bignonia (*Bignoniaceae*)

capreolata CCCN CRHN EBee WCot WSHC
- 'Dragon Lady' SKHP

lindleyana see *Clytostoma calystegioides*
tweedieana see *Macfadyena unguis-cati*
unguis-cati see *Macfadyena unguis-cati*

Bilderdykia see *Fallopia*

Billardiera (*Pittosporaceae*)

cymosa CTsd MOWG
longiflora ♀H3 CBcs CHid CMac CSBt CTri EBee ECou ELan EPfP EUJe IArd ITim LBMP LRHS MAsh MGil MGos MOWG MRav NLar NSoo SEND SLim SPer SPoG SWvt WHil WKif WPat WSHC
- 'Cherry Berry' CBcs CFlo CMac EBee ELan EPfP LRHS NLar SLim SPer SPoG SRms SWvt WSHC
- 'Fructu-albo' CBcs CFlo EBee ELan EPfP EWes LRHS NLar SLon SPer SWvt

Billbergia (*Bromeliaceae*)

'Borracho' new LAir NLos
'Carnaval' new LAir
'Casa Blanca' new LAir
'Deja Vu' new LAir
distachya var. ***maculata*** new NLos
elegans new LAir
'Flamenco' new LAir
'Fosters Striate' new NLos
'Gerda' new LAir
'Hallelujah' new LAir
'Las Manchas' new LAir
manarae new LAir
nutans CHll EBak ESwi EUJe IBlr IMou LEdu NLos SChr SEND SPlb WSFF
- var. ***schimperiana*** EShb

* - 'Variegata' (v) CCon CHll EShb EUJe NLos SChr WCot

'Pink Patches' new LAir
pyramidalis ♀H1a NLos XBlo
I - 'Variegata' (v) IBlr
× ***windii*** ♀H1a CHEx EBak NLos

Biserrula (*Papilionaceae*)

pelecinus WCot

Bismarckia (*Arecaceae*)

nobilis CCCN LPal

Bistorta see *Persicaria*

Bituminaria (*Papilionaceae*)

bituminosa WCot
- HH&K 174 WSHC

blackberry see *Rubus fruticosus*

blackcurrant see *Ribes nigrum*

Blechnum (*Blechnaceae*)

alpinum see *B. penna-marina* subsp. *alpinum*
auratum new GLin

	brasiliense ♀H1a	ESwi ISha NLos
§	***chilense*** ♀H4	CBcs CBty CDTJ CDes CHEx CLAP EFtx EPfP EWes GBin GCal GCra IBlr LEdu LPal LRHS MMoz NLos SArc SBig SGSe SKHP SPlb SRms WCru WMoo WPat
	discolor	CLAP
	fluviatile	CDTJ CLAP EFtx MMoz NLos SGSe
	gibbum	CBty EFtx LPal
	- 'Silver Lady'	ISha NLos
	magellanicum misapplied	see *B. chilense*
	magellanicum (Desv.) Mett.	SBig SKHP
	minus	CBty
	novae-zelandiae	LRHS NLos
	nudum	CBty CDTJ CKel EFtx ESwi LPal NLos SGSe
	palmiforme new	GLin
	penna-marina ♀H4	CBty CCCN CExl CKel CLAP CTal ECou EFer EFtx ELon GAbr GBin GCal GMaP LEdu LPal LRHS MMoz MRav NBir NLos SCob WFib WMoo XLum
§	- subsp. ***alpinum***	CLAP ECha GEdr GKev NWad SGSe SKHP WMoo
	- - BR 68 new	GEdr
	- 'Cristatum'	CLAP GAbr GEdr SGSe
	punctulatum	ISha
	spicant ♀H6	Widely available
	tabulare misapplied	see *B. chilense*
	tabulare (Thunb.) Kuhn	CBcs CDTJ CKel EFtx EPfP GGal NLos WPGP
	wattsii	CDes

Blepharocalyx (*Myrtaceae*)

§	***cruckshanksii***	CCCN CExl CSde EBee ELon ETwe IDee LRHS NLar SEle WBor WPGP WPat
	- 'Heaven Scent'	see *B. cruckshanksii*

Blephilia (*Lamiaceae*)

	ciliata	SPhx

Bletilla (*Orchidaceae*)

	sp.	NDav
	hyacinthina	see *B. striata*
	ochracea	CExl LAma
	Penway Paris gx	CTal
	sinensis	CExl
§	***striata*** ♀H4	CAby CBct CCon CDes CExl CHel CTri CTsd ECho EPot GKev LAma LEdu LRHS MNrw SDeJ WPGP XLum
	- ***alba***	see *B. striata* f. *gebina*
	- 'Albostriata'	CBct CCon CExl ECho ELan LAma WCot XLum
§	- f. ***gebina***	CCon CDes CExl CHel CTal CTri CTsd ECho EPot GKev LEdu LRHS SDeJ WPGP
	- - variegated (v)	GKev LEdu
	- var. ***japonica***	IGor
	- 'Kuchi-beni'	GKev LAma
	- 'Lips'	GKev
	- 'Soryu'	GKev LAma
	Yokohama gx	CTal

Bloomeria (*Asparagaceae*)

	crocea	ECho
	- var. ***aurea***	ECho GLin
	- var. ***montana***	ECho

blueberry see *Vaccinium corymbosum*

Blumea (*Asteraceae*)

	balsamifera	CHab

Bocconia (*Papaveraceae*)

	cordata	see *Macleaya cordata* (Willd.) R. Br.
	microcarpa	see *Macleaya microcarpa*

Boehmeria (*Urticaceae*)

	biloba	SDix
	nivea	WCot
	platanifolia	IMou
	tricuspis	IMou WCot

Boenninghausenia (*Rutaceae*)

	albiflora	CPne
	- B&SWJ 1479	WCru
	- BWJ 8141 from China	WCru
	- CC 7147 new	EWld
	- pink-flowered B&SWJ 3112	WCru
	japonica B&SWJ 11186	WCru

Bolax (*Apiaceae*)

	glebaria	see *B. gummifer*
§	***gummifer***	ECho EPot GEdr WAbe

Bolboschoenus (*Cyperaceae*)

§	***maritimus***	SMea

Boltonia (*Asteraceae*)

	asteroides	GCra LRHS MMuc SMrm SPer SWat WRHF XLum
	- var. ***latisquama***	GMaP GQue LSou MAvo MRav MWat NCGa NLar SHar SMad WBor WHal WHil
	- - 'Nana'	SGSe
	- - 'Snowbank'	ELan GCal MSpe NDov
	decurrens	CBod EBee GCal IMou MSpe WBor
	- 'Warrior's Blush'	MNrw
	incisa	see *Kalimeris incisa*

Bolusanthus (*Papilionaceae*)

	speciosus	SPlb

Bomarea (*Alstroemeriaceae*)

	acutifolia	CFil SKHP WCot
	- B&SWJ 9094	WCru
	- B&SWJ 9130	WCru
	- B&SWJ 10388	WCru
	aff. ***andreana*** B&SWJ 10617	WCru
	boliviensis	WCot WCru
	caldasii	see *B. multiflora*
	costaricensis B&SWJ 10467	WCru
	distichifolia	CExl WCot WCru
§	***edulis*** ♀H1c	CDes CPne CRHN EWld SBrt WCot WHil WKif
	- B&SWJ 9017	LEdu WCru
	- F&M 104	CExl
	frondea	see *B. multiflora*
	aff. ***frondea*** B&SWJ 10681	WCru
	hirsuta B&SWJ 10774	WCru
	hirtella	see *B. edulis*

§ ***multiflora*** ♀H2	CBcs CCCN CCon CExl EBee GCal MOWG NLos SKHP WBor WCot WCru WSHC
patacocensis JCA 13987	WCot
salsilla ♀H1c	CAvo CCCN CFil EBee NLos SKHP WSHC

Bombax (*Malvaceae*)

ceiba	SPlb

Bongardia (*Berberidaceae*)

chrysogonum	CAvo ECho EPot LLHF LRHS WCot

Bonia (*Poaceae*)

§ ***solida***	CHEx EPla ERod MMoz MMuc MWht SEND

borage see *Borago officinalis*

Borago (*Boraginaceae*)

laxiflora	see *B. pygmaea*
officinalis	CArn CHby CUse ELau ENfk EPfP GPoy MHer MNHC NBir NPri SBch SRms SVic WJek
- 'Alba'	CBre CUse ELau ENfk MNHC SIde SRms WJek
- 'Bill Archer' (v)	CNat
§ ***pygmaea***	CArn CExl CHid CSpe CUse ELan GCal LEdu MHer MNrw NBir NSti SRms WGwG WJek WMoo

Borinda (*Poaceae*)

KR 4558	ERod
KR 5287 **new**	MWht
KR 5600	MWht
KR 5950	ERod
KR 6438 **new**	MWht
KR 6439 **new**	MWht
KR 7346	MWht
KR 7662 **new**	MWht
albocerea ♀H4	EPfP EPla ERod MWht
- Yunnan 1	ERod
- Yunnan 2	CDTJ CEnt EPla ERod MMoz
- Yunnan 3a	CDTJ CEnt EPla ERod
- Yunnan 3b	ERod
boliana	SBig
frigida	CDTJ CEnt
- KR 4059	ERod MWht
fungosa	ESwi IBoy
grossa KR 5931	MWht
lushuiensis	EPla
- Yunnan 4	CDTJ CEnt EPla MWht
macclureana KR 5051	MWht
- KR 5177 from Gyala, Nepal	ERod ESwi MWht
- KR 5602	ERod
- KR 5950	ERod
- KR 6236	ESwi
- KR 6243	ERod
- KR 6400 from Show La	ESwi
- KR 6438 from Pasm Tso	ESwi
aff. ***macclureana*** KR 6900 **new**	MWht
papyrifera	CEnt ERod WPGP
- CS 1046	EPla MWht
scabrida ♀H4	CDTJ CEnt ERod MAvo MMoz MWht WPGP
- 'Asian Wonder'	CBod EPla EUJe LRHS MBlu NLar SPoG

Boronia (*Rutaceae*)

heterophylla	CBcs CCCN CSde CTsd EPfP IDee IVic LRHS MOWG SEle SPoG
- 'Ice Charlotte'	CBcs CCCN IDee

Bossiaea (*Papilionaceae*)

riparia	SPlb

Bothriochloa (*Poaceae*)

§ ***bladhii***	CKno EPPr
caucasica	see *B. bladhii*

Bougainvillea (*Nyctaginaceae*)

'African Sunset'	SPlb
'Alexandra'	SPre
glabra ♀H1c	SPre

Boussingaultia (*Basellaceae*)

baselloides Hook.	see *Anredera cordifolia*

Bouteloua (*Poaceae*)

curtipendula	CBod SGSe
§ ***gracilis***	CAby EAJP EBee EHoe LEdu LRHS MSCN NWsh SGSe SMad SMea WWEG XLum

Bouvardia (*Rubiaceae*)

ternifolia	CSpe CWGN ESwi EUJe LSou MHol MNrw MSCN SPoG WCot

Bowiea (*Asparagaceae*)

volubilis	EBee

Bowkeria (*Stilbaceae*)

sp.	CCCN
cymosa	SPlb SVen
verticillata	CHII WBor

Boykinia (*Saxifragaceae*)

aconitifolia	CMac GLog IMou MRav NLar NRya SMad WCru WMoo
elata	see *B. occidentalis*
heucheriformis	see *B. jamesii*
§ ***jamesii***	WAbe
lycoctonifolia	EBee LEdu NLar
major	EBee
§ ***occidentalis***	MMHG WCru WMoo WPtf XLum
rotundifolia	GJos NBir WCru WMoo
tellimoides	see *Peltoboykinia tellimoides*

boysenberry see *Rubus* 'Boysenberry'

Brachychilum see *Hedychium*

Brachychiton (*Malvaceae*)

acerifolius	SPlb
populneus	SPlb

Brachyelytrum (*Poaceae*)

japonicum	EPPr NLar

Brachyglottis (*Asteraceae*)

§ ***bidwillii***	CBcs IDee IVic WHor
- 'Basil Fox'	WAbe
§ ***compacta***	ECou ELan EPfP LRHS SLon SPer SPoG
compacta × monroi	ECou

	'County Park'	ECou
	Dunedin Group	WHar
	- 'Drysdale'	EAEE EBee ELan EPfP LRHS SBod SHil SKHP SLon SRGP SWvt
§	- 'Moira Reid' (v)	CExl CTsd
§	- 'Sunshine' ♀H4	CDoC CDul CSBt CTri EBee ECrN ELan EPfP IVic LRHS MGos MJak MRav MSwo MWat NPer NPri NSoo NWea SCob SEND SHil SLim SPer SPlb SPoG SRGP SRms SWvt
	'Frosty'	EAEE ECou ECrN
	greyi misapplied	see *B.* (Dunedin Group) 'Sunshine'
	greyi ambig.	EPla
§	***greyi*** (Hook. f.) B. Nord.	CAco CMac COtt EPfP MWhi SGol
	greyi* × *repanda	CDoC
	huntii	SVen
	huntii* × *stewartii	SEND
	laxifolia misapplied	see *B.* (Dunedin Group) 'Sunshine'
§	***monroi***	CBcs CMac CSBt CTsd ECou EHoe ELan EPfP IVic LRHS MRav SGol SKHP SLon SPer SVen
	- 'Clarence'	ECou
	repanda	CBcs EWld
	- 'Purpurea'	CBcs
	- var. ***rangiora***	CTsd
§	***rotundifolia***	CCCN
	'Silver Waves'	ECou
I	'Sunshine Improved'	CBcs EHoe
	'Sunshine Variegated'	see *B.* (Dunedin Group) 'Moira Reid'
	Walberton's Silver Dormouse = 'Walbrach'PBR ♀H4	CSBt EAEE EBee EPfP LRHS MBri MGos NPri SPoG SRkn STPC WCot

Brachyotum (*Melastomataceae*)

ledifolium new	CPne

Brachypodium (*Poaceae*)

pinnatum	EPPr
sylvaticum	CHab SEND

Brachyscome (*Asteraceae*)

'Blue Brazil' new	LAst
iberidifolia 'Brachy Blue'	LAst
'Metallic Blue'	NPri
rigidula	CPBP GKev
Surdaisy Strawberry Pink = 'Bonbrapi'PBR	LAst

Brachystachyum (*Poaceae*)

densiflorum	ERod

Bracteantha see *Xerochrysum*

Brahea (*Arecaceae*)

armata	CBrP CDTJ CPHo EPfP EShb LPal SPlb WCot
dulcis	NLos
edulis	CCCN CPHo LPal NLos
'Super Silver'	NLos WCot

Brassaia see *Schefflera*

Brassica (*Brassicaceae*)

	juncea new	SVic
	nigra	CArn
	oleracea	CAgr SVic WHer
	- var. ***ramosa*** new	WCot
*	***rapa*** var. ***japonica***	MNHC SHDw

Bravoa (*Agavaceae*)

geminiflora	see *Polianthes geminiflora*

Brighamia (*Campanulaceae*)

insignis	CCCN

Brillantaisia (*Acanthaceae*)

kirungae	CCCN

Brimeura (*Asparagaceae*)

§	***amethystina*** ♀H5	CAvo CExl CPom ECho GBin GKev LEdu SDeJ SPhx WCot WThu
	- 'Alba'	CAvo ECho GKev SDeJ SPhx WCot

Briza (*Poaceae*)

maxima	CKno CTri EHoe LEdu NGdn NSti SPhx WHer WTou
media	Widely available
- 'Golden Bee'	CKno CWCL EHoe ELon EPPr EPfP LEdu LRHS MMHG NDov NLar SMad
- 'Limouzi'	CBod CCon CElw CKno CWCL EBee EHoe ELon EPPr GCal LEdu LRHS MAvo NSti NWsh SMad SMea XLum
- 'Russells'PBR	CBod CHid CKno EBee EHoe ELan EPPr EPfP LPot LRHS MAvo NWad NWsh SHil SMea SPer SPoG SRms SWvt WGrn
subaristata	EAJP EPPr LPal MWhi
triloba	LRHS MMHG NWsh SMea

Brocchinia (*Bromeliaceae*)

hechtioides new	NLos

Brodiaea (*Asparagaceae*)

§	***californica***	EBee ECho GKev WCot
	- NNS 00-109	WCot
	- NNS 06-102	WCot
	- 'Babylon' new	GKev
	coronaria	WCot
	'Corrina'	see *Triteleia* 'Corrina'
	elegans	ECho
	ida-maia	see *Dichelostemma ida-maia*
	laxa	see *Triteleia laxa*
	pallida	WCot
	peduncularis	see *Triteleia peduncularis*
	stellaris	ECho

Bromus (*Poaceae*)

erectus	CHab
inermis 'Skinner's Gold' (v)	EBee EHoe EPPr NLar SMea WCot WWEG

Broussonetia (*Moraceae*)

kazinoki	CArn
papyrifera	CAbP CBcs CDul CMCN EBtc EGFP ELan GBin IVic SPer WPGP
- 'Billardii'	NLar
- 'Laciniata'	EBee IDee SMad WCot

Browallia (*Solanaceae*)

from Sikkim	CSpe

Bruckenthalia see *Erica*

Brugmansia ✿ (*Solanaceae*)

	Name	Suppliers
	'Angel' (d) **new**	MNai
	'Angels Applause' (d) **new**	MNai
	'Angels Cloud' (d) **new**	MNai
	'Angels Daydream' (d) **new**	MNai
	'Angels Endless Summer' (d) **new**	MNai
	'Angels Exotic' (d) **new**	MNai
	'Angels Fantasy' (d) **new**	MNai
	'Angels Glamour' (d) **new**	MNai
	'Angels Honeymoon' (d) **new**	MNai
	'Angels Innovation' (d) **new**	MNai
	'Angels Inspiration' (d) **new**	MNai
	'Angels Love' (d) **new**	MNai
	'Angels Moonlight' (d) **new**	MNai
	'Angels Paradise' (d) **new**	MNai
	'Angels Phenomenal' (d) **new**	MNai
	'Angels Prima Donna' (d) **new**	MNai
	'Angels Proud' (d) **new**	MNai
	'Angels Sensation' (d) **new**	MNai
	'Angels Shredded Dress' (d) **new**	MNai
	'Angels Surprise' (d) **new**	MNai
	'Angels Swingtime' (d) **new**	MNai
	'Anja' (d) **new**	MNai
	'Apricot Queen'	MNai
	'Apricot Queen Variegated' (v) **new**	MNai
§	***arborea***	CBcs CDTJ
§	- 'Knightii' (d) 🏆H1c	CDTJ MNai
	- 'Rosea' variegated (v) **new**	ELan
	- variegated (v) **new**	ELan
	aurea	CCCN CHEx EUJe SAdn
	- 'Citronella' **new**	MNai
	'Bergfee' (d) **new**	MNai
	'Bergische Symphonie' (d) **new**	MNai WOth
	'Birgit' (d) **new**	MNai
	'Bolero' (d) **new**	MNai
	'Borner Gold' **new**	MNai
	'Bridesmaid' (d) **new**	MNai
	'Canarybird' **new**	MNai
	× ***candida***	CCCN CHEx MNai SAdn
	- 'Angels Summertime' (d) **new**	MNai
	- 'Angels Sunsilk' (d) **new**	MNai
	- 'Blush'	EUJe
	- 'Double White' (d) **new**	MNai
§	- 'Grand Marnier' 🏆H1c	CDTJ CHEx CHll WOth
	- 'Maya'	MNai
	- 'Pink Perfektion' (d) **new**	MNai
	- 'Plena'	see *B. arborea* 'Knightii'
	- f. ***plena*** 'Angels Flight' (d)	MNai
	- - 'Angels Flight Variegated' (v/d) **new**	MNai
	- - 'Salmon Perfektion' (d)	MNai
	- 'Rosalla' **new**	MNai
§	- 'Variegata' (v)	CCCN CDTJ CHll
	'Caribbean Night' **new**	MNai
	'Carousel' (d) **new**	MNai
	'Cerise Baby' **new**	MNai
	'Cerise Wonder' **new**	MNai
	'Creamsickle' (d) **new**	MNai
	'Dalen's Pink Amour' (d) **new**	MNai
	'Dalen's Princess' (d) **new**	MNai
	'Dark Rossetta' **new**	MNai
	'Day Dreams' (d) **new**	MNai
	'Dottie' **new**	MNai
	'Double Dark Rossetta' (d) **new**	MNai
	'Dream Angel' (d) **new**	MNai
	'Elfi' (d) **new**	MNai
	'Exotic Variegated Pink' (v) **new**	MNai
	'Fandango' (d) **new**	MNai
	'Fascination' (d) **new**	MNai
	'Flieder' **new**	MNai
	'Flowerdream' (d)	EUJe
	'Frosty Pink'	MNai
	'Gelber Riese' **new**	MNai
	'Golden Princess' **new**	MNai
	'Goldtraum' **new**	MNai
	'Grand Marnier' **new**	MNai
	'Grazie' **new**	MNai
	'Herzenbrücke' **new**	MNai
§	× ***insignis***	CHll
	- 'Pink Delight'	MNai
§	- pink-flowered	SEND
	'Kani Spirit' **new**	MNai
	'Kleine Aap' **new**	MNai
	'Kongmansia' **new**	MNai
	'L'Amour' **new**	WOth
	'Lemon Giant' **new**	MNai
	'Lilac 1' **new**	MNai
	'Lilac Touch' **new**	MNai
	'Lime Wonder' **new**	MNai
	'Logee's Species' (d) **new**	MNai
	'Louise' **new**	MNai
	'Lovely Lady' (d) **new**	MNai
	'Marie Stöppler' (d) **new**	MNai
	meteloides	see *Datura inoxia*
	'Midnight Passion' **new**	MNai
	'Midsummer Magic' (d) **new**	MNai
	'Miss Emily Mackenzie' **new**	WOth
	'Morgensonne'	WOth
	'Mystic Fire' **new**	MNai
	'Painted Lady' **new**	WOth
	'Pink Flamingo' **new**	MNai
	'Pink Honour' **new**	MNai
	'Pink Lady'	MNai
	'Pink Smitty' (d) **new**	MNai
	'Prince of Colombia' **new**	MNai
	'Red Devil' **new**	MNai
	rosei	see *B. sanguinea* subsp. *sanguinea* var. *flava*
§	***sanguinea***	CCCN CHEx CHll IDee SEND SPlb WOth
	- red-flowered	CHEx
	- 'Rosea'	see *B.* × *insignis* pink-flowered
§	- subsp. ***sanguinea*** var. ***flava***	CHEx
	'Schloss Burg' **new**	MNai
	'Shredded Fantasy' (d) **new**	MNai
	'Snowbank' (v) **new**	MNai
	'Sonja' (d) **new**	MNai
	'Splashes' **new**	MNai
§	***suaveolens*** 🏆H1c	CBcs CHll ELan EUJe MNai
	- pink-flowered	EShb
	- ***rosea***	see *B.* × *insignis* pink-flowered
	- 'Variegata' (v)	EShb
	- yellow-flowered	EShb
	suaveolens × ***versicolor***	see *B.* × *insignis*

'Super Pink' **new** — MNai
'Tangie Tigress' **new** — MNai
'Tante Erna' (d) **new** — MNai
'Thea's Liebling' (d) **new** — MNai
'Tropicana' (d) **new** — MNai
'Variegata Sunset' — see *B.* × *candida* 'Variegata'
versicolor misapplied — see *B. arborea*
§ ***versicolor*** Lagerh. — CCCN
'Violet Crush' **new** — MNai
'Wildfire' (d) **new** — MNai
'Wuppergold' (d) **new** — MNai
'Wupperstolz' (d) **new** — MNai
* 'Yellow Trumpet' — ELan

Brunfelsia (*Solanaceae*)

americana — CCCN MOWG
calycina — see *B. pauciflora*
eximia — see *B. pauciflora* 'Eximia'
jamaicensis — MOWG
lactea — CCCN
§ ***pauciflora*** ♀H1c — CCCN ELan
§ - 'Eximia' — SPer
- 'Floribunda' — MOWG

Brunia (*Bruniaceae*)

albiflora — SPlb

Brunnera ✿ (*Boraginaceae*)

§ ***macrophylla*** — Widely available
- 'Agnes Amez' — IMou
- 'Aimee Angus' **new** — EPPr
- 'Alba' — see *B. macrophylla* 'Betty Bowring'
§ - 'Betty Bowring' — Widely available
- 'Blaukuppel' — CLAP EWes GBin GCal NBir SBod WCAu WPtf
- 'Dawson's White' (v) — CBcs CLAP CWCL ECha ECtt ELan EPfP EPla EPri GBuc GEdr GJos GMaP IKil LBMP LRHS MCot MGos MLHP NBid NBir NGdn NLar SCob SPer SRGP SRms SWvt WFar
- 'Diane's Gold' [PBR] — EBee ECtt MPnt NLar SMDP
- 'Emerald Mist' [PBR] (v) — EBee ECtt EPfP GBin MAsh MGos NLar NSti SPad SPoG SWvt
- 'Gordano Gold' (v) — EHoe NBir WCot
- 'Green Gold' (v) — EBee NLar SPoG
- 'Hadspen Cream' (v) ♀H6 — Widely available
- 'Inspector Morse' — SWvt
- 'Jack Frost' [PBR] ♀H6 — Widely available
- 'Jennifer' **new** — WCAu
- 'King's Ransom' [PBR] (v) — CBct CNor CWGN ECtt NLar NSti SPoG
- 'Langford Hewitt' (v) — MNrw
- 'Langtrees' — CBct CBod CMac EBee ECha EHoe EPla GAbr GBin GBuc GCal GCra LRHS MCot MHol MMuc NBir NGdn NOrc SEND SWat WHea WKif WWEG
- 'Looking Glass' [PBR] ♀H6 — Widely available
- 'Marley's White' — CLAP ELan LLHF NLar SBch SGbt
§ - 'Mister Morse' [PBR] (v) — Widely available
- 'Sea Heart' **new** — GBin
- 'Silver Heart' **new** — SCob
- 'Silver Lace' **new** — IFro
- 'Silver Wings' — CBod CElw CWCL EAEE EBee ECtt EPfP EPla EWTr EWll GEdr GKev LRHS LSou MBel MBri MGos NBir NGdn NLar NSti NWad SGol SPoG SWat WCAu WFar
- 'Spring Yellow' — CBod ECtt NLar
'Mrs Morse' [PBR] — see *B. macrophylla* 'Mister Morse'
sibirica — CLAP EBee EPPr EWes NBid

Brunsvigia (*Amaryllidaceae*)

bosmaniae — ECho WCot
gregaria — WCot
josephinae LAV 30394 — WCot
marginata — ECho
pulchra — ECho WCot
radula 'Vanrhynsdorp' — ECho
radulosa — ECho WCot
rosea 'Minor' — see *Amaryllis belladonna*
striata — ECho

Bryonia (*Cucurbitaceae*)

dioica — CArn GPoy NMir

Bryophyllum see *Kalanchoe*

Buddleja ✿ (*Scrophulariaceae*)

HCM 98.017 from Chile — WPGP
agathosma — CExl CFil MOWG SLon WKif WLav WSHC
albiflora — SLon WLav
alternifolia ♀H5 — Widely available
- 'Argentea' — CBcs CDoC EBee ELan EPfP EWTr LRHS MBNS MRav NLar SKHP SPer SRGP SWvt WCot WLav WSHC XSen
asiatica ♀H2 — CHid IDee MOWG SLon WLav
- B&SWJ 11278 — WCru
auriculata — CBcs CDul CExl CHll CSde EBee ELan EPfP LRHS MOWG SDix SKHP SLon SPlb SVen WLav
'Autumn Surprise' — SLon
'Blue Chip' [PBR] (Lo and Behold Series) — CDoC EPfP GBin LBuc LRHS MAsh MBri MGos MJak MPkF NSoo SLim SLon SPoG SRms SWvt WLav
* 'Blue Trerice' — CExl
caryopteridifolia — EBtc GQui SEND SLon WCot
colvilei — CBcs CDoC CDul ELan EPfP GCal GGal GKin IArd IDee LAst NSoo SBrt SLon SWvt
- B&SWJ 2121 — WCru
- GWJ 9399 — WCru
- 'Kewensis' — CExl CHGN CHid CNec CRHN CWld ETwe EWTr EWes GCal GGal NLar SEND SLon SVen WBor WCFE WCru WLav WPat WSHC
cordata — CFil SLon
- B&SWJ 10433 — WCru
- F&M 220 — WPGP
coriacea — SLon
§ ***crispa*** — CBcs CExl CHid CSpe EBee ECha ELan EPfP GCal LRHS MOWG SEND SLon SPer SRkn SVen SWvt WFar WKif WPGP WSHC XSen
- var. ***farreri*** — CHGN CHid SLon
crotonoides subsp. ***amplexicaulis*** — SLon
curviflora f. ***venenifera*** — SLon
- - B&SWJ 6036 — WCru
'David Griffin' — LRHS
davidii — CArn CCVT NPol NWea SCob
- B&SWJ 8083 — WCru
- Adonis Blue = 'Adokeep' [PBR] — CBcs CNec CWCL LBuc LRHS MBri SLon STPC WLav

- 'African Queen' CAni LRHS SLim SLon SRGP WLav
§ - 'Autumn Beauty' CAni SLon WLav
- 'Autumn Delight' **new** SLon
- 'Bath Beauty' CAni
- 'Beijing' see *B. davidii* 'Autumn Beauty'
- 'Bishop's Velvet' CAni EAEE
- 'Black Knight' ℽH5 Widely available
- 'Blue Eyes' **new** WLav
- 'Blue Horizon' ℽH5 CAni LRHS NLar SLon SRGP WCot WLav WMoo WRHF
- 'Border Beauty' CAni CNec LRHS SCob SLon WLav
- 'Boskoop Beauty' CAni
- 'Brown's Beauty' CAni
- 'Butterfly Heaven'[PBR] WLav
- Buzz Series LBuc NHol SLon
- - Buzz Ivory = 'Tobuivo' CBct CEnd CMac CNec ELan ELon ESwi LRHS LSou MBri NHol NPri SHil SLim SLon SMDP SPoG WHil WLav
- - Buzz Lilac ELan LRHS NHol SLon
- - Buzz Magenta = 'Tobudpipur'[PBR] CBct CBod CEnd CMac CMea CNec CNor CRos ELan ELon LBMP LRHS LSou MBri NEgg NHol NPri SCob SEle SHil SLim SLon SPad SPoG SWvt WHil WLav
- - Buzz Sky Blue = 'Tobuskyblu' CMac CRos EPla LBMP LRHS LSou NEgg NHol NPri SEle SHil SLim SMDP SPad SPoG WLav
- - Buzz Violet = 'Tobudviole' CBct CHid CMac CMea CRos ELan ELon GBin LRHS LSou MBri NHol NPri SBod SLim SLon SWvt WLav
- Camberwell Beauty = 'Camkeep' (English Butterfly Series) ℽH5 CDoC CHll CNec CSBt LBuc LRHS MBri SLon WLav
- 'Car Wash' CAni
- 'Castle Blue' LRHS SLon
- 'Castle School' CAni CSam WLav
§ - 'Charming' CDul WMoo WSHC
- 'Clive Farrell' see *B. davidii* 'Autumn Beauty'
- 'Corinne Tremaine' WHer
- 'Cotswold Blue' **new** WLav
- 'Darent Valley' ℽH5 SLon
- 'Dartmoor' ℽH5 Widely available
- 'Dart's Ornamental White' CNec MRav SLon WLav
- 'Dart's Papillon Blue' CAni SLon WLav
- 'Dart's Purple Rain' CAni CNec LRHS SLon WLav
- 'Dubonnet' CAni SLon WLav
- 'Dudley's Compact Lavender' CAni
- 'Ecolonia' CAni SLon WLav
- 'Ellen's Blue' CExl CFil CNec LRHS WLav
- 'Empire Blue' CAni CBcs CDoC CDul CNec CSBt ECtt EPfP GKin LRHS MGos NBir NPer NSoo NWea SCob SEND SPer SPlb SPoG SRGP SRms SWat SWvt
- 'Fair Lady' WLav
- 'Fascinating' CAni CNec GCal MRav NBir SLon WLav
- 'Flaming Violet' CAni SLon WLav
- 'Florence' CNec LLHF LRHS MBri MWat NEgg NLar SLon SRGP WMoo
- 'Fortune' CAni
- 'Foxtail' WLav
- 'Glasnevin Hybrid' CAni CNec LRHS NLar SDix SLon WLav
- 'Gonglepod' CAni CNec LRHS SLon WLav
- 'Greenway's River Dart' CAni SLon
- 'Grey Dawn' WLav
- 'Griffin Blue' MAsh WLav
- 'Gulliver'[PBR] LRHS MWat NLar SGol SLon WFar WLav
- 'Harlequin' (v) Widely available
- 'Île de France' CAni CBcs CNec NLar NWea SLon SRms WLav
- 'Leela Kapila' SLon
- 'Les Kneale' CAni CNec SLon WLav
- 'Lilac Moon' WLav
- 'Lyme Bay' CAni
- Marbled White = 'Markeep'[PBR] (English Butterfly Series) CNec CSBt EBee LBuc LRHS MBri SLon STPC WLav WMoo
- Masquerade = 'Notbud' (v) MRav SLon
- Moonshine = 'Buddma' **new** LSou
§ - Nanho Blue = 'Mongo' Widely available
- 'Nanho Petite Indigo' see *B. davidii* Nanho Blue
- 'Nanho Petite Plum' see *B. davidii* Nanho Purple
- 'Nanho Petite Purple' see *B. davidii* Nanho Purple
§ - Nanho Purple = 'Monum' ℽH5 CAni CDoC CMHG CMac CNec COtt CTri EBee ELan EPfP LAst LRHS MBri MGos MRav NLar SGol SLim SLon SPer SPlb SPoG SRGP SRms XSen
- Nanho White = 'Monite' ℽH5 EHoe ELan EPfP LRHS SGol SLon SPer SPoG SRms
- var. ***nanhoensis*** CAni CDul SEND SGol WFar WLav
- - blue-flowered EPfP NWad SLon SPer
- 'Orchid Beauty' CAni SLon WLav
- 'Orpheus' CAni CNec SLon WLav
- 'Panache' CNec EPfP LRHS MAsh SLon WLav
- 'Peace' CMac CTri EWTr MRav NLar SLon SPoG WLav
- Peacock = 'Peakeep'[PBR] (English Butterfly Series) CNec CSBt LBuc MAsh MBri NEgg SPoG STPC WLav
- 'Persephone' SLon WLav
- 'Petite Indigo' see *B. davidii* Nanho Blue
- 'Pink Beauty' LAst MBlu SRGP WFar
- 'Pink Charming' see *B. davidii* 'Charming'
- 'Pink Pearl' CAni LRHS SEND SLon WLav
- 'Pink Spreader' CAni LRHS SLon WLav
- 'Pixie Blue' CAni LBMP LRHS MAsh NLar SLon WLav
- 'Pixie Red' CAni LBMP LBuc LRHS MAsh MHer NLar SEND WLav
- 'Pixie White' LBuc LRHS MAsh NLar SEND SGol WLav
- Purple Emperor = 'Pyrkeep' (English Butterfly Series) CNec LBuc MBri NBir SLon SPoG STPC WLav
- 'Purple Friend' CAni SLon WLav
- 'Purple Prince' CAni
- 'Red Admiral' CAni LLHF LRHS MAsh SLon SRGP
- Rêve de Papillon Blue = 'Minpap3' WLav
- Rêve de Papillon = 'Minpap' CNec LRHS MAsh WLav
- 'Royal Purple' CAni SLim SWvt
- 'Royal Red' ℽH5 Widely available
- 'Royal Red Variegated' (v) CTsd
- 'Saith Ffynnon Early' WSFF
- 'Santana' (v) CAni CBcs CBod CDul CMac CNec EBee EHoe ELon EPfP EWes LAst LRHS LSou MRav NEgg NHol NLar SEle SGol SPoG SRms SWvt WCFE WCot WMoo WPat XSen

- 'Shapcott Blue' CAni
- 'Shire Blue' WLav
- 'Southcombe Splendour' CAni LRHS
- 'Summer Beauty' CAni CDul MBlu SLon WLav
- 'Summer House Blue' LRHS SLon WLav
- 'Twotones' WLav
- 'Variegata' (v) CAni MAsh SLon SWvt WLav
- 'White Ball' EHoe ELan NLar SLon WLav
- 'White Bouquet' CAni CCVT CSBt EAEE EPfP GKin LAst LRHS MHer MSwo MWat NWea SEND SPer SRGP SWvt WLav XSen
- 'White Cloud' CAni ECrN GQui LRHS SRms WGwG
- 'White Harlequin' (v) SLon WCFE
- 'White Profusion' ♀H5 Widely available
- 'White Wings' CNec LRHS SLon WLav
- 'Widecombe' CAni
- 'Windtor' CNec LRHS

§ ***delavayi*** CExl ECre SEND WCru
fallowiana misapplied see *B.* 'West Hill'
fallowiana Balf. f. & W.W. Sm. ELan GQui LRHS WLav
- ACE 2481 LRHS
- BWJ 7803 WCru
- var. ***alba*** ♀H5 CDoC CHGN CMac ECrN ELan EPfP ETwe LRHS MAsh MRav NLar SLon SPer WPGP WSHC
- 'Bishop's Violet' CTsd
'Flower Power' see *B.* × *weyeriana* 'Bicolor'
forrestii WCru
globosa ♀H5 Widely available
- RCB/Arg C-11 WCot
- 'Cally Orange' GCal WGwG
- 'Lemon Ball' MBlu NPer SLon WLav
glomerata EShb SLon
- 'Silver Service' EBee ELan LRHS SKHP WCot
heliophila see *B. delavayi*
indica SLon WLav
japonica SLon
- B&SWJ 8912 WCru
* ***knappii*** new ETwe
× ***lewisiana*** 'Margaret Pike' SLon
'Lilac Chip' (Lo and Behold Series) MPkF NSoo
limitanea SLon
lindleyana Widely available
aff. ***lindleyana*** EWTr
- B&SWJ 11478 WCru
'Lochinch' ♀H5 Widely available
longifolia SLon XSen
'Longstock' SLon
'Longstock Silver' SLon
loricata CDoC CExl CHGN CTsd EBee EPfP GBin GQui IDee LRHS MOWG NSoo SEND SKHP SLon SPlb WCot WLav WPGP WPat
macrostachya GLin
- HWJ 602 WCru
- PAB 4198 new LEdu
- WWJ 12016 WCru
§ ***madagascariensis*** ♀H2 CRHN MOWG NLar SLon SPlb SVen
'Malvern Blue' CAni
megalocephala B&SWJ 9106 WCru WPGP
'Miss Ruby'PBR ♀H5 CDoC LBuc LRHS MBri MPkF SHil WLav
§ 'Morning Mist'PBR CBcs CDoC CExl CMHG CMac CNec COtt CSBt CWGN EBee EHoe ELan EPfP GBin LLHF LRHS MBri MOWG NEgg NHol NLar NPri SGol SLon SPoG SRms SWvt WCot WPGP
myriantha CExl SLon WPGP XSen
nappii SLon
nicodemia see *B. madagascariensis*
nivea CExl CHid CMHG ETwe MOWG NSoo SLon WLav XSen
- B&SWJ 2679 WCru
- pink-flowered SLon
officinalis ♀H2 CExl CSde MOWG SLon WLav
paniculata SLon
- GWJ 9286 from Sikkim new WCru
parvifolia SLon
- MPF 148 WLav
× ***pikei*** 'Hever' SRms XSen
'Pink Delight' ♀H5 Widely available
'Pink Perfection' CAni WFar
'Pride of Hever' MOWG SDys
'Pride of Longstock' LRHS SLon SPoG
'Purple Chip' (Lo and Behold Series) new LRHS
saligna SLon
'Salmon Spheres' SLon WLav
salviifolia CBcs CExl CHid CMac CSde CTsd EBee ELan GGal LRHS MBlu NLar NSoo SEND SPlb SVen WGwG WHer WLav WPGP
- white-flowered SLon WPGP
Silver AnniversaryPBR see *B.* 'Morning Mist'
stachyoides MOWG WLav
stenostachya CExl SLon
sterniana see *B. crispa*
'Sugar Plum' CNec CSBt EPfP LRHS SLon
tibetica see *B. crispa*
tubiflora MOWG SLon WLav
venenifera B&SWJ 895 WCru
§ 'West Hill' ♀H5 SLon WLav
× ***weyeriana*** CDul ECtt EPfP GGal GQui MGil MMuc MNrw MSwo NBir NSoo SPad SPlb SWvt WOut
§ - 'Bicolor' CNec EPPr EPfP EWTr LRHS MNrw NLar SLon SPoG SRms WLav
- 'Boy Blue' SLon WLav
- 'Golden Glow' CTri ECrN EPfP GBin NLar SLon SWvt WLav WSFF
- 'Honeycomb' GBin MGos NLar
- 'Lady de Ramsey' SEND
- 'Moonlight' CBcs CExl CNec ELan ETwe GBin LRHS SLon SPer WCot WLav
- 'Pink Pagoda'PBR CNec EPfP LRHS SLon SPoG
- 'Sungold' ♀H4 Widely available
'Winter Sun' SLon
yunnanensis CBcs GCal NLar SLon
- B&SWJ 8146 WCru

Buglossoides (*Boraginaceae*)

§ ***purpurocaerulea*** CHll CSpe ECha ELan EPfP LSun MLHP MNrw MWhi NBid NChi WCot WHea WSHC XLum

Bukiniczia (*Plumbaginaceae*)

cabulica CSpe GKev WAbe

Bulbine (*Asphodelaceae*)

SH 74 CCse

abyssinica	ECho
alooides	ECho WCot
annua misapplied	see *B. semibarbata*
bulbosa misapplied	see *B. semibarbata*
capitata 'Bloemfontein'	ECho
caulescens	see *B. frutescens*
§ ***frutescens***	CBod CDoC CHll MHer SBHP SMad SVen WJek
- 'Hallmark'	CCCN
latifolia	CCCN
narcissifolia 'Ladybrand'	ECho
§ ***semibarbata***	CCCN

Bulbinella (*Asphodelaceae*)

angustifolia	ECho MHer
cauda-felis	WCot
- 'Tulbagh'	ECho
eburniflora	ECho
elata	WCot
gibbsii var. ***balanifera***	ECho
graminifolia 'Clanwilliam'	ECho
hookeri	CExl CHel EBee ECho EWld GBee GBin GEdr GKev ITim LRHS MHer NChi SRms WHal WThu
latifolia	ECho
- subsp. ***doleritica***	ECho
- subsp. ***latifolia***	IBlr
nutans	CDes EBee ECho WPGP
punctulata 'Piketberg'	ECho

Bulbinopsis see *Bulbine*

Bulbocodium (*Colchicaceae*)

vernum	ECho EPot GKev LAma LLHF NMin SDeJ

bullace see *Prunus insititia*

Bunias (*Brassicaceae*)

orientalis	CAgr LEdu

Bunium (*Apiaceae*)

bulbocastanum	CAgr CSpe IMou LEdu SDix SHDw XLum

Buphthalmum (*Asteraceae*)

salicifolium	CSam EBee ELan EPfP MMuc NBro NGdn SEND SPer SRms SWat WCot WWtn XLum
- 'Alpengold'	ECha GMaP NBre NLar
- 'Dora'	ECtt WCot
- 'Sunwheel'	LRHS SRms
speciosum	see *Telekia speciosa*

Bupleurum (*Apiaceae*)

angulosum	NBir
- copper-leaved	see *B. longifolium*
falcatum	ECGP ECha LRHS NDov WCot WWFP
fruticosum	CBcs CFil CSpe EBee ELan EPfP GBin LRHS MAsh NSoo SCob SDix SEND SKHP SLon SMad SPer SPoG SSpi WCot WPGP WPat XSen
§ ***longifolium***	CElw CMea CPom CSpe EBee EWes LEdu LRHS MNrw NBir NChi SKHP SMad SMrm WSHC
- subsp. ***aureum***	SPhx
- 'Bronze Beauty' **new**	GEdr
- bronze-leaved	MAvo
ranunculoides	SPhx XLum
rotundifolium	CSpe LEdu SPhx
spinosum	SMad XSen
tenue	CArn

Burchellia (*Rubiaceae*)

capensis	SPlb

Bursaria (*Pittosporaceae*)

spinosa	CCCN CHll

Butia (*Arecaceae*)

capitata	CAbb CBcs CCCN CDTJ CPHo LPal SArc
§ - var. ***odorata***	SPlb
odorata	see *B. capitata* var. *odorata*
yatay	LPal NLos SBig

Butomus (*Butomaceae*)

umbellatus	CBAq CBen CRow CWat ECha EHon EPfP EWay GQue MNrw MRav MSKA MWts NBir NPer SRms SWat WMAq WWtn XLum
- f. ***albiflorus***	MSKA
- 'Rosenrot'	CRow EWay LLWG
- 'Schneeweisschen'	EWay GQue LLWG MNrw MWts NLar

butternut see *Juglans cinerea*

Buxus ✿ (*Buxaceae*)

sp.	MJak
aurea 'Marginata'	see *B. sempervirens* 'Marginata'
'Green Mound'	LBMP
'Green Velvet'	EPfP
harlandii hort.	CMen SRiv
japonica 'Nana'	see *B. microphylla*
§ ***microphylla***	MHer NWad NWea SGol
- 'Asiatic Winter'	see *B. microphylla* var. *japonica* 'Winter Gem'
§ - 'Compacta'	CMen LLHF MHer NWad SRiv WCot WPat WThu
- 'Curly Locks'	EPla NWad
- 'Faulkner' ♀H5	CCVT EAEE ELan EPfP LBuc LRHS LTop MAsh MGos MJak SCob SGol SPer SRiv SRms WGrf WMoo
- Golden Dream = 'Peergold'PBR	NLar SRms
- 'Golden Triumph'PBR	EBee EPfP SRms
- 'Green Pillow'	MHer SRiv
- var. ***insularis***	see *B. sinica* var. *insularis*
- var. ***japonica*** 'Morris Midget'	NWad
- - 'National'	NLar
§ - - 'Winter Gem'	MHer MRav NLar
- 'John Baldwin'	SRiv
- var. ***sinica***	LTop
'Newport Blue'	see *B. sempervirens* 'Newport Blue'
riparia	EPla
sempervirens	Widely available
§ - 'Angustifolia'	EPla MHer MRav NWad SMad
- 'Arborescens'	CNWT MBri
- 'Argentea'	see *B. sempervirens* 'Argenteo-variegata'
§ - 'Argenteo-variegata' (v)	EPfP IFoB MJak SGol
- 'Aurea'	see *B. sempervirens* 'Aureovariegata'

	- 'Aurea Maculata'	see *B. sempervirens* 'Aureovariegata'
	- 'Aurea Marginata'	see *B. sempervirens* 'Marginata'
	- 'Aurea Pendula' (v)	CJun
§	- 'Aureovariegata' (v)	EBee EPfP EShb LRHS LTop MGos MHer MRav NLar SBod SPer SRiv SRms WMoo
	- 'Bentley Blue'	LTop NWea
	- 'Blauer Heinz'	ELan EWTr IVic MHer MRav SRiv WMoo
	- 'Bowles's Blue'	EWes
I	- 'Brilliantissima'	WMoo
	- clipped ball	EPfP MGos NLar SGol SLim SRiv SRms
	- clipped bird	SRiv
	- clipped cone	SGol SRiv SRms
	- clipped pyramid	EPfP MGos NLar SGol SLim SRiv SRms
	- clipped spiral	SGol SRiv SRms
	- 'Elegans'	IFoB LRHS
§	- 'Elegantissima' (v) ♀H5	Widely available
	- 'Fiesta'	SRms
	- 'Gold Tip'	see *B. sempervirens* 'Notata'
§	- 'Graham Blandy' ♀H5	IVic MHer SGol SRiv
	- 'Green Balloon'	EPfP LBuc
	- 'Greenpeace'	see *B. sempervirens* 'Graham Blandy'
	- 'Handsworthensis'	CLnd CTri NLar NWea SEND SRms WMoo
	- 'Japonica Aurea'	see *B. sempervirens* 'Latifolia Maculata'
	- 'King Midas'	IVic
	- 'Kingsville'	see *B. microphylla* 'Compacta'
	- 'Kingsville Dwarf'	see *B. microphylla* 'Compacta'
	- 'Latifolia Macrophylla'	SLon
§	- 'Latifolia Maculata' (v) ♀H5	CAbP CDoC EPfP LRHS MHer NPer SEND SPoG SRiv WRHF
	- 'Longifolia'	see *B. sempervirens* 'Angustifolia'
§	- 'Marginata' (v)	CArn CPne EPla IFoB LRHS LTop SGol SLon WHar
	- 'Memorial'	LTop MHer NWad SMHy SRiv
	- 'Myosotidifolia'	NEoE SRiv WCot
	- 'Myrtifolia'	MHer
§	- 'Newport Blue'	NLar
§	- 'Notata' (v)	IFoB MAsh WHar WMoo
	- 'Parasol'	MHer
	- 'Prostrata'	NWad
	- 'Rosmarinifolia'	MHer MRav
	- 'Rotundifolia'	ELan SEND WGrf WMoo
	- 'Silver Beauty' (v)	LBMP
	- 'Silver Variegated'	see *B. sempervirens* 'Elegantissima'
	- 'Suffruticosa'	Widely available
	- 'Suffruticosa Variegata' (v)	SRms SWvt
	- 'Twisty'	WFar
	- 'Vardar Valley'	NEoE SRiv
*	- 'Variegata' (v)	ECrN MSwo
	- 'Waterfall'	MHer
§	***sinica*** var. ***insularis***	EPla
	- - 'Justin Brouwers'	MHer SRiv
	- - 'Tide Hill'	LTop MHer SRiv

C

Cacalia (*Asteraceae*)

plantaginea	see *Arnoglossum plantagineum*

Cachrys (*Apiaceae*)

alpina	SPhx

Caesalpinia (*Caesalpiniaceae*)

gilliesii ♀H1c	CBcs CSpe ETwe MOWG NLos SBrt SPlb WCot
mexicana	CSpe
pulcherrima ♀H1b	CCCN SPlb
spinosa	CBcs SPlb

Caiophora (*Loasaceae*)

coronata	SPlb

Caladium (*Araceae*)

'Candidum' (v)	SDeJ
'Carolyn Whorton'	SDeJ
'Florida Cardinal' (v)	SDeJ
'Freida Hemple'	SDeJ
'White Christmas' (v)	SDeJ

Calamagrostis (*Poaceae*)

	sp.	MAsh
	× ***acutiflora***	XLum
	- 'Avalanche'	CKno ECha EHoe EPPr EPla EShb EWes LRHS MWhi NWsh WWEG
	- 'Eldorado' (v)	WCot
	- 'Karl Foerster'	Widely available
	- 'Overdam' (v)	Widely available
	- 'Stricta'	EBee EPPr NWsh WWEG
	- 'Waldenbuch'	CKno
	argentea	see *Stipa calamagrostis*
	arundinacea	CElw CExl CMac CSpe SDix SPlb WMoo WPGP XLum
	'Avalanche'	CKno GBin GCal GQue MAsh NOak
§	***brachytricha*** ♀H7	Widely available
	- 'Mona'	NDov
	canadensis	EPPr
	emodensis	CAby CMea CSam CSpe CWCL EBee ECha EHoe EPPr MAvo MMoz MWhi NBid NOak NWsh SMad WCot WGrn WHea WMoo WPGP WWEG
	epigejos	CKno LEdu WHrl
	foliosa <u>new</u>	EPPr
	nutkaensis	EPPr
	splendens misapplied	see *Stipa calamagrostis*
	splendens Trin.	LPla NDov
	varia	CKno EBee EHoe GBin SMrm WHrl

Calamintha (*Lamiaceae*)

	alpina	see *Acinos alpinus*
§	***ascendens***	CArn EBee WMoo
	clinopodium	see *Clinopodium vulgare*
*	'Fritz Kuhn'	WWEG
§	***grandiflora***	CArn CBod CMea ECha ELan GJos GPoy ITim LEdu MHer MMuc MNHC MNrw MRav MWat MWhi NBir NPer SPer SPlb SRms WHea WJek WMoo
	- 'Elfin Purple'	EBee EPfP
	- 'Variegata' (v)	ECtt ELan ENfk EPPr EPfP MPie SPoG WCAu
	'Harrogate'	NDov
§	***menthifolia***	NBre NLar WJek
§	***nepeta***	CArn CHab CMea ECha ENfk EPla GMaP LAst LRHS MHer MNFA

		MNHC NBro SCob SEND SPhx SPlb SPoG SRms SWat WCAu WJek WMoo WOut
	- subsp. ***glandulosa***	ECGP WMoo
	- - ACL 1050/90	EBee WHoo
	- - 'White Cloud'	CSpe EBee ECGP ECtt ELan EPla GQue LLWP MRav NBir SPoG WCAu WHea WMoo
	- 'Gottfried Kuehn'	LPla MRav
§	- subsp. ***nepeta***	COtt ELan ELon EPfP IMou MCot MHer MLHP MRav MWat NDov NSti SPer WFar WHal WWEG XLum
	- - 'Blue Cloud'	CFis CSam CSpe EBee ECha EPfP EPri MAvo MRav MSpe MWat NBir NDov SPhx SPtp WCAu WFar WMoo WWEG
	- 'Weisse Riese'	CMea SPhx
	nepetoides	see *C. nepeta* subsp. *nepeta*
	officinalis misapplied	see *C. ascendens*
	sylvatica	see *C. menthifolia*
I	- 'Menthe'	LPla
	vulgaris	see *Clinopodium vulgare*

calamondin see *Citrus × microcarpa*

Calandrinia (*Portulacaceae*)

*	***ranunculina***	CPBP
	sibirica	see *Claytonia sibirica*
	umbellata	EDAr LBMP MAsh WIce
	- 'Ruby Tuesday'	NPri XLum

Calanthe (*Orchidaceae*)

	alismifolia	EFEx
	arcuata	EFEx
	arisanenesis	EFEx
	aristulifera	EFEx GKev
	bicolor	see *C. striata*
	discolor	CDes EBee EFEx GKev LAma WCot
	- subsp. ***amamiana***	EFEx
	- var. ***flava***	see *C. striata*
	- subsp. ***tokunoshimensis***	EFEx
	fargesii	WCot
	graciliflora	EFEx
	Hizen gx	GKev
	Kozu gx	GKev LEdu
	mannii	EFEx
	nipponica	CBct EBee EFEx GKev LAma
	reflexa	EFEx GKev LAma
	sieboldii	see *C. striata*
§	***striata***	CBct EFEx GKev WCot
	sylvatica	EBee GKev WCot
	Takane gx	GKev
	tricarinata	CBct EBee EFEx GKev LAma
	triplicata	GKev

Calathea (*Marantaceae*)

	argyrophylla 'Exotica'	XBlo
	louisae 'Maui Queen'	XBlo
§	***majestica*** ♀H1b	XBlo
	makoyana ♀H1b	XBlo
	ornata	see *C. majestica*
	picturata 'Argentea' ♀H1b	XBlo
	roseopicta ♀H1b	XBlo
	- 'Rosastar'	XBlo
	rufibarba ♀H1b	NGBl XBlo
*	***stromata***	XBlo
	veitchiana 'Medaillon'	XBlo
	zebrina ♀H1b	XBlo
	'Zoizia'	XBlo

Calceolaria (*Calceolariaceae*)

	acutifolia	see *C. polyrhiza* Cav.
	andina new	GKev
	arachnoidea	EBee GEdr SKHP SPlb
§	***biflora***	ECho GKev
	- 'Goldcap'	ECho SMrm
	- 'Goldcrest Amber'	SPlb
	corymbosa	GKev
	falklandica	ECho GBin NSla SRms
	filicaulis	GKev
	fothergillii	GKev GLog WAbe
	'Goldcrest'	ECho LRHS SRms
	integrifolia ♀H1c	CAbb CBcs CDTJ CExl CSpe CTri ECtt ELan MGil MSCN NSoo SAdn SEND SPer SRms WAbe WBor
	- bronze	MSCN SPer
	- 'Gaines' Yellow'	EBee GCal
	'John Innes'	ECho
	'Kentish Hero'	CSpe CTsd GBin GCal SDys WAbe
	pavonii new	MGil
	aff. ***pavonii***	CRHN
	perfoliata B&SWJ 10638	WCru
	plantaginea	see *C. biflora*
§	***polyrhiza*** Cav.	ECho GKev
	rugosa	see *C. integrifolia*
	tenella	ECho NSla WAbe
	uniflora var. ***darwinii***	ECho GKev WAbe
	'Walter Shrimpton'	ECho EPot EWes WAbe

Calendula (*Asteraceae*)

	arvensis	CCCN
	'Bronze Beauty'	CSpe
	officinalis	CArn CUse ELau ENfk GPoy MHer MNHC SIde SPav SRms SVic SWvt WJek WSFF
	- 'Art Shades'	CWCL
	- 'Calypso Orange' (Calypso Series)	CWCL
	- Fiesta Gitana Group	WJek
	- 'Touch of Red Buff' (Touch of Red Series)	CSpe
	'Tarifa'	SEND

Calibanus (*Asparagaceae*)

	hookeri	EShb

Calibrachoa (*Solanaceae*)

	(Cabaret Series) Cabaret Apricot = 'Balcabapt'	NPri
	- Cabaret Bright Red = 'Balcabrite' new	NPri
	- Cabaret Deep Blue = 'Balcabdebu'PBR	NPri
	- Cabaret Deep Yellow = 'Balcabdepy' new	NPri
	- Cabaret Hot Pink = 'Balcabhopi'PBR	NPri
	- Cabaret White = 'Balcabwit' new	NPri
	(Can-can Series) Can-can Black Cherry new	NPri
	- Can-can Apricot = 'Balcanapt'	NPri

- Can-can Rose Star = 'Balcanrost'	NPri
(Million Bells Series) Million Bells Trailing Blue = 'Sunbelkubu'PBR	LAst
- Million Bells Trailing Ice = 'Sunbelkuriho'PBR	LAst
- Million Bells Trailing Lavender Vein = 'Sunbelbura'PBR	LSou
- Million Bells Trailing Lemon	LSou
(MiniFamous Series) MiniFamous Double Blush Pink = 'Kleca08164'	LAst
- MiniFamous Double Lemon = 'Kleca09204'PBR	LAst
- MiniFamous Double Nostalgia	LAst
(Superbells Series) Superbells Amarena = 'Uscal33703'PBR	LAst
- Superbells Apricot Punch = 'Uscali41308'	LAst
- Superbells Cherry Punch **new**	LAst
- Superbells Cherry Star **new**	LAst
- Superbells Double Rose = 'Us08cj0202' **new**	LAst
- Superbells Double Ruby = 'Uscal83901' **new**	LAst
- Superbells Gold **new**	LAst
- Superbells Imperial Purple = 'Uscali100'PBR	LAst LSou
- Superbells Lemon Slice = 'Uscal5302m' **new**	LAst NPri
- Superbells Orange = 'Uscali41109'	LAst LSou
- Superbells Pink = 'Uscali11'PBR	LAst LSou
- Superbells Red = 'Uscali28'PBR	NPri
- Superbells Royal Blue = 'Uscali4'PBR	LAst
- Superbells White (2007) = 'Uscal1651'	LAst
- Superbells Yellow = 'Uscali53002'	LAst

Calla (*Araceae*)

aethiopica	see *Zantedeschia aethiopica*
palustris	CBAq CBen CRow CWat EBee EHon EWay MSKA MWts NPer SRms SWat WMAq

Calliandra (*Mimosaceae*)

'Dixie Pink'	CCCN
eriophylla	SPlb
portoricensis	CCCN
surinamensis	CCCN
tweediei ♀H1c	CCCN MOWG

Callianthemum (*Ranunculaceae*)

anemonoides	LLHF WAbe WCot
coriandrifolium	GEdr
kernerianum	GEdr WAbe

Callicarpa (*Lamiaceae*)

acuminata	CFil
americana	CExl NLar
- var. ***lactea***	CMCN
bodinieri	CHll WHar
- var. ***giraldii***	GBin MRav NLar SGol
- - 'Profusion' ♀H5	Widely available
'Cardinal' **new**	CJun
cathayana	NLar
dichotoma	CBcs CExl NLar
- f. ***albifructa***	ETwe
- 'Issai'	EPfP ESwi ETwe LRHS NLar WPat
- 'Variegata' (v)	CJun
japonica	CExl CMen NLar
- B&SWJ 12621	WCru
- f. ***albibacca***	ESwi
- 'Heavy Berry'	NLar
- 'Koshima-no-homate'	NLar
- 'Leucocarpa'	CBcs CExl CHel CMac ELan EPfP ESwi EWTr MRav NLar SPer SPoG
- var. ***luxurians*** B&SWJ 8521	WCru
kwangtungensis	CBcs EPfP ESwi ETwe MMuc NLar
mollis	CBcs CExl
shikokiana	NLar
× ***shirasawana***	NLar
aff. ***tikusikensis*** B&SWJ 7127	WCru
Van den Broek selection	NLar
yunnanensis	NLar

Callirhoe (*Malvaceae*)

involucrata	SBrt SMad WHrl XLum
- var. ***tenuissima***	GCal SMad

Callisia (*Commelinaceae*)

fragrans	EOHP EShb

Callistemon (*Myrtaceae*)

acuminatus	CCCN
'Awanga Dam'	ECou
brachyandrus	SVen
'Burgundy'	MOWG
'Candy Pink'	MOWG
citrinus	CBcs CHel CHll CTri CWSG ECou EPfP EPri SEND SPlb SRms WGrn WHar
- 'Albus'	see *C. citrinus* 'White Anzac'
- 'Angela'	MOWG
- 'Firebrand'	LRHS MAsh
- 'Splendens' ♀H3	Widely available
§ - 'White Anzac'	CDoC CMac CSde ELan EMil EPfP LRHS MOWG SEND SPoG
comboynensis	CCCN
glaucus	see *C. speciosus*
'Hannah's Child'	MOWG
'Happy Valley'	ECou MOWG
'Havering Gold'	ECou
'Havering Pink'	ECou
'Havering Red'	ECou
'Inferno'	LRHS NEgg
'Injune'	MOWG
'Kings Park Special'	MOWG
laevis hort.	see *C. rugulosus*
linearis ♀H2	CBcs CMac CSde CTri ECou ECrN ELan EPfP LRHS MAsh MHer MHin

	MOWG SEND SLim SLon SPlb SRms SWvt WSHC
macropunctatus	SPlb SVen
'Masotti'[PBR]	LRHS MPkF SPoG
'Mauve Mist'	CCCN CDoC CHll ELan EPfP EPri GBin LRHS MOWG SPoG SVen WGrn
'Millie Marsden'	MOWG
pachyphyllus	MOWG
- var. ***viridis***	MOWG
pallidus	CBcs CCCN CHEx CHel CMac CTsd ECou ELan EPfP IDee LRHS MAsh MOWG MRav SDys SEND SPer SPlb SPoG SVen
- 'Candle Glow'	MOWG
- 'Father Christmas'	MOWG
paludosus	see *C. sieberi* DC.
pearsonii 'Rocky Rambler'	MOWG
'Perth Pink'	CBcs CCCN CDoC CSde ELan EPfP LRHS MOWG SLim SVen
phoeniceus	MOWG
- 'Pink Ice'	MOWG
pinifolius	SPlb SVen
- 'Sockeye'	MOWG
'Pink Champagne'	MOWG
§ ***pityoides***	CExl ECou MOWG SVen
- from Brown's Swamp, Australia	ECou
recurvus	MOWG
'Red Clusters'	CMac ELan EPfP IArd LRHS MAsh MJak MOWG NPri SEle SWvt
'Reeve's Pink'	MOWG
rigidus	CBcs CChe CDoC CHEx CHll CMHG CTri CTsd ELan EPfP EPri GAbr IArd LRHS MGos MMuc MRav NLar SEle SPer SVen SWvt
§ ***rugulosus***	CCCN EPla MOWG SVen SWvt
salignus ♀H2	CBcs CCCN CDoC CDul CMac CTri CTsd EPfP GLin LPal LRHS MHer MOWG MRav NEgg NLar SEle SLim SPer SVen
sieberi misapplied	see *C. pityoides*
§ ***sieberi*** DC.	CBcs CDoC CHel CTsd ELan EPfP LRHS MMuc MOWG NBir NLar SEND SLim SPlb
- purple-flowered	MOWG
§ ***speciosus***	CDul MOWG NLar SPlb
subulatus	CHEx ECou GGal MOWG SArc SPlb
- 'Crimson Tail'	ECrN NLar SEND SPtp
I - 'Packer's Selection'	ECou MOWG
'Taree Pink'	MOWG
viminalis	CBcs CCCN LPal MOWG SPlb
- 'Captain Cook'	CHel CMac ECou IDee LRHS MOWG NEgg NLar SRms SVen SWvt WGrn
- 'Endeavor'	CCCN SLim
- 'Hannah Ray'	EUJe MOWG
- Hot Pink = 'Kkho1'[PBR]	EPla LRHS MPkF NPri SCoo SHil SLim
- 'Little John'	CSde LRHS MAsh MOWG SPad SWvt
- 'Malawi Giant'	MOWG
'Violaceus'	SPlb SVen
viridiflorus	CMCN ECou GGal SEND SPlb WGwG
- 'County Park Dwarf'	ECou
'White Anzac'	see *C. citrinus* 'White Anzac'

Callistephus (*Asteraceae*)

chinensis	SVic

Callitriche (*Plantaginaceae*)

sp.	WSFF
autumnalis	see *C. hermaphroditica*
brutia subsp. ***hamulata***	LLWG
§ ***hermaphroditica***	CBAq
§ ***palustris***	CBen MSKA MWts
stagnalis	WMAq
verna	see *C. palustris*

Callitropsis see *Chamaecyparis*

× ***leylandii***	see × *Cuprocyparis leylandii*
nootkatensis	see *Xanthocyparis nootkatensis*

Calluna ✿ (*Ericaceae*)

sp.	CAco
vulgaris	SWhi WOut
- 'Adrie'	SWhi
- 'Alba Elongata'	see *C. vulgaris* 'Mair's Variety'
§ - 'Alba Rigida'	CFst
- 'Alexandra'[PBR] (Garden Girls Series)	IVic SCoo SPoG
- 'Alicia'[PBR] (Garden Girls Series) ♀H7	LRHS SCoo SPoG SWhi
- 'Allegro'	EAEE EPfP MMuc SCoo SWhi
- 'Amethyst'[PBR] (Garden Girls Series)	LRHS MJak MMuc SPoG SWhi
- 'Amilto'	CFst SPer SWhi
- 'Anette'[PBR] (Garden Girls Series)	MJak SCoo SWhi
- 'Annabel' (d)	SWhi
- 'Annegret'	see *C. vulgaris* 'Marlies'
- 'Annemarie' (d) ♀H7	CBcs CFst CSBt EPfP SCoo SPlb SWhi
- 'Anne's Goldzwerg'	CFst
- 'Anne's Zwerg'	CFst
- 'Anthony Davis'	SWhi
- 'Aphrodite'[PBR] (Garden Girls Series)	CFst LRHS SWhi
- 'Arina'	MAsh SCoo SWhi
- 'Athene'[PBR] (Garden Girls Series)	CFst SPer SWhi
- 'Aurea'	MJak
- 'Beoley Crimson'	SCoo
- 'Beoley Gold' ♀H7	CSBt CTri EPfP MAsh NHol SCoo SWhi
- 'Beoley Silver'	SCoo SWhi
- 'Blazeaway'	CTri EPfP MAsh MJak SCoo SWhi
- 'Bonfire Brilliance'	CSBt NHol
- 'Bonita'[PBR] (Garden Girls Series)	CFst SPer SWhi
- 'Boskoop'	IVic MAsh NHol SWhi
- 'C.W. Nix'	CSBt
- 'Con Brio'	CFst CSBt SCoo SWhi
- 'Cottswood Gold'	SCoo
- 'County Wicklow' (d) ♀H7	CTri EPfP MMuc NHol SCoo SWhi
- 'Cuprea'	EPfP MJak SCoo SWhi
- 'Dark Beauty'[PBR] (d) ♀H7	CBcs CFst CSBt EPfP IVic MAsh NHol SCoo SPer SWhi
- 'Dark Star' (d) ♀H7	CFst CSBt EPfP MAsh MMuc NHol SCoo SWhi
- 'Darkness' ♀H7	CBcs CFst CTri EPfP MAsh MJak SCoo SWhi
- 'David Hagenaars'	SWhi
- 'Disco Queen' **new**	SWhi
- 'Dunnet Lime'	SPlb

	Name	Suppliers
	– 'Easter-bonfire'	SCoo SWhi
	– 'Elsie Purnell' (d) 🏆H7	CFst EPfP MAsh NHol SCoo SPlb SWhi
	– 'Feuerwerk'	SCoo
	– 'Firefly' 🏆H7	CFst CSBt EAEE EPfP MJak MMuc NHol NWea SCoo SPer SWhi
	– 'Flamingo'	MMuc SCoo SWhi
	– 'Forest Fire'	CFst SWhi
	– 'Foxii Nana'	CFst NHol SWhi
	– 'Fred J. Chapple'	MJak SWhi
	– 'Galaxy' PBR **new**	CFst
	– Garden Girls Series	MMuc
	– 'Glenfiddich'	CSBt MAsh
	– 'Gold Haze'	CTri MAsh NHol SCoo SWhi
	– 'Gold Knight'	EPfP MAsh SCoo
	– 'Golden Carpet'	CFst CSBt MAsh NHol
	– 'Golden Fleece'	CFst
	– 'Golden Turret'	MAsh
	– 'Grey Carpet'	CFst
	– 'Guinea Gold'	MAsh
§	– 'H.E. Beale' (d)	CTri EPfP MJak NHol SCoo
	– 'Hammondii Aureifolia'	SPlb SWhi
	– 'Hammondii Rubrifolia'	SWhi
	– 'Highland Rose'	SPlb
	– 'J.H. Hamilton' (d)	CTri MAsh NHol SCoo SWhi
	– 'Jan Dekker'	MAsh SPer SWhi
	– 'Joan Sparkes' (d)	SPer
	– 'Johnson's Variety'	SCoo
	– 'Josefine'	SWhi
	– 'Joy Vanstone'	EPfP
	– 'Kerstin' 🏆H7	CFst CSBt MMuc NHol SCoo SPlb SWhi
	– 'Kinlochruel' (d) 🏆H7	CBcs CFst CSBt CTri EPfP MAsh NHol SPer SPlb SWhi
	– 'Kirby White'	MAsh SPlb SWhi
	– 'Klaudine' PBR (Garden Girls Series)	CFst IVic
	– 'Larissa' PBR (Garden Girls Series)	SPer
	– 'Lemon Queen'	CFst
	– 'Leprechaun'	SWhi
	– 'Leslie Slinger'	SCoo SWhi
	– 'Loch Turret'	SPer
	– 'Long White'	CFst SWhi
	– 'Madonna' PBR (Garden Girls Series)	SWhi
§	– 'Mair's Variety'	SCoo
	– 'Marleen'	MJak SWhi
§	– 'Marlies'	SWhi
	– 'Melanie' (Garden Girls Series)	NHol SCoo SWhi
	– 'Mrs Pat'	MAsh
	– 'Multicolor'	MAsh NHol
§	– 'My Dream' (d)	CSBt EPfP SCoo
	– 'Nana Compacta'	CFst
	– 'October White'	CFst
	– 'Orange Queen'	CSBt
	– 'Peter Sparkes' (d) 🏆H7	CBcs CSBt EPfP MAsh MMuc NHol SCoo SWhi
	– 'Pink Alicia' PBR (Garden Girls Series)	LRHS
	– 'Pink Beale'	see *C. vulgaris* 'H.E. Beale'
	– 'Purple Passion'	EPfP SCoo
	– 'Radnor' (d)	CSBt
	– 'Ralph Purnell'	SCoo
	– 'Rebecca's Red'	LRHS
	– 'Red Beauty'	CBcs CFst SPer SWhi
	– 'Red Favorit' (d)	CFst SPer SWhi
	– 'Red Fred'	SCoo
	– 'Red Haze'	EPfP NHol SCoo
	– 'Red Pimpernel'	EPfP SCoo SWhi
	– 'Red Star' (d)	NHol
	– 'Reini'	SWhi
	– 'Rigida Prostrata'	see *C. vulgaris* 'Alba Rigida'
	– 'Robert Chapman' 🏆H7	CFst CSBt CTri MAsh NHol SPer SWhi
	– 'Rosalind' ambig.	EPfP
	– 'Rosalind, Underwood's'	EPfP NHol
	– 'Rosann' **new**	SPer
	– 'Rosita' PBR	CFst
	– 'Roswitha'	CFst
	– 'Roter Oktober'	SWhi
	– 'Ruby Slinger'	NHol SWhi
	– 'Ruth Sparkes' (d)	NHol
	– 'Safari' **new**	CFst
	– 'Sandy' PBR (Garden Girls Series)	LRHS SPer SPoG SWhi
	– 'Schurig's Sensation' (d)	IVic
	– 'Serlei Aurea'	CSBt EPfP MAsh
	– 'Silvana' PBR **new**	CFst
	– 'Silver Fox'	CFst
	– 'Silver Knight'	CSBt EPfP MAsh MJak NHol SCoo SPlb SWhi
	– 'Silver Queen' 🏆H7	CFst MAsh MJak NHol SWhi
	– 'Silver Rose'	SWhi
	– 'Sir John Charrington'	CFst CSBt EPfP MAsh NHol SWhi
	– 'Sister Anne' 🏆H7	CFst CSBt EPfP MJak MMuc SCoo SWhi
	– 'Snowball'	see *C. vulgaris* 'My Dream'
	– 'Sonja' (d)	IVic
	– 'Spitfire'	MAsh
	– 'Spring Cream' 🏆H7	CBcs CFst MAsh MMuc NHol SCoo SPoG SWhi
	– 'Spring Torch'	CBcs CFst CSBt MAsh MJak NHol SCoo SPoG SWhi
	– 'Stefanie'	SWhi
	– 'Strawberry Delight' (d)	EPfP SCoo
	– 'Sun Sprinkles' **new**	CFst
	– 'Sunrise'	EPfP
	– 'Sunset'	CFst SWhi
	– 'Theresa' (Garden Girls Series)	CFst SPer
	– 'Tib' (d) 🏆H7	CSBt MAsh SWhi
	– 'Tricolorifolia'	EPfP MAsh SCoo SWhi
	– 'Velvet Fascination' 🏆H7	EPfP SCoo SWhi
	– 'White Coral' (d) 🏆H7	EPfP IVic SCoo SWhi
	– 'White Lawn'	CFst MMuc NHol SWhi
	– 'Wickwar Flame' 🏆H7	CBcs CFst CSBt EPfP MAsh MJak MMuc NHol SCoo SPlb SWhi
	– 'Winter Chocolate'	CSBt EPfP MAsh NHol SCoo SWhi
	– 'Yellow Beauty' PBR	CFst
	– 'Yvette's Gold'	CFst SWhi
	– 'Yvette's Silver'	CFst

Calocedrus (*Cupressaceae*)

	Name	Suppliers
§	***decurrens*** 🏆H6	CAco CBcs CDoC CDul CLnd CMac CMen CTho EHul EPfP EPla EUJe MBlu NWea SLim SPoG
	– 'Aureovariegata' (v) 🏆H6	CBcs CLnd EHul EPla MBri NPCo SCoo
	– 'Berrima Gold' 🏆H6	CDoC NLar SLim
§	– 'Depressa'	CKen
	– 'Intricata'	CKen SLim
	– 'Maupin Glow' (v)	NLar SLim
	– 'Nana'	see *C. decurrens* 'Depressa'
	– 'Pillar'	CKen NLar

Calochortus (*Liliaceae*)

albus	ECho
- var. ***rubellus***	ECho
aureus	ECho
caeruleus	ECho
'Cupido'PBR	CExl GKev LAma
invenustus	ECho
luteus Douglas ex Lindl.	EPot
- 'Golden Orb'PBR	CExl ECho GKev LAma SDeJ
splendens 'Violet Queen'	ECho GKev LAma
superbus	ECho EPot GKev SDeJ
'Symphony'PBR	CExl ECho EPot GKev LAma SDeJ
venustus	ECho EPot GKev LAma SDeJ
- 'Burgundy'	ECho EPot SDeJ
vestae	WCot

Calomeria (*Asteraceae*)

§ ***amaranthoides***	WJek

Calonyction see *Ipomoea*

Caloscordum see *Allium*

Calothamnus (*Myrtaceae*)

quadrifidus	ECou
- yellow-flowered	MOWG
validus	SPlb

Calpurnia (*Papilionaceae*)

aurea	SPlb

Caltha (*Ranunculaceae*)

howellii	see *C. leptosepala* subsp. *howellii*
introloba	SWat
laeta	see *C. palustris* var. *palustris*
leptosepala	CRow EBee EWTr EWay GEdr GKev LLHF NLar
§ - subsp. ***howellii***	EBee GKev
- - NNS 07-87	GKev
natans	EWay LLWG
palustris	Widely available
- var. ***alba***	Widely available
- 'Auengold'	EBee LLWG
- 'Auenwald'	LLWG
- 'Flore Pleno' (d) ♀H7	Widely available
- 'Honeydew'	CDes CRow EWay LLWG WCot WSHC
- 'Marilyn'	LLWG
- 'Multiplex' (d)	ECtt GBin GBuc SRot
- Newlake hybrid	LLWG
- 'Pallida Plena' (d) **new**	SCob
§ - var. ***palustris***	CBAq CBen CBre CRow ECha EHon ELan EUJe EWay GCal MWts SWat WWtn
- - 'Plena' (d)	CBAq CWat EPla EWay LRHS MCot MSKA SGol SPoG
- var. ***radicans***	CRow EWay GEdr
- - 'Flore Pleno' (d)	CRow WWtn
- 'Stagnalis'	CRow MSKA MWts
- 'Yellow Giant'	MSKA
polypetala Hochst. ex Lorent	CCon CWat GCal GJos MSCN MSKA NPer SMad SWat WMAq
- from Turkey	SGSe
sagittata	WSHC

Calycanthus (*Calycanthaceae*)

fertilis	see *C. floridus* var. *glaucus*
floridus	Widely available
- 'Athens'	CBcs CJun NLar
§ - var. ***glaucus***	EPfP LRHS MAsh MGil SHil WSHC
- - 'Purpureus'	CBcs CJun MBlu MBri NLar
- var. ***laevigatus***	see *C. floridus* var. *glaucus*
- 'Michael Lindsay'	CJun MBri NLar
mohrii	NLar
occidentalis	CAgr CArn CBcs CDul CMCN CSpe EPPr MBlu MMuc SBrt WCFE

Calylophus (*Onagraceae*)

§ ***serrulatus***	MMuc

Calystegia (*Convolvulaceae*)

'Angel's Trumpets'	SKHP
§ ***hederacea*** 'Flore Pleno' (d)	SMad
japonica 'Flore Pleno'	see *C. hederacea* 'Flore Pleno'
soldanella NNS 99-85	WCot

Calytrix (*Myrtaceae*)

tetragona	SPlb

Camassia ✿ (*Asparagaceae*)

'Blue Candle'	EPot ERCP LAma SPhx
'Blue Heaven'	CMea CRos EBee ERCP LAma LRHS SDeJ SPhx
cusickii	CBod CBro CExl CTca CTri CWCL EBee ECho ECtt ELan EPfP EPot ERCP GKev IFro LAma LPot LRHS MBri MCot MNrw NBir NLar SDeJ SPer WCot
- white-flowered	IFoB NChi
- 'Zwanenburg'	CTca EBee ERCP GKev WCot
esculenta Lindl.	see *C. quamash*
'John Treasure' (d) **new**	MAvo
leichtlinii misapplied	see *C. leichtlinii* subsp. *suksdorfii*
leichtlinii (Baker) S.Watson	see *C. leichtlinii* subsp. *leichtlinii*
'Alba' misapplied	
* - 'Alba Plena'	MNrw NBir
I - 'Atrocaerulea'	GMaP
- 'Blue Wave'	ERCP NWad SBch
§ - subsp. ***leichtlinii***	Widely available
- 'Magdalen'	MAvo
- 'Plena' (d)	ECha
- 'Sacajawea'	CAvo CMea CTca EBee ERCP LAma LBuc LRHS MAvo SBch SDeJ
- 'Semiplena' (d)	CAvo CBro CMea CTca EBee ECtt EPfP ERCP LAma LRHS MBel MCot MNrw NSti SDix SPhx WBor WCot WHoo WShi
§ - subsp. ***suksdorfii***	GCra LBuc WCot
- - 'Alba'	CBod LRHS
- - Caerulea Group	Widely available
- - 'Electra'	CAvo ECha SMHy
- - 'Lady Eve Price'	SMHy
§ ***quamash***	CArn CAvo CBro CHel CTca CWCL EBee ECha ELan EPfP EPot ERCP GKev LAma LEdu LLWG LRHS MBel MBri MCot NBir SCob SDeJ SRms WFar WShi XLum
- 'Blue Melody' (v)	CAvo CBro CMea CSam CTca EBee ECtt EPot ERCP GKev GMaP IFro LEdu SDeJ
- 'Orion'	CBro EBee LRHS WCot

Camellia ✿ (*Theaceae*)

'Adorable' (*pitardii* hybrid)	LRHS
'Alpen Glo'	MPkF
'Annette Carol'	CDoC

'April Blush' SCog
'Ariel's Song' CDoC
'Auburn White' see *C. japonica* 'Mrs Bertha A. Harms'
'Baby Bear' MPkF
'Barbara Clark' (*reticulata* × *saluenensis*) CDoC LRHS MAsh SCog SCoo
'Bertha Harms Blush' see *C. japonica* 'Mrs Bertha A. Harms'
'Bett's Supreme' CDoC
'Black Lace' ♀H5 CTrh CTri EPfP LRHS MAsh MMuc SArc SCam SCog SCoo SEND SHil
'Blissful Dawn' CBcs CTrh
'Bonnie Marie' CDoC SCam SCog
'Canterbury' CDoC LRHS MPkF
'Champêtres Spring Awakening' MPkF
chekiangoleosa new CPne
'China Lady' (*granthamiana* × *reticulata*) SCam
'Christmas Daffodil' (*japonica* hybrid) MPkF
'Cinnamon Cindy' CDoC LRHS MPkF
'Cinnamon Sensation' LRHS MPkF SCog
'Congratulations' COtt CSBt
'Contessa Lavinia Maggi' see *C. japonica* 'Lavinia Maggi'
'Cornish Snow' (*cuspidata* × *saluenensis*) ♀H4 CBcs CDoC CDul CSBt CTri ELan GGal MGos NLar NSoo SCam SCog SPer SSpi
'Cornish Spring' (*cuspidata* × *japonica*) ♀H4 CCCN CDoC CHel CSBt CTrh CTsd LRHS MGos SCam SCog SPer
'Crimson Candles' ♀H5 LRHS MPkF SCam
'Cupido' new CWSG
cuspidata SCam SCog
'Czar' see *C. japonica* 'The Czar'
'Dainty Dale' CDoC SCam
'Delia Williams' see *C.* × *williamsii* 'Citation'
'Den Burton' (*japonica* × *reticulata*) SCam
'Diana's Charm' CDoC
'Doctor Clifford Parks' (*japonica* × *reticulata*) ♀H4 CDoC CTrh SCam
'Donckelaeri' see *C. japonica* 'Masayoshi'
edithae LRHS
'El Dorado' (*japonica* × *pitardii*) CDoC
'Elizabeth Bolitho' SCam
'Extravaganza' (*japonica* hybrid) ♀H5 CHel CTrh IArd SCam
'Fairy Blush' CDoC LRHS MPkF
'Fairy Wand' CDoC LRHS MPkF
'Fascination' SWvt
'Felice Harris' (*reticulata* × *sasanqua*) CDoC SCog
'Festival of Lights' MPkF
'Fiesta Grande' MPkF
'Fire 'n' Ice' CDoC
'Forty-niner' (*japonica* × *reticulata*) CBcs LRHS
'Fox's Fancy' CDoC
'Fragrant Pink' CDoC CTrh
'Francie L' (*reticulata* × *saluenensis*) ♀H4 CDoC CMac EPfP SCam SCog SSta
'Free Spirit' CTrh
'Freedom Bell' ♀H5 CDoC CHel CMHG CTrh EPfP GGal GKin LRHS MAsh MBri MPkF SCog SCoo
'Gay Baby' CDoC MPkF
'Golden Anniversary' see *C. japonica* 'Dahlohnega'
grijsii CExl CTrh
handelii CExl
'Happy Anniversary' COtt CSBt SWvt
§ ***hiemalis*** 'Bonanza' CTrh LRHS MPkF
- 'Chansonette' CDoC ELon SCog
§ - 'Dazzler' CBcs LRHS MGos SCam SCog
- 'Interlude' MPkF
- 'Kanjirō' CDoC SCam
- 'Shishigashira' CTrh
- 'Shōwa-no-sakae' CDoC LRHS MPkF SCog
§ - 'Sparkling Burgundy' ♀H5 CBcs CDoC ELon EPfP LRHS MGos NSoo SCam SCog SMDP SPoG
'High Fragrance' LRHS MPkF
'Hooker' CDoC LRHS MAsh SCoo
'Ice Follies' SCam
'Imbricata Rubra' see *C. japonica* 'Imbricata'
'Inspiration' (*reticulata* × *saluenensis*) ♀H4 CDoC CMac COtt CSam CTrh EPfP GKin MBri MGos NLar NSoo SCam SCog SPer
japonica CAco SEWo SPre
- 'Aaron's Ruby' CDoC COtt ELon LRHS SCam SCog
- 'Ada Pieper' CTrh
- 'Adelina Patti' ♀H5 CBcs CDoC CMHG CTrh ELon SCog
- 'Adolphe Audusson' ♀H5 Widely available
§ - 'Akashigata' ♀H5 CBcs CDoC ELon EPfP LRHS SCog SLim SSta WHar
- 'Alba Plena' ♀H5 CTrh LRHS NSoo SCog SWvt
- 'Alba Simplex' CDoC CDul CMac CTrh ELan EPfP IVic MBri MJak NPri SCam SCob SCog SSta
- 'Alexander Hunter' ♀H5 CDoC LRHS SCam SCog
- 'Alison Leigh Woodroof' CDoC
§ - 'Althaeiflora' CBcs CDoC ELon LRHS SCam SCog
- 'Amazing Graces' CDoC
- 'Anemoniflora' CBcs CDoC EPfP LRHS SCam SCog
- 'Angel' CBcs SCam WBor
- 'Angello' LRHS
- 'Ann Sothern' CBcs
- 'Annette Gehry' CBcs
- 'Annie Wylam' ♀H5 CTrh
- 'Apollo 14' COtt
- 'Apollo' ambig. CBcs CDoC LRHS MBri MGos SPer
- 'Apollo' Paul, 1911 MSwo SCam SCog
§ - 'Apple Blossom' CTrh CTsd LRHS
- 'Arajishi' misapplied see *C. japonica* subsp. *rusticana* 'Beni-arajishi'
* - 'Augustine Supreme' CMac
- 'Australis' ♀H5 SCam
- 'Ave Maria' ♀H5 CDoC CTrh LRHS
- 'Baby Pearl' SCam
- 'Baby Sis' CDoC LRHS
- 'Ballet Dancer' ♀H5 CDoC ELon SCam SCog
- 'Bambino' CDoC
- 'Barbara Woodroof' CBcs
- 'Baron Gomer' see *C. japonica* 'Comte de Gomer'
- 'Baronne Leguay' SCam
- 'Beau Harp' CDoC LRHS SCam
- 'Bella Lambertii' SCog
- 'Bella Romana' SCam
- 'Benten-kagura' (v) CDoC
- 'Berenice Boddy' ♀H5 CBcs CDoC LRHS
- 'Berenice Perfection' CDoC SCog
- 'Betty Foy Sanders' CTrh
- 'Betty Robinson' CDoC LRHS
- 'Betty Sheffield' CDoC COtt LRHS MAsh SCog

	Cultivar	Suppliers
	– 'Betty Sheffield Pink'	LRHS SCam
	– 'Betty Sheffield Supreme'	CBcs
	– 'Betty's Beauty'	LRHS
	– 'Black Magic'	CTrh LRHS
	– 'Black Tie'	CDoC CTrh CWSG ELan ELon LRHS MBri MGos NEgg NSoo SCam SCog
	– 'Blackburnia'	see *C. japonica* 'Althaeiflora'
	– 'Blaze of Glory'	SCog
§	– 'Blood of China'	CBcs CDoC CSBt ELan LRHS MBri MGos MMuc NSoo SCam SCog SCoo SHil
	– 'Bob Hope' ♀H5	CBcs CDoC CTrh CTri LRHS MAsh
	– 'Bob's Tinsie' ♀H5	CBcs CDoC CMHG CSBt LRHS MGos MPkF NLar
§	– 'Bokuhan' ♀H5	CDoC MPkF
	– 'Bonomiana'	NLar
	– 'Bright Buoy'	CDoC LRHS
	– 'Brushfield's Yellow'	CBcs CDoC CMHG COtt CSBt CTrh CTsd EBee ELan ELon EPfP IArd LMil LRHS MAsh MBri MGos NLar SCam SCog SCoo SPer SSta
	– 'Bush Hill Beauty'	see *C. japonica* 'Lady de Saumarez'
§	– 'C.M. Hovey' ♀H5	CMHG CMac LRHS
	– 'C.M. Wilson'	CDoC CMac SCog
	– 'Campsii Alba'	CDoC CTsd
	– 'Can Can'	CDoC ELon SCog
	– 'Candy Apple'	CTrh
	– 'Candy Stripe'	CDoC
	– 'Captain Blood'	CDoC
	– 'Cara Mia'	CBcs CDoC CTsd LRHS SCam
	– 'Carolyn Tuttle'	LRHS
	– 'Carter's Sunburst' ♀H5	CBcs CDoC ELan EPfP SCog
	– 'Cassandra'	EPfP SHil
	– 'Chandleri Elegans'	see *C. japonica* 'Elegans'
	– 'Charlotte de Rothschild'	CTrh CTri
	– 'Cheryll Lynn'	CDoC
	– 'Cinderella'	CDoC LRHS SCog
	– 'Clarke Hubbs'	CDoC
	– Classique = 'Kerguelen'PBR	LRHS MBri MPkF SCog SPoG
	– 'Colonel Firey'	see *C. japonica* 'C.M. Hovey'
	– 'Commander Mulroy' ♀H5	CDoC CTrh SCam
§	– 'Comte de Gomer'	CDoC ELan ELon EPfP LRHS MBri MGos SCog
	– 'Conspicua'	CBcs
	– 'Contessa Samailoff'	CDoC
§	– 'Coquettii' ♀H5	CBcs LRHS
	– 'Coral Pink Lotus'	CDoC
	– 'Coral Queen'	CDoC
	– 'Cornish Excellence'	CDoC CHel
	– 'Curly Lady'PBR	MBri MMuc NPri WMoo
§	– 'Dahlohnega'	CDoC COtt CSBt CTrh ELon LRHS MAsh MGos MPkF SCam
	– 'Daikagura'	CBcs CDoC
	– 'Dainty'	CBcs
	– 'Daitairin'	see *C. japonica* 'Dewatairin'
	– 'Daphne du Maurier'	LRHS
	– 'Dark of the Moon'	CDoC LRHS MAsh
	– 'Dear Jenny'	CBcs
	– 'Debutante'	CBcs CDoC CMac COtt ELon MGos SCam SCog
	– 'Deep Secret' ♀H5	CDoC
	– 'Desire' ♀H5	CBcs CDoC CHel CMHG CSBt CTrh CTsd CWSG EPfP LMil LRHS MAsh MBri MPkF NLar SCam SCog SCoo SPoG
	– 'Devonia'	CBcs SCog
§	– 'Dewatairin' (Higo)	CBcs CDoC MGos SCam SCog
	– 'Diddy's Pink Organdie'	LRHS
	– 'Dixie Knight'	CBcs CDoC LRHS MGos SCam SCog
	– 'Dobreei'	CMac
	– 'Doctor Burnside'	CBcs CDoC CHel CTrh LRHS SCam SCog
	– 'Doctor King'	CWSG EPfP LRHS MBri NPri NSoo SPoG
	– 'Doctor Tinsley' ♀H5	CDoC LRHS MAsh NPri SCoo
	– 'Dolly Dyer'	CDoC
	– 'Dona Herzilia de Freitas Magalhaes'	CBcs CDoC ELon MGos SCam SCog
	– 'Dona Jane Andresson'	SCam
	– 'Donckelaeri'	see *C. japonica* 'Masayoshi'
	– 'Donnan's Dream'	CTrh
	– 'Drama Girl' ♀H5	CBcs CDoC CTsd LRHS SCam SCog
	– 'Duc de Bretagne'	SCog
	– 'Duchesse Decazes'	CBcs
	– 'Ed Combatalade'	CDoC
	– 'Edelweiss'	CDoC ELon SCam SCog
	– 'Effendee'	see *C. sasanqua* 'Rosea Plena'
§	– 'Elegans'	CBcs CDoC ELon EPfP LMil LRHS MBri SCam SCog SCoo SLim SPer SPoG SWvt
	– 'Elegans Champagne'	EPfP
	– 'Elegans Splendor'	CDoC
	– 'Elisabeth'	CDoC LRHS
	– 'Elizabeth Arden'	CTsd
	– 'Elizabeth Cooper'	CTrh
	– 'Elizabeth Dowd'	SCog
	– 'Elizabeth Hawkins'	CTrh LRHS MAsh MMuc NCGa
	– 'Emily Wilson'	CDoC
	– 'Emmett Pfingstl'	SCam
	– 'Emperor of Russia'	CBcs CDoC LRHS
	– 'Eric Baker'	CDoC SCam
	– 'Erin Farmer'	CBcs
	– 'Eugène Lizé'	SCam
	– 'Eximia'	EPfP LRHS SCam
	– 'Fanny'	SCog
	– 'Fashionata'	CDoC
	– 'Feast Perfection'	CDoC
	– 'Finlandia Variegated'	CDoC ELon SCam SCog
	– 'Fire Dance'	CDoC
	– 'Fire Falls' ♀H5	CDoC CMHG
	– 'Firebird'	CBcs
	– 'Flamingo'	CDoC
	– 'Flashlight'	CDoC EPfP LRHS
§	– 'Fleur Dipater'	LRHS SCam SCob
	– 'Flowerwood'	SCog
	– 'Forest Green'	CDoC
	– 'Frans van Damme'	CBcs
	– 'Fred Sander'	CBcs CDoC ELon LRHS MGos SCam SCog
	– 'Frosty Morn'	CDoC
§	– 'Gigantea'	LRHS SCam
	– 'Giuditta Rosani'	CDoC LRHS
	– 'Gladys Wannamaker'	SCog
	– 'Glen 40'	see *C. japonica* 'Coquettii'
	– 'Gloire de Nantes' ♀H5	CTrh SCam SCog
	– 'Gold Tone'	CDoC ELon MGos SCam
*	– 'Golden Wedding' (v)	SCog
	– 'Goshozakura'	CDoC
	– 'Grace Albritton' (d) **new**	MPkF
	– 'Grace Bunton'	CBcs CDoC ELon MGos SCam SCog
	– 'Granada'	SCog
	– 'Grand Prix' ♀H5	CDoC ELon MGos NLar SCam SCog SPer

	Cultivar	Suppliers
	- 'Grand Slam' 🏆H5	CBcs CDoC SCam
	- 'Grand Sultan'	CDoC
	- 'Guest of Honor'	CBcs CDoC COtt LRHS
	- 'Guilio Nuccio' 🏆H5	CBcs CDoC CHel COtt CTri EBee ELan ELon EPfP IArd LMil LRHS MBri NEgg NPri SCam SCog SCoo SLim SPer
	- 'Gus Menard'	SCam
	- 'Gwenneth Morey'	CBcs CDoC
	- 'H.A. Downing'	CDoC SCam
§	- 'Hagoromo' 🏆H5	CBcs CDoC CSBt CTrh CTsd ELan LRHS SCam
	- 'Hakugan'	EPfP NLar NSoo
§	- 'Hakurakuten' 🏆H5	CDoC CTrh CTri SCog
	- 'Hanafūki'	CDoC LRHS SCam SCog
	- 'Haru-no-utena'	CTrh MPkF
	- 'Hatsuzakura'	see *C. japonica* 'Dewatairin'
	- 'Hawaii'	CBcs CDoC CMac CTrh ELon LRHS SCam SCog
	- 'Her Majesty Queen Elizabeth II'	CDoC
	- Herme	see *C. japonica* 'Hikarugenji'
	- 'High Hat'	CBcs SCog
	- 'High, Wide 'n' Handsome'	CDoC
§	- 'Hikarugenji'	CDoC LRHS SCog
	- 'Hinomaru'	CDoC CMac
	- 'Hiryū'	MBri
	- 'Holly Bright'	CTrh MPkF
	- 'Honeyglow'	CDoC
	- 'Ichisetsu'	SCog
§	- 'Imbricata'	CTrh LRHS MAsh MMuc SCog
	- 'Italiana Vera'	LRHS MAsh
	- 'J.J. Whitfield'	CMac
	- 'Jack Jones Scented'	CMHG
	- 'Janet Waterhouse'	CBcs
§	- 'Japonica Variegata' (v)	CDoC LRHS
	- 'Jean Clere'	CDoC SCog
	- 'Jennifer Turnbull'	CDoC
	- 'Jessie Katz'	CDoC
	- 'Jingle Bells'	CBcs
	- 'Jitsugetsusei'	CDoC
	- 'Joseph Pfingstl' 🏆H5	CDoC CTri EPfP LRHS MBri MMuc NLar SCam SCog SEND
	- 'Jovey Carlyon'	CBcs LRHS
	- 'Joy Sander'	see *C. japonica* 'Apple Blossom'
	- 'Juan XXIII' **new**	SHil
	- 'Julia France'	SCog
	- 'Juno'	LRHS SCoo
	- 'Jupiter' Paul, 1904 🏆H5	CBcs CDoC CHel CMac COtt CTri EPfP SCam SCog WHar
	- 'Kellingtoniana'	see *C. japonica* 'Gigantea'
	- 'Kenny'	CBcs
	- 'Kentucky'	LRHS SCam
	- 'Kick-off'	CBcs CTrh SCog
	- 'Kimberley'	CBcs CDoC MPkF SCog
	- 'King Size'	CDoC MGos
	- 'King's Ransom'	CDoC CMac CTsd LRHS
	- 'Kingyoba-shiro-wabisuke'	CDoC
	- 'Kingyo-tsubaki'	CDoC SCam SSta
	- 'Kitty Berry'	CTrh
	- 'Kokinran'	CDoC SCam
§	- 'Konronkoku' 🏆H5	CBcs CDoC LRHS
	- 'Kouron-jura'	see *C. japonica* 'Konronkoku'
	- 'Kramer's Beauty'	COtt
	- 'Kramer's Supreme' 🏆H5	CBcs CCCN CDoC CDul ELon LRHS MBri SCog SCoo SGol SHil
§	- 'Kumasaka'	CTri LRHS
	- 'La Pace Rubra'	SCam
	- 'Lady Campbell'	CTri EPfP MBri NPri NSoo SCam
	- 'Lady Clare'	see *C. japonica* 'Akashigata'
§	- 'Lady de Saumarez'	CBcs CDoC CMac COtt
	- 'Lady Erma'	CBcs
	- 'Lady Loch'	CTrh SCam
	- 'Lady Marion'	see *C. japonica* 'Kumasaka'
	- 'Lady McCulloch'	LRHS
	- 'Lady Saint Clair'	CDoC
	- 'Lady Vansittart'	CDoC CTrh ELan EPfP GGal LRHS MAsh MBri MGos MPkF SCam SCog SCoo SLim SPer SPoG SSta
§	- 'Lady Vansittart Pink'	CMac
	- 'Lady Vansittart Red'	see *C. japonica* 'Lady Vansittart Pink'
	- 'Lady Vansittart Shell'	see *C. japonica* 'Yours Truly'
	- 'Lady Vere de Vere' (d)	CDoC
	- 'Latifolia'	SCam
	- 'Laura's Red'	CTsd
	- 'Laurie Bray'	NSoo SCog
§	- 'Lavinia Maggi' 🏆H5	CBcs CDoC CTri ELan ELon EPfP LMil LRHS MAsh MBri NPri SCam SCog SCoo SHil SPoG SReu SRms SSta
	- 'L'Avvenire'	SCog
	- 'Lemon Drop'	CBcs COtt CTrh
	- 'Leonora Novick'	CDoC SCog
	- 'Lillian Rickets'	CDoC
	- 'Lily Pons'	CDoC CTrh
	- 'Little Bit'	CBcs CDoC CMHG ELon MGos SCam SSta
	- 'Little Man'	COtt LRHS
	- 'Lovelight' 🏆H5	CHel CTrh LRHS
	- 'Lucy Hester'	CDoC
	- 'Ludgvan Red'	LRHS
	- 'Lulu Belle'	SCog
	- 'Mabel Blackwell'	ELon SCam
	- 'Madame de Strekaloff'	CMac CSBt SCam
	- 'Madame Hahn'	CDoC
	- 'Madame Lebois'	CBcs CDoC SCam
	- 'Madame Martin Cachet'	SCog
	- 'Madge Miller'	LRHS
	- 'Magnoliiflora'	see *C. japonica* 'Hagoromo'
	- 'Maiden's Blush'	CMac COtt
	- 'Man Size'	CDoC
	- 'Manuroa Road'	LRHS
	- 'Margaret Davis' 🏆H5	CCCN CDoC CHel COtt CSBt CWSG EBee ELan ELon EPfP LRHS MAsh MBri MPkF NEgg NPri NSoo SCam SCoo SHil SLim WFar
	- 'Margaret Davis Picotee'	CBcs CMHG CTrh SCog SPer
	- 'Margaret Rose'	SCam
	- 'Margaret Short'	CDoC CTsd
	- 'Margherita Coleoni'	CBcs
	- 'Marguérite Gouillon'	CBcs CDoC SSta
	- 'Marian Mitchell'	SCam
	- 'Mariana'	CDoC ELon SCog
	- 'Marinka'	CBcs
	- 'Mariottii Rubra'	CMac
	- 'Marjorie Magnificent'	LRHS MAsh SCoo
	- 'Mark Alan'	CDoC LRHS
	- 'Maroon and Gold'	CDoC LRHS SCog
	- 'Mars' 🏆H5	CBcs SCam SCog SPer
	- 'Mary Alice Cox'	CDoC
	- 'Mary Costa'	CBcs CDoC CTrh
§	- 'Masayoshi' 🏆H5	CBcs CSBt LRHS MAsh SCam SCog
	- 'Mathotiana Alba'	CDoC CMac CTri CTsd ELan EPfP MGos MMuc SCam SCog SPer
§	- 'Mathotiana Rosea'	CMac NLar SCam

	– 'Mathotiana Supreme'	CDoC SCam SCog
	– 'Matilija Poppy' **new**	CTrh
	– 'Matterhorn'	CTrh
	– 'Mattie Cole'	CDoC SCam
	– 'Mercury' 🏆H5	CBcs CMac EPfP GGGa SCog
	– 'Mercury Variegated' (v)	CMHG
	– 'Mermaid'	CDoC LRHS
	– 'Midnight'	CBcs CDoC CMHG LRHS MAsh SCoo
	– 'Midnight Magic'	CTrh CTri LRHS MAsh
	– 'Midnight Serenade'	CDoC LRHS
	– 'Midnight Variegated'	MPkF
	– 'Midsummer's Day'	CBcs
§	– 'Mikenjaku'	CBcs CDoC LRHS SCog
	– 'Miriam Stevenson'	SCam
	– 'Miss Charleston'	CBcs CHel SCog
	– 'Miss Lyla'	MMuc
	– 'Modern Art'	MPkF
	– 'Momiji-gari'	CDoC
	– 'Monsieur Faucillon'	CBcs
	– 'Monstruosa Rubra'	see *C. japonica* 'Gigantea'
	– 'Monte Carlo'	CDoC SCam SCog
	– 'Moonlight'	CDoC
	– 'Moshe Dayan'	CDoC LRHS MAsh SCog SCoo
	– 'Moshio'	CDoC
§	– 'Mrs Bertha A. Harms'	CDoC LRHS MGos SCam SCog
	– 'Mrs Charles Cobb'	LRHS
	– 'Mrs D.W. Davis'	CBcs CDoC EPfP SCam
	– 'Mrs Swan'	MBri NPri
	– 'Mrs William Thompson'	LRHS SCam
	– 'Nagasaki'	see *C. japonica* 'Mikenjaku'
	– 'Nigra'	see *C. japonica* 'Konronkoku'
	– 'Nioi-fubuki' (Higo)	CDoC
	– 'Nobilissima' 🏆H5	CBcs CDoC CMac CTrh CTri CWSG EBee EPfP LMil MBlu MBri MJak MMuc NLar NSoo SCam SCog SCoo SPer SPoG WFar
	– 'Nokogiriba-tsubaki'	MPkF
	– 'Nuccio's Cameo' 🏆H5	CBcs CDoC CTrh LMil LRHS MAsh MBri NPri SCoo
	– 'Nuccio's Gem' 🏆H5	CDoC CMHG ELan EPfP LRHS MAsh SCoo SGol
	– 'Nuccio's Jewel' 🏆H5	CDoC CSBt CTrh ELon EPfP LRHS MAsh SCam SCog WMoo
	– 'Nuccio's Pearl' 🏆H5	CBcs CDoC EPfP LRHS MAsh SCog SCoo
	– 'Nuccio's Pink Lace'	CDoC CTri LRHS
	– 'Olga Anderson'	CDoC
	– 'Onetia Holland'	CBcs CDoC EPfP MGos SCam SCog SLim
	– 'Oo-La-La'	CTrh LRHS MPkF
	– 'Optima'	CBcs CDoC ELon LRHS SCam SCog SCoo
	– 'Orandakō'	SCob SHil
	– 'Paul Jones Supreme'	CDoC
	– 'Paulette Goddard'	SCam
	– 'Paul's Apollo'	see *C. japonica* 'Apollo' Paul, 1911
	– 'Peachblossom'	see *C. japonica* 'Fleur Dipater'
	– 'Pearl Harbor'	SCam
	– 'Pensacola Red'	CDoC
	– 'Pink Champagne'	MBri
	– 'Primavera'	CTrh SCam SCog
	– 'Prince Murat'	CDoC LRHS
	– 'Princess Baciocchi'	SCam
	– 'Princess du Mahe'	CMac
	– 'R.L. Wheeler' 🏆H5	CBcs CDoC CSBt CTri EPfP LRHS MBri NPri SCog SCoo SPoG
	– 'Raspberry Ripple'	MPkF
	– 'Red Dandy'	CDoC SCam SCog
	– 'Red Red Rose'	CDoC LRHS
	– 'Reg Ragland'	CDoC MGos SCog
	– 'Roger Hall'	CBcs CDoC CTrh LRHS MBri SCoo SPoG
	– 'Rosa Baroveira Nella'	NLar NSoo
	– 'Rosularis'	CDoC ELon SCog
	– 'Royal Velvet'	CDoC CTrh
	– 'Rubescens Major'	CBcs
	– 'Ruddigore'	CTrh
§	– subsp. ***rusticana***	CBcs CDoC SCog
	– – 'Arajishi' misapplied	see *C. japonica* subsp. *rusticana* 'Beni-arajishi'
	– – 'Arajishi' Ko'emon	SCam
§	– – 'Beni-arajishi'	LRHS
	– – 'Reigyoku' (v)	CBcs CDoC
	– 'Sabiniana'	LRHS
	– 'Saint André'	CMac LRHS MAsh SCoo
	– 'San Dimas' 🏆H5	CDoC CTrh LRHS MGos MPkF SCam SCog
	– 'Saturnia'	CDoC ELon LRHS MMuc WBor
	– 'Sawada's Dream'	CDoC SCog
	– 'Scented Red'	CDoC
	– 'Scentsation' 🏆H5	CDoC CMHG CTri MBri SCog SHil
	– 'Sea Foam'	LRHS
	– 'Sea Gull'	CTrh
	– 'Senator Duncan U. Fletcher'	CDoC
	– 'Shikibu'	CTrh
	– 'Shiragiku'	CBcs CDoC EPfP SCog
	– 'Shiro Chan'	CDoC ELon MGos SCam SCog
	– 'Shirobotan'	CDoC ELon LRHS MAsh SCam SCog SCoo
	– 'Silver Anniversary' 🏆H5	CBcs CDoC CMHG COtt CSBt CTrh CTri ELan ELon EPfP LMil LRHS MAsh MGos NEgg NLar NPri NSoo SCam SCog SCoo SLim SPer SPoG SReu SWvt
	– 'Silver Chalice' **new**	MAsh
	– 'Silver Ruffles'	CDoC CTrh ELon LRHS SCam
	– 'Silver Waves'	MPkF
	– 'Something Beautiful'	CDoC
	– 'Souvenir de Bahuaud-Litou' 🏆H5	CDoC SCam SCog
	– 'Spencer's Pink'	CDoC
	– 'Splendens Carlyon'	LRHS SCoo
	– 'Spring Fever'	SCam
	– 'Spring Fling'	CTrh
	– 'Spring Formal'	CTrh
	– 'Spring Frill'	CWSG SCam
	– 'Stacy Susan'	MPkF
	– 'Strawberry Blonde'	SCog WFar
	– 'Strawberry Parfait'	CBcs CDoC COtt
	– 'Strawberry Swirl'	CBcs SCog
	– 'Sugar Babe'	CDoC CTrh LRHS SCog SCoo WHar
	– 'Suibijin'	SSpi
	– 'Sunset Glory'	SCam
	– 'Sweetheart'	SCog
	– 'Sylva' 🏆H5	EUJe GGGa GGal NSoo
	– 'Sylvia'	CMac
	– 'Takanini'	CBcs CDoC CTrh MPkF
	– 'Tama Electra'	MPkF
	– 'Tama-no-ura'	CDoC CTrh
	– 'Tammia'	CDoC COtt LRHS
	– 'Tarō'an'	CDoC GGal
	– 'Teresa Ragland'	CDoC SCam
	– 'Teringa'	CDoC
§	– 'The Czar'	CBcs

	Cultivar	Suppliers
	- 'The Mikado'	CDoC LRHS SCog
	- 'Tickled Pink'	CDoC
	- 'Tiffany'	CBcs CDoC ELon LRHS SCam SCog SCoo
	- 'Tinker Bell'	CDoC ELon MGos SCam SCog
	- 'Tinker Toy'	CTrh
	- 'Tom Pouce'	LRHS MPkF
	- 'Tom Thumb' 🏆[H5]	CDoC CTrh LRHS SRms
	- 'Tomorrow'	CBcs CDoC CTsd MMuc NEgg SCam SCog
	- 'Tomorrow Park Hill'	CBcs SCog
§	- 'Tomorrow Variegated' (v)	SCam
	- 'Tomorrow's Dawn'	CDoC
	- 'Touchdown'	SCam
	- 'Tregye'	CBcs
	- 'Trewithen White'	CDoC LRHS
§	- 'Tricolor' 🏆[H5]	CBcs CDoC CMHG CMac COtt CSBt CTrh ELon LRHS MAsh MGos MMuc SCam SCog SCoo
	- 'Tricolor Red'	see *C. japonica* 'Lady de Saumarez'
	- 'Trinkett'	CDoC
	- 'Valtevareda'	CDoC
	- variegated (v)	SCog
	- 'Victor Emmanuel'	see *C. japonica* 'Blood of China'
	- 'Ville de Nantes'	LRHS
	- 'Virginia Carlyon'	CBcs CDoC
	- 'Visconti Nova'	LRHS
	- 'Vittorio Emanuele II'	CDoC CTrh LRHS SCoo
	- 'Volcano'	CDoC MPkF
	- 'Volunteer' **new**	SPoG
	- 'Vosper's Rose'	CDoC
	- 'Warrior'	CDoC SCog
	- 'Wheel of Fortune'	LRHS MAsh
	- 'White Nun'	CBcs SCog
	- 'White Perfection'	SArc
	- 'White Swan'	CMac COtt CSBt LRHS MAsh SCoo
	- 'White Tinsie'	LRHS
	- 'Wilamina' 🏆[H5]	CDoC CMHG
	- 'Wildfire'	LRHS
	- 'William Bartlett'	CTrh MBri SPoG
	- 'William Honey'	CTrh
	- 'Wisley White'	see *C. japonica* 'Hakurakuten'
	- 'Witman Yellow'	CTrh
§	- 'Yours Truly'	CDoC CMac COtt CTrh CTsd LRHS MAsh SCog
	- 'Yukimi-guruma'	CDoC
	'John Tooby'	CDoC COtt
	'Jury's Yellow'	see *C.* × *williamsii* 'Jury's Yellow'
	'Kichō'	MPkF
	'Lasca Beauty' (*japonica* × *reticulata*)	CTrh
	'Leonard Messel' (*reticulata* × (× *williamsii*)) 🏆[H5]	CBcs CDoC CMHG CMac CTrh CTri EPfP GGal LRHS MAsh MBri MPkF NLar SCam SCog SCoo SPer SReu
	'Liz Henslowe'	CTsd
	'Mandalay Queen' (*reticulata* hybrid)	SCam
	'Maud Messel' (*reticulata* × (× *williamsii*))	SCam
	'Milo Rowell'	CDoC
	'Mimosa Jury'	CDoC LRHS
	'Monticello'	CDoC
	'Mystique'	see *C. reticulata* 'Mystique'
	'Nicky Crisp' (*japonica* × *pitardii*)	CDoC CTrh LRHS MPkF
	'Nijinski' (*reticulata* hybrid)	CDoC
	'Nikisi Kerin'	NSoo
	'Nonie Haydon' (*pitardii* hybrid)	CDoC
	oleifera	CExl CTrh NLar
	'Phyl Doak' (*reticulata* × *saluenensis*)	CDoC
	'Pink Goddess'	MPkF
	'Pink Icicle' (*oleifera* hybrid)	CWSG ELon
	'Pink Spangles'	see *C. japonica* 'Mathotiana Rosea'
	pitardii	CDoC
	- 'Snippet'	CDoC
	'Polar Ice'	CDoC SCog
	'Polyanna'	CDoC SCog
	'Portuense'	see *C. japonica* 'Japonica Variegata'
	'Quintessence' (*japonica* × *lutchuensis*)	CDoC CTrh LRHS SCog
	'Red Crystal' **new**	CTrh
	reticulata Lindl.	CPne
	- 'Captain Rawes'	SCam
	- 'Mary Williams'	NLar NSoo SCoo
	- 'Miss Tulare'	CDoC
§	- 'Mystique'	CDoC
	- 'Satsuma-kurenai'	LRHS
	'Rose du Steir' (*reticulata* hybrid)	MPkF
	rosiflora 'Roseaflora Cascade'	CDoC
	rusticana	see *C. japonica* subsp. *rusticana*
I	***sasanqua*** 'Alba'	CMac CTri
	- 'Baronesa de Soutelinho'	ELon SCam SCog
	- 'Bettie Patricia'	SCog
	- 'Bonanza'	see *C. hiemalis* 'Bonanza'
	- Borde Hill form	SCam
	- 'Briar Rose' **new**	CDul
	- 'Brocéliande'	MPkF
	- 'Cleopatra'	EPfP NSoo
	- 'Cotton Candy'	CDoC
	- 'Crimson King' 🏆[H4]	CDoC CTrh LRHS MAsh
	- 'Dazzler'	see *C. hiemalis* 'Dazzler'
	- 'Dwarf Shishi' **new**	CTrh
	- 'Early Pearly'	CDoC LRHS
I	- 'Exquisite'	CDoC
	- 'Flamingo'	see *C. sasanqua* 'Fukuzutsumi'
	- 'Fragrans'	ELon MGos SCam SCog SMDP
	- 'Fuji-no-mine'	ELon SCog
§	- 'Fukuzutsumi'	CSBt
	- 'Gay Border'	LRHS
	- 'Gay Sue'	CDoC CTrh SCam
	- 'Hiryū'	LRHS MBri SCam SPoG
	- 'Hugh Evans' 🏆[H4]	CBcs CDoC COtt CTrh ELan ELon EPfP LRHS SCam SCog SCoo SMDP SSta
	- 'Jean May' 🏆[H4]	CBcs CDoC ELan ELon EPfP LRHS MBri NSoo SCam SCog SCoo SPer WCot
	- 'Kenkyō'	ELon SCam SCog SPer SSta
	- 'Maiden's Blush'	LRHS MBri SCog WCot
	- 'Mignonne'	CTrh
	- 'Narumigata' 🏆[H4]	CAbP CBcs CDoC CDul CMac CTrh CTsd ELon EPfP LRHS MBlu MBri MGos NSoo SCam SCog SPoG SSta
	- 'New Dawn'	SCam SCog
	- 'Nyewoods'	CMac
	- 'Papaver'	SCam SCog
	- 'Paradise Audrey'	LMil LRHS
	- 'Paradise Belinda'[PBR]	EPfP LMil LRHS
	- 'Paradise Blush'	CBcs CDoC LRHS SCog
	- 'Paradise Glow'	CBcs CDoC LMil LRHS SCam

Name	Suppliers
- 'Paradise Helen'	LRHS SCam
- 'Paradise Hilda'	CBcs CDoC LRHS
- 'Paradise Little Liane'PBR	CBcs CDoC SCog
- 'Paradise Pearl'	CDoC EPfP LMil LRHS SCog SSpi
- 'Paradise Petite'PBR	SCog
- Paradise Sayaka = 'Parsay'	CDoC
- 'Paradise Venessa'PBR	CBcs CDoC EPfP LRHS SCam
- 'Peach Blossom'	CBcs
- 'Plantation Pink'	CTrh ELan EPfP LRHS MBri NSoo SCam SCog SRkn WCot
- 'Rainbow'	CAbP CBcs CDoC CTrh ECre ELan ELon EPfP GGal LRHS MAsh MBri MPkF SCam SCoo SSta
- 'Rosea'	CMac ELon LRHS SCam SCog
§ - 'Rosea Plena'	CBcs SCam
- 'Sasanqua Rubra'	CMac SCam SCog SMDP
- 'Sasanqua Variegata' (v)	CTrh ELon MPkF SCam SCog
- 'Setsugekka'	CDoC LRHS SCog
- 'Shishigashira' Nihon Engei Kai Zasshi, 1894	SCog
- 'Snowflake'	SCam SSta
- 'Souvenir de Claude Brivet'	CDoC
- 'Sparkling Burgundy'	see *C. hiemalis* 'Sparkling Burgundy'
- 'Tanya'	CDoC CTrh
- 'Versicolor'	EPfP LRHS MBri MPkF NSoo
- 'Winter's Joy'	CBcs
- 'Winter's Snowman'	CBcs CDoC LRHS SCam SCog
'Satan's Robe' (*reticulata* hybrid)	CDoC MGos SCog
'Scented Sun'	CTrh
'Scentuous' (*japonica* × *lutchuensis*)	CDoC
'Show Girl' (*reticulata* × *sasanqua*) ♀H4	SCam SCog
§ ***sinensis***	CBcs CCCN CTrh CTsd ELon GPoy LRHS NLar SCam SPlb SPre
- var. ***assamica***	CCCN SPre
- var. ***sinensis***	CCCN
'Sir Victor Davis'	CDoC
'Snow Flurry'	CBcs CTrh CWSG LRHS MAsh SCam SCog
'Spring Festival' (*cuspidata* hybrid) ♀H4	CDoC CMHG CSBt CTrh LRHS MMuc MPkF SCog
'Spring Mist' (*japonica* × *lutchuensis*)	CDoC CMHG CTrh
'Sugar Dream'	CDoC CTrh
'Superscent'	CTrh
'Survivor'	LRHS MPkF
'Swan Lake'	COtt LRHS MAsh MBri NPri SCog
'Sweet Emily Kate' (*japonica* × *lutchuensis*)	CDoC LRHS MPkF
'Sweet Jane'	LRHS MPkF
'Sweet Olive' (d) **new**	MPkF
'Tamzin Coull' (d) **new**	MPkF
'Tarōkaja' (wabisuke)	SCam
thea	see *C. sinensis*
'Tinsie'	see *C. japonica* 'Bokuhan'
'Tiny Princess' (*fraterna* × *japonica*)	CMac
'Tom Knudsen' (*japonica* × *reticulata*) ♀H4	CDoC CTrh LRHS
'Tomorrow Supreme'	see *C. japonica* 'Tomorrow Variegated'
transnokoensis ♀H4	CExl CMac CTrh LRHS MPkF
'Tricolor Sieboldii'	see *C. japonica* 'Tricolor'
'Tristrem Carlyon' (*reticulata* hybrid)	CTri EBee EPfP LRHS
'Valley Knudsen' (*reticulata* × *saluenensis*)	SCog
× ***vernalis*** 'Star Above Star'	CMHG
- 'Yuletide'	CDoC CTrh LRHS MAsh MPkF SCam SCog
'Volcano'	CDoC
× ***williamsii*** 'Angel Wings'	LRHS
- 'Anticipation' ♀H5	Widely available
- 'Anticipation Variegated'	LRHS
- 'Ballet Queen'	CBcs CDoC CSBt SCam
- 'Ballet Queen Variegated'	CDoC ELon SCog
- 'Bartley Number Five'	CMac
- 'Beatrice Michael'	CBcs CMac
- 'Blue Danube'	CBcs
- 'Bow Bells'	CDoC CDul CTri ELan
- 'Bowen Bryant' ♀H5	CTrh GGGa GGal LRHS SCog
- 'Brigadoon' ♀H5	CBcs CDoC COtt CTri EPfP GGGa GGal LRHS MBri SCog
- 'Burncoose'	CBcs
- 'Burncoose Apple Blossom'	CDoC
- 'Buttons 'n' Bows'	CDoC MPkF SCog
- 'C.F. Coates'	CDoC MGos SCam SCog
- 'Caerhays'	CBcs
- 'Carolyn Williams'	CBcs
- 'Celebration'	CBcs COtt CSBt
- 'Charlean'	CDoC SCam
- 'Charles Colbert'	CDoC LRHS
- 'China Clay' ♀H5	CDoC CHel EPfP LRHS SCam
§ - 'Citation'	CBcs CMac SCog
- 'Clarrie Fawcett' ♀H5	CDoC
- 'Contribution'	CTrh
- 'Coral Delight'	MPkF
- 'Crinkles'	CDoC SCam
- 'Daintiness' ♀H5	CDoC SCog
- 'Dark Nite'	CMHG
- 'Debbie' ♀H5	Widely available
- 'Debbie's Carnation'	CDoC LRHS
- 'Donation' ♀H5	Widely available
- 'Dream Boat'	CDoC LRHS MPkF
- 'E.G. Waterhouse'	CBcs CDoC CSBt CTrh CTri ELan ELon EPfP GKin LRHS MAsh MGos MJak NLar NSoo SCam SCog SPoG SSta
- 'E.T.R. Carlyon' ♀H5	CDoC CTrh CTri EPfP LRHS MAsh MBri NLar NPri SCog SCoo SLim SPoG
- 'Edward Carlyon' **new**	LRHS
- 'Elegant Beauty' ♀H5	CBcs CDoC COtt CTrh ELon LRHS NLar SCam SCog SPer
- 'Elizabeth Anderson'	CTrh CTsd
- 'Elizabeth de Rothschild'	GGGa NSoo
- 'Ellamine'	CBcs
- 'Elsie Jury' ♀H5	CBcs CDoC CMac COtt CTri ELan GKin LRHS MGos NLar SCam SCog SGol SPer
- 'Exaltation'	CDoC SCog
- 'Fiona Colville'	CDoC
- 'Francis Hanger'	CBcs CDoC CTrh LRHS SCam SCog SPer
- 'Galaxie'	CBcs CDoC SCog
- 'Gay Time'	CBcs LRHS MAsh SCog
- 'George Blandford' ♀H5	CBcs CMac GGal
- 'Glenn's Orbit' ♀H5	CDoC NLar SCam SCog
- 'Golden Spangles' (v)	CDoC CMac ELan EPfP GKin LRHS MGos MMuc SCam SCog SLim SPer
- 'Grand Jury'	LRHS

– 'Gwavas'	CBcs CCCN CDoC CTrh LRHS MAsh SCog SCoo
– 'Hilo'	CDoC SCam
– 'Hiraethlyn'	CBcs
– 'J.C. Williams' ♀H5	CBcs CMac CTri EPfP LRHS MMuc SCog SEND
– 'Jamie'	CDoC
– 'Jean Claris'	CDoC
– 'Jenefer Carlyon'	CBcs CDoC
– 'Jill Totty'	CTrh
– 'John Pickthorn'	CBcs
– 'Joyful Bells'	LRHS
– 'Jubilation'	LRHS
– 'Julia Hamiter' ♀H5	CDoC LRHS
§ – 'Jury's Yellow' ♀H5	CBcs CCCN CDoC CHel CSBt CTrh CTri ELan ELon EPfP GGGa LMil LRHS MAsh MBri MMuc NEgg NLar NPri NSoo SCam SCog SCoo SHil SLim SPer SPoG SSta SWvt
– 'Lady's Maid'	CBcs
– 'Laura Boscawen'	CDoC CTrh
– 'Les Jury' ♀H5	CBcs CDoC CMHG COtt CSBt CTrh LMil LRHS NLar SCog SLim
– 'Little Lavender'	CDoC
– 'Lucky Star' (d) **new**	MPkF
– 'Margaret Waterhouse'	CBcs SCam SCog
– 'Marjorie Waldegrave'	LRHS MAsh
– 'Mary Christian'	CBcs GGal SSta
– 'Mary Larcom'	CBcs
– 'Mary Phoebe Taylor' ♀H5	CBcs CDoC GGal NLar SCog SCoo SLim
– 'Mirage'	CDoC CTrh SCam
– 'Moira Reid'	CDoC
– 'Monica Dance'	CBcs CDoC
– 'Muskoka' ♀H5	CBcs
– 'New Venture'	CBcs
– 'Night Rider'	CDoC MPkF
– 'Phillippa Forward'	CMac
– 'Pink Wave'	LRHS
– 'Red Dahlia'	CBcs
– 'Rendezvous'	CDoC CTrh SCam SCog
– 'Rose Bouquet'	CDoC
– 'Rosemary Williams'	CBcs CMac
– 'Ruby Bells'	CMHG
– 'Ruby Wedding' (d) ♀H5	CBcs CDoC COtt CSBt CTrh CTsd EPfP LMil LRHS MAsh MBri NEgg NLar NPri NSoo SCog SCoo SLim SPer SPoG SWvt
– 'Saint Ewe' ♀H5	CBcs CDoC CHel CSBt CTrh CTri ELan EPfP GGal LRHS MAsh MBri MGos SCam SCog SCoo SPer
– 'Saint Michael'	CBcs CDoC
– 'Sayonara'	CBcs SCog
– 'Senorita' ♀H5	CDoC CTrh ELon MBri NLar NPri SCam SCog
– 'Shocking Pink'	LRHS MAsh
– 'Sun Song'	SCog
– 'Taylor's Perfection'	SCam
– 'The Duchess of Cornwall'	CDoC LRHS SCam
– 'Tiptoe'	CDoC CTrh
– 'Toni Finlay's Fragrant' **new**	CTrh
– 'Tulip Time'	LRHS MPkF
– 'Twinkle Star'	LRHS
– 'Waltz Time'	CDoC SCam
– 'Water Lily' ♀H5	CBcs CDoC CTri ELon EPfP LRHS MAsh NLar SCam
– 'Wilber Foss'	CDoC ELon LRHS MGos MMuc SCam SCog SEND
– 'William Carlyon'	LRHS
– 'Winter Gem'	MPkF
– 'Wynne Rayner'	CDoC
– 'Yesterday'	COtt MBri MMuc NPri
'Winter's Charm'	LRHS
'Winter's Dream'	SCog
'Winter's Interlude'	CDoC LRHS SCog
'Winter's Joy'	SCog
'Winter's Toughie'	LRHS SCog
'Winter's Waterlily' **new**	COtt
'Winton' (*cuspidata* × *saluenensis*)	CBcs CDoC
'Yoimachi' (*fraterna* × *sasanqua*)	CDoC CTrh

Camissonia (*Onagraceae*)

bistorta 'Sunflakes'	CSpe

Campanula ✿ (*Campanulaceae*)

sp.	WCot
RCB AM 13	WCot
from Sicily **new**	WCot
from Zigana Pass, Turkey **new**	CPBP
abietina	see *C. patula* subsp. *abietina*
alata	ELan LRHS MNrw NBir SRms SWat WMoo WOut XLum
§ ***alliariifolia***	Widely available
– DHTU 0126	WCru
– 'Ivory Bells'	see *C. alliariifolia*
I ***alpestris*** 'Silver Bells'	MSCN
alsinoides **new**	GEdr
americana	EWTr XLum
ardonensis	NSla
arvatica	EACa ECho EPot GMaP LRHS NHar
– 'Alba'	GMaP
aucheri	see *C. bellidifolia* subsp. *aucheri*
barbata	CCon EACa EBee ECho EPfP MWat SIgm WAbe WMoo
'Belinda'	CPBP EPot
bellidifolia	LLHF NSla
§ – subsp. ***aucheri***	EWTr GEdr
– subsp. ***saxifraga***	GEdr
§ ***betulifolia*** ♀H5	CSam EACa EPot GEdr NSla
'Birch Hybrid'	CFis EACa ECho ECtt ELan GCrg LRHS MMuc SRms XLum
'Blithe Spirit'	WAbe
'Blue Octopus' **new**	IBoy SCob
bononiensis	LLHF NWad SRms XLum
'Bumblebee'	WAbe
'Burghaltii' ♀H7	CAby EACa ELan GBee GCal NLar SHar WOut WWEG
'Cantata'	CPBP EPot WAbe
§ ***carnica***	ECho XLum
carpatha white-flowered **new**	CPBP WHar
carpatica ♀H5	ECho EPfP NBro NGdn SPlb SRms SWat WFar WHar XLum
– f. ***alba***	ECho LRHS NGdn SPlb SWat XLum
– – 'Bressingham White'	EACa
§ – – 'Weisse Clips'	EAEE ECho ECtt ELan EPfP GBin GKin GMaP LAst LRHS MAsh NEgg NGdn NHol NPri SCob SPer SPoG SRms SWvt WFar
– 'Albescens' **new**	EWoo
§ – 'Blaue Clips'	CBcs ECho ECtt ELan EPfP GKin GMaP IFoB LAst LRHS MAsh MGos

NEgg NGdn NPri SCob SPer SPoG SRms SWvt WFar
- Blue Clips — see *C. carpatica* 'Blaue Clips'
- 'Blue Moonlight' — EACa ECho LRHS
- 'Caerulea' — COtt
- 'Chewton Joy' — CTri EACa ECho LLHF LRHS
- dwarf — EACa
- 'Karpatenkrone' — EACa GBin
- 'Kathy' — EPot GBuc GCrg
* - var. ***pelviformis*** — SMHy
- var. ***turbinata*** — ECho NSla SRms
- - 'Foerster' — EACa ECho GCrg LRHS XLum
- - 'Isabel' — EACa ECho LLHF LRHS XLum
- - 'Jewel' — EACa ECho LRHS
- White Clips — see *C. carpatica* f. *alba* 'Weisse Clips'
cephallenica — see *C. garganica* subsp. *cephallenica*
§ ***chamissonis*** — ECho EPot LLHF NWad
- 'Major' — EWes
- 'Oyobeni' — EACa NHar
§ - 'Superba' ♀^{H5} — EACa ECho NRya WAbe
choruhensis — EPot LLHF SPlb
§ ***cochlearifolia*** ♀^{H5} — CSpe CTri EBee ECho EDAr EPfP EWTr GAbr GJos GMaP LRHS MAsh MLHP MMuc SBch SEND SPoG WHoo XLum
- var. ***alba*** — CSpe CTri EDAr MHer MMuc NRya SBch SEND SRms WHoo XLum
- - 'White Baby' (Baby Series) — EACa ECho ECtt ELon EPfP EPot LRHS NWad SPoG XLum
- 'Bavaria Blue' — ECho ELon GJos NHol NWad SMrm XLum
- 'Blue Baby' (Baby Series) — ECho ECtt EPfP GJos MHer SPoG SRms SRot
- 'Blue Wonder' — GBin GCrg
- 'Elizabeth Oliver' (d) ♀^{H5} — CBod CTri EACa ECho ECtt EDAr EPau EPot GCal GCrg GMaP LRHS MHer MHol NBir SPlb SRms WFar WHoo WIce WRHF
- 'Flore Pleno' (d) — WFar
- 'R.B. Loder' (d) — LRHS MHer WAbe
- 'Tubby' — ECho EPot LLHF LRHS MHer SRms
- 'Warleyensis' — see *C.* × *haylodgensis* W. Brockbank 'Warley White'
collina — CTri EACa LLHF WCFE XLum
'Covadonga' — CMea CPBP EACa ECho LLHF LRHS SBch WAbe WThu
cretica — MHol WRHF
'Crystal' — CDes ECtt MAvo MNrw MSpe SMHy
dasyantha — see *C. chamissonis*
dolomitica — EACa EBee GKev LLHF
'E.K. Toogood' — CCon CElw EACa ECho ECtt MWat SRms XLum
'Faichem Lilac' — GCra LLHF NEoE
fenestrellata — EACa SRms XLum
- subsp. ***fenestrellata*** — EPot
§ - subsp. ***istriaca*** — GKev
finitima — see *C. betulifolia*
foliosa — EACa
fragilis — ECho IFoB WAbe
- 'Hirsuta' — ECho
garganica ♀^{H5} — EACa ECho EPfP EWoo GKev GMaP LAst LRHS MAsh MMuc MRav SEND SRms SVic SWvt WFar WMoo XLum
- 'Aurea' — see *C. garganica* 'Dickson's Gold'
- 'Blue Diamond' — EACa ECho IVic NLar
§ - subsp. ***cephallenica*** — CElw EACa NBro
§ - 'Dickson's Gold' — Widely available
- 'Erinus Major' — EACa IVic XLum
- 'Hirsuta' — ECho
- subsp. ***istriaca*** — see *C. fenestrellata* subsp. *istriaca*
- 'Major' — ECho LAst SPoG
- 'Mrs Resholt' — ECtt ESwi EWll EWoo LAst LRHS NLar SWvt
- 'W.H. Paine' ♀^{H5} — EACa ECho ECtt IFoB IGor NLar NSla WAbe WHoo
'Glandore' — EACa XLum
glomerata — CExl CWld GAbr GJos MHer NBir NBro NGBl NMir WBrk WFar WOut XSen
- var. ***acaulis*** hort. — EACa EAJP EPfP GKev LEdu LRHS NLar WFar WWtn XLum
- var. ***alba*** — CBcs CBod CCon CSpe EACa EAEE ECtt ELan EPfP EPla GJos GMaP LRHS MLHP SCob SMrm SPer SPlb SPoG SWat WCAu WGwG WMnd WWEG XLum
§ - - 'Schneekrone' — ECha WFar
- Bellefleur Blue (Bellefleur Series) **new** — EACa
- 'Caroline' — Widely available
- Crown of Snow — see *C. glomerata* var. *alba* 'Schneekrone'
- var. ***dahurica*** — CBod CCon ELon LRHS NLar XLum
- 'Emerald' — EACa EBee LRHS MHer NLar SRms WFar
- 'Freya'^{PBR} — SCob WFar WHil
- 'Joan Elliott' — EACa EBee ECha ECtt EShb GBuc LEdu MNFA MWat
- 'Purple Pixie' — LRHS SRms
- 'Superba' ♀^{H7} — Widely available
grossekii — CCon EBee LLHF LRHS
hakkiarica — EBee WCot
'Hannah' — EACa ECho EPot LRHS
hawkinsiana — EPot
× ***haylodgensis*** misapplied — see *C.* × *haylodgensis* 'Plena'
§ × ***haylodgensis*** W. Brockbank 'Marion Fisher' (d) — CPBP ECtt EPot WAbe WHoo
§ - 'Plena' (d) — ECho ECtt ELan EPot LRHS SRms WAbe WHoo WKif
§ - 'Warley White' (d) — ECho XLum
- 'Yvonne' — CBod EACa ECtt EPot GCrg SBod
hercegovina 'Nana' — CPBP EPot ITim WAbe
hierapetrae — WAbe
'Hilltop Snow' — NHar
hofmannii — CTsd ELan GJos GKev NWad
hypopolia — CPBP WAbe
§ ***incurva*** — CSpe EACa EBee ELan EWld GJos GKev WAbe WMoo
× ***innesii*** — see *C.* 'John Innes'
isophylla ♀^{H2} — ECho
- 'Alba' ♀^{H2} — ECho
Jenny = 'Harjen'^{PBR} — CWGN EBee SHar
'Joe Elliott' — CPBP NSla WAbe
§ 'John Innes' — CPBP
kemulariae — EDAr LLHF WCot XLum
- 'Alba' — ITim
'Kent Belle' ♀^{H7} — Widely available
khasiana — EBee GKev
komarovii — WCot
lactiflora — CAby CElw CMac EACa EBee ECha EPla GAbr GCra IFoB ITim LRHS

	MCot MLHP NEgg SPer WCAu WFar WMoo WWEG XLum
- ***alba***	see *C. lactiflora* white-flowered
- 'Alba' ♀H7	COtt CUse EACa EBee ECha EPfP GBin GMaP IBoy IVic LSun MAvo MBel MHol MTis SCob WMnd
- 'Avalanche'	ECtt MBNS NLar NOrc WHil
- 'Blue Cross'	EBee
- 'Border Blues'	EACa ECtt MBri WFar
- 'Dixter Presence'	SMHy
- dwarf pink-flowered	EACa EBee EPfP
- 'Favourite'	CCon CSpe ECtt EWoo MNrw NGdn
- hybrids	CBod GJos
- 'Lidie's Choice'	CSam
- 'Loddon Anna' ♀H7	Widely available
- 'Moorland Rose'	WMoo
- 'Pouffe'	CHid COtt EACa EAEE EBee ECtt ELan EPfP EPla GMaP IVic LRHS MHol MNrw MPro MRav NBro NGdn NLar SGbt SMrm SPer SWat SWvt
- 'Prichard's Variety' ♀H7	Widely available
- 'Superba' ♀H7	ECtt IVic SMad
- 'Violet'	SWat
- 'White Pouffe'	EACa ECtt ELan EPfP EPla EWTr GBin GMaP IVic LRHS MLHP MPro NChi NLar SGbt SMrm SPer SPoG SWat WCAu WFar
§ - white-flowered	ECha GBin NBir SMrm SPer SWat
latifolia	EACa GJos LPot LRHS MCot MLHP NBid NMir NOrc SPer SRms WMoo WShi
- var. ***alba***	EBee ELan EPfP GCra GJos LRHS MMuc NGdn SEND SPav SPer SRms WHal WWEG
* - 'Amethyst'	LSun
- blue-flowered	NChi
- 'Brantwood'	CFis EBee EPfP GAbr LRHS MRav NLar SPad SRms SWat WMnd
- 'Gloaming'	ECtt GBBs LRHS
- var. ***macrantha***	EBee ELan ELon EPfP EWTr GMaP LRHS MWat NSoo NSti SPer SWat SWvt WMoo WWEG
- - 'Alba'	ECtt EWTr GLog GMaP IPot MHol MRav NLar WCot WMoo WWEG
latiloba	CElw CMHG MLHP WBrk WCot WKif
§ - 'Alba' ♀H7	EBee ELan GCal GCra MCot NEgg NLar NWad WBrk
- 'Hidcote Amethyst'	CAby CSpe CUse CWGN EACa ECtt ELan ELon EPfP GAbr GBuc GCal IKil LRHS LSun MCot MHol MRav MSpe MWhi NBid NBir NChi NGdn NLar SPer WMnd
- 'Highcliffe Variety' ♀H7	CUse EACa ECtt ELan EPfP GBuc GCra MBel MHol MRav NLar SGSe SPer WCot WMnd
* - 'Highdown'	GBuc
- 'Percy Piper' ♀H7	ELan GBuc LRHS MRav NBro NLar
linifolia Scop.	see *C. carnica*
'Lynchmere'	CMea WAbe
makaschvilii	CHid CPla CSpe EACa EBee GEdr GKev MHer MPie MSpe NLar SGSe SMrm SRkn WCot WSHC XSen
makaschvilii* × *trachelium new	WCot
'Marion Fisher'	see *C.* × *haylodgensis* W. Brockbank 'Marion Fisher'
medium	CBod LAst
'Misty Dawn'	MAvo WCot
moesiaca	GKev WHil
'Monic'	EPfP
muralis	see *C. portenschlagiana*
myrtifolia	WAbe
nitida	see *C. persicifolia* var. *planiflora*
'Norman Grove'	EPot
ochroleuca	CMea CSpe EBee GBin IMou SGSe SWat WCFE WCot WNPC
- 'Mevrouw von Vollenhove' new	EBee MBri WCot
odontosepala from Iran	EPPr NLar
'Oliver's Choice'	WHrl
olympica misapplied	see *C. rotundifolia* 'Olympica'
oreadum	EPot
orphanidea	IMou
ossetica	EBee ECtt ELan MLHP WBor
patula	EACa NLar WKif XLum
§ - subsp. ***abietina***	NLar
'Paul Furse'	ECtt MSpe NCGa NSti SHar WWEG
pendula	EBee EWes GBee GJos MBNS SRot XLum
persicifolia	Widely available
- var. ***alba***	Widely available
§ - 'Alba Coronata' (d)	EWoo SRms WHar
- 'Alba Plena'	see *C. persicifolia* 'Alba Coronata'
- 'Azure Beauty'	CSpe EBee ECtt ELan NCGa NLar WCot
- 'Beau Belle'	LSou NLar
§ - 'Bennett's Blue' (d)	EPfP MRav SRms SWat
- 'Blue Bell'	COtt MWat
- 'Blue Bloomers' (d)	CLAP ECtt EPri EWes GBin IKil LRHS MBel MNFA MRav MSCN NSbr NWad SMrm SRms WBrk WCFE WCot WHal XLum
- blue cup-in-cup (d)	ELon WPtf
- 'Blue-eyed Blonde'PBR (v)	ECtt LSou NLar
- blue-flowered	IFoB SGSe SPlb
- 'Boule de Neige' (d)	WWEG
- 'Caerulea Coronata'	see *C. persicifolia* 'Coronata'
* - 'Caerulea Plena' (d)	EWoo
§ - 'Chettle Charm'PBR	Widely available
- 'Cornish Mist'	CBod CCon CExl CHel CUse EACa EBee ECtt ELan EPfP GBin LPla MHol MPie NLar WCot WRHF
§ - 'Coronata' (d)	GCra NLar
- cup and saucer blue (d)	GCra
- double blue-flowered (d)	NBro
- double white-flowered (d)	ELan
- 'Fleur de Neige' (d)	MRav WCot WWEG
- 'Frances' (d)	WCot
- 'Gawen'	CMac CWCL EACa EBee ECtt EPla GMaP MTis NBre SGbt SMrm SPtp WCot
- 'George Chiswell'PBR	see *C. persicifolia* 'Chettle Charm'
- 'Grandiflora'	EAJP
- 'Grandiflora Alba'	EAJP NLar NWad XLum
§ - 'Hampstead White' (d)	GCal NBro NLar WHil WWEG
- 'Hetty'	see *C. persicifolia* 'Hampstead White'
- 'Kelly's Gold'	ELon LRHS NBir NLar SRms WWEG
- 'La Belle' (d)	COtt EBee LSou MNrw NLar WCot
- 'La Bello'PBR	EBee MNrw
- 'La Bonne Amie' (d)	EBee GBin IBoy IKil NLar SPoG XEll
- 'Moerheimii' (d)	EPfP
- 'Perry's Boy Blue'	NPer

§	– var. ***planiflora***	CPBP MWat
	– – f. ***alba***	MWat WAbe
	– – 'Coerulea'	WAbe
	– 'Powder Puff' (d)	CHel CUse EPfP GBin MHol NPCo WCot
	– 'Pride of Exmouth' (d)	ELan IBoy LPot MHer MRav NLar WMnd WWEG
	– subsp. ***sessiliflora*** 'Alba'	see *C. latiloba* 'Alba'
	– 'Snowdrift'	SRms
	– Takion Series	CSpe
	– – 'Takion Blue'	EBee GBin LRHS MPro NPri SPoG
	– – 'Takion White'	EPfP LRHS MPro SPoG
	– 'Telham Beauty' misapplied	CSBt EBee ELan EPfP EPla LRHS MRav SPer SRms SWvt WMnd
	– 'Telham Beauty' ambig.	CBod COtt MCot NEgg NGBl SCob SPad SRkn SWvt WWEG XLum
	– 'Telham Beauty' D.Thurston	CAby MWhi NLar
	– 'White Bell'	SMrm
	– 'Wortham Belle' misapplied	see *C. persicifolia* 'Bennett's Blue'
	– 'Wortham Belle' ambig.	MRav
	– 'Wortham Belle' Blooms	ECtt LRHS MBNS NEgg
	petrophila	WAbe
	pilosa	see *C. chamissonis*
	– 'Superba'	see *C. chamissonis* 'Superba'
	'Pink Octopus'[PBR]	Widely available
	planiflora	see *C. persicifolia* var. *planiflora*
§	***portenschlagiana*** ♀[H5]	Widely available
	– 'Biokovo'	XLum
	– 'Blue Ocean'	GBin
	– 'Blue Sky' **new**	NPri
	– 'Catharina'	EACa LRHS MBri SHil SPoG
	– 'Lieselotte'	CElw CPBP EPot LLHF
	– 'Major'	EACa LAst LBMP WGwG WMoo
	– 'Resholdt's Variety'	CMea CSam EACa ECho ECtt EDAr ELan EPfP GMaP LRHS MCot MMuc MRav SEND SRms WMoo XLum
	poscharskyana	Widely available
	– 'Blauranke'	EACa EWes XLum
	– 'Blue Gown'	EACa GCrg GMaP MNFA XLum
	– 'Blue Waterfall'	CWGN EACa EAEE LRHS LSun MBNS NCGa NDov SPoG WCot XLum
	– 'E.H. Frost'	CElw EACa ECho ECtt EDAr ELan EPPr EPfP EWTr GKev GMaP IBoy MCot MMuc MWat NBro NRya SEND SPer SRGP SRms SWvt WBrk WMnd WMoo XLum
I	– 'Freya'	XLum
	– 'Lilacina'	EACa EPPr
	– 'Lisduggan Variety'	CElw EACa EBee ECtt EDAr EPPr EWes GMaP IBoy MHer MNFA NBro NLar SRms WBrk WCot WIce WMoo XLum
	– 'Nana Alba'	EACa EPPr
	– 'Pinkins'[PBR]	EACa
	– 'Stella'	EACa ECha ECho ECtt ELan EPPr EPfP EWoo IBoy LRHS MAvo MRav NBro NDov SPer SRGP SWvt WHoo WMoo XLum
	– 'Trollkind'	EACa EPPr XLum
	– variegated (v)	EHoe
	– white-flowered	CTri ECho ELan
	× ***pseudoraineri*** hort.	EACa ECho EWes LRHS
	pulla	CPBP CSpe EACa ECho EDAr ELan ELon GCrg GEdr LRHS NSla SCob SPoG SRms SRot WAbe WIce
	– 'Alba'	EACa ECho LRHS NSla WAbe
	× ***pulloides*** hort. 'G.F. Wilson' ♀[H5]	EACa ECho ECtt EPot EWld GMaP NLar SRkn
	– 'Jelly Bells'[PBR]	EACa ECtt IPot NLar
	punctata	CMHG CSpe GKev LEdu LRHS MCot NBro NSti SWat WFar WGwG WMoo
	– f. ***albiflora***	MNrw MSpe WFar WMnd
	– – 'Nana Alba'	GEdr
	– 'Alina's Double' (d)	MNrw MSCN MSpe MTis NLar WCot WWEG
	– 'Cherry Pie'	EPfP
	– dwarf	CPBP
	– 'Einhorn JP'	IVic
	– 'Golddrache JP'	IVic
	– 'Hexe JP'	IVic
	– var. ***hondoensis***	EBee MLHP
	– hose-in-hose (d)	MMHG WGwG
	– 'Hot Lips'	CMac EPPr EPfP SRGP WWEG
*	– var. ***howozana***	GKev
	– var. ***microdonta*** B&SWJ 5553	WCru
	– 'Milly'	IVic
	– 'Moorgeist JP'	IVic
*	– 'Nana'	GEdr
	– 'Nasachtal'	IVic
	– 'Pantaloons' (d)	CMac CSpe LRHS NLar SPoG SRms WCot
	– 'Pink Chimes'	IVic LSou MBNS MHol NLar
	– 'Plum Wine'	MSpe
	– 'Pumpernickel JP'	IVic
	– 'Reifrock'	IVic SMrm
	– 'Rosea'	SRms
	– f. ***rubriflora***	CBod CSpe ECtt ELan EPfP EPla GCra LRHS MCot MNrw MWat NEgg NOrc NSoo SCob SMrm SPer SRms WBor WCAu WMnd WWEG XLum
	– – 'Beetroot'	IKil IVic MHer MTis NLar WHrl
	– – 'Bowl of Cherries'	CSpe ECtt ELan EPfP ESwi IVic LRHS LSou MMHG NLar SRkn SRms SRot
	– – 'Cherry Bells'	ECtt EPfP IVic
	– – 'Vienna Festival'	CSBt NLar WCot
	– – 'Wine 'n' Rubies'	EBee ECtt GBee MAvo WCot
	– 'Seejungfrau JP'	IVic
I	– 'Silver Bells'	EBee ECtt EPfP SRms WFar WHil
	– 'Troll JP'	IVic
	– 'Wedding Bells'	CAby EACa EBee ELan EPri LAst MHer MHol MSpe MTis NLar NSti SCob SRkn SRms WWEG
	– 'Weisser Schwan JP'	IVic
	– 'Weisser Turm JP'	IVic
I	– 'White Bells'	ELan EPPr MJak
	– white hose-in-hose (d)	MNrw WBrk XLum
	'Purple Sensation'[PBR]	CAbP CSpe EBee ECtt EPfP LSou MAvo MBel MBri MNrw NCGa NLar NSti WCot
	pusilla	see *C. cochlearifolia*
	pyramidalis	CSpe EACa EBee ELan EPfP GJos NGBl SBod SPav SPlb SRms WWEG XLum
	– 'Alba'	CSpe EACa ELan EPfP GJos NGBl SPav SPlb WWEG XLum
	raddeana	EACa EBee SBrt WBrk
	raineri ♀[H5]	ECho EPot WAbe
*	– 'Alba'	ECho WAbe
	– 'Nettleton Gold'	ECho EPot LRHS
§	***rapunculoides***	GJos GKev SWat WCFE XLum
§	– 'Afterglow'	WCot

- 'Alba'	EACa XLum
rapunculus	CArn MNHC WCot XLum
recurva	see *C. incurva*
rhomboidalis Gorter	see *C. rapunculoides*
rhomboidalis L.	XLum
rigidipila	WHer
rotundifolia	CArn CWld EACa EAJP ECho ELan EPfP GAbr GEdr GJos GLog MCot MHer MMuc MNHC NGBl SEND SGSe SIde SPhx SPlb SWat WBrk WPtf XLum
- var. ***albiflora***	CElw EWes WAbe
- 'Jotunheimen'	WAbe
§ - 'Olympica'	EWoo MMuc WHoo
- 'Superba'	ECho
- 'Thumbell Blue' **new**	WHar
- 'White Gem'	CMea EACa EBee EPfP GJos LRHS NBre WHoo WPtf
'Royal Wave'	CAbP CUse ECtt GEdr IPot MHol NDov NLar SCob WCot
rupestris	LLHF
rupicola	WAbe
'Samantha'	EACa ECtt ELon GBin IBoy LRHS MAvo SHar SRGP WHoo XEll
'Sarastro'	Widely available
sarmatica	EACa EBee EPfP GKev MNFA NBid SRms
- 'Hemelstraling'	NLar
sartorii	SIgm
'Senior'	CUse ECtt EPPr EWoo IVic MHol SHar WCot
'Serafinental'	IVic
sibirica 'Royal Wedding' **new**	IPot
speciosa	EBee
'Stansfieldii'	EACa ECho LLHF LRHS
suanetica	GMaP
subramulosa	see *C. cochlearifolia*
'Summer Nights'	NCGa
'Summer Pearl'	CPBP ECtt
'Summertime Blues' [PBR]	ECtt IBoy LSou NLar
§ 'Swannables'	CPou EACa LLHF LRHS MAvo MNFA MRav NCGa NChi WOut
takesimana	CBro CDoC CSpe ECtt ELan EPfP GAbr GKin LEdu LRHS MLHP NBro NEgg NSti SPad SPer SRms SWvt WMnd WMoo WWEG XLum
- B&SWJ 8499	WCru
I - 'Alba'	GBBs LBMP WFar WHea WMoo
- 'Beautiful Trust'	CLAP EBee MCot MSpe SGSe WCot
- 'Bellringers' **new**	MMuc
- 'Elizabeth'	Widely available
- 'Elizabeth II' (d)	EPPr LAst WCot WPtf
- 'Feenrock JP' **new**	XLum
- purple-flowered	CBod WWtn
thyrsoides	EACa EBee GKev MCot SPav XLum
'Timsbury Perfection'	EPot NHar WAbe
tommasiniana 🏆^{H5}	WAbe
trachelium	CMHG EACa EBee ELon GJos GKev LRHS MHer MNHC MRav NMir SWat WCot WFar WHer WMoo WOut WWEG XLum
- f. ***alba***	CLAP EBee IFro IMou LRHS MMuc NLar SEND SGbt SWat WCot WMoo
- - 'Alba Flore Pleno' (d)	CLAP LEdu SMHy
- 'Bernice' (d)	Widely available
- lilac-blue-flowered	SWat
- 'Purple Break' **new**	MHol WCot
- 'Snowball'	CMac
tridentata	GEdr
troegerae	NSla
'Tymonsii'	ECho LLHF NBir
'Van-Houttei'	CDes EBee EWes WCot
versicolor	CSpe EACa MMuc SRms
vidalii	see *Azorina vidalii*
'Viking' [PBR]	IPot
waldsteiniana	CPBP WAbe
wanneri	GJos
- 'Violet Belle'	LRHS
'Warley White'	see *C.* × *haylodgensis* W. Brockbank 'Warley White'
'Warleyensis'	see *C.* × *haylodgensis* W. Brockbank 'Warley White'
'White Octopus' **new**	IBoy SCob
× ***wockei*** 'Puck'	CHid EACa ECho ECtt EPot GCrg LLHF LRHS SIgm WAbe
zangezura	EACa EDAr GJos GKev IKil SGbt XLum
zoysii	WAbe

Campanula × *Symphyandra* see *Campanula*

Campanumoea see *Codonopsis*

Campsis (*Bignoniaceae*)

grandiflora	CArn CBcs CFlo CSBt CSPN CWGN ELan EPfP LRHS MJak SPer SRms SWvt WCFE
radicans	CArn CBcs CHel CMac CRHN ECrN ELan EPfP LRHS MJak MSwo SLon SPer SPlb
- 'Atrosanguinea'	SVen
- 'Flamenco'	CBcs CDoC CMac CSPN CWCL EBee ELan EUJe LRHS NLar SAdn SCoo SLim SVen SWvt
§ - f. ***flava*** 🏆^{H4}	CBcs CDoC CFlo CMac COtt CTri EBee ELan EPfP LRHS MBlu MGos MJak NLar NPla SLim SPer SPoG SVen SWvt WSHC
- 'Indian Summer'	CBcs CFlo COtt CSBt CSPN CWGN ELon EPfP LRHS LSou MBri MGos MRav NLar SCoo
- 'Stromboli'	CAco EPfP
- 'Yellow Trumpet'	see *C. radicans* f. *flava*
× ***tagliabuana*** Dancing Flame = 'Huidan' [PBR]	CWGN EBee LRHS
- 'Madame Galen' 🏆^{H4}	Widely available

Camptosema (*Papilionaceae*)

praeandinum	WPGP

Camptosorus see *Asplenium*

Camptotheca (*Nyssaceae*)

acuminata	WPGP
- NJM 11.049 **new**	WPGP

Campylandra see *Tupistra*

Campylotropis (*Papilionaceae*)

macrocarpa	WSHC

Canarina (*Campanulaceae*)

canariensis 🏆^{H2}	CCCN CFil CPne ECho MOWG SVen

- from Anaga Mountains, Tenerife **new** CLak
- from Los Silos, Tenerife **new** CLak

Candollea see *Hibbertia*

Canna ✿ (Cannaceae)

'Adam's Orange' CDTJ CHEx XBlo
'Alaska' ♀H3 SAdu
'Alberich' SHaC
altensteinii CDTJ SAdu SHaC SPlb XBlo
'Ambassador' LAma SAdu SDeJ
'Ambassadour' SAdu SHaC
'Angel Pink' SAdu
'Annei-Rubra' SAdu
'Anthony and Cleopatra' (v) WCot
'Argentina' SAdu SHaC
'Assaut' SAdu SHaC XTur
'Atlantis' XBlo
'Australia' CDTJ EUJe SAdu SHaC XBlo
'Austria' SAdu
'Baron Seguier' XLum
'Bethany' ♀H3 SAdu
'Black Knight' CBod CCon ECGP LAma LPal MSCN SAdu SDeJ SHaC XBlo XTur
'Bonfire' CDTJ CHEx
'Bonnezeaux' XTur
brasiliensis CCon CHll SAdu SHaC XBlo
'Brillant' LAma SAdu SDeJ SHaC XTur
'Britannia' **new** SAdu
'Caballero' SHaC XLum
'Caliméro' SHaC XTur
'Canary' XBlo
'Carnaval' SHaC XTur
'Centenaire de Rozain-Boucharlat' SAdu SDeJ SHaC SPlb XLum XTur
'Champion' SAdu XTur
'Chocolate Sunrise' **new** SAdu
'Chouchou' SHaC XTur
I 'Citrina' XBlo
§ 'City of Portland' LAma XTur
§ 'Cleopatra' CCCN EBee LAma SAdu SHaC XBlo XTur
coccinea SArc
compacta **new** SHaC
'Corail' XTur
'Corrida' XLum
'Corsica' (Island Series) SAdu
'Creamy White' SHaC XBlo
'Député Hénon' **new** SAdu
'Di Bartolo' XBlo
'Durban' Hiley, orange-flowered see *C.* 'Phasion'
'Durban' ambig. CHel CWGN EPfP LAma LPal XTur
'E. Neubert' SAdu SHaC
edulis CDTJ CHEx SAdu
- purple-leaved SAdu
§ × ***ehemanii*** ♀H3 CDTJ EUJe SAdu SDix SHaC
'En Avant' SPlb XTur
'Endeavour' CHEx EUJe MSKA SAdu SHaC
'Erebus' ♀H3 EUJe MSKA SAdu SDix SHaC
'Ermine' EUJe
'Étoile du Feu' XBlo XTur
'Evening Star' XTur
'Extase' XTur
'Fatamorgana' SHaC
'Felix Ragout' XTur
* 'Felix Roux' XTur
'Feuerzauber' SHaC XTur
'Fiesta' SHaC
Firebird see *C.* 'Oiseau de Feu'
flaccida SAdu SHaC
'Flame' XBlo
§ 'Florence Vaughan' SAdu
'Foulquier' XLum
'General Eisenhower' ♀H3 SAdu SHaC
generalis* × *indica SHaC
glauca SAdu SDix SHaC
'Gnom' SAdu SDeJ SHaC
'Golden Girl' SAdu
'Golden Lucifer' EBee LAma
'Golden Orb' SHaC
'Gran Canaria' SAdu
'Grand Duc' XTur
'Grand Large' XLum
'Grande' CCon SAdu SHaC SPlb
'Grandiose' **new** SHaC
'Heinrich Seidel' CHll SAdu
Henlade hybrids CDTJ
'Henlade Pink' SAdu
'Henlade Red' SAdu
'Hercule' SAdu
'Horn' XTur
'Hossegor' XLum
'Hungaria' SAdu
hybrids SHaC
'Ibis' XTur
'Ibiza' (Island Series) SAdu
'Indiana' **new** SHaC
indica CAbb CDTJ CHel SAdu SArc SHaC SPlb
- 'Kreta' (Island Series) SAdu
- 'Purpurea' CDTJ CHEx EUJe SAdu SDix SHaC SPlb
- 'Red King Rupert' CCCN
- 'Russian Red' ♀H3 SAdu SHaC
- Tropicanna Gold = 'Mactro'PBR CCCN EPfP SAdu SPoG
'Ingeborg' XTur
'Intrigue' EUJe SAdu
iridiflora misapplied see *C.* × ***ehemanii***
iridiflora Ruiz & Pav. CDTJ CHEx CSpe SArc
'Italia' SAdu
jacobiniflora SAdu SHaC
'Jivago' SHaC XTur
'Kalimpong' CDTJ
I 'King Humbert' (blood-red) CBcs CDTJ CHEx EPfP XBlo
King Humbert (orange-red) see *C.* 'Roi Humbert'
'King Midas' see *C.* 'Richard Wallace'
'Königin Charlotte' SAdu SDeJ SHaC
'La Bohème' (Grand Opera Series) LAma
'La France' SAdu
'La Gloire' XTur
La Source = 'Turcalsou' (Grand Opera Series) XTur
latifolia SHaC
'Lesotho Lil' CHll SAdu SHaC
'Libération' XLum XTur
'Liberté' see *C.* 'Wyoming'
'Lion Rouge' XLum
'Lippo's Kiwi' SAdu
'Llanthony' SAdu
'Lolita' SHaC XTur
'Louis Cayeux' ♀H3 LAma SHaC XTur

'Louis Cottin'	CBcs CCCN CDTJ EPfP LAma SAdu XTur
'Love Child' **new**	SAdu
'Lucifer'	CBod CCCN CHEx LAma NPer NPri XLum
lutea	CHEx SHaC XBlo
'Madame Angèle Martin'	XBlo XTur
'Madeira' (Island Series)	EUJe SAdu
'Malawiensis Variegata'	see *C.* 'Striata'
'Marabout'	SAdu XTur
'Montaigne'	SHaC XLum
'Moonshine'	CBod CCCN
'Musifolia' ♀H3	CDTJ CHEx EUJe EWes SAdu SDix SHaC XBlo
'Mystique' ♀H3	EWes SAdu SDix SHaC
'Ointment Pink'	XBlo
§ 'Oiseau de Feu'	XLum
'Oiseau d'Or'	XLum XTur
'Orange Beauty'	SAdu
'Orange Perfection'	CCon
'Orange Punch'	SAdu XTur
'Orchid'	see *C.* 'City of Portland'
'Osric'	CSpe
'Panache'	CDTJ CHEx EUJe SAdu SHaC WCot
paniculata	SHaC
'Payton'	LLWG
'Peach Pink'	XBlo
'Pearlescent Pink'	XBlo
'Perkeo'	SHaC
§ 'Phasion' (v) ♀H3	CCCN CHll CSpe ELan EPfP EUJe EWes LAma LPal MSCN NPer NPla SAdu SDix SHaC SPoG WCot XBlo
'Picadore'	XTur
'Picasso' ♀H3	CBcs CCCN CDTJ CExl CHEx LAma XBlo
'Pink Champagne'	XBlo
'Pink Futurity' (Futurity Series)	CCCN
'Pink Perfection'	SHaC
'Pink Sunburst' (v)	SAdu
'Plantagenet'	XTur
'Plaster Pink'	XBlo
'Pony' **new**	XTur
'President'	LAma SAdu SHaC XBlo XLum
'Pretoria'	see *C.* 'Striata'
'Pretoria Variegata'	see *C.* 'Striata'
'Prince Charmant'	SHaC XTur
'Pringle Bay' (v)	SAdu
'Professor Lorentz'	see *C.* 'Wyoming'
'Puck'	SHaC XTur
'Ra' ♀H3	MSKA SHaC
'Red Cherry' **new**	XTur
'Red Stripe' **new**	SAdu
§ 'Richard Wallace'	CExl SAdu SHaC SPlb XBlo
'Robert Kemp'	SHaC
§ 'Roi Humbert'	SAdu SHaC
'Roi Soleil'	SHaC XLum XTur
'Roitelet'	CHEx
'Roma'	SAdu SHaC
'Rosemond Coles'	CHEx SAdu SHaC XBlo
'Saladin'	SHaC XLum
'Saumur'	SHaC XTur
Savennières = 'Turcasav'	XTur
'Sémaphore'	CHel EBee EUJe SAdu WCot XBlo
'Shenandoah' ♀H3	SAdu SHaC
'Singapore Girl'	SAdu SHaC
'Snow-white'	XBlo
'Soudan'	CDTJ SAdu
speciosa	CDTJ SPlb XBlo
'Statue of Liberty'	SAdu
'Strasbourg'	NPer SAdu XLum XTur
'Strawberry Pink'	XBlo
'Striata' misapplied	see *C.* 'Stuttgart'
§ 'Striata' (v) ♀H3	CCCN CDTJ CHEx CSpe CWGN EPfP EUJe LPal SAdu SEND SHaC SMad WCot XBlo XTur
'Striped Beauty' (v)	CCCN CDTJ EUJe LAma SAdu
§ 'Stuttgart' (v)	CDTJ CSpe ESwi EWes SAdu SHaC XTur
'Summer Gold'	XBlo
'Summer Joy'	SHaC
'Sunset'	WCot
'Tafraout'	XTur
'Tali'	SAdu SHaC
'Talisman'	LAma XBlo
'Taney'	EUJe MSKA SHaC
'Taroudant'	SHaC XLum XTur
'Tenerife' (Island Series)	SAdu
'Tricarinata'	CHEx
'Triomphe'	SHaC
(Tropical Series) 'Tropical Blanc' **new**	XTur
- 'Tropical Bronze Scarlet'	SAdu SHaC
- 'Tropical Jaune' **new**	XTur
- 'Tropical Orange' **new**	XTur
- 'Tropical Red'	SAdu SHaC
- 'Tropical Rose'	SAdu SHaC XTur
- 'Tropical Rouge' **new**	XTur
- 'Tropical Salmon'	SAdu SHaC
- 'Tropical White'	SAdu SHaC
- 'Tropical Yellow'	SAdu SHaC
Tropicanna	see *C.* 'Phasion'
Tropicanna Black = 'Lon01'PBR	EPfP SAdu
tuerckheimii	SAdu SHaC
'Valentine'	ECGP WCot
'Vanilla Pink'	XBlo
'Verdi' ♀H3	EBee LAma SAdu SHaC
warscewiczii	CDTJ CExl SAdu SHaC
'Weymouth'	CDTJ SAdu
'Whithelm Pride' ♀H3	SAdu SDeJ SHaC
'Wintzer's Colossal'	SAdu
'Woodbridge Pink'	XBlo
§ 'Wyoming' ♀H3	CBcs CBod CCCN CDTJ CHEx ECGP EUJe LAma LPal SAdu SDeJ SEND SHaC XBlo XTur
'Yara'	SAdu SDeJ SHaC
'Yellow Humbert' misapplied	see *C.* 'Richard Wallace', *C.* 'Cleopatra', *C.* 'Florence Vaughan'
'Yellow Humbert'	SAdu XTur
'Zoodikers!' **new**	SAdu

Cantua (*Polemoniaceae*)

buxifolia ♀H2	CAbb CBcs CCCN CDes CExl CHel CHid CHll CPne ECre LRHS MOWG
- 'Alba'	CBcs CCCN CHid ESwi
- 'Dancing Oaks'	WCot

Cape gooseberry see *Physalis peruviana*

Capnoides see *Corydalis*

Capparis (*Capparaceae*)

spinosa	CCCN
- subsp. ***rupestris***	SPlb WJek

Capsicum (*Solanaceae*)

annuum	CCCN SVic
- 'Ancho' **new**	SVic
- var. ***annuum*** (Longum Group) cayenne	CCCN
- - - jalapeno	SVic
- - - 'Joe's Long Cayenne' **new**	SVic
- - - 'Ring of Fire' **new**	SVic
- - - 'Serrano' **new**	SVic
- - 'Marconi Rosso' **new**	SVic
- - 'Prairie Fire' ♀H1c	CCCN
- 'Apache' ♀H1c	CCCN SEND SPre
- 'Cayenne Red' **new**	SVic
- var. ***glabriusculum*** **new**	SVic
- 'Hungarian Hot Wax' ♀H1c **new**	SVic
- 'Las Cruces Cayenne' **new**	SVic
- 'Numex Big Jim' **new**	SVic
- 'Numex Garnet' **new**	SVic
- 'Numex Piñata' **new**	SVic
- 'Numex Primavera' **new**	SVic
- 'Numex Twilight' **new**	SVic
- 'Peter Pepper' **new**	SVic
- 'Pinocchio's Nose' **new**	SVic
baccatum 'Aji Limon' **new**	SVic
- 'Aji Omnicolor' **new**	SVic
- 'Christmas Bell' **new**	SVic
chinense (Habanero Group) 'Habanero Caribbean Red' **new**	SVic
- - 'Naga Morrich' **new**	SVic
- 'Numex Suave Orange' **new**	SVic
- 'Numex Suave Red' **new**	SVic
frutescens Tabasco Group	SVic
'Rodeo' **new**	SVic

Caragana (*Papilionaceae*)

CC 3945	CExl
arborescens	CAgr CDul CMCN EBee ELan EPfP NLar NWea SEND SPer SPlb
- 'Lorbergii'	CEnd GBin MBlu NLar SPer
- 'Pendula'	CAco CMac ELan ESwi GBin LAst MAsh NEgg NLar SCoo SLim SPer
- 'Walker'	CEnd CMac ELan GBin MAsh MBlu MBri MGos NHol NLar NWea SCoo SLim SPer
aurantiaca	NLar
pygmaea	NLar

carambola see *Averrhoa carambola*

caraway see *Carum carvi*

Cardamine ✿ (*Brassicaceae*)

asarifolia misapplied	see *Pachyphragma macrophyllum*
bulbifera	CLAP EBee ELon EPPr GBin LEdu MAvo NRya WCot WCru WSHC
bulbosa	GBuc
californica	EPPr MAvo NRya WCru WMoo
concatenata	WCru
digitata	EBee NCGa
diphylla	CDes CLAP EBee LEdu MAvo SKHP WCot WCru
- 'American Sweetheart'	CExl
- 'Eco Cut Leaf'	CAby CDes CExl EBee WCru
- 'Eco Moonlight'	WCru
aff. ***diphylla***	CTal WCot
enneaphylla	CLAP NBid
glanduligera	CElw EBee ECha ELon EPPr EPri GBuc GEdr LEdu MAvo MMoz MNrw SMrm WCot WCru WSHC
§ ***heptaphylla***	CAby CAvo CLAP ECha ECho ELon GBin GKev IGor WSHC
- from the Pyrenees	GCal NLar
- 'Big White'	GBuc GCal MAvo NCGa WPnP
- Guincho form	CLAP EPPr WCot
- white-flowered	CLAP GMaP
§ ***kitaibelii***	CAby CLAP CTal GBin GCal LEdu NLar WCot WCru
latifolia Vahl	see *C. raphanifolia*
macrophylla	CLAP EBee GBin LEdu SWat WCot WSHC
- CD&R 561	NCGa
- 'Bright and Bronzy'	CExl GBin IMou WCru
maxima	LEdu WCru
pachystigma	GBuc
pentaphylla ♀H5	CBro CSpe ECho ELan ELon EPPr EPla EPot GAbr GBin GBuc GKev GMaP IFro IGor LEdu MCot MNHC NBir NHar SPhx WCot
- bright pink-flowered	CLAP WCot
pratensis	CArn CBAq CWat CWld EHon GJos MCot MHer MNHC MSKA NMir SPhx SWat WHer WMoo WSFF WShi
- 'Diane's Petticoat'	MAvo MHer MNrw WHoo
- 'Edith' (d)	CLAP EBee MMoz MNrw
- 'Flore Pleno' (d)	CAby CBct CBre ECha EPfP GBuc GCal GMaP IFro LEdu MAvo MHer MHol MNrw NBid NBir NBro NCGa NLar NSla SWat WSFF
- - white-flowered (d) **new**	LEdu
- 'William' (d)	MAvo MNrw
quinquefolia	CDes CElw CLAP CMea CPom ECha ELon GBuc LEdu LRHS MBel MCot MMoz MNrw NCGa NLar SDys SMrm WBrk WCot WCru WOut
§ ***raphanifolia***	CBre CDes CExl EBee GAbr GBin GCal IFro IMou LLWG MAvo NBid NBro NRya NSti SKHP SWat WBor WMoo WOut WPGP
- PAB 204	LEdu
trifolia	CAby CElw CMac CTal EBee ECha EPPr GBin GCal GMaP IFro IMou LEdu MRav NBir NBro NRya SWat WCot WCru WMoo
waldsteinii	CDes CElw CExl CLAP CSpe CTal EBee ECho EPPr GBuc GEdr LEdu MMoz NCGa WCru WSHC
yezoensis B&SWJ 4659	EBee WCru

cardamon see *Elettaria cardamomum*

Cardiandra (*Hydrangeaceae*)

alternifolia B&SWJ 5719	WCru
- B&SWJ 5845	WCru
- B&SWJ 6177	WCru
- B&SWJ 6354	WCru
- subsp. ***moellendorffii***	CExl CFil
- 'Pink Geisha'	WCru
amamiohshimensis	WCru
formosana	CExl CFil
- B&SWJ 2005	WCru

– 'Crûg's Abundant'	WCru
– 'Hsitou'	WCru
– 'Hsitou Splendour'	WCru

Cardiocrinum ✿ (*Liliaceae*)

	cathayanum	GEdr GKev
	cordatum	ECho
	– B&SWJ 2812	WCru
	– B&SWJ 4841	WCru
	– B&SWJ 5427	WCru
	– B&SWJ 6336	WCru
	– var. ***glehnii***	CCCN ECho GBuc GKev
	– – B&SWJ 4722	WCru
	– – B&SWJ 4758	WCru
	– – B&SWJ 10827 new	WCru
	– red-veined	MNrw
	giganteum	CBcs CBct CBro CCCN CDes CHEx CHid CSpe CTal CTca EBee ECho GAbr GBin GBuc GCal GCra GEdr GKev LAma LRHS MNrw NBid NLar WAbe WCru WPnP XLum
	– B&SWJ 2419	WCru
	– GWJ 9219 from Sikkim	WCru
	– HWJK 2158 from Nepal	WCru
	– var. ***yunnanense***	ECho EPfP GAbr GBuc GEdr GLin NBid WCru WPGP

cardoon see *Cynara cardunculus*

Carduncellus (*Asteraceae*)

mitissimus	GEdr

Carduus (*Asteraceae*)

benedictus	see *Cnicus benedictus*

Carex (*Cyperaceae*)

	acuta	MSKA
	– 'Variegata' (v)	CBAq CBen CMac CRow CWat EHoe EShb GMaP IFro LLWG MMoz MWts NBro NOak WMoo WWtn
	acutiformis	NMir
	alba	CKno EPPr WCot
	'Amazon Mist'	COtt MBri NWsh WFar
	appalachica	EPPr
	arenaria	CKno GBin
	atrata	EHoe EPla WHrl
§	– subsp. ***pullata***	GCal
	– – KEKE 494	EBee
	aurea	EPPr IFoB
	baccans	CExl ECou GCal SBrt SGSe
	bebbii	EPPr
	berggrenii	CSde ECou EHoe ELan EPPr GBin LPot SPlb
	brizoides	IMou
	brunnea	CMac SHDw
	– 'Jenneke' (v)	LRHS SGSe SHDw SLim SWvt
	– 'Variegata' (v)	EHoe SHDw
	buchananii	Widely available
	– 'Firefox' new	MWhi
	– 'Green Twist'	EShb LPla
	– 'Red Rooster'	COtt EWoo MWat WHar WRHF
	– 'Viridis'	ELan GBin XLum
	chathamica	CPom GKev LRHS SVen
	'China Blue'	MMoz SGSe
	ciliatomarginata 'Treasure Island' (v)	WCot
	colchica	XLum
	comans	EPPr EPfP NBro
	– from Dunedin, New Zealand	EPPr
	– 'Bronze Perfection'	SMea XLum
	– bronze-leaved	Widely available
	– 'Copper Green'	SMea
	– 'Dancing Flame'	CWCL ELon NWsh
	– 'Frosted Curls'	Widely available
	– red-leaved	CBcs CBod CWCL NLar SRms
	– 'Small Red'	see *C. comans* 'Taranaki'
§	– 'Taranaki'	MBNS SCoo
	conica	MWat
	– 'Hime-kan-suge'	see *C. conica* 'Snowline'
	– 'Kiku-sakura' (v)	EPPr
§	– 'Snowline' (v)	CMac CMea EHoe ELan EPla EShb GAbr GKev GMaP LEdu LLWP LRHS MMoz NBro NLar NWsh SGSe SGol SWvt XLum
	crinita	EPPr
	cristatella	EPPr
	dallii	SGSe WHrl
	davalliana	EBee
	davisii	EPPr
	depauperata	EHoe
	dioica	LLWG
	dipsacea	CKno CMac CWCL EHoe EPPr EShb GMaP LRHS MMoz MNrw NWad NWsh WHal
	– 'Dark Horse'	CKno EHoe MMuc SEND SMea WPtf
	dissita	GAbr
	divulsa	CKno NDov
	– subsp. ***leersii***	EPPr
§	***dolichostachya***	CSBt EPPr EPla GKev LEdu LRHS
	'Kaga-nishiki' (v)	SLim WPtf
	duthiei	see *C. atrata* subsp. *pullata*
§	***elata*** 'Aurea' ♀H6	Widely available
	– 'Bowles's Golden'	see *C. elata* 'Aurea'
	– 'Knightshayes'	CKno EBee MWhi NLar SGSe WCot
	'Evergold'	see *C. oshimensis* 'Evergold'
	firma 'Variegata' (v)	GEdr MWat WThu
	flacca	CHab CKno EHoe EPPr GBin WBor XLum
	– 'Bias' (v)	EPla MMoz
	– 'Blue Zinger'	CKno WWEG
§	– subsp. ***flacca***	EBee MMoz NSti SMea
	flagellifera	CBcs CBod CHEx CMac COtt CSde CSpe CTri CWCL EBee EHoe ELon EPPr EPfP EShb GCal GMaP LRHS MLHP MMuc MWhi NBir SCob SEND SMrm SPlb WWEG
	– 'Auburn Cascade'	NWad SPtp WPtf
	– 'Coca-Cola'	NOak SGSe WRHF
	– 'Kiwi'	EAEE EShb
	flava	CBAq CKno EHoe EPPr
	fortunei	see *C. morrowii* Boott
	fraseri	see *Cymophyllus fraserianus*
	fraserianus	see *Cymophyllus fraserianus*
	glauca Bosc. ex Boott	see *C. glaucescens*
	glauca Scop.	see *C. flacca* subsp. *flacca*
§	***glaucescens***	CWCL EPPr
	'Gold Fountains'	see *C. dolichostachya* 'Kaga-nishiki'
	granularis	EPPr
I	'Grayassina'	EPPr
	grayi	CDes CPom CWCL EHoe LEdu LLWG LRHS MBlu MSKA NLar NOak SGSe SPlb SPtp WBor XLum
	'Ice Dance' (v)	Widely available

	kaloides	EHoe EPPr XLum
	'Kan-suge'	see *C. morrowii* Boott
*	***leformeri***	XLum
	limosa	LLWG
	lupulina	GBin NOak
	lurida	EPfP MBNS XLum
	- 'Silver'	EPPr MBNS
	mertensii NNS 07-98	EPPr
	Milk Chocolate = 'Milchoc'[PBR] (v)	EPfP MBri MGos NOak SCob
	morrowii misapplied	see *C. oshimensis*
§	***morrowii*** Boott	CWCL EPPr
I	- 'Fisher's Form' (v)	CKno CTri ELan EPPr EPla MMoz MRav NLar NWsh SCob SGSe SWvt WGrn WWEG
	- 'Gilt' (v)	EHoe EPPr EPla MBNS NWad
	- 'Nana Variegata' (v)	CTri NBir
	- 'Pinkie'	WPtf
	- var. ***temnolepis***	IMou
	- - 'Silk Tassel' (v)	EPPr SGSe WWEG
	- 'Variegata' (v)	EHoe ELan EPPr EPla EWoo GCal GMaP LAst MJak MMoz MMuc NBir NSti SGol SRms XLum
	muehlenbergii	EPPr
	muricata	EPPr
	muskingumensis	CBAq CBen CExl CKno CWCL EHoe ELan EPPr EPfP EShb GBin GCal LEdu NBro NOak NWsh SDix SLim SMad WMoo WPnP WWEG
	- 'Ice Fountains' (v)	EPPr WWEG
	- 'Little Midge'	CKno CMac EPPr EShb GBin GCal LEdu MBri NOak WWEG
	- 'Little Titch'	SMHy
	- 'Oehme' (v)	CBod CKno CWCL EBee EPPr EShb GBin LEdu LLWG LRHS NBid NHol NWad SGSe WPtf WWEG
	- 'Silberstreif' (v)	CKno EBee EPPr EShb GBin LEdu MMuc NLar XLum
	nigra (L.) Reichard	CBAq EHon EPPr XLum
§	- 'On-line' (v)	CKno EPPr LRHS MMoz
	- 'Variegata'	see *C. nigra* 'On-line'
	No 1, Nanking (Greg's broad leaf)	MMoz
	No 4, Nanking (Greg's thin leaf)	EPPr MMoz
	normalis	EPPr
	obnupta	CKno EPPr
	ornithopoda 'Aurea'	see *C. ornithopoda* 'Variegata'
§	- 'Variegata' (v)	EBee GBin NBro NHol NWsh WMoo WWEG
§	***oshimensis***	EPPr MMoz WCot
	- Everest = 'Fiwhite'[PBR] (v)	CKno COtt EShb GBin LBMP NWad SCob SMad SPoG WCot WRHF
§	- 'Evergold' (v) ♀H7	Widely available
	- 'Everillo'[PBR]	CKno ESwi LBMP MAsh NWad SMad SPoG WCot WRHF
	- 'Everoro' (v) new	WCot
	- 'Variegata' (v)	NBir
	otrubae	CHab XLum
	panicea	CKno CSBt CWCL EBee EHoe EPPr EPla EShb LLWG MMoz MSKA SGSe WMoo
	paniculata	XLum
	parviflora	SMea
	pendula	Widely available
	- 'Cool Jazz' (v)	EPPr MSKA
	- 'Moonraker' (v)	EHoe EPPr EPla ESwi MSKA NOak NWad WCot WWEG
	petriei	CWCL EBee ECha ELon LLWP WCot XLum
	phyllocephala	EShb
	- 'Sparkler' (v)	EHoe EPfP EUJe LRHS SGSe SPad SWvt XLum
	plantaginea	EBee EHoe EPPr EShb GBin LEdu WMoo WWEG
	praegracilis	CKno EPPr
	Pritchard's selection (v)	IFro
	projecta	EPPr
	pseudocyperus	CBAq CBen EHoe EHon GBin MMoz MSKA MWts NPer NWsh SWat WMoo WPnP
	punctata	XLum
	remota	CKno EHoe EPPr EShb SMea
	riparia	CBAq EPla MMoz MMuc MSKA NPer SMea SWat WShi
	- 'Bowles's Golden'	see *C. elata* 'Aurea'
	rostrata	MMuc SEND
	sabynensis	see *C. umbrosa* subsp. *sabynensis*
*	***saxatilis*** 'Variegata' (v)	EWoo
	scaposa KWJ 12304 new	WCru
	secta	CKno ECou EPPr EPfP GBin GMaP IMou LPla LRHS MNrw NDov SGSe SHDw WMoo
	- from Dunedin, New Zealand	EPPr
	siderosticha	EPla WSHC
	- 'Banana Boat'	see *C. siderosticha* 'Golden Falls'
§	- 'Golden Falls' (v)	LEdu LRHS NOak SGSe SMad SPtp
	- 'Golden Fountains'	WCot
	- 'Old Barn'	EBee
	- 'Shima-nishiki' (v)	EBee EPfP LRHS NOak
	- 'Variegata' (v)	CHEx CTsd EBee EHoe ELan ELon EPPr EPla EShb GCal GKev LEdu NBir NBro NLar NOak NSti NWsh SGSe SLim WBor WWEG WWtn
	'Silver Sceptre' (v)	CChe EAEE EHoe EPPr EShb GMaP LRHS MBNS MBri MGos NSti NWad NWsh SLim SPlb SWvt WBrk WHar WMoo
	'Silver Streams'	WWEG
	solandri	CKno LEdu NWsh SGSe SHDw XLum
	spissa	MNrw
	stricta Gooden. 'Bowles's Golden'	see *C. elata* 'Aurea'
	stricta Lam.	MMuc
	sylvatica	EHoe
	tenuiculmis	CWCL EBee EPPr LRHS NOak NSti NWad NWsh SGSe SPtp WCot WWEG XLum
	testacea	Widely available
	- dark-leaved	EPfP
	- 'Limeshine' new	EWes
	- 'Old Gold'	ELan EWes NOak SMad SPlb WMoo
	- 'Prairie Fire'	CSpe LRHS WGrn
	texensis	EPPr
	'The Beatles'	EHoe EPPr EShb EWoo NBir
	'Triffid'	WPtf
	trifida	CHEx CKno ECou EHoe MNrw
	- 'Chatham Blue'	CBod CHid GBin MMoz SEND
*	- 'Glauca'	CWCL
	- 'Rekohu Sunrise'[PBR] (v)	CBct CKno EBee ELon EPfP ESwi LRHS SGSe SLon SPoG WCot
	umbrosa subsp. ***sabynensis*** 'Thinny Thin' (v)	EBee EPPr EShb
	vulpina	EPPr

Carica (*Caricaceae*)

	papaya (F)	XBlo
	- 'Babaco'	CCCN
	pubescens	SPlb

Carissa (*Apocynaceae*)

	grandiflora	see *C. macrocarpa*
§	***macrocarpa*** (F)	CCCN
	- 'Boxwood Beauty'	NSoo

Carlina (*Asteraceae*)

	acanthifolia	SPhx
	acaulis	CArn ECho ELan SPlb SRot
	- subsp. ***acaulis***	GPoy
	- 'Bronze Form' **new**	EBee
	- var. ***caulescens***	see *C. acaulis* subsp. *simplex*
§	- subsp. ***simplex***	ECha NPri SRot
	- - bronze-leaved	CBod SMad SPhx
	vulgaris 'Silver Star'	SPhx

Carmichaelia (*Papilionaceae*)

	'Abundance'	ECou
	'Angie'	ECou
	angustata 'Buller'	ECou
	appressa	ECou
	- 'Ellesmere'	ECou
	astonii	ECou
	- 'Ben More'	ECou
	- 'Chalk Ridge'	ECou
	australis	WSHC
	'Clifford Bay'	ECou
	enysii	LLHF
	fieldii 'Westhaven'	ECou
	flagelliformis 'Roro'	ECou
	kirkii	ECou
	monroi	ECou
	- 'Rangitata'	ECou
	- 'Tekapo'	ECou
	odorata	CExl ECou
	- 'Lakeside'	ECou
	- 'Riverside'	ECou
	petriei	ECou SMad
	- 'Aviemore'	ECou
	- 'Lindis'	ECou
	- 'Pukaki'	ECou
	'Spangle'	ECou
	stevensonii	MBlu WPGP
	'Tangle'	ECou
	uniflora	ECou
	williamsii	ECou

× *Carmispartium* see *Carmichaelia*

Carpenteria (*Hydrangeaceae*)

	californica	CJun CSBt CTri EBee ELan EPfP ETwe EWTr GKev LAst LRHS MBri MGos NPri SCob SEND SSpi SWvt WFar WPat
	- 'Bodnant' ♀H4	CDul ELan ETwe LRHS MAsh MBri MGos NSoo SEle SHil SPoG SWvt WFar WPGP
	- 'Elizabeth' ♀H4	CAbP CBcs CJun CSBt CWGN ELan EPfP LRHS MAsh SSpi SSta WCFE WPGP WPat
	- 'Eskimo'	LRHS SWvt
	- 'Ladhams' Variety'	CBcs CDul CJun CMac EPfP LRHS MGos MRav SEle SPer SRkn SWvt

Carpinus ✿ (*Betulaceae*)

	sp.	CMen SWvt
	betulus ♀H6	Widely available
*	- 'A. Beeckman'	SGol
	- 'Columnaris'	CDul CLnd CTho EPla
*	- 'Columnaris Nana'	LLHF MPkF WCot WPat
§	- 'Fastigiata' ♀H6	CBcs CCVT CDoC CDul CEnd CLnd CMCN CMac CNWT CSBt CTho ECrN ELan EPfP EPla LAst LBuc MGos NEgg NPri NWea SCob SCoo SEWo SGol SSta SWvt WHar WMou
	- 'Frans Fontaine'	CCVT CDoC CDul CEnd CLnd CMCN CTho EBee EPfP EPla IArd MBlu MBri MGos NLar NWea SCoo SEWo SGol SLim SPer WHar
	- 'Globus'	MBlu
	- 'Incisa'	WMou
	- 'Lucas'	EBee MBlu SBir SGol WMou
	- 'Monument'	MPkF
	- 'Pendula'	CAco CDul CEnd CTho EBee EPla IArd IDee MBlu SWvt WPat
	- 'Purpurea'	CDul CEnd CLnd MBlu MGos NLar
	- 'Pyramidalis'	see *C. betulus* 'Fastigiata'
	- 'Quercifolia'	CDul EBee
	caroliniana	CDul CLnd CMCN EPfP SBir WMou
	- 'Sentinel Dries'	MBlu MBri
	cordata	CDul MBlu SSta
	coreana	CMCN SBir
	fangiana	CDul CEnd CExl CTho EPfP IVic MBlu SKHP WPGP WPat
	fargesii	see *C. viminea*
	henryana	CExl CMen EBtc SBir
	japonica ♀H6	CDul CEnd CLnd CMCN CMen EBee EPfP LRHS MBlu MBri NLar SBir SCoo SEWo SMad SSta
	- B&SWJ 10803	WCru
	- B&SWJ 11072	WCru
	kawakamii CWJ 12412	WCru
	- CWJ 12449	WCru
	laxiflora	CExl CMen
	- B&SWJ 10809	WCru
	- B&SWJ 11035	WCru
	- var. ***longispica*** B&SWJ 8772	WCru
	- var. ***macrostachya***	see *C. viminea*
	omeiensis KR 280 **new**	WPGP
	orientalis	CMCN SBir
	- PAB 3865	LEdu
	polyneura	SBir SSta WPGP
	pubescens	WPGP
	- 'Abbotsbury'	SSta
	rankanensis	SSta
	- RWJ 9839	WCru
	× ***schuschaensis***	EBtc
	shensiensis	CDul WPGP
	tschonoskii B&SWJ 10800	WCru
	turczaninowii	CDul CMCN CMen NLar SBir SSta
§	***viminea***	CEnd CExl CMCN SSta

Carpobrotus (*Aizoaceae*)

§	***edulis***	CCCN CDTJ SArc SEND SVen WHer XLum
	- var. ***edulis***	CHEx
	- var. ***rubescens***	CCCN CHEx
	muirii	CCCN SVen
	sauerae	CCCN

Carpodetus (*Rousseaceae*)

serratus CBcs IVic WPGP

Carrierea (*Salicaceae*)

calycina CBcs IVic WPGP

carrot see *Daucus carota*

Carthamus (*Asteraceae*)

tinctorius CArn MNHC SPav SRms SVen

Carum (*Apiaceae*)

carvi CArn CBod ELau ENfk GPoy MHer MNHC SIde SRms SVic WJek
petroselinum see *Petroselinum crispum*

Carya ✿ (*Juglandaceae*)

cordiformis CAco CTho MBlu
illinoinensis (F) CAgr CBcs EGFP MBri WPGP
- 'Carlson No 3' seedling (F) CAgr
- 'Colby' seedling (F) CAgr
- 'Cornfield' (F) CAgr
- 'Lucas' (F) CAgr

laciniosa (F) CTho EPfP WPGP
- 'Henry' (F) CAgr
- 'Keystone' seedling (F) CAgr

ovata (F) CAgr CBcs CDul CLnd CTho EPfP MBlu SSpi WPGP
- 'Grainger' seedling (F) CAgr
- 'Neilson' seedling (F) CAgr
- 'Weschcke' seedling (F) CAgr
- 'Yoder No 1' seedling (F) CAgr

tomentosa EPfP NLar WPGP

Caryophyllus see *Syzygium*

Caryopteris ✿ (*Lamiaceae*)

× ***clandonensis*** CAco CMac ECtt MGil MWat NBir
- 'Arthur Simmonds' ♀H4 CTri ECha ELan SCob SPer
- 'Dark Knight' CMea COtt CSpe CTsd EBee ECtt ELan EPfP LAst LBuc LRHS LSun MAsh MBri MCot MWat SBod SCob SDys SEle SHil SMDP SPoG SWvt WFar WHoo
- 'Ferndown' COtt ELon NLar SEND SPoG SRms
- aff. 'Ferndown' **new** CArn
- 'First Choice' ♀H5 CMac ECrN ECtt ELan EPPr EPfP LAst LRHS LSqu MAsh MGos NSoo SDys SLim SPer SPoG SRkn SWvt WSHC
- 'Gold Giant' LRHS MAsh SPoG
- Grand Bleu = 'Inoveris'PBR CDoC CDul CMac CSBt ELan EPfP LRHS MBri MGos NLar SGbt SGol SPoG SWvt WPat
- 'Heavenly Baby' ♀H4 EPfP LRHS MAsh SKHP SLon SPoG
- 'Heavenly Blue' Widely available
- Hint of Gold = 'Lisaura'PBR ♀H4 CDoC ELan EPfP LRHS MAsh MBri SPoG STPC
- 'Kew Blue' CBcs CDul CMac COtt CSBt EHoe ELan EPfP EShb IVic LBMP LRHS MAsh MGos MHer MSwo MWat NLar SCob SCoo SGol SLim SLon SPer SRms SSta SWvt WSHC XSen
- 'Longwood Blue' EPfP LRHS MAsh SRms
- Petit Bleu = 'Minbleu'PBR EBee LRHS MPkF
- Sterling Silver = 'Lissilv'PBR ♀H4 CDoC CMac EHoe EPfP LRHS MAsh SCob SPer SPoG SRms
- 'Summer Gold' CMac MAsh
- 'Summer Sorbet'PBR (v) ♀H4 CDoC CMac COtt CWGN EBee ECrN EHoe ELan EPfP EPla EWes LRHS MAsh MBri MGos MTPN MWat NLar SCoo SEND SGol SLim SPer SPoG SRms SWvt WHar
- 'White Surprise'PBR CBcs CMac CWGN ELan EMil EPfP EPla LAst LRHS MBri MPkF NEgg SGol SPoG WCot
- 'Worcester Gold' ♀H4 Widely available

divaricata CMCN SBrt WHil
- 'Electrum' CDes LSou
- 'Jade Shades' EBee LSou

§ ***incana*** EPfP SPer
- 'Autumn Pink'PBR EPfP
- 'Blue Cascade' EBtc ELan EPla MRav NLar SRms WGrn WPat
- 'Delft Blue' **new** CChe
- § 'Jason'PBR ELon MBri MPkF MWat NLar SCob SPoG SWvt WHil WRHF
- Sunshine BluePBR see *C. incana* 'Jason'

mastacanthus see *C. incana*

Caryota (*Arecaceae*)

mitis CCCN
- 'Himalaya' LPal NLos

Cassandra see *Chamaedaphne*

Cassia (*Caesalpiniaceae*)

corymbosa Lam. see *Senna corymbosa*
marilandica see *Senna marilandica*
nemophila SPlb

Cassinia (*Asteraceae*)

fulvida CBcs EHoe SVen
leptophylla CBcs
- 'Avalanche Creek' ECou

vauvilliersii EBee SEND SEle SVen
'Ward Silver' ECou EHoe EWes

Cassinia × *Helichrysum* (*Asteraceae*)

hybrid WKif

Cassiope ✿ (*Ericaceae*)

'Askival Arctic Fox' ITim
'Askival Freebird' see *C.* Freebird Group
'Askival Snowbird' ITim NHar
'Askival Snow-wreath' see *C.* Snow-wreath Group
'Askival Stormbird' ITim
'Badenoch' ECho GBin
'Edinburgh' ♀H5 ECho GBin NHar NWad WThu
fastigiata WAbe
§ Freebird Group NHar
lycopodioides 'Beatrice Lilley' GBin NHar NLar WThu
- 'Jim Lever' NHar WAbe
- 'Rokujō' ITim

mertensiana ECho
- 'California Pink' NHar NWad
- var. ***californica*** ITim NLar NWad WThu
- var. ***gracilis*** NHar NLar NWad WThu

'Muirhead' ♀H5 ECho NHar NLar WThu
'Randle Cooke' ♀H5 ECho NHar WIce WThu
selaginoides GBin
- LS&E 13284 WAbe WThu

§ Snow-wreath Group ITim
tetragona ITim WAbe
wardii ITim NWad

Castanea ✿ (*Fagaceae*)

'Bouche de Bétizac' (F)	CAgr
crenata	CAgr CDul
dentata	CBcs
'Maraval' (F)	CAgr CTho ERea MBlu MBri MCoo SGol WHar
'Maridonne' (F)	CAgr
'Marigoule' (F)	CAgr EPom ERea MCoo SPer WHar
'Marlhac' (F)	CAgr
'Marsol' (F)	CAgr MCoo SGol
mollissima	CBcs
'Précoce Migoule' (F)	CAgr
sativa	Widely available
§ - 'Albomarginata' (v) ♀H6	CEnd EBee EPfP MAsh MBlu MBri SPoG
- 'Anny's Red'	MBlu SPer
- 'Anny's Summer Red'	CDul EUJe
- 'Argenteovariegata'	see *C. sativa* 'Albomarginata'
- 'Aspleniifolia'	CDul
- 'Aureomarginata'	see *C. sativa* 'Variegata'
- 'Belle Epine' (F)	CAgr
- 'Bournette' (F)	CAgr
* - 'Doré de Lyon'	CAgr
- 'Marron Comballe' (F)	CAgr
- 'Marron de Goujounac' (F)	CAgr
- 'Marron de Lyon' (F)	CAgr CDul CEnd CHab CTho EPfP EPom IVic MBri NWea SVic
- 'Regal' (F)	EPom
§ - 'Variegata' (v)	CBcs CMCN ELan SPer

Castanopsis (*Fagaceae*)

sclerophylla	CBcs WPGP
sieboldii	CBcs

Castanospermum (*Papilionaceae*)

australe	CArn

Castilleja (*Orobanchaceae*)

integra	SPlb
miniata	CDes SPlb WAbe
sulphurea new	CDes

Casuarina (*Casuarinaceae*)

cunninghamiana	SPlb

Catalpa ✿ (*Bignoniaceae*)

bignonioides ♀H6	CAco CBcs CCVT CDul CHEx CHab CLnd CMCN CTho CTri CTsd ECrN ELan EPfP EPla EWTr GKin LEdu LPal MBri MSwo NWea SCob SEND SGol SPad SPer SPlb SWvt WMou
- 'Aurea' ♀H6	Widely available
- 'Nana'	EBee LPal WHar WPat
- 'Purpurea'	see *C.* × *erubescens* 'Purpurea'
- 'Variegata' (v)	ELon EPfP LRHS MAsh NWea WPat
bungei	CAco CCVT CTho MBlu SArc SGol
§ × ***erubescens***	CBcs CDul CEnd CLnd CMCN
'Purpurea' ♀H6	CMac CTho EBee ELan ELon EPfP EPla EUJe LAst LRHS MAsh MBlu MBri MGos MRav NLar SCob SLim SPoG SWvt WHar WPGP WPat
fargesii f. ***duclouxii*** ♀H5	CBcs CDul CEnd EBee EPfP IVic MBlu WPGP
ovata	CMCN CTho
- 'Slender Silhouette'	NLar
speciosa ♀H6	CDul CMCN CTho SVen
- 'Frederik'	NLar
- 'Pulverulenta' (v)	CDul EBee EPla LLHF SBig WCot WPat

Catananche (*Asteraceae*)

caerulea	CDoC CMea CSBt CTri EAJP ECha ELan EPfP LPot LRHS MBel MBri MHer MNHC MSCN MSpe NEgg NPri SCob SMrm SPad SPer SPoG SWvt WHar WHoo WMoo WSHC XLum
- 'Alba'	CMea EAJP ECha ELan EPfP IFoB LPot LRHS MBel MNrw NBir SCob SMrm SPad SPer SPoG SWvt WHar WMoo
- 'Amor Blue'	EPfP LRHS
- 'Bicolor'	MHer MSpe WMoo
- 'Major' ♀H5	ELan LRHS SHil SRms
caespitosa	SIgm

Catha (*Celastraceae*)

edulis	CArn GPoy WHfH WJek

Catharanthus (*Apocynaceae*)

roseus ♀H1c	EOHP

Catopsis (*Bromeliaceae*)

morreniana new	LAir

Caulokaempferia (*Zingiberaceae*)

petelotii	LEdu
- B&SWJ 11818	WCru

Caulophyllum (*Berberidaceae*)

thalictroides	EPPr IMou LEdu SRot WCru WMoo WPnP WSHC
- subsp. ***robustum***	WCru

Cautleya ✿ (*Zingiberaceae*)

cathcartii	CExl LEdu
- 'Tenzing's Gold'	CDes WCru WSHC
§ ***gracilis***	CDTJ CExl EBee EPfP EUJe GCal IBlr MMoz MNrw NSoo SBig
- BWJ 7843 new	WCru
- NJM 09.105	WPGP
- 'Crûg Gold' new	LEdu WCru
- var. ***gracilis*** new	NLos
- var. ***robusta*** new	NLos
lutea	see *C. gracilis*
spicata	CAby CBct CCCN CDTJ CDoC CHEx CHel CSpe CTsd ECho EUJe GKev IBlr MMoz NLos NSoo SBHP SBig
- CC 3676	CExl
- 'Arun Flame'	LEdu WCru
- 'Crûg Canary'	LEdu WCru
* - var. ***lutea***	CBct CHEx LEdu WBor
- 'Robusta'	CAvo CExl CHEx EBee GCal GCra IBlr LEdu MNrw SGSe SMad WBor WCot WCru WPGP

Cayratia (*Vitaceae*)

japonica B&SWJ 6636	WCru
§ ***thomsonii*** BWJ 8123	WCru

Ceanothus ✿ (*Rhamnaceae*)

sp.	CAco
'A.T. Johnson'	ECrN SGol SRms

americanus	CArn
arboreus	SArc
- 'Trewithen Blue' ♀[H4]	CBcs CBod CDul CHel CMac COtt CSBt CTsd ELan EPfP LAst LRHS MAsh MBri MGos MRav MSwo NEgg NPri NSoo SCob SEND SGbt SHil SLim SPer SPoG SWvt
'Autumnal Blue' ♀[H4]	Widely available
'Blue Cushion'	CBcs CDoC COtt CTri CWSG LRHS MAsh MGos MJak SLim SLon SWvt
'Blue Diamond'[PBR]	NLar
'Blue Jeans'	LRHS MMuc NLar
'Blue Mound' ♀[H4]	Widely available
'Blue Sapphire'[PBR]	CBcs CDoC CWGN EAEE ELan ELon EPfP LRHS MAsh MGos MRav NLar NPri SPer SWvt
'Burkwoodii' ♀[H4]	CBcs CDoC CSBt EPfP LAst LRHS MAsh MGos MRav NEgg SCob SLim SPer SPoG SWvt
'Cascade' ♀[H4]	CBcs COtt MGos MWat SLim SLon SPer SPlb WHar
'Centennial'	MRav
'Concha' ♀[H4]	Widely available
§ ***cuneatus*** var. ***rigidus***	WSHC
'Cynthia Postan'	EPfP LRHS LSou MAsh MHer NEgg NLar SCob SMad
'Dark Star' ♀[H4]	CDoC CSBt CTri CWGN CWSG ELon EPfP LBMP LRHS MAsh MGos MOWG NHol SBod SCob SEND SLim SPoG SSta SWvt
'Delight'	CAco CBcs EPfP
× ***delileanus*** 'Gloire de Versailles' ♀[H4]	CBcs CDoC CDul CTri EAEE ELan ELon EPfP LBMP LRHS MGos MRav MSwo NLar SCob SGol SPer SWvt WSHC
- 'Henri Desfossé'	ELan EPfP ETwe LRHS MRav MSwo NLar SCob SPer SPoG WKif
- 'Topaze' ♀[H4]	CDul ELan EPfP LRHS MOWG MRav NLar SGol SLon WHar WKif
dentatus misapplied	see *C.* × *lobbianus*
dentatus Torr. & A.Gray	SPlb
'Diamond Heights'	see *C. griseus* var. *horizontalis* 'Diamond Heights'
'Edinburgh'	COtt NEgg
El Dorado = 'Perado' (v)	SPoG
gloriosus 'Anchor Bay'	EPfP LRHS
- 'Emily Brown'	CBcs CDoC CRos MRav NLar
griseus	MAsh
§ - var. ***horizontalis*** 'Diamond Heights' (v)	CBcs CMac EPfP MAsh SPer
- - 'Silver Surprise'[PBR] (v)	ELan EPfP LBuc LRHS MAsh MGos NEgg NLar SLim SRms
- - 'Yankee Point'	CBcs CDoC CMac CSBt ECrN EPfP LRHS MAsh MBri MGos MRav MSwo MWat NLar NSoo SCoo SEND SLim SPlb SPoG SVen SWvt
- 'Kurt Zadnik'	LRHS
impressus	CTri EPfP LRHS MAsh SHil SPer SVen SWvt
'Italian Skies'	CBcs CDoC COtt CRos CSBt CWSG ELan EPfP LAst LBMP LRHS MAsh MGos MSwo NEgg NLar NSoo SCob SCoo SGol SLim SLon SPer SPlb SPoG SWvt
'Joan Mirov'	NLar
'Lemon and Lime'[PBR]	LBuc LRHS
§ × ***lobbianus***	CTri
'Madagascar'	LBMP MAsh SCoo SPoG WFar
microphyllus **new**	COtt
× ***pallidus***	WHar
- 'Elan'	ETwe
- 'Marie Simon'	CBcs ELan EPfP EWTr LRHS MAsh MGos SCob SGol SPer SPoG SRms SWvt WCFE WHar WKif
- 'Perle Rose' ♀[H4]	CBcs CBod EAEE EPfP LLHF LRHS MGos MOWG NLar SPer WKif WSHC
papillosus	IArd SBrt
§ 'Pershore Zanzibar'[PBR] (v)	CBcs CBod CChe CDoC CMac COtt CSBt EHoe ELan EPfP EPla EShb LAst LBMP LBuc LRHS MGos MRav MSwo NLar NPri SCoo SEND SGol SLim SPer SPoG SRms SWvt
'Pin Cushion'	EPfP LRHS MAsh
'Point Millerton'	see *C. thyrsiflorus* 'Millerton Point'
'Popcorn'	CDoC
prostratus	SMad
- var. ***prostratus*** **new**	WAbe
'Puget Blue' ♀[H4]	Widely available
'Ray Hartman'	NLar
repens	see *C. thyrsiflorus* var. *repens*
rigidus	see *C. cuneatus* var. *rigidus*
'Skylark' ♀[H4]	Widely available
'Snow Flurries'	see *C. thyrsiflorus* 'Snow Flurry'
'Snow Showers'	SEND
'Southmead' ♀[H4]	CDoC CTri ECrN ELan EPfP LBMP LRHS MGos MSwo NEgg SHil SLim SPer WHar
thyrsiflorus	CTri SRms SWvt WHar
§ - 'Millerton Point'	EPfP LRHS MAsh NLar SCoo SLim WHar
- 'Mystery Blue' ♀[H4]	EMil EPfP LRHS SHil SPoG
§ - var. ***repens*** ♀[H4]	Widely available
§ - 'Snow Flurry'	EPfP ETwe LBMP MSwo NEgg
'Tilden Park'	LRHS MAsh
'Tuxedo'[PBR]	LBMP MAsh MRav WCot
× ***veitchianus***	CSBt ELan EPfP LRHS SEND
'Victoria'	CDoC CEnd EAEE EBee MWat NLar NSoo SHil SRGP SRms WHar
'Zanzibar'[PBR]	see *C.* 'Pershore Zanzibar'

Cedrela (*Meliaceae*)

sinensis	see *Toona sinensis*

Cedronella (*Lamiaceae*)

§ ***canariensis***	CArn CBod CPrp CUse ENfk GPoy MHer MNHC SWat WJek
mexicana	see *Agastache mexicana*
triphylla	see *C. canariensis*

Cedrus (*Pinaceae*)

atlantica	CAco CDul CLnd CMac CMen EHul EPla NWea SEND SGol WMou
- 'Aurea' ♀[H6]	CDul EBee ESwi MBri MGos MJak NLar NPCo NWea SSta WHar
- 'Fastigiata'	CDul EHul MAsh MGos NLar SLim
- Glauca Group	Widely available
- - 'Glauca Pendula' ♀[H6]	CAco CCVT CDoC CDul EBee ECrN EHul MBlu MBri MGos NEgg NLar NPCo NWea SGol SLim SSta WHar
- - 'Silberspitz'	CKen NLar
- 'Pendula'	MAsh SMad
- 'Sahara Frost'	NLar
- 'Saphir Nymph'	CKen MAsh NLar SLim
brevifolia	NLar

- 'Epstein' NLar
- 'Hillier Compact' CKen NLar
- 'Kenwith' CKen NLar

deodara ♀H6 Widely available
- 'Albospica' (v) MAsh SWvt
- 'Argentea' EPla
- 'Aurea' ♀H6 CDoC CKen CTho EHul EPfP MAsh MBri MGos NEgg NHol NLar SGol WFar WHar
- 'Aurea Pendula' **new** CAco
- 'Blue Dwarf' CKen
* - 'Blue Mountain Broom' CKen
- 'Blue Snake' CKen IVic
- 'Blue Surprise' SLim
- 'Bush's Electra' NLar
- 'Devinely Blue' CKen SLim
- 'Feelin' Blue' ♀H6 CDoC CKen EHul EPla LRHS MAsh MBri MJak NEgg NLar NPCo SBod SLim SMad SWvt WFar
- 'Gold Cascade' SLim
- 'Golden Horizon' CDoC CKen CMen EHul MAsh MBri NEgg NPCo SLim WFar
- 'Golden Jubilee' SGol
- 'Karl Fuchs' LRHS NLar
- 'Kelly Gold' EBee EPla
- 'Klondyke' MAsh
- 'Lime Glow' SLim
- 'Nana' CKen
- 'Pendula' ♀H6 CAco CKen EHul NWea SLim
- 'Pygmy' CKen
- 'Roman Candle' NPCo WFar
- 'Silver Mist' CKen
- 'Silver Spring' NLar WFar

libani ♀H6 CAco CCVT CDoC CDul CLnd CMCN CTho EBee ECrN EHul ELan EPfP EPla EUJe EWTr LRHS MAsh MBlu MMuc NLar NWea SEND SGol SLim SPlb SWvt WFar WHar WMou
- 'Blue Angel' NLar SLim
- 'Comte de Dijon' NLar
- 'Fontaine' NLar
- 'Glauca' **new** CAco EWTr
- 'Home Park' CKen
- 'May' NLar
- Nana Group CAco CKen NPCo
- 'Pendula' **new** WFar
- 'Sargentii' CKen EHul NLar NPCo
- 'Taurus' NLar

Ceiba (*Malvaceae*)

pentandra SPlb

Celastrus (*Celastraceae*)

dependens CWJ 12478 WCru
flagellaris B&SWJ 8572 WCru
hookeri B&SWJ 11667 WCru
kusanoi CWJ 12445 WCru
orbiculatus CBcs CDoC ELan EPPr LRHS MRav SLon SPer WBor WHar
- 'Diana' (f) CMac
- 'Hercules' (m) CMac
- Hermaphrodite Group ♀H6 EWTr MMuc SDix SEND SKHP WSHC
- var. ***papillosus*** B&SWJ 591 WCru
- var. ***punctatus*** CWJ 12439 WCru

scandens CMac SPhx SPlb

stephanotiifolius B&SWJ 4727 WCru

Celmisia (*Asteraceae*)

allanii IBlr WAbe
angustifolia ♀H5 GKev
argentea WAbe
bellidioides EPot NSla WAbe
coriacea misapplied see *C. semicordata*
coriacea (G. Forst.) Hook. f. GBin
'David Shackleton' IBlr
densiflora IBlr
- silver-leaved IBlr

discolor GKev WAbe
'Edrom' GKev
'Eggleston Silver' NBir NEgg
glandulosa GCra
gracilenta WAbe
hectorii IBlr WAbe
hectorii × ***ramulosa*** WAbe
hookeri GBin ITim
lyallii GKev
petiolata GKev
prorepens EPot
ramulosa EPot ITim
- var. ***tuberculata*** IBlr

§ ***semicordata*** GCra IBlr NSla
- subsp. ***semicordata*** GKev
- subsp. ***stricta*** IBlr

sessiliflora GKev WAbe
spectabilis EPot
- subsp. ***magnifica*** ITim

verbascifolia GKev
§ ***walkeri*** IBlr
webbiana see *C. walkeri*

Celosia (*Amaranthaceae*)

argentea var. ***cristata*** (Plumosa Group) Kimono Series LAst

Celsia see *Verbascum*

× *Celsioverbascum* see *Verbascum*

Celtica see *Stipa*

Celtis (*Cannabaceae*)

australis CBcs CLnd EBtc LEdu MGos SEND
biondii NLar
bungeana NLar
caucasica CFil
choseniana B&SWJ 12774 **new** WCru
occidentalis CDul ELan
sinensis CMen

Cenolophium (*Apiaceae*)

denudatum CDes CSam CSpe EPPr GBin LEdu LRHS MMuc MPie NChi NDov SPtp WPGP WPtf

Centaurea ✿ (*Asteraceae*)

HH&K 271 NBid
RCB AM 6 WCot
W&B BG B-1 **new** WCot
albonitens WCot
alpestris MSpe NLar SPhx WPGP

	'Amethyst on Ice'	LBuc LRHS
§	***atropurpurea***	CDes CSpe EBee EPfP EWes GQue LPot LRHS MMuc MSpe MWat NBid NLar SHar SPhx SPlb WHea WHrl WPGP
	bagadensis	MSpe
	bella	Widely available
	- 'Katherine' (v)	MSpe
	benoistii misapplied	see *C. atropurpurea*
	benoistii ambig.	CSpe MAvo MRav
	benoistii ambig. × ***orientalis*** ambig.	SPhx
	'Blewit'	CAby CDes CElw MAvo MSpe WOut WPGP
	cana	see *C. triumfettii* subsp. *cana*
	candidissima misapplied	see *C. cineraria*
	'Caramia'	CDes ECtt MAvo MBri MSpe NBid SPad
	carniolica SDR 5443	EBee GKev
	cheiranthifolia	CDes EPPr MAvo MNrw MSpe NBid NBir SHar WBrk WPGP XSen
§	***cineraria***	ECre SPhx
	- subsp. ***cineraria*** ♀H3	CSpe SEND WCot
	cyanus	CHab MHer MNHC SVic WJek
	- 'Black Ball'	CSpe MNHC SPhx
	- 'Blue Ball'	CSpe
	- 'Pinkie' (d)	MNHC
	cynaroides	see *Stemmacantha centaureoides*
	dealbata	CMac COtt EAJP EBee ELon EPfP GJos IFoB LRHS MBel MLHP MMuc MSpe NBro NLar NMir NOrc NPri SCob SEND SPhx WHar WMoo WWEG XLum
	- 'Steenbergii'	CMac CWld ELan GCal LLWP MSpe NBid NBir NGdn NPer NSti SGSe SPer SPoG WCot WMnd
	debeauxii subsp. ***nemoralis***	NLar
	declinata RCB UA 18	WCot
	deflexa new	GKev
	fischeri Willd.	WPGP
	glastifolia	CDes GCal LEdu MSpe WPGP
	gymnocarpa	see *C. cineraria*
	hypoleuca	NBid
	jacea	GKev GQue MMuc MSpe NBid NDov NLar SPhx WCot WOut
	'John Coutts'	Widely available
	'Jordy'	CWGN EBee ECtt EPPr EPfP GBin GBuc IPot MAvo MBel MSpe MTis NCGa NChi NLar SCob SMrm SPhx WBrk WCAu WFar WKif WOut WPtf
	karabaghensis	EBee GCal MSpe WPGP
	kotschyana	EBee LPla WPGP
	macrocephala	Widely available
	microptilon new	EBee
	mollis	NBid
	montana	Widely available
	- 'Alba'	Widely available
	- 'Amethyst Dream' PBR	IPot NLar
	- 'Amethyst in Snow'	CHel ECtt GBin IPot LSun MAvo MBri MSpe NHol NLar NWad SCob SPoG WBor
	- 'Black Sprite'	CMea CNor CPar CWGN EBee ECtt EPfP LRHS MBel MBri MNrw NDov NLar NSti SHar STPC WBrk WFar WHil WNPC WOut
§	- 'Carnea'	CAby CElw CPom GCra GMaP MBel MSpe NBir NChi NLar NSbr SPhx WBrk WCAu WFar WMoo WOut WWEG
	- 'Elworthy Glacier'	CElw
	- 'Gold Bullion'	CSpe EBee ECtt ELan ELon EPfP EWes GMaP LRHS MAvo MHer MHol MRav MSpe NBid NLar SMad SMrm WSHC
	- 'Grandiflora'	EBee ELon MJak MPie
	- 'Joyce'	CElw MAvo MSpe MTis NBid NLar WOut WSHC
	- 'Lady Flora Hastings'	CBre CCse CElw CKno CPom CSpe EBee LRHS MSpe NBid WPGP
	- 'Lilac Heart'	MTis
	- lilac-flowered	NBid
	- 'Ochroleuca'	CDes CElw MBel MSpe NBid WPGP
	- 'Parham'	CBod ECtt ELan ELon GCal LBMP LLWP LRHS LSou MBel MMuc MNrw MRav MSpe MWat NEgg NSti SPlb SPoG WMnd WMoo WSHC
	- 'Purple Heart'	CAby CDes EBee ECtt ELon IPot MBel MBri MHer MNrw MSpe MTis NLar NPri SMrm SRot WCAu WCot
	- 'Purple Prose'	CElw MSpe
	- 'Purpurea'	CDes CElw CPom MSpe WOut
	- 'Rosea'	see *C. montana* 'Carnea'
*	- ***violacea***	NBid
	- 'Violetta'	MAvo MSpe MTis NBid NBir WMoo
	montana × ***triumfettii***	SHar WSHC
	nervosa	see *C. uniflora* subsp. *nervosa*
	nigra	CArn CHab CWld EPfP GJos MSpe NDov NLar NMir SMrm SPhx WMoo WOut WSFF
	- var. ***alba***	CBre NBid
	- 'Elstead'	MSpe
	- subsp. ***rivularis***	MMuc NBid XLum
	nogmovii	MAvo MSpe
	orientalis	CBod CSpe EPla EWes GCal IBoy LSou MSpe NLar SPhx WBor WHoo
	pannonica subsp. ***pannonica*** HH&K 259	NBid WSHC
	phrygia	MBel MMuc MSpe
	pterocaula RCB/TQ 18 new	WCot
	pulcherrima	LRHS MMuc MSpe NDov SCob SEND SPhx XSen
	'Pulchra Major'	see *Stemmacantha centaureoides*
	pumilio	GKev
	rupestris	EBee EPfP MSpe SPhx
	ruthenica	MBel MMuc MSpe NDov SCob SKHP SPer SPhx SPlb WCot
	salicifolia	MSpe NBir
	salonitana RCB AM 1	WCot
	scabiosa	CArn CHab CWld IBoy MHer MNHC MSpe NBid NBir NLar NMir SPhx
	'Silver Feather'	LBuc LRHS MBri
	simplicicaulis	CSam MAsh MSpe SBch SHar SMrm SRms WHoo WSHC XSen
	thracica	EBee WCot
	triumfettii	CPBP
§	- subsp. ***cana***	XSen
I	- - 'Rosea'	MSpe WBrk
	- 'Hoar Frost'	CDes MAvo MSpe MTis NDov WPGP
	- subsp. ***stricta***	CPrp MSpe
	uniflora	EBee XSen

§ – subsp. ***nervosa***	ELon NBid NBro NLar XLum
vallesiaca	WOut
woronowii	MSpe

Centaurium (*Gentianaceae*)

erythraea	CArn CWld GPoy MHer MMuc
scilloides	GCrg NSla WAbe

Centella (*Apiaceae*)

§ ***asiatica***	CArn EOHP GPoy LEdu WJek

Centradenia (*Melastomataceae*)

sp.	LAst
inaequilateralis	CCCN

Centranthus (*Caprifoliaceae*)

§ ***lecoqii***	EPPr EWes LPla SPhx WCot
§ ***ruber***	Widely available
§ – 'Albus'	Widely available
– 'Atrococcineus'	ECha MAvo MMuc
– 'Bubblegum Pink' **new**	SMrm
– var. ***coccineus***	CBcs CBod EBee ELan EPfP EPla GAbr GBin GKin GMaP LBMP LRHS LSun MJak MRav MWat NPri NSoo SCob SEND SHil SMrm SPhx SRot SWat WCAu WCot WGwG WWEG
– mauve-flowered misapplied	see *C. lecoqii*
– mauve-flowered	NBir
– 'Nettleton'	CNat
– 'Roseus'	EBee EPfP LRHS WMoo
– 'Snowcloud'	EBee ECtt ENfk EPfP MNHC SRms
'White Cloud'	SPad WJek

Centropogon (*Campanulaceae*)

§ ***ayavacensis*** subsp. ***ayavacensis*** B&SWJ 10663	WCru
cordifolius B&SWJ 10282	WCru
costaricae B&SWJ 10455	WCru
ferrugineus B&SWJ 10665	WCru
hirsutus B&SWJ 10657	WCru
aff. ***valerii*** B&SWJ 10341	WCru
willdenowianus	see *C. ayavacensis* subsp. *ayavacensis*

Cephalanthera (*Orchidaceae*)

falcata	EFEx
longibracteata	EFEx

Cephalanthus (*Rubiaceae*)

occidentalis	CDul EBee GBin IVic LLWG LRHS LSou MAsh MBNS MBlu NLar SLim SPer SPoG WBor WCFE

Cephalaria (*Caprifoliaceae*)

§ ***alpina***	EPPr EPfP LRHS MAsh MHer MNFA MNrw SGSe SHar SPhx SRms SWat WBrk WCot XLum
caucasica	see *C. gigantea*
dipsacoides	LPla MSpe SKHP SMHy SPhx SRms WMoo
§ ***flava***	EBee LRHS
galpiniana	SPlb
§ ***gigantea***	Widely available
graeca	see *C. flava*
leucantha	CArn CFis EBee GBin NLar SPhx WMoo
litvinovii	CElw SPhx
natalensis	LEdu
tatarica hort.	see *C. gigantea*
tchihatchewii	EBee NLar WCot
transsylvanica W&B BG J-1 **new**	WCot

Cephalotaxus (*Taxaceae*)

harringtonia var. ***drupacea***	CDoC
– 'Fastigiata'	CDoC CDul EHul IArd IDee LRHS MBri MGos NLar NWea SLim SPoG
– 'Gimborn's Pillow'	NLar NWea
– 'Korean Gold'	SLim
sinensis	CMCN

Cerastium (*Caryophyllaceae*)

alpinum	ECho IFoB SRms
– var. ***lanatum***	ECho EWes XLum
arvense 'Compactum'	XLum
biebersteinii	XLum
fontanum	CHab
tomentosum	CNec ECho EPfP GAbr GBin LPot MMuc NPri SEND SPer SPlb SPoG
– var. ***columnae***	ECha ECho EHoe EWes XLum

Ceratonia (*Caesalpiniaceae*)

siliqua	CBcs SPlb

Ceratophyllum (*Ceratophyllaceae*)

demersum	CBAq CBen CWat EHon EWay MSKA MWts SWat WMAq WSFF
submersum	LLWG

Ceratostigma (*Plumbaginaceae*)

abyssinicum	ELan GCal LEdu SEND
asperrimum B&SWJ 7260	WCru
'Autumn Blue'	EPfP LRHS
capensis	CMac
griffithii	CBcs CDoC CDul CMac COtt EAEE EBee EHoe ELan EPfP LBMP LRHS MAsh MRav MSwo NLar SCoo SEND SGol SLim SPer SPoG SRms SVen SWvt WGwG WKif WSHC XLum XSen
– wild-collected	GCal
§ ***plumbaginoides*** ♀H4	Widely available
willmottianum ♀H4	Widely available
– BWJ 8140	WCru
– Desert Skies = 'Palmgold'PBR	CBcs CMac ELan EPfP NLar SGol SLim SPer SWvt
– Forest Blue = 'Lice'PBR ♀H4	CDoC CMac COtt CRos CSBt ELan EPfP LAst LRHS MAsh MBri MGos MRav NLar NPri SCob SCoo SEle SHil SLim SPer SPoG SWvt WPat

Cercidiphyllum ✿ (*Cercidiphyllaceae*)

japonicum ♀H5	Widely available
– 'Boyd's Dwarf'	CJun CRos ELan LLHF LRHS MAsh NLar SPoG SSta WAbe
– 'Chameleon' (v)	NLar
– 'Herkenrode Dwarf'	NLar
– 'Heronswood Globe' ♀H5	CJun EPfP MBlu NLar SSta
– 'Kreukenberg Dwarf'	CJun NLar SSta
– 'Lisa Ann' **new**	NPCo
– f. ***miquelianum***	NLar SSta
– 'Morioka Weeping'	CAco CDoC CJun CTho MPkF NLar SChF SSta WPGP
– 'Peach'	CJun NLar SSta

§ - f. ***pendulum*** ♀H5	Widely available
- - 'Amazing Grace'	CAco CTho MBlu NLar SSta
- 'Raspberry'	CJun NLar SSta
- Red Fox	see *C. japonicum* 'Rotfuchs'
§ - 'Rotfuchs'	CAco CBcs CEnd CJun CLnd CMCN CMac CRos EBee ELan EPfP EWTr GBin GKin IVic LRHS MAsh MBlu MBri MGos MPkF NLar SCob SHil SPoG SSpi SSta WFar WHar WPat
- 'Ruby'	CJun MBlu NLar SChF WPGP
- 'Strawberry'	CBcs CJun MBlu NLar SSta
- 'Tidal Wave'	CJun NLar SSta
- 'Titania'	NLar SSta
magnificum	CBcs CDoC CEnd CExl CMCN IDee MBlu NLar WPGP
- f. ***pendulum***	see *C. japonicum* f. *pendulum*

Cercis ✿ (*Caesalpiniaceae*)

canadensis	CAco CBcs CDul CMCN CWGN EPfP MGos MMuc NEgg NLar NWea SCob SLim SPer WPat
- 'Ace of Hearts'PBR	EPla MPkF NLar NTre SSta
- f. ***alba***	CBcs ESwi WMou
- - 'Royal White'	CDul CJun EPfP ETwe IArd LRHS MBlu NTre
- 'Appalachian Red'	CAco CJun CTho ESwi MBlu MGos NTre SKHP WCot
- 'Cascading Hearts'	CBcs ESwi LRHS NLar NTre
- 'Flame'	CJun NLar NTre SKHP SSta WPat
- 'Forest Pansy' ♀H5	Widely available
- 'Hearts of Gold'PBR	CAco CRos CTho CWGN EBee EBtc EPfP EPla EWTr LRHS MAsh MGos MPkF MRav NLar NTre SHil SKHP SLon SPoG WHar WMou
- Lavender Twist = 'Covey'	CBcs CEnd CWSG EBee ELan EPfP EPla ESwi LRHS MBlu MBri MGos NLar NTre SCob SGol SKHP SLon SPoG WHar WMou WPat
- Little Woody = 'Litwo'PBR	MPkF NLar NTre SGol
- 'Melon Beauty'	ESwi NLar SKHP WPat
- 'Merlot'	NTre NWea
- 'Pauline Lily'	NLar NTre
- 'Pink Heartbreaker'	SGol
- 'Ruby Falls' ♀H5	EBee LRHS MBri NLar NTre NWea SCob SPoG
- 'Rubye Atkinson'	CJun NLar SSpi
- 'Silver Lining' (v) new	NTre
- 'Tennessee Pink'	CJun NLar NTre
- var. ***texensis*** 'Oklahoma'	CJun ESwi MGos MPkF NLar NTre SKHP WHar WMou
- - 'Texas White'	CBcs CEnd CJun EPfP MPkF NLar NTre SGol SKHP SLim SPoG WHar WPat
- - 'Traveller'	NLar NTre SGol
- 'Whitewater' (v) new	NTre
chinensis	LLHF NLar SPer WMou
- B&SWJ 12665 new	WCru
- NJM 11.047 new	WPGP
- f. ***alba***	CTho MGos
- 'Avondale' ♀H5	Widely available
- 'Don Egolf' ♀H5	CJun EUJe MBlu MGos MPkF NLar NTre SGol SKHP SSta
- 'Shirobana'	CDul EBee NLar NTre
chingii	CExl WPGP
gigantea	NLar WPGP WPat
griffithii	LLHF NLar SSta
occidentalis	LEdu SSta
racemosa	CExl WPGP
siliquastrum	Widely available
- f. ***albida***	CTho ECrN ELan EPfP EWes LRHS SKHP SPer
- 'Bodnant' ♀H4	CTho EPfP EPla EWes IArd IDee LLHF LRHS MBlu MBri MGos NLar NTre SHil SSta WHar WPGP WPat
- 'White Swan'	CAco CJun CTho EWes NTre
yunnanensis	NLar

Cerinthe (*Boraginaceae*)

glabra	SPlb
major	SWvt
- 'Kiwi Blue'	CHll
- 'Purpurascens'	CSpe CWCL ELan EPfP LBMP MNHC NWad SEND SMrm SPer SPhx SPoG WKif
- 'Yellow Gem'	ELan

Ceropegia (*Apocynaceae*)

§ ***linearis*** subsp. ***woodii*** ♀H1c	EShb
woodii	see *C. linearis* subsp. *woodii*

Cestrum (*Solanaceae*)

aurantiacum	EShb
auriculatum	MOWG
× ***cultum***	CHll EShb
- 'Cretan Pink'	CCCN MOWG
- 'Cretan Purple'	CBcs CCCN CHGN CHll ELan ELon EPfP EShb IDee LRHS MOWG NSoo SEND SPoG SWvt WKif WSHC
diurnum × ***nocturnum***	EShb
§ ***elegans***	CDoC CExl CHEx CHel CHll CTsd EBee ELon EPfP IDee LRHS MOWG NSoo SEND SLon SWvt
fasciculatum	EShb MOWG
'Newellii' ♀H1c	CBcs CCCN CDoC CExl CHel CMHG CRHN EBak EBee ELan ELon EPfP EShb EUJe LRHS MOWG NSoo SEND SPlb SVen SWvt WKif WSHC
nocturnum	CCCN CHll CPne EBak EShb MOWG
parqui ♀H3	CAbb CBcs CCCN CHll CTsd ELan EPfP EUJe LRHS MGil MOWG SDix SEND SLon SMad SWvt WJek WKif WSHC
psittacinum	CExl
purpureum (Lindl.) Standl.	see *C. elegans*
roseum	CExl
- B&SWJ 10255 from Oaxaca State, Mexico	WCru
* ***splendens***	MOWG

Ceterach see *Asplenium*

officinarum	see *Asplenium ceterach*

Chaenomeles (*Rosaceae*)

sp.	CWSG
× ***californica***	CAco
cathayensis	CAgr CDul CTho NLar WHer WPGP
§ ***japonica***	CAco MMuc SEND
- 'Chojubai'	CMen
- 'Cido'	CAgr LBuc MCoo
- 'Orange Beauty'	LRHS NHol SPer
- 'Sargentii'	CMac EPfP LBuc MBlu MJak NBro NLar SGol
lagenaria	see *C. speciosa*

Madame Butterfly = 'Whitice' — CDoC EBee EPfP LRHS MAsh MBri MMuc MRav NEgg SCob SGol SLim SPer SPoG SRms
maulei — see *C. japonica*
'Orange Star' — CEnd
sinensis — see *Pseudocydonia sinensis*
§ ***speciosa*** — NWea
- 'Apple Blossom' — see *C. speciosa* 'Moerloosei'
- 'Brilliant' — EPfP
- 'Cardinalis' — CMac
- 'Contorta' — LRHS MAsh WFar
- 'Eximia' — LRHS
- 'Falconnet Charlet' (d) — EWTr LRHS MBri MRav SRms
- 'Flocon Rose' — EPfP LRHS
- 'Friesdorfer' — LRHS
- 'Geisha Girl' (d) ♀H6 — CBcs CDoC CEnd CHel CMac COtt CSBt EBee EPfP EWTr LAst LRHS MAsh MBri MGos MRav MSwo MWat NPri SCob SGbt SGol SHil SLim SPer SPoG SRms SWvt WFar WPat
- 'Grayshott Salmon' — NLar
- Hot Fire = 'Minvesu' — CDoC EBee EPfP LRHS MBri
- 'Kinshiden' — EPfP LRHS NLar
- 'Knap Hill Radiance' — SLim
§ - 'Moerloosei' ♀H6 — Widely available
- 'Nivalis' — Widely available
- 'Rubra Grandiflora' — LRHS
- 'Simonii' (d) — CBcs EPfP MRav NWea
- 'Snow' — MAsh MSwo SRms
- 'Umbilicata' — MBlu SPer SRms
- 'Winter Snow' (d) — SPer
- 'Yukigotan' (d) — CDoC LLHF LRHS MBri NLar SCob SGol SHil SWvt WPat
× ***superba*** — IBoy
- 'Boule de Feu' — CTri MCoo
- 'Cameo' (d) — CChe CEnd ELon EPfP LRHS MAsh MBNS MRav NLar NSoo SGol SRms WBor WFar
- 'Coquelicot' — NLar
- 'Crimson and Gold' ♀H6 — Widely available
- 'Elly Mossel' — CMac NLar WFar
- 'Ernst Finken' — NLar
- 'Etna' — WFar
- 'Fascination' — NLar
- 'Fire Dance' — CDul CHll MSwo NLar SGol SPer
- 'Fusion' — CAgr
- 'Hollandia' — SRms
- 'Issai White' — MRav NLar
- 'Jet Trail' — CBcs CMac CSBt EAEE ECrN ELan EPfP LRHS MAsh MBri MGos MJak MRav MSwo NLar SCob SGol SHil SLim SRms SWvt WFar
- 'Knap Hill Scarlet' — CDoC CHel EBee ELan EPfP GGal LBMP LRHS MAsh MBri MGos NSoo SCob SEND SLim SPer SPoG SRms SWvt
- 'Lemon and Lime' — ELan LRHS MAsh MGos MRav NLar SLon SRms
- 'Nicoline' ♀H6 — CBcs CDoC CDul EAEE EPfP IBoy LRHS MGos NEgg SCob SLim WMoo
- 'Orange Trail' — MBri
- 'Pink Lady' ♀H6 — Widely available
- 'Pink Trail' — MBri NLar SRms
- 'Red Joy' — EBee EPfP EPla LRHS MBri NLar WGrn
- 'Red Trail' — MRav
- 'Rowallane' ♀H6 — CHll ELan EPfP MRav
- 'Salmon Horizon' — EPfP EWTr IArd NLar
- 'Tortuosa' — EBee LRHS NLar WGrn
'Toyo-nishiki' — MBlu

Chaenorhinum (*Plantaginaceae*)

§ ***origanifolium*** — ECho SBch SPlb
- 'Blue Dream' — CSpe ECho EPfP GKev IPot LRHS MAsh SCob SPoG SWvt WIce WMoo
- 'Dreamcatcher' — EPfP

Chaerophyllum (*Apiaceae*)

hirsutum — CRow IMou
- 'Roseum' — Widely available

Chamaebatiaria (*Rosaceae*)

millefolium — SBrt

Chamaecyparis ✿ (*Cupressaceae*)

formosensis — CKen
lawsoniana — CAco CDul EHul NWea WMou
- 'Allumii Aurea' — see *C. lawsoniana* 'Alumigold'
- 'Allumii Magnificent' — CDul
§ - 'Alumigold' — MAsh MGos MJak
- 'Alumii' — CAco CMac EHul MAsh MGos MJak NWea
- 'Aurea' — CDul
- 'Aurea Densa' ♀H6 — CKen CSBt CTri EHul EPfP MAsh MGos
- 'Bleu Nantais' ♀H6 — CKen EHul LBee MAsh MGos SCoo SLim SPoG
- 'Blom' — CKen EHul
§ - 'Blue Gown' — EHul LBee
- 'Blue Surprise' — CKen EHul MJak
- 'Brégéon' — CKen NLar
- 'Broomhill Gold' ♀H6 — CDoC CSBt EHul LBee MAsh MGos NPri SCoo SLim SPoG WBor
- 'Caudata' — CKen NLar
- 'Chantry Gold' — EHul
§ - 'Chilworth Silver' ♀H6 — CSBt EHul LBee LRHS MAsh SRms
- 'Columnaris' — CAco CBcs CDoC EPfP LAst LBee MBri MJak NEgg NWea SCoo SPoG
- 'Columnaris Aurea' — see *C. lawsoniana* 'Golden Spire'
- 'Columnaris Glauca' — CMac EHul MAsh MGos NEgg NLar NWea SCoo SPer
- 'Cream Crackers' — EHul
- 'Cream Glow' — CKen CSBt MAsh MGos
- 'Croftway' — EHul
- 'Dik's Weeping' ♀H6 — CDoC NLar NWea SLim
- 'Duncanii' — EHul
- 'Dutch Gold' — EHul MAsh MGos
- 'Eclipse' — CKen
- 'Elegantissima' ambig. — CKen CMac
- 'Ellwoodii' ♀H6 — CDul CMac COtt CSBt CTri EHul EPfP LAst LRHS MGos MJak NPri NWea SCoo SLim SPer SRms
I - 'Ellwoodii Glauca' — SPlb
- 'Ellwood's Empire' — EHul
- 'Ellwood's Gold' ♀H6 — CBcs CDoC CDul CMac CSBt EHul ELan EPfP LBee LRHS MAsh MBri MGos MJak NPri NWea SPer SPlb SPoG SRms
- 'Ellwood's Gold Pillar' ♀H6 — COtt EHul EPla LBee MAsh MBri MGos NHol SLim WBor WGor
§ - 'Ellwood's Nymph' — CKen MAsh
- Ellwood's Pillar = 'Flolar' ♀H6 — CDoC CMac EHul EPla LAst LBee LRHS MBri MGos NLar SCoo SLim WCFE WGor

	- 'Ellwood's Pygmy'	CMac
	- 'Ellwood's Silver'	MAsh
	- 'Ellwood's Silver Threads'	CMac LBee
*	- 'Ellwood's Treasure'	MBri
	- 'Ellwood's Variegata'	see *C. lawsoniana* 'Ellwood's White'
§	- 'Ellwood's White' (v)	CMac CSBt EHul EPfP SPoG
	- 'Emerald Spire'	MAsh
	- 'Erecta Aurea'	EHul
	- 'Erecta Viridis'	CBcs MJak NEgg NWea
	- 'Ericoides'	EHul
	- 'Filiformis Compacta'	EHul
	- 'Filip's Golden Tears'	MAsh SLim
	- 'Fleckellwood'	EHul MAsh
	- 'Fletcheri' ♀H6	CMac EHul NWea
	- 'Fletcheri Aurea'	see *C. lawsoniana* 'Yellow Transparent'
	- 'Fletcher's White'	EHul
	- 'Forsteckensis'	CKen EHul NLar NWea
I	- 'Forsteckensis Aurea'	CDoC NLar
	- 'Fraseri'	NWea
	- 'Gimbornii' ♀H6	CDul EHul EPla LBee SLim
	- 'Glauca'	CDul
	- 'Globosa'	MGos
	- 'Gnome'	CDoC CKen CMac EHul LAst NHol SCoo SLim SPoG WThu
§	- 'Golden Pot'	CDoC COtt CSBt EHul LBee SCoo
§	- 'Golden Queen'	EHul
	- 'Golden Showers'	EHul
§	- 'Golden Spire'	MGos
	- 'Golden Triumph'	EHul
	- 'Golden Wonder' ♀H6	EHul MAsh MJak NLar SCoo
	- 'Goldfinger'	NLar
	- 'Grayswood Feather' ♀H6	CDoC EHul LBee MAsh SPlb
	- 'Grayswood Gold'	EHul
	- 'Grayswood Pillar'	EHul MGos
	- 'Green Globe' ♀H6	CDoC CKen CMen CSBt EHul LBee MAsh SLim WThu
§	- 'Green Hedger'	CDul CSBt NWea
§	- 'Green Pillar'	CDul LAst LBee NEgg SCoo
	- 'Green Spire'	see *C. lawsoniana* 'Green Pillar'
	- 'Hogger's Blue Gown'	see *C. lawsoniana* 'Blue Gown'
	- 'Imbricata Pendula' ♀H6	CDoC CKen IDee MBlu NLar SLim SMad WBor
	- 'Ivonne' ♀H6	EHul MGos MJak
	- 'Jackman's Green Hedger'	see *C. lawsoniana* 'Green Hedger'
	- 'Jackman's Variety'	see *C. lawsoniana* 'Green Pillar'
	- 'Jeanette'	CKen
	- 'Kelleriis Gold'	EHul
	- 'Killarny Salmon'	CMac
	- 'Kilmacurragh' ♀H6	CDul CMac MAsh MGos NWea WCFE
	- 'Kilworth Column'	CDoC NLar NWea
	- 'Kingswood'	CDoC
	- 'Knowefieldensis'	CMac
	- 'Lane' misapplied	see *C. lawsoniana* 'Lanei Aurea'
	- 'Lane' den Ouden	MRav NEgg
§	- 'Lanei Aurea' ♀H6	MGos MJak NWea SPoG
	- 'Lemon Pillar'	COtt
	- 'Lemon Queen'	CDul LBee
	- 'Little Spire' ♀H6	CDoC EPla EUJe LRHS MBri MGos NLar SLim SPoG
	- 'Lutea'	CMac EHul MGos
§	- 'Lutea Nana'	CMac EHul MAsh NLar
	- 'Luteocompacta'	LBee
*	- 'MacPenny's Gold'	CMac
	- 'Minima Argentea'	see *C. lawsoniana* 'Nana Argentea'
	- 'Minima Aurea' ♀H6	CDoC CDul CKen CMac CSBt EHul EPfP EPla LAst LBee MAsh MBri MGos MJak NEgg NWea SLim SPer SPoG WCFE
	- 'Minima Glauca' ♀H6	CMac EHul EPfP LAst MBri MJak NEgg NWea SCoo SRms
*	- 'Moonsprite' ♀H6	CKen EHul LAst NLar SCoo SLim SPoG
	- 'Nana'	CMac
	- 'Nana Albospica' (v)	EHul LBee MBri MGos
§	- 'Nana Argentea'	CKen CMac EHul EPla SPoG
	- 'Nana Lutea'	see *C. lawsoniana* 'Lutea Nana'
	- 'Nicole'	EHul LAst MAsh MBri MGos NWea SCoo SLim
	- 'Nidiformis'	EHul NWea
	- 'Nyewoods'	see *C. lawsoniana* 'Chilworth Silver'
	- 'Nymph'	see *C. lawsoniana* 'Ellwood's Nymph'
	- 'Pagoda'	MAsh
	- 'Pearly Swirls' (v) **new**	NLar
§	- 'Pelt's Blue'	CAco CBcs CDoC CDul CSBt EHul MGos NLar
	- 'Pembury Blue' ♀H6	CDoC CDul EHul EPfP LBee LRHS MAsh MGos MJak MRav NEgg NLar NWea SCoo SLim SPer SPoG
	- Pot of Gold	see *C. lawsoniana* 'Golden Pot'
	- 'Pottenii'	CMac EHul LBee MAsh MGos NWea
	- 'Pygmaea Argentea' (v) ♀H6	CKen CMac CSBt EHul ELan EPla LBee MAsh MBri MGos NEgg NWea SLim SPoG SRms WCFE
	- 'Pygmy'	EHul NLar NWea
	- 'Rijnhof'	EHul LBee
	- 'Rimpelaar'	CDoC NWad SPoG
	- 'Silver Queen' (v)	CKen
	- 'Silver Threads' (v)	COtt EHul ELan EPfP EPla LBee LRHS MAsh MBri MGos SPoG
	- 'Silver Tip' (v)	EHul SLim
	- 'Snow Flurry' (v)	CKen EHul SLim
	- 'Snow White' PBR (v) ♀H6	COtt EHul EPla LBee LRHS MAsh MBri MGos NHol SCoo SLim SPoG
	- 'Springtime' PBR	COtt CSBt EHul EPla LBee LRHS MAsh MBri
	- 'Stardust' ♀H6	CBcs CDoC CDul CSBt EHul ELan MAsh MGos MJak MRav NEgg NPri SCoo
	- 'Stewartii'	CDul NEgg NWea
*	- 'Summer Cream'	EHul
	- 'Summer Snow' (v) ♀H6	CDoC EHul EPfP EPla MGos NHol NPri SCoo SLim
	- 'Sunkist'	SLim
	- 'Tamariscifolia'	CDoC EHul WCFE
	- 'Tilford'	EHul
	- 'Treasure' (v)	COtt CSBt EHul EPla MAsh MGos
	- 'Van Pelt'	see *C. lawsoniana* 'Pelt's Blue'
	- 'Waterfall'	SMad
	- 'Westermannii' (v)	CMac MGos
	- 'White Spot' (v)	EHul MGos NPri
	- 'Winston Churchill'	MGos
	- 'Wisselii' ♀H6	CDoC CKen CMac EHul LAst MGos NLar NWea SCoo SLim SRms WCFE
	- 'Wisselii Nana'	CKen EHul
	- 'Wissel's Saguaro' ♀H6	CDoC CKen IVic MGos NLar SLim
	- 'Witzeliana'	CDul NLar
	- 'Yellow Queen'	see *C. lawsoniana* 'Golden Queen'
	- 'Yellow Success'	see *C. lawsoniana* 'Golden Queen'
§	- 'Yellow Transparent'	CMac MBri
	- 'Yvonne'	CDoC CDul EPfP EPla LRHS MAsh MBri NLar SCoo SLim SPoG
	× ***leylandii***	see × *Cuprocyparis leylandii*

	Name	Suppliers
	nootkatensis	see *Xanthocyparis nootkatensis*
	obtusa 'Albovariegata' (v)	CKen
	- 'Arneson's Compact'	CKen
	- 'Aurea'	CDoC SCoo
	- 'Aurora' ♀H7	CKen ELan MAsh SLim WGor
	- 'Bambi'	CDoC CKen WAbe WThu
	- 'Barkenny'	CKen
	- 'Bartley'	CKen
	- 'Bassett'	CKen
	- 'Bess'	CKen
	- 'Brigitt'	CKen
	- 'Buttonball'	CKen
	- 'Caespitosa'	WAbe
	- 'Chabo-yadori'	CDoC EHul NLar
	- 'Chilworth'	CDoC CKen NWad
	- 'Chima-anihiba'	CKen
	- 'Chirimen'	CDoC CKen NLar NWad SLim
	- 'Clarke's Seedling'	CDoC CKen
	- 'Confucius'	CDoC EHul MGos
	- 'Corley Gold'	NLar
§	- 'Crippsii' ♀H7	CBcs CDoC CMac
	- 'Crippsii Aurea'	see *C. obtusa* 'Crippsii'
	- 'Dainty Doll'	CDoC CKen NHol NLar NWad
	- 'Densa'	see *C. obtusa* 'Nana Densa'
	- 'Draht'	CDoC MGos NLar
	- 'Draht Hexe'	CKen
	- 'Elf'	CKen
	- 'Ellie B'	CKen
	- 'Ericoides'	CKen
	- 'Erika'	NLar
	- 'Fernspray Gold' ♀H7	CDoC CDul CKen CMac CTri EHul EPfP EPla LRHS MAsh MBri MGos NEgg NLar SCoo SLim SPer SPoG
	- 'Flabelliformis'	CKen NWad
	- 'Gitte' **new**	SLim
	- 'Gnome'	CKen CMen
	- 'Gold Fern'	CKen
	- 'Golden Fairy'	CDoC CKen NLar
	- 'Golden Filament' (v)	CKen
	- 'Golden Nymph'	CDoC CKen
	- 'Golden Sprite'	CDoC CKen WAbe
	- 'Goldilocks'	EHul
	- 'Gracilis Aurea'	CKen CMac
	- 'Green Cushion'	CKen
	- 'Green Diamond'	CKen
	- 'Hage'	CKen
	- 'Hannah'	NLar
	- 'Hypnoides Nana'	CKen
	- 'Intermedia'	CDoC CKen WAbe
	- 'Ivan's Column'	CKen
	- 'Junior'	CKen
	- 'Juniperoides'	CKen WThu
	- 'Juniperoides Compacta'	WAbe
	- 'Kamarachiba' ♀H7	CDoC CKen CSBt EHul EPla LBee MAsh NLar SCoo SPoG
	- 'Kerdalo'	NLar
	- 'Konijn'	EHul
	- 'Kosteri' ♀H7	CDoC CKen CMac EHul ELan LBee LPot MAsh NHol SCoo
	- 'Kyoto Creeper'	CKen
	- 'Leprechaun'	WAbe
	- 'Limerick'	CKen
	- 'Little Markey'	CKen
	- 'Lucas' PBR	CDoC NLar
	- 'Marian'	CKen NLar
§	- 'Mariesii' (v)	CKen
	- 'Melody'	CKen
	- 'Meroke'	NLar
	- 'Minima'	CKen
	- 'Nana' ♀H7	CDoC CKen CMac CMen LBee NHol NWad SRms
	- 'Nana Aurea' ♀H7	CDoC CMac CSBt EHul EPfP EPla LRHS MAsh MJak NHol NPCo WGor
§	- 'Nana Densa'	CDoC CKen CMac
	- 'Nana Gracilis' ♀H7	CDoC CDul CKen CMen CSBt EHul ELan EPfP EPla EUJe IVic LAst LRHS MAsh MBri MGos MJak NEgg NPCo NWad NWea SBod SCoo SLim SPoG
I	- 'Nana Gracilis Aurea'	CMen EHul
I	- 'Nana Lutea' ♀H7	CDoC CKen EHul EPfP EPla LBee MAsh MGos NHol NWad SLim
	- 'Nana Rigida'	see *C. obtusa* 'Rigid Dwarf'
	- 'Nana Variegata'	see *C. obtusa* 'Mariesii'
	- 'Pygmaea'	CSBt EHul MGos SCoo SLim
§	- 'Rigid Dwarf'	CDoC CKen EHul LBee SLim
	- 'Snowflake' (v)	CDoC CKen NWad
	- 'Snowkist' (v)	CKen
	- 'Spiralis'	CKen
	- 'Split Rock'	NLar
	- 'Stoneham'	CKen
	- 'Tempelhof'	CKen EHul MAsh NEgg NLar SCoo SLim
	- 'Tetragona Aurea'	CBcs CMac EHul NWad
	- 'Timothy'	CMac
	- 'Tonia' (v)	CKen EHul EPla SLim
	- 'Tsatsumi'	CDoC NLar
	- 'Tsatsumi Gold' ♀H7	CDoC CKen EHul EPfP MPkF NLar SCoo SLim SPoG
	- 'Verdon'	CKen
	- 'Wissel'	CKen
	- 'Wyckoff'	CKen
	- 'Yellowtip' (v)	CKen EPfP MAsh NPCo
	pisifera Endl. 'Aurea Nana' misapplied	see *C. pisifera* 'Strathmore'
	- 'Avenue'	EHul
	- 'Baby Blue'	EHul ELan EPfP EPla MGos SCoo SLim SPoG
	- 'Blue Globe'	CKen
	- 'Boulevard' ♀H7	CAco CBcs CDoC CDul CJun CMac CSBt EHul ELan EPfP EPla LAst LBee LRHS MAsh MGos MJak NEgg NPri NWea SLim SPer WBor
	- 'Compacta Variegata' (v)	MAsh NEgg SRms
	- 'Curly Tops' ♀H7	CSBt EHul NHol SCoo SLim
	- 'Devon Cream'	NEgg
	- 'Filifera'	CMac CSBt SCoo
	- 'Filifera Aurea' ♀H7	CKen CMac EHul EPfP EPla LBee MGos MJak NEgg NHol NWea SCoo WCFE
	- 'Filifera Aureovariegata' (v)	EHul
	- 'Filifera Nana'	EHul ELan LRHS MGos SLim SPoG
	- 'Filifera Nana Aurea'	see *C. pisifera* 'Golden Mop'
	- 'Filifera Sungold'	see *C. pisifera* 'Sungold'
	- 'Fuiri-tsukomo'	CKen
	- 'Gold Cushion'	CKen
	- 'Gold Dust'	see *C. pisifera* 'Plumosa Aurea'
	- 'Gold Spangle'	CKen EHul
§	- 'Golden Mop'	CKen EHul NLar
	- 'Green Pincushion'	CKen CMen
	- 'Hime-himuro'	CKen
	- 'Hime-sawara'	CKen CMen
	- 'Lime Tart'	CKen
	- 'Nana'	CKen CMen EHul EPla MAsh MBri NHol

I - 'Nana Albovariegata' (v) CDoC MAsh WThu
- 'Nana Aurea' new NWad
- 'Nana Aureovariegata' (v) CDoC CSBt EHul LBee MBri
I - 'Nana Compacta' CMac SRms
- 'Nana Variegata' (v) CMac LBee NWad
I - 'Parslorii' CKen
- 'Pici' CKen
§ - 'Plumosa Aurea' CKen EHul MAsh NWea
- 'Plumosa Aurea Compacta' CKen
- 'Plumosa Aurea Nana' MAsh
I - 'Plumosa Aurea Nana Compacta' CMac
- 'Plumosa Aurescens' CDoC CMac
I - 'Plumosa Compacta Nana' new SRms
§ - 'Plumosa Compressa' ♀H7 CDoC CKen EHul EUJe NWad
- 'Plumosa Densa' see *C. pisifera* 'Plumosa Compressa'
- 'Plumosa Flavescens' EHul
I - 'Plumosa Juniperoides' CKen EHul MBri
§ - 'Plumosa Rogersii' EHul
I - 'Pygmaea Tsukumo' NLar
- 'Rogersii' see *C. pisifera* 'Plumosa Rogersii'
- 'Silver and Gold' (v) EHul
- 'Silver Lode' (v) CKen
- 'Snow' (v) CKen
- 'Snowflake' CKen EHul
- 'Spaan's Cannon Ball' CKen
- 'Squarrosa Dumosa' CKen EHul
I - 'Squarrosa Lombarts' CMac CSBt EHul SRms
- 'Squarrosa Lutea' CKen
- 'Squarrosa Sulphurea' CSBt EHul EPfP MBri
§ - 'Strathmore' EHul NWad
§ - 'Sungold' ♀H7 CDoC CKen CSBt EHul EPla LRHS MAsh MGos SCoo SLim SPoG SRms
- 'Tama-himuro' CKen
- 'Teddy Bear' MBri NLar NPCo
- 'True Blue' EHul EPla WGor
- 'White Beauty' (v) EPla
thyoides 'Andelyensis' CMac CSBt EHul MBri
- 'Aurea' EHul
- 'Blue Rock' new SLim
- 'Conica' MAsh
- 'Ericoides' CKen CTri EHul LBee SPlb
- 'Little Jamie' CKen
- 'Red Star' see *C. thyoides* 'Rubicon'
§ - 'Rubicon' CMac CSBt EHul EPfP EPla LBee LRHS MAsh MBri NEgg SLim SPoG
- 'Top Point' EPla LAst LBee MAsh SCoo SPoG
- 'Variegata' (v) EHul

Chamaecytisus (*Papilionaceae*)

hirsutus see *Cytisus hirsutus*
- var. ***demissus*** see *Cytisus demissus*
proliferus see *Cytisus proliferus*
purpureus see *Cytisus purpureus*
- 'Incarnatus' see *Cytisus purpureus* 'Atropurpureus'
supinus see *Cytisus hirsutus*

Chamaedaphne (*Ericaceae*)

calyculata CBcs
- 'Nana' NHar

Chamaedorea (*Arecaceae*)

elegans ♀H1a LPal
erumpens see *C. seifrizii*
metallica misapplied see *C. microspadix*
§ ***microspadix*** CPHo LPal SChr
radicalis CBrP CPHo NLos SChr
§ ***seifrizii*** LPal

Chamaemelum (*Asteraceae*)

§ ***nobile*** CArn CBod CHby CPrp CTri CUse CWld ELau ENfk EPfP GPoy MBri MHer MMuc MNHC NGdn NPri SEND SPlb SRms SVic WJek
- dwarf SMor SVic
- dwarf, double-flowered (d) CUse LEdu
- 'Flore Pleno' (d) Widely available
- 'Treneague' Widely available

Chamaenerion (*Onagraceae*)

§ ***angustifolium*** SWat WSFF
§ - 'Album' CAby CDes CElw CMea CSpe ECha ELan EPfP LEdu LRHS MBel MMuc MNrw MRav NBid NBir NSti SEND SPad SPer SPhx SPoG SWat WCot WHal WMoo WPGP WPtf WSFF WSHC
- 'Isobel' MRav WCot
- 'Stahl Rose' CAby CElw CHid CMea EPfP EWes LPla MCot NSti SGbt SMrm SPhx SWat WCot WSHC
§ ***dodonaei*** CFis ELan EWes IMou LPla SPhx WCot
§ ***fleischeri*** MMuc SEND

Chamaepericlymenum see *Cornus*

Chamaerops (*Arecaceae*)

excelsa misapplied see *Trachycarpus fortunei*
excelsa Thunb. see *Rhapis excelsa*
humilis ♀H4 CAbb CAco CBcs CBrP CHEx EPfP ESwi EUJe LPal LRHS MGos NPla NPri NSoo SArc SChr SEND SHil SPlb SPoG STrG WCot
§ - var. ***argentea*** CBrP CDTJ CPHo LPal LRHS MGos SChr SPlb WCot
- var. ***cerifera*** see *C. humilis* var. *argentea*
- 'Vulcano' CDTJ LPal SChr

Chamaespartium see *Genista*

Chamaesphacos (*Lamiaceae*)

ilicifolius misapplied see *Siphocranion macranthum*

Chamelaucium (*Myrtaceae*)

uncinatum CCCN MOWG

Chamerion see *Chamaenerion*

Chasmanthe (*Iridaceae*)

aethiopica EBee EPri
bicolor CExl CPrp CTca EBee EPri IDee
floribunda CHEx CPrp CTca EBee EPri GKev
- var. ***duckittii*** CCon CPrp EBee ECho EPfP GKev
- 'Saturnus' EBee GKev

Chasmanthium (*Poaceae*)

§ ***latifolium*** CBod CKno CSde ECha EHoe ELan ELon EPPr EPla EShb EUJe LRHS MBrN MBri MMoz SCob SGSe SGol SMrm SPoG WBor WCot WSHC WWEG WWFP XLum
- 'Golden Spangles' CKno
- 'River Mist' (v) EBee ELon LRHS MAvo SCob SPad SPoG

laxum CBod SMea

Cheilanthes (*Pteridaceae*)

argentea CBty ISha
bonariensis WCot
distans ISha SRms
lanosa CBty CCCN CHid CLAP EBee EFer EWes ISha LRHS NLos SGSe SPlb WCot
sinuata ISha
tomentosa CBty CCCN CLAP ISha LPal LRHS
wootonii WAbe
wrightii ISha

Cheiranthus see *Erysimum*

Cheirolophus (*Asteraceae*)

benoistii misapplied see *Centaurea atropurpurea*
benoistii (Humb.) Holub CSpe EBee MRav SKHP WSHC

Chelidonium (*Papaveraceae*)

japonicum see *Hylomecon japonica*
majus CArn GEdr GPoy GQui MHer NMir WHer WSFF
- 'Flore Pleno' (d) CBre GJos NBid NBro WHer WTou
- var. ***laciniatum*** WCot

Chelone (*Plantaginaceae*)

barbata see *Penstemon barbatus*
§ ***glabra*** Widely available
lyonii EBee ELan NLar SPad SPhx WMoo WShi
- 'Pink Temptation' EBee MMoz MWat
obliqua Widely available
- var. ***alba*** see *C. glabra*
- 'Forncett Foremost' GQui
- 'Ieniemienie' EBee LEdu
- 'Pink Sensation' WFar
I 'Pink Turtle' EBee GBin

Chelonopsis (*Lamiaceae*)

moschata CLAP EBee GBin GEdr LEdu MHer SBrt SMad SPlb WMoo WPGP
yagiharana CAby CDes NBid SHar WMoo WOut

Chenopodium (*Amaranthaceae*)

ambrosioides CArn
bonus-henricus CAgr CArn CHab CHby ENfk GPoy LPot MCoo MHer MNHC SIde SRms WHer WJek
capitatum **new** CUse
foliosum **new** MNHC
giganteum CUse MNHC SHDw WJek

cherimoya see *Annona cherimola*

cherry, Duke see *Prunus* × *gondouinii*

cherry, sour or morello see *Prunus cerasus*

cherry, sweet see *Prunus avium*

chervil see *Anthriscus cerefolium*

chestnut, sweet see *Castanea sativa*

Chiastophyllum (*Crassulaceae*)

§ ***oppositifolium*** ♀H5 CBcs CSam CTri EBee ECha ECho EDAr ELan EPfP ETwe GAbr GEdr GJos GKev ITim LAst LRHS MHol MLHP MMuc MRav NBid SPlb SRms WKif WMoo WSHC XLum
- 'Frosted Jade' see *C. oppositifolium* 'Jim's Pride'
- 'Jane's Reverse' (v) EBee WCot
§ - 'Jim's Pride' (v) ECha ECho ECtt EHoe EWes EWll GAbr GBuc GEdr GKev GMaP MHer MPie MRav NHar NPer SPlb SRGP SRms SRot WIce WKif WMoo WSHC
simplicifolium see *C. oppositifolium*

Chiliotrichum (*Asteraceae*)

diffusum MMuc
- 'Lanceolatum' **new** GAbr

Chilopsis (*Bignoniaceae*)

linearis CArn
- var. ***linearis*** SPad

Chimonanthus ✿ (*Calycanthaceae*)

fragrans see *C. praecox*
nitens CBcs CMCN NLar
§ ***praecox*** Widely available
- 'Brockhill Goldleaf' NLar
- 'Grandiflorus' ♀H5 CEnd CJun EPfP LRHS MBri SPoG SSta WPGP WPat
- 'Luteus' ♀H4 CBcs CEnd CJun ELan EPfP LRHS MBri MGos SPoG SSpi SSta WCot WPGP WPat
- 'Sunburst' CJun
- 'Trenython' ♀H4 CEnd CJun WPat
yunnanensis misapplied IArd
yunnanensis W.W. Sm. see *C. praecox*

Chimonobambusa (*Poaceae*)

KR 7592 MWht
hookeriana misapplied see *Himalayacalamus falconeri* 'Damarapa'
macrophylla f. ***intermedia*** EPla
§ ***marmorea*** CDTJ CEnt EPla ERod MMoz MMuc MWht SBig
- 'Variegata' (v) CDTJ EPla ERod ESwi MMoz
§ ***quadrangularis*** CBcs CDTJ CDoC CEnt EPfP EPla ERod ESwi IMou MMoz MWht SBig
- 'Nagaminei' (v) ERod
- 'Suow' (v) CDTJ
- 'Tatejima' ERod
tumidissinoda CDTJ CEnt EPfP EPla ERod ESwi IMou MMoz MWhi MWht SBig

Chinese chives see *Allium tuberosum*

Chiogenes see *Gaultheria*

Chionanthus (*Oleaceae*)

retusus CBcs CDul CMCN EBee EPfP ETwe LRHS MPkF NLar SHil SKHP SPer SSpi
- 'Arnold's Pride' **new** NLar
- 'Tokyo Tower' CJun
virginicus CBcs CDoC CDul CJun CMCN ECrN ELan EPfP EPla ETwe EWTr GBin IArd LRHS MBlu MGil MMuc MRav NEgg NLar SKHP SPer SPlb SPoG SSpi

Chionochloa (*Poaceae*)

conspicua CAby CBod EBee GAbr GBee GBin GCal GKev MAvo MMuc NBid NBir SGSe SMea WPGP
- subsp. ***conspicua*** WCot
- 'Rubra' see *C. rubra*
flavescens EHoe GBin MAvo MMuc
flavicans CSpe IMou MHin SMad SMea
§ ***rubra*** ♀H7 CBcs CElw CKno CSpe EBee EHoe ELan EPla EWes GBin GCal GMaP IMou MAsh MAvo MMoz MRav SGSe SMad WCot WMoo WPGP WWFP
- PAB 67 LEdu
- subsp. ***cuprea*** CAby CBod GBin

Chionodoxa ✿ (*Asparagaceae*)

cretica see *C. nana*
§ ***forbesii*** CBro CWCL ECGP ECho EPfP EPot EShb GKev LRHS NBir SDeJ SPer SRms WShi
- 'Alba' ECho
- 'Blue Giant' ECho ELan EPot ERCP
- 'Rosea' ECho LAma
- Siehei Group see *C. siehei*
- 'Tmoli' ECho
- 'Violet Beauty' ECho GKev LRHS SBch SDeJ
- 'Zwanenburg' ECho
gigantea see *C. luciliae* Gigantea Group
luciliae misapplied see *C. forbesii*
luciliae ambig. CAvo ECho LRHS SEND
luciliae Boiss. ♀H5 CAby CBro EPfP LAma MBri SPer
- 'Alba' CHVG ECho LRHS SBod SDeJ SPer
§ - Gigantea Group ECho GKev
- - 'Alba' EPot GKev
§ ***nana*** ECho
'Pink Giant' CAvo CBro ECho ELan EPfP EPot ERCP EShb GKev LAma LRHS SDeJ WBor XLum
sardensis ♀H5 CBro CHVG CPrp ECho EPot ERCP GKev LAma LRHS SDeJ SPhx WShi
§ ***siehei*** ♀H5 ECho
'Valentine Day' EPot

Chionographis (*Melanthiaceae*)

japonica EFEx WCru

Chionohebe (*Plantaginaceae*)

pulvinaris NSla WAbe

× *Chionoscilla* (*Asparagaceae*)

§ ***allenii*** ECho EPot SPhx WCot

Chiranthodendron (*Malvaceae*)

pentadactylon **new** SPlb

Chirita (*Gesneriaceae*)

'Aiko' WDib
'Candy' WDib
'Chastity' WDib
'Diane Marie' WDib
'Erika' WDib
flavimaculata WDib
heterotricha WDib
'Keiko' WDib
linearifolia WDib
linearifolia* × *sinensis WDib
linearifolia* × *sinensis 'Latifolia' WDib
longgangensis WDib
'New York' WDib
sinensis ♀H1c WDib
- 'Hisako' WDib
speciosa 'Crûg Cornetto' WCot WCru
'Stardust' WDib
'Sweet Dreams' WDib
tamiana WDib

Chironia (*Gentianaceae*)

baccifera SPlb

× *Chitalpa* (*Bignoniaceae*)

tashkentensis CBcs CEnd EPfP ESwi MTPN
- 'Morning Cloud' MBlu
- 'Pink Dawn' ESwi LRHS MBlu MBri SPad
- Summer Bells = 'Minsum' CDoC ELon WCot

chives see *Allium schoenoprasum*

Chlidanthus (*Amaryllidaceae*)

fragrans CCCN ECho GKev SDeJ SEND XLum

Chloranthus (*Chloranthaceae*)

fortunei CDes CLAP
- 'Domino' WCot
glaber B&SWJ 11102 **new** WCru
- var. ***flavus*** see *Sarcandra glabra* f. *flava*
henryi WCot
japonicus GBuc GEdr WCru
oldhamii CTal
- B&SWJ 2019 GEdr LEdu WCru
serratus GEdr WCru

Chloris (*Poaceae*)

distichophylla see *Eustachys distichophylla*

Chlorogalum (*Asparagaceae*)

pomeridianum CFil CLak

Chlorophytum (*Asparagaceae*)

comosum EShb SEND SVic
- 'Aureomarginata' (v) SEND
- 'Variegatum' (v) ♀H2 EShb NGBl SEND SPre SRms
- 'Vittatum' (v) ♀H2 EShb NGBl SRms
krookianum CCon CDes WCot
macrophyllum EShb
nepalense B&SWJ 2528 WCru
saundersiae CExl

Choisya (*Rutaceae*)

× ***dewitteana*** 'Aztec Gold'PBR **new** CRos EPla LRHS MAsh MGos SCob SHil
- 'Aztec Pearl' ♀H4 Widely available
- Golden Gift = 'Lismarty'PBR LRHS SSpi
- Goldfingers = 'Limo'PBR CBcs CDul CMac CWGN EBee ELan EPfP EShb LAst LRHS MBri MGos MRav NEgg NHol NLar NPri SCob SCoo SGbt SLim SLon SPer SPoG SWvt
- White Dazzler = 'Londaz'PBR ♀H4 Widely available
'Royal Lace' **new** LBuc LRHS SLon
ternata ♀H4 Widely available

- Moonshine = 'Walcho'PBR — EBee NLar
- Moonsleeper PBR — see *C. ternata* Sundance
- Snow Flurries = 'Lisflurry'PBR — CRos ELan EPfP LLHF LRHS MAsh MRav SPoG
§ - Sundance = 'Lich'PBR ♀H4 — Widely available

Chondrosum (*Poaceae*)

gracile — see *Bouteloua gracilis*

Chordospartium see *Carmichaelia*

Chorisia (*Bombacaceae*)

speciosa — CCCN SPlb

Chorizema (*Papilionaceae*)

cordatum ♀H2 — ECou SVen
dicksonii — SPlb

Chronanthus see *Cytisus*

Chrysalidocarpus see *Dypsis*

Chrysanthemopsis see *Rhodanthemum*

Chrysanthemum ✿ (*Asteraceae*)

E.H. Wilson s.n. — WCot
'Action Bronze' (22) — EPfP
'Agnes Ann' (21d) — EWoo MNrw
'Alan Foxall Yellow' (3b) — MCms
'Albert's Yellow' (21d) — EWoo
'Alec Bedser' (25a) — NHal
'Alehmer Rote' (21) — MNrw WWEG
'Alex Young' (25b) — MCms
'Aline' (21) — EWoo MNrw
'Alison' (29c) — ELon EWoo MNrw
'Alison's Dad' — MNrw
'Allouise' (25b) ♀H3 — NHal
'Allouise Pink' (25b) — MCms
'Allyson Peace' (14a) — MCms NHal
alpinum — see *Leucanthemopsis alpina*
'Amber Gigantic' (1) — NHal
'Amber Matlock' (24b) — MCms
'American Beauty Lemon' (5b) — MCms
'American Beauty White' (5b) — MCms
'Anastasia' (21c) — CHid EBee ECtt ELon GCal LRHS MNrw MRav NSti WBor WWEG
'Anderton' (6b) **new** — MCms
'Angela Blundell' (19b) — WCot
'Angela Cosimini' (25b) — MCms
'Angelic' (21b) ♀H4 — EBee EWoo
'Anne Ratsey' (21) — CHVG CSam MNrw WBrk
'Anne, Lady Brocket' (21d) — ECtt EWoo MNrw NWsh
'Anthony Peace' (25b) — MCms NHal
'Antigua'PBR — MCms
'Apollo' H. Shoesmith — EWoo LLHF MNrw WCot
'Apollo' (21) — NCGa SPhx WHoo
'Apricot' — see *C.* 'Cottage Apricot'
'Apricot Chessington' (25a) — MCms NHal
'Apricot Courtier' (24a) — MCms NHal
'Apricot Enbee Wedding' — see *C.* 'Bronze Enbee Wedding'
'Apricot Mundial' (6b) **new** — MCms
arcticum L. — see *Arctanthemum arcticum*
argenteum — see *Tanacetum argenteum*
'Astro' (25b) — NHal
'Aunt Millicent' (21d) ♀H4 — EWoo LLHF MNrw NHal SPhx WCot
'Balcombe Perfection' (5a) — MCms NHal
balsamita — see *Tanacetum balsamita*
Barbara = 'Yobarbara' (22) — NHal
'Beacon' (5a) ♀H2 — NHal
'Beechcroft' (29Rub) — MNrw
'Belle' (21d) — EWoo MNrw
'Beppie Bronze' (29e) — MCms
'Beppie Purple' (29e) — MCms
'Beppie Red' (29e) — MCms
'Beppie Rose' (29e) — MCms
'Beppie Yellow' (29e) — MCms
'Best Man' (29d) — MCms
'Betty' (21) — EWoo
'Bill Holden' (14a) — MCms NHal
'Bill Wade' (25a) — NHal
'Billy Bell' (15a) — MCms NHal
'Blanche Poitevene' (5b) — EMal
'Bob Green' (13b) — MCms
'Bobby Swinburn' (13b) — NHal
'Branroyal'PBR — NLar
Bravo = 'Yobra' (22c) ♀H3 — NHal
* 'Breitner's Supreme' — ECtt MNrw WWEG
'Brennpunkt' — EWoo MNrw
'Bretforton Road' — ECtt MNrw WCot
'Brierton Violet' (17b) — NHal
'Brightness' (21) — EWoo MNrw
'Bronze Cassandra' (5b) ♀H2 — MCms NHal
'Bronze Darren Pugh' (3b) **new** — NHal
'Bronze Dee Gem' (29c) — MCms NHal
§ 'Bronze Elegance' (21b) ♀H4 — CTri ECtt EWoo LRHS MNrw NBir NGdn NSti NWsh SRms
§ 'Bronze Enbee Wedding' (29d) ♀H3 — MCms NHal
'Bronze Gigantic' (1) — NHal
'Bronze Matlock' (24b) — NHal
'Bronze Max Riley' (23b) ♀H3 — MCms NHal
'Bronze Mayford Perfection' (5a) ♀H2 — NHal
'Bronze Mei-kyo' — see *C.* 'Bronze Elegance'
'Bronze Talbot Parade' (29c) ♀H3 **new** — MCms
'Bronze William Florentine' (15a) — MCms
'Brown Eyes' (21b) ♀H4 — EWoo
'Bryony Wade' (13b) **new** — MCms NHal
'Buff William Florentine' (15a) **new** — MCms
burnt orange-flowered — CAby MNrw
'Burntwood Belle' (3b) — MCms
'Buxton Ruby' — EWoo
'Candy John Wingfield' (14b) **new** — MCms
'Capel Manor' — EBee EWoo LLHF MNrw WCot
'Capella' (10a) **new** — MCms
'Carlene Welby' (25b) — MCms
'Carmine Blush' (21d) ♀H4 — EWoo MNrw SPhx WBrk WCot
'Casablanca' (25a) — NHal
'Cassandra' (5b) ♀H2 — MCms NHal
'Charles Tandy Yellow' (15b) — MCms
'Chelsea Physic Garden' — CAby EBee EWoo IGor MNrw SPhx WCot WWEG
'Chempak Rose' (14b) — MCms
'Cherry Chessington' (25a) — MCms NHal

	Name	Suppliers
	'Cherry Riley's Dynasty' (14a)	MCms
	'Chesapeake Primrose' (10a) **new**	MCms
	Chesapeake = 'Yochesapeake'[PBR] (10a)	MCms NHal
	'Chesswood Beauty' (7b) **new**	MCms
	'Chestnut Talbot Maid' (29c)	MCms
	'Chestnut Talbot Parade' (29c) ♀H3	MCms
	'Chloe Ball' (13b)	MCms
	'Christmas' **new**	MNrw
	'Christopher Lawson' (24b)	MCms NHal
	'Cinderella'	WMnd WWEG
	cinerariifolium	see *Tanacetum cinerariifolium*
	'Clapham Delight' (23a)	MCms NHal
	'Clara Curtis' (21d)	Widely available
	'Clare Louise' (24b)	MCms
	'Clarksdale' (15b)	MCms NHal
	coccineum	see *Tanacetum coccineum*
	'Colsterworth'	MNrw
	'Contralto' (22)	EWoo
	'Coral Reef' (10b)	MCms NHal
	'Corinna' (21d)	GBin
	'Cornetto' (25b)	MCms NHal
	corymbosum	see *Tanacetum corymbosum*
§	'Cottage Apricot' (21)	ECGP EWoo LRHS MBNS MLHP MNrw MRav SRms
	'Cottage Bronze'	MNrw
	'Cottage Lemon'	MNrw
	'Cottage Pink'	see *C.* 'Emperor of China'
	'Cottage Yellow'	EWoo
	'Courtier' (24a)	NHal
	'Cousin Joan' (21d) ♀H4	EBee EWoo LLHF MNrw NCGa SPhx WCot
	'Cream Elegance' (9c)	NHal
	'Cream John Hughes' (3b)	MCms
	'Cream Patricia Millar' (14b)	NHal
	'Cream Talbot Maid' (29c)	MCms
	'Cream Talbot Parade' (29c) ♀H3	MCms
	'Cream West Bromwich' (14a)	MCms
	Dana = 'Yodana' (25b) ♀H3	NHal
	Dance = 'Fidance'[PBR]	MCms
	'Dance Red'	MCms
	Dance Salmon = 'Fidancesal'[PBR]	MCms
	'Dance Sunny'	MCms
	'Dance White'	MCms
	'Daniel Cooper' (21d) ♀H4	EBee EWoo MNrw SBch
	'Daphne' (21d)	EWoo
	'Darren Pugh' (3b)	MCms NHal
	'David Cooper' **new**	SBch
	'Dee Gem' (29c) ♀H3	MCms NHal
	'Delianne'	MCms
	'Delianne Yellow'	MCms
	'Delistar'[PBR] **new**	MCms
	'Delistar Bronze' **new**	MCms
	'Delistar Cream'[PBR] **new**	MCms
	'Delistar Lemon' **new**	MCms
	'Delistar Lilac' **new**	MCms
	'Delistar Mint' **new**	MCms
	'Delistar Pink' **new**	MCms
	'Delistar Pink Star' **new**	MCms
	'Delistar Saffira' **new**	MCms
	'Delistar Sunny' **new**	MCms
	'Delta' (5b)	NHal
	'Delta Copper Bronze' (9d)	NHal
	'Delta Crimson' (29d)	NHal
	'Delta Yellow' (29)	NHal
	'Denise Oatridge' (5a) **new**	MCms
	'Dennis Fletcher' (25a)	NHal
	'Dennis Gill' (25b)	MCms
	'Dennis Turner' (25b) **new**	MCms
	'Dennis Turner Primrose' (15b) **new**	MCms
	'Dernier Soleil' **new**	XLum
	'Deva Glow' (25a)	MCms
	'Dixter Orange'	GCal
§	'Doctor Tom Parr' (21c)	CExl ELan EWoo MNrw
	'Don't Start' (7a)	MCms
	'Doreen Hall' (15a)	NHal
	'Doreen Statham' (4b)	MCms NHal
	'Doris Ozols' (25a)	NHal
	'Dorothy Stone' (25b)	NHal
	'Dorridge Crystal' (24a)	MCms NHal
	'Downpour' (10a) **new**	MCms
	'Dublin'	MCms
	'Duchess of Edinburgh' (21d)	CFis EBee ECtt ELan EPfP EWoo GBin LRHS LSun MNrw NSoo SDys SPhx XLum
	'Dulwich Pink' (21d) ♀H4	EWoo WCot
	'Dutchy'[PBR]	MCms
	'Early Yellow'	EBee ELon EWoo MNrw WCot
	'Edelweiss' (21)	CAby
	'Edmund Brown' **new**	WCot
	'Edward Shaw' (5a)	MCms
	'Egret' (23b)	MCms NHal
	'Elegance' (9c)	NHal
	'Elizabeth Lawson' (5b)	NHal
	'Elizabeth Shoesmith' (1)	NHal
§	'Emperor of China' (21)	CAby CElw ECha ECtt EWoo IGor LSun MNrw MRav NHal SPhx SRms WBor WMnd WWEG XLum
	'Enbee Wedding' (29d) ♀H3	MCms NHal
	'Energy'[PBR] (9)	MCms
	'Esther' (21d)	EWoo MNrw NCGa SMad
	'Eva Allen' (25b)	MCms
	'Fairweather' (3b)	MCms NHal
	'Fairweather Peach' (3b)	MCms
	'Feeling Green Dark'[PBR]	MCms
	'Fleur de Lis' (10a)	MCms
	foeniculaceum	see *Argyranthemum foeniculaceum*
	'Fondant'	NHal
	'Foxtrot'[PBR] ♀H3	NLar
	'French Rose'	MNrw
	'Froggy'[PBR] (9)	MCms
	frutescens	see *Argyranthemum frutescens*
	'Gala Burgundy'	EPfP NLar
	'Gambit' (24a)	NHal
	'Geoff Aird' (15b)	NHal
	'Geoff Amos' (3b)	MCms NHal
	'Geoff Brady' (5a)	MCms NHal
	'George Griffiths' (24b) ♀H3	MCms NHal
	'Gigantic' (1)	NHal
	'Gillette' (23b)	MCms
	'Ginger Nut' (25b)	MCms
	'Ginger Nut Yellow' (25b)	MCms

'Gladys Emerson' (3b)	MCms NHal
'Gold Enbee Wedding' (29d) ♀H3	MCms
'Gold Marianne'	XLum
'Gold Mundial' (6b) ♀H2 **new**	MCms
'Golden Cassandra' (5b) ♀H2	MCms NHal
'Golden Chalice' (12a)	NHal
'Golden Courtier' (24a)	MCms NHal
'Golden Gigantic' (1)	NHal
'Golden Masons' (7b) **new**	MCms
'Golden Mayford Perfection' (5a) ♀H2	MCms NHal
'Golden Plover' (22)	NHal
'Golden Rain' (10a) ♀H2	MCms NHal
'Golden Splendour' (10a) **new**	MCms
'Golden Wedding' (21)	MNrw
'Golden William Florentine' (15a)	MCms
'Golden Woolman's Glory' (7a)	NHal
'Goldengreenheart' (21d) ♀H4	EBee ECtt EShb EWoo LLHF MNrw WBrk WHoo
'Goldmarianne' (21)	GBin
'Goodlife Sombrero' (29a) ♀H3	MCms
'Goshu Penta' (10a)	MCms
'Grandchild' (21c) ♀H4	MNrw NHal
'Hanenburg'	NHal
haradjanii	see *Tanacetum haradjanii*
'Harold Lawson' (5a)	MCms NHal
'Harry Gee' (1)	NHal
'Harry Tolley' (14b)	MCms
* 'Hazel' (21)	EWoo
'Heather James' (3b)	MCms NHal
'Hebe' (21d)	EBee
'Heide' (29c) ♀H3	NHal
'Helen Louise' (25b)	MCms NHal
'Herbie McCauley' (24b) **new**	MCms
'Herbstbrokat'	EBee GBin XLum
'Hesketh Knight' (5b) ♀H2	MCms NHal
'Hoagy' (29d)	NHal
'Holly Elizabeth' (14a)	MCms
Holly = 'Yoholly' (22b) ♀H3	NHal
'Honey Enbee Wedding' (29d)	MCms NHal
'Horningsea Pink' (19d)	ECGP WBor
'Imp' (21e) ♀H4	EWoo
indicum	SVic
'Innocence' (21d) ♀H4	CFis ECtt ELan EWoo IGor MNrw MRav NGdn SHar WBrk WHoo WWEG
'Isabellrosa' (21d) ♀H4	GBin
'Janet South'	EWoo MNrw
'Jante Wells' (21b) ♀H4	MNrw WBor WWEG
'Jenny Wren' (12a)	NHal
'Jessie Cooper' misapplied	see *C.* 'Mrs Jessie Cooper' (21)
'Jimmy Simpson' (25b) **new**	MCms NHal
'Jimmy Tranter' (14b)	NHal
'Joan Waugh' (14b)	MCms
'John Harrison' (25b)	MCms NHal
'John Hughes' (3b)	MCms NHal
'John Lowry' (24a)	MCms NHal
'John Riley' (14a)	NHal
'John Wingfield' (14b)	MCms NHal
'John Wingfield Honey' (14b)	MCms
'John Wingfield Pearl' (14b)	MCms
'Jolie Rose'	WCot
'Joyce Fountain' (24a)	MCms NHal
'Joyce Frieda' (13b)	MCms NHal
'Julia' (28)	EPfP MNrw
'Julia Arnold' **new**	WHoo
'Julia Peterson'	MHer WBrk WCot WHoo
'Julie Lagravère' (28)	EWoo MNrw WPtf XLum
'Karen Taylor' (29c) ♀H3	NHal
'Kath Stephenson' (7b)	MCms NHal
'Kath Stephenson Honey' (7b)	MCms
'Kath Stephenson Peach' (7b)	MCms
'Kath Stephenson Primrose' (7b)	MCms NHal
'Kath Stephenson Rose' (7b)	MCms NHal
'Kath Stephenson Salmon' (7b)	MCms
'Katie Jane' (7b)	NHal
'Kay Woolman' (13b)	MCms NHal
'Kay Woolman Yellow' (13b)	MCms
'Killerton Tangerine'	MNrw
'Kiyomi-no-meisui'	MCms NHal
'Kleiner Bernstein'	MNrw
'La Damoiselle'	WCot
§ 'Lady in Pink' (21)	EWoo MNrw
'Lady Manito'	EWoo
'Lakelanders' (3b)	NHal
'Lava' (10a) **new**	MCms
'Leo' (21b) ♀H4	EBee EWoo
leucanthemum	see *Leucanthemum vulgare*
'Lexy'PBR (9)	MCms
'Lexy Red'PBR (9)	MCms
'Lilac Chessington' (25a)	MCms NHal
Linda = 'Lindayo' (22c) ♀H3	NHal
'L'Innocence' (21)	CAby
'Little Dorrit' (21f) ♀H4	EWoo
'Liverpool Festival' (23b)	MCms
'Lollipop'PBR (9)	MCms
'Lorna Wood' (13b)	MCms NHal
'Louise' (25b)	MNrw
'Louise Park' (24a)	MCms
'Lucy' (29a)	MCms NHal
'Lucy Simpson' (21d)	EWoo SBch
'Lundy' (2)	NHal
'Lydia Mannion' (7b)	MCms
'Lynn Johnson' (15a)	MCms
Lynn = 'Yolynn' (22c) ♀H3	NHal
macrophyllum	see *Tanacetum macrophyllum* (Waldst. & Kit.) Sch.Bip.
'Malcolm Perkins' (25a)	MCms NHal
'Mancetta Comet' (29a)	NHal
'Mancetta Symbol' (5a)	MCms
'Mandarin'	EWoo
maresii	see *Rhodanthemum hosmariense*
'Margaret Dear' (25a) **new**	MCms
'Margery Fish'	MNrw
'Marion' (25a)	MNrw WCot
'Mark Woolman' (1)	NHal
'Mary' (21f)	EWoo MNrw NHal
'Mary Stoker' (21d)	CAby EBee ECtt ELan ELon EPfP EPri EWoo LRHS LSun MNrw MPie

	MRav NCGa NHal NLar NSoo SPer WAul WCAu WMnd WWEG XLum
'Mary's Miracle' (24a)	MCms
'Mason's Bronze' (7b)	MCms
'Matlock' (24b)	NHal
'Mauve Gem' (21f) ♀H3	MNrw NHal
mawii	see *Rhodanthemum gayanum*
'Max Riley' (23b) ♀H3	MCms NHal
maximum misapplied	see *Leucanthemum* × *superbum*
maximum Ramond	see *Leucanthemum maximum* (Ramond) DC.
'Maxine Charlton' (24b)	MCms
'Maxine Johnson' (25b)	NHal
'May Shoesmith' (5a) ♀H2	NHal
'Maybach' (9)	MCms
'Mayford Perfection' (5a) ♀H2	MCms NHal
'Mei-Kyō' (28b) ♀H4	CFis CMea CTri ECtt EWoo IGor LRHS MNrw SRms WBor WBrk WHil WWEG
'Membury' (24b)	NHal
'Michelle Preston' (13b)	NHal
'Millennium' (25b) ♀H3	MCms NHal
'Millie Mathews' (14b)	MCms
'Misty Cream' (25b)	MCms
'Misty Golden' (25b)	MCms
'Misty Lemon' (25b)	MCms
'Moonlight' (29d/K)	MRav
'Moonlight' (24a) **new**	LRHS
'Morning Star' (12a)	NHal
'Mount Fuji' (10b) **new**	MCms
§ 'Mrs Jessie Cooper' (21d) ♀H4	CAby CHGN EBee EWoo GBee GQue MNrw NLar SDys SMrm SRms WCot WHoo WPtf WWEG
'Mrs Jessie Cooper No 1'	NCGa NWsh SBch
'Mrs Jessie Cooper No 2'	MNrw
'Mundial' (6) **new**	MCms
'Mundial Peach' (6b) **new**	MCms
'Mundial Rose' (6b) **new**	MCms
'Mundial Ruby' (6b) **new**	MCms
'Muriel Odell' (7b)	MCms
'Music' (23b)	NHal
'Muxton Sable' (10a)	MCms NHal
'Myss Carol' (29c) ♀H3	NHal
'Myss Debbie' (29e)	NHal
'Myss Dorothy' (29c)	NHal
'Myss Eliza' (29c)	MCms
'Myss Goldie' (29c)	MCms
'Myss Marion' (29c) ♀H3	EWoo
'Myss Rihanna' (29c)	MCms NHal
'Myss Saffron' (29c) ♀H3	NHal
'Nancy Perry' (21d)	CSam EWoo GBee MNrw MRav XLum
'Nantyderry Sunshine' (28b) ♀H4	ELon LLHF LRHS MNrw MPie NWsh SPhx WCot WMnd WWEG
'Naru' (9c)	NHal
'Naru Crimson' (9c)	NHal
'Natalie Sarah' (29d) ♀H3	MCms NHal
'Nell Gwynn' (21d)	EWoo MNrw NHal
Nicole = 'Yonicole' (22c) ♀H3	NHal
nipponicum	see *Nipponanthemum nipponicum*
'Olwyn' (4b)	MCms
'Orange Allouise' (25b)	MCms NHal
'Orange Enbee Wedding' (29d)	NHal
pacificum	see *Ajania pacifica*
'Paloma Redeye' (29d)	NHal
'Paloma Regent' (29d)	NHal

'Paloma Rose' (29d) **new**	NHal
parthenium	see *Tanacetum parthenium*
'Patricia Millar' (14b)	MCms NHal
'Patricia Millar Cerise' (14b)	MCms
'Patricia Millar Coral' (14b)	MCms
'Patricia Millar Orange' (14b)	MCms
'Patricia Millar Yellow' (14b)	MCms
'Paul Boissier' (30Rub)	CAby CFis ECtt EWoo MNrw NLar NSti SPhx WBor WMnd WWEG
'Paul Cornelius' (24b) **new**	NHal
'Pauline White' (15a)	MCms
'Peach Courtier' (24a)	NHal
'Peach Enbee Wedding' (29d) ♀H3	MCms NHal
'Peach John Wingfield' (14b)	MCms NHal
'Pearl Celebration' (24a)	MCms
'Pearl Enbee Wedding' (29d) **new**	MCms
'Pennine Bullion'	NHal
'Pennine Marie' (29a) ♀H3	MCms
'Pennine Oriel' (29a) ♀H3	MCms NHal
'Pennine Point' (19c)	NHal
'Pennine Polo' (29d) ♀H3	NHal
'Pennine Ranger' (29d)	NHal
'Pennine Swan' (29c)	NHal
'Pennine Sweetheart' (29c) ♀H3	MNrw
'Penny's Yellow'	LLHF WBrk
'Perry's Peach' (21d) ♀H4	EWoo LLHF MNrw NCGa NHal NPer SPhx
'Peter Rowe' (23b)	MCms NHal
'Peterkin'	CMac EBee ECtt ELon EWoo LRHS WWEG XLum
'Picasso'	MNrw
'Pink Anemone'	EWoo
'Pink John Wingfield' (14b)	NHal
'Pink Progression'	see *C.* 'Lady in Pink'
'Pink Splendour' (10a) ♀H2	NHal
'Pocahontas' (10a) **new**	MCms
'Poesie'	WCot
'Polar Gem' (3a)	MCms NHal
'Pot Black' (14b)	MCms
'President Osaka'	MNrw
'Primrose Allouise' (24b) ♀H3	NHal
'Primrose Chessington' (25a)	MCms
'Primrose Courtier'	see *C.* 'Yellow Courtier'
'Primrose Dorothy Stone' (25b)	NHal
'Primrose Egret' (23b) **new**	MCms
'Primrose Enbee Wedding' (29d) ♀H3	MCms NHal
'Primrose Fairweather' (3b)	MCms
'Primrose John Hughes' (3b)	MCms NHal
'Primrose Mayford Perfection' (5a) ♀H2	NHal
'Primrose Pauline White' (15a) **new**	MCms
'Primrose Pennine Oriel' (29a)	MCms
'Primrose Sam Vinter' (5a)	NHal
'Primrose West Bromwich' (14a)	MCms NHal

Cultivar	Suppliers
'Princess' (21d)	LLHF
'Promise' (25a)	NHal
'Purleigh White' (28b)	ECtt ELon EWoo MLHP MNrw NSti WCot WWEG
'Purple Chempak Rose' (14b)	MCms NHal
'Ralph Lambert' (1)	NHal
'Raquel' (21)	MNrw
'Red Balcombe Perfection' (5a)	MCms NHal
'Red Chempak Rose' (14b)	MCms
'Red Goodlife Sombrero' (29a) **new**	MCms
'Red Louise Park' (14a)	MCms
'Red Mayford Perfection' (5a)	MCms NHal
'Red Pennine Gift' (29c)	NHal
'Red Regal Mist' (25b)	MCms
'Red Shirley Model' (3a)	MCms NHal
'Redbreast' (12a)	NHal
'Regal Mist Purple' (25b)	MCms NHal
I 'Rhumba'	WCot
'Riley's Dynasty' (14a)	MCms
'Ringdove' (12a)	NHal
'Rita McMahon' (29d) ♀H3	NHal
'Robeam' (9c) ♀H2	NHal
Robin = 'Yorobi' (22c)	NHal
'Roen Sarah' (29c)	NHal
'Romantica' **new**	MNrw
'Romany' (2)	CElw
'Rose Enbee Wedding' (29d)	MCms NHal
'Rose Madder'	EWoo LPot MNrw WCot
'Rose Mayford Perfection' (5a) ♀H2	MCms NHal
'Rose Patricia Millar' (14b)	MCms NHal
'Rose Talbot Parade' (29c) **new**	MCms
'Rosetta'	MNrw WCot
roseum	see *Tanacetum coccineum*
'Rosy Yoigloo'[PBR]	MWat
'Roy Bevan' (29d)	MCms
'Roy Coopland' (5b) ♀H2	MCms
'Royal Command' (21a)	MNrw WCot
'Royal Sport'	EWoo
rubellum	see *C. zawadskii*
'Ruby Enbee Wedding' (29d) ♀H3	MCms NHal
'Ruby Glow' (7b)	MCms
'Ruby Mound' (21c) ♀H4	EWoo MNrw NHal SDys SHar SPhx WCot
'Ruby Raynor' (21d) ♀H4	EWoo MNrw NHal SDys WCot
'Rumpelstilzchen' (21d)	CMea ECtt EWoo MNrw NWsh WWEG
'Salhouse Dream' (10a)	MCms NHal
'Salhouse Joy' (10a)	MCms NHal
'Salmon Allouise' (25b)	NHal
'Salmon Enbee Wedding' (29d) ♀H3	NHal
'Salmon Fairweather' (3b)	MCms
'Salmon John Wingfield' (24b)	MCms
'Salmon Patricia Millar' (14b) **new**	MCms
'Salmon Pauline White' (15a)	MCms
'Salmon Talbot Maid' (29c)	MCms
'Salmon Talbot Parade' (29c) ♀H3	MCms
'Sam Vinter' (5a)	NHal
'Samba'	WCot
'Sarah Louise' (25b)	NHal
'Savanna Charlton' (25a)	MCms
'Sea Urchin' (21f) ♀H3	MNrw NHal SDys
'Seaton's Ashleigh' (10b) **new**	MCms
'Seaton's Galaxy' (10a)	MCms NHal
'Senkyo Karyu' (10a)	MCms
'Senkyo Kenshin' (10a)	MCms NHal
'Sheffield'	EWoo XLum
'Sheila Coles' (7b)	MCms NHal
'Sheila Harris' (3b)	MCms
'Shenley Orange'	EWoo LLHF
'Shining Light' (21f)	EWoo LLHF MNrw
'Shirley Primrose' (1)	NHal
'Sound' (9d)	MCms
'Southway Sheba' (29d) ♀H3	MCms NHal
'Southway Sheba Bronze' (29d)	MCms NHal
'Southway Shimmer' (29d)	NHal
'Southway Shiraz' (29d)	NHal
'Southway Sloe' (29d)	MCms NHal
'Southway Spectacular' (29d)	NHal
'Southway Strontium' (29d)	NHal
'Spartan Canary' (21d) ♀H4	EWoo
'Spartan Display'	EWoo
'Spartan Linnet'	EWoo
'Spartan Raspberry' (21d)	EWoo
'Spartan Seagull' (21d)	EWoo MNrw
'Stallion'[PBR] (9)	MCms
'Starlet' (21f) ♀H4	EWoo NHal
'Steve Packham' (23b) **new**	NHal
'Stockton' (3b) ♀H2	MCms NHal
'Stratford Pink' (21d)	EWoo
'Suffolk Pink'	ECtt EShb EWoo MNrw
Sundoro = 'Yosun' (22d)	NHal
'Sunny John Wingfield' (14b) **new**	MCms
Swan = 'Fiswan'[PBR] (9)	MCms
'Syllabub' (21f) ♀H3	ECtt MNrw
'Symphony' (10a)	MCms NHal
'Talbot Maid' (29c)	MCms
'Talbot Parade' (29c) ♀H3	MCms
'Talbot Parade Pink' (29c)	MCms
'Tapestry Rose' (21d)	CMea EWoo MNrw NCGa SPhx WBor WHoo
'Terracotta' (29c)	NHal
'Terry Brook' (29e)	MCms NHal
'Terry Morris' (7b)	MCms
'Thoroughbred' (24a)	NHal
'Tickle Pink' (29f/K)	MNrw
'Tom Parr'	see *C.* 'Doctor Tom Parr'
'Tom Snowball' (3b)	MCms
'Topsy' (21d) ♀H4	ELon EWoo
'Tracy Waller' (24b)	NHal
'Trident' (2)	NHal
Triumph = 'Yotri' (22)	NHal
uliginosum	see *Leucanthemella serotina*
'Uri'	CAby CFis EBee EWoo SPhx
'Vagabond Prince'	ELon EWoo MNrw NCGa WBor WBrk WHoo
'Venice' (24b)	NHal
'Venus' (21)	NCGa WCot
'Venus One' (7)	ECtt EWoo MNrw NHal SPhx
'Vibrant' (9c) ♀H2	NHal

'Viking' (9)	MCms
'Vulcano Dark' (9)	MCms
'Warm Yoigloo'PBR	SPoG
'Wedding Day' (29k)	EWoo MNrw
'Wedding Sunshine' (21)	MNrw
welwitschii	see *Glebionis segetum*
'Wembley' (24b)	MCms
'Wendy Tench' (21d)	ECtt EWoo NWsh
'West Bromwich' (14a)	MCms
weyrichii	CPBP EBee ECho EWTr GCrg IKil LEdu NLar SBch SRms WWEG
'White Allouise' (25b) ♀H3	MCms NHal
'White Beppie' (29e)	MCms
'White Cassandra' (5b)	MCms NHal
'White Denise Oatridge' (5a) new	MCms
'White Enbee Wedding' (29d)	MCms NHal
'White Fairweather' (3b)	MCms NHal
'White Gem' (21f)	NHal
'White Gloss' (21e)	LLHF MNrw SPhx
'White Pearl Celebration' (24a)	MCms
'White Tower' (27)	EWoo MNrw
'Wilder Charms'	WHil
'William Florentine' (15a)	MCms NHal
'Wills Wonderful' (21d) ♀H4	EWoo
'Win' (9c)	NHal
'Wind Dancer' (10a) new	MCms
'Winning's Red' (21)	EWoo NCGa SMad WCot
'Woolman's Glory' (7a)	MCms NHal
'Woolman's Glory Red' (7a)	MCms
'Woolman's Star' (3a)	MCms NHal
'Woolman's Venture' (14b)	MCms NHal
'Yellow Allouise' (25b)	MCms
'Yellow American Beauty' (5b) ♀H2	MCms
'Yellow Billy Bell' (15a)	NHal
'Yellow Clapham Delight' (23a)	MCms NHal
§ 'Yellow Courtier' (24a)	MCms NHal
'Yellow Duke of Kent' (1)	NHal
'Yellow Egret' (23b)	MCms NHal
'Yellow Enbee Wedding' (29d)	MCms NHal
'Yellow Goodlife Sombrero' (29a) new	MCms
'Yellow Heide' (29c) ♀H3	NHal
'Yellow John Hughes' (3b) ♀H2	MCms NHal
'Yellow John Wingfield' (14b)	MCms NHal
'Yellow May Shoesmith' (5a)	NHal
'Yellow Mayford Perfection' (5a) ♀H2	NHal
'Yellow Pennine Oriel' (29a) ♀H3	MCms NHal
'Yellow Spider' (10a)	MCms NHal
'Yellow Starlet' (21f) ♀H4	EWoo LLHF MNrw
'Yellow Talbot Parade' (29c)	MCms
'Yellow Woolman's Glory' (7a)	MCms
yezoense	MNrw SRms
- B&SWJ 10872	WCru
- 'Roseum'	ECtt
'Yonashville'	SRms
§ ***zawadskii***	CMac SRms

Chrysocephalum (*Asteraceae*)

'Desert Flame'	LRHS

Chrysogonum (*Asteraceae*)

australe	LRHS
virginianum	CMea EWes LRHS SBch SPer WFar WWEG
- 'Golden Acres' new	ECtt

Chrysopogon (*Poaceae*)

gryllus	EBee WPGP

Chrysopsis (*Asteraceae*)

§ ***mariana***	WOld
villosa (Pursh) Nutt. ex DC.	see *Heterotheca villosa*

Chrysosplenium (*Saxifragaceae*)

alternifolium	GEdr
davidianum	CBre CSam EBee EPot EWld GCal GEdr GJos GKev IMou NLar NSla WBor WCot WCru WMoo WSHC
- SBEC 233	CExl
flagelliferum B&SWJ 8902	WCru
hebetatum B&SWJ 9835	WCru
lanuginosum	GEdr
var. ***formosanum***	
- - B&SWJ 6979	ESwi WCru
macrophyllum	CDes CExl CTal EBee EPPr EWld GCal GKev GMaP IGor IMou LEdu MAvo MMHG MPie MTPN NLar SHar WBor WCot WCru WSHC
macrostemon var. ***shiobarense*** B&SWJ 6173	WCru
oppositifolium	ECha NMir WSFF WShi

Chusquea (*Poaceae*)

breviglumis misapplied	see *C. culeou* 'Tenuis'
culeou ♀H4	CAbb CBcs CDoC CEnt CHEx CHid EPfP EPla IDee LEdu LPal MAvo MGos MMoz MWht SBig SPlb SSta
- 'Breviglumis'	see *C. culeou* 'Tenuis'
§ - 'Tenuis'	ERod
- weeping	CDTJ
delicatula from Machu Picchu, Peru	CExl CFil
gigantea ♀H3	CDTJ CEnt CExl CFil CHid EPfP EPla ERod ESwi MMoz MWht SBig WPGP
montana	EPla
mulleri F&M 104A from Mexico	CExl
nigricans	CFil
quila	MMoz

Cicerbita (*Asteraceae*)

BWJ 7891 from China	CSpe WCru
§ ***alpina***	GAbr NBid SPlb
bourgaei	MMuc
macrorhiza CC 6912	GKev
plumieri	EWes GAbr MMuc WCot WFar WMoo WPtf
- 'Blott' (v)	WCot

Cichorium (*Asteraceae*)

intybus	CArn CHby CPom CSpe CWld ELan ELau ENfk GAbr GPoy LSun

MBel MCot MHer MNHC NBir NCGa NMir NPri SIde SPer SPlb SPoG SRms SVic WHrl WJek WMoo WSHC
- f. ***album*** — EBee ECha ECtt EWTr LRHS MBel MCot SWat WPtf
- 'Palla Rossa' ♀H4 — SRms
- 'Roseum' — CBod CMos ECha ECtt ELan EWTr GKin LRHS MBel MCot NCGa SBod SHar SPoG SWat WHrl

Cicuta (*Apiaceae*)

virosa — LLWG

Cimicifuga see *Actaea*

acerina — see *Actaea japonica*
americana — see *Actaea podocarpa*
cordifolia (DC.) Torrey & A.Gray — see *Actaea cordifolia*
cordifolia Pursh — see *Actaea podocarpa*
foetida — see *Actaea cimicifuga*
racemosa var. ***cordifolia*** — see *Actaea cordifolia*
- 'Purpurea' — see *Actaea simplex* Atropurpurea Group
ramosa — see *Actaea simplex* 'Prichard's Giant'
rubifolia — see *Actaea cordifolia*
simplex var. ***matsumurae*** — see *Actaea matsumurae*

Cineraria (*Asteraceae*)

maritima — see *Senecio cineraria*

Cinnamomum (*Lauraceae*)

camphora — CBcs CExl CHEx SPlb WHfH

Cionura (*Asclepiadaceae*)

oreophila — ELan GCal LRHS SKHP WPGP WSHC

Circaea (*Onagraceae*)

alpina — EBee
lutetiana — WHer
- 'Caveat Emptor' (v) — NBid WCot

Cirsium (*Asteraceae*)

arvense — WSFF
* ***atroroseum*** — SWat
canum — GQue
ciliatum — EBee
diacantha — see *Ptilostemon diacantha*
helenioides — see *C. heterophyllum*
§ ***heterophyllum*** — CHid CPom EBee EWld GQue LEdu MMuc NChi NLar SHar WCot WHil
- PAB 067 — LEdu
japonicum 'Mura-kumo' (v) — WCot
- 'Pink Beauty' — MHol SPhx WWEG
- 'Rose Beauty' — EBee WBor
'Mount Etna' — CBod CMHG EBee ELan EPla GKin GQue LRHS LSun MBNS MMuc MSpe NDov NGdn SEND SPoG
oleraceum — LEdu NBid NLar
purpuratum — MNrw WCot
rivulare 'Atropurpureum' — Widely available
- 'Trevor's Blue Wonder' **new** — GBin IBoy MBel MHol SPer SPoG WCot WPtf
tuberosum — CAby LEdu NDov SKHP SPhx
vulgare — WSFF

Cissus (*Vitaceae*)

antarctica ♀H1c — CCCN EShb SEND
pedata B&SWJ 2371 — WCru
rhombifolia ♀H1c — EOHP EShb SEND
- 'Ellen Danica' ♀H1c — EShb
§ ***striata*** — CBcs CDoC CHEx CMac CWCL EBee ELon EShb IBoy LRHS MGil MRav NChi SEND SLim SWvt WSHC

Cistus ✿ (*Cistaceae*)

sp. — CAco
acutifolius misapplied — see *C. inflatus*, *C.* × *pulverulentus*
× ***aguilarii*** — CBcs CHEx CSBt CTri LAst MRav SPhx WSHC XSen
- 'Maculatus' ♀H4 — CBcs CDoC CDul CExl CHel CSam ELan EPfP LRHS MMuc NLar SCoo SEle SMad SPer SPoG SWvt WKif WPGP
albidus — CArn SVen XSen
algarvensis — see *Halimium ocymoides*
'Ann Baker' — WRHF
'Anne Palmer' — see *C.* × *fernandesiae* 'Anne Palmer'
× ***argenteus*** 'Blushing Peggy Sammons' — ELan NLar SVen SWvt XSen
- Golden Treasure = 'Nepond' (v) — SWvt
- 'Paper Moon' — EWTr NLar SVen
§ - 'Peggy Sammons' — CDoC CDul COtt ECha ELan EPfP EWTr LBMP LPot LRHS MAsh MGos MMuc MOWG NLar SCob SEND SLim SPer SPhx SWvt WHar WSHC XSen
- 'Silver Ghost' — EPfP LRHS SLim SVen SWvt
- 'Silver Pink' misapplied — see *C.* × *lenis* 'Grayswood Pink'
- 'Silver Pink' ambig. — Widely available
- 'Stripey' — XSen
'Blanche' — see *C. ladanifer* 'Blanche'
× ***bornetianus*** 'Jester' ♀H4 — CSBt EPfP EWTr LRHS MAsh NLar SVen SWvt WBor
× ***canescens*** — SVen XSen
- f. ***albus*** — WKif XSen
§ ***clusii*** — NLar
- subsp. ***multiflorus*** — XSen
× ***corbariensis*** — see *C.* × *hybridus*
creticus — CDoC CExl CSam EWTr LAst LRHS MAsh MBri MGos MOWG NEgg SHil SLon SPoG SRms SVen SWvt WKif
- subsp. ***corsicus*** — XSen
§ - subsp. ***creticus*** — EBee ELan EPfP MRav SCoo SPer
§ - subsp. ***incanus*** — WCot
× ***crispatus*** — XSen
§ - 'Warley Rose' — GMaP SIgm WKif XLum
crispus misapplied — see *C.* × *pulverulentus*, *C.* × *purpureus*
§ ***crispus*** L. — ELan SEND SGol
- 'Prostratus' — see *C. crispus* L.
- 'Sunset' — see *C.* × *pulverulentus* 'Sunset'
§ × ***cyprius*** ♀H4 — CArn ELan EPfP GBin LRHS MGos MJak MWat SDix SEND SPer SRms SWvt
§ - var. ***ellipticus*** 'Elma' ♀H4 — ELan EPfP EWTr LRHS MAsh NLar SPer XSen
§ × ***dansereaui*** — CMac COtt CSBt EAEE LRHS NLar SVen SWvt
- 'Decumbens' ♀H4 — CChe CDul COtt CSde CTri CTsd EBee ELan EPfP LRHS MAsh MBNS

	MBri MJak MRav MSwo NEgg NLar SArc SCoo SGbt SHil SPer SPhx SPoG SWvt WPGP
- 'Jenkyn Place' $\mathbb{Y}^{H4}$	CBod CDoC GMaP IVic MBNS MMuc NLar SPer SPoG WKif
× ***dubius***	SVen XSen
'Elma'	see *C.* × *cyprius* var. *ellipticus* 'Elma'
'Enigma'	CDoC
§ × ***fernandesiae*** 'Anne Palmer'	EPfP LLHF LRHS MAsh MNHC NLar SPoG SRGP
× ***florentinus*** misapplied	see × *Halimiocistus* 'Ingwersenii'
× ***florentinus*** ambig.	SVen XLum
§ × ***florentinus*** Lam.	GMaP XSen
- 'Fontfroide'	MMuc SEND SVen
* - 'Tramontane'	XSen
formosus	see *Halimium lasianthum* subsp. *formosum*
'Gordon Cooper' $\mathbb{Y}^{H4}$	MMuc NLar SPoG WBor
× ***heterocalyx*** 'Chelsea Bonnet'	CBod COtt GMaP MBNS MMuc NLar SCoo SEND SLim SPoG XSen
heterophyllus	SVen
'Highlights'	EPfP LRHS MAsh
hirsutus Lam. 1786	see *C. inflatus*
- var. ***psilosepalus*** misapplied	see *C. inflatus*
§ × ***hybridus***	Widely available
- 'Gold Prize' (v)	CMHG COtt CWGN ELan NLar SWvt WGrn
- Little Miss Sunshine = 'Dunnecis'^{PBR} (v)	LBMP LRHS MAsh MGos NHol NLar SHil SPoG SRms SWvt
- Rospico = 'Rencis'^{PBR} (v)	SIgm
incanus	see *C. creticus* subsp. *incanus*
§ ***inflatus***	XSen
ingwerseniana	see × *Halimiocistus* 'Ingwersenii'
'Jessamy Beauty'	SVen WHar WIce
'Jessamy Bride'	SVen
'Jessamy Charm'	SPhx
ladanifer misapplied	see *C.* × *cyprius*
ladanifer ambig.	CMac ECha SArc WKif
ladanifer L.	CBcs CDoC COtt CSBt CSde CTri ELan EPfP GPoy LRHS MRav MSwo SPer SWvt WHar XSen
§ - 'Blanche'	CDoC EPfP EWTr LLHF NLar SEND SPer SSpi SWvt WKif
§ - 'Paladin'	LRHS
- Palhinhae Group	see *C. ladanifer* var. *sulcatus*
- 'Pat'	COtt ELan EPfP LRHS MAsh NBir NLar SPer SPoG SSpi SWvt
§ - var. ***sulcatus***	ELan EPfP LRHS
lasianthus	see *Halimium lasianthum*
laurifolius	CDul CPne EPfP LRHS MGos NBir NLar SCob SEND SKHP SPer SVen SWvt XLum XSen
- subsp. ***atlanticus***	XSen
× ***laxus*** 'Snow White' $\mathbb{Y}^{H4}$	CDoC CWGN EBee EPfP LAst MGos NLar NPer SLim SLon
× ***ledon***	XSen
§ × ***lenis*** 'Grayswood Pink' $\mathbb{Y}^{H4}$	CDoC CExl COtt CTri EBee ECrN ELan EPfP EWTr LRHS MAsh MGos MMuc MSwo NEgg NLar NSoo SBch SBod SEND SIgm SLim SPer SPhx SPlb SVen SWvt WHar XLum
libanotis	COtt SVen
- 'Major'	XSen
× ***longifolius***	see *C.* × *nigricans*
× ***loretii*** misapplied	see *C.* × *dansereaui*
× ***loretii*** Rouy & Foucaud	see *C.* × *stenophyllus*
× ***lucasii***	XSen

× ***lusitanicus*** Maund	see *C.* × *dansereaui*
'Merrist Wood Cream'	see × *Halimiocistus wintonensis* 'Merrist Wood Cream'
monspeliensis	CAbP CMac EPfP LRHS LSun MAsh MBNS MMuc SEND SLon SPer XSen
- 'Vicar's Mead'	CCCN MBNS MMuc SEND
monspeliensis × ***salviifolius***	see *C.* × *florentinus* Lam.
§ × ***nigricans***	XSen
× ***oblongifolius***	SWvt XSen
× ***obtusifolius*** misapplied	see *C.* × *nigricans*
× ***obtusifolius*** ambig.	ELan LRHS MRav SKHP
× ***obtusifolius*** Sweet	EPfP WPGP XSen
§ - 'Thrive' $\mathbb{Y}^{H4}$	EPfP LRHS MBri MGos SCoo SHil
ocymoides	see *Halimium ocymoides*
× ***pagei***	XSen
'Paladin'	see *C. ladanifer* 'Paladin'
palhinhae	see *C. ladanifer* var. *sulcatus*
parviflorus misapplied	see *C.* × *lenis* 'Grayswood Pink'
parviflorus Lam.	WSHC
aff. ***parviflorus***	MOWG
* × ***pauranthus*** 'Natacha'	XSen
'Peggy Sammons'	see *C.* × *argenteus* 'Peggy Sammons'
× ***platysepalus***	SPhx
populifolius	CMHG CMac ECha EPfP LLHF LRHS NLar SGol SPer SWvt
- var. ***lasiocalyx***	see *C. populifolius* subsp. *major*
§ - subsp. ***major***	EPfP EWTr LRHS MOWG SKHP WPGP
psilosepalus misapplied	see *C. inflatus*
§ × ***pulverulentus***	CExl CTri ECha MMHG SVen XSen
* - Delilei Group	XSen
- - 'Fiona'	XSen
§ - 'Sunset' $\mathbb{Y}^{H4}$	Widely available
- 'Warley Rose'	see *C.* × *crispatus* 'Warley Rose'
§ × ***purpureus*** $\mathbb{Y}^{H4}$	Widely available
- 'Alan Fradd'	Widely available
- 'Betty Taudevin'	see *C.* × *purpureus*
- f. ***strictus***	EPfP LRHS SVen XSen
× ***rodiaei*** 'Jessabel'	EPfP EWTr LRHS MAsh MRav NLar SCoo SPer SWvt WPGP
- 'Jessica'	NLar
rosmarinifolius	see *C. clusii*
'Ruby Cluster'	CCCN LRHS MMuc NLar
sahucii	see × *Halimiocistus sahucii*
salviifolius	CAbP CArn CCCN MOWG SVen XSen
- 'Avalanche'	MRav WAbe
- 'Gold Star'	ELan NLar
- 'May Snow'	EHoe LRHS MAsh
- 'Prostratus'	CSde ELan EPfP LRHS SWvt WPGP
'Silver Pink'	see *C.* × *argenteus* 'Silver Pink'
× ***skanbergii***	CHEx CMac CTri ELan EPfP MGos MLHP MMuc MOWG MRav MWat NBir NLar SDix SEND SMrm SPer SPoG WCFE XLum XSen
'Snow Fire' $\mathbb{Y}^{H4}$	CCCN CDoC CWSG EBee ELan EPfP LRHS MAsh MGos MMuc MWat NEgg NEoE NLar NSoo SBod SCoo SEle SWvt WGrn WHar
§ × ***stenophyllus***	EPfP SPer
'Stripey'	SVen
× ***tephreus***	XSen
'Thrive'	see *C.* × *obtusifolius* 'Thrive'
tomentosus	see *Helianthemum nummularium* subsp. *tomentosum*
× ***verguinii***	SDix XSen

villosus	see *C. creticus* subsp. *creticus*
wintonensis	see × *Halimiocistus wintonensis*

Citharexylum (*Verbenaceae*)

quadrangulare Jacq.	see *C. spinosum*
spicatum	CExl CFil WBor
§ ***spinosum***	CHll

citrandarin see *Citrus reticulata* × C. trifoliata

citrange see *Citrus* × *insitorum*

citrangequat see *Citrus* × *georgiana*

citremon see *Citrus* × *limon* × C. trifoliata

× *Citrofortunella* see *Citrus*

mitis	see *Citrus* × *microcarpa*

citron see *Citrus medica*

Citronella (*Icacinaceae*)

§ ***gongonha***	SVen
mucronata	see *C. gongonha*

Citrullus (*Cucurbitaceae*)

colocynthis	CArn
lanatus 'Charleston Gray' new	SVic

Citrus (*Rutaceae*)

sp.	CCCN
§ × ***aurantiifolia*** (F)	CCCN EPfP SCit SPre SVic
- key lime	see *C.* × *aurantiifolia*
× ***aurantium*** 'Aber's Narrowleaf' (F)	SCit
- subsp. ***bergamia***	see *C.* × *limon*
- 'Bouquet de Fleurs'	see *C.* × *aurantium* (Sour Orange Group) 'Bouquet'
- 'Gou-tou Cheng' (F)	SCit
§ - Grapefruit Group (F)	CCCN SPre SVic
- - 'Foster' (F)	SCit
- - 'Golden Special' (F)	SCit SVic
- - 'Marsh' (F)	SCit
- - 'Oroblanco' (F) new	SCit
- - 'Red Blush' (F/S)	SCit
- - 'Star Ruby' (F/S)	CCCN SCit
- - 'Wheeny'	see *C. maxima* 'Wheeny'
- 'Robinson' (F) new	SCit
§ - (Sour Orange Group) 'Bouquet' (F)	SCit
- - 'Bouquetier de Nice' (F)	SCit
- - 'Chinotto' (F)	SCit
- - 'Seville' (F)	SCit
- - 'Smooth Flat Seville' (F)	SCit
§ - Sweet Orange Group (F)	CCCN LRHS SCit SHil SPre SVic
§ - - 'Baia' (F/S)	SCit
- - 'Embiguo' (F)	SCit
- - 'Fukumoto' (F)	CCCN
- - 'Jaffa'	see *C.* × *aurantium* (Sweet Orange Group) 'Shamouti'
- - 'Lane Late' (F)	CCCN SCit
§ - - 'Malta Blood' (F)	SCit
- - 'Maltaise Sanguine'	see *C.* × *aurantium* (Sweet Orange Group) 'Malta Blood'
- - 'Navelate' (F)	SCit
- - 'Navelina' (F/S)	CCCN CDoC SCit SPre
- - 'Newhall' (F/S)	NLar SCit
- - 'Salustiana' (F/S)	SCit
§ - - 'Sanguinelli' (F)	CCCN SCit
§ - - 'Shamouti' (F)	SCit
- - 'Spanish Sanguinelli' (F)	see *C.* × *aurantium* (Sweet Orange Group) 'Sanguinelli'
- - 'Succari' (F)	SCit
- - 'Tarocco' (F)	SCit
- - 'Valencia' (F)	CCCN SCit SVic
- - 'Valencia Late' (F)	LRHS
- - 'Washington'	see *C.* × *aurantium* (Sweet Orange Group) 'Baia'
- - 'Washington Navel'	see *C.* × *aurantium* (Sweet Orange Group) 'Baia'
§ - (Tangelo Group) 'Minneola' (F)	SCit
§ - - 'Nova' (F/S)	CCCN SCit
- - 'Orlando' (F)	SCit
- - 'Ugli' misapplied	see *C.* × *aurantium* (Tangelo Group) 'Minneola'
- - 'Ugli' (F)	SCit
- (Tangor Group) 'Ellendale' (F)	SCit
- - 'Murcott' (F)	SCit
bergamia	see *C.* × *limon*
'Buddha's Hand'	see *C. medica* 'Fingered'
calamondin	see *C.* × *microcarpa*
deliciosa	see *C. reticulata* 'Willowleaf'
× ***floridana*** 'Eustis' (F)	SCit SPre
§ ***hystrix***	CCCN CDoC ELan NLar NPla SCit SPre
× ***insitorum*** 'C-35'	SCit
- 'Carrizo' (F)	SCit
- 'Swingle' (F)	SCit
§ ***japonica*** (F) ♀H1c	CDoC EPfP LRHS SCit SHil SPre
- Hong Kong kumquat (F) new	SCit
- 'Nagami' (F)	SPre
kinokuni	see *C. japonica*
'Kucle' (F) new	SCit
'Kulci' (F)	CCCN
kumquat	see *C. japonica*
'La Valette' (F)	CCCN SPre
× ***latifolia*** (F/S)	CCCN CDoC EPfP LRHS SCit SPre
- 'Bearss' (F)	SCit
- variegated (v)	SPre
latipes Hook. f. & Thomson ex Hook. f.	see *C. hystrix*
limetta	CCCN SVic
limettioides (F)	CArn SCit SPre
§ × ***limon*** (F)	CHEx CUse LRHS SCit SHil
- 'Eureka'	see *C.* × *limon* 'Garey's Eureka'
- 'Eureka Variegated' (F/v)	SCit
- 'Fino' (F)	CCCN SCit
- 'Four Seasons' (F)	see *C.* × *limon* 'Garey's Eureka'
§ - 'Garey's Eureka' (F)	CCCN CDoC ELan EPfP NLar SCit SPre
- 'Imperial' (F)	SCit
- 'Improved Meyer'	see *C.* × *limon* 'Meyer'
- 'Lemonade' (F)	SCit
- 'Lisbon' (F)	SCit
- 'Lunario' (F) new	SCit
§ - 'Meyer' (F) ♀H2	CBcs CCCN CHll CTri ELan EPfP LRHS NLar SCit SPre
- 'Ponderosa' (F)	SCit
- 'Quatre Saisons'	see *C.* × *limon* 'Garey's Eureka'
- 'Rangpur' (F)	SCit
- 'Sfusato d'Amalfi' (F) new	SCit
- 'Siracusano' (F) new	SCit

- 'Variegata' (F/v) ♀H2	CCCN SCit
- 'Verna' (F)	CCCN SCit
- 'Villa Franca' (F)	SCit SVic
- 'Yen Ben' (F)	SCit
- 'Zagara Bianca' **new**	SCit
× ***limonia***	see *C.* × *limon*
'Lipo' (F)	CCCN NLar SPre
macrophylla	SCit
madurensis	see *C. japonica*
§ ***maxima*** 'Wheeny' (F)	SCit
medica 'Cidro Digitado'	see *C. medica* 'Fingered'
- var. ***digitata***	see *C. medica* 'Fingered'
- 'Ethrog' (F)	SCit SPre
§ - 'Fingered' (F)	SCit SPre
- var. ***sarcodactylis***	see *C. medica* 'Fingered'
× ***meyeri***	see *C.* × *limon*
§ × ***microcarpa*** (F) ♀H1c	CCCN CDoC LRHS NLar SCit SHil SPre
- Philippine lime	see *C.* × *microcarpa*
§ - 'Tiger' (F/v)	SCit
- 'Variegata'	see *C.* × *microcarpa* 'Tiger'
× ***mitis***	see *C.* × *microcarpa*
× ***nobilis*** Lour.	see *C. reticulata* 'Willowleaf'
- var. ***inermis***	see *C. japonica*
- Ortanique Group	see *C.* × *aurantium* Sweet Orange Group
× ***obovata*** (F)	SPre
§ - 'Fukushu' (F)	CCCN SCit
× ***paradisi***	see *C.* × *aurantium* Grapefruit Group
- 'Wheeny'	see *C. maxima* 'Wheeny'
'Pursta' (F)	CCCN
§ ***reticulata*** (F)	CCCN LRHS SPre
- 'Clausellina' (F/S)	SCit
- var. ***deliciosa***	see *C. reticulata* 'Willowleaf'
- 'Fina' (F/S)	SCit
- 'Hashimoto' (F/S)	SCit
- 'Hernandina' (F)	CCCN
- Mandarin Group (F)	CDoC EPfP LRHS
- - 'Clementine' (F)	CDoC EPfP LRHS SPre
- - 'De Nules' (F/S)	CCCN SCit
- - 'Encore' (F)	SCit
- - 'Esbal' (F)	CCCN
- - 'Fortune' (F)	SCit
- - 'Fremont' (F) **new**	SCit
- 'Marisol' (F/S)	SCit
- 'Miyagawa' (F)	CCCN SCit
- 'Nour' (F)	SCit
- 'Nova'	see *C.* × *aurantium* (Tangelo Group) 'Nova'
- 'Okitsu' (F/S)	CCCN SCit
- 'Owari' (F/S)	SCit
§ - 'Willowleaf' (F)	SCit
satsuma	see *C. reticulata*
sinensis	see *C.* × *aurantium* Sweet Orange Group
- 'Jaffa'	see *C.* × *aurantium* (Sweet Orange Group) 'Shamouti'
- 'Washington'	see *C.* × *aurantium* (Sweet Orange Group) 'Baia'
× ***taitensis*** 'Otaheite' (F)	CCCN
§ - rough lemon (F)	SCit
- Schaub rough lemon	see *C.* × *taitensis* rough lemon
§ ***trifoliata***	CAgr CArn CBcs CCCN CDoC CDul ELan EPfP ETwe IDee LRHS MBlu MGil MRav SArc SCit SMad SPer SPlb SVic WSHC
- 'Flying Dragon'	IVic SCit SMad
unshiu	see *C. reticulata*
volkameriana	see *C.* × *limon*

Cladium (*Cyperaceae*)

mariscus	XLum

Cladothamnus see *Elliottia*

Cladrastis (*Papilionaceae*)

§ ***kentukea***	CBcs CDul CLnd CMCN CTho EBee ELan EPfP EPla EUJe EWTr LRHS MBlu MBri MRav NLar WHar
§ - 'Perkins Pink'	MBlu MBri
- 'Rosea'	see *C. kentukea* 'Perkins Pink'
lutea	see *C. kentukea*
sikokiana	CFil
sinensis	CBcs CExl CFil EPfP EPla MBlu SKHP WPGP

Clarkia (*Onagraceae*)

* ***repens***	CSpe

Clavinodum (*Poaceae*)

§ ***oedogonatum***	MWht

Claytonia (*Portulacaceae*)

alsinoides	see *C. sibirica*
lanceolata NNS 08-88 **new**	GKev
§ ***perfoliata***	CArn GPoy MNHC WHer
§ ***sibirica***	CAgr CArn CElw IMou LPot LSou MMoz WBor XLum
- f. ***albiflora***	CElw MMoz MPie WBor WCot WMoo
virginica	ECho LAma MMoz WFar WMoo

Clematis ✿ (*Ranunculaceae*)

BWJ 7630 from China	WCru
CC 711	CExl
CC 4710	CExl
CC 5904	GKev
NJM 11.075 from Guizhou, China **new**	WPGP
'Abigail' (Vt)	NHaw
Abilene = 'Evipo027'	CFlo EPfP LBuc LRHS LSqu NPri NTay SPoG SWCr
'Abundance' (Vt) ♀H6	CDoC CFlo CRHN CSPN CWCL LBMP LRHS MAsh MBri NHol NTay SDix WFar
acuminata	WCru
var. ***sikkimensis*** B&SWJ 7202	
addisonii	CSPN NHaw
afoliata	ECou WThu
afoliata × ***forsteri***	ECou
'Akaishi' (EL)	NTay
akebioides	NHaw
Alabast = 'Poulala' PBR (EL) ♀H6	CLng CSPN MBri SCoo SPoG
Alaina = 'Evipo 056'	LBuc LSqu NTay SLon SPoG SWCr
'Alba Luxurians' (Vt)	CBcs CCon CDoC CFlo CRHN CSPN CSam CTri CWCL ELan EPfP LRHS MAsh MBri MGos MLHP NHol NTay SDix SLim SPer SPoG SWCr
'Albert' (A)	NTay
'Albiflora' (A)	CLng CSPN NTay
'Albina Plena' (A/d)	LRHS NPri SLon
'Aleksandrit' (EL)	NHaw
'Alice Fisk' (EL)	CSPN LRHS MBri MSwo NHaw SLim

	Name	Suppliers
	'Aliide' (LL) **new**	NHaw
	'Alionushka' (I) 🏆H6	CRHN ELan EPfP LRHS MBri NLar SLim SPer SPoG SWCr WSHC
	Alita = 'Evipo070' (Vt) **new**	NTay
	'Allanah' (LL)	ELon LRHS NHaw SCoo SLim SPoG WHar
	alpina	GGal GKev GKin IBoy LSun MAsh MRav NHaw NPer SCob SEWo SPlb SPre SWvt
	- 'Albiflora'	see *C. sibirica*
	- 'Columbine White'	see *C.* 'White Columbine'
I	- 'Odorata' (A)	CSPN NHaw
§	- 'Pamela Jackman' (A) 🏆H6	CDoC CMac CSPN ELan LBMP LRHS MAsh MBri MJak MMuc NEgg NTay SCoo SDix SEND SLim SPer SPoG SRkn SWCr SWvt WFar
	- pink-flowered	GKev
	- 'Stolwijk Gold' (A)	CSPN CWGN MBlu NHaw NTay SRms
	alternata	CWGN EBee
	'Amelia' (I)	SMDP
	'Amelia Joan' (Ta)	MWat
	'Amethyst Beauty' (A)	EPfP LBuc LRHS
	Amethyst Beauty = 'Evipo043'	LSqu NTay SLon SWCr
	'Andante' (I) **new**	CWGN
	'Andromeda' (EL)	CLng CSPN LRHS MBri NHaw NTay SDix SWCr
	Aneta = 'Evipo055'	CFlo CWGN NTay
	Angela = 'Zoang'PBR (EL)	NTay
	Angelique = 'Evipo017' (EL)	CFlo CLng COtt CRos CSPN CWGN EPfP LRHS LSqu NPri NTay SCoo SLon SPer SWCr
§	***angustifolia***	EBee
	'Anita' (Ta)	CFlo EBee EPfP NHaw NTay SLim SMDP
	Anna Louise = 'Evithree'PBR (EL) 🏆H6	CLng COtt CRos CSPN CWCL EPfP LRHS LSqu MBri NTay SCoo SLim SLon SPer SWCr
	'Annabel' (EL)	CSPN MAsh
	Anniversary = 'Pynot' (EL)	SCoo
	'Aotearoa' (LL) 🏆H6	IPot MBri NHaw
	'Aphrodite' (I)	CCon
	'Aphrodite Elegafumina' (I)	CCon CRHN CWGN LRHS NHaw SWCr
	'Apollonia' **new**	CWGN IPot
	'Apple Blossom' (Ar)	Widely available
	'Arabella' (I) 🏆H6	CFlo COtt CRHN CSPN CWCL CWGN ELan ELon EPfP EShb LRHS MAsh MBri NLar NPri NTay SLim SPer SPoG SRkn SWCr SWvt WHar WSHC
§	Arctic Queen = 'Evitwo'PBR (EL) 🏆H6	CFlo CLng CRos CSPN EPfP LBuc LRHS LSqu MAsh MBri NPri NTay SCoo SLon SPoG SWCr WHar
	armandii	Widely available
	- 'Enham Star'	LRHS MBri MGos
§	- 'Little White Charm'	EBee LRHS MBri SKHP SWCr
	- 'Meyeniana'	see *C. armandii* 'Little White Charm'
I	- 'Snowdrift'	CBcs CFlo CSBt CSPN CWSG ELan EPfP LRHS MAsh MGos MSwo NLar NTay SCob SKHP SPer SPoG SRms SWCr
	× ***aromatica***	CCon CFlo CSPN CWGN EAEE ELan EPfP LRHS NTay SCoo
	'Asao' (EL)	CLng ELan EPfP IBoy LRHS MBri MMuc NTay SCoo SPer SPoG SWCr
	'Ascotiensis' (LL)	CLng CRHN CSPN EPfP LRHS MBri NHaw NTay SCoo SLim SLon SPer SPoG SWCr
	'Ashva' (LL)	CWGN
	'Aureolin' (Ta)	CSPN
	Avant-garde = 'Evipo033'PBR (Vt)	CFlo CLng COtt CRos CSPN CWCL CWGN ELan EPfP EUJe LRHS LSqu NTay SLon SWCr
§	Aztek = 'Daihelios' (Ta)	CSPN LRHS NTay SCoo
	Baby Doll = 'Zobadol' (EL)	CWGN NTay
	Baby Star = 'Zobast' (EL)	NTay
§	'Bagatelle' (LL)	CLng CSPN LRHS MBri MGos NHaw
	'Bal Maiden' (Vt)	CRHN NHaw
§	'Ballerina in Blue' (A/d)	IPot
	'Barbara' (LL)	NTay
	'Barbara Dibley' (EL)	CFlo CLng CTri LRHS MAsh NHaw SCoo SLim
	'Barbara Harrington'PBR (LL)	CLng COtt LRHS NHaw SLon SWCr
	'Barbara Jackman' (EL)	CLng CMac LRHS MAsh MSwo NTay SCoo SLon SWCr
	'Beata' (LL)	MGos NHaw
	'Beauty of Worcester' (EL)	CCon CMac CSPN CWSG ELan ELon EPfP LRHS MAsh MSwo NHaw NTay SCoo SDix SLim SPer
	'Bees' Jubilee' (EL)	CBcs CMac CWSG ELan ELon LRHS MAsh MSwo NBir NLar NTay SLim SPer SPoG SWCr SWvt
	'Belle Nantaise' (EL)	NTay SCoo SRms
	'Belle of Woking' (EL)	CLng CSPN ELan ELon LRHS MAsh NTay SCoo SLim SPer SPoG SWCr SWvt
	'Bells of Emei Shan'	NTay
	'Ben's Beauty' (A)	CFlo
	'Berry Red' (A)	CWGN
	'Best Wishes'PBR	LRHS NTay SLon SPoG SWCr
§	'Beth Currie' (EL)	CLng CSPN EPfP LRHS SWCr
	'Betina'	see *C.* 'Red Beetroot Beauty'
	'Betty Corning' (Vt)	CFlo CLng CRHN CSPN CWGN EBee ELan EPfP LRHS MBri MGos NTay SCoo SLon SPoG SRms SWCr SWvt
	BijouPBR	see *C.* Thumbelina
	'Bill MacKenzie' (Ta) 🏆H6	CFlo CHVG CMHG CMac CSam CTri ELan EPfP LBMP LRHS MAsh MBri MGos MRav MWat NHol NPri NTay SCob SDix SLim SPer SPoG SRms SWCr SWvt WSHC
	'Black Prince' (Vt)	CFlo CRHN CWGN ELan EPfP IPot LRHS MBri NHaw NLar NTay SLim SLon SMDP SPoG SRms
	'Black Tea' (LL)	CDul CSPN IPot LRHS NHaw NTay SLim SLon SWCr
§	'Błękitny Anioł' (LL) 🏆H6	CFlo CLng CMac CRHN CSPN CWGN EBee LRHS MAsh MBri MLHP NLar NTay SCoo SPer SPoG SWCr WBor
	Blue Angel	see *C.* 'Błękitny Anioł'
	'Blue Belle' (Vt)	CRHN ELan SLon WFar
	'Blue Bird' (A/d)	CBcs CWCL IPot MAsh NTay SRms
	Blue Blood	see *C.* 'Königskind'
	'Blue Boy' (EL)	see *C.* 'Elsa Späth'
	'Blue Boy' (I)	see *C.* × *diversifolia* 'Blue Boy' (I)
	'Blue Dancer' (A)	CBcs CLng COtt EPfP LRHS MBri MGos NLar NTay SPoG SWCr
	'Blue Eclipse' (A)	CFlo CSPN CWGN MBri NHaw NHol NTay
	'Blue Eyes' (EL)	CSPN ELon MBri NHaw NTay SLim
§	'Blue Light'PBR (EL/d)	CFlo CSPN CWGN ELan LRHS NLar NTay

Blue Moon = 'Evirin'PBR (EL)	CLng EPfP LRHS MBri NLar NTay SCoo SLon SWCr
Blue Pirouette = 'Zobluepi'PBR (I)	IPot LRHS MBri MJak
Blue Rain	see *C.* 'Sinii Dozhd'
'Blue Ravine' (EL)	EPfP LRHS MBri NLar NTay SCoo
Blue River = 'Zobluerive'PBR	CWGN ELan
§ 'Blushing Ballerina' (A/d)	MBri
'Bolam Belle' (Vt) **new**	NHaw
Bonanza = 'Evipo031'PBR (Vt)	CLng CRos EPfP LRHS LSqu MBri NLar NTay SCoo SDix SLon SPer SPoG SWCr
× ***bonstedtii*** 'Crépuscule' (H)	MCot SMDP
Bourbon = 'Evipo018'PBR (EL)	CLng ELan EPfP LRHS LSqu NPri NTay SCoo SLon SPoG SWCr
brachyura B&SWJ 8854	WCru
'Brocade' (Vt)	CRHN CSPN NHaw
'Broughton Bride' (A)	CFlo CLng CSPN CWGN MBri NHol NTay SMDP WHar
'Broughton Star' (M/d) ♀H4	CFlo CMac COtt CRHN CSBt CSPN CWCL ELan EPfP IBoy LRHS MAsh MBlu MBri MGos MRav MSwo NBir NHol NPCo NTay SLim SLon SPoG SRkn SRms SWvt WBor WHar
'Brunette' (A)	CFlo CSPN EBee ELan EPfP IPot LRHS MAsh MBri NHaw NLar NTay SLon SWCr
buchananiana Finet & Gagnep.	see *C. rehderiana*
buchananiana DC. B&SWJ 8333a	WCru
'Buckland Beauty' (V)	CFlo CLng CSPN CWGN LRHS NHaw SMDP
'Buckland Cascade'	SMDP
'Buckland Pixie' (Vt) **new**	NHaw
'Burford Bell' (V)	NHaw
'Burford Princess' (Vt)	CRHN NHaw
'Burford White' (A)	CSPN MBri NLar
'Burma Star' (EL)	CFlo CWGN EPfP LRHS MBri NTay
'By the Way' (M)	SMDP
Caddick's Cascade	see *C.* 'Semu'
calycina	see *C. cirrhosa* var. *balearica*
§ ***campaniflora***	CSPN EPla EShb GCal NHaw
'Candida' (EL)	MBri
'Candleglow' (A)	MBri NHaw
'Candy Stripe'	CLng LRHS NTay SCoo SPoG SWCr
'Capitaine Thuilleaux'	see *C.* 'Souvenir du Capitaine Thuilleaux'
'Cardinal Wyszynski'	see *C.* 'Kardynał Wyszyński'
'Carmencita' (Vt)	CRHN CSPN EBee NHaw SCoo SLon
'Carnaby' (EL)	CBcs COtt CSPN CWCL ELan ELon EPfP LRHS MAsh MBri MJak NPri NTay SCoo SLim SPoG SWCr SWvt WHar
'Carnival Queen' (EL)	CSPN
'Carol Klein' (I) **new**	NHaw
'Carol Leeds' (Vt)	NHaw
'Caroline' (LL)	CSPN CWGN NHaw NTay SDix
× ***cartmanii*** hort. 'Avalanche'PBR (Fo/m)	CFlo CSPN ELan EPfP GBin LRHS MBri MGos NLar NPri NTay SCoo SLim SLon SPoG SWCr SWvt
- 'Joe' (Fo/m) ♀H4	CBcs CFlo CLng ELan EPfP EWes GAbr LRHS NTay SCoo SPoG SWCr SWvt WIce
- 'Joe' × *marmoraria* (Fo)	ECho MAsh SWCr

- Michiko = 'Evipo044' (Fo) **new**	LRHS NTay
- Tai Yang = 'Evipo045'	LRHS
- 'White Abundance'PBR (Fo/f)	LRHS NLar SPoG
× ***cartmanii*** hort. × ***petriei*** (Fo)	ECho
Cassis = 'Evipo020'PBR	CLng COtt CSPN ELan EPfP LRHS LSqu MBri NTay SCoo SLon SPer SWCr
'Catherine Clanwilliam' (T)	CWGN SMDP
'Celebration'PBR Godfrey (EL)	CFlo NTay SLim SPoG
Cezanne = 'Evipo023'PBR (EL)	CFlo CLng COtt CRos CSPN ELan EPfP LRHS LSqu MGos NPri NTay SCoo SLon SPer SWCr
'Chacewater' (Vt)	CRHN
'Chalcedony' (EL)	CSPN CWGN NTay
Chantilly = 'Evipo021'PBR	CFlo CLng COtt CSPN ELan EPfP LBuc LRHS LSqu NPri NTay SCoo SLon SPer SWCr
'Charissima' (EL)	CSPN CWGN LRHS NLar SCoo SWCr
'Charlie Brown' (LL)	CRHN NHaw
'Chatsworth' (Vt)	CRHN CWGN EPfP LRHS NHaw SLon SWCr
Chelsea = 'Evipo100' **new**	LRHS LSqu NTay SLon SPoG SWCr
CherokeePBR	see *C.* Ooh La La
Chevalier = 'Evipo040' (EL)	ELan EPfP LRHS NTay SLon SPer SPoG SWCr
chiisanensis	WSHC
- B&SWJ 4560	WCru
- B&SWJ 8800	WCru
- B&SWJ 12725 **new**	WCru
- 'Korean Beauty' (A)	MSCN
- 'Lemon Bells' (A)	ELan EPfP LRHS MAsh SCoo SLon SWCr
- 'Love Child' (A)	ELan IPot NTay
chinensis misapplied	see *C. terniflora*
chinensis Osbeck PAB 3751	LEdu
- RWJ 10042	WCru
Chinook = 'Evipo013'PBR	CLng LRHS SLim
chrysantha	see *C. tangutica*
chrysocoma misapplied	see *C. spooneri*
chrysocoma Franch.	SMDP
'Cicciolina' (Vt)	CRHN NHaw
cirrhosa	CTri LRHS MAsh SCob SWCr
§ - var. ***balearica***	CBcs CDoC CFlo CMac CSPN CTri CWCL ELan EPfP LRHS MAsh MBri MGos MRav MSwo NTay SDix SEND SLim SPer SPoG SWCr SWvt
- 'Ourika Valley'	CWGN ELon EPfP LRHS MAsh MBri NLar NTay
- var. ***purpurascens*** 'Freckles' ♀H4	Widely available
- - 'Lansdowne Gem'	CFlo CMac CSPN CWGN LRHS NLar NTay SKHP SMDP SPoG SWCr SWvt
- 'Wisley Cream' ♀H4	CBcs CFlo CMac COtt CSPN CWCL ELan EPfP LRHS MAsh MBri MJak MSwo NLar NTay SCob SCoo SEND SKHP SLim SPer SPoG SRms SWCr SWvt
clarkeana misapplied	see *C. urophylla* 'Winter Beauty'
§ ***columbiana*** var. ***tenuiloba***	GKev
- - 'Ylva' (A)	NHaw WAbe
'Columbine' (A)	CDul EBee LRHS MBri MSwo NTay SDix SPer SPoG

'Columella' (A)	MGos NHaw NLar
'Comtesse de Bouchaud' (LL) ♀H6	CDoC CFlo CMac COtt CSPN CTri CWCL EBee ELan ELon EPfP EShb LRHS MAsh MBri MGos MMuc MRav NPri NTay SDix SLim SPer SPoG SWCr WBor
Confetti = 'Evipo036'[PBR] (Vt)	CFlo CLng EBee EPfP LRHS MBri NTay SLim SLon SPoG
'Congratulations' (EL)	ELon LRHS SLim
connata	GQui
- B&SWJ 2956 **new**	WCru
aff. ***connata*** GWJ 9431 from West Bengal	WCru
- HWJK 2176 from Nepal	WCru
'Constance' (A) ♀H6	CFlo CLng CMac CSPN CWCL EBee EPfP LRHS MBri NHaw NLar NTay SCoo SPer SPre SRms SWCr WFar
'Continuity' (M)	CWGN NTay
'Cora' (I)	CWGN
'Cornish Spirit' (Vt)	CRHN
'Corona' (EL)	CLng CSPN ELon EPfP LRHS MBri MMuc SCoo
'Côte d'Azur' (H)	CBcs CCse CExl CMac GCal MNrw
'Countess of Lovelace' (EL)	CBcs CSPN ELan EPfP MBri NTay SCoo
County Park hybrids (Fo)	ECou
'Cragside' (A)	MMuc
§ 'Crimson King' (LL)	MBri NHaw NLar
'Crinkle'[PBR] (M)	CCCN SPoG
§ ***crispa***	NHaw
§ Crystal Fountain = 'Evipo038'[PBR] (EL)	CFlo CLng COtt CSPN CWCL CWGN ELan EPfP LBuc LRHS LSqu MBri NTay SCoo SLim SLon SPer SPoG SWCr
'Danae' (Vt)	NHaw
Dancing Queen = 'Zodaque'[PBR] (EL)	MBri NTay
Dancing Smile = 'Zodasmi'[PBR]	NTay
'Daniel Deronda' (EL) ♀H6	CDoC CFlo CSPN CWCL CWGN CWSG ELan ELon IBoy IPot LRHS MAsh MBri MMuc NBir NTay SCoo SDix SLim SPer SPoG SWCr
'Dark Eyes' (Vt)	CSPN CWGN IPot
'Dark Secret' (A)	MBri NHaw NHol NTay
'Dawn' (EL)	CCCN CFlo CLng CSPN LRHS MBri NTay SCoo SPer SWCr
'De Vijfhoeven' (Vt)	NHaw
'Débutante' (EL)	NHaw
'Denny's Double' (EL/d)	CSPN CWGN LRHS NTay
'Destiny' (EL)	CWGN
Diamantina = 'Evipo039'[PBR] (EL)	CFlo EPfP LBuc LRHS LSqu NPri NTay SLon SPer SPoG SWCr
'Diana' (LL)	NHaw
Diana's Delight = 'Evipo026' (EL)	EPfP LRHS LSqu NTay SLon SPer SPoG SWCr
dioscoreifolia	see *C. terniflora*
§ × ***diversifolia***	CRHN NHaw SDix SWvt
§ - 'Blue Boy' (I)	CRHN CSPN NHaw SLon
- 'Heather Herschell' (I)	CFlo CRHN CSPN NHaw SMDP
§ - 'Hendersonii' (I)	CFlo CWCL EAEE ELan GBuc LRHS MBri MCot MRav MSwo MWat NBir SPer SWat SWvt WCot
§ - 'Olgae' (I)	CExl CSPN NHaw
'Doctor Mary' (V) **new**	NHaw
'Doctor Penelope'[PBR] (M)	WNPC
'Doctor Ruppel' (EL)	CFlo CMac COtt CSPN CWCL EBee ELon EPfP IBoy LRHS MAsh MBri MMuc MSwo NBir NPri NTay SDix SLim SPer SWCr
'Dominika' (LL)	NHaw
'Dorath'	CWGN LRHS NHaw NTay SPoG SWCr
'Dorothy Barbara' (M)	SMDP
'Dorothy Walton'	see *C.* 'Bagatelle'
'Double Cross'	ECou
'Double Delight' (M)	CFlo CWGN WNPC
'Duchess of Albany' (1897) (T)	CFlo CLng CSPN CTri ELan EPfP LRHS MAsh MBri MGos NEgg NHol SPer SWCr
'Duchess of Edinburgh' (EL)	CBcs CMac EBee ELan ELon EPfP IBoy LRHS MAsh MBri MGos MMuc MSwo NEgg NHol NTay SDix SLim SPoG SWCr SWvt WHar
'Duchess of Sutherland' (EL)	NHaw SDix
'Dulcie'	NHaw
× ***durandii*** ♀H6	CBcs CFlo COtt CRHN CSPN CSpe CWCL EBee ELan EPfP LRHS MAsh MBri MGos MRav NTay SCoo SPer SPoG SWCr SWvt WCot
'Dutch Sky' (LL)	CWGN MBri
'Early Sensation' (Fo/f)	CBcs CFlo CSPN CTri ELan ELon EPfP EUJe LRHS MAsh MBri NTay SCoo SLim SPer SPoG SPre SWCr SWvt
East River = 'Zoeastri'[PBR] (I)	ELan IPot
'Eclipse' (H)	NHaw
'Edith' (EL) ♀H6	MBri NHaw NLar NTay
'Edomurasaki' (EL)	MBri
'Edouard Desfossé' (EL)	CLng MBri
'Edward Prichard'	CFlo CSPN EPfP MAsh NTay SDix SMDP
'Eetika' (LL)	CRHN NHaw
'Ekstra' (LL)	NHaw
'Eleanor' (Fo/f)	ECou GEdr
'Elf' (Vt)	CWGN SMDP
'Elfin' (Fo/v)	ECou
'Elizabeth' (M) ♀H4	Widely available
§ 'Elsa Späth' (EL)	CExl CLng CMac COtt CSPN CTri ELan EPfP LRHS MAsh MBri NTay SLim SPer SPoG SWCr SWvt
'Elten' (M)	CSPN
'Elvan' (Vt)	CRHN NHaw NLar
'Ember' (I)	CWGN
'Emilia Plater' (Vt)	CRHN LRHS MBri NHaw NTay SLon
Empress = 'Evipo011'[PBR] (EL)	CFlo CLng CSPN EBee ELan EPfP LRHS LSqu NTay SLon SWCr
'Entel' (Vt)	CRHN NHaw
× ***eriostemon***	see *C.* × *diversifolia*
'Ernest Markham' (LL) ♀H6	CBcs CDoC CMac COtt CSPN CWCL ELan EPfP IBoy LRHS MAsh MBri MGos MJak MSwo NEgg NPri NTay SDix SLim SPer SPoG SWCr SWvt
Esme = 'Evipo048' **new**	NTay
'Esperanto' (LL)	NHaw
'Essex Star' (Fo)	ECou
'Étoile de Malicorne' (EL)	MBri
'Étoile de Paris' (EL)	MBri
'Étoile Rose' (Vt)	CCon CMac CRHN CSPN CTri CWCL EBee ELan EPfP IPot LBMP LRHS MAsh NHaw NHol NTay SCoo SDix SLim SLon SPer SPoG SWCr

	'Étoile Violette' (Vt) 🏆H6	Widely available
	Evening Star = 'Evista' (EL)	EPfP MBri
	Exciting = '20exci' (EL) **new**	NTay
	'Eximia'	see *C.* 'Ballerina in Blue'
	'Fair Rosamond' (EL)	MBri NHaw NLar NTay
	'Fairy' (Fo/f)	ECou
	Fairy BluePBR	see *C.* Crystal Fountain
	'Fairydust' (Vt)	NHaw
	× ***fargesioides***	see *C.* 'Paul Farges'
	fasciculiflora	CMHG
	- KWJ 12160	WCru
	- L 657	EPfP WCru WPGP
	'Fascination'PBR (I)	CFlo CWGN MBri NHaw NTay SMDP
	fauriei	WSHC
	Filigree = 'Evipo029'PBR	CFlo CLng COtt CRos CSPN LBuc LRHS MGos NTay SPoG SWCr
	'Firefly' (EL)	EBee
	'Fireworks' (EL)	CFlo CSPN CWGN EPfP IBoy LRHS MAsh MBri MRav NEgg NLar NTay SLim SPer SPoG SWCr
	'Flamingo' (EL)	CWCL
	flammula	CCon CFlo CMac CSPN ELan EPfP LRHS MAsh MBlu MBri MRav NTay SDix SPer SPoG SRms SWCr SWvt
	- 'Rubra Marginata'	see *C.* × *triternata* 'Rubromarginata'
	Fleuri = 'Evipo042'PBR (EL)	CFlo CLng CSPN CWCL EPfP LBuc LRHS NPri NTay SCoo SLon SPer SPoG SWCr
	florida	CWGN SWvt
	- 'Bicolor'	see *C. florida* var. *florida* 'Sieboldiana'
	- var. ***flore-pleno*** 'Plena' (d)	CCCN CFlo CLng CSPN CWCL ELan EPfP LRHS MAsh NEgg NTay SPoG SWCr
§	- var. ***florida*** 'Sieboldiana' (d)	CBcs CFlo CSPN CWCL CWGN CWSG ELan EPfP LRHS MAsh MBri NTay SLim SPoG SRkn SWCr SWvt WFar
	- var. ***normalis*** Pistachio = 'Evirida'PBR (LL)	CCCN CFlo CLng CSPN CWCL CWGN EPfP LRHS LSqu MAsh MGos NLar NTay SLim SLon SPoG SWCr
	'Floris V' (I)	MCot NHaw NLar
	'Fluffy Duck' (Vt/d)	NHaw
	foetida × 'Lunar Lass' (Fo)	ECho
	foetida × ***petriei***	ECho
	'Fond Memories' (EL)	CFlo EPfP IPot LRHS MBri NLar NTay SLon SPoG SWCr
	Forever Friends = 'Zofofri'PBR (LL)	CWGN IPot LRHS NTay SLon SWCr
	'Forget-me-not NLP1'	MBri NLar WHar
	forrestii	see *C. napaulensis*
§	***forsteri***	CSPN WSHC
	'Foxtrot' (Vt)	CRHN
	'Foxy' (A) 🏆H6	CFlo CLng MBri NLar NTay SLon
	'Fragrant Joy' (Fo/m)	ECou
	'Fragrant Oberon' (Fo)	CFlo ECou NTay SMDP SWvt
	'Fragrant Spring' (M)	CSBt CSPN CWGN ELon IBoy LRHS MMuc NLar NTay SLim SMDP SPoG SWCr
	'Frances Rivis' (A) 🏆H6	CFlo CMac CSPN CWCL ELan EPfP LRHS MAsh MBlu MBri MMuc MRav MSwo NLar NTay NWea SDix SPer SPoG SRms SWCr
	'Frankie' (A) 🏆H6	CFlo CLng COtt CSPN EBee ELan EPfP LRHS MAsh MBri MGos MHer NTay SCoo SWCr
	Franziska Maria = 'Evipo008' (EL)	CFlo CLng EPfP LRHS LSqu MAsh MBri MGos NTay SCoo SLon SWCr
	'Frau Mikiko' (EL)	MGos
	'Freda' (M) 🏆H6	CRHN CTri CWGN ELan EPfP LRHS MAsh MBlu MBri MRav NHol NTay SDix SLim SPer SPoG SWCr WFar
	fremontii	GKev NHaw
	'Fryderyk Chopin' (EL)	CSPN EBee NHaw NLar
	'Fujimusume' (EL) 🏆H6	CFlo CLng CSPN CWGN IPot LRHS MAsh NHaw NTay SPoG SWCr
	fujisanensis B&SWJ 11370	WCru
	'Fukuzono'	LRHS NHaw NTay SDix SWCr
	fusca misapplied	see *C. japonica*
	fusca Turcz.	GBin
	- dwarf	CWGN
§	- var. ***fusca***	WSHC
	- var. ***kamtschatica***	see *C. fusca* Turcz. var. *fusca*
	'Gabrielle' ambig.	MBri
	GalorePBR	see *C.* Vesuvius
	'Garnet' (V)	NHaw
	Gazelle = 'Evipo014'PBR	CLng LRHS NTay SKHP
	'Generał Sikorski' (EL)	CBcs CFlo CMac CSPN ELan EPfP LRHS MAsh MBri MGos NTay SCoo SLim SPer SWCr SWvt
	'Geoffrey Tolver' (LL)	NHaw
	'Georg' (A/d)	NHaw
	'Georg Ots' (LL)	NHaw
	Giant Star = 'Gistar'PBR (M)	CLng EBee IBoy LRHS NLar NPer SLim SPoG SRkn WNPC
	'Gillian Blades' (EL) 🏆H6	CFlo CLng COtt CSPN ELan EPfP LRHS MAsh MBri MGos NHaw NTay SCoo SWCr SWvt
§	'Gipsy Queen' (LL) 🏆H6	CBcs CMac CSPN CWCL ELan ELon EPfP IBoy LRHS MAsh MBri MGos NTay SDix SLim SPer SPoG SWCr SWvt
	'Gisela' (EL) **new**	LRHS
	Giselle = 'Evipo051' **new**	LSqu NTay SLon SPoG SWCr
	'Gladys Picard' (EL)	MBri NHaw
	glauca Turcz.	see *C. intricata*
	glaucophylla	WCru WSHC
	'Golden Harvest' (Ta)	NLar
	Golden Tiara = 'Kugotia'PBR (Ta) 🏆H6	CSPN CWGN GBin MBri NLar NTay SRms WCot
	'Gothenburg' (M)	MBri
	'Grace' (Ta)	EPfP NHaw NLar
	gracilifolia BWJ 8002 **new**	WCru
I	'Grandiflora' (F)	COtt WFar
	grandiflora	SLim SRms
	'Grandiflora Sanguinea' (Vt)	NTay
	grata misapplied	see *C.* × *jouiniana*
	'Gravetye Beauty' (T)	CFlo CMac COtt CRHN CSPN ELan EPfP LRHS MAsh MBri MGos NHol NTay SDix SLon SPer SPoG SRms SWCr SWvt
§	'Grażyna' (LL)	NTay
	grewiiflora B&SWJ 2956	WCru
	'Guernsey Cream' (EL)	CCon CFlo CSPN CWCL EPfP LRHS MAsh MBri NLar NTay SCoo SDix SLim SPoG SRkn SWCr
	Guiding Promise = 'Evipo053'	CLng LRHS NTay SLon
	'Gunta' (LL) **new**	NHaw
	'H.F.Young' (EL)	CFlo CLng CSPN ELan EPfP LRHS MAsh MBri MGos MMuc NLar NTay SCoo SDix SPer SWvt
	haenkeana	NHaw

	Name	Suppliers
	'Hagley Hybrid' (LL)	CDoC CDul CMac COtt CSPN CWCL EBee ELan EPfP LRHS MAsh MBri MGos MJak MMuc MRav NEgg NLar NTay SDix SLim SPer SPoG SRms SWCr SWvt
	'Hakuōkan' (EL)	CSPN EPfP LRHS MBri NLar SCoo
	'Hakuree' K. Ozawa (I)	MLHP SMDP
	'Hanaguruma' (EL)	CSPN MBri
	'Hanajima' (I)	SMDP
	'Happy Anniversary' (EL)	LBuc MBri NLar NTay
§	Happy Birthday = 'Zohapbi'PBR (LL)	NTay
	Harlow Carr = 'Evipo004'PBR	CLng CMac EPfP LRHS MBri NTay SCoo SLim SRms SWCr
	Havering Hybrids (Fo)	ECou
	'Hayate' **new**	CWGN
	'Helios'	see *C.* Aztek
	'Helsingborg' (A) H6	CFlo CLng COtt CSPN EBee ELan EPfP LRHS MAsh MBri NPri NTay SCoo SPoG SRms SWCr
I	'Hendersonii' (I)	CFlo GBuc MNFA
	hendersonii Koch	see *C.* × *diversifolia* 'Hendersonii'
	hendersonii Stand.	see *C.* × *diversifolia*
I	'Hendersonii Rubra' (Ar)	CSPN
	'Hendryetta'PBR (I)	LRHS MBri SMDP SWvt
	henryi	EShb MAsh MBri MMuc NTay
	- B&SWJ 3402	WCru
	'Henryi' (EL)	CFlo CMac CSPN CTri CWCL EBee ELan EPfP LRHS MBri MRav MSwo NEgg SDix SPer SPoG SWCr
	henryi var. ***morii*** B&SWJ 1668	WCru
	heracleifolia	CCon CMac CPou EAJP ECtt GLog LRHS MWhi NLar SGSe WBor WWEG XLum
	- Alan BloomPBR	see *C. tubulosa* Alan Bloom
	- 'Blue Dwarf'	MGos SMDP WAbe
	- 'Cassandra'	CFlo CWGN CWld EAEE ECtt ELon EPfP EPla EShb GCal GLog LRHS MCot MWhi NCGa NOrc SBod SChF SMDP SPoG WGwG
	- 'China Purple'	CExl GBin LRHS MSCN NLar SMDP
	- var. ***davidiana***	see *C. tubulosa*
	- 'Pink Dwarf' (H)	CWGN NLar NTay SMDP WAbe
	- 'Roundway Blue Bird' (H)	NHaw SMDP
	'Herbert Johnson' (EL)	NHaw
	hexapetala Forster	see *C. forsteri*
	hexapetala Pall	see *C. angustifolia*
	hexasepala	see *C. forsteri*
	hirsutissima	SBrt
	'Honora' (LL)	CFlo CSPN CWGN LRHS MAsh MBri NTay SCoo
	'Horn of Plenty' (EL)	LRHS MBri NHaw
	'Huldine' (LL) H6	CBcs CLng CRHN CSPN ELan EPfP LRHS MAsh MBri MRav NTay SDix SLon SPer SWCr SWvt
	'Huvi' (LL)	CWGN MGos NHaw
	'Hybrida Sieboldii' (EL)	EUJe SCoo
	Hyde Hall = 'Evipo009'PBR (EL)	CFlo CLng CMac CRos CSPN CWGN ELan EPfP LRHS LSqu MAsh MBri MGos NTay SCoo SLim SLon SPer SRms SWCr
	'Hythe Egret' (Fo)	ECho LLHF
	I Am a Little Beauty = 'Zolibe' (Vt)	CRHN NHaw NTay
	I am Lady J = 'Zoiamlj' (Vt)	IPot NHaw
	I Am Lady Q = 'Zoiamladyq'PBR (Vt)	CRHN CWGN NHaw NTay
	I Am Red Robin = 'Zorero'PBR (A)	CSPN MBri NTay
	ianthina var. ***kuripoensis***	NHaw WSHC
	- - B&SWJ 700	WCru
	'Ibi' (EL)	CWGN
	Ice Blue = 'Evipo003'PBR (Prairie Series) (EL)	CLng CRos ELan EPfP LRHS LSqu MBri NPri NTay SCoo SLim SLon SPoG SWCr
	'Ice Queen' (EL)	MAsh
	'Ingrid Biedenkopf' (Vt)	NHaw
	Inspiration = 'Zoin'PBR (I)	CSPN ELan MBri NLar SCoo
	integrifolia	CExl CPou CSpe ELan EPfP IFoB MBel MBri MHer NLar NPer NTay SRms WCot WHoo WWEG
	- RCB UA 10	WCot
	- from Lake Baikal, Russia **new**	GKev
I	- 'Alba'	CCon CFlo CSPN ECtt LRHS MBri NBir NHaw NTay SCoo SRms
	- 'Blue Ribbons' (I)	WSHC
	- 'Budapest' (I)	NHaw
	- 'Hendersonii' Koch	see *C.* × *diversifolia* 'Hendersonii'
	- mid-blue-flowered	MGos
	- 'Olgae'	see *C.* × *diversifolia* 'Olgae'
	- 'Ozawa's Blue' (I)	CWGN EAEE MBNS MLHP
	- white-flowered	see *C. integrifolia* 'Alba'
	'Intermedia Rosea' (I)	NChi
§	***intricata***	CExl
	'Iola Fair' (EL)	NHaw
	ispahanica	NHaw
	'Iubileinyi-70' (LL)	NHaw
	'Ivan Olsson' (EL)	IPot
	'Jackmanii' (LL) H6	CBcs CMac COtt CTri EBee EPfP IBoy LRHS MAsh MBri MGos MJak NWea SCoo SEND SLim SPoG SWCr SWvt WHar
	'Jackmanii Alba' (EL)	ELan ELon EPfP LRHS MAsh MBri SCoo SLim SPoG SWCr
	Jackmanii Purpurea = 'Zojapur'PBR (LL)	LRHS
	'Jackmanii Superba' misapplied	see *C.* 'Gipsy Queen'
	'Jackmanii Superba' ambig. (LL)	CFlo CMac CSPN CWCL CWSG ELan EPfP LRHS MAsh MBri MGos MMuc MRav MSwo NEgg NPer NPri NTay SDix SLim SPer SPoG SWCr
	'Jacqueline du Pré' (A) H6	CBcs CFlo CMac CSPN CWCL EBee ELan EPfP MBri NHaw NTay SMDP
	'James Mason' (EL)	CSPN MBri
	'Jan Fopma'PBR (I)	CWGN LRHS NTay SMDP
	'Jan Lindmark' (A/d)	CLng LRHS MAsh MBri NLar NTay SCoo SPre SWCr
§	'Jan Paweł II' (EL)	ELan LRHS MBri SCoo SPer
	'Janny' (A)	IPot
§	***japonica***	NHaw WSHC
	- B&SWJ 11204	WCru
	'Jean Caldwell' (Vt)	NHaw
	'Jenny' (M/d)	CFlo LRHS SMDP SPoG SWCr
	'Jenny Caddick' (Vt)	MGos NHaw
	'Jessica' (EL)	see *C.* 'Kjell'
	Jessica = 'Evipo012'PBR	CLng LRHS
	Jewel of MerkPBR	see *C.* Happy Birthday
	'Jingle Bells' (C)	CFlo CLng CMac COtt EPfP LBMP LRHS MAsh MBri NLar NTay SCoo SLim SLon SPoG SWCr
	'Joan Baker' (Vt)	CRHN
	John Howells = 'Zojohnhowells'PBR (Vt)	CFlo MBri NTay SLon
	'John Huxtable' (LL) H6	CFlo CLng LRHS MBri NHaw NTay

	Name	Suppliers
	John Paul II	see *C.* 'Jan Paweł II'
	'John Treasure' (Vt)	CRHN LRHS NHaw NLar NTay SMDP
	'John Warren' (EL)	LRHS MAsh MBri NHaw NTay SCoo SLim SPer SWCr
	'Jolly Jake' (Vt)	CFlo
	Josephine = 'Evijohill'PBR (EL)	CFlo CLng COtt CSPN CWCL CWGN EPfP EUJe LRHS LSqu MAsh MBri MGos NLar NPri NTay SCoo SLim SPer SPoG SRkn SWCr SWvt WHar
§	× ***jouiniana***	MRav SEND SWvt WSHC
	- 'Chance' (H)	NHaw NTay
	'Julka' (EL)	CFlo NHaw NTay
	'June Pyne' (EL)	MBri
	'Justa' (Vt)	NHaw
	'Juuli' (I)	LRHS MBri
	'Kaaru' (LL)	CRHN CSPN
	'Kacper' (EL)	NHaw
	'Kaen' (EL)	NTay
	'Kaiu' (V)	CFlo CSPN CWGN LRHS NHaw NTay SLim SMDP SWCr
§	'Kakio' (EL)	CLng LRHS MAsh MBri NTay SDix SLim SPer SPoG SWCr
I	'Kamilla' (EL)	CWGN
§	'Kardynał Wyszyński' (EL)	MBri
§	'Kasmu' (Vt)	NHaw
	'Kathleen Dunford' (EL)	MBri NHaw NTay SCoo
	'Kathryn Chapman' (Vt)	CRHN NHaw
	'Kaunitar' (LL) **new**	NHaw
	'Ken Donson' (EL) ♀H6	MBri SCoo
	'Ken Pyne' (LL)	CFlo
	'Kermesina' (Vt) ♀H6	CCon CRHN EBee ELan EPfP IBoy LRHS MAsh MBri SCoo SDix SLim SPoG SRms SWCr
	'Ketu Õde' (LL) **new**	NHaw
	'Kiev' (Vt)	NHaw
	'Killifreth' (Vt)	CRHN NHaw
	'King Edward VII' (EL)	MBri
	Kingfisher = 'Evipo037'PBR (EL)	CFlo CRos CSPN ELan EPfP LBuc LRHS LSqu NPri NTay SCoo SLon SPoG SWCr
	'Kinju Atarashi' (LL)	NTay
	'Kiri Te Kanawa' (EL)	CSPN ELon LRHS MBri NLar NTay
§	'Kjell' (EL)	NTay
	'Kommerei' (LL)	NHaw
§	'Königskind' (EL)	CSPN NLar
	koreana	MAsh WCru
	- B&SWJ 8431 **new**	WCru
	'Külli' (LL) **new**	NHaw
	ladakhiana	GQui NHaw SMDP WPGP
	- CC 7134 **new**	ITim
	- CC 7135 **new**	EWld
	'Lady Betty Balfour' (LL)	CMac CSPN LRHS MBri NTay SCoo SWvt
	'Lady Bird Johnson' (T)	CFlo EPfP LRHS NTay SCoo SWCr
	'Lady Caroline Nevill' (EL)	MBri
	'Lady Londesborough' (EL)	MBri MMuc NHaw NTay SCoo SDix
	'Lady Northcliffe' (EL)	CLng CSPN CTri LRHS MAsh MBri NTay SDix
	'Lambton Park' (Ta) ♀H6	CCon CRHN LRHS NHaw NLar NTay SMDP
	lasiandra	NHaw
	'Last Dance' (Ta)	CRHN
	Lasting Love	see *C.* 'Grażyna'
	'Lasurstern' (EL) ♀H6	CBcs CExl CFlo CMac CSPN CTri ELan EPfP LRHS MAsh MBri NTay SDix SPer SPoG SWCr SWvt WFar
	'Lavender Twirl'	CRHN
	'Lawsoniana' (EL)	CMac MBri
	'Lemon Chiffon' (EL)	CLng CSPN LRHS NHaw NTay
	Liberation = 'Evifive'PBR (EL)	CLng LRHS MBri NLar NTay SCoo SLim SLon SPoG SWCr
§	***ligusticifolia***	NHaw
	'Lilacina Floribunda' (EL)	NHaw
	'Lilactime' (EL)	NHaw
	'Lincoln Star' (EL)	CLng CMac ELon LRHS MAsh MBri SDix SLim SPoG SWvt
	'Little Bas' (Vt)	CRHN MBri NHaw NLar NTay SLon
	'Little Butterfly' (Vt)	CRHN NHaw
	'Little Mermaid' (EL)	CFlo
	'Little Nell' (Vt)	CCCN CRHN CSPN ELan EPfP LRHS MAsh NTay SCoo SDix SLon
I	'Longiflora'	CFlo
	'Lord Herschell'	CFlo CSPN CWGN LRHS MBri SMDP
	'Lord Nevill' (EL)	EPfP LRHS MBri
	'Louise Pummell' (Fo)	ECou
	'Louise Rowe' (EL)	CFlo CLng ELan LRHS MBri NHaw NTay SWCr
	loureiroana HWJ 663	WCru
	'Love Jewelry' (EL)	NHaw
	'Lunar Lass' (Fo/f)	CFlo EBee ECho NTay WAbe
	'Lunar Lass Variegata' (Fo/v)	ECho LLHF
	'Luxuriant Blue' (Vt)	CRHN NHaw NTay
	'M. Koster' (Vt)	CDoC CRHN NHaw SLon SRms
	macropetala (d)	CBcs CLng CSBt ELan EPfP GKev LAst LRHS MAsh MGos MMuc MRav MWhi NTay SDix SPer SWCr
	- 'Alborosea'	see *C.* 'Blushing Ballerina'
	- 'Blue Lagoon'	see *C. macropetala* 'Lagoon' Jackman 1959
	- 'Lagoon' Jackman 1956	see *C. macropetala* 'Maidwell Hall' Jackman
	- 'Lagoon' ambig.	SWCr
§	- 'Lagoon' Jackman 1959 (A/d) ♀H6	CSPN LRHS MAsh MBri MSwo NHol NTay SCoo SPoG
	- 'Maidwell Hall' ambig.	SPer
§	- 'Maidwell Hall' Jackman (A/d)	CSPN CTri EPfP IPot MAsh MGos NTay
	- 'Wesselton' (A/d) ♀H6	CFlo CSPN CTri EBee EPfP LBMP LRHS MAsh MBri NHaw NTay SPre SRms SWCr
	- 'White Moth'	see *C.* 'White Moth'
	'Madame Baron-Veillard' (LL)	CLng LRHS MBri SCoo
	'Madame Edouard André' (LL)	CLng CSPN EPfP LRHS MAsh MBri NTay SCoo SPoG SWCr
	'Madame Grangé' (LL) ♀H6	CSPN LRHS MBri NHaw SCoo
	'Madame Julia Correvon' (Vt) ♀H6	Widely available
	'Madame le Coultre'	see *C.* 'Mevrouw Le Coultre'
	'Majojo' (Fo)	GEdr LLHF
	mandschurica	GCal GKev NHaw NLar XLum
	'Margaret Hunt' (LL)	CSPN ELan IBoy MBri NHaw NTay
	'Mari' (LL) **new**	NHaw
	'Maria' (Kivistik) (LL) **new**	NHaw
	'Maria Băsescu' **new**	NTay
	'Maria Cornelia'PBR (Vt)	CRHN CWGN NTay
	'Marie Boisselot' (EL) ♀H6	CBcs CFlo CMac CSPN CTri CWCL ELan EPfP IBoy LRHS MAsh MBri MMuc MRav MSwo NPri NTay SDix SPer SPoG SWCr SWvt
	'Marinka'	EBee
	'Marjorie' (M/d)	CBcs CDoC COtt CSPN CTri CWSG ELan EPfP GKin IBoy LRHS MAsh

		MBri MGos MRav NEgg NTay SLim SPer SPoG SRms SWCr WFar
	'Markham's Pink' (A/d) ♀H6	Widely available
	marmoraria	EAEE ECho LRHS SRms
	- 'Timpany Treasure' **new**	ITim
	marmoraria* × *petriei	ECho
	'Marmori' (LL)	CWGN NHaw
	'Mary Habberley' (Vt) **new**	NHaw
	'Mary Rose'	see *C. viticella* 'Flore Pleno'
§	'Maskarad' (Vt)	MBri
	Masquerade (Vt)	see *C.* 'Maskarad'
I	'Masquerade' (EL)	MBri
	maximowicziana	see *C. terniflora*
	'Mayleen' (M) ♀H4	CPou CSBt CTri EPfP IBoy LRHS MAsh MBri MRav NEgg NTay SCoo SLim SPer SPoG SRms SWCr SWvt
I	'Melodie' (Vt)	NHaw
§	'Mevrouw Le Coultre' (EL)	MJak
	meyeniana var. ***insularis*** B&SWJ 6700	WCru
	Mienie Belle = 'Zomibel'PBR (T)	CWGN IPot NHaw
	'Mikelite' (Vt)	MGos NHaw
	'Miniseelik' (LL)	NHaw NTay
	'Minister' (EL)	MBri
	'Minuet' (Vt) ♀H6	CRHN CSPN EPfP LRHS MAsh MGos NTay SCoo SDix SLon SPer SWvt
	Miranda = 'Floclemi'PBR (I)	CWGN SMDP
	'Miriam Markham' (EL)	MBri
	'Miss Bateman' (EL)	CDoC CFlo CMac COtt CSPN CTri CWCL CWSG ELan EPfP LRHS MAsh MBri MGos MMuc NTay SDix SLim SPer SPoG SWCr WBor
	'Miss Christine' (M)	CFlo ELan NTay SMDP
	'Mister Hans Horn' (Vt)	NHaw
	Mon Amour = 'Zomoa' (EL)	CWGN NTay
	'Moniuszko' (EL)	CWGN
	montana	CExl CSBt GGal MAsh SCob SDix SEWo
	- B&SWJ 6724 from Taiwan	WCru
	- B&SWJ 6930	WCru
	- var. ***alba***	see *C. montana* var. *montana*
	- 'Alexander' (M)	CPou EPfP LRHS SWCr
	- var. ***grandiflora*** (M) ♀H4	CDul CMac CSam CWSG EBee ELan EPfP GKin LBuc LPot LRHS MBri MJak MMuc MPro NBir NPri NTay SCob SEND SLim SPer SPoG SRms SWCr SWvt
§	- var. ***montana***	EAEE MAsh MGos MJak SCob SPer SPoG
I	- 'Peveril'	CSPN
	- var. ***rubens*** misapplied	see *C. montana* var. *montana*
	- var. ***rubens*** E.H.Wilson	CDoC CSBt CTri ELan EPfP GGal LRHS MBri MSwo NHol NWea SDix SPlb
I	- - 'Odorata' (M)	GKin LRHS MRav NTay SCoo SLim SPoG WHar
	- - 'Pink Perfection' (M)	CDoC CMac CWSG EBee ELan EPfP GKin LRHS MAsh MBri NTay SCob SCoo SLim SPer SPoG SWCr SWvt WFar WHar
	- - 'Tetrarose' (M) ♀H4	Widely available
I	- 'Rubens Superba' (M)	COtt CTri GKin MPro NPri NTay SRms SWCr WFar
	- var. ***sericea***	see *C. spooneri*
	- 'Superba' (M)	MBri
§	- var. ***wilsonii***	CFlo CSPN CSam ELan EPfP GKin LRHS MBri MMuc MRav MSwo NTay SDix SMDP SPoG SRms SWCr SWvt
	'Monte Cassino' (EL)	CSPN CWGN EBee NTay
	'Moonbeam' (Fo)	ECou GEdr ITim MRav NOrc
	Moonfleet = 'Evipo046' (LL)	CLng LRHS MGos NTay SWCr
§	'Moonlight' (EL)	MAsh
	'Moonman' (Fo)	ECou LLHF
	Morning Cloud	see *C.* 'Yukikomachi'
	'Morning Heaven' (Vt)	NHaw
	Morning Star = 'Zoklako'PBR (EL)	CWGN
	Morning Yellow = 'Cadmy'PBR (M)	CCCN IBoy LRHS
	'Mrs Cholmondeley' (EL) ♀H6	CMac CSPN ELan EPfP LRHS MAsh MBri MGos MSwo NPri NTay SLim SPer SPoG SWCr
	'Mrs George Jackman' (EL) ♀H6	CFlo CLng CSPN CWCL LRHS NLar NTay SCoo
	'Mrs James Mason' (EL)	EBee NHaw
	'Mrs N.Thompson' (EL)	CMac COtt CSPN CTri CWCL ELan ELon IBoy LRHS MAsh MBri NBir NEgg NHol NPer NTay SDix SLim SPer SPoG SWCr
	'Mrs P.B.Truax' (EL)	LRHS NTay
	'Mrs Robert Brydon' (H)	ECtt NLar NTay SRms
	'Mrs Spencer Castle' (EL)	CSPN
	'Mrs T. Lundell' (Vt)	CRHN CSPN MGos NHaw
	'Multi Blue' (EL)	CBcs CFlo COtt CWSG ELan ELon EPfP EUJe IBoy LRHS MAsh MBri MGos MMuc NTay SLim SPer SPoG SRkn SRms SWCr WHar
	'My Angel'PBR (Ta)	CSPN ELan NHaw NLar NTay
§	***napaulensis***	CFlo CSPN CTri CWCL EPfP NHaw SMDP WCru WSHC
I	'Natacha' (EL)	NHaw NTay SCoo
	'Natascha' (EL)	CLng CSPN LRHS MBri SWCr SWvt
	'Negritianka' (LL)	CSPN EPfP LRHS MBri NHaw
	'Negus' (LL)	NHaw
	'Nelly Moser' (EL) ♀H6	Widely available
	'Nelly Moser Neu' (EL)	NTay
	'New Dawn' (M)	CSPN NHaw
	'New Love'PBR (H)	CSPN NHaw NLar NTay
	'Niobe' (EL) ♀H6	CBcs CMac COtt CSPN CWCL ELan EPfP EShb EUJe IBoy LRHS MAsh MBri MGos MMuc MSwo NHol NPri NTay SCob SDix SLim SPer SPoG SRms SWCr WFar
	'North Star' (EL)	EPfP NTay
	North Star (LL)	see *C.* 'Põhjanael'
	nutans var. ***thyrsoidea***	see *C. rehderiana*, *C. veitchiana*
	'Ocean Pearl' (A)	CFlo MBri NLar NTay
	Octopus = 'Zooct'PBR (A)	CFlo NTay
	'Odoriba' (V)	CWGN LRHS NHaw SMDP
	'Olimpiada-80' (EL)	NHaw
	'Omoshiro' (EL)	CWGN IPot LRHS NHaw NTay
§	Ooh La La = 'Evipo041'PBR (EL)	CFlo CLng COtt CRos CSPN CWCL ELon EPfP LBuc LRHS NPri NTay SCoo SPer SPoG SWCr
	orientalis misapplied	see *C. tibetana* subsp. *vernayi*
	orientalis L.	EBee GCra SCoo SWvt
	- 'Orange Peel'	see *C. tibetana* subsp. *vernayi* var. *vernayi* 'Orange Peel'
*	- 'Rubromarginata' (Ta)	MBri
	- 'Sherriffii'	see *C.* 'Sherriffii'
	- var. ***tenuiloba***	see *C. columbiana* var. *tenuiloba*
	orientalis* × *tangutica	SWvt

	Name	Suppliers
	otophora **new**	NHaw
	'Paala' (EL)	NHaw
	'Pagoda' (Vt)	CDoC CRHN EBee EPfP MBri SCoo SLon SMDP SRms
	Palette = 'Evipo034'[PBR] (Vt)	CLng LRHS MBri NTay SLon
	'Pamela' (F)	NHaw NTay
§	'Pamela Jackman' (Vt)	MBri
	'Pamela Jackman'	see *C. alpina* 'Pamela Jackman', *C.* 'Pamela Jackman' (Vt)
	'Pamiat Serdtsa' (I)	ELon NHaw
	'Pangbourne Pink' (I) ♀H6	CFlo CSPN CWCL EPfP LRHS MBri NHaw NTay SCoo SWCr
	paniculata Thunb.	see *C. terniflora*
	paniculata J.G. Gmel var. ***lobata***	NTay
	'Paradise Queen' (EL)	LBuc MBri NLar NTay
	'Parasol' (EL)	MBri
	Parisienne = 'Evipo019'[PBR] (EL)	CFlo CLng COtt CSPN EPfP LRHS LSqu NPri NTay SCoo SLon SPer SPoG SWCr
	parviflora DC.	see *C. campaniflora*
	parviloba var. ***bartlettii*** B&SWJ 6788	WCru
	'Pastel Princess' (EL)	NHaw
	patens	CCse
	- 'Korean Moon' (EL)	WCru
§	- 'Manshuu Ki' (EL)	CFlo CSPN ELon EPfP LRHS SRms
	- 'Yukiokoshi' (EL)	IPot
§	'Paul Farges' (Vb) ♀H6	CSPN CWGN GLog MBri MNrw NHaw NTay SMDP
	'Pauline' (A/d) ♀H6	CBcs LRHS MBri NTay SCoo SLim SWCr
	'Pendragon' (Vt)	CRHN NHaw
	'Pennell's Purity' (LL)	CFlo NHaw NTay
	Peppermint = 'Evipo005'[PBR] (d)	CFlo CLng CRos CSPN ELan EPfP LRHS LSqu NTay SCoo SLon SWCr
	'Perida' (LL)	CWGN
	'Perle d'Azur' (LL)	CBcs CMac CRHN CSPN CTri CWCL ELan ELon EPfP LAst LRHS MAsh MBri MSwo NEgg NTay SDix SLim SPer SPoG SRms SWCr WFar
	'Perrin's Pride' (Vt)	CLng LRHS MBri MGos NHaw NLar NTay SCoo SWCr
	Petit Faucon = 'Evisix'[PBR] (I) ♀H6	CFlo CLng COtt CWCL EPfP LRHS LSqu MBri MGos NLar NTay SCoo SLim SPer SPoG SWCr SWvt
	petriei	ECou WThu
	'Peveril Pearl' (EL)	NTay
	'Peveril Pristine' (Vt)	CWGN
	'Peveril Profusion' (T)	SMDP
	Picardy = 'Evipo024'[PBR] (EL)	CFlo CLng COtt CRos CSPN EPfP LRHS LSqu NPri NTay SCoo SLim SPer SPoG SWCr
I	'Picton's Variety' (M)	CSPN CTri MBri NHaw
	'Piilu' (EL)	COtt CSPN CWGN ELan LRHS LSou MAsh MBNS MBri NHaw NLar NTay SCoo SLim SMDP SPoG SRkn SWCr
	'Pille' (LL) **new**	NHaw
	Pink Champagne	see *C.* 'Kakio'
	'Pink Fantasy' (LL)	CFlo CLng CRHN CSPN CTri LRHS MAsh MBri NLar NTay SCoo SLim SRkn SWCr
	'Pink Flamingo' (A) ♀H6	CLng CSPN CWCL ELan EPfP LRHS MBri NTay SCoo SLim SPoG SRkn SWCr WBor
	'Pink Ice' (I)	CSPN LRHS NHaw NTay
	'Pirko' (Vt)	NHaw
§	***pitcheri***	NHaw SMDP
	'Pixie' (Fo/m)	CFlo CLng CSPN EBee ECou ELan ELon EPfP LRHS MGos NLar NTay SCoo SLim SPoG
	pogonandra	NHaw
§	'Põhjanael' (LL)	CSPN MBri NLar
	Polar Bear[PBR]	see *C.* Arctic Queen
	'Poldice' (Vt) ♀H6	CRHN
	'Polish Spirit' (LL) ♀H6	CDoC CFlo CMac COtt CRHN CSPN CTri CWCL ELan EPfP LAst LBMP LRHS MBri MGos MMuc NHol NTay SEND SLon SPer SPoG SRkn SWCr SWvt WFar
	potaninii	CCon GCra NSti
	- 'Summer Snow'	see *C.* 'Paul Farges'
	'Praecox' (H) ♀H6	CRHN CWCL CWld EAEE EBee ELan EPfP EPla LRHS MBri MCot MWhi NBir NSti NTay SDix SPer SPoG WCot
	Pretty in Blue = 'Zopre'[PBR] (F)	MBri SWvt
	'Primrose Star'[PBR]	see *C.* 'Star'
	'Prince Charles' (LL) ♀H6	CFlo CPou CRHN CSPN CTri ELan EPfP MAsh MBri MJak NHaw NLar NTay SCoo SDix SLim SPer SPoG SWCr SWvt
§	'Princess Diana' (T) ♀H5	CFlo COtt CRHN CSPN CSam CTri CWGN EBee ELan IPot LBuc LRHS MAsh MBel MBlu MJak MSwo NHol NTay SCoo SLim SPer SPoG SRms SWCr SWvt
	Princess Kate = 'Zoprika' (T)	CWGN IPot NTay SPoG
§	'Princess of Wales' (1875) (EL)	NLar SLon SWvt
	'Prinsesse Alexandra'[PBR] (EL)	NTay
	'Propertius' (A)	CFlo CSPN CWGN LRHS MGos NHaw NTay SMDP
	'Proteus' (EL)	CLng CSPN EBee ELan ELon EPfP LRHS MAsh MBri MGos NTay SCoo SLim SWCr WHar
	psilandra CWJ 12377	WCru
	'Purple Haze' (Vt)	CRHN NHaw
	'Purple Princess' (H)	NTay
	'Purple Spider' (A/d)	CFlo CMac CSPN EPfP MAsh MBlu MBri MLHP NHaw NLar NTay SCoo
	'Purpurea Plena Elegans' (Vt/d) ♀H6	CBcs CCon CMac CRHN CSam CTri CWCL EBee ELan ELon EPfP IBoy LAst LRHS MAsh MBri MSwo NEgg NHol NTay SDix SLim SPer SPoG SWCr SWvt WBor
	quadribracteolata	NHaw
	Queen Mother = 'Zoqum' (Vt)	CWGN EPfP IPot
	'Radar Love' (Ta)	LSun
	'Radiance'	CWGN
	'Ragamuffin' (EL/d)	MGos
	'Ramona' (LL)	CLng LRHS NHaw SWCr
	ranunculoides	NHaw
	'Rapture' (T)	MBri
	Rebecca = 'Evipo016'[PBR] (EL)	CFlo CLng COtt CSPN CWCL CWGN ELan EPfP EUJe LBuc LRHS LSqu MBri NPri NTay SCoo SLon SPer SPoG SWCr
	recta	CSPN ECtt EWTr MNrw NLar
	- 'Lime Close' seedlings	CAby
	- 'Purpurea' (F)	CFlo CMea EHoe ELan EPfP EWTr GKev IPot LRHS MNrw NBid NBir

		NChi NSti NTay SChF SDix SEND SPer SPoG SWCr WHoo XLum
	- 'Velvet Night' (F)	CSpe ECtt ESwi GBuc MAvo MBNS MBel MCot NEgg NLar SMDP WCot
§	'Red Beetroot Beauty' (A)	CSPN
	'Red Cooler'	see *C.* 'Crimson King'
	'Red Pearl' (EL)	CFlo LRHS MBri NTay SWCr
I	'Red Star' (d)	EPfP NTay
	Reflections = 'Evipo035' (LL)	EPfP LRHS LSqu NTay SLon SWCr
§	***rehderiana*** ♀H5	CCon CRHN CSPN CSam ELan EPfP LRHS MBlu MBri NBir NSti NTay SChF SDix SWvt WCot WHea WPGP WSHC
	'Reiman' (LL)	NHaw
	'Remembrance' (LL)	CFlo EPfP MBri
	repens Veitch	see *C. montana* var. *wilsonii*
	'Rhapsody' ambig.	CLng EPfP MAsh MBri MGos NTay SCoo SWCr
	'Rhapsody' B. Fretwell (EL)	CSPN LRHS NHaw
	'Ribble Red' (V) **new**	NHaw
	'Richard Pennell' (EL) ♀H6	LRHS MAsh SLim SWCr
	'Richard's Picotee' (Vt)	NHaw
	'Rising Star'	EBee NHaw
	'Ristimägi' (LL)	NHaw
	'Robud' PBR (M/d)	NPer
	'Roelie' (Vt)	NHaw
	'Roko-Kolla' (LL)	EBee NHaw
	'Romance' (Vt)	MBri
	'Romantika' (LL)	CFlo CSPN ELan IBoy IPot LRHS MAsh MBri NHaw NTay SCoo
	'Rooguchi' (I)	CFlo CWGN EBee MBri NHaw SDix
I	'Rosea' (I)	CSPN EPfP LRHS NTay
I	'Rosea' (Vt)	NHaw
	Rosemoor = 'Evipo002' PBR (EL)	CFlo CLng COtt CRos CSPN CWCL CWGN EPfP LBuc LRHS LSqu MAsh MBri NTay SCoo SLim SLon SWCr SWvt
	'Rosy O'Grady' (A) ♀H6	CWCL MAsh MBri NLar NTay SRms
	'Rosy Pagoda' (A)	ELan LRHS MBri NHaw NLar NTay SLim
	'Rouge Cardinal' (LL)	CFlo CMac CSPN CWSG ELan ELon EPfP IBoy LRHS MAsh MBri MGos MJak NEgg NTay SDix SLim SPer SPoG SRms SWCr
	'Royal Velours' (Vt)	CDoC CFlo CRHN CSPN CTri ELan EPfP LRHS MAsh MBri MGos NHol NTay SCoo SDix SLim SPer SPoG SWCr
	Royal Velvet = 'Evifour' PBR (EL)	CSPN LRHS MBri NTay SCoo
	'Royalty' (EL)	CLng CSPN EBee ELan EPfP LRHS MAsh MBri MJak NBir NTay SCoo SWCr
	'Rubens Superba'	see *C. montana* 'Rubens Superba'
	'Ruby' (A)	CLng CSPN ELan EPfP LRHS MAsh MMuc NTay SCoo SPer SRms
	'Ruby Glow' (EL)	CLng EBee EPfP LRHS NTay SCoo SWCr
	'Ruby Wedding' ambig.	CFlo CWGN EPfP LBuc MBri NTay SMDP SWvt
	'Rüütel' (EL)	CFlo ELon LRHS MAsh MBri NHaw NTay SCoo SMDP
	'Saalomon' (LL)	NHaw
	'Sally Cadge' (EL)	NHaw
	'Samantha Denny' (EL)	CSPN
	Samaritan Jo = 'Evipo075' **new**	LRHS LSqu NTay SPoG SWCr
	'Sander' (H)	SMDP
	'Saturn' (EL)	MGos
	Savannah = 'Evipo015' PBR (Vt)	CLng LRHS SLim
	'Scartho Gem' (EL)	CLng COtt LRHS MBri SCoo SWCr
	'Sealand Gem' (EL)	MBri NHaw
§	'Semu' (LL)	CSPN CWGN NHaw
	'Serenata' (EL)	MBri
	serratifolia	GLog MWhi SDix SPlb
	- B&SWJ 8458 from Korea	WCru
I	'Sherriffii' (Ta)	SWvt
	'Shikoo' (EL)	CWCL NTay WHlf
	Shimmer = 'Evipo028' (LL)	EPfP LBuc LRHS LSqu NTay SLon SWCr
	'Shirayukihime' (EL)	NLar
§	'Shiva' (A)	MBri
	'Shooun' (EL)	MBri
	'Sialia' (A/d)	CFlo CSPN
§	***sibirica***	EPfP MBri
	'Signe' (Vt)	see *C.* 'Kasmu'
	'Siirus' (EL)	NHaw
	'Silver Moon' (EL)	CFlo CLng CSPN EPfP LRHS MAsh MBri NLar NTay SCoo
	simensis	LEdu
	'Simplicity' (A)	CSPN MBri
	simsii Small	see *C. pitcheri*
	simsii Sweet	see *C. crispa*
	'Sinee Plamia' (LL)	NHaw
§	'Sinii Dozhd' (I)	CWCL EPfP NHaw
	'Sir Eric Savill' (M)	SMDP
	'Sir Garnet Wolseley' (EL)	MBri SDix
	'Sir Trevor Lawrence' (T)	CSPN LRHS NHaw
	'Sireen' (LL) **new**	NHaw
	smilacifolia	WPGP
	NJM 10.094 **new**	
	aff. ***smilacifolia*** HWJ 1049 **new**	WCru
	'Snow Queen' (EL)	CCon CFlo CLng CSPN ELon EPfP LRHS MBri NTay SLim SPoG SRms
	'Snowbird' (A/d)	CFlo CSPN LRHS NHaw NTay SPer SPoG SWCr
	'Snowdrift'	see *C. armandii* 'Snowdrift'
	'Södertälje' (Vt)	CRHN EPfP MBri SCoo
	'Sonnette' (V)	CFlo CWGN NHaw
	'Souvenir de J.L. Delbard' (EL)	NTay
§	'Souvenir du Capitaine Thuilleaux' (EL)	ELon LRHS MBri NTay
	'Special Occasion' (EL)	CLng COtt CSPN CWGN LRHS MBri NHaw NLar NTay SCoo SPoG SWCr
	Spiky = 'Zospi' PBR (A/d)	CFlo
§	***spooneri***	CTri NTay SCoo SLim SPoG SWvt
	'Sputnik' (I)	CWGN NHaw
	stans	CExl CHel CPou EBee IFro LLHF LRHS NLar SMDP SWCr
	- B&SWJ 5073	WCru
	- B&SWJ 6345	WCru
§	'Star' PBR (M/d)	CSPN ELan EPfP LRHS MBri MSwo NLar NTay SPer SPoG
	'Star of India' (LL)	CLng COtt EPfP LRHS MBri MGos NTay SCoo SLim SPer SPoG WBor
	Star River = 'Zostarri' PBR (I)	ELan
I	'Starfish' (EL)	NHaw
	'Starlight' (M)	ELon LRHS NTay SLim
	'Stasik' (LL)	NHaw
	'Stephanie' (A)	CFlo CSPN

Name	Suppliers
Still Waters = 'Zostiwa'PBR (EL)	CSPN CWGN LRHS NTay
Sugar Candy = 'Evione'PBR (EL)	CLng MAsh MBri NTay SCoo SLim SWCr
Summer Snow	see *C.* 'Paul Farges'
Summerdream = 'Zosumdre' (EL)	IPot NTay
'Sundance' (Ta)	CSPN SMDP
Sunny Sky = 'Zosusk'PBR (Vt)	CFlo NHaw NTay
'Sunrise' (M/d)	CSPN LRHS MBri MSwo NHaw NLar NTay
'Sunset' (EL) 🏆H6	CLng ELon LRHS MBri MGos MMuc NLar NTay SCoo SLim SWCr
'Swedish Bells' (I)	CWGN
'Sweet Scentsation' (F)	CFlo EPfP MBri NHaw NLar
'Sweet Summer Love' (F) **new**	CWGN
I 'Sweetheart' (I)	ELan EPfP NTay
'Sylvia Denny' (EL)	ELan EPfP MAsh MBri
'Sympatia' (LL)	NHaw
'Syrena' (LL)	NHaw
szuyuanensis B&SWJ 6791	WCru
- CWJ 12455	WCru
'Tage Lundell' (A)	CFlo CSPN EBee EPfP MBri NLar
'Tango' (Vt)	CRHN NHaw
§ ***tangutica***	Widely available
'Tapestry' (I)	NHaw
'Tartu' (EL)	NHaw
tashiroi purple-flowered B&SWJ 7005	WCru
- 'Yellow Peril'	WCru
Tekla = 'Evipo069' **new**	NTay
'Teksa' (LL)	NHaw
Temptation = 'Zotemp'PBR (EL)	CSPN NTay
tenuiloba	see *C. columbiana* var. *tenuiloba*
§ ***terniflora***	EPfP NHaw SKHP WHar
- B&SWJ 5751	WCru
'Teshio' (EL)	IPot NHaw
texensis	NHaw WSHC
- 'The Princess of Wales'	see *C.* 'Princess Diana'
'The Bride' (EL)	CSPN CWGN LRHS
The Countess of Wessex = 'Evipo 073'	EPfP LRHS LSqu NTay SPoG SWCr
'The First Lady' (EL)	CSPN MBri
'The President' (EL) 🏆H6	CDul CMac COtt CSPN CTri CWCL CWSG ELan EPfP IBoy LBMP LRHS MBri MGos MJak MSwo NEgg NPri NTay SCob SDix SLim SPer SPoG SRms SWCr WFar
'The Princess of Wales' (EL)	see *C.* 'Princess of Wales' (1875) (EL)
'The Princess of Wales' (T)	see *C.* 'Princess Diana' (T)
'The Vagabond' (EL)	CSPN ELan EPfP LRHS MAsh MBri NHaw NLar NTay SCoo SLim SPoG SWCr
§ Thumbelina = 'Evipo030'PBR (EL)	CLng COtt CWCL LBuc LRHS MGos NTay SPoG SWCr
thunbergii misapplied	see *C. terniflora*
tibetana	NHaw
- 'Black Tibet' (Ta)	CWGN
§ - subsp. ***vernayi***	CMHG
- - 'Glasnevin Dusk' (Ta)	SMDP WSHC
- - var. ***laciniifolia*** 'Tibetan Gem' (Ta) **new**	IPot
§ - - var. ***vernayi*** 'Orange Peel' LS&E 13342 (Ta)	CBcs CDoC SEND

Name	Suppliers
'Tie Dye' (LL)	CWGN ELan EPfP NHaw NTay
'Tiiu' (LL) **new**	NHaw
'Tinkerbell'	see *C.* 'Shiva'
'Toki' (EL)	CWGN
tongluensis GWJ 9358	WCru
- HWJK 2368	WCru
'Tranquility'	CWGN SMDP
'Treasure Trove' (Ta)	CSPN SMDP
'Triinu' (Vt)	NHaw
§ × ***triternata*** 'Rubromarginata'	CCon CDoC CFlo CMac CRHN CSPN CSam CWGN ELan ELon EPfP LRHS MAsh MBri MGos MJak MRav NTay SDix SLim SLon SPer SPoG SRkn SRms SWCr
'Tsunami Child' (M)	IMou
'Tsuzuki' (EL)	CSPN
§ ***tubulosa***	CSPN SMDP
§ - Alan Bloom = 'Alblo'PBR (H)	LRHS
- 'Wyevale' (H)	CFlo CHel CMac CSPN EAEE ELan ELon EPfP EPla LRHS MCot MRav NSti NTay SCoo SDix SMDP SPer SPoG WAul WCot
'Twilight' (EL)	CFlo CLng CSPN EPfP LRHS MAsh MBri NTay SWCr
Twinkle Bell = 'Wer01'	NTay
Twinkle = 'Zotwi' (I)	CWGN IPot
uncinata B&SWJ 11368	WCru
- CWJ 12373	WCru
'Uno Kivistik'PBR (LL) **new**	NHaw
§ ***urophylla*** 'Winter Beauty'	CDoC CFlo CWCL EBee ELan MBri NTay SMDP SPoG WPGP
urticifolia B&SWJ 8651	WCru
- B&SWJ 8852	WCru
'Utopia' (EL)	CSPN CWGN
'Valge Daam' (LL)	CWGN NHaw
'Valle' (LL) **new**	NHaw
'Van Gogh' (M)	SMDP
'Vanessa' (LL)	CRHN
'Vanso'PBR	see *C.* 'Blue Light'
§ ***veitchiana***	NHaw
'Venosa Violacea' (Vt) 🏆H6	CCon CFlo CRHN CSPN ELan EPfP LRHS MAsh MRav NHaw NHol NTay SCoo SDix SPer SPoG SRms SWCr
'Vera' (M)	CSPN LRHS NTay SCoo SLim
vernayi	see *C. tibetana* subsp. *vernayi*
'Veronica's Choice' (EL)	CFlo CSPN ELan LRHS MBri MGos NHaw NTay
Versailles = 'Evipo025'PBR (EL)	CLng EPfP LRHS NTay SLim SWCr
versicolor	WSHC
§ Vesuvius = 'Evipo032'PBR (Vt)	CLng EPfP LRHS MBri NTay SCoo SLim SLon SWCr
'Vetka'PBR (LL)	NHaw
Victor Hugo = 'Evipo007'PBR (LL)	CFlo CLng EBee LRHS NLar NTay SCoo
'Victoria' (LL) 🏆H6	CRHN CSPN LRHS MBri NHaw NTay SCoo SWCr
Viennetta = 'Evipo006'PBR (d)	CFlo CLng CSPN CWCL CWGN EPfP LRHS LSqu MGos NTay SCoo SLon SRms SWCr
'Vihma' (LL) **new**	NHaw
'Ville de Lyon' (LL)	CBcs CFlo COtt CRHN CSPN CWCL CWSG ELan EPfP GGal IBoy LRHS MAsh MBri MGos MJak MMuc NEgg NTay SDix SLim SPer SPoG SWCr WHar
'Vince Denny' (Ta)	EBee MBri NHaw SMDP

Vino = 'Poulvo'PBR (EL)	CLng LRHS MBri NHaw NTay SCoo SLim
'Viola' (LL)	CFlo CSPN CWGN ELon LRHS MBri NHaw NTay SDix SMDP
'Violet Charm' (EL)	MBri
viorna	NHaw WCru
virginiana misapplied	see *C. vitalba*
virginiana Hook.	see *C. ligusticifolia*
§ ***vitalba***	CArn CWld ECrN NHaw NTay NWea WHer WSFF
- SDR 6610	GKev
viticella	CRHN GKev MBri NHaw WCot
- subsp. ***campaniflora***	see *C. campaniflora*
§ - 'Flore Pleno' (Vt/d)	CFlo CRHN CSPN EBee ELon EPfP IPot LRHS NHaw NTay SLon SWCr
- 'Hågelby Blue' (Vt)	NHaw
- 'Hågelby Pink' (Vt) ♀H6	CRHN CWGN EBee NHaw
- 'Hågelby White' (Vt)	CWGN NHaw
- 'Hanna' (Vt)	CRHN NHaw
- 'Mary Rose'	see *C. viticella* 'Flore Pleno'
'Vivienne'	see *C.* 'Beth Currie'
'Voluceau' (Vt)	CLng CPou CRHN ELan LRHS SRms SWCr
'Vostok' (LL)	MGos NHaw NTay
'Vyvyan Pennell' (EL)	CBcs CFlo CMac COtt CSPN CTri CWSG ELan EPfP EUJe IBoy LBMP LRHS MAsh MBri MSwo NEgg NLar NTay SLim SPer SPoG SWCr SWvt WFar
'W.E. Gladstone' (EL)	LRHS NTay SDix
Wada's Primrose	see *C. patens* 'Manshuu Ki'
'Walenburg' (Vt) ♀H6	CRHN CWGN NHaw SLon
'Walter Pennell' (EL)	CBcs LRHS SCoo
'Warsaw' (Ta)	COtt NLar SWCr
'Warszawska Nike' (EL) ♀H6	CLng CMac CRHN ELan EPfP LBMP LRHS MAsh MBri MGos NTay SCoo SLim SPer SPoG
'Warwickshire Rose' (M)	CFlo CLng CMac CRHN CSPN CTri CWGN ELan LRHS MAsh MWat NHaw NTay SLim SPoG SWCr WHar
'Wedding Day' (EL)	CFlo NLar NTay
'Wee Willie Winkie' (M)	LRHS SCoo
'Westerplatte' (EL)	CFlo CLng CRHN CSPN CWGN EPfP MBri MGos NHaw NTay SLim SMDP SPoG SWCr WHar
'Whirligig' (A)	CSPN
§ 'White Columbine' (A) ♀H6	ELan LRHS MBri NTay SDix SLim SPer SPoG
'White Lady' (A/d)	NHaw
'White Magic'PBR (Vt)	CRHN
§ 'White Moth' (A/d)	CSPN ELan MAsh NHaw NHol SLim SPoG
'White Satin' (A)	EPfP LRHS SRms SWCr
'White Swan' (A/d)	CSPN MAsh MBri NHol NLar SCoo
'White Wings' (A/d)	CFlo
'Will Goodwin' (EL) ♀H6	CBcs CLng COtt CWCL ELan EPfP LRHS MBri SLim SRms
'William Kennett' (EL)	ELan EPfP IBoy LRHS MBri MJak SMDP
williamsii	SMDP
'Willy' (A)	CBcs CLng COtt CSPN EBee ELan EPfP LBMP LRHS MAsh MBri MGos MMuc MSwo NLar NTay SDix SLim SPer SRms SWCr
Wisley = 'Evipo001'PBR (Vt) ♀H6	CBcs CLng CSPN EPfP LRHS MBri MGos NLar NTay SLim SLon SWCr
'Xerxes' misapplied	see *C.* 'Elsa Späth'
'Yatsuhashi' ambig.	CCon
'Yellow Queen' Holland	see *C. patens* 'Manshuu Ki'
'Yellow Queen' Lundell/ Treasures	see *C.* 'Moonlight'
§ 'Yukikomachi' (EL)	CSPN NHaw NTay
yunnanensis	WPGP
'Yvonne Hay'	SMDP
Zara = 'Evipo062'	ELan LRHS LSqu NTay SLon SPoG SWCr
'Zephyr' (Vt)	NHaw

Clematopsis see *Clematis*

Clementsia see *Rhodiola*

Cleome (*Cleomaceae*)

hassleriana 'Helen Campbell' ♀H2	CSpe
Senorita Rosalita = 'Inncleosr'PBR	NPri

Clerodendrum (*Lamiaceae*)

bungei	Widely available
- PAB 8953 **new**	LEdu
- 'Pink Diamond' (v)	CCCN CDoC CWGN ELan EPfP EThi EUJe EWes LRHS LSou MGos MPkF NLar SKHP SLim SMDP SPer SPoG SWvt
§ ***chinense*** var. ***chinense*** (d) ♀H1b	CCCN CHll
- 'Pleniflorum'	see *C. chinense* var. *chinense*
colebrookianum B&SWJ 6651	WCru
fragrans var. ***pleniflorum***	see *C. chinense* var. *chinense*
myricoides 'Ugandense' ♀H1b	CCCN CHll CRHN EShb MOWG SMrm WSFF
philippinum	see *C. chinense* var. *chinense*
speciosissimum	MOWG
aff. ***subscaposum*** WWJ 11735	WCru
thomsoniae ♀H1b	EShb WSFF
trichotomum	CBcs CDul CEnd CExl CLnd CMCN CSam CSpe CTho CTri EPfP EUJe IArd LRHS NLar SLim SLon SPer WBor
- var. ***fargesii*** ♀H4	Widely available
- - 'Carnival' (v) ♀H4	CAbP CBcs CCCN CDul CExl CMac EBee ELan EPfP ETwe EWes LRHS MAsh MBri MGos NLar SChF SKHP SLim SMDP SMad SPer SPoG SWvt WCot WPat
- 'Purple Blaze'	EPfP ETwe
- 'Purple Haze'	CJun NLar
- 'Shiro'	WCru
wallichii	CSpe EShb

Clethra ✿ (*Clethraceae*)

acuminata	GKin NLar
alnifolia	CBcs CDul CExl CMHG MPkF SRms WCFE WCot WFar
- 'Anne Bidwell'	EWTr MBlu NLar
- 'Creel's Calico' (v)	NLar
- 'Fern Valley Pink'	CCCN CMac EBee ELon GKin LLHF LRHS NLar SRms WFar
- 'Hokie Pink'	GKin NLar
- 'Hummingbird' ♀H5	CCCN CDoC CEnd CExl CMac ELan EPfP GKin IDee LRHS MAsh MBlu NLar NPCo SChF SLim SPad SPoG SSpi SWvt WFar WSHC

- 'Paniculata' — CDoC ELon EPfP LRHS MMuc MNHC SBod WBor
- 'Pink Spires' — CAco CDoC CExl CWld ECrN EWTr GKin LSou MMHG MMuc MRav NLar SCob SCoo SEle SMad
- 'Rosea' — CTri GKin GQui MMHG MPkF
- 'Ruby Spice' 🏆H5 — CBcs CCCN CEnd CExl CJun CMac EBee ELan ELon GBin GGGa GKin IDee LAst LRHS MAsh MBlu NLar SLim SPer SPoG SWvt
- 'September Beauty' — CJun NLar
- 'Sixteen Candles' — GGGa GKin NLar
- Vanilla Spice = 'Caleb' **new** — NLar

arborea — CBcs NLar
barbinervis 🏆H5 — CBcs CDoC CExl CTho EPfP GGGa GKin IDee IVic LRHS MBlu MGil NLar SPer WPGP WSHC
- B&SWJ 11562 — WCru

delavayi Franch. — CBcs CCCN CDoC CFil EBee EPfP GGGa GQui IDee NLar SKHP SSpi
- SBEC 1513 — CExl
- Stone's hardy strain — SKHP

fargesii — CExl CFil EPfP GKin NLar
luzmariae **new** — CFil
mexicana — CFil
monostachya — CExl GGGa NLar
pringlei — CFil NLar WPGP WSHC
tomentosa 'Cottondale' — CJun NLar

Cleyera (*Pentaphylacaceae*)

fortunei — see *C. japonica* 'Fortunei'
- 'Variegata' — see *C. japonica* 'Fortunei'

japonica — CDoC
- § 'Fortunei' (v) — CCCN CMHG CMac ETwe LRHS SHil SSta
- var. ***japonica*** — WPGP
- 'Tricolor' (v) — CBcs CDoC MPkF

Clianthus ✿ (*Papilionaceae*)

maximus — GDun
§ ***puniceus*** 🏆H3 — CAbb CBcs CExl CHel CHll CMHG CPom CSpe CTsd EBee EPfP GDun IBoy LRHS MOWG NSoo SEle SGbt SIgm SPer SPlb SPoG SWvt WCot WSHC
- § 'Albus' 🏆H3 — CBcs CExl CHEx CHGN CHel CHll CSpe EBee EPfP GDun IBoy IDee LRHS MGil MOWG SPer SPoG SWvt WCot
- 'Flamingo' — see *C. puniceus* 'Roseus'
- 'Kaka King' — CBcs EWes MGil SPoG
- 'Red Admiral' — see *C. puniceus*
- 'Red Cardinal' — see *C. puniceus*
- § 'Roseus' 🏆H3 — CBcs CExl EPfP EUJe IVic LRHS SPer SPoG WCot
- 'White Heron' — see *C. puniceus* 'Albus'

Clinopodium (*Lamiaceae*)

ascendens — see *Calamintha ascendens*
calamintha — see *Calamintha nepeta*
grandiflorum — see *Calamintha grandiflora*
§ ***vulgare*** — CArn CHab CSpe EBee MHer MNHC NMir WJek WMoo WOut

Clintonia (*Liliaceae*)

andrewsiana — ECho EWes WCru
udensis — WCru
- HWJK 2339 from Nepal — WCru

umbellulata — GCal WCru
uniflora — EBee ECho EWes

Clivia ✿ (*Amaryllidaceae*)

caulescens — WCot
gardenii — WCot
gardenii* × *miniata — WCot
miniata 🏆H1c — CAbb CBcs CTca CTsd ECho EWoo SAdn SMrm SPlb SRms WCot
- 'Arturo's Yellow' **new** — WCot
- 'Ato-Shan' **new** — WCot
- 'Aurea' — CSpe EWoo
- Belgian hybrids **new** — WCot
- 'Beverley's Delight' — WCot
- broad-leaf, variegated (v) **new** — WCot
- broad-leaved — EWoo
- broad-leaved, dark orange-flowered — EWoo
- var. ***citrina*** 🏆H1c — CTca ECho LAma WCot
- 'Citrina Spider' — CFwr
- Daruma Group — WCot
- green-centred — EWoo WCot
- hybrids — SEND
- 'Light of Buddha' (v) — WCot
- 'Orange Spider' — CFwr
- pastel shades — CFwr EWoo WCot
- 'Striata' (v) — WCot
- 'Vico Yellow' — CTsd EWoo
- 'Wide Leaf Monk' — WCot

nobilis 🏆H1c — SPlb WCot
robusta — WCot
'San Marcus Yellow' × 'Solomone Yellow' — WCot

Clusia (*Clusiaceae*)

rosea — CCCN

Clytostoma (*Bignoniaceae*)

§ ***calystegioides*** — CCCN CHll CRHN

Cneorum (*Rutaceae*)

tricoccon — SKHP

Cnicus (*Asteraceae*)

§ ***benedictus*** — CArn

Cnidium (*Apiaceae*)

officinale — GPoy

Cobaea (*Polemoniaceae*)

pringlei — CRHN WPGP WSHC
- CD&R 1323 — WCot

scandens 🏆H2 — CCCN CDTJ CSpe ELan EShb SPer
- f. ***alba*** — CSpe EShb SPer

cobnut see *Corylus avellana*

Coccoloba (*Polygonaceae*)

uvifera — SPlb

Cocculus (*Menispermaceae*)

laurifolius — ETwe EUJe
§ ***orbiculatus*** — CExl
- B&SWJ 535 — WCru

trilobus — see *C. orbiculatus*

Cochlearia (*Brassicaceae*)

armoracia see *Armoracia rusticana*
officinalis CArn ELau MHer WHer

Cocos (*Arecaceae*)

plumosa see *Syagrus romanzoffiana*
weddelliana see *Lytocaryum weddellianum*

Codonanthe (*Gesneriaceae*)

gracilis WDib
'Paula' WDib

× *Codonatanthus* (*Gesneriaceae*)

'Golden Tambourine' WDib
'Sunset' WDib
'Tambourine' WDib

Codonopsis (*Campanulaceae*)

HWJK 2105 from Nepal WCru
affinis HWJCM 70 WCru
- HWJK 2151 WCru
benthamii GWJ 9352 WCru
bhutanica GKev
cardiophylla EBee EWld GCal NLar
clematidea CCon CSpe EBee ECha ECho EPfP EWld GCal GKev MNHC MNrw NEgg NLar NSum SGSe SPhx SPlb SWvt WWEG
- 'Lilac Eyes' SGSe WWtn
convolvulacea misapplied see *C. grey-wilsonii*
- 'Alba' see *C. grey-wilsonii* 'Himal Snow'
- Forrest's form see *C. forrestii* Diels
convolvulacea ambig. GKev
convolvulacea Kurz var. **hirsuta** B&SWJ 7812 WCru
'Dangshen' see *C. pilosula*
dicentrifolia NLar
- HWJCM 267 WCru
forrestii misapplied see *C. grey-wilsonii*
§ **forrestii** Diels CPne ECho EWld NHar
- BWJ 7776 WCru
- BWJ 7847 WCru
§ **grey-wilsonii** ♀H5 CAby CBro CCon CPne ECho GEdr GKev MNrw NSum
- B&SWJ 7532 WCru
§ - 'Himal Snow' CAby CPne ECho EWld GEdr WCru
inflata GWJ 9442 WCru
javanica FMWJ 13329 **new** WCru
kawakamii EPot
- B&SWJ 1592 WCru
- RWJ 10007 WCru
§ **lanceolata** CAby EWld GCal SBrt SGSe
- B&SWJ 562 WCru
meleagris ambig. CCon
mollis ECho NSum
nepalensis Grey-Wilson see *C. grey-wilsonii*
ovata CPne NBro NLar SPhx
§ **pilosula** EWld GKev GPoy SBrt SGSe WSHC
- BWJ 7910 WCru
§ **rotundifolia** var. **angustifolia** WCru
- var. **grandiflora** EWld GKev
silvestris see *C. pilosula*
subsimplex BWJ 7502 WCru
tangshen misapplied see *C. rotundifolia* var. *angustifolia*
tangshen Oliv. CArn GKev WSHC
ussuriensis see *C. lanceolata*
vinciflora CPne ECho EWld GEdr GKev WAbe
viridiflora CCon WCru
viridis HWJK 2435 WCru

Coffea (*Rubiaceae*)

arabica CCCN SPlb SPre

coffee see *Coffea*

Coincya (*Brassicaceae*)

wrightii PJL 20098 CHid

Colchicum (*Colchicaceae*)

agrippinum ♀H4 CAvo CBro CTal CTca ECha ECho EPot GBin MRav NBir NRog NRya WHoo WThu
'Antares' ECha NRog
atropurpureum ECho LAma
'Autumn Herald' ECho ELan GKev LAma NRog
'Autumn Queen' ♀H5 CTca ECho GKev NRog
§ **autumnale** CArn CAvo CBro CHab ECho EPot GKev GPoy LAma NRog NRya SDeJ WShi
- 'Alboplenum' CTca ECho ERCP GKev LAma NBir NRog
- 'Album' CAvo CBro CTca ECho EPot ERCP GKev LAma NBir SPer WShi
- 'Atropurpureum' ECho EPot NRog
- var. **major** hort. see *C. byzantinum* Ker Gawl.
- var. **minor** hort. see *C. autumnale*
§ - 'Nancy Lindsay' ♀H5 CBro CTal ECho EPot NRog WCot WShi XEll
- 'Pannonicum' see *C. autumnale* 'Nancy Lindsay'
§ - 'Pleniflorum' (d) ECho GKev LAma NRog
* - **roseum** ECho
- 'Roseum Plenum' see *C. autumnale* 'Pleniflorum'
baytopiorum ECho GKev NRog
- from Turkey ECho
'Beaconsfield' NRog
§ **bivonae** ECho EPot
- 'Apollo' ECho GKev NRog
§ **boissieri** ECho
bornmuelleri misapplied see *C. speciosum* var. *bornmuelleri* hort.
bornmuelleri Freyn CBro ECho EPot GKev LAma NRog
bowlesianum see *C. bivonae*
byzantinum ambig. NRog
§ **byzantinum** Ker Gawl. ♀H5 CBro EPot GKev LAma NBir SDeJ
- **album** see *C. byzantinum* 'Innocence'
§ - 'Innocence' ECho EPot GKev NRog WCot
cilicicum ECho LAma NRog
- Bowles's form ECho
- 'Purpureum' CTca ECho EPot GKev LAma NRog
'Conquest' see *C.* 'Glory of Heemstede'
corsicum ECho GKev WThu
cupanii ECho GKev
- var. **pulverulentum** ECho NRog
davisii CTal ECho NRog
'Dick Trotter' ECho NRog SDeJ
'Disraeli' ECho EPot GKev NRog
falcifolium ECho NRog
§ **giganteum** ECho LAma NRog SPer
§ 'Glory of Heemstede' ECho GKev NRog WCot
'Gracia' NRog
graecum ECho
'Harlekijn' ECho EPot ERCP NRog
hungaricum ECho EPot NRog
- f. **albiflorum** ECho EPot GKev NRog

	- 'Valentine'	EPot
	- 'Velebit Star'	ECho GKev NRog
	illyricum	see *C. giganteum*
	'Jaroslavna' **new**	NRog
	'Jochem Hof'	LEdu NRog
	kesselringii	GKev NRog
	laetum misapplied	see *C. parnassicum*
	laetum Stev.	NRog
	'Lilac Bedder'	ECho NRog
	'Lilac Wonder'	ECho ELan EPfP GKev LAma MRav NRog SDeJ SEND WCot
	longifolium	see *C. neapolitanum*
	lusitanum	LAma
	luteum	NRog
	macrophyllum	LAma NRog
	minutum	ECho NRog
	munzurense	NRog
§	***neapolitanum***	NRog
	'Neptun' **new**	NRog
	parlatoris	ECho NRog
§	***parnassicum***	ECha ECho NRog WThu
	'Pink Goblet' ♀H5	CBro LAma
	'Poseidon'	ECho NRog
	procurrens	see *C. boissieri*
	pusillum	GKev NRog
	'Rosy Dawn' ♀H5	CBro CTca ECha ECho GKev NRog
	sfikasianum	ECho
	sibthorpii	see *C. bivonae*
	speciosum ♀H5	CAvo CBro ECho ELan EPot GKev LAma NBir NRog
	- 'Album' ♀H5	CAvo CBro ECha ECho EPfP EPot ERCP GAbr GKev LAma NBir NRog SDeJ
	- 'Atrorubens' ♀H5	ECha ECho GKev
I	- var. ***bornmuelleri*** hort.	ECho
	- 'Dombai' **new**	NRog
	- var. ***illyricum*** hort.	see *C. giganteum*
	szovitsii 'Tivi'	ECho NRog
	- white-flowered	ECho
	tenorei ♀H4	CTal ECho EPot GKev LAma NBir NRog
	'The Giant'	CBro ECho EPfP EPot GKev LAma NRog SDeJ
	triphyllum	NRog
	'Violet Queen'	ECho EPot GAbr GKev LAma NRog
	'Waterlily' (d) ♀H5	CAvo CBro CTca CWCL ECho ELan EPfP EPot ERCP GBin GKev LAma NBir NRog SDeJ WCot WHoo
	'William Dykes'	ECho NRog
	'Zephyr'	ECho LAma

Coleonema (*Rutaceae*)

§	***pulchellum***	CCCN CHEx CHel CSpe SVen
	pulchrum misapplied	see *C. pulchellum*
	'Sunset Gold'	COtt CSpe SPlb

Coleus see *Solenostemon, Plectranthus*

Colignonia (*Nyctaginaceae*)

	ovalifolia B&SWJ 10644	WCru

Colletia (*Rhamnaceae*)

	armata	see *C. hystrix*
	cruciata	see *C. paradoxa*
§	***hystrix***	CBcs CMac CTri CTsd ELon IVic NLar SArc SMad
	- RCB RA S-3	WCot
	- 'Rosea'	CMac GCal MBlu SKHP
§	***paradoxa***	CBcs CCCN CDoC ELan EPfP LAst SArc SKHP SMad SPoG
	paradoxa* × *spinosissima	SMad
	ulicina	SVen

Collinsonia (*Lamiaceae*)

	canadensis	CArn LEdu

Collomia (*Polemoniaceae*)

	grandiflora	WCot

Colocasia (*Araceae*)

	affinis var. ***jeningsii***	CCon CDTJ
	antiquorum	see *C. esculenta*
§	***esculenta*** ♀H1a	CCon CDTJ CHEx EBee EUJe MSKA NLos SPlb XBlo
	- 'Black Coral' **new**	SPad
	- 'Black Magic'	CBct CDTJ CHel CHll ECtt EUJe IKil LAma LRHS NSoo SBig SDix SPad XBlo
	- 'Blue Hawaii'	LRHS
	- burgundy-stemmed	CDTJ LAma SBig
	- 'Diamond Head'	CWGN ESwi EUJe LRHS
	- 'Fontanesii'	CDTJ CHEx EUJe MPkF
	- 'Hawaiian Eye'	LRHS
	- 'Hilo Bay'	CHel ESwi LRHS
	- 'Hilo Beauty'	XBlo
	- 'Illustris'	CDTJ LLWG
	- 'Mammoth' **new**	EUJe
	- 'Pineapple Princess' (v)	ECtt LRHS
	- 'Ruffles'	EUJe
	- 'Sangria'	EUJe
	fallax	CCon CHEx
	formosana B&SWJ 6909	WCru
	gaoligongensis	CCon
	gigantea	CDTJ
	- 'Thailand Giant' **new**	EUJe
	'Himalayan Dragon'	SKHP

Colquhounia (*Lamiaceae*)

	coccinea	CArn CHel CHll CMHG CSde GGal MBlu MGil MRav NLar SBrt SLon WSHC
	- Sch 2458	WPGP
§	- var. ***mollis*** B&SWJ 7222	WCru
	- var. ***vestita*** misapplied	see *C. coccinea* var. *mollis*
	- var. ***vestita*** ambig.	CBcs CTsd EBee EPfP LRHS SEND

Columnea (*Gesneriaceae*)

	'Aladdin's Lamp'	WDib
	× ***banksii*** ♀H1c	WDib
§	'Broget Stavanger' (v) ♀H1c	WDib
	'Chanticleer' ♀H1c	WDib
I	'Firedragon'	WDib
	'Gavin Brown'	WDib
	gloriosa	EBak
	'Inferno'	WDib
	'Katsura'	WDib
	'Merkur'	WDib
I	'Midnight Lantern'	WDib
	'Rising Sun'	WDib
	schiedeana	WDib
	'Sherbert'	WDib
	'Stavanger' ♀H1c	WDib
	'Stavanger Variegated'	see *C.* 'Broget Stavanger'

Colutea (*Papilionaceae*)

arborescens	CBcs CExl ELan LRHS MBlu MGil MGos MMuc NWea SEND SPer SPlb SPoG
cilicica	EGFP
× ***media***	CPom CTsd ECre
- 'Copper Beauty'	CBcs ELan LRHS NLar SPer WPat
orientalis	CCCN CSde

Colvillea (*Caesalpiniaceae*)

racemosa	SPlb

Comarum see *Potentilla*

Combretum (*Combretaceae*)

fruticosum	CCCN

Commelina (*Commelinaceae*)

coelestis	see *C. tuberosa* Coelestis Group
dianthifolia	LEdu SRms WPtf
- 'Electric Blue'	ELan LRHS SVic
robusta	CSpe WCot
tuberosa	MAvo NWad
- B&SWJ 10353	WCru
- blue-flowered	SDeJ
§ - Coelestis Group	CAby CSpe ECha MPie SDys SRms WKif WSHC
- - 'Sleeping Beauty'	MSpe WHea
virginica L.	SMad

Conandron (*Gesneriaceae*)

ramondoides B&SWJ 8929	WCru

Conanthera (*Tecophilaeaceae*)

campanulata	EBee

Conicosia (*Aizoaceae*)

pugioniformis	SVen

Coniogramme (*Pteridaceae*)

japonica	WFib

Conium (*Apiaceae*)

maculatum	CArn
- 'Golden Nemesis' (v)	WCot

Conoclinium (*Asteraceae*)

§ ***coelestinum***	CBod EBee SBrt XLum

Conopodium (*Apiaceae*)

majus	SRms WOut WShi

Consolida (*Ranunculaceae*)

ajacis Giant Imperial Series **new**	SVic

Convallaria ✿ (*Asparagaceae*)

japonica	see *Ophiopogon jaburan*
keiskei	EPPr MAvo WHil WWEG
I - 'Marginata' (v)	WCot
majalis ♀H7	Widely available
- 'Albostriata' (v)	CBct CFwr CLAP CRow CTal CUse ECho EHoe ELan EPPr EUJe GAbr GKev GMaP LPal LRHS MHol MNrw MRav NBir NSti SGSe WCot WHer WHoo WPnP
- 'Berlin Giant'	NRya SDeJ
- 'Blush'	CAvo
- 'Bordeaux'	CBro CExl CNec EBee EPPr MHer NLar NPCo WCot
- 'Bridal Choice'	EBee ELan GBin GKev NLar
- 'Dorien'	CBct CBre EPPr IMou
- 'Flore Pleno' (d)	SGSe WWEG
- 'Géant de Fortin'	CAvo CBct CBro CCon CExl CLAP ECho EPot GCal GEdr MMoz MRav NBir NLar NMyG SBch WCot WWEG
- 'Gerard Debureaux'	see *C. majalis* 'Green Tapestry'
- 'Gold Leaf'	CAvo
§ - 'Green Tapestry' (v)	CBct CRow MAvo
- 'Haldon Grange' (v)	CDes CLAP EPPr
- 'Hardwick Hall' (v)	CBct CCse CExl CLAP CRow CTal EBee ECho EHoe EPot GEdr GKev NMyG WAul WCot WWEG XEll
- 'Hitschberger Riesenperle'	XLum
- 'Hofheim' (v)	CLAP CRow LEdu MAvo WCot WHal WWEG
- 'Prolificans'	CBct CCon CCse CLAP CTal EBee ECho ECtt EPPr EPfP GKev LSou MAvo MRav NBir NLar NSti WCot WHil WPnP
- var. ***rosea***	Widely available
- 'Rosea Plena' (d) **new**	EWoo
- 'Silbercconfolis' (v) **new**	WCot
- 'Variegata' (v)	CAvo EPot LBMP MLHP NMyG SBch SMad WThu WWEG
- 'Vic Pawlowski's Gold' (v)	CBct CDes CExl CLAP CMac ELon EPPr GEdr MAvo MMoz NSla WPGP WSHC
transcaucasica	EBee GKev

Convolvulus (*Convolvulaceae*)

althaeoides	CFis CMea ECho ELan EPri SEND SPhx WSHC
§ - subsp. ***tenuissimus***	CSpe EWes
§ ***boissieri***	EPot WAbe XEll XSen
cantabrica	LRHS MMuc SGSe SPhx XLum XSen
chilensis	CCCN
cneorum ♀H4	Widely available
- 'Snow Angel'	CEnd LRHS LSou SWvt
compactus	XSen
elegantissimus	see *C. althaeoides* subsp. *tenuissimus*
humilis	ECho
lineatus	ECho EWes
mauritanicus	see *C. sabatius*
nitidus	see *C. boissieri*
§ ***sabatius*** ♀H3	CCCN CHEx CHel CSam CSde CTri ECho ECtt ELan EPfP EPot EWoo LAst MCot SEND SLim SPer SPlb SPoG SVen SWvt WCFE XLum XSen
- dark-flowered	CCCN CSpe ECho SMrm
- 'Moroccan Beauty' PBR	CSpe ECtt LSou
thunbergii **new**	WCot

× *Cooperanthes* see *Zephyranthes*

Cooperia see *Zephyranthes*

Coprosma (*Rubiaceae*)

acerosa 'Hawera'	CBcs
- 'Live Wire' (f)	ECou
atropurpurea (f)	ECou
- (m)	ECou

'Autumn Orange' (f)	ECou
'Autumn Prince' (m)	ECou
baueri misapplied	see *C. repens*
'Beatson's Gold' (f/v)	CBcs CDTJ CExl CHGN CHll CTsd ELan EShb IVic LRHS SEND SLim SWvt WGrn WSHC
'Black Cloud'	CBcs LRHS
'Blue Pearls' (f)	ECou
'Blue Skies'	NHar WThu
brunnea	ECou
- (f)	WThu
- (m)	WThu
- 'Blue Beauty' (f)	ECou
- 'Violet Fleck' (f)	ECou
'Bruno' (m)	ECou
'Cappuccino'	CBcs EShb
cheesemanii (f)	ECou
'Coppershine'	CExl
× ***cunninghamii*** (f)	ECou
× ***cunninghamii*** × ***macrocarpa*** (m)	ECou
depressa	ECou WThu
- 'Orange Spread' (f)	ECou
'Evening Glow'^{PBR} (f/v)	CCCN CDTJ CDoC CHel CSBt CWSG EAEE ELan EShb EUJe IVic LRHS MAsh MBri MGos NSoo SEle SHil SLim SRms WHar
'Fire Burst'^{PBR} (f/v)	CBcs CCCN CWSG EAEE EBee ELan EShb EUJe LBuc LRHS MAsh MBri MGos SHil SLim SLon SRms WHar
grandifolia	ECou
'Green Globe'	CHll
'Hinerua' (f)	ECou
'Inferno' **new**	EMil LRHS SEle SHil
'Karo Red'^{PBR} (v)	CBcs ELan SLim SRms
I × ***kirkii*** 'Kirkii' (f)	CHll
- 'Variegata' (f/v)	CBcs CSde CTsd EBee ECou EPfP EShb LRHS SEND SLim
'Lemon and Lime'^{PBR} (v)	CDoC EBee ELan EUJe LBuc LRHS MAsh MGos NSoo SEle SHil SPoG SRms WHar
'Lemon Drops' (f)	ECou
macrocarpa (f)	ECou
- (m)	ECou
parviflora red-fruited (f)	ECou
'Pearly Queen' (f)	ECou
petriei	ECou WThu
- 'White Pearls'	WThu
propinqua (f)	ECou
- (m)	ECou
- var. ***latiuscula*** (m)	ECou
- - (f)	ECou
quadrifida	ECou
'Rainbow Surprise'^{PBR} (v)	CCCN CExl CSBt EAEE ELan LRHS MBri MGos NEgg NSoo SHil SLim SRms WHar
§ ***repens***	CBcs CExl EShb SPlb SVen
- (f)	ECou
- (m)	ECou
- 'County Park Plum' (v)	CBcs ECou
- 'County Park Red'	ECou
- 'Exotica' (f/v)	ECou
- 'Marble King' (m/v)	ECou
- 'Marble Queen' (m/v) ♀H2	CBcs ECou
- 'Midnight Martini' (v)	LRHS SHil SPoG
- 'Orangeade' (f)	ECou
- 'Pacific Lady'	ECou
- Pacific Night = 'Hutpac'^{PBR} (m)	CDoC CSBt ECou ELan EUJe IVic LBuc LRHS MAsh MBri MGos NPri SHil SLon
- Pacific Sunset = 'Jwncopps' (v)	LRHS MAsh NSoo SEle SLon
- 'Painter's Palette' (m)	ECou SVen
- 'Picturata' (m/v) ♀H2	ECou EShb
- 'Pina Colada'^{PBR} (v)	CSBt LBuc LRHS SEle SHil SPoG
- 'Pink Splendour' (m/v)	CBcs ECou
- 'Rangatiri' (f)	ECou
- 'Variegata' (m/v)	ECou
rigida	ECou
- 'Ann' (f)	ECou
- 'Tan' (m)	ECou
robusta	ECou
- 'Tim Blunt' (m)	ECou
- 'Variegata' (m/v)	ECou
'Roy's Red' (m)	EShb LRHS SEND SPoG
rugosa (f)	CExl ECou
'Scarlet O'Hara' **new**	SEle
'Snowberry' (f)	ECou
'Tequila Sunrise'	LBuc LRHS NEgg SEle SHil
'Translucent Gold' (f)	ECou
'Violet Drops' (f)	ECou
virescens (f)	ECou
'Walter Brockie'	CHGN CHll CSde

Coptis (*Ranunculaceae*)

japonica	GPoy WCru
- var. ***dissecta***	WCru
- var. ***major***	CDes EBee WCru WSHC
omeiensis	WCru
quinquefolia	CTal
- B&SWJ 1677	WCru
ramosa B&SWJ 6000	WCru
- B&SWJ 6030	WCru
trifolia	WCru

Corallospartium see *Carmichaelia*

Cordyline ✿ (*Asparagaceae*)

australis ♀H3	Widely available
- 'Albertii' (v) ♀H3	CCCN MBri SArc SEND
- 'Atlantic Green'	LRHS MGos SHil
- 'Atropurpurea'	CCCN MWat
- 'Black Night'	CCCN
- Burgundy Spire = 'Jel01'^{PBR}	EPfP LBuc LRHS
- 'Claret'	CBcs COtt
- 'Coffee Cream'	CCCN
- 'Karo Kiri'	SMad
- 'Olive Fountain'	CCCN
- 'Peko'^{PBR}	CCCN
- 'Pink Champagne'	CCCN ELan LRHS MGos MSwo SCob SLim
- Pink Passion = 'Seipin'^{PBR}	CCCN EPfP LBuc LRHS MBri NSoo
- 'Pink Stripe' (v)	CCCN CDoC ELan EPfP MBri SLim SWvt
- 'Purple Heart'	CCCN MSwo
- Purpurea Group	CBcs CDTJ ELan LRHS MGos SEND SPer SPlb WFar
- 'Red Sensation'	CCCN CHEx LRHS SWvt
- 'Sparkler'	CCCN EPfP LRHS MBri MGos SCob
- 'Sundance' ♀H3	CBcs CBod CDoC COtt EPfP LRHS MAsh MBri MGos MSwo NPer SCob SEND SLim SPoG SRms SWvt

- 'Torbay Dazzler' (v) ♀H3	CAbb CBcs CBod CDoC CHEx COtt CSBt ELan EPfP IVic LPal LRHS MAsh MBri MGos MJak NEgg NPla NPri SCob SEND SHil SLim SPer SPoG SWvt WFar
- 'Torbay Red' ♀H3	CCCN CDoC CMac EPfP LRHS MAsh MBri NPri SPer SWvt
- 'Torbay Sunset'	CCCN LRHS
- 'Variegata' (v)	MWat
'Autumn'	CCCN
banksii	CTsd IDee
'Cardinal'PBR	CBcs
'Cherry Sensation' (v)	CBod LBuc LRHS SHil
'Dark Star'	CCCN CDTJ SLim
'Eurostar'	CCCN
'Eurostripe'PBR	LRHS MBri
Festival Grass = 'Jurred'	LRHS
'Firecracker'	CCCN LRHS MBri SHil
fruticosa 'Red Edge' ♀H1b	XBlo
§ ***indivisa***	CBcs CBrP CCCN CDTJ CTsd EUJe IDee NLos SArc SPlb WPGP
kaspar	CCCN CTsd
obtecta	CCCN CTsd
- bronze-leaved	CTsd
pumilio	LRHS
'Purple Sensation'	CBcs CCCN LRHS
'Purple Tower' ♀H3	MJak
'Red Bush'	XBlo
'Red Heart'	CCCN LRHS NEgg
'Red Star'	CAbb CBcs CCCN CEnd COtt CSBt CWGN CWSG EPfP LPal LRHS MBri MJak MSwo NPer SCob SHil SPoG SWvt WFar
Renegade = 'Tana'PBR	LRHS NPri
'Southern Splendour'	CCCN EAEE ELan EPfP ESwi LBuc LRHS MBri MGos NPri SHil SPoG
§ ***stricta***	CHEx
'Sunrise' (v)	CEnd CWGN EUJe LRHS MBri SHil
terminalis	see *C. fruticosa*

Coreopsis (*Asteraceae*)

'Astolat'	CBod EAEE EPla LSou MRav SPer
auriculata Cutting Gold	see *C.* 'Schnittgold'
- 'Elfin Gold'	EDAr
- 'Nana'	MNrw NBre
- 'Superba'	MRav
- 'Zamphir'	EBee EPfP MNrw WCot
'Autumn Blush'	NLar
'Baby Gold'	see *C. lanceolata* 'Sonnenkind' (unblotched)
Baby Sun	see *C.* 'Sonnenkind' (red-blotched)
'Calypso' (v)	EWes LBuc LRHS SMad
'Cherry Pie' **new**	SCob
'Citrine' **new**	CWGN NPri WHlf
'Cosmic Eye' (Big Bang Series)	NCGa
'Cranberry Ice'	CWGN NLar
'Desert Coral' **new**	WHlf
'Dream'	SRkn
'Fool's Gold' **new**	EBee
'Fruit Punch'	LRHS MPro
'Full Moon'PBR (Big Bang Series)	CBod NLar SMrm STPC WFar XLum
'Galaxy' (Big Bang Series) **new**	MAsh
'Garnet'	WHlf
'Golden Pompom'PBR (d)	EBee LSou
grandiflora	NEgg SHar
- 'Bernwode' (v)	CMac LSou NLar SWvt
- 'Domino'	EAJP EBee LSun
- 'Early Sunrise' ♀H5	COtt CSBt EBee ECtt EPfP EShb IBoy LPot LRHS MAsh MBri MNHC NBir NGBl NPer SGbt SPoG SWvt WHar WWEG XLum
- Flying Saucers = 'Walcoreop'PBR	EPfP LBuc LRHS SCoo SPoG
- 'Heliot'	LPot MBri
- 'Illico'	EBee MBri
- 'Mayfield Giant'	CCon CSBt EBee ELan EPla MNrw NPri SPer SRms SWvt WHrl
- 'Presto' (d)	CNor SPad
- 'Rising Sun'	ELan MBri NPri
- 'Sunburst'	EPfP NBre XLum
- 'Sunfire'	LRHS MBri MHer SHil
- 'Sunray'	CBcs CDoC CSBt ECtt EPfP EPla LRHS MBri MGos NGdn NPri SHil SMrm SPlb SPoG SRms SWvt WCAu WMoo XLum
- 'Tetra Riesen'	NBre
'Jethro Tull'	EBee LSou SPoG
'Jive'PBR (Coloropsis Series)	CSpe CWGN SCob
lanceolata	LPal NBre
- 'Goldfink'	MRav SRms
- 'Goldteppich'	EBee EPfP LRHS
- 'Little Sundial'	LSou MBri
§ - 'Sonnenkind' (unblotched)	GMaP XLum
- 'Walter'	EPla LSou MAsh MNrw NDov NEgg SPoG WCot WGwG WWEG XLum
'Limbo' (Coloropsis Series)	SCob
'Limerock Passion'PBR	EPfP LRHS LSou MBNS SRkn
'Limerock Ruby'PBR	CUse ECtt EPau GMaP LRHS LSou MHol SCob SPer SRkn SWvt WHar XLum
Little Penny = 'Rp1' (Pie Series) **new**	MAvo MPro
major	EBee MMuc
'Mango Punch'	CSpe MAvo MPro
maximiliani	see *Helianthus maximiliani*
'Moonlight'PBR	CUse
'Pineapple Pie' **new**	SCob
'Pink Sapphire' **new**	WHlf
'Pinwheel'	LSou WHlf
pubescens	LSou
- 'Sunshine Superman'	EBee ELan
'Pumpkin Pie' **new**	LRHS MPro SCob
rosea 'American Dream'	CBod CSBt ELan EPfP EPla GMaP LAst LRHS NBir NGdn NLar SGSe SPer SPlb SRms SWvt WCAu WGwG WMnd WRHF XLum
- 'Heaven's Gate'PBR	LAst SCob
- 'Nana'	XLum
- 'Sweet Dreams'PBR	CUse SRkn
'Route 66'PBR **new**	WFar
'Ruby Frost'	CBod MAvo MHol
'Rum Punch'PBR	CSpe
'Sangria'PBR	SPoG
§ 'Schnittgold'	NBre SHar
Solanna Golden Sphere **new**	MBri
I 'Sonnenkind' (red-blotched)	EBee LRHS NBre
'Star Cluster' (Big Bang Series)	MAvo MBri SPoG
'Sterntaler'	CCon CMea EBee ECtt ELon EPPr EPfP LRHS LSun MBri NPri SPad SPoG SWvt WWEG XLum
Sun Child	see *C.* 'Sonnenkind' (red-blotched)

	'Tequila Sunrise' (v)	MNrw
	tinctoria	CArn MNHC SRms
	tripteris	CAby ELan EPfP LPla MMuc SEND SGSe SMad SPhx WMoo XLum
	- 'Mostenveld'	EBee
	verticillata	CMac EBee ECha GCal MBrN MGos MHer MWat NLar NPer SDix SRms WCAu WHal WOld
	- Crème Brûlée = 'Crembru'PBR	ECtt EPau EWes SCoo SRkn
I	- 'Golden Gain'	ECtt EPla GBuc MArl NGdn WFar WGwG WMnd WWEG
	- 'Golden Shower'	see *C. verticillata* 'Grandiflora'
§	- 'Grandiflora' ♀H5	CBcs CBod CPrp EAEE ELan EPfP EPla GMaP LRHS MRav NGdn NHol NWad SHar SPer WFar WMnd XLum
	- 'Limerock Dream'PBR	LSou MBNS SCob SHar
	- 'Moonbeam'	Widely available
	- 'Old Timer' ♀H5	SDix
	- 'Ruby Red'	CAbP LRHS MBri
	- 'Sunbeam'	ELon SCob
	- 'Tweety'	WFar
	- 'Zagreb' ♀H6	Widely available

coriander see *Coriandrum sativum*

Coriandrum (*Apiaceae*)

*	***citratus***	ELau
	sativum	CArn ENfk GPoy MHer MNHC NPri SIde SPoG SRms
	- 'Leisure'	SVic
	- 'Santo'	ELau
	- 'Slobolt'	ELau

Coriaria ✿ (*Coriariaceae*)

	arborea	WCru
	intermedia B&SWJ 019	WCru
	japonica	ETwe NLar SVen WCru
	- B&SWJ 2833	WCru
	- subsp. ***intermedia*** B&SWJ 3877	WCru
	kingiana	WCru
§	***microphylla***	WCru
	- B&SWJ 8999	WCru
	myrtifolia	NLar WCru
	nepalensis	NLar WCru
	- BWJ 7755	WCru
	pteridoides	WCru
	ruscifolia	WCru
	- HCM 98178	WCru
	sarmentosa	WCru
	terminalis var. ***xanthocarpa***	GCal NLar WCru
	- - GWJ 9204	WCru
	- - HWJK 2112c	WCru
	thymifolia	see *C. microphylla*

Cornus ✿ (*Cornaceae*)

	alba misapplied	see *C. sericea*
	alba L.	CCVT CDoC CDul CLnd ECrN EWTr MHer MRav NHed NWea SCob SEWo SRms WMou
	- 'Argenteovariegata'	see *C. alba* 'Variegata'
	- 'Atrosanguinea' **new**	WWtn
	- 'Aurea' ♀H7	Widely available
	- Baton Rouge = 'Minbat'PBR	CNec ELon EPfP LRHS MAsh MBri SWvt
	- 'Cream Cracker'PBR (v)	EBee MRav
	- 'Elegantissima' (v) ♀H7	Widely available
	- 'Gouchaultii' (v)	CBcs CMac CRos EPfP EPla GKin LRHS MRav NLar NSoo SGol SHil SPer SRms WFar WMoo
	- 'Hessei' misapplied	see *C. sanguinea* 'Compressa'
	- 'Hessei' Hesse	WPat
	- Ivory Halo = 'Bailhalo'PBR	EAEE EBee EMil EPfP LRHS MAsh MBri MRav NLar NWea SLim SPer SPoG
	- 'Kesselringii'	Widely available
	- Red Gnome = 'Regnzam'	ELon LLHF MAsh WPat
	- 'Siberian Pearls'	ELan GKin MBlu NLar
§	- 'Sibirica' ♀H7	Widely available
	- 'Sibirica Variegata' (v) ♀H7	CDoC CMac CWSG EBee ELon EPfP GCra GKin LRHS MAsh MBlu MGos NEgg SCob SHil SLim SPer SPoG SSpi SWvt WCFE WHar WMoo
	- 'Spaethii' (v) ♀H7	Widely available
§	- 'Variegata' (v)	EPla LAst WFar
	- 'Westonbirt'	see *C. alba* 'Sibirica'
	- 'Wintersun'	NLar
	alternifolia	CBcs CCVT CMCN CTho EAEE ELan EWTr WMou
§	- 'Argentea' (v) ♀H6	Widely available
	- 'Brunette'	CJun MBlu NLar
	- Golden Shadows = 'Wstackman'PBR (v) **new**	EBee LRHS NLar SPoG WHor
	- 'Golden Surprise'	CJun
	- 'Goldfinch' (v) **new**	CJun MBlu
	- 'Moonlight' (v) **new**	CJun
	- Pinky Spot = 'Minpinky' **new**	NLar
	- 'Silver Giant' (v)	CJun GBin MBri NLar NPCo
	- 'Variegata'	see *C. alternifolia* 'Argentea'
	- 'Yellow Spring'	CJun NLar
	amomum	CAbP EBtc NLar
	- 'Lady Jane'	NLar
	angustata	SKHP
	- 'Full Moon'	CJun
	'Ascona'	CBcs CEnd CJun MBri NLar SPer SSta
	Aurora = 'Rutban' (Stellar Series)	CJun MBlu NLar SGol
	canadensis	Widely available
	candidissima Marshall	see *C. racemosa*
	capitata	CAby CBcs CDoC CDul CHel CHid CJun CMac CTsd EBee EPfP ESwi ETwe EWTr GKev IDee IMou LRHS MGos SEND SKHP WCru WFar WPGP
	- subsp. ***emeiensis***	CJun
	- 'Foreness Fog' (v)	SEND
§	Celestial = 'Rutdan' (Stellar Series)	CJun LRHS MBri NLar SGol SKHP
	'Celestial Shadow'	CBcs LBuc MBri MGos MPkF SGol
	'Centennial'	LRHS
	chinensis	ETwe SSta SWvt
	'Constellation' (Stellar Series)	CJun MAsh SGol
	controversa	CBcs CCVT CDul CLnd CMCN COtt CTri ECrN ELan EPfP EPla EWTr GBin MBlu MBri MWat NWea SEND SEWo SGol SLim SSpi SSta SWvt WHar
I	- 'Aurea'	LRHS
	- 'Candlelight'	MBlu NLar
	- 'Carpe Diem' **new**	MBri

	Name	Suppliers
§	– 'Frans Type' (v)	CJun
	– 'Green Carpet'	NLar
	– 'Laska' new	CJun MBri NLar WPGP
	– 'Lucia' new	CJun NLar
I	– 'Marginata Nord'	NLar
	– 'Pagoda'	CJun MBlu MGos NLar
	– 'Troya Dwarf'	CJun NLar
	– 'Variegata' (v) ♀H5	Widely available
	– 'Variegata' Frans type	see *C. controversa* 'Frans Type'
	– 'Winter Orange'	CJun NLar
	'Dorothy'	CJun NLar
	'Eddie's White Wonder' ♀H5	Widely available
	florida	CAco CDul CLnd CMCN CTho ESwi EWTr MMHG MMuc NWea SPer WHar
	– 'Alba Plena' (d)	CJun
	– 'Appalachian Spring'	CTho
	– 'Apple Blossom'	CJun CMac CMen NPCo
	– 'Aurea' × ***kousa***	MPkF
	– 'Autumn Gold'	SSta
	– Cherokee Brave = 'Comco No 1'	CBcs CJun CMen CTho ESwi LMil LRHS MAsh MGos NPCo SGol SPoG SSta
	– 'Cherokee Chief'	CBcs CDul CEnd CJun CMac CMen COtt CTho CTri GKin IVic MGos MPkF NPCo WHar
	– 'Cherokee Daybreak'	see *C. florida* 'Daybreak'
	– 'Cherokee Princess'	CJun LRHS MAsh SGol SPoG SSta
	– 'Cherokee Sunset'	see *C. florida* 'Sunset'
	– 'Cloud Nine'	CBcs CDoC CJun CMen CTho GKin MGos MPkF NPCo SSpi WHar
§	– 'Daybreak' (v) ♀H5	CBcs CJun ESwi LRHS MAsh MBri MGos MPkF SHil SPer WHar
	– 'Eternal Dogwood' (d)	ESwi SGol
	– 'First Lady' (v)	CJun CMac CMen NPCo SSpi
	– 'Fragrant Cloud'	SWvt
	– 'G.H. Ford' (v)	NLar
	– 'Golden Nugget' (v)	CJun
	– 'Granary Gold'	SSta
	– 'Junior Miss'	CEnd
	– 'Moonglow'	CJun
	– 'Pendula'	CJun
	– 'Pink Flame' (v)	CJun SSta
	– f. ***pluribracteata*** (d)	NLar
	– var. ***pringlei***	CJun
	– 'Purple Glory'	CJun NLar SPer
	– 'Pygmaea'	NLar
	– 'Rainbow' (v) ♀H5	CAbP CBcs CJun CMac GKin LRHS MAsh MBri MGos MPkF NWea SHil SPoG WHar
	– 'Red Giant'	CAbP CBcs CJun
	– f. ***rubra***	CBcs CLnd CTri ELan ESwi GKin LRHS MGos MMuc MRav NPCo SPer
	– 'Spring Day'	CMac CMen NPCo
	– 'Spring Song'	CJun CMac CMen NPCo
	– 'Springtime'	CJun
	– 'Stoke's Pink'	CEnd CJun CMac CMen NPCo
§	– 'Sunset' (v)	CBcs CEnd CJun CMen LRHS MAsh MGos NLar NPCo SSta SWvt WHar
	– 'Sweetwater'	CJun
	– subsp. ***urbiniana***	WPGP
	– 'Variegata'	GKin
	– 'White Cloud'	CJun
	'Gloria Birkett'	CAbP CJun ELan EPfP LMil LRHS MAsh NEgg NPCo SSpi
	'Gold Splash' (v) new	NPCo
	hemsleyi	EPla
	hessei misapplied	see *C. sanguinea* 'Compressa'
	hongkongensis	LRHS MAsh NLar WPGP
	– B&SWJ 11700	WCru
	– HWJ 1033	EPfP WPGP
	– subsp. ***gigantea*** KWJ 12225	WCru
	– subsp. ***tonkinensis*** B&SWJ 11791	WCru
	'Jerry Mundy'	CMac IVic
	'Kelsey Dwarf'	see *C. sericea* 'Kelseyi'
	'Kenwyn Clapp'	CJun
	kousa	CCVT CDoC CMCN CMHG CMac CTho ELan EPfP GKin MJak NEgg NLar SCob SPer SPlb WFar WHar WMou
	– B&SWJ 12610 from Korea	WCru
	– 'Akabana'	CJun
	– 'Akatsuki'	CJun MPkF SSta
	– 'All Summer'	CJun MBri
	– 'Angyo Issai'	NLar
	– 'Autumn Rose'	CJun EPfP NLar
	– 'Beni-fuji'	CJun NLar
	– 'Big Apple'	CJun CRos LLHF LMil LRHS MBri NLar SBir
	– 'Blue Shadow'	CJun MBri NLar SSta
	– 'Boldre Beauty'	SSpi
	– 'Bonfire' (v)	CJun MBri
	– 'Bultinck's Beauty'	NLar
	– 'Bultinck's Giant'	NLar
	– 'Bush's Pink'	CJun
	– 'Cherokee'	CJun
	– 'China Dawn' (v)	CJun MBri SSta
	– var. ***chinensis***	Widely available
	– – 'Bodnant Form'	CAby CEnd CJun CMac CTho ESwi NLar NPCo SSta WBor
	– – 'China Girl' ♀H5	Widely available
	– – 'Claudia'	EPfP IVic MBri NLar SSta
	– – 'Great Star'	LRHS MAsh
	– – 'Greta's Gold' (v)	CJun SSta
	– – 'Ikone'	IVic
	– – 'PVG' new	CJun
	– – 'Snowflake'	CJun
	– – 'Spinners'	CJun MBri
	– – 'Summer Stars'	CJun
	– – 'Tri-Splendor' new	MBri
	– – 'White Dusted' (v)	CJun EPfP MBlu NLar
	– – 'White Fountain'	EPfP LRHS MBri MPkF MPnt NLar WHar
	– – 'Wieting's Select'	CJun IDee IVic MBlu MBri MPkF NLar
	– – 'Wisley Queen' ♀H5	CAbP CJun CMHG CRos EPfP LMil LRHS MAsh SSta WPGP
	– 'Claudine'	CJun
	– 'Copacabana'[PBR] new	MBlu
	– 'Doctor Bump'	CJun
	– 'Doubloon'	CJun WPat
	– 'Dwarf Pink'	CJun
	– 'Ed Mezitt'	CJun NLar
	– 'Eline'[PBR]	MPkF NLar
	– 'Elizabeth Lustgarten'	CJun MBlu MPkF SSta
	– 'Eurostar'	IArd IVic MBri NLar
	– 'Eva'[PBR]	MPkF
	– 'Fanfare'	CJun NLar
	– 'Fernie's Favourite'	CJun MBri
	– Galilean = 'Galzam'	CJun MBri MPkF
	– 'Gay Head'	CJun
I	– 'Girard's Nana'	CJun
	– 'Gold Cup' (v)	CJun MBri MPkF SSta

	Plant	Suppliers
	- 'Gold Star' (v)	CBcs CEnd CJun CMac ELan LMil LRHS MBlu MGos MPkF NLar NPCo SPoG SSta
	- 'Greensleeves'	CJun EPfP LLHF LMil LRHS MBri SSta
	- 'Heart Throb'	CAco CJun MBri MGos NLar SGol
	- 'Highland'	CJun
	- 'John Slocock' ♀H5	CJun MBri NLar
	- 'Kim'	MBri NLar
	- 'Kreutzdame'	CJun MBlu MBri NLar
	- 'Laura'	NPCo SSta
	- 'Little Beauty'	CJun
	- 'Lizzie P'	NLar
	- 'Lustgarten Weeping'	CJun NLar
	- 'Madame Butterfly'	CJun IDee LRHS MBlu MBri NLar NPCo
	- 'Marwood Dawn'	CMHG SSta
	- 'Marwood Twilight'	CMHG
	- 'Melanie'PBR	GQue MBlu MPkF
	- 'Milky Way'	CDul CJun CLnd CMCN CTho EPfP ESwi EWTr GBin MAsh MBlu MBri MGos MPkF MRav NLar NPCo SGol SSpi WPat
	- 'Milky Way Select'	CBcs CJun LRHS MGos
	- 'Minuma'	NLar
	- 'Miss Petty'	CJun MBri MPkF NLar
	- 'Miss Satomi' ♀H5	Widely available
	- 'Moonbeam'	CJun NLar WPat
	- 'Mount Fuji'	CJun CMHG MBlu NLar SSta
	- 'National'	CJun LMil MAsh MBri MGos MPkF NLar SSta WPat
	- 'Nicole'	CDoC EPla LRHS MBri NLar WPat
	- 'Ohkan'	CJun
	- 'Pevé Limbo' (v)	CJun NLar
	- 'Pevé Satomi Compact'	MBri NLar
	- 'Pink Lips' **new**	MBri
	- 'Polywood'	CJun MBri NLar
	- 'Radiant Rose'	CJun MBri MPkF NLar SBir SSpi SSta
	- 'Rasen'	CJun NLar
	- 'Rel Whirlwind'	CJun NLar
*	- 'Robert'	MBri NLar
	- 'Rosea'	CJun
	- Samaratin = 'Samzam' (v)	CBcs CEnd CJun MBri MGos MPkF SGol SKHP SSta
	- 'Satomi Akatuki' (v)	CJun NLar
	- 'Schmetterling'	CJun MBlu NLar WPat
	- 'Silver Pheasant' (v)	MBri
	- 'Snowbird'	CJun MBri
	- 'Snowboy' (v)	CBcs CDul CEnd CJun CMac MBlu NPCo SMad
	- 'Snowflurries'	CJun MBri
	- 'Southern Cross'	CJun GBin
	- 'Square Dance'	CJun MBri
	- 'Steeple'	CJun MBri
	- 'Summer Fun' ♀H5	CJun CRos LRHS SPoG SSta
	- 'Summer Gold' (v)	MPkF
	- 'Summer Majesty'	CJun
	- 'Sunsplash' (v)	CJun SSta
	- 'Temple Jewel' (v)	CJun MBri
	- 'Teresa' **new**	MBri
	- 'Teutonia' ♀H5	CJun IArd IDee IVic MBri MGos NLar SHil SSta
	- 'Trinity Star'	CJun MBri
	- 'Triple Crown'	CJun WPat
	- 'Tsukubanomine'	CJun CLnd MBri NLar
	- 'Vale Milky Way' (v)	NLar
	- 'Weaver's Weeping'	CJun MPkF NLar
	- 'Weisse Fontäne'	CJun NLar
	- 'White Dream'	CJun NLar
	- 'White Giant'	CJun SPoG
	- 'Willy Boy'	WHor
	- 'Wolf Eyes' (v) ♀H5	CBcs CJun MAsh MBlu MPkF NLar NPCo SGol SSpi SSta
	macrophylla Wall.	EPfP WCru
	- MSF 821	WPGP
	mas	Widely available
	- 'Aurea' (v) ♀H6	CAbP CBcs CJun ELan EPfP LRHS MAsh MBlu MBri MGos MRav NEgg NLar NPCo SGol SLim SPer SPoG SSpi SSta WPat
§	- 'Aureoelegantissima' (v)	CJun CMac LRHS MAsh MBri NLar SPer SSpi WPat
	- 'Devin' (F)	NLar
	- 'Elegant' (F)	CAgr
	- 'Elegantissima'	see *C. mas* 'Aureoelegantissima'
	- 'Golden Glory' ♀H6	CJun CLnd EPfP MBri NLar SKHP WHor
	- 'Gourmet' (F)	CAgr
	- 'Happy Face'	NLar
	- 'Hillier's Upright'	CJun
	- 'Jolico' (F) ♀H6	CAgr CJun LEdu MBlu NLar SKHP
	- 'Kasanlaker' (F)	CAgr NLar
	- 'Pancharevo' (F)	CAgr
	- 'Pioneer' (F)	CJun NLar
	- 'Redstone' (F)	CJun
	- 'Schönbrunner Gourmet Dirndl' (F)	MCoo
	- 'Shan' (F)	CAgr
	- 'Shumen' (F)	CAgr
	- 'Spring Glow'	CJun NLar
	- 'Titus' (F)	NLar
	- 'Variegata' (v) ♀H6	CAbP CBcs CDul CJun CMCN CMac EBee EPfP LRHS MAsh MBlu MBri MGos NLar NPCo SKHP SPer SSpi WPat
	- 'Xanthocarpa'	CJun NLar
	- 'Yellow'	CAgr
	'Norman Hadden' ♀H5	Widely available
	nuttallii	CDul CTho CTri ELan EPfP MGos MMuc SPer SWvt
	- 'Colrigo Giant'	CJun
	- 'Gold Spot' (v)	CJun CMac NPCo NWea
	- 'Monarch'	CJun CTho ESwi ETwe SKHP WPat
	- 'North Star'	CJun NLar
	- 'Portlemouth'	CEnd CJun GKin LRHS NLar
	- 'Zurico'	CJun MPkF NLar
	oblonga **new**	CExl
	officinalis	CAgr CDul CMCN EPfP IMou LEdu LRHS NLar SKHP SWvt
	- 'Kintoki' ♀H6	ESwi MBri NLar SKHP
	'Ormonde' ♀H5	CJun EPfP NLar NPCo SSpi SSta WPGP
	'Pink Blush'	CJun
	'Porlock' ♀H5	CDul CJun CMCN EPfP IArd LRHS MAsh MBri NLar SHil SWvt WPat
	pumila	CJun NLar
§	***racemosa***	EBtc NLar
	rugosa	EBtc NLar
I	× ***rutgersiensis***	LRHS
	- Galaxy	see *C.* Celestial
	Ruth Ellen = 'Rutlan' (Stellar Series)	CJun NLar
	sanguinea	CBcs CCVT CDul CHab CLnd CTri ECrN EPfP LBuc MJak MMuc MRav MSwo NWea SCob SEWo SGol SPer SVic WHar WMou
§	- 'Anny'	CJun MBlu WPat

- 'Anny's Winter Orange' ♀H6	CJun
§ - 'Compressa'	EPfP EPla MGil MRav NLar
- 'Magic Flame' ♀H6	CJun ELon EMil EPfP LRHS MBri NLar WPat
- 'Midwinter Fire'	Widely available
- 'Winter Beauty'	CJun CSBt EPfP EUJe LBMP MAsh MBlu NEgg NLar NSoo NWea SLon SWvt WCFE WHar WPat WWtn
- 'Winter Flame'	see *C. sanguinea* 'Anny'
§ ***sericea***	SRms WMoo
- 'Bud's Yellow'	ELon EPfP LRHS MBlu MBri SHil
- 'Cardinal'	CHGN CRos ELon EPfP ESwi LRHS MAsh MBri NLar SHil
- 'Flaviramea' ♀H7	Widely available
- 'Hedgerows Gold' (v) ♀H7	CRos EBee ELan ELon EMil EPfP LRHS MAsh MBri SHil SPoG WCot WPat
§ - 'Kelseyi'	CMac EBee EPfP MRav NLar SCob WMoo
- Kelsey's Gold = 'Rosco'	MAsh WPat
- subsp. ***occidentalis*** 'Sunshine'	NEoE NLar
§ - 'White Gold' (v)	CDoC EAEE EHoe ELon EPfP EWTr MBri MRav NEoE NLar NSoo SMad SPer SPoG WMoo
- 'White Spot'	see *C. sericea* 'White Gold'
Stardust = 'Rutfan' (Stellar Series)	CJun
Stellar Pink = 'Rutgan' (Stellar Series)	CBcs CJun CTho LRHS MAsh MBri MGos MPkF NLar SGol SKHP
stolonifera	see *C. sericea*
suecica	CTal NHar
× ***unalaschkensis***	LLHF
- NNS 08-101	GKev
Venus = 'Kn30 8'PBR	CJun ELan EPfP LBuc LRHS MBlu MBri MPkF SLon SSta
walteri	CBcs EBtc
- B&SWJ 8776	WCru

Corokia (*Argyrophyllaceae*)

buddlejoides	CBcs CHGN CMHG CSde CTsd ECou NLar SEND WFar
'Coppershine'	CMHG
cotoneaster	Widely available
- 'Boundary Hill'	ECou
- 'Brown's Stream'	ECou
- 'Hodder River'	ECou
- 'Swale Stream'	ECou
- 'Wanaka'	ECou
macrocarpa	ECou
× ***virgata***	CAbP CChe CTri CTsd ECou ELan EPfP GBin GGal LRHS NLar SArc SWvt WSHC
- 'Bronze King'	LPal LRHS MOWG SPer SVen
- 'Bronze Lady'	ECou
- 'Cheesemanii'	ECou
- 'County Park Lemon'	ECou
- 'County Park Orange'	ECou
- 'County Park Red'	ECou
- 'Frosted Chocolate'	CMHG CSde CTsd EBee ECou ELan EPfP IVic LLHF LRHS MOWG SEND SKHP SLim SPoG SVen SWvt WGrn
- 'Geenty's Green'	ECou LRHS
- 'Havering'	ECou
- 'Pink Delight'	ECou EPfP ESwi MAsh MRav
- 'Red Wonder'	CMHG CMac EBee ELan EPfP IVic LRHS SEND SLim SPoG SVen WGrn
- 'Silver Ghost'	ECou
- 'Sunsplash' (v)	CBcs CDoC CMac CTsd EBee ECou EPfP ESwi LBMP LLHF LRHS MAsh MPkF NLar SEND SEle SPoG SWvt WGrn
I - 'Virgata'	ECou
- 'Yellow Wonder'	CBcs CMHG EBee ESwi LRHS NLar SEND SLim SWvt

Coronilla (*Papilionaceae*)

comosa	see *Hippocrepis comosa*
coronata	LRHS
emerus	see *Hippocrepis emerus*
glauca	see *C. valentina* subsp. *glauca*
minima	XSen
'Nan Hicks'	EWld
valentina	CDoC CRHN CSPN MGil SDix WSHC
- 'Clotted Cream'	CHid
§ - subsp. ***glauca*** ♀H4	CDul CMac CSBt CSde CTri EBee ELan EPfP LRHS MGil MMuc MWat SEND SLim SPer SPoG SRms SVen SWvt WAbe WOut WPat XLum XSen
- - 'Brockhill Blue'	EBee IVic LRHS WCot
- - 'Citrina' ♀H4	Widely available
* - - 'Pygmaea'	SRms WCot
- - 'Variegata' (v)	CBcs CDoC CMac COtt CSPN CTri CWld EBee EHoe ELan EPfP LBMP LRHS MCot MGil MRav SEND SLim SLon SMrm SPer SPoG SRms SVen WCot
varia	see *Securigera varia*

Correa (*Rutaceae*)

aemula	MOWG
alba	CCCN CDoC CExl EPfP
- 'Pinkie' ♀H2	CExl CSde CTsd ECou MOWG WAbe WCot
alba* × *backhouseana	MOWG
backhouseana ♀H2	CAbb CBcs CCCN CDoC CExl CHll CMac CSde CTri CTsd ECou ELan EPfP GCal IDee IVic LPot LRHS MOWG NLar SEle SVen WSHC
- 'Mount Congreve'	MOWG
- 'Peaches and Cream'	CCCN IVic SEle SRkn
decumbens	MOWG
'Dusky Bells' ♀H2	CAbb CBcs CCCN CDoC CHll CSde CTri CTsd ECou EPfP IDee IVic LBMP LRHS MAsh MOWG SEND SEle SLim SMrm SPlb SPoG SRkn SVen
'Dusky Maid'	CCCN CExl
'Federation Belle'	CCCN CDoC ECou MOWG SPlb SVen
glabra	MOWG SEle
'Gwen'	CDoC
'Harrisii'	see *C.* 'Mannii'
'Inglewood Gold'	ECou
'Ivory Bells'	ECou EPfP
lawrenceana	CExl CFil CTsd SEND SVen WPGP
- var. ***grampiana*** new	SVen
§ 'Mannii' ♀H2	CBcs CCCN CDoC CExl CTsd ECre ELan ELon EPfP IDee IVic LRHS MOWG SEle SPoG WSHC
'Marian's Marvel' ♀H2	CCCN CDoC CExl CSde CTsd ECou ECre EPfP LBMP MAsh MOWG SEND SEle SPoG SRkn SVen WAbe
'Peachy Cream'	CAbb CCCN CDoC CTsd EPfP LRHS

	'Poorinda Mary'	ECou MOWG
	pulchella 🏆H2	CDoC CExl CTri SEle
	- orange-flowered	MOWG
	- 'Pink Mist'	CDoC ECou MOWG WAbe
	reflexa 🏆H2	CDoC CExl
	- var. ***nummulariifolia***	ECou LBMP MAsh MGil MOWG WAbe
	- var. ***reflexa***	CExl
	- - 'Mary's Choice'	CDoC
*	- ***virens***	CExl
	schlechtendalii	CCCN ECou SEle

Cortaderia ✿ (*Poaceae*)

	argentea	see *C. selloana*
	fulvida misapplied	see *C. richardii* (Endl.) Zotov
§	***fulvida*** (Buchanan) Zotov 🏆H6	EWes IArd IDee NWsh SMad SWvt WCot WGrf
	jubata 'Candy Floss'	see *C. selloana* 'Candy Floss'
	richardii misapplied	see *C. fulvida* (Buchanan) Zotov
	richardii ambig.	CBod CCon CExl EHoe GBin IMou MMuc NBir SMad SWvt WHrl
§	***richardii*** (Endl.) Zotov 🏆H5	CAby CBcs CKno EBee ECha ESwi EWes IDee IMou LRHS MAvo MHin MWhi SArc WCru WMnd WPGP
	- Brown's strain	LSun WCot
§	***selloana***	CAco CBcs CBod CDul CHEx CTri IBoy MGos MJak MRav NBir SArc SCob SGol SPlb
§	- 'Albolineata' (v)	CBcs ELon EWes MMuc MWht SEND SLim SPoG SWvt
§	- 'Aureolineata' (v) 🏆H5	CBcs CDoC CMac CSde CWCL ELan EPfP GMaP IVic LRHS MGos MHin MMuc NBid SEND SLim SPer SPoG SWvt
§	- 'Candy Floss'	CKno
	- 'Evita'PBR 🏆H5	CKno ECtt MBri SMad SWvt
	- 'Gold Band'	see *C. selloana* 'Aureolineata'
	- 'Golden Goblin'PBR	EHoe
	- 'Icalma'	CSde EPPr
	- 'Monstrosa' 🏆H5	MMuc SEND SMad
	- 'Patagonia' 🏆H5	EHoe EPPr
	- 'Pink Feather'	CTsd EPfP MMuc SEND SPer
	- 'Pointe du Raz'	SWvt
	- 'Pumila' 🏆H5	Widely available
	- 'Rendatleri'	CBcs CDoC ELan SCoo SLim SPoG SWvt
	- 'Rosea'	CBod EPfP MGos MJak NGdn NLar SCob SGol
	- 'Silver Fountain' (v)	ELan EPfP LRHS MAsh
	- 'Silver Stripe'	see *C. selloana* 'Albolineata'
	- 'Splendid Star'PBR (v)	CBcs EHoe LRHS MAsh MBri MGos MJak NLar SLim SMad SPoG SWvt
	- 'Sunningdale Silver' 🏆H5	CDoC CMac ECha ECtt ELan ELon EPfP LRHS MBri MGos MMuc SCob SEND SLim SMad SPer SPoG SWvt
*	- 'White Feather'	CBod NGdn SCob SLim SPer WHar
	Toe Toe	see *C. richardii* (Endl.) Zotov

Cortusa (*Primulaceae*)

	brotheri	EBee ECho
*	***caucasica***	EBee GKev
*	- 'Alba'	GKev
	matthioli	ECho EWld GBin GEdr GKev SRms WFar
	- 'Alba'	CCon ECho NLar SRms
	- var. ***congesta***	GEdr GKev
	- subsp. ***pekinensis***	CCon ECho EDAr GKev MLHP MPnt NBid NLar SGSe SRms WPnP
	- - var. ***sachalinensis***	GKev
	turkestanica	ECho GEdr GKev LLHF

Corydalis ✿ (*Papaveraceae*)

	anthriscifolia	CLAP EWes MMHG WCot
	'Blackberry Wine'	CExl EBee ECtt EPfP GBuc LRHS MPnt NLar SPad WOut
	'Blue Panda'	see *C. flexuosa* 'Blue Panda'
	'Bronze Beauty'	WFar WMoo
	bulbosa misapplied	see *C. cava*
	bulbosa (L.) DC.	see *C. solida*
	buschii	CLAP CPBP EBee ECho ELon GBin GBuc GEdr GKev NHar NLar NMyG
	'Canary Feathers'PBR	ECtt GEdr LRHS MBNS MHol NLar NPri
	cashmeriana	GKev LRHS NBid WAbe WHal
	- 'Kailash'	EBee LRHS
	cashmeriana × ***flexuosa***	CBro CLAP ECho WAbe
	caucasica	ECho GBuc
	- var. ***alba*** misapplied	see *C. malkensis*
§	***cava***	CLAP EBee ECho EPot LAma SPhx WShi
	- 'Albiflora'	CLAP ECho EPot SPhx
	- subsp. ***cava***	ECho
	cheilanthifolia	CExl CRow CSpe EPfP EWld IMou LEdu LPla SRms XLum
	'Craigton Blue'	CLAP EBee EPPr GBuc GEdr IMou IPot NHar WAbe
	curviflora	GKev
	- subsp. ***rosthornii***	CExl EWes
	- - 'Blue Heron'	CSpe ECtt GEdr IPot MPnt NCGa SHar
	davidii	CExl
	decipiens Schott, Nyman & Kotschy	see *C. solida* subsp. *incisa*
I	***decipiens*** misapplied	CPom ECho EPot
I	- purple-flowered	ECho
	densiflora	ECho
	'Early Bird'	ECtt
	elata	CLAP CSpe EWes GAbr GBin GBuc GEdr IFro LRHS LSou MArl MBel MBri MCot MMuc MNrw NBid NBir NChi SPhx SPoG WCot WCru WHal WHoo WOut WPtf WSHC
	- 'Blue Summit'	CLAP ECtt EPPr IMou LRHS
	elata × ***flexuosa***	IMou
	elata × ***flexuosa*** clone 1	CCse CExl CLAP GEdr
	flexuosa 🏆H5	CSpe ECho EPfP GBin MArl MNrw WAbe WBor WSHC XLum
	- CD&R 528	IFro NRya
	- 'Balang Mist'	CExl CLAP NHar
	- 'Blue Dragon'	see *C. flexuosa* 'Purple Leaf'
§	- 'Blue Panda'	CExl EPPr EWes GBuc GKev GMaP MNrw NLar WCru
	- 'China Blue'	Widely available
	- 'Golden Panda' (v)	CBct NLar
	- 'Hale Cat'	ECtt EPPr
	- 'Hidden Purple'	CHid
	- 'Nightshade'	CExl EWld LLHF NBid WCot WHoo
I	- 'Norman's Seedling'	EBee EPPr IVic WPGP
	- 'Père David'	CBod CMac COtt CSBt CSpe CWCL EBee ECha ECho ELan EPPr EPfP GBin ITim LRHS MHer MWat NBir NCGa NMyG NPCo SPlb SPoG SWvt WCru WPnP WSHC WWEG XLum
§	- 'Purple Leaf'	Widely available
	'Golden Spinners'	IVic
	'Heavenly Blue'	GKev

heterocarpa	IMou
incisa	ECho ERCP LAma
- B&SWJ 4417	WCru
'Kingfisher'	CDes CLAP CWCL LEdu NHar NLar NSla WAbe
leucanthema DJHC 752	CDes CExl CLAP
- 'Silver Spectre' (v)	CExl LLHF LRHS WMoo
linstowiana	CSpe WCot
- CD&R 605	CExl CLAP
§ ***lutea***	CBcs CBod EBee EPfP IFoB IFro MMuc NBir NPer NPri NWad SEND SRms WCot WMoo
magadanica	MMoz
§ ***malkensis*** ♀H5	CPom CWCL EBee ECho EPot GBin GBuc LLHF MAvo NBir NRya WCot WThu
'Maya' (v)	XLum
moorcroftiana	CExl
nobilis	CSpe ECho IFoB LLHF SPhx
ochotensis	IMou LRHS
§ ***ochroleuca***	CElw CRow CSpe EPot GCal LPla NLar WMoo
ophiocarpa	CSpe EHoe ELan GCal WHil WMoo
pachycentra	CExl WAbe
paczoskii	ECho GBuc GKev LRHS MNrw
pseudofumaria alba	see *C. ochroleuca*
pumila	ECho
'Rainier Blue'	IVic
rosea 'American Dream'	CWCL
'Ruksans Red' **new**	CWCL
'Sapphire' **new**	CBro
scandens	see *Dactylicapnos scandens*
scouleri	IMou NBir
shimienensis	CPom
- 'Berry Exciting'PBR	CAby CBct CLAP CWGN EBee ECtt ELon EPfP GBuc LRHS LSou MBNS MHol NPer SPoG
siamensis	IFoB IMou
- B&SWJ 7200	WCru
§ ***solida***	CAvo CBro CPom EBee ECho ECtt ELan EPfP EPot GAbr ITim LAma LEdu LRHS MPie MRav NLar NRya SDeJ SPhx WCot WShi
- 'Advocet' **new**	GEdr
- 'Evening Shade' **new**	GEdr
- 'Fire Bird'	ECho GEdr
- 'Firecracker'	CBro ECho LLHF LRHS SPhx
- 'Frodo'	ECho LAma
- 'Galah'	ECho
- 'Gandalf'	NHar
- 'Gaviota' **new**	GEdr
§ - subsp. ***incisa*** ♀H5	ECho EPot GKev SDeJ SPhx
- lilac-flowered	IFoB
- 'Moonlight Shade'	ECho
- 'Purple Beauty'	ECho EPot MNrw SPhx
- 'Purple Bird'	CAvo
§ - subsp. ***solida***	CLAP ECho EPot GBin GKev NBir NRya SPhx WCot
- - from Penza, Russia	GKev LLHF
- - 'Beth Evans'	CBro CWCL ECha ECho ELon EPPr EPot ERCP EShb GAbr GBin GBuc GKev LAma LEdu LLHF MCot MHer MNrw NBir NCGa NHar NLar NWad SDeJ SMad SPhx WBor WCot WWEG
- - 'Blushing Girl'	ECho GEdr LAma
- - 'Dieter Schacht' ♀H5	EPPr EPot ITim LAma LLHF NLar WAbe
- - 'Evening Shade'	ECho GEdr LAma
- - 'George Baker' ♀H5	Widely available
- - 'Lahovice'	WAbe WCot
- - Prasil Group	EPot GEdr GKev SPhx WBor
- - 'White Knight'	ECho LAma WCot
- f. ***transsylvanica***	see *C. solida* subsp. *solida*
- 'White King'	WCot
- 'White Swallow'	GEdr
'Spinners'	CDes CElw CFis CLAP EBee ECha ECtt ELon EPPr GCal GKev GLog IMou IVic NMyG WPnP WSHC WWEG XLum
stipulata B&SWJ 2951	WCru
taliensis	CExl GLog
temulifolia 'Chocolate Stars'	CSpe CWGN ECtt EWld GEdr LEdu LLHF LPla MBNS MHol MPie NCGa NSti WCot WSHC WWFP
tomentella	NSla
'Tory MP'	CBct CDes CExl CHid CLAP CPne CPom CSam CSpe EBee EPPr GEdr IFro LRHS MNrw MPie NBid NCGa NChi NHar NMyG WHoo WPGP
transsylvanica hort.	see *C. solida* subsp. *solida*
turtschaninovii	SKHP
vittae	ECho IFoB
wendelboi	IFoB
'Wildside Blue'	CLAP
wilsonii	CExl IFoB

Corylopsis ✿ (*Hamamelidaceae*)

glabrescens	CHGN CJun LRHS
- var. ***gotoana***	CJun EPfP LRHS MAsh NLar SSpi SSta WPat
- - 'Chollipo'	CAbP CBcs LRHS NLar SSta
- 'Lemon Drop'	CJun NLar
glandulifera	CJun
himalayana	WAbe
multiflora	SSpi
pauciflora ♀H5	CBcs CDoC CDul CEnd CJun CMHG CTho CTri ELan EPfP IDee IVic LRHS MAsh MRav NEgg NLar NPri SChF SCob SGol SKHP SLim SPer SPoG SSpi WPGP
platypetala	see *C. sinensis* var. *calvescens*
- var. ***laevis***	see *C. sinensis* var. *calvescens*
sinensis	EPfP
§ - var. ***calvescens***	CBcs CJun CTho EPfP
§ - - f. ***veitchiana*** ♀H5	CJun CSam EPfP IArd IDee LRHS MAsh NLar
§ - var. ***sinensis*** ♀H5	CDoC CDul CJun CTho ELon EPfP IVic LAst LRHS MAsh NLar SLon SPoG WAbe
- - 'Spring Purple'	CAbP CBcs CEnd CJun CMac EPfP ETwe IDee IVic LRHS NLar SChF SHil SKHP SSpi SSta WCot WPGP WPat
- 'Veitch's Purple'	CJun NLar
spicata	CBcs CDul CJun IArd IDee LRHS MBlu MRav NEgg NLar SCob SGol SLim WPat
- 'Red Eye'	CJun IVic NLar
veitchiana	see *C. sinensis* var. *calvescens* f. *veitchiana*
willmottiae	see *C. sinensis* var. *sinensis*
'Winterthur'	SSta

Corylus ✿ (*Betulaceae*)

sp.	MAsh

avellana (F)	CAco CBcs CCVT CDoC CDul CHab CLnd CMac CTho CTri ECrN EPfP EPom GAbr LAst LBuc MBri MGos MJak NEgg NHed NLar NWea SCob SEWo SPer SPre SVic WHar WMou
- 'Anny's Purple Dream'[PBR] new	NLar
- 'Anny's Red Dwarf'	IArd NLar
- 'Aurea'	CAco CBcs CDoC CDul CEnd CSBt CTho CTri EBee ECrN ELan EPfP EPla EUJe GBin LBuc LRHS MAsh MBlu MBri MGos MRav NLar NWea SCob SLim SPer SSta SWvt
- 'Bollwylle'	see *C. maxima* 'Halle'sche Riesennuss'
§ - 'Butler' (F)	CAgr CDul CMac CTho CTri ERea IArd MBri MJak SDea SKee WHar
- 'Casina' (F)	CAgr CTho
- 'Contorta' ♀H6	Widely available
- 'Corabel' (F)	CAgr MBri
- 'Cosford' (F)	CAgr CCVT CDul CMac CSBt CTho CTri ECrN EPla EPom ERea GTwe IArd LBuc LEdu LRHS MBlu MBri MGos NLar NOra SDea SEWo SGol SKee SPer SWvt WHar
§ - 'Ennis' (F)	CAgr MBri NOra SDea SKee WHar
§ - 'Fuscorubra' (F)	CJun EPla EPom MRav NLar SWvt
- 'Gustav's Zeller' (F)	CAgr
§ - 'Heterophylla'	CDul EBee EPfP EPla MBri NLar SSta WHar WPat
- 'Laciniata'	see *C. avellana* 'Heterophylla'
§ - 'Lang Tidlig Zeller' (F)	CAgr ERea LRHS MBri MCoo NOra NWea
- 'Louis Berger' (F)	MCoo
- 'Merveille de Bollwyller'	see *C. maxima* 'Halle'sche Riesennuss'
- 'Nottingham Prolific'	see *C. avellana* 'Pearson's Prolific'
- 'Pauetet' (F)	CAgr
§ - 'Pearson's Prolific' (F)	CAgr CSBt GTwe LBuc MMuc SDea SEND SGol SKee
- 'Pendula'	EBee EPla MAsh MBlu SCoo WCot WHar WPat
- 'Princess' (F) new	SVic
- 'Purpurea'	see *C. avellana* 'Fuscorubra'
- 'Red Majestic'[PBR] ♀H6	Widely available
- 'Tonda di Giffoni' (F)	CAgr MCoo
- 'Webb's Prize Cob' (F)	CAgr CDul CLnd ERea GBin GTwe IArd LEdu MBlu MJak MMuc NLar SDea SEND SGol SKee SVic
colurna ♀H5	CCVT CDul CMCN CMac EBee ECrN EPfP IArd LEdu MBlu MGos NLar NWea SCoo SGol SPer WHar WMou
× ***colurnoides***	IDee
- 'Chinoka' (F)	CAgr MCoo WHar
- 'Freeoka' (F)	CAgr MCoo WHar
Early Long Zeller	see *C. avellana* 'Lang Tidlig Zeller'
fargesii new	WPGP
maxima (F)	CDul CLnd CMac CTri EPom GTwe MSwo NWea SDea
- 'Butler'	see *C. avellana* 'Butler'
- 'Ennis'	see *C. avellana* 'Ennis'
- 'Fertile de Coutard'	see *C. maxima* 'White Filbert'
- 'Frühe van Frauendorf'	see *C. maxima* 'Red Filbert'
- 'Garibaldi' (F)	NLar
- 'Grote Lambertsnoot'	see *C. maxima* 'Kentish Cob'
- 'Gunslebert' (F)	CAgr CCVT CDul CMac CSBt CTho CTri ECrN ERea GTwe LRHS MBri NOra SDea SKee SPoG WHar
- Halle Giant	see *C. maxima* 'Halle'sche Riesennuss'
§ - 'Halle'sche Riesennuss' (F)	CAgr EPla ERea GTwe MBri MMuc NLar NOra SEND SKee WHar
§ - 'Kentish Cob' (F)	CAgr CBcs CDul CMac CSBt CTho ECrN ELan EPfP EPom ERea GTwe IArd LBuc LRHS MBri MGos MWat NLar SDea SEWo SKee SLim SPer SPoG SRms SVic SWvt WHar WMou
- 'Lambert's Filbert'	see *C. maxima* 'Kentish Cob'
- 'Longue d'Espagne'	see *C. maxima* 'Kentish Cob'
- 'Monsieur de Bouweller'	see *C. maxima* 'Halle'sche Riesennuss'
- 'Nottingham Cobnut' (F) new	SVic
- 'Purple Filbert'	see *C. maxima* 'Purpurea'
§ - 'Purpurea' (F)	Widely available
§ - 'Red Filbert' (F) ♀H6	CDul CEnd CHab CTho EPom ERea GTwe IArd LEdu MAsh MBlu MBri NLar NOra SCoo SGol SKee SLim SSta WHar WPat
- 'Red Zellernut'	see *C. maxima* 'Red Filbert'
- 'Spanish White'	see *C. maxima* 'White Filbert'
§ - 'White Filbert' (F)	CHab GTwe SKee WHar
- 'White Spanish Filbert'	see *C. maxima* 'White Filbert'
- 'Witpit Lambertsnoot'	see *C. maxima* 'White Filbert'
'Nottingham Early' (F)	NLar
sieboldiana B&SWJ 11056	WCru
'Te Terra Red'	CDul CJun CMCN EBee MAsh MBlu MBri SLon WHar
tibetica new	LEdu

Corymbia see *Eucalyptus*

Corynabutilon see *Abutilon*

Corynephorus (*Poaceae*)

canescens	NBir WWEG

Corynocarpus (*Corynocarpaceae*)

laevigatus	CBcs ECou MBri

Cosmos (*Asteraceae*)

§ ***atrosanguineus***	Widely available
- Chocamocha = 'Thomocha'[PBR]	CAvo CBcs CCCN CChe CHel CHid CSpe CWCL CWGN ECtt EPfP EUJe GMaP IBoy LAst MPro NCGa NLar NPri SCob SHil SMrm SPer SPoG SRot WBor
- 'New Choco'[PBR] new	LSou
bipinnatus 'Antiquity'	NPri SPhx
- 'Purity'	CSpe SPhx
- 'Sea Shells' (mixed)	CWCL
- (Sonata Series) 'Sonata Carmine'	LSou NPri SPoG
- - 'Sonata Pink'	LSou NPri SPoG
- - 'Sonata White'	CSpe LAst LSou NPri SPoG
caudatus	WJek
peucedanifolius	CSpe NGBl
- 'Flamingo'	EPfP ERCP SDeJ
'Razzmatazz Pink' new	NPri
sulphureus 'Bunte Lichter'	CSpe

Cosmos × *Dahlia* (*Asteraceae*)

'Mexican Black'	ECtt ERCP NJRG WCot WPGP

costmary see *Tanacetum balsamita*

Cotinus ✿ (*Anacardiaceae*)

americanus	see *C. obovatus*
§ ***coggygria***	CAco CArn CBcs CDoC CDul CMCN CMac CWSG EBee ECrN ELan EPfP LPal MBri MMuc MRav MSwo MWat NLar NWea SCob SEND SGol SPer SWvt WFar WHar XSen
- Golden Spirit = 'Ancot'PBR 🏆H5	Widely available
- Green Fountain = 'Kolcot'PBR	EBee EMil
- 'Kanari'	CJun NLar WPat
- 'Nordine'	WPat
- 'Notcutt's Variety'	MRav
- 'Old Fashioned'PBR	MGos MPkF WMou
- 'Pink Champagne'	CJun EPfP MAsh NLar SSta WPat
- Purpureus Group	EPfP SGol
- 'Red Beauty'	CJun NLar
- 'Royal Purple' 🏆H5	Widely available
- Rubrifolius Group	CBcs EPfP SEND SGol SPer SWvt
- Selection	EPfP
- Smokey Joe = 'Lisjo'PBR	EPfP LRHS MAsh SLon SPoG SSta SWvt WHar
- 'Smokey Joe Purple'	LSou
- 'Velvet Cloak'	CAbP CJun EBee ELan EPfP GKin LRHS MGos MPkF NLar SLon SWvt WMou
- 'Young Lady'PBR 🏆H5	CBcs CDoC CMac COtt CSBt ELon EPfP EUJe EWes GBin LAst LBMP LRHS LSou MAsh MBlu MBri MPkF NEoE NLar SCob SCoo SGol SMad SPer SWvt WFar WHar WPat
Dusky Maiden = 'Londus'PBR	CSBt ELon EPfP GBin LLHF LRHS MAsh MBri MGos NLar SCob SLon SPoG WPat
'Flame' 🏆H5	CBcs CDul CJun ELan ELon EPfP EUJe EWTr LRHS MAsh MBri MGos MRav NLar SCob SGbt SHil SKHP SLim SPer SPoG SWvt WFar WPat
'Grace'	Widely available
§ ***obovatus***	CJun CMCN EBtc ELon EPfP IArd LLHF LRHS MBlu MPkF MRav NLar SSpi SSta WPGP WPat

Cotoneaster ✿ (*Rosaceae*)

SDR 5804	GKev
SDR 5841	GKev
acuminatus	SRms
adpressus	CAco SCob
§ - 'Little Gem'	ECho NHar NLar
- var. ***praecox***	see *C. nanshan*
- 'Tangstedt'	SGol
- 'Tom Thumb'	see *C. adpressus* 'Little Gem'
affinis	SRms
albokermesinus	SRms
ambiguus	NLar
amoenus	NLar SRms
- AC 829	MSnd
- 'Fire Mountain'	NEoE
§ ***apiculatus***	NLar SRms
§ ***ascendens***	SRms
assamensis	SRms
§ ***astrophoros***	CMac MBlu NHar NLar
atropurpureus	NLar SRms
§ - 'Variegatus' (v) 🏆H6	CBcs CDul CMac CTri ECrN EHoe ELan ELon EPfP EPla LRHS MAsh MBri MGos MJak MMuc NEgg NLar NPer SCob SCoo SEND SHil SLim SPer SPoG SRms SWvt WFar WMoo
aurantiacus new	NLar
boisianus	NLar SRms
bradyi	SRms
§ ***bullatus***	CDul CTri EPfP MMuc NLar SPer SRms WHil
- 'Firebird'	see *C. ignescens*
- f. ***floribundus***	see *C. bullatus*
- var. ***macrophyllus***	see *C. rehderi*
bumthangensis	SRms
buxifolius blue-leaved	see *C. lidjiangensis*
- 'Brno'	see *C. marginatus* 'Brno'
- f. ***vellaeus***	see *C. astrophoros*
camilli-schneideri	SRms
canescens	NLar SRms
chadwellii new	NLar
chungtiensis	NLar
cinnabarinus	SRms
§ ***cochleatus***	LAst SRms
§ ***congestus***	CDul CSBt MSwo MWat SPlb SRms WHar XLum
- 'Nanus'	CMea ELan GCrg GEdr
conspicuus	CBcs LAst SPer SRms
- AC 3176	MSnd
- 'Decorus' 🏆H6	CDoC CDul CSBt EAEE EPfP LAst LRHS MBri MGos MJak MMuc MSwo NEgg NLar NWea SCob SEND SGol SHil SLim SPer SPlb SPoG SWvt WHar WMoo
- 'Leicester Gem'	SRms
- 'Red Glory'	CMac
cooperi	SRms
cordifolius	MBlu NLar SRms
cornifolius	SRms
crispii	NLar
cuspidatus	MBlu NLar
dammeri	Widely available
§ - 'Major'	LBuc SPoG WFar
§ - 'Mooncreeper'	CWSG MMuc SCob SEND WHar
- 'Oakwood'	see *C. radicans* 'Eichholz'
- var. ***radicans*** misapplied	see *C. dammeri* 'Major'
dielsianus	NLar NWea SRms
divaricatus	EPfP NLar NWea SPer SRms
duthieanus 'Boer'	see *C. apiculatus*
elatus	SRms
elegans	SRms
emeiensis	NLar SRms
encavei new	NLar
'Erlinda'	see *C.* × *suecicus* 'Erlinda'
'Exburiensis'	CBcs CBod CCVT CDoC CDul ECrN EPfP LAst MAsh MBri MGos MMuc MRav NLar SCob SEND SGol WFar WHar
falconeri	SRms
fastigiatus	SRms
flinckii	SRms
floccosus	NWea
floridus	SRms
forrestii	SRms
franchetii	Widely available
cf. ***franchetii*** new	COtt
frigidus	SRms
- 'Cornubia' 🏆H6	Widely available
- 'Saint Monica'	MBlu
gamblei	SRms
ganghobaensis	SRms

	– B&L 12234	WCru
	glabratus	SRms
	glacialis	SRms
	glaucophyllus	IArd SEND SRms
§	***glomerulatus***	NLar SRms
	gracilis	SRms
	granatensis	NLar SRms
	harrovianus	NLar SRms
I	***hedegaardii*** 'Fructu Luteo'	SRms
	henryanus	SRms
	– 'Corina'	SRms
	'Herbstfeuer'	see *C. salicifolius* 'Herbstfeuer'
	'Highlight'	see *C. pluriflorus*
§	***hjelmqvistii***	LBuc NLar SRms
	– 'Robustus'	see *C. hjelmqvistii*
	– 'Rotundifolius'	see *C. hjelmqvistii*
	hodjingensis	SRms
	horizontalis	Widely available
	– 'Variegatus'	see *C. atropurpureus* 'Variegatus'
	– var. ***wilsonii***	see *C. ascendens*
	hualiensis	SRms
	– B&SWJ 3143	WCru
	humifusus	see *C. dammeri*
	hummelii	SRms
§	'Hybridus Pendulus'	CAco CBcs CCVT CDoC CDul CMac CSBt CTri CWSG EBee ECrN ELon LAst LRHS MAsh MBri MGos MJak MRav NEgg NLar NPri NWea SLim SPer SPoG SRms SWvt WHar WJas
§	***hylmoei***	SRms
	hypocarpus	SRms
	ignavus	SRms
§	***ignescens***	NLar NWea SRms
	ignotus	SRms
	incanus	NLar
	induratus	SRms
	insculptus	SRms
	insolitus	NLar
	integerrimus	SRms
§	***integrifolius***	MMuc NLar SEND SRms WMoo
	kangdingensis	SRms
	kingdonii new	NLar
	kweitschoviensis	NLar
	lacteus ♀H6	Widely available
	lancasteri	SRms
	langei	SRms
	laxiflorus	SRms
§	***lidjiangensis***	SRms
§	***linearifolius***	GCra
	lucidus	NLar SRms
	ludlowii	SRms
	magnificus	SRms
§	***mairei***	NLar NWea SRms
	marginatus Lindl. ex Loudon	SRms
§	– 'Blazovice'	SRms
§	– 'Brno'	SRms
	marquandii	NLar SRms
§	***meiophyllus***	MBlu NLar
	melanocarpus	NLar
	meuselii	NLar SRms
	meyeri new	NLar
	microphyllus misapplied	see *C. purpurascens*
	microphyllus ambig.	CBcs EAEE EPla SCob
	microphyllus Wall. ex Lindl.	CDul CTri LRHS MGos NWea SDix SPer SPoG WMoo
	– NICE 004	WCFE
	– var. ***cochleatus*** (Franch.) Rehder & E.H. Wilson	see *C. cochleatus*
	– var. ***cochleatus*** ambig.	NSla
	– 'Donard Gem'	see *C. astrophoros*
	– 'Teulon Porter'	see *C. astrophoros*
	– var. ***thymifolius*** misapplied	see *C. linearifolius*
	– var. ***thymifolius*** (Lindl.) Koehne	see *C. integrifolius*
	– var. ***thymifolius*** ambig.	LRHS
	milkedandaensis	SRms
	miniatus	SRms
	mirabilis	SRms
	monopyrenus	SRms
	'Mooncreeper'	see *C. dammeri* 'Mooncreeper'
	morrisonensis	SRms
	moupinensis	GLog SRms
	– BWJ 8167	WCru
	mucronatus	NLar SRms
§	***nanshan***	CAbP NLar NWea SRms WHar
	– 'Boer'	see *C. apiculatus*
	naoujanensis	EPfP MBri NLar
	– 'Berried Treasure'	EPfP LRHS SHil
	newryensis	SRms
	nitens	NLar SRms
	nitidifolius	see *C. glomerulatus*
	nohelii	SRms
	notabilis	SRms
	nummularioides	SRms
	nummularius Fisch. & C.A. Mey.	SRms
	obscurus	SRms
	obtusus Wall. ex Lindl.	SRms
	ogisui new	NLar
	omissus	NLar
	pangiensis	SRms
	pannosus	SRms
	paradoxus	SRms
	parkeri	NLar SRms
	pekinensis	SRms
	permutatus	see *C. pluriflorus*
	perpusillus	SRms
§	***pluriflorus***	NLar SRms
	poluninii	NLar SRms
	polycarpus	SRms
	praecox 'Boer'	see *C. apiculatus*
	procumbens	SRms
	– 'Queen of Carpets' ♀H6	CAco CBod CDoC ELan EPfP IBoy LRHS MAsh MBri MGos MRav MWhi NEgg SCoo SHil SLim SPoG SRms SWvt WMoo
	– 'Streib's Findling'	see *C.* 'Streib's Findling'
	prostratus	SRms
	przewalskii	SRms
	pseudo-obscurus	SRms
§	***purpurascens***	CSBt
	pyrenaicus misapplied	see *C. congestus*
	qungbixiensis	SRms
	raboutensis new	NLar
	racemiflorus	SRms
§	***radicans*** 'Eichholz'	MGos NWad
§	***rehderi***	CMHG NLar SRms
	rokujodaisanensis	NLar
	roseus	SRms
	'Rothschildianus' ♀H6	Widely available
	rugosus	SRms
	salicifolius	CTri MSwo NLar NWea SEND SRms WFar

- Autumn Fire	see *C. salicifolius* 'Herbstfeuer'
§ - 'Avonbank'	CDoC CEnd NLar WHar
- 'Brno Orangeade'	SRms
- 'Gnom' ♡H6	CDul CMac ELan EPfP LRHS MAsh MGos MMuc MRav NBir NEgg SCob SEND SPer SPoG SRms WHar WMoo
§ - 'Herbstfeuer'	MRav MSwo SRms WMoo
- Park Carpet	see *C. salicifolius* 'Parkteppich'
§ - 'Parkteppich'	NWea
- 'Pendulus'	see *C.* 'Hybridus Pendulus'
- 'Pink Champagne' ♡H6	CMac MRav
- 'Repens'	CDoC EPfP MWhi NPla NWad NWea SCob SGol SLim SPer SPoG SRms WHar
- var. ***rugosus***	see *C. hylmoei*
salwinensis	SRms
sandakphuensis	SRms
Saphyr Green = 'Belka'PBR **new**	EAEE
scandinavicus	SRms
schantungensis	NLar SRms
schlechtendalii 'Blazovice'	see *C. marginatus* 'Blazovice'
- 'Brno'	see *C. marginatus* 'Brno'
schubertii	SRms
serotinus misapplied	see *C. meiophyllus*
serotinus Hutch.	SRms
shannanensis	SRms
shansiensis	SRms
sherriffii	NLar SRms
sikangensis	SRms
simonsii ♡H6	CBcs CCVT CDoC CDul CLnd CMac EBee ECrN ELan EPfP LBuc LRHS MGos MJak NHol NLar NWad NWea SCob SGol SPer SPoG SRms WHar
§ ***splendens***	SRms
- 'Sabrina'	see *C. splendens*
spongbergii	SRms
staintonii	SRms
sternianus ♡H6	EPfP SRms
- ACE 2200	EPot
§ 'Streib's Findling'	IBoy MAsh SCob SGol
suavis	SRms
subacutus	SRms
subadpressus	SRms
× ***suecicus*** 'Coral Beauty' ♡H6	CBod CCVT CDoC COtt CTri EBee EPfP EPla EShb LAst LBuc LRHS MAsh MGos MJak MSwo MWat NEgg NHol NLar NPri SCob SGol SLim SPer SPoG SRms SWvt WHar WMoo
§ - 'Erlinda' (v)	SRms
- 'Ifor'	SRms
- 'Juliette' (v) ♡H6	EHoe LRHS MAsh MMuc NLar SCob SCoo SLim
- 'Skogholm'	CBcs CDul ELan EPfP EPla LRHS MAsh MGos MMuc NWea SCob SPer SRms WHar
taoensis	SRms
tardiflorus	SRms
tauricus	SRms
teijiashanensis	SRms
tengyuehensis	SRms
thimphuensis	SRms
tomentellus	WCFE
tomentosus	SRms
turbinatus	NLar SRms
'Valkenburg'	SRms
vandelaarii	NLar SRms
veitchii	NLar SRms
verruculosus	SRms
villosulus	SRms
vilmorinianus	SRms
wardii misapplied	see *C. mairei*
wardii W.W. Sm.	GGal SRms
washanensis **new**	NLar
× ***watereri***	CBod CCVT COtt EAEE ECrN ELon MJak MMuc MSwo NWea SEND SHil WJas
- 'Avonbank'	see *C. salicifolius* 'Avonbank'
- 'Cornubia'	see *C. frigidus* 'Cornubia'
- 'John Waterer'	EPfP SPer SPoG
- 'Pendulus'	see *C.* 'Hybridus Pendulus'
wilsonii	SRms
yalungensis	SRms
yinchangensis	SRms
zabelii	SRms

Cotula (*Asteraceae*)

coronopifolia	CBAq CBen CWat EHon NPer SWat
hispida ambig.	SIgm SPtp
§ ***hispida*** (DC.) Harv.	CTri CUse CWCL ECho EDAr EHoe EPot GMaP MAsh MHer MWat NPer NRya SPoG SRms WIce WJek XLum
lineariloba (DC.) Hilliard	ECha ECho EWes
minor	see *Leptinella minor*
'Platt's Black'	see *Leptinella squalida* 'Platt's Black'
potentilloides	see *Leptinella potentillina*
pyrethrifolia	see *Leptinella pyrethrifolia*
squalida	see *Leptinella squalida*

Cotyledon (*Crassulaceae*)

chrysantha	see *Rosularia chrysantha*
gibbiflora var. ***metallica***	see *Echeveria gibbiflora* var. *metallica*
oppositifolia	see *Chiastophyllum oppositifolium*
orbiculata	CHEx CTal SDix SPlb
- 'Silver Waves'	MCot
simplicifolia	see *Chiastophyllum oppositifolium*

Crambe (*Brassicaceae*)

cordifolia ♡H5	Widely available
maritima	Widely available
- 'Lilywhite'	CAgr LEdu SVic
tatarica	GJos

cranberry see *Vaccinium macrocarpon*, *V. oxycoccos*

Crassula ✿ (*Crassulaceae*)

anomala	see *C. atropurpurea* var. *anomala*
arborescens	EShb EUJe SChr
argentea	see *C. ovata*
§ ***atropurpurea*** var. ***anomala***	SChr
- subsp. ***arborescens*** 'Blue Mist'	SEND
'Buddha's Temple'	CSuc
coccinea	EShb SPlb
columella	CSuc
elegans subsp. ***elegans***	CSuc
multicava	CHEx CHel
muscosa	CSuc SChr SPlb SRot
obtusa	SRot

	orbicularis	WCot
§	***ovata*** ♀H2	CDoC CHEx EBak EOHP EPfP NPer NPla SChr SEND SPlb SPre SVen WThu
	- 'Blue Bird'	LToo
	- 'Horn Tree'	CSuc
	- 'Variegata' (v)	EBak WCot
	perfoliata	EOHP SRot WCot
	var. ***falcata*** ♀H2	
	perforata 'Variegata' (v)	MAvo SRot
	portulacea	see *C. ovata*
§	***sarcocaulis*** ♀H3	CBcs CHEx CHVG CTri ECho ELan ELon GCrg GEdr GMaP MAsh SPlb SPoG SRms SRot SVen WAbe WIce WSHC XSen
I	- 'Alba'	GEdr
	sedifolia	see *C. setulosa* 'Milfordiae'
	sediformis	see *C. setulosa* 'Milfordiae'
	setulosa	SPlb
§	- 'Milfordiae'	CTri ECho NBir NRya
	socialis	WAbe
	- 'Major'	SChr
	tetragona	SEND
*	***tomentosa*** 'Variegata' (v)	EShb

+ *Crataegomespilus* (*Rosaceae*)

'Jules d'Asnières'	NLar

× *Crataegosorbus* (*Rosaceae*)

miczurinii 'Ivan's Belle'	CAgr

Crataegus (*Rosaceae*)

	sp.	SWvt
	F&M 196	WPGP
	arnoldiana	CAgr CDul CLnd CTri EBee ECrN EPfP MAsh MCoo MMuc MWat NLar NWea SCoo SEND
	'Autumn Glory'	CEnd CLnd EBee ECrN
	azarolus var. ***aronia*** new	WCot
	chrysocarpa	EPfP
	chungtienensis SDR 5104	GKev
	coccinea misapplied	see *C. intricata*
	coccinea ambig.	NWea
§	***coccinea*** L.	CAgr CLnd CNWT CTho EBee MAsh SCoo
	coccinioides	EPfP
	cordata	see *C. phaenopyrum*
	crus-galli misapplied	see *C. persimilis* 'Prunifolia'
	crus-galli L.	CCVT CDul CLnd ECrN EPfP LAst MAsh MBri NLar NWea SPer WJas
	dahurica	EPfP
	dsungarica	EPfP
	× ***durobrivensis***	CAgr CDul CLnd EPfP MBri
	ellwangeriana	CAgr ECrN EPfP SDix
	- 'Fire Ball'	MBlu
	gemmosa	MAsh NWea
	greggiana	EPfP
	× ***grignonensis*** ♀H6	CBcs CDul CLnd CTho ECrN MAsh WJas
§	***intricata***	NWea
	jonesiae	EPfP
	laciniata misapplied	see *C. orientalis*
§	***laevigata***	CCVT NWea SCob
	- 'Coccinea Plena'	see *C. laevigata* 'Paul's Scarlet'
	- 'Crimson Cloud' ♀H6	Widely available
	- 'Gireoudii'	CDul LAst MGos NSti WJas
	- 'Mutabilis'	CTri EWTr SGol
§	- 'Paul's Scarlet' (d) ♀H6	Widely available
	- 'Pink Corkscrew'	EPfP ETwe LLHF MBlu MGos WPat
	- 'Plena' (d)	CBcs CDoC CDul CLnd CMac CSBt CTri EBee ECrN EPfP LAst MGos MRav MSwo MWat NWea SCrf SEWo SGol SLim SPer SWvt WHar
	- 'Rosea'	GKin
	- 'Rosea Flore Pleno' (d) ♀H6	Widely available
	× ***lavalleei***	CCVT CDul CLnd CMCN CTri ECrN ELan LAst MMuc MRav MSwo NWea SCoo SEND SLon
	- 'Aurora'	NLar
	- 'Carrierei' ♀H6	CDul CTho EPfP EWTr IVic MBri NWea SCoo SEWo SPoG WCot WMou
	mexicana	see *C. pubescens* f. *stipulacea*
	mollis	CAgr CTho ECrN EPfP
	monogyna	Widely available
§	- 'Biflora'	CDul CEnd CLnd CTho CTri EBee MAsh MCoo MGos NLar NWea SLim
	- 'Compacta'	LLHF MBlu WPat
	- 'Praecox'	see *C. monogyna* 'Biflora'
	- 'Stricta'	CCVT CDul CLnd CSBt ECrN EPfP EPla IDee MMuc SEND SGol
	- 'Variegata' (v)	ECrN
	× ***mordenensis*** 'Toba' (d)	CDul CLnd EPfP SGol
	nigra	CDul
§	***orientalis*** ♀H6	CCVT CDul CEnd CLnd CMCN CTho CTri ECrN EPfP IArd LRHS MAsh MBri MCoo MGos NLar NWea SCoo SLim WHar WJas WMou
	oxyacantha misapplied	see *C. laevigata*
	pedicellata	see *C. coccinea* L.
§	***persimilis*** 'Prunifolia' ♀H6	Widely available
	- 'Prunifolia Splendens'	CCVT EBee EWTr GBin LBuc LRHS MBri SCoo WPat
§	***phaenopyrum***	CDul CLnd CTho EPfP MBri
	pinnatifida	EPfP
	- var. ***major***	CDul CEnd EPfP LEdu MBri MCoo
	- - 'Big Golden Star'	CAgr CTho ECrN EPfP MBlu MCoo NLar SCoo
	'Praecox'	see *C. monogyna* 'Biflora'
	prunifolia	see *C. persimilis* 'Prunifolia'
	pseudoheterophylla	EPfP
§	***pubescens*** f. ***stipulacea***	CDul CTho ECrN EPfP
	punctata	CTho EPfP
	- f. ***aurea***	EPfP MBlu
	sanguinea	EPfP
	schraderiana	CAgr CDoC CDul CLnd CTho EBtc EPfP IVic MBri NLar NWea SCoo WHar
	submollis	CLnd
	succulenta 'Jubilee' PBR	EBee MCoo
	- var. ***macracantha***	CMCN EPfP
	tanacetifolia	CAgr CDul CTho EPfP MBlu MBri WPGP
	viridis 'Winter King'	EPfP SLim
	wattiana	CDul CLnd EBee ELan EPfP

× *Crataemespilus* (*Rosaceae*)

grandiflora	CDul CLnd

Crawfurdia (*Gentianaceae*)

pasquieri	GLin

Cremanthodium (*Asteraceae*)

arnicoides	EBee
brunneopilosum new	GKev

ellisii CC 7220 **new** GKev

Crenularia see *Aethionema*

Crepis (*Asteraceae*)

aurea ECho
incana ♀H4 CMea CPla ECho ECtt GCrg NChi NSla NWad SRms WAbe
- 'Pink Mist' GBin NLar
rubra WHil

Crinitaria see *Aster*

Crinodendron (*Elaeocarpaceae*)

hookerianum ♀H4 Widely available
- 'Ada Hoffmann' CBcs CDoC CEnd CExl CMac CTsd CWSG EBee ELan ELon EPfP GCal GKin IVic LRHS MBlu MBri MGos MPkF NLar NSoo SChF SEle SKHP SLim SWvt WBor WSHC
patagua CBcs CCCN CExl CHid CTsd EBee ELon EPfP EPri ESwi ETwe GBin IDee LRHS MMuc NLar NSoo SBrt SEND SEle SPlb SPoG SVen WSHC

Crinum (*Amaryllidaceae*)

sp. CMac
amoenum CCCN EBee ECho GBin WCot
asiaticum WCot
§ ***bulbispermum*** CPrp ELan WCot
campanulatum CDes
capense see *C. bulbispermum*
'Carolina Beauty' CDes WCot
'Cintho Alpha' SDeJ SPer
'Elizabeth Traub' WCot
'Ellen Bosanquet' CCCN CCon CTca EBee ELan GBin LRHS WCot
'Emma Jones' WCot
'Hanibal's Dwarf' CFil WCot WPGP
moorei CAvo CBro CCon CTca ECho IVic LEdu SChr WPGP
- f. ***album*** CCCN CFil CTca EBee
'Ollene' WCot
§ × ***powellii*** CBcs CBod CBro CExl CPrp CTca CTsd EBak ECha ECho ELan ELon EPfP EWTr GCal LAma LEdu LRHS MNrw MRav MWat SDeJ SEND SMad SPer SRms WCot WWFP
- 'Album' CAvo CBod CBro CDes CHEx CPrp CTca CTri EBee ECha ECho ELan ELon EPfP EWes GCra LAma LEdu LRHS MRav NWad SDeJ SEND SMad SPer SRms SSpi WCot WPGP
- 'Harlemense' CDes EBee
- 'Krelagei' **new** CDes
- 'Longifolium' see *C. bulbispermum*
- 'Roseum' see *C.* × *powellii*
'Sangria' WCot
'Summer Nocturne' WCot
variabile WCot
'White Queen' WCot
yemense misapplied IMou

Criogenes see *Cypripedium*

Crithmum (*Apiaceae*)

maritimum CArn CEls GPoy MNHC SPlb SRms WJek

Crocosmia (*Iridaceae*)

'Anna Marie' **new** ECtt
'Anniversary' IBlr
'Apricot' CTca ECrc IBal
'Apricot Surprise' ELon
aurea misapplied see *C.* × *crocosmiiflora* 'George Davison' Davison
aurea ambig. EShb GCal LRHS
aurea (Pappe ex Hook.f.) Planch. CPou IBlr
- from Swaziland GCal IBal
- subsp. ***aurea*** CTca IBlr
- - 'Maculata' IBlr
- subsp. ***pauciflora*** IBlr
'Auricorn' CTca IBlr LEdu
'Auriol' IBlr NCot
'Aurora' NGdn
'Beth Chatto' CTca ECrc IBal
'Bowland Blaze' MAvo
Bressingham Beacon = 'Blos' IBlr LRHS MSpe
'Bressingham Blaze' CBre CMHG CTca ECrc IBal IBlr LRHS NGdn NHol WHil
Bridgemere hybrid ECrc NHol
Bright Eyes = 'Walbreyes'PBR LBuc LRHS
'Buttercups' CMea EPot EWoo
'Cadenza' IBal IBlr NHol
'Carnival' IBlr
'Cascade' IBal IBlr
'Chinatown' IBal IBlr NHol WHil
'Chrome' CSam
'Chrome Spray' IBlr
'Citronella' misapplied see *C.* × *crocosmiiflora* 'Honey Angels'
'Comet' Knutty CTca ECrc GCal IBal IBlr LRHS MAvo WMoo
'Cornish Copper' CTca SMad
× ***crocosmiiflora*** CHEx CTca CTri IBlr SPlb SRms WBrk WMoo WShi
- 'A.E.Amos' ECrc
- 'A.J. Hogan' CPrp CTca IBal IBlr NHol
- 'African Glow' CTca EBee ECrc IBal LEdu
- 'Amber Sun' IBlr
- 'Amberglow' CElw CExl IBal IBlr MAvo NHol NPer
- 'Apricot Queen' CTca IBlr NHol
- 'Autumn Gold' ECrc IBlr
- 'B.A.Walker' ECrc
- 'Baby Barnaby' CBre CDes
- 'Babylon' Widely available
- 'Bicolor' CTca IBal IBlr WHil
- 'Burford Bronze' CPrp CTca IBal IBlr NHol
- 'Butterball' **new** LRHS SHil
- 'Buttercup' CSam CTca ECrc ECtt EPfP GKev IBal IBlr IKil LRHS MAvo MCot NHol SRkn WMoo WOut WWEG
- 'Canary Bird' CBro CSam ECtt IBal IBlr NGdn NHol WBrk
- 'Cardinale' IBlr
§ - 'Carmin Brillant' ♀H4 CBod CBro CSam CTca EAEE EBee ECha ECtt ELon EPfP ERCP GKev IBlr LAma LEdu LRHS MBri MPro MWhi NHol NSoo SCob SGSe SHil SMad SPoG SRms WMoo
- 'Challa' CTca ECtt
- 'Citrina' CTca MNrw

	– 'Citronella' J.E. Fitt	CBro CExl CSam CTri ECrc EPfP GMaP GQue LRHS MBel MRav MWhi NGdn NHol
§	– 'Coleton Fishacre'	Widely available
§	– 'Columbus'	CAvo CMos CSam CTca ECrc ELon EPfP EPri GKev IBal IBlr LRHS LSou MAvo MPro MSCN NHol SGSe SPer SRms WHil WMoo WWEG
	– 'Colwall'	IBal IBlr
	– 'Comet'	IBal
	– 'Constance'	CBro CSam CTca ECrc ECtt IBal IBlr LRHS MAvo NBid NGdn NHol WBrk WHil
	– 'Corona'	CPrp CTca IBal IBlr MAvo NHol
	– 'Corten'	IBlr
§	– 'Croesus'	CTca IBal IBlr MRav
	– 'Custard Cream'	CPrp CSpe CTca ECrc IBlr LRHS NHol
	– 'D.H. Houghton'	IBlr
	– 'Daisy Hill'	IBlr
	– 'David Fitt'	MAvo
	– 'Debutante'	CDes CPrp CTca ECrc EPri IBal IBlr NHol WSHC
§	– 'Diadème'	CSam CTca
	– 'Dusky Maiden'	CMac CTca ECrc ECtt EHoe EPri GCal GKin GMaP IBal IBlr LAst LRHS LSou MRav MSwo NHol SRms SWvt
	– 'Dwarf Gold'	IBal
§	– 'E.A. Bowles'	CPou CTca ECrc IBlr
	– 'Eastern Promise'	CBre CTca ELon IBal IBlr MAvo
	– 'Eclatant'	IBlr
	– 'Elegans'	ECrc ECtt IBal IBlr
§	– 'Emily McKenzie'	Widely available
	– 'Etoile de Feu'	IBlr
	– 'Fantasie'	ECrc IBal
	– 'Festival Orange'	ECrc IBlr
	– 'Fire Jumper'	CDes CTca EBee IBal MAvo
	– 'Firebrand'	IBlr
	– 'Fireglow'	CTca ECtt IBal IBlr
	– 'George Davison' misapplied	see *C.* × *crocosmiiflora* 'Golden Glory', *C.* 'Sulphurea'
§	– 'George Davison' Davison	Widely available
	– 'Gillian'	ECrc
	– 'Gloria'	CTca ECrc IBal MAvo SGSe
	– 'Golden Glory' misapplied	see *C.* × *crocosmiiflora* 'Diadème'
§	– 'Golden Glory' ambig.	CBod CExl COtt CPrp CTca CWCL ELan ELon EPla EWoo GBuc GKev IBal IBlr MSwo MWat NBir NPri SCob SEND SGSe SRms WHar
	– 'Goldfinch'	CPrp EBee ECrc IBlr WHil WWEG
	– 'Goldie'	CTca ECrc MAvo
	– 'Hades'	IBlr
	– 'Harvest Sun'	IBlr
	– 'His Majesty'	CBro CSam CSpe CTca ECrc IBal IBlr NHol WHil
	– 'Hoey Joey'	ECrc
§	– 'Honey Angels'	Widely available
	– 'Honey Bells'	ECrc WBrk
	– 'Irish Dawn'	ECrc IBal IBlr NHol NWad
§	– 'Jackanapes'	CDes CTca ECtt ELan GCal GKev IBal IBlr LRHS MLHP STPC
	– 'Jackanapes VI'	IBal
	– 'James Coey' misapplied	see *C.* × *crocosmiiflora* 'Carmin Brillant'
	– 'James Coey' J.E. Fitt	EAEE ECha EHoe EPfP GKin IFoB MLHP NGdn NLar NPCo SMrm WMoo
§	– 'Jessie'	CTca IBlr
	– 'Judith'	CTca IBlr
	– 'Kapoor'	IBlr
	– 'Kiautschou'	CTca CWCL IBal IBlr NGdn NHol
	– 'Lady Hamilton'	CCon CElw CExl CSam CTca GCal GCra IBal IBlr LRHS MAvo MRav NCGa NHol WHil WMoo WOut WWEG
	– 'Lady McKenzie'	see *C.* × *crocosmiiflora* 'Emily McKenzie'
	– 'Lady Oxford'	CTca ECrc IBal IBlr NHol WHil
	– 'Lambrook Gold'	CAvo ECrc IBlr
	– 'Lord Nelson'	CExl CTca IBal NHol
	– 'Loweswater'	ECrc MAvo
	– 'Lutea'	ECtt IBal
	– 'Marjorie'	ECrc
	– 'Mars'	CElw ECrc EWes IBal IFoB MAvo NGdn SRkn
	– 'Mephistopheles'	CPrp CTca IBlr MAvo NHol
	– 'Merryman'	CTca ECrc IBal
	– 'Météore'	ECtt EPfP GQue LRHS MBNS WWEG
	– 'Morgenlicht'	CTca NHol
	– 'Moses'	CTca
	– 'Mount Usher'	CCon CCse CTca ECrc GCal IBal IBlr NHol
§	– 'Mrs Geoffrey Howard'	CSam CTca IBal IBlr LRHS NHol SRms WCru
	– 'Mrs Morrison'	see *C.* × *crocosmiiflora* 'Mrs Geoffrey Howard'
	– 'Newry Seedling'	see *C.* × *crocosmiiflora* 'Prometheus'
	– 'Nimbus'	CTca IBal IBlr WHil
§	– 'Norwich Canary'	CMHG CTca ECha ECtt EPfP EPri GBuc GCra GKev IBal IBlr LEdu LRHS MRav NBir NGdn NHol WCot WHil WMoo WOut WWEG
	– 'Olympic Fire'	ECrc IBlr NHol
	– 'Olympic Sunrise'	CTca
	– 'Pepper'	IBlr
	– 'Ping Pong'	CTca
	– 'Plaisir'	CTca IBal IBlr NBid NHol
	– 'Polo'	CSam CTca CWCL IBal
	– 'Princess'	see *C. pottsii* 'Princess'
§	– 'Princess Alexandra'	IBlr
	– 'Prolificans'	ECrc IBlr
§	– 'Prometheus'	CTca IBal IBlr NHol
	– 'Queen Alexandra' misapplied	see *C.* × *crocosmiiflora* 'Princess Alexandra'
§	– 'Queen Alexandra' J.E. Fitt	CTca ECha IBlr WHal WMoo
	– 'Queen Charlotte'	CTca ECrc IBal IBlr
	– 'Queen Mary II'	see *C.* × *crocosmiiflora* 'Columbus'
	– 'Queen of Spain'	CTca IBal IBlr LRHS WHil WWEG
	– 'Rayon d'Or'	ECrc IBlr
	– 'Red King'	EBee EPfP GKev IBal IBlr LRHS MBri NLar WHil WMoo WRHF
	– 'Red Knight'	IBlr
	– 'Rheingold' misapplied	see *C.* × *crocosmiiflora* 'Diadème'
	– 'Rose Queen'	IBlr
	– 'Saint Clements'	CTca IBal IBlr NHol
	– 'Saracen'	CBod CMac CMea CTca EAEE ECtt EPla GBuc GCal GKin IBal IBlr IBoy LEdu LRHS LSou MBNS MHol SKHP SMrm SPoG WAul WMoo
	– 'Severn Seas'	ECrc ECtt
	– 'Sir Mathew Wilson'	IBal IBlr
	– 'Solfatare' ♀H4	Widely available
	– 'Solfatare Coleton Fishacre'	see *C.* × *crocosmiiflora* 'Coleton Fishacre'

	- 'Star of the East' ♀H4	Widely available
	- 'Starbright'	IBlr
	- 'Starfire'	ECrc
	- 'Sultan'	CExl IBlr WMoo
	- 'Tiger's Eye'	CTca
	- 'Twilight Fairy Gold' new	ECtt GBin MHol WCot
	- 'Venus'	CBre CHel CTca ECtt ELon IBal IBlr LPla MAvo NHol WHil WMoo WOut
	- 'Vesuvius'	ECrc GCal IBlr WSHC
	- 'Vic's Yellow'	ECrc
	- 'Voyager'	ECtt ELon ERCP GKev IBal IBlr LRHS NHol NLar SDeJ WOut
	- Wasdale strain	ECrc
	- 'Zeal Tan'	CElw CExl CMHG CSam CTca ECtt ELan ELon EPri GBin GCal IBal IBlr LEdu LRHS MBNS MNFA NEgg NLar NSti SMrm WCot WMoo
§	× ***crocosmioides***	CTca IBlr WHil
	- 'Castle Ward Late'	CPrp CTca EAEE ECrc ECtt EPfP GBin GCal GCra GQue IBal IBlr MAvo MWhi NHol NLar SMrm SRms WCot WMoo
	- 'Mount Stewart Late'	IBlr
§	- 'Vulcan' Leichtlin	CMac CTca IBlr LRHS WHil
	'Darkleaf Apricot'	see *C.* × *crocosmiiflora* 'Coleton Fishacre'
	'Devil's Advocate'	CTca
	'Eggs and Bacon' new	ECrc
	'Eldorado'	see *C.* × *crocosmiiflora* 'E.A. Bowles'
	'Elegance'	IBlr
	'Ellenbank Canary'	CTca MAvo
	'Ellenbank Firecrest'	CDes CTca EBee MAvo NCGa
	'Ellenbank Goldcrest'	NLar
	'Ellenbank Skylark'	MAvo
	'Emberglow'	Widely available
	'Fandango'	IBal IBlr NHol
	'Fernhill'	ECrc IBlr
	'Fire King' misapplied	see *C.* × *crocosmiiflora* 'Jackanapes'
	'Fire King' ambig.	ECrc EPot ERCP IBal NLar NSti SWvt WHil
	'Fire Sprite'	IBlr
	'Firecracker'	IBlr
	'Firefly'	IBlr
	'Flaire'	IBlr
	'Fleuve Jaune'	CTca ECrc
	'Forest Fire'	IBal LLHF LSou
	fucata	IBlr
	- 'Jupiter'	see *C.* 'Jupiter'
	fucata × ***paniculata***	CTca IBal
	'Fugue'	CTca IBlr NCot
	'Fusilade'	IBlr
	'Gold Sprite'	IBlr
	'Golden Ballerina' PBR	EBee ECtt EWes GBin IBal LBMP LSou MWat NCGa SGSe SHar SPoG SRkn
	'Golden Dew'	CTca ECrc ECtt EPfP GQue MBNS NCGa SKHP WCot WMoo
	Golden Fleece *sensu* Lemoine	see *C.* × *crocosmiiflora* 'Coleton Fishacre'
	'Harlequin'	CElw CPrp CTca IBal
	'Harmonia'	CDes CTca EBee
	'Hellfire'	CHVG CPar CSam CTca ECtt ELon IBal LEdu LLHF LRHS MAvo MBNS MBri MNrw NGdn NSti SMad SRms WCot WMoo
	'Highlight'	ECrc IBal IBlr MAvo NHol
	'Jennine'	IBal
	'Jenny'	MAvo
	Jenny Bloom = 'Blacro' PBR	EBee LRHS NChi
	'John Boots'	CHel ECtt ELon GBuc GKev IBal LRHS MCot NBid NHol NLar SRms WHil
§	'Jupiter'	CBre CSam CTca CWCL GCal IBal MAvo MMuc MRav NChi NHol NLar SEND WHil
	'Kathleen'	ECrc
	'Krakatoa'	CHVG CHll CPrp CTca ECrc GBin IBal LBMP LLHF MAvo MBel SGSe SKHP SRkn SWvt WMoo
	'Lady Wilson' misapplied	see *C.* × *crocosmiiflora* 'Norwich Canary'
	'Lana de Savary'	CPrp CTca EWes GCal IBal IBlr NBid NHol NWad WCot
	'Late Cornish'	see *C.* × *crocosmiiflora* 'Queen Alexandra' J.E. Fitt
	'Late Lucifer'	CHEx CTca CTri GCal IBlr SDix SMHy
	× ***latifolia***	see *C.* × *crocosmioides*
	'Lemon Spray'	CTca IBlr
	'Limpopo'	Widely available
	'Lowen Daa'	CTca
	'Lucifer' ♀H5	Widely available
	Lucifer's Children	EPfP MPro
	'Malahide Castle Red'	SMad WMoo
	'Mandarin'	ECrc IBlr
	'Marcotijn'	CTca IBal IGor
	masoniorum ♀H4	Widely available
	- from Satan's Nek, South Africa	CTca
	- 'African Dawn'	CTca ECrc ECtt
	- 'Amber'	IBlr
	- 'Dixter Flame'	IBlr IFoB SDix WOut
	- 'Firebird'	CHel CTca GCra IBal IBlr IGor LRHS MHol NHol SRms WCot
	- 'Flamenco'	IBlr
	- 'Golden Swan'	SRms
	- Holehird strain	ECrc
	- 'Kiaora'	IBlr
	- 'Moira Reid'	IBal IBlr NHol
	- red-flowered	IBlr
	- 'Rowallane Apricot'	IBlr
	- 'Rowallane Orange'	CPrp CTca IBal IBlr NHol
	- 'Rowallane Yellow' ♀H4	CPrp CTca EBee GCal IBal IBlr IMou LRHS NCGa NHol SMHy WCot WSHC
	- 'Sherbert Orange' new	MAvo
	- Slieve Donard selection	CTca ECrc IBal
	- 'Sunflare'	IBlr
	- 'Tropicana'	IBlr
	mathewsiana	IBlr
	mathewsiana × ***paniculata***	CTca
	'Mex'	MAvo WCot
	'Minotaur'	IBlr
	'Miss Scarlet'	EPfP LBuc LRHS
	'Mistral'	CCCN CCon CHel COtt CTca ECtt EPot GAbr GBuc GKev IBal IBlr LAst LRHS NHol NLar WMoo
	'Moorland Blaze'	WMoo
	'Mount Stewart'	see *C.* × *crocosmiiflora* 'Jessie'
	'Mr Bedford'	see *C.* × *crocosmiiflora* 'Croesus'
	'Mullard Pink'	CTca ECrc
	'Okavango' PBR	CBre CBro CMac CPrp CTca ECtt ELon EPri GAbr GQue IBal LSun MAvo MBNS MCot MHol MNrw NLar NPCo SGSe SKHP SMrm WCot WFar WHil
	Old Hat	see *C.* 'Walberton Red'

	'Orange Devil'	CBre ECtt GKin IBal IBlr LLHF MBNS WHil
	'Orange River'	MAvo
	'Orangeade'	CTca ECtt IBal IBlr NHol SRms
	'Pageant'	ECrc
§	***paniculata***	CMac CPou CTca ECtt GAbr GBin MNFA NBid SArc WBrk WMoo WOut WShi
	- from Howick	CTca
	- from Kologha	CTca
	- brown/orange-flowered	IBlr
	- 'Cally Greyleaf'	GCal MAvo WCot
	- 'Cally Sword'	GCal IBal MAvo
	- 'Major'	CTri IBlr
	- 'Natal'	CPrp CTca ECtt IBal NHol
	- red-flowered	CTca IBlr SWvt
	- triploid	IBlr
	aff. ***paniculata***	IBlr
	'Paul's Best Yellow'	CDes CEnd CHel CMea CPar CSam CTca ECGP ECtt ELon EWes GAbr IBal LLHF LRHS LSun MAvo MBNS MTis NPCo NSti SHar SMad SMrm SPer SWvt WCot WHoo
	pearsei	CTca IBlr
	'Phillipa Browne'	CSde CTca ECtt IBal SGSe WCot WMoo
	pottsii	CTca IBal IBlr WHil WPtf WWEG
	- CD&R 109	CPou
	- 'Culzean Pink'	CElw CExl CHVG CPrp CTca GBin GCal IBal IBlr LPla MLHP NBid NBir NCot NHol NLar NPCo WOut
	- deep pink-flowered	IBlr IGor WMoo
	- 'Grandiflora'	IBlr
§	- 'Princess'	ECrc ECtt IBal
	- tall	CTca IBal MSpe
	'Quantreau'	IBlr
	'Queen Alexandria'	LRHS
	'R.W. Wallace'	CTca IBal
	'Red Star'	IBal
	rosea	see *Tritonia disticha* subsp. *rubrolucens*
	'Rowden Bronze'	see *C.* × *crocosmiiflora* 'Coleton Fishacre'
	'Rowden Chrome'	see *C.* × *crocosmiiflora* 'George Davison' Davison
	'Ruby Velvet'	IBlr
	'Rubygold'	CPrp IBlr
	'Saffron Queen'	IBlr
	'Saturn'	see *C.* 'Jupiter'
	'Scarlatti'	CTca IBal IBlr NHol
	'Scarlet Wonder'	CTca
	'Severn Sunrise' ♀H5	Widely available
	'Shocking'	IBlr MAvo
	'Sonate'	CTca
	'Sorento'	IBlr
	'Spitfire'	CExl CSam CTca ECha ECtt ELan GAbr GQue IBal IBlr LRHS MArl MAvo MRav NHol SGSe SWvt
§	'Sulphurea'	CExl CPou CSam ECtt EPfP IBal IBlr MSpe NHol SDix
	'Sunzest'	CTca ECrc MAvo
	'Suzanna' **new**	ECtt
	'Tamar Double Red'	CTca
	'Tamar Glow'	CTca
	'Tamar New Dawn'	CTca
	'Tamar Peace'	CTca
	'Tangerine'	ECrc
	'Tangerine Dream'	IBlr
	'Tangerine Queen'	CTca ECrc IBal IBlr LRHS NHol WHil WMoo
	'Tiger'	CElw CTca ECrc
	'Toccata'	IBlr
	'Twilight Fairy Crimson' **new**	CAbb CWGN ECrc ECtt GBin
I	'Vulcan' A. Bloom	CTca IBal IBlr MAvo
	'Vulcan' Leichtlin	see *C.* × *crocosmioides* 'Vulcan' Leichtlin
§	'Walberton Red'	CDes CTca ECrc EWes IBal MAvo NWad SKHP SMad
	Walberton Yellow = 'Walcroy'PBR	CHVG EPfP LBuc LRHS SMHy SMad
	'Zambesi'PBR	CDes CMac CTca ECtt ELon GQue IBal MAvo MBNS MBri MCot MNrw NCGa SKHP WHil
	'Zeal Giant'	CRow CTca ECrc ECtt IBal IBlr NHol
	'Zeal Remembrance'	CTca
	'Zeal Unnamed'	CCon CPrp CTca ECrc GBee IBal IBlr NHol

Crocus ✿ (*Iridaceae*)

	'Advance'	ECho EPot ERCP LAma MBri SDeJ WShi
§	***albiflorus***	EPot
	ancyrensis	ECho EPot GKev SDeJ
	- 'Golden Bunch'	ECho SBch SDeJ WShi
§	***angustifolius*** ♀H5	ECho EPot GKev SDeJ
	- bronze-tinged	NMin
	- 'Minor'	EPot
	antalyensis	ECho
	'Ard Schenk'	ECho GKev LAma LRHS
	asturicus	see *C. serotinus* subsp. *salzmannii*
	asumaniae	ECho NRog
	- white-flowered **new**	NRog
	'Aubade'	ECho EPot GKev
	aureus	see *C. flavus* subsp. *flavus*
	banaticus ♀H5	ECho EPot GKev LLHF NHar NRog
	- 'Early Bird' **new**	NRog
	- 'Snowdrift'	NHar
	baytopiorum	ECho
	biflorus	ECho
	- 'Blue Pearl' ♀H5	CAvo CBro ECho EPfP EPot GKev MBri NBir SBch SDeJ SPhx WCot WShi
	- subsp. ***melantherus***	NRog
	- 'Miss Vain'	ECho EPot ERCP GKev LAma MBri
	- 'Serevan'	EPot
	- subsp. ***tauri***	ECho
	- subsp. ***weldenii***	ECho
	- - 'Albus'	ECho EPot LAma
	- - 'Fairy'	ECho EPot LAma
	'Blue Bird'	ECho EPot LAma
	boryi	ECho LRHS NRog
	cambessedesii	ECho NRog
	cancellatus	SDeJ
§	- subsp. ***cancellatus***	ECho EPot GKev LAma NRog
	- var. ***cilicicus***	see *C. cancellatus* subsp. *cancellatus*
	- subsp. ***damascenus*** **new**	NRog
	- subsp. ***lycius***	ECho EPot NRog
	- subsp. ***mazziaricus***	NRog
	- subsp. ***pamphylicus***	NRog
	candidus var. ***subflavus***	see *C. olivieri* subsp. *olivieri*
	cartwrightianus ♀H4	GKev LRHS NRog WShi
	- 'Albus' misapplied	see *C. hadriaticus*
	- 'Albus' Tubergen ♀H4	EPot GKev NRog SDeJ
	- 'Marcel' **new**	NRog

	Name	Suppliers
	- 'Michel' **new**	NRog
	chrysanthus ♀H5	CHab
	- 'Cream Beauty' ♀H5	CAvo CBro ECho EPfP EPot GKev LAma LRHS MBri NBir SDeJ WShi
	- 'E.A. Bowles' misapplied	see *C. chrysanthus* 'E.P. Bowles'
§	- 'E.P. Bowles'	ECho LAma MBri
	- var. ***fuscotinctus***	ECho EPfP EPot LAma MBri SDeJ
	- 'Sunspot'	EPot
	- 'Uschak Orange'	ECho
	- 'Warley'	ECho
	- 'Zwanenburg Bronze' ♀H5	ECho EPfP GKev SDeJ WShi
	'Cloth of Gold'	see *C. angustifolius*
	clusii	see *C. serotinus* subsp. *clusii*
	corsicus ♀H4	ECho EPot
	dalmaticus	EPot
	danfordiae	ECho
	'Dorothy'	EPot GKev
	'Dutch Yellow'	see *C.* × *luteus* 'Golden Yellow'
	etruscus ♀H5	ECho
	- 'Rosalind'	ECho
	- 'Zwanenburg' ♀H5	ECho EPot GKev LAma SDeJ
	'Fantasy'	ECho WShi
	flavus	ECho
§	- subsp. ***flavus*** ♀H5	ECho EPot LAma WShi
	fleischeri	ECho EPot LAma
	'Flower Record'	ECho GKev LAma NBir SDeJ
	'Gipsy Girl'	CAvo EPfP EPot ERCP LAma MBri
	'Golden Mammoth'	see *C.* × *luteus* 'Golden Yellow'
	'Goldilocks' ♀H5	EPot GKev LAma SDeJ
	goulimyi ♀H4	CBro CTal ECho EPot GKev LAma LRHS NRog SDeJ
	- 'Albus'	see *C. goulimyi* subsp. *goulimyi* 'Mani White'
§	- subsp. ***goulimyi*** 'Mani White' ♀H4	CTal
	- subsp. ***leucanthus***	NRog
	'Grand Maître'	CAvo LAma MBri SDeJ
§	***hadriaticus*** ♀H4	ECho EPot GKev LAma LRHS NRog
	- var. ***chrysobelonicus***	see *C. hadriaticus*
	- subsp. ***hadriaticus*** f. ***lilacinus***	EPot
	- 'Jumbo'	NRog
	'Herald'	LAma
	heuffelianus subsp. ***heuffelianus***	EPot WShi
	imperati subsp. ***imperati*** var. ***albus***	WAbe
	- subsp. ***suaveolens***	EPot
	- - 'De Jager'	ERCP LAma
	'Jānis Rukšans'	CAvo
	'Jeanne d'Arc'	CAvo CBro ECho EPfP EPot GKev LAma MBri NBir SDeJ WShi
	'Jeannine'	ECho EPot SDeJ
	× ***jessoppiae***	ECho
	karduchorum	ECho EPot LAma NRog
	'King of the Striped'	ECho LAma SDeJ SPer
	korolkowii	ECho GKev LAma
	- 'Golden Nugget'	EPot
	- 'Kiss of Spring'	ECho EPot
	kosaninii	ECho NMin
	- 'April View'	EPot NMin
	kotschyanus ♀H5	ECho
	- 'Albus'	ECho NRog SDeJ
	- subsp. ***cappadocicus***	NRog
§	- subsp. ***kotschyanus***	ECho EPot NRog SDeJ
	- 'Reliance'	ECho NRog
	kotschyanus × ***ochroleucus***	ECho
	'Ladykiller' ♀H5	CAvo CBro ECho EPot ERCP GKev LAma MBri NMin SPhx WShi
	laevigatus ♀H3	ECho NRog
	- CE&H 612	EPot
	- 'Fontenayi'	ECho EPot ERCP GKev NRog
	'Large Yellow'	see *C.* × *luteus* 'Golden Yellow'
§	***ligusticus*** ♀H5	CAvo CBro ECho EPot LAma
	- 'Millesimo' **new**	NRog
	longiflorus ♀H4	ECho EPot LRHS NRog
§	× ***luteus*** 'Golden Yellow' ♀H5	CAvo EPfP EPot GKev LAma WShi
	malyi ♀H4	ECho NMin
	- 'Sveti Roc'	EPot
	mathewii	ECho EPot
	- 'Dream Dancer'	EPot
	medius	see *C. ligusticus*
	minimus	ECho EPot ERCP LAma LLHF
	'Negro Boy'	ECho EPot LAma SBch
	niveus	CBro ECho EPot GKev LAma LLHF LRHS NRog WAbe WCot
	nudiflorus	ECho EPot GKev LAma LLHF NRog
	ochroleucus	ECho EPot GKev NRog SDeJ
	olivieri	ECho
	- subsp. ***balansae***	ECho
	- - 'Zwanenburg'	ECho EPot
§	- subsp. ***olivieri***	ECho
	- - 'Little Tiger'	ECho
	oreocreticus	NRog
	pallasii	ECho
	- subsp. ***dispathaceus*** **new**	NRog
	paschei	EPot
	'Peter Pan'	CAby
	'Pickwick'	CAby CAvo ECho EPfP EPot LAma MBri NBir SDeJ WShi
	'Prins Claus'	ECho EPfP EPot ERCP LAma MBri SBch SDeJ SPer
	'Prinses Beatrix'	NMin
	pulchellus ♀H4	CAvo ECho EPot ERCP GKev LAma NRog SDeJ
	- 'Albus'	ECho EPot NRog
	- 'Inspiration'	NRog
	- 'Michael Hoog'	ECho NRog
	'Purple Heart'	NRog
	'Purpureus'	see *C.* 'Purpureus Grandiflorus'
§	'Purpureus Grandiflorus'	CBro EPot SDeJ
	'Queen of the Blues'	CBro EPot SDeJ
	'Remembrance'	CAby CAvo CBro ECho EPfP EPot GKev LAma NBir SDeJ WShi
	reticulatus	ECho EPot
	- subsp. ***reticulatus***	EPot
	robertianus	NRog
	- HOA 9856	EPot
	'Romance'	CAvo CBro EPot GKev LAma MBri SDeJ
	'Ruby Giant'	CAvo CBro ECho EPfP EPot ERCP GKev LAma MBri NBir SDeJ SPer SPhx WShi
	rujanensis	ECho
	salzmannii	see *C. serotinus* subsp. *salzmannii*
	sativus	CArn CAvo CBod CBro CPrp CTca CTsd ECho ELan EPot ERCP GKev GPoy LAma NBir NRog SDeJ SVic
	'Saturnus'	EPot LAma
§	***serotinus*** subsp. ***clusii***	ECho LAma NRog
§	- subsp. ***salzmannii***	ECho LAma NRog
	- - f. ***albus***	NRog
	- - 'Erectophyllus'	NRog
	sibiricus	see *C. sieberi*

§ ***sieberi*** ♀H5	EPot
- 'Albus'	see *C. sieberi* 'Bowles's White'
- subsp. ***atticus***	ECho
- - 'Firefly'	ECho EPfP EPot GKev LAma SDeJ
§ - 'Bowles's White' ♀H5	CBro ECho EPot GKev SDeJ
- 'Hubert Edelsten' ♀H5	ECho LAma
- 'Ronald Ginns'	EPot
- subsp. ***sublimis*** 'Tricolor' ♀H4	CAvo CBro CTca ECho EPfP EPot GKev LAma MBri NBir NWad SDeJ SPer
- 'Violet Queen'	LAma
'Snow Bunting' ♀H5	CAvo CBro CTca ECho EPfP EPot GKev LAma NBir SDeJ SPer WShi
speciosus ♀H4	CAvo CBro CTca EPfP LAma MLHP NBir SDeJ SPer WShi
- 'Aino'	ECho NRog
- 'Aitchisonii'	ECho EPot GKev LAma LRHS NRog
- 'Albus' ♀H4	CAvo CBro ECho EPot ERCP GKev NRog SDeJ WShi
- 'Artabir'	ECho EPot GKev LRHS NRog SDeJ
- 'Cassiope'	ECho EPot GKev LAma LRHS NRog SDeJ
- 'Conqueror'	CBro ECho EPfP EPot ERCP GKev LAma LRHS NRog SDeJ
- 'Oxonian'	CBro ECho GKev LAma NRog
- subsp. ***speciosus***	ECho EPot NBir NRog SDeJ
- subsp. ***xantholaimos***	NRog
'Spring Beauty'	CAvo EPfP ERCP SDeJ SPer
susianus	see *C. angustifolius*
suterianus	see *C. olivieri* subsp. *olivieri*
thomasii	NRog
tommasinianus ♀H5	CAvo CBro CHab CTca ECho EPot LAma LLWP MBri MRav NBir SDeJ SPhx SRms WShi
- 'Albus'	ECho EPot LAma WShi
- 'Barr's Purple'	ECho EPot GKev LAma SDeJ
- 'Claret'	ECho
- 'Eric Smith'	EPot
- 'Lilac Beauty'	ECho EPfP EPot LAma
- 'Pictus'	ECho LAma LLHF WShi
- 'Roseus'	CAvo CDes ECho EPot ERCP GKev LAma NMin SDeJ SPhx WCot WShi
- 'Whitewell Purple'	CAvo CBro ECho EPot ERCP GKev LAma MBri NBir SDeJ WShi
tournefortii ♀H3	ECho LRHS NRog
* - 'Albus'	ECho
'Vanguard' ♀H5	CAvo CBro ECho EPfP EPot LAma SDeJ
veluchensis	ECho LLHF
veneris	ECho NRog
vernus	ECho GKev
- subsp. ***albiflorus***	see *C. albiflorus*
- 'Graecus'	ECho EPot
- 'Michael's Purple'	ECho
- Uklin strain	ECho
- subsp. ***vernus*** 'Grandiflorus'	see *C.* 'Purpureus Grandiflorus'
versicolor 'Picturatus'	ECho EPot ERCP LAma LLHF NMin SDeJ
vitellinus	EPot
'White Triumphator'	LAma
'Yalta'	CAvo ECho ERCP GKev
'Yellow Giant'	SDeJ
'Yellow Mammoth'	see *C.* × *luteus* 'Golden Yellow'
'Zenith'	ECho EPot
'Zephyr' ♀H4	CBro ECho EPot NRog SDeJ
zonatus	see *C. kotschyanus* subsp. *kotschyanus*

Croomia (*Stemonaceae*)

heterosepala	WCru

Crossyne (*Amaryllidaceae*)

flava new	NRog

Crotalaria (*Papilionaceae*)

laburnifolia ♀H2	CCCN

Crowea (*Rutaceae*)

exalata × ***saligna***	CExl

Crucianella (*Rubiaceae*)

stylosa	see *Phuopsis stylosa*

Cruciata (*Rubiaceae*)

§ ***laevipes***	NMir

Crusea (*Rubiaceae*)

coccinea	CSpe WCot
- 'Crûg Crimson'	WCru

Cryptantha (*Boraginaceae*)

paradoxa	CPBP

Cryptanthus (*Bromeliaceae*)

alagoanus new	LAir
bivittatus new	LAir
- 'Pink Starlight' (v) ♀H1a	LAir
Black Mystic Group	LAir
bromelioides	LAir
marginatus new	LAir
'Red Star' new	LAir

Cryptocarya (*Lauraceae*)

alba	CDul GBin SVen

Cryptogramma (*Pteridaceae*)

crispa	WHer

Cryptomeria ✿ (*Cupressaceae*)

fortunei	see *C. japonica* var. *sinensis*
japonica	CAco CDul CMen CTho ELau EPfP MBlu MMuc SEND SWvt WMou
- Araucarioides Group	NPCo
- 'Aurea'	EUJe
- 'Bandai-sugi' ♀H6	CKen CMac CMen EHul EPfP EUJe GKin MGos NHol NLar SLim SRms
- 'Barabits Gold'	MGos
- 'Birodo'	CKen
- 'Black Dragon'	SLim
- 'Compressa'	CDoC CKen EHul EPfP LBee MAsh MGos NWad SRms
§ - 'Cristata'	CBcs CDoC CMac ELan ESwi LRHS MGos MPkF NPCo SLim SRms
- 'Dacrydioides'	CDoC GKin NLar SLim
- 'Dinger'	CKen NLar
- Elegans Group	CBcs CDul CMac CSBt EHul ELan EPfP EPla EUJe LRHS MBri MGos NEgg NLar NWea SCoo SEND SLim SPer SPoG SRms WMou
- 'Elegans Aurea'	CCVT EHul ELan MAsh MBri SWvt
- 'Elegans Compacta' ♀H6	CDoC CMac CSBt EHul ELan GBin LBee LRHS MBri MMuc NLar NWea SLim SPoG SRms SWvt
- 'Elegans Nana'	LBee SRms
- 'Elegans Viridis' ♀H6	MJak SLim SPer WHar

I	- 'Elegantissima' new	CCVT
	- 'Globosa Nana' ♀H6	CAco CDul EHul EPfP LAst LBee LPal MGos NEgg NHol SArc SCoo SLim SPoG
	- 'Golden Promise' ♀H6	CBcs NHol NWad SCoo SLim SPer SWvt
	- Gracilis Group	CDoC
	- 'Jindai-sugi'	GKin NLar
	- 'Kamasan' new	NLar
	- 'Karl Fuchs'	SLim
	- 'Kilmacurragh'	CKen
	- 'Knaptonensis' (v)	CDoC
	- 'Kohui-yatsubusa'	CKen
	- 'Koshiji-yatsubusa'	NLar
	- 'Koshyi'	CKen
	- 'Little Champion'	CDoC CKen SLim
	- 'Little Diamond'	CKen NPCo
	- 'Little Sonja'	CKen SLim
	- 'Little Yoko'	CKen
	- 'Lobbii Nana' hort.	see *C. japonica* 'Nana'
	- 'Monstrosa'	NLar
§	- 'Nana'	CDoC CMac EHul EPfP
	- 'Osaka-tama'	CKen
	- 'Pipo'	CKen
	- 'Pygmaea'	NHol NLar NWad SRms
	- 'Rasen-sugi'	GKin IDee IVic MGos NLar
	- 'Rein's Dense Jade'	SLim
	- 'Sekkan-sugi' ♀H6	CBcs CCVT CDoC CDul CMac EHul EPfP EPla ESwi GBin GKin IArd LAst LBee MGos NLar NPCo SCoo SLim SPoG SWvt WBor
	- 'Sekka-sugi'	see *C. japonica* 'Cristata'
§	- var. ***sinensis***	CBod
§	- 'Spiralis' ♀H6	CDoC CKen CMac EHul ELan EPfP EPla EUJe GKin LAst LBee MAsh MGos NEgg NHol NLar NWad NWea SCoo SLim SPer SPoG SRms SWvt
§	- 'Spiraliter Falcata'	CBod CDoC NLar
§	- 'Tansu'	CDoC CKen
	- 'Tenzan-sugi' ♀H6	CDoC CKen MGos NHol NWad SLim WThu
	- 'Tilford Gold'	EHul MGos NHol
	- 'Toda'	CKen
	- 'Vilmorin Gold'	MGos NHol
	- 'Vilmoriniana' ♀H6	CDoC CKen CMen CTri EPfP EPla GKin LRHS MBri MGos MMuc NEgg NHol NLar SCoo SEND SLim SPer SPoG SWvt WMoo
	- 'Winter Bronze'	CKen
	- 'Yatsubusa'	see *C. japonica* 'Tansu'
	- 'Yore-sugi'	see *C. japonica* 'Spiralis', 'Spiraliter Falcata'
	- 'Yoshino'	CKen SLim
	sinensis	see *C. japonica* var. *sinensis*

Cryptostegia (*Apocynaceae*)

	grandiflora	CCCN

Cryptotaenia (*Apiaceae*)

	japonica	CHby CPou GPoy LEdu MHer MNHC SRms WHer WJek
	- f. ***atropurpurea***	CSpe EBee EHoe LEdu MNrw SDix SGSe

Ctenanthe (*Marantaceae*)

	lubbersiana ♀H1b	XBlo
	oppenheimiana	XBlo

Cucubalus (*Caryophyllaceae*)

	baccifer	CArn EWld NLar

Cudrania see *Maclura*

cumin see *Cuminum cyminum*

Cuminum (*Apiaceae*)

	cyminum	CArn ELau SVic

Cunninghamia (*Cupressaceae*)

	konishii	CExl
§	***lanceolata***	CAco CBcs CDTJ CDoC CDul CKen CMCN CMac CTho EPfP GKin SMad SSpi SSta WBor WPGP
	- 'Glauca'	CAco CExl CJun CTho IVic
	sinensis	see *C. lanceolata*
	unicaniculata	see *C. lanceolata*

Cunonia (*Cunoniaceae*)

	capensis	CExl

Cuphea (*Lythraceae*)

	caeciliae	CSam
	cyanea	CMHG SDix
	'Firecracker'	LAst
	hyssopifolia ♀H1c	CHll EShb SWvt
	- 'Alba'	CCCN EShb SWvt
	- pink-flowered	CCCN
	- red-flowered	CCCN
	- 'Rosea'	SEND SWvt
§	***llavea*** 'Georgia Scarlet'	CCCN
	- 'Tiny Mice'	see *C. llavea* 'Georgia Scarlet'
I	***macrophylla*** hort.	CHll
	maculata	CCCN
	'Regal Purple'	CPla
	'Torpedo'	NPri
	viscosissima	CSpe MCot

× *Cupressocyparis* see × *Cuprocyparis*

Cupressus (*Cupressaceae*)

	arizonica new	LPal
	- var. ***arizonica*** 'Arctic'	CDoC
	- var. ***glabra*** 'Angaston'	SLim
	- - 'Aurea'	CAco CMac EHul MAsh NPCo SGol SLim
	- - 'Blue Ice'	CAco CBcs CDoC CDul CMac CTho EHul MAsh MGos NPCo SLim SPoG SWvt WHar WMou
	- - 'Compacta'	CKen
I	- - 'Fastigiata'	CAco CCVT CDoC EHul EPfP
	- 'Pyramidalis' ♀H5	EPfP SEND SGol
I	- 'Sulfurea'	MBri
	cashmeriana ♀H3	CAco CBcs CDTJ CDoC CTho ELan IVic SLim SMad
	× ***leylandii***	see × *Cuprocyparis leylandii*
	lusitanica 'Brice's Weeping'	CKen NPCo SLim
	- 'Glauca Pendula'	CDoC
	- 'Pygmy'	CKen
	macrocarpa	CBcs CCVT CDoC CDul CTho EHul SEND
	- 'Compacta'	CKen
	- 'Gold Spread'	EHul SLim
	- 'Goldcrest' ♀H4	CBcs CCVT CDoC CDul CMac ECrN EHul ELan LBee LRHS MBri MGos NBir NPri NSoo NWea SEWo

SGol SLim SPer SPoG SWvt WCFE WMou
- 'Golden Cone' NPCo
- 'Golden Pillar' CDoC EHul SWvt
- 'Greenstead Magnificent' SLim
- 'Horizontalis Aurea' EHul
- 'Lohbrunner' CKen
- 'Lutea' CDoC

I - 'Pendula' SLim
- 'Pygmaea' CKen
- 'Sulphur Cushion' CKen
- 'Wilma' ♀H4 CSBt EHul LAst LBee LRHS MAsh MBri MGos SCoo SEND SGol SLim SPoG SWvt
- 'Woking' CKen

nootkatensis see *Xanthocyparis nootkatensis*
sempervirens CDul CMCN CTsd EHul ELan EUJe LPal SPlb
- 'Bolgheri' SBig
- 'Garda' CDoC
- 'Green Pencil' CKen
- 'Pyramidalis' see *C. sempervirens* Stricta Group
- var. ***sempervirens*** see *C. sempervirens* Stricta Group

§ - Stricta Group CAco CBcs CCVT CDul CMCN CTho EHul EPfP EWTr LPal NLar SArc SEND SEWo SGol WCFE
- 'Swane's Gold' CBcs CDoC CDul CKen EHul MAsh NPCo WCFE
- 'Totem Pole' CAco CCVT CKen CSBt CTho CTri EHul ELan EPfP EUJe LBee LPal LRHS MAsh MGos SCoo SEND SPoG SWvt

torulosa WGrf

× *Cuprocyparis* (*Cupressaceae*)

§ ***leylandii*** Widely available

I - '2001' CCVT CDoC CMac SGol SLim WMou
- 'Blue Jeans' PBR MMuc SEND

§ - 'Castlewellan' CAco CBcs CCVT CDoC CDul CMac COtt CSBt CTri EHul EPfP LBuc MAsh MBri MGos MJak MMuc NHed NSoo NWea SCob SEND SGol SLim SPer SPoG SWvt WFar WHar WMou
- Excalibur Gold = 'Drabb' PBR CDoC NPri NWea
- 'Ferngold' MAsh
- 'Galway Gold' see × *C. leylandii* 'Castlewellan'
- 'Gold Rider' ♀H6 CDoC CMac EHul MAsh MGos MMuc NEgg NWea SCob SCoo SEND SGol SMad SPer SPoG SWvt WHar

§ - 'Harlequin' (v) CMac SEND SWvt
- 'Herculea' CDoC
- 'Leighton Green' WMou
- 'Naylor's Blue' CMac
- 'Olive's Green' SWvt
- 'Robinson's Gold' CMac EHul GQui MMuc NWea SGol SLim WHar WMou
- 'Variegata' see × *C. leylandii* 'Harlequin'

* - 'Viridis' **new** CAco
- 'Winter Sun' WCFE

Curculigo (*Hypoxidaceae*)

capitulata XBlo
crassifolia B&SWJ 2318 WCru
- HWJ 683 from Vietnam **new** WCru

Curcuma ✿ (*Zingiberaceae*)

alismatifolia SDeJ
longa CArn SPre
roscoeana LAma SDeJ
zedoaria 'Bicolor Wonder' CCCN
- 'Pink Wonder' CCCN
- 'White Wonder' CCCN SDeJ

Curtonus see *Crocosmia*

Cussonia (*Araliaceae*)

paniculata CDTJ CWGN EUJe WCot
spicata CDTJ SPlb

custard apple see *Annona cherimola*, *A. reticulata*

Cyananthus (*Campanulaceae*)

incanus GEdr
integer misapplied see *C. microphyllus*
lobatus ♀H5 LLHF
- 'Albus' EPot WAbe
- giant CTal GEdr NHar WAbe

lobatus* × *microphyllus CTal GCrg GEdr WAbe

§ ***microphyllus*** ♀H5 EPot GCrg GEdr NHar NSla WAbe

***microphyllus* × 'Sherriff's Variety'** NHar
sherriffii EPot GJos IFoB WAbe
spathulifolius WAbe

Cyanella (*Tecophilaeaceae*)

orchidiformis NRog

Cyathea (*Cyatheaceae*)

australis CBty CDTJ CKel ESwi IDee SPlb
brownii ISha
cooperi CDTJ CKel EFtx ESwi WFib

* - 'Brentwood' ESwi ISha NLos

dealbata CDTJ CKel GBin
dregei SPlb
incisoserrata EFtx
medullaris CKel EFtx
smithii CDTJ CKel
tomentosissima CDTJ CKel EFtx

Cyathodes (*Ericaceae*)

colensoi see *Leucopogon colensoi*
fraseri see *Leucopogon fraseri*
parviflora see *Leucopogon parviflorus*

Cycas (*Cycadaceae*)

media LPal
panzhihuaensis CBrP LPal SPlb
revoluta ♀H2 CAbb CBrP CCCN CDoC EPfP EUJe LPal NLos SArc SChr SEND SMad SPlb STrG XBlo
revoluta* × *taitungensis CBrP

§ ***rumphii*** CBrP LPal

taitungensis CBrP
thouarsii see *C. rumphii*

Cyclamen ✿ (*Primulaceae*)

abchasicum see *C. coum* subsp. *caucasicum*
africanum CBro ECho EPot GKev LAma LRHS MAsh
africanum* × *hederifolium ECho

§	***alpinum***	CBro ECho EPot GKev LAma LRHS MAsh SDeJ
	- 'Nettleton White'	MAsh
	balearicum	CBro ECho EPot GKev LAma LRHS MAsh
	cilicium 🏆^{H3}	CBro ECho EPfP EPot ERCP GBuc GKev LAma LRHS MAsh WCot WHoo WShi XEll
	- f. ***album***	CBro ECho EPot GBuc GKev LAma LLHF LRHS MAsh
	- patterned-leaved	ECho
	colchicum	ECho MAsh
§	***coum*** 🏆^{H5}	Widely available
	- var. ***abchasicum***	see *C. coum* subsp. *caucasicum*
§	- subsp. ***caucasicum***	MAsh
	- subsp. ***coum***	CBro ECho
	- - f. ***albissimum***	GBuc
	- - - 'George Bisson'	MAsh
	- - - 'Golan Heights'	MAsh
	- - f. ***coum*** Pewter Group 🏆^{H5}	ECho GBuc GKev WCot
	- - - - 'Blush'	GBuc
	- - - - 'Maurice Dryden' 🏆^{H5}	CBro CLAP ECho EPot GKev LAma LRHS MAsh WHoo
	- - - - red-flowered	WPat
	- - - - 'Tilebarn Elizabeth'	MAsh NBir WHoo
	- - - 'Roseum'	CAvo GBuc
	- - - Silver Group	CAvo CBro ECho EWoo LRHS NRya WHoo
	- - - - red-flowered	WHoo
	- - magenta-flowered	WHoo
	- - f. ***pallidum*** 'Album'	CAvo CWCL ECho EPot EWoo GKev LAma LPal LSun SDeJ SMrm SPer WHoo WPat
	- dark pink-flowered	CAvo CLAP ECho WHoo
	- hybrid	ERCP
	- marble-leaved	ECho WHoo
	- plain-leaved	CLAP
	- red-flowered	CLAP ECho
I	- 'Rubrum'	GKev
	- 'Something Magic'	LSou
	creticum	ECho MAsh
	cyprium	CBro ECho GKev LRHS MAsh
	- 'E.S.'	ECho MAsh WThu
	- 'Galaxy'	MAsh
	× ***drydeniae***	MAsh
	elegans	MAsh
	europaeum	see *C. purpurascens*
	fatrense	see *C. purpurascens* subsp. *purpurascens* from Fatra, Slovakia
	graecum	CBro CPne ECho EPot GKev LLHF LRHS MAsh WCot WHil WThu XEll
	- subsp. ***candicum***	MAsh
	- subsp. ***graecum*** f. ***album***	CBro ECho EPot GKev LRHS MAsh
	- - f. ***graecum*** 'Glyfada'	EPot GKev MAsh
§	***hederifolium*** 🏆^{H5}	Widely available
	- S&L 175/1	WCot XLum
	- 'Amaze Me'	LEdu LSou MPie WCot
	- arrow-head	CLAP ECho
	- var. ***confusum***	WCot
	- var. ***hederifolium*** f. ***albiflorum*** 🏆^{H5}	CAvo CBro CTri ECho EWoo GKev LEdu NWad SDeJ WCot WHil WHoo WPat WPnP XLum
	- - - 'Album'	CWCL MAvo
	- - - Bowles's Apollo Group	GBuc
	- - - 'Linnett Stargazer'	WCot
	- - - 'Nettleton Silver'	see *C. hederifolium* var. *hederifolium* f. *albiflorum* 'White Cloud'
	- - - 'Perlenteppich'	GMaP
	- - - silver-leaved	SDys
§	- - - 'White Cloud' 🏆^{H5}	CLAP ECho MAsh WCot WHoo
	- - f. ***hederifolium*** Bowles's Apollo Group	CHid CLAP GBuc
	- - - 'Fairy Rings'	MAsh
	- - - 'Ruby Glow'	CWCL GBuc LRHS MAsh NBir WPat WThu
	- - - Silver Cloud Group 🏆^{H5}	CBro CHid CLAP GBuc MAsh NBir WHoo WPat
	- - - 'Stargazer'	LLHF
	- 'Lysander'	MAsh
	- 'Pewter Mist'	LAma
	- 'Rose Pearls'	SRot
	- Silver-leaved Group	ECho GKev SRot
	- - 'Silver Leaf Pink'	GMaP NWad
	- - 'Silver Leaf White'	GMaP NWad
	× ***hildebrandii***	LLHF
	ibericum	see *C. coum* subsp. *caucasicum*
	intaminatum	CBro ECho EPot GKev LAma LLHF LRHS MAsh XEll
	- plain-leaved	WThu
	latifolium	see *C. persicum*
	libanoticum	CBro ECho EPot GKev LAma LRHS MAsh XEll
	mirabile 🏆^{H4}	CBro CPne ECho EPot GBuc GKev LAma LLHF LRHS MAsh SDeJ WThu
	- f. ***mirabile*** 'Tilebarn Nicholas'	ECho MAsh WCot
	- f. ***niveum*** 'Tilebarn Jan'	ECho MAsh
	neapolitanum	see *C. hederifolium*
	orbiculatum	see *C. coum*
	parviflorum	MAsh
§	***persicum***	CBro CWCL ECho GBuc GKev LRHS MAsh
	- white-flowered	ECho MAsh
	pseudibericum 🏆^{H4}	CBro ECho EPot GKev LAma LLHF LRHS MAsh SDeJ WThu
	- f. ***roseum***	MAsh
§	***purpurascens***	CBro ECho GBuc GKev LLHF MAsh WHoo WPat WThu
	- var. ***fatrense***	see *C. purpurascens* subsp. *purpurascens* from Fatra, Slovakia
§	- subsp. ***purpurascens*** from Fatra, Slovakia	GKev
	repandum	CAvo CBro ECho EPot GKev LAma LLHF LRHS MAsh WHer
	- 'Pelops' misapplied	see *C. rhodium* subsp. *peloponnesiacum*
	- subsp. ***repandum*** f. ***album***	MAsh
§	***rhodium*** subsp. ***peloponnesiacum***	ECGP MAsh
	- subsp. ***rhodium***	MAsh
	- subsp. ***vividum***	MAsh
	rohlfsianum	CBro ECho GKev LRHS MAsh NMin XEll
	× ***schwarzii***	MAsh
	'Trena' **new**	SDeJ
	trochopteranthum	see *C. alpinum*
	× ***wellensiekii***	MAsh
	× ***whiteae***	MAsh

Cyclea (*Menispermaceae*)

polypetala KWJ 12157	WCru

Cydonia ✿ (*Rosaceae*)

japonica	see *Chaenomeles japonica*
oblonga (F)	CBcs ECrN
- 'Agvambari' (F)	SKee
- 'Aromatnaya' (F)	ERea WHar
- 'Bereczki'	see *C. oblonga* 'Bereczki'
§ - 'Bereczki' (F)	NLar
- 'Champion' (F)	CAgr CHab ECrN ERea GTwe LBuc MCoo NEgg NOra SKee SVic WHar
- 'Early Prolific' (F)	SEND
- 'Ekmek' (F)	SKee
- 'Isfahan' (F)	ERea SKee
- 'Krymsk' (F)	CAgr
- 'Leskovac' (F)	CAgr EPom ERea NLar NOra
§ - 'Lusitanica' (F)	CAgr CHab CLnd ECrN ELan ERea GTwe NLar NOra SKee WHar
- 'Meech's Prolific' (F)	CAgr CDul CHab CLnd CTho CTri ECrN EMil EPom ERea GTwe LAst LRHS MAsh MBri MGos MRav MWat NLar NOra NWea SDea SFam SKee SLim SPer SPoG WHar
- pear-shaped (F)	CHab ECrN NEgg SPer
- Portugal	see *C. oblonga* 'Lusitanica'
- 'Rea's Mammoth' (F)	CHab ERea NLar
- 'Seibosa' (F)	SKee
- 'Serbian Gold' (F)	CDoC CDul CTho ECrN EPom ERea GQue GTwe LAst LRHS MAsh MBri NLar NOra WHar
- 'Shams' (F)	SKee
- 'Smyrna' (F)	NLar WHar
- 'Sobu' (F)	SKee
- 'Vranja' misapplied	see *C. oblonga* 'Bereczki'
- 'Vranja' ambig. (F)	MAsh
- 'Vranja' Nenadovic (F) 🏆H5	Widely available

Cylindropuntia (*Cactaceae*)

imbricata	SPlb XLum XSen
leptocaulis	XSen
versicolor	XSen
× ***viridiflora***	XSen

Cymbalaria (*Plantaginaceae*)

aequitriloba 'Alba'	GAbr
§ ***hepaticifolia***	SBrt SPlb
§ ***muralis***	ECho ECtt GAbr MHer WBor WHer WIce XLum
- 'Albiflora'	see *C. muralis* 'Pallidior'
§ - 'Globosa Alba'	WBor
- 'Kenilworth White'	WCot WMoo
- 'Nana Alba'	MMuc MSCN
§ - 'Pallidior'	ECho
§ ***pallida***	CPBP MAsh MMuc SBch SEND SPlb WMoo
- 'Alba'	EWTr WMoo
§ ***pilosa***	ECtt NLar
'Snow Wave'	ECtt LSou

Cymbopogon (*Poaceae*)

citratus	CArn CBod CCCN CTsd CUse ENfk GPoy MNHC SHDw SIde SRms SVic WJek
flexuosus	CCCN ELau MHer WJek
martini	GPoy
nardus	CArn GPoy

Cymophyllus (*Cyperaceae*)

§ ***fraserianus***	CDes CFil CHEx EBee GBin

Cynanchum (*Apocynaceae*)

acuminatifolium	GCal
ascyrifolium	EBee GEdr WCot

Cynara (*Asteraceae*)

§ ***baetica*** subsp. ***maroccana***	SBrt WHil
cardunculus 🏆H6	Widely available
- ACL 380/78	SWat
- 'Bianco Avorio' **new**	SVic
I - 'Cardy'	NCGa
- dwarf	SMHy
- subsp. ***flavescens*** from La Gomera **new**	SBrt
I - 'Florist Cardy'	NLar
- 'Gobbo di Nizza'	ELau LEdu WHer
- 'Porto Spineless'	WFar
§ - Scolymus Group	CBcs CHEx CMea EHoe EWes GPoy IBoy IGor LRHS MBri MNHC MRav MWat NPri SEND SPav SPhx SPoG SVic WHer WWEG
- - 'Carciofo Violetto Precoce'	LEdu WHer
- - 'Gigante di Romagna'	WHer
- - 'Gros Camus de Bretagne'	MAvo WCot XLum
- - 'Gros Vert de Lâon' 🏆H5	CBcs ELan ELau LRHS WCot
- - 'Imperial Star'	ELau
- - 'Large Green'	NLar
- - 'Monica Lynden-Bell'	WCot
- - 'Purple Globe'	CArn ELau LEdu SMrm
- - 'Romanesco'	ELau SVic
- - 'Rouge d'Alger' **new**	WCot
- - 'Tavor'	EPla SVic WCot
- - 'Vert Globe'	CSBt ELau ENfk LEdu MWat NPer NPri SMrm SPad SVic SWvt WHil
- - 'Violet de Provence'	CSBt ELau LEdu
- - 'Violetto di Chioggia' 🏆H4	ELau LEdu WHer
* ***gomerensis*** **new**	WCot
hystrix misapplied	see *C. baetica* subsp. *maroccana*
scolymus	see *C. cardunculus* Scolymus Group
syriaca	SBrt XSen

Cynodon (*Poaceae*)

aethiopicus	CDes EBee EHoe LEdu WCot

Cynoglossum (*Boraginaceae*)

amabile 🏆H3	SPhx
- f. ***roseum*** 'Mystery Rose'	CHVG
dioscoridis	SPhx
grande	EBee SBrt
nervosum	EBee ELan EPPr LAst MLHP MMuc MRav SEND SPer SPoG WCot WWEG
officinale	CArn MHer WSFF

Cynosurus (*Poaceae*)

cristatus	CHab NMir

Cypella (*Iridaceae*)

aquatilis	EWay LLWG
herbertii	CDes CPom WHil

peruviana WHil

Cyperus (*Cyperaceae*)

§ ***albostriatus*** CCCN EShb

- 'Nanus' SGSe

alternifolius misapplied see *C. involucratus*

alternifolius L. CBAq CBen EHon EPfP EUJe LPal MHin MSKA SArc WMAq WMoo

- 'Compactus' see *C. involucratus* 'Nanus'

'Chira' NWsh

diffusus misapplied see *C. albostriatus*

§ ***eragrostis*** CArn CBAq EHoe GCal LPot MWts SDix SPlb SWat WGrn WMAq WMoo

esculentus CAgr CArn LEdu

fuscus NWsh WMoo

glaber IBoy MBNS

haspan misapplied see *C. papyrus* 'Nanus'

haspan L. MSKA

§ ***involucratus*** ♀H1c CHEx EBak EShb EWay MMuc MSKA MWts SEND SGSe SMad SWat WMoo

§ - 'Nanus' EShb

longus CBAq CBen CWat EHoe EHon EPPr GCal MMuc MWts NPer SEND SWat WMAq XLum

papyrus ♀H1a CDTJ LPal MHin MSKA SArc SBig XBlo

§ - 'Nanus' ♀H1a XBlo

- 'Perkamentus'PBR LLWG

prolifer LLWG

rotundus MBri

vegetus see *C. eragrostis*

Cyphanthera (*Solanaceae*)

tasmanica ECou

Cyphomandra see *Solanum*

Cypripedium (*Orchidaceae*)

acaule GEdr

Achim gx GEdr XFro

Aki gx GEdr XFro

- 'Pastel' GEdr XFro

× ***andrewsii*** GEdr

Anna gx new GEdr XFro

Annette gx GEdr

Bärbel Schmidt gx GEdr

× ***barbeyi*** see *C.* × *ventricosum*

Barry Phillips gx new GEdr

Bernd gx GEdr

Bill gx GEdr

Birgit gx pastel-flowered GEdr XFro

Boots gx new GEdr

calceolus CCon

Carol Ilene gx GEdr

Chauncey gx GEdr

Cleo Pinkepank gx GEdr

× ***columbianum*** GEdr

corrugatum see *C. tibeticum*

Dawn Edwards gx new GEdr

Dietrich gx ♀H5 GEdr XFro

Emil gx GEdr XFro

fasciolatum GEdr

flavum GBin GEdr GKev

formosanum ♀H3 GEdr LAma SKHP

Gisela gx GEdr LAma XFro

- 'Pastel' GEdr

Hank Small gx ♀H3 GEdr XFro

Hans Erni gx GEdr

henryi GKev LAma

Inge gx GEdr XFro

Ingrid gx GEdr XFro

Irene gx GEdr XEll

Ivory gx GEdr

japonicum GKev

James Armitage gx new GEdr

Jens gx new GEdr

Judith Merrick gx GEdr

Julia Barclay gx GEdr

Kathleen Anne Green gx GEdr

kentuckiense ♀H5 CCCN CCon GEdr GKev LRHS

Kristi Lyn gx GEdr XFro

Lothar Pinkepank gx GEdr

Lucy Pinkepank gx GEdr

macranthos GEdr

- 'Hotei' GEdr

- var. ***hotei-atsumorianum*** Sadovsky GEdr

- John Hagger Group new XFro

- var. ***speciosum*** GEdr

Maria gx GEdr XFro

Memoria Gerd Kohls gx GEdr

Memoriam Shawna Austin gx GEdr

Michael gx ♀H5 GEdr XFro

- 'Pastel' GEdr

Neil Lancaster gx new GEdr

Otto gx GEdr

parviflorum GEdr

§ - var. ***pubescens*** GEdr LAma

'Parville' LRHS

Paul gx GEdr XFro

Peter gx GEdr XFro

Philipp gx ♀H5 GEdr XFro

Pixi gx GEdr

Pluto gx GEdr XFro

pubescens see *C. parviflorum* var. *pubescens*

'Pueblo' LRHS

Rascal gx GEdr

reginae ♀H5 CCCN CCon GEdr LAma LRHS SKHP XEll

- f. ***album*** GEdr LRHS

Renate gx GEdr

- pastel-flowered XFro

Rhodopis gx GEdr

Sabine gx ♀H5 GEdr XFro

- pastel-flowered GEdr XFro

Sebastian gx GEdr XFro

segawae LAma

Selston High School gx new GEdr

Siggi gx new GEdr

Sunny gx GEdr

§ ***tibeticum*** GEdr

Tilman gx GEdr XFro

Tower Hill gx GEdr

Ulla Silkens gx ♀H5 GEdr LAma XEll XFro

Ursel gx GEdr XFro

§ × ***ventricosum*** GEdr XFro

- 'Pastel' XFro

Victoria gx GEdr XFro

Werner Frosch gx GEdr

Cyrilla (*Cyrillaceae*)

racemiflora CMac

Cyrtanthus (*Amaryllidaceae*)

	'Alaska'	ECho
§	***brachyscyphus***	ECho EShb
	breviflorus	ECho WPGP
	'Edwina'	CCCN ECho
§	***elatus*** ♀H1c	CPne CSpe ECho EWll LEdu WCot
	- 'Cream Beauty'	ECho
	- 'Pink Diamond'	ECho WCot
	- pink-flowered	ECho
	'Elizabeth'	CCCN ECho
	eucallus **new**	WCot
	mackenii	ECho EShb WPGP
	- var. ***cooperi***	CAby CPne
	- cream white-flowered	CCCN ECho
	- 'Himalayan Pink'	CCCN EBee ECho
	- orange-flowered	ECho
	- pink-flowered	CAbb
	- red-flowered	CAbb CCCN ECho
	- white-flowered	ECho
	- yellow-flowered	ECho
	montanus	ECho WCot
	obliquus	WCot
	parviflorus	see *C. brachyscyphus*
	purpureus	see *C. elatus*
	sanguineus	ECho WCot
	smithiae	ECho
	speciosus	see *C. elatus*

Cyrtomium (*Dryopteridaceae*)

§	***caryotideum***	CBty CLAP ISha
§	***falcatum*** ♀H2	Widely available
	- 'Rochfordianum'	CBty CCCN GBin ISha LRHS MRav MWat WFib
§	***fortunei*** ♀H3	CBod CHid CKel CLAP EFer ELan ELon EPfP EUJe GBin IDee LPal LRHS MGos MMuc MRav NBid NGdn NLos SEND SGSe SPer SPoG SRms WCFE WFib WMoo WPnP XLum
	- var. ***clivicola***	CBty CKel EBee EPfP EShb ISha LPal LPot LRHS MGos MMoz MRav NLar SPad SPtp WCot XLum
	macrophyllum	CLAP GLin LPal LRHS

Cystopteris ✿ (*Woodsiaceae*)

bulbifera	CLAP MNFA
dickieana	CLAP GBin WFib
fragilis	EFer WFib
moupinensis	EFtx
- B&SWJ 6767	WCru

Cytisopsis (*Papilionaceae*)

pseudocytisus subsp. ***reeseana*** **new**	CPBP

Cytisus (*Papilionaceae*)

	sp.	CAco
	'Andreanus'	see *C. scoparius* f. *andreanus*
	'Apricot Gem'	LRHS MBri NLar
	× ***beanii*** ♀H5	EBee ELan EPfP LRHS MAsh NLar SLon
	'Boskoop Glory'	NEgg NLar
	'Boskoop Ruby' ♀H5	CDoC CMac CSBt EBee EPfP GKin LBMP LRHS MAsh MBri MJak MWat NEgg NHol NPri NSoo SCob SHil SPer SWvt WBor WHar
	'Burkwoodii' ♀H5	CBcs CDoC CDul ELan EPfP LRHS MSwo MWat NEgg SPoG WFar
	canariensis	see *Genista canariensis*
	'Compact Crimson'	LRHS
	'Cottage'	WAbe
§	***decumbens***	MAsh
§	***demissus*** ♀H4	WAbe
	'Dorothy Walpole'	EBee WFar
	'Dukaat'	NLar
	'Eastern Queen'	EBee
	filipes **new**	GKin
	'Garden Magic' **new**	EBee
	'Golden Cascade'	CBcs CWCL ELan LBMP LRHS MAsh NEgg SLim
	'Goldfinch'	CDoC CSBt ELan LRHS MJak MSwo NHol NLar NSoo SCob SPad WFar
§	***hirsutus***	CExl SRms
	'Hollandia' ♀H5	CBcs CSBt EPfP GKin LBMP MMuc MRav SGol
	× ***kewensis*** ♀H5	ELan EPfP LRHS MAsh MGos MRav NLar NWea SPer SRms
	- 'Niki'	EPfP LRHS MAsh MMuc NLar SPer WRHF
	'Killiney Red'	ELan
	'Killiney Salmon'	GKin MMuc MRav
	'La Coquette'	EPfP LRHS MBri SPlb
	'Lena' ♀H5	CDoC CMac CSBt EPfP GKin LRHS MBri MGos MMuc MWat NBir NEgg NHol NLar NPri NSoo SCob SGol SHil SLim SPoG WFar WHar
	'Luna'	EPfP SHil
	maderensis	see *Genista maderensis*
	'Maria Burkwood'	MMuc NLar NSoo
	'Minstead'	ELan SPer
	'Mrs Norman Henry'	NLar
	'Newry Seedling'	CMac
	nigricans 'Cyni' ♀H5	CWld ELan ELon ESwi IArd LAst LRHS MAsh MMuc SPer SPoG
	oromediterraneus	EBee
	'Palette'	CAco MMuc
	'Porlock'	see *Genista* 'Porlock'
	× ***praecox***	CMac ELon LAst LRHS MAsh NEgg SGol SPlb SPoG WFar WHar
	- 'Albus'	CBcs CDoC CDul CMac ELan EPfP LAst LRHS MAsh MBri MGos MJak MRav NHol NSoo SCob SHil SPer WFar WHar
	- 'Allgold' ♀H5	CBcs CDoC CDul CMac CSBt CTri CWCL ELon EPfP LRHS MAsh MBri MGil MMuc MRav NEgg NHol NPri NWea SCob SEND SGol SHil SLon SPer SPoG SRms SWvt WFar
	- 'Canary Bird'	see *C.* × *praecox* 'Goldspeer'
	- 'Frisia'	WFar
§	- 'Goldspeer'	CAco MWat
	- 'Lilac Lady'	LRHS
	- 'Warminster' ♀H5	EPfP GKin MBri MMuc MRav NWea SEND SPer SRms
§	***proliferus***	CExl
§	***purpureus***	ELan EPfP MRav SPer WPat WSHC
	- f. ***albus***	EPfP
§	- 'Atropurpureus'	EPfP NWea
	racemosus	see *Genista* × *spachiana*
	Red Favourite	see *C.* 'Roter Favorit'
	'Red Wings'	MMuc SPer
§	'Roter Favorit'	EPfP WRHF
	scoparius	CArn CDul NWea
§	- f. ***andreanus***	CDoC CTri EPfP MJak SPer
	- 'Cornish Cream'	CDul CSBt ELan EPfP LRHS NEgg SPer

- 'Firefly'	CBcs CMac
- 'Fulgens'	CWCL EPfP
- 'Golden Sunlight'	CSBt EPfP MJak MSwo
- Monarch strain	GJos
× ***spachianus***	see *Genista × spachiana*
supinus	see *C. hirsutus*
'White Lion'	CMac
'Windlesham Ruby'	CExl EBee ELan EPfP LRHS NLar SLim SPer WFar
'Zeelandia' ♀H5	CMac EPfP LRHS MBri MWat NHol SCob SPer WFar

D

Daboecia ✿ (*Ericaceae*)

	cantabrica	MMuc
§	- f. ***alba***	CSBt MBri NWad SWhi
	- - 'Creeping White'	CFst
	- - 'David Moss'	MMuc NWad
I	- - 'Early Bride'	CFst
	- 'Alberta White'	CFst IVic SWhi
	- 'Amelie'PBR	CFst IVic SWhi
	- 'Arielle'	CFst SWhi
	- 'Atropurpurea'	CFst CSBt NWad SWhi
	- 'Bicolor'	CFst
	- 'Blueless'	SWhi
	- f. ***blumii*** 'Pink Blum'	CFst
	- - 'Purple Blum'	CFst
	- - 'White Blum'	CFst SPer SWhi
	- 'Bubbles'	CFst
	- 'Celtic Star'	CFst
	- 'Chaldon'	CFst
	- 'Charles Nelson' (d)	SWhi
	- 'Cinderella'	IVic SWhi
	- 'Covadonga'	CFst
	- 'Cupido'	CTsd IVic
	- 'Glamour'	CFst SPer
I	- 'Globosa Pink'	NWad
	- 'Graceful Muxoll' **new**	CFst
	- 'Heather Yates'	CFst
	- 'Hookstone Purple'	NWad SWhi
	- 'Praegerae'	CTri SWhi
	- 'Rainbow' (v)	CFst SWhi
	- subsp. ***scotica*** 'Ben'	CFst
	- - 'Cora'	CFst
	- - 'Ellen Norris'	CFst
	- - 'Golden Imp'	CFst SWhi
	- - 'Goscote'	MGos
	- - 'Jack Drake'	CFst MBri SWhi
	- - 'Katherine's Choice'	CBcs CFst NWad SWhi
	- - 'Red Imp'	CFst
	- - 'Robin'	CFst
	- - 'Silverwells' ♀H5	CBcs MAsh MBri SWhi
	- - 'William Buchanan' ♀H5	CFst GAbr GJos MAsh MBri NWad SCoo SWhi
	- - 'William Buchanan Gold' (v)	MBri
	- 'Stardust Muxoll' **new**	CFst
	- 'Tinkerbell'	CFst GJos SWhi
	- 'Vanessa'PBR	CFst IVic
	- 'Waley's Red' ♀H5	NWad SWhi

Dacrycarpus (*Podocarpaceae*)

§	***dacrydioides***	CBcs CBrP ECou LEdu
	- 'Dark Delight'	ECou

Dacrydium (*Podocarpaceae*)

bidwillii	see *Halocarpus bidwillii*
cupressinum	CBcs CDoC SPlb WThu
franklinii	see *Lagarostrobos franklinii*
laxifolium	see *Lepidothamnus laxifolius*

Dactylicapnos (*Papaveraceae*)

	macrocapnos	CCon CSpe IDee IFro WBor WCru
	platycarpa **new**	WPGP
§	***scandens***	CRHN EPfP MSCN SBrt SMad
	- GWJ 9438	WCru
	- 'Shirley Clemo'	CExl
	torulosa	WTou
§	***ventii***	EWld
	- GWJ 9376	WCru

Dactylis (*Poaceae*)

glomerata	CHab SVic WSFF
- 'Variegata' (v)	MMuc NBid SEND SHDw

Dactylorhiza (*Orchidaceae*)

	sp.	NDav
	alpestris	CCon SKHP
	aristata	EFEx
	× ***braunii***	ECha
§	***elata*** ♀H5	GAbr IBlr LAma WCot
	- Duguid's	WThu
§	***foliosa*** ♀H4	CCCN CTsd GCra IBlr
§	***fuchsii***	CCCN CCon CMil EPot GBin GKev LEdu MMoz MNrw NPCo NRya NSla SKHP WHer WSFF
	- pink-flowered	CCon
	× ***grandis***	IBlr
	hybrid	LEdu
	incarnata	NBid
§	***maculata***	CCon CHid ELan EPfP LAma LRHS WBor WHer
	maderensis	see *D. foliosa*
§	***majalis***	CCon LAma MNrw WSFF XEll
	mascula	see *Orchis mascula*
	praetermissa	CCCN CCon LRHS SKHP
	- subsp. ***praetermissa*** hybrid	SKHP
	purpurella	CCon GAbr GJos NRya

Dahlia ✿ (*Asteraceae*)

	'A la Mode' (LD)	CWGr
	'Abba' (SD)	CWGr ECtt
	'Abbie' (SD)	NHal
	'Abingdon Ace' (SD)	CWGr SGbt
	'Abridge Alex' (SD)	CWGr
	'Abridge Ben' (MinD)	CWGr
	'Abridge Florist' (SWL)	CWGr
	'Abridge Natalie' (SWL)	CWGr
	'Abridge Primrose' (SWL)	CWGr
	'Abridge Taffy' (MinD)	CWGr
I	'Acapulco' (S-c)	ERCP
	'Adelaide Fontane' (MD)	CWGr
	'Admiral Rawlings' (SD)	CWGr
	'African Garden' (SD) **new**	CSut
	'Aimie' (MinD)	CWGr
	'Aitara Caress' (MinC)	NHal SGbt WPhe
	'Aitara Cloud' (MinC)	CWGr
	'Akita' (Misc)	CWGr NBri SGbt WPhe
	'Aladdin's Lamp' (SWL) **new**	NJRG
	'Alauna Clair-Obscur' (Fim)	CWGr ERCP WPhe
	'Albert Schweitzer' (MS-c)	CWGr SGbt

	Name	Suppliers
	'Alfred C' (GS-c)	CWGr
	'Alfred Grille' (MS-c)	SDeJ SGbt SMrm SPer
	'Alf's Mascot' (MD)	NJRG WPhe
	'Aljo' (MS-c)	CWGr
	'All Triumph' (MinS-c)	CWGr
	'Allan Snowfire' (MS-c)	LAyl NHal
	'Allan Sparkes' (SWL) 🏆H3	CWGr
	'Alloway Candy' (Misc)	ERCP
	'Alloway Cottage' (MD)	CWGr NHal SGbt WPhe
	'Almand's Climax' (GD) 🏆H3	CWGr SGbt WPhe
	'Almand's Supreme' (GS-c)	CWGr
	'Alpen Beauty' (Col)	CWGr
	'Alpen Fern' (Fim)	CWGr
	'Alpen Mildred' (SS-c)	CWGr
	'Alpen Sun' (MinS-c)	CWGr
	'Alstergruss' (Col)	CWGr
	'Alva's Doris' (SS-c) 🏆H3	CWGr LAyl
	'Alva's Lilac' (SD)	CWGr
	'Alva's Supreme' (GD) 🏆H3	CWGr LAyl NHal WPhe
	'Amanda Jarvis' (SC)	CWGr
	'Amanjanca' (MinS-c)	CWGr
	'Amaran Guard' (LD)	CWGr
	'Amaran Relish' (LD)	CWGr SGbt
	'Amaran Return' (GD)	CWGr
	'Amaran Royale' (MinD)	CWGr
	'Amaran Troy' (SWL)	CWGr
I	'Amazone' (DwB)	LRHS SPoG
	'Amber Banker' (MC)	CWGr SGbt WPhe
	'Amber Festival' (SD)	NHal
	'Amber Quartz' (Misc)	SMrm
	'Amberglow' (MinBa)	CWGr LAyl
	'Amberley Joan' (SD)	CWGr
	'Amberley Victoria' (MD)	CWGr
	'Ambition' (SS-c)	CAvo CWGr ERCP
	'Amelia's Surprise' (LD)	CWGr
	'American Copper' (GD)	CWGr
	American Pie = 'Vdtg26'PBR (Dark Angel Series) (Sin)	LRHS SDeJ
	'Amethyst' (SD)	CWGr
	'Amgard Delicate' (LD)	CWGr SGbt
	'Amgard Rosie' (SD)	CWGr
	'Amira' (SBa)	CWGr NHal
	'Amorangi Joy' (SC)	CWGr
	'Amy Cave' (SBa)	LAyl NHal
	'Anchorite' (SD)	CWGr
	'Andrea Clark' (MD)	NHal WPhe
	'Andrea Lawson' (Ba)	NHal WPhe
	'Andrew Lockwood' (Pom)	CWGr
	'Andrew Mitchell' (MS-c)	CWGr NHal WPhe
	'Andries' Amber' (MinS-c)	CWGr
	'Andries' Orange' (MinS-c)	CWGr ECtt
	'Anelog' (MinBa)	NHal
	'Angora' (SD/Fim)	SGbt
	'Anita Summerhayes' (Misc)	CWGr
	'Anja Doc' (MS-c)	CWGr
	'Ann Breckenfelder' (Col) 🏆H3	ECtt ERCP EUJe NHal NJRG SDix SMrm WPhe WWEG
	'Annika' (Sin)	SDeJ
	'Anniversary Ball' (MinBa)	LAyl
	'Another Pet'	see *D.* 'Mystic Enchantment'
	'Apache' (MS-c/Fim)	CAby ERCP SDeJ SGbt SPer
	'Apache Blauw' (Fim)	ERCP
	'Apple Blossom' (MC)	SGbt
I	'Appleblossom' (Col)	CWGr
	'Apricot Honeymoon Dress' (SD)	CWGr
	'April Dawn' (MD)	CWGr
	'April Heather' (Col) 🏆H3	NHal WWEG
	'Arabian Night' (SD)	CAby CAvo CBcs CSpe CSut CWGr ECtt ELan ERCP LAyl LRHS LSun MNrw NBri NHal NLar SDeJ SEND SGbt SMrm SPer WCot WPhe WWEG
	'Arc de Triomphe' (MD)	CWGr
	'Arlequin' (LD)	CWGr SGbt
	'Arnhem' (SD)	CWGr
	'Arthur Godfrey' (GD)	CWGr
	'Arthur Hankin' (SD)	CWGr
	'Arthur's Delight' (GD)	CWGr
	'Asahi Chohje' (Anem) 🏆H3	CWGr
	'Askwith Ian' (MD) **new**	NHal
	'Askwith Joan' (MD) **new**	NHal
	'Aspen' (MinS-c)	CWGr
	'Athalie' (SC)	CWGr
	'Athelston John' (SC)	CWGr
	'Atilla' (SD)	CWGr
I	'Atlanta' (SD)	CWGr SGbt
	'Aubrey Keyse' (SD)	CWGr
	'Audacity' (MD)	CWGr LAyl SGbt
	'Audrey R' (SWL)	CWGr
	'Aurora's Kiss' (MinBa)	CWGr ERCP NHal SGbt
	'Aurwen's Violet' (Pom)	CWGr LAyl NHal WPhe
	australis	CSpe CWGr
	- B&SWJ 10208	WCru
	- B&SWJ 10358	WCru
	- B&SWJ 10389	WCru
	'Autumn Fairy' (D)	ERCP SDeJ
	'Autumn Lustre' (SWL)	CWGr
	'Avignon' (LD)	CBod CSut NBri SDeJ WBrk
	'Avoca Amanda' (MD)	NHal WPhe
	'Avoca Comanche' (SS-c)	NHal
	'Avoca Cree' (SS-c) **new**	CWGr
	'Avoca Salmon' (MD)	NHal
	'Avon Snowflake' (MinC)	NHal
	'Awaikoe' (Col)	CWGr
	'Aylett's Dazzler' (MinD/DwB)	CWGr
	'B.J. Beauty' (MD)	CWGr LAyl NHal NJRG WPhe
	'Babette' (S-c)	SMrm
	'Baby Fonteneau' (SS-c)	CWGr
	'Baby Royal' (SD)	CWGr
	'Babylon' (GD)	SGbt
§	'Babylon Brons' (LD)	ERCP SGbt
	'Babylon Bronze'	see *D.* 'Babylon Brons'
	'Babylon Lila' (MD) **new**	SGbt
§	'Babylon Paars' (MD)	LRHS SDeJ SGbt
	'Babylon Purple'	see *D.* 'Babylon Paars'
	'Babylon Rose' (GD)	LRHS SGbt
	'Ballego's Glory' (MD)	CWGr SGbt
	'Bambino' (Lil)	CWGr
	'Banker' (MC)	CWGr
	'Bantling' (MinBa)	CWGr ECtt ERCP SGbt
	'Barbara' (MinBa)	CWGr
	'Barbara Schell' (GD)	CWGr
	'Barbara's Pastelle' (MS-c)	CWGr NJRG SGbt WPhe
	'Barbarry Ball' (SBa)	CWGr
	'Barbarry Balloon' (SBa) **new**	NHal
	'Barbarry Banker' (MinD)	LAyl
	'Barbarry Bluebird' (MinD)	NHal SGbt
	'Barbarry Carousel' (SBa)	CWGr
	'Barbarry Cascade' (SD)	CWGr
	'Barbarry Chevron' (MD)	CWGr
	'Barbarry Cosmos' (SD)	CWGr
	'Barbarry Dominion' (MinD)	CWGr

Cultivar	Suppliers
'Barbarry Flag' (MinD)	CWGr
'Barbarry Gem' (MinBa)	CWGr
'Barbarry Ideal' (MinD)	CWGr
'Barbarry Melody' (SD)	NHal
'Barbarry Monitor' (MinBa)	CWGr SGbt
'Barbarry Noble' (MinD)	CWGr
'Barbarry Olympic' (SBa)	CWGr
'Barbarry Oracle' (SD)	CWGr
'Barbarry Parade' (MinD) **new**	NHal
'Barbarry Pimpernel' (SD)	CWGr
'Barbarry Pinky' (SD)	CWGr
'Barbarry Pip' (MinD) **new**	NHal
'Barbarry Polo' (MinD)	CWGr
'Barbarry Quest' (MinD)	CWGr
'Barbarry Red' (MinD)	CWGr
'Barbarry Sultan' (MinD) **new**	NHal
'Barbarry Sunbeam' (MinD) **new**	NHal
'Barbarry Triumph' (MinD)	CWGr
'Barbette' (MinD)	CWGr
'Baret Joy' (LS-c)	CWGr NHal
'Bargaly Blush' (MD)	NHal
'Baron Ray' (SD)	CWGr
'Barry Williams' (MD)	SGbt
'Bart' (SD)	CWGr
'Bayou'[PBR] (Misc)	ERCP NJRG SGbt
'Beacon Light' (SD)	CWGr
'Bedford Sally' (MD)	CWGr
'Bednall Beauty' (Misc/DwB) ♀H3	CHll CSpe CWCL CWGr ECtt ELan EUJe EWes LRHS NJRG WCot WPhe WWEG
'Bell Boy' (MinBa)	SGbt
'Bella S' (GD)	CWGr
'Belle Epoque' (MC)	CWGr
'Belle Moore' (SD)	CWGr
'Belle of Barmera' (GD)	CWGr
'Berger's Rekord' (S-c)	CSut CWGr
'Berliner Orange' (MD)	ERCP
'Bernice Sunset' (SS-c)	CWGr
'Berolina' (MinD)	CWGr
'Berwick Wood' (MD)	CWGr NHal SGbt
'Bess Painter' (SD)	CWGr
'Beth's Chaplet' (Sin)	WCot
'Betty Ann' (Pom)	CWGr
'Bicentenary' (SD)	CWGr
'Biddenham Fairy' (MinD)	CWGr
'Biddenham Strawberry' (SD)	CWGr SGbt
'Biddenham Sunset' (MS-c)	CWGr
'Big Orange' (GD)	CWGr
'Bilbao'[PBR] (Jumbo Collection) (D) **new**	NBri
'Bill Holmberg' (GD)	CWGr SGbt
'Bingo' (MinD)	CWGr SGbt
'Bishop of Auckland'[PBR] (Misc)	CAby CAvo CWGN CWGr ECtt EPfP EPot ERCP EWoo LRHS SDeJ SGbt SHil SMrm SPoG WCot WPhe
'Bishop of Cambridge' (Sin)	WPhe
'Bishop of Canterbury'[PBR] (P)	CPrp CWGr ECtt EPfP LRHS NHal NSoo SDeJ SGbt SHil SPoG WPhe
'Bishop of Dover' (Sin)	EPfP EPot LRHS SDeJ SGbt WBrk WPhe
'Bishop of Lancaster' (Misc)	CWGr NLar
'Bishop of Leicester' (Misc)	CWGr ECtt EPfP EPot LRHS NLar NSoo SDeJ SGbt SHar WPhe
'Bishop of Llandaff' (P) ♀H3	Widely available
'Bishop of Oxford' (Misc)	CAby CHVG CWGr ELan EPfP EPot ERCP LRHS SDeJ SGbt SHil SPoG WPhe
'Bishop of York' (Misc)	CAby CAvo CPrp CSpe CWGr ECtt EPfP EPot LRHS NGdn NSoo SDeJ SGbt SHil SPoG WBrk WPhe
'Bishop Peter Price' (Sin)	CWGr
'Bitsa' (MinBa)	CWGr SMrm
'Bitter Lemon' (SD)	CWGr
'Black Beauty' ambig.	CSpe
'Black Fire' (SD)	CWGr ECtt
'Black Jack' (SD)	ERCP NHal WPhe
'Black Monarch' (GD)	CWGr NHal SGbt
'Black Narcissus' (MC)	CWGr SGbt SPer WPhe
I 'Black R Jack' **new**	NJRG
'Black Spider' (SS-c)	CWGr
'Black Star' (Sin)	EPfP
'Black Touch' (Fim)	CWGr ERCP WPhe
'Black Wizard' (MS-c)	EWoo
'Blackberry Ripple' (SS-c)	CWGr ERCP NPri
'Blaze' (MD)	CWGr
'Bliss' (SWL)	CWGr
'Bloemfontein' (SD)	CWGr
'Bloodstone' (SD)	CWGr SGbt
'Bloom's Amy' (MinD)	CWGr
'Bloom's Graham' (SS-c)	CWGr
'Bloom's Kenn' (MD)	CWGr SGbt
'Blue Beard' (SS-c)	CWGr
'Blue Bell' (MD)	ERCP
'Blue Boy' (SD)	ERCP SPer
'Blue Diamond' (MC)	CWGr
'Blue Record' (MS-c/DwB)	ERCP
'Blue Wish' (WL) **new**	NJRG
'Bluesette' (SD)	CWGr
'Blyton Lady in Red' (MinD)	NHal NJRG WPhe
'Blyton Romance' (SD) **new**	NHal
'Blyton Softer Gleam' (MinD) ♀H3	NHal NJRG SGbt WPhe
'Bob Fitzjohn' (GS-c)	CWGr
'Bokay' (SWL)	CWGr
'Bonaventure' (GD)	CWGr NHal
'Bonesta' (MinD)	CWGr LRHS NBri WPhe
'Bonny Blue' (SBa)	CWGr
'Boogie Woogie' (Anem)	CWGr SDeJ
'Boom Boom White' (MinBa)	ERCP
'Bora Bora' (SS-c)	NBri
'Border Princess' (SC/DwB)	SGbt
'Border Triumph' (DwB)	CWGr
'Boy Scout' (MinBa)	CWGr
'Bracken Lorelei' (SWL)	NHal NJRG
'Brackenhill Flame' (SD)	CWGr
'Brackenridge Ballerina' (SWL)	CWGr LAyl NHal NJRG SGbt WPhe
'Brandaris' (MS-c)	CWGr SGbt
'Brandon James' (MinD)	ERCP SDeJ
'Brandysnap' (SD)	CWGr SGbt
'Brantwood' (Sin)	CWGr
Braveheart = 'Vdtg67'[PBR] (Dark Angel Series) (Sin)	LRHS SDeJ
'Brian's Dream' (MinD)	LAyl NHal WPhe
'Bride's Bouquet' (Col)	ERCP LRHS
'Bridge View Aloha' (MS-c) ♀H3	CWGr SGbt WPhe
'Bridgette' (SD)	CWGr
'Bright Eyes' (Sin)	CAvo ERCP WPhe
'Bristol Petite' (MinD)	CWGr

'Brookfield Delight' (Sin/Lil) ♀H3 CWGr
'Brookfield Rachel' (MinBa) CWGr
'Brookfield Rene' (MinD) CWGr
'Brookfield Snowball' (SBa) CWGr
'Brookfield Sweetie' (DwB/Lil) CWGr
'Bryce B. Morrison' (SD) CWGr
'Bryn Terfel' (GD) NHal SGbt WPhe
'Bud Flanagan' (MD) CWGr
'Bull's Pride' (GD) CWGr
'Butterball' (MinD/DwB) SDeJ
* 'Buttercup' (Pom) CWGr
'By George' (GD) CWGr
'Caballero' (SWL) CWGr
'Café au Lait' (GD) CWGr EPfP ERCP IPot LRHS NBri SDeJ SGbt SPer
'Calgary' (SD) CWGr
'Camano Ariel' (MC) CWGr
'Camano Choice' (SD) CWGr
'Camano Passion' (MS-c) CWGr
'Camano Poppet' (SBa) CWGr
'Camano Regal' (MS-c) CWGr
'Cambridge' (D) **new** NBri
'Cameo' (WL) CWGr NHal NJRG SGbt WPhe
campanulata CWGr
'Campos Philip M' (GD) CWGr
'Canary Fubuki' (Fim) CWGr ERCP SDeJ SGbt
I 'Candy' (SD) CWGr
'Candy Cane' (MinBa) CWGr
Candy Eyes PBR see *D.* 'Zone Ten'
'Candy Hamilton Lilian' (SD) CWGr
'Candy Keene' (LS-c) CWGr NHal
'Caproz Jerry Garcia' (MD) CWGr
'Capulet' (SBa) CWGr
'Careless' (SD) CWGr
'Caribbean Fantasy' (D) NSoo
'Carolina Moon' (SD) CWGr LAyl NHal SGbt
'Carol's Spanish Dancer' (MinC) NHal
'Carstone Firebox' (Col) LAyl NHal
'Carstone Ruby' (SD) NHal
'Carstone Sunbeam' (SD) CWGr
'Carstone Suntan' (MinC) CWGr
'Carstone Valiant' (MinBa) NHal
'Castle Drive' (MD) CWGr
'Catherine Deneuve' (Misc) CWGN CWGr SGbt
'Cha Cha' (SS-c) SGbt
'Chanson d'Amour' (SD) CWGr
'Charles de Coster' (MD) CWGr
'Charles Dickens' (SBa) CWGr
'Charlie Briggs' (SBa) NHal
'Charlie Dimmock' (SWL) ♀H3 NHal NJRG SGbt WPhe
'Charlie Two' (MD) CWGr NHal WPhe
'Chat Noir' (MS-c) CAvo ECtt ERCP LRHS SGbt WPhe
'Chee' (SWL) CWGr
'Cheerio' (SS-c) CWGr LAyl WPhe
'Cherry Wine' (SD) CWGr
'Cherrywood Turnpike' (SD) CWGr
'Cherubino' (Col) CWGr
'Cherwell Goldcrest' (SS-c) CWGr NHal SGbt WPhe WWEG
'Cherwell Skylark' (SS-c) NHal
'Chic en Rouge' (Misc) LSou
'Chilson's Pride' (SD) CWGr SGbt
'Chiltern Amber' (SD) CWGr
'Chiltern Fantastic' (SC) CWGr
'Chiltern Sylvia' (MinS-c) CWGr
'Chimborazo' (Col) CWGr EUJe LAyl SDix SGbt WPhe
'Chinese Lantern' (SD) CWGr
'Chloe's Keene' (LS-c) CWGr
'Christine' (SD) SPer WPhe
I 'Christine' (SWL) CWGr SGbt WPhe
'Christmas Carol' (Col) CWGr ECtt NHal NJRG
'Christmas Star' (Col) CWGr
'Christopher Nickerson' (MS-c) CWGr SGbt
'Christopher Taylor' (SWL) NHal SGbt WPhe
'Citizen' (MS-c) WPhe
'Clair de Lune' (Col) ♀H3 CAby CWCL CWGr ECtt ERCP LRHS MCot NHal NJRG NLar SGbt SMrm WCot
'Claire Diane' (SD) CWGr
'Clara May' (Fim) CWGr
I 'Clarion' (Sin) CHVG CWGr
'Classic A.1' (MC) CWGr
'Classic Poème' PBR (Misc) ERCP
'Classic Rosamunde' PBR (Misc) CHVG CWGr NHal NJRG
'Classic Summertime' (Misc) CWGr
§ 'Classic Swanlake' PBR (Misc) CAvo CWGr ERCP EWoo NJRG WPhe
'Claudette' (D) ECtt WPhe
'Clearview Irene' (MS-c) NHal
coccinea CExl CFil CSpe CWGr MCot SDix SGbt SMHy WPGP
– NJM 05.072 WPGP
– hybrids NSti WHil
– var. ***palmeri*** CAvo CFil WPGP XEll
'Cocktail' (S-c) CWGr
'Colac' (LD) CWGr
'Color Spectacle' (LS-c) CSut CWGr
'Colour Magic' (LS-c) CWGr
'Coltness Gem' (Sin/DwB) CWGr
'Comet' (Anem) CWGr
'Como Polly' (LD) CWGr
I 'Concordia' (SD) CWGr
'Connie Bartlam' (MD) CWGr
'Contessa' (SWL) CWGr SDeJ WPhe
'Coral' (SD) CWGr
'Coral Jupiter' (GS-c) CWGr WPhe
'Coral Strand' (SD) CWGr
'Cornel' (SBa) CWGr ERCP LAyl NHal NJRG SGbt
'Cornel Brons' (MinBa) ERCP
'Cornish Minx' (Pom) CWGr
'Cornish Ruby' (Sin) CBod CCon CHel EPfP
'Corona' (SS-c/DwB) SDeJ
'Coronella' (MD) CWGr SGbt
'Cortez Silver' (MD) CWGr
'Cortez Sovereign' (SS-c) CWGr
'Corton Bess' (SD) CWGr
'Corton Olympic' (GD) CWGr
'Corydon' (SD) CWGr
'Country Boy' (MS-c) CWGr
'Coupe de Soleil' (SD) **new** CSut
'Craigowan' (MS-c) NHal WPhe
'Crazy Legs' (MinD) CWGr SGbt
'Crazy Love' (SD) EBee
'Cream Alva's' (GD) ♀H3 CWGr
'Cream Beauty' (SWL) CWGr
'Cream Elegans' (SS-c) CWGr
'Cream Moonlight' (MS-c) CWGr SGbt WPhe
'Cream Reliance' (SD) CWGr
'Crève Coeur' (GD) CWGr
'Crichton Cherry' (MinD) CWGr

Name	Suppliers
'Crichton Honey' (SBa)	CWGr
'Croesus' (GS-c)	CWGr
'Crossfield Allegro' (SS-c)	CWGr
'Crossfield Anne' (MinD)	CWGr
'Crossfield Ebony' (Pom)	CWGr
'Crossfield Festival' (LD)	CWGr
'Croydon Ace' (GD)	CWGr
'Croydon Jumbo' (GD)	CWGr
'Croydon Snotop' (GD)	CWGr
'Croydon Superior' (GD)	SGbt
'Cryfield Harmony' (MinBa)	CWGr ERCP
'Cryfield Keene' (LS-c)	CWGr
'Cryfield Max' (SC)	CWGr
'Cryfield Rosie' (SBa)	CWGr
'Culdrose' (SD)	SGbt
'Curate' (Misc)	CWGr
'Curiosity' (Col)	NJRG
'Currant Cream' (SBa)	CWGr SGbt
cuspidata **new**	CFil
'Cycloop' (SS-c)	CWGr
'Cynthia Chalwin' (MinBa)	CWGr
'Czar Willo' (Pom)	CWGr
'Czardas' (MC)	GCal
'D. Day' (MS-c)	CWGr
'Daddy's Choice' (SS-c)	CWGr
Dahlietta Jenny^{PBR}	see *D.* 'Jenny'
'Daily Mail' (GD)	CWGr
'Daleko Jupiter' (GS-c)	CWGr NHal
'Daleko National' (MD)	CWGr
'Daleko Tangerine' (MD)	CWGr
'Dana Audrey' (MinC)	CWGr
'Dana Dream' (MinS-c)	CWGr
'Dana Iris' (SS-c)	CWGr
'Dana Sunset' (SC)	CWGr
'Dancing Queen' (S-c)	CWGr
I 'Dandy' (Col)	CWCL
'Danjo Doc' (SD)	CWGr SGbt
'Dannevirke' (Sin)	CWGr LRHS
'Danum Belle' (SD)	CWGr
'Danum Chippy' (SD)	CWGr
'Danum Fancy' (SD)	CWGr
'Danum Gail' (LD)	CWGr
'Danum Hero' (LD)	CWGr
'Danum Rhoda' (GD)	CWGr
'Danum Torch' (Col)	CWGr ECtt SGbt
'Dark Desire' (Sin/DwB)	CAvo CSpe CWCL CWGN CWGr ECtt EWoo WCot
'Dark Fubuki' (Fim)	ERCP
'Dark Spirit' (MinD)	CHVG ECtt SGbt
'Dark Splendour' (MC)	CWGr
'Dark Stranger' (MC)	CWGr
'Darkarin' (Misc)	SPer
'Darlington Diamond' (MS-c)	CWGr
'Darlington Jubilation' (SS-c)	CWGr
'Davar Jim' (SS-c)	CWGr
'Davenport Anita' (MinD)	CWGr
'Davenport Honey' (MinD)	CWGr
'Davenport Sunlight' (MS-c)	CWGr
'Dave's Snip' (MinD)	CWGr
'David Digweed' (SD)	CWGr NHal SGbt
'David Howard' (MinD) ♀H3	CHVG CWGr ECtt ELan EPfP EPla ERCP EUJe EWoo LAst LAyl LRHS MBri MWat NBri NHal NJRG NSoo SDix SGbt SMrm SPer SWvt WCot WFar WPhe WWEG
'David's Choice' (MinD)	CWGr
'Dawn Chorus' (MinD)	CWGr
'Dawn Sky' (SD)	LAyl
'Daytona' (SD)	CWGr
'Deborah's Kiwi' (SC)	CWGr NHal SGbt WPhe
'Debra Anne Craven' (GS-c)	CWGr NHal
'Decorette' (DwB/SD)	CWGr SGbt
'Decorette Rose' (MinD/DwB)	CWGr
'Deep Impact' (Fim) **new**	SMrm
'Deepest Yellow' (MinBa)	CWGr SDeJ SGbt
'Demi Schneider' (Col)	CWGr
'Dentelle de Venise' (MC)	CWGr
'Deuil du Roi Albert' (MD)	CWGr
'Deutschland' (MD)	CWGr
'Devon Elegance' (SS-c)	CWGr
'Devon Joy' (MinD)	CWGr
'Devon Liam' (LS-c)	CWGr
'Devon Temptation' (SC)	CWGr
'Diamond Jubilee' (MinD)	SPer
'Diamond Rose' (Anem/DwB)	CWGr
'Diamond Wedding' (SD)	SGbt
'Diamond Years' (SD)	SGbt
'Diana Gregory' (Pom)	CWGr SGbt
'Dick Westfall' (GS-c)	CWGr
'Dikara Jodie' (MD)	NHal
'Dikara Kent' (MinBa) ♀H3	WWEG
'Dikara Moon' (MD)	NHal WPhe
'Dikara Superb' (MinD)	NHal WPhe
'Dilys Ayling' (Col) **new**	NHal
I 'Disneyland' (Col)	SGbt
dissecta	CExl CFil EBee
- F&M 191	WPGP
'Doc van Horn' (LS-c)	CWGr
'Doctor Arnett' (GS-c)	CWGr
'Doctor Caroline Rabbitt' (SD)	CWGr SGbt
'Doctor John Grainger' (MinD)	CWGr EBee LRHS
'Don Hill' (Col) ♀H3	CWGr NJRG WCot WPhe
'Doris Bacon' (SBa)	CWGr
'Doris Day' (SC)	CWGr NHal SGbt
'Doris Rollins' (SC)	CWGr
'Dottie D.' (SBa)	CWGr
'Double Dream Fantasy' (Misc)	LRHS
'Dovegrove' (Sin) ♀H3	CWGr
'Downham Royal' (MinBa)	CWGr ERCP
Dracula = 'Vdtg17'^{PBR} (Dark Angel Series) (Sin)	ERCP
Dragon Ball = 'Vdtg31'^{PBR} (Dark Angel Series) (Sin)	LRHS SDeJ
'Dream Seeker' (Col) **new**	MBri
Dreamy Inspire (Misc)	NLar
'Dreamy Moonlight' (Dreamy Series) (Sin)	NLar
'Drummer Boy' (LD)	CWGr
'Duddon Grace' (SWL)	LAyl NHal
'Duet' (MD)	CSut CWGr ECtt NBri SGbt
'Dusky Harmony' (SWL)	CWGr SGbt
'Dutch Boy' (SD)	CWGr
'Dutch Explosion' (SS-c)	WPhe
'Dutch Triumph' (LD)	CWGr
'Earl Haig' (LD)	CWGr
'Earl Marc' (SC)	CWGr
'Early Bird' (SD)	CWGr
'Early Harvest' (MD)	SGbt
'Easter Sunday' (Col)	CHVG CWGr

	'Eastwood Moonlight' (MS-c)	CWGr NHal SGbt WPhe
	'Eastwood Star' (MS-c)	CWGr
	'Edge of Joy' (D)	ERCP
	'Edinburgh' (SD)	CWGr ERCP NBri SDeJ SGbt
	'Edith Jones' (Col)	CWGr NJRG
	'Edith Mueller' (Pom)	CWGr
	'Edna C' (MD)	CWGr
	'Edwin's Sunset' (WL) ♀H6	NHal WPhe
	'El Cid' (SD)	CWGr
	'El Paso' (SD)	CWGr
	'Elaine Huston' (MS-c) **new**	NJRG
	'Eldon Wilson' (Misc)	CWGr
	'Elga' (SS-c)	ERCP
	'Elgico Leanne' (MC)	CWGr SGbt
	'Elizabeth Snowden' (Col)	CWGr NJRG
	'Ella Britton' (MinD)	LRHS
	'Ellen Huston' (Misc/DwB) ♀H3	CHVG CWGr ECtt ERCP NHal SGbt WCot WPhe
	'Elma E' (LD)	CWGr ERCP LAyl NHal WPhe
	'Elmbrook Chieftain' (GD)	CWGr
	'Elmbrook Rebel' (GS-c)	CWGr
	'Embrace' (SC)	LAyl NHal NJRG WPhe
	'Emma's Coronet' (MinD)	CWGr
	'Emmie Lou' (MD)	CWGr
	'Emory Paul' (LD)	CWGr ERCP
	'Emperor' (MD)	CWGr
	'Enfield Salmon' (LD)	CWGr
	'Engadin' (MD)	CWGr
	'Engelhardt's Matador' (MD)	ECtt ERCP EUJe LRHS MCot MHol NJRG SGbt SMrm WCot
	'Enid Adams' (SD)	CWGr
	'Eric's Choice' (SD)	CWGr
	'Ernie Pitt' (SD)	CWGr
	'Esau' (GD)	CWGr
	'Etheral' (Sin)	CAvo CWGr
	'Eunice Arrigo' (LS-c)	CWGr
	'Eveline' (SD)	CAby CHVG CWGr ERCP SGbt WPhe
	'Evelyn Foster' (MD)	CWGr
	'Evelyn Rumbold' (GD)	CWGr SGbt
	'Evelyn Taylor' (SS-c) **new**	NJRG
	'Evening Lady' (MinD)	CWGr
I	'Evita' (Anem) **new**	NJRG
	excelsa	CHll
	- B&SWJ 10238	WCru
	- 'Penelope Sky'	WCru
	'Excentrique' (Misc)	CWGr ECtt NJRG
	'Exotic Dwarf' (Sin/Lil) ♀H3	ECtt NHal NJRG
	'Explosion' (SS-c)	CWGr
	'Extase' (MD)	CWGr
	'Eye Candy' (Sin)	LRHS NJRG WPhe
	'Fabula' (Col)	CWGr LRHS
	'Fairfield Frost' (Col)	NHal
	'Fairway Pilot' (GD)	CWGr
	'Fairway Spur' (GD)	NHal WPhe
	'Fairy Queen' (MinC)	CWGr SGbt
	'Falcon's Future' (MS-c)	CWGr
§	'Famoso' (Col)	CAby CSut ERCP
	'Fantastico' (Col)	CSut CWGr ERCP WBor
	'Fascination' (P) ♀H3	CAby CBcs CHVG CWGr ECGP ECtt ERCP LAyl LRHS MCot MPro MSCN NJRG NLar SDeJ SGbt SMrm WHoo WWEG
	'Fascination Aus' (Col)	CWGr
	'Fashion Monger' (Col)	CWGr ECtt ERCP NHal NJRG SGbt
	'Fata Morgana' (Anem)	CWGr NJRG SGbt
	'Ferncliffe Illusion' (LD)	CWGr ERCP SGbt
*	'Fernhill Suprise' (SD)	CWGr
	'Festivo' (Col)	CWGr LRHS
	'Feu Céleste' (Col)	CWGr
	'Fidalgo Blacky' (MinD)	CWGr
	'Fidalgo Bounce' (SD)	CWGr
	'Fidalgo Climax' (LS-c/Fim)	CWGr
	'Fidalgo Magic' (MD)	CWGr
	'Fidalgo Snowman' (GS-c)	CWGr
	'Fidalgo Splash' (MD)	CWGr
	'Fidalgo Supreme' (MD)	CWGr LAyl
	'Fiesta' (Pom)	SDeJ
	Figaro Series (Misc/DwB)	NPri
	'Figurine' (SWL) ♀H3	CWGr NJRG
	'Fille du Diable' (LS-c)	CWGr SGbt
	'Finchcocks' (SWL) ♀H3	CWGr LAyl
	'Fiona Stewart' (SBa)	CWGr
	'Fire and Ice' (Misc)	CHVG CWGr EBee WBor WHil
	'Fire Mountain' (MinD)	CHVG ERCP LAyl NHal NJRG
	'Firebird' (MS-c)	see *D.* 'Vuurvogel'
	'Firebird' (Sin)	CWGr
	'Firebrand' ambig. (S-c)	SGbt
	'Firepot' (WL)	ERCP MBri SGbt SMrm
	'First Lady' (MD)	CWGr
	'Flame On' (MC) **new**	MWat
	'Fleur' (Fim)	see *D.* 'Fleurel'
	'Fleur Mountjoy' (Col)	CWGr
§	'Fleurel'[PBR] (Fim)	ERCP SDeJ SMrm SPer
	'Floorinoor' (Anem)	NJRG SGbt WPhe
*	'Florence Vernon' (MinBa)	CWGr
	'Flutterby' (SWL)	CWGr
	'Fontmell Kaz' (Col)	NJRG SGbt
	'Formby Art' (SD) **new**	NHal
	'Formby Supreme' (MD)	CWGr SGbt
	'Forrestal' (MS-c)	CWGr
	'Fortuna' (Col)	CWGr ERCP
	'Frank Holmes' (Pom)	CWGr
	'Frank Lovell' (GS-c)	CWGr
	'Franz Kafka' (Pom)	CAvo CWGr ERCP LRHS NJRG SDeJ WPhe
	'Frau Louise Mayer' (SS-c)	CWGr
	'Fred Wallace' (SC)	CWGr
	'Freelancer' (LC)	CWGr SGbt
	'Freestyle' (SC)	CWGr NJRG
§	'Freya's Paso Doble' (Anem) ♀H3	CWGr LAyl NJRG SGbt
	'Freya's Thalia' (Sin/Lil)	CWGr
	'Frigoulet' (SC)	CWGr ERCP SGbt
	'Fringed Star' (MS-c)	CWGr NBri
	'Funfair' (MD)	CWGr
	'Funny Face US' (D)	CWGr
	'Furswood Park' (Pom) **new**	NJRG
	'Fusion' (MD) ♀H3	CWGr SGbt SHar WCot
	'Fuzzy Wuzzy' (MD)	ERCP
	'G.I. Joe' (LD)	SGbt
	'Gala Parade' (SD)	CWGr
	'Gale Lane' (Pom)	CWGr
	(Gallery Series) 'Gallery Art Deco'[PBR] (SD) ♀H3	CWGr ERCP LRHS MPro NHal SGbt SHil
	- 'Gallery Art Fair'[PBR] (MinD) ♀H3	CWGr ERCP LRHS MBri NHal SDeJ SHil
	- 'Gallery Art Nouveau'[PBR] (MinD) ♀H3	CWGr ERCP LRHS MPro NHal NSoo SHil WCot
	- 'Gallery Bellini'[PBR] (SD)	LRHS MBri MPro SDeJ
	- 'Gallery Cézanne'[PBR] (MinD)	CWGr MBri SGbt
	- 'Gallery Cobra'[PBR] (MinD)	ERCP
	- 'Gallery La Tour'[PBR] (MinD) ♀H3	SDeJ

Cultivar	Suppliers
– 'Gallery Leonardo'PBR (SD) ♀H3	CWGr SDeJ
– 'Gallery Matisse'PBR (SD)	CWGr LRHS
– 'Gallery Monet'PBR (SD)	CWGr NSoo
– 'Gallery Pablo'PBR (SD) ♀H3	CWGr LRHS MPro SGbt SHil
– 'Gallery Pinto'PBR (MinD) **new**	LRHS SHil
– 'Gallery Rembrandt'PBR (MinD) ♀H3	CWGr NSoo
– 'Gallery Renoir'PBR (SD) ♀H3	CWGr LRHS SHil
– 'Gallery Rivera'PBR (MinD)	ERCP SDeJ SHil
– 'Gallery Salvador'PBR (SD)	CWGr ERCP SGbt
– 'Gallery Valentin'PBR (MinD) **new**	LRHS MPro
– 'Gallery Vermeer'PBR (MinD)	CWGr SGbt
'Gamelan' (Anem/DwB)	CWGr
'Garden Festival' (SWL)	CWGr ERCP WPhe
'Garden Party' (MC/DwB) ♀H3	CWGr LAyl
'Garden Princess' (SC/DwB)	CWGr SGbt
'Garden Wonder' (SD)	CBod CWGr NBri SDeJ SMrm
'Gargantuan' (GS-c)	CWGr
'Garnet Quartz' (Misc)	EBee
Gateshead Festival	see *D.* 'Peach Melba' (SD)
'Gaudy' (GD)	CWGr
'Gay Princess' (SWL)	CWGr LAyl
'Gay Triumph' (GS-c)	CWGr
'Geerlings' Babette' (SBa)	ERCP
'Geerlings' Beatrice' (MinBa)	CWGr
'Geerlings' Cupido' (SWL)	CWGr NHal SGbt WPhe
'Geerlings' Indian Summer' (MS-c)	CWGr NHal
'Geerlings' Moonlight' (MD)	CWGr
'Geerlings' Sorbet' (MS-c)	CAby LAyl NHal SGbt WPhe
'Geerlings' Yellow' (SS-c)	CWGr
'Gelber Vulkan' (LS-c)	SGbt
'Gemma Darling' (GD)	CWGr
'Gemma's Place' (Pom)	CWGr
'Genova' (MinBa)	CAvo ERCP SGbt
'Gentle Giant' (GD)	CWGr
'Gerald Grace' (LS-c)	CWGr
'Gerlos' (MD)	CWGr
'Gerrie Hoek' (SWL)	CAvo CWGr ECtt ERCP EWoo IPot NBri SDeJ SGbt WPhe
'Gillwood Terry G' (SC)	NHal WPhe
'Gilt Edge' (MD)	CWGr
'Gina Lombaert' (MS-c)	CWGr SEND
'Ginger Willo' (Pom)	CWGr
'Gipsy Night' (MinBa)	CAvo ERCP SDeJ
'Giraffe' (DblO)	CAby CWGr ERCP LRHS SGbt WHlf
'Glad Huston' (SS-c/DwB)	CWGr
'Glenbank Honeycomb' (Pom)	WWEG
'Glenbank Paleface' (Pom)	CWGr
'Glenbank Twinkle' (MinC)	CWGr
'Glengarry' (SC)	CWGr
'Globular' (MinBa)	CWGr
'Glorie van Heemstede' (SWL) ♀H3	CWGr ERCP LAyl NHal SDeJ SEND SGbt WPhe
'Glorie van Noordwijk' (MinS-c)	ERCP SDeJ SGbt WPhe
'Glory' (LD)	CWGr
'Glow Orange' (MinBa)	CWGr
'Go American' (GD)	CWGr NHal WPhe
'Gold Crown' (LS-c)	CWGr SDeJ
'Golden Charmer' (SC)	CWGr
'Golden Emblem' (MD)	ECtt NBri SDeJ
'Golden Fizz' (MinBa)	CWGr
'Golden Glitter' (MS-c)	CWGr
'Golden Heart' (MS-c)	CWGr
'Golden Impact' (MS-c)	CWGr
'Golden Leader' (SD)	CWGr
'Golden Scepter' (MinD)	CWGr ERCP SDeJ SGbt
'Golden Torch' (MD)	NBri
'Golden Turban' (MD)	CWGr
'Goldfield' (MD)	CWGr
'Goldie Gull' (Anem)	NJRG
'Goldilocks' (S-c)	CWGr
'Goldorange' (SS-c)	CWGr
'Good Earth' (MC)	CWGr SDeJ
'Good Hope' (MinD)	CWGr
'Good Intent' (MinBa)	CWGr
'Goshen Beauty' (SWL)	CWGr
'Goya's Venus' (SS-c)	CWGr
'Grace Rushton' (SWL)	CWGr
'Gracie S' (MinC)	CWGr NJRG
'Grand Prix' (GD)	CSut CWGr ERCP SDeJ SGbt
'Grand Willo' (Pom)	CWGr
'Grenadier' (SD) ♀H3	CWGr ECtt ERCP EWoo LAyl LRHS MHol NJRG NLar SDix SGbt SMrm WBrk WCot WWEG
'Grenidor Pastelle' (MS-c)	CWGr NHal NJRG WPhe
'Gretchen Heine' (SD)	CWGr
'Grock' (Pom)	CWGr
'Gunyuu' (GD)	CWGr
'Gurtla Twilight' (Pom)	CWGr NHal NJRG WPhe WWEG
'Gute Laune' (MinS-c)	CWGr
'Gwyneth' (SWL)	NJRG WPhe WWEG
'Gypsy Boy' (LD)	CWGr LAyl
'Gypsy Girl' (SD)	CWGr SGbt
'Hallmark' (Pom)	CWGr NJRG
'Hallwood Coppernob' (MD)	CWGr
'Hallwood Satin' (MD)	CWGr
'Hallwood Tiptop' (MinD)	CWGr
'Hamari Accord' (LS-c) ♀H3	CWGr LAyl
'Hamari Bride' (MS-c) ♀H3	CWGr
'Hamari Girl' (GD)	CWGr NHal SGbt
'Hamari Gold' (GD) ♀H3	CWGr NHal SGbt WPhe
'Hamari Katrina' (LS-c)	CWGr WPhe
'Hamari Rosé' (MinBa) ♀H3	CWGr NHal SGbt
'Hamari Sunshine' (LD)	NHal SGbt
'Hamilton Amanda' (SD)	CWGr
'Hamilton Lillian' (SD) ♀H3	CWGr
'Hans Ricken' (SD)	CWGr
'Hapet Charmant' (WL)	NHal WPhe
'Hapet Ideal' (SS-c)	NHal WPhe
'Hapet Pearl' (MinBa)	NHal
'Hapet Pom' (Pom)	NHal WPhe
'Hapet Vinete' (Pom) **new**	NHal
* 'Happy Birthday' (SS-c)	CWGr
'Happy Caroline' (MinD)	CWGr
'Happy Halloween' (SD)	CWGr
'Happy Melody' (MinBa)	CWGr
(Happy Single Series)	CWGr ERCP NSoo SDeJ WHil
Happy Single Date = 'HS Date'PBR (Sin)	
– Happy Single First Love = 'HS First Love'PBR (Sin)	CWGr ERCP LRHS MBri SDeJ
– Happy Single Flame = 'HS Flame'PBR (Sin) ♀H3	CWGr EBee ERCP LRHS MBri NSoo

- Happy Single Juliet = 'HS Juliet'PBR (Sin)	CWGr ERCP MBri SDeJ
- Happy Single Kiss = 'HS Kiss'PBR (Sin)	MPro
- Happy Single Party = 'HS Party'PBR (Sin)	CAvo CWGr LRHS MBri SDeJ
- Happy Single Princess = 'HS Princess'PBR (Sin) ♀H3	ERCP LRHS MBri
- Happy Single Romeo = 'HS Romeo'PBR (Sin)	CWGr LRHS MBri NSoo SDeJ WHil
- Happy Single Wink = 'HS Wink'PBR (Sin) ♀H6	CWGr ERCP LRHS LSou MBri MPro NPri NSoo SDeJ WHil WPhe
'Happy Tip Purple' (Sin)	LRHS
'Happy Tip Red' (Sin)	LRHS MPro
'Haresbrook' (Sin)	NGdn
'Harriet G' (SWL)	NHal NJRG WPhe
'Harvest' (Fim)	CWGr
'Harvest Brownie' (Sin/Lil)	CWGr
§ 'Harvest Imp' (Sin/Lil)	CWGr
§ 'Harvest Samantha' (Sin/Lil) ♀H3	CWGr NHal
'Haseley Bridal Wish' (MC)	CWGr
'Haseley Miranda' (SD)	CWGr
'Hayley Jayne' (SC)	CWGr ERCP NBri NJRG SGbt WPhe
'Heather Huston' (MD)	CWGr
'Heather Jean' (Col) **new**	NJRG
'Hello There' (MS-c)	CWGr
'Helma Rost' (SS-c)	CWGr
'Henriette' (MC)	CWGr
'Herbert Smith' (D)	SEND
'Hexton Copper' (SBa)	CWGr SGbt
'Highgate Bobby' (SBa)	CWGr
'Highgate Lustre' (MS-c)	CWGr
'Highgate Torch' (MS-c)	CWGr
'Highness' (MinS-c)	CWGr
'Hilda Clare' (Col)	CWGr
'Hildepuppe' (Pom)	CWGr
'Hillcrest Amour' (SD)	CWGr SGbt
'Hillcrest Bobbin' (SBa)	CWGr
'Hillcrest Camelot' (GS-c)	CWGr
'Hillcrest Candy' (MS-c)	NHal NJRG SGbt WPhe
'Hillcrest Carmen' (SD)	CWGr
'Hillcrest Cheryl' (SinO)	NHal
'Hillcrest Contessa' (MinBa)	CWGr
'Hillcrest Delight' (MD)	NHal SGbt
'Hillcrest Desire' (SC) ♀H3	LAyl
'Hillcrest Divine' (MinD)	CWGr
'Hillcrest Fiesta' (MS-c)	CWGr
'Hillcrest Hannah' (MinD)	CWGr NHal
'Hillcrest Heights' (LS-c)	CWGr
'Hillcrest Jake' (MS-c)	NHal
'Hillcrest Jessica J' (MC)	CWGr
'Hillcrest Kismet' (MD)	LAyl NHal WPhe
'Hillcrest Matt' (SD) **new**	NJRG
'Hillcrest Pearl' (MD)	CWGr
'Hillcrest Regal' (Col) ♀H3	CWGr SGbt
'Hillcrest Royal' (MC) ♀H3	CWGr LAyl NHal SDix SGbt
'Hillcrest Suffusion' (SD)	CWGr
'Hillcrest Ultra' (SD)	CWGr
'Hindu Star' (MinBa)	CWGr
hjertingii **new**	CWGr
'Hockley Nymph' (SWL)	CWGr
'Holland Festival' (GD)	CWGr SGbt
'Hollyhill Big Pink' (GS-c)	SGbt
'Home Run' (Sin)	CWGr
'Homer T' (LS-c)	CWGr
'Honey' (Anem/DwB)	CWGr
'Honeymoon Dress' (SD)	CWGr
'Honeypot' (MinBa)	SGbt
'Honka' (SinO) ♀H3	CWGr ECtt ERCP LAyl LRHS NHal NJRG NSti SDeJ WCot WPhe
'Honka Fragile' (SinO)	ERCP
'Honka Orange' (SinO) **new**	ERCP
'Honka Pink Edge' (SinO) **new**	NJRG
'Honka Red' (SinO)	CAby EPfP ERCP NHal
'Honka Rose' (SinO) **new**	ERCP NJRG
'Honka Surprise' (SinO)	CAby CWGr ECtt ERCP EUJe MCot NJRG SDeJ SMrm WCot
'Honka White' (SinO)	CAby ERCP
'Honor Francis' (Misc)	WCot WWEG
I 'Hootenanny' (Col)	NHal WPhe
'Horst Athalie' (SC)	CWGr
'Hot Chocolate' (MinD)	CWGr NJRG SGbt
'Hugh Mather' (MWL)	CWGr
'Hugs 'n' Kisses' (D)	EPfP
'Hulin's Carnival' (MinD)	CWGr
'Hy Clown' (SD)	CWGr
'Hy Wine Frost' (Col) **new**	NJRG
'Ian Hislop' (Sin) **new**	CWGr
'Ice Cube' (MD)	ERCP SDeJ
'Ice Queen' (SWL)	CWGr
'Ida Gayer' (LD)	CWGr
'I-lyke-it' (SS-c)	CWGr
'Imagion' (SD)	EPfP
'Imp'	see *D.* 'Harvest Imp'
'Imperial Palace' (C)	CHVG
imperialis	CCon CDTJ CHEx CHll CWGr LEdu LRHS SBig SDix SGbt
- B&SWJ 8997	WCru
- 'Alba' (B)	CWGr
- pink double-flowered (B)	CExl CFil
'Impression Famosa'	see *D.* 'Famoso'
'Inca' (Anem)	WPhe
'Inca Dambuster' (GS-c)	CWGr NHal SGbt WPhe
'Inca Glamour' (LD)	CWGr
'Inca Matchless' (MD)	CWGr
'Inca Panorama' (MD)	CWGr
'Inca Royale' (LD)	CWGr
'Inca Spectrum' (GS-c)	CWGr
'Inca Streamline' (S-c)	CWGr
'Inca Vanguard' (GD)	CWGr
'Inca Vulcan' (GS-c)	CWGr
'Independence' (LD)	SGbt
'Inglebrook Jill' (Col)	CWGr
'Inland Dynasty' (GS-c)	CWGr
'Inn's Gerrie Hoek' (MD)	CWGr
'Iola' (LD)	CWGr
'Irene van der Zwet' (Sin)	CWGr
'Iris' (Pom)	CWGr
'Islander' (LD)	CWGr
'Ivanetti' (MinBa)	CWGr NHal SGbt WPhe
'J.R.G.' (Misc) ♀H3 **new**	NJRG
'Jack Hood' (SD)	CWGr SGbt
'Jack O'Lantern' (Col)	CWGr
'Jackie Magson' (SS-c)	CWGr
'Jacqueline Tivey' (SD)	CWGr
'Jaldec Jerry' (GS-c)	CWGr
'Jaldec Joker' (SC)	CWGr
'Jamaica' (MinWL)	CWGr SGbt
'Jamie' (SS-c)	CWGr
'Jan Cardew' (MinD)	CWGr
'Jan Lennon' (MS-c)	CWGr

I	'Jan van Schaffelaar' (Pom)	ERCP SDeJ
	'Janal Amy' (GS-c)	NHal SGbt WPhe
	'Jane Cowl' (LD)	CWGr
	'Jane Horton' (Col)	CWGr SGbt
	'Janet Beckett' (LC)	CWGr
	'Janet Howell' (Col)	CWGr
	'Japanese Waterlily' (SWL)	CWGr
	'Jazzy' (Col)	CWGr
	'Je Maintiendrai' (GD)	CWGr
	'Jean Fairs' (MinWL) ♀H3	CWGr SGbt
	'Jean Marie'PBR (MD)	ERCP
	'Jean Melville' (MinD)	CWGr
	'Jean Shaw' (GD)	NHal
	'Jeanne d'Arc' (GC)	CWGr EPfP
	'Jean's Carol' (Pom)	CWGr
	'Jennie' (Fim)	CWGr
§	'Jenny'PBR (Dahlietta Select Series) (Misc)	SGbt
	'Jersey Beauty' (MD)	CWGr
	'Jescot Buttercup' (SD)	CWGr
	'Jescot India' (MinD)	CWGr
	'Jescot Jess' (MinD)	CWGr
	'Jescot Jim' (SD)	CWGr
	'Jescot Julie' (DblO)	CAvo ERCP LAyl
	'Jescot Lingold' (MinD)	CWGr SGbt WPhe
	'Jescot Redun' (MinD)	CWGr
	'Jessica' (S-c)	CWGr
	'Jessie G' (SBa)	CWGr NJRG
	'Jessie Ross' (MinD/DwB)	CWGr
	'Jill Doc' (MD)	CWGr
	'Jill's Delight' (MD)	CWGr
	'Jim Branigan' (LS-c)	CWGr NHal
	'Jive' (Anem)	SDeJ
	'Joan Beecham' (SWL)	CWGr
	'Joan Walker' (SD)	CWGr
	'Joanne Taylor' (SWL) **new**	NJRG
	'Jocondo' (GD)	CWGr NHal SGbt
	'Joe Swift' (Sin)	CWGr
	'Johann' (Pom)	CWGr NHal
	'John Butterworth' (LD)	CWGr
	'John Hill' (GD) **new**	NHal
	'John Street' (SWL)	CWGr
	'John's Champion' (MD)	CWGr
	'Jomanda' (MinBa) ♀H3	CWGr NHal NJRG SGbt WPhe
	'Josie Gott' (MinBa) ♀H3	NJRG SGbt WPhe
	'Jowey Linda' (MinBa)	WPhe
	'Joy Donaldson' (MC)	CWGr
	'Joyce Green' (GS-c)	CWGr SGbt
	'Joyce Margaret Cunliffe' (SD)	CWGr
	'Juanita' (MS-c)	CWGr
	'Jules Dyson' (Misc)	SDys
	'Julie One' (DblO)	CAvo CWGr SGbt
	'Julie's Delight' (MS-c) **new**	CWGr
	'Julio' (MinBa)	CWGr
	'Jura' (SS-c)	CWGr EPfP
	'Juul's Allstar' (SinO) ♀H3	CWGr
	'Kaiser Wilhelm' (SBa)	CWGr
	'Karenglen' (MinD) ♀H3	CWGr NHal NJRG SGbt
	'Kari Quill' (SC)	CWGr
	'Karma Amanda'PBR (SD)	CWGr
	'Karma Bon Bini'PBR (SC)	CAby SGbt WPhe
	'Karma Choc'PBR (SD)	CAby CAvo CSpe CWGr EBee EPfP ERCP IPot LRHS MSCN NPri SEND SGbt SMrm SPer WCot WFar WHoo WPhe
	'Karma Corona'PBR (SC)	CWGr SGbt
	'Karma Fuchsiana' (SD)	CWGr ERCP LRHS NPri SGbt WPhe
	'Karma Irene'PBR (SD)	ERCP WPhe
	'Karma Lagoon'PBR (SD)	CWGr ERCP LRHS SGbt WPhe
	'Karma Maarten Zwaan'PBR (SWL)	CWGr WPhe
	'Karma Naomi'PBR (SD)	CWGr ERCP SGbt WPhe
	'Karma Pink Corona'PBR (SC)	WPhe
	'Karma Prospero'PBR (SD)	ERCP WPhe
	'Karma Red Corona'PBR (SC)	SDeJ SGbt WPhe
	'Karma Sangria'PBR (SC)	CWGr LRHS SDeJ SGbt WPhe
	'Karma Serena'PBR (SD)	SDeJ WPhe
	'Karma Ventura'PBR (SD)	CWGr
	'Karma Yin Yang' (SD)	SGbt WPhe
	'Karras 150' (SS-c)	CWGr
	'Kasasagi' (Pom)	CWGr
	'Kate Mountjoy' (Col)	CWGr SGbt
	'Kathryn's Cupid' (MinBa)	CWGr
	'Katie Dahl' (MinD)	NHal
	'Katisha' (MinD)	CWGr
	'Kayleigh Spiller' (Col)	SGbt
	'Keith's Choice' (MD)	CWGr NHal SGbt
	'Keith's Pet' (Sin) ♀H3	CWGr
	'Kelsea Carla' (SS-c) ♀H3	CWGr
	'Kelvin Floodlight' (GD)	CHVG CWGr NBri NPri SDeJ SGbt SMrm SPer WPhe
	'Kennemerland' (MS-c)	EPfP SDeJ SGbt
	'Kenora Canada' (MS-c)	CWGr
	'Kenora Challenger' (LS-c)	CWGr NHal NJRG SGbt WPhe
	'Kenora Christmas' (SBa)	CWGr
	'Kenora Clyde' (GS-c)	CWGr
	'Kenora Frills' (Fim)	NHal
	'Kenora Jubilee' (LS-c)	NHal SGbt WPhe
	'Kenora Lisa' (MD)	CWGr
	'Kenora Macop-B' (Fim)	CWGr IPot NHal WPhe
	'Kenora Moonbeam' (MD)	CWGr
	'Kenora Ontario' (LS-c)	CWGr
	'Kenora Sunburst' (LS-c)	CWGr
	'Kenora Sunset' (MS-c) ♀H3	CWGr LAyl NHal SGbt
	'Kenora Superb' (LS-c)	CWGr SGbt WPhe
	'Kenora Valentine' (LD) ♀H3	CWGr LAyl NHal SGbt WPhe
	'Ken's Coral' (SWL)	CWGr
	'Ken's Flame' (SWL)	CWGr SGbt
	'Ken's Rarity' (SWL)	NJRG SGbt
	'Key West' (LD)	CWGr
	'Kidd's Climax' (GD) ♀H3	CWGr ERCP WPhe
	'Kikoski' (GC)	SGbt
	'Kilburn Fiesta' (MS-c)	NHal WPhe
	'Kilburn Rose' (WL)	NHal WPhe
	'Kilmorie' (SS-c)	NHal WPhe
	'Kim Willo' (Pom)	CWGr
	'Kingston' (MinD)	CWGr SGbt
	'Kismet' (SBa)	CWGr
	'Kiss' (MinD)	CWGr MBri
	'Kiss Me' (SD)	EPfP
	'Kit Kat' (LC)	CWGr
	'Kiwi Brother' (SS-c)	CWGr
	'Kiwi Cousin' (SC)	CWGr
	'Kiwi Gloria' (SC)	CWGr NHal NJRG WPhe
	'Kiwi Sister' (SS-c)	CWGr
	'Klondike' (MS-c)	CWGr ERCP NJRG WPhe
I	'Knockout'PBR (Sin) ♀H3	CWGr EPfP ERCP LRHS LSou MGos NBri NSoo SHar SPoG
	'Kochelsee' (MinD)	CWGr
	'Kogane Fubuki' (Fim)	CWGr
	'Kotare Jackpot' (SS-c)	CWGr
	'Kung Fu' (SD)	CWGr
I	'Kyoto' (SWL)	CWGr LRHS SGbt
	'L.A.T.E.' (MinBa)	NHal NJRG SGbt

	'La Cierva' (Col)	CWGr
	'La Gioconda' (Col)	CWGr
	'La Recoleta' (D)	ERCP
	'Lady Linda' (SD)	CWGr NHal SGbt
	'Lady Orpah' (SD)	CWGr
	'Lady Sunshine' (SS-c)	CWGr
	'Lakeland Polly' (Pom) **new**	CWGr NJRG
	'Lambada' (Anem)	CWGr
	'L'Ancresse' (MinBa)	LAyl NHal NJRG
	'Larkford' (SD)	CWGr
	'Last Dance' (MD)	CWGr
	'Laura Marie' (MinBa)	CWGr
	'Laura's Choice' (SD)	CWGr
	'Lauren Kitchener' (Misc) **new**	NJRG
	'Lavender Chiffon' (MS-c)	CWGr
	'Lavender Freestyle' (SC)	CWGr
	'Lavender Leycett' (GD)	CWGr
	'Lavender Line' (SS-c)	NHal
	'Lavender Nunton Harvest' (SD)	CWGr
	'Lavender Perfection' (GD)	CWGr
	'Lavengro' (GD)	CWGr
	'Le Baron' (SD)	CSut ERCP WPhe
	'Le Castel' (SWL) ♀H3	CWGr SDeJ
	'Le Patineur' (MD)	CWGr
	'Le Vonne Splinter' (GS-c)	CWGr
	'Leander' (GS-c)	CWGr
	'Lemon Cane' (Misc)	CWGr
	'Lemon Elegans' (SS-c) ♀H3	NHal
	'Lemon Meringue' (SD)	CWGr ECtt SGbt
*	'Lemon Puff' (Anem)	CWGr
	'Lemon Zing' (MinBa)	LAyl NHal SGbt
	'Leopold Chloe' (SD) **new**	NHal
	'Leslie's Willo' (Pom)	WWEG
	'Lexington' (Pom)	CWGr
	'Leycett' (GD)	CWGr
	'Liberator' (GD)	CWGr
	'Libretto' (Col)	CWGr
	'Life Force' (GD)	CWGr SGbt
	'Life Size' (LD)	CWGr
	'Light Music' (MS-c)	CWGr
	'Lilac Athalie' (SC)	CWGr
	'Lilac Bull' (MinD)	LRHS
	'Lilac Marston' (MinD) ♀H3	NHal WPhe
	'Lilac Shadow' (S-c)	CWGr
	'Lilac Taratahi' (SC) ♀H3	CSam CWGr LAyl
	'Lilac Time' (MD)	CWGr ERCP NBri SDeJ SGbt WPhe
	'Lilac Willo' (Pom)	CWGr
	'Lilian Alice' (Col)	CHVG
	'Lilianna W' (Sin) **new**	NJRG
	'Lilliput Orange' (Sin) **new**	NJRG
	'Linda's Baby' (MinBa)	SMrm
	'Linda's Chester' (SC)	CWGr
	'Linda's Diane' (SD)	CWGr
	'Lisa' (WL)	CWGr
	'Lismore Carol' (Pom)	CWGr NHal WPhe
	'Lismore Moonlight' (Pom)	CWGr LAyl NHal
	'Lismore Robin' (MinD)	NHal
	'Lismore Sunset' (Pom)	SGbt
	'Lismore Willie' (SWL) ♀H3	CWGr NJRG WPhe
	'Little Dorrit' (Sin/Lil)	CWGr NJRG
	'Little Fawn' (SS-c)	CWGr
	'Little Glenfern' (MinC)	CWGr
	'Little John' (Sin/Lil)	CWGr
	'Little Lamb' (MS-c)	CWGr
	'Little Laura' (MinBa)	CWGr
	'Little Matthew' (Pom)	CWGr SGbt
	'Little Reggie' (SS-c)	CWGr
	'Little Robert' (MinD)	CAvo CWGr ERCP NBri SGbt WPhe
	'Little Sally' (Pom)	CWGr SGbt
	'Little Scottie' (Pom)	CWGr
	'Little Shona' (MinD)	CWGr
	'Little Snowdrop' (Pom)	CWGr SGbt
	'Little Tiger' (MinD)	CWGr
I	'Little William' (MinBa)	SGbt WPhe
	'Liz' (LS-c)	CWGr
	'Lloyd Huston' (GS-c)	CWGr
	'Lois Walcher' (MD)	CWGr
	'Lorona Dawn' (SinO)	ERCP LAyl NJRG
	'Loud Applause' (SC)	CWGr
	'Louis V' (Fim)	SGbt
	'Lucky Devil' (MD)	CWGr
	'Lucky Number' (MD)	CWGr ERCP
	'Ludwig Helfert' (S-c)	CWGr SEND
	'Lupin Dixie' (SC)	CWGr
	'Lyn Mayo' (SD)	CWGr
	'Mabel Ann' (GD)	CWGr LAyl NHal WPhe
	'Madame de Rosa' (LS-c)	LAyl NHal
	'Madame Elisabeth Sawyer' (SS-c)	CWGr
	'Madame Simone Stappers' (WL)	CWGr ECtt EUJe LRHS WWEG
	'Madame Vera' (SD)	CWGr
	'Madelaine Ann' (GD)	CWGr
	'Maelstrom' (SD)	CWGr
	'Mafolie' (GS-c)	CWGr
	'Magenta Magenta' (MinD)	LAyl SGbt
	'Magenta Magic' (Sin/DwB)	NHal
	'Magenta Star' (Sin) ♀H3	CAvo CWGr SGbt WPhe
	'Magic Moment' (MS-c)	CWGr
	'Magnificat' (MinD)	CWGr
	'Maisie Mooney' (GD)	CWGr
	'Majestic Athalie' (SC)	CWGr
	'Maldiva' (D) **new**	ERCP
	'Malham Portia' (SWL)	CWGr
I	'Mambo' (Anem)	SDeJ
	'Mandy' (MinD)	CWGr
	'Manhattan Island' (MD)	ERCP NBri
	'Marble Ball' (MinD)	CWGr ERCP SDeJ SGbt
	'Margaret Ann' (MinD)	CWGr
	'Margaret Brookes' (LD)	CWGr
	'Margareth Kleene' (MD)	ERCP
	'Marie' (SD)	CWGr
	'Marie Schnugg' (SinO) ♀H3	CAvo CWGr NJRG SGbt
	'Mariposa' (Col)	CWGr
	'Marissa' (SWL)	CWGr
	'Mark Damp' (LS-c)	CWGr
	'Mark Hardwick' (GD)	CWGr
	'Mark Lockwood' (Pom)	CWGr
	'Market Joy' (SS-c)	CWGr
	'Marla Lu' (MC)	CWGr
	'Marlene Joy' (Fim)	CWGr SGbt WPhe
	'Mars' (Col)	CWGr NJRG SGbt
	'Marshmallow Sky' (Col)	CWGr
	'Marston George' (MinB) **new**	NHal
	'Martin's Yellow' (Pom)	NHal
	'Mary Eveline' (Col)	EBee ECtt NHal
	'Mary Evelyn' (SC)	ERCP MSCN SGbt SMrm
	'Mary Partridge' (SWL)	CWGr
	'Mary Pitt' (MinD)	CWGr SGbt
	'Mary Richards' (SD)	CWGr
	'Mary's Jomanda' (SBa) ♀H3	CWGr NHal SGbt WPhe WWEG
	'Mascot Maya' (MD) **new**	NJRG
	'Master Michael' (Pom)	CWGr

Name	Suppliers
'Matador' (D)	EPfP
'Matchless' (C)	CWGr
'Matilda Huston' (SS-c)	CWGr LAyl NHal
'Matt Armour' (Sin)	CWGr
'Maureen Hardwick' (GD)	CWGr SGbt
'Maureen Jones' (Col) **new**	NJRG
(Maxi Series) 'Maxi Colima' (D/DwB) **new**	MPro
- 'Maxi Morelia' (D/DwB) **new**	MPro
- 'Maxi Novia' (D/DwB) **new**	MPro
- 'Maxi Tampico' (D/DwB)	LRHS MPro
- 'Maxi Topia' (D/DwB) **new**	MPro
'Maxime' (SD)	ERCP
'Maxine Bailey' (SD)	CWGr
'Maya' (SD)	IPot
'Mayan Pearl' (O) ♀H3	LAyl SGbt
'Mayan Swan' (SS-c)	SGbt
'Mediterranee' (D) **new**	ERCP
'Megan Dean' (MinBa)	NHal WPhe
'Meiro' (SD)	CWGr
'Melanie Jane' (MS-c)	CWGr
'Melody Bolero'PBR (MinD) **new**	CWGr
'Melody Dixie'PBR (MinD)	ERCP LRHS
'Melody Dora'PBR (SD)	CWGr LRHS MBri
'Melody Gipsy'PBR (SS-c)	CWGr
'Melody Harmony'PBR (SD) ♀H3	EPfP ERCP
'Melody Latin'PBR (D)	LRHS
'Melody Mambo'PBR (MinD) **new**	LRHS MBri
'Melody Swing'PBR (D)	CWGr LRHS
'Melton' (MinD)	CWGr
merckii	CCon CExl CFil CSpe CWGr EWes EWoo LRHS MCot MNrw MRav NSti SHar SPtp
- 'Alba' (B)	CExl CFil CSpe
- compact	CFil
- 'Edith Eddleman' (B)	CFil
'Mevrouw Clement Andries' (Fim)	ERCP
'Mexico Mogul' (MD)	SGbt
'Michael J' (MinD)	CWGr
'Michigan' (MinD)	CWGr
'Mick' (SC)	CWGr
'Mick's Peppermint' (MS-c)	CWGr SGbt
'Midas' (SS-c)	CWGr
'Midnight' (Pom)	CWGr SGbt
'Midnight Star' (SinO) **new**	NJRG
'Mies' (Sin)	CWGr
'Mignon Silver' (Sin/DwB)	CWGr
'Milk Shake' (SD) **new**	NPri
'Mingus Alex' (Fim)	CWGr
'Mingus Gregory' (LS-c)	CWGr
'Mingus Kyle D' (SD)	CWGr
* 'Mingus Max'	ERCP
'Mingus Nichole' (LD)	CWGr
'Mingus Randy' (LS-c)	SPer
'Mingus Toni' (SD)	ERCP
'Mini' (Sin/Lil)	CWGr
'Mini Red' (MinS-c)	CWGr
'Minley Carol' (Pom)	CWGr LAyl NHal
'Minley Iris' (Pom)	CWGr
'Miramar' (SD)	CWGr
'Mish-Mash' (Fim/MS-c)	CWGr
'Miss Blanc' (SD)	CWGr
'Miss Campbell' (Ba)	NJRG
'Miss Ellen' (Misc) ♀H3	CWGr
'Miss Rose Fletcher' (SS-c)	CWGr
'Miss Swiss' (SD)	CWGr
'Misterton' (MD)	CWGr SGbt
'Mistill Beauty' (SC)	CWGr
'Mistill Delight' (MinD)	CWGr
'Mistral' (Fim)	ECtt
mollis	CFil
'Mom's Special' (LD)	CBod CWGr ERCP
'Monet Mystique' (SWL)	SGbt
'Monet Sunlight' (SWL)	SGbt
'Monk Marc' (SC)	CWGr
'Monrovia' (MinBa)	CWGr
'Moonfire' (Misc/DwB) ♀H3	CAby CHel CWCL CWGN CWGr ECtt ELan EPfP ERCP EUJe LAyl LBMP LRHS MBri NHal NJRG SDix SGbt SMrm SPer WCot WHoo WPhe WWEG
'Moonglow' (LS-c)	CWGr ERCP
'Moor Place' (Pom)	CWGr NHal NJRG SGbt WPhe WWEG
'Moray Susan' (SWL)	CWGr
'Moret' (SS-c)	CWGr
'Morley Lass' (SS-c)	CWGr
'Morning Dew' (SC)	CWGr
'Motto' (LD)	CWGr
'Mr Optimist' (SD)	SPer
'Mrs A. Woods' (MD)	CWGr
'Mrs Black' (Pom)	CWGr
'Mrs Eileen' (GD)	ERCP SGbt WPhe
'Mrs George Le Boutillier' (LD)	CWGr
'Mrs H. Brown' (Col)	SGbt
'Mrs McDonald Quill' (LD)	CWGr SGbt
'Mrs Silverston' (SD)	CWGr
'München' (MinD)	CWGr SDeJ SGbt
'Murdoch' (D)	ECtt EWoo LRHS WCot
'Murillo' ambig.	CWGr LAyl
'Murray May' (LD)	CWGr
'Murray Petite' (SS-c)	CWGr
'Musette' (MinD)	CWGr SGbt
'My Joy' (Pom)	CWGr
'My Love' (SS-c)	CSut CWGr ERCP NBri SEND SGbt WPhe
'My Neddy' (SD)	NJRG SGbt
'Myama Fubuki' (Fim)	ERCP
'Myrtle's Folly' (Fim)	ERCP
'Mystery Day' (MD)	CBod CWGr SMrm
Mystic Desire	see *D.* 'Scarlet Fern'
§ 'Mystic Enchantment'PBR (Sin)	EBee LRHS LSou SPoG
Mystic Illusion	see *D.* 'Knockout' (Sin)
Mystic Mars	see *D.* 'Scarlet Fern'
'Nagano' (MinD)	CWGr SDeJ WPhe
'Nancy H' (MinBa)	CWGr
'Naples' (SD) **new**	EWoo
'Nargold' (Fim)	CWGr LAyl
'Narrow's Tricia' (MS-c)	WPhe
'Natal' (MinBa)	ECtt ERCP NBri SDeJ
'Natalie G' (MinD) **new**	NJRG
'Nathalie's Wedding' (SWL)	ERCP
'Nationwide' (SD)	CWGr
'Neal Gillson' (MD)	CWGr
neglecta	CWGr
'Nellie Geerlings' (Sin)	CWGr
'Nenekazi' (Fim)	CWGr
'Nepos' (SWL)	CWGr NJRG SGbt WPhe

	'Nescio' (Pom)	CWGr ERCP SDeJ
	'Nettie' (MinBa)	CWGr
	'New Baby' (MinBa)	CWGr ERCP SGbt
	'New Dimension' (SS-c)	CWGr
	'Newsham Wonder' (SD)	CWGr
	'Nicolette' (MWL)	CWGr
	'Night Editor' (GD)	CWGr
I	'Night Queen' (MinBa)	ERCP
	'Nina Chester' (SD)	CWGr
	'Nippon' (Sin)	EBee EPfP LRHS
	'Nonette' (SWL)	CWGN CWGr EBee ECtt SGbt WCot
	'Norbeck Dusky' (SS-c)	CWGr
	'Noreen' (Pom)	CWGr NHal WPhe
	'Norman Lockwood' (Pom)	CWGr
	'Northland Primrose' (SC)	CWGr
	'Northwest Cosmos' (Sin) ♀H3	CWGr
§	'Nuit d'Eté' (MS-c)	CAby CHVG CSpe CWGr ECGP ERCP EWoo LAyl LRHS NHal SGbt WPhe
	'Nuland's Josephine' (MinBa) **new**	NHal NJRG
	'Nunton Form' (SD)	CWGr
	'Nunton Harvest' (SD)	CWGr
	'Nymphenberg' (SWL) **new**	CWGr
	'Oakwood Diamond' (SBa)	CWGr
	'Oakwood Goldcrest' (SS-c)	CWGr NHal WPhe
	'Old Boy' (SBa)	CWGr
	'Old Gold' (SD)	CWGr SGbt
I	'Olivia' (Col) **new**	CWGr NJRG
	'Olivia Mari' (WL) **new**	NHal
	'Omo' (Sin/Lil) ♀H3	NJRG
	'Onesta' (SD)	CWGr ERCP LRHS SDeJ WPhe
	'Only Love' (MS-c)	CWGr
	'Onslow Michelle' (SD)	CWGr
	'Onslow Renown' (LS-c)	CWGr
	'Optic Illusion' (SD)	CWGr
	'Opus' (SD)	CWGr SGbt
	'Orange Cushion' (MinD)	CWGr
	'Orange Explosion' (Misc)	SGbt
	'Orange Fubuki' (SD)	ERCP
	'Orange Keith's Choice' (MD)	CWGr
	'Orange Mullett' (MinD/DwB)	CWGr
	'Orange Nugget' (MinBa)	CWGr SDeJ
	'Orange Pathfinder' (Misc) **new**	CWGr
I	'Orange Queen' (MC)	CWGr SGbt
	'Oranjestad' (SWL)	CWGr
	'Orchid Princess' (MS-c)	ERCP
	'Orel' (Col)	CWGr SGbt
	'Oreti Bliss' (SC)	LAyl NHal
	'Oreti Classic' (MD)	NHal
	'Oreti Duke' (Pom)	CWGr
	'Orfeo' (MC)	CHVG CWGr ECtt ERCP MNrw SDeJ SGbt
	'Oriental Dream' (D)	LRHS
I	'Orion' (MD)	CWGr
	'Ornamental Rays' (SC)	CWGr
	'Osaka' (SD)	CWGr
	'Osirium' (SD)	ERCP SPer
	'Ossie Latham' (Sin)	CWGr LRHS SGbt
	'Othello' (MS-c)	CWGr
	'Otto's Thrill' (LD)	ERCP
	'Pacific Argyle' (SD)	NHal
	'Paint Box' (MS-c)	CWGr
	'Painted Girl' (D)	ERCP
	'Pale Excentrique' (Sin/DwB) **new**	NJRG
	'Pale Roxy' **new**	NJRG
	'Pam Howden' (SWL)	NHal NJRG SGbt WPhe
	'Pamela' (SD)	CWGr
	'Pari Taha Sunrise' (MS-c)	CWGr
	'Parkflamme' (MinD)	CWGr
	'Park Princess' (SC/DwB)	CHVG CSut CWGr LAyl NBri NGdn NHal NSoo SDeJ SGbt SMrm
	'Park Record' (S-c) **new**	NBri
	'Parkland Rave' (SS-c)	CWGr
	'Paroa Gillian' (SC)	CWGr
	'Paso Doble' misapplied	see *D.* 'Freya's Paso Doble'
	'Pat Knight' (Col)	CWGr NJRG
	'Pat Mark' (LS-c)	CWGr LAyl
	'Pat 'n' Dee' (SD)	CWGr
	'Pat 'n' Perc' (Col)	NJRG SGbt
	'Patricia' (Col)	NHal
	'Paul Chester' (SC)	CWGr
	'Paul Critchley' (SC)	CWGr
	'Paul Smith' (SBa)	CWGr
	'Peace Pact' (SWL)	CWGr NJRG
	'Peach Athalie' (SC)	CWGr
	'Peach Brandy' (MinWL)	SMrm
	'Peach Cupid' (MinBa)	CWGr
	'Peach Delight' (MS-c)	NHal SGbt
§	'Peach Melba' (SD)	CWGr NHal WPhe
	'Peaches and Cream'PBR (MinD)	NSoo
	'Peachette' (Misc/Lil)	CWGr
	'Pearl of Heemstede' (SD) ♀H3	CWGr LAyl NHal WPhe
	'Pearl Sharowean' (MS-c)	CWGr
	'Pearson's Ben' (SS-c)	CWGr NJRG
	'Pearson's Patrick' (S-c)	CWGr
	'Pembroke Levenna' (MinBa)	NHal
	'Penhill Autumn Shade' (LS-c)	NJRG SGbt
	'Pennsclout' (GD)	CWGr
	'Pennsgift' (GD)	CWGr
	'Pensford Marion' (Pom)	CWGr
	'Perfect Partner' (Sin)	CWGr
	'Perfectos' (MC)	CWGr
	'Peter' (MinD)	ECtt SGbt
	'Peter Nelson' (SBa)	CWGr
	'Petit Byoux' (DwCol)	CWGr
	'Petite Harvest' (Misc/DwB) **new**	NJRG
	'Petite Sunrise' (Sin) **new**	NJRG
	'Petite Sunset' (Misc/Lil) **new**	NJRG
	'Pfitzer's Joker' (SC)	CAby
	'Pianella' (SS-c)	CWGr SGbt
	'Pineapple Lollipop' (MinBa)	CWGr
	'Pineholt Princess' (LD)	CWGr
	'Pinelands Pam' (Fim)	CWGr
	'Pinelands Princess' (Fim)	ERCP EUJe SGbt
	'Pink Attraction' (MinD)	CWGr
	'Pink Carol' (Pom)	NJRG
	'Pink Giraffe' (DblO) ♀H3	CAby CWGr ERCP LRHS SGbt
	'Pink Honeymoon Dress' (SD)	CWGr
	'Pink Isa'PBR (MinD) **new**	CWGr ERCP
	'Pink Jupiter' (GS-c)	CWGr NHal SGbt
	'Pink Katisha' (MinD)	CWGr

'Pink Kerkrade' (SC) CWGr
'Pink Leycett' (GD) CWGr
'Pink Loveliness' (SWL) CWGr
'Pink Pastelle' (MS-c) 🏆H3 NHal SGbt WPhe
'Pink Preference' (SS-c) CWGr
'Pink Risca Miner' (SBa) CWGr
'Pink Robin Hood' (SBa) CWGr
'Pink Sensation' (SC) 🏆H3 CWGr
'Pink Shirley Alliance' (SC) CWGr LAyl
'Pink Skin' (MD) ECtt EWoo LRHS SDeJ
'Pink Sylvia' (MinD) CWGr
'Pink Symbol' (MS-c) CWGr
pinnata B&SWJ 10240 WCru
'Piperoo' (MC) CWGr SGbt
'Piper's Pink' (SS-c/DwB) CWGr ECtt LRHS SGbt
'Pippa' (MinWL) CWGr
'Playa Blanca' (SC/DwB) MWat NSoo SGbt SMrm
'Playboy' (GD) CWGr
'Plum Surprise' (Pom) CWGr
'Polka' (Anem) NJRG SDeJ SGbt
'Polly Peachum' (SD) CWGr
'Polventon Supreme' (SBa) CWGr
'Polyand' (LD) CWGr
'Pontiac' (SC) CAvo CWGr LAyl SGbt
'Pooh' (Col) see *D.* 'Pooh - Swan Island'
§ 'Pooh - Swan Island' (Col) 🏆H3 CHVG CWGr EBee ERCP EUJe LAyl MAvo NHal NJRG SMrm WCot WPhe
'Popular Guest' (Fim) CWGr
'Pot Black' (MinBa) CWGr
'Potgeiter' (MinBa) CWGr
'Pow Wow' (Anem) **new** EWoo
'Prefect' (MS-c) CWGr
'Prefere' (Sin) CWGr
'Preference' (SS-c) CWGr ERCP SDeJ SGbt
'Preston Park' (Sin/DwB) 🏆H3 CWGr LAyl NHal
Pretty Woman = 'Vdtg43'^{PBR} (Dark Angel Series) (Sin) LRHS
'Priceless Pink' (Misc) **new** ERCP
Pride of Berlin see *D.* 'Stolz von Berlin'
'Prime Minister' (GD) CWGr
'Primrose Diane' (SD) CWGr
'Primrose Rustig' (MD) CWGr
'Prince Valiant' (SD) CWGr
I 'Princess' (Col) SDeJ
'Princess Marie José' (Sin) CWGr
'Princesse Elisabeth' (MinD) ERCP
'Princesse Gracia' (MinD) ERCP
'Princesse Laetitia' (MinD) ERCP
'Prinzessin Irene von Preussen' (SD) CWGr
'Procyon' (SD) CSut CWGr NBri NSoo SGbt WPhe
'Prom' (Pom) CWGr
'Promise' (Fim) CWGr ECtt ERCP
aff. ***pteropoda*** F&M 312 WPGP
'Punky' (Pom) CWGr
'Purbeck Lydia' (LS-c) CWGr
'Purpinca' (Anem) CWGr
'Purple Flame'^{PBR} (SD) **new** ERCP
'Purple Gem' (SS-c) CBod CWGr ERCP EUJe LAst NSoo SGbt SMrm WPhe
'Purple Haze' (Misc) EPfP ERCP WPhe
'Purple Pearl' (MD) ERCP NHal
'Purple Petite' (Sin) **new** NJRG
'Purple Puff' (Anem) NHal NJRG
'Purple Sensation' (SS-c) CWGr
'Purple Splash' (SWL) CWGr
'Purple Taiheyō' (GD) CWGr
'Purpurröschen' CWGr
purpusii **new** CWGr
aff. ***purpusii*** B&SWJ 10321 WCru
'Pussycat' (SD) CWGr
'Quel Diable' (LS-c) CWGr
'Quick Step' (Anem) NJRG
'Rachel de Thame' (Sin) CWGr
'Rachel's Place' (Pom) CWGr
I 'Radjah' (Pom) **new** NPri
'Raffles' (SD) CWGr LAyl
'Ragged Robin' (Misc) CSpe CWGN ECtt LRHS
'Raiser's Pride' (MC) NHal WPhe
'Raspberry Ripple' (SS-c) CWGr
* 'Raymond Guernsey' ECtt
'Rebecca Lynn' (MinD) CWGr
'Rebecca's World' (SD) **new** CSut
'Red Alert' (MinBa) CWGr
'Red and White' (SD) CWGr SGbt
'Red Arrows' (SD) CWGr
'Red Balloon' (SBa) CWGr
'Red Cap' (MinD) CWGr
'Red Carol' (Pom) CWGr
'Red Diamond' (MD) CWGr NHal
'Red Fubuki' (SD) SDeJ
'Red Highlight' (LS-c) CWGr
'Red Kaiser Wilhelm' (SBa) CWGr
'Red Majorette' (SS-c) CWGr SDeJ
'Red Pathfinder' (Sin) **new** NJRG
'Red Pimpernel' (SD) CWGr
'Red Pygmy' (SS-c) CWGr SDeJ
'Red Riding Hood' (MinBa) CWGr
'Red Schweitzer' (MinD) CWGr
'Red Velvet' (SWL) CWGr
'Reddy' (DwLil) CWGr
'Reedly' (SD) CWGr
'Reese's Dream' (GD) CWGr
'Regal Boy' (SBa) CWGr
'Reginald Keene' (LS-c) CWGr NHal
'Renato Tozio' (SD) CWGr
'Reputation' (LC) CWGr SGbt
'Requiem' (SD) CWGr ECtt ERCP NJRG
'Reverend P. Holian' (GS-c) CWGr SGbt
'Revive' (Misc) CWGr
'Rhanna Tammy' (GD) **new** NHal
'Rhonda' (Pom) NHal WPhe WWEG
'Richard Marc' (SC) CWGr
'Richard S' (LS-c) NHal
'Richstone' (MD) **new** CWGr
'Riisa' (MinBa) CWGr
'Rip City' (SS-c) CAvo CSpe CWGr ERCP MCot WCot WPhe
'Risca Miner' (SBa) CWGr
'Rita Easterbrook' (LD) CWGr
'Rita Shrimpton' (Misc) CWGr NJRG
'Roan' (MinD) CWGr
'Robann Royal' (MinBa) CWGr
'Robert Too' (MinD) CWGr
'Robin Hood' (SBa) CWGr
'Rocco' (MinBa) ERCP SGbt WBor WPhe
'Rockcliffe Billy' (SS-c) **new** NJRG
'Rockcliffe Gold' (MS-c) CWGr
'Romance' (MinC) CWGr
'Rosalinde' (S-c) CWGr
'Rose Jupiter' (GS-c) CWGr NHal
'Rose Quartz' (Misc) SMrm
'Rose Tendre' (MS-c) CWGr

	Cultivar	Suppliers
	'Rosella' (MD)	CWGr SDeJ SGbt WPhe
	'Rosemary Webb' (SD)	CWGr SGbt
	'Rossendale Lewis' (MinD)	NHal
	'Rossendale Luke' (SD)	CWGr
	'Rossendale Natasha' (MinBa)	NHal SGbt
	'Rossendale Stephanie' (MD) **new**	NHal
	'Rosy Cloud' (MD)	CWGr
	'Rothesay Castle' (MinD/DwB)	CWGr
	'Rothesay Herald' (SD/DwB)	CWGr
	'Rothesay Reveller' (MD)	CWGr
	'Rothesay Robin' (SD)	WPhe
	'Rothesay Rose' (SWL)	CWGr
	'Rotonde' (SC)	CWGr
I	'Roxy' (Sin/DwB)	CAby CBcs CHel CWGr EBee ECtt ELan EPfP ERCP GMaP LAst LAyl LRHS MAvo MBri MCot MNrw NGdn NHal NJRG SGbt WCot WHoo WPhe
	'Royal Mail' (MinD)	SGbt
	'Royal Visit' (SD)	CWGr SGbt
	'Royal Wedding' (LS-c)	CWGr
	'Ruby Murray' (MinD) ♀H3 **new**	LAyl
	'Ruby Puff' (Anem)	CWGr
	'Ruby Red' (MinBa)	CWGr
	'Ruby Wedding' (MinD)	CWGr SGbt
	rudis	CExl CFil CWGr WPGP
	'Ruskin Andrea' (SS-c)	LAyl NHal WPhe
	'Ruskin Avenger' (MS-c) **new**	NJRG
	'Ruskin Belle' (MS-c)	CWGr
	'Ruskin Bride' (MS-c)	NHal
	'Ruskin Buttercup' (MinD)	CWGr SGbt
	'Ruskin Charlotte' (LS-c)	CWGr NJRG
	'Ruskin Diana' (SD)	CWGr NHal WPhe
	'Ruskin Dynasty' (SD)	CWGr
	'Ruskin Emil' (SS-c)	CWGr
	'Ruskin Gypsy' (SBa)	CWGr
I	'Ruskin Harmony' (S-c)	CWGr NHal WPhe
	'Ruskin Limelight' (MC)	NHal
	'Ruskin Marigold' (SS-c)	CWGr NHal
	'Ruskin Myra' (SS-c)	CWGr LAyl NHal WPhe
	'Ruskin Petite' (MinBa)	CWGr
	'Ruskin Respectable' (SS-c)	WPhe
	'Ruskin Sensation' (MS-c)	NHal WPhe
*	'Ruskin Tangerine' (SBa)	NHal SGbt
	'Russell Turner' (SS-c)	CWGr
	'Rustig' (MD)	CWGr
	'Rusty Hope' (MinD)	CWGr
	'Ryecroft Brenda T' (SD)	NHal NJRG WPhe
	'Ryecroft Claire' (MinD)	NHal
	'Ryecroft Crystal' (SS-c)	NHal
	'Ryecroft Delight' (MinBa)	NHal
	'Ryecroft Ice' (LD)	NHal SGbt WPhe
	'Ryecroft Jan' (MinBa) ♀H3	CWGr NHal NJRG WPhe
	'Ryecroft Jim' (Anem)	NHal
	'Ryecroft Laura' (MinBa)	NHal
	'Ryecroft Magnum' (MD)	CWGr
	'Ryecroft Pixie' (MinC) **new**	NHal
	'Ryecroft Rebel' (MD)	NHal WPhe
	'Ryecroft Sparkler' (MinC)	NHal SGbt
	'Ryecroft Yellow Orb' (SBa) **new**	NHal
	'Ryecroft Zoe' (SS-c)	NHal
	'Ryedale Pinky' (SD)	CWGr
	'Ryedale Prince' (GD)	CWGr
	'Ryedale Rebecca' (GS-c)	CWGr
	'Safe Shot' (MD)	CWGr
	'Saint Croix' (GS-c)	CWGr
	'Saint-Saëns' (S-c)	ERCP SDeJ
	'Sakura Fubuki' (Fim)	ERCP
	'Saladin' (Misc)	CWGr
	'Salmon Athalie' (SC)	CWGr
	'Salmon Hornsey' (SD)	CWGr
	'Salmon Wheels' (Col) **new**	NJRG
	'Sam Hopkins' (SD)	ERCP LAyl NHal WPhe
	'Sam Huston' (GD)	CWGr SGbt
	'Samantha'	see *D.* 'Harvest Samantha'
	'Sandia Rose' (WL) **new**	NHal
	'Sandia Shomei' (SWL) **new**	EWoo
	'Sandra' (MinD)	ERCP
	'Sans Souci' (GC)	CWGr
	'Santa Claus' (MD)	CWGr SGbt
	'Sarah' (MinS-c)	ECtt EPla EUJe LRHS SBod WHoo
	'Sarah G' (LS-c)	CWGr
	'Sarah Thomas' (Col)	CWGr
	'Sarum Aurora' (SD)	CWGr
	'Sascha' (SWL) ♀H3	LAyl NHal
	'Sassy' (MinD)	CWGr SGbt
	'Scarborough Ace' (MD)	CWGr
	'Scarlet Comet' (Anem)	CWGr
§	'Scarlet Fern' (Sin)	CWGr LRHS WPhe
	'Scarlet Kokarde' (MinD)	CWGr
	'Scarlet O'Hara' (MinD) **new**	NJRG
	'Scarlet Rotterdam' (MS-c)	CWGr
	'Scarlet Star' (SS-c)	CWGr
	'Scarlett Claire' (Col)	CWGr
	'Scaur Sunrise' (SD) **new**	NJRG
	'Scaur Swinton' (MD)	CWGr LAyl NHal SGbt
	'Schweitzer's Kokarde' (MinD)	CWGr
	'Scottish Impact' (MinS-c)	CWGr
	'Scura' (Sin)	ERCP
	'Seattle' (SD)	CWGr NBri
	'Seduction' (MinD)	EPfP ERCP
	'Seirō' (MS-c)	SGbt
	'Severin's Triumph' (LD)	CWGr
	'Shandy' (SS-c)	LAyl
	'Shannon' (SD)	CWGr
	'Sheila Mooney' (LD)	CWGr
	'Shep's Memory' (SWL) ♀H3	CWGr NJRG
	'Sherwood Monarch' (GS-c)	CWGr
	'Sherwood Titan' (GD)	CWGr
	'Sherwood's Peach' (LD)	CWGr
	'Shirley' (LD)	CWGr
	'Shirley Pillman' (Misc)	CWGr
	'Shooting Star' (LS-c)	CWGr NBri
	'Show 'n' Tell' (Fim)	ERCP SGbt WPhe
	'Shy Princess' (MC)	CWGr
	'Siedlerstolz' (SD)	CWGr
	'Silver City' (LD)	CWGr NHal SGbt WPhe
	'Silver Years' (MD)	CWGr
	'Sir Alf Ramsey' (GD)	CWGr LAyl NHal SGbt WPhe
	'Sisa' (SD)	CWGr
	'Skipley Spot' (SD)	CWGr
	'Skipper Rock' (GD)	CWGr
	'Sky High' (SD)	CWGr
	'Small World' (Pom) ♀H3	CWGr LAyl NHal WWEG
	'Smokey' (MD)	CWGr
	'Smoky O' (MS-c)	CWGr
	'Smoots' (Fim)	CWGr

	Name	Suppliers
	'Sneezy' (Sin)	CWGr
	'Snip' (MinS-c)	CWGr
	'Snoho Tammie' (MinBa)	CWGr
	'Snow Cap' (SS-c)	CWGr SDeJ
	'Snow Fairy' (MinC)	CWGr
	'Snow White' (Sin/DwB)	CWGr
	'Snowbound' (LD)	SGbt
	'Snowflake' (SWL)	CWGr ERCP SDeJ
	'Snowfox' (Anem) **new**	NJRG
	'Snowstorm' (MD)	CWGr SGbt
	'Snowy' (MinBa)	CWGr
	'So Dainty' (MinS-c) ♀H3	CWGr LAyl
	'Song of Olympia' (SWL)	CWGr
	'Sonia Henie' (SBa)	CWGr
	'Sophie Taylor' (SinO) **new**	NJRG
	sorensenii	CWGr
	'Sorrento Flush' (SD)	WPhe
	'Soulman' (Anem)	CSpe CWGr EWoo NJRG SGbt WBrk
	'Sourire de Crozon' (SD)	CWGr
	'Souvenir d'Eté' (Pom)	CWGr SDeJ
	'Spanish Conquest' (MinD)	SGbt
	'Sparkler' (SS-c)	CWGr ERCP
	'Spartacus' (LD)	CWGr LAyl NHal WPhe
	'Spassmacher' (MS-c)	CWGr
	spectabilis **new**	CWGr
	'Spectacular' (SD)	CWGr SGbt
	'Spencer' (SD)	CWGr
	'Spike' (LS-c)	SGbt
	'Spikey Symbol' (MS-c)	CWGr
	'Sprinter' (C)	CWGr
	'Staleen Condesa' (MS-c) ♀H3	NHal SGbt
	'Star Child' (SinO)	CWGr
	'Star Elite' (MC)	CWGr NBri
	'Star Surprise' (SC)	CWGr SDeJ
	Star Wars (Dark Angel Series) (Sin)	ERCP SDeJ WPhe
	'Starlight Keene' (LS-c)	CWGr
	'Starry Night' (MinS-c)	CWGr
	'Star's Favourite' (MC)	CHVG ERCP
	'Star's Lady' (SC)	CWGr
	'Stefan Bergerhoff' (MinD)	CWGr
	'Stellyvonne' (LS-c/Fim)	CWGr
	'Stevie D' (SD) ♀H3	CWGr SGbt
§	'Stolz von Berlin' (MinBa)	CWGr ERCP SDeJ SGbt
	'Stoneleigh Cherry' (Pom)	LAyl
	'Stoneleigh Joyce' (Pom)	CWGr
	'Storm Warning' (GD)	CWGr
	'Storrs Julie' (Pom) **new**	NJRG
	'Striped Vulcan' (MS-c) **new**	CAby
	'Sue Mountjoy' (Col)	CWGr
	'Sue Willo' (Pom)	CWGr
	'Suffolk Fantasy' (SD)	CWGr
	'Suffolk Punch' (MD)	LAyl
	'Sugar Diamond' (SC)	ERCP
	'Suitzus Julie' (Misc)	CWGr
	'Summer Festival' (SD)	CWGr SGbt
	'Summer Night' (M-Sc)	see *D.* 'Nuit d'Eté'
	'Summer Nights' (Misc) **new**	CWGr NJRG
	'Summer's End' (SWL)	CWGr
	'Sunlight' (SBa)	CWGr
	'Sunlight Pastelle' (MS-c)	CWGr
	'Sunny Boy' (MinD)	NBri
	'Sunray Glint' (MS-c)	CWGr
	'Sunray Silk' (MS-c)	CWGr
I	'Sunshine' (Sin)	ECtt LRHS
	'Sunshine Girl' (Col) **new**	NJRG
	'Super Rays' (MC)	CWGr
	'Super Trouper' (SD)	CWGr
	'Superfine' (SC)	CWGr
	'Sure Thing' (MC)	CWGr
	'Susan Carey' (LS-c) ♀H3	WPhe
	'Susan Gilbert' (Col) **new**	NHal
	'Susan Gilliott' (MS-c)	NHal
I	'Suzanne' (Col) **new**	NJRG
	'Suzette' (SD/DwB)	CWGr SGbt
	'Swallow Falls' (SD)	CWGr
	'Swan Lake'	see *D.* 'Classic Swanlake'
	'Swanvale' (SD)	SGbt
	'Sweet Content' (SD)	CWGr SGbt
	'Sweet Sensation' (MS-c)	CWGr
	'Sweetheart' (SD)	CWGr NJRG
	'Swiss Miss' (MinBa)	CWGr
I	'Sylvia' (SBa)	CWGr ERCP NBri NJRG SMrm WPhe
	'Sylvia's Desire' (SC)	CWGr
	'Symbol' (MS-c)	CWGr
	'Sympathy' (SWL)	CWGr
	'Syston Harlequin' (SD)	CWGr
	'Syston Sophia' (Ba)	CWGr
	'Tahiti Sunrise' (MS-c)	CWGr
	'Tahoma Hope' (Misc) **new**	CWGr
	'Tahoma Moonshot' (SinO)	CWGr
	'Tahoma Tom Tom' (MS-c)	NHal
	'Tally Ho' (Misc) ♀H3	CHVG CHel CWGr ECGP ECtt EPfP LRHS NJRG SDys WCot WWEG
	'Tam Tam' (MinBa)	CWGr EPfP
	'Tamburo' (SS-c) **new**	ERCP
	'Tapestry' (Sin)	CWGr SGbt WPhe
	'Taratahi Ruby' (SWL) ♀H3	CWGr ERCP NHal NJRG WPhe
	'Taratahi Sunrise' (MS-c)	CWGr
	'Tartan' (MD)	CWGr
	Taxi Driver = 'Vdtg57'PBR (Dark Angel Series) (Sin)	LRHS
	'Teamarie Butterscotch' (Misc) **new**	NJRG
	'Teesbrooke Audrey' (Col)	CWGr ECtt LAyl NHal WPhe
	'Teesbrooke Red Eye' (Col)	CWGr ERCP NHal NJRG SGbt WPhe
	'Temptress' (SS-c)	CWGr
	tenuicaulis	CCon CDTJ CExl CWGr GGal SBig
	– F&M 257	CFil
	– F&M 355	CFil
	'Terracotta' (DwB)	NHal
	'Thais' (Col)	NJRG
	'Thames Valley' (MD)	CWGr
	'The Baron' (SD)	CWGr
	'The Phantom' (Anem)	ERCP NJRG WBor
	'Thelma Clements' (LD)	CWGr
	'Theo Sprengers' (MD)	CWGr
	'Thika' (SD)	CWGr
	'Thomas A. Edison' (MD)	CAvo CWGr ERCP SDeJ SGbt
	'Thoresby Jewel' (SD)	CWGr
I	'Tiara' (SD)	CWGr
	'Tiffany Lynn' (SinO)	CWGr
	'Tiger Eye' (MD)	CWGr SGbt
	'Tiger Tiv' (MD)	CWGr
	'Tinker's White' (SD)	CWGr
	'Tioga Spice' (Fim)	CWGr
I	'Tiptoe' (MinD)	LAyl NHal
	'Tisa' (Pom)	NHal
	'Toga' (SWL)	CWGr
	'Tohsuikyoh' (Misc)	CWGr SGbt
	'Tommy Doc' (SS-c)	CWGr

	'Tommy Keith' (MinBa)	CWGr
	'Tomo' (SD)	LAyl NHal
	'Top Affair' (MS-c)	CWGr
	'Top Choice' (GS-c)	CWGr
	'Top Totty' (MinD)	NHal
I	'Topaz Puff' (Anem)	CWGr
	'Topmix' (Sin)	SDeJ
	'Topmix Mama' (Sin) **new**	NJRG
	'Topmix Pink' (Sin)	SDeJ
	'Topmix Purple' (Sin) **new**	NJRG
	'Topmix Red' (Sin)	NJRG SDeJ
	'Topmix Reddy' (Sin) **new**	NJRG
I	'Topmix Rose' (Sin) **new**	NJRG
	'Topmix White' (DwB)	SDeJ
	'Topmix Yellow' (DwB)	NJRG SDeJ
	'Toto' (Anem)	ERCP
	'Towneley Class' (SD)	CWGr
	'Trampolene' (SS-c)	CWGr
	'Trelyn Daisy' (Col) ♀H3	CWGr
	'Trelyn Kiwi' (SS-c) ♀H3	CWGr NHal NJRG SGbt WPhe
	'Trelyn Rebecca' (Col)	NHal WPhe
	'Trelyn Rhiannon' (SC) ♀H3	CWGr WPhe
	'Trelyn Seren' (SinO)	LAyl NHal WPhe
	'Trendy' (SD)	CWGr
	'Trengrove Autumn' (MD)	CWGr SGbt
	'Trengrove Jill' (MD)	CWGr
	'Trengrove Millennium' (MD)	CWGr NHal NJRG SGbt
	'Trengrove Tauranga' (MD)	CWGr
	'Trevor' (Col)	CWGr ECtt SGbt
	'Tricolor' ambig.	MSCN
	'Trooper Dan' (S-c) **new**	NHal
	'Trotter's Jo-Anne' (MS-c)	CWGr
	'Troy Dyson' (Misc)	SDys
	'Truly Scrumptious' (MS-c)	SGbt
	'Tu-tu'	CWGr SGbt
	tubulata	CFil
	'Tudor 1' (Misc/DwB)	NHal
	'Tui Avis' (MinC)	CWGr NJRG
	'Tui Orange' (SS-c)	CWGr
	'Tula Rosa' (Pom)	CWGr
	'Tutankhamun' (Pom)	CWGr
	'Twiggy' (SWL)	CWGr SGbt
	'Twilight Time' (MD)	CWGr SDeJ WPhe
*	'Twinkle Stars'	SDeJ
	'Twyning's After Eight' (Sin) ♀H3	CAby CAvo CExl CHVG CHel CSpe CWGN CWGr ECtt ELan EPfP ERCP EWoo LAyl LRHS LSun MBri MCot NHal NJRG NSti SDix SDys SGbt SMrm WBor WCot WHoo WPhe
	'Twyning's Aniseed' (Sin)	CWGr
	'Twyning's Black Cherry' (MinD)	CWGr
	'Twyning's Candy' (Sin)	CWGr
	'Twyning's Chocolate' (Sin)	CWGr
	'Twyning's Peppermint' (Sin)	CWGr
	'Twyning's Pink Fish' (Col) ♀H3	CWGr
	'Twyning's Revel' (Sin)	CAvo CWGr
	'Twyning's Smartie' (Sin)	CSut CWGr
	'Twyning's White Chocolate' (Sin)	CWGr
	'Tyrell' (D)	EPfP
	'Uchuu' (GD)	CWGr
	'Uncle Hankey' (SD) **new**	ERCP
	'Union Jack' (Sin)	CWGr
	'United' (SD)	CWGr
	'Usugesho' (LD)	CWGr
	'Vader Abraham' (MinD)	CWGr
	'Vaguely Noble' (SBa)	CWGr
	'Val Saint Lambert' (MC)	CWGr
	'Vancouver' (Misc)	ERCP SDeJ
	'Variace' (MinBa)	CWGr
	'Velda Inez' (MinD)	CWGr
	'Vera's Elma' (LD)	CWGr
	'Veritable' (MS-c)	CSut NBri
	'Vesuvius' (MD)	CWGr
	'Vicky Crutchfield' (SWL)	WCot
	'Vicky Jackson' (SWL)	CWGr
	'Victory Day' (LC)	CWGr
	'Vigor' (SWL)	CWGr
	'Vino' (Pom)	CWGr
	'Vivex' (Pom)	CWGr
	'Vivian Russell' (WL) **new**	NJRG
	'Vulcan' (S-c)	CWGr ERCP SGbt WPhe
§	'Vuurvogel' (MS-c)	CWGr ERCP NBri SDeJ
	'Walter Hardisty' (GD)	CWGr
	'Walter James' (SD)	CWGr
	'Waltzing Mathilda' (Misc)	ERCP
	'Wanda's Capella' (GD)	CWGr WPhe
	'Wanda's Moonlight' (GD)	CWGr
	'Wandy' (Pom)	CWGr
	'War of the Roses' (SD)	WHer
	'Warkton Willo' (Pom)	CWGr
	'Warmunda' (MinBa)	CWGr
	'Wendy' (MinBa)	CWGr
	'Wendy Spencer' (MinD)	CWGr
	'Wendy's Place' (Pom)	CWGr
	'Wennie' (Anem)	CWGr
	'Westerton Folly' (SBa)	NHal
	'Westerton Lilian' (SS-c) **new**	NHal
	'Weston Aramac' (SS-c)	CWGr
	'Weston Buccaneer' (MinC)	NHal WPhe
	'Weston Corsair' (MinC) **new**	NJRG
	'Weston Forge' (SC)	CWGr
	'Weston Kelpie' (MinC)	NJRG
	'Weston Miss' (MinS-c)	CWGr NHal NJRG
	'Weston Nugget' (MinC)	CWGr
	'Weston Pirate' (MinC) ♀H3	CWGr LAyl NHal NJRG WPhe WWEG
	'Weston Princekin' (MinS-c)	CWGr
	'Weston Spanish Dancer' (MinC) ♀H3	CWGr ERCP LAyl NHal NJRG SGbt WPhe
	'Weston Stardust' (MinC) ♀H3	NHal NJRG WPhe
	'Weston Sunup' (MinC)	NJRG
	'Weston Tea-time' (MinC)	CWGr
	'Weston Torero' (MinC)	CWGr
	'Wheels' (Col)	CWGr NJRG
	'White Alva's' (GD) ♀H3	CWGr LAyl NHal SGbt WPhe
	'White Aster' (Pom)	CWGr ERCP
	'White Ballerina' (SWL)	LAyl NHal SGbt WPhe
	'White Ballet' (SD) ♀H3	CWGr LAyl SGbt
	'White Cameo' (SWL)	CWGr
	'White Charlie Two' (MD)	NHal
	'White Hunter' (SD)	CWGr
	'White Katrina' (LS-c)	WPhe
	'White Klankstad' (SC)	CWGr
	'White Knight' (MinD)	NHal
	'White Linda' (SD)	CWGr NHal
	'White Magenta Star' (Sin)	CWGr
	'White Moonlight' (MS-c)	LAyl NHal WPhe
	'White Nettie' (MinBa)	CWGr SGbt

'White Onesta' (SD) SDeJ WPhe
'White Perfection' (LD) CWGr ECtt EPfP ERCP SDeJ
'White Rustig' (MD) CWGr
'White Star' (MS-c) ERCP SDeJ
'White Swallow' (SS-c) NHal
'Who Dun It' (MD) ERCP
'Wicky Woo' (SD) CWGr
'Wildwood Marie' (SWL) CWGr NJRG
'William B' (GD) CWGr
'William John' (Pom) CWGr
'Williamsburg' (SS-c) CWGr
'Willo's Borealis' (Pom) CWGr NHal WPhe
'Willo's Night' (Pom) CWGr
'Willo's Surprise' (Pom) CWGr NHal SGbt WWEG
'Willo's Violet' (Pom) CWGr NHal NJRG SGbt WPhe WWEG
'Willowfield Mick' (LD) CWGr
'Wine & Roses' (SWL) SGbt
'Winholme Diane' (SD) CWGr NHal WPhe
'Winkie Colonel' (GD) CWGr
'Winnie' (Pom) CWGr
'Winsome' (SWL) CWGr
'Winston Churchill' (MinD) CWGr
'Winter Springs' (S-Sc) ERCP WPhe
'Wise Guy' (GD) CWGr
'Wishes n Dreams' (Sin) NJRG
'Wisk' (Pom) CWGr
'Wittem' (MD) CWGr
'Witteman's Best' (LS-c) CWGr ERCP MCot NBri SGbt WPhe
'Witteman's Superba' (SS-c) ♀H3 CWGr NHal SDix
'Wizard of Oz' (MinBa) CWGr ERCP WPhe
'Woodbridge' (Sin) CWGr SGbt
'Woodside Finale' (MinD) NHal
'Wootton Carnival' (SC) CWGr
'Wootton Cupid' (MinBa) ♀H3 CWGr
'Wootton Impact' (MS-c) ♀H3 NHal WPhe
'Wootton Phebe' (SD) CWGr
'Wootton Windmill' (Col) CWGr
'Worton Blue Streak' (SS-c) CWGr ERCP SGbt
'Worton Revival' (MD) CWGr
'Worton Superb' (SD) CWGr
'Wyndal Horizon' (MS-c) **new** CWGr
'Yamabiraki' (GD) **new** CWGr
'Yellow Abundance' (SD) CWGr
'Yellow Baby' (Pom) CWGr
I 'Yellow Bird' (Col) CWGr
'Yellow Galator' (MC) CWGr SGbt
'Yellow Hammer' (Sin/DwB) ♀H3 CWGr LAyl NHal SGbt
'Yellow Linda's Chester' (SC) CWGr
'Yellow Lorona Dawn' (Col) **new** NJRG
'Yellow Pages' (SD) CWGr
'Yellow Passions' (MD) ERCP
'Yellow Pet' (SD) CWGr
'Yellow Spiky' (MS-c) CWGr
'Yellow Star' (MS-c) ERCP EUJe SDeJ
'Yellow Vulcan' (GS-c) CWGr
'Yelno Enchantment' (SWL) LAyl
'Yelno Petite Glory' (MinD) CWGr
'York and Lancaster' (MD) CWGr SGbt
'Yukino' (Col) CWGr
'Zagato' (MinD) CWGr
'Zakuro-hime' (SD) CWGr
I 'Zelda' (LD) CWGr
'Zest' (MinD) CWGr
§ 'Zone Ten' PBR (Sin/DwB) CAby LRHS LSou MGos SHar SPoG WBor
'Zorro' (GD) ♀H3 CWGr ERCP NHal SGbt WPhe
'Zurich' (SS-c) CWGr

Daiswa see *Paris*

Dalea (*Papilionaceae*)

purpurea SPhx
– 'Stephanie' LRHS

damson see *Prunus insititia*

Danae (*Asparagaceae*)

§ ***racemosa*** ♀H5 CBcs CFil CTri EBee ELan EPfP MGil MGos MMuc MRav SArc SEND SRms SSpi SWvt WCot WCru WPGP

Danthonia (*Poaceae*)

§ ***cincta*** **new** WCot

Daphne ✿ (*Thymelaeaceae*)

DJHC 98164 from China WCru
acutiloba CJun GKev
– 'Fragrant Cloud' CExl CJun EWes SChF
albowiana CJun LLHF LRHS
alpina CJun
altaica CJun
arbuscula ♀H5 CJun EPot MWat SIgm WAbe
– subsp. ***arbuscula*** f. ***albiflora*** CJun
– 'Diva' CJun
– 'Muran Pride' CJun
– f. ***radicans*** CJun
arbuscula × ***cneorum*** var. ***verlotii*** CJun
arbuscula × 'Leila Haines' see *D.* × *schlyteri*
arisanensis B&SWJ 6983 WCru
aurantiaca **new** GKev
bholua CAbP CHll CJun EPfP GCal GGal LRHS
I – 'Alba' CJun EPfP SSta WPGP
– 'Darjeeling' CExl CHll CJun EPfP LRHS SKHP WPGP
– var. ***glacialis*** 'Gurkha' ♀H4 CExl CJun EPfP SKHP WPGP
– 'Hazel Edwards' **new** LRHS
– 'Jacqueline Postill' ♀H4 Widely available
– 'Limpsfield' CJun LRHS SCoo SSta
– 'Penwood' **new** CJun
– 'Peter Smithers' CExl CJun EPfP LRHS SSta WPGP
– 'Wisley Purple' CJun
blagayana CJun ECho NBir SIgm SRms WThu
– 'Brenda Anderson' CJun EPot WAbe
'Bramdean' see *D.* × *napolitana* 'Bramdean'
× ***burkwoodii*** EBee SCob
– 'Albert Burkwood' CJun
– 'Astrid' (v) CBcs CJun LRHS MGos MJak NLar SCob SLon
– 'Briggs Moonlight' (v) MAsh NLar
§ – 'Carol Mackie' (v) CJun LRHS SIgm
– 'G.K. Argles' (v) CJun MAsh
I – 'Gold Sport' CJun SChF
– 'Gold Strike' (v) CJun
– 'Golden Treasure' CJun MAsh SChF WPat

	Name	Suppliers
	- 'Lavenirii'	CJun
	- 'Somerset' ♀H4	CBcs CJun ELan GKev MGos MSwo NLar NWea SCob
§	- 'Somerset Gold Edge' (v)	CJun
§	- 'Somerset Variegated' (v)	SChF WThu
	- 'Variegata' broad cream edge	see *D.* × *burkwoodii* 'Somerset Variegated'
	- - broad gold edge	see *D.* × *burkwoodii* 'Somerset Gold Edge'
	- - narrow gold edge	see *D.* × *burkwoodii* 'Carol Mackie'
	calcicola 'Gang-ho-ba'	CJun WThu
	caucasica	CJun
	circassica	CJun SChF
	cneorum	CBcs CJun EPot IVic MGos MWat
	- 'Benaco'	CJun
	- 'Blackthorn Triumph'	CJun WAbe
	- 'Eximia' ♀H5	CJun LRHS WAbe
	- 'Klaus Patzner'	CJun
	- 'Lac des Gloriettes'	CJun
	- 'Puszta'	CJun MAsh WAbe
	- var. ***pygmaea***	CJun EPot
	- - 'Alba'	CJun
	- 'Rubra'	LRHS
	- 'Ruby Glow'	CJun
	- 'Variegata' (v)	CJun EPot GEdr
	- 'Velký Kosir'	CJun MWat SChF WAbe
	- var. ***verlotii***	EPot
	collina	see *D. sericea* Collina Group
	domini	GKev
	× ***eschmannii*** 'Jacob Eschmann'	CJun
	'Forarch'	CJun
	genkwa	CJun WThu
	giraldii	CJun
	gnidioides	CJun
	'Guardsman'	CJun MAsh WAbe
	× ***hendersonii***	CJun
	- 'Appleblossom'	CJun SChF WAbe
	- 'Aymon Correvon'	CJun MAsh WThu
	- 'Blackthorn Rose'	CJun WAbe
	- 'Ernst Hauser'	CJun GKev WAbe WIce WThu
	- 'Fritz Kummert'	CJun WAbe WThu
	- 'Jeanette Brickell'	CJun WAbe WThu
	- 'Kath Dryden'	CJun SIgm WAbe
	- 'Marion White'	CJun WAbe
	- 'Rosebud'	CJun WThu
	- 'Solferino'	CJun MAsh
	'Hinton'	CJun
	× ***houtteana***	CJun
	× ***hybrida***	CJun
	japonica 'Striata'	see *D. odora* 'Aureomarginata'
	jasminea	CJun ECho WAbe
	jezoensis	CJun LRHS SSta
	× ***jintyae*** 'Pink Cascade'	CJun
	juliae	CJun WAbe
	kamtschatica	CJun
	'Kilmeston Beauty'	CJun
	kosaninii	CJun
	× ***latymeri*** 'Spring Sonnet'	CJun SChF SIgm WAbe
	laureola	CJun EPfP GPoy MMHG NBid NBir NLar NPer SPer
	- 'Kingsley Green'	CJun
	- 'Margaret Mathew'	CJun EPfP EPot NLar SChF
	- subsp. ***philippi***	CBcs CJun CMac ELan EPfP ETwe GKev LRHS MAsh MBlu MGil MGos NLar SKHP
	'Leila Haines'	CJun NLar
	longilobata	GKev
	× ***mantensiana*** 'Audrey Vockins'	CJun
	- 'Manten'	CJun
	× ***mauerbachii*** 'Perfume of Spring'	CJun SChF
	'Meon'	see *D.* × *napolitana* 'Meon'
	mezereum	CTri ECho GKev GMaP GPoy IFoB ITim LRHS MAsh MBri MGil MGos NChi NWea SChF SCob SGol SLim SWvt WCFE WHar WHil WPGP
	- PAB 7643 **new**	LEdu
	- f. ***alba***	CBcs CJun ECho GKev MAsh MGos NChi SChF SRms SWvt WAbe WCFE
	- - 'Bowles's Variety'	CJun EPot MAsh
	- 'Rosea'	ECho MAsh SRms
	- var. ***rubra***	CBcs CJun CMac CWSG ELan GKin LRHS MGos MJak MRav MSwo SPer WAbe
	× ***napolitana*** ♀H4	CJun SChF
§	- 'Bramdean'	CJun
§	- 'Meon'	CJun MAsh WAbe WThu
	odora	CBcs CJun CWSG EBee EPfP LRHS MSwo SCob SLim
§	- f. ***alba***	CCCN CJun CMac
	- - 'Sakiwaka'	CCCN CExl CJun SKHP WPat
§	- 'Aureomarginata' (v) ♀H4	Widely available
	- 'Clotted Cream' (v)	CJun MAsh
	- 'Geisha Girl' (v)	CJun MAsh MGos
	- var. ***leucantha***	see *D. odora* f. *alba*
	- 'Limelight' (v)	CJun
	- 'Mae-jima' (v)	CExl CJun EBee ELan EPfP LRHS MAsh NLar SLon SPer
	- 'Marginata'	see *D. odora* 'Aureomarginata'
	- Marianni = 'Rogbret' (v)	CWSG ELon ETwe EUJe GKev MJak NCGa NLar SGol SMad SWvt WCot
	- Rebecca = 'Hewreb' (v)	CBct CBod EPfP LBuc LRHS MAsh MBri SHil SLon SPoG
	- var. ***rubra***	CCCN CCon CJun CMac GKev LLHF
	- 'Sunshine'	SSta
	- 'Walberton' (v)	EPfP LRHS MBri
	oleoides	CJun NLar
	papyracea	CExl CFil
	petraea	CJun WAbe
	- 'Cima Tombea'	CJun
	- 'Corna Blacca'	CJun
	- 'Garnet'	CJun WAbe
	- 'Grandiflora'	CJun WAbe
	- 'Lydora'	CJun
	- 'Persebee'	CJun
	- 'Punchinello'	CJun
	- 'Tuflungo'	CJun
	Pink Fragrance = 'Blapink'PBR	CBcs EPfP MAsh SKHP SPer SPoG
	'Pink Star'	CJun
	pontica	CBcs CJun EBee EPfP IDee LRHS MAsh NLar SDix SKHP SSpi WPGP
	× ***reichsteinii*** **new**	GKev
	retusa	see *D. tangutica* Retusa Group
	'Richard's Choice'	CJun
	× ***rollsdorfii*** 'Arnold Cihlarz'	CJun GKev WAbe
	- 'Wilhelm Schacht' ♀H5	CAbP CJun IVic MAsh SChF WAbe WThu
	× ***rossetii*** 'Rossetii'	CJun
	'Rosy Wave'	CJun SChF
§	× ***schlyteri***	CJun
	- 'July Glow' **new**	EPot GEdr

- 'Lovisa Maria' CJun EPot SIgm WAbe
sericea CJun
§ - Collina Group CAbP CJun WIce
'Spring Beauty' CJun EPfP
'Spring Herald' CJun
'Stasek' (v) CJun
× ***suendermannii*** 'Franz Suendermann' WAbe
× ***susannae*** 'Anton Fahndrich' CJun NLar WThu
- 'Cheriton' ♀H5 CJun EPot LRHS NLar WAbe WThu
- 'Tage Lundell' CJun IVic
- 'Tichborne' CAbP CJun EPot SChF WThu
tangutica ♀H5 CBcs CExl CJun CMac CTri ECho ELan EPfP ETwe EWTr GKev LRHS MAsh MGil MGos NBir NHol NLar SCoo SEND SKHP SPoG SRkn SRms SSpi WAbe WKif
- 'Golden Thread' (v) new EPfP SPer
§ - Retusa Group ♀H5 CExl CJun CWCL ECho ELan ELon EOHP EPot GAbr GBin GEdr GKev LEdu LRHS MGil MHer NBir NLar NRya SIgm SPer SRms
× ***transatlantica*** 'Beulah Cross' (v) CAbP CJun ELan LRHS MAsh SChF SLon
- Eternal Fragrance = 'Blafra'PBR ♀H5 CAbP CCCN CEnd CExl CWGN ELan ELon EPfP EPot EUJe LLHF LRHS LSqu MAsh MGos NLar SCoo SKHP SLim SLon SPer SPoG SSpi SSta WPGP
- 'Jim's Pride' SChF WPat
- 'Summer Ice' (v) new WAbe
'Valerie Hillier' CJun GKev LRHS
velenovskyi CJun
× ***whiteorum*** 'Beauworth' CJun WAbe WOld
- 'Kilmeston' CJun WAbe
- 'Warnford' CJun
wolongensis 'Kevock Star' CExl GKev

Daphniphyllum (*Daphniphyllaceae*)

KWJ 12244 from northern Vietnam WCru
aff. ***angustifolium*** B&SWJ 8225 WCru
- B&SWJ 11804 WCru
- WWJ 12020 WCru
glaucescens WCru
subsp. ***oldhamii*** var. ***kengii*** B&SWJ 6872
- - - B&SWJ 7119 WCru
- - var. ***oldhamii*** B&SWJ 7056 WCru
- - - CWJ 12351 WCru
himalaense new SMad
humile see *D. macropodum* var. *humile*
aff. ***longeracemosum*** B&SWJ 11788 WCru
- NJM 10.147 new WPGP
macropodum CBcs CCCN CFil CHEx CMCN EBee EPfP GBin LRHS NLar SArc SDix SKHP SSpi SVen WCru WPGP
- B&SWJ 581 WCru
- B&SWJ 2898 WCru
- B&SWJ 6809 from Taiwan WCru
- B&SWJ 8507 from Ulleungdo, South Korea WCru
- B&SWJ 8763 from Cheju-do, Korea WCru
- B&SWJ 11489 from Yakushima, Japan WCru
- dwarf WCru
§ - var. ***humile*** B&SWJ 11232 WCru
majus B&SWJ 11744 WCru
paxianum B&SWJ 9755 WCru
pentandrum B&SWJ 6888 WCru
- B&SWJ 7056 WCru
- CWJ 12393 WCru
- RWJ 9836 WCru
teysmannii B&SWJ 11110 from Japan WCru
- B&SWJ 11112 WCru
- B&SWJ 11358 from Japan WCru
aff. ***teysmannii*** CWJ 12350 from Taiwan WCru

Darlingtonia (*Sarraceniaceae*)

californica ♀H3 EFEx WSSs

Darmera (*Saxifragaceae*)

peltata ♀H6 Widely available
- 'Nana' CHEx EBee ECha EPfP GBuc GCal LBMP MWts NBid NHol NLar NMyG SWat WFar WMoo

Darwinia (*Myrtaceae*)

taxifolia MOWG

Dasylirion (*Asparagaceae*)

§ ***acrotrichum*** CDTJ CExl EShb SArc
berlandieri CExl
cedrosanum CDTJ CJun SPlb
glaucophyllum CJun
gracile Planchon see *D. acrotrichum*
longissimum CBrP CCCN EShb LPal SChr
miquihuanense SMad
- F&M 301A WPGP
- F&M 321 EBee WPGP
quadrangulatum LPal SPlb
serratifolium EUJe LPal
texanum IDee LEdu
wheeleri ♀H2 CBrP LPal SPlb

date see *Phoenix dactylifera*

Datisca (*Datiscaceae*)

cannabina CArn CDTJ EBee ECha EPPr GBin GCal IMou LPla NChi SBrt SDix SMHy SMad SMrm WMoo WPGP WSHC

Datura (*Solanaceae*)

arborea see *Brugmansia arborea*
cornigera see *Brugmansia arborea*
'Double Blackcurrant Swirl' CSpe
ferox CArn
§ ***inoxia*** CSpe
meteloides see *D. inoxia*
rosea see *Brugmansia* × *insignis* pink-flowered
rosei see *Brugmansia sanguinea*
sanguinea see *Brugmansia sanguinea*
stramonium CArn EBtc WCot
suaveolens see *Brugmansia suaveolens*
versicolor see *Brugmansia versicolor* Lagerh.
- 'Grand Marnier' see *Brugmansia* × *candida* 'Grand Marnier'

Daubenya (*Asparagaceae*)

alba	EСho
aurea	ECho
- var. ***coccinea***	ECho
marginata	ECho
namaquensis	ECho

Daucus (*Apiaceae*)

carota	CArn CHab LEdu NMir SVic WHer WSFF

Davallia (*Davalliaceae*)

canariensis ♀H1c	CMen EFtx
mariesii ♀H2	CMen ISha NLos
- B&SWJ 4448	WCru
- var. ***stenolepis***	CMen
tasmanii	CMen
trichomanoides	CBty CMen NLos
- f. ***barbata***	CMen EFtx

Davidia (*Nyssaceae*)

involucrata ♀H5	Widely available
- 'Sonoma'	CLnd MBlu NLar WHor
- var. ***vilmoriniana*** ♀H5	CBcs CDoC CWCL ELan EPfP LRHS MAsh MBlu MGos SLim SPer SPtp

Daviesia (*Papilionaceae*)

cordata	SPlb
* ***ovalifolia***	SPlb
pectinata	SPlb

Debregeasia (*Urticaceae*)

longifolia	SVen
- WWJ 11686	WCru

Decaisnea (*Lardizabalaceae*)

fargesii	Widely available
- B&SWJ 8070	WCru

Decodon (*Lythraceae*)

verticillatus	LLWG

Decumaria (*Hydrangeaceae*)

barbara	CBcs CMac MMuc NLar SLim WCru WSHC
- 'Vicki'	NBro NLar
sinensis	EPfP ESwi EUJe LRHS MMuc SHil SKHP SLon SPoG SSpi WCru WSHC

Deinanthe (*Hydrangeaceae*)

bifida	CDes CExl CMil EBee EPfP EWes LRHS SMad WCru WPGP
- B&SWJ 5436	EWld WCru
- B&SWJ 5551	WCru
- B&SWJ 5655	LEdu NLar WCru
- 'Pink-Kii'	WCru
- 'Pink-Shi'	WCru WSHC
bifida* × *caerulea	CLAP WCru
'Blue Blush'	WCru
caerulea	CLAP CMil ECho GCra GKev IGor IMou LEdu NLar SKHP WCru WPGP WSHC
- 'Blue Wonder'	CExl CLAP LLHF MNrw
- white-flowered **new**	IMou

Delonix (*Caesalpiniaceae*)

decaryi	SPlb
regia	SPlb

Delosperma (*Aizoaceae*)

from Graaf Reinet, South Africa	GEdr NSla
from Ouberg Pass **new**	CPBP
from Sani Pass, South Africa	ECtt EPot GCrg GEdr NSla WAbe
§ ***aberdeenense*** ♀H3	CHEx SChr XLum
alpinum	ECho EPot EWes GEdr
ashtonii	CCCN EWes NSla XLum
basuticum	NSla
'Basutoland'	see *D. nubigenum*
'Beaufort West'	EPot NSla WIce XLum
congestum	CCCN CPBP CTal ECho EDAr EPot EWll GEdr NRya SMad WAbe WHal WIce XLum
I - 'Album'	CTal EWes GEdr SMad WIce
- 'Gold Nugget' ♀H3	EAEE ECho LRHS
* - white-flowered	ECho EDAr EPot WAbe
cooperi	CCCN CTri ECho ECtt EDAr EPfP EPot EUJe GBin LAst LRHS LSou MSCN SChr SIgm SPlb SRot SVen WBor WIce WPnn XLum XSen
dyeri Red Mountain = 'Psdold'	GEdr XLum
ecklonis	GKev
Fire Spinner = 'P001s' **new**	WHlf
floribundum Sequins = 'Balosquin' **new**	CAbb
- 'Starburst'	EDAr EWll MHol NRya
- 'Stardust'	EWes
jansei **new**	NSla
(Jewel of Desert Series) 'Jewel of Desert Garnet' **new**	CAbb ECtt SPad
- 'Jewel of Desert Moon Stone' **new**	ECtt
- 'Jewel of Desert Peridott' **new**	ECtt
- 'Jewel of Desert Topaz' **new**	CAbb ECtt
§ 'John Proffitt'	CCCN GKev SPlb XLum
karrooicum	GEdr
lavisiae	ELon NSla SPlb
'Lesotho Pink'	EWes
lineare	XLum
Mesa Verde = 'Kelaidis'	ECtt
§ ***nubigenum***	CTal CTri ECho ECtt EPot EUJe GAbr GCrg GEdr GKev MAsh SPlb SPoG
'Ruby Coral'	ECtt EPot
sphalmanthoides	EPot GEdr WAbe
sutherlandii ♀H3	CTal ECho EDAr EPfP GAbr GBin NPri SRot XLum
- 'Peach Star'	CCCN EDAr EWll GEdr SBch WIce
Table Mountain	see *D.* 'John Proffitt'

Delphinium ✿ (*Ranunculaceae*)

sp.	MLHP SVic
'After Midnight'	CNMi
'Ailsa'	CNMi
'Alice Artindale' (d)	CDes EBee EWes EWld IFoB SMrm WCot
'Ann Woodfield'	CNMi
'Ariel' ambig.	LRHS
Astolat Group	CBcs COtt CSBt CTri ELan EPfP EPla GJos GMaP IBoy LBMP LRHS MBri MGos MWat NBir NHol NLar NSoo SPer SPoG SWvt WCAu WHar

'Atholl' ♀H5 CNMi
'Bambi' CNMi
Belladonna Group CWCL ELan EPfP WHar
- 'Atlantis' ECha LRHS MAsh NLar
- 'Casa Blanca' EBee EPfP GMaP LRHS NLar
- 'Cliveden Beauty' CWCL EPfP GMaP LRHS NLar
§ - 'Janny Arrow' LRHS
- 'Piccolo' ECha MAsh NLar
- 'Pink Sensation' see *D.* × *ruysii* 'Pink Sensation'
- 'Völkerfrieden' IBoy LRHS MNrw MRav NLar
× ***bellamosum*** EPfP GMaP LRHS MNrw
'Berghimmel' LRHS
'Beryl Burton' CNMi
Black Knight Group Widely available
'Black Pearl' ECtt IKil
'Black-eyed Angels' (New Millennium Series) IPot LSun SCob SGbt
'Black-eyed Sailors' (New Millennium Series) new LRHS
'Blauwal' LRHS
'Blue Arrow' see *D.* 'Blue Max Arrow', *D.* (Belladonna Group) 'Janny Arrow', *D.* 'Kings Blue Arrow'
Blue Bird Group CBcs COtt CSBt CTri ELan EPfP EPla GJos GMaP LBMP LRHS MGos MJak MWat NMir NSoo SGbt SPer SPoG WHoo
'Blue Butterfly' see *D. grandiflorum* 'Blue Butterfly'
'Blue Dawn' ♀H5 CNMi
Blue Fountains Group CSBt EPfP SPoG SRms
'Blue Jay' CBcs CTri EPfP EWoo MWat NBir
'Blue Lace' IPot LRHS
§ 'Blue Max Arrow' LRHS
'Blue Mirror' SRms
'Blue Nile' ♀H5 CNMi
'Blue Oasis' CNMi
Blue River CBcs
Blue Springs Group NGdn
'Blue Tit' CNMi
'Bob Geldof' CNMi
'Boudicca' CNMi
'Bruce' ♀H5 CNMi
'Butterball' CNMi
Cameliard Group CBcs CSBt ELan EPfP EPla LBMP LRHS MWat NLar SPer SPoG
'Cameliard' (Pacific Hybrid Series) COtt
'Can-Can' ♀H5 CNMi
carolinianum SBrt
ceratophorum WCru
var. ***ceratophorum*** BWJ 7799
'Chelsea Star' CNMi LRHS
'Cher' CNMi
'Cherry Blossom' EPfP NLar
'Christel' LRHS NLar
'Claire' CNMi
'Conspicuous' ♀H5 CNMi
'Coral Sunset'PBR (d) LBuc MBri NPri
'Crown Jewel' LRHS
'Darling Sue' CNMi
'Diamant'PBR IKil LRHS
'Dreaming Spires' SRms
drepanocentrum HWJK 2263 WCru
'Dunsden Green' CNMi
Dusky Maidens Group CMea ELan IFoB LRHS LSun SGbt SPoG
dwarf, dark blue-flowered LRHS
elatum GCal
- 'Blushing Brides' (New Millennium Series) LRHS SPoG
- 'Dasante Blue' NPri NSir
- 'Double Innocence' (New Millennium Series) (d) IPot LRHS
- 'Morning Lights' (New Millennium Series) LRHS SPoG
- 'Sweet Sensation' CMos ECtt IBoy LBuc LRHS NLar
- 'Sweethearts' (New Millennium Series) ♀H5 LSun
'Elizabeth Cook' ♀H5 CNMi SMrm
'Elmfreude' IBoy LRHS
'Emily Hawkins' ♀H5 CNMi
exaltatum LBMP
'Fanfare' CNMi
'Faust' ♀H5 CNMi LRHS
'Fenella' ♀H5 CNMi
'Finsteraarhorn' GBin IKil LRHS MAvo MNrw
'Florestan' CNMi
'Foxhill Nina' ♀H5 CNMi
'Franjo Sahin' CNMi
Galahad Group CBcs CSBt CTri ECtt ELan EPfP EPla EWoo GMaP MBri MJak MWat NBir NGdn NHol NSoo SPer SPlb SPoG WCAu WHar WHoo
'Galahad' (Pacific Hybrid Series) COtt
'Galileo' ♀H5 CNMi
'Gemini' CNMi
'Gemma' CNMi
'Gillian Dallas' IKil
glaciale HWJK 2299 WCru
'Gossamer' CNMi ECtt IKil
grandiflorum 'Blauer Spiegel' new MPro
§ - 'Blauer Zwerg' MNHC SPoG
§ - 'Blue Butterfly' CSpe EPfP LBMP LRHS SPlb SPoG WSHC
- Blue Dwarf see *D. grandiflorum* 'Blauer Zwerg'
- 'Delfix' LRHS
- (Summer Series) 'Summer Blues' LRHS MBri SRot
- - 'Summer Colors' new MAsh
- - 'Summer Nights' EPfP LRHS MBri MPro WHar
- - 'Summer Stars' GJos LRHS MBri
* - 'Tom Pouce' EAJP
- 'White Butterfly' LRHS
'Green Twist' (New Millennium Series) LRHS SCob SPoG
(Guardian Series) 'Guardian Blue' LRHS NPri SHil
- 'Guardian Lavender' LRHS NPri SHil
- 'Guardian White' LRHS NPri SHil
Guinevere Group CBcs CSBt ECtt EPfP EPla GJos MBri NBir SPer SPoG WCAu
- 'Lady Guinevere' COtt IBoy
'Guy Langdon' CNMi
halteratum CSpe
'Highlander Blueberry Pie' EBee ECtt IBoy LRHS
'Highlander Crystal Delight' ECtt LRHS
'Honey Pink' CNMi
I 'Independence' IKil LRHS
'Innocence' CMea LRHS SCob
'Jenny Agutter' CNMi
'Kathleen Cooke' CNMi
'Kestrel' ♀H5 CNMi COtt

	King Arthur Group	CBcs CBod CSBt CWCL ELan EPfP EPla GJos LBMP MGos MWat NSoo SPer SPoG
§	'Kings Blue Arrow'PBR	LRHS
	'La Bohème'	NLar
	'Lanzenträger'	LRHS
	'Leonora'	CNMi
	'Loch Leven'	CNMi
	'Lord Butler' ♀H5	CNMi LRHS SMrm
	'Lucia Sahin' ♀H5	CNMi
	maackianum	GCal IMou LLHF NLar WCot
	Magic Fountains Series	IFoB NGBl SPlb SPoG SVic
	- 'Magic Fountains Cherry Blossom'	EPfP SPoG
	- 'Magic Fountains Dark Blue'	EPfP GMaP NEgg NLar SPoG
	- 'Magic Fountains Deep Blue'	NLar
	- 'Magic Fountains Lavender'	EPfP NLar
	- 'Magic Fountains Lilac Pink'	EPfP SPoG
	- 'Magic Fountains Lilac Rose'	LRHS
	- 'Magic Fountains Pure White'	EPfP LRHS NEgg
	- 'Magic Fountains Sky Blue'	EPfP SPoG
	'Margaret' ♀H5	CNMi
	'Marilyn Clarissa'	CNMi
	'Merlin' ambig.	LRHS
	'Michael Ayres' ♀H5	CNMi
	micropetalum CNDS 031	WCru
	'Mighty Atom'	CNMi IKil
	'Min' ♀H5	CNMi
	'Misty Mauves' (New Millennium Series) (d)	LRHS
	'Molly Buchanan'	CNMi
	'Moon Light' (Highlander Series) (d)	EBee LBuc NLar
	'Moonlight Blues' (New Millennium Series)	LSun SGbt
	'Morgentau'	LRHS
	'Mother Teresa'	CNMi
	'Mrs Newton Lees'	IKil LRHS NLar
	'Ned Rose'	IKil
	'Ned Wit'	IKil
	nudicaule	SPlb
	- 'Laurin'	LRHS
	- 'Redcap' **new**	MAsh MPro
	'Oliver' ♀H5	CNMi
	'Ouvertüre'	LRHS
	oxysepalum	LLHF
	Pacific hybrids	CWCL EPfP MHer NLar SRms SWvt WHar
	'Pagan Purples' (New Millennium Series) (d)	IFoB IPot LRHS
	'Patricia Johnson'	CNMi
	Percival Group	EPfP
	'Pericles'	CNMi
	'Pink Punch' (New Millennium Series)	ELan IPot SCob
	Pink River = 'Barfourtythree'PBR	CBcs
	'Pink Ruffles'	CNMi
	'Plagu Blue'PBR	NLar
	Princess Caroline = 'Odabar'PBR	CBcs
	'Purple Passion' (New Millennium Series)	ELan EPfP IPot LRHS LSun SCob SPoG
	pylzowii	EWld
	'Raymond Lister'	MAvo
	'Red Caroline'	CBcs
	requienii	CBgR CSpe MMuc MNHC NSti
	'Rona'	CNMi
	Round Table Mixture	CTri
	'Royal Aspirations' (New Millennium Series)	CMea ELan IPot LRHS LSun SCob SGbt SPoG
	'Ruby'	CNMi
	'Ruby Tuesday'	CNMi
§	× ***ruysii*** 'Pink Sensation'	NLar
	'Sandpiper'	CNMi
	'Schönbuch'	LRHS
	'Secret'PBR	LRHS WCot
	'Shieldbearer' **new**	LRHS
	'Silver Jubilee'	CNMi
	'Sky Sensation'	IBoy LRHS
	'Snow Queen Arrow'	LRHS
	'Sommerabend'	LRHS
	'Sooty'	CNMi
	'Spindrift' ♀H5	CNMi
	stapeliosmum B&SWJ 2954	WCru
	- HWJK 2179	WCru
	staphisagria	CArn
	'Starlight'PBR	LRHS
	'Strawberry Fair'	LRHS NLar
	Summer Skies Group	CBcs CSBt CTri CWCL ELan EPfP EPla EWoo GJos LRHS MBri MWat NBir NSoo SPer SPoG WCAu WHoo
	'Summerfield Diana'	CNMi
	'Summerfield Oberon'	WCot
	'Sungleam' ♀H5	ECtt IKil
	'Sunkissed' ♀H5	CNMi
	'Sunny Skies' (New Millennium Series)	ELan LRHS SPoG
	'Susan Edmunds'PBR (d)	CNMi
	sutchuenense	CPom
	- BWJ 7867	WCru
	'Sweetheart' **new**	LRHS
	tatsienense	EPot IFoB SRms
	'Tiger Eye'	CNMi
	tricorne	EBee
	'Trudy'	CNMi
	'Vanessa Mae'	CNMi
	'Walton Benjamin'	CNMi
	White River = 'Barfourtyfive'PBR	CBcs
	'White Swan'	EPfP
	'Wishful Thinking'PBR	MBri
	Woodfield strain	WHrl
	'Yvonne'	LRHS NLar
	'Zauberflöte'	LRHS

Dendranthema see *Chrysanthemum*

	pacificum	see *Ajania pacifica*

Dendriopoterium see *Sanguisorba*

Dendrobenthamia see *Cornus*

Dendrocalamus (*Poaceae*)

	asper	XBlo
	calostachys	SPlb
	giganteus	XBlo
§	***strictus***	XBlo

Dendromecon (*Papaveraceae*)

rigida CBcs EPfP LRHS SKHP WPGP WSHC

Dendropanax (*Araliaceae*)

trifidus B&SWJ 11230 WCru

Dennstaedtia (*Dennstaedtiaceae*)

punctilobula CLAP

Dentaria see *Cardamine*

pinnata see *Cardamine heptaphylla*
polyphylla see *Cardamine kitaibelii*

Deparia see *Athyrium*

Dermatobotrys (*Scrophulariaceae*)

saundersii ECre

Derwentia see *Parahebe*

Deschampsia (*Poaceae*)

cespitosa CBod CKno EAEE EPPr EPfP LPot LRHS MWat SCob SPhx SPlb WCot WMoo WWEG XLum
- Bronze Veil see *D. cespitosa* 'Bronzeschleier'
§ - 'Bronzeschleier' Widely available
- 'Coral Cloud' GQue
- 'Fairy's Joke' see *D. cespitosa* var. *vivipara*
- 'Garnet Schist' GQue SPhx
- Gold Dust see *D. cespitosa* 'Goldstaub'
- Golden Dew see *D. cespitosa* 'Goldtau'
- Golden Pendant see *D. cespitosa* 'Goldgehänge'
- Golden Shower see *D. cespitosa* 'Goldgehänge'
- Golden Veil see *D. cespitosa* 'Goldschleier'
§ - 'Goldgehänge' CSam EHoe EPla NBir WWEG XLum
§ - 'Goldschleier' CAby CPrp CSam EBee ECha EPPr EPfP EPla GBin GCal GMaP GQue LEdu LPal LRHS MTis NGdn NWsh SCob SPhx SWvt WMoo XLum
§ - 'Goldstaub' EPPr
§ - 'Goldtau' Widely available
- 'Mill End' CKno
- 'Morning Dew' MBri WFar
- 'Northern Lights' (v) ELan ELon EPfP LRHS LSun MBel MBri MMuc NBro NSti SLim SPer SPoG SRms SWvt WPtf WWEG
- 'Pixie Fountain' CKno EDAr EPPr GQue LRHS LSun MWat NOak SPhx SPtp WWEG
- 'Schottland' CKno ELon EPPr GBin LEdu NDov
- 'Tardiflora' CKno EPPr
- 'Tauträger' CKno ELon EPPr GQue XLum
§ - var. ***vivipara*** EHoe EPPr EPla GBin NBro SGSe
- 'Waldschatt' CKno
- 'Willow Green' GCal SCoo
flexuosa EHoe LRHS NBir NWsh SPhx
- 'Tatra Gold' CSBt CWCL ECha EHoe ELan ELon EPfP EPla GMaP LBMP LRHS MAsh MMuc MRav NBir NBro NGdn NOak NPri NSti SCob SGSe SLim SPer SPoG SRot SWvt WWEG
holciformis 'Marin' CKno

Desfontainia (*Loganiaceae*)

§ ***spinosa*** ♀H4 Widely available
- 'Harold Comber' CMac GKin WCru WHor
- f. ***hookeri*** see *D. spinosa*

Desmanthus (*Mimosaceae*)

illinoensis SBrt

Desmodium (*Papilionaceae*)

callianthum CMac LRHS SBrt WSHC
canadense EBee MNrw NLar SPhx
cuspidatum SPhx
var. ***longifolium***
§ ***elegans*** CBcs CExl CHEx EBee ELan EPfP ETwe LRHS MBri NLar SBrt SKHP SVen WHer WPGP WSHC
paniculatum SBrt WSHC
praestans see *D. yunnanense*
sessilifolium SPhx
tiliifolium see *D. elegans*
§ ***yunnanense*** CExl CHEx WSHC

Deuterocohnia (*Bromeliaceae*)

brevifolia ♀H2 CFil EBee WCot WPGP
longipetala RCB/Arg L-5 WCot
lotteae new WCot

Deutzia ✿ (*Hydrangeaceae*)

CC 4548 CExl
CC 4550 CExl
bhutanensis WCru
HWJK 2180 new
'Bright Eyes' new WPGP
calycosa GQui
- B&SWJ 7742 WPat
- BWJ 8007 WCru
- 'Dali' CDoC CExl CFil SDys
aff. ***calycosa*** SIN 1878 GLin
chunii see *D. ningpoensis*
compacta CMCN SLon WPGP
- GWJ 9202 WCru
- GWJ 9203 WCru
- GWJ 9339 WCru
- 'Lavender Time' CDoC CExl CMac EPfP EWTr NLar SWvt
cordatula B&SWJ 3720 WCru
- B&SWJ 6917 WCru
corymbosa MRav
crenata B&SWJ 8886 WCru
- B&SWJ 8896 WCru
- B&SWJ 8924 WCru
- 'Flore Pleno' see *D. scabra* 'Plena'
- var. ***heterotricha*** B&SWJ 5805 WCru
- - B&SWJ 8879 WCru
- var. ***nakaiana*** WPat
- - B&SWJ 11184 WCru
- - 'Nikko' see *D. gracilis* 'Nikko'
§ - 'Pride of Rochester' (d) ♀H5 CAco CBcs CMCN EAEE ECrN GKin LRHS LSou MBri MGos MRav NLar SCob SEle SGol SLim SPoG SWvt WGrn
'Dark Eyes' CExl CFil
discolor 'Major' CExl CFil WPGP WPat
× ***elegantissima*** SRms
- 'Fasciculata' CBod ELan EPfP LRHS NLar SPer SWvt WBor
- 'Rosealind' ♀H5 CBcs CDul CExl CMac CTri EBee ELan EPfP GKin IArd LRHS LSou MGos MMuc MRav SEND SLim SPer SRms SWvt WCFE WKif WPat WSHC
glabrata B&SWJ 617 GQui WCru

	Name	Suppliers
	- B&SWJ 8427	WCru
	glomeruliflora BWJ 7742	WCru
	gracilis	CBod CDoC CSBt EAEE ELan EPfP EWTr GGal GKin GQui IArd LPot LRHS MAsh MGos MRav MSwo NSoo SPad SPer SPoG WFar WHar
	- B&SWJ 8927	WCru
	- 'Carminea'	see *D.* × *rosea* 'Carminea'
§	- 'Nikko' ♀H4	CBcs CExl CHel CMCN CMac CMea COtt EBee ECho ELan EShb EWes GKin LRHS MAsh MBri MGos MHer MMuc MRav MWhi NLar SGol SHil SPlb SPoG SWvt WKif WSHC
	- var. ***ogatae*** B&SWJ 8911	WCru
	- 'Rosea'	see *D.* × *rosea*
	grandiflora	NChi WPGP
	'Hillieri'	CFil
	hookeriana	EBee EPfP EWTr LBuc LLHF LRHS MBri SWvt
	× ***hybrida*** 'Contraste' ♀H5	CMac SPer
	- 'Joconde' ♀H5	CExl WFar
	- 'Magicien'	Widely available
	- 'Mont Rose' ♀H5	Widely available
§	- 'Strawberry Fields' ♀H5	Widely available
	'Iris Alford'	CDoC CExl EPfP LRHS MBri SChF SHil SLon WFar WPGP
	× ***kalmiiflora***	CExl CJun CMac CSBt CTri ETwe GBin GKin GQui MAsh MBri MJak MRav NLar SPer SRms WFar
	× ***lemoinei***	MJak
	longifolia	CMCN WPGP WPat
	- 'Veitchii'	CSBt GQui MGil MRav
	- 'Vilmoriniae'	MRav
	× ***magnifica***	CBcs CDul GQui NLar SGbt SRms
	- 'Nancy'	GKin
	- 'Rubra'	see *D.* × *hybrida* 'Strawberry Fields'
	× ***maliflora***	CFil
	maximowicziana B&SWJ 11567	WCru
	monbeigii ♀H5	CDoC CExl CFil EPfP EWTr LLHF LRHS MRav SWvt WKif
	- BWJ 7728	WCru
	multiradiata	CExl CFil WPGP
§	***ningpoensis***	CExl CFil ETwe EWTr GQui NLar SPer WBor WCFE WPGP WPat
	paniculata B&SWJ 8592	WCru
	parviflora var. ***barbinervis*** B&SWJ 8478	WCru
	'Pink Pompon'	see *D.* 'Rosea Plena'
	prunifolia B&SWJ 8588	WCru
	pulchra	CAbP CDoC CDul CMCN CPom EPfP EWTr IDee LRHS MRav SLon SMrm SPer SPoG SSpi WPGP WPat
	- B&SWJ 3870	WCru
	- B&SWJ 6908	WCru
	- pink-tinged **new**	WPGP
	purpurascens BWJ 7859	WCru
	- 'Alpine Magician' **new**	COtt
	rehderiana	CFil
§	× ***rosea***	CDul EPfP LAst LRHS MAsh MWat SRms WKif WRHF
	- 'Campanulata'	CExl EPfP MAsh MSwo
§	- 'Carminea'	SPlb SRms WPat
§	'Rosea Plena' (d)	CDoC CExl CMac CSBt ECrN ELan EPfP EWTr GKin LBuc LRHS MAsh MBri MGos NLar SEle SLim SWvt WFar WPat
	rubens	LLHF WPat
	scabra	CAco CDul CTri
	- B&SWJ 11127	WCru
	- B&SWJ 11168	WCru
	- B&SWJ 11178	WCru
§	- 'Candidissima' (d) ♀H5	CDul CMac GQui MGil MRav SCob SPer WPat WRHF
	- 'Codsall Pink' ♀H5	CFil MRav
§	- 'Plena' (d)	CExl ECrN ELan EPfP GKin NLar NSoo SPer SPoG WCFE
	- 'Pride of Rochester'	see *D. crenata* 'Pride of Rochester'
	- 'Punctata' (v)	EHoe MAsh MMuc SEND SRms
	- 'Robert Fortune'	SPlb
	- 'Variegata' (v)	CDul CMac
	setchuenensis	CMac GQui SSpi WPat WSHC
	- PAB 7449 **new**	LEdu
	- var. ***corymbiflora*** ♀H5	CBcs CDoC CDul CExl CHel CSam CTri ECre EPfP EWTr IArd IDee LRHS MSwo NLar SPoG SWvt WFar WKif WPGP
	taiwanensis	SGol WPGP WPat
	- B&SWJ 6858	WCru
	- CWJ 12443	WCru
	- CWJ 12459	WCru
	'Tourbillon Rouge'	EPfP LRHS NLar WBor
*	***vidalii***	GGal
	× ***wellsii***	see *D. scabra* 'Candidissima'
	× ***wilsonii***	SRms

Dianella ✿ (*Hemerocallidaceae*)

	Name	Suppliers
	brevicaulis	ECou
	caerulea	CBcs CHel CMac EBee ECou ELan EPri IBoy IMou LEdu MNrw MOWG NBir NLar
	- 'Caspar Blue'	LPal
	- Cassa Blue = 'Dbb03'PBR	CBod CHll EPfP LRHS MSpe NSoo SPad SPer SPoG
	- 'Kulnura'	ECou
	- Little Jess = 'Dcmp01'PBR	CExl EAEE EBee SPoG
	- 'Variegata'	see *D. tasmanica* 'Variegata'
	ensifolia	LEdu
	nigra	CBcs CExl ECou IMou LEdu
	- 'Margaret Pringle' (v)	CBcs CExl ECou SEND
	revoluta	CCon ECou
	- Baby Bliss = 'Dtn03'PBR	CKno WCot
	- Little Rev = 'Dr5000'PBR	EBee EPfP ESwi NSoo
	'Silver Streak' (v)	CBod NSoo
	tasmanica	Widely available
	- from Logan	EBee GCal
	- 'Emerald Arch'	ELan ESwi SPer
	- 'Prosser'	ECou
	- Tasred = 'Tr20'PBR	CExl ELan EPfP ESwi EUJe NSoo SPer SPoG
§	- 'Variegata' (v)	CCCN CCon CDTJ CExl ECou ELan NLar SEND SGSe

Dianthus ✿ (*Caryophyllaceae*)

	Name	Suppliers
	sp.	SVic
	AC&W 2116	ECtt
	'Alan Titchmarsh' (p)	CWCL ECtt EPfP EPla LRHS MGos MTis NCGa NEgg SPoG SWvt
	'Albert Hill' (p)	LAll
	'Albus Plenus' (p) **new**	MJak
	'Aldridge Yellow' (b)	LAll
	'Alfriston' (b) ♀H6	LAll
	'Alice' (p)	LAll
	'Alice Lever' (p)	WAbe
§	'Allen's Maria' (p)	LAll

	Plant	Suppliers
	'Allspice' (p)	CFis MRav WHoo
	Allwoodii Group (p)	NNor
	- 'Doris' (p)	EPla SHil
	Allwoodii Alpinus Group (p)	NGdn SRms XLum
	'Allwood's Celebration' (p)	LAll
	'Allwood's Crimson' (pf)	LAll
	'Allwood's Delight' (p)	LAll
	alpinus ♀[H6]	GCrg GJos ITim NSla
	- 'Albus' (p)	GCrg GKev NWad
	- 'Joan's Blood' (p) ♀[H5]	ECho GBuc GCrg GKev WAbe
	'Alyson' (p)	LAll
	amurensis	ECho EPPr GCal MLHP NNor SPhx WSHC XLum
	- 'Andrey' (p)	NNor
	anatolicus	CTri ECho EDAr MHer NGdn XLum
	'Anders Apollo' (p)	CNMi
	'Anders Cream Princess' (pf)	CNMi
	'Anders Fay Seagrave' (p)	LAll
	'Anders Irene Ann' (pf)	CNMi
	'Anders Kath Phillips' (pf) ♀[H2]	CNMi
	'Anders Melody' (p)	LAll
	'Anders Patricia Griffiths' (p)	CNMi LAll
	'Anders Royal Purple' (pf)	CNMi
	'Andrew Morton' (b)	LAll
	'Angela Carol' (pf)	CNMi
	'Angelo' (b)	LAll
	'Ann Franklin' (pf) ♀[H2]	CNMi
	'Annabelle' (p)	LAll
	'Annette' (p)	ECho EDAr GCrg GEdr LRHS MAsh NGdn NHol SRGP SWvt
	'Annie Claybourne' (pf)	CNMi
	Apollo = 'Klepol' (pf) **new**	LAll
	'Apricot Sue' (pf)	CNMi LAll
	Arctic Star	see *D.* 'Devon Arctic Star'
	arenarius	CCon GKev LAll LEdu NGdn SPhx SPlb XLum
	- 'Little Maiden' (p)	GEdr LSun NCGa NGdn SPhx WIce
	'Argus'	IGor LAll
	armeria	CBgR CFis WHer WOut
	arpadianus	GKev
	- var. ***pumilus***	EPot LLHF
	'Arthur Leslie' (b)	LAll
§	× ***arvernensis*** (p) ♀[H4]	ECha ECho EPot SBch
	- 'Albus'	ECho
	'Audrey Robinson' (pf)	CNMi
	'Aurora' (b)	LAll
	'Auvergne'	see *D.* × ***arvernensis***
	'Averiensis'	see *D.* 'Berlin Snow'
	'Baby Treasure' (p)	ECtt
	'Badenia' (p)	ECha
	'Bailey's Celebration' (p)	ECtt EPla LRHS MTis NCGa SRGP WMnd
	'Barbara Norton' (p)	ECtt
	barbatus	MNrw SVic
	- SDR 6404	GKev
	- 'Black Adder'	CSpe
I	- 'Darkest of All'	CSpe MMuc SEND
	- 'Heart Attack' (p) **new**	WCot
	- Midget Group (p,a) **new**	CBod
	- 'Monksilver Black' (p,a) **new**	MHol SMrm WCot
	- Nigrescens Group (p,a) ♀[H7]	CBre CHVG CSpe SPhx
I	- 'Sooty' (p,a)	CBod CTsd EDAr
	- 'Super Parfait Strawberry' (Super Parfait Series)	LRHS
	- 'Tuxedo Black'	WMoo
	'Barley Sugar' (pf)	CNMi
§	'Bat's Double Red' (p)	LAll
	'Becky Robinson' (p) ♀[H6]	CNMi LAll
	Belen = 'Barbelen'[PBR] (pf) **new**	LAll
	'Belmont Duchess' (p)	LAll
	'Belmont Ruby Wedding' (p)	CNMi
§	'Berlin Snow' (p)	CPBP ECho EPot GCrg
	'Bernard' (pf) **new**	LAll
	'Betsy' (pf) **new**	LAll
	'Betty Miller' (b)	LAll
	'Betty Morton' (p) ♀[H6]	ECtt IFoB WKif
	'Betty's Choice' (pf)	CNMi
	'Bill Smith' (pf)	CNMi
	'Blue Hills' (p)	ECho GKev
	'Blue Ice' (b)	LAll
	'Blush'	see *D.* 'Souvenir de la Malmaison'
	'Bobby' (p)	LAll
	'Bob's Highlight' (pf)	CNMi
	'Bookham Gleam' (b)	LAll
	'Bookham Grand' (b)	LAll
	'Bookham Heroine' (b)	LAll
	'Bookham Lad' (b)	LAll
	'Border Special' (b)	LAll
	'Bouquet Purple' (p)	CSpe
	'Bovey Belle' (p)	LAll
	'Bramdean' (pf) **new**	CNMi
	brevicaulis	WAbe
	- subsp. ***brevicaulis***	LLHF
	'Brian Tumbler' (b) ♀[H6]	LAll
	'Bridal Veil' (p)	LAll SBch WHer
	'Brilliance' (p)	MSCN WMoo
	'Brilliant'	see *D. deltoides* 'Brilliant'
	'Brilliant Star' (p) ♀[H6]	ECho ECtt LRHS MWat SEND SWvt WIce
	'Brockenhurst' (pf) **new**	CNMi
	'Brympton Red' (p)	CFis ECha LAll
	'Bryony Lisa' (b) ♀[H6]	LAll
	caesius	see *D. gratianopolitanus*
	'Calipso' (pf) **new**	LAll
	callizonus	LLHF
	'Calypso' (pf)	CTri
	'Calypso Star' (p)	ECho ECtt NGdn SPoG
	'Cameron' (pf)	LAll
	'Camilla' (b)	CNMi
	'Can-can' (pf)	ECho ECtt
	'Candy Clove' (b)	LAll
	Candy Floss[PBR]	see *D.* 'Devon Flavia'
	'Candy Spice' (p)	MRav
	'Carbrooke Village' (p) **new**	SGSe
§	'Carmine Letitia Wyatt'[PBR] (p) ♀[H6]	ECtt LRHS NCGa SPoG
	Carole = 'Licar' (pf) **new**	LAll
	carthusianorum	CAby CArn CKno CSpe EWTr GQue LAll LEdu LPla LRHS MCot MNFA NDov NGdn NSti SCob SGSe SPhx SPlb SRms SWat SWvt WKif WPGP WSHC WWEG WWFP XLum
I	- 'Rupert's Pink' (p)	NGdn SWvt
	caryophyllus	CArn ENfk SVic
	- 'Citrien'[PBR] (pf)	LRHS
	- 'Princess'[PBR] (pf)	NPri
	Cassandra = 'Bardranasca' (pf) **new**	LAll
	'Charles' (p)	LAll
	'Charles Edward' (p)	LAll
	'Charles Musgrave'	see *D.* 'Musgrave's Pink'
	Charlie = 'Hilcharly' (pf)	LAll

	Name	Suppliers
	'Chastity' (p)	LAll LLHF WHoo
	Cheddar pink	see *D. gratianopolitanus*
	'Cheerio' (pf)	LAll
	'Cherry Clove' (b)	LAll
	'Cherry Pie' (p)	LRHS
	'Cheryl'	see *D.* 'Houndspool Cheryl'
	'Chesswood Dorothy Cottam' (b)	LAll
	'Chetwyn Ruth Gillies' (pf)	CNMi
	'Chianti Double' (p)	LAll
	chinensis 'Black and White' (p,a)	CSpe
I	- 'Valentine' (p,a) **new**	LAll
	'Chris Crew' (b) ♀H6	LAll
	'Christopher' (p)	LAll
	'Clara' (pf)	CNMi
	'Clara's Lass' (pf)	CNMi
	'Clare' (p)	LAll
	'Claret Joy' (p) ♀H6	CBcs ECtt EPfP LAll LRHS MMuc SEND
	'Clifford Pipperoo' (pf)	LAll
	'Clunie' (b)	LAll
§	'Cockenzie Pink' (p)	LAll SBch WHer
	Coconut Sundae = 'Wp 05 Yves' (p)PBR	ECtt ELan ELon EPfP EWll GBin LRHS MCot MSCN NNor SRot
	'Constance' (p)	LAll
	'Constance Finnis'	see *D.* 'Fair Folly'
	'Consul' (b)	LAll
	'Conwy Silver' (p)	WAbe
	'Conwy Star' (p)	WAbe
	'Coral Reef'PBR (p)	ECtt ELan LRHS NNor SPoG
	'Coronation Ruby' (p) ♀H6	LAll
	'Cosmic Swirl Pink' (p)	MHol
	'Coste Budde' (p)	WSHC
	Cracker = 'Wp10 Sab06'PBR (Early Bird Series) (p)	GAbr
	'Cranmere Pool' (p) ♀H6	CBcs ECtt ELan EPfP LRHS NGdn NNor SEND SPoG SWvt WRHF WWEG
	'Cream Sue' (pf)	CNMi
	'Crimson Chance' (p)	EPot NSla
	'Crimson Warrior' (pf)	CNMi
	'Crock of Gold' (b)	LAll
	'Crompton Bride' (pf)	CNMi
	'Crompton Classic' (pf)	CNMi
	'Crompton Princess' (pf)	CNMi
	cruentus	LRHS SPhx SPtp SWvt WWEG
	'D.D.R.'	see *D.* 'Berlin Snow'
	'Dad's Favourite' (p)	CFis LAll WHer
	'Dainty Dame' (p) ♀H4	CSpe CTal CTri ECho EPfP LAll LRHS LSun MNHC SBch
	'Dancing Queen'PBR (p)	MTis MWat NNor
	'Daphne' (p)	LAll
	'Dark Farida' (pf) **new**	LAll
	'Dark Star' (p)	ECho
	'Dartington Double' (p)	ECho SEND
	'David' (p)	LAll NSoo SCob
	'David Russell' (b) ♀H6	LAll
	'David Saunders' (b) ♀H6	LAll
	'Dawn' (b)	LAll
	'Dawn' (pf)	ECho
	'Daydream' (pf)	MNrw
	'Dedham Beauty'	MPie SEND WCot WWEG
	deltoides ♀H5	CArn CTre ECha ECho ENfk EPfP LEdu MAsh MBel MMuc MNHC SPlb SRms WJek WPtf
	- 'Albus' (p)	ECha EPfP GKev NGdn WMoo
	- 'Arctic Fire' (p)	ECho EDAr EPfP GJos NGdn NHol WMoo
	- 'Bright Eyes' (p)	ECho MWat
§	- 'Brilliant' (p)	CTri EAJP ECho GJos LAll LAst NGdn NHol SPhx SRms WWEG
	- 'Broughty Blaze'	GCrg
	- 'Canta Libra'	MLHP
	- 'Dark Eyes' (p)	EWes
	- 'Erectus' (p)	EPfP
	- Flashing Light	see *D. deltoides* 'Leuchtfunk'
§	- 'Leuchtfunk' (p)	ECho ECtt EDAr EPfP GJos LAst MJak NNor SPoG WMoo WRHF WWEG
I	- 'Luneburg Heath Maiden Pink' (p)	NGdn SPhx
	- Microchips Group (p)	WMoo
	- 'Nelli' (p)	ECho NGdn WMoo
	- red-flowered (p)	SVic
	- 'Shrimp' (p)	EAJP NGdn
	'Dennis' (p)	LAll
	'Desert Song' (b)	LAll
	'Desmond'	EPfP
§	'Devon Arctic Star' (p)	CMea CTal CTri ECho ELan EWTr EWoo GBin GMaP LRHS SPoG SRms SRot SWvt
	'Devon Cream'PBR (p)	ECtt ELan LAst LRHS MWat NEgg WMnd
	'Devon Dove'PBR (p) ♀H6	CMea CSBt CTri ECGP ECtt ELan EPfP EPla LRHS MRav MWat NCGa NEgg
§	'Devon Flavia'PBR (Scent First Series) (p) ♀H6	ELan GBin LAst LBMP LRHS LSou MAvo MTis SEND SPoG
	'Devon General'PBR (p)	CTri
	'Devon Glow' (p)	EPfP
	'Devon Magic'PBR (p)	ECtt ELan MTis
§	'Devon Sapphire' (p) ♀H6	CMea CTal ELan EWoo MTis WIce
	'Devon Wizard'PBR (p) ♀H6	CSBt ECtt EPfP EPla LRHS MMuc MRav MSpe MTis NCGa NDov NEgg NNor SEND
§	'Devon Xera' (p) ♀H6	MTis SRms
	'Dewdrop' (p)	CMea CTri ECho EWTr LAll MAsh MHer MMuc NBir NGdn SBch SEND WHal
	'Diana'	see *D.* Dona
	'Diana Lavender Picotee' (p,a)	LRHS
	'Diane' (p) ♀H6	ELan EPfP LAll LPal LRHS NEgg SPoG SWvt WHar WMnd
*	'Diane Cape'	LAll
	'Diplomat' (b)	LAll
	'Doctor James Dennison' (pf)	CNMi
§	Dona = 'Brecas' (pf)	SRGP
	'Dora' (p)	ECho LRHS
	'Doreen Hodgson' (p)	LAll
	'Doris' (p) ♀H6	Widely available
	'Doris Allwood' (pf)	CNMi CSBt EMal LAll
	'Doris Elite' (p)	LAll
	'Doris Galbally' (b)	LAll
	'Doris Majestic' (p)	LAll
	'Doris Ruby'	see *D.* 'Houndspool Ruby'
	'Doris Supreme' (p)	LAll
	'Double Lace'	LRHS SLon
	Dubai = 'Bardibua' (pf) **new**	LAll
	'Dubarry' (p)	CTri
	'Duchess of Fife' (p)	EPfP
	'Duchess of Roxburghe' (pf)	EMal LAll
	'Duchess of Westminster' (M)	EMal LAll
	'Duke of Norfolk' (pf)	EMal LAll
	'Dunkirk Spirit' (pf)	CNMi

	Name	Suppliers
	'Dusky' (p)	CNMi
	'Dusky Janelle' (pf)	CNMi
	'Earl Kelso' (pf) **new**	EMal
	'Earl of Essex' (p)	LAll
	'Edenside Scarlet' (b)	LAll
	'Edenside White' (b)	LAll
	'Edna' (p)	LAll
	'Edward Allwood' (pf)	LAll
	'Edwin Cross' (b)	LAll
	'Eileen' (p)	LAll
	'Eileen Lever' (p)	CPBP EPot IFoB ITim MWat WAbe
	'Eileen Neal' (b) ♀H6	LAll
	'Eileen O'Connor' (b) ♀H6	LAll
	'Eira Wen' (p)	WAbe
	'Eleanor Parker' (p)	WAbe
	'Eleanor's Old Irish' (p)	CUse ECtt ELon LRHS MBel MHol MPie SEND WCot WHoo WMnd WWEG
	'Elfin Star' (p)	ECho
	'Elizabethan' (p)	CFis CSpe MCot SDys
*	'Elizabethan Pink' (p)	LAll
	'Ellen Ladd' (pf)	CNMi
	'Elsie Ketchen' (pf)	CNMi
	'Emile Paré' (p)	CFis
	'Emjay' (b)	LAll
	'Emmeline Pankhurst' (pf) **new**	CNMi
	'Emperor'	see *D.* 'Bat's Double Red'
	erinaceus	ECho GCrg GJos
	- var. ***alpinus***	EPot GBin
	- Duguid's	WAbe WThu
	'Erycina' (b)	LAll
	'Ethel Hurford' (p)	WHoo
	'Eva Humphries' (b)	LAll
	'Evelyn Berry' (p) **new**	CNMi
	'Evening Star' (p) ♀H6	CTal CTri ECho EWoo GBin LRHS SPoG SWvt WIce
	'Eve's Holly' (pf)	CNMi
	'Exquisite' (b)	LAll
§	'Fair Folly' (p)	IGor LAll WHer
	Fancy Fuego = 'Bargofanfu'[PBR] (pf)	LAll
	'Farnham Rose' (p)	LAll
	'Fenbow Nutmeg Clove' (b)	SDix
	'Fettes Mount' (p)	LPla MWhi WCot
	'Feuerhexe' (p)	EPot GCrg
	Fiesta = 'Lontocia' (pf) **new**	LAll
	'Fimbriatus' (p)	WHoo
	'Fiona' (p)	LAll
	Fire Star	see *D.* 'Devon Xera'
	'Firestar' (p)	CTri ELan LRHS MAsh MWat SHil SRot SWvt
	'First Lady' (b)	LAll
	Fizzy = 'Wp08 Ver03'[PBR] (Early Bird Series) (p)	CMea CTal ELan EPfP LBMP LRHS SHil
	'Flanders' (b) ♀H6	LAll
	'Flashdance' (pf)	CNMi
	'Fleur' (p)	LAll
	Fleurette = 'Kofleur'[PBR] (pf) **new**	LAll
	'Florence Franklin' (pf)	CNMi
	'Floristan Mix' (p,a)	NNor
	'Forest Princess' (b)	LAll
	'Forest Sprite' (b)	LAll
	'Forest Treasure' (b)	LAll
	'Forest Violet' (b)	LAll
	'Forge Pink'	LLHF
	'Fortuna' (p)	LAll

	Name	Suppliers
	Foxtrot = 'Hilfox' (pf) **new**	LAll
	'Fragrant Ann' (pf) ♀H6	CNMi LAll
	'Fragrant Phyllis' (pf)	CNMi
	'Frances Isabel' (p)	LAll
	'Frank Bruno' (pf)	CNMi
	'Freda' (p)	LAll
	'Freda Woodliffe' (p)	ECtt GCrg SBch WAbe
	'Freya' (pf)	LAll
	freynii	ECho EPot EWes GKev WAbe
*	- var. ***nana***	GKev
*	'Frilly'	LBMP LRHS SHil
	fringed pink	see *D. superbus*
	furcatus	GKev
	'Fusilier' (p)	CTal CTri ECho ECtt EDAr EPfP GAbr GBuc GCrg GKev GMaP LAll LRHS LSun MAsh SEND SHar SRot SWvt
	'Gail Graham' (b)	LAll
	'Gail Tilsley' (b)	LAll
	'Garland' (p)	CMea CTri
	'Gaydena' (b)	LAll
	giganteus	WSHC
	'Gingham Gown' (p)	ECtt EPot LAll NBir
*	***glacialis elegans***	GKev
	'Gold Dust' (p)	ECtt EPot EWTr LAll SBch
	'Gold Embrace' (pf) **new**	CNMi
	'Golden Cross' (b) ♀H6	LAll
	'Grace's Scarlet Clove' (b)	LAll
	'Grandma Calvert' (p)	LAll
	graniticus	EPot
	'Gran's Favourite' (p) ♀H6	CBcs CSBt CTri CUse ECtt ELan EPfP EPla EWoo GAbr LAll LAst LPot LRHS MCot MGos MMuc MTis MWat NEgg NGdn NNor SEND SHil SPlb SPoG SRGP SWvt WGwG
§	***gratianopolitanus*** ♀H5	CArn CBod CPBP CTri EDAr ENfk EPfP GJos GKev LAll LEdu MHer MNHC MRav NBid WGwG
	- 'Albus'	MHer
	- 'Babi Lom' **new**	GCrg
	- dwarf	SIgm WAbe
	- 'Grandiflorus'	SPhx
*	- 'Karlik' (p)	GKev
	- 'Rosenfeder' (p)	SPhx
§	- 'Tiny Rubies' (p)	CTal EDAr GCrg SDys WAbe
	'Greensides' (p)	LAll
	'Grey Dove' (b) ♀H6	LAll
	'Greytown' (b)	GCal
	'Gypsy Star' (p)	ECho SPoG
	haematocalyx 'Alpinus'	see *D. haematocalyx* subsp. *pindicola*
§	- subsp. ***pindicola***	LLHF WAbe
	'Hannah Gertsen' (p)	LAll
	'Hannah Louise' (b) ♀H6	LAll
	'Harkell Special' (b)	LAll
	Harvey = 'Hilharvey' (pf) **new**	LAll
	'Hayden' (pf)	CNMi
	'Hayley's Choice' (b)	LAll
	'Haytor Rock' (p) ♀H6	EPfP LRHS MTis NCGa NNor WGwG
	'Haytor White' (p) ♀H6	CBcs CTri EPfP LAll MWhi NSoo SCob WWEG
	'Hazel Ruth' (b) ♀H6	LAll
	'Heath' (p) **new**	LAll
	'Helen' (p)	ELon LAll
	'Helena Hitchcock' (p)	LAll
	'Herbert's Pink' (p)	SPhx

'Hercules' (pf) **new**	CNMi
'Hereford Butter Market' (p)	EBee
'Hidcote' (p)	CTri LLHF LRHS SIgm
'Hidcote Red'	ECho
'Highland Fraser' (p)	WKif
Highland hybrids	SGbt
'Hope' (p)	LAll
'Hot Spice' (p)	SPoG
§ 'Houndspool Cheryl' (p) ♀H6	CTri EPfP LAll SRGP
§ 'Houndspool Ruby' (p) ♀H6	CBcs EPfP LAll
hyssopifolius	CArn
'Ian' (p)	LAll
Iced Gem = 'Wp06 Fatima'PBR (Scent First Series) (p)	ELan ELon EPfP LRHS LSou MTis NNor SHil SPoG SRot
'Icomb' (p)	WHoo
'Inchmery' (p)	IGor LAll LRHS WHer WHoo
'India Star'PBR (p) ♀H6	CTal CTri EPfP LRHS MTis MWat NEgg SEND SRms SRot WIce
'Inglestone' (p)	CTri
'Inshriach Dazzler' (p) ♀H5	CPBP CTal ECho ECtt EPot GCrg GMaP LLHF LRHS MAsh MHer NEgg NHar NHol SRot WAbe WHal
'Irene' (pf) **new**	LAll
'Irene Della-Torré' (b) ♀H6	LAll
'Jacqueline Ann' (pf) ♀H2	CNMi
'James Portman' (p)	ELon
'Janelle Welch' (pf)	CNMi
'Janet Walker' (p)	GMaP
'Jess Hewins' (pf)	CNMi LAll
Jet Set = 'Hiljet' (pf) **new**	LAll
'Joanne' (pf)	CNMi
'Joanne's Highlight' (pf)	CNMi
'Joe Vernon' (pf)	CNMi
'Joy' (p) ♀H6	EPfP LAll LAst SPoG WWEG
'Julian' (p)	LAll
'Julie Ann Davis' (b)	LAll
'Kathleen Hitchcock' (b) ♀H6	LAll
'Kessock Charm' (p)	MNrw
'Kesteven Kirkstead' (p) ♀H6	LAll MNrw
'Kim' (p)	NDov
knappii	CFis SPhx WHer XLum
- 'Yellow Harmony' (p,a)	ELon LAll MLHP
'La Bourboule' (p) ♀H5	CMea CTri ECho ECtt EDAr GAbr GCrg GEdr LRHS MWat SBch
'La Bourboule Alba' (p) ♀H5	CTri ECho ECtt EPot GCrg MAsh SBch
'Laced Joy' (p)	LAll
'Laced Monarch' (p)	CBcs ECtt ELan EPfP EPla GCra LAll LRHS MCot MMuc NCGa NEgg NNor SEND SMrm SPlb SPoG WGwG WWEG
'Laced Mrs Sinkins' (p)	CNMi LAll
'Laced Prudence'	see *D.* 'Prudence'
'Laced Romeo' (p)	LAll
'Laced Treasure' (p)	LAll
'Lady Granville' (p)	IGor LAll SBch
Lady in Red = 'Wp04 Xanthe'PBR (p)	CSBt ECtt ELan EPfP LRHS MTis MWhi NNor
Lady Madonna = 'Wp04 Opal'PBR (p) ♀H6	ELan
'Lady Wharncliffe' (p)	SBch
'Lady Windermere' (M)	EMal LAll
'Lancing Monarch' (b)	LAll
'Lancing Supreme' (p)	EWTr LAll
'Langford Manor' (pf) **new**	CNMi
'Laura' (p)	LAll
'Lavender Lady' (pf)	CNMi
'Layla Jane' (p) **new**	CNMi
'Leatham Pastel' (pf)	CNMi
'Lege Marrone' (pf) **new**	LAll
'Lemsii' (p) ♀H6	NGdn
'Leslie Rennison' (b)	LAll
'Letitia Wyatt' (p) ♀H6	CMea LRHS MWat MWhi SPoG SRGP
'Leuchtkugel' (p)	CPBP ECho LLHF WAbe
'Lily Lesurf' (b)	LAll
Lily the Pink = 'Wp05 Idare'PBR (p) ♀H6	ELan LRHS MTis
'Lime Crush' (pf)	CNMi
'Linfield Annie's Fancy' (pf)	CNMi
'Linfield Doreen Ashmore' (p)	LAll
'Linfield Dorothy Perry' (p) ♀H6	LAll
'Linfield Isobel Croft' (p)	LAll
'Linfield Julie' (p)	LAll
'Linfield Kathy Booker' (p) ♀H5	LAll
'Linfield Pink Margaret' (p)	CNMi LAll
'Little Ben' (p)	LAll
'Little Jock' (p)	CTal ECho ECtt EDAr EPot GCrg GEdr LAll LRHS LSun MAsh MHer MWat SBch SPlb
'Liz Rigby' (b)	LAll
'London Brocade' (p)	LAll
'London Glow' (p)	CNMi LAll
'London Lovely' (p)	LAll
'London Poppet' (p)	LAll
'Lord Nuffield' (b)	LAll
lumnitzeri	XLum
'Lustre' (b)	LAll
'Madonna' (pf)	WHer
Maggie = 'Shemway' (pf) **new**	LAll
'Maisie Neal' (b) ♀H6	LAll
'Mandy' (p)	LAll
'Manon des Sources' (pf)	CNMi
'Margaret Taylor' (p)	CNMi LAll
'Maria'	see *D.* 'Allen's Maria'
'Marielle' (pf)	LAll
'Marjery Breeze' (p)	LAll
'Marmion' (M)	EMal LAll
'Mars' (p)	ECho
'Ma's Choice' (p)	LAll
'Matthew' (p)	WHoo
'Maudie Hinds' (b)	LAll
'Maxine' (pf) **new**	CNMi
'Maybole' (b)	LAll
'Maybush' (pf) **new**	CNMi
'Megan' (pf) **new**	LAll
Memories = 'WP11 Gwe04' (p)	LBMP LBuc LRHS MTis
'Mendip Hills' (b)	LAll
Mendlesham Minx = 'Russmin'PBR (p)	CTal ECho EDAr ELan EPfP LAll LRHS MTis SRms SWvt
'Merlin Clove' (b)	COtt
'Messines Pink' (p)	LAll
'Michael Saunders' (b) ♀H6	LAll
microlepis	ECho EDAr GKev NGdn NSla WAbe
- f. ***albus***	GKev NSla

– ED 791562	NGdn
– var. ***musalae***	ECho LLHF
– 'Rivendell' (p)	ECho WAbe
'Mike Briggs' (b)	LAll
'Miss Farrow' (p)	LRHS SPhx
'Miss Sinkins' (p)	CTri IFoB
'Miyu' (pf) **new**	LAll
Mojácar = 'Barjamocar' (pf) **new**	LAll
'Mondriaan' (pf)	EBee
'Monica Wyatt' (p) ♀H6	CBcs ECtt ELan EPfP EPla LRHS NCGa NEgg SPoG WWEG
'Montrose Pink'	see *D.* 'Cockenzie Pink'
'Monty Allwood' (p)	LAll
'Moor Editha' (p)	CNMi
Morning Star = 'Devon Winnie'[PBR] (p)	CTal MAsh MTis
Mother of Pearl = 'Wp10 Ele04'[PBR] (Perfume Pinks Series) (p)	ELan LRHS
'Moulin Rouge' (p) ♀H6	CTri CWCL ECtt ELan EPfP EPla GAbr GCra LRHS MTis NDov SBod SPoG WWEG
'Mrs Macbride' (p)	LAll
'Mrs Roxburgh' (p)	CSam
'Mrs Sinkins' (p)	Widely available
'Murray Douglas' (p)	IGor
'Murray's Laced Pink' (p)	MWhi
'Musgrave's Pink' (p)	CFis ECha LAll MRav SBch
'Musgrave's White'	see *D.* 'Musgrave's Pink'
myrtinervius	CCon ECho EDAr NGdn
'Mystic Dawn' (b)	LAll
Mystic Star	see *D.* 'Devon Sapphire'
'Napoleon III' (p)	LAll
nardiformis	XLum
'Natalie Saunders' (b) ♀H6	LAll
'Nautilus' (b)	LAll
neglectus misapplied	see *D. pavonius*
'Neon Star'[PBR] (p) ♀H5	CTri ECho EDAr ELan GBuc GEdr GKev LRHS MTis MWat SHil SPoG SRms SRot
'Night Star' (p) ♀H6	CTal ECho ELan EPfP EWoo GBin GKev GMaP LPot LRHS MHol NEgg SBch SEND SRot WPtf
nivalis	EPot GKev
noeanus	see *D. petraeus* subsp. *noeanus*
'Nomie' (pf)	CNMi
'Northland' (pf)	CNMi EMal LAll
Novella = 'Hilnovel' (pf) **new**	LAll
'Nyewoods Cream' (p)	CMea CTri ECho EPot GCrg MHer NGdn NHar NWad SBch
§ 'Oakington' (p)	CTri GCrg
'Oakington Rose'	see *D.* 'Oakington'
'Oakwood Billy Boole' (p)	CNMi
'Oakwood Candy' (p)	CNMi
'Oakwood Erin Mitchell' (p)	CNMi
'Oakwood Romance' (p)	CNMi
'Oakwood Sweetheart' (p)	LAll
'Old Blush'	see *D.* 'Souvenir de la Malmaison'
'Old Clove Red' (b)	CUse
'Old Crimson Clove' (b)	SBch
'Old French Red' (pf)	EMal
'Old Red Clove' (p)	CHVG CSpe ECtt GAbr MBel MCot MPie NSti WCot
§ 'Old Square Eyes' (p)	IGor LAll MNrw SHar
'Old Velvet' (p)	GCal LAll MNrw SBch
'Oliver' (p)	LAll
'Orange Maid' (b)	LAll
'Owston Third Avenue' (p)	LAll
'Oxford Magic' (p)	LAll
'Painted Lady' (p)	LAll
'Paisley Gem' (p)	LAll
Passion = 'Wp Passion'[PBR] (Scent First Series) (p)	EBee ECtt ELan EPfP GBin LRHS LSou LSun MBel MHer MHol MPie MTis MWat NNor SEND SHil SPoG WCot
§ ***pavonius*** ♀H6	EWes MAsh NGdn
'Peach' (p)	SEND
'Pendle Doris Delight' (p)	LAll
'Pendle Mrs Riley' (p)	CNMi
'Pennine Reflections' (b)	LAll
'Peter Wood' (b) ♀H6	LAll
§ ***petraeus***	EWes NGdn WThu
§ – subsp. ***noeanus***	LLHF WHal
'Petticoat Lace' (p)	LAll
'Phantom' (b)	LAll
Phantom = 'Hilphan'[PBR] (pf) **new**	LAll
'Pheasant's Eye' (p)	LAll WHer
* 'Picton's Propeller' (p)	GBuc
Pierrot = 'Kobusa' (pf)	CNMi
'Pike's Pink' (p) ♀H5	CSpe CTal CTri ECho EDAr ELan EPfP EPot EWoo GCrg LAll LRHS LSun MAsh MHer MMuc MWat NBir NGdn SEND WWEG
pindicola	see *D. haematocalyx* subsp. *pindicola*
pinifolius	IFro SBrt
'Pink Doris' (pf)	CNMi
'Pink Fantasy' (b)	LAll
'Pink Fizz'	EWll LRHS MTis
'Pink Jewel' (p)	CMea ECha EDAr EPot GKev LAll MAsh MNHC SBch
'Pink Mrs Sinkins' (p)	LAll MHer MLHP MNrw
'Pink Pearl' (b)	LAll
'Pixie' (b)	EPot
'Pixie Star'[PBR] (p) ♀H6	CTal ECho EPfP SPoG SRot WIce
plumarius	CArn IFro LAll MLHP WHer XLum
– 'Albiflorus'	XLum
Popstar = 'Wp04 Esther' (p)	CTal EWll MTis SGbt SRms
'Pretty' (p)	LAll
Pretty Flamingo[PBR]	see *D.* 'Carmine Letitia Wyatt'
'Prince Charming' (p)	ECho MAsh
'Princess of Wales' (M)	EMal LAll
'Priory Pink' (p)	LAll
§ 'Prudence' (p)	LAll
'Pudsey Prize' (p)	CPBP EPot GCrg WAbe
'Purple Jenny' (p)	LAll
'Queen of Hearts' (p)	CTri ECho MMuc SEND
§ 'Queen of Henri' (p)	EBee ECho LRHS
'Queen of Sheba' (p)	IGor LAll SBch WHer WHoo WKif
'Rachel' (p)	LAll
'Raggio di Sole' (pf)	CNMi
'Rainbow Loveliness' (p,a)	LAll WOut
'Ralph Gould' (p)	ECho
'Raspberry Parfait' (p,a)	LRHS
'Raspberry Ripple' (p)	CTal
Raspberry Sundae = 'Devon Yolande'[PBR] (p)	ECtt ELan EPfP GBin LBMP LRHS SEND SHil SPoG WBor WRHF
Rebekah = 'Wp09 Mar05'[PBR] (Early Bird Series) (p)	CBod CMea CTal LAst LRHS MAvo SHil
'Red Diamonds' (pf) **new**	LAll
'Red Star'[PBR] (p) ♀H6	ECho ELan GJos LRHS MAsh SRot WIce

'Reine de Henri' see *D.* 'Queen of Henri'
'Richard Pollak' (b) LAll
'Ringwood Belle' (pf) new CNMi
'Rizalene' (p) CNMi
'Robert Allwood' (pf) LAll
'Robin Ritchie' (p) WHoo
'Robina's Daughter' GAbr
Romance = 'Wp09 Wen04'PBR (Scent First Series) (p) ELan LRHS LSou MTis SHil
'Romsey' (pf) new CNMi
'Roodkapje' (p) XLum
'Rose de Mai' (p) CFis CNMi CSam LAll SBch WHoo
'Rose Joy' (p) ♀H6 EPfP LRHS
§ 'Rose Monica Wyatt'PBR (p) ♀H6 LRHS
Rosebud = 'Wp08 Ros03'PBR (Early Bird Series) (p) CTal LBMP LRHS SHil
'Rötkappchen' (p) ELon WCot
'Ruby' see *D.* 'Houndspool Ruby'
'Ruby Doris' see *D.* 'Houndspool Ruby'
rupicola WCot
'Sam Barlow' (p) IGor LAll
'Santa Claus' (b) LAll
Scarlet Beauty = 'Hilbeau' WMoo
'Seraphina' (pf) new CNMi
'Seren Wen' (p) WAbe
serotinus EPot WCot XLum
Sherbet = 'Wp08 Ros03'PBR (Early Bird Series) (p) CTal ELan EPfP SHil
Shooting Star = 'Wp04 Flores'PBR (p) ELan LRHS MTis SRms
'Shot Silk' (pf) LAll
'Show Aristocrat' (p) LAll
'Show Beauty' (p) LAll
Show Girl = 'Hilshow' (pf) LRHS
Show Girl = 'Wp08 Uni02'PBR (Scent First Series) (p) ELan LSou MTis MWat
'Show Glory' (p) LAll
'Show Harlequin' (p) LAll
'Show Satin' (p) LAll
Silver Star = 'Wp10 Hel01'PBR (p) CTal LRHS MTis SHil
Sindy = 'Mizindi' (pf) new LAll
'Singapore Girl' (Kiwi Series) (p) CWGN
* 'Six Hills' NWad
Slap 'n' Tickle = 'Wp05 Pp22'PBR (Scent First Series) (p) EBee ECtt ELon LRHS LSou MTis NPri SHil SPoG SRot
'Solomon' (p) CFis IGor LAll
'Sops-in-wine' (p) CSam ECha ECtt LAll MSCN
§ 'Souvenir de la Malmaison' (M) EMal LAll
'Spangle' (b) LAll
'Spencer Bickham' (p) MNrw
spiculifolius CFis EWTr SPhx
'Spinfield Joy' (b) ♀H6 LAll
'Spirit' (pf) LAll
'Spring Star' (p) ECtt SRot WJek
'Square Eyes' see *D.* 'Old Square Eyes'
squarrosus ECho EPot WAbe
* - ***alpinus*** ECho
- 'Nanus' see *D.* 'Berlin Snow'
'Starburst'PBR (p) CBod CTal ECho EWll GBin LRHS MTis WIce
Stardust = 'Wp07 Opr04'PBR (Early Bird Series) (p) CTal LAst LRHS WIce
'Stargazer' (Whetman Stars Series) (p) new MTis
Starlight = 'Hilstar' (pf) CMea LRHS SRms
'Starry Eyes' (p) ♀H6 CSam CTal ECho ELan GBin GCrg GEdr GMaP LRHS NPri SRms SRot SWvt
'Storm' (pf) CNMi EMal LAll
stramineus GKev
'Strawberries and Cream' (p) ECtt LRHS NEgg NOrc SPoG
strictus WCot
* - subsp. ***pulchellus*** GEdr
subacaulis EDAr GAbr IFoB NGdn XLum
- subsp. ***brachyanthus*** GJos
- - 'Murray Lyon' WThu
suendermannii see *D. petraeus*
Sugar Plum = 'Wp08 Ian04'PBR (Scent First Series) (p) ELan EPfP EWll LSou MTis
'Summerfield Adam' (p) LAll
'Summerfield Amy Francesca' (p) LAll
'Summerfield Blaze' (p) LAll
'Summerfield Blush' (p) LAll
'Summerfield Daniel' (b) LAll
'Summerfield Debbie' (p) LAll
'Summerfield Emma Louise' (p) LAll
'Summerfield Jo' (p) LAll
'Summerfield Rebecca' (p) LAll
SummertimePBR see *D.* 'Rose Monica Wyatt'
'Sunray' (b) LAll
'Sunstar' (b) LAll
§ ***superbus*** CMHG MNrw NNor SBch SHar SPhx WMoo XLum
- 'Crimsonia' (p) WOut
I - 'Primadonna' GQue
'Supernova' (pf) CMea CTal LBMP MTis
'Susan' (p) LAll
'Susannah' (p) LAll
* 'Susan's Seedling' (p) LAll
'Swanlake' (p) LAll
'Sway Lass' (p) SEND
'Sweet Cecille' (pf) CNMi
'Sweet Sue' (b) LAll
'Sweetheart Abbey' (p) IGor
sylvestris WOut
- dwarf EPot
'Tamsin Fifield' (b) ♀H6 LAll
'Tatra Blush' (p) GCal
'Tatra Fragrance' (p) CCse GCal LAll
'Tatra Ghost' (p) LAll SDys
'Tayside Red' (M) EMal LAll
'Tempest' (pf) new LAll
'Terracotta' (pf) new LAll
'Terranova' (pf) CNMi
'Thora' (M) EMal LAll
Tickled Pink = 'Devon Pp 11'PBR (Scent First Series) (p) ECtt ELan ELon EPfP EWll LBMP LRHS LSou MWat NPri SHil SPoG
'Tiny Rubies' see *D. gratianopolitanus* 'Tiny Rubies'
'Tony's Choice' (pf) CNMi
'Tracy Jardine' (pf) CNMi
'Treasure' (p) LAll
'Trevor' (p) LAll

tristis	XLum
'Tropic Butterfly' (p)	LPot
'Tudor'	ELon MNrw
turkestanicus	NNor WPtf
Tyrolean trailing carnations	LAll
'Uncle Teddy' (b) ♀H6	LAll
'Unique' (p)	IGor LAll
'Ursula Le Grove' (p)	WHer
'Valda Wyatt' (p) ♀H6	CBcs ELan EPfP EPla LAll LAst MCot NCGa NEgg NNor NSti SEND SPoG SWvt WGwG WMnd
'Vic Masters'	SBch
'Violet Clove' (b)	LAll
'Violet Yates' (pf) **new**	CNMi
'W.A. Musgrave'	see *D.* 'Musgrave's Pink'
'Waithman Beauty' (p)	CTri ECtt LAll WHoo
'Waithman's Jubilee' (p)	LAll
'Warden Hybrid' (p)	CTri ECho ECtt GCrg LAst LRHS MNHC NGdn NWad SPoG SWvt WAbe
'Waterloo Sunset'PBR (p)	CMea CSBt MTis
'Weetwood Double' (p)	LPot SBch
Wellington = 'Hilwelling' (pf) **new**	LAll
'Welton Raspberry Ice' (p)	LAll
'Wessex' (pf) **new**	CNMi
weyrichii	ECho EPot
'Whatfield Anona' (p)	LAll
'Whatfield Beauty' (p)	ECho ECtt
'Whatfield Brilliant' (p)	ECho
'Whatfield Cancan' (p) ♀H6	CBod CMea CTal ECho ECtt ELan EPot GMaP LAll LRHS MNHC NEgg NGdn NHol SBch SPoG SWvt WJek
'Whatfield Cyclops' (p)	ECho LAll
'Whatfield Dawn' (p)	ECho
'Whatfield Dorothy Mann' (p)	ECho LAll
'Whatfield Fuchsia Floss' (p)	LAll
'Whatfield Gem' (p)	CTal ECho ECtt ELan ELon EPfP GCrg LAll MNHC MWat NGdn SIgm SWvt WHoo
'Whatfield Joy' (p)	CTal ECho ECtt ELan EPfP GCrg LAll LRHS MHer NGdn
'Whatfield Magenta' (p) ♀H6	CSam ECho ECtt ELan EPot GCrg LAll LRHS MWat SBch SPoG WAbe
'Whatfield Mini' (p)	LAll SBch
'Whatfield Miss' (p)	LAll SBch
'Whatfield Misty Morn' (p)	ECho LAll
'Whatfield Nine Star' (p)	ECho
'Whatfield Peach' (p)	LAll
'Whatfield Pretty Lady' (p)	ECho LAll
'Whatfield Rose' (p)	ECho EPot
'Whatfield Ruby' (p)	ECho ELan GJos LAll
'Whatfield Supergem' (p)	ECho EPot
'Whatfield White' (p)	ECho ECtt LAll
'Whatfield White Moon' (p)	ECho
'Whatfield Wisp' (p)	CPBP CTri ECho EPfP EPot GEdr MRav NBir SBch
'White and Crimson' (p)	LAll
'White Joy'PBR (p) ♀H6	ELan MRav
'White Ladies' (p)	LAll MRav
'Whitehill' (p)	ECho ITim MHer
'Whitesmith' (b) ♀H6	LAll
'Widecombe Fair' (p) ♀H6	CTri ELan EPfP LAll MTis SPoG
'Yellow Alice' (b)	LAll
'Zebra' (b)	LAll

Diapensia (*Diapensiaceae*)

lapponica var. ***obovata***	NHar WAbe

Diarrhena (*Poaceae*)

japonica	MMoz

Diascia (*Scrophulariaceae*)

'Alice Cap'	SBch
'Andrew'	SBch
barberae 'Belmore Beauty' (v)	EWes
- 'Blackthorn Apricot' ♀H4	CBod CHel EAEE EBee ECha ELan EPfP EPla EWoo GBin GMaP LRHS NDov NLar SPer SPlb SPoG SRms SWvt WGwG XEll
§ - 'Ruby Field' ♀H4	CMea EBee ECha ELan EPfP LRHS SPer SPoG SRms SWvt
Blue Bonnet = 'Hecbon'	SBch SWvt
'Bluebelle' (Maritana Series)	LAst MCot
'Blush'	see *D. integerrima* 'Blush'
'Candy Floss'	SBch
Coral Belle = 'Hecbel'PBR ♀H3	ECho EWoo GBin LRHS LSou
'Denim Blue'	CSpe EDAr EPfP NLar WHea
elegans misapplied	see *D. fetcaniensis, D. vigilis*
'Emma'	NDov SMHy SWvt
felthamii	see *D. fetcaniensis*
§ ***fetcaniensis***	CMea CPne CPrp EBee EPfP GMaP LRHS MCot MHer NEgg SPer WHal WKif
- 'Daydream'	LBuc MPie SBch WHrl
flanaganii misapplied	see *D. vigilis*
(Flying Colours Series) Flying Colours Appleblossom = 'Diastara'	EPfP SPoG
- Flying Colours Apricot = 'Diastina'	EPfP
- Flying Colours Red = 'Diastonia'	EPfP SPoG
'Frilly' ♀H3	ECtt
'Hector Harrison'	see *D.* 'Salmon Supreme'
Ice Cracker = 'Hecrack'	CMea ELan LRHS SRms
Iceberg = 'Hecice'	NDov SWvt
§ ***integerrima*** ♀H4	CTal ECha MCot SIgm
- 'Alba'	see *D. integerrima* 'Blush'
§ - 'Blush'	CSpe NDov
- 'Ivory Angel'	see *D. integerrima* 'Blush'
integrifolia	see *D. integerrima*
'Jacqueline's Joy'	CMea NPer
'Joyce's Choice' ♀H3	ECho LRHS SRms
'Katherine Sharman' (v)	EWes
'Lilac Belle' ♀H3	EDAr ELan LRHS NBir NEgg SPlb SPoG SRms
'Lilac Mist' ♀H3	NPer
lilacina × ***rigescens***	GBee
Little Dancer = 'Pendan'PBR	GBin LAst LSou MCot MSCN NLar SLon
'Little Dazzler'	EPfP GBin
Little Dreamer = 'Pender'PBR	LAst NLar
Little Drifter = 'Pendrif'PBR	LSou NLar
Little Maiden = 'Penmaid'PBR	GBin NLar
Little Tango = 'Pentang'PBR	CBod CPrp LAst LSou MCot NLar SRms WCot WRHF
personata	CAby CBod CHll CMea CPne CPrp CSam CSpe ECtt GBin

	GCal ITim LBMP LLHF LPla MCot MHer MHol MNrw MPie NDov SMHy SPer SPhx WBor WBrk WCot WSHC
- 'Hopleys'	ECre EWes LRHS MAvo MSCN NCGa WHea WWEG
'Peter'	NDov
Pink Panther = 'Penther'	NLar SWvt
'Pitlochrie Pink'	GBin
Red Ace = 'Hecrace'PBR	EPfP LAst MCot NPer SWvt
Redstart = 'Hecstart'	NGdn SWvt
rigescens ♀H3	CCon CHEx CHel CPne CPrp CSpe CWCL ECtt ELan GBin MHer NLar NPer NSoo SPer SPlb SPoG SWvt WBor WCFE WSHC
§ - 'Anne Rennie'	LRHS SWvt
- pale-flowered	see *D. rigescens* 'Anne Rennie'
Romeo Orange = 'Balromor' (Romeo Series)	NPri
'Ruby Field'	see *D. barberae* 'Ruby Field'
'Rupert Lambert' ♀H3	EWes NDov SBri
§ 'Salmon Supreme'	ELan LRHS NPer SPoG SRms
'Twinkle' ♀H3	ECho LRHS NBir NPer SRms
* 'Twins Gully'	EWes
§ ***vigilis*** ♀H3	CExl CMea EPfP EPot GBee LRHS NBro NCGa SRms WHal WPnn WWEG
Whisper Lavender Pink = 'Balwhislapi' (Whisper Series)	CBod
White Belle = 'Penbel'PBR	LAst

Dicentra ✿ (*Papaveraceae*)

CC 4452	CExl
'Adrian Bloom'	CExl ECtt EPfP GBuc MCot MWat SMrm SPer SWvt WFar WMoo
'Aurora'	CBod EBee ECtt ELon EPfP GBin GBuc LAst LRHS MBri MRav MTis NGdn NLar NSti SCob SPer SPoG SWvt WMoo
'Boothman's Variety'	see *D.* 'Stuart Boothman'
'Bountiful'	CMac ECtt EPau EPla LSou MRav NGdn SBod SWvt WGwG WWtn
'Brownie'	GBuc
'Burning Hearts'PBR	CMos CWCL CWGN ECtt EWoo GBin IKil LLHF LRHS LSou MPnt MPro SPer WHil
canadensis	CLAP GBuc GKev MAvo NLar WAbe WCru WHal
'Candy Hearts'PBR	EBee ECtt ELan NGdn NLar SGol
chrysantha	see *Ehrendorferia chrysantha*
cucullaria	CAby CElw CHel CLAP CPBP CTal CWCL EBee ECho ELon EPPr EPot GAbr GBuc GKev ITim LRHS MNrw MRav NHar NLar WAbe WCru WFar
- 'Pink Punk'	CTal CWCL EBee LLHF MNrw NHar NLar
- 'Pittsburg'	CAby CDes EBee EPPr GBuc MNrw
eximia misapplied	see *D. formosa*
eximia ambig.	MHol
eximia (Ker Gawl.) Torr. 'Alba'	see *D. eximia* 'Snowdrift'
§ - 'Snowdrift'	CLAP ECtt ELan EPfP LRHS MCot MTis NLar SRms WMoo
'Fire Island'PBR	ECtt MBri NCGa
'Firecracker'	ECtt MBri MPnt
§ ***formosa***	CBcs CHel CTri ECha ELan EPfP EPla GKev IFro LAst LRHS MLHP NBro NGdn NOrc NPri NSoo SPlb SRms WMoo
- f. ***alba***	GAbr GCra GLog GMaP NBir SRms WCru WFar WKif
- 'Bacchanal' ♀H5	Widely available
- 'Cox's Dark Red'	CExl CLAP EWes GBuc GKev LLHF SKHP
- 'Langtrees' ♀H5	CMac CSam ECha EPau GBuc MLHP MRav NBro NLar SGSe SRms SWvt WCru WFar WHea WHrl WMoo WOut
- 'Moorland Pearl' **new**	WOut
- subsp. ***oregana***	CLAP EPPr IGor SKHP WHal
- - 'Rosea'	EPPr
- Snowflakes = 'Fusd'	EWes MRav
- 'Spring Gold'	CBod EBee ECha ELon EPPr LRHS LSun NLar WMoo
- 'Spring Magic'	EBee EPPr LRHS MRav NLar
'Ivory Hearts'PBR	CWGN EBee ELan EWoo GKev IKil LRHS MAvo MBri MCot NLar NSti SPer
§ 'Katie'	EPPr
'Katy'	see *D.* 'Katie'
'King of Hearts'	Widely available
'Luxuriant' ♀H5	CBcs CBod COtt CSBt ECtt ELan EPfP GBuc GKev LAst LRHS MCot MGos MHol MRav SCob SMrm SPer SPoG SRms SRot SWvt WMoo
macrantha	see *Ichthyoselmis macrantha*
'Pearl Drops'	ELan GLog GMaP IFro LRHS MCot MMoz MRav NBid NLar SRms WMoo
peregrina	WAbe
'Red Fountain'PBR	CBod CWCL ECtt IPot MBri NLar NSti WFar
scandens	see *Dactylicapnos scandens*
spectabilis	see *Lamprocapnos spectabilis*
'Spring Morning'	CElw CMHG CSam CTal EAEE ECtt EPPr EPau EPla LRHS NOrc WHoo
§ 'Stuart Boothman' ♀H5	CMac CSam CSpe CWCL ECtt ELan ELon EPfP GBuc GMaP LAst LRHS MCot MLHP MRav MSpe MTis NBro NCGa NGdn NLar NPri SPer SPoG SRms SWvt WFar WKif WMoo
thalictrifolia	see *D. scandens*
ventii	see *Dactylicapnos ventii*

Dichelachne (*Poaceae*)

crinita	SMea

Dichelostemma (*Asparagaceae*)

congestum	CAvo ECho GKev SDeJ
§ ***ida-maia***	CAvo CWCL EPot GKev IFro MCot SDeJ
- 'Pink Diamond'	EBee GKev SDeJ
volubile	ECho
- 'Pink Giant'	SDeJ

Dichocarpum (*Ranunculaceae*)

§ ***dicarpon*** B&SWJ 11555	WCru

Dichondra (*Convolvulaceae*)

argentea 'Silver Falls'	CSpe EShb ESwi LAst LBMP LSou NPri SCoo SPer SPoG
§ ***micrantha***	EShb
repens misapplied	see *D. micrantha*

Dichopogon (*Anthericaceae*)

strictus	ECou WSFF

Dichroa (*Hydrangeaceae*)

febrifuga	CAbb CBcs CDoC CExl CHEx CHGN CHll CMil CTsd EBee EPfP LRHS SEle SWvt WCru WPGP
- B&SWJ 2367	WCru
- HWJK 2430	WCru
- NJM 10.042 **new**	WPGP
- pink-flowered	CHEx
hirsuta B&SWJ 8207 from Vietnam	WCru
aff. ***hirsuta*** B&SWJ 8371 from Laos	WCru
versicolor B&SWJ 6565	WCru
- B&SWJ 6605 from Thailand	WCru
aff. ***yunnanensis*** B&SWJ 9734	WCru

Dichromena see *Rhynchospora*

Dichrostachys (*Mimosaceae*)

cinerea	SPlb

Dicksonia ✿ (*Dicksoniaceae*)

antarctica 🏆H3	CAbb CBcs CDoC CHEx CHel CKel CSBt CSam CTsd EPfP ERod EUJe EWes GAbr IBal LPal LRHS MGos SArc SChr SEND SGSe SHil SPad SPoG SWvt WCot WFib WPGP WPat
fibrosa 🏆H3	CDTJ CKel EFtx ISha
lanata	EFtx
sellowiana	CDTJ CKel
squarrosa 🏆H3	CCCN CDTJ CKel

Dicliptera (*Acanthaceae*)

§ ***sericea***	CCCN CHll EShb MCot MSCN SBch SRkn WHil WOut WPGP
suberecta	see *D. sericea*

Dictamnus ✿ (*Rutaceae*)

albus	CArn CBcs CHll CTri CWCL EBee ECha ELan EPfP EWTr EWoo GMaP LAst LEdu LRHS LSun MCot MNrw MRav NPri SBrt SKHP SMHy SPer SPoG SWat SWvt WCAu
- var. ***albus*** 🏆H6	IBoy SWvt WAul
§ - var. ***purpureus*** 🏆H6	CWCL EAEE ECha ELan EPfP GBin GMaP GPoy IBoy LAst LRHS LSun MBel MMuc MNrw MRav NEgg SKHP SPer SPoG SRms SWat SWvt WAul WCot WKif WWEG
* - var. ***roseus***	IMou
* - ***turkestanicus***	GCal
fraxinella	see *D. albus* var. *purpureus*

Didymochlaena (*Dryopteridaceae*)

lunulata	see *D. truncatula*
§ ***truncatula***	XBlo

Dierama ✿ (*Iridaceae*)

sp.	WHil
adelphicum	LLHF
ambiguum	CWCL EBee NLos XLum
argyreum	CBod CCCN CElw CMac CPla CTsd CWCL EAJP EBee EPri EWTr GBin ITim LRHS MMuc NLar SBrt SGSe SPad SPoG SRot WHil XLum
'Ballyrogan Red'	IBlr
Barr hybrids	CBro CWCL GAbr WHil
'Black Knight'	CExl IBlr
'Blackberry Bells'	CSam CWCL CWGN ELon GBin LAst MAvo NLar NLos WHil
Blue Belle = 'Rowblu'PBR	IBal IVic LBuc LRHS NPri WHlf
'Blush'	IBlr
'Buckland White'	WPGP
'Candy Stripe'	CPla CWCL EBee IBal WHil
'Carmine'	CWCL
'Cherry Chimes'	EPfP
'Cinnamon Fairy'	EBee EPfP IBal MBri
cooperi	CElw CPou CTca EBee IBlr NBir WWEG
'Coral Belle' **new**	IBal
'Coral Bells'	CDes CKno GCal IBal LBuc NPri
'Cosmos'	CExl CWCL EPri EUJe LRHS MHer MMuc MWhi SEND WHil
'Delicacy'	IBlr
'Desire'	IBlr
dissimile	EBee
'Donard Legacy'	IBlr
§ ***dracomontanum***	Widely available
- JCA 3.141.100	WPGP
- dwarf, pale pink-flowered	LRHS
dracomontanum × ***pulcherrimum***	SMad
dubium	IBlr
ensifolium	see *D. pendulum*
erectum	CBcs CBod CCCN CHel CHid CMac CTsd CWCL EBee EPri GBin MMuc NLar NLos SGSe SRot
formosum	CCon EBee WPGP
galpinii	CBod CCCN CHel CPla CWCL EBee ELan EPri LLHF MMuc NLos WPGP
grandiflorum	CPou IBlr
'Guinevere'	Widely available
igneum	Widely available
- CD&R 278	CExl CPou ELon GBuc
insigne	CCCN CHel CHid EBee ESwi EWTr GBin LRHS NLar NLos WHil
'Iris'	IBlr
jucundum	CHel CWCL EBee EWTr GBuc
'Juno'	CMac
'Knee-high Lavender'	CDes WPGP
'Lancelot'	CBcs CElw CExl CKno COtt ECtt IBal IBlr LRHS MBNS MBri NBir NCGa NPri SWvt WFar WKif
latifolium	CHid IBlr MNrw
'Mandarin'	IBlr
medium	ELon SWat WPGP WWEG
'Milkmaid'	CExl IBlr
'Miranda'	CKno EBee ECtt EPri IBal LRHS MBNS MMuc NLar NPri
mossii	CBcs CCCN CCon CExl CHel CHid CMHG CMac CTsd CWCL EBee ELan EPri EWTr GBin IBlr LRHS NLar NLos SGSe SPlb SRot SVen WHil WPGP XLum
nixonianum	IBlr
'Painted Lady'	CWCL EBee EPfP IBal LBuc LRHS MBri NPri SKHP SLon
pallidum	CExl
'Pamina'	CExl CPrp IBlr
'Papagena'	IBlr
'Papageno'	IBlr

pauciflorum	CAbb CCCN CCon CExl CHel CHid CPrp CWCL EPri GBin IKil MNrw NBir NLos SRot SWat WPGP WSHC WWEG
§ ***pendulum***	CBro ELan GBBs IBlr LRHS MNrw MRav SWvt WFar WWEG
pictum	IBlr
'Pink Rocket'	CWCL MHer NHol
Plant World hybrids	ELon SGSe
Plant World Jewels	CWCL NLos
'Pretty Flamingo'	CExl CHel CPrp IBlr
'Puck'	CDes EBee GCal IBlr ITim MRav WPGP
pulcherrimum	Widely available
- var. ***album***	CCCN CHel CWCL ELan IBlr LRHS MBel MHer MNrw MWhi NLos WHil WPGP
- 'Blackbird'	CBcs CCCN CCon CDes CExl CHel CSam CWCL EAJP ELan EPri GAbr IBlr IBoy LAst LRHS MAvo MBel MHer MMuc NHol NLar NLos SGSe SKHP SPoG SWvt WHil WPGP
- dark cerise seedlings **new**	MAvo NDov
- dark pink-flowered	IBoy SGSe
- 'Falcon'	IBlr
- 'Flamingo'	IBlr
- 'Merlin'	CElw CExl CKno CPou EBee ECtt ELon EWoo GMaP IBal IBlr IBoy LRHS MBri NBir NGdn NPri SCob SVen SWvt WGwG
- pale-flowered	ECha
- 'Peregrine'	IBoy
- 'Redwing'	IBlr
- Slieve Donard hybrids	CBod CWCL GBuc LAst NLos SMad WFar WHrl WMnd
pumilum misapplied	see *D. dracomontanum*
'Queen of the Night'	IBlr
reynoldsii	CAbb CBcs CBod CCCN CCon CExl CHel CHid CMac CPla CTsd CWCL EBee ELan EPri IBlr IVic LRHS MBel MMuc MWhi SGSe SPlb SPoG SRkn SVen WKif WPnP
robustum	CAbb CExl CPou CWCL IBlr LRHS MNrw SMad WHoo WPGP
'Sarastro'	CExl IBlr
'September Charm'	IBlr
sertum	EBee
'Spring Dancer'	CWCL EHoe MHer NHol NLos SGSe SPlb
'Tamino'	IBlr
'Tiny Bells'	EDAr GBin GCal GKev MBri SMHy
'Titania'	GCal IBal IBlr
trichorhizum	CBod CCCN CCon CExl CHel CPla CPrp CWCL ELan EPri GBin GKev IBlr LPla LRHS SGSe WPGP WWEG
'Tubular Bells'	IBlr
'Violet Ice'	IBlr
'Westminster Chimes'	IBlr
'Zulu Bells'	ELon

Diervilla ✿ (*Caprifoliaceae*)

middendorffiana	see *Weigela middendorffiana*
rivularis 'Troja Black'	EPPr NLar
§ ***sessilifolia***	CBcs CHGN CMac EBee EPPr IDee LAst MRav SLon WCot WFar WMoo
- 'Butterfly'	CMac EPPr LSou NLar WMoo
- Cool Splash = 'Lpdc Podaras' (v)	CMHG CMac CWGN EBee ELan EMil EPPr EPla LBuc LRHS MAsh SPoG SWvt WCot
× ***splendens***	CExl CMHG EHoe ELan EPPr EPfP EWTr GAbr IDee LRHS MBNS MBlu MSwo NLar SEND SPer SPoG SWvt

Dietes (*Iridaceae*)

bicolor	CAbb CBod CDes CExl CHEx CPrp CTca CTre EPri LEdu LRHS LSou SChr SGSe WSHC
grandiflora	CAbb CArn CBod CCse CDes CExl CHEx CHll CPne CPrp CTca ECho ESwi SGSe WCot
§ ***iridioides***	CHel CPrp CTca EBee ECho ESwi ETwe GKev LRHS WCot
robinsoniana	CSpe

Digitalis ✿ (*Plantaginaceae*)

sp.	SVic
'Albino'	EPfP LRHS
ambigua	see *D. grandiflora*
apricot hybrids	see *D. purpurea* 'Sutton's Apricot'
canariensis	CAbb CCCN CDTJ CHEx CHel CHll CRHN CSpe EUJe LRHS MHin SDix SEle SPlb SVen WCFE
cariensis	GKev
ciliata	GKev
Dalmation Series, mixed **new**	NSir
'Danielle'	CSpe
davisiana	CExl EWld GLog MNHC WMoo
dubia	EPfP WAbe
'Elsie Kelsey'	ECtt NBir SWvt
eriostachya	see *D. lutea*
ferruginea ♀H7	Widely available
- 'Gelber Herold'	CLAP GMaP NLar SHar SPhx WFar
- 'Gigantea'	CLAP ECtt ELan EWoo GBin GQue LAst LEdu MBNS MHin MSCN SCob SHar SPlb SWat WWEG WWtn
fontanesii	SBrt
'Foxtrot'	CRos EPfP LBuc LRHS SHil
× ***fulva***	NBir
'Glory of Roundway'	CLAP CMos ECtt EWld IBoy LBMP LEdu LSou MBel SPer SPoG STPC WCot WWEG
§ ***grandiflora*** ♀H5	Widely available
aff. ***grandiflora***	IBoy
- 'Carillon'	ELan EPfP GBin GJos IFoB LAst MBel NBir NLar SCob SGSe SRot WHoo
- 'Cream Bell'	EPfP LRHS MHol WHar
heywoodii	see *D. purpurea* subsp. *heywoodii*
Illumination Series	EPfP MTis
- Illumination Apricot **new**	LBuc LRHS SPoG
- Illumination Chelsea Gold **new**	CHid
- Illumination Pink = 'Tmdgfp001'	CAby CHid CRos CWGN LBuc LRHS NPri SPoG STPC
- Illumination Raspberry **new**	LBuc LRHS SPoG
isabelliana	CCCN
'John Innes Tetra'	MNrw SPad SPtp WHoo
kishinskyi	see *D. parviflora*
laevigata	CCon GBin LEdu NBro SEND SPav WMnd WMoo
- subsp. ***laevigata***	SPtp
- white-flowered	ESwi GBin MCot NSti WCot
lamarckii misapplied	see *D. lanata*
§ ***lanata***	CArn EBee ECtt ELan EPfP EPla GKev LAst LRHS MBNS MNHC NGdn NOrc SGSe SPav SPer SPhx SPlb SPtp SRms WMnd WWEG

	- 'Café Crème'	CLAP LRHS MPro WHar
§	***lutea***	Widely available
	- SDR 6377	GKev
	- SDR 6413	GKev
I	- 'Aurea'	LPla
§	- subsp. ***australis***	GJos
	- 'Flashing Spires' (v)	CPla
	× ***mertonensis*** ♀H5	Widely available
	- 'Raspberry'	CLAP
	- 'Summer King'	COtt ECtt ELan EWld GJos LSun MAsh MWat NPri SMrm WFar WHil
	micrantha	see *D. lutea* subsp. *australis*
	obscura	CBod ECho GCal IFoB LRHS MHer SEND SPhx SPlb SVen WMnd
	orientalis	see *D. grandiflora*
§	***parviflora*** Jacq.	CSam ECha ECtt ELan EPPr EPfP GAbr GBin GCra GJos GKev IBoy LEdu LPal LRHS MAvo MBNS MMuc NBro NChi SBrt SEND SPav WMnd WMoo WPGP WWEG WWtn
	- 'Milk Chocolate'	CAby CBcs CLAP CMHG CSpe ECtt ELan EPfP GBin GBuc GJos GQue IBoy LRHS MCot MHer MHin MNHC MWat NBir NEgg NLar SBHP SCob SGSe SKHP SPtp
	'Pink Chapel'	ECtt
	'Polkadot Pandora' **new**	LRHS
	'Polkadot Pippa'	LRHS SHil WHlf
	purpurea	CArn CHab CWld ELan ENfk EPfP EWoo GKev GPoy LPal MHer MLHP MMuc MNHC NMir NPri SCob SIde SMrm SPlb SPoG WBrk WJek WMoo WOut WSFF WWFP
	- 'Alba'	see *D. purpurea* f. *albiflora*
§	- f. ***albiflora***	Widely available
	- - 'Anne Redetzky'PBR	CSpe LRHS WCot
	- Camelot Series	CNec LRHS LSqH SHar SVic
	- - 'Camelot Cream'	ELan EPfP LBMP LRHS MBri NLar SWvt
	- - 'Camelot Lavender'	COtt ELan EPfP LBMP LRHS MBri NLar SMrm SWvt
	- - 'Camelot Rose'	ELan EPfP LBMP LRHS MBri NLar SWvt
	- - 'Camelot White'	COtt ELan EPfP LRHS MBri NLar
*	- 'Campanulata Alba'	MBel
	- 'Candy Mountain'	LRHS
	- 'Chedglow' (v)	CNat
	- (Dalmatian Series) 'Dalmatian Cream' **new**	CBod MAsh
	- - 'Dalmatian Peach' **new**	MAsh
	- - 'Dalmatian Purple'	CBod LBMP LRHS MAsh NPri SHil
	- - 'Dalmatian Rose' **new**	MAsh
	- - 'Dalmatian White'	LAst LRHS MAsh NPri SHil WHlf
	- Excelsior Group	CBcs CBod CMac CSBt CTri CWCL EAEE ECtt EPfP GJos GMaP IBoy LAst LRHS MBri MJak MWat NHol NMir SCob SPer SPoG SRms SVic SWvt WHar WWEG XLum
	- Excelsior Group (Suttons; Unwins) ♀H7	ECtt MRav
	- Foxy Group	EAJP EPfP LRHS MJak MNHC SPoG WHar WWEG
	- - 'Foxy Apricot'	EPla SPtp SWvt
	- - 'Foxy Pink'	ELan GBin SPtp
	- Giant Spotted Group	ECtt EPfP LRHS SPoG
	- Glittering Prizes Group	SWat
	- (Gloxinioides Group) 'The Shirley' ♀H7	WMoo
§	- subsp. ***heywoodii***	ELan EWTr WMoo WWEG
	- 'Pam's Choice'	Widely available
	- 'Pam's Split'	LRHS SMrm
	- 'Primrose Carousel'	EAJP LRHS MCot NEgg NLar SCob SMrm STPC
	- 'Serendipity'	EPfP LBuc LRHS MBri SHil
	- 'Snow Thimble'	CAby CBod CLAP COtt EAJP ELan EShb GJos IBoy LRHS LSun MAvo MBri MTis NLar STPC WWEG
§	- 'Sutton's Apricot' ♀H7	Widely available
	- white cen-type mutant	NChi
	purpurea × ***thapsi***	WWEG
	'Red Skin'	CLAP CPom GBin GJos MBel MMuc MSCN NLar SGSe SPad WMoo WRHF
	'Saltwood Summer'	EPfP LRHS MBri
	sceptrum	CCCN CExl CHEx SPlb SVen WPGP
	'Spice Island'	CBod CLAP CMos ECtt ELon ESwi GBin GJos IBoy LEdu LPal LRHS LSou MBri MCot MHol NCGa NDov NLar NSti SCob SPer SPoG STPC WCot
*	***stewartii***	ELan EWes GCra GLog WMoo
	'Strawberry Fayre'	GJos
	thapsi	CBod ELan EPfP GJos LRHS NChi SBrt SEND WMoo WWEG XLum
	- 'Spanish Peaks'	LSou
	trojana	EAJP ECtt GKev IFoB SDix
	- 'Helen of Troy'	CLAP ELan SKHP SPtp
	viridiflora	CExl ECtt NBro

Dilatris (*Haemodoraceae*)

ixioides	CLak
pillansii	CLak

dill see *Anethum graveolens*

Dimorphotheca (*Asteraceae*)

cuneata **new**	WHil

Dionaea ✿ (*Droseraceae*)

	muscipula	CHew EECP SKHP SPlb WSSs
	- 'Akai Ryu' ♀H3	NLos WSSs
	- 'B52'	WSSs
	- (Dentate Traps Group) 'Dentate Traps'	WSSs
*	- f. ***heterodoxa*** **new**	NLos
	- large clone **new**	NLos
	- long-toothed **new**	NLos
	- 'Pink Venus' **new**	NLos
	- 'Royal Red'	CHew NLos WSSs
	- 'Sawtooth'	NLos WSSs
	- shark-toothed	NLos
	- Slack's red clone **new**	NLos
	- 'South West Giant' ♀H3 **new**	NLos
	- 'Spider'	EECP NLos
	- upright **new**	NLos

Dionysia (*Primulaceae*)

'Annielle'	WAbe
archibaldii	WAbe
aretioides ♀H5	WAbe
- 'Bevere'	WAbe
- 'Phyllis Carter'	ECho
bryoides	WAbe
'Charlson Emma'	WAbe
'Charlson Gem'	WAbe
'Charlson Jake'	WAbe
'Charlson Petite'	WAbe
'Charlson Pip'	WAbe

'Charlson Primrose'	WAbe
'Corona'	WAbe
curviflora	WAbe
'Emmely'	WAbe
'Eric Watson'	WAbe
'Ewesley Iota'	WAbe
'Ewesley Kappa'	WAbe
'Ewesley Theta'	WAbe
'Geist'	WAbe
janthina	WAbe
'Judith Bramley'	WAbe
lamingtonii	WAbe
'Lycaena'	WAbe
'Monika'	WAbe
'Pascal'	WAbe
sarvestanica new	WAbe
tapetodes	WAbe
- 'Brimstone'	WAbe
- 'Peter Edwards'	WAbe
'Tess'	WAbe
'Yellowstone'	WAbe
'Zdeněk Zvolánek' new	WAbe

Dioon (*Zamiaceae*)

califanoi	CBrP
caputoi	CBrP
edule 🏆H1b	CBrP LPal SPlb
- var. ***angustifolium***	CBrP
merolae	CBrP
rzedowskii	CBrP
spinulosum	CBrP SBig

Dioscorea (*Dioscoreaceae*)

araucana	LSou
batatas	CAgr CArn CUse LEdu
deltoidea	CExl
japonica	CAgr CUse LEdu
quinqueloba	WCru
villosa	CArn LEdu

Diosma (*Rutaceae*)

ericoides	SEND SWvt
- 'Pink Fountain'	CAbb EPfP EWTr LRHS SEle SPoG
- 'Sunset Gold'	CAbb CBod CSpe CWGN EPfP LBuc LRHS SCoo SEle SPoG

Diosphaera (*Campanulaceae*)

asperuloides	see *Trachelium asperuloides*

Diospyros (*Ebenaceae*)

austroafricana	CFil SPlb
glabra new	SVen
* ***hyrcanum***	NLar
kaki (F)	CBcs CMCN EPfP NLar NPla SEWo WPGP
- 'Fuyu' (F)	CAgr
- 'Kostata' (F)	CAgr
- 'Mazelii' (F)	CAgr WPGP
lotus	CAgr CBcs CMCN ESwi LEdu LRHS NLar SPlb
- (f)	CAgr
- (m)	CAgr
lycioides	SPlb
'Nikita's Gift'	CAgr
ramulosa	SPlb
rhombifolia	CBcs NLar
'Russian Beauty'	CAgr
virginiana (F)	CAgr CBcs CMCN NLar SPlb SSpi
- 'Early Golden' (F)	CAgr
- 'Meader' (F)	CAgr

Diostea (*Verbenaceae*)

juncea new	MGil

Dipcadi (*Asparagaceae*)

ciliare	CLak
marlothii 'Bloemfontein'	ECho
serotinum	ECho
- subsp. ***lividum***	WPGP
viride	CLak
white-flowered	CLak

Dipelta (*Caprifoliaceae*)

floribunda 🏆H5	CBcs CDul CExl CFil CJun CMCN CMac ELan EPfP EPla LRHS MBlu MBri NLar SBrt SKHP SPer WPGP WPat
ventricosa	CAbP CBcs CExl CFil CJun ELan EPfP LRHS MBlu NLar SChF SSpi WPGP WPat
yunnanensis	CBcs CExl CJun ELan EPfP IDee LRHS NLar SKHP SWvt WPGP WPat

Diphylleia (*Berberidaceae*)

cymosa	CAby CLAP CTal ECha GCal MRav SPhx WCot WCru
- red-marked	CDes
grayi	WCru
sinensis	CExl WCru

Dipidax see *Onixotis*

Diplacus see *Mimulus*

Dipladenia see *Mandevilla*

Diplarrena (*Iridaceae*)

§ ***latifolia***	CNor EBee GBBs GCal IBlr LRHS NCGa SGSe WPtf
- Helen Dillon's form	IBlr
moraea	CAbP CAby CMac CWCL EBee ECho GAbr GBBs GBin GCal IBlr IKil LEdu MBel NCGa NSbr WPGP WSHC
- ***minor***	IBlr
- 'Slieve Donard'	IBlr
- West Coast form	see *D. latifolia*

Diplopanax (*Cornaceae*)

stachyanthus	WCru
B&SWJ 11803 new	

Diplotaxis (*Brassicaceae*)

muralis	CArn ELau WJek
tenuifolia	ELau ENfk MNHC SRms

Dipsacus (*Caprifoliaceae*)

§ ***fullonum***	CArn CBod CHab ENfk EPfP GJos MBri MHer MNHC NDov NMir NPri SEND SIde SRms WHer WJek WSFF
inermis	CSam ECha NBid NLar
japonicus	SKHP
- HWJ 695	SPhx WCru
pilosus	CBgR CPom NDov
sativus	NLar
strigosus	SPhx
sylvestris	see *D. fullonum*

Dipteracanthus see *Ruellia*

Dipteronia (*Aceraceae*)

sinensis CBcs CMCN EPla MBri WPGP

Disa (*Orchidaceae*)

aurata NDav
Bride's Dream gx NDav
Child Safety Transvaal gx NDav
Constantia gx NDav
Diores gx NDav
- 'Inca City' NDav
- 'Inca Gold' NDav
- 'Inca Princess' NDav
- 'Inca Warrior' NDav
Diorosa gx NDav
Foam gx NDav
Ivan Watson gx NDav
Kalahari Sands gx NDav
Kewbett gx NDav
Kewdior gx NDav
Kewensis gx 'Alice' NDav
- 'Ann' NDav
- 'May' NDav
- 'Milkmaid' NDav
- 'Ruth' NDav
Reheat gx NDav
Riette gx NDav
Robert Parkinson gx new NDav
Sealord gx NDav
Tracey Parkinson gx NDav
tripetaloides NDav
Unidiorosa gx NDav
'Tracey' new
uniflora NDav
- carmine-flowered NDav
- pink-flowered NDav
- red-flowered new NDav
Unifoam gx NDav
- 'Firebird' NDav
Unilangley gx NDav
Watsonii gx 'Bramley' NDav
- 'Candy' NDav
- 'Don' new NDav
- 'Sandra' NDav

Disanthus (*Hamamelidaceae*)

cercidifolius ♀H5 CAbP CBcs CJun CMCN CMac EPfP GBin GKin IArd IDee LRHS MBlu MBri MPkF NLar SPer SPoG SSpi WPGP
- 'Ena-nishiki' (v) IArd MBlu NLar WPGP

Discaria (*Rhamnaceae*)

chacaye LEdu WPGP
toumatou SVen

Diselma (*Cupressaceae*)

archeri CDoC CKen SCoo SLim
- 'Read Dwarf' CKen

Disepalum (*Annonaceae*)

petelotii B&SWJ 11690 new WCru

Disphyma (*Aizoaceae*)

crassifolium SChr

Disporopsis (*Asparagaceae*)

B&SWJ 229 from Taiwan WCru
B&SWJ 1864 from Taiwan WCru
aspersa CHEx CLAP CSpe EBee ECho EPPr EWld GEdr ITim LEdu MAvo NBir WCru WPGP
- tall CBct CExl WCru
fuscopicta CBct CLAP EBee EPPr LEdu MAvo MPie WCru WWEG
longifolia CLAP
- B&SWJ 5284 WCru
- HWJ 861 CDes
luzoniensis IMou
- B&SWJ 3891 CBct CExl ESwi GEdr LEdu WCru
'Min Shan' CExl CTal ELon
* ***nova*** EPPr
§ ***pernyi*** Widely available
- B&SWJ 1864 CBct EPPr GEdr
- 'Bill Baker' CBct EBee EPPr LEdu MAvo
aff. ***pernyi*** CCon
taiwanensis IMou LEdu
- B&SWJ 3388 CBct GEdr WCru
undulata CBct EPPr IMou LEdu NBid WCru

Disporum (*Colchicaceae*)

austrosinense B&SWJ 9777 WCru
bodinieri CBct CExl WPnP
- BWJ 8128 WCru
- DJHC 765 WCru
cantoniense CBct CCon EPri IMou LEdu WCru WFar
- B&L 12512 CExl CLAP
- B&SWJ 1424 WCru
- B&SWJ 9715 WCru
- DJHC 98485 LEdu MMoz SKHP
I - 'Aureovariegata' CBct ETwe LEdu WCot
- var. ***cantoniense*** f. ***brunneum*** B&SWJ 5290 WCru
- var. ***multiflorum*** B&SWJ 11252 WCru
- - B&SWJ 11291 WCru
- var. ***sikkimense*** B&SWJ 2337 WCru
- - B&SWJ 2358 LEdu WCru
- - PAB 4973 new LEdu
- var. ***y-tiense*** HWJ 1045 WCru
hookeri see *Prosartes hookeri*
kawakamii B&SWJ 350 WCru
- RWJ 10103 CBct WCru
lanuginosum see *Prosartes lanuginosa*
leschenaultianum B&SWJ 9484 WCru
- B&SWJ 9505 WCru
leucanthum CTal WCru
- B&SWJ 2389 WCru
longistylum LEdu SGSe
- B&SWJ 2859 WCru
- L 1564 CBct ESwi LEdu WCru
- L 2164 new ETwe
- 'Green Giant' CBct CDes CExl CLAP CTal EBee EPfP GEdr GKev IDee IFoB LEdu LSou MSCN NLar WFar WHil WPnP WPtf
- 'Night Heron' CBct CExl CTal IFoB IMou LEdu WCot WFar WPnP

lutescens CTal WCru
maculatum see *Prosartes maculata*
megalanthum CBct CExl CLAP IFoB LEdu MMoz WCru
- CD&R 2412B CExl CTal EPPr
menziesii see *Prosartes smithii*
nantouense CTal
- B&SWJ 359 CBct LEdu WCru
- B&SWJ 6812 WCru
oreganum see *Prosartes hookeri* var. *oregana*
sessile EBee ECho LEdu WCru
- AGSJ 146 GBuc
- B&SWJ 2824 WCru
I - 'Aureovariegatum' (v) ECho WCru
- 'Awa-no-tsuki' (v) GEdr
- 'Cricket' GEdr
- 'Kinga' (v) GEdr
- f. ***macrophyllum*** B&SWJ 4316 WCru
I - 'Robustum Variegatum' (v) EBee
- 'Variegatum' (v) CAby CExl CHEx CNor CPom CTal EBee ECho ELan ELon EPPr EPfP EPla IMou LEdu LRHS NLar SGSe SPhx WBor WCru WFar WPGP WPnP
- var. ***yakushimense*** ECho LEdu
shimadae B&SWJ 399 WCru
smilacinum CDes CTal NLar SGSe WCru
- B&SWJ 713 CBct WCru
* - 'Aureovariegatum' (v) LEdu WCru
- pink-flowered WCot WCru
smithii see *Prosartes smithii*
taiwanense B&SWJ 1513 WCru
- B&SWJ 2018 WCru
tonkinense B&SWJ 11672 WCru
- B&SWJ 11814 WCru
- HWJ 882 WCru
trabeculatum CBct WCru
- 'Nakafu' IMou LEdu WCru
uniflorum CAby CAvo CBct CLAP CPom CTal ECho EPPr EPfP LEdu LRHS MMHG MNrw NBid SMHy WSHC
- B&SWJ 651 CBct LEdu WCru
- B&SWJ 872 WCru
- B&SWJ 4100 WCru
viridescens CBct EBee EPPr LEdu SKHP WCru
- B&SWJ 4598 WCru

Distylium (*Hamamelidaceae*)

myricoides NLar WPat
racemosum CBcs CMac EPfP ETwe IVic MBlu NLar SSta WSHC

Dittrichia (*Asteraceae*)

viscosa WCot

Diuranthera see *Chlorophytum*

Dizygotheca see *Schefflera*

Dobinea (*Anacardiaceae*)

vulgaris B&SWJ 2532 WCru

Dodecatheon (*Primulaceae*)

sp. MSCN
alpinum GKev NHar
- subsp. ***alpinum*** EBee
amethystinum GKev
'Aphrodite'PBR CBod LLWG NLar WFar
austrofrigidum GEdr NCGa NHar
clevelandii GEdr GKev
- subsp. ***insulare*** LLHF
- subsp. ***patulum*** ECho LRHS
conjugens EWld GKev LLHF
cusickii see *D. pulchellum* subsp. *cusickii*
dentatum ♀H5 CElw CPBP GEdr GKev LEdu NHar SBrt WAbe WFar
- subsp. ***dentatum*** GKev
NNS 07-166 **new**
- subsp. ***utahense*** NHar
frigidum GEdr WAbe
§ ***jeffreyi*** CBod ECho EPPr GBuc GEdr GKev LEdu LRHS MNrw NCGa NLar NSum WAbe WBor WFar
- 'Rotlicht' WHil
* × ***lemoinei*** WAbe
§ ***meadia*** ♀H5 Widely available
- from Cedar County, USA WAbe
- f. ***album*** ♀H5 CBro ECho ELan EPfP EPot GAbr LAma LEdu LRHS MBel MMoz MNrw NCGa NHol NLar NMyG NSum NWad SKHP SPer SWvt WPnP
- 'Aphrodite' EPfP
* - 'Goliath' GAbr GJos NSum
- membranaceous WAbe
- 'Queen Victoria' ECho GBuc GEdr LEdu NLar SKHP WFar
- red shades GBuc NSum
mixed **new** SMrm
pauciflorum misapplied see *D. pulchellum*
pauciflorum (Dur.) E. Greene see *D. meadia*
poeticum SPlb
- NNS 00-259 NCGa
§ ***pulchellum*** ♀H5 CBro EBee ECho EDAr GEdr GKev IBoy LLWG LRHS MNrw NRya WIce
- ***album*** ECho
§ - subsp. ***cusickii*** LEdu
- subsp. ***monanthum*** GKev
NNS 08-122 **new**
- subsp. ***pulchellum*** 'Red Wings' ECho EPot IBoy LLHF LRHS NBir NHar NLar SKHP WHoo
- ***radicatum*** see *D. pulchellum*
- 'Sooke Variety' WAbe
radicatum see *D. pulchellum*
redolens GBuc
tetrandrum see *D. jeffreyi*

Dodonaea (*Sapindaceae*)

viscosa CBcs ECou SPlb
- (f) ECou
- (m) ECou
- 'Purpurea' CBcs CDoC CExl CHGN COtt CTsd EUJe IVic LPal LRHS SLim SPoG SVen

Doellingeria (*Asteraceae*)

scabra see *Aster scaber*

Dolichos (*Papilionaceae*)

purpureus see *Lablab purpureus*

Dombeya (*Malvaceae*)

× ***cayeuxii*** SVen
wallichii CCCN

Dondia see *Hacquetia*

Doodia (*Blechnaceae*)

media	CBty GBin ISha LRHS SPlb

Doronicum (*Asteraceae*)

austriacum	NBid
- PAB 5641 **new**	LEdu
carpetanum	GKev
subsp. ***kuepferi*** **new**	
caucasicum	see *D. orientale*
§ ***columnae***	CBcs
cordatum	see *D. columnae*
§ × ***excelsum*** 'Harpur Crewe'	CPrp LEdu MRav NPer
'Finesse'	COtt GCal GJos LRHS LSun SRms
'Little Leo'	CMea COtt ELan EPfP GJos GMaP LRHS NLar NPri NSoo SPoG SRGP SRms WHil WRHF
§ ***orientale***	ELan EPfP GJos SEND SPer SPoG SWat
- 'Leonardo'	EBee LRHS WHar
- 'Leonardo Compact'	LPot
- 'Magnificum'	CSBt EBee EPfP GMaP LRHS MBNS MBri MWat NGBl NMir SMrm SPoG SRms WCot WHar
pardalianches	CArn CFis GCal MMuc WHal WRHF
- 'Goldstrauss'	EBee
plantagineum 'Excelsum'	see *D.* × *excelsum* 'Harpur Crewe'

Doryanthes (*Doryanthaceae*)

excelsa	CHEx
palmeri	CBrP

Dorycnium see *Lotus*

Douglasia see *Androsace*

vitaliana	see *Vitaliana primuliflora*

Dovyalis (*Salicaceae*)

caffra (F)	XBlo

Doxantha see *Macfadyena*

Draba (*Brassicaceae*)

acaulis	WAbe
aizoides	ECho EDAr LRHS SPlb SRms XLum
aizoon	see *D. lasiocarpa*
bruniifolia	NHar
bryoides	see *D. rigida* var. *bryoides*
'Buttermilk'	WAbe
cusickii	GKev
cuspidata	CTal
dedeana	GJos WAbe
densifolia	IFoB
imbricata	see *D. rigida* var. *imbricata*
'John Saxton'	EPot WAbe
§ ***lasiocarpa***	XLum
longisiliqua ♀H4	LLHF WAbe
mollissima	EPot WAbe
- 'Göteborg'	EPot
oligosperma	EDAr IFoB
oreades	CPBP
ossetica	WAbe
§ ***rigida*** var. ***bryoides***	WThu
* - var. ***imbricata***	GCrg NSla
- - f. ***compacta***	EPot
rosularis	EDAr EPot GJos WAbe
× ***salomonii***	EPot
scardica	see *D. lasiocarpa*
ventosa	WAbe
yunnanensis	WAbe

Dracaena ✿ (*Asparagaceae*)

cochinchinensis	SPlb
draco ♀H1c	CArn EShb MHin SPlb WCot XBlo
fragrans Deremensis Group	XBlo
indivisa	see *Cordyline indivisa*
'Lemon Lime Tips'	XBlo
marginata (v) ♀H1b	XBlo
- 'Tricolor' (v) ♀H1b	XBlo
stricta	see *Cordyline stricta*

Dracocephalum (*Lamiaceae*)

argunense	SPhx SRms WCot
* - 'Album'	GKev
- 'Blue Carpet'	LEdu NLar
- 'Fuji Blue'	CExl EDAr EPfP EWes SPoG WIce XLum
- 'Fuji White'	CExl SPhx SPoG
austriacum	LRHS SBrt
botryoides	CPBP MMuc SPhx
calophyllum var. ***smithianum***	IMou
forrestii	EBee
grandiflorum	GEdr MMHG SBrt SPhx XLum
hemsleyanum	LLHF
mairei	see *D. renatii*
multicaule **new**	GKev
peregrinum 'Blue Dragon'	SPhx
prattii	see *Nepeta prattii*
§ ***renatii***	LLHF SPhx
rupestre	EBee GEdr SPhx
ruyschiana	ELan EWes GEdr MMHG SPhx XLum
- 'Blue Moon'	NLar
sibiricum	see *Nepeta sibirica*
* ***tataricum***	LRHS
virginicum	see *Physostegia virginiana*
wendelboi	NBir

Dracunculus (*Araceae*)

canariensis	WCot
muscivorus	see *Helicodiceros muscivorus*
§ ***vulgaris***	CAby CHel CHid CPom EBee ECho EPfP EPot ESwi EUJe GKev MMoz SDix SEND SPlb WCot

Dregea (*Apocynaceae*)

sinensis	CBcs CCCN CHel CHll CRHN ECre ELan EPfP EShb EWTr EWes LRHS MOWG MRav SEND SKHP SPer SPoG SWvt WPGP WSHC
- 'Brockhill Silver'	EPfP LRHS SKHP SWvt
- 'Variegata' (v)	EWes

Drepanostachyum (*Poaceae*)

falconeri J.J.N. Campbell. ex D. McClintock	see *Himalayacalamus falconeri*, *Himalayacalamus falconeri* 'Damarapa'
hookerianum	see *Himalayacalamus hookerianus*
§ ***khasianum***	CExl WPGP

Drimia (*Asparagaceae*)

angustifolia ambig.	ECho
anomala	CLak
basutica	CLak
elata	CLak
involuta	CLak
mzimvubuensis	CLak
sphaerocephala	CLak
uniflora	CLak

Drimiopsis (*Asparagaceae*)

maculata	LToo MPie WCot

Drimys (*Winteraceae*)

andina	CExl EPfP MMuc
aromatica	see *Tasmannia lanceolata*
colorata	see *Pseudowintera colorata*
granadensis var. ***grandiflora*** B&SWJ 10777	WCru
* ***latifolia***	CBcs CHEx IDee
winteri ♀H4	Widely available
§ - var. ***chilensis***	CExl EPfP LRHS SSpi WCru WPGP
- Latifolia Group	see *D. winteri* var. *chilensis*
- var. ***winteri*** new	SRms

Drosanthemum (*Aizoaceae*)

hispidum	ECho ELan EPfP LRHS MAsh SBHP SPlb SPoG WAbe
speciosum	ECho
* ***sutherlandii***	ECho

Drosera ✿ (*Droseraceae*)

admirabilis	CHew
aliciae ♀H3	CHew EECP
andersoniana	EFEx
androsacea	CHew
ascendens	CHew
binata	CHew EECP
§ - subsp. ***dichotoma*** ♀H3	CHew NLos
- 'Extrema'	CHew NLos
- 'Giant' new	NLos
- 'Multifida'	CHew
browniana	EFEx
bulbigena	EFEx
bulbosa subsp. ***bulbosa***	EFEx
- subsp. ***major***	EFEx
callistos	CHew
capensis	CHew SPlb
- 'Albino' ♀H3	CHew EECP
dichotoma	see *D. binata* subsp. *dichotoma*
dichrosepala	CHew EECP
echinoblastus	CHew
enodes	CHew
ericksoniae	CHew
erythrorhiza	EFEx
- subsp. ***collina***	EFEx
- subsp. ***erythrorhiza***	CHew EFEx
- subsp. ***magna***	EFEx
- subsp. ***squamosa***	EFEx
filiformis	NLos
- var. ***filiformis***	CHew EECP
- var. ***tracyi***	NLos
gigantea	EFEx
graniticola	EFEx
helodes	CHew
heterophylla	EFEx
lasiantha	CHew
leioblastus	CHew
loureiroi	EFEx
macrantha	EFEx
- subsp. ***macrantha***	EFEx
macrophylla subsp. ***macrophylla***	EFEx
mannii	CHew
marchantii subsp. ***prophylla***	EFEx
menziesii subsp. ***basifolia***	EFEx
- subsp. ***menziesii***	EFEx
- subsp. ***thysanosepala***	EFEx
modesta	EFEx
nidiformis	CHew
orbiculata	EFEx
paleacea subsp. ***trichocaulis***	CHew
peltata	EFEx
platypoda	EFEx
pulchella	CHew
pycnoblasta	CHew
pygmaea	CHew
ramellosa	EFEx
roseana	CHew
rosulata	EFEx
rotundifolia	WHer
salina	EFEx
sargentii	CHew
scorpioides	CHew EECP
slackii ♀H3	CHew
stelliflora	CHew
stolonifera subsp. ***compacta***	EFEx
- subsp. ***humilis***	EFEx
- subsp. ***porrecta***	EFEx
- subsp. ***rupicola***	EFEx
- subsp. ***stolonifera***	EFEx
tubaestylus	EFEx
zonaria	EFEx

Drosophyllum (*Drosophyllaceae*)

lusitanicum	CHew

Dryandra (*Proteaceae*)

formosa	CTre SPlb

Dryas (*Rosaceae*)

drummondii	ECho LLHF WAbe
§ ***integrifolia***	WAbe
- 'Greenland Green'	WAbe
octopetala ♀H5	CArn CMea ECho GJos GKev LRHS MWat NChi SPoG SRms SWvt WAbe
- subsp. ***hookeriana***	LLHF
§ - 'Minor' ♀H5	EPot NHar WAbe
× ***suendermannii*** ♀H5	CMea EBee EPfP EPot GCrg GEdr GMaP LLHF NHar NSla SBch WAbe
tenella misapplied	see *D. octopetala* 'Minor'
tenella Pursh	see *D. integrifolia*

Dryopteris ✿ (*Dryopteridaceae*)

aemula	EFer SRms
§ ***affinis*** ♀H5	CBty CLAP CMac EAEE ECha EPfP ERod EWoo GMaP LBuc LPal LRHS MBri MCot MGos MMoz MWat NPri SCob SPer SPoG SRms WCot WFib WShi XLum

	Name	Suppliers
	- 'Angustata Crispa' new	MWat
§	- subsp. ***borreri***	SRms
	- subsp. ***cambrensis***	ISha
	- - 'Crispa Barnes'	WPGP
	- - 'Insubrica'	EFer
	- 'Congesta'	CKel CLAP
	- 'Congesta Cristata'	CLAP CTal EFer GMaP LPal SRot
	- Crispa Group	CBod CLAP EHon GBBs LRHS MMoz SCob WGrf WWEG
§	- 'Crispa Gracilis' ♀H5	CKel CLAP EFtx ELan ERod GBin ISha LPal MMoz NBir NEgg NHol WGrf
*	- 'Crispa Gracilis Congesta'	CBty CWCL GEdr MRav MWhi NGdn NWad SGSe WCot WFib WPat
§	- 'Cristata' ♀H5	Widely available
	- 'Cristata Angustata' ♀H5	CBty CLAP CTal EFer ELan EPfP MMoz NBid NGdn NHol SRms WBor WFib WMoo WPGP
	- 'Cristata The King'	see *D. affinis* 'Cristata'
	- 'Grandiceps Askew'	EFer SRms WFib
*	- ***kerryensis***	MWhi
	- 'Pinderi'	CBty CLAP EBee GBin ISha LSun MMoz SCob SRms WGrf WRHF
	- Polydactyla Group	CLAP
	- - 'Polydactyla Dadds'	CBty CLAP EFtx LLHF NLar NMyG WWEG
	- - 'Polydactyla Mapplebeck' ♀H5	CLAP NBid SRms WFib
	- 'Revoluta'	SGSe
	- 'Revolvens'	CLAP EFer
	atrata misapplied	see *D. cycadina*
	atrata (Wall. ex Kunze) Ching	CDTJ CKel CWCL EWTr LPal LRHS NLar SPoG XLum
	× ***australis***	CDes CLAP ISha NLos
	austriaca	see *D. dilatata*
	bissetiana	ISha
	blanfordii	WPGP
	- from Kashmir	ISha
	borreri	see *D. affinis* subsp. *borreri*
	buschiana	CBty CLAP EBee EFtx LPal MMuc MRav NLar WCot
	carthusiana	CLAP EFer GBin NLar XLum
	- 'Cristata'	EFer
	celsa	ISha NLos
	championii	CCCN CLAP ISha LRHS
	clintoniana	CLAP EFer GBin GEdr LRHS MMoz WCot WPGP
	× ***complexa***	CBty ISha NLos
	- 'Stablerae' ♀H7	CLAP EFer EFtx GBin MWhi WFib WPGP
	- 'Stablerae' crisped ♀H7	NMyG WFib
	coreanomontana	CBty
	crassirhizoma ♀H6	CCCN CKel CLAP EBee GBin ISha LRHS MMoz SGSe SMDP WPtf WRHF
	cristata	CLAP CWCL EBee EPfP WMoo XLum
§	***cycadina*** ♀H4	CLAP CTal EBee EFer EFtx ELan EPPr EPfP ERod EShb EUJe GBin ISha LRHS MBri MGos MMoz MWat NBid NBir NLos SCob SPtp WFib WGrf WMoo WPnP
	cystolepidota	EFer
§	***dilatata*** ♀H6	ECha EFer EFtx ELan EPfP ERod LPal LRHS MMuc MRav SGSe SRms WFib WHal WShi
	- 'Crispa Whiteside' ♀H6	CBty CLAP CWCL EAEE EBee EFer EFtx ELan EPfP ERod LBMP LEdu LRHS MBri MMoz MRav MWat MWhi NLar SHil SPlb WCot WFib WGrf WMoo WPGP WPat WWEG
	- 'Grandiceps'	CLAP CMac EFer WFib
	- 'Jimmy Dyce'	CBty CLAP ISha LRHS
	- 'Lepidota Crispa Cristata'	CLAP EBee WPat
	- 'Lepidota Cristata' ♀H6	CBty CLAP CWCL EFtx ELan EPPr ERod MMuc NGdn NLos NMyG SGSe SRms WFib WMoo
	- 'Lepidota Grandiceps'	CLAP
*	- 'Recurvata'	CLAP ISha LLHF NLar
	erythrosora ♀H4	Widely available
	- 'Brilliance' ♀H5	CCCN CLAP GQue ISha LRHS LSou SMDP SMrm WCot WRHF
	- var. ***koidzumiana***	ISha
	- var. ***prolifica***	CBod CBty CKel CLAP EBee EFtx ELan EPfP GMaP ISha LPal LRHS MBri MGos MMoz NBir NEgg NLar NPri SBod SPoG WFib WGrf WPat
	× ***euxinensis***	CLAP
	filix-mas ♀H7	Widely available
	- 'Barnesii'	CBod CLAP CWCL EFer ELan ERod GBin ISha LRHS MMuc NLar SEND SGol SPlb WWEG
	- 'Crispa'	CBty CLAP LRHS SGol SRms WFib
	- 'Crispa Congesta'	see *D. affinis* 'Crispa Gracilis'
	- 'Crispa Cristata' ♀H7	CBty CLAP CWCL EBee EFer EFtx ELan EPfP ERod EUJe GMaP IKil LLWG LRHS MBri MRav NBid NBir SCob SGSe SPoG SRms WFib WGrf WWEG XLum
	- 'Crispatissima'	EBee
	- 'Cristata' ♀H7	CLAP CTal EBee EFer ELan EPfP LPot MJak MMoz MMuc NOrc SEND SRms WMoo
	- Cristata Group	EFer
*	- - 'Cristata Grandiceps'	EFer
	- - 'Cristata Jackson'	CLAP MWhi SPlb
	- - 'Cristata Martindale'	CBty CLAP NBid NMyG SRms WFib
	- - 'Fred Jackson'	CLAP WFib
	- 'Depauperata'	CLAP WPGP
	- 'Furcans'	CLAP EBee
	- 'Grandiceps Wills' ♀H7	NBid WFib
	- 'Linearis'	EFer EHon ELan EWoo ISha LAst LRHS MCot MGos MWhi SGSe SRms WFib
	- 'Linearis Congesta'	WPGP
	- 'Linearis Polydactyla' ♀H7	CBty CLAP CMac CWCL EFer EFtx ELan EPPr EPfP LPal LRHS MMoz MMuc MRav NGdn NHol NLar NLos NMyG SCob SEND SPoG SPtp WGrf WMoo WPnP XLum
	- 'Parsley'	CLAP ISha
*	- Polydactyla Group	ECha MRav MWat NEgg SCob
I	- 'Revolvens'	MWhi WFib
	goldieana	CDTJ CLAP CTal EBee ECha EFer EFtx EWTr GMaP ISha LRHS MMuc NBid NBir NLar NMyG WFar WFib WGrf WMoo WPnP WWEG XLum
	hirtipes misapplied	see *D. cycadina*
	hondoensis	EFtx
	intermedia	ISha
	labordei	ISha LRHS
	lacera	ISha
	lepidopoda	CBty EFtx GLin LPal LRHS LSun SGSe SMDP WPtf WRHF
	ludoviciana	CBty ISha
	marginalis	CDTJ CKel CLAP GBin LRHS MMoz NLar SCob WMoo

oreades WCot
pacifica CLAP
paleacea CLAP
pseudofilix-mas ISha
pseudomas see *D. affinis*
pycnopteroides EFtx
× ***remota*** ISha NLos
× ***separabilis*** ISha
sieboldii 🏆H6 CBty CCon CLAP CTal CWCL EFer ERod EShb EUJe ISha LPal LRHS MBri NBid NBir NCGa NGdn NLar SEND SGSe SPoG SRms WMoo WPGP XLum
stewartii CLAP GEdr LLHF NLar WWEG
sublacera EFtx
tokyoensis 🏆H6 CDTJ CLAP GBin ISha LRHS MMoz NLar WPGP
uniformis CLAP EFer
wallichiana 🏆H5 Widely available
- F&M 107 WPGP

Duchesnea (*Rosaceae*)

chrysantha see *D. indica*
§ ***indica*** MRav SEND WHea WMoo WOut XLum
§ - 'Harlequin' (v) CExl
* - 'Snowflake' (v) WMoo
- 'Variegata' see *D. indica* 'Harlequin'

Dudleya (*Crassulaceae*)

brittonii 🏆H3 new SMad

Dugaldia (*Asteraceae*)

hoopesii see *Hymenoxys hoopesii*

Dulichium (*Cyperaceae*)

arundinaceum LLWG
- 'Tigress' LLWG

Dunalia (*Solanaceae*)

australis see *Iochroma australe*
- blue-flowered see *Iochroma australe* 'Bill Evans'
- white-flowered see *Iochroma australe* 'Andean Snow'

Duranta (*Verbenaceae*)

§ ***erecta*** CCCN CHll EShb
§ - 'Geisha Girl' CCCN
- 'Sapphire Swirl' see *D. erecta* 'Geisha Girl'
- 'Variegata' (v) CCCN
- white-flowered SVen
plumieri see *D. erecta*
repens see *D. erecta*
serratifolia CCCN

Duvernoia see *Justicia*

Dyckia (*Bromeliaceae*)

brevifolia WCot
'Cherry Coke' WCot
frigida WCot WGrn
goehringii new WCot
jonesiana new WCot
leptostachya WCot WGrn
marnier-lapostollei WCot
'Morris Hobbs' WCot
* ***polyphylla*** new WCot
remotiflora SChr
velascana WCot

Dypsis (*Arecaceae*)

§ ***decaryi*** CCCN LPal XBlo
lutescens 🏆H1a LPal XBlo

Dysosma see *Podophyllum*

E

Ecballium (*Cucurbitaceae*)

elaterium CArn CDTJ CFil LEdu SIde WCot WPGP

Eccremocarpus (*Bignoniaceae*)

scaber CBcs CWCL ELan EPfP IDee LBMP LRHS MGil MNrw NPer SEND SLim SMrm WHea
- 'Carmineus' EPfP EWld
- 'Coccineus' EUJe
- cream-flowered ESwi NLar
- orange-flowered ESwi
- red-flowered NLar SPoG
- 'Tangerine' CSpe
- 'Tresco Cream' CSpe

Echeandia (*Asparagaceae*)

formosa B&SWJ 9147 WCru

Echeveria ✿ (*Crassulaceae*)

affinis CBod CDTJ EUJe SRot
'Afterglow' CSuc
agavoides 🏆H1c CDTJ MRav WCot
- 'Lipstick' new WCot
albicans CSuc SPlb
amoena CDoC
ballsii new WCot
* 'Black Prince' CDTJ CDes CDoC ELan MHer NPer SPlb SRot WCot WPGP
'Blue Prince' CDoC
'Blue Waves' CSuc WCot
* ***cana*** CDTJ CDoC SRot
cante 🏆H2 SPlb
carnicolor CSuc
'Chrissy 'n' Ryan' CDoC
coccinea ELan
colorata 🏆H2 WCot
- f. ***brandtii*** CDoC
'Corymbosa' WCot
'Crûg Ice' WCru
'Crystal Maze' new CSuc
'Curly Locks' WCot
cuspidata × ***setosa*** var. ***ciliata*** CSuc
'Derenceana' CDoC
× ***derosa*** CDTJ
difractens new WCot
'Dondo' CSuc
'Doris Taylor' CSuc
'Duchess of Nuremberg' CBod CDoC CHel EUJe SPlb SRot
elegans 🏆H2 CBod CDTJ CDoC CHEx CHel EPfP EUJe LSou LSun NWad SArc SPlb
'Galaxy Mars' (Galaxy Hybrids Series) CDoC
'Ghost Buster' WPGP
§ ***gibbiflora*** var. ***metallica*** EPfP

	× ***gilva*** ♀H2	CSuc
*	– 'Red'	LSun MHol WCot
	glauca Baker	see *E. secunda* var. *glauca*
	harmsii	CDoC CSuc
	'Hens and Chicks'	CHEx
	hyalina RE 614	CDoC
	'Ileen'	CDoC
	lilacina ♀H2	CDoC EUJe SMrm SPlb SRot WPGP
	lutea RE 502	CDoC
	'Mahogany'	CDoC WCot WGrn
	'Mauna Loa'	CDTJ EBee EWes LRHS WGrn
	maxonii B&SWJ 10396	WCru
	'Meridian'	CHEx
	minima ♀H2	CSuc WCot
	montana B&SWJ 10277	WCru
	multicaulis	CSuc
	nodulosa	CSuc WCot
	nuda	CSuc
	'Paul Bunyon'	CSuc
	peacockii	MHer MSCN SMrm SPlb
	'Perle d'Azur'	CHEx
	'Perle von Nürnberg' ♀H2	CAbb SMad SPlb
	prolifica	CSuc
	pulidonis ♀H1c	CDoC EPfP MHer
	purpusorum	SPlb
	'Ramillette'	CSuc
	'Ron Evans'	CDoC
	rosea ♀H1c	WCot
	runyonii 'Topsy Turvy' ♀H2	CDTJ CDoC CHEx EPfP SRot
	'Scorpio' **new**	CSuc
	secunda	CAbb SPlb
§	– var. ***glauca***	CDTJ CDes CHEx CHel ELan EShb NBir SEND WPGP
	– – 'Compton Carousel' **new**	WCot
*	– – 'Gigantea'	NDov NPer WPGP
	setosa ♀H1c	CDTJ EPfP WCot
	– var. ***ciliata***	EShb
	– var. ***deminuta***	CSuc
	shaviana ♀H2	CDTJ EUJe SRot WCot
	– RE 581	CDoC
	subsessilis	WCot
	– RE 163	CDoC
	'Telstar' **new**	CSuc
	'Violet Queen'	CDoC

Echinacea ✿ (*Asteraceae*)

§	'Adam Saul'	LRHS STPC
§	'After Midnight'[PBR] (Big Sky Series)	EBee ECtt IBoy
	'Aloha'	NLar
	'Amazing Dream'	ECtt IBoy
	'Amber Mist' (Mistical Series)	EBee
	angustifolia	CArn CBod ENfk EPfP GPoy LRHS MHer SPhx WJek
§	'Art's Pride'[PBR]	MGos SCob SPer
	'Cheyenne Spirit' mixture **new**	CBod MAsh SPhx
	'Coral Reef'	ECtt
	'Cranberry Cupcake' (d)	ECtt
	Crazy Pink	see *E.* 'Adam Saul'
	Crazy White	see *E.* 'Noam Saul'
	'Daydream'	ECtt LSou
	Double Scoop Bubblegum = 'Balscblum'	CUse EBee
	Double Scoop Orangeberry = 'Balscoberr'	CUse
	Double Scoop Raspberry = 'Balsceras' (d) **new**	EBee SMrm
	'Eccentric' (d) **new**	CWGN IBoy MHol
	'Emily Saul'[PBR]	see *E.* 'After Midnight' (Big Sky Series)
	'Evan Saul'[PBR]	see *E.* 'Sundown'
	'Evening Glow' **new**	CWGN MSCN
	'Ferris Wheel' (Carnival Series) **new**	SCob
	'Flame Thrower'[PBR]	CMos CUse CWGN ECtt LSou NLar SPoG
	'Garden Emotion' **new**	MSCN
	'Gemini Pink'	LRHS
	'Green Envy'[PBR]	CBcs CUse CWGN EBee ECtt ELan EPfP EWoo GQue IBoy LRHS MBNS MBel MNrw NLar NSti SCob SKHP SPoG WCAu WCot
	'Green Jewel'	CUse CWGN EBee ECtt EUJe EWoo LRHS MBel MCot MPie NDov NPri SCob WCAu WCot WPtf
	'Greenline' **new**	EBee ECtt
	'Guava Ice'	LLHF MHol NPri
	'Gum Drop'	CUse EBee LRHS SPoG
§	'Harvest Moon'[PBR] (Big Sky Series)	CBcs CHel CHid CMac CUse CWGN EBee ECtt EPfP LBMP LRHS NPri NSti SCob SKHP SMrm SPer SPoG SWvt WCot WFar
	'Heavenly Dream'[PBR]	ECtt ELon
	'Hot Lava'[PBR]	CMos CWGN EBee ECtt LRHS LSou NDov SBod SMrm SPoG
	'Hot Papaya'[PBR] (d)	CBod CWCL CWGN ECtt EWoo IBoy IPot LLHF LSou MBNS MBri MHol SCob SMad SPer WCot
	'Hot Summer'[PBR]	CBcs CHel CPar CUse CWGN EBee EWoo IPot LRHS MAvo MBri NDov NLar SCob SGbt SPoG STPC
	'Irresistible' (d)	CMos CNor CWGN EBee IPot
	'Jupiter' (Big Sky Series)	ECtt
	'Katie Saul'[PBR]	see *E.* 'Summer Sky'
	'Little Angel' **new**	ECtt
	'Mac 'n' Cheese'[PBR]	EBee LRHS SCob WCot
	'Mama Mia'	CPar CUse CWGN ECtt LRHS NLar SGbt SPoG
	Mango Meadowbrite = 'CBG Cone3'	EPfP LRHS
	'Marmalade'[PBR]	CBcs CWGN EBee LLHF LRHS LSou MHol NCGa SCob WCAu
	'Matthew Saul'[PBR]	see *E.* 'Harvest Moon'
	'Maui Sunshine'[PBR]	CUse EBee ECtt SHar
	'Maya Raya' **new**	IBoy
	'Meditation'	CUse EBee WCot
§	'Noam Saul'	LRHS
	Orange Meadowbrite[PBR]	see *E.* 'Art's Pride'
	'Orange Passion' **new**	CWGN ECtt LRHS
	pallida	CArn CBod CKno CNec CSam CSpe EBee ELan EPfP EPri EShb GPoy LEdu LRHS MBel MNFA MWhi NDov NGdn SEND SGSe SKHP SPer SPhx SWvt WJek WWEG XLum
	– 'Hula Dancer'	CHel EAJP NGdn SHar SPhx WWEG
	paradoxa	CArn CHid ELan EPfP EPri GPoy LRHS MCot MMuc NGdn SEND SGSe SPav SPer SPhx SPlb SPtp SWvt WWEG XLum
	– var. ***paradoxa***	EAJP SPtp
	– 'Yellow Mellow'	EPfP
	paradoxa × ***purpurea***	IBoy
	'Piccolino'	CAbP CUse CWGN ECtt LLHF MHol MPie WCot
	'Pink Mist' (Mistical Series)	EBee

Pixie Meadowbrite = 'CBG Cone 2'	CAbP CWGN EBee ECtt GQue IKil MNrw MPie SHar WCot WPGP
§ ***purpurea***	Widely available
- 'Alaska'PBR	IBoy LSou NGdn NLar SGol
- 'Alba'	EPfP LBMP LRHS SHil WCot XLum
- 'Augustkönigin'	CKno EBee LRHS MNrw NDov
- 'Avalanche'PBR	EBee ELon LSou
- 'Baby Swan Pink'	CWld LRHS SHil SPhx
- 'Baby Swan White'	CBod CRos EBee ELon GBin LRHS NLar SHil WCot WFar WWEG
- Bressingham hybrids	CNec EPla EUJe LRHS MRav MWat SMrm SPer WWtn
- 'Catharina'PBR	CWGN EBee ECtt
- 'Coconut Lime'PBR	CWGN EPfP LRHS LSou SPer
- dark-stemmed	LPla
- Doppelganger	see *E. purpurea* 'Doubledecker'
§ - 'Doubledecker'	CHel CWCL EBee EPfP GBin IBoy LLHF MHol MWat NGdn NSoo SGbt SGol SPoG SWat WCAu WFar WHar XLum
- Elton Knight = 'Elbrook'PBR ♀H7	ECtt LRHS MBri SDix SKHP STPC SWvt
- 'Fancy Frills'	ECtt LSou
- 'Fatal Attraction'PBR	Widely available
- 'Firebird'PBR	ECtt LRHS MNrw SCob SGbt
- 'Fragrant Angel'PBR	ECtt ELon EPfP LRHS NLar SKHP SWat SWvt WCot
- 'Green Eyes'	ECtt NLar
- 'Green Jewel'PBR	GBin LSou LSun MAsh MNrw SGbt SGol
- 'Happy Star'	EPla LRHS SHil
- 'Hope'PBR	CBod CPar EBee ECtt LRHS LSou MMHG NLar WCAu
- 'Jade'	CAbP EBee GQue LRHS MBNS MCot NGdn NLar SWat WCot
- 'JS Purple Prairie' **new**	IPot
- 'Kim's Knee High'PBR	CKno CMea COtt ECtt ELan EPfP EWoo GMaP LRHS LSou MBel MCot MPie NGdn NLar SCob SGol SPer SWat SWvt WCot WPGP
- 'Kim's Mop Head'	CKno ECtt ELan EPfP EWes LRHS MCot MRav NGdn NLar NOrc WCot
§ - 'Leuchtstern'	CKno EPfP LRHS NBir NGdn SWat WWEG XLum
- 'Lilliput'PBR	ECtt NLar
- 'Little Giant'	ELon
- 'Little Magnus'PBR	CHel CKno CWld ECtt LRHS MAsh NPri SPoG
- 'Lucky Star'	EPfP LRHS SPhx WCFE
- 'Magnus'	Widely available
- 'Magnus Superior'	CHel EAEE LRHS LSou LSun NDov SHil SPhx WHoo
- 'Maxima'	CAbP ECtt LRHS MNrw
- 'Meringue'PBR	IBoy SCob SPoG
- 'Merlot'PBR	ECtt LRHS LSou
- 'Milkshake'PBR	CWGN EBee LLHF LRHS LSou
- 'Mistral'	EBee LRHS
- 'Pica Bella'	COtt CWGN ECtt EPfP LRHS LSou MSCN
- 'Pink Double Delight'PBR	LRHS MRav NGdn SWat
- 'Pink Glow'	NDov
- 'Pink Poodle'PBR	CPar EBee EPri IBoy
- 'Pink Sorbet'PBR	NLar
- 'Polar Breeze'PBR	LRHS
- (PowWow Series) PowWow White = 'Pas709018' **new**	MBri NPri WCAu
- - PowWow Wild Berry = 'Pas702917'	IPot LRHS MBri NPri NSir SCob
- 'Prairie Splendor'	EPfP LRHS MHol NDov SPhx
- 'Primadonna Deep Rose'	CNec IFro LEdu NGBl SRot SVic
- Primadonna (mixed)	ELon
- 'Primadonna White'	LRHS NPri SRot WWtn
- 'Purity'PBR	ECtt LRHS SPoG WCAu
- 'Razzmatazz'PBR (d)	CAbP CMac COtt EBee ECtt ELan EWes IBoy MGos MHol MNrw MPie NGdn NSti SGol SPer SWat SWvt WCot
- 'Red Baron'	EBee MSCN
- 'Red Knee High'	ECtt MBri
- 'Robert Bloom'	CAbP ECtt GQue NBir SWvt
- 'Rubinglow'	ECtt IBoy MTis NBir NLar SWvt
- 'Rubinstern'	Widely available
- 'Ruby Giant' ♀H7	CCon CKno CUse ECtt ELan EWoo GBin GMaP IBoy LRHS LSou LSun MBel MGos MNFA MPie MTis NEgg NLar NPri NSti SGbt SPer SPoG WCot WWEG
- 'Southern Belle' **new**	IPot SMad
- 'The King'	GKev LRHS NGdn NLar
- 'Tom Thumb' **new**	EBee
- 'Verbesserter Leuchtstern'	NLar
- 'Vintage Wine'PBR	CCon CKno CMac CUse ECtt ELan ELon EPfP EWoo GAbr GMaP GQue ITim LPla LRHS LSun MBel MNrw MTis NEgg NLar NPCo NPri NSti SCob SPer SPoG SWvt WCot
- 'Virgin'PBR	EBee EWoo IPot MAvo NDov NLar
- 'White Lustre'	ECha EPfP SRms
- White Natalie = 'Norwhinat'PBR	EBee
- 'White Swan'	Widely available
'Quills and Thrills' (Prairie Pillars Series)	CWGN ECtt IPot SCob
'Raspberry Tart'	ECtt LRHS LSou
'Raspberry Truffle' **new**	ECtt MSCN WHlf
'Satin Nights' (Prairie Stars Series) **new**	NCGa
(Secret Series) 'Secret Joy' (d) **new**	WHlf
- 'Secret Love' (d) **new**	SCob
- 'Secret Lust' (d)	ECtt
- 'Secret Passion' (d)	CUse CWGN EBee ECtt LRHS NCGa SGbt
- 'Secret Pride' (d) **new**	SCob
simulata	MMuc MNFA SPhx
'Solar Flare' (Big Sky Series)	CPar EBee ECtt LRHS MBri
(Sombrero Series) 'Sombrero Hot Coral'	CUse EBee MAsh
- 'Sombrero Salsa Red'	CUse MAsh SMrm
- 'Sombrero Sandy Yellow'	CUse EBee MAsh
'Starlight'	see *E. purpurea* 'Leuchtstern'
'Strawberry Shortcake'	EBee
'Summer Breeze'	NDov
'Summer Cloud' **new**	CMos
'Summer Cocktail'	IPot SPoG
'Summer Passion'	SGol
'Summer Salsa'	CAbP CUse EUJe LLHF MHol NPCo SMrm WCot
§ 'Summer Sky'PBR (Big Sky Series)	ECtt EPfP LRHS MBNS NLar
'Summer Sun'PBR	LRHS NLar
§ 'Sundown'PBR (Big Sky Series)	CBod CMac CPar CUse EBee ECtt EPfP EPla GMaP IBoy IPot LRHS

	MBNS MWhi NLar SCob SGbt SMrm SPoG WCAu
'Sunrise'[PBR] (Big Sky Series)	Widely available
'Sunset'[PBR] (Big Sky Series)	CAbP ECtt ELon EWes GBin GMaP LLHF LRHS MBNS MBri MGos NEgg SPoG SWat SWvt
'Tangerine Dream'	CUse ECtt EPfP MAsh SBod SCob SPoG WCAu
tennesseensis	CArn SPhx WPGP
- 'Rocky Top'	CBcs EPfP LRHS MNFA SKHP SPhx
'Tiki Torch'[PBR]	CBod CHel CMea CPar CUse ECtt ELon EWes LRHS MAvo NPCo NPri SCob SMrm SPer SPoG WCot
'Tomato Soup'[PBR]	Widely available
'Twilight'[PBR] (Big Sky Series)	CUse ECtt LRHS MBri MNrw NOrc
'White Mist' (Mistical Series)	EBee
'White Spider' **new**	SCob

Echinops (*Asteraceae*)

sp.	WWtn
RCB/TQ H-2	WCot
albus	see *E.* 'Nivalis'
babatagensis	EBee
§ ***bannaticus***	CBcs CBod CSBt NBid SCob
* - 'Albus'	EBee WFar
- 'Blue Globe'	CBod CMHG CUse EBee EHoe ELan EPfP GCal IBoy LRHS LSun MGos MHol NChi NDov NGdn NHol SBod SCob SPhx SPoG WCAu WFar WMnd WWEG XLum
- 'Star Frost'	EBee ELan EPfP GQue LRHS NLar SMrm SPhx
- 'Taplow Blue'	Widely available
commutatus	see *E. exaltatus*
§ ***exaltatus***	LPla NBir
maracandicus	EBee GCal WCot
§ 'Nivalis'	CBre LRHS
* ***perringii***	GCal
ritro misapplied	see *E. bannaticus*
§ ***ritro*** L. 🏆H7	CTri EAJP EBee ECha ECtt ELan ELon EPfP LAst LPal LRHS MArl MBel MCot MMuc MWat NBro NGBl NPri SEND SMrm SPer SPlb SPoG SRms SWvt WBrk WFar XLum XSen
- subsp. ***ruthenicus*** 🏆H7	ELan EWTr MRav
- - 'Platinum Blue'	ECtt ELon LRHS NEgg SPad SPhx SRms
- 'Veitch's Blue' misapplied	see *E. ritro* L.
- 'Veitch's Blue'	Widely available
sphaerocephalus	NBir SMrm SPlb
- 'Arctic Glow'	CBod CMHG CMac CPou EBee ECha ECtt EHoe ELan EPfP GBin GMaP LRHS LSun MBri MCot MWhi NDov NGdn NLar SCob SEND SPer SPlb SWvt WFar WMnd WWtn XLum
terscheckii	LPal
tjanschanicus	LRHS NLar SEND

Echinospartum (*Papilionaceae*)

sp.	CArn

Echium (*Boraginaceae*)

amoenum	MNrw SPhx
bethencourtianum **new**	SVen
'Blue Steeple'	MSCN NLos
boissieri	CCCN ELan WOut
§ ***candicans*** 🏆H1c	CAbb CBcs CCCN CCon CHEx CSde CSpe CTre CUse ECre ELan IBoy IDee NLos SArc SVen
decaisnei	SVen
subsp. ***decaisnei***	
fastuosum	see *E. candicans*
gentianoides	SPlb SVen
italicum	CCCN
lusitanicum	CCCN
onosmifolium	SVen
pininana 🏆H2	CAbb CBcs CBod CDoC CHEx CHid CPla CTre CTsd ECre ELan EUJe EWll IBoy IDee LRHS NLos SArc SChr SEND SIde SMad SPav SPhx SVen
- 'Snow Tower'	CBod CCCN CDTJ CPla ELan LRHS NLos SMad SVen
'Pink Fountain'	CCCN CDTJ CPla ECre ELan LRHS MSCN NLos WHil
rosulatum	CCCN
russicum	CArn CCCN CFis CSpe EBee ELan IBoy IDee MSpe SPad SPav SPhx SPlb WCot
strictum	CCCN
sventenii	SPlb
tuberculatum	SPhx WMoo
virescens	SVen
vulgare	CArn CCCN CHab CWld ELan ENfk MHer MNHC NLar NMir NPri SBch SIde WHer WHfH WJek WOut WPnn WSFF
- 'Blue Bedder' 🏆H7	SPhx WCot WSFF
- Drake's form	SPhx
webbii	MMHG SVen
wildpretii 🏆H1c	CCCN CCon CDTJ CPla ECre ELan EUJe MHin NLos SIgm SPlb SVen
- subsp. ***wildpretii***	SPav

Edgeworthia (*Thymelaeaceae*)

§ ***chrysantha***	CBcs CExl CHGN CJun EBee ELan EPfP ETwe GBin LPal LRHS MGos MTPN NLar SBig SChF SHil SPoG
I - 'Grandiflora'	CJun EBee GBin LRHS MBri MGos MPkF NLar SMad WPGP
§ - 'Red Dragon'	CJun NLar
- f. ***rubra*** hort.	see *E. chrysantha* 'Red Dragon'
papyrifera	see *E. chrysantha*

Edraianthus (*Campanulaceae*)

croaticus	see *E. graminifolius*
dalmaticus	EPot
dinaricus	EPot
§ ***graminifolius***	XLum
- subsp. ***graminifolius***	LLHF
owerinianus	LLHF WAbe
pilosulus **new**	WAbe
§ ***pumilio*** 🏆H5	CPBP EPot GKev NSla SIgm SRms WAbe
§ ***serpyllifolius***	EPot GKev NSla
- 'Major'	WAbe
tenuifolius	WIce
- 'Albus'	GKev

Egeria (*Hydrocharitaceae*)

§ ***densa***	CBen

Ehrendorferia (*Papaveraceae*)

§ ***chrysantha***	SIgm

Ehretia (*Boraginaceae*)

anacua	CBcs
dicksonii	CBcs CHEx IVic
rigida	SPlb

Eichhornia (*Pontederiaceae*)

crassipes	CBAq CBen MSKA MWts
- 'Major'	NPer

Elaeagnus (*Elaeagnaceae*)

	angustifolia	CAco CAgr CBcs CDul EPfP MCoo MGos NLar SCob SPer SRms
	- Caspica Group	see *E.* 'Quicksilver'
	argentea Pursh	see *E. commutata*
§	***commutata***	CBcs CDul CMac ECrN EHoe EPfP MBlu MWhi NLar SPer WHar
	- 'Zempin'	EPfP
§	× ***ebbingei*** ♀H5	Widely available
	- 'Coastal Gold' (v)	CBcs CDoC CDul COtt CSde EBee EPfP LBMP LRHS MAsh MGos MJak SGol SLim SRms WFar WRHF
I	- 'Compacta'	LRHS LSou SHil
	- 'Gilt Edge' (v) ♀H5	Widely available
	- Gold Splash	CDoC CMac EPfP LRHS SGol SPoG
	= 'Lannou' (v)	SWvt
	- 'Limelight' (v)	Widely available
	- 'Moonlight'	EPfP LRHS MAsh
	- 'Salcombe Seedling'	CCCN
	- 'Viveleg'PBR (v)	EPfP LRHS MBri SCob SEWo SHil
	glabra	GGal
	- 'Reflexa'	see *E.* × *reflexa*
	macrophylla	CMac EBee EPfP
	multiflora	CDoC CDul SPer WPGP
	- 'Sweet Scarlet' new	CAgr
	parvifolia	CCCN
	pungens 'Argenteovariegata'	see *E. pungens* 'Variegata'
	- 'Aureovariegata'	see *E. pungens* 'Maculata'
	- 'Dicksonii' (v)	LRHS MAsh NLar SLon SPer SRms
	- 'Forest Gold' (v)	ELan EPfP LRHS MAsh
	- 'Frederici' (v)	CBcs CDoC CMac EBee EHoe ELan LAst LBMP LRHS MAsh MRav NLar SCob SPer SPoG SWvt WRHF
	- 'Goldrim' (v)	EPfP
	- 'Hosoba-fukurin' (v)	EBee ELan EPla LBuc LRHS MAsh NLar SLon
§	- 'Maculata' (v)	Widely available
§	- 'Variegata' (v)	CBcs CMac NBir SPer
§	'Quicksilver'	Widely available
§	× ***reflexa***	WPGP
	× ***submacrophylla***	see *E.* × *ebbingei*
	umbellata	CAco CBcs CExl CTho EPfP LEdu MBlu NLar SPer WPat WSHC
	- CWJ 12835 new	WCru
	- 'Amber' (F)	CAgr
	- 'Big Red' (F)	CAgr
	- var. ***borealis*** 'Polar Lights'	NLar
	- 'Brilliant Rose' (F)	CAgr
	- 'Garnet' (F)	CAgr
	- 'Hidden Springs' (F)	CAgr
	- 'Jewel' (F)	CAgr
	- 'Late Scarlet' (F)	CAgr
	- 'Newgate' (F)	CAgr
	- 'Red Cascade' (F)	CAgr LEdu
	- 'Ruby' (F)	CAgr LEdu
	- 'Sweet 'n' Tart' (F)	CAgr

Elaeocarpus (*Elaeocarpaceae*)

sylvestris var. ***ellipticus***	LEdu WPGP

Elatostema (*Urticaceae*)

rugosum	CHEx

elderberry see *Sambucus nigra*

Elegia (*Restionaceae*)

capensis	CAbb CBod CCCN CCon CDTJ CDoC CExl CHEx CHel CTre NLos SPlb SPoG WPGP
cuspidata	NLos
elephantina	CTre NLos
equisetacea	CTre NLos
filacea	NLos
macrocarpa	CCCN NLos SPlb
spathacea	CCon
tectorum ♀H2	CAbb CCon CHEx CHel CTre EAEE LRHS MGos NLos SGSe SHDw SPlb
- dwarf	CTre

Eleocharis (*Cyperaceae*)

acicularis	CBAq CWat MSKA
parvula	MSKA

Eleorchis (*Orchidaceae*)

japonica	GKev

Elettaria (*Zingiberaceae*)

cardamomum	CArn EOHP EShb GPoy LEdu SPre WJek

Eleutherococcus (*Araliaceae*)

sp.	CArn
divaricatus B&SWJ 5027 new	WCru
giraldii BWJ 8091 new	WCru
hypoleucus B&SWJ 5532	WCru
nakaianus B&SWJ 5027	WCru
pictus	see *Kalopanax septemlobus*
senticosus	GCal GPoy
- B&SWJ 4568	WCru
septemlobus	see *Kalopanax septemlobus*
sessiliflorus B&SWJ 4528 new	WCru
- B&SWJ 8457	WCru
- B&SWJ 8618	WCru
sieboldianus	MRav SEND
- 'Variegatus' (v)	CBcs CSpe EBee EHoe ELan ELon EPfP ESwi EUJe GBin LAst LRHS MRav NLar WCFE WHer WSHC WWFP
trifoliatus RWJ 10108	WCru

Elingamita (*Primulaceae*)

johnsonii	ECou

Elisena (*Amaryllidaceae*)

longipetala	see *Hymenocallis longipetala*

Elliottia (*Ericaceae*)

pyroliflora	WAbe

Ellisiophyllum (*Plantaginaceae*)

pinnatum	SBrt
- B&SWJ 197	CDes LEdu WCru WPGP

Elmera (*Saxifragaceae*)

racemosa	EPau

Elodea (*Hydrocharitaceae*)

canadensis	CBAq MSKA NBir WMAq
densa	see *Egeria densa*

Elsholtzia (*Lamiaceae*)

fruticosa	CArn
stauntonii	CArn CBcs EBee ECha ELan GPoy IDee IVic LRHS MHer NLar SBch SBrt SLon SPer SRms SWvt WBor WJek XLum

Elymus (*Poaceae*)

arenarius	see *Leymus arenarius*
canadensis	EHoe EPPr
- f. ***glaucifolius***	CCon
cinereus from Washington State, USA	WPGP
glaucus misapplied	see *E. hispidus*
§ ***hispidus*** ♀H6	CBod CSpe EPPr MBlu MBri MLHP NDov SPer WCFE WCot
§ ***magellanicus***	Widely available
- 'Blue Sword'	ELan LRHS MBri MGos SHil SLon SRkn SRms
riparius	EPPr
sibiricus	EPPr
villosus	EPPr
- var. ***arkansanus***	EPPr
virginicus	EBee EPPr

Embothrium ✿ (*Proteaceae*)

coccineum	CBcs CFil CPne EPfP GKin LSou MGil MMuc SEND SPlb WPGP WPat
* - var. ***andina*** new	MGil
- Lanceolatum Group	CAby CBcs CDoC CEnd CHel CHll CTsd ELon EPfP EUJe GKin LRHS MBlu MPkF SArc SLim SPer SSpi SSta SWvt WAbe WBor WPat
- - 'Inca Flame'	CCCN EPfP LRHS MAsh SPoG SWvt
- - 'Ñorquinco'	CBcs GGal WCru
- Longifolium Group	CCCN EPfP IBlr WPGP

Emmenopterys (*Rubiaceae*)

henryi	CBcs EPfP IArd MBlu NLar SMad WCot WPGP

Empetrum (*Ericaceae*)

nigrum	GPoy WThu
rubrum	MGil

Empodium (*Hypoxidaceae*)

namaquensis new	NRog
plicatum	NRog

Encephalartos ✿ (*Zamiaceae*)

altensteinii	CBrP LPal
caffer	CBrP
cycadifolius	CBrP
ferox	CBrP LPal
horridus	CBrP
lanatus	CBrP
lebomboensis	CBrP LPal
lehmannii	CBrP LPal
natalensis	CBrP LPal
senticosus	LPal
villosus	CBrP LPal

Endymion see *Hyacinthoides*

Enkianthus ✿ (*Ericaceae*)

campanulatus ♀H5	Widely available
- var. ***campanulatus*** f. ***albiflorus***	CBcs GKin IVic MMuc NLar
I - 'Hollandia'	GKin MMuc
I - 'Pagoda'	IArd MBri
- var. ***palibinii***	CAbP EPfP GGGa GKin LRHS MAsh NLar SSpi
- 'Red Bells'	CDoC CDul EPfP GBin GKin LRHS MAsh MMuc NLar SSta SWvt WFar
- 'Red Velvet'	CBcs GKin NLar
- 'Ruby Glow'	IVic
- 'Showy Lantern' new	NLar
- var. ***sikokianus***	EPfP GGGa GKin NLar
- 'Sinsetu' new	NLar
* - 'Variegatus' (v)	LRHS MAsh
- 'Venus'	CBcs GKin NLar
- 'Victoria'	CBcs NLar
- 'Wallaby'	CBcs LRHS NLar WAbe
cernuus f. ***rubens*** ♀H5	CBcs EPfP GBin GGGa GKin ITim NLar
chinensis	CAbP CBcs EPfP GGGa LRHS MAsh MBri MMuc
deflexus	GGGa LRHS MAsh NLar SSpi WPGP
perulatus ♀H5	CBcs CDul CMac GKin LRHS MGil MGos MMuc NLar SPer SSpi SSta WFar
serrulatus	GGGa

Ensete (*Musaceae*)

gilletii	XBlo
- from Malawi	XBlo
- from Mozambique	XBlo
glaucum	CDTJ CDoC GCal LPal
§ ***ventricosum*** ♀H1c	CCCN CDTJ CDoC CHll EUJe NLos SArc SEND XBlo
§ - 'Maurelii' ♀H1c	CCCN CDTJ CDoC CHEx CHel CHll CSpe ESwi EUJe LPal NLos NPla NSoo SArc SDix SEND SPer SPoG WCot WPGP
- 'Rubrum'	see *E. ventricosum* 'Maurelii'
- 'Tandarra Red'	CAbb CDoC ESwi

Entelea (*Malvaceae*)

arborescens	CHEx ECou EShb SPlb

Eomecon (*Papaveraceae*)

chionantha	CCon CDes CExl CHEx CSam CSpe CWCL GAbr GBuc GCal GCra GEdr LEdu MLHP MRav NBid SBrt WCru WHer WMoo WPGP WWEG XLum

Epacris (*Ericaceae*)

impressa	WAbe
microphylla	ITim
serpyllifolia	WThu

Ephedra (*Ephedraceae*)

sp.	SArc
andina new	IMou
chilensis	MGil XLum
distachya	GPoy
equisetina	CArn IFro
fedtschenkoi	XSen

gerardiana IFro LRHS
– var. ***sikkimensis*** GEdr WOld XLum
intermedia RCB/TQ K-1 WCot
§ ***major*** XSen
minuta MSCN
monosperma GEdr WThu
nebrodensis see *E. major*
nevadensis CArn GPoy WHfH
sinica CArn GPoy
viridis CArn XSen

Epigaea (*Ericaceae*)

asiatica WAbe
gaultherioides GGGa

Epilobium (*Onagraceae*)

angustifolium see *Chamaenerion angustifolium*
– f. ***leucanthum*** see *Chamaenerion angustifolium* 'Album'
californicum misapplied see *Zauschneria californica*
canum see *Zauschneria californica* subsp. *cana*
dodonaei see *Chamaenerion dodonaei*
fleischeri see *Chamaenerion fleischeri*
garrettii see *Zauschneria californica* subsp. *garrettii*
glabellum misapplied MSCN NSla SEND WCFE
glabellum G. Forst. CSpe MMuc WKif
hirsutum 'Album' EWTr GMaP MHer
microphyllum see *Zauschneria californica* subsp. *cana*
rosmarinifolium see *Chamaenerion dodonaei*
septentrionale see *Zauschneria septentrionalis*
villosum see *Zauschneria californica* subsp. *mexicana*

Epimedium ✿ (*Berberidaceae*)

Chen Yi 8 from Jian Xi, China WCot
from Yunnan, China CDes CLAP CPom IFoB WPGP
from Jian Xi, China GEdr
acuminatum CCon CCse CElw CFil CLAP EFEx GEdr LEdu MNrw NLar NMyG WMoo WPGP WSHC XPou
– L 575 CDes CElw CExl CFil
– 'Galaxy' CDes CExl CFil CJun CLAP CMil LEdu WPGP
– 'Night Mistress' XPou
– 'Quinquin' IMou
– yellow-flowered CC 011415 XPou
'Akakage' CExl CLAP GBuc
'Akebono' Widely available
Alabaster = 'Conalba' SGol
alpinum CFil CFis CMac EBee EPPr EWTr GKev GLog IFro LEdu LRHS SHar SKHP SPer WMoo XLum
'Amanogawa' CDes CJun CMil CPom GEdr IFoB LEdu WPGP
'Amber Queen'PBR CHel CLAP CMil EBee EPfP GEdr IFoB IGor LEdu LLHF LLWG LSun MMHG NCGa NHar NPCo NSti NWad SCob SMHy SMrm SPhx WCAu WCot WFar
'Anju' GEdr
'Arctic Wings'PBR CLAP CMil EPfP GEdr NGdn
'Asiatic Hybrid' CJun CLAP WHal
'Autumn Raspberry' CJun
baojingense new XPou
'Beni-goromo' GEdr
'Beni-kujaku' CDes CJun CLAP EBee GEdr IFoB
'Beni-yushima' GEdr
'Black Sea' CElw CJun CLAP CSpe EPPr EPot GBuc IFoB IGor IMou MNrw NCGa SCob SGol XPou
borealiguizhouense CC 020711 XPou
brachyrrhizum CDes CExl CJun CMil CPom LLHF NLar WPGP
– CPC 940447 XPou
– 'Elfin Magic' IFoB
brevicornu CPom GEdr SKHP WPGP
– Og 82.010 CExl CFil CJun XPou
– Og 88.010 CJun XPou
'Buckland Spider' CDes CLAP EBee EPPr GEdr IFoB MNrw WPGP
campanulatum LLHF
– Og 93.087 CExl CFil CJun
× ***cantabrigiense*** CBro CMac CTal ECtt EPla ESwi GBuc GEdr GKev GMaP MRav NLar SRms XLum
chlorandrum CAby IFoB LEdu WPGP
– Og 93.003 XPou
– Og 94.003 CDes EBee
creeping yellow EBee LSou
cremeum see *E. grandiflorum* subsp. *koreanum*
davidii CDes CFil EPPr GEdr LEdu MNrw NLar NMyG SKHP WHal WPGP WSHC
– CPC 960079 CExl EBee XPou
– EMR 4125 CElw CExl CJun CLAP NCGa XPou
– dwarf CExl
dewuense XPou
diphyllum CExl CFil CPom CTsd EBee GEdr IFoB IVic WHal WPGP XPou
dolichostemon CElw CLAP IFoB
– Og 81.010 CJun XPou
'Domino' XPou
ecalcaratum CDes CLAP CMil CPom EBee LEdu MNrw WPGP
– Og 93.082 CExl CJun XPou
– spurred XPou
'Egret' new CDes
elongatum CLAP
– CC 12906 XPou
'Emperor' see *E.* 'Phoenix'
'Enchantress' CElw CJun CLAP CMil CPom CTal EWTr EWld IFoB MCot MNrw NLar WHal WHoo
epsteinii CAby CDes CFil CLAP CMil CTal EBee EPPr GEdr IFoB LEdu LLHF MNrw SKHP WCot WPGP
– CPC 940347 CExl CJun IVic XPou
fangii CExl IFoB SKHP
– CC 022008 XPou
fargesii CDes CExl CFil EBee GEdr IFoB LEdu MNrw NCGa NMyG WPGP
– Og 93.057 CTal XPou
– 'Pink Constellation' CDes CExl CFil CJun CPom GEdr ITim LEdu SBch WPGP XPou
'Fire Dragon'PBR CLAP EPfP GEdr IFoB LLHF MAvo MBNS NMyG
flavum CFil EBee SKHP WPGP
– Og 92.036 CDes CExl CJun XPou
'Flowers of Sulphur'PBR CLAP EBee EPfP GEdr
franchetii CCon CExl GEdr IFoB SKHP
– 'Brimstone Butterfly' CDes CExl CFis CJun EPPr GEdr SKHP WCot WPGP XPou

	Name	Suppliers
	'Fukujuji'	CLAP GEdr
	'Genpei'	GEdr
	'Golden Eagle'	CDes CExl CJun CPom EBee EWes MNrw
§	***grandiflorum*** 🏆H5	CBcs CBod CElw CPla CTri ELan ELon EPfP EWTr GBuc GEdr GLog NBir NLar NMyG SCob SPer WPnP WWEG
	- 'Akagiza Kura'	XPou
	- 'Album'	CLAP
	- 'Bandit'	GEdr IFoB
	- 'Beni-chidori'	CJun CLAP GEdr
	- 'Circe'	XPou
	- 'Crimson Beauty'	CJun CLAP ECha WHal WHoo WSHC
	- 'Crimson Queen'	EBee IFoB LEdu MNrw WPGP
	- f. ***flavescens*** Aomori forms	XPou
	- - Number 1 CC 940549	XPou
	- 'Freya'	CDes CExl IFoB WSHC XPou
§	- var. ***higoense***	CJun GEdr WHal WPGP XPou
	- - 'Saturn' **new**	CDes
	- 'Jennie Maillard'	WCot
	- 'Koji'	CLAP EBee IFoB NLar WSHC
§	- subsp. ***koreanum***	CLAP CPla ECha EFEx GEdr IFoB
	- 'La Rocaille'	CLAP EBee EWld XPou
	- lilac-flowered	CLAP WHal
	- lilac-pink-flowered	SMHy
	- 'Lilafee'	Widely available
	- 'Mount Kitadake'	CLAP WAbe
	- 'Mugawa-gen-pan'	XPou
	- 'Nanum' 🏆H5	CDes CJun CPBP CSpe EBee ECho GBuc MNrw NHar SKHP WAbe WPGP WThu
	- pink-flowered	MCot
	- 'Purple Prince'	CDes CExl CLAP CTal EBee WPGP XPou
	- 'Queen Esta'	CDes CExl CJun CLAP CMil EBee IFoB LEdu MNrw WPGP WSHC XPou
	- 'Red Beauty'	CBod CHel CLAP CWCL ELan ELon EWTr GBin GEdr IFoB LRHS LSou MAvo MCot MNrw WGrn WGwG
	- 'Red Queen' **new**	CMac
	- 'Rose Queen' 🏆H5	CAby CDes CHel CSam ECha ELan ELon EPfP EPla EThi GMaP LBMP LRHS MBri MRav NBir NMyG NSti SCob SWvt WFar WMoo
	- 'Roseum'	CLAP CMac CMil ESwi IFoB MMoz SGSe SWvt
	- 'Rubinkrone'	GBuc GEdr GMaP IMou MNrw
	- 'Sirius'	CJun CLAP MNrw
	- f. ***violaceum***	CJun CLAP EBee WCFE WSHC
	- 'White Beauty'	WSHC
	- 'White Queen' 🏆H5	CCon CElw CJun EBee EPPr IFoB LLHF SMHy WCot WHal
	- 'Wildside Red'	CJun
	- 'Yellow Princess'	CDes CJun CLAP EBee XPou
	- 'Yubae'	GEdr IFoB
	'Hagoromo'	GEdr
	'Hakubai'	GEdr
	'Harugasumi'	GEdr
	'Heavenly Purple'	CJun
	higoense	see *E. grandiflorum* var. *higoense*
	'Hina Matsuri' **new**	GEdr
	hunanense	XPou
	ilicifolium	CDes CFil CJun EBee LEdu WPGP
	- Og 93.020	XPou
	'Jean O'Neill'	CDes CLAP EBee LEdu SGSe WCot WPGP
	'Jenny Pym'	EBee
	'Kaguyahime'	CJun CMil EPPr IFoB WSHC
	'King Prawn'	CDes
	'Kodai Murasaki' **new**	XPou
	'Koki'	GEdr
	koreanum 'Harold Epstein'	XPou
	'Korin' **new**	XPou
	'Kotobuki'	GEdr XPou
	latisepalum	CDes CLAP CPne CPom CTal EBee GEdr LEdu MNrw NCGa WCot WPGP
	- Og 91.002	CJun
	- Og 93.009	XPou
	'Lemon Meringue Pie'	CJun
	leptorrhizum	CElw CExl CFil CJun CLAP EBee EPPr EWTr EWld GBuc GEdr IFoB IVic LEdu MNFA MNrw NCGa NHar NLar NMyG SKHP WCot WHal
	- Og Y.44	CExl WSHC XPou
	- 'Mariko'	CDes CExl CJun CMil CPom LEdu WPGP XPou
	lishihchenii	CDes CExl CFil CJun CTal GEdr WPGP
	- CC 95007	XPou
	- Og 93.024	XPou
	'Little Shrimp'	CJun CTal CTri EBee GMaP LLHF LRHS MNFA MNrw NLar WSHC
	macranthum	see *E. grandiflorum*
	macrosepalum	GEdr XPou
	membranaceum	CAby CCon CFil CMil EBee GEdr GKev LEdu LLHF NCGa SKHP WHal WPGP XPou
	- Og 93.047	CExl CJun EPPr GEdr
	mikinorii	CExl
	- CC 990001	XPou
*	***milianthemum*** **new**	GEdr
	'Milky Way' **new**	CDes
	'Mine-no-fubuki'	GEdr
	'Myojo' **new**	GEdr
	myrianthum	CDes CJun LEdu WPGP XPou
	ogisui	CAby CDes CElw CLAP CMil CPom IFoB LEdu SMHy WPGP WThu
	- Og 91.001	CExl CFil CJun EBee MNrw SKHP XPou
§	× ***omeiense*** 'Akame'	CDes CExl CJun CMil EPPr WPGP XPou
	- 'Emei Shan'	see *E.* × *omeiense* 'Akame'
	- 'Myriad Years'	XPou
	- 'Pale Fire Sibling'	CDes CJun
	- 'Stormcloud'	CDes CElw CExl CFil CJun CMil CPom EBee EPPr MNrw WPGP XPou
	pauciflorum	CFil EBee EPPr EWTr GEdr LEdu NHar NMyG WPGP XPou
	- Og 92.123	CExl CJun CLAP
	× ***perralchicum***	CBro CJun CTri ECha GKev IFro MLHP NLar WSHC
	- 'Fröhnleiten'	Widely available
	- 'Lichtenberg'	CDes EBee XPou
	- 'Wisley'	CElw CJun CSam EWes
	perralderianum	CHEx CMac CSam CTal EPot GMaP MBel MCot MNrw SRms WHal WPnP XLum
	- 'Weihenstephan'	LRHS MMoz WPnP
§	'Phoenix'	CDes CExl EBee WCot WPGP

	'Pink Champagne'	CDes EPfP GEdr LEdu SMrm WCot WFar
	'Pink Elf'PBR	CLAP CMil CMos ECGP EPfP EWoo GEdr IFoB LLHF MNrw MPie NCGa NLar NOrc NSti SRms WCAu WCot WFar WHil
	pinnatum	ECho GMaP WHal XLum
§	- subsp. ***colchicum*** 🏆H7	CJun CLAP CWCL ELan EPfP EWTr GBuc GLog LEdu LRHS MCot MRav NGdn NLar SCob SDix SPer WCot WFar WPnP XEll
	- - L 321	CDes GEdr WPGP
	- ***elegans***	see *E. pinnatum* subsp. *colchicum*
	platypetalum	CFil CLAP CMil SBrt WCot WPGP
	- Og 93.085	CExl CJun XPou
	pubescens	IFoB
	- Og 91.003	CExl CFil CJun WPGP
	pubigerum	CDes CJun CSam EAEE EWTr GAbr GBuc GEdr IFro LEdu LRHS MBri MNFA NLar NMyG NPCo SEND SWvt WCAu WHal XEll XPou
	reticulatum	GEdr
	rhizomatosum	EPPr GEdr GMaP LLHF NMyG WPGP WSHC
	- Og 92.114	CJun WCot XPou
	× ***rubrum*** 🏆H7	Widely available
	- 'Galadriel' new	GBin
	- 'Sweetheart' new	GEdr
	sagittatum	CLAP EFEx
	- 'Warlord'	XPou
	'Sakura-maru'	GEdr
	'Sasaki'	CLAP EWTr GBin GBuc IFoB MNrw NLar XEll
	sempervirens	CJun CLAP WHal
	- 'Cream Sickle'	GEdr
	- 'Okuda's White'	CDes EBee WPGP
	- var. ***sempervirens***	CLAP
	- 'Violet Queen' new	XPou
	- violet-flowered new	CDes
	- 'White Purity'	XPou
	× ***setosum***	CJun WHal
	'Shiho'	EBee GBin GEdr MNrw
	shuichengense CC 030175	XPou
	'Sphinx Twinkler'	see *E.* 'Spine Tingler'
§	'Spine Tingler'	CHel CMil ESwi EUJe GBin GEdr LEdu MSCN NPCo SCob SPoG WCot XPou
	'Spinners' new	EBee
	'Starcloud'	GBin LRHS WGrn
	stellulatum	GEdr
	- long-leaved CC 970051	XPou
	- 'Wudang Star'	CDes CExl CFil CJun CLAP CMil CPom EWes IFoB IMou IVic WPGP XPou
	- 'Yukiko'	XPou
	sutchuenense CC 990394	XPou
	'Suzuka'	GEdr LEdu
	'Tama-no-genpei'	CDes CJun CPom GEdr IFoB LEdu WPGP
	'Tanima-no-yuki'	GEdr
	'The Giant'	XPou
	'Tokiwa-gozen'	GEdr
	'Totnes Turbo'	CDes
	× ***versicolor***	CExl SCob
	- 'Cherry Tart'	CLAP
	- 'Cupreum'	CJun CLAP EBee GBuc LRHS
§	- 'Discolor'	CAby CDes CElw CFis CLAP CPom CTal ECha EPPr NBir SMHy XPou
	- 'Neosulphureum'	CBro CDes CLAP EPPr WPGP WSHC WThu XPou
	- 'Sulphureum' 🏆H7	Widely available
	- 'Versicolor'	see *E.* × *versicolor* 'Discolor'
	× ***warleyense***	Widely available
	- 'Orangekönigin'	CElw CWCL EBee ELon EPfP GBin GMaP IFoB LAst LBMP LRHS MBri MMuc MNFA MNrw MRav NBro NLar NMyG NSti SEND SGol WBor WCAu WFar WHal WPnP XLum
	'William Stearn'	CDes CExl CJun CLAP GEdr XPou
	wushanense	CFil CLAP EPPr EWTr GEdr LEdu XPou
	- CC 014193	XPou
	- Og 93.019	CExl CJun XPou
	- 'Caramel'	CAby CDes CExl CJun CLAP CMil CPom EBee GEdr IFoB LEdu SKHP WPGP WSHC XPou
	- spiny-leaved CC 014631	XPou
	'Yachimata-hime'	GEdr
	'Yōkihi'	GEdr XPou
	× ***youngianum***	IFoB NEgg
	- 'Beni-kujaku' new	XPou
	- 'Merlin'	CElw CJun CLAP CMil EBee EPfP GBuc GEdr IFoB MBri NSti WHal WSHC XPou
	- 'Niveum' 🏆H5	Widely available
	- 'Roseum'	CBcs CElw CTal CWCL EHoe ELon EPfP EShb GAbr GKev GKin IFoB IKil LPal LRHS MBel MCot MRav NCGa NLar NSti SCob SGSe SKHP SPer SPlb SPoG SWvt WGwG WPnP
	- 'Shikinomai'	CExl CJun CLAP EPPr EPot
	- 'Tamabotan'	CDes CLAP CMil EBee GEdr MNrw MRav XPou
§	- 'Typicum'	CElw CLAP GBuc WSHC
	- 'Yenomoto'	CJun CLAP
	- 'Youngianum'	see *E.* × *youngianum* 'Typicum'
	zhushanense	CDes CTal GEdr LEdu WCot
	- CC 022403 new	XPou

Epipactis (*Orchidaceae*)

	Catalina gx	GEdr
	gigantea	CAvo CBro CCon EBee ECha ECho ELan GBin GEdr GKev LRHS MHer MNrw MRav NDav WPGP
	gigantea × ***veratrifolia***	see *E.* Lowland Legacy gx
	helleborine	WHer
§	**Lowland Legacy gx**	GEdr
	- 'Edelstein'	MNrw
	- 'Frankfurt'	GEdr
	palustris	GEdr LRHS MNrw NDav WHer WPnP
	Passionata gx Light Royals Group new	GEdr
	royleana	GEdr
	Sabine gx	CAby GEdr
	- 'Frankfurt'	EWld MNrw
	thunbergii	EFEx GEdr
	- yellow-flowered	GEdr

Epipremnum (*Araceae*)

pinnatum 'Marble Queen' (v)	XBlo

Episcia (*Gesneriaceae*)

dianthiflora	WDib
'San Miguel'	WDib

Equisetum ✿ (*Equisetaceae*)

- ***arvense*** CArn
- 'Bandit' (v) CDes CNat MAvo SMad WMoo
- × ***bowmanii*** CNat
- * ***camtschatcense*** EWay SArc SBig SMad SPlb XLum
- × ***dycei*** CNat
- ***fluviatile*** CNat MSKA
- ***giganteum*** LLWG
- ***hyemale*** CBAq CBen CKno EHoe EWay GQue LRHS MMuc MSKA MWts NOak NPer NSti SArc SCob SPlb WCot WMoo WWtn XLum
- § - var. ***affine*** CNat CRow EBee ELan EPla EWll LEdu MSKA SCob WMAq
- - var. ***robustum*** see *E. hyemale* var. *affine*
- ***pratense*** CNat
- ***ramosissimum*** var. ***japonicum*** LEdu MMuc NLos NPla SCob SWat
- ***robustum*** SCob
- ***scirpoides*** CBAq EBee EFer EHoe EWay MSKA MWts NPer NWad SPlb SWat WMAq WMoo XLum
- ***telmateia*** LEdu SMad
- ***variegatum*** EBee EFer

Eragrostis (*Poaceae*)

- RCB/Arg S-7 EBee WCot
- ***airoides*** misapplied see *Agrostis montevidensis*
- ***airoides*** ambig. CBod WMoo
- ***chloromelas*** EPPr
- ***curvula*** CBod CElw CKno CMea CWCL ECha EHoe EPPr GAbr LRHS MAvo MBel MRav MWhi NBir NChi NGdn NOak NWsh SEND SGSe SMrm SPhx WMoo XLum
- - S&SH 10 CDes CElw EPPr SMHy WPGP
- - 'Totnes Burgundy' CAby CBod CDes CExl CKno CWCL EBee ECha EPPr EPfP LRHS MAvo MNrw SMea SPhx SRms WMoo WPGP
- ***elliottii*** CBod CKno ECha EPPr EShb LBMP LRHS MAvo NWsh SEND SHDw SMea SMrm WWEG
- - 'Wind Dancer' CSde EPPr WHar
- ***prolifera*** IMou
- 'Silver Needles' see *Agrostis canina* 'Silver Needles'
- ***spectabilis*** CBod CCon CKno CSBt CSde EBee ELan EPfP LBMP MWhi NGdn NLar NWsh SDix SGSe SMea SMrm WMoo XLum
- ***trichodes*** CBod CCon CKno EBee EHoe LEdu MAvo NWsh SGSe SMea SMrm WCot

Eranthemum (*Acanthaceae*)

- ***pulchellum*** ♀H1b ECre

Eranthis (*Ranunculaceae*)

- ***cilicica*** see *E. hyemalis* Cilicica Group
- § ***hyemalis*** ♀H5 CBro CMea CSpe CTca ECho ELan ELon EPfP GBin GKev LAma LRHS MCot MWat SDeJ SPhx SWvt WBor WCot WHoo WShi
- § - Cilicica Group CBro ECho ELan EPot GEdr GKev GMaP IFro LRHS NLar SDeJ SPer SPhx WCot WShi
- - 'Flore Pleno' (d) ECho EPot GEdr
- - 'Grünling' ECho EPot
- - 'Orange Glow' ECho GEdr
- - 'Schwefelglanz' CAvo CBro ECho EPot GEdr
- § - Tubergenii Group CBro ECho EPot
- - - 'Guinea Gold' ♀H5 CTca ECho
- ***pinnatifida*** EFEx GEdr WCru
- × ***tubergenii*** see *E. hyemalis* Tubergenii Group

Ercilla (*Phytolaccaceae*)

- ***volubilis*** CBod CExl CFil CHel CRHN CWGN EPfP GCal IDee LRHS MGil SEND WCru WSHC

Eremophila (*Scrophulariaceae*)

- § ***debilis*** ECou
- ***glabra*** SVen
- 'Kilbara Carpet' ECou
- ***longifolia*** SPlb
- ***maculata*** ECou
- - pale pink-flowered MOWG
- - 'Peaches and Cream' MOWG
- 'Yellow Trumpet' ECou

Eremostachys (*Lamiaceae*)

- ***laciniata*** XSen

Eremurus (*Asphodelaceae*)

- ***altaicus*** JCA 0.443.809 WCot
- 'Brutus' EBee
- ***bungei*** see *E. stenophyllus* subsp. *stenophyllus*
- ***cristatus*** JCA 0.444.029 WCot
- 'Disco' EBee
- 'Emmy Ro' EBee LAma LRHS NLar WCot
- 'Foxtrot' EBee
- ***fuscus*** JCA 0.444.043 WCot
- 'Grace' LAma NLar
- 'Helena' LAma LRHS
- ***himalaicus*** CAvo CBro CCon EBee ELan EPot ERCP GBin GKev LAma LRHS MCot MHer NLar SCob SDeJ SPer SPhx
- 'Image' EBee
- × ***isabellinus*** 'Cleopatra' CAvo CBod CWCL EBee EPfP EPot ERCP GKev GMaP LAma LRHS MBNS MBel MGos MHer SCob SDeJ SPer SPhx
- - 'Obelisk' EBee LAma LRHS
- - 'Pinokkio' CAvo CWCL EBee EPot GKev LAma MHer SDeJ
- - Ruiter hybrids CBod ELan EPfP GKev GMaP LAma LAst LRHS MCot MGos MNrw NLar SEND SPer
- - Shelford hybrids CAvo CBcs ELan GKev LAma SDeJ SPhx
- - 'Tropical Dream' CAvo MAvo
- 'Jeanne-Claire' LAma LRHS NLar
- 'Joanna' LAma LRHS NLar
- ***lactiflorus*** WCot
- 'Line Dance' EBee LAma
- 'Luca Ro' EBee NLar
- 'Moneymaker' CAvo CWCL EBee EPot LAma
- 'Oase' EBee LAma LRHS SDeJ
- 'Paradiso' EBee
- ***regelii*** JCA 444.083 WCot
- 'Rexona' LAma MBNS SDeJ
- ***robustus*** ♀H7 CAvo CBcs CBro CCon CWCL ELan EPot ERCP LAma LRHS MAvo MHer MNrw NLar SDeJ SPer SPhx SPlb

'Roford'	MNrw
'Romance'	EBee EPot ERCP GKev LAma MBNS MBel MNrw NLar SCob SDeJ
'Rumba'	EBee LAma
'Samba'	LAma
stenophyllus ♀H6	CAvo CBod CBro CTri CWCL EPot ERCP GBin GKev LRHS MPkF NLar SDeJ SPhx SPoG WCot
§ - subsp. ***stenophyllus***	CBcs EBee EPfP GMaP IBoy LAst MHer MNrw NPer NPri NSbr SPer
'Tap Dance'	EBee LAma
'White Beauty Favourite'PBR	ERCP GKev
zenaidae JCA 0.444.409	WCot

Erepsia (*Aizoaceae*)

lacera	SPlb

Erianthus see *Saccharum*

Erica ✿ (*Ericaceae*)

aestiva	SPlb
alopecurus	SPlb
andevalensis f. ***albiflora***	CFst
arborea	CBcs SPlb
- var. ***alpina*** ♀H5	CDoC CTri EPfP GAbr GGal LRHS SCob SPer SPoG SWhi
§ - - f. ***aureifolia*** 'Albert's Gold' ♀H5	CFst CSBt CTri ELan EPfP GAbr LRHS MBri NHol SCob SCoo SPoG SWhi
- 'Arbora Gold'	see *E. arborea* var. *alpina* f. *aureifolia* 'Albert's Gold'
- 'Arnold's Gold'	see *E. arborea* var. *alpina* f. *aureifolia* 'Albert's Gold'
- 'Estrella Gold' ♀H5	CBcs CDoC CFst CSBt CTri ELan EPfP GAbr LRHS NHol SCob SCoo SPoG SWhi
- 'Golden Joy' **new**	CFst
australis f. ***albiflora*** ♀H2 'Mr Robert'	CFst GCal
- 'Holehird'	CFst
- 'Riverslea' ♀H4	CFst CTri GCal LRHS SCob SPoG SWhi
- 'Trisha'	CFst
caffra	CTre SPlb
canaliculata ♀H2	CBcs
carnea 'Adrienne Duncan' ♀H7	SCoo SRms SWhi
- f. ***alba*** 'C.J. Backhouse'	SRms
- - 'Golden Starlet' ♀H7	CFst CSBt CTri EPfP MAsh MJak NHol NWea SCoo SPer SRms SWhi
- - 'Ice Princess' ♀H7	ELan EPfP MAsh SCoo SRms SWhi
- - 'Isabell' ♀H7	CBcs CFst CSBt EPfP IVic MAsh SCoo SRms SWhi
- - 'Rosalinde Schorn'	SRms
- - 'Schneekuppe'	SWhi
- - 'Schneesturm'	SRms
- - 'Snow Queen'	SRms
- - 'Springwood White' ♀H7	CFst CSBt CTri ELan EPfP MAsh MMuc NHol SEND SLon SRms SWhi
- - 'Whitehall'	CFst SCoo SRms SWhi
- - 'Winter Snow' ♀H7	CFst CSBt ELan SCoo SPer SRms SWhi
- 'Amy Doncaster'	see *E. carnea* 'Treasure Trove'
- 'Ann Sparkes' ♀H7	CBcs CFst CSBt CTri ELan EPfP MAsh NHol SCoo SPer SRms SWhi
- 'Atrorubra'	SWhi
- f. ***aureifolia*** 'Aurea'	SCoo SRms
- - 'Barry Sellers'	SRms
§ - - 'Bell's Extra Special'	EPfP SRms
- - 'Foxhollow' ♀H7	CBcs CFst CTri EPfP IArd MAsh MJak NHol SCoo SRms SWhi
- - 'Gelber Findling'	SRms
- - 'Hilletje'	CFst SRms SWhi
- - 'January Sun'	SRms
- - 'Westwood Yellow' ♀H7	CSBt MAsh NHol SRms SWhi
- 'Aztec Gold' **new**	CFst
- 'Beoley Pink'	SRms
- 'Challenger' ♀H7	ELan EPfP MAsh SCoo SLon SRms SWhi
- 'Clare Wilkinson'	SRms
- 'Claribelle'	CFst
- 'December Red'	CFst ELan EPfP MAsh MMuc SCoo SEND SRms SWhi
- 'Diana Young'	SCoo SWhi
- 'Dømmesmoen'	CFst SRms
- 'Dorset Sunshine'	CFst
- 'Early Red'	SRms
- 'Eileen Porter'	SEND
- 'Eva' ♀H7	CBcs CFst IVic SRms SWhi
- 'Foxhollow Fairy'	SPer SRms
- 'Gracilis'	SRms
- 'Heathwood'	MAsh SRms SWhi
- 'James Backhouse'	CTri
- 'Jason Attwater'	SRms
- 'Jennifer Anne'	SRms
- 'John Kampa'	SRms
- 'John Pook'	SCoo SRms
- 'King George'	CFst CTri SRms SWhi
§ - 'Kramer's Rubin'	CFst SRms
- 'Lena'	see *E.* × *darleyensis* 'Lena'
- 'Lesley Sparkes'	CFst
- 'Lohse's Rubin'	NWea SRms SWhi
- 'Loughrigg' ♀H7	CTri MAsh MJak NHol SCoo SRms SWhi
- 'March Seedling' ♀H7	CFst EPfP MAsh NHol SCoo SLon SPer SRms SWhi
- 'Margery Frearson'	SRms
I - 'Martin'	SRms
- 'Memory'	SWhi
- 'Myretoun Ruby' ♀H7	CBcs CFst CSBt CTri EPfP MAsh NHol SCoo SPer SRms SWhi
- 'Nathalie' ♀H7	CFst CSBt IVic MAsh SCoo SRms SWhi
- 'Pink Cloud'	CFst
- 'Pink Mist'	SRms SWhi
- 'Pink Spangles' ♀H7	CBcs CFst CSBt CTri MAsh MJak SCoo SPer SRms SWhi
- 'Pirbright Rose'	SRms
- 'Polden Pride'	SRms
- 'Praecox Rubra'	EPfP NHol SCoo SRms
- 'Queen Mary'	SRms
- 'Queen of Spain'	MAsh SRms
- 'R.B. Cooke'	EPfP MAsh MJak SCoo SRms
- 'Robert Jan'	SRms
- 'Rosalie' ♀H7	CFst EPfP IArd MAsh MMuc SCoo SPer SRms SWhi
- 'Rosantha'	CFst SRms
- 'Rosea'	SPlb
- 'Rosy Morn'	SRms
- 'Rotes Juwel'	SRms
- 'Rubinteppich'	SRms
- 'Ruby Glow'	MJak NHol
- 'Scatterley'	SRms
- 'Schatzalp'	SRms
- 'Sherwood Creeping'	SRms
- 'Smart's Heath'	SRms
- 'Springwood Pink'	CSBt CTri NHol SRms SWhi

- 'Tanja' CFst SWhi
§ - 'Treasure Trove' CFst SWhi
- 'Viking' MAsh
- 'Vivellii' ♀H7 CFst CTri MAsh MJak NHol SCoo SRms SWhi
- 'Walter Reisert' SRms
- 'Wentwood Red' SRms
- Whisky see *E. carnea* f. *aureifolia* 'Bell's Extra Special'
- 'Winter Beauty' MJak NHol
- Winter Rubin see *E. carnea* 'Kramer's Rubin'
- 'Wintersonne' ♀H7 CFst EPfP MMuc SRms SWhi
cerinthoides **new** CTre
ciliaris 'Bretagne' SWhi
- 'Corfe Castle' CFst SWhi
- 'David McClintock' CFst SWhi
- 'Globosa' SWhi
- 'Ram' SWhi
cinerea SWhi
- f. ***alba*** 'Alba Minor' CFst MAsh SWhi
- - 'Celebration' SWhi
- - 'Domino' MAsh
- - 'Hookstone White' SWhi
- 'Atropurpurea' MAsh
- 'Atrorubens' CFst
- f. ***aureifolia*** 'Apricot Charm' CSBt
- - 'Fiddler's Gold' MAsh SWhi
- - 'Golden Charm' SWhi
- - 'Golden Drop' CFst CSBt MAsh
- - 'Golden Hue' MAsh
- - 'Goldilocks' CFst
- - 'Summer Gold' SWhi
- 'Bucklebury Red' CFst
- 'C.D. Eason' ♀H7 CFst CSBt CTri EPfP IVic MAsh SCoo SWhi
- 'Cevennes' SWhi
- 'Champs Hill' CFst
- 'Discovery' CFst SWhi
- 'Eden Valley' CFst SCoo SWhi
- 'Glasnevin Red' IVic
- 'Glencairn' MMuc SWhi
- 'John Ardron' CFst
- 'Joseph Murphy' CBcs CFst
- 'Joyce Burfitt' CFst
- 'Katinka' CBcs CFst IVic SWhi
- 'Lilac Time' CFst
- 'Lime Soda' SWhi
- 'Mrs E.A. Mitchell' SPlb
- 'My Love' CFst SWhi
- 'Ockham' **new** CFst
- 'P.S. Patrick' SWhi
- 'Pentreath' MMuc SWhi
- 'Pink Ice' ♀H7 CFst CTri EPfP MAsh NHol SWhi
- 'Providence' CFst
- 'Purple Beauty' SWhi
- 'Purple Robe' SWhi
- 'Rosita' CFst SWhi
- 'Roter Kobold' SWhi
- 'Sandford Heritage' **new** CFst
- 'Sandpit Hill' CFst
- 'Sherry' CFst NHol SWhi
- 'Stephen Davis' ♀H7 NHol SCoo SWhi
- 'Ted Oliver' CFst
- 'Velvet Night' ♀H7 CSBt MAsh NHol SWhi
- 'Vivienne Patricia' CFst SWhi
cooperi SPlb
curviflora SPlb
× ***darleyensis*** GGal
- 'Alba' see *E.* × *darleyensis* f. *albiflora* 'Silberschmelze'
- f. ***albiflora*** 'Ada S. Collings' MAsh SRms
- - 'Bing' CFst SCoo
- - 'N.R. Webster' SRms
§ - - 'Silberschmelze' CSBt CTri EPfP MAsh MJak MMuc SCoo SEND SRms SWhi
- - 'White Glow' CTri MAsh SRms
- - 'White Perfection' ♀H6 CBcs CFst CSBt EPfP IArd IVic MAsh MJak NHol SCoo SPer SPoG SRms SWhi
- 'Archie Graham' SRms
- 'Arthur Johnson' ♀H6 CFst CSBt CTri MAsh SRms SWhi
§ - f. ***aureifolia*** 'Eva Gold' PBR CFst SWhi
- - 'Jack H. Brummage' CSBt CTri MAsh SRms SWhi
- - 'Mary Helen' CSBt EPfP MAsh NHol SCoo SRms SWhi
- - 'Moonshine' CFst SRms SWhi
- - 'Tweety' CBcs CFst SRms
- 'Aurélie Brégeon' CFst SRms
- 'Bert' CFst SCoo
- 'Cherry Stevens' see *E.* × *darleyensis* 'Furzey'
§ - 'Darley Dale' CFst CSBt ELan EPfP MAsh MJak MMuc SCoo SEND SLon SPoG SRms SWhi
- 'Epe' CFst SRms
- 'Eva' PBR see *E.* × *darleyensis* f. *aureifolia* 'Eva Gold'
§ - 'Furzey' ♀H6 CSBt EPfP MAsh NHol NWea SCoo SRms SWhi
- 'George Rendall' CSBt CTri EPfP MAsh SCoo SRms
- 'Ghost Hills' ♀H6 CSBt EPfP MAsh MJak SCoo SPoG SRms SWhi
- 'Golden Perfect' CFst
- 'Irish Treasure' CFst
- 'J.W. Porter' ♀H6 EPfP MJak MMuc SCoo SEND SLon SRms SWhi
- 'James Smith' SRms
- 'Jenny Porter' ♀H6 CSBt ELan EPfP SCoo SLon SWhi
- 'Katia' PBR (Winter Belles Series) CFst SPer SWhi
- 'Kramer's Rote' ♀H6 CFst CSBt CTri ELan EPfP MJak NHol SCoo SPer SPoG SRms SWhi XLum
§ - 'Lena' CFst SWhi
- 'Lucie' PBR (Winter Belles Series) CFst SWhi
- 'Margaret Porter' CFst EPfP MAsh SCoo SWhi
- Molten Silver see *E.* × *darleyensis* f. *albiflora* 'Silberschmelze'
- 'Phoebe' PBR (Winter Belles Series) CFst SWhi
- 'Pink Perfection' see *E.* × *darleyensis* 'Darley Dale'
- 'Rubina' PBR **new** CFst SWhi
- 'Snow Surprise' **new** SWhi
- 'Spring Surprise' PBR ♀H6 CFst EPfP SCoo SPer SWhi
- 'W.G. Pine' SRms
- 'White Spring Surprise' SWhi
- 'Winter Surprise' CFst SWhi
- 'Winter Treasure' CFst
discolor CTre
erigena f. ***alba*** 'Brian Proudley' CFst
- - 'W.T. Rackliff' ♀H5 CBcs CSBt EPfP MAsh NHol SCoo SRms SWhi

- f. ***aureifolia*** 'Golden Lady'	CFst CSBt MAsh NHol SCoo SRms SWhi
- - 'Thing Nee'	CFst SRms SWhi
- 'Brightness'	CSBt EPfP MAsh NHol SCoo
- 'Irish Dusk' ♀H5	CBcs CSBt CTri EPfP MAsh NWea SCoo SEND SRms SWhi
- 'Rosslare'	CFst
- 'Superba'	MAsh SRms SWhi
glauca var. ***elegans***	CDes
- var. ***glauca***	SPlb
§ × ***griffithsii*** 'Heaven Scent'	SWhi
- 'Jacqueline'	SWhi
- 'Valerie Griffiths'	NHol SWhi
'Heaven Scent'	see *E.* × *griffithsii* 'Heaven Scent'
× ***krameri*** 'Rudi'	IVic
lusitanica ♀H2	CFst LRHS SPoG
- f. ***aureifolia*** 'George Hunt'	CFst ELan EPfP LRHS MAsh SLon SPer SPoG
- Great Star	see *E. lusitanica* 'La Vasterival'
§ - 'La Vasterival'	CFst
- 'Sheffield Park'	CFst EPfP LRHS MAsh SPer SPoG
mackayana f. ***eburnea*** 'Doctor Ronald Gray'	CFst
- - 'Shining Light'	CFst SWhi
- 'Errigal Dusk'	CFst
- 'Galicia'	SWhi
- f. ***multiplicata*** 'Ann D. Frearson' (d)	CFst
- - 'Plena' (d)	CFst WHer
mammosa ♀H2	CTre SPlb
mediterranea misapplied	see *E. erigena*
nabea new	CDes
× ***oldenburgensis*** 'Ammerland' ♀H6	SCoo SRms SWhi
patersonii	CDes SPlb
perspicua	SPlb
platycodon	CFst
subsp. ***maderincola*** f. ***aureifolia*** 'Levada Gold'	
scabriuscula new	CTre
sessiliflora	CTre
spiculifolia 'Balkan Rose'	GCal
straussiana	SPlb
× ***stuartii*** 'Irish Lemon' ♀H5	CFst CSBt NHol SWhi
- 'Irish Orange'	CSBt NHol SWhi
taxifolia	CDes
terminalis 'Thelma Woolner'	SWhi
tetralix	SWhi
- f. ***alba*** 'Alba Mollis' ♀H7	CFst CSBt MAsh SWhi
- f. ***aureifolia*** 'Ruth's Gold'	NHol
- 'Con Underwood'	CFst CSBt SWhi
- 'Riko'	CFst SWhi
- 'Samtpfötchen'	CFst
- 'Silver Bells'	CSBt
- f. ***stellata*** 'Pink Star' ♀H7	CFst NHol SWhi
- 'Tina'	SWhi
vagans f. ***alba*** 'Cornish Cream' ♀H6	EPfP NHol SWhi
- - 'Diana's Gold'	SRms
- - 'Golden Triumph'	CFst SWhi
- - 'Kevernensis Alba' ♀H6	NWad SWhi
- f. ***aureifolia*** 'Valerie Proudley' ♀H6	CSBt MAsh NHol
- - 'Yellow John'	CFst SRms SWhi
- 'Birch Glow' ♀H6	EPfP SWhi
- 'Fiddlestone'	SWhi
- 'Keira'	CFst SRms SWhi
- 'Lyonesse' ♀H6	MAsh MMuc NHol SWhi
- 'Mrs D.F. Maxwell' ♀H6	CBcs CFst CSBt MAsh MMuc NHol SWhi
- 'Mrs Donaldson'	CFst
- 'Saint Keverne'	CFst CSBt IArd IVic MMuc NHol SWhi
- 'Summertime'	CFst
× ***veitchii***	MMuc
- 'Exeter' ♀H5	CFst CSBt CTsd ELan EPfP LRHS MAsh SPer SWhi
- 'Gold Tips' ♀H5	CFst CSBt EPfP LRHS SWhi
- 'Pink Joy'	SWhi
versicolor	SPlb
verticillata	CTre
× ***watsonii*** 'Claire Elise'	CFst SWhi
- 'Dawn'	SWhi
- 'H. Maxwell'	SWhi
- 'Mary'	SWhi
- 'Pink Pacific'	CFst SWhi
× ***williamsii*** 'Ken Wilson'	CFst SWhi
woodii	SPlb

Erigeron ✿ (*Asteraceae*)

acris subsp. ***angulosus***	GKev
'Adria'	CBod EBee ECtt LLHF LRHS MBNS MMuc MSpe SEND SPer WMnd WWEG
annuus	CSpe NCGa NDov
aurantiacus	MNrw NBro WCot WHal
aureus 'Canary Bird' ♀H4	EPot NSla WAbe
- 'The Giant'	WAbe
'Azure Beauty'	ELan
Azure Fairy	see *E.* 'Azurfee'
§ 'Azurfee'	CSBt ELan EPfP GMaP MBNS MHol MWat NBir NLar NPri SGSe SPer SPoG SWvt WFar WMoo
Black Sea	see *E.* 'Schwarzes Meer'
'Blue Beauty'	CMac EPfP LRHS
borealis	GAbr
'Charity'	MRav WBrk
chrysopsidis	MHer
- 'Grand Ridge'	ECho LLHF LRHS WAbe
compositus	CTri SRms
§ - var. ***discoideus***	EDAr NSla SPlb WHoo
- 'Rocky'	CBod ECho MMuc
Darkest of All	see *E.* 'Dunkelste Aller'
deep pink-flowered	CHEx
'Dignity'	CBod ECGP ELan GBuc LLHF MBrN MMuc MRav MSpe NHol NSoo SEND SWvt WBrk WFar WWEG
'Dimity'	CMea ECha NBir NBre WFar WHal
'Dominator'	MNrw WCot
I 'Dunkelste Aller'	CBod CMea CPrp CSam ELan EPfP GBin GMaP LRHS LSou MRav MSpe NLar NPri SCob SGbt SPer SPoG SRms SWvt WWEG
* ***ereganus***	NBre
flettii	ECho GKev
'Foersters Liebling' ♀H5	EBee GBin MBel MNrw WWEG
formosissimus	GBin
'Four Winds'	CAbP ECho ECtt ELan EWes GKev LRHS MRav NGdn WBrk WWEG
'Gaiety'	NBre
glaucus	CBod CCCN CSBt ECho GBee GEdr GJos GKev LRHS MMuc MRav NGdn SEND SMad WBrk WFar

- 'Albus'	ELon LRHS NLar WBor WFar
- 'Elstead Pink'	CTri ECtt ELan MBri WFar
- large-flowered new	LRHS
- 'Roger Raiche'	CMea MRav
- 'Rose Purple'	CFis
- 'Roseus'	CBcs SEND
- 'Sea Breeze'	CBod CCCN CNec CPrp ECtt ELon EWll GEdr GJos GMaP LRHS MBNS MBel MBri MHol MLHP NDov NPri NSir SBod SCob SGbt SHil SMrm SPoG SRms SWvt WBor WHoo
- 'Sennen'	WBrk
- 'Viewpoint Blue'	ELon LRHS
howellii	NBre
§ ***karvinskianus*** ♀H4	Widely available
- 'Kew Profusion' new	LRHS SHil
- 'Stallone'	LSun MAvo NPri
leiomerus	LBee LLHF
linearis	LLHF
'Mrs F.H. Beale'	LSou MSpe SRGP WCot
mucronatus	see *E. karvinskianus*
multiradiatus	GCal
'Nachthimmel'	CAby NBre NGdn
philadelphicus	CDes CElw IGor MNrw NBir NBro WHal
'Pink Beauty'	SKHP
Pink Jewel	see *E.* 'Rosa Juwel'
'Profusion'	see *E. karvinskianus*
pygmaeus	LLHF
pyrenaicus Rouy	see *Aster pyrenaeus*
'Quakeress'	CAby CBod CElw CPrp ECtt EPfP EPri GBin GBuc GMaP IKil LRHS MMuc MNrw MRav MSpe NGdn SEND SMrm SWvt WBrk WFar WWEG XLum
§ 'Rosa Juwel'	CSBt CTri ECtt ELan EPfP GBin GMaP LRHS MBNS MHol MRav NBir NHol NPri SPer SPoG SRms SWvt WFar WMnd WMoo
'Rotes Meer'	CMac EBee MRav
rotundifolius 'Caerulescens'	see *Bellis caerulescens*
salsuginosus misapplied	see *Aster sibiricus*
§ 'Schneewittchen'	CBod CSam EBee ELan EPfP MBNS MBel MMuc MPie MRav MSpe NCGa SRms SWvt WWEG
§ 'Schwarzes Meer'	EBee LPla MSpe WCot
scopulinus	ITim LLHF SBch WAbe WHal
simplex	ECho LRHS
'Sincerity'	XLum
'Snow Queen'	SWvt
Snow White	see *E.* 'Schneewittchen'
'Sommerneuschnee'	GBin LPla NDov SPhx WMnd
speciosus NNS 07-195	GKev
- 'Grandiflora'	MHol
'Strahlenmeer'	MSpe NBre
trifidus	see *E. compositus* var. *discoideus*
uniflorus	LLHF SRms
vagus	ITim
'Wayne Roderick'	CBod ELan EPfP LAst LRHS NPri SRGP
'White Quakeress'	CElw CFis CMea MRav SMrm WCot
'Wuppertal'	MSpe

Erinacea (*Papilionaceae*)

§ ***anthyllis*** ♀H5	WAbe WThu
pungens	see *E. anthyllis*

Erinus (*Plantaginaceae*)

alpinus ♀H4	CTri ECho ECtt EDAr GAbr GJos GKev MLHP MWat NBir NSla SRms WCot XLum
- var. ***albus***	ECho GJos SRms WHoo XLum
- 'Doktor Hähnle'	ECho EDAr GJos GMaP NRya SRms WHoo XLum

Eriobotrya (*Rosaceae*)

'Coppertone'	see × *Rhaphiobotrya* 'Coppertone'
deflexa	CBcs CHEx EBee
japonica (F)	CAbb CArn CBcs CCCN CDul CHEx CTho ELan EPfP ETwe EUJe LPal LRHS MGos MMuc NLar NLos NPla SArc SCoo SEND SPer SPlb SPtp SSta SVic WHer WPGP
- 'Gold Nugget' (F)	XBlo
- 'Mrs Cookson' (F)	MBri
- 'Oliver' (F)	MBri

Eriocapitella see *Anemone*

Eriocephalus (*Asteraceae*)

africanus	CBod SPlb WJek

Eriogonum (*Polygonaceae*)

alatum	WCot
alleni	WCot
- 'Little Rascal' new	EBee
cespitosum	LLHF SIgm WAbe
ovalifolium	SIgm
umbellatum	ECho EPot GKev SIgm
- subsp. ***covillei***	CPBP
- var. ***porteri***	GKev
- var. ***torreyanum***	CMea

Eriophorum (*Cyperaceae*)

angustifolium	CBAq CBen CWat EHoe EHon EPla MSKA MWts SPlb SWat WMAq WPnP WWtn XLum
chamissonis	MWts
latifolium	LLWG MSKA MWts SGSe XLum
rousseauianum	MSKA
vaginatum	CRow EHoe EWay LLWG MSKA SGSe XLum

Eriophyllum (*Asteraceae*)

lanatum	CFis EBee ECha EPfP NBid NGBl SHar WWEG XLum
* - 'Pointe'	WSHC

Eritrichium (*Boraginaceae*)

aretioides	SPlb
howardii	GKev
nipponicum new	GKev

Erodium (*Geraniaceae*)

absinthoides	LRHS XSen
- var. ***amanum***	see *E. amanum*
'Almodovar'	WCot
§ ***amanum***	CSpe EWes
balearicum	see *E.* × *variabile* 'Album'
'Bidderi'	XSen
'Candy Store'	LRHS
'Carmel'	XSen
'Caroline'	CMea SBch WHoo
carvifolium	CHid

§ ***castellanum*** EBee GKev LLHF SMrm
celtibericum EPot XSen
- 'Javalambre' XSen
- 'Peñagolosa' XSen
'Cézembre' WCot XSen
chamaedryoides see *E. reichardii*
- 'Roseum' see *E.* × *variabile* 'Roseum'
§ ***cheilanthifolium*** XSen
- 'David Crocker' WAbe
chrysanthum CElw CSam CTri ECha ECho ECtt EDAr EPfP EPot EWTr EWoo GBuc GJos GMaP ITim MPnt NChi NLar SEND SMrm SRot SWvt XLum XSen
- (f) WFar
- (m) NRya
- 'Arcadia' CMea SPhx
- pink-flowered CSpe ECtt EPot MMuc SEND SMrm SRot
corsicum ECho
- 'Album' ECho LLHF
'County Park' ECha EPPr MLHP NLar SHar SRms XSen
daucoides misapplied see *E. castellanum*
'Fran's Delight' CMea CPBP ECtt EPot GJos SBch WAbe WHoo
'Freedom' XEll
'Fripetta' WIce XSen
'Gini's Choice' WCot
glandulosum ♀H5 CUse ECho EPfP MAsh MMuc NLar SBch SEND SPtp SRms SRot XLum XSen
- 'Marie Poligné' XSen
'Grey Blush' SMHy WKif
gruinum CHid SPhx
guicciardii XSen
guttatum misapplied see *E.* 'Katherine Joy'
guttatum (Desf.) Willd. EPot EWTr EWld SRms
hymenodes L'Hér. see *E. trifolium*
'Julie Ritchie' WHoo
§ 'Katherine Joy' ECtt EPot EWes MHer NRya SBch SRGP SRot XSen
× ***kolbianum*** SMHy WAbe WCot WHoo WPnn XSen
- 'Natasha' CMHG ECtt EPPr EPot EWes GBuc GMaP MHer MMuc NSla SEND SPoG SRGP WAbe WIce WKif XSen
'Las Meninas' CMea ECtt WCot
× ***lindavicum*** GCrg NChi WPnn XSen
macradenum see *E. glandulosum*
manescavii Widely available
'Marchants Mikado' WKif
'Maryla' CMea WAbe WIce
'Merstham Pink' ELon GMaP SRms XLum XSen
'Mesquita' CMea
'Pallidum' CSam
pelargoniiflorum CFis CHid CSpe ELan EPfP EWTr LRHS MCot NLar SEND SMrm SRms SWvt WKif WPnn
'Peter Vernon' MHer XSen
petraeum see *E. cheilanthifolium*
subsp. ***crispum*** misapplied
- subsp. ***petraeum*** MSpe
'Pickering Pink' EBee NLar
'Pippa Mills' SBch
'Princesse Marion' MLHP XSen
* 'Purple Haze' EBee MSCN SRms SRot WFar
§ ***reichardii*** CTri ECho ECtt LRHS MBrN SPoG SRms WCFE
- 'Album' CTal ECho GCrg LRHS MAsh MMuc MSCN SEND SMrm SPoG WHoo WPnn
- 'Bianca' EPfP
* - 'Rubrum' CElw ECho MAsh
'Robertino' WAbe
rodiei EWes
§ ***rupestre*** ECho ECtt SRms SRot WIce
'Sarck' XSen
sibthorpianum XSen
'Souvenir d'Hélène' XSen
'Spanish Eyes' CBod CWGN ECtt GCrg IPot LRHS LSou NPri SMrm SRot SWvt WCot WHoo WKif
'Stephanie' CFis CMHG ECho ECtt ELan EPPr EPot EWes MHer MMuc SEND WAbe WIce XSen
supracanum see *E. rupestre*
'Tiny Kyni' XSen
trichomanifolium misapplied see *E. cheilanthifolium*
trichomanifolium L'Hér. EWes
§ ***trifolium*** ECho ELan EPfP EWld LSun MHer SBch SPhx WHea
× ***variabile*** WFar
§ - 'Album' ECho EPfP GCrg GMaP LAst LRHS MHer NEgg NPri NSla SRms SRot SWvt WAbe WBrk WFar
I - 'Bishop's Form' CMea CNec ECho ECtt ELon EPfP GCrg GJos GMaP IPot LAst LRHS MAsh MHer NEgg NRya NSbr SMrm SPoG SRGP SRms SRot SWvt WAbe WBrk WCFE WFar WHoo WIce
- 'Candy' CTal ELon MHer WBrk
- 'Derek' ECho SRGP
- 'Flore Pleno' (d) CBod ECho ELan EPfP EWes GMaP ITim LRHS MHer SPoG SRms SRot WBrk WRHF
- 'Red Rock' CTri
§ - 'Roseum' ♀H4 ECho ECtt ELan ELon EPfP MMuc MSCN NPri NSla SEND SPlb SRms WBrk
- 'Timpany Seedling' ITim
'Whitwell Superb' XSen

Erpetion see *Viola*

Eruca (*Brassicaceae*)

vesicaria ENfk
- subsp. ***sativa*** CSpe ELau GPoy MHer MNHC SIde SVic

Eryngium ✿ (*Apiaceae*)

NJM 09.072 WPGP
§ ***agavifolium*** Widely available
- giant WPGP
alpinum CBcs CHel CSpe ECha ECho ELan GKev GMaP IBoy LAst MGos MMuc MSCN NBir SCob SKHP SMrm SPer SRms SRot WCAu WFar
- 'Amethyst' LRHS NBro WFar
- 'Blue Jacket' NSti
- 'Blue Star' CExl CHel CSpe EBee ECtt ELan ELon EWoo GBin GBuc LRHS NLar SMad WCFE WCot WWEG
- 'Holden Blue' MAvo
- 'Slieve Donard' see *E.* × *zabelii* 'Donard Variety'
- 'Superbum' CSpe ECtt GCal GLog LRHS MNrw SRms SWat

	amethystinum	CCse ELon EPri LRHS SMrm WHoo XLum
	biebersteinianum	see *E. caeruleum*
	'Blue Jackpot'	EPfP EWes MAvo MBel MNrw
	'Blue Spikes' new	EBee
	'Blue Steel'	EBee LLHF
	bourgatii	Widely available
	– Graham Stuart Thomas's selection	CAbP CAby CElw CEnd CExl CMHG CSpe CUse ECtt ELan EPPr EWes GAbr GMaP LRHS MBel MCot MHol NBir NLar NPCo SPad SPer SRms WCot WHoo WHrl WPGP WWEG
	– 'Oxford Blue' ♀H5	CElw GBin GMaP MHer NLar NSla SGSe SKHP SWvt
	– 'Picos Amethyst'	CBcs CBct CMac CWCL ELon EPfP LRHS MGos NLar NSti SCob SCoo SGSe SKHP SRms WSHC
	– 'Picos Blue'[PBR]	Widely available
	bromeliifolium misapplied	see *E. agavifolium*, *E. eburneum*
	bromeliifolium ambig.	LRHS
§	***caeruleum***	MNrw
	campestre	CArn MAvo
	caucasicum	see *E. caeruleum*
	'Cobalt Star'	MAvo MRav NLar WHoo
	creticum	NBro NChi
	cymosum B&SWJ 10267	WCru
	decaisneanum misapplied	see *E. pandanifolium*
	deppeanum F&M 54	WPGP
	– NJM 05.031	LEdu
	Dove Cottage hybrid	MAvo NDov
	ebracteatum var. ***poterioides***	LPla SMHy SMad SPhx
§	***eburneum***	CBod CCon ECha EPfP EWes GCal GMaP LRHS NBro NChi SKHP SMad
	aff. ***eburneum***	CMac
	'Electric Haze'	CBod CSam ECtt GBuc LRHS LSou
	elegans var. ***elegans***	CCon
	foetidum	CArn
§	***giganteum*** ♀H7	Widely available
	– 'Silver Ghost' ♀H7	CAby CBod CExl CHel CSam CSpe CUse ECtt EWll EWoo GMaP LRHS LSun MBel NChi NDov NGdn NLar NPri NSti SKHP SPhx SWat SWvt WCot WWEG
	gracile B&SWJ 10205	WCru
	– B&SWJ 10351	WCru
	– B&SWJ 10441	WCru
	'Green Jade'	LRHS
	guatemalense B&SWJ 8989	WCru
	– B&SWJ 10322	WCru
	– B&SWJ 10420	WCru
	horridum misapplied	see *E. eburneum*
	horridum ambig.	EWes MNrw NChi NLar NLos SArc WMnd
	horridum Malme	WCot
	humile B&SWJ 10464	WCru
	'Indigo Star'	MAvo
	'Lapis Blue'	MAvo
	leavenworthii	LRHS
	maritimum	CArn CEls CPou EBee EPla GPoy MHer MNHC NLar SPlb
	Miss Willmott's ghost	see *E. giganteum*
	monocephalum	EBee
	× ***oliverianum*** ♀H6	CBod CMea CSpe ECtt ELan EPfP GBuc GCal GKev LRHS MAvo MBel MCot MHol MLHP MRav MTis NBir NChi NLar NPCo SDix SMad SPer SWat SWvt WCot WHoo
	palmatum	NChi
§	***pandanifolium*** ♀H3	CCon CHEx CHel CKno ELan EUJe EWTr EWes GCal LEdu NSoo SArc SEND SGSe SKHP SMad SPlb SPoG SWvt WMnd
	– 'Physic Purple'	CAby CSpe MAvo SPhx
	'Pen Blue' new	LBuc MGos SCob
	planum	Widely available
	– 'Bethlehem'	NLar SWat
§	– 'Blauer Zwerg'	CKno MAvo NLar
	– 'Blaukappe'	CExl CMea EAEE EBee ELon EPfP EWoo LRHS LSun MMuc MNFA NLar SEND SKHP SMrm SPhx SRms
*	– 'Blue Candle'	NLar
	– Blue Dwarf	see *E. planum* 'Blauer Zwerg'
	– 'Blue Glitter'	CBod EBee ELon LRHS LSun NLar SPhx SWvt
	– 'Blue Hobbit'	Widely available
	– 'Blue Ribbon'	LSou
	– 'Flüela'	EWes GBuc GCal LRHS NEgg SWat
	– 'Jade Frost'[PBR] (v)	Widely available
	– 'Little Blue Wonder'[PBR]	NHol
	– 'Naughty Jackpot' (v)	EBee NLar
	– 'Paradise Jackpot'[PBR]	SRms
	– 'Seven Seas'	CCon MBNS NEgg
	– 'Silver Salentino'	CBod ELon WHil WOut
	– 'Silver Stone'	SRms
	– 'Sunny Jackpot'[PBR]	NSti
	– 'Tetra Petra'	LRHS SRms
	– 'Tiny Jackpot'	CWGN GMaP IBoy NLar
	– 'White Glitter'	EBee
	proteiflorum	EPfP LRHS NChi SKHP SMad SPhx SPlb
	– F&M 224	WPGP
	serbicum	GCal SMHy WCot
	serra	EWes LRHS MCot NLos
	tricuspidatum	ECtt LRHS
	× ***tripartitum*** ♀H5	CBcs CElw CTri ECha ECtt ELan EPPr EPfP GMaP LAst LRHS MNFA MRav MWat NBro NEgg NLar SBod SMrm SPhx SPoG SRkn SWat SWvt
*	***umbelliferum***	GCal IMou MBNS SKHP
	variifolium	Widely available
	– 'Miss Marbel'	CNec COtt EPfP LSun MWat SRms WSHC
	venustum	EBee EUJe EWTr LRHS SMad
	viviparum new	WFar
	yuccifolium	CCon EPfP EWes GCal LEdu MAvo NLar SDix SMrm SPhx SPlb SWvt WHil XLum
	× ***zabelii***	ECha NBir NChi WBor
	– 'Big Blue'	CBct CBod ELon EWTr GBin LRHS LSun MAsh MAvo MHol MPro MTis NLar NPCo SMad SMrm WCot
	– 'Blaue Ritter'	SKHP SWat
§	– 'Donard Variety'	COtt ECtt GBBs GBuc GCal LRHS MAvo NLar NPCo SWat
	– 'Forncett Ultra'	GCal MNrw NChi
	– 'Jewel'	SWat
	– 'Jos Eijking'[PBR]	Widely available
	– 'Violetta'	IGor MCot NLar SWat

Erysimum ✿ (*Brassicaceae*)

allionii misapplied	see *E.* × *marshallii*
'Andy's Oranges and Lemons' (v)	WCot

'Apricot Delight'	see *E.* 'Apricot Twist'
§ 'Apricot Twist'	Widely available
arkansanum	see *E. helveticum*
asperum	GJos IFro
'Audrey's Pink'	WHoo
'Bowles's Mauve' ♀H4	Widely available
'Bowles's Purple'	SRms SWvt
'Bowles's Yellow'	GCal WCot
'Bredon'	CElw NPer
'Butterscotch'	MMHG WHoo
capitatum var. ***purshii***	CPBP WAbe
caricum	WAbe
cheiri	CArn MHer
- 'Baden-Powell' (d)	GCal
- 'Bloody Warrior' (d)	CElw WCot
- 'Harpur Crewe' (d)	NPer SRms WHer
'Constant Cheer'	CMea CSBt CWCL ECtt ELan ELon
	EPfP IFoB MAvo MCot MMuc NPer
	SCob SEND SPer SRGP SRkn SRms
	SWvt WCAu WHil WHoo WKif
'Cotswold Gem' (v)	EHoe ELan ELon LSou MHer MMuc
	NPer SEND SLim SWvt WCot
'Dawn Breaker'	ECtt MRav WCot
'Dorothy Elmhirst'	see *E.* 'Mrs L.K. Elmhirst'
'Emm's Variety'	ECtt
'Gold Rush'	GJos
'Gold Shot'	GJos
'Golden Gem'	ECho ELan EPfP
'Golden Jubilee'	ECho ECtt EPPr GBuc LRHS SRms
	WIce
'Hector's Gatepost'	EWTr SRGP
§ ***helveticum***	ECho MMuc SBod SRms
'Jacob's Jacket'	ECha ECtt MBNS MHer NPer
'Jenny Brook' PBR	LSun
'John Codrington'	GBin NPer WKif
'Jubilee Gold'	WWEG
kotschyanum	ECho EPot GCrg NSla SRms WIce
'Lemon Light' new	WHoo
linifolium	SRms
- 'Little Kiss Lilac'	GJos
§ - 'Variegatum' (v)	CBod CCCN CSBt EBee ECtt ELan
	EPfP LPot LRHS MCot NLar NPer
	SCob SPer SPoG SRot XLum
- - peach-flowered (v)	NSbr SPad
§ × ***marshallii***	GJos
'Moonlight'	EPot GBuc GMaP MHer MRav NBir
	SRms WHoo
§ 'Mrs L.K. Elmhirst'	ELon MMHG NPer
mutabile	CTri EPfP MRav WHal
- 'Variegatum' (v)	CAby
'My Old Mum'	LSou
'Orange Flame'	CMea ECha ECho ELon GCrg MHer
	MMuc NPer SEND WHoo
'Orange King'	WIce
'Orange Zwerg'	MMuc WIce
'Paintbox' new	WHlf
'Parish's'	CElw CHVG CSpe CWld WWFP
'Parkwood Gold'	ECho EPot GJos GKev
'Pastel Patchwork'	CBod CSpe ECtt LAst WCot
perofskianum	GKev
Perry's hybrid	NPer
'Perry's Peculiar'	NPer
'Perry's Surprise'	NPer
'Perry's Variegated' (v)	NPer
'Plant World Lemon'	CAby CBod CHGN ELon NLar
'Poppet'	CSpe
§ ***pulchellum***	ECha GKev
pumilum DC.	see *E. helveticum*
pusillum	WAbe
'Ray's Early Giants' (mixed)	CPla
rupestre	see *E. pulchellum*
'Ruston Royal'	ECha
Rysi Bronze	LRHS
= 'Innrysibro' PBR	
Rysi Gold = 'Innrysigol' PBR	SPoG
Rysi Moon	GBin MAvo
scoparium	ECha ELon
'Sissinghurst Variegated'	see *E. linifolium* 'Variegatum'
'Spice Island'	EPfP
'Sprite'	CMea CTri MMuc NPer SEND
'Starbright'	CWCL
'Stars and Stripes' (v)	ECtt LRHS LSou SRkn
Sunburst = 'Listrace'	CAby CMea CWGN ECtt LRHS LSou
	MTis SPoG WCAu WCot
'Sweet Sorbet'	EPfP NLar SRkn SWvt
Walberton's Fragrant Star	EPfP LBuc LRHS MAsh SPoG SRms
= 'Walfrastar' (v)	
Walberton's Fragrant	EPfP LRHS MAsh MBri SCoo
Sunshine = 'Walfrasun'	
'Wenlock Beauty'	CFis SRms
'Winter Joy'	EPfP LLHF LRHS MBNS NLar
Winter Orchid	CSpe CWGN GBin LRHS NLar WCot
Winter Rouge	CMea CWCL LBMP LRHS
Winter Sorbet	ECtt ELon EPfP LRHS NLar
= 'Inneryws' PBR	

Erythraea see *Centaurium*

Erythrina (*Papilionaceae*)

abyssinica	SPlb
amazonica	SPlb
arborescens	SPlb
× ***bidwillii***	CCCN WPGP
crista-galli ♀H3	CBcs CCCN CDTJ CHll CPom CSde
	CSpe EBee ELan EPfP ESwi LRHS
	MPie SPlb WCot WPGP
flabelliformis	SPlb
guatemalensis	SPlb
herbacea	SPlb
§ ***humeana***	SPlb
latissima	SPlb
lysistemon	SPlb
princeps	see *E. humeana*
rubrinervia	SPlb
speciosa	SPlb
vespertilio	SPlb

Erythronium ✿ (*Liliaceae*)

albidum	CLAP ECho GBuc GKev IBlr LAma
americanum	CArn CLAP ECho GKev IBlr LAma
	MNrw NRog SKHP WAbe
'Apple Blossom'	ECho IBlr
'Ballyrogan's Blaze'	IBlr
'Beechpark'	IBlr
'Blush'	ECho IBlr
'Bronze Beauty'	IBlr
'Californian Star'	IBlr
californicum ♀H5	CCon CLAP ECho GBuc IBlr LRHS
	NHar NRog
- J&JA 13216	CLAP
- 'Ballyrogan Bronze Bounty' new	IBlr
- 'Brimstone'	IBlr
- 'Brocklamont Inheritance'	IBlr
- 'Bronze Edge'	IBlr
- 'Dark Delight'	IBlr

	- 'Harvington Snowgoose'	see *E.* 'Harvington Snowgoose'
	- Plas Merdyn form	IBlr
	- 'Purple Heart'	IBlr
	× ***revolutum***	
	- 'Stellar'	IBlr
	- 'White Beauty' ♀H5	Widely available
	californicum	IBlr NRog
	× ***hendersonii***	
	'Carol Scott'	IBlr
	caucasicum	CLAP NRog
	citrinum	GBuc LLHF NRog
	- J&JA 13462	CLAP
	- subsp. ***citrinum***	GBuc
	- var. ***roderickii***	NRog
	citrinum* × *hendersonii	IBlr NRog
	'Citronella'	CBro CCon CLAP GBuc GKev IBlr NRog WAbe
	cliftonii hort.	see *E. multiscapideum* Cliftonii Group
	'Craigton Beauty' **new**	IBlr
	'Craigton Cover Girl'	IBlr
	'Craigton Cream'	IBlr
	'Delicacy'	ECha IBlr
	dens-canis ♀H5	Widely available
	- JCA 470.001	CLAP
	- from Slovenia	CLAP
	- 'Charmer'	ECho GEdr MNrw NRog
	- 'Frans Hals'	CCon CLAP ECho EPot GBuc GCra GEdr GKev IPot MNrw NRog SKHP WHal
	- large-flowered	IBlr
	- 'Lilac Wonder'	EBee ECho EPot GBuc GEdr GKev GMaP IPot LAma LEdu MAvo MNrw NRog NWad SDeJ SKHP
*	- 'Moerheimii' (d)	ECho EPot GEdr GKev IBlr NRog
	- var. ***niveum***	GEdr IBlr NRog
	- 'Old Aberdeen'	CAvo CLAP IBlr LRHS MNrw NRog
	- 'Pink Perfection'	EBee ECho GEdr GKev LEdu MNrw NMin NRog SDeJ
	- 'Purple King'	EBee ECGP ECho EPot GBuc GEdr GKev GMaP IPot LAma MAvo MNrw NHol NRog NWad SDeJ
	- 'Rose Queen'	ECho EPot GBuc GKev GMaP IPot LAma MAvo MNrw NMin NRog NWad SDeJ WHal
*	- 'Semi-plenum' (d)	IBlr
	- 'Snowflake'	CAvo CBro CLAP ECho EPot GBuc GEdr GKev LAma LEdu LRHS MAvo MNrw NBir NHol NMin NRog NWad SDeJ SKHP WAbe
	- 'White Splendour'	ECho IBlr MNrw NRog
	- white-flowered, from Serbia	ECho
	'Eirene'	IBlr
	elegans	ECho GBuc NRog
	'Flaire' **new**	IBlr
	'Flash'	IBlr
§	***grandiflorum***	CLAP ECho NRog
	- M&PS 007	CLAP
	- subsp. ***chrysandrum***	see *E. grandiflorum*
§	'Harvington Snowgoose'	CAvo CLAP IBlr LLHF LRHS NHar SKHP SPoG
	helenae	CLAP ECho IBlr NRog WAbe
	hendersonii	CAvo CLAP ECho GBuc LRHS NHar NRog SKHP WAbe
	- J&JA 12945	CLAP
	'Hidcote Beauty' **new**	LLHF LRHS
	howellii	CLAP SKHP
	- J&JA 13441	CLAP
	'Janice'	IBlr
	japonicum	ECho EFEx EPot LAma MNrw NRog
	'Jeanette Brickell'	CLAP GBuc IBlr
	'Jeannine'	EPot GBuc IBlr
	'Joanna'	CTal GBuc IBlr MNrw NRog
	'John Brookes'	IBlr
	'Kinfauns Pink'	CWCL EBee EPot GBuc GEdr IBlr LLHF NHar NRog
	klamathense	EPot
	'Kondo'	CCon CHel CTri ECho EPfP EPot GKev GMaP IBlr LAma LRHS NBir NHol NLar NRog NWad SPer WAbe
	'Lavender Eye'	IBlr
	'Margaret Mathew'	CLAP IBlr WAbe
	'Minnehaha'	GBuc
	montanum	ECho
§	***multiscapideum***	CLAP ECho GBuc LLHF WCot
	- NNS 02-166	WCot
§	- Cliftonii Group ♀H4	CLAP GBuc SKHP WAbe WCot
	'Oregon Encore'	IBlr
	oregonum	CLAP ECha ECho GBuc GKev IBlr LLHF LRHS MNrw NHar NRog
	- 'Ballyrogan Yellow' **new**	IBlr
	- subsp. ***leucandrum***	CLAP
	- - 'The Giant'	IBlr
	- subsp. ***oregonum***	SKHP
	- - NNS 01-202	WCot
I	- 'Sulphur Form'	CLAP
	oregonum	IBlr
	× ***revolutum*** **new**	
	'Pagoda' ♀H5	Widely available
	purdyi	see *E. multiscapideum*
	revolutum ♀H5	CBro CLAP CWCL ECho EPot GBuc GEdr GKev GMaP IBlr LAma LRHS MNrw NHar NRog SChF SKHP SRot WCru
	- from God's Valley	IBlr MNrw
	- 'Ballyrogan White Blusher' **new**	IBlr
	- 'Dark Dapple'	IBlr
	- 'Guincho Splendour'	IBlr
I	- 'Inshriach Form'	IBlr
	- Johnsonii Group	ECho WAbe WCru
	- 'Knightshayes'	CAvo EBee GBuc IBlr LRHS NHar SKHP
	- 'Knightshayes Pink'	CLAP IBlr LLHF NBir WShi
	- 'Pink Beauty'	NRog
	- Plas Merdyn form	IBlr
	- 'Rose Beauty'	ECho
	- 'Wild Salmon'	CLAP EBee LLHF LRHS NHar SKHP
	'Rippling Waters'	IBlr
	'Rosalind'	IBlr NRog WAbe
	sibiricum	ECho NRog
	'Spring Fresh' **new**	IBlr
	'Sundisc'	ECha ECho GBuc IBlr NRog WAbe
	'Sunshine'	IBlr
	'Susannah'	IBlr LRHS NHar
	tuolumnense ♀H5	CBro CCon CLAP CTal CWCL ECho EPot GBuc GEdr GKev GMaP IBlr LAma MCot MMoz MNrw NRog NWad SDeJ SPhx WAbe WCot
	- EBA clone 2	IBlr
	- EBA clone 3	IBlr
	- Plas Merdyn form	IBlr
	- 'Spindlestone'	GBuc GEdr IBlr LRHS SKHP
	umbilicatum	ECho EPot GEdr IBlr
	'White Star'	IBlr
	'Winifred Loraine' **new**	IBlr

Escallonia ✿ (*Escalloniaceae*)

	sp.	CAco
	'Alice'	SCob SPer
§	***alpina***	MGil
	- SDR 7016	GKev
	'Apple Blossom' ♀H5	Widely available
§	***bifida*** ♀H4	CDoC CDul CHGN ECre LRHS SDix SPhx
	'C.F. Ball'	CBcs CTri ELan EPfP GKin LBMP LBuc LRHS MAsh MSwo NEgg NPla NWea SEND SGol SRms WMoo
	'Compacta Coccinea'	LRHS MBri
	'Dart's Rosy Red'	MBri WMoo
	'Donard Beauty'	SRms
	'Donard Brilliance'	SGol SRms
	'Donard Radiance' ♀H5	CBcs CBod CDoC CDul CMac CSBt ELan EPfP EShb LRHS MBri NLar NWad NWea SCob SGol SLim SPer SPoG SRms SWvt WMoo
	'Donard Seedling'	CBcs CBod CCVT CDoC CDul EBee ECrN ELan EPfP GKin LAst LBuc LRHS MAsh MGos MMuc MSwo NEgg NPer NWea SCob SGol SLim SPer SRms SWvt WMoo
	'Donard Star'	EPfP NLar NWad NWea WCFE WHar
	'Donard White'	CBod EPfP NLar SPoG
	'Edinensis'	EAEE EPfP NLar SLim SRms WMoo
	'Everest'	EPfP LRHS MAsh MMuc SLon
	× ***exoniensis***	SRms
	fonkii	see *E. alpina*
	'Hopleys Gold'PBR	see *E. laevis* 'Gold Brian'
	illinita	NLar
	'Iveyi' ♀H4	Widely available
	'Jamie'PBR	EAEE EShb LLHF WMoo
§	***laevis***	LRHS
§	- 'Gold Brian'PBR	CDul CMac COtt EHoe ELan EPfP LRHS MAsh MGos MJak MWat NLar SCob SGol SPer
	- 'Gold Ellen' (v)	Widely available
	'Langleyensis' ♀H5	CMac CTri GGal SGol SRms WHar
	montevidensis	see *E. bifida*
	organensis	see *E. laevis*
	'Peach Blossom' ♀H5	CBod CDoC CDul COtt ELan ELon EPfP GKin LRHS MAsh MLHP MMuc MSwo NBir NEgg NHol SCob SCoo SEND SGol SLim SPer SPoG SRms
	'Pink Elle' **new**	EBee LRHS MBri
	'Pink Pyramid'	LRHS
	'Pride of Donard' ♀H5	CAco CBod CSBt EPfP GKin LRHS MGos SRms
	punctata	see *E. rubra*
	Red Carpet = 'Loncar'PBR	EAEE ELon LAst LRHS NSoo SLon WMoo WNPC
	'Red Dream'	CSBt CWSG EBee EPfP LBMP LRHS MAsh MBri MGos MSwo NLar NWad SCoo SEWo SHil SPoG SRms SWvt
	'Red Elf'	CMac EBee ELan EPfP GKin LAst LRHS MBri MGos MWat NEgg SBod SCoo SHil SPer SPlb SPoG SRms SWvt
	'Red Hedger'	CBod COtt CSBt CTsd EAEE ELan EShb GGal MRav NSoo SCob SRms WMoo
	'Red Knight'	MAsh NEgg NHol WNPC
	'Red Robin'	SPoG
	resinosa	CBod CExl CTsd SArc SPlb SRms SVen WJek
	revoluta	CTri MGil
§	***rubra*** SDR 7052	GKev
	- 'Crimson Spire' ♀H5	CBcs CDoC CDul COtt CSBt CTri EBee ECrN EPfP GKin LRHS MAsh MBri MGos MMuc MRav MWat NBir NEgg NWea SCob SEND SGbt SHil SLim SPer SPlb SPoG SRms WMoo
	- 'Ingramii'	NWea SEND
	- var. ***macrantha***	Widely available
*	- - ***aurea***	NPla
	- 'Pygmaea'	see *E. rubra* 'Woodside'
§	- 'Woodside'	ECho EPfP LLHF NWad SGol SRms
	'Silver Anniversary'	MSwo
	'Slieve Donard'	CMac EPfP MRav NWad NWea SLim SLon SRms
	tucumanensis	SPlb SVen
	'Ventnor'	SPlb SVen WPGP
	virgata	MGil

Eschscholzia (*Papaveraceae*)

californica	MBel
- 'Alba'	CSpe
- 'Gini's Cream'	CSpe WHil
- 'Ivory Castle'	SMrm SPhx
- 'Jersey Cream'	CSpe
- 'Red Chief'	SMrm SPhx

Espeletia (*Asteraceae*)

aff. ***summapacis*** B&SWJ 10766	WCru

Esterhuysenia (*Aizoaceae*)

alpina	CPBP WAbe

Eucalyptus ✿ (*Myrtaceae*)

aggregata	SArc SKin WEuc
alpina	SPlb
amygdalina	SPlb
apiculata	WEuc
approximans	SKin WEuc
archeri	CDTJ CDul CTho ELan EPfP LRHS MBri MGos MMuc MWhi NLar NSoo SEND SHil SKin WCot WEuc
baeuerlenii	SKin
caesia ♀H2	SPlb
camaldulensis	SPlb
camphora	CCCN CTsd EBee ESwi MMuc SEND SKin
cinerea	SBig SKin SPlb WEuc
citriodora	CWCL MHer SPlb
coccifera	CBcs CSBt CTsd ELan EPfP EUJe LRHS MMuc NPer SBig SEND SKin SPlb WCot WEuc
cordata	ELan SKin WPGP
crenulata	SKin WEuc
crucis subsp. ***crucis***	SPlb
cypellocarpa	SPlb
dalrympleana ♀H4	CMHG CMac ELan EPfP EUJe IDee LRHS MGos NLar NPer SBig SEND SHil SKin SLim SPer SPlb SRms WCot WEuc WHar WPGP
deanei	WEuc
debeuzevillei	see *E. pauciflora* subsp. *debeuzevillei*
delegatensis	CMHG NPer SKin WEuc

	divaricata	see *E. gunnii* subsp. *divaricata*
	erythrocorys	SPlb
	eximia	SPlb
*	- 'Nana'	SPlb
	ficifolia	CDTJ IDee
	fraxinoides	SPlb
	gamophylla	SPlb
	glaucescens	CAco CMHG ELan EPfP IDee LRHS SArc SEWo SHil SKin SPer WEuc
	globulus	CWCL SPlb
	- subsp. ***bicostata*** new	WEuc
	goniocalyx	EPfP WEuc
§	***gregsoniana***	CDul EPfP EUJe GGal SKin SPlb WEuc
	gunnii ♀H5	Widely available
	- Azura = 'Cagire'PBR	COtt LRHS MPkF SLon
§	- subsp. ***divaricata***	EPfP MBri SKin WEuc
	johnstonii	CAco CDul IDee NSoo SKin SPer
	kitsoniana	ELan SKin WEuc
	kruseana	SPlb
	kybeanensis	SKin WCot WEuc
§	***lacrimans***	WEuc
	leucoxylon subsp. ***megalocarpa***	SPlb
	ligustrina	SKin WEuc
	macarthurii	SKin
	macrocarpa	SPlb
	mannifera subsp. ***elliptica***	SKin WEuc
	mitchelliana	SKin WEuc
	moorei	WEuc
	- var. ***nana***	CDTJ
	neglecta	SKin WEuc
	nicholii	CBcs CDul CSpe EBee EHoe ELan EPfP EUJe EWes IDee LRHS MGos MMuc NSoo SCoo SEND SKin SLim WCot WEuc
	niphophila	see *E. pauciflora* subsp. *niphophila*
	nitens	CAco CDTJ CTsd SBig SKin SPlb WEuc
§	***nitida***	SKin WEuc
	nova-anglica	SKin
	obliqua	WEuc
	parviflora	SKin
	parvula	CAco CCCN CDoC CMac EPfP MWhi NLar SCoo SEND WEuc
	pauciflora	CCCN CDoC CSBt CTsd ELan EUJe IDee MGos MMuc SPer
§	- subsp. ***debeuzevillei*** ♀H5	CDoC EPfP SArc SBig SKin WEuc
	- subsp. ***hedraia***	SKin
	- var. ***nana***	see *E. gregsoniana*
§	- subsp. ***niphophila*** ♀H5	Widely available
	- - 'Pendula'	see *E. lacrimans*
	- subsp. ***pauciflora***	WEuc
	- - from Mount Buffalo, Australia new	WEuc
	perriniana	CAco CBcs CDul CLnd CMHG ECrN ELan EPfP EPla EUJe IDee LRHS MBri MGos MWhi NSoo SBig SCoo SEND SHil SKin SLim SPer SPlb SPoG SWvt WEuc WFar
	pulchella	WEuc
	pulverulenta	CMac SKin SPlb WEuc
	- 'Baby Blue'	LRHS SHil SKin SWvt WEuc
	regnans	SKin WEuc
	risdonii	SKin WEuc
	rodwayi	IDee SKin WEuc
	rossii	SPlb
	rubida	CCCN CMHG GAbr SKin WEuc
	sideroxylon	SPlb
	- 'Rosea'	SPlb
	simmondsii	see *E. nitida*
	stellulata	SKin WEuc
	stricta	SKin WEuc
	sturgissiana	WEuc
	subcrenulata	CDul ELan EPfP SKin WEuc
	tetraptera	SPlb
	torquata	SPlb
	urnigera	SKin WEuc
	vernicosa	SKin WEuc
	viminalis	CAco SKin

Eucharidium see *Clarkia*

Eucharis (*Amaryllidaceae*)

§	***amazonica*** ♀H1b	CCCN ECho LAma SDeJ SPav
	grandiflora misapplied	see *E. amazonica*

Eucomis ✿ (*Asparagaceae*)

	AlohaPBR	see *E.* 'Leia'
	autumnalis misapplied	see *E. zambesiaca*
§	***autumnalis*** (Mill.) Chitt. ♀H3	CBro CHEx CTsd ECho EPot ERCP GKev LAma LRHS SDeJ SPav SPlb
	- subsp. ***autumnalis*** 'Peace Candles'	CTca
	'Baby Coral'	CAvo
	bicolor ♀H3	Widely available
	- 'Alba'	CAvo CExl CTca ECho GKev LAma
	- 'Stars and Stripes'	WCru WHil
	'Cabernet Candles'	CTca
§	***comosa*** ♀H3	CAvo CBro CHEx CHll CPrp CSam CTal CTca EBee ERCP EShb GKev LAma LEdu LRHS SDeJ SMad SPav WWEG
	- 'Cornwood'	CAvo CTca
	- 'First Red'	WPGP
	- green-leaved	CTca
	- 'Kilimanjaro'	CTca EBee GKev WHil
	- 'Lotte'	CTca EBee GKev
	- 'Oakhurst'	CAby CBct CDoC CHel CKno CMos ECtt ESwi LRHS SPad SPtp WHil
	- purple-leaved	CAvo CHEx EShb
	- 'Sparkling Burgundy' ♀H6	Widely available
	- 'Sparkling Rosy'	ECho ERCP GKev SCob
	- var. ***striata***	CAby CDes
	'Frank Lawley'	CDes
	'Freckles'	CMos LSou SPad
	humilis	CTca XEll
	- 'Twinkle Stars'	EPot GKev MBri SCob
	'John Huxtable'	GCal
	'John Treasure'	SMHy
	'Joy's Purple'	CBro CPar CTca EPri LRHS
§	'Leia'PBR	CTca GKev LRHS
	montana	CBro CPar CPrp CTca EBee ECho EPot GKev LAma WCot WPGP
	pallidiflora ♀H3	CAvo CHEx CTal LEdu SMHy WPGP
	'Pink Gin'	CAvo
	'Playa Blanca'	CTca
	pole-evansii	CBro CCon CExl CPar CPne CTal CTca EAEE ELan EPla EPri EUJe GKev IGor IVic LAma MMHG MRav SDeJ SMrm WCru WPtf WWEG
	- 'Burgundy'	GBin
I	- 'Purpurea'	CExl GCal WCot
	punctata	see *E. comosa*
	regia	CTca

- JCA 3.230.709	WCot
'Swazi Pride'	CTca
'Tugela Ruby'PBR	CTca
undulata	see *E. autumnalis* (Mill.) Chitt.
vandermerwei ♀H3	CAvo CBro CDes CPne CTal CTca EBee ECho EPot ERCP GKev LAma SDeJ SKHP SPlb WPGP
- 'Octopus'	CCCN CExl CKno CPrp CTca ECho ELan EPfP ESwi EUJe GBin GKev LSou MGos MHer MPie WCot WWEG
§ ***zambesiaca***	CAvo CTal CTca EBee GCal LAma SMHy WWEG
- JCA 3.230.709	WCot
- JCA 3.231.010	WCot
- 'White Dwarf'	ECho SPer WHil
'Zeal Bronze'	CMHG CTal CTca EPfP GCal GCra

Eucommia (*Eucommiaceae*)

ulmoides	CBcs CDul CMCN EBtc EPfP IArd IDee NLar WPGP

Eucrosia (*Amaryllidaceae*)

bicolor	CAby

Eucryphia ✿ (*Cunoniaceae*)

cordifolia	CAbP CBcs CDoC CMac GKin IDee MBlu
§ ***cordifolia* × *lucida***	CBcs CCCN ELan GGal
glutinosa ♀H4	CCCN EPfP GGGa GKin IDee LRHS MAsh SSpi WCru
- 'Miniature'	EPfP SChF WPGP
× ***hillieri*** 'Winton'	CMHG GQui
× ***intermedia***	CExl CMac CWSG EPfP GKin NLar SRms SSpi SSta
- 'Rostrevor' ♀H4	CBcs CDul CExl CJun CMHG CMac CTho ELan EPfP GBin GGGa GGal GQui IDee LRHS MBlu MBri MGil MGos MMuc NLar SPoG SReu SSta WSHC
lucida	CCCN CTho ELan LLHF LRHS MMuc NLar
- 'Ballerina' ♀H4	CBcs CMHG CMac CTho ELon GKin IDee LRHS MAsh MGos SChF SCoo SPoG SSpi WPGP
- 'Dumpling'	CExl WPGP
- 'Gilt Edge' (v)	CBcs GKin LLHF LRHS
- 'Leatherwood Cream' (v)	WHor
- 'Pink Cloud'	CBcs CDoC CDul CEnd CExl CMac CTho ELan EPfP GKin GQui IDee IVic LRHS MBlu NLar SLim SSta SWvt WPGP
- 'Pink Whisper'	see *E. milliganii* subsp. *pubescens* 'Pink Whisper'
- 'Spring Glow' (v)	CExl LLHF LRHS MAsh SPoG
milliganii	CAbP CDoC CDul CFil CMac ELan EPfP GGGa GQui LRHS MBlu MRav SRms SSpi WPGP
§ - subsp. ***pubescens*** 'Pink Whisper'	WPGP
moorei	CBcs CCCN CExl CMac GGGa WPGP
× ***nymansensis***	CHab SArc SRms SSpi
- 'George Graham'	CMHG GGGa
- 'Nymans Silver' (v)	CJun ELan GGGa LLHF LRHS MAsh
- 'Nymansay' ♀H4	Widely available
'Penwith' misapplied	see *E. cordifolia* × *E. lucida*
'Penwith' ambig.	CTsd GKin GQui IDee MMuc

Eugenia (*Myrtaceae*)

uniflora	CCCN

Eumorphia (*Asteraceae*)

prostrata	WNPC
sericea	CFis

Eunomia see *Aethionema*

Euodia (*Rutaceae*)

daniellii	see *Tetradium daniellii*
hupehensis	see *Tetradium daniellii* Hupehense Group

Euonymus ✿ (*Celastraceae*)

B&L 12543	EWes
CC 4522	CExl
NJM 09.109 **new**	WPGP
NJM 10.106 **new**	WPGP
alatus	Widely available
- B&SWJ 8794	WCru
- var. ***apterus***	EPfP MBri WGrn
- 'Blade Runner' **new**	EPfP LRHS
- Chicago Fire	see *E. alatus* 'Timber Creek'
- 'Ciliodentatus'	see *E. alatus* f. *striatus*
- 'Compactus' ♀H5	Widely available
§ - 'Fire Ball'	CJun
- Little Moses = 'Odom'	NLar
* - 'Macrophyllus'	CJun EPfP MBri
- 'Rudy Haag'	CJun
- 'Select'	see *E. alatus* 'Fire Ball'
- 'Silver Cloud'	EPfP NLar
§ - f. ***striatus*** **new**	NLar SBrt WPat
§ - 'Timber Creek'	CJun EPfP IDee LEdu LLHF MBlu NLar WPat
americanus	EPfP MBlu NLar
- var. ***angustifolius*** B&SWJ 12905 **new**	WCru
- 'Evergreen'	EPfP
- narrow-leaved	CJun EPfP
bungeanus	EPfP WPat
- B&SWJ 8782 from South Korea **new**	WCru
- 'Dart's Pride'	CJun EPfP NLar
- 'Fireflame'	CJun WPat
* - var. ***mongolicus***	EPfP
- 'Pendulus'	CJun MBlu SCoo
- var. ***semipersistens***	CJun WCru
carnosus	CJun
- CWJ 12425 **new**	WCru
chibae B&SWJ 11159	WCru
§ ***clivicola***	CJun NLar
'Copper Wire'	EHoe
cornutus var. ***quinquecornutus*** ♀H5	CJun CMCN ELan EPfP EPla MBlu NLar SBrt WPGP WPat
'Den Haag'	CJun EPfP NLar
europaeus	Widely available
- from Slovakia	WCru
- f. ***albus***	CJun CTho EPfP LRHS NLar
- 'Atropurpureus'	CMCN CTho EPfP NLar
- 'Atrorubens'	CJun
- 'Aucubifolius' (v)	CMac
* - 'Aureus'	CNat
- 'Brilliant'	CJun EPfP NLar
* - f. ***bulgaricus***	EPfP
- 'Chrysophyllus'	EPfP MBlu
- 'Howard'	EPfP NLar

Name	Suppliers
- var. ***intermedius***	CJun EPfP EPla MBlu MBri NLar
- 'Miss Pinkie'	CEnd
- 'Red Cascade' 𝕐H5	Widely available
- 'Scarlet Wonder'	CJun EPfP
- 'Thornhayes'	CTho EPfP NLar
farreri	see *E. nanus*
fimbriatus	CJun SEND
fortunei	LEdu
- Blondy = 'Interbolwi'PBR (v)	CDoC CDul COtt CTri ELan EPfP LAst LBMP LRHS MAsh MBri MGos MJak MMuc MSwo NEgg NLar NPri SCob SCoo SEND SGol SLim SPoG SRms
- 'Canadale Gold' (v)	COtt EPfP LRHS MAsh NHol NPri SLon SPoG
- 'Coloratus'	CMac ECrN EPfP MBlu MSwo SEND SPer
- 'Country Gold'	WFar
- 'Dart's Blanket'	CDul ELan EPPr EPfP MRav SCob SEND
- 'Emerald Gaiety' (v) 𝕐H5	Widely available
- 'Emerald 'n' Gold' (v) 𝕐H5	Widely available
- 'Emerald Surprise' (v) 𝕐H5	EPfP SRGP
- 'Gaiety Silver'	IBoy
- 'Gold Spot'	see *E. fortunei* 'Sunspot'
- 'Gold Tip'	see *E. fortunei* 'Golden Prince'
- Golden Harlequin = 'Hoogi'PBR (v)	COtt CSBt LRHS MAsh MBri MPkF NWad SPoG SWvt
§ - 'Golden Pillar' (v)	EHoe EPla
§ - 'Golden Prince' (v)	CMac EHoe MRav MSwo SRms
- Goldy = 'Waldbolwi'PBR	LRHS NLar NSoo SGol SHil SPoG
- 'Harlequin' (v)	CBcs CMac CSBt CWGN EBee EHoe ELan ELon EShb LBuc LRHS MAsh MBlu MGos MJak MRav NBir SGol SLim SPer SPoG SRms SWvt WFar
- 'Heins Silver'PBR	LRHS NSoo
- 'Hort's Blaze'	EPPr
- 'Kewensis' 𝕐H5	CDoC CHid CMac ELan EUJe GCal GEdr LRHS MSCN MWhi SArc SCob SPoG WCru
- 'Longwood'	LRHS
- 'Minimus'	CDul CTri EPPr EPla MSwo SCob WBor WPGP XLum
* - 'Minimus Variegatus' (v)	ECho EPPr EShb SPlb
§ - var. ***radicans***	EWld
- 'Sheridan Gold'	CTri MRav
- 'Silver Gem'	see *E. fortunei* 'Variegatus'
- 'Silver Pillar' (v)	EHoe
- 'Silver Queen' (v)	Widely available
- 'Silverstone'PBR (v)	EPfP LRHS SPoG
- 'Sunshine' (v)	EBee ELan EPfP LRHS MAsh SLon SPoG
§ - 'Sunspot' (v)	CBcs CBod CMac ELan MGos MJak MMuc MSwo SEND SRms WHar WRHF
- 'Tustin'	EAEE EPPr
§ - 'Variegatus' (v)	SRms
- 'Wolong Ghost' 𝕐H5	CDoC CExl CHel EMil EPPr GKin IArd IDee LRHS MBlu MGos NLar SGol SKHP SWvt WCot WPat
frigidus	EPfP
- var. ***elongatus*** GWJ 9378 new	WCru
grandiflorus	CJun EBee EPfP EPla NLar SCoo WFar
- 'Red Wine'	CJun CTho EBee ELon EPfP EPla ESwi ETwe LEdu LRHS NLar SKHP WPGP WPat
- f. ***salicifolius***	CJun EPfP
hamiltonianus	CMCN EBtc ECrN EPfP EWTr LRHS MMuc SEND SSpi
- NJM 11.006 new	WPGP
- 'Fiesta'	CJun
- subsp. ***hians***	see *E. hamiltonianus* subsp. *sieboldianus*
- 'Indian Summer'	CJun ELon EPfP ETwe LRHS MAsh NLar SCoo SKHP SSpi WPGP WPat
- 'Koi Boy'	CJun EBee EPla MAsh
- 'Miss Pinkie'	CJun EPfP IVic MAsh NLar SCoo WPat
- 'Pink Delight'	CJun
- 'Poort Bulten'	CJun
- 'Popcorn'	CJun EPfP WPat
- 'Rainbow'	CJun EPfP
- 'Red Chief'	CJun EPfP
- 'Red Elf'	CJun NLar
- 'Rising Sun'	CJun EBee EPfP NLar SMad
§ - subsp. ***sieboldianus***	CDul CExl CJun GBin MRav WPat
- - B&SWJ 10941	WCru
- - PAB 5337 new	LEdu
- - 'Calocarpus'	CJun EPfP SCoo
- - 'Coral Charm'	CJun EPfP NLar
* - - var. ***yedoensis*** f. ***koehneanus***	EPfP
- 'Snow'	CJun EBee EPla WCot WPat
- 'Winter Glory'	CJun MMHG
- var. ***yedoensis***	see *E. hamiltonianus* subsp. *sieboldianus*
japonicus	CBcs CBod CDoC CDul CMac CTri ECrN EPfP SArc SBod SCob SEND SEWo SPer
- 'Albomarginatus' (v)	CBcs CTri EHoe EPfP LRHS MJak SEND SRms
§ - 'Aureomarginatus'	CAco LRHS
- 'Aureopictus'	see *E. japonicus* 'Aureus'
- 'Aureovariegatus'	see *E. japonicus* 'Ovatus Aureus'
§ - 'Aureus' (v)	CAco CBcs CDoC CSBt CTsd EPfP LAst LRHS NPri NSoo SCoo SEND SLon SPer WHar
- 'Benkomasaki'	EPfP
- 'Bravo' (v)	CDoC CDul ECrN EHoe EPfP IVic LRHS MAsh MBri MGos NLar SCob SCoo SEWo SHil SLim SPoG SWvt WFar
- 'Chollipo' (v) 𝕐H5	ELan EPfP EPla LRHS MAsh SEND SHil SPoG
- 'Compactus'	SCoo
- 'Duc d'Anjou' misapplied	see *E. japonicus* 'Viridivariegatus'
- 'Duc d'Anjou' Carrière (v)	EBee EHoe ELan EPfP EWes MRav SEND SPoG
- 'Elegantissimus Aureus'	see *E. japonicus* 'Aureomarginatus'
- Exstase = 'Goldbolwi'PBR (v)	SPoG WCot
- 'Francien' (v)	EBee LRHS SHil
- 'Gold Queen'PBR	LRHS NLar
- 'Golden Maiden' (v)	ELan EPfP LRHS MAsh SLim SLon SPoG SRms SWvt
- 'Golden Pillar'	see *E. fortunei* 'Golden Pillar'
- Green Millenium = 'Minmil'PBR new	LRHS
- 'Green Rocket'	EBee EPfP EShb GBin LRHS MBri MRav SGol SHil SLim SPoG WFar WPat
- 'Green Spider'	SPoG
- 'Grey Beauty'	ELon EShb NLar
- 'Happiness'PBR	MPkF SLim

- 'Hibarimisake' (v) EPfP
- 'Kathy'[PBR] ELon EPfP LRHS LSqu MAsh NSoo SCob SHil SLim SPoG SRGP
§ - 'Latifolius Albomarginatus' (v) CTsd ELan EPfP MRav MSwo SPer SWvt
- 'Luna' see *E. japonicus* 'Aureus'
- 'Macrophyllus Albus' see *E. japonicus* 'Latifolius Albomarginatus'
- 'Maiden's Gold' COtt CSBt
- 'Marieke' see *E. japonicus* 'Ovatus Aureus'
- 'Microphyllus' CDoC MRav NEgg SRms
§ - 'Microphyllus Albovariegatus' (v) CBcs CDoC CDul CMac CSBt CTri ELan EPfP LAst LRHS MGos NSoo SCob SEND SHil SLim SRms SWvt WFar
§ - 'Microphyllus Aureovariegatus' (v) CDoC ELan EPfP LRHS MAsh MMuc NLar NSoo SHil WHar
- 'Microphyllus Aureus' see *E. japonicus* 'Microphyllus Pulchellus'
§ - 'Microphyllus Pulchellus' (v) CBcs CDoC CMac CSBt EBee ECrN EPfP LRHS MAsh MGos SEND SHil SWvt
- 'Microphyllus Variegatus' see *E. japonicus* 'Microphyllus Albovariegatus'
§ - 'Ovatus Aureus' (v) ♀H5 CDoC CDul CExl CMac CSBt CTri EBee ELon EPfP LAst LRHS MGos MRav NLar NSoo SCob SEND SGol SHil SLim SPer SPlb SPoG SRms SWvt WFar
- 'Président Gauthier' (v) CAco CDoC EAEE EBee MBri MGos SCob SCoo SLim SPer SWvt WCFE
- 'Pulchellus Aureovariegatus' see *E. japonicus* 'Microphyllus Aureovariegatus'
I - 'Pyramidatus' EPfP
- 'Rokujo' GEdr
- 'Silver King' CMac
- 'Silver Krista' (v) NLar
- 'Susan' (v) ♀H5 CDoC CMac EShb MAsh SRGP
§ - 'Viridivariegatus' (v) LRHS
kachinensis B&SWJ 11668 WCru
kiautschovicus 'Berry Hill' NLar
- 'Manhattan' NLar
latifolius CJun CMCN EPfP IMou LEdu WPat
§ ***laxiflorus*** GWJ 9351 **new** WCru
- HWJ 890 **new** WCru
lucidus CBcs CExl CHll EBee SSpi
maackii NWea
macropterus CJun EPfP
maximowiczianus EPfP NLar WPat
mexicanus CFil
morrisonensis CJun WPat
- B&SWJ 3700 WCru
myrianthus CJun EPfP ETwe EUJe EWes MBlu NLar
§ ***nanus*** CJun NLar WSHC WThu
- var. ***turkestanicus*** CFil GKin LRHS SBrt SLon SRms WOld
obovatus NLar
oxyphyllus ♀H5 CDul CJun CMCN CTho EBee EPfP EPla IArd MBri NLar SEND WCru WPat
- 'Waasland' CJun EPfP
phellomanus ♀H5 CDoC CDul CTho EBee EPfP GKin LRHS MAsh MBlu MGil MGos MPkF MRav NLar SCoo SKHP SPoG SWvt WCot WFar WPGP
- 'Silver Surprise' (v) CJun ELon EPfP WPat
Pierrolino = 'Heespierrolino'[PBR] LRHS MRav SCoo
§ ***planipes*** Widely available
- B&SWJ 8660 **new** WCru
- 'Dart's August Flame' CJun EPfP
- 'Sancho' ♀H5 CJun EPfP MBri WPat
porphyreus GWJ 9377 **new** WCru
quelpaertensis CJun
radicans see *E. fortunei* var. *radicans*
'Rokojō' LLHF WPat
'Rokojō Variegated' (v) WCot
rongchuensis 'Cliuicolus' see *E. clivicola*
rosmarinifolius see *E. nanus*
rubescens see *E. laxiflorus*
sachalinensis misapplied see *E. planipes*
sachalinensis (F. Schmidt) Maxim. B&SWJ 10835 WCru
sacrosanctus CJun MBlu
sanguineus CJun SSpi
sieboldianus ETwe
var. ***sanguineus***
- - B&SWJ 11140 WCru
- - B&SWJ 11386 WCru
spraguei NLar
- CWJ 12446 WCru
tingens CJun NLar
trapococcus EPfP
vagans EPfP WCot
verrucosus CJun NLar
vidalii EPfP
wilsonii CDoC COtt LRHS NLar
yedoensis see *E. hamiltonianus* subsp. *sieboldianus*

Eupatoriadelphus see *Eupatorium*

Eupatorium ✿ (*Asteraceae*)

B&SWJ 9052 from Guatemala WCru
FMWJ 13428 from Northern Vietnam **new** WCru
album misapplied see *Ageratina altissima*
album L. NBid SWat
altissimum SRms
aromaticum see *Ageratina aromatica*
atrorubens see *Bartlettina sordida*
cannabinum CArn CHab EHon ELan EShb GLog GPoy IFoB MBNS MHer MMuc MNHC MRav NBir NMir NPer SEND SGSe SPav SWat WHfH WSFF
§ - f. ***albiflorum*** SPhx
- 'Album' see *E. cannabinum* f. *albiflorum*
- f. ***cannabinum*** 'Flore Pleno' (d) CAby CMac CPrp ECtt ELan ELon EPfP IBoy MAvo MBel MHer MRav NBir NGdn NLar SPhx SWat WCot WMnd WSFF WWtn XLum
- - 'Spraypaint' (v) WSFF
capillifolium ♀H3 CAby EBee ECtt ESwi EWes SDix SHar SMrm SPhx WCot WWEG
chinense CSpe
coelestinum see *Conoclinium coelestinum*
dubium 'Baby Joe'[PBR] CWGN ECtt IPot LRHS MNrw NPCo
- 'Little Joe' EBee EPPr LEdu MWhi WCAu WWEG
fistulosum EBee
- f. ***albidum*** **new** WWFP
- - 'Bartered Bride' CKno EBee ECtt EWes GCal MAvo WCot
- - 'Ivory Towers' LBMP LRHS LSun SPtp WPtf WWEG

- - 'Massive White' ♀H6	CCon GCal NBir NSti
- 'Berggarten'	GCal
- 'Carin'	WSFF
fortunei	CArn
- 'Fine Line' (v)	CKno EPPr LSou WSFF WWEG
- 'Pink Elegance' (v)	CBod EBee ECtt EPla EShb LRHS SPoG SRms WMnd WWEG
- 'Pink Frost' (v)	MAsh WHil
japonicum	GPoy
ligustrinum	see *Ageratina ligustrina*
lindleyanum	CKno EBee
maculatum	MHer MSCN NGdn NLar WHrl
- Atropurpureum Group	Widely available
- - 'Ankum's August'	IMou
- - 'Gateway'	CBod EBee ECtt ELon GCal LRHS NBre NLar SWvt WHil WHoo WMnd WMoo WSFF WWtn
- - 'Glutball'	CKno ELon GCal IMou LBMP LPla LRHS MNrw NChi SMad WWEG
- - 'Little Red'	GBin WSFF
- - 'Orchard Dene' ♀H6	SMHy
- - 'Phantom' PBR	CBod EBee ECtt ELon EWoo GQue IPot LRHS MBri MWts NCGa NLar SPoG WMoo WPtf
- - 'Purple Bush' ♀H6	CKno EBee ECtt ELon EPPr EWTr GBee GBin GCal GQue LRHS NEgg NPCo SPhx SWvt WSFF WWEG
- - 'Red Dwarf'	CBod ECtt ELon GQue IKil IPot LEdu MBel SCob SHar SWvt WWEG
- - 'Riesenschirm' ♀H6	Widely available
makinoi	WCru
var. ***oppositifolium*** B&SWJ 8449	
micranthum	see *Ageratina ligustrina*
perfoliatum	CArn CKno GPoy MNrw NBre NLar SPhx WSFF
purpureum	Widely available
- 'Album'	CTri MBel SPhx SWvt
rugosum	see *Ageratina altissima*
weinmannianum	see *Ageratina ligustrina*

Euphorbia ✿ (*Euphorbiaceae*)

'Abbey Dore'	SPhx WCot
aeruginosa new	LToo
ambovombensis	LToo
amygdaloides	ECtt SWat SWvt WOut
- 'Craigieburn'	CBod EWes GBuc GCra LRHS MAsh MGos MRav SPoG WPGP
- 'Frosted Flame' PBR	CSpe
§ - 'Purpurea'	Widely available
§ - var. ***robbiae***	Widely available
- - dwarf	EWes
- - 'Pom Pom'	LSou
- - 'Redbud'	EWes LSou
- 'Rubra'	see *E. amygdaloides* 'Purpurea'
- 'Winter Glow'	CSpe
aureoviridiflora	LToo
baselicis	CPla CPom CSpe EWes SEND
biglandulosa Desf.	see *E. rigida*
Blackbird = 'Nothowlee' PBR	Widely available
'Blue Dome'	CSpe
'Blue Haze'	CAby CDes CPom NLar WCot
Breathless Blush = 'Balbreblus' PBR	WCot
caerulescens	LToo
capitulata	SBrt
cashmeriana	EBee
- CC&McK 607	EWes
ceratocarpa	CFil CPom CSpe ECtt EWes EWoo GMaP LPla LRHS LSou NWit SEND SIgm SMad WCot WSHC
characias	CArn CBcs CHEx CMac ECtt EPfP EPla EWoo IBoy LRHS LSun MCot MJak MLHP MRav NPer SPer SPhx SRms SWvt WBrk WCot WMnd WWEG XLum XSen
- 'Black Pearl'	CBcs CBod CHel CRos ECrN ECtt EPfP LRHS MAvo MBel MBri MGos MPnt MWat NSbr SGbt SGol SHil SLim SPer SPoG SRkn SWvt WFar WWEG
- 'Blue Wonder'	CExl ECtt ELan EPfP GAbr GBin GMaP LBMP LRHS MAvo MGos MHol NEgg NGdn NLar NWit WCot
- subsp. ***characias***	CBod GMaP NLar SEND
- - 'Blue Hills'	ECtt WWEG
- - 'Burrow Silver' (v)	CCon MRav NEgg SPer SWvt
- - 'Humpty Dumpty'	CBod CExl CUse EBee ECrN ECtt ELan ELon EPfP GMaP IBoy LRHS LSqH MAsh MBri MGos MWat NGdn NLar NPer NSoo SCob SPer SRms SWvt WCot
- 'Dwarf Black Pearl'	ECtt WWEG
- 'Forescate'	CUse EBee EPfP GBin
- 'Freckles' (v) new	MAvo
- 'Glacier Blue' PBR	CBct CSpe CWGN LAst LRHS MAsh MPro SCob SPoG WNPC
- 'Goldbrook'	CWCL ECtt EHoe EPfP EPla LRHS MRav NGdn NLar
- 'Kestrel' (v)	WCot
- 'Portuguese Velvet' ♀H7	CBod CExl CHel CWCL ECtt ELan ELon EPfP EUJe LPla LRHS MCot MNFA MRav NLar NPri NWit SKHP SLim SPhx SPoG SPtp WCot WWEG
- Silver Swan = 'Wilcott' PBR (v) ♀H2	Widely available
- 'Tasmanian Tiger' PBR (v)	CBct CUse CWGN ECtt EWes GMaP LAst LRHS LSou MBri MGos MHol MPnt NBir SEle SGol SKHP SMDP SPad SPoG SRms SWvt WCot WNPC WRHF
- subsp. ***wulfenii***	Widely available
- - 'Bosahan' (v)	CExl
- - 'Emmer Green' (v)	CExl CHel ECtt ELon EWes GAbr GMaP IKil LRHS MAvo MHol MMHG NLar NSti NWit SMrm WCot WWEG
- - 'Jimmy Platt'	SRms WCot
§ - - 'John Tomlinson' ♀H4	MRav WCFE
- - Kew form	see *E. characias* subsp. *wulfenii* 'John Tomlinson'
- - 'Lambrook Gold' ♀H4	CSam CWCL GCra MRav NLar NPer SMad WCot WWEG
- - - seed-raised	see *E. characias* subsp. *wulfenii* Margery Fish Group
§ - - Margery Fish Group	CWCL LRHS MCot NBir
- - 'Perry's Tangerine'	EWes NPer
§ - - 'Purple and Gold'	ECtt EWes MAvo NWit SWvt WWEG
- - 'Purpurea'	see *E. characias* subsp. *wulfenii* 'Purple and Gold'
- - 'Shorty' new	ECtt
- - var. ***sibthorpii***	IBoy
- - 'Silver Shadow'	WCot
- - 'Thelma's Giant'	MAvo NWit
- - 'Westacre Giant'	EWes

clavarioides* var. *truncata	WCot
'Copton Ash'	CSpe EBee EWes GBin SKHP WNPC XSen
corallioides	ECha IFro LRHS NLar NPer NSti SPer WHer
§ ***cornigera*** ♀H6	CElw EBee ECha EPfP GBin GBuc LRHS MAvo MMuc MSpe NBid NGdn NLar NSti NWit SEND SPhx SWat WCru WFar
- 'Goldener Turm'	CBod ECtt EPfP ESwi GBin GBuc GCal LPla LRHS LSou MBri MSCN NDov NWit SDix SPer WCot WFar
croizatii	LToo
cylindrifolia* var. *tubifera	LToo
cyparissias	CBcs ECha ELan EWoo MLHP MRav NBir NGdn NLar SMrm SPav SRms WBrk WFar XLum XSen
- 'Betten'	see *E.* × *gayeri* 'Betten'
- 'Bushman Boy'	SMrm
- 'Clarice Howard'	see *E. cyparissias* 'Fens Ruby'
§ - 'Fens Ruby'	Widely available
- 'Orange Man'	CBod CNec CTca ECtt EPfP EPla EWes LBMP LRHS LSou NBro NEgg NGdn NLar SMrm SPoG SVen SWat SWvt WAul WBrk WFar WWEG
- 'Purpurea'	see *E. cyparissias* 'Fens Ruby'
- 'Red Devil'	NWit WWEG
- 'Tall Boy'	EWes
decaryi **new**	LToo
decidua	LToo
deflexa	EBee EWes MAvo
dendroides	LRHS
'Despina'[PBR]	LRHS SBod SMrm
didiereoides **new**	LToo
§ ***donii***	EWes MAvo NWit SDix XEll
- HWJK 2405	WCru
- 'Amjillasa'	SDix SMHy WCot
dulcis	CBre NBro NWit
- 'Chameleon'	CSBt ECtt EHoe ELan ELon EPfP GCal MCot MGos MRav NBid NBir NLar NPer SGol SPlb SRms SRot SWat SWvt WBrk WCot WFar WMoo WWEG
'Efanthia'[PBR]	CEnd CKno CUse ELon EWes GBin LRHS LSou MAvo NLar SHil SMrm WCot
enormis	LToo
epithymoides	see *E. polychroma*
esula Baker's form	NWit
Excalibur = 'Froeup'[PBR]	CBod CExl CKno CMac CWCL ELan ELon GBin IVic MBNS MMuc MNrw MRav NBir NLar NSti SBod SEND SPer SPoG SPtp SRkn SRms SWvt
fischeriana B&SWJ 8575	WCru
flavicoma	GCal
fragifera	NWit
§ × ***gayeri*** 'Betten'	EBee LPla
glauca	ECou SKHP
globosa **new**	LToo
'Golden Foam'	see *E. stricta*
'Grey Hedgehog'	LSou SHar SRms WNPC
griffithii	CHll GGal IFoB NBro SWat WFar WMoo WWtn
- 'Dixter' ♀H7	Widely available
- 'Dixter Flame'	IFoB MWat NWit
- 'Fern Cottage'	CElw EWes MAvo WMnd
- 'Fireglow'	Widely available
- 'King's Caple'	ELon EWes GBin LRHS NLar SPoG WCru
- 'Wickstead'	CPom GBin MLHP
groenewaldii	LToo
'Helena'[PBR] (v)	CExl NLar SRms SWvt WHil
horrida ♀H2	LToo SPlb
hyberna	SWat
hypericifolia Diamond Frost = 'Inneuphe'[PBR]	CSpe ESwi LBMP LSou MCot SRkn WCot
ingens	CAbb SPlb
jacquemontii	IFoB NLar WCot
'Jade Dragon'	LRHS SWvt
jolkinii	CExl
Kalipso = 'Innkalff'	LRHS NLar SHil SRot
knobelii	LToo
'Lambrook Silver'	SRkn
lathyris	CArn CBre MLHP NLar NPer NWit SRms SVic
longifolia misapplied	see *E. cornigera*
longifolia D. Don	see *E. donii*
longifolia Lam.	see *E. mellifera*
margalidiana	EWes MAvo NWit
× ***martini***	Widely available
- 'Aperitif'[PBR]	LPal
- 'Ascot Rainbow'[PBR] (v)	Widely available
- 'Baby Charm'	EAEE EBee ECtt ELon EUJe GBin GCal GKin IPot LRHS MAsh MGos NLar SHil SMrm SPoG SRms WFar WNPC
- 'Cherokee'	WCot
- 'Colibri' **new**	MBel MPnt
- dwarf	CCon
- 'Helen Robinson'	WCot
- Helena's Blush = 'Inneuphhel' (v)	EPfP
- 'Kolibri'	EBee MBri SPoG SWvt
- 'Little John'	CRos LRHS MBri
- 'Rudolph'[PBR] **new**	CBod ECtt EPfP LRHS MAsh
- Tiny Tim = 'Waleutiny'	ECtt EPPr EPfP GBin LRHS MAsh SPoG SWvt
- 'Walberton's Red Flush'	EPfP LRHS
§ ***mellifera*** ♀H2	Widely available
meloformis ♀H2	LToo
milii ♀H1b	EBak
moratii	LToo
myrsinites ♀H4	Widely available
nereidum	EWes NWit
nicaeensis	GCal LPla LRHS SEND SPer SPhx WCot XLum XSen
- subsp. ***glareosa***	NWit
obesa ♀H2	LToo
oblongata	GBin NLar NWit SEND WCot
palustris ♀H7	Widely available
- 'Walenburg's Glorie'	CWCL ECha ELan EWTr EWoo GBin GQue IBoy MNrw MRav NSti NWit SWat WCot WKif
- 'Woodchippings'	WCot
- 'Zauberflöte'	ELon SRms
paralias	WCot WHer
× ***pasteurii***	CBod CCon CDTJ EPfP EWes EWld GCal LSou MNHC MNrw NBir NLos NWit SPhx WCot WPGP
- 'Devil's Honey'	CHid WCot
- 'John Phillips'	CExl CMHG EBee EPfP IVic LRHS MAvo SChF WGrf WPGP
- 'Phrampton Phatty'	LRHS WCot WPGP
pekinensis	SKHP

pentagona SVen
pilosa 'Major' see *E. polychroma* 'Major'
pithyusa CSpe ECha ELan MRav SEND WCot WSHC XLum XSen
platyclada LToo
§ ***polychroma*** Widely available
- 'Bonfire'PBR ECtt LRHS LSun MAvo MBri NLar SPoG
§ - 'Candy' CBod EBee ECha EPfP LSqH MNHC SMrm WFar
- compact NWit
- 'First Blush' (v) MAsh NWit
- 'Geisha' **new** EWes
- 'Golden Fusion' EPfP LBuc LRHS MAsh MAvo MBri WFar
§ - 'Lacy' (v) CDoC EWes NBir NGdn NWit SKHP
§ - 'Major' ♀H6 CExl EBee WCot WKif
- 'Midas' CWCL GBin MNrw NWit SDix SMrm
- 'Purpurea' see *E. polychroma* 'Candy'
* - 'Senior' GBin LRHS NLar
- 'Variegata' see *E. polychroma* 'Lacy'
portlandica SVen WHer
§ × ***pseudovirgata*** SMrm
pulcherrima SPre
pulvinata LToo
Redwing = 'Charam'PBR ♀H5 CBcs CKno CMac CUse ECtt EHoe ELan EPfP EWoo IKil LBuc LRHS LSou MAvo MBri MGos MHol MRav NLar NPri NSti NWit SGol SLim SPer SPoG SWvt WCot
reflexa see *E. seguieriana* subsp. *niciciana*
§ ***rigida*** ♀H6 CAby CBod CBro CDes CPom CSpe EBee EHoe ELan EPfP EUJe EWes GCal GJos LPla MAvo SEND SIgm SMrm SPhx WCot WPGP WWEG XSen
robbiae see *E. amygdaloides* var. *robbiae*
'Roundway Titan' EBee LRHS SSpi SWvt WSHC
sarawschanica ECha GQue LPla LRHS NWit SMad SPhx
schillingii ♀H5 EHoe ELan EPfP EWTr GCra GMaP LRHS MRav NLar SDix SPer SPhx SPlb SPoG SPtp SRms SWvt WCru WWEG
schoenlandii LToo
seguieriana ECha NLar SPhx
§ - subsp. ***niciciana*** GBin IMou WHoo
sepulta **new** LToo
serrulata Thuill. see *E. stricta*
sikkimensis ♀H5 CBod CExl CMHG CWCL ECha ELan EWes GCal IMou LRHS NEgg NPer SRms WCru
- 'Crûg Contrast' WCru
soongarica NWit
spinosa NWit SPlb XSen
stellispina LToo
§ ***stricta*** CBgR CFil CPom NWad SBod
stygiana CCon CExl CHel CPne CPom CSam CSpe ELon EUJe EWes GBin GCal IBoy LRHS SMrm SPlb WCot WCru WSHC
- subsp. ***santamariae*** CFil
- subsp. ***stygiana*** CFil
tirucalli EShb
uralensis see *E.* × *pseudovirgata*
valdevillosocarpa CBod SPhx WFar
'Velvet Ruby' CUse GBin LSou NWit SWvt WCot WNPC
viguieri LToo
villosa Waldst. & Kit. ex Willd. GBin LEdu NWit
§ ***virgata*** EWes NWit
× ***waldsteinii*** see *E. virgata*
wallichii misapplied see *E. donii*
wallichii Kohli see *E. cornigera*
wallichii ambig. CSam
wallichii Hook. f. CExl EPfP GCal MNrw NOrc SKHP SPhx
'Whistleberry Garnet' CMac CWCL EAEE EBee EPfP EWoo LBMP LLHF LRHS LSou NSti SDix SEND SKHP SLim SPoG SWvt WNPC

Euptelea (*Eupteleaceae*)

franchetii see *E. pleiosperma*
§ ***pleiosperma*** NLar SSpi
polyandra EPfP NLar SBrt

Eurya (*Pentaphylacaceae*)

japonica 'Moutiers' (v) WCot
- 'Variegata' misapplied see *Cleyera japonica* 'Fortunei'

Euryops (*Asteraceae*)

abrotanifolius CCCN SVen
§ ***acraeus*** ♀H4 CMea CSBt ECho EPot EWes GCrg GEdr WAbe
brachypodus **new** SVen
§ ***chrysanthemoides*** CCCN CDoC CHEx CSde EShb SEND SVen
- 'Sonnenschein' LAst SPtp
evansii Schltr. see *E. acraeus*
lateriflorus SPlb
pectinatus ♀H3 CBcs CBod CCCN CDTJ CDoC CExl CHEx CHel CSde CTca CTri CTsd ELan EPfP EShb GGal IVic LAst LRHS MOWG MSCN SEND SPtp SVen SWvt
tenuissimus SVen
tysonii CTca EPot EWes SPlb SVen
virgineus CCCN CDoC CExl SPlb SVen

Euscaphis (*Staphyleaceae*)

japonica B&SWJ 11359 **new** WCru

Eustachys (*Poaceae*)

§ ***distichophylla*** NWsh

Eustrephus (*Philesiaceae*)

latifolius ECou

Eutaxia (*Papilionaceae*)

obovata ECou

Eutrochium see *Eupatorium*

Ewartia (*Asteraceae*)

planchonii EPot NSla WAbe

Exochorda (*Rosaceae*)

alberti see *E. korolkowii*
giraldii var. ***wilsonii*** CExl CMac EBee EPfP LRHS MBlu MNHC MRav NLar NSoo SWvt
§ ***korolkowii*** LRHS MAsh NLar
× ***macrantha*** COtt LRHS
- 'Irish Pearl' CExl

§	- 'Niagara'	CMac EPfP GBin LRHS LSqu MPkF NLar SCob
	- Snow Day Surprise	see *E.* × *macrantha* 'Niagara'
	- 'The Bride' ♀H6	Widely available
	racemosa	EPfP MMuc NLar SPer
	serratifolia	CBcs EPfP LRHS MMuc SPoG
	- 'Snow White'	CJun EPfP EWes GKin IArd LRHS MBlu NLar SLon SPoG SWvt

F

Fabiana (*Solanaceae*)

	foliosa 'Cliftonville Limelight' **new**	WAbe
	imbricata	CAbP ELon EPfP LLHF LRHS MGil SLon SPer SPlb WAbe WCot
	- 'Prostrata'	CBcs EBee LRHS SVen WThu
	- f. ***violacea*** ♀H4	CExl CHel CHll CSBt CTri CTsd EBee EPfP LLHF LRHS MMuc SEND SPer SPoG SWvt WKif
	- - dark-flowered **new**	CBcs
	nana	WAbe

Fagopyrum (*Polygonaceae*)

	from India	GCal
	cymosum	see *F. dibotrys*
§	***dibotrys***	EBee ECha EWld LEdu

Fagus ✿ (*Fagaceae*)

§	***crenata***	CMen MBlu
	- 'Mount Fuji'	CMen LLHF NPCo SBir
	engleriana	CExl CMCN SBir
	grandifolia subsp. ***mexicana***	SBir
	japonica	SBir
	- var. ***multinervis***	SBir
	longipetiolata	CExl
	lucida	CExl
	orientalis	CAco CMCN SBir
	- 'Iskander'	IArd MBlu MBri NLar
	sieboldii	see *F. crenata*
	sylvatica ♀H6	Widely available
	- 'Albovariegata' (v)	CMCN
	- 'Aniek'	MBri SGol
	- 'Ansorgei'	CEnd EPla LAst MBlu MPkF
	- 'Arcuata'	SBir
	- Atropurpurea Group	Widely available
	- 'Aurea Pendula'	CAco CEnd CMCN MBlu SBir WPat
	- 'Bicolor Sartini'	MBlu
	- 'Birr Zebra'	CEnd
	- 'Black Swan'	CDul CLnd CMCN EBee GBin IArd LLHF MBlu MBri MGos NEgg NHol NLar NPCo SBir SLon SPoG
	- 'Brathay Purple'	MBlu
	- 'Cochleata'	CMCN
	- 'Cockleshell'	MBlu SBir
	- 'Cristata'	MBlu
§	- 'Dawyck' ♀H6	CBcs CDoC CDul CLnd CMac COtt CSBt CTho ECrN ELan EPfP EPla MBri MGos NEgg NLar NPCo NWea SBir SCob SGol SLau SLim SPer WMou
	- 'Dawyck Gold' ♀H6	CBcs CDoC CDul CEnd CLnd CMCN CMac COtt CTri EBee GKin IVic MAsh MBlu MBri MGos NEgg NPCo NWea SBir SCob SGol SLau SPer WHar
	- 'Dawyck Purple' ♀H6	CAco CBcs CDoC CDul CEnd CLnd CMCN CMac COtt CTho CTri EPfP EWTr GKin IVic LAst MAsh MBlu MBri MGos NEgg NWea SBir SCob SGol SPer
	- 'Eugen'	SBir
	- 'Fastigiata' misapplied	see *F. sylvatica* 'Dawyck'
	- 'Felderbach'	SBir
	- 'Franken' (v)	CAco LLHF MBlu SBir
	- 'Greenwood'	LLHF MBlu NLar
	- var. ***heterophylla***	CLnd CSBt CTho NWea
	- - 'Aspleniifolia' ♀H6	CAco CBcs CDul CEnd CMCN CMac EBee ECrN ELan EPfP EPla ESwi GKin MBlu MBri MGos NPCo SBir SCoo SGol SLau SPer WMou
	- - 'Incisa'	MBlu
	- - f. ***laciniata***	MBlu
	- 'Horizontalis'	MBlu
	- 'Luteovariegata' (v)	CEnd
	- 'Mercedes'	CDoC CDul CMCN LLHF MBlu NPCo WPat
	- 'Pendula' ♀H6	CAco CBcs CDoC CDul CEnd CLnd CMCN CMac COtt CSBt CTho EBee ECrN ELan EPfP EPla MGos MSwo NEgg NPCo NWea SGol SLau SPer WHar WMou
	- 'Prince George of Crete'	CDul CMCN
	- 'Purple Fountain' ♀H6	CAco CDoC CDul CEnd CMCN EBee ELan EPla LAst MAsh MBlu MBri MGos MWat NLar SBir SLau SLim
	- Purple-leaved Group	see *F. sylvatica* Atropurpurea Group
	- 'Purpurea Pendula'	CAco CBcs CCVT CEnd CMCN CMac COtt CSBt CTri ELan EPfP GKin IVic LAst MAsh MBri MGos MJak MSwo NEgg NPCo NWea SCoo SGol SLau SLim SPer SPoG WHar
§	- 'Purpurea Tricolor' (v)	CDul CEnd CMCN CMac ECrN EWTr MAsh MBlu MGos NWea SBir SCoo SPer WMou
	- 'Red Obelisk'	see *F. sylvatica* 'Rohan Obelisk'
	- 'Riversii' ♀H6	CAco CBcs CDoC CDul CEnd CLnd CMCN COtt CTho CTri ECrN ELan EPfP GKin LAst MAsh MBri MGos NWea SPer WHar
	- 'Rohan Fastigiate' **new**	EPla
	- 'Rohan Gold'	CEnd CMCN SGol
	- 'Rohan Minaret'	SGol
§	- 'Rohan Obelisk'	CAco CDul CEnd CMCN CTho ELan EPla EWTr IArd MBlu NLar NPCo SBir SGol SPoG
I	- 'Rohan Pyramidalis'	CEnd
	- 'Rohan Trompenburg'	CMCN MBlu
	- 'Rohan Weeping'	MBlu SBir
	- 'Rohanii'	CBcs CDoC CDul CEnd CLnd CMCN CTri EBee ELan EPfP GKin LAst MGos NPCo SBir SLau SPer WHar
	- 'Roseomarginata'	see *F. sylvatica* 'Purpurea Tricolor'
	- 'Rotundifolia'	CDul MBlu NPCo SGol
	- 'Spaethiana'	EWTr GKin
	- 'Striata'	LLHF NPCo
	- 'Sychrov'	SBir
	- f. ***tortuosa***	MPkF NPCo

	- 'Tricolor' misapplied (v)	see *F. sylvatica* 'Purpurea Tricolor' (v)
	- 'Tricolor' ambig. (v)	SLau
	- 'Tricolor' (v)	CBcs CLnd COtt CSBt ELan EPla LLHF NHol NPCo SGol
	- 'Viridivariegata' (v)	CMCN
	- 'Zlatia'	CDul CLnd CMCN CSBt ELan EPfP MBlu MGos MPkF NLar NWea SBir SGol SLau

Fallopia (*Polygonaceae*)

	aubertii	see *F. baldschuanica*
§	***baldschuanica***	CBcs CChe CMac COtt CSBt CTri EBee ELan EPfP LBuc LRHS MAsh MGos MJak MMuc MSwo NEgg NPri NWea SEND SLim SLon SPer SPlb SPoG SWvt WHar
§	***japonica*** var. ***compacta***	WMoo XLum
	- - 'Fuji Snow'	see *F. japonica* var. *compacta* 'Milk Boy'
§	- - 'Milk Boy' (v)	EShb
	- - 'Variegata' misapplied	see *F. japonica* var. *compacta* 'Milk Boy'
§	***multiflora***	CArn CBod LEdu
	- var. ***hypoleuca***	SCoo SLim SPoG
	- - B&SWJ 120	WCru

Farfugium (*Asteraceae*)

§	***japonicum***	CHEx MBel
	- B&SWJ 884	WCru
	- 'Argenteum' (v)	SMad WCot
§	- 'Aureomaculatum' (v) ♀H3	CCon CHEx CTal ECtt EPfP LEdu
	- 'Bumpy Ride'	WCot
	- 'Crispatum'	CAbP CCon CTal EPfP LAst LEdu WWEG
	- double-flowered (d)	WCru
	- var. ***formosanum*** B&SWJ 7125	WCru
	- - CWJ 12356	WCru
	- 'Kaimon Dake'	WCot
	- 'Kinkan' (v)	WCot
I	- 'Nanum'	CHEx
	- 'Ryuto'	WCot
I	- 'Tsuwa-buki'	WCot
	'Last Dance'PBR	NLar
	tussilagineum	see *F. japonicum*

Fargesia (*Poaceae*)

	from Jiuzhaigou, China	CDTJ CEnt EPfP ERod EUJe GBin LPal MAvo MBri MMoz MMuc MWht NLar NWsh SBig SEND WPGP
	adpressa	EPla MWht
	angustissima	CDTJ CEnt CExl CFil EPfP EPla ERod MMuc MWht SBig SEND
	confusa	CDTJ
	denudata	CDTJ CEnt CFil EPla ERod SBig
	- L 1575	CExl EPla MMoz MWht
	- Xian 1	CDTJ EPla MMoz WPGP
	dracocephala	CDoC CEnt CExl CFil EPla ERod ESwi GBin LEdu LRHS MAvo MBrN MMoz MMuc MWht SBig SEND WMoo WPGP
	- 'White Dragon'	CExl CFil SMad
	ferax	EPla
§	***murielae*** ♀H4	CDoC CEnt CFil CHEx ELan EPau EPfP EPla ERod MGos MJak MMoz MMuc MWhi MWht NGdn NLos SArc SCob SEND SPlb SPoG WMoo
	- 'Amy'	NLar
	- 'Bimbo'	CBod CEnt EPfP EPla ERod ESwi LPal LRHS MWhi MWht NLar SCob WMoo
	- 'Dana Jumbo'	LRHS
	- 'Grüne Hecke'	ERod MWht SBig
	- 'Harewood'	CFil MMoz MWht SWvt
	- 'Joy'	GBin NLar WMoo
	- 'Jumbo'	CEnt CSBt ELan ELon EPfP EPla ERod ESwi EUJe LPal LRHS MAvo MBri MGos MMoz MWhi MWht NGdn NWsh SBig SPer SPoG SRms SWvt
	- 'Kranich'	NLar
	- 'Lava'	MBri
	- 'Mae'	CDTJ MWht
	- 'Pinocchio'	MBri
	- 'Simba'	Widely available
	- 'Vampire'	ERod EUJe LRHS MBri SBig
	- 'Willow'	MBri
	murieliae 'Superjumbo'PBR	EPla LPal
*	***nepalensis***	ESwi
§	***nitida***	CAbb CBcs CDoC CDul CEnd CEnt CSBt ELan EPfP ERod IFro LRHS MBri MGos MJak MMoz MWht SCob SPoG SRms SWvt WHer WMoo WPGP
	- 'Eisenach'	MMoz
	- 'Great Wall'	EUJe LPal MBri MGos MWht
	- Jiuzhaigou 1	see *F.* Red Panda
	- 'Jiuzhaigou 2'	EPla
	- 'Jiuzhaigou 4'	CExl CFil WPGP
	- 'Jiuzhaigou 8'	WPGP
	- 'Jiuzhaigou Genf'	CFil WPGP
	- 'Nymphenburg'	CEnd MBri MMoz SBig
	perlonga	EPla
	- Yunnan 6	ERod MMoz WPGP
§	Red Panda = 'Jiu' ♀H4	CExl CFil EPla LPal LRHS SPoG
	robusta ♀H4	CAbb CChe CDTJ CEnt CHel ELan EPfP EPla ERod LRHS MAvo MBrN MBri MMoz MMuc MWhi MWht NGdn NLar NLos SBig
	- 'Campbell'	EPla LPal MMoz
	- 'Ming Yunnan'	LEdu
	- 'P. King'	ERod MWht
	- 'Pingwu'	CBod CDTJ CEnt EPla ERod GBin LPal MGos MWht SBig
	- 'Red Sheath'	CEnt CExl CJun EPla ERod MMoz MWht WPGP
	- 'Wolong'	CDoC CExl EPla ERod MMoz MWht WPGP
	rufa ♀H4	CAbb CEnt CExl CFil CHEx CHel EPPr EPfP EPla ERod EUJe LPal LRHS MAvo MBlu MBrN MGos MJak MMoz MMuc MWhi MWht NLar SBig SEND WPGP
	spathacea misapplied	see *F. murielae*
	utilis	CEnt ERod MMoz MMuc MWht SEND
	yulongshanensis	EPla ERod MWht

Farsetia (*Brassicaceae*)

	clypeata	see *Fibigia clypeata*

Fascicularia (*Bromeliaceae*)

	andina	see *F. bicolor*
§	***bicolor***	Widely available
§	- subsp. ***bicolor***	CFil CMac CPne IBoy NLos SMad
§	- subsp. ***canaliculata***	CAbP CFil CHEx CHid IBlr LEdu MNrw SChr SKHP SPad WCot WPGP

kirchhoffiana see *F. bicolor* subsp. *canaliculata*
litoralis see *Ochagavia litoralis*
pitcairniifolia misapplied see *F. bicolor* subsp. *bicolor*
pitcairniifolia (Verlot) Mez see *Ochagavia litoralis*

× *Fatshedera* (*Araliaceae*)

lizei ♀H3 CBcs CDoC CDul CHEx CMac CSde CTri EBee ECrN ELon EPfP EUJe LRHS MAsh MBel MRav SArc SDix SEND SPer SPlb SPoG SWvt
§ - 'Annemieke' (v) ♀H3 CBcs CDoC CHEx CRHN ELan ELon EPfP EUJe LRHS MAsh MMuc MRav SEND SPer SPoG WBor
- 'Lemon and Lime' see × *F. lizei* 'Annemieke'
- 'Maculata' see × *F. lizei* 'Annemieke'
- 'Variegata' (v) ♀H3 CMac CSde EBee EBtc ELan EPfP EUJe LAst LRHS MAsh MBel MGos MMuc SDix SEND SPer SWvt WCFE

Fatsia (*Araliaceae*)

§ ***japonica*** ♀H5 Widely available
- 'Annelise' (v) SEND SPoG
- 'Moseri' CExl ELan ESwi NGdn NLar SWvt WCot
- 'Spider's Web' (v) CAbb CExl CHel CHid CWGN ECtt ELan ELon ESwi EUJe LBMP LRHS MNrw MRav MSCN SBig SDix SPad SPer SPoG WCot WGrn
- 'Variegata' (v) ♀H3 CAbb CBcs CMac ELan EPfP ESwi LRHS MAsh MBri MGos MPie MRav SCob SEND SHil SLim SLon SPer SPoG WCot
papyrifera see *Tetrapanax papyrifer*
polycarpa CDTJ CExl CFil WPGP
- B&SWJ 7144 CExl WCru
- RWJ 10133 WCru
- deeply cut leaf BWJ 12499 WCru

Fedia (*Valerianaceae*)

cornucopiae CArn

Feijoa see *Acca*

Felicia (*Asteraceae*)

§ ***amelloides*** CCCN LAst SEND SPlb
- 'Blue Eyes' LAst
- 'Santa Anita' CTri SVen
§ - variegated (v) CCCN ECtt LAst MBri MSCN NPer SDix SEND
§ ***amoena*** CTri
- 'Variegata' (v) CCCN CTri
capensis see *F. amelloides*
coelestis see *F. amelloides*
echinata CCCN
filifolia blue-flowered SVen
fruticosa CHll
natalensis see *F. rosulata*
pappei see *F. amoena*
§ ***petiolata*** CTri EWes MNrw NSti
§ ***rosulata*** ECho GCrg GEdr MBrN MHer NBro NLar SBrt SRot WHal WIce
uliginosa EWes GCrg SPlb WIce
wrightii new GEdr

Fenestraria (*Aizoaceae*)

rhodalophylla subsp. ***aurantiaca*** ♀H2 LToo

fennel see *Foeniculum vulgare*

fenugreek see *Trigonella foenum-graecum*

Ferraria (*Iridaceae*)

LP 18095 WCot
§ ***crispa*** ECho NRog WCot
- var. ***nortieri*** NRog WCot
divaricata CDes NRog WCot
- subsp. ***arenosa*** new NRog
schaeferi NRog WCot
undulata see *F. crispa*

Ferula (*Apiaceae*)

chiliantha see *F. communis* subsp. *glauca*
§ ***communis*** CArn CMea CSpe ECGP ECha ELan EPfP GBin GCra IBoy LRHS SDix SEND SPav SPhx SPlb WJek
- 'Gigantea' see *F. communis*
§ - subsp. ***glauca*** CArn CMea EWes SDix WPGP
- - B&SWJ 12999 new WCru
'Giant Bronze' see *Foeniculum vulgare* 'Giant Bronze'
szowitsiana new NDov
tingitana 'Cedric Morris' ECha GCra SDix

Ferulago (*Apiaceae*)

sylvatica PAB 2875 new LEdu

Festuca (*Poaceae*)

actae XLum
amethystina CBod CKno EHoe EShb LRHS MNFA NGdn SEND SMea SPhx SRot WMoo WWEG XLum
- 'Aprilgrün' XLum
arundinacea CHab MMoz SEND
californica CKno EPPr
coxii CHid WCot
curvula subsp. ***crassifolia*** EPla EShb
durissima XLum
'Eisvogel' EPPr
elegans EPPr XLum
eskia EAEE EHoe EPPr LRHS XLum
filiformis CHab
gamisansii XLum
§ ***gautieri*** EPPr GBin SMea XLum
- 'Hobbit' new CBod
- 'Pic Carlit' GBin XLum
gigantea CBod CHab SEND XLum
glacialis XLum
- 'Czakor' XLum
glauca Vill. CAco CBcs CBod ELan EPfP EShb GMaP LPot MBNS MGos MRav MWat NGdn NOak SGSe SLim SPer SPlb SRms WHea WWEG
I - 'Auslese' CExl EPPr EShb NGdn
- 'Azurit' EHoe EPPr EWes NWad SPoG
§ - 'Blaufuchs' COtt EAEE ELan EPfP EPla EWes GMaP LRHS MAsh MAvo MBlu MGos NWad SLim SPer SPlb SWvt WFar WWEG XLum
§ - 'Blauglut' EBee EPfP LRHS MBri MRav SRms WRHF
- Blue Fox see *F. glauca* 'Blaufuchs'
- Blue Glow see *F. glauca* 'Blauglut'

	- 'Elijah Blue'	Widely available
	- 'Golden Toupee'	CTsd ECha EHoe ELan EPfP EWes LRHS MAsh MBlu MGos NBir NEgg NSti SGSe SLim SPer SPlb SPoG SWvt WWEG XLum
	- 'Harz'	EHoe EPla XLum
	- 'Intense Blue'	CAbP CKno EPfP EWes LRHS SHil SMad SPoG SRms STPC
*	- ***minima***	CCCN NWsh WGrn WWEG
	- 'Pallens'	see *F. longifolia*
	- Sea Urchin	see *F. glauca* 'Seeigel'
§	- 'Seeigel'	EPPr LRHS NWad
	- Select	see *F. glauca* 'Auslese'
	- 'Seven Seas'	see *F. valesiaca* 'Silbersee'
	- 'Silberreiher'	EPPr WWEG
	- 'Solling'	XLum
	- 'Uchte'	CWCL ELan EPPr WWEG
	'Hogar'	EPPr LPal
	idahoensis	EShb
	- 'Tomales Bay'	CKno
§	***longifolia***	EPPr
	mairei	CKno EBee ECha EHoe EPPr SPhx XLum
	novae-zelandiae	CWCL
	ovina	CHab EPfP GBin WSFF
	- var. ***gallica***	NWsh
	- 'Söhrewald'	EPPr
*	- 'Tetra Gold'	SWvt
	paniculata	CKno EHoe EPPr XLum
	- subsp. ***spadicea***	XLum
	pratensis	CHab
	punctoria	CBod MMuc SMea
	rubra	CHab CKno WSFF XLum
	scoparia	see *F. gautieri*
	'Siskiyou Blue'	CKno EPPr WWEG
	tatrae	EBee MBel WCot
	tolucensis NJM 09.071	WPGP
	valesiaca	SMea XLum
	- var. ***glaucantha***	EPPr MMuc NGdn WWEG XLum
§	- 'Silbersee'	EAEE EHoe EPPr GBin SRms
	- Silver Sea	see *F. valesiaca* 'Silbersee'
	violacea	EPPr
	vivipara	EHoe LEdu NBid
*	'Willow Green'	SPlb

Fibigia (*Brassicaceae*)

§	***clypeata***	CUse XLum
I	- 'Select'	CSpe

Ficus (*Moraceae*)

	afghanistanica	ERea
I	***binnendijkii*** 'Alii'	WCot
	carica (F)	CCCN EUJe MBri SArc SEWo SLon SPad
	- 'Abicou' (F)	ERea
	- 'Adam' (F)	CCCN ERea LEdu SEND
	- 'Alma' (F)	ERea
	- 'Angélique' (F)	ERea
I	- 'Bauern Feige' (F)	SRms
	- 'Beall' (F)	CCCN
	- 'Bellone' (F)	CCCN
	- 'Black Ischia' (F)	CCCN CHel ERea SDix
	- 'Black Jack' (F)	ERea
	- 'Black Neck Lady' (F)	LRHS MGos
	- 'Bornholm' (F)	NLar SPre
	- 'Bourjassotte Grise' (F)	CAgr CHel ERea SDea
	- 'Brogiotto' (F)	CCCN
	- 'Brown Turkey' (F) ♀H4	Widely available
	- 'Brunswick' (F)	CAgr CCCN CDul CHel CHll ELan ELon EPfP EPom ERea EUJe EWTr GTwe LEdu LRHS NLar SDix SEND SKee SLim SRms WCot WFar
	- 'Califfo Blue' (F)	CSut SRms
	- 'Castle Kennedy' (F)	CCCN CHel ERea GTwe
	- 'Celeste' (F)	CBcs CCCN SRms
	- 'Col de Dame Blanc' (F)	ERea
	- 'Col de Dame Noir' (F)	ERea
	- 'Colummaro Black Apulia' (F)	CCCN
	- 'Colummaro White Apulia' (F)	CCCN
	- 'Continental' (F)	LRHS MGos
	- 'Dalmatie' (F)	CAgr CCCN ELan EPfP ERea LRHS MGos SEND SRms WPGP
§	- 'Desert King' (F)	ERea
I	- 'Digitata' (F)	MBlu
	- 'Digredo' (F)	CCCN
	- 'Dorée de Porquerolles' (F)	CCCN
	- 'Drap d'Or' (F)	ERea
	- 'Excel' (F)	ERea
	- 'Figue d'Or' (F)	ERea
	- 'Filacciano' (F)	CCCN
	- 'Flanders' (F)	CCCN
	- 'Goutte d'Or' (F)	CAgr CCCN EPfP ERea SDea
	- 'Green Ischia' (F)	CCCN ERea
	- 'Grise de Marseille' (F)	CCCN
	- 'Grise de Saint Jean' (F)	CCCN ERea
	- 'Ice Crystal' (F) ♀H5	EBee ECrN ELan EPfP EPla ERea EShb LRHS MBlu SPoG SRms WPGP
	- 'Kadota' (F)	CCCN IDee
	- 'King'	see *F. carica* 'Desert King'
*	- 'Laciniata' (F)	MBri
	- 'Lisa' (F)	ERea
	- 'Little Yellow Wonder' (F)	ERea
	- 'LSU Purple' (F)	ERea
	- 'Madeleine des Deux Saisons' (F) **new**	EPom
	- 'Malta' (F)	GTwe
	- 'Marseillaise' (F)	EPfP GTwe SDea
	- 'Melanzana' (F)	CCCN
	- 'Morena' (F)	CSut SRms
	- 'Moscatel' (F)	CCCN
	- 'Napolitana' (F)	ERea
	- 'Neck Lady White' (F)	LRHS MGos
	- 'Negrétte de Porquerolles' (F)	CCCN
	- 'Nero' (F)	ELon SGol
	- 'Newlyn Harbour' (F)	ELon
	- 'Noire de Caromb' (F)	CAgr CCCN EPfP ERea LRHS SKee SRms
	- 'Noire de Provence'	see *F. carica* 'Reculver'
	- 'Osborn's Prolific' (F)	ECrN EPfP MAsh SEND SGol SWvt
	- 'Panachée' (F)	CCCN CSut EPom ERea SRms
	- 'Peter's Honey' (F)	ERea
	- 'Petite Nigra' (F)	ERea
	- 'Pied de Boeuf' (F)	CCCN
	- 'Pinet' (F)	LRHS MGos
	- 'Porthminster' (F)	CHEx
	- 'Précoce de Dalmatie' (F)	CTho NLar SRms
	- 'Précoce Ronde de Bordeaux' (F)	ERea SEND
	- 'Quinta' (F)	CCCN
§	- 'Reculver' (F)	SEND
	- 'Ronde de Bordeaux' (F)	CCCN
	- 'Rouge de Bordeaux' (F)	CCCN EPom ERea LRHS MAsh SDea SPlb SRms

- 'Safi' (F) CCCN
- 'Saint Johns' (F) CHel SDea
- 'San Pedro Miro' (F) ERea
- 'Sugar 12' (F) ERea
- 'Sultane' (F) CAgr ERea
- 'Texas Everbearing' (F) ERea
- 'Verte d'Argenteuil' (F) CCCN
- 'Violetta'PBR (F) MBri
- 'Violette Dauphine' (F) CHel EPfP ERea LEdu
- 'Violette de Bordeaux' (F) ERea
- 'Violette de Sollies' (F) ERea SVic
- 'Violette Normande' (F) MAsh SEND
- 'Violette Sepor' (F) ERea
- 'White Adriatic' (F) CBcs ERea SRms
- 'White Genoa' see *F. carica* 'White Marseilles'
- 'White Ischia' (F) CHel ERea

§ - 'White Marseilles' (F) CAgr CCCN ECrN ERea LRHS MBri SDea SEND SKee SRms WPGP

- 'Zidi' (F) CCCN

microcarpa LPal

pubigera CExl

pumila ♀H1c CHEx EShb

- 'Variegata' (v) ♀H1c CHEx EShb

tikoua CFil

fig see *Ficus carica*

filbert see *Corylus maxima*

Filipendula ✿ (*Rosaceae*)

alnifolia 'Variegata' see *F. ulmaria* 'Variegata'

camtschatica CCon CRow ECha ELan LEdu MCot NBid NLar SMrm WPGP WWtn

- B&SWJ 10987 WCru
- RBS 0224 NLar
- 'Rosea' MRav

digitata 'Nana' see *F. multijuga*

hexapetala see *F. vulgaris*

- 'Flore Pleno' see *F. vulgaris* 'Multiplex'

'Kahome' CMea CPrp CRow EAJP ELon EShb GMaP IFoB LLWG LRHS MSCN NBid NBir NGdn NLar NOrc SCob SPer SPhx SWat WHil WMoo WPnP WWEG

kiraishiensis EBee

- B&SWJ 1571 WCru

§ ***multijuga*** GCal IFoB LLWG MSCN NHol NLar NWad WBor WMoo

- B&SWJ 10950 **new** WCru
- var. ***yezoensis*** B&SWJ 10828 IMou WCru

palmata ECha LLWG MLHP NBre SWat WMoo

- 'Digitata Nana' see *F. multijuga*
- dwarf CDes
- 'Elegantissima' see *F. purpurea* 'Elegans'
- 'Göteborg' EBee
- 'Nana' see *F. multijuga*
- 'Rosea' CMac LLWG MMoz NBir
- 'Rubra' CTri GCra LRHS MRav NGdn

purpurea CKno CSBt ECha ELon IBlr MBri MMuc SBod SEND SRms WCru WMoo

- f. ***albiflora*** LLWG MBri WMoo

§ - 'Elegans' EBee ECha ELon GBin LLWG LRHS MLHP NBid NHol SCob SPer SRms SWat WMoo WPnP

- 'Pink Dreamland' SPhx

* - 'Plena' (d) NLar

'Queen of the Prairies' see *F. rubra*

'Red Umbrellas' CBod EBee ELon MBri

§ ***rubra*** CRow IFro MCot WSFF

§ - 'Venusta' ♀H5 Widely available

- 'Venusta Magnifica' see *F. rubra* 'Venusta'

rufinervis B&SWJ 8611 WCru

§ ***ulmaria*** CArn CBen CHab CHby CWat CWld EBee EHon ELau ENfk GJos GMaP GPoy MCot MHer MMuc MNHC MWts NMir SIde SWat WHer WHfH WJek WMoo WOut WPnP WSFF WShi XLum

- 'Aurea' CBod CCon CMac CNor CRow CTri CWCL EBee ECha ECtt EHoe ELan GAbr GMaP LEdu LRHS MAvo MLHP MRav MWat NBid NLar SPer SRms WCot WFar WMoo WSHC WWEG
- 'Flore Pleno' (d) CBre CCon EBee LLWG LRHS MRav NBid SPer SWat WCot WFar WHil
- 'Rosea' IBlr MBel MHer

§ - 'Variegata' (v) CBen CPrp EBee ECtt EHoe ELan GBuc IFoB LBMP LRHS NBid NGdn NLar SPer SRms WFar WHfH WMoo WPnP WWEG

§ ***vulgaris*** CArn CHab LRHS MBel MLHP MMuc MNHC NBro NMir NSbr SWat WHer WHfH WJek WWEG

- 'Flore Pleno' see *F. vulgaris* 'Multiplex'
- 'Grandiflora' CBre EBee

§ - 'Multiplex' (d) CMac CSpe ECha ELan GMaP LLWG LRHS MHer MMuc MRav MSpe MWts NBid NBir NLar NRya NSti SEND SRms WFar WMoo XLum

- 'Plena' see *F. vulgaris* 'Multiplex'
- 'Rosea' NBre

Firmiana (*Malvaceae*)

simplex EShb ESwi ETwe EUJe IDee SPad WPGP

Fitzroya (*Cupressaceae*)

cupressoides CBcs CDoC CMac CTho GBin IArd SLim WThu

- 'Borde Hill' (f) WThu
- 'Westonbirt' (m) WThu

Foeniculum (*Apiaceae*)

vulgare Widely available

- 'Bronze' see *F. vulgare* 'Purpureum'
- var. ***dulce*** CUse ENfk SIde

§ - 'Giant Bronze' EBee LRHS MAvo SCob SPhx WCot WGrn

§ - 'Purpureum' Widely available

- 'Smokey' ECha MRav
- 'Sweet Florence' SVic

Fontanesia (*Oleaceae*)

fortunei EBtc

phillyreoides CBcs

Fontinalis (*Fontinalaceae*)

antipyretica CBAq

Forsythia (*Oleaceae*)

'Arnold Dwarf' ECrN NBir SRms

'Beatrix Farrand' ambig. COtt CTri MWat NWea SEND SRms

'Beatrix Farrand' K. Sax	MMuc NLar
'Fiesta' (v)	EPfP EPla LAst LRHS MAsh MGos MRav MSwo NLar NPCo SPer SPoG WCot
giraldiana	MSwo SLon SRms
Gold Tide[PBR]	see *F.* Marée d'Or
'Golden Bells'	WHar
'Golden Nugget'	CMac ELan EPfP LBuc LRHS MAsh SLon SPoG WCFE WFar
'Golden Times' (v)	CMac EWes LAst LBuc LPot MAsh MGos MSwo NHol NSoo NWea SCoo SPoG SWvt
× ***intermedia***	CAco IBoy
- 'Arnold Giant'	MBlu
- 'Goldrausch'	ELan LRHS MAsh NLar SHil
- 'Goldzauber'	NWea
- 'Josefa' (v)	ELon
- 'Lynwood Variety' 🏆H5	Widely available
- Minigold = 'Flojor'	CHel CMac CNec CSBt EBee EPla MSwo MWat NSoo SRms
- 'Spectabilis'	CDul EPfP LBuc NSoo NWea SCob SCoo SGol SLim WFar
- 'Spectabilis Variegated' (v)	CMHG MBNS NEoE
- 'Spring Glory'	MHer
- Week End = 'Courtalyn'[PBR] 🏆H5	CBod CEnd CNec EPfP LBuc LRHS MAsh MBri MMuc MWat NHol NLar NSoo SCob SEND SGol SHil SLon SPlb WFar
'Kanarek' **new**	NLar
× ***mandshurica*** **new**	IDee
§ Marée d'Or = 'Courtasol'[PBR] 🏆H5	ELon IVic LRHS MAsh MGos MRav NLar NWea SLon SPer SPoG
Mêlée d'Or = 'Courtaneur'	SGol
Melissa = 'Courtadic'	NWea
ovata 'Tetragold'	NWea
'Paulina'	NLar WAbe
suspensa	CMac CTri EPfP NWea SPlb SRms
- f. ***atrocaulis***	CDul
- 'Nymans'	MBri MRav NSti SEND
§ - 'Taff's Arnold' (v)	CExl
- 'Variegata'	see *F. suspensa* 'Taff's Arnold'
viridissima	NWea
- 'Bronxensis'	CMac CTal ECho LLHF MAsh NBir NLar WAbe WPat
- var. ***koreana*** 'Kumsom' (v)	EBee NLar SLim SPoG
- 'Weber's Bronx'	NLar NWea WAbe

Fortunella (*Rutaceae*)

× ***crassifolia***	see *Citrus japonica*
'Fukushu'	see *Citrus* × *obovata* 'Fukushu'
hindsii	see *Citrus japonica*
margarita	see *Citrus japonica*

Fothergilla (*Hamamelidaceae*)

gardenii	CBcs CJun ELan EPfP LRHS MBlu MGos MRav NLar SPer SWvt
- 'Blue Mist'	CAbP CDoC CEnd CExl CJun EBee ELan ELon EPfP GQue IVic LRHS MAsh SKHP SPer SPoG WPat
- 'Brian Upchurch' **new**	NLar
- 'Harold Epstein'	NLar
- 'Suzanne'	NLar
- 'Zundert'	NLar
'Huntsman'	CCCN CTho EBee EPfP
× ***intermedia*** Beaver Creek = 'Klmtwo'	NLar
- 'Blue Shadow'	CBcs CJun EPfP EUJe LRHS MGos MPkF MRav NLar SGol SKHP
- 'Mount Airy' 🏆H5	CDoC CJun CMCN EBee EPfP LRHS MBri MPkF NLar SKHP SSta
- 'Red Licorice'	CJun EPfP NLar
- 'Sea Spray'	CJun NLar
- 'Windy City'	CJun MBri NLar
major 🏆H5	CBcs CDul CJun EBee ELan EPfP GKin IDee LRHS MAsh MBlu MGos MJak NEgg NLar NPri SHil SPer SPoG SReu SWvt WFar WPat
- 'Bulkyard'	CJun
- Monticola Group	CDoC CDul CEnd CJun CTho ELan EPfP LRHS MAsh MGos MMuc NSoo SLim SPer SSpi SSta

Fouquieria (*Fouquieriaceae*)

columnaris	SPlb
splendens	SPlb

Fragaria (*Rosaceae*)

from Taiwan	WHer
alpina	see *F. vesca* 'Semperflorens'
- 'Alba'	see *F. vesca* 'Semperflorens Alba'
× ***ananassa*** 'Albion'[PBR] (F)	CSBt SPer
- 'Alice'[PBR] (F) 🏆H6	CAgr CMac EPom LBuc LEdu LRHS
- 'Anablanca' (F)	CSut EPom LRHS
- 'Aromel' (F) 🏆H6	EPfP LBuc LRHS
- 'Bogota' (F)	LRHS
- 'Bolero' (F)	MBri
- 'Buddy' (F) **new**	CSut EPom NPri SBmr SPer
- 'Calypso' (F)	CSBt LBuc SDea SFrt SPer
- 'Cambridge Favourite' (F) 🏆H6	CAgr CMac CSBt CTri EMil EPfP EPom GTwe LBuc LRHS MBri MGos MJak NPri SDea SEND SFrt SPlb WHar
- 'Cambridge Vigour' (F)	LRHS
- 'Christine' (F)	CAgr CSut EMil EPom LRHS SDea
- 'Darselect'[PBR] (F)	EPom
- 'Elegance'[PBR] (F)	EPom GTwe SFrt SRms
- 'Elsanta' (F)	CSBt CTri EMil EPfP EPom GTwe IArd LBuc LEdu LRHS NEgg NPri SDea SPer WHar
- 'Elvira' (F)	EPfP
- 'Eros'[PBR] (F)	LBuc
- 'Fenella'[PBR] (F)	CMac EPom GTwe
- 'Flamenco'[PBR] (F)	EPom LEdu LRHS NWad
- 'Florence'[PBR] (F)	CAgr CSBt CTri EPfP EPom GTwe LBuc LEdu LRHS MBri SDea SFrt SPer
- 'Florian' (F) **new**	LEdu
- (Fragoo Series) Fragoo Deep Rose = 'Tarpan' (F)	LRHS
- - Fragoo Pink = 'Pikan' (F) **new**	LRHS
- - Fragoo White = 'Belton' (F) **new**	LRHS
- Fraise des Bois	see *F. vesca*
- 'Frau Mieze Schindler' (F)	EPom SFrt
- 'Fruitful Summer' (F)	LBuc LRHS
- 'Gariguette' (F)	EPom
- 'Hapil' (F) 🏆H6	CTri EMil EPfP EPom GTwe LBuc LEdu
- 'Honeoye' (F) 🏆H6	CAgr CSBt EMil EPfP EPom GAbr GTwe LBuc LEdu LRHS MBri NWad SEND SPer WHar
- 'Judibell'[PBR] (F)	LRHS SFrt
- 'Korona'[PBR] (F)	CMac EPom
- 'Loran' (F)	LRHS

	- 'Lucy'PBR (F)	SFrt
	- 'Malling Opal'PBR (F)	EPom
	- 'Malwina'PBR (F)	CSut EPom SVic
	- 'Manille' (F) new	EPom
	- 'Merlan'PBR (F) new	SRms
	- 'Mount Everest' (F)	LBuc
	- 'Pandora' (F)	LEdu
	- 'Pegasus'PBR (F) ♀H6	CAgr CSBt EPfP EPom GTwe LBuc LRHS NPri
	- Pink Panda = 'Frel'PBR (F)	CBod CMac CTri EAEE EBee ELan EPla LRHS MBel MGos MRav NEgg NGdn NLar SPer SPoG WJek WWFP
	- pink-flowered (F)	GAbr LPot MBel
	- 'Rabunda' (F)	LRHS
	- Red RubyPBR	see *F.* × *ananassa* 'Samba'
	- 'Redgauntlet' (F)	EPfP GTwe LBuc LRHS
	- 'Rhapsody' (F) ♀H6	GTwe LRHS
	- 'Rosie'PBR (F)	SDea
	- 'Royal Sovereign' (F)	CMac CSut CTri EPom GTwe LEdu NBir SVic
§	- 'Samba'PBR (F)	CBod EAEE EPla GLog LRHS MBel MNrw NDov NGdn SPer SPoG
	- 'Senga Sengana' (F)	SVic
	- 'Sonata'PBR (F)	EPom LRHS NWad
	- 'Sophie'PBR (F)	LEdu LRHS
	- 'Sweetheart' (F)	CSut LRHS
	- 'Symphony'PBR (F) ♀H6	CAgr CSBt EPfP EPom LBuc LRHS MBri SFrt SPer
	- 'Temptation' (F)	LRHS
	- 'Totem' (F)	GTwe
§	- 'Variegata' (v)	CTri EAEE EBee EPla MRav SPer SPoG WHea WMoo
	'Bowles's Double'	see *F. vesca* 'Multiplex'
	chiloensis (F)	IFro LEdu
	- 'Chaval' (F)	CHid ECha EPPr IMou MRav NChi WMoo
	- 'Variegata' misapplied	see *F.* × *ananassa* 'Variegata'
	daltoniana	GCra
	indica	see *Duchesnea indica*
	'Lipstick'	EBee NLar
	moschata	CAgr
	nubicola	CAgr GPoy
	'Variegata'	see *F.* × *ananassa* 'Variegata'
§	***vesca*** (F)	CAgr CArn CBcs CWld ELan EPfP GPoy MHer MNHC NMir NPri SFrt SIde SPlb SRms SVic WGwG WJek WOut WSFF WShi
	- 'Alexandra' (F)	CArn CPrp ELau ENfk EPPr ERea SIde WHar
	- 'Alpina Scarletta' (F)	ENfk
	- 'Alpine Yellow' new	EWTr
	- 'Baron Solemacher' (F)	ERea SHDw SPhx WHer
	- 'Capron Royale' (F) new	CAgr
	- 'Flore Pleno'	see *F. vesca* 'Multiplex'
	- 'Fructu Albo' (F)	CAgr CArn CBre CRow GLin WMoo
	- 'Golden Alexandra' (F)	ECha EWes MHer NEoE WHer WOut WWFP
	- 'Golden Surprise'	SHDw
	- 'Mara des Bois'PBR (F)	EPom SRms
	- 'Monophylla' (F)	CRow SIde WHer
§	- 'Multiplex' (d)	CRow MRav NChi WBor WHer WOut
§	- 'Muricata'	CBre CRow LEdu
	- 'Pineapple Crush' (F)	WHer
	- 'Plymouth Strawberry'	see *F. vesca* 'Muricata'
	- 'Reine des Vallées' (F) new	ERea
	- 'Scarlet Beauty' (F) new	EPom
§	- 'Semperflorens' (F)	WRHF
§	- 'Semperflorens Alba' (F)	CAgr
	- 'Variegata' misapplied	see *F.* × *ananassa* 'Variegata'
	- 'Variegata' ambig. (v)	EHoe LLWG WWEG
	virginiana	CAgr
	- subsp. ***glauca***	EPPr
	viridis	CAgr

Francoa (*Francoaceae*)

	appendiculata	GAbr NBir WHer WMoo
	Ballyrogan strain	IBlr
	'Confetti'	CAbP CExl IKil
	'Purple Spike'	see *F. sonchifolia* Rogerson's form
	ramosa	CCon CTri IBlr NBro SDix WKif WMoo
*	- 'Alba'	CSpe
	sonchifolia	Widely available
	- 'Alba'	GKev WMoo
	- 'Doctor Tom Smith'	WCot
	- 'Pink Bouquet'	CKno CMac CMos EBee GBin SHar WOut
	- 'Pink Giant'	CBod EPla GBin GBuc GCal GKev MHer WHil WMoo
§	- Rogerson's form	CAby CElw CSam CTri ELon IMou IVic LRHS MBri NBir NChi SDix SGSe WCot WMoo WWEG

Frangula (*Rhamnaceae*)

§	***alnus***	CArn CCVT CDul CHab CTri ECrN EShb LBuc MBlu MGos NWea SEWo WFar WMou WSFF
	- 'Aspleniifolia'	EPfP LRHS MBlu MMuc MPkF MRav NLar SMad WCFE WPat
	- 'Fine Line'	MBri MPkF NLar
	- 'Minaret'	MBlu
	- 'Ron Williams'	MBlu

Frankenia (*Frankeniaceae*)

	laevis	SRms
	thymifolia	CTri ECho LSun MAsh MHer MSCN MWat SEND SIgm SPlb WRHF XLum

Franklinia (*Theaceae*)

	alatamaha	CBcs IDee IVic MBlu MBri WPGP

Fraxinus ✿ (*Oleaceae*)

	americana	CDul CMCN NWea
	- 'Autumn Purple'	CDul CEnd CMCN CTho EBee EPfP MAsh NWea WMou
	angustifolia	CMCN
	- 'Raywood' ♀H6	CCVT CDoC CDul CEnd CLnd CMCN CMac CTho CTri EBee ECrN ELan EPfP EWTr LAst LBuc MAsh MGos MMuc MSwo NWea SCob SEND SGol SPoG WMou
	anomala	CDul
	chiisanensis B&SWJ 12719 new	WCru
	chinensis	CDul CLnd CMCN
	excelsior	CAco CCVT CDoC CDul CHab CLnd CMac CSBt CTho CTri ECrN EPfP LBuc MAsh MBri MGos MJak MMuc NHed NWea SCob SEND SEWo SGol WMou
	- 'Althena'	CDul
	- 'Aurea Pendula'	CDul CEnd CMac MGos
	- 'Crispa'	NLar
	- f. ***diversifolia***	CDul CLnd MBri
	- 'Jaspidea' ♀H6	CCVT CDoC CDul CEnd CLnd CMCN CMac CTho ECrN ELan EPfP

	ERod LAst MAsh MBri MGos MMuc MSwo NWea SCob SEND SGol
- 'Nana'	LLHF
- 'Pendula'	CAco CCVT CDul CEnd CLnd CMac CTsd EBee ECrN ELan NWea SGol WMou
- 'R.E. Davey'	CDul
- variegated (v)	CMac
- 'Westhof's Glorie' ♀H6	CCVT CDoC CDul
insularis var. ***henryana***	CDul CMCN
latifolia	CMCN
mariesii	see *F. sieboldiana*
nigra 'Fallgold'	CEnd
ornus	CArn CCVT CDul CLnd CMCN CMac CTri ECrN ELan EPfP LAst LEdu MMuc MSwo NWea SEND
- 'Arie Peters'	CDul
- 'Obelisk'	EBee EBtc EWTr MAsh MBri
- 'Rotterdam'	EBee
pennsylvanica	CDul CLnd CMCN
- 'Variegata' (v)	CLnd EBee
quadrangulata	CDul
§ ***sieboldiana***	CDul CLnd CMCN EPfP MBri
sogdiana Potamophila Group	CFil
velutina	CDul
xanthoxyloides	CDul

Freesia (*Iridaceae*)

alba Foster	see *F. lactea*
alba Watson	see *F. caryophyllacea*
§ ***caryophyllacea***	NRog
corymbosa	NRog
fucata	ECho
grandiflora	CExl CHll ECho WCot
grandiflora × ***laxa***	CDes
'Grumpy' **new**	LRHS
§ ***lactea***	CDes ECho
§ ***laxa*** ♀H3	CExl CSpe CTal CTri CUse ECho EPri LEdu LRHS NLos WAbe WCot
- var. ***alba*** ♀H3	CExl CSpe CUse ECho EPri LLWP WAbe
- blue-flowered	ECho WAbe
- 'Joan Evans'	CSpe ECho LLHF SBch
- red-spotted	CExl ECho
- ***viridiflora***	ECho
leichtlinii	NRog
refracta **new**	NRog
- 'Worcester'	ECho
'Tootsie' **new**	LRHS
viridis	CDes CExl EBee ECho NRog
xanthospila	NRog WCot

Fremontodendron (*Malvaceae*)

sp.	CHel
'California Glory' ♀H4	CBcs CDoC CDul CMac CWSG EPfP EUJe IDee LAst LBMP LRHS MAsh MBlu MGil MGos MWat NPla NPri NSoo SArc SEle SGbt SGol SHil SPer SPoG SVen SWvt
californicum	CTri EBee ELan MBri NLar SEND SLim SPlb WFar
'Dara's Gold'	LRHS
'Pacific Sunset'	CBcs EPfP MGos MRav SGol
'Tequila Sunrise' ♀H4	CDoC CJun CWGN LLHF

Freylinia (*Scrophulariaceae*)

cestroides	see *F. lanceolata*
§ ***lanceolata***	CBcs CCCN SPlb SVen WCot
tropica	CHll GFai WCot
visseri	GFai MOWG

Fritillaria ✿ (*Liliaceae*)

acmopetala ♀H4	CAvo CBro CCon CPom CTal CWCL ECho EPot ERCP GBuc GKev ITim LAma MNrw NMin SDeJ WIce
- 'Brunette'	EPot LAma
- subsp. ***wendelboi***	ECho EPot GKev LAma
affinis	CWCL ECho EPot GBin GBuc
- NNS 00-336	WCot
- 'Sunray'	LAma
§ - var. ***tristulis***	CWCL
- 'Vancouver Island'	LAma
amana	CTca CWCL ECho EPot ERCP GKev LLHF NMin WCot
- 'Cambridge' ♀H4	WCot
- 'Goksan Gold'	ECho
- yellow-flowered	EPot
arabica	see *F. persica*
armena	GKev
assyriaca	EPot GBuc
aurea	LAma
- 'Golden Flag'	ECho EPot GKev LAma LLHF
biflora	ECho EPot LAma
- 'Martha Roderick'	ECho GKev LAma SDeJ
§ ***bithynica***	ECho LAma
bucharica	ECho EPot GKev LAma NMin
- 'Nurek Giant'	ECho
camschatcensis	CBro CHel CWCL ECho EFEx EPfP EPot ERCP GBin GBuc GEdr GKev GMaP LAma LRHS MAvo NBir NHar SDeJ SPhx WAbe WCru
- 'Alaska'	NHar
- 'Aurea'	ECho GBuc NHar SPhx
- black-flowered	CAby ECho NHar
- double-flowered (d)	CCon ECho GBuc
- f. ***flavescens***	EFEx GBuc GEdr LAma
- green-flowered	CAby
carduchorum	see *F. minuta*
carica	ECho EPot
citrina	see *F. bithynica*
§ ***crassifolia*** subsp. ***kurdica***	ECho EPot GKev ITim
davisii	ECho EPfP EPot GKev IFro LAma LLHF WCot
eduardii	ECho EPot GKev LAma
elwesii	ECho EPot ERCP GKev ITim LAma LLHF SDeJ
* ***glauca*** 'Golden Flag'	LLWG
- 'Goldilocks'	LAma SDeJ
graeca	ECho EPot GBuc GKev LAma NMin SDeJ
- subsp. ***graeca***	GBuc
hispanica	see *F. lusitanica*
imperialis ♀H6	ECGP MBri
- 'April Flame'	LAma
- 'Argenteovariegata' (v)	LAma
- 'Aureomarginata' (v)	LAma
- 'Aurora'	EPot ERCP GKev LAma LRHS MBri NLar NPer SDeJ WFar
- 'Garland Star'	GKev LAma LRHS NLar
- 'Grenadier'	LAma
- var. ***inodora***	LAma
- 'Inodora Purpurea'	LAma
- 'Lutea'	CAvo CHel CTca ELan ERCP GKev LAma LRHS SPhx SPoG WFar

- 'Maxima'	see *F. imperialis* 'Rubra Maxima'
- 'Maxima Lutea' ♀H6	CBro ELan EPfP EPot ERCP LSun MBri NLar SDeJ SPer SPoG
- 'Orange Brilliant'	LAma
- 'Prolifera'	GKev LAma SDeJ
- 'Rubra'	CTca EPfP ERCP GKev LAma NLar SPer WFar
§ - 'Rubra Maxima'	CBro CHel CTca ELan EPfP EPot ERCP GKev LRHS LSun SDeJ
- 'Slagzwaard'	GKev LAma
- 'Striped Beauty'	EPot GKev LAma SDeJ
- 'Sulpherino'	LAma
- 'The Premier'	GKev LAma SDeJ
- 'William Rex'	CAvo CHel EPot ERCP GKev LAma LRHS LSun SDeJ SPhx SPoG
involucrata	ECho WCot
japonica var. ***koidzumiana***	EFEx LAma
karadaghensis	see *F. crassifolia* subsp. *kurdica*
kotschyana	ECho EPot LAma
lanceolata	see *F. affinis* var. *tristulis*
latakiensis	ECho EPot
§ ***lusitanica***	ITim
meleagris ♀H5	Widely available
- 'Artemis'	GBuc
- var. ***unicolor*** subvar. ***alba*** ♀H5	CAvo CBro ECho ERCP GBuc GKev LLWG MBri MWat NHol SDeJ SPer SPhx WShi
- - - 'Aphrodite'	EPot NBir
michailovskyi	CHel CHid CTri CWCL ECho EPfP EPot ERCP GBuc GKev LAma LRHS MNrw SDeJ SRms WFar
minima	ECho
§ ***minuta***	ECho EPot ERCP LAma NMin SDeJ
montana	ECho
nigra Mill.	see *F. pyrenaica*
olivieri	ECho
pallidiflora ♀H5	CBro CTca CWCL ECho EPot ERCP GBuc GCra GKev IFro LAma MBri NBir SDeJ SPhx WCot
§ ***persica***	ECha ECho EPfP EPot ERCP GKev LAma LRHS MBri MNrw SCob SPhx
- 'Adiyaman' ♀H4	ELan SDeJ
- 'Alba'	SDeJ
- 'Chocolate'	CWCL
- 'Ivory Bells'	ECho ELan EPot ERCP LAma LRHS SDeJ SKHP
- 'Ivory Queen'	CBro
- 'Midnight Bells'	ECho
pinardii	ECho EPot LAma
- 'Ole Sonderhause'	ECho LAma
pontica ♀H4	CAvo CBro CCon CWCL ECho EPot ERCP GBuc GKev ITim LAma LLWG MNrw SDeJ SPhx
pudica	ECho LAma WAbe
* - 'Fragrant'	ECho
- 'Giant'	ECho EPot GKev NMin SDeJ
purdyi	ECho
§ ***pyrenaica*** ♀H5	CWCL ECho GCra LAma LLHF SPhx
raddeana	ECho EPot ERCP GKev LAma SDeJ SPhx
reuteri	ECho LAma
rhodocanakis	NMin
rubra major	see *F. imperialis* 'Rubra Maxima'
ruthenica	ECho
sewerzowii	ECho EPot LAma
stenanthera	ECho EPot LAma
tachengensis	see *F. yuminensis*
thunbergii	CTal ECho GKev LAma LLHF SPhx WCot
tuntasia subsp. ***tuntasia***	CTal WCot
uva-vulpis	CAby CCon CMea CTca ECho ECtt ELon EPfP EPot ERCP GKev LAma LLWG LRHS MNrw NBir SDeJ SPhx WFar
verticillata	CBro ECha EPot GKev LAma SPhx WCot WCru
whittallii	ECho EPot GKev LAma
- 'Green Light'	NMin
§ ***yuminensis***	LAma

Fuchsia ✿ (*Onagraceae*)

'A.M. Larwick'	EBak
'A.W. Taylor'	EBak
'Aalt Hillie van de Veen'	WOth
'Abbé Farges' (d)	CLoc CWVF EBak EPts SVic WOth WRou
'Abbigayle Reine' (v)	CDoC
'Abigail' ambig.	CWVF
'Achievement' ♀H4	CLoc LCla MJac SVic
'Adalbert Bogner' (d)	CDoC
'Adinda' (T) ♀H1c	EPts LCla WRou
'Ailsa Garnett' (d)	EBak
'Aintree'	CWVF
'Airedale'	CWVF
'Aisen'	WRou
'Aladna's Sander' (d)	CWVF
'Alan Ayckbourn'	CWVF WOth
'Alan Titchmarsh' ♀H2	CDoC EPts LCla SLBF
'Alaska' (d)	CLoc EBak SVic
'Albertina'	SVic WOth
'Albertus Schwab'	LCla
'Alde'	CWVF WOth
'Alderford'	SLBF
'Alf Thornley' (d)	CWVF WOth
'Alice Ashton' (d)	EBak
'Alice Blue Gown' (d)	CWVF
'Alice Doran'	CDoC LCla
'Alice Hoffman' (d) ♀H4	CAby CCCN CLoc CMac COtt CSBt CWCL CWVF EBak EBee ELan EPfP EPla EPts LAst LRHS MAsh MGos MJac NEgg NLar SEND SHil SLBF SLim SPer SPoG SVic WFar WRou
'Alice Mary' (d)	EBak
'Alice Sweetapple' (d)	CWVF
'Alice Travis' (d)	EBak
'Alicia Sellars'	SLBF WRou
'Alipat'	EBak
'Alison Ewart'	CLoc CWVF EBak MJac SVic
'Alison Patricia' ♀H2	CWVF EBak LAst LCla MJac SLBF SVic WOth WRou
'Alison Reynolds' (d)	CWVF
'Alison Ruth Griffin' (d)	MJac
'Alison Ryle' (d)	EBak
'Alison Sweetman' ♀H2	CWVF MJac
'Allen Jackson'	LCla WOth
'Aloha'	WOth
alpestris	CDoC EBak GCal LCla SVic
'Alton Waters' (d/v)	WOth
'Alwin' (d)	CWVF
'Alyce Larson' (d)	CWVF EBak MJac SVic
'Alyssa May Garcia' (d)	EPts SLBF WOth WRou
'Amazing Grace' (d)	MJac
'Amazing Maisie' (d)	SLBF WOth
'Ambassador'	EBak SVic

Name	Suppliers
'Amelia Rose' **new**	SLBF
'Amelie Aubin'	CLoc CWVF EBak SVic
'America'	CWVF
'Amerika' (d)	WOth
'Amigo' ambig.	EBak
§ ***ampliata***	CDoC LCla
'Amy'	MJac
'Amy Lye'	CLoc EBak SVic
'Amy Ruth'	CWVF
§ 'Andenken an Heinrich Henkel' (T)	CDoC CLoc CWVF EBak SVic WRou
'André Le Nostre' (d)	CWVF EBak SVic
'Andreas Schwab'	LCla
andrei	LCla
'Andrew'	EBak
'Andrew Carnegie' (d)	CLoc
'Andrew Hadfield'	CWVF SVic WOth
'Angela Dawn'	WRou
'Angela King'	SLBF WOth WRou
'Angela Leslie' (d)	CLoc EBak SVic
'Angela Rippon'	CWVF MJac
'Angel's Flight' (d)	EBak
'Angel's Kiss' (E)	CDoC LCla SLBF
'Angie' **new**	WOth
'Angie Baby'	WOth
'Anhaltiner' **new**	WOth
'Anita' (d)	CDoC CLoc CWVF EPts LAst MJac SLBF SVic WOth WRou
'Anjo' (v)	CWVF
'Ann Howard Tripp'	CLoc CWVF EPts MJac SVic WRou
'Ann Lee' (d)	EBak
'Anna Louise'	WOth
'Anna of Longleat' (d)	CWVF EBak LAst MJac
'Annabel' (d) ♀H4	CCCN CDoC CLoc CTri CWVF EBak EPts LAst LCla MJac SLBF SVic WRou
'Anneke de Keijzer'	CDoC LCla WOth
'Annie den Otter'	WOth
'Annie Geurts'	CDoC
'Annie Hall' (E) **new**	WOth
'Annie M.G. Schmidt'	EPts LCla WRou
'Anniek Geerlings' (T)	WOth
'Another Little Cracker'	WRou
'Ant and Dec' (d/v)	MJac
'Anthea Day' (d)	CLoc
'Anthonie Sherwood' (T)	WRou
'Antigone'	SLBF WOth
'Apart' **new**	WOth
'Aphrodite' (d)	CLoc CWVF EBak
'Applause' (d)	CLoc CWVF EBak EPts SVic
aprica misapplied	see *F.* × *bacillaris*
aprica Lundell	see *F. microphylla* subsp. *aprica*
'Apricot Ice'	CLoc SVic
'Arabella'	CWVF
'Arabella Improved'	CWVF SVic
arborea	see *F. arborescens*
§ ***arborescens***	CBcs CDoC CHll CLoc CWCL CWVF EBak EWld LCla MCot MHer SDys SMrm SVic WJek WRou
- B&SWJ 10475	WCru
'Arcadia Gold' (d)	CWVF SVic
'Arcady'	CLoc CWVF
'Arels Nina' **new**	WOth
'Ariel' (E)	CDoC LRHS SVic WOth WRou
'Arkie'	MJac
'Arlendon' (d)	CWVF
'Army Nurse' (d) ♀H4	CDoC CLoc COtt CWCL CWVF ELan ELon EPfP EPts LRHS MBri MGos NBir NLar SEND SHil SLBF SVic WOth WRou
'Arthur Baxter'	EBak
'Ashley'	CDoC LCla
'Ashley and Isobel'	CWVF
'Ashtede'	SLBF
'Ashville'	SLBF WOth WRou
'Atahualpa' (T)	CDoC WOth
'Athela'	EBak
'Atlantic Star'	CWVF MJac
'Atlantis' (d)	CWVF
'Atomic Glow' (d)	EBak SVic
'Aubergine'	see *F.* 'Gerharda's Aubergine'
'Audrey Hepburn'	CWVF
'Auenland'	MJac
'Aunt Juliana' (d)	EBak
'Auntie Jinks' ♀H2	CDoC CWVF EBak LAst MJac SLBF SVic WOth
'Aurora Superba'	CLoc CWVF EBak SLBF
'Australia Fair' (d)	CWVF EBak
§ ***austromontana***	EBak
'Autumnale' ♀H2	CDoC CLoc CWVF EBak EPts SLBF SPoG SVic WOth WRou
'Avalanche' ambig. (d)	CDoC CLoc EBak SLBF
'Avalanche' Henderson (d) **new**	WOth
'Avocet'	CLoc EBak
'Avon Celebration' (d)	CLoc
'Avon Gem'	CLoc
'Avon Glow' (d)	CLoc
'Avon Gold'	CLoc
'Awake Sweet Love' (T) **new**	EPts WOth
ayavacensis	LCla
'Aylisa Rowan' (E)	SLBF
'Azure Sky' (d)	MJac
'Baby Blue Eyes' ♀H4	CDoC CWVF ELan ELon EPfP LRHS MAsh SVic WOth
'Baby Bright'	CWVF LCla WRou
'Baby Brooke'	WOth WRou
'Baby Chang'	WOth
'Baby Pink' (d)	CWVF
'Baby Thumb' (v)	EPts
'Babyface' Tolley (d)	SVic
§ × ***bacillaris*** (E)	CAbb CDoC CHGN EBak EWes GCal MHer SEND SLBF SPoG
§ - 'Cottinghamii' (E)	CDoC EWld SPlb WOth WSHC
§ - 'Reflexa' (E)	CAbP CCCN LSou WOth
'Baden Powell' (E)	SVic
'Bagworthy Water'	CLoc
'Baker's Tri' (T)	EBak
'Balkonkönigin'	CLoc CWVF EBak
'Ballerina Dreams'	LAst
'Ballerina Girl' (E)	SLBF
'Ballet Girl' (d) ♀H2	CLoc CWVF EBak SLBF
'Bambini'	CWVF EPts
'Banks Peninsula'	GBin GQui
'Barbara'	CLoc CWVF EBak EPts LCla MJac SVic
'Barbara Evans'	SLBF
'Barbara Norton'	CDoC
'Barbara Pountain' (d)	CWVF
'Barbara Reynolds'	WOth
'Barbara Windsor'	CWVF MJac
'Barry's Queen'	see *F.* 'Golden Border Queen'
'Bart Comperen' (d)	WRou
'Bartje'	SLBF
'Bashful' (d)	CDoC EPts LCla SVic

	Name	Suppliers
	'Beacon'	CDoC CLoc CMac COtt CWVF EBak EPfP EPts LAst LCla LRHS MJac NGBl SLBF SPoG SVic WRou
	'Beacon Rosa' ♀H4	CLoc CWVF ELon EPfP EPts LAst LCla LRHS MJac SLBF SPoG SVic WRou
	'Bealings' (d)	CWVF SVic
	'Beautiful Dreamer' (d) **new**	CDoC
	'Beauty of Bath' (d)	CLoc EBak
	'Beauty of Clyffe Hall' Lye	CDoC EBak WOth
	'Beauty of Exeter' (d)	CWVF EBak WOth
	'Beauty of Meise' (d)	CDoC
	'Beauty of Prussia' (d)	CLoc CWVF
	'Beauty of Purbeck' (d) **new**	WOth
	'Beauty of Swanley'	EBak
	'Beauty of Trowbridge'	CWVF LCla WOth
	'Belinda Jane'	WOth
	'Bella Forbes' (d) ♀H2	EBak
	'Bella Rosella' (California Dreamers Series) (d) ♀H2	CDoC EPts LAst MJac SCoo SLBF
	'Belsay Beauty' (d)	CWVF MJac
	'Belvoir Beauty' (d)	CLoc
	'Ben de Jong'	LCla SLBF WRou
	'Ben Jammin'	CLoc CWVF EPfP EPts LRHS SEND SVic WRou
	'Ben-Ben' **new**	SLBF
	'Beninkust'	WOth
	'Béranger' Lemoine, 1897 (d)	EBak
	'Berba's Happiness' (d)	CWVF
	'Berba's Trio'	WOth
	'Berliner Kind' (d)	CWVF EBak
	'Bermuda' (d)	CWVF
	'Bernadette' (d)	CWVF
	'Bernie's Big-un' (d)	MJac
	'Bernisser Hardy' ♀H4	EPts LCla LRHS SLBF SLim WOth XLum
	'Beryl Clarke' (v)	EPts
	'Bessie Girl'	CDoC
	'Bessie Kimberley' (T)	LCla
	'Beth Robley' (d)	CWVF
	'Betsy Huuskes'	SLBF
	'Betsy Ross' (d)	EBak
	Betty = 'Shabetty'PBR (Shadowdancer Series)	LAst
	'Beverley'	CWVF EBak EPts
	'Bewitched' (d)	EBak
	'Bianca' (d)	CWVF SVic
	'Bicentennial' (d)	CLoc CWVF EBak EPts LAst MJac SVic
	'Big Slim'	WOth
	'Billy'PBR	CDoC
	'Billy Green' (T) ♀H2	CDoC CLoc CWVF EBak EPts LCla MHer MJac SVic WRou
	'Billy P'	LAst
	'Bishop's Bells' (d)	CWVF SVic
	'Bittersweet' (d)	SVic
	'Black Beauty' (d)	CWVF
	'Black Country 21'	SLBF WOth
	'Black Prince'	CDoC CWVF SVic WOth
	'Black to the Future'	WOth
	'Blackmore Vale' (d)	CWVF
	'Blacky' (d)	CCCN CDoC EBak EUJe GBin LAst LSou MSCN NPri SDys SEND SMrm SVic
I	'Blanche Regina' (d)	CWVF MJac
	'Bland's New Striped'	CDoC EBak EPts LSou SLBF WOth
	'Blaze Away' (d)	LAst MJac
	'Blood Donor' (d)	MJac
	'Blowick'	CWVF MJac WOth
	'Blue Angel' (d)	LAst MJac WOth
	'Blue Beauty' (d)	EBak
	'Blue Bush'	CWVF EPts MJac SVic WOth
	'Blue Butterfly' (d)	CWVF EBak WOth
	'Blue Gown' (d)	CDoC CLoc CWVF EBak SVic
	'Blue Lace' (d)	CDoC SVic
	'Blue Lagoon' ambig. (d)	CWVF
	'Blue Lake' (d)	CWVF
	'Blue Mink'	EBak
	'Blue Mirage' (d)	CLoc CWVF LAst SVic
	'Blue Mist' (d)	EBak
	'Blue Pearl' (d)	CWVF EBak
	'Blue Pinwheel'	CWVF EBak
	'Blue Satin' (d)	LAst WOth
	'Blue Sleighbells'	WOth
	'Blue Tit'	LCla
	'Blue Veil' (d)	CLoc CWVF MJac SCoo SVic WOth
	'Blue Waves' (d)	CLoc CSBt CWVF EBak MJac SVic
	'Blush o' Dawn' (d)	CLoc CWVF EBak EPts SVic
	'Bob Bartrum'	EPts
	'Bob Pacey'	CWVF
	'Bobby Boy' (d)	EBak
	'Bobby Dazzler' (d)	CWVF
	'Bobby Shaftoe' (d)	EBak
	'Bobby Wingrove'	EBak
	'Bobby's Girl'	EPts
	'Bobolink' (d)	EBak
	'Bob's Best' (d)	CWVF EPts MJac
	'Boerhaave'	EBak
	boliviana Britton	see *F. sanctae-rosae*
	boliviana ambig.	CBcs MHer WOth WRou
§	***boliviana*** Carrière	CDoC CHEx CHII CLoc CWVF EBak LCla
§	- var. ***alba*** ♀H2	CDoC CHII CLoc EBak EPts LCla SVic WOth
	- var. ***boliviana***	CRHN SVic
	- var. ***luxurians*** 'Alba'	see *F. boliviana* Carrière var. *alba*
	- f. ***puberulenta*** Munz	see *F. boliviana* Carrière
	'Bon Accorde'	CLoc CWVF EBak EPts SLBF WRou
	'Bon Bon' (d)	CWVF EBak SVic
	'Bonita' (d)	CWVF SVic
	'Bonnie Lass' (d)	EBak
	'Bora Bora' (d)	CWVF EBak SVic
	'Borde Hill' (d)	EPts
	'Border Princess'	EBak
	'Border Queen' ♀H4	CLoc CWVF EBak EPts MJac MSCN SLBF SVic WOth
	'Border Raider'	WOth
	'Border Reiver'	CWVF EBak SVic
	'Börnemann's Beste'	see *F.* 'Georg Börnemann'
	'Bouffant'	CLoc SVic
	'Bountiful' Munkner (d)	CLoc CWVF
	'Bow Bells'	CDoC CLoc CWVF MJac SVic WOth
	'Boy Marc' (T) ♀H1c	CDoC LCla
	'Braamt's Glorie'	CDoC WRou
	'Brandt's 500 Club'	CLoc EBak
	'Breckland'	EBak
	'Breeders' Delight'	CWVF
	'Breeder's Dream' (d)	EBak
	'Breevis Minimus'	SLBF
	'Brenda' (d)	CWVF EBak
	'Brenda White'	CLoc CWVF EBak SVic WOth WRou
	'Brentwood' (d)	EBak
	'Brian C. Morrison' (T)	LCla
	'Brian G. Soanes'	EBak
	'Brian Kimberley' (T)	LCla
	'Brian McFetridge' (d)	WOth WRou

'Bridal Veil' (d)	EBak
'Bridesmaid' (d)	CWVF EBak SVic
'Brigadoon' (d)	EBak
'Brighton Belle' (T)	CDoC CWVF
'Brilliant' ambig.	COtt CWVF
'Brilliant' Bull, 1865	CLoc EBak LCla
'British Jubilee' (d)	CWVF SVic WOth
'British Sterling' (d)	WOth
'Brixham Orpheus'	CWVF
'Bronze Banks Peninsula'	CDoC
'Brookwood Belle' (d) ℽH3	CWVF EPts LCla MJac SLBF
'Brookwood Joy' (d)	CWVF
'Brutus' ℽH4	CDoC CLoc CWVF EBak EPfP EPts LRHS MAsh MSCN MWat NGBl SCoo SLBF SPoG SVic WFar WOth WRou
'Bryan Breary' (E)	LCla WOth WRou
'Buddha' (d)	EBak
'Bugle Boy'	CDoC LCla WRou
'Bunny' (d)	CWVF EBak SVic
'Burgundy Velvet' **new**	WOth
'Buster' (d)	LCla
'Buttercup'	CLoc CWVF EBak SVic
'Butterfly Dance' **new**	WOth
'C.J. Howlett'	EBak
'Caballero' (d)	EBak
'Caesar' (d)	CWVF EBak
'Caledonia'	CDoC EBak WOth
'Callaly Pink'	CWVF
'Cambridge Louie'	CWVF EBak
campos-portoi	CDoC CFil LCla WPGP
'Candlelight' (d)	EBak
'Candy Bells' (d)	CSBt
canescens misapplied	see *F. ampliata*
'Canny Bob'	MJac WOth
'Canopy' (d)	CWVF
'Cape Cornwall' **new**	CDoC
'Capri' (d)	CWVF EBak
'Cara Mia' (d)	CDoC CLoc
'Caradela' (d)	CLoc MJac WRou
'Cardinal'	CLoc
'Cardinal Farges' (d)	CDoC CLoc CWVF SLBF SVic
'Careless Whisper'	CDoC LCla SLBF
'Carioca'	EBak
'Carl Drude' (d)	SVic
'Carla Johnston' ℽH2	CLoc CWVF EPts MJac SVic WRou
'Carl's Brummagem Beauty'	MJac
'Carmel Blue'	CCCN CDoC CLoc LAst LCla LRHS SVic
'Carmen' Lemoine (d)	CDoC
'Carnoustie' (d)	EBak
'Carol Grace' (d)	CLoc
'Carol Nash' (d)	CLoc
'Caroline'	CLoc CWVF EBak EPts SVic WOth WRou
'Caroline's Joy'	MJac SCoo
'Cascade'	CLoc CWVF EPts MJac SLBF
'Caspar Hauser' (d)	CWVF SLBF SVic
'Catharina' (T)	CDoC
'Catherine Bartlett'	CWVF
'Cathie MacDougall' (d)	EBak
'Cecile' (d)	CCCN CDoC CWVF EPts LAst LCla MJac SLBF SVic
'Celadore' (d)	CWVF
'Celebration' (d)	CLoc CWVF
'Celia Smedley' ℽH3	CDoC CLoc CWVF EBak EPts LAst LCla MJac SLBF SVic WRou
'Celtic Beauty' **new**	CDoC
'Centerpiece' (d)	EBak
'Ceri'	CLoc
'Cerrig'	SVic
'Champagne Celebration'	CLoc WOth
'Champion'	XLum
'Chancellor' (d)	CWVF
'Chandleri'	CWVF SLBF SVic
'Chang' ℽH2	CDoC CLoc CWVF EBak LCla SLBF SVic WOth WRou
'Chantelle Garcia' (d)	EPts SLBF WRou
'Chantry Park' (T)	LCla
'Chapel Rossan' (E)	SLBF WRou
'Charisma'	SVic
'Charles Edward' (d)	CDoC
'Charles Welch'	EPts
Charlie Dimmock = 'Foncha'[PBR] (d)	CLoc
'Charlie Gardiner'	CWVF EBak
'Charlie Girl' (d)	EBak SVic
'Charming'	CDoC CLoc CWVF EBak LRHS MAsh MJac SVic WOth
'Chartwell'	WOth
'Chatt's Delight'	SLBF
'Checkerboard' ℽH3	CDoC CLoc CWVF EBak EPts LAst LCla MHer MJac MSCN SLBF SVic WOth WRou
'Cheers' (d)	CWVF
'Chelsea Louise'	EPts
'Chenois Godelieve'	CDoC
'Cherry Lee' **new**	SLBF
'Cherry Pie'	CDoC
'Cherry Pop' (E)	WRou
'Chessboard'	CLoc
'Chillerton Beauty' ℽH4	CDoC CLoc CTri CWVF ELan ELon EPts LCla LRHS MJac NLar SEND SLBF SPer SVic WMnd WOth
'Chilli Red'	EPts
'China Doll' (d)	CWVF EBak
'China Lantern'	CLoc CWVF EBak SVic
'Chor Echo'	CDoC WOth
'Chris Bright'	MJac WRou
'Chris Joiner'	WRou
'Chris Tarrant' (d)	EPts
'Christina Becker'	SVic
'Christine Bamford'	CDoC CWVF
'Churchtown'	CWVF
cinerea	LCla
'Cinnabarina' (E)	CLoc SVic WOth
'Cinque Port Liberty' (d)	SLBF
'Cinvenu'	LCla
'Cinvulca'	LCla
'Circe' (d)	CWVF EBak
'Circus'	EBak
'Circus Spangles' (d)	CLoc
'Citation'	CLoc CWVF EBak SVic
'City of Adelaide' (d)	CLoc
'City of Leicester'	CWVF
'Clair de Lune'	CWVF EBak SVic
'Claire Oram'	CLoc
'Claudia' (d)	LAst LCla MJac SLBF WRou
'Cliantha' (d)	CDoC WRou
'Clifford Gadsby' (d)	EBak
'Cliff's Hardy'	CDoC LCla SVic
'Cliff's Own'	SVic
'Cliff's Unique' (d)	CWVF EPts
'Clifton Beauty' (d)	CWVF MJac
'Clifton Belle' (d)	CWVF
'Clifton Charm'	EPts LCla MJac SVic

	Plant	Suppliers
	'Clipper'	CWVF
	'Cloth of Gold'	CLoc CWVF EBak MJac SVic
	'Cloverdale Jewel' (d)	CDoC CWVF EBak SVic WOth
	'Cloverdale Joy'	EBak
	'Cloverdale Pearl'	CDoC CWVF EBak SPoG SVic WOth
	'Coachman' 🏆H4	CLoc CWVF EBak EPts LAst LCla SLBF SVic WOth WRou
	coccinea	CDoC CTsd WOth
	× ***colensoi***	CDoC ECou LCla WRou
*	- var. ***purpurascens***	WOth
	'Collingwood' (d)	CLoc CWVF EBak
	'Come Dancing' (d)	CDoC CWVF SVic
	'Comet' Banks	CWVF
I	'Comet' Tiret (d)	CLoc EBak
	'Comperen Lutea' (d)	CDoC
	'Conchetta Garcia'	SLBF WRou
	'Conchilla' (d)	EBak
	'Connie' (d)	EBak SVic
	'Connor's Cascade'	SLBF
	'Conspicua' 🏆H4	CDoC CWVF EBak ELon SLBF SVic WOth
	'Constable Country' (d)	CWVF
	'Constance' (d)	CDoC CLoc CWVF LCla MJac SLBF SVic WOth
	'Constance Comer'	MJac WRou
	'Constellation' ambig.	CWVF
	'Constellation' Schnabel, 1957 (d)	CLoc EBak
	'Coombe Park'	MJac
	'Coquet Bell'	CWVF EBak
	'Coquet Dale' (d)	CWVF EBak
	'Coral Baby' (E)	LCla SLBF WRou
	'Coral Rose' (d)	SVic
	'Coral Seas'	EBak
	'Coralle' (T) 🏆H1c	CCCN CDoC CLoc CWVF EBak EPts LCla MHer MJac MSCN SLBF SVic WOth WRou
	'Corallina' 🏆H4	CDoC CLoc EBak MMuc SEND SVic WOth WPnn
*	***cordata*** B&SWJ 9095	WCru
	- B&SWJ 10325	WCru
	cordifolia misapplied	see *F. splendens*
	'Core'ngrato' (d)	CLoc CWVF EBak
	'Cornelia Smith' (T)	CDoC LCla
	'Cornwall Calls' (d)	EBak
	'Corsage' (d)	CWVF SVic
	'Corsair' (d)	EBak SVic
	corymbiflora misapplied	see *F. boliviana* Carrière
	corymbiflora Ruíz & Pav.	CDoC EBak SVic
	'Cosmopolitan' (d)	EBak
	'Costa Brava'	CLoc EBak
	'Cotta Bright Star'	CDoC CWVF LCla
	'Cotta Carousel'	LCla
	'Cotta Christmas Tree'	CDoC LCla SLBF WRou
	'Cotta Fairy'	CWVF
	'Cotta Vino'	SVic
	'Cottinghamii'	see *F.* × *bacillaris* 'Cottinghamii'
	'Cotton Candy' (d)	CLoc CWVF SVic
	'Countdown Carol' (d)	EPts
	'Countess of Aberdeen'	CWVF EBak SLBF
	'Countess of Maritza' (d)	CLoc CWVF
	'Court Jester' (d)	CLoc EBak
	'Cover Girl' (d)	EBak EPts
	'Coxeen'	EBak
	'Crackerjack'	CLoc EBak
	'Crescendo' (d)	CLoc CWVF
	'Crinkley Bottom' (d)	EPts MJac SLBF
	'Crinoline' (d)	EBak
	'Crosby Serendipity'	CLoc
	'Crosby Soroptimist'	CWVF MJac
	'Cross Check'	CWVF
	'Crusader' (d)	CWVF
	'Crystal Blue'	EBak SVic
	'Crystal Stars' (d)	SVic
	'Cumbrian Lass'	WOth WRou
	'Cupid'	EBak
	'Curly Q'	EBak SVic
	'Curtain Call' (d)	CWVF EBak SVic
	cylindracea misapplied	see *F.* × *bacillaris*
	'Cymon' (d)	CWVF
	'Cymru' (d)	SVic
	'Dainty'	EBak
	'Dainty Lady' (d)	EBak
	'Daisy Bell'	CLoc CWVF EBak LCla MJac SVic WOth
	'Dalton'	EBak
	'Dana Samantha'	EPts
	'Dancing Bloom'	EPts
	'Dancing Flame' (d) 🏆H3	CDoC CLoc CWVF EBak EPts LAst LCla MJac SLBF SVic WRou
	'Daniel Pfaller' (d)	MJac
	'Danielle'	WRou
	'Danish Pastry'	CDoC CWVF
	'Danny Boy' (d)	CLoc CWVF EBak SVic
	'Dark and Delicious' (Mojo Series) **new**	WOth
	'Dark Eyes' (d) 🏆H4	CCCN CLoc CWVF EBak LAst MJac SLBF SPer SVic WOth
	'Dark Mystery' (d)	WOth
	'Dark Secret' (d)	EBak
	'Dark Treasure' (d)	CDoC
	'Daryn John Woods'	CDoC LCla WOth
	'David' 🏆H4	CDoC CLoc CSde CWVF ELon EPfP EPts LAst LCla MJac SEND SLBF WHil WOth WRou
	'David Alston' (d)	CLoc CWVF EBak
	'David Lockyer' (d)	CLoc CWVF SVic
	'David Savage' (d)	LCla
	'Dawn'	EBak WOth
	'Dawn Fantasia' (v)	CLoc EPts
	'Dawn Redfern' (d)	CWVF
	'Dawn Sky' (d)	EBak
	'Dawn Star' (d)	CDoC CLoc CWVF MJac SVic WOth
	'Dawn Thunder' (d)	SVic
	'Day Star'	EBak
	'De Groot's Dream'	WOth
	'De Groot's Floriant'	LCla
	'De Mijnlamp' (d)	CDoC
	'Debby' (d)	EBak
	'Deben Petite' (E)	LCla
	'Deborah Jane'	SLBF
	'Deborah Street' (d)	CLoc
	'Debron's Black Cherry' **new**	SLBF
§	***decussata*** Ruíz & Pav.	EBak
	'Dee Copley' (d)	EBak
	'Deep Purple' (d)	CLoc LAst MJac SCoo SLBF
	'Delia Smith' (d)	EPts
	'Delicate Purple'	EPts WRou
	'Delilah' (d)	CWVF
	'Delphobe' **new**	EPts WOth
	'Delta's Bride'	SLBF
	'Delta's Dream'	CWVF WOth
	'Delta's Drop'	SVic
	'Delta's Fellow'	WOth
	'Delta's Groom'	LCla SLBF WRou

Name	Suppliers
'Delta's Ko' (d)	SVic
'Delta's Parade' (d)	CDoC WOth
'Delta's Rien'	SVic
'Delta's Sara'	CDoC COtt EPfP LAst LBuc LRHS MBri MJac SHil SLim SLon SPoG WFar WHar WRou
'Delta's Song'	WRou
'Delta's Symphonie' (d)	CWVF
'Delta's Wonder'	SVic
'Dennis Cartwright'	MJac
§ ***denticulata*** Υ^{H2}	CDoC CLoc CWVF EBak EPts LCla LRHS MHer SLBF SVic WOth
'Derby Imp'	CWVF
'Desperate Daniel'	EPts
'Devonshire Dumpling' (d) Υ^{H2}	CCCN CDoC CLoc CTsd CWVF EBak EPts LAst MJac SLBF SVic WRou
'Dharlah' (T) **new**	WOth
'Diablo' (d)	EBak
'Diamond Celebration' (d)	WOth
'Diamond Wedding'	SVic WOth
'Diana' (d)	EBak
'Diana Wills' (d)	CWVF
'Diana Wright'	CDoC
Diana, Princess of Wales = 'Fucdpw'[PBR]	LAst
'Diane Brown'	CWVF
'Diane Stephens'	SLBF WRou
'Didi' (d) **new**	WOth
§ 'Die Schöne Wilhelmine'	SVic
'Dilly-Dilly' (d)	CWVF
'Dipton Dainty' (d)	CLoc EBak SVic
'Display' Υ^{H4}	CLoc COtt CWVF EBak EPfP EPts LAst LCla LRHS MAsh MBri MGos MJac NPer SHil SLBF SPoG SVic WHar
'Doc'	CDoC EPts SVic
'Docteur Topinard'	CLoc EBak
'Doctor'	see *F.* 'The Doctor'
'Doctor Becky Reynolds' (d)	WRou
'Doctor Foster' Υ^{H4}	CDoC CLoc CTri EBak SPoG SVic
'Doctor Mason'	CWVF
'Doctor Olson' (d)	CLoc EBak
'Doctor Robert'	CWVF EPts MJac SVic
'Doctor Sat Sandilands' (d)	WRou
'Dodo'	LCla SLBF
'Doffie' **new**	WOth
§ 'Dollar Prinzessin' (d) Υ^{H4}	CDoC CLoc CMac COtt CWVF EBak EPfP EPts EShb LAst LCla LRHS MAsh MBri MGos MJac NPer SHil SLBF SLim SMrm SPlb SVic WFar WRou
'Dominyana'	CDoC EBak LCla
'Don Peralta'	EBak
'Dopy' (d)	EPts SVic
'Doray'	CDoC SLBF WOth WRou
'Doreen Redfern'	CLoc CWVF MJac SVic
'Doreen Stroud' (d)	CWVF
'Doris Joan'	SLBF
'Dorothea Flower'	CLoc CWVF EBak WOth
'Dorothy'	EPts LCla SLBF
'Dorothy Ann'	LCla SLBF
'Dorothy Cheal'	CWVF
'Dorothy Clive'	WRou
'Dorothy Day' (d)	CLoc
'Dorothy Hanley' (d)	CCCN CDoC CLoc EPts LAst LRHS LSou MAsh MJac SLBF SVic WOth WRou
'Dorothy Oosting' (d)	CDoC
'Dorothy Shields' (d)	CWVF MJac WOth
'Dorrian Brogdale' (T)	LCla
'Dorset Abigail'	CWVF
'Dorset Delight' (d)	CWVF
'Dragon Moon' (d)	CDoC
'Drake 400' (d)	CLoc
'Drama Girl' (d)	CWVF
'Drame' (d)	CDoC CWVF EBak SVic WHea
'Drum Major' (d)	EBak
'Du Barry' (d)	EBak
'Duchess of Albany'	CLoc EBak
'Duchess of Cornwall' (d)	EPts
'Duet' (d)	SVic
'Duke of Wellington' Haag, 1956 (d)	CLoc
'Dulcie Elizabeth' (d)	CWVF EBak MJac
'Dusky Beauty'	CWVF SVic WRou
'Dusky Rose' (d)	CLoc CWVF EBak MJac SVic
'Dutch Kingsize'	WOth
'Dutch Mill'	CLoc CWVF EBak
'Duyfken'	CWVF
'Dying Embers'	CDoC CLoc MSCN SVen WOth WRou
'Dymph Werker van Groenland' (E)	LCla
'East Anglian'	CLoc EBak WOth
'Easter Belle'	LRHS
'Easter Bonnet' (d)	CLoc CWVF
'Ebb 'n' Flow'	EBak
'Ebbtide' (d)	CLoc EBak
'Echo'	CWVF
'Ed Largarde' (d)	EBak
'Eden Lady'	CLoc
'Eden Princess'	CWVF MJac
'Eden Rock' (d)	CLoc WOth
'Edith' ambig.	EPts WRou
'Edith' Brown (d)	LCla SLBF
'Edith Emery' (d)	CDoC
'Edna May'	CWVF
'Edna W. Smith'	CWVF
'Eileen Raffill'	EBak
'Eileen Saunders'	EBak
'El Camino' (d)	CWVF
'El Cid'	CLoc EBak SVic
'Elaine Ann'	EPts MJac
'Elaine Taylor' (d)	MJac
'Eleanor Clark'	WOth
'Eleanor Grace' **new**	WOth
'Eleanor Leytham'	CWVF EBak SVic
'Eleanor Rawlins'	EBak WRou
'Elfin Glade'	CLoc CWVF EBak SVic
'Elfrida' (d)	CDoC
'Elfriede Ott' (T) Υ^{H1c}	CLoc EBak LCla
'Elizabeth' ambig.	WOth
'Elizabeth' Whiteman, 1941	EBak
'Elizabeth Honnorine'	SVic
'Elizabeth Travis' (d)	EBak
'Ellen Morgan' (d)	CWVF EBak
'Elma'	LCla MJac
'Elsa' (d)	CWVF SVic
'Elsie Mitchell' (d)	CWVF
§ 'Emile de Wildeman' (d)	CWVF EBak
'Emily'	WOth
'Emily Austen'	CWVF
'Emma Alice' (d)	CWVF
'Emma L. Falconer' **new**	WRou
'Emma Louise' (d)	WOth
'Empress of Prussia' Υ^{H4}	CDoC CLoc CWVF EBak EPts SLBF SVic WOth

Name	Suppliers
'Enchanted' (d)	CWVF EBak
encliandra (E)	WRou
- subsp. ***encliandra*** (E)	CDoC
§ 'Enfant Prodigue' (d)	CLoc SDix SLBF SMrm SVic
'English Rose' (d)	CWVF
'Enstone'	see *F. magellanica* var. *molinae* 'Enstone'
'Erich Mehlis'	WOth
'Eric's Hardy' (d)	CDoC
'Eric's Majestic' (d)	MJac
'Erika Köth' (T)	LCla WOth
'Erna van Wiele' new	CDoC
'Ernest Rankin'	SVic
'Ernie'[PBR]	CDoC EPts LAst SLBF WOth
'Ernie Bromley'	CWVF WOth
'Ernie Wise' (d)	MJac SCoo
'Eroica'	SVic
'Eruption'	CDoC CLoc LAst MCot
'Estelle Marie'	CLoc CWVF EBak SVic
'Eternal Flame' (d)	CWVF EBak EPts SVic
'Ethel May' (d)	MJac
'Eusebia' (d)	SVic
'Eva Boerg' ♀H4	CCCN CLoc CTri CWVF EBak LAst SVic WKif
'Evelyn Stanley' (d)	CWVF
§ 'Evelyn Steele Little'	EBak
'Evening Sky' (d)	EBak
'Evensong'	CLoc CWVF EBak SVic
excorticata	CAbb CBcs CDoC CExl CTsd ECre GBin LEdu LRHS MCot SPlb
'Fabian Franck' (T)	LCla WRou
'Fairy Lavender'	LAst
'Falklands' (d)	EPts SLBF
'Falling Stars'	CLoc CWVF EBak SVic
'Falmouth'	CDoC
'Fan Dancer' (d)	EBak
'Fancy Pants' (d)	CLoc CWVF EBak SVic
'Fanfare'	CDoC EBak LCla SVic
'Fascination'	see *F.* 'Emile de Wildeman'
'Fashion' (d)	EBak
'Favourite'	EBak
'Felicity Kendal' (d)	SCoo
'Feltham's Pride'	CWVF
'Fenman'	CWVF SVic
'Festival Lights' (E)	SLBF WRou
'Festoon'	EBak
'Fey' (d)	CWVF
'Ffion'	CDoC EPts WOth
'Fiery Spider'	EBak SVic
'Finn'	CDoC CWVF EPts
'Fiona'	CLoc CWVF EBak SVic WOth
'Fiona Pitt' (E)	WOth
'Fiorelli Flowers' (d)	CDoC
'Fire Mountain' (d)	CLoc SVic
'Firecracker'[PBR]	see *F.* 'John Ridding'
'Firefly'	SVic
'Firelite' (d)	EBak
'Firenza' (d)	CWVF
'First Kiss' (d)	CWVF
'First Lady' (d)	CWVF
'First Lord'	CWVF
'First Success' (E)	CDoC CWVF LCla SVic WOth WRou
'Flair' (d)	CLoc CWVF WOth
'Flame'	EBak
'Flamenco Dancer' (California Dreamers Series) (d)	CLoc
'Flamingo' (d)	SVic
'Flash' ♀H4	CLoc CTri CWVF EBak ELan EPfP EPts LCla MJac MRav SLBF SPoG SVic WOth WRou
'Flashlight'	CDoC CWVF EPfP EWld LAst LCla MJac SCoo WOth
'Flat Jack o' Lancashire' (d)	CDoC SLBF
'Flavia' (d)	EBak
'Fleur de Picardie'	SLBF
'Flirtation Waltz' (d)	CLoc CWVF EBak MJac SVic
'Flocon de Neige'	EBak
'Flogman'	LCla
'Floral City' (d)	CLoc EBak
'Florence May Joiner'	WRou
'Florence Taylor' (d)	CWVF
'Florence Turner'	EBak WOth
'Florentina' (d)	CLoc CWVF EBak SVic
'Florrie's Gem' (d)	SLBF
'Flowerdream' (d)	CWVF
'Flyaway' (d)	EBak
'Fly-by-night' (d)	CWVF
'Flying Cloud' (d)	CDoC CLoc CWVF EBak SVic WOth
'Flying Scotsman' (d)	CLoc CWVF EBak EPts SCoo SVic WOth
'Folies Bergères' (d)	EBak
'Foolke'	EBak
'Forget-me-not'	CLoc CWVF EBak SVic WOth
'Fort Bragg' (d)	CWVF EBak
'Fountains Abbey' (d)	CWVF
'Four Farthings' (d)	EPts
'Foxgrove Wood' ♀H4	CWCL CWVF EBak ELon EPts SLBF WOth WRou
'Foxtrot' (d)	CWVF
'Foxy Lady' (d)	CWVF
'Frances Haskins'	WOth
'Frank Saunders'	CWVF LCla SLBF
'Frank Unsworth' (d)	CWVF EPts MJac
'Frankfurt 2006'	MJac
'Frankie's Magnificent Seven' (d)	EPts
'Franz von Zon'	LCla SLBF WRou
'Frau Hilde Rademacher' (d)	CWVF EBak EPts SLBF SVic
'Frauke'	SVic
'Fred Hansford'	CDoC CWVF
'Fred Swales' (T)	WOth
'Fred's First' (d)	SVic
'Freefall'	EBak
'Friendly Fire' (d)	CLoc
'Frosted Flame'	CLoc CWVF EBak LAst LCla MJac SLBF
'Frozen Tears'	EPts WOth
'Frühling' (d)	EBak
'Fuchsiade '88'	CLoc CWVF EBak SLBF WRou
'Fuchsiarama '91' (T) ♀H2	CDoC CWVF WRou
'Fudzi San' (T)	WRou
'Fuji-san'	ELon EPts
'Fuksie Foetsie' (E)	CDoC WOth
fulgens (T) ♀H2	CDoC GCal LCla WRou
* - 'Variegata' (T/v)	CDoC CLoc EPts LCla WOth WRou
'Fulpila'	CDoC LCla SLBF
'Für Elise' (d)	EBak
'Gala' (d)	EBak
'Galadriel'	CDoC WOth
'Garden News' (d) ♀H4	CDoC CLoc COtt CWCL CWVF EPfP EPts LAst LCla LRHS MAsh MBri MJac MSCN NGBl NPer SHil SLBF SPer SVic WFar WHar WRou
'Garden Week' (d)	CDoC CWVF SVic

Name	Suppliers
'Gartenmeister Bonstedt' (T) ♀H1c	CLoc CWVF EBak EWld LCla SVic
'Gary Rhodes' (d)	EBak MJac SCoo
'Gay Anne' (d)	WOth
'Gay Fandango' (d)	CLoc CWVF EBak
'Gay Future'	WOth
'Gay Parasol' (d)	LAst MJac SVic
'Gay Paree' (d)	EBak
'Gay Señorita'	EBak
'Gay Spinner' (d)	CLoc
gehrigeri	EBak
'Gemma Fisher' (d)	EPts
Gene = 'Goetzgene'[PBR] (Shadowdancer Series)	LAst LSou SCoo
'Général Monk' (d)	CDoC CWVF EBak EPts LAst SVic
'General Wavell' (d)	SVic
'Genii' ♀H4	Widely available
'Geoff Oke'	CDoC SLBF WOth
'Geoffrey Smith' (d)	EPts
§ 'Georg Börnemann' (T) ♀H2	CLoc EBak MJac
'George Allen White' (d)	CWVF
'George Barr'	CDoC LRHS
'George Johnson'	CDoC
'George Travis' (d)	EBak
'Georges Remy'	WOth
§ 'Gerharda's Aubergine'	CLoc CWVF WOth
'Gerharda's Katja' **new**	CDoC
'Gesneriana'	CLoc EBak
'Ghislaine' (d)	CDoC
'Giant Pink Enchanted' (d)	CLoc EBak
'Gilda' (d)	CWVF MJac SVic
'Gillian Althea' (d)	CWVF
'Gilt Edge' (v)	CLoc
I 'Gina'	WOth
'Gina Bowman' (E)	EPts LCla SLBF WRou
Ginger = 'Goetzginger'[PBR] (Shadowdancer Series)	LAst LSou SCoo
'Gipsy Princess' (d)	CLoc
'Girls' Brigade'	CWVF
'Glad B'	WRou
'Gladiator' (d)	CMac EBak SVic
'Gladys Godfrey'	EBak
'Gladys Lorimer'	CDoC CWVF EPfP EPts LRHS
'Gladys Miller'	CLoc
glazioviana ♀H2	CDoC CSde CWVF EPts GCal LCla MHer SLBF SVen WOth WRou
'Glenby' (d)	CWVF
'Glendale'	CWVF
'Glitters'	CWVF EBak
§ 'Globosa'	CAgr EBak WOth
'Glow'	EBak WOth
'Glowing Embers'	EBak
'Glowing Lilac' (d)	EPts
'Gold Brocade'	ELan EPfP
'Gold Crest'	EBak
'Gold Leaf'	CWVF
'Golden Anniversary' (d)	CLoc CWVF EBak MJac SVic WRou
'Golden Arrow' (T)	LCla SVic WCot
§ 'Golden Border Queen'	CLoc EBak
'Golden Dawn'	CLoc CWVF EBak SVic
– 'Golden Girl'	SLBF
'Golden Herald'	SLBF
'Golden la Campanella' (d/v)	CDoC CLoc
'Golden Lena' (d/v)	CWVF
'Golden Marinka' (v) ♀H2	CLoc EBak SVic
'Golden Swingtime' (d)	MJac SVic
'Golden Treasure' (v)	CLoc CWVF
'Golden Vergeer' (v)	SLBF
'Golondrina'	CWVF EBak
'Good Girl'	WOth
'Goody Goody'	EBak SVic
'Gordon's China Rose'	LCla
'Gota'	WRou
'Göttingen' (T)	EBak
'Governor Pat Brown' (d)	EBak
'Grace Bell' **new**	CDoC
'Grace Darling'	CDoC CWVF EBak
gracilis	see *F. magellanica* var. *gracilis*
'Graf Witte'	CWVF SVic
'Grand Duke' (T/d)	CWVF
'Grand Prix' (d)	SVic
'Grandad Fred' (d)	SLBF
'Grandad Hobbs' (d)	LCla SLBF
'Grandma Sinton' (d)	CLoc CWVF
'Grandpa Jack' (d)	SLBF
'Granny Charlton'	WCFE
'Grasmere'	WOth
'Grayrigg'	CDoC ELon EPts LCla SLBF WOth
'Great Ouse' (d)	EPts
'Great Scott' (d)	CLoc
'Green 'n' Gold'	EBak
'Greenpeace'	SLBF SVic
'Greta' (T)	CDoC
'Grey Lady' (d)	SVic
'Groene Kan's Glorie'	SVic
'Grumpy'	CWVF EPts SVic WOth
'Gruss aus dem Bodethal'	CLoc CWVF EBak EPts SLBF
'Guinevere'	CWVF EBak
'Gunar Reich' (d)	WOth
'Gustave Doré' (d)	EBak
'Guy Dauphine' (d)	EBak
'Guy-Ann Mannens'	CDoC
'Gwen Dodge'	SVic
'Gypsy Girl' (d)	CWVF
'H.G. Brown'	EBak
'Hage Pinokkio'	WOth
'Hampshire Blue'	CDoC CWVF WOth
'Hanna' (d)	LRHS
'Hannah Louise' (d)	EPts
'Hans Callaars'	CDoC LCla
'Happiness' (d)	SVic
'Happy'	CDoC CWVF EPts LCla MSCN SVic
'Happy Anniversary'	CLoc SVic WOth
'Happy Fellow'	CDoC CLoc EBak WOth
'Happy Wedding Day' (d)	CDoC CLoc CWVF EPts LAst MJac SCoo SVic
'Hapsburgh'	EBak
'Harbour Lites'	SLBF WRou
'Harlow Car'	CDoC CWVF EPts WOth
'Harlow Perfection'	CDoC
'Harmony' Niederholzer, 1946	EBak
'Harry Dunnett' (T)	EBak
'Harry Gray' (d) ♀H2	CDoC CLoc CWVF EBak EPts LAst MJac SVic
'Harry Lye'	WOth
'Harry Pullen'	EBak
'Harry Taylor' (d)	EPts
'Harry's Sunshine'	SLBF
'Harti's Olivia'	CDoC
hartwegii	CDoC LCla MHer
'Harvey's Reward'	SLBF WOth
'Hastings'	CDoC
'Hathersage' (d)	EBak
hatschbachii ♀H2	CDoC CSde CTsd EWes GCal LCla MCot MHer SBrt SDix SLon SPlb

	SPoG SVen WHil WOth WPGP WPnn
'Haute Cuisine' (d)	CLoc SVic
'Hawaiian Sunset' (d)	CLoc CWVF EPts SLBF WRou
'Hawkshead' ♀H4	Widely available
'Hayley Jay' (d)	CDoC SLBF WRou
'Hazel' (d)	CWVF SVic WOth
'Hazel Elizabeth' **new**	WRou
'Heart Throb' (d)	EBak
'Hebe'	EBak
'Heidi Ann' (d) ♀H4	CDoC CLoc CWVF EBak EPts LAst LRHS MAsh MRav SLBF SVic
'Heidi Blue' (d)	SLBF
§ 'Heidi Weiss' (d)	CLoc CWVF
'Heinrich Henkel'	see *F.* 'Andenken an Heinrich Henkel'
'Helcom' **new**	WRou
'Helen Clare' (d)	CLoc CWVF EBak
'Helen Gair' (d)	CWVF
'Helen Lang'	EPts
'Helen Storer' **new**	MJac
'Hellen Devine'	CWVF
'Helston Flora' (d) **new**	CDoC
'Hemsleyana'	see *F. microphylla* subsp. *hemsleyana*
'Hendrikje Stoffels' (d)	WOth
'Henkelly's Chloris'	WOth
'Henkelly's Gitano'	WOth
'Henkelly's Hermine' **new**	WOth
'Henkelly's Trubia' **new**	WOth
'Henning Becker' ♀H3	CDoC CWVF ELan ELon
'Henri Poincaré'	EBak
'Henrieke Dimi' (d)	CDoC
'Herald' ♀H4	CDoC CWCL CWVF EBak EPfP LRHS LSou MAsh MBri MGos SHil SLBF SVic WOth
'Herbé de Jacques'	see *F.* 'Mr West'
'Heri Trevally'	WOth
'Heritage' (d)	CLoc EBak
'Herman de Graaff' (d)	SLBF
'Hermiena'	CDoC CLoc CWVF EPts SLBF SVic WOth
'Heron'	EBak
'Herps Kipkar'	WOth
'Herps Martina'	WOth
'Herps Pierement'	SLBF WRou
'Herps Vierspan' **new**	CDoC
'Hessett Festival' (d)	CWVF EBak
'Heston Blue' (d)	CWVF
'Hettenheuvel'	WOth
'Heydon'	CWVF
'Hi Jinks' (d)	EBak
hidalgensis	see *F. microphylla* subsp. *hidalgensis*
'Hidcote Beauty' ♀H2	CLoc CWVF EBak LCla SLBF SVic WOth
'Hidden Treasure'	WRou
'Highland Pipes'	LCla SVic
'Hilary'	WRou
'Hilda May Salmon'	CWVF
'Hindu Belle'	EBak
'Hinnerike' (E)	CWVF LCla SVic
'Hiroshige' (T)	LCla
'His Excellency' (d)	EBak
'Hobson's Choice' (d)	CWVF SLBF
'Holly's Beauty' (d)	CLoc EPts LAst
'Hollywood Park' (d)	EBak
'Horsforth Beauty'	WOth
'Horsforth Dream' **new**	WOth

'Horsforth in Bloom'	WOth WRou
'Hot Coals'	CWVF EPts MJac SVic WRou
'Howlett's Hardy' ♀H4	CDoC CLoc CWVF EBak NLar SVic WMnd WOth
'Huet's Baraketh'	WOth
'Huet's Kwarts'	CDoC
'Huet's Turkoois'	CDoC
'Hula Girl' (d)	CWVF EBak MJac
'Huntsman' (d)	CCCN
'I Love You'	WOth
'Ian Leedham' (d)	EBak
'Ian Storey'	CDoC
'Ice Cream Soda' (d)	EBak
'Iceberg'	CWVF EBak SVic
'Icecap'	CWVF SVic
'Iced Champagne'	CLoc CWVF EBak MJac
'Ichiban' (d)	CLoc
'Ida' (d)	EBak
'Igloo Maid' (d)	CLoc CWVF EBak SVic
'Imogen Faye' (d)	SLBF WRou
'Impala' (d)	CWVF
'Imperial Fantasy' (d)	CWVF
'Impudence'	CLoc CWVF EBak
'Impulse' (d)	CLoc
'Independence' (d)	SVic
'Indian Maid' (d)	CWVF EBak
'Insulinde' (T)	CWVF EPts LCla MHer MJac SLBF
'Interlude' (d)	EBak
'Iolanthe' (T)	CWVF
'Iona'	WRou
'Irene L. Peartree' (d)	CWVF LCla
'Irene Sinton' (d)	CDoC MJac
'Iris Amer' (d)	CLoc CWVF EBak
'Isis' Lemoine	WRou
'Island Sunset' (v) **new**	SLBF
'Isle of Purbeck'	SVic
'Italiano' (d)	CWVF MJac SVic
'Ivana van Amsterdam'	WRou
'Jack Acland'	CWVF
'Jack Shahan' ♀H2	CCCN CLoc CWVF EBak LAst LCla MJac SLBF WOth
'Jack Siverns'	WOth
'Jack Stanway' (v)	CDoC CWVF WOth
'Jackie Bull' (d)	CWVF EBak
'Jackpot' (d)	EBak
'Jackqueline' (T)	CWVF
'Jadi Messingtetra' **new**	CDoC WOth
'Jadi Netbotia' **new**	CDoC
'Jamboree' (d)	EBak
'James Bamber'	WOth WRou
'James Lye' (d)	CWVF EBak WOth
'James Travis' (E/d)	CDoC EBak LCla WOth WRou
'Jan Bremer'	SVic
'Jan Weijeb' **new**	CDoC
'Jandel'	CWVF
'Jane Humber' (d)	CWVF
'Jane Lye'	EBak
'Janice Perry's Gold' (v)	CLoc CNor MJac
'Janie' (d)	CDoC EPfP LBuc LRHS MAsh SVic
'Jap Vantveer' (T)	LCla
'Jasper Marnix'	WOth
'Jasper's Zuurstok' **new**	WOth
'Jaunty Jack'	SLBF WOth
'Javelin'	CDoC WOth
'Jean Baker'	CDoC
'Jean Campbell'	EBak
'Jean Frisby'	CLoc WOth
'Jean Taylor'	EPts WRou

Plant	Suppliers
'Jean Webb' (v)	WCot
'Jeeves' (d) **new**	WOth
'Jennifer'	EBak MJac
'Jennifer Ann'	LAst SLBF WOth
'Jenny May'	CLoc EPts LCla WOth
'Jenny Sorensen' ♀H2	CWVF
'Jess'	LCla SLBF WOth
'Jessie Pearson'	CWVF
'Jessimae'	CWVF
'Jester' Holmes (d)	CLoc WOth
'Jet Fire' (d)	EBak
'Jezebel' (d)	SVic
'Jiddles' (E)	LCla WRou
'Jill Holloway' (T)	SLBF
'Jill Whitworth'	CDoC WPnn
'Jim Coleman'	CWVF SVic
'Jim Dodge' (d)	EPts
'Jim Hawkins'	EBak
'Jim Muncaster'	CWVF
'Jim Watts'	CDoC WOth
jimenezii	CDoC
'Jimmy Cricket' (E)	SLBF WOth
'Joan Barnes' (d)	CWVF
'Joan Cooper'	CLoc CWVF EBak SLBF SVic WOth
'Joan Goy'	CWVF MJac SVic
'Joan Knight'	CLoc
'Joan Margaret' (d)	MJac
'Joan Morris'	SLBF
'Joan Pacey'	CWVF EBak
'Joan Smith'	EBak
'Joan Waters' (d)	CWVF
'Joanna Lumley' (d)	CDoC EPts MJac
'Joanne'	WOth
'Jo-Anne Fisher' (d)	EPts
'Joan's Delight'	SVic WOth
'Joe Kusber' (d)	CWVF EBak
'Joel'	WOth
'John Bartlett'	CLoc
'John Green'	CDoC
'John Grooms' (d)	CLoc SVic WRou
'John Lockyer'	CLoc CWVF EBak
'John Maynard Scales' (T) ♀H2	CWVF LCla MJac WRou
'John Nicholass'	SLBF WOth
§ 'John Ridding' PBR (T/v) ♀H1c	CLoc EPts LBuc SPoG
'John Suckley' (d)	EBak
'John Wright'	CDoC LCla
'Jomam'	CWVF
'Jon Oram'	CLoc CWVF
'Jonny Wilkinson'	MJac
'Jorma van Eijk' (d)	CDoC
'Jose's Joan' (d)	CWVF SVic
'Jotu'	WOth
'Joy Patmore'	CLoc CWVF EBak SLBF
'Joyce Adey' (d)	CWVF
'Joyce Sinton'	CLoc CWVF
'Joyce Wilson' (d)	EPts
'Judith Coupland'	CWVF
'Judith Louise' **new**	WOth
'Juella'	WRou
'Jülchen'	CWVF
'Jules Daloges' (d)	EBak
'Julie Marie' (d)	CWVF MJac
'June Gardner'	CWVF
'Jungle'	CDoC LCla SLBF WOth
'Jungle Baby' **new**	WOth
I 'Juno' Kennett	EBak
juntasensis	CDoC WOth
'Jupiter Seventy'	EBak
'Just Pilk'	SLBF
'Just Pink' (E)	CDoC WOth
'Justin's Pride'	CDoC
'Kaleidoscope' (d)	EBak
'Kaley Jackson'	WRou
'Kames Bay'	WOth WRou
'Karen Isles' (E)	CDoC LCla SLBF
'Karen Louise' (d)	CLoc
'Kate Taylor' (d)	SLBF
'Kate Wieteska' (E)	WRou
'Kath van Hanegem'	CLoc SLBF WOth WRou
'Kath Wilson'	LAst
'Kathryn Maidment'	SVic
'Katie' **new**	WOth
'Katie Rogers'	EPts
'Katinka' (E)	CDoC CWVF LCla SLBF WOth
'Katjan'	LCla SLBF WOth WRou
'Katrina' (d)	CDoC CLoc EBak
'Katrina Thompsen'	CLoc CWVF EPts SLBF WOth WRou
'Katy Flynn'	CLoc CWVF WOth WRou
'Katy James'	WRou
'Keepsake' (d)	EBak
'Kegworth Carnival' (d)	CWVF
'Ken Goldsmith' (T)	CWVF
'Ken Jennings'	CWVF
'Ken Tudor'	MJac
'Kenny Holmes'	CWVF
'Kenny Walkling'	LCla SLBF
'Ken's Pixie' **new**	MJac
'Kernan Robson' (d)	CLoc CWVF EBak
'Keystone'	EBak
'Kilili'	WOth
'Kim Joiner'	WRou
'Kimberly' (d)	EBak
'King of Bath' (d)	EBak
'King of Hearts' (d)	EBak
'King's Ransom' (d)	CLoc CWVF EBak SVic
'Kiss 'n' Tell'	CWVF MJac
'Kit Oxtoby' (d)	CDoC CWVF MJac SLBF WOth
'Kiwi' (d)	EBak
'Knockout' (d)	CWVF SVic
'Kobold'	SLBF WOth
'Kolding Perle'	CWVF SLBF
'Komeet'	CDoC
'Krommenie'	WOth
'Kuniko Atarashi' (d)	EPts
'Kwintet'	CWVF EBak MJac
'La Bianca'	EBak
'La Campanella' (d) ♀H2	CCCN CDoC CLoc CWVF EBak EPts LAst MJac SVic
'La Fiesta' (d)	EBak
'La France' (d)	EBak
'La Neige' ambig.	CWVF
'La Neige' Lemoine (d)	EBak
'La Porte' (d)	CLoc CWVF
'La Rosita' (d)	EBak
I 'La Traviata' Blackwell (d)	EBak
'Lace Petticoats' (d)	EBak SVic
'Lady Beth' (d)	SVic
'Lady Boothby' ♀H4	Widely available
'Lady Framlingham' (d)	EPts
'Lady in Black' **new**	WRou
'Lady in Grey' (d)	MJac SVic
'Lady in Red' (d)	WRou
'Lady Isobel Barnett'	CLoc CWVF EBak MJac SLBF SVic WOth

	Name	Suppliers
	'Lady Kathleen Spence'	CWVF EBak SVic WOth
	'Lady Patricia Mountbatten'	CWVF SVic WOth WRou
	'Lady Ramsey'	EBak
	'Lady Rebecca' (d)	CLoc
	'Lady Thumb' (d) ♀H3	Widely available
	'Laepines'	WOth
	'Laing's Hybrid'	CWVF EBak
	'Lakeland Princess'	EBak
	'Lakeside'	EBak
	'Lambada'	CDoC CLoc LAst SLBF WRou
	'Lancashire Lad' (d)	MJac
	'Lancashire Lass'	CWVF WOth
	'Lancelot'	EBak
	'Land van Beveren'	SLBF WOth
	'Landgoed Hulshorst' **new**	WOth
	'Lapshead White'	CExl
	'Lark' (T)	CWVF
	'Lassie' (d)	CLoc CWVF EBak
	'Last Chance' (E)	SLBF
	'Launceston Lady Carole Anne' **new**	WRou
	'Laura' ambig.	CWVF SVic WOth WRou
I	'Laura' (Dutch)	CLoc EPts LCla SLBF
	'Laura Cross' (E)	CDoC SLBF WOth WRou
	'Lauren'	CDoC WRou
	'Lavender Kate' (d)	CWVF EBak
	'Lazy Lady' (d)	CWVF EBak
	'Lechlade Apache'	LCla
	'Lechlade Bullet'	LCla
	'Lechlade Chinaman'	SVic
	'Lechlade Debutante'	LCla WOth
	'Lechlade Fairy' (E)	WRou
	'Lechlade Gorgon'	CDoC CWVF LCla SLBF
	'Lechlade Magician'	CDoC EPts LCla SLBF
	'Lechlade Maiden'	CWVF
	'Lechlade Martianess'	CDoC LCla SVic WOth
	'Lechlade Potentate'	LCla
	'Lechlade Tinkerbell' (E)	CDoC LCla
	'Lechlade Violet' (T)	LCla SVic
	lehmanii	LCla
	'Len Bielby' (T)	CWVF LCla
	'Lena' (d) ♀H2	CDoC CLoc CMac CTri CWVF EBak EPts MJac SLBF SMrm SPer SPlb SVic
	'Lena Dalton' (d)	CLoc CWVF EBak SVic
	'Leonhart von Fuchs'	WOth
	'Leonora'	CDoC CLoc CWVF EBak SLBF SVic WRou
	'Lesley' (T)	CWVF LCla
	'Lesley's Wonder'	MJac
	'Leslie Bowman'	LCla SLBF WRou
	'Lett's Delight' (d)	CWVF EPts
	'Letty Lye'	EBak
	'Leverhulme'	see *F.* 'Leverkusen'
§	'Leverkusen' (T)	CDoC CLoc EBak LCla MJac WOth
I	'Liebesträume' Blackwell (d)	EBak
	'Liebriez' (d) ♀H4	EBak SVic
	'Liemers Lantaern'	CWVF
	'Likalin'	CWVF
	'Lilac'	EBak
	'Lilac Lustre' (d)	CLoc CWVF EBak SVic
	'Lilac Mist'	SLBF
	'Lilac Queen' (d)	EBak
	'Lilian'	WOth
	'Lillian Annetts' (d) ♀H2	CWVF MJac SLBF WOth WRou
	'Lillibet' (d)	CLoc CWVF EBak
	'Lime Lite' (d)	MJac
	'Linda Goulding'	CWVF EBak SVic
	'Linda Grace'	MJac
	'Linda Hinchliffe'	MJac
	'Linda Rosling' (d)	CDoC
	'Lindisfarne' (d)	CLoc CWVF EBak MJac WOth
	'Lindsey Victoria' (d)	SVic
	'Lionel'	WOth WRou
	'Lipstick'	SLBF
	'Lisa' (d)	EPts
	'Little Beauty'	CWVF SVic WOth
	'Little Boy Blue'	EPts
	'Little Brook Gem'	SLBF
	'Little Catbells' (E)	SLBF WRou
	'Little Cracker'	LBuc
	'Little Gene'	EBak
	'Little Margaret'	WRou
	'Little Nan'	SLBF
	'Little Ouse' (d)	CWVF
	'Little Scamp'	SLBF
	'Little Tony' **new**	SLBF WRou
	'Liz' (d)	EBak
	'Lochinver' (d)	CWVF
	'Loeky'	CDoC CLoc CWVF EBak SVic WOth
	'Logan Garden'	see *F. magellanica* 'Logan Woods'
	'Lolita' (d)	CWVF EBak
	'London 2000'	LCla MJac SLBF WOth WRou
	'London Eye'	WOth WRou
	'London in Bloom'	SLBF
	'Lonely Ballerina' (d)	CLoc CWVF
	'Long Distance' (T)	CDoC LCla
	'Long Wings'	LCla SVic
	'Lord Byron'	CLoc EBak
	'Lord Jim'	LCla
	'Lord Lonsdale'	CWVF EBak EPts LCla SVic WRou
	'Lord Roberts'	CLoc CWVF SLBF
	'Lorelei'	CDoC
	'Lorna Swinbank'	CWVF SVic
	'Lorraine's Delight' (d)	SVic
	'Lottie Hobby' (E) ♀H3	CLoc CMac CTsd CWVF EPfP EPts EShb LCla MLHP SVic WCot WOth WRou
	'Louise Emershaw' (d)	CWVF EBak MJac SVic
	'Louise Nicholls'	MJac
	'Loulabel'	SVic
	'Lovable' (d)	EBak
	'Loveliness'	CLoc CWVF EBak SVic
	'Lovely Linda'	SLBF
	'Love's Reward' ♀H2	CLoc CWVF MJac SLBF SVic WRou
	'Lower Raydon'	EBak
I	'Loxensis'	CDoC CWVF EBak SVic
	loxensis misapplied	see *F.* 'Speciosa', *F.* 'Loxensis'
	loxensis Kunth	WOth
	'Loxhore Lullaby' (E)	LCla
	'Loxhore Minuet' (T)	LCla
	'Loxhore Posthorn' (T)	CDoC LCla
	'Lucinda'	CWVF
	'Lucky Strike' (d)	EBak
	Lucy = 'Goetzlucy' (Shadowdancer Series)	EBak
	'Lucy Locket'	MJac
	'Lunter's Klokje'	WOth
	'Lustre'	CWVF EBak SVic
I	'Lycioides'	LCla WOth
	lycioides misapplied	see *F.* 'Lycioides'
§	***lycioides*** Andrews	EBak WOth
	'Lydia'	WOth
	'Lye's Excelsior'	EBak
	'Lye's Own'	EBak SLBF

	Name	Suppliers
	'Lye's Unique' ♀H3	CDoC CLoc CWVF EBak EPts LCla MJac SLBF SVic WOth
	'Lynette' (d)	CLoc
	'Lynn Cunningham'	CDoC
	'Lynn Ellen' (d)	EBak
	'Lynne Marshall'	WOth
	'Lynne Patricia' (d)	EPts SLBF WOth
	'Mabel Greaves' (d)	CWVF
	'Mac Wagg'	WRou
	'Machu Picchu'	CLoc CWVF EPts LCla SVic WOth WRou
	macrophylla	WMoo
	'Madame Butterfly' (d)	CLoc
	'Madame Cornélissen' (d) ♀H4	CLoc CMac CSBt CTri CWVF EBak EBee ELan EPfP EPts LAst LRHS MAsh MBri MRav NLar SCob SCoo SHil SLBF SLim SPer SPoG SVic WFar WRou XLum
	'Madame Eva Boye'	EBak
	magellanica ♀H4	CAby CBcs CDoC CTsd CUse MGil MLHP MMuc NPer NWea SPer SVic WMoo WPnn
I	- 'Alba Aureovariegata' (v)	CMac EPfP SPer SVic WFar XLum
	- 'Alba Variegata' (v)	WFar
	- 'Americana Elegans'	CDoC
	- 'Angel's Teardrop'	CDoC
	- 'Folius Aureus' **new**	WFar
§	- var. ***gracilis*** ♀H4	CAgr CDoC CHEx CLoc CSde CTri CWVF EPfP LRHS MLHP NBro SCoo SVic WMoo WOth WPnn WRou
	- - 'Aurea' ♀H4	CBcs CMac CSde CTsd CWVF ELan EPfP LCla LRHS MHer MRav SCoo SDix SLBF SPer SPoG SVic WMoo WOth
	- - 'Purple Mountain'	EPfP LRHS SPoG
§	- - 'Tricolor' (v) ♀H4	CDoC CTsd EPfP EPts EWes LBMP LCla LRHS MMuc NLar SEND SLBF SRms SVic WCFE WPnn
	- - 'Variegata' (v) ♀H4	CDoC CTsd EBak EPfP LCla LRHS MGos MRav SDix SVic WPnn
	- 'Lady Bacon'	CDoC ELon EPts EWes GCal MCot MMuc SDys SEND SLBF SMHy WOth WRou WSHC
§	- 'Logan Woods'	CAby CDoC ELon GKin SLBF SMrm
	- 'Longipedunculata'	CDoC
	- var. ***magellanica***	SCob
	- var. ***molinae***	CAby CDoC CDul CLoc CTri CWVF EBak ECrN ELan EPfP EPts EShb EWoo GKin LCla LRHS MBlu MNrw MSwo NBid NChi NPer SCob SPer SPlb SPoG WFar WMnd WMoo WPnn
§	- - 'Enstone' (v)	ELon
	- - 'Golden Sharpitor' (v)	CCCN LAst WFar WRou
	- - 'Mr Knight's Blush'	CDul
§	- - 'Sharpitor' (v) ♀H2	CDoC CSde CTsd EBak ELan ELon EPfP LRHS MAsh NPer SPer SVic WFar WKif WMoo WRou WSHC
	- 'Mountain Gold'	LAst
	- var. ***myrtifolia***	CDoC CTsd
	- 'Pumila'	CAby CDoC EWes GCal MHer MLHP SCoo SMHy SRot SVic WAbe WHal WThu
	- ***purpurea***	LRHS
	- 'Red Mountain'	EWes
	- 'Sea Spray'	CDoC
	- 'Seahorse'	CDoC
§	- 'Thompsonii' ♀H4	CDoC ECGP SMHy
§	- 'Versicolor' (v)	Widely available
	'Magenta Flush'	CDoC CWVF
	'Magic Flute'	CLoc CWVF MJac SVic
	'Maharaja' (d)	EBak
	'Maik Luijten' (d)	CDoC
	'Major Heaphy'	CDoC CWVF EBak MHer
	'Making Waves'	WRou
	'Malibu Mist' (d)	CWVF
	'Mama Bleuss' (d)	EBak
	'Mancunian' (d)	CWVF
I	'Mandarin' Schnabel	EBak
	'Mandi Oxtoby' (T)	LCla
	'Mantilla' (T)	CLoc CWVF EBak LCla MJac SVic
	'Maori Pipes' (T)	WOth
	'Marbled Sky'	SVic
	'Marcel Michiels' (d)	CDoC
	'Marcia'[PBR] (Shadowdancer Series)	CLoc LAst
	'Marcus Graham' (d)	CLoc CWVF EBak SCoo SVic WRou
	'Marcus Hanton' (d)	CWVF
	'Mardi Gras' (d)	EBak
	'Margaret' (d) ♀H4	CDul CLoc CTri CWVF EBak EPts SEND SLBF SVic WFar WRou
	'Margaret Bird'	LCla
	'Margaret Brown' ♀H4	CDoC CLoc CTri CWVF EBak LCla LRHS SLBF SVic WOth WRou
	'Margaret Davidson' (d)	CLoc
	'Margaret Pilkington'	CDoC CWVF SVic WOth
	'Margaret Roe'	CDoC CWVF EBak MJac
	'Margaret Susan'	EBak
	'Margaret Viscountess Thurso' **new**	SLBF
	'Margarite Dawson' (d)	SVic
	'Margery Blake'	EBak
	'Maria Landy'	CWVF MJac SLBF WOth
	'Maria Mathilde' (d)	SLBF
	'Maria Shaw' **new**	EPts
	'Marilyn Olsen'	CWVF
	'Marin Belle'	EBak
	'Marin Glow' ♀H3	CLoc CWVF EBak SLBF SVic
	'Marina Kelly'	WRou
	'Marinka' ♀H2	CLoc CWVF EBak EPts LAst LCla MJac SLBF SVic WOth
	'Mark Kirby' (d)	CWVF EBak
	'Marlies de Keijzer' (E)	CDoC EPts LCla SLBF SVen WRou
	Martha = 'Goetzmart'[PBR] (Shadowdancer Series)	LAst WBor
	'Martina'	SLBF
I	'Martin's Choice Improved'	WOth
	'Martin's Inspiration'	CDoC LCla
	'Martin's Sylvia' **new**	CDoC
	'Martin's Trompet' **new**	CDoC
	'Martin's Yellow Surprise' (T)	LCla SLBF SVic
	'Marty' (d)	EBak
	'Mary' (T) ♀H1c	CDoC CLoc CWVF EPts LCla SLBF SVic WOth WRou
	'Mary Lockyer' (d)	CLoc EBak
	'Mary Poppins'	CWVF SVic
	'Mary Reynolds' (d)	CWVF
	'Mary Thorne'	EBak
	'Mary's Millennium'	CWVF
	'Masquerade' (d)	EBak
	'Mauve Beauty' (d)	CWVF SLBF
	'Mauve Wisp' (d)	SVic
	'Mavis Enderby'	MJac SLBF
	'Max Jaffa'	CWVF
I	'Maxima'	EPts LAst LCla SLBF

	Name	Suppliers
	'Maxima's Baby'	CDoC
	'Maxine's Smile' **new**	SLBF
	'Mayblossom' (d)	CWVF
	'Mayfield'	CWVF
	'Mazda'	CWVF
	'McGee's Chocolate Mint'	SLBF
	'Meadowlark' (d)	CWVF EBak
	'Medard's Botsaert' (d)	CDoC
	'Meditation' (d)	CLoc
	'Melanie'	SVic WOth
	'Melissa Heavens'	CWVF
	'Melody'	EBak SVic
	'Melody Ann' (d)	EBak
	'Melting Moments' (d)	SCoo WRou
	'Mendocino Rose'	SVic
	'Menna'	CDoC
	'Mephisto' ♀H2	CWVF
	'Merel' **new**	EPts
	'Merlin'	CDoC LCla
	'Merry Mary' (d)	CWVF EBak
	'Mersty' (d)	SLBF
I	'Mexicali Rose' Machado	CLoc
	'Michael' (d)	CWVF EPts
	'Michael Wallis' (T)	CDoC LCla SLBF WOth
	'Michelle Wallace'	SVic
	michoacanensis misapplied	see *F. microphylla* subsp. *aprica*
	michoacanensis Sessé & Moç. (E) B&SWJ 9027	WCru
	- B&SWJ 9148	WCru
	'Micky Goult' ♀H2	CDoC CLoc CWVF EPts MJac SLBF SVic WOth WRou
	'Microchip' (E)	LCla
	microphylla (E)	CAby CBcs CDoC CElw CExl CHel CLoc CWVF EBak ELon GCal IDee NBro SIgm SVic WRou
	- B&SWJ 10331	WCru
§	- subsp. ***aprica*** (E)	LCla
	- - B&SWJ 9101	WCru
	- - 'Dolly's Dress'	WCru
	- 'Cornish Pixie'	CDoC
§	- subsp. ***hemsleyana*** (E)	CDoC CExl SVic
	- - B&SWJ 10478	WCru
	- - 'Silver Lining'	WCru WSHC
	- - 'Sprite' (E/v)	WRou
§	- subsp. ***hidalgensis*** (E)	CDoC LCla WRou
§	- subsp. ***minimiflora*** (E)	SVic
	- subsp. ***quercetorum*** (E)	CTsd WOth
	- 'Variegata' (E/v)	EWes
	'Midas'	CWVF
	'Midnight Sun' (d)	EBak
	'Midwinter'	CWVF SVic WOth
	'Mieke Meursing' ♀H2	CLoc CWVF EBak MJac
	'Miep Aalhuizen'	CDoC LCla WOth
	'Mike Oxtoby' (T)	CWVF
	'Millennium'	CLoc EBak EPts MJac SCoo SVic WRou
	'Millie Butler'	CWVF
	'Ming'	CLoc
	'Mini' **new**	WOth
	'Miniature Jewels' (E)	SLBF
	minimiflora misapplied	see *F.* × *bacillaris*
	minimiflora Hemsl.	see *F. microphylla* subsp. *minimiflora*
	'Minirose'	CWVF EPts SLBF WOth
	'Minnesota' (d)	EBak
	'Miramere'	EPts
	'Mischief'	SVic
	'Miss California' (d)	CLoc CWVF EBak

	Name	Suppliers
	'Miss Great Britain'	CWVF
	'Miss Muffett' (d)	EPts
	'Miss Vallejo' (d)	EBak
	'Mission Bells'	CDoC CLoc CWVF EBak EPts SVic
	'Misty Blue' (d)	SVic
	'Misty Haze' (d)	CWVF SVic
	Mojo Series	CDoC
	'Molesworth' (d)	CWVF EBak MJac
	'Money Spinner'	CLoc EBak
	'Monica Dare' (T) ♀H1c	CDoC
	'Monsieur Thibaut' ♀H4	SPer
	'Monte Rosa' (d)	CWVF
	'Montevideo' (d)	CWVF
	'Mood Indigo' (d)	CDoC CWVF MJac SLBF SVic WOth
	'Moonbeam' (d)	CLoc
	'Moonglow'	MJac
	'Moonlight Sonata'	CLoc CWVF EBak
	'Moonraker' (d)	CWVF SVic
	'Moorland Beauty' (d) **new**	WOth
	'More Applause' (d)	CLoc
	'Morning Light' (d)	CLoc EBak SVic
	'Morning Mist'	EBak
	'Morrells' (d)	EBak
	'Moth Blue' (d)	CWVF EBak
	'Mountain Mist' (d)	CWVF SVic
	'Moyra' (d)	CWVF
	'Mr A. Huggett'	CLoc CWVF EPts SLBF WOth
	'Mr W. Rundle'	EBak SVic
§	'Mr West' (v)	EAEE LSou MCot SVic WMoo
	'Mrs Churchill'	CLoc
	'Mrs Lawrence Lyon' (d)	EBak
	'Mrs Lee Belton' (E)	CDoC LCla SLBF
	'Mrs Lovell Swisher' ♀H4	CWVF EBak LCla SVic WOth
	'Mrs Marshall'	CWVF EBak SLBF
	'Mrs Popple' ♀H4	Widely available
	'Mrs W. Castle'	SVic
	'Mrs W.P. Wood' ♀H4	CLoc CWVF ELon LRHS MSCN SVic WOth WRou
	'Mrs W. Rundle'	CLoc CWVF EBak SLBF WOth
	'Muriel' (d)	CLoc CWVF EBak
	'Murru's Pierre Marie' (d)	SLBF
	'My Delight'	CWVF
	'My Fair Lady' (d)	CLoc CWVF EBak
	'My Honey'	WOth
	'My Kath' (d)	WRou
	'My Little Cracker'	CDoC WRou
	'My Mum'	LCla SLBF WRou
	'My Pat'	SLBF WRou
	'My Reward' (d)	CWVF
	'Naaldwijk 800'	WOth
	'Nancy Lou' (d)	CLoc CWVF MJac SLBF SVic
	'Nanny Ed' (d)	CWVF
	'Natasha Lynn' (d)	WOth WRou
	'Natasha Sinton' (d)	CCCN CDoC CWVF LAst MJac
	'Nathan Rhys'	EPts SLBF WOth WRou
	'Native Dancer' (d)	CWVF EBak
	'Nautilus' (d)	EBak
	'Neapolitan' (d)	CDoC SLBF
	'Neck'	LCla
	'Nell Gwyn'	CLoc CWVF EBak SVic
	'Nellie Nuttall' ♀H2	CLoc CWVF EBak EPts SLBF SVic
	'Neopolitan' (E)	CLoc EPts LCla SVic WOth WRou
	'Nephele' **new**	EPts
	'Nettala'	CDoC SVic WOth
	'Neue Welt'	CDoC CWVF EBak
	'New Fascination' (d)	EBak
	'New Millennium' (d)	CDoC
	'Niamh Jane Allen' (d)	WRou

Name	Suppliers
'Nice 'n' Easy' (d)	LRHS MJac
'Nicki Fenwick-Raven' (E)	LCla
'Nicki's Findling'	CDoC CWVF EPts LCla MJac WRou
'Nicola'	EBak
'Nicola Jane' (d)	CDoC CWVF EBak EPts LCla MJac SHar SLBF SVic WRou
'Nicola Storey'	CDoC
'Nicolette'	CWVF MJac
'Nightingale' (d)	CLoc EBak
§ ***nigricans*** B&SWJ 10664	WCru
'Nina Wills'	EBak
'Niobe' (d)	EBak
'Niula'	CDoC LCla
'No Name' (d)	EBak
'Noblesse' **new**	CDoC
'Nonchalance' (T)	CDoC LCla
'Noor'	WOth
'Norman Welton'	MJac SLBF
'Normandy Bell'	EBak SVic
'Northern Jewel'	SLBF
'Northern Pride' (d)	WOth
'Northilda'	SVic
'Northumbrian Belle'	EBak
'Northumbrian Pipes'	CDoC LCla WOth
'Northway'	CLoc CWVF MJac SVic
'Norvell Gillespie' (d)	EBak
'Novato'	CDoC EBak
'Novella' (d)	CWVF EBak
'Nuance'	CDoC LCla WOth
'Nunthorpe Gem' (d)	CDoC
'O Sole Mio'	SVic
obconica (E)	CDoC
'Obcylin' (E)	CDoC EPts LCla
'Ocean Beach'	CDoC EPts
'Oetnang' (d)	CTri SCoo
'Oh Carol' (E)	LCla SLBF WOth WRou
'Old Somerset' (v)	CCCN SVic
'Olga Storey'	CDoC
'Olive Moon' (d)	WOth
'Olive Smith'	CWVF EPts LCla MJac WRou
'Olympia'	WOth
'Olympic Lass' (d)	EBak WOth
'Olympic Sunset'	SVic WOth
'Oosje' (E)	LCla SVic WRou
'Oostveens Thymen' **new**	WOth
'Opalescent' (d)	CLoc CWVF SVic
'Orange Crush'	CLoc CWVF EBak MJac WOth
'Orange Crystal'	CWVF EBak MJac SLBF SVic
'Orange Drops'	CLoc CWVF EBak EPts SVic WOth
'Orange Flare'	CLoc CWVF EBak SLBF SVic
'Orange Heart'	LCla
'Orange King' (d)	CLoc CWVF LAst
'Orange Mirage'	CLoc CWVF EBak SLBF SVic
'Orange Star' (E)	CDoC LCla WRou
'Orangeblossom'	SLBF WOth
'Oranje van Os'	CWVF
'Orient Express' (T) ♀H1c	CDoC CLoc CWVF MJac SVic WOth
'Oriental Sunrise'	CWVF
'Ornamental Pearl' (v)	CLoc CWVF EBak WOth
'Orwell' (d)	CWVF
'Oso Sweet'	CWVF
'Other Fellow'	CDoC CWVF EBak EPts LCla MJac SLBF SVic WOth
'Oulton Empress' (E)	LCla SLBF WRou
'Oulton Fairy' (E)	SLBF
'Oulton Hoya' (E) **new**	WOth
'Oulton Painted Lady'	WRou
'Oulton Red Imp' (E)	LCla SLBF WRou

Name	Suppliers
'Oulton Travellers Rest' (E)	SLBF
'Oulton Tu-Fu' (E)	WOth
'Our Carol'	SLBF
'Our Claire'	WRou
'Our Darling'	CWVF
'Our Hilary'	SLBF WOth
'Our Kid'	SLBF
'Our Nan' (d)	MJac
'Our Pamela'	MJac
'Our Shep' (d)	WRou
'Our Spencer'	SLBF
'Our Ted' (T)	EBak EPts
'Our William'	SLBF
'Overbecks'	see *F. magellanica* var. *molinae* 'Sharpitor'
'P.E. King' (d)	SLBF
'Pabbe's Belle' **new**	WOth
'Pabbe's Kirrevaalk'	WOth
'Pabbe's Klompnoagel'	WOth
'Pacific Grove' Greene	see *F.* 'Evelyn Steele Little'
'Pacific Grove' Niederholzer (d)	EBak
'Pacific Queen' (d)	EBak
'Pacquesa' (d)	CWVF EBak SVic
'Padre Pio' (d)	CWVF EBak MJac
'Pam Plack'	CDoC LCla SLBF WOth
'Pamela Knights' (d)	EBak
'Pamela Wallace'	WOth
'Pam's People'	LCla
'Pan' (T)	WOth
'Pan America' (d)	EBak
'Panache' (d)	LCla
'Pangea' (T)	CDoC
paniculata (T) ♀H2	CCCN CDoC CRHN CWVF EBak EPts IDee LCla MCot MHer SLBF WCot WCru
'Panique'	CDoC LCla
'Pantaloons' (d)	EBak
'Pantomine Dame' (d)	CWVF
'Panylla Prince'	LCla SLBF WRou
'Papa Bleuss' (d)	CWVF EBak
'Papoose' (d)	CDoC EBak LCla SLBF SVic
'Parkstone Centenary' (d)	CWVF
'Party Frock'	CDoC CLoc CWVF EBak WOth
parviflora misapplied	see ***F. × bacillaris***
parviflora Lindl.	see *F. lycioides* Andrews
'Pastel'	EBak
'Pat Meara'	CLoc EBak
'Pathétique' (d)	CLoc
'Patience' (d)	CDoC CWVF EBak SLBF
'Patio King'	EBak
'Patio Princess' (d)	CDoC CLoc CWVF EPts LAst
'Patricia' Wood	EBak
'Patricia Hodge'	CDoC WOth WRou
'Patty Evans' (d)	CWVF EBak
'Patty Sue' (d)	WRou
'Paul Cambon' (d)	EBak
'Paul Fisher'	CDoC
'Paul Roe' (d)	MJac
'Paula Jane' (d) ♀H2	CWVF LAst MJac SLBF SVic
'Pauline Rawlins' (d)	CLoc EBak
'Paulus'	WRou
'Peace' (d)	EBak
'Peachy' (California Dreamers Series) (d)	CDoC CLoc LAst SCoo
'Peachy Keen' (d)	EBak
'Peacock' (d)	CLoc
'Pearly Gates'	WOth

	Name	Suppliers
	'Pearly King' (d)	WOth
	'Pearly Queen' (d)	WOth
	'Peasholm'	WOth WRou
	'Pee Wee Rose'	EBak SVic
	'Peggy Burford' (T)	LCla
	Peggy = 'Goetzpeg'[PBR] (Shadowdancer Series)	LAst LSou SCoo
	'Peggy King'	CDoC EBak SVic
	'Peloria' (d)	CLoc EBak
	'Pennine'	WOth
	'People's Princess'	MJac
	'Peper Harow'	EBak
	'Pepi' (d)	CWVF EBak
	'Peppermint Candy' (d)	CWVF MJac
	'Peppermint Stick' (d)	CLoc CWVF EBak SVic
	'Percival's' **new**	CDoC
	'Perky Pink' (d)	EBak EPts
	'Perry Park'	CWVF EBak MJac SVic
	'Perry's Jumbo'	NPer
	perscandens	CBcs CDoC CExl LCla
	'Personality' (d)	EBak
	'Peter Bielby' (d)	CWVF
	'Peter Crookes' (T)	CWVF
	'Peter Grange'	EBak
	'Peter Meredith'	MJac WOth WRou
	'Peter Pan'	CWVF
	petiolaris	LCla
	- B&SWJ 10675	WCru
	'Petit Four'	CWVF WOth
	'Petite' (d)	EBak
	'Phaidra' (T)	CDoC LCla WOth WRou
	'Pharaoh'	CLoc
	'Phénoménal' (d)	CWVF EBak
	'Phil's Pill'	SLBF
	'Phryne' (d)	EBak SVic
	'Phyllis' (d) ♀H4	CDoC CLoc CWVF EBak EPts LCla LRHS MJac SEND SLBF SVic WRou
	'Piet G. Vergeer'	WOth WRou
	'Piet van der Sande'	CDoC LCla
	'Piggelmee'	CDoC WOth
	'Pinch Me' (d)	CWVF EBak SVic
	'Pink Aurora'	CLoc
	'Pink Ballet Girl' (d)	CLoc EBak SVic
	'Pink Bon Accord'	CLoc CWVF SVic
	'Pink Cloud'	CLoc EBak
	'Pink Cornet'	LCla
	'Pink Darling'	CLoc EBak
	'Pink Dessert'	EBak
	'Pink Fairy' (d)	EBak
	'Pink Fandango' (d)	CLoc
	'Pink Fantasia' ♀H2	CLoc CWVF EBak EPts LAst LCla MJac SLBF SVic WOth WRou
	'Pink Flamingo' (d)	EBak
	'Pink Galore' (d) ♀H2	CLoc CWVF EBak LAst MJac SLBF
	'Pink Goon' (d)	SLBF SVic
	'Pink Haze'	SVic
	'Pink Jade'	CWVF EBak
	'Pink la Campanella'	CDoC CWVF EBak LAst
	'Pink Marshmallow' (d) ♀H4	CDoC CLoc CWVF EBak MJac SLBF SVic
	'Pink Panther' (d)	CDoC
	'Pink Pearl' Bright (d)	EBak
	'Pink Profusion'	EBak
	'Pink Quartet' (d)	CLoc CWVF EBak WCot
	'Pink Rain'	CWVF MJac
	'Pink Slippers'	CLoc
	'Pink Spangles'	CDoC CWVF SVic
	'Pink Sprite'	WOth WRou
	'Pink Temptation'	CLoc CWVF EBak SVic
	'Pinwheel' (d)	CLoc EBak
	'Piper' (d)	CDoC CWVF
	'Piper's Vale' (T)	CDoC LAst MJac SLBF WOth
	'Pirbright'	CWVF
	'Pixie'	CDoC CLoc CWVF EBak MJac SLBF SVic
	'Playboy' (d)	SVic
	'Playford'	CWVF EBak
	'Plenty'	EBak SVic
	'Plumb Bob' (d)	CWVF
	'Polskie Fuksji'	CDoC
	'Pop Whitlock' (v)	CWVF SVic
	'Poppet'	CWVF WOth
	'Popsie Girl'	SLBF WOth WRou
	'Port Arthur' (d)	EBak
	'Postiljon'	CWVF EBak
	'Postman'	CDoC
	'Powder Puff' ambig.	CWVF
	'Powder Puff' Hodges (d)	CLoc SVic
	'Prelude' Blackwell	CLoc
I	'Prelude' Kennett (d)	EBak
	'President'	CDoC EBak LRHS
	'President B.W. Rawlins'	EBak
	'President Barrie Nash'	CLoc
	'President Carol Gubler' (d)	SLBF
	'President George Bartlett' (d) ♀H2	CDoC CLoc EPts MJac SLBF WOth WRou
	'President Jim Muil'	SLBF
	'President Joan Morris' (d)	SLBF
	'President John Porter'	MJac SLBF
	'President Leo Boullemier'	CWVF EBak MJac SVic
	'President Margaret Slater'	CLoc CWVF EBak SVic
	'President Moir' (d)	SLBF WOth
	'President Norman Hobbs'	CWVF
	'President Roosevelt' (d)	CDoC
	'President Stanley Wilson' (d)	EBak EPts
	'President Wilf Sharp' (d)	SVic
	'Preston'	CMac
	'Preston Guild' ♀H3	CLoc CWVF EBak NPer SDys SVic WOth WRou
	'Pride of the West'	EBak
	'Prince of Orange'	CLoc EBak SVic
	'Princess Dollar'	see *F.* 'Dollar Prinzessin'
	'Princessita'	CWVF EBak WOth
	procumbens	CBcs CCCN CDoC CExl CHel CLoc CWVF EBak ECou EPfP EPts EUJe GCal IDee LCla MCot MHer SBrt SLBF WOth WRou
	- 'Argentea'	see *F. procumbens* 'Wirral'
	- 'Variegata'	see *F. procumbens* 'Wirral'
§	- 'Wirral' (v)	CDoC CLoc CTsd ITim WOth WRou
	'Prodigy'	see *F.* 'Enfant Prodigue'
	'Profusion' ambig.	SVic
	'Prosperity' (d) ♀H3	CDoC CLoc CWVF EBak EPfP EPts LCla LRHS MJac SLBF SVic WOth WRou
	'Pumila'	CExl CMac EBee ELan EPfP EPts LRHS SDix SVic WPat
	'Purbeck Mist' (d)	CWVF
	'Purperklokje'	CWVF EBak SVic
	'Purple Emperor' (d)	CLoc
	'Purple Heart' (d)	CLoc EBak
	'Purple Lace'	SVic
	'Purple Rain'	CDoC EPts
	'Purple Splendour' (d)	CDoC

'Pussy Cat' (T)	CLoc CWVF EBak SVic
'Putney Pride'	EPts
'Put's Folly' 🏆H2	CWVF EBak MJac WOth
putumayensis	EBak
'Quasar' (d)	CCCN CDoC CLoc CWVF EPts LAst MJac SLBF SVic
'Queen Esther'	WOth
'Queen Mabs'	EBak
'Queen Mary'	CLoc EBak
'Queen of Bath' (d)	EBak SVic
'Queen of Derby' (d)	CWVF
'Queen of Hearts' Kennett (d)	SVic
'Queen of Mercia' **new**	MJac
'Queen's Park' (d)	EBak
'Query'	EBak SVic
'R.A.F.' (d)	CLoc CWVF EBak EPts SVic WRou
'Rachel Craig' (d)	WRou
'Radings Gerda' (E)	LCla SLBF WRou
'Radings Karin'	CDoC WRou
'Radings Mia' (T)	SLBF
'Radings Michelle'	CWVF WOth WRou
'Rahnee'	CWVF
'Rainbow'	CWVF
'Ralph Storey' **new**	CDoC
'Ralph's Delight' (d)	CWVF
'Rambling Rose' (d)	CLoc CWVF EBak MJac
'Rams Royal' (d)	CDoC CWVF
'Raspberry' (d)	CLoc CWVF EBak SVic
'Raspberry Ripple' (d)	WOth WRou
'Raspberry Sweet' (d)	CWVF
'Ratae Beauty'	CWVF
'Ratatouille' (d)	WOth
ravenii	WOth
'Ray Redfern'	CWVF
'Razzle Dazzle' (d)	EBak
'Reading Show' (d)	CWVF EPts SLBF
'Rebecca Williamson' (d)	CWVF MJac
'Rebeka Sinton' (v)	CLoc EBak
'Red Ace' (d)	WOth
'Red Jacket' (d)	CWVF EBak
'Red Petticoat'	CWVF
'Red Rain'	CWVF
'Red Ribbons' (d)	EBak
'Red Rover'	WRou
'Red Shadows' (d)	CLoc CWVF EBak
'Red Spider'	CCCN CLoc CWVF EBak LAst SCoo SVic WOth
'Red Sunlight'	CDoC
'Red Wing'	CLoc
'Reflexa'	see *F.* × *bacillaris* 'Reflexa'
'Reg Gubler'	SLBF
'Regal'	CLoc
'Regal Robe' (d)	CDoC
regia subsp. ***regia***	LCla
– subsp. ***reitzii***	CDoC CDul EWes LCla XLum
– subsp. ***serrae***	CBcs WOth
'Remember Carole Anne' (d)	SLBF WOth WRou
'Remember Eric'	CDoC WOth
'Remember Tommy Struck'	CDoC
'Remembering Claire' **new**	EPts WOth
'Remembrance' (d)	EPts LCla SLBF
'Remus' (d)	SVic
'Rene Schwab'	LCla
'Renée-Madeleine'	WOth
'Requiem'	CLoc
'Reverend Doctor Brown' (d)	EBak
'Reverend Frank Pagden'	WOth WRou
'Rhapsody' ambig.	SVic
I 'Rhapsody' Blackwell (d)	CLoc
'Rhona Foster' **new**	CDoC
'Riccartonii' 🏆H6	Widely available
'Richard John' (v)	SVic
'Ridestar' (d)	CLoc CWVF EBak
'Rigoletto'	SVic
'Rijs 2001' (E)	CDoC SLBF WRou
'Rina Felix'	WOth
'Ringwood Gold'	SVic
'Ringwood Market' (d)	CWVF EPts MJac SCoo SVic
'Rita Mary'	WRou
'Rivendell'	EPts
'Riverdancer Claire'	WOth
'Robert Lutters'	SVic
'Rocket Fire' (California Dreamers Series) (d)	SVic
'Roesse Belinda' (d)	CDoC
'Roesse Callisto'	CDoC
'Roesse Duck'	WOth
'Roesse Juliet'	CDoC
'Roesse Meton'	WOth
'Roesse Peacock' (d)	CDoC
'Roesse Sextans'	CDoC WRou
'Roesse Tricolor'	CDoC
'Roger de Cooker' (T)	CDoC CLoc EPts LCla SVic WOth WRou
'Rohees Lava'	SLBF
'Rohees Leada' (d)	SLBF
'Rohees New Millennium' (d)	SLBF
'Rohees Tethys' (d)	SLBF
'Rolla' (d)	CWVF EBak
'Rolt's Ruby' (d)	CWVF SVic
'Roman City' (d)	CLoc SVic
'Romance' (d)	CWVF
'Romany Rose'	CLoc
'Ronald L. Lockerbie' (d)	CLoc CWVF SVic
'Rondo'	MJac
'Ron's Pet' **new**	WOth
'Roos Breytenbach' (T)	CCCN CDoC LAst LCla MJac WOth WRou
'Rosamunda' (d)	CLoc
'Rose Aylett' (d)	EBak
'Rose Bradwardine' (d)	EBak
'Rose Churchill' (d)	MJac
'Rose Fantasia' 🏆H2	CLoc CWVF EPts LAst MJac SLBF WRou
'Rose of Castile'	CLoc EBak EPts LCla MJac SLBF SVic WRou
'Rose of Castile Improved' 🏆H4	CWVF EBak LCla MJac WOth
'Rose of Denmark'	CCCN CLoc CWVF EBak MJac SCoo SLBF WOth
'Rose Reverie' (d)	EBak
'Rose Winston' (d)	SCoo
rosea misapplied	see *F.* 'Globosa'
rosea Ruíz & Pav.	see *F. lycioides* Andrews
'Rosebud' (d)	EBak
'Rosecroft Beauty' (d)	CWVF EBak SVic
Rosella = 'Goetzrose' PBR (Shadowdancer Series)	LAst
'Roselynne'	WOth
'Rosemarie Higham'	MJac SCoo WOth
'Rosemary Day'	CLoc
'Roswitha'	SLBF
'Rosy Bows'	CWVF

'Rosy Frills' (d)	CWVF MJac SVic
'Rosy Morn' (d)	CLoc EBak
'Roualeyn's White Gold' (d)	SLBF WRou
'Rough Silk'	CLoc CWVF EBak
'Roy Castle' (d)	CWVF
'Roy Walker' (d)	CWVF
'Royal Academy' (d)	EPts WRou
'Royal and Ancient'	CWVF
'Royal Mosaic' (California Dreamers Series) (d)	CDoC MJac
'Royal Orchid'	EBak
'Royal Purple' (d)	EBak
'Royal Serenade' (d)	CWVF
'Royal Touch' (d)	EBak
'Royal Velvet' (d) 🏆^{H2}	CCCN CDoC CLoc CWVF EBak EPts LAst LRHS MAsh MJac SLBF SVic WRou
'Rubra Grandiflora'	CWVF EBak LCla SDys SLBF WOth WRou
'Ruby Wedding' (d)	CWVF SLBF
'Ruddigore'	CWVF
'Ruffles' (d)	CWVF EBak
'Rufus' 🏆^{H4}	CDoC CLoc CMac CWVF EBak ELan EPfP EPts LCla MJac SLBF SVic WRou
'Ruth'	SVic WOth
'Ruth King' (d)	CWVF EBak WOth
'S'Wonderful' (d)	CLoc EBak
'Sabrina'	WRou
'Sailor'	EPts SVic
'Salmon Cascade'	CWVF EBak EPts LCla MJac SLBF
'Salmon Glow'	CWVF MJac SVic
'Sam Sheppard'	SLBF
'Samantha Reynolds'	WOth
'Samson' (d/v)	EBak
'San Diego' (d)	CWVF
'San Francisco'	EBak
'San Leandro' (d)	EBak
'San Mateo' (d)	EBak
§ ***sanctae-rosae***	CDoC EBak LCla
'Sandboy'	CWVF EBak
'Sanrina'	CDoC
'Santa Cruz' (d)	CDoC CMac CWVF EBak SLBF SVic
'Santa Lucia' (d)	CLoc EBak
'Santa Monica' (d)	EBak
'Sapphire' (d)	EBak
'Sappho Phaoon' (T) **new**	EPts WOth
'Sara Helen' (d)	CLoc EBak
'Sarah Brightman' (d)	CDoC CLoc MJac
'Sarah Eliza' (d)	EShb SCoo
'Sarah Jane' (d)	EBak SVic
'Sarah Louise'	CWVF
'Sarong' (d)	EBak
'Satellite'	CLoc CWVF EBak SVic
'Saturnus' 🏆^{H4}	CDoC CWVF EBak LRHS MAsh SPoG
'Saxondale Sue'	SVic
scabriuscula	CDoC LCla
scandens	see *F. decussata* Ruíz & Pav.
'Scarcity'	CWVF EBak SVic
'Scarisbrick' **new**	WOth
'Scarlet Jester' **new**	EPts
'Schneeball' (d)	EBak SVic
'Schneewitcher'	CDoC EPts
'Schneewittchen' Klein	EBak
'Schönbrunner Schuljubiläum' (T)	EBak
'Schöne Hanaurin'	SLBF
'Schöne Wilhelmine'	see *F.* 'Die Schöne Wilhelmine'
'Scotch Heather' (d)	CWVF
'Sea Shell' (d)	CWVF EBak
'Seaforth'	EBak
'Sealand Prince'	CDoC CWVF LCla SVic
'Seattle Blue' (T/d)	SLBF
'Sebastopol' (d)	CLoc
'Selma Lavrijsen'	WOth
'Sensation' **new**	WOth
serratifolia Hook.	see *F. austromontana*
serratifolia Ruíz & Pav.	see *F. denticulata*
'Seventh Heaven' (d)	CDoC CLoc CWVF LAst MJac SCoo
'Shady Blue'	CWVF
'Shangri-La' (d)	EBak
'Shanley'	CWVF SVic
'Sharon' (d) **new**	WOth
'Sharon Leslie'	WRou
'Sharpitor'	see *F. magellanica* var. *molinae* 'Sharpitor'
'Shawna Ree' (E)	WOth
'Sheila Crooks' (d)	CWVF EBak
'Sheila Kirby'	CWVF
'Sheila Steele' (d)	CWVF
'Shelford'	CDoC CLoc CWVF EBak EPts MJac SLBF SVic WOth WRou
'Shell Pink'	SVic
'She's a Beauty'	MJac
'Shirley Halladay' (d)	LCla
'Shirley'^{PBR} (Shadowdancer Series)	LAst LSou SCoo
'Shirley Teece' **new**	EPts
'Shooting Star' (d)	EBak
'Showfire'	EBak
'Showtime' (d)	CWVF
'Shrimp Cocktail'	CLoc LRHS MSCN WRou
'Shuna Lindsay'	LCla WOth
'Siberoet' (E)	CDoC LCla SLBF
'Sierra Blue' (d)	CLoc CWVF EBak
'Silver Anniversary' (d)	SVic
'Silver Dawn' (d)	WOth
'Silver Dollar'	SVic
'Silverdale'	CDoC EPts
'Simon J. Rowell'	LCla
simplicicaulis	CDoC EBak LCla
'Sincerity' (d)	CLoc SVic
'Siobhan'	CWVF
'Siobhan Evans' (d)	SLBF
'Sir Alfred Ramsey'	CWVF EBak
'Sir David Jason'	MJac
'Sir Ian Botham' (d)	MJac
'Sir Matt Busby' (d)	EPts LAst MJac WRou
'Siren' Baker (d)	EBak
'Sister Ann Haley'	EPts
'Sister Sister' (d)	SLBF WRou
'Sleepy'	EPts SVic
'Sleigh Bells'	CLoc CWVF EBak SVic WOth
'Small Pipes'	CWVF
'Smarty'	WRou
'Smokey Mountain' (d)	SVic
'Sneezy'	CDoC EPts SVic
'Snow Burner' (California Dreamers Series) (d)	CLoc LAst
'Snow White' (d)	SVic
'Snowbird' (d)	SLBF
§ 'Snowcap' (d) 🏆^{H4}	CCCN CDoC CLoc CWVF EBak EPfP EPts GKin LAst LCla LRHS MAsh MGos MJac NPer SCoo SHil SLBF SLim SPoG SVic WFar WRou
'Snowdon' (d)	CWVF

	Name	Suppliers
	'Snowdrift' Colville (d)	CLoc
	'Snowdrift' Kennett (d)	EBak
	'Snowfall'	CWVF
	'Snowfire' (d)	CLoc CWVF SCoo SVic WOth
	'Snowflake' (E)	CDoC EPts LCla SLBF WBor WOth WRou
	'Softpink Jubelteen'	WOth
	'Son of Thumb' ♀H4	CDoC CLoc CWVF EPfP EPts LAst LBMP LRHS MAsh MJac MRav SCob SLBF SLim SPer SVic WRou
	'Sonata' (d)	CLoc CWVF EBak SVic
	'Sophie Grace'	WOth
	'Sophie Louise'	CWVF EPts SLBF WOth WRou
	'Sophie Strawson'	WRou
	'Sophisticated Lady' (d)	CLoc CWVF EBak EPts SVic
	'South Crofty' **new**	CDoC
	'South Gate' (d)	CLoc CWVF EBak EPts LAst SVic
	'South Seas' (d)	EBak
	'Southlanders'	EBak
	'Space Shuttle'	CLoc LCla SLBF WRou
	'Sparky' (T)	CLoc CWVF EPts LCla WOth WRou
§	'Speciosa'	CDoC EBak LCla WRou
	'Spion Kop' (d)	CCCN CWVF EBak LAst
§	***splendens*** ♀H2	CCCN CDoC CLoc EBak IDee LCla MCot NPer SLBF
	– B&SWJ 10469	WCru
	'Squadron Leader' (d)	CWVF EBak EPts
	'Squirtie' **new**	SLBF WRou
	'St Ives Bay' **new**	CDoC
	'Stan'	WOth
	'Stanley Cash' (d)	CLoc CWVF SVic
	'Star Wars'	CDoC CLoc EPts MJac WOth WRou
	'Stardust'	CDoC CWVF EBak WOth
	'Steeley' (d)	SVic
	'Stella Ann' (T)	CWVF EBak EPts LCla WRou
	'Stella Marina' (d)	EBak
	'Straat Cumberland'	LCla
	'Straat Futami' (E)	CDoC EPts LCla
	'Straat Kobe' (T)	CDoC LCla
	'Straat La Plata'	LCla
	'Straat Magelhaen'	LCla WOth
	'Straat of Plenty'	CDoC LCla
	'Strawberry Daiquiri' (d)	WOth
	'Strawberry Delight' (d)	CLoc CWVF EBak MJac SVic
	'Strawberry Sundae' (d)	CLoc CWVF EBak
	'String of Pearls'	CLoc CWVF MJac SLBF SVic
	'Stuart Joe'	CWVF
	'Sue'	SLBF WOth
	'Sue Joiner'	WRou
	'Suffolk Splendour' (d)	EPts
	'Sugar Almond' (d)	CWVF
	'Sugar Blues' (d)	EBak
	'Sugar Plum Fairy' (E)	WRou
	'Summerdaffodil'	CDoC WOth
	'Sunbeam Hillary' (Sunbeam Series)	WOth
	'Sunkissed' (d)	EBak
	'Sunny'	CDoC
	'Sunny Jim'	SVic
	'Sunny Smiles'	CWVF
	'Sunray' (v)	CLoc CWVF EBak ELon LBuc LRHS MAsh MGos NEgg SCoo SHil SLim SPoG SPtp SVen WCot WOth
	'Sunset'	CLoc CWVF EBak
	'Supersport' (d)	SVic
	'Superstar'	CWVF SVic
	'Susan Ford' (d)	CWVF
	'Susan Green'	CWVF EBak MJac SLBF
	'Susan McMaster'	CLoc
	'Susan Olcese' (d)	CWVF EBak
	'Susan Travis'	CLoc CWVF EBak SVic
	'Swanley Gem' ♀H2	CLoc CWVF EBak SLBF SVic
	'Swanley Pendula'	CLoc
	'Swanley Yellow'	CWVF EBak SVic
	'Sweet Hollie'	SLBF WRou
	'Sweet Leilani' (d)	EBak
	'Sweet Sarah' (E)	EPts WOth
I	'Sweetheart' van Wieringen	EBak
	'Swingtime' (d) ♀H2	CCCN CLoc CWVF EBak EPts LAst LCla MJac SLBF SVic WRou
	sylvatica misapplied	see *F. nigricans*
	sylvatica Benth.	CDoC
	'Sylvia Barker' ♀H2	CWVF LCla SLBF WOth WRou
	'Sylvia Rose' (d)	CWVF
	'Sylvia's Choice'	EBak
	'Symphony'	CLoc CWVF EBak
	'T.S.J.' (E)	CDoC LCla
	'T'Vöske' (d/v)	WOth
	'Taco'	CDoC LCla
	'Taddle'	CWVF SLBF
	'Taffeta Bow' (d)	CLoc SLBF SVic
	'Taffy' (d)	EBak
	'Tamerus Nandoe'	WRou
	'Tamworth'	CLoc CWVF EBak MJac SVic
	'Tangerine'	CLoc CWVF EBak SVic WCot
	'Tanya Bridger' (d)	EBak WOth
	'Tarra Valley'	CDoC LCla SVic WOth
	'Task Force'	CWVF SVic
	'Taudens Heil'	WOth
	'Tausendschön' (d)	CLoc
	'Ted Perry' (d)	CWVF
	'Temptation' ambig.	CWVF
	'Temptation' Peterson	CLoc EBak WOth
	'Tennessee Waltz' (d) ♀H2	CDoC CLoc CWVF EBak EPts SLBF SVic WRou
	'Tess' **new**	SLBF
	tetradactyla misapplied	see *F. × bacillaris*
	'Texas Longhorn' (d)	CLoc CWVF EBak SVic
	'Thalia' (T) ♀H1c	CCCN CDoC CHEx CLoc CWVF EBak EPfP EPts EUJe LAst LCla MBri MCot MHer MJac NEgg NPri SLBF SMrm SPer SPlb SPoG SVic WOth WRou
	'Thamar'	CDoC CLoc CWVF EPts SVic WOth WRou
	'That's It' (d)	EBak SVic
	'The Aristocrat' (d)	CLoc EBak
§	'The Doctor'	CLoc CWVF EBak
	'The Jester' (d)	EBak
	'The Madame' (d)	CWVF EBak
	'The Tarns'	CWVF EBak SVic WOth
	'Théroigne de Méricourt'	EBak
	'Thilco'	CDoC
	'Thomas' (d)	EPts
	'Thompsonii'	see *F. magellanica* 'Thompsonii'
	'Thornley's Hardy'	MRav SVic
	'Three Cheers'	CLoc EBak
	'Three Counties'	EBak
	'Thumbelina'	CDoC LRHS
	'Thunderbird' (d)	CLoc CWVF EBak
	thymifolia (E)	CWVF GCra LRHS MHer SDys SMHy WKif WOth
	– subsp. ***thymifolia*** (E)	CDoC CTsd
	'Tiara' (d)	EBak
	'Tickled Pink'	WRou
	'Tiffany' Reedstrom (d)	EBak
	'Tillingbourne' (d)	SLBF

'Time After Time'	CLoc WRou
'Timlin Brened' (T)	CWVF EBak WRou
'Timothy Titus' (T) 🏆H1c	LCla
'Ting-a-ling'	CLoc CWVF EBak SVic
'Tinker Bell' Hodges	EBak SVic
'Tintern Abbey'	CWVF
'Tjinegara'	CDoC LCla
'Toby Bridger' (d)	CLoc EBak
'Toby Foreman'	SLBF
'Tolling Bell'	CWVF EBak
'Tom Goedeman'	LCla
'Tom H. Oliver' (d)	EBak
'Tom Knights'	EBak WOth
'Tom Thorne'	EBak
'Tom Thumb' 🏆H4	Widely available
'Tom West' misapplied	see *F.* 'Mr West'
'Tom West' Meillez (v)	CDoC CHEx CLoc CMHG COtt CSBt CWVF EBak EHoe EPts LAst LCla MHer MJac MRav MSCN SLBF SLim SPtp WFar WOth WRou
'Tom Woods'	CWVF
'Tomarama' (E)	WOth WRou
'Ton Ten Hove'	CDoC LCla
'Tony Talbot'	MJac
'Tony's Treat' (d)	EPts
'Toos'	SVic
'Topaz' (d)	CLoc EBak
'Topper' (d)	CWVF
'Torch' (d)	CLoc CWVF EBak SVic
'Torchlight'	CWVF EPts LCla
'Torvill and Dean' (d)	CLoc CWVF EPts LAst MJac SLBF
'Tosca'	CDoC CWVF
'Town Crier'	SLBF
'Tracid' (d)	SVic
'Trail Blazer' (d)	CLoc CWVF EBak MJac
'Trailing King'	WOth
'Trailing Queen'	EBak MJac
'Trase' (d)	CDoC CWVF EBak SVic
'Traudchen Bonstedt' (T) 🏆H1c	CLoc CWVF EBak LCla SVic
'Traviata'	see *F.* 'La Traviata' Blackwell
'Treasure' (d)	EBak
'Treslong'	WOth
'Tricolor'	see *F. magellanica* var. *gracilis* 'Tricolor'
'Trientje'	LCla SLBF
'Trimley Bells'	EBak
triphylla (T)	EBak MHer
'Trish's Triumph'	EPts WOth
'Tristesse' (d)	CLoc CWVF EBak
'Troika' (d)	EBak
'Troon'	CWVF
'Tropic Sunset' (d)	CDoC
'Tropicana' (d)	CLoc CWVF EBak SVic
'Troubador' Waltz (d)	CLoc
'Trudi Davro'	CDoC LAst MJac SCoo
'Trudy'	CDoC CWVF EBak EPts SVic WOth
'Truly Treena' (d)	SLBF
'Trumpeter' ambig.	CWVF
'Trumpeter' Fry	SVic
'Trumpeter' Reiter (T)	CLoc EBak EPts LCla MJac WRou
'Tubular Bells' (T)	LCla WOth
'Tuonela' (d)	CLoc CWVF EBak
'Turkish Delight'	WOth WRou
'Tutti-frutti' (d)	CLoc
'Twinkling Stars'	CWVF MJac SVic WOth
'Twinny'	CWVF EPts
'Two Tiers' (d)	CWVF
'U.F.O.'	CWVF SVic
'Ullswater' (d)	CWVF EBak WOth
'Ultramar' (d)	EBak
'Uncle Charley' (d)	CDoC EBak SVic
'Uncle Steve' (d)	EBak SVic
'University of Liverpool'	CLoc MJac
'Upward Look'	EBak
'Valda May' (d)	CWVF
'Vale of Belvoir'	SVic
'Valentine' (d)	EBak
'Valerie Ann' (d)	EBak SVic
'Valerie Bradley'	EPts
'Valiant'	EBak
'Vanessa Jackson'	CLoc CWVF MJac SVic
'Vanessa Wright' **new**	CDoC
'Vanity Fair' (d)	CLoc EBak
'Variegated Lottie Hobby' (E/v)	CDoC WOth
'Variegated Procumbens'	see *F. procumbens* 'Wirral'
'Variegated Swingtime' (v)	EBak LAst
'Veenlust'	EBak
'Velvet Crush'	EPts LAst WRou
'Vendeta'	CDoC LCla WOth
'Venus Victrix'	EBak WOth
venusta	CDoC EBak LCla
'Vera Garcia'	CDoC EPts SLBF WRou
'Versicolor'	see *F. magellanica* 'Versicolor'
'Victory' Reiter (d)	EBak
'Ville de Paris' **new**	WOth
'Vincent van Gogh' (T)	WOth
'Vintage Dovercourt'	LCla
'Violet Bassett-Burr' (d)	CLoc EBak
'Violet Gem' (d)	CLoc
'Violet Rosette' (d)	CWVF EBak SVic
Violetta = 'Goetzviol' (Shadowdancer Series)	CDoC LAst LSou SCoo WRou
'Viva Ireland'	EBak
'Vivien Colville'	CLoc SVic
'Vivien Harris' **new**	CDoC
'Vobeglo'	CWVF
'Vogue' (d)	EBak
'Voltaire'	EBak
'Voodoo' (d)	CCCN CDoC CLoc CWVF EBak EPts LAst LCla SCoo SVic
vulcanica André	LCla
'Vyvian Miller'	CWVF
'W.P. Wood'	CDoC
'Wagtails White Pixie'	EBak
'Waldfee' (E)	CDoC LCla WRou
'Waldis Alina'	WRou
'Waldis Billy'	WRou
'Waldis Grafin'	WRou
'Waldis Isobel'	WRou
'Waldis Maja'	WRou
'Waldis Spezi'	CDoC LCla
'Walsingham' (d)	CWVF EBak WOth
'Walton Jewel'	EBak
'Walz Bella'	LCla
'Walz Blauwkous' (d)	CWVF
'Walz Estafette' (d)	SVic
'Walz Fluit'	MJac
'Walz Freule'	CWVF MJac WOth
'Walz Harp'	CWVF WOth
'Walz Jubelteen' 🏆H2	CDoC CLoc CWVF ELon EPts LCla MJac SAdn SLBF SVen SVic WOth WRou
'Walz Lucifer'	CWVF LCla SLBF
'Walz Mandoline' (d)	CWVF SVic
'Walz Nugget'	CDoC

'Walz Panfluit'	LCla
'Walz Polka'	CDoC LCla
'Walz Sitar'	WOth
'Walz Toeter' **new**	WOth
'Walz Triangel' (d)	SVic
'Walz Trompet'	CDoC
'Walz Tuba'	CDoC
'Wapenveld 150'	LCla
'Wapenveld's Bloei'	CDoC EPts LCla SLBF
'War Paint' (d)	CLoc EBak
'Warm Night' **new**	CDoC
'Warton Crag'	CWVF SVic
'Water Color' **new**	SLBF
'Water Nymph'	CLoc LAst MHer SLBF SVic WOth WRou
'Wattenpost'	SLBF
'Wave of Life'	CWVF
'Waveney Gem'	CLoc CWVF EBak LCla MJac SLBF WOth
'Waveney Queen'	CWVF SVic WOth
'Waveney Sunrise'	CWVF MJac SVic WOth
'Waveney Unique'	CWVF
'Waveney Valley'	CWVF EBak
'Waveney Waltz'	CWVF EBak
'Wedding Bells' ambig.	SVic
'Welsh Dragon' (d)	CLoc CWVF EBak WOth
'Wendy' Catt	see *F.* 'Snowcap'
'Wendy Bendy'	SLBF WRou
'Wendy Hebdon'	WRou
'Wendy's Beauty' (d)	CDoC CLoc EBak EPts MJac
'Wentworth'	CWVF SVic
'Wessex Belle' (d/v)	CWVF
'Westham'	LCla
'Westminster Chimes' (d)	CLoc CWVF
'Wharfedale' 🏆H4	ELon EPts EWTr MJac SLBF SVic WOth
'What's-it' (E)	LCla SLBF
'Whickham Blue'	CWVF
'Whirlaway' (d)	CLoc CWVF EBak SVic
'White Academy' **new**	EPts
'White Ann'	see *F.* 'Heidi Weiss'
'White Bride' (d)	SVic
'White Clove'	CDoC SVic WOth WRou
'White Galore' (d)	CWVF EBak SVic
'White Général Monk' (d)	CDoC
'White Gold' (v)	EBak
'White Joy'	EBak
'White King' (d)	CLoc CWVF EBak LAst SVic WRou
'White Pixie' 🏆H4	CDoC EPts MJac SLBF SVic
'White Queen' ambig.	CWVF
'White Queen' Doyle	EBak
'White Spider'	CLoc CWVF EBak SVic WOth
'White Veil' (d)	CWVF
'Whiteknights Amethyst'	CDoC WOth
'Whiteknights Blush'	CCse CDoC CExl EPfP EWes GCal GQui LRHS SMrm
'Whiteknights Cheeky' (T)	CWVF EBak EPts LCla SVic
'Whiteknights Pearl' 🏆H3	CDoC CTsd CWVF ECha EPfP EPts LAst LCla MLHP MMuc SDys SEND SLBF SMHy SVic WHar WOth WPnn
'Whiteknights Ruby' (T)	WOth
'Whitton Starburst'	LCla
'Wicked Queen' (d)	SVic
'Widnes Wonder'	SLBF WRou
'Widow Twanky' (d)	CWVF
'Wigan Peer' (d)	CDoC EPts MJac SLBF WOth WRou
'Wight Magic' (d)	MJac
'Wild and Beautiful' (d)	CWVF SVic
'Wilf Langton'	SLBF WOth WRou
'Wilhelmina Schwab'	LCla
'Willeke Smit' (d)	CDoC
'Willow Tinsdale'	CDoC LRHS LSou SLim
'Willy Nijhuis' (T)	WOth
'Wilma van Druten'	CDoC LCla
'Wilson's Colours'	EPts LCla
'Wilson's Joy'	MJac
'Wilson's Pearls' (d)	CWVF SLBF
'Wilson's Sugar Pink'	EPts LCla MJac WOth
'Win Oxtoby' (d)	CWVF
'Windhapper'	LCla SLBF
'Windmill'	CWVF
'Wine and Roses' (d)	EBak
'Wingrove's Mammoth' (d)	SVic
'Wings of Song' (d)	CWVF EBak
'Winjim' (T)	WRou
'Winston Churchill' (d) 🏆H2	CDoC CLoc CWVF EBak LAst MJac SCoo SVic WOth
'Winter's Touch'	WOth
'Witchipoo'	SLBF
'Woodnook' (d)	CWVF
'Woodside' (d)	SVic
'Wyre Light' (E)	SLBF
'Yattendon Lady' **new**	SLBF
'Ymkje'	CDoC EBak
'Yolanda Franck'	LAst
'York Manor'	EShb
'Yvonne Schwab'	CDoC LCla
'Zeebrook'	SVic
'Zeeuwse Parel' **new**	WOth
'Zellertal'	CDoC
'Zeta'	CDoC
'Zets Bravo'	CDoC
'Ziegfield Girl' (d)	EBak SVic
'Zifi'	SLBF
'Zulu King'	CDoC SVic WOth
'Zulu Queen'	SVic WOth
'Zus Liebregts' (d)	CDoC WOth
'Zwarte Dit'	WOth
'Zwarte Snor' (d)	CWVF

Fumaria (*Papaveraceae*)

capreolata	WSFF
lutea	see *Corydalis lutea*
officinalis	CArn

Furcraea (*Asparagaceae*)

bedinghausii	see *F. parmentieri*
§ ***foetida***	CCCN
gigantea	see *F. foetida*
longaeva misapplied	see *F. parmentieri*
macdougalii	SPlb
§ ***parmentieri***	CBcs CCCN CCon CDTJ CExl CHEx CHGN CHll CPne CTsd EBee GBin LEdu NLos SArc SPlb
selloa var. ***marginata*** (v)	CDoC CHEx MHin

Gahnia (*Cyperaceae*)

sieberiana	SPlb

Gaillardia (*Asteraceae*)

aristata 'Maxima Aurea'	EBee EPfP MSpe NBre SPhx

'Arizona Sun'	EAJP LPal LRHS MHer NPri SCob SHil SPad SVic
'Bijou'	EBee LSun SWvt
'Dwarf Goblin'	NGBl
§ 'Fackelschein'	IBoy MSpe XLum
'Fanfare'PBR	CWGN EBee ECtt LAst LSou MGos NSir SCoo
Goblin	see *G.* × *grandiflora* 'Kobold'
'Golden Queen'	XLum
× ***grandiflora*** 'Amber Wheels'	EPfP MSpe NCGa SPhx
- 'Arizona Apricot' **new**	NPri
- 'Arizona Red Shades' **new**	LRHS NPri
- 'Bremen'	MSpe XLum
- 'Burgunder'	CBod CSBt CSpe EAJP ELan EPfP EPla EWoo LAst LRHS LSou LSun MBri MPie MSpe NGBl NPri NSoo SBod SCob SPer SPhx SPoG SWvt WCAu WHar XLum
- 'Dazzler'	CBod CSBt EAEE EBee ELan EPfP EPla LAst LRHS SMrm SPer SPoG WMoo XLum
- (Gallo Series) 'Gallo Dark Bicolor' **new**	LRHS
- - 'Gallo Fire' **new**	LRHS
- - 'Gallo Peach' **new**	LRHS
- - 'Gallo Yellow' **new**	LRHS
- - 'Gallo Yellow Trumpet' **new**	LRHS
§ - 'Goldkobold'	XLum
§ - 'Kobold'	CBcs CMac COtt CSBt CTsd EBee ELan ELon EPfP EPla GMaP IBoy LAst LRHS LSun MBri NHol NLar NSoo SPer SPlb SPoG SWvt WHar XLum
- 'Mesa Yellow'	NPri
- (Sunburst Series) Sunburst Burgundy Picotee = 'Granretip'PBR	LRHS
- - Sunburst Burgundy	LRHS SHil
- - Sunburst Orange = 'Granoran'PBR	LRHS SHil
- - Sunburst Yellow = 'Granyel'PBR	LRHS SHil
- 'Tizzy'PBR	MPie
- 'Tokajer'	EBee ELan EPfP LRHS MSpe NBre SPhx XLum
'Naomi Sunshine'	SHar
§ 'Oranges and Lemons'PBR	EBee ECtt LSou SCob SHar WCAu
peach-flowered **new**	LRHS
'Red Sun'	CWGN NLar
Saint ClementsPBR	see *G.* 'Oranges and Lemons'
'Solar Flare' **new**	SCob
Torchlight	see *G.* 'Fackelschein'
Yellow Goblin	see *G.* × *grandiflora* 'Goldkobold'

Galactites (*Asteraceae*)

tomentosa	EHoe ELan SPav
- white-flowered	CPla

Galanthus ✿ (*Amaryllidaceae*)

'Acton Pigot No. 3'	CAvo
'Alison Hilary'	GEdr LRHS MAsh
× ***allenii***	CBro GKev
alpinus var. ***bortkewitschianus***	CAvo
'Anne of Geierstein'	IFoB WCot
'Annette'	LAma NMyG
'Ann's Millenium Giant' **new**	CBro
'Armine'	CElw IFoB LRHS WCot
'Art Nouveau'	CAvo
'Atkinsii' ♀H5	CAvo CBgR CBro CElw CLAP CRos CWCL ECho EPot EWoo GAbr GEdr IFoB IGor LAma LRHS MAsh MRav MWat NBir NMyG WCot WFar WHoo WShi
'Autumn Beauty'	CBro LRHS
'Babraham Scented' **new**	GEdr
'Backhouse Spectacles'	ITim
'Barbara's Double' (d)	CAvo CBgR CLAP MAsh
'Benhall Beauty'	CElw
'Bertram Anderson' ♀H5	GEdr MAsh WCot
'Bess'	CAvo CElw CSna IFoB LRHS
'Bill Bishop'	CBro EWoo IFoB LRHS MAsh WCot
'Bitton' ambig.	NPol
'Blewbury'	IFoB
'Brenda Troyle'	CBro CElw CLAP ECho EPot GAbr GBin GEdr IGor LRHS MAsh MHom NMyG NPol WCot WFar
'Byfield Special'	CAvo IFoB
byzantinus	see *G. plicatus* subsp. *byzantinus*
'Castlegar'	IFoB
caucasicus misapplied	see *G. elwesii* var. *monostictus*
caucasicus ambig.	GAbr IFoB NPol
- 'Comet'	see *G. elwesii* 'Comet'
- var. ***hiemalis*** Stern	see *G. elwesii* Hiemalis Group
'Charlotte' **new**	LRHS
'Cicely Hall'	CDes IFoB
'Clare Blakeway-Phillips'	CLAP LRHS
corcyrensis spring-flowering	see *G. reginae-olgae* subsp. *vernalis*
- winter-flowering	see *G. reginae-olgae* subsp. *reginae-olgae* Winter-flowering Group
'Cordelia' (d)	CElw CLAP GAbr IFoB LRHS MAsh NMyG
'Cornwood Gem'	CAvo IFoB
'Cowhouse Green'	CAvo
'Curly'	CAvo CDes IFoB MAsh
'Desdemona' (d)	CAvo CBro CLAP EPot GAbr LLHF LRHS NMyG WCot WFar
'Ding Dong'	CAvo IFoB
'Dionysus' (d)	CBgR CBro CExl CLAP EPot EWes EWoo GAbr GEdr IGor LLHF LRHS MHom NBir NMyG WBrk WFar WShi
'Drummond's Giant'	IFoB
§ ***elwesii*** ♀H5	CBro CTri ECho ELan EPfP EPot ERCP GKev IFoB IGor LAma LRHS MWat NBir NPol SDeJ SPoG SRms WCot WFar WHoo WShi
- 'Abington Green'	CSna
- 'Broadleigh Gardens'	LRHS
- 'Cedric's Prolific'	ECha EWoo IFoB IGor LRHS NMyG WFar
- 'Cinderdine' **new**	ITim
§ - 'Comet' ♀H5	CAvo CElw GBuc IFoB LRHS MAsh WFar
- 'Daphne's Scissors'	CAvo CElw CSna GEdr
- 'David Shackleton'	CElw IFoB LRHS MAsh
- 'Early Twin'	WCot
- Edward Whittall Group	CLAP
- 'Elmley Lovett'	CElw
- var. ***elwesii*** 'Fred's Giant'	GMaP
- - 'Kite'	LRHS
- - 'Magnus'	CLAP NBir
- - 'Maidwell L'	CBro CSna LRHS
- - 'Sibbertoft Magnet'	CAvo CDes IFoB

*	- 'Flore Pleno' (d)	NPol
	- 'Godfrey Owen'	CDes IFoB
	- 'Green Brush'	IFoB LRHS
	- 'Grumpy'	GEdr MAsh
§	- Hiemalis Group	CBro EPot LRHS MHom WCot
	- - 'Barnes'	WCot
	- 'J. Haydn'	ECho LAma NMyG
	- 'Jessica'	CAvo IFoB
	- 'Kyre Park'	GEdr MAsh
	- 'Long 'drop'	GEdr IFoB
	- 'Mandarin'	CElw
	- 'Marielle'	EPPr
	- 'Marjorie Brown'	CFis ITim LRHS NMyG
	- 'Milkwood'	see *G. elwesii* 'Mrs Macnamara'
§	- var. ***monostictus*** ♀H5	CAvo CBro ECha ECho IFoB LLHF LRHS WBrk WFar WShi
	- - 'G. Handel'	ECho IFoB LAma LLHF LRHS NMyG
	- - 'Grayswood' **new**	GEdr
	- - 'Green Tips'	CAvo
	- - 'H. Purcell'	ECho GEdr LAma LLHF LRHS
	- - late-flowering	ECho
	- - 'Lord Monostictus' **new**	CAvo
	- - 'Miller's Late'	CAvo
	- - 'Rogers Rough'	SDys
	- - 'Warwickshire Gemini'	CDes
§	- 'Mrs Macnamara'	CDes EWoo GEdr IFoB LRHS MAsh WFar
	- November-flowering **new**	WCot
	- 'Penelope Ann'	GEdr
	- 'Peter Gatehouse'	CDes
§	- 'Ransom's Dwarf'	CDes
	- 'Sickle'	CSna
	- 'Sir Edward Elgar'	LAma LLHF LRHS
	- 'Three Leaves'	CAvo IFoB
	- 'Washfield Colesbourne'	see *G.* 'Washfield Colesbourne'
	aff. ***elwesii*** var. ***monostictus***	WFar
	'Erway'	MHom
I	'Excelsis' **new**	CAvo
	'F63'	IFoB
	'Falkland House'	CElw GEdr
	'Faringdon Double' (d)	CAvo LRHS MAsh
	'Fieldgate Prelude'	CAvo GEdr
	'Fieldgate Superb'	IFoB
	'Fieldgate Tiffany' **new**	CAvo
	'Fly Fishing' **new**	CAvo
	fosteri	CBro ECho GEdr LRHS
	'G71' (d)	IFoB
	'Galadriel'	CAvo
	'Galatea'	CAvo CBro CLAP CSna EWes EWoo GAbr LRHS MAsh MHom SDys WFar
	'George Elwes'	CAvo
	'Ginns'	CLAP EWoo IFoB
	'Gloria' **new**	MAsh
§	***gracilis***	CAvo CBre CBro CExl CLAP ECho LRHS NPol
	- 'Highdown'	CElw CLAP IFoB LRHS MAsh MHom
	- hybrid **new**	LRHS
	- Kew	CElw
	- 'Vic Horton'	CElw LRHS WThu
	graecus misapplied	see *G. gracilis*
	graecus Orph. ex Boiss.	see *G. elwesii*
	'Grande Juge'	IFoB
	'Grayling'	see *G. plicatus* 'Percy Picton'
	Greatorex double (d)	CLAP
	'Green Arrow' **new**	CAvo
	'Green Man'	CAvo IFoB
	'Green Necklace'	CAvo
	'Greenfields'	CSna IFoB IGor MAsh
	'Heffalump' (d)	CAvo IFoB MAsh
	'Hercule' **new**	CAvo
	'Hill Poë' (d)	CBro CElw CLAP EPot GEdr IFoB LRHS MAsh MHom MWat NMyG
	'Hippolyta' (d)	CAvo CBro CElw CLAP ECha EPot EWoo GAbr GEdr IFoB IGor LAma LRHS MAsh MHom NMyG NPol SKHP SMrm WCot WShi
	'Hobson's Choice'	LRHS
	'Honeysuckle Cottage'	CAvo
	× ***hybridus*** 'Merlin' ♀H5	CBro CElw IFoB IGor LRHS NMyG WCot WFar
	- 'Robin Hood'	CAvo CDes CLAP IFoB LRHS
	'Icicle'	CAvo
§	***ikariae*** Bak.	CElw EPfP
	- subsp. ***ikariae*** Butt's form	NPol
	- Latifolius Group	see *G. platyphyllus*
	- subsp. ***snogerupii***	see *G. ikariae* Bak.
	'Imbolc'	CAvo GEdr IFoB LRHS
	'Irish Green'	CAvo IFoB
	'Jacquenetta' (d)	CAvo CBro CElw CLAP CSna GEdr IFoB IGor ITim LRHS MCot MHom NMyG
	'James Backhouse'	LRHS WHoo WShi
	'John Gray'	CBro CSna GEdr IFoB MAsh
	'Ketton'	CBro CElw CSna EWoo GEdr IFoB LRHS NRya
	'Kildare'	CAvo IFoB
	'Kingston Double' (d)	CBgR CLAP
	krasnovii **new**	LRHS
	'Lady Beatrix Stanley' (d) ♀H5	CAvo CBro CElw CLAP ECha EPot GAbr GEdr IFoB LLWP MAsh MHom NMyG WCot WFar
	'Lapwing'	CAvo IFoB LRHS MAsh
	latifolius Rupr.	see *G. platyphyllus*
	'Lavinia' (d)	CAvo CElw CLAP EWes GEdr MAsh MHom WFar
	'Lerinda'	IFoB LRHS
	'Limetree'	CElw CLAP EPri EWes EWoo ITim LRHS MHom NCot NPol WFar
	'Little Ben'	GMaP
	'Little John'	LRHS WBrk
	'Little Magnet'	CAvo
	'Longstowe'	MAsh
	'Louise Ann Bromley'	CAvo
	lutescens	see *G. nivalis* Sandersii Group
	'Lyn'	CBro GEdr NBir
	'Magnet' ♀H5	CAvo CBgR CBro CElw CLAP ECho ELon EPot EWoo GAbr GEdr IGor LAma LRHS MAsh MHom MWat NBir NMyG NPol SKHP WBrk WCot WFar WHoo WShi
	aff. 'Magnet'	GMaP SMrm
	'Maidwell'	IFoB
	'Melanie Broughton'	CAvo CDes IFoB
	'Mighty Atom'	CBro CDes CLAP GAbr WBrk
	'Moccas'	CElw CSna MHom
	'Modern Art'	CAvo IFoB MAsh
	'Mrs Backhouse No 12'	IFoB LRHS
	'Mrs Thompson'	CAvo CDes CElw GEdr IFoB LRHS MAsh
	'Mrs Wrightson's Double' (d)	CDes
	'Natalie Garton'	CAvo IFoB
	'Neill Fraser'	GEdr MHom

	Name	Suppliers
	'Nerissa' (d)	GEdr
	nivalis ♀H5	Widely available
	- 'Alice's Late'	CBgR
	- 'Anglesey Abbey'	CAvo CElw EWes GEdr IFoB MHom
	- 'April Fool'	MHom
	- 'Ballynahinch'	ITim
	- 'Bitton'	CLAP GEdr
	- 'Blonde Inge'	GEdr IFoB MAsh
	- 'Chedworth'	CElw WBrk
	- 'Dreycott Greentip'	IFoB
	- 'Elfin'	CAvo CElw IFoB MAsh
	- 'Fuzz'	CAvo
	- subsp. ***imperati***	CExl
	- 'Lutescens'	see *G. nivalis* Sandersii Group
	- 'Major Pam'	IFoB
	- 'Maximus'	LRHS WShi
	- 'Melvillei'	MAsh
	- f. ***pleniflorus*** (d)	CTca ECho GKev MAsh SPoG WHil
	- - 'Blewbury Tart' (d)	CAvo CBro CElw CLAP CSna EWoo GEdr IFoB WBrk
	- - 'Flore Pleno' (d) ♀H5	CBro CExl CWCL EPfP EPot ERCP IFoB LAma LLWP LRHS MMuc NCot NRya SDeJ SEND SMrm SPer SRms WBrk WCot WHoo WShi
	- - 'Lady Elphinstone' (d)	CAvo CBro CDes CLAP CRow CSna IFoB LLHF MAsh MHom NMyG NPol NRya WCot
	- - 'Pusey Green Tips' (d)	CAvo CBro CElw CLAP EPot IFoB NMyG NPol WCot
	- - 'Walrus' (d)	MAsh
§	- - 'Wonston Double' (d)	CAvo IFoB
	- Poculiformis Group	CElw CLAP MAsh
	- - 'Snow White' **new**	LRHS
	- cf. Poculiformis Group **new**	CElw
§	- Sandersii Group	GMaP IFoB
§	- Scharlockii Group	CAvo CElw IGor MAsh MHom WBrk
	- 'Sibbertoft White'	MAsh
	- 'Tiny'	IFoB MHom WFar
	- 'Tiny Tim'	MAsh
	- 'Virescens'	CLAP IFoB
	- 'Viridapice'	CAvo CBro CElw CExl ECha ECho EPot GKev GMaP IFoB IGor LAma LRHS MAsh MWat NBir NPol SDeJ SKHP WCot WFar WHoo WShi
	- 'White Dream'	IFoB WShi
	'Nothing Special'	MAsh
	'Ophelia' (d)	CAvo CBro EPot EWoo GAbr GEdr IGor LRHS MAsh MHom MWat NMyG NPol SKHP WBrk WFar WHoo
	'Orion'	CDes
	'Orleton'	CDes
	'Peg Sharples'	IFoB MHom
	peshmenii	ECho
§	***platyphyllus***	CExl LRHS
	plicatus ♀H5	CAvo CBro CElw EPot GAbr LRHS MCot MHom NMyG NPol WBrk WCot WHoo WShi
	- from Coton Manor	MCot
	- 'Augustus'	CAvo CBro CElw EPot EWes GEdr IFoB IGor LRHS MAsh MHom NMyG WCot WHoo
	- 'Baxendale's Late'	CAvo CLAP
	- 'Bill Clark'	IFoB
	- 'Bolu Shades'	IFoB
§	- subsp. ***byzantinus***	CBro MHom WThu
	- 'Colossus'	CBro ECho EWes IFoB WCot
	- 'Diggory'	CAvo GEdr IFoB MAsh
	- 'Duckie'	CAvo GEdr
	- 'Edinburgh Ketton'	LRHS
	- 'Florence Baker'	CAvo
	- 'Gerard Parker'	CAvo IFoB LRHS
	- 'Green Teeth' **new**	MAsh
	- 'Greenpeace'	CSna
	- 'Henham No. 1' **new**	LRHS
	- 'John Long'	CAvo GEdr
	- 'Limey'	EWoo
	- 'Madelaine' **new**	MAsh
§	- 'Percy Picton'	CAvo
	- 'Sally Pasmore'	CAvo
	- 'Sophie North'	CElw CLAP IFoB LLHF NPol
	- 'The Pearl'	IFoB
	- 'Three Ships' ♀H5	CAvo GEdr IFoB LRHS
	- 'Trym'	CDes IFoB NPol
	- 'Warham'	CBro CElw EPot GAbr IFoB IGor LRHS MHom NMyG WCot
	- 'Warham Rectory'	LRHS
	- 'Wendy's Gold' ♀H5	CAvo CBro CSna IFoB MAsh
	- 'Woodtown'	IMou
	'Primrose Warburg'	CAvo CDes IFoB MAsh
	'Ransom's Dwarf'	see *G. elwesii* 'Ransom's Dwarf'
	reginae-olgae	ECho GKev IFoB MHom
	- subsp. ***reginae-olgae*** ♀H3	EPot
§	- - Winter-flowering Group	CBro
§	- subsp. ***vernalis***	EPot IFoB NMyG WCot
	'Reverend Hailstone'	CAvo IFoB LRHS
	'Richard Ayres' (d)	CAvo IFoB LRHS
	rizehensis	CAvo CLAP IFoB LRHS MHom NMyG
	- Baytop 34474	IFoB
	'Rodmarton'	IFoB
	'S. Arnott' ♀H5	CAvo CBro CElw CExl CLAP ECha ECho EPot ERCP EWoo GAbr GBuc GKev IFoB IGor LAma LRHS MAsh MWat NBir NPol NRya SDeJ WBrk WCot WFar WHoo
	'Saint Anne's'	CElw CSna GEdr IFoB MHom
	'Scharlockii'	see *G. nivalis* Scharlockii Group
	'Seagull'	CElw
	'Sentinel'	CAvo CElw
	'Silverwells'	CSna GEdr IFoB
	'Sir Herbert Maxwell'	ITim MAsh
	'Spindlestone Surprise'	CAvo EWoo GEdr
	'Sprite' **new**	CAvo
§	'Straffan' ♀H5	CAvo CBro CElw ECho EPot IFoB IGor LRHS MHom NMyG NPol WBrk WCot
	'Sutton Courtenay'	CAvo CElw CSna
	'The O'Mahoney'	see *G.* 'Straffan'
	'Titania' (d)	CBro GEdr IFoB IGor LRHS MAsh MHom WShi
	'Trotter's Merlin'	CElw
	'Trymming' **new**	CAvo
	'Tubby Merlin'	CElw CLAP EWoo IFoB
	'Uncle Dick'	CAvo
	× ***valentinei*** 'Compton Court'	CBro IFoB ITim
§	'Washfield Colesbourne'	CElw EWoo
	'Washfield Warham'	CAvo CElw ECha EWoo ITim MAsh NMyG
	'Wasp'	CAvo MAsh
	'White Admiral'	SKHP
	'White Dreams'	IFoB LRHS
	'White Swan' Ballard (d)	CElw EWes ITim LRHS

'William Thomson'	CSna LRHS
'Winifrede Mathias'	CBgR CElw CLAP LRHS MAsh
'Wisley Magnet'	LRHS
'Wonston Double'	see *G. nivalis* f. *pleniflorus* 'Wonston Double'
woronowii ♀H5	CBro CElw CLAP CTca CTri ECho EPfP EPot GKev IFoB LAma LRHS MHom MWat NBir NMyG SDeJ SPer WBrk WCot WFar

Galax (*Diapensiaceae*)

aphylla	see *G. urceolata*
§ ***urceolata***	ECho IBlr MNrw

Galega (*Papilionaceae*)

bicolor	NBir SRms SWat
'Duchess of Bedford'	GBin
× ***hartlandii***	CExl
- 'Alba' ♀H7	ELon EWes GBin IBlr LRHS MArl MCot SHar SMHy SWat WCot WHoo WSHC WWtn
- 'Lady Wilson' ♀H7	CPom ECtt ELon EWes EWld GBin MArl MLHP SHar WCot WHoo WHrl WOut
'Her Majesty'	see *G.* 'His Majesty'
§ 'His Majesty'	CDes ECtt IFro MAvo MCot MLHP MRav WCot WHoo WPGP
officinalis	Widely available
- 'Alba'	CBod CPrp ECtt ELan EPfP GJos LEdu LPot MAvo MBel MBrN MHer MNHC SPer WHer WHrl WKif WMoo
- 'Lincoln Gold'	MTPN
orientalis	CDes EBee ECtt EWes LEdu MArl MCot MRav WCot WMoo WPGP WSHC

Galeobdolon see *Lamium*

Galeopsis (*Lamiaceae*)

tetrahit	WSFF

Galium (*Rubiaceae*)

cruciata	see *Cruciata laevipes*
mollugo	CArn CHab
§ ***odoratum***	Widely available
verum	CArn CHab ENfk GJos GPoy MCoo MHer MMuc MNHC NMir SIde

Galtonia (*Asparagaceae*)

candicans ♀H4	Widely available
- 'Moonbeam' (d)	EBee GKev
princeps	CBro CSam CTca EBee ECha GBin GCra IMou LRHS WHil WPGP
regalis	CExl CTca WPGP
viridiflora	CAvo CBro CTca CWld EBee ECha ELan EPla EPot ERCP GBin GCal GGal GKev IBoy LEdu LRHS MNrw NChi NWad SDeJ WCot WHil XLum

Galvezia (*Plantaginaceae*)

speciosa	MCot

Gamblea (*Araliaceae*)

pseudoevodiifolia B&SWJ 11707	WCru

Garcinia (*Clusiaceae*)

mangostana	CCCN

Gardenia (*Rubiaceae*)

augusta	see *G. jasminoides*
'Crown Jewel' **new**	EPfP
florida L.	see *G. jasminoides*
grandiflora	see *G. jasminoides*
§ ***jasminoides*** ♀H1c	CArn CBcs CCCN EBak MBri
- 'Kleim's Hardy'	Widely available
magnifica	MOWG
'Perfumed Petticoats'	WHlf

garlic see *Allium sativum*

garlic, elephant see *Allium ampeloprasum* 'Elephant'

Garrya ✿ (*Garryaceae*)

elliptica	CBcs CDul CMac COtt EBee EPfP GGal LRHS MAsh MBri MGos NPri NWea SCob SEND WFar WHar
- (f)	MJak MSwo SWvt
- (m)	CDoC CTri ELon LAst MBlu NLar SGol SLim
- 'James Roof' (m) ♀H4	Widely available
× ***issaquahensis*** 'Glasnevin Wine' (m) ♀H4	CAbP CDul CJun ELan ELon EPfP IArd LRHS MAsh MBri MGos SCoo SLim SPoG
- 'Pat Ballard' (m)	EPfP
× ***thuretii***	CBcs CDul LAst MBri NLar SEND SPer

Gasteria ✿ (*Asphodelaceae*)

bicolor var. ***liliputana*** ♀H2	SPlb
carinata var. ***verrucosa***	EShb MSCN SPlb
ellaphieae	LToo
excelsa	LToo
nitida var. ***nitida*** variegated (v)	WCot
'Smokey'	EShb

× *Gaulnettya* see *Gaultheria*

Gaultheria ✿ (*Ericaceae*)

NJM 10.032 **new**	WPGP
adenothrix	WThu
antarctica	WThu
cardiosepala	WThu
crassa 'John Saxton'	WAbe
cuneata	ECho GEdr LRHS MAsh NHar WThu
forrestii	CExl
- BWJ 7809 **new**	WCru
hispidula	ECho
itoana	ECho GEdr GJos GKev NHar WThu
miqueliana	GEdr WThu
§ ***mucronata***	CDul EPfP MAsh MJak NWea WFar
- (m)	CMac CSBt CTri CWSG EPfP LRHS MGos MMuc NEgg NWad SPer SRms WFar
- SDR 7051	GKev
- 'Alba' (f)	MJak
- 'Bell's Seedling' (f/m) ♀H6	CBcs CDoC CDul CTri EBee ELan EPfP LRHS MAsh MMuc NBir NEgg NLar SCob SGbt SPer SPoG
- 'Cherry Ripe' (f)	CMac MMuc
- 'Crimsonia' (f) ♀H6	CBcs CMac EPfP SPer SRms
- 'Indian Lake'	NWad
- 'Lilacina' (f)	CMac MAsh

- 'Lilian' (f)	CSBt EPfP NWad
- Mother of Pearl	see *G. mucronata* 'Parelmoer'
- 'Mulberry Wine' (f) ♀H6	CBcs CSBt CTri ELan MMuc NEgg NHol SPer
§ - 'Parelmoer' (f)	CSBt SPer
- 'Pink Pearl' (f) ♀H6	SRms
- red-berried (f)	MJak
- 'Rosea' (f)	MJak
§ - 'Signaal' (f)	CBcs EBee EPfP LRHS MAsh NEgg NLar NWad SCob SPer
- Signal	see *G. mucronata* 'Signaal'
§ - 'Sneeuwwitje' (f)	CBcs CDul EPfP LRHS MAsh MMuc NBir SPer
- Snow White	see *G. mucronata* 'Sneeuwwitje'
- 'Thymifolia' (m)	EPfP
- white-berried (f)	MMuc
- 'Wintertime' (f) ♀H6	CMac SRms
§ ***myrsinoides***	WThu
'Pearls'	NHar NWad WAbe WThu
'Pink Champagne'	ITim
procumbens	Widely available
- 'Very Berry'	CBod EShb NWad WFar
prostrata	see *G. myrsinoides*
pumila	LEdu NHar
schultesii	WThu
shallon	CAgr CBcs CSBt EPfP MJak MMuc NLar SPer SRms SWvt WFar
sinensis	NHar
- lilac-berried	WThu
tasmanica	ECou
tetramera	CExl
thymifolia	NWad WThu
trichophylla	NHar
× ***wisleyensis***	LRHS SLon SRms
- 'Pink Pixie'	LRHS MAsh NLar
- 'Ruby'	CMac
- 'Wisley Pearl'	CBcs IBlr MMuc SCoo WFar
yunnanensis	CExl

Gaura (*Onagraceae*)

lindheimeri ♀H4	CAby CMea CSBt CSpe EBee ECha ELan EPfP EWTr LRHS MCot MHer SBch SPer SWvt WCAu WCFE WHar WHoo WMnd WOut XLum XSen
- Belleza Series	CWCL EPfP LRHS MBri MNrw SHil
- 'Blaze'PBR	LRHS
- Cherry Brandy = 'Gauchebra'PBR	CBod EAEE EBee ECtt ELan EPfP EPla IPot LRHS LSun MBel MBri MCot SHil SWvt WHar
- 'Chiffon' **new**	SHar
- 'Corrie's Gold' (v)	CAby EAEE EBee ECha ECtt EHoe ELan EPfP LRHS MHer SPer WMnd
- 'Crimson Butterflies'PBR	EPfP
- deep rose-flowered **new**	LRHS
§ - 'Heather's Delight'	MRav
- In the Pink	see *G. lindheimeri* 'Heather's Delight'
- 'Jo Adela' (v)	ECha EPfP
- Karalee Petite = 'Gauka'	CWCL EPfP
- Karalee Petite ImprovedPBR	see *G. lindheimeri* Lillipop Pink
- Karalee Pink	MBri
- Karalee White = 'Nugauwhite'PBR	CBod CHel CWCL EPfP LAst LRHS MBri NLar SCoo SHil SPer SPoG
§ - Lillipop Pink = 'Redgapi'PBR	CAby ELon EPfP LBMP MAvo MBrN MBri NLar SCob SMrm SPoG
- 'My Melody'PBR (v)	CWCL
- 'Occitania' (v)	XLum
- Papillon = 'Nugaupapil'PBR	CBod ECtt ELon LBMP MAvo SMrm SPer SPoG
- 'Passionate Blush'PBR	CBcs CBod CChe CMos EAEE ECtt EPfP EPla LRHS LSou MGos SLon SPad SPoG SRms
- 'Passionate Pink'PBR	LRHS
- 'Passionate Rainbow'PBR (v)	CMos CWCL EHoe EPfP LRHS SHil SPoG SRms
- 'Pink Dwarf'	EPfP IPot SAdn
- Pink Fountain = 'Walgaupf' **new**	LRHS
- 'Pink Gin'	LSou
- 'Rosyjane'	Widely available
- 'Ruby Ruby'	SHar
- short	WSHC
- 'Siskiyou Pink'	CBcs CSBt CWCL EAEE EBee ECha ECtt EHoe ELan EPfP EPla LPal LRHS MWat NSoo SAdn SBod SCob SMad SPer SWat SWvt WCFE WGwG WMnd XLum
- Snow Fountain = 'Walsnofou'	LRHS
- 'Summer Breeze'	EAJP LRHS LSun MWat NGBl SPhx
- 'The Bride'	CBod CTri EAEE EBee ECtt EPfP EPla LRHS MAvo MBel MMuc MNHC MRav MWat SAdn SBod SGbt SPav SPer SWvt
- 'Tutti Frutti'	LRHS LSou SPoG
- 'Vanilla'	CKno CWCL LRHS LSou SPoG
I - 'Variegata' (v)	CWCL LRHS SHil SRms
- 'Whirling Butterflies'	CKno CSpe CWCL ECGP ECtt ELan ELon EPfP GMaP LRHS MWat SCob SMad SPer SWat SWvt WWEG
- 'White Dove'	CBod IPot LRHS
- 'White Heron'	MNrw
sinuata	CAby SHar

Gaylussacia (*Ericaceae*)

baccata (F)	CMac

Gazania (*Asteraceae*)

'Aztec'	CCCN
'Bicton Orange'	CCCN CSam ECtt SCoo SVen
'Big Kiss White Flame' (Kiss Series)	LBuc SPoG
'Big Kiss Yellow Flame' (Kiss Series)	LBuc SPoG
'Blackberry Ripple'	CCCN SCoo
'Blackcurrant Ice'	MCot
'Christopher'	SCoo
'Christopher Lloyd'	CCCN ECtt
'Cookei'	CSpe
'Cornish Pixie'	CCCN
'Cream Beauty'	MCot
(Daybreak Series) 'Daybreak Rose Stripe'	NGBl
- 'Daybreak Red Stripe'	NGBl
'Jamaica Ginger'	SMrm
'Kiss Bronze Star' (Kiss Series)	SVen
krebsiana	CCCN
'Lemon Beauty'	ECtt
'Magic'	CCCN SCoo
Nahui = 'Suga119' (Sunbathers Series)	CCCN
'Orange Beauty'	ELan
rigens 'Variegata' (v)	CCCN ELan

Rumi = 'Suga116' (Sunbathers Series)	CCCN
Sunset Jane = 'Sugaja'PBR (Sunbathers Series)	CCCN
Sunset Jane Lemon Spot = 'Sugajale' (Sunbathers Series)	CCCN
'Talent'	SEND
Tiger Eye = 'Gazte'PBR (v)	CCCN LAst LSou
Toptokai = 'Suga407' (Sunbathers Series)	CCCN
Totonaca = 'Suga212' (Sunbathers Series)	CCCN LAst

Geissorhiza (Iridaceae)

aspera	ECho
bracteata	ECho
brehmii 'Rawsonville'	ECho
darlingensis	ECho
imbricata	ECho
- subsp. ***bicolor***	ECho
inequalis	ECho
inflexa	ECho
monanthos	ECho
ornithogaloides	ECho
- subsp. ***marlothii***	ECho
radians	ECho
rosea	ECho
splendidissima	ECho

Gelasine (Iridaceae)

azurea	see *G. elongata*
§ ***coerulea***	WHil
§ ***elongata***	SBrt

Gelidocalamus (Poaceae)

fangianus	see *Ampelocalamus mocrophyllum*

Gelsemium (Gelsemiaceae)

rankinii	EBee LRHS
sempervirens 🏆H1c	CArn CCCN CHll CRHN EBee LRHS MOWG SBrt SLim SPoG

Genista (Papilionaceae)

aetnensis 🏆H5	CDul EBee ELan EPfP MGil SArc SEND SMad SRms
§ ***canariensis*** 🏆H1c	CExl CSBt
carinalis	GJos
cinerea	WCFE
decumbens	see *Cytisus decumbens*
'Emerald Spreader'	see *G. pilosa* 'Yellow Spreader'
fragrans	see *G. canariensis*
hispanica	CBcs CDul CSBt ELan EPfP GGal MGos NLar SCob SEND SLim SPer SRms SWvt WCFE
humifusa	see *G. pulchella*
lydia 🏆H5	Widely available
§ ***maderensis***	LRHS SHil
pilosa	EPot MAsh
- 'Goldilocks'	LRHS MMuc
- 'Lemon Spreader'	see *G. pilosa* 'Yellow Spreader'
- var. ***minor***	NLar NSla SBch WAbe
- 'Procumbens' 🏆H5	CMea GEdr MHer
- 'Vancouver Gold'	CBcs CMac ELan EPfP MBri MGos MRav SPer SRms
§ - 'Yellow Spreader'	CBcs MAsh MSwo
§ 'Porlock' 🏆H3	CBcs CDoC CDul CExl CMac CSBt CTri EPfP GGal IDee LBMP LRHS MAsh MBri MMuc MRav SEND SHil SLim
§ ***pulchella***	CTri GCrg
sagittalis	CTri GJos LRHS MMuc NBir SPer WWFP
§ × ***spachiana*** 🏆H1c	CEnd CTri NSoo SPoG
subcapitata	WAbe
tinctoria	CArn CHab EOHP GJos GPoy MCot MHer WHer
§ - 'Flore Pleno' (d) 🏆H6	ECho NEoE
- 'Humifusa'	EPot
- 'Moesiaca'	WAbe
- 'Plena'	see *G. tinctoria* 'Flore Pleno'
- 'Royal Gold' 🏆H6	EBee MRav NWad SPer SPlb
villarsii	see *G. pulchella*

Gentiana ✿ (Gentianaceae)

sp.	LLWG
§ ***acaulis*** 🏆H5	CMea CPla ECho EDAr ELan EPfP EPot GKev GMaP LRHS MAsh MWat NGdn NHar NLar NSla SBch SPlb SRms WAbe
- f. ***alba***	EPot WThu
- 'Belvedere'	EPot WAbe
- 'Coelestina'	WThu
- 'Dinarica'	see *G. dinarica*
- 'Holzmannii'	IVic WAbe
- 'Krumrey'	EPot GEdr
- 'Luna'PBR **new**	NLar
- 'Max Frei'	NHar
I - 'Maxima Enzian'	GEdr
- 'Rannoch'	EPot GEdr
- 'Stumpy'	GEdr
- 'Trotter's Variety'	WAbe
- 'Undulatifolia'	EPot
- 'Velkokvensis'	EPot IVic
'Alex Duguid'	GEdr IVic LRHS NHar
'Amethyst'	EPot GEdr LRHS NHar SPer SPoG WAbe
angulosa misapplied	see *G. verna* 'Angulosa' hort.
angustifolia	GKev WAbe XEll
- Frei hybrid	GKev
'Ann's Special'	GEdr
asclepiadea 🏆H5	CLAP CSpe CTal CTri ECho ELan GAbr GCra GEdr GKev LEdu LRHS MBri MNrw NBid NBir NCGa NLar SGSe SMad SPoG SRms SSpi WBor WKif WSHC
- 'Alba'	CCon CLAP GCal GEdr GKev LEdu NBid SGSe SRms WCFE
- 'Knightshayes'	CCon CLAP EBee GKev LLHF NLar
- pale blue-flowered	SGSe
- 'Pink Cascade'	SGSe
- 'Pink Swallow'	CLAP EBee GEdr GQue MSCN NLar NMyG SGSe WWEG
- 'Rosea'	GEdr GKev MNrw
'Balmoral'PBR	GMaP NHar
'Barbara Lyle'	WAbe
bavarica var. ***subacaulis***	SPlb
× ***bernardii***	see *G.* × *stevenagensis* 'Bernardii'
'Berrybank Dome'	GEdr GMaP LRHS
'Berrybank Sky'	GAbr GEdr GMaP LRHS
'Berrybank Snowflakes'	GMaP
'Berrybank Star'	GEdr GMaP
bisetaea	SRms
'Blauer Diamant'	GEdr
'Blauer Stern'	IVic
'Blauer Zwerg'	GEdr

	Name	Suppliers
	'Blue Flame'	GEdr
	'Blue Heaven'	EPot GEdr
	'Blue Magic'PBR	EBee LRHS
	'Blue Sea'	LRHS
	'Blue Silk' ♀H5	EPot EWes GEdr GKev IVic LRHS NHar SPoG WAbe
	brachyphylla	WAbe
	'Braemar'PBR	GMaP NHar
	'Cairngorm'	GEdr LRHS NHar
	'Carmen'	GEdr
	× ***caroli***	WAbe
	clusii	WAbe
	'Compact Gem'	EPot GEdr NHar WAbe
§	***cruciata***	EWTr GEdr MMHG NLar
§	***dahurica***	ECho GEdr NGdn NLar XLum
	'Dark Hedgehog'	GEdr
	decumbens	GKev
	depressa	EPot GEdr GKev WAbe
	'Devonhall'	GEdr IVic NHar NWad
	'Diana'PBR	LRHS NLar
§	***dinarica***	ECho EPot NHar
	- 'Colonel Stitt'	GEdr WThu
	- 'Frocheneite'	EPot
	'Dumpy'	EPot GEdr
	'Elehn'	GEdr NHar
	'Elizabeth'	GEdr
	'Ettrick'	GEdr IVic
	'Eugen's Allerbester' (d)	GEdr GKev GMaP IVic LRHS NHar NHol NRya NWad SPer SPoG WAbe
	'Eugen's Bester'	NHar
	farreri	WAbe
	- Silken Star Group	WAbe
	fetissowii	see *G. macrophylla* var. *fetissowii*
	'Gellerhard'	GEdr
	georgei	EPot LLHF
	'Gewahn'	GEdr IVic NHar
I	'Glamis Strain'	LRHS NHar
	'Glen Moy'	GEdr
	'Glendevon'	GEdr WAbe
§	***gracilipes***	GKev MWat NSla SPlb SRms XLum
	- 'Yuatensis'	see *G. macrophylla* var. *fetissowii*
	'Henry'	GEdr WAbe
	hexaphylla	GEdr
	Inshriach hybrids	LRHS
	'Inverleith'	GEdr LRHS NHol SPlb
	'Iona'PBR	GMaP NHar
	'Joan Ward'	LRHS SPer
	'John Aitken'	GEdr
	'Juwel'	GEdr
	'Kobold'	GEdr
	kochiana	see *G. acaulis*
	kurroo var. ***brevidens***	see *G. dahurica*
	lagodechiana	see *G. septemfida* var. *lagodechiana*
	ligustica	EPot
	'Little Diamond'PBR	LRHS NLar
	'Lucerna'	EPfP GEdr LRHS
	lutea	GAbr GCal GPoy LLHF SMad SRms
	× ***macaulayi***	CPla
	- 'Blue Bonnets'	GEdr
	- 'Elata'	IVic NWad
	- 'Kidbrooke Seedling'	EWes GEdr GKev GMaP LRHS WAbe
	- 'Kingfisher'	CPla GEdr IVic LRHS NBir WAbe
§	- 'Wells's Variety'	LRHS
§	***macrophylla*** var. ***fetissowii***	LLHF
	makinoi 'Marsha'PBR	CHll GEdr LRHS MMHG NCGa NLar SPoG
	- 'Royal Blue'	EBee GAbr LRHS
	'Margaret'	GEdr WAbe
	'Maryfield'	GEdr
	'Melanie'	GEdr NHar
	'Multiflora'	LRHS
	'Mystic'PBR **new**	NLar
	occidentalis	EPot
	'Oktoberfest'	GEdr
	ornata	LRHS
	paradoxa ♀H5	GKev LLHF NSla SBrt WAbe
	paradoxa × ***septemfida***	GKev
	phlogifolia	see *G. cruciata*
	pneumonanthe	LRHS NLar SPlb
	pumila	WAbe
	subsp. ***delphinensis***	
	purdomii	see *G. gracilipes*
	'Saphir'PBR **new**	SPer
	'Sapphire Blue' **new**	GEdr
	saxosa	EPfP EPot GCrg ITim LRHS NBir NSla WAbe WIce
	scabra	LRHS
	- 'Zuikorindo'	NLar
	'Selektra'	GEdr IVic
	septemfida ♀H5	EDAr GKev LRHS MAsh MBri MJak MWat NBir NSla SPlb SRms WHoo WKif
	- 'Alba'	LLHF
	- var. ***kolakovskyi***	LLHF
§	- var. ***lagodechiana*** ♀H5	LLHF LRHS SRms XLum
	'Serenity'	GEdr IVic LRHS NHar NLar NWad WAbe
	'Shot Silk' ♀H5	EWes GAbr GEdr GJos GMaP LRHS MGos NBir NHar NHol SPoG WAbe WIce
	'Silken Giant'	GEdr WAbe
	'Silken Night'	GEdr NHar WAbe
	'Silken Seas'	GEdr NHar NWad WAbe
	'Silken Skies' ♀H5	GEdr NHar WAbe
	'Silken Surprise'	WAbe
	sino-ornata ♀H5	CPla CTri ECho GAbr GMaP MAsh MBri NCGa SRms WAbe WIce
	- SDR 5127	MGos
	- 'Alba'	CPla
	- 'Angel's Wings'	GEdr LRHS
	- 'Bellatrix'	GEdr IVic NHar
	- 'Blautopf'	GEdr IVic
	- 'Brin Form'	SRms
	- 'Downfield'	GKev LRHS
	- 'Edith Sarah'	GEdr IVic
	- 'Gorau Glas' **new**	WAbe
	- 'Mary Lyle'	GEdr
	- 'Oha'	GEdr IVic
	- 'Purity'	GEdr LRHS NHar WAbe
	- 'Starlight'	GEdr NHar
I	- 'Trotter's Form'	EWes
	- 'Weisser Traum'	GEdr IVic LRHS NHar NHol NLar SPer
	- 'White Wings'	GEdr
	'Sir Rupert'	GEdr IVic NHar
	'Sternschuppe'	GKev
	× ***stevenagensis***	CPla LRHS
§	- 'Bernardii'	GEdr NHar WAbe
	- dark-flowered	WAbe
	straminea	LLHF
	'Strathmore' ♀H5	EWes GAbr GEdr GKev GMaP LRHS NBir NHar SPer SPlb WAbe
	'Suendermannii'	GKev
	syringea	WAbe

szechenyii LLHF
ternifolia 'Cangshan' GEdr WAbe
- 'Dali' GKev NHar
'The Caley' GEdr GMaP NHar
tibetica CArn CCon GPoy XLum
- PAB 2357 LEdu
triflora var. ***japonica*** NLar WWEG
'True Blue' **new** SPad
veitchiorum GKev LLHF WAbe
verna ECho EDAr EPfP EPot EWes LRHS NPri NSla SPoG WAbe
- 'Alba' GEdr WAbe
§ - 'Angulosa' ♀H5 MAsh
- subsp. ***angulosa*** (Bieb.) V.E.Avet. WIce
- subsp. ***oschtenica*** WAbe
- subsp. ***tergestina*** WAbe
'Violette' GEdr LRHS NWad
waltonii EWes
wellsii see *G.* × *macaulayi* 'Wells's Variety'
wutaiensis see *G. macrophylla* var. *fetissowii*

Geranium ✿ (*Geraniaceae*)

from Bambashata, Altai Mountains NCot
aconitifolium misapplied see *G. palmatum*
aconitifolium L'Hér. see *G. rivulare*
'Adam Moreland' WOut
'Adi' **new** WCot
'Alan Mayes' CBod CElw CMac CNec ECtt EPPr EPla EWoo GBin GBuc GKin LRHS LSou MBri MNFA NGdn SBod SRGP WCra WFar WPtf
'Alan's Blue' NChi
albanum CElw EPPr GLog LLWP MMuc SDix SRGP WMoo
anemonifolium see *G. palmatum*
'Ann Folkard' ♀H7 Widely available
'Anne Thomson' ♀H7 CBod CElw CNec CSpe CWCL ECtt EPPr GBuc GKin GMaP LBMP LRHS LSou MBel MLHP MNFA MNrw MWhi NBid NBir NChi NDov SGbt SRGP WBrk WCra WCru WHrl WMoo WPnP
× ***antipodeum*** 'Chocolate Candy'PBR LRHS MGos
- (*G. sessiliflorum* subsp. *novae-zelandiae* 'Nigricans' × *G. traversii* var. *elegans*) SRms
- 'Pink Spice'PBR CWGN EWoo GKin LBuc LRHS MGos SRms
- 'Sea Spray' CMHG NBro WMnd
aristatum ECGP EPPr EWes GCal MNFA MNrw MRav NBir SGbt SRGP WCru WMoo
armenum see *G. psilostemon*
asphodeloides CBod CElw IFro MBNS MNrw MWhi NBid NBir NCot SGbt SPav SRGP WBrk WFar WMnd WMoo WPnP
- subsp. ***asphodeloides*** white-flowered CElw SRGP WMoo
- 'Starlight' NBid
atlanticum Hook. f. see *G. malviflorum*
'Azure Rush' **new** CUse EBee ECtt IPot LRHS LSqH NSir SPoG SRms WCra
'Azzurro' CBod EBee LRHS MAsh WHil
'Baby Blue' see *G. himalayense* 'Baby Blue'
'Bertie Crûg' CAby CBod ECtt EHoe ELon LLHF NBir NLar SMrm SPer SPoG SRms SRot SWat SWvt
biuncinatum IFro
'Blue Boy' NLar
'Blue Cloud' ♀H7 Widely available
'Blue Pearl' EPPr MAvo NBir NSti SRGP WMoo
§ Blue Sunrise = 'Blogold'PBR ♀H7 Widely available
'Blushing Turtle'PBR CBod EBee NCot NLar NSti WCra
'Bob's Blunder' CUse ECtt EPfP EPts LRHS MBNS MBel MNrw MSCN SMrm SPoG SRGP SRms SWvt WCot WCra WFar WHoo
bohemicum SRGP WHer
- 'Orchid Blue' CSpe SWvt WCra
'Brookside' ♀H7 Widely available
'Buckland Beauty' CExl EWes
'Buxton's Blue' see *G. wallichianum* 'Buxton's Variety'
caeruleatum EBee EPPr GCal NLar
caffrum CPla IFro SPlb SRGP
canariense see *G. reuteri*
candicans misapplied see *G. lambertii*
§ × ***cantabrigiense*** CMac CRos CSBt ECtt IFro LRHS MHer MNrw NBir NBro NLar NPer NSti SMrm SRms WBrk WCru WHea WMoo
- 'Berggarten' EBee EPPr GBin SRGP WBrk WPtf
- 'Biokovo' Widely available
- 'Cambridge' CBcs CBod CMHG CNec CPrp EAJP EBee ECha ECtt ELan EPPr EPfP GAbr GKin LRHS MCot MRav MSwo MWhi NCot SCob SPer SWat SWvt WBrk WCra WFar WMnd WMoo WPnP
- 'Hanne' **new** EBee EPPr
- 'Harz' EPPr WBrk
- 'Hilary Rendall' **new** EPPr
- 'Karmina' CBod CFis CRos EBee EPPr EPfP EPla GCal LRHS MNFA MWhi SBod SHil SWat WCra WHoo WMoo WWEG XLum
- 'Rosalina' EPPr WBrk
- 'Show Time' EPPr WBrk
- 'St Ola' CBod CHVG EBee ECtt EPPr EPfP GBuc GMaP LRHS MNFA MNrw MRav NBro NChi NCot NEgg NGdn SCob SRGP WBrk WCot WCra WCru WHoo WMnd WMoo WPGP WPtf WWEG
- 'Vorjura' EBee EPPr SMHy WBrk
- 'Westray'PBR CBod CHVG CMac CMea CNec EBee ECtt EPPr EPfP EShb GBuc GLog GMaP LAst LSou MBel MHol MMuc NGdn NLar NPri NSti SCob SEND SMrm SRkn SRms SWvt WCra WIce
'Catherine Deneuve' STPC
'Chantilly' CBod CFis CLAP EBee ECtt EPPr EPfP EWTr LRHS MAvo MNrw NBir WCra WCru WGwG WMoo WPtf
'Chipchase Castle' NChi
christensenianum B&SWJ 8022 WCru
cinereum CNec ECho
- 'Apple Blossom' see *G.* × *lindavicum* 'Apple Blossom'

Name	Suppliers
– 'Elizabeth'	ECtt GBuc
– subsp. ***nanum***	see *G. nanum*
– 'Sateene' PBR	EPPr GMaP LRHS SRms SRot WCra
(Cinereum Group) 'Alice' PBR	CMos EBee EPPr GMaP IPot LLHF MBNS NHar NLar NSti SRms SRot WCra
– 'Ballerina' ♀H5	Widely available
– 'Carol'	CWGN EAEE ECtt EPPr EWes GKin LRHS LSou MBNS MRav MSpe NHar NLar NSti SWvt WCra WFar WHoo
– 'Lambrook Helen'	CExl CFis
– 'Laurence Flatman'	CExl CKno CPla CUse ECtt EPfP EPri EWoo GBuc GMaP LAst LBMP LRHS LSou MAsh MGos NBid NEgg NHar NRya NSla SRms SRot SWat WAbe WCra WHoo WMnd
– 'Lizabeth' PBR	ECtt EPPr GBin LSou NHar NLar SMrm WCra
– 'Penny Lane' PBR	WCra
– 'Purple Pillow'	CMos CSpe CWGN ECtt ELan EPPr EWoo IPot LAst LLHF LRHS LSou MBri MCot MRav MSCN NHar NLar NSti SGol SPer SRGP SRms SRot STPC SWvt WCAu WCra WFar
– René Macé = 'Progera'	LRHS SRkn WCAu
– Rothbury Gem = 'Gerfos' PBR ♀H5	ECtt MAsh MRav MSCN NChi SKHP SWvt
– 'Signal'	ECtt EPPr MAsh MSCN NHar NLar WCra
§ – 'Thumbling Hearts'	CMos CWGN EBee IPot MBri WCAu
– Thumping Heart	see *G.* (Cinereum Group) 'Thumbling Hearts'
'Claridge Druce'	see *G.* × *oxonianum* 'Claridge Druce'
clarkei 'Kashmir Pink'	Widely available
§ – 'Kashmir White'	Widely available
– 'Mount Stewart'	CExl CHid EBee EPfP SMad WCru WPGP
– (Purple-flowered Group) 'Kashmir Purple'	Widely available
– Raina 82.83	MNrw
clarum B&SWJ 10246	WCru
collinum	EPPr NBir NCot SRGP WCru
'Colour Carousel'	EBee GBin
'Coombland White'	CCon CExl CHid ECtt GBuc LBMP LSou MAvo MMuc MNrw NLar NSti SKHP SMrm SPer SPoG SRGP WCot WCra WMoo WPnP WRHF
'Coquet Island' **new**	EBee EPPr
'Criss Canning'	EBee EPPr
'Cyril's Blue'	EBee NChi
'Cyril's Fancy'	EBee EPPr
dahuricum	WCru
dalmaticum ♀H5	Widely available
– 'Album'	CHel EBee ECho ECtt ELan EPPr EPfP EPot GBuc LRHS MRav NRya SBch SRGP SRms SWat WAbe WCru
– 'Bressingham Pink'	EBee ECtt EPPr
– 'Bridal Bouquet'	ECtt EPot LLHF NChi NCot NSla
– 'Stades Hellrosa'	EPPr
dalmaticum × ***macrorrhizum***	see *G.* × *cantabrigiense*
'Danny Boy' ♀H7	EBee
delavayi misapplied	see *G. sinense*
'Deux Fleurs' **new**	MAvo
'Devon Pride'	CElw EBee EPPr
'Dilys' ♀H7	CElw CPrp EBee ELan EPPr GBuc MLHP MNFA MNrw NBir NChi NDov NGdn NLar SRGP WCra WCru WHal WMoo WPnP
'Distant Hills'	CDes EBee EPPr SRGP
'Diva'	EBee EPPr EPfP LLHF SRGP
donianum	NSla
'Double Jewel'	see *G. pratense* 'Double Jewel'
Dragon Heart = 'Bremdra' PBR	CBod CLAP ECtt EWoo IPot MAvo MBri MPnt NLar NSti SKHP SMrm SPoG STPC WCAu WCra WPtf
Dreamland = 'Bremdream' **new**	EBee EWoo LSou STPC
'Dusky Crûg'	Widely available
'Dusky Gem'	SIgm
'Dusky Rose'	CAby CHel CLAP CMos CPrp CSpe ECtt ELan EWoo LBuc NLar SHar SRGP SRot WFar
'Edith May'	EBee
'Elizabeth Ross'	MAvo WCra
'Elke'	Widely available
'Ella'	CWGN
'Elworthy Eyecatcher'	CDes CElw MNrw SRGP WPGP
'Elworthy Tiger'	CElw WCra
'Emily'	SRGP
endressii ♀H7	CBre CElw CNec ECha ECho EPfP GAbr GLog GMaP LPot MBNS MCot MHer MMuc NBro NPer NPol SCob SEND SPlb SRGP SRms SWvt WCra WHar WMoo WPtf WWEG XLum
– 'Album'	see *G.* 'Mary Mottram'
– 'Castle Drogo' ♀H7	EPPr SRGP
– 'Prestbury White'	see *G.* × *oxonianum* 'Prestbury Blush'
– 'Rose'	MAvo
– 'Wargrave Pink'	see *G.* × *oxonianum* 'Wargrave Pink'
erianthum	GMaP IMou MLHP NLar SRGP WCru WMoo
– 'Axeltree'	WCot
– 'Cally Pearl'	GCal
– 'Calm Sea'	CDes WCru WMoo
– 'Neptune'	CDes WCru WWEG
– 'Pale Blue Yonder'	EBee
eriostemon Fischer	see *G. platyanthum*
'Eureka Blue'	ECtt LRHS NCot NLar
'Eva'	MTis WPnP
'Expression' PBR	see *G.* 'Tanya Rendall'
'Extravaganza'	EBee EWes WCra
'Farncombe Cerise Star'	CElw WCra
§ ***farreri***	CExl ECho EPot LLHF LRHS NBir WOut
'Fay Anna'	EPfP WFar WHil
'Foundling'	NDov
fremontii	EWld
goldmannii	SKHP
gracile	CFis EBee GMaP LRHS LSou MNrw NBir SRGP WBrk WCru WMoo WPtf
– 'Blanche'	EPPr MNrw
– 'Blush'	CElw EPPr MNFA WCra
– 'Golden Gracile'	see *G.* 'Mrs Judith Bradshaw'
grandiflorum	see *G. himalayense*
'Grasmere'	ECtt
'Gwen Thompson'	WOut
gymnocaulon	CMac EPPr GKin LRHS SRGP WCru
gymnocaulon × ***platypetalum***	EBee NCot
'Harmony'	EBee EPPr
harveyi	CMea ELan EWes NChi SPhx SRGP WKif

	Name	Suppliers
	hayatanum	LRHS
	- B&SWJ 164	NLar WCru WMoo
§	***himalayense***	CBcs CMHG CNec ECha ELan EPfP LAst LRHS MBNS MLHP MMuc MRav MWat NBir NBro SEND SPlb SRGP SRms SRot SWat WCra WFar WMoo WPnP WWEG XLum
	- CC 1957 from Tibetan border	CExl EPPr
	- ***alpinum***	see *G. himalayense* 'Gravetye'
§	- 'Baby Blue'	CElw CMos EBee ECtt ELon EPPr GBuc GCal GCra LRHS MAvo MNFA MNrw NCot NGdn NLar NSti SRGP WBrk WCAu WCra WCru WMoo WPnP WPtf
	- 'Birch Double'	see *G. himalayense* 'Plenum'
	- 'Derrick Cook'	CBod CCon CDes CElw CLAP CPrp EBee ECtt EPPr EPfP GBuc MAvo MNFA MSpe MTis MWhi NCot NSti SMrm SPoG STPC WBrk WCAu WCra WHal WHoo
	- 'Devil's Blue'	EPPr SRGP WPtf
§	- 'Gravetye'	Widely available
	- 'Irish Blue'	CElw EBee EPPr EWoo GBee GBuc GCal GCra IGor LRHS MSpe NCot NLar NPol NSti SRGP WCru WMoo WPnP WPtf
	- ***meeboldii***	see *G. himalayense*
	- 'Pale Irish Blue'	EBee GCal NCot
§	- 'Plenum' (d)	Widely available
	ibericum misapplied	see *G.* × *magnificum*
	ibericum ambig.	SRms
	ibericum Cav.	CSBt CTri LRHS NBre SPav SRGP SRms
	- 'Blue Springs'	ECtt LAll
	- subsp. ***ibericum***	CMac EPPr WPtf
	- subsp. ***jubatum***	EPPr MNrw SGbt SRms WCru
	- - 'White Zigana'	CAby CFis CUse EAEE EBee ECtt EPPr EPfP EWoo LRHS MWhi NLar NPCo SRms WCra WFar WPnP WWtn
	- subsp. ***jubatum*** × ***renardii***	SWvt
	- var. ***platypetalum*** misapplied	see *G.* × *magnificum*
	- var. ***platypetalum*** Boiss.	see *G. platypetalum* Fisch. & C.A. Mey.
§	- 'Ushguli Grijs'	EBee EPPr IMou NCot NLar WCot
	ibericum × ***libani***	CDes EBee
	incanum	CAbP CMHG EBee ELon EWes GCal NBir SBrt SRGP SVen
	- var. ***incanum***	SBch
	- white-flowered	SRGP
	'Ivan' 🏆H7	CBod CElw CLAP CMos EBee ECtt EPPr GBuc LRHS NChi NLar SRGP WCot WCra WCru WHoo WMoo WPnP
	'Ivybridge Eyeful'	CDes
	'Jean Armour'	CDes ECtt EPla GBuc LRHS NDov NLar SPoG SRGP WCra WFar WGwG WPGP
	'Johnson's Blue'	Widely available
	'Jolly Bee'PBR	see *G.* Rozanne
	'Joy'	CBod CLAP CPrp CUse EBee ECtt EPPr GBin GBuc LRHS LSou LSun MAvo MCot MNrw MRav NBir NCGa NChi NEgg NLar NSti NWad SRGP SRms WCot WCra WMoo WPnP
§	'Kanahitobanawa'	CDes EBee WCot WSHC
	'Karen Wouters'	EPPr MTis NCot
	'Kashmir Blue'	CBod CExl ECtt ELan EPPr EPfP GMaP LRHS MTis NCot NLar SWat SWvt WCAu WCra WFar WKif WMoo WPnP WPtf WWEG
	'Kashmir Green'	CLAP CUse ECtt EPfP LLHF MBNS NSti WCra WMoo WPnP
§	'Khan'	CFis EPPr IFro LRHS MAvo NCot NEoE SDys SMHy SRGP WCra WCru
	'Kirsty'	EBee EWes
	kishtvariense	GCal IMou MNrw MRav NSti WCru
	koraiense	WMoo
	- B&SWJ 797	WCru
	- B&SWJ 878	CExl EBee WCru
	koreanum misapplied	see *G. hayatanum*
	koreanum ambig.	CPla NLar WMoo
	- B&SWJ 602	CExl WCru
	krameri	IMou NLar
	- B&SWJ 1142	CExl WCru
	'Lakwijk Star'	CBod IPot MBri NCot NLar WCra
§	***lambertii***	EWes GBuc GCal NBir
	- 'Swansdown'	GBuc GCal
I	***libani***	ELon EPPr LLWP MCot NBid NSti WBrk WCot WSHC
	- RCB RL B-2	CDes WCot WCra
	libani × ***peloponnesiacum***	WPGP
	'Light Dilys'	EBee EPPr NDov
	'Lilac Ice'	CMos ECtt GMaP MAsh NLar SCob WCra
§	× ***lindavicum*** 'Apple Blossom'	CMea MAsh MSCN NSla WFar
	- 'Gypsy' 🏆H5	CMea SBch
	linearilobum subsp. ***transversale***	SRot WPnP
§	'Little David'	CElw EBee NLar
	'Little Devil'	see *G.* 'Little David'
	'Little Gem'	CElw EBee EPPr LRHS NChi NLar SBch WCra WFar WHoo WMoo
	lucidum	NCot WOut WPtf WSFF
	'Luscious Linda'	MAvo NLar WPnP
	'Lydia'	EBee SRGP
§	***macrorrhizum***	CArn CBod CSBt ECrN ELon EPfP GKev GKin IFro LEdu LSun MCot MLHP MRav MWat MWhi NBro NCGa SRms SWat WCAu WFar WHar WHil WWEG XLum
	- AL & JS 90179YU	CHid EPPr
	- 'Album'	CBre CElw ECha ELan ELon EPPr GMaP LRHS MAsh MBel MBri MNFA MSpe MSwo MWat NBid NBro NChi SPhx SWat WBrk WCot WCru WMoo WPtf WWEG
	- 'Bevan's Variety'	Widely available
	- 'Bulgaria'	EPPr WCra
	- 'Cham-ce'	EPPr WBrk
	- 'Czakor'	Widely available
I	- 'De Bilt'	EWes WBrk
	- 'Freundorf'	EBee EPPr EWes GCal NCot WBrk WCra WOut
	- 'Glacier' **new**	EWes
	- 'Ingwersen's Variety' 🏆H7	Widely available
	- 'Lohfelden'	CLAP EPPr EWes GBuc GCal SRGP WCru
	- 'Mount Olympus'	see *G. macrorrhizum* 'White-Ness'
	- 'Mytikas'	EPPr WBrk WPtf
	- 'Pindus'	CBod CLAP CPrp EBee EPPr GAbr GBuc LRHS MNFA NLar NSti SPoG SRGP WCra WCru WFar WPtf

	Name	Suppliers
	- 'Prionia'	EPPr NCot WBrk
	- 'Purpurrot'	WBrk WWEG
	- 'Ridsko'	EPPr GCal LPla NBro SRGP WBrk WCru
	- ***roseum***	see *G. macrorrhizum*
	- 'Rotblut'	EPPr SRGP WBrk
	- 'Sandwijck'	EBee EPPr MAvo
	- 'Snow Sprite'	CMea CPla EPPr EPot LLHF MHer NEoE NLar WBrk WCra WHrl XLum
	- 'Spessart'	CUse EBee ELan ELon EPPr EPfP EWoo GMaP LBMP LPal LRHS MBri MGos MMuc NBid NLar SCob SEND SGbt SPer SPhx SPoG SWvt WBrk WCra WHar WRHF WWEG XLum
	- 'Variegatum' (v)	CNec EBee ELan GMaP LEdu LPot MNFA NBir SRGP SRms WBrk WCot WMnd WWEG
	- 'Velebit'	EPPr SRGP WBrk WCru XLum
§	- 'White-Ness' ♀[H7]	Widely available
	macrostylum	WCot WCru
I	- 'Caeruleum'	WPtf
	- 'Leonidas'	EPPr WCot WPnP
	- 'Talish'	EPPr
	- 'Uln Oag Triag'	EPPr
	maculatum	CArn CElw EPfP LRHS MCot MMHG MNrw MRav NSti SRGP SWat WCru WHal WPnP
	- from Kath Dryden	EPPr
	- f. ***albiflorum***	CLAP EBee ELan ELon EPPr EPfP EWTr EWoo LRHS LSun MBel MNFA MNrw MWhi NChi NLar NSti SMrm SRGP WBrk WCra WCru WMoo WPnP
	- 'Beth Chatto'	Widely available
	- 'Elizabeth Ann'[PBR] ♀[H7]	CElw CLAP CSam CWGN EBee ECtt EPPr EWoo GAbr LBMP LSou MNrw MTis NGdn NLar NSti NWad SPoG WCot WCra WFar WMoo WPGP WPnP WWEG
	- 'Espresso'	Widely available
	- purple-flowered	EPPr
	- 'Putnam County'	EBee EPPr
	- 'Shameface'	EPPr WMoo
	- 'Silver Buttons'	CDes EBee
	- 'Smoky Mountain'	EPPr
	- 'Spring Purple'	CDes CElw EBee EPPr MAvo NChi NLar WCra
	- 'Sweetwater'	EPPr
	- 'Vickie Lynn'	EBee EPPr NChi WCra
	maderense ♀[H3]	Widely available
	- 'Guernsey White'	CBod CCon NLos SMrm WOut
	- white-flowered	CSpe
§	× ***magnificum*** ♀[H7]	Widely available
	- 'Blue Blood'	CAbP CAby CBod CElw CLAP COtt EBee ECtt EPPr EPfP EPla GAbr GCal LRHS LSou MBNS MCot NGdn NPCo NSti SMrm SWvt WCot WCra WPtf WWEG
	- 'Ernst Pagels'	NCot WOut
	- 'Hylander'	EPPr
	- 'Peter Yeo'	EBee EPPr MNFA SRGP WPtf
	- 'Rosemoor'	CBod CElw CHid CNec COtt ECtt ELan EPPr EPfP GBin GBuc GCal IKil LRHS MWhi NEoE SMrm SPer SPtp WCot WCra WHoo WMnd WPtf XLum
	- 'Vital'	XLum
	magniflorum	EWes GKev NBid NGdn
	'Maître Hugo'	EBee NCot
§	***malviflorum***	CFis CMHG ECha ELan EPPr LLWP NCot SBrt WCot WCru WHea WHoo
	- from Spain	EWes WSHC
	- pink-flowered	EPPr
§	'Mary Mottram'	CElw EPPr WCot WCra
	'Mavis Simpson' ♀[H4]	Widely available
	maximowiczii	WPtf
	'Maxwelton'	EBee
	'Melinda'[PBR]	CBod CUse EBee ECtt EPPr EWoo MHol MNrw MTis NCot NDov NLar NMir SMrm WCAu WCot WCra WPtf WRHF
	'Memories'[PBR]	CMos ECtt LRHS MBNS SRms
	'Menna Bach'	MAvo WCra
	'Meryl Anne'	SRGP WPtf
	microphyllum	see *G. potentilloides*
	'Midnight Clouds'	CMos CUse CWGN EBee ECtt EPfP MAvo NCGa NSti WCra WFar WPtf
	molle	NBir WSFF
	× ***monacense***	EBee ELan IFoB IMou LEdu LRHS MBNS MWat SHar SRGP SWat WCra WCru WGwG WMoo WOut WPnP WWtn
	- var. ***anglicum***	CCon ECtt EPPr EPfP GMaP LRHS MWhi NLar WCra WMoo
	- - 'Eric Clement' **new**	EBee
	- 'Anne Stevens'	EBee WPtf
	- 'Claudine Dupont'	CElw EBee EPPr IFro NCot NWad WCot WPtf
	- dark-flowered	WMoo
	- 'Emma White'	EBee EPPr
	- var. ***monacense*** 'Breckland Fever'	EBee EPPr NCot SRGP WCra
§	- - 'Muldoon'	CUse EPPr EPfP EPla NBir SRGP WMoo WPnP
*	'Money Peniche'	XEll
	'Mourning Widow'	see *G. phaeum* 'Lady in Mourning'
	'Mrs Jean Moss'	EBee EPPr EWes NCot
§	'Mrs Judith Bradshaw'	EBee MNrw NChi NCot
§	***nanum***	WAbe
	napuligerum misapplied	see *G. farreri*
	'Natalie'	EBee EPPr LRHS
	nepalense	SRGP SRms
	'Nicola'	CElw EPPr IFro MNFA NLar SRGP WCra
	'Nimbus' ♀[H7]	Widely available
	nodosum	Widely available
	- 'Blueberry Ice'	CElw MAvo
	- 'Clos du Coudray'	EBee EPPr EWoo MAvo NCot NLar WCra
	- 'Dark Heart'	MCot WCra
	- dark-flowered	see *G. nodosum* 'Swish Purple'
	- 'Darkleaf'	EBee
	- 'Hexham Big Eyes'	CElw EWes MAvo
	- 'Hexham Face Paint'	EPPr
	- 'Hexham Feathers' **new**	CElw
	- 'Hexham Freckles'	EPPr
	- 'Hexham Lace'	CElw EPPr
	- 'Julie's Velvet'	CElw LEdu SBch WBor WHoo WPGP
	- pale-flowered	see *G. nodosum* 'Svelte Lilac'
	- 'Pascal'	EPPr
	- 'Saucy Charlie'	SBch
	- 'Silverwood'	CElw CLAP EBee EPPr EWoo GCal LSou MAvo MNFA MTis NChi NSti SBch SPoG WCot WCra WHoo WWFP
	- 'Simon'	SRGP

§	- 'Svelte Lilac'	CBod CElw EAEE EPPr EPfP EWTr LAst LRHS LSou MNFA MNrw NBro NDov NHol SPoG SRGP SWat WBrk WCra WCru WMoo WPnP
§	- 'Swish Purple'	CElw EPPr NLar SRGP WCru WMoo WPGP WPnP
	- 'Tony's Talisman'	EBee
	- 'Whiteleaf'	CElw CMac CMea EPPr GCal MAvo MNFA NChi SRGP WCru WFar WHal WMoo WPGP WPnP
	- 'Wreighburn House White' **new**	EBee
	'Northumberland Lavender Queen'	EBee
	'Nunwood Purple'	EBee EPPr EWes MAvo MNFA WCra WPtf
	ocellatum	GAbr IFro MMuc
	'Old Rose'	LRHS MNFA SRGP WCru
§	***orientalitibeticum***	CCon CExl CMHG CPrp CSpe ECtt EPPr GAbr GKev IFro MCot MHer MMuc NBid NLar SEND SKHP SMad WCot WCra WMoo WWEG
	'Orion' ♀H7	Widely available
	'Orkney Blue'	CElw EPPr WCru
	Orkney Cherry = 'Bremerry'PBR	CMac CUse EBee ECtt EPfP EWTr GBin LLHF MBel NDov NSti SPoG SRkn SRms
	'Orkney Dawn'	WPnP
	'Orkney Mist'	EBee
	'Orkney Pink'	ECtt EPPr EPfP LEdu NSti SPoG SRGP SWat
	'Out of the Blue'	WOut
	× ***oxonianum***	CNec NCot WMoo
	- 'A.T. Johnson' ♀H7	Widely available
	- 'Andy's Star'	EBee
	- 'Ankum's White'	CLAP EBee
	- 'Anmore'	SRGP
	- 'Beholder's Eye' ♀H7	CPrp EPPr MMuc NLar SRGP WPnP WPtf WWEG
	- 'Breckland Sunset'	EBee EPPr NLar SRGP
	- 'Bregover Pearl'	CBre CElw EPPr SRGP WMoo
	- 'Bressingham's Delight'	LRHS SRGP
	- 'Buttercup'	EPPr SRGP
	- Caborn hybrids	LLWP
I	- 'Cally Seedling'	EBee EWes GCal
	- 'Chocolate Strawberry'	EBee EPPr EWes WCra
§	- 'Claridge Druce'	Widely available
	- 'Coronet'	CCon GCal SRGP WCra WMoo
	- 'Cream Chocolate' **new**	EBee EPPr
	- 'David Rowlinson'	EPPr
	- 'Diane's Treasure'	EBee
	- 'Elworthy Misty'	CElw EPPr SRGP
	- 'Frank Lawley'	CPrp LLWP NBid SRGP WMoo
§	- 'Fran's Star' (d)	SRGP WCru
	- 'Hexham Pink'	EBee EPPr EWes NChi SRGP
	- 'Hollywood'	EBee ELan EPPr EPfP NLar NPer SRGP SRms WCra WMoo WPtf WWEG
	- 'Iced Green Tea'	EPPr
	- 'Julie Brennan'	EBee GAbr LRHS
	- 'Kate Moss'	EPPr EWes NSti SRGP
	- 'Katherine Adele'	CMos CUse EBee ECha ECtt EPPr EPfP EWes GCal LPla LSou MAvo MMuc MSpe MTis NCot NLar NSti SEND SRGP SRms WCra WFar
§	- 'Kingston'	CElw EBee EPPr
	- 'Königshof'	EPPr EWes
	- 'Kurt's Variegated'	see *G.* × *oxonianum* 'Spring Fling'
	- 'Lace Time'	CAby CBod CBre CCon CUse EBee ECtt EPPr EPla GBuc GKin LRHS MSpe NEgg SPer SPoG SRGP SRms WCra WGwG WMnd WMoo
	- 'Lady Moore'	EPla LRHS NBro SRGP WMoo WPtf
	- 'Lambrook Gillian'	CFis EPPr SRGP WBrk
	- 'Lasting Impression'	EPPr SRGP
	- 'Laura Skelton'	CElw EBee
	- 'Little John'	EWes
	- 'Maid Marion'	EPPr EWes
	- 'Maurice Moka'	ECtt MAsh MTis NLar WCra
	- 'Miriam Rundle'	EPPr SRGP WCru WMoo WWEG
	- 'Moorland Jenny'	CElw WMoo
	- 'Moorland Star'	WMoo
	- 'Mrs Molly Kisby'	EBee
	- 'Music from Big Pink'	EBee EPPr EWes WCra
	- 'Pat Smallacombe'	EBee WMoo
	- 'Patricia Josephine'	WCAu
	- 'Pearl Boland'	EBee EPPr SRGP
	- 'Phantom'	EBee EPPr WCra
	- 'Phoebe Noble'	CBre CElw CPrp EBee EPPr LRHS MNrw NLar SRGP WMoo
	- 'Phoebe's Blush'	EPPr GCal GQue SRGP
	- 'Pink Cluster'	CLAP
	- 'Pink Lace'	LSou
§	- 'Prestbury Blush'	CElw EPPr NCot SRGP
	- 'Prestbury White'	see *G.* × *oxonianum* 'Prestbury Blush'
	- 'Raspberry Ice'	EBee EWes WCra
	- 'Rebecca Moss'	CPrp ECtt ELan EPPr GAbr GCra LRHS NSti SMrm SRGP WCra WCru WOut WPtf WWEG
	- 'Robin's Ginger Nut'	EBee EWes
	- 'Robin's Red Eye'	EPPr
	- 'Rose Clair'	CCon CNec ELan EPPr EPfP LRHS MBri MWhi NBir NLar SRGP WCra WCru WMnd WMoo WWEG
	- 'Rosenlicht'	CPrp EAEE EBee EPPr EWoo GKin LRHS MRav NLar SRGP WCra WCru WHoo WMnd WMoo WPtf XLum
	- 'Rothbury Sarah'	EBee
	- 'Sandy'	EWes
§	- 'Spring Fling' (v)	ECtt EWes LPla NWad SRGP
	- 'Stillingfleet Keira'	EBee NSti SRGP
	- 'Summer Surprise'	EPPr EWes WCra WCru
	- 'Susan'	EPPr EWes
	- 'Susie White'	EPPr SRGP WCru
§	- f. ***thurstonianum***	Widely available
	- - 'Armitageae'	EPPr SRGP
	- - 'Breckland Brownie'	CElw EBee EPPr EWes MAvo SRGP WCra
	- - 'Crûg Star'	WCru
	- - 'David McClintock'	EBee SRGP WMoo
	- - 'Red Sputnik'	EBee EPPr SRGP
	- - 'Sherwood'	CSde EPPr GCal GQue MSpe NBro NSti SRGP WCra WMoo
	- - 'Southcombe Double' (d)	CLAP CMos CNec CPla CWCL ECtt ELan EPPr GCra LSou SPer SPoG SRGP SRms WCra WCru WGwG WMoo WPtf WWEG
§	- - 'Southcombe Star'	EBee EPPr GAbr GCal NBro NGdn SRGP WCru WMoo WPtf WWEG
	- - 'Sue Cox'	EPPr NLar
	- - 'White Stripes'	EBee EPPr MAvo
	- 'Trevor's White'	CLAP EBee EPPr LLWP LRHS MNFA SRGP WCru
	- 'Wageningen' ♀H7	CBod CBre CNec EBee EPPr GCal LPla LRHS LSou MBri MNFA NDov

		NGdn NLar SEND SMrm SRGP SRms WCot WCra WCru WHoo WMoo
	– 'Walter's Gift'	CBod CNec ECtt EPPr EPla EPri EShb EWoo LLWP LRHS LSou MAvo MHer MRav MWhi NBir NBro NCGa NChi NDov NLar NPer WBrk WCra WCru WHoo WMoo WWtn
§	– 'Wargrave Pink'	Widely available
	– 'Waystrode'	EBee EPPr SRGP
	– 'Westacre White'	EPPr EWes WCra
	– 'Whitehaven'	SRGP
	– 'Whiter Shade of Pale'	EBee EPPr
	– 'Winscombe'	EPfP GCal SRGP WMoo WWEG
§	***palmatum*** ♀H4	Widely available
	palustre	EBee EPPr GLog MMuc MNrw NCot SRGP WCot WMoo WPtf
	'Pastel Clouds'	WFar
	Patricia = 'Brempat' ♀H7	Widely available
	peloponnesiacum	CElw EAEE EPPr EWes GQue LRHS MAsh MNFA NLar NOrc NWad SPoG WMoo WPtf
	'Perfect Storm'	CLAP CUse ECtt LLHF NLar
	phaeum	Widely available
	– from Ploeger	NCot
	– 'Acorn Bank'	EBee
	– 'Advendo'	EBee EPPr NCot
	– 'Album'	Widely available
	– 'Alec's Pink'	EBee EPPr LLWP NCot SHar WCra WPtf
	– 'All Saints'	EBee EPPr LEdu SRGP
	– 'Angelina'	EBee EPPr NCot WCra WPtf
	– 'Aureum'	see *G. phaeum* 'Golden Spring'
	– 'Basket of Lavender' **new**	EBee
	– 'Blauwvoet'	EPPr LBMP NChi NCot WPtf
	– 'Blue Shadow'	CElw CLAP EBee EPPr LEdu MAvo SRGP WPtf
	– 'Caborn Lilac'	LLWP
	– 'Calligrapher'	CElw EPPr LLHF NChi NCot SRGP WCra WMoo
	– 'Chocolate Chip'	EPPr NCot WPtf
	– 'Conny Broe' (v)	CLAP
	– 'Dark Angel' **new**	EBee
	– 'Dark Dream'	EBee
	– dark-flowered	NCot
	– 'David Bromley'	NCot WCru
	– 'David Martin'	EBee EPPr NCot
	– 'Enid'	EPPr
	– 'George Stone'	EPPr WPtf
	– 'Golden Samobor'	CElw EPPr
§	– 'Golden Spring'	EBee EPPr MAvo NCot NEoE SRGP WOut
	– 'Green Ghost'	EBee EPPr
	– 'Hector's Lavender'	EBee NCot SRGP WOut
	– var. ***hungaricum***	EBee EPPr SRGP WCra WPtf
	– 'James Haunch'	EPPr WCra
	– 'Judith's Blue'	EBee EPPr NChi NCot
	– 'Klepper'	EPPr GBin
§	– 'Lady in Mourning'	CExl EBee EPPr GCal LPla MNFA NChi SRGP SRms SWat WCru WMoo
	– 'Lavender Pinwheel'	CBod CMos CPrp EBee EPfP MBri MSpe MTis NCot SPer SPoG WHil WPtf
	– 'Lilacina'	ECha WPtf
	– 'Lily Lovell'	Widely available
	– 'Lisa' (v)	CLAP EPPr MAvo MNrw NCot SMHy WCot WCra
	– 'Little Boy'	EPPr
	– var. ***lividum***	CBre EPfP GMaP LLWP MRav NCot SRGP SRms WFar WPnP XLum
	– – 'Joan Baker'	CBre CFis CSam EBee EPPr LPla MNFA NChi NCot NGdn NSti SDys SRGP WCru WMoo WOut WPnP WWEG
	– – 'Majus'	EBee ECtt ELan EPPr EPfP EPyc LLWP LPla LRHS WFar WMoo
	– 'Lustige Witwe' (v) **new**	WCot
	– 'Maggie's Delight' (v)	SRGP
	– 'Marchant's Ghost'	IFro LPla MAvo NGdn SMHy
	– 'Margaret Wilson' (v)	CCon CDes CMos CUse CWGN EBee ECtt EPPr EWes GAbr GCal LBMP LEdu LRHS MAvo MNrw MSpe NGdn NLar NPCo NSti SPer SPoG SRGP WCot WMoo WPnP WPtf WSHC
	– 'Mierhausen'	EBee EPPr NCot WPtf
	– 'Mojito' (v)	WCot
	– 'Moorland Dylan'	WMoo WOut
	– 'Mottisfont Rose'	CLAP NCot SBch
	– 'Mourning Widow'	see *G. phaeum* 'Lady in Mourning'
	– 'Mrs Charles Perrin'	CElw CFis WPtf
	– 'Night Time'	EBee EPPr WPtf
	– 'Nightshade'	EBee EPPr
	– 'Our Pat' ♀H7	CDes CLAP EBee EPPr MAvo NChi WCot
	– var. ***phaeum***	WPtf
	– – 'Langthorns Blue'	CWCL EBee ELan EPPr EWes LEdu LRHS MNrw SRGP SWvt WCra
	– – 'Samobor'	Widely available
	– 'Phantom of the Opera' (v)	EBee EPPr NCot
I	– 'Ploeger de Bilt'	EBee EPPr
	– purple-flowered	NCot
	– 'Rachel's Rhapsody'	CElw EBee EPPr MAvo NCot SRGP WCra
	– 'Raven'	CLAP CMos EBee ECtt EPPr EWoo MAvo NChi NCot NLar WCra WPtf
	– 'Ray of Light'	EPPr
	– 'Rise Top Lilac'	EBee NCot WPGP WPtf
	– 'Robin's Angel Eyes'	EBee
	– 'Rose Air'	EPPr MAvo SRGP WMoo
	– 'Rose Madder'	CCon CElw CPrp EPPr EPyc GBuc GCal LEdu LLWP LPla MNrw NChi SPhx SRGP WCru WGwG WMoo
	– 'Rothbury Ruby' **new**	EBee EPPr
	– 'Saturn'	EPPr WPtf
	– 'Séricourt'	CDes WCot WCra
	– 'Shadowlight'	CBod ECtt EPPr NCot NLar NSti SPoG WCra WFar WPtf
	– 'Slatina'	EPPr WPtf
	– 'Springtime' PBR	CMos EBee EPPr LLHF MBNS MSpe NCot NGdn NLar WCra
	– 'Stillingfleet Ghost'	EBee EPPr LEdu MNrw NChi NCot NSti
	– 'Taff's Jester' (v)	LPla NHol SRGP WCot
	– 'Trevor's Recall'	EBee
	– 'Tyne Mist'	EPPr
§	– 'Variegatum' (v)	CBre CMac EBee EHoe ELan EPPr GMaP IFro MSpe NBir NBro NCot SGSe SRGP WCru WHer WMoo
	– 'Vintage Dave'	WOut
	– 'Walküre'	EPPr EWes EWoo NCot NLar
	'Philippe Vapelle'	Widely available
	'Pink Carpet'	NDov
	'Pink Delight'	CElw MNrw SBch
	'Pink Ghost'	WPtf
	'Pink Penny'	CBod CLAP EBee ECtt EPPr EPfP LRHS SRGP WCra WMoo WPtf

§ ***platyanthum***	EPPr MNrw MWhi SRGP WCru WPtf
- var. ***reinii***	LSun WCru
- 'Russian Giant'	EPPr
platypetalum misapplied	see *G.* × *magnificum*
platypetalum Franch.	see *G. sinense*
§ ***platypetalum*** Fisch. & C.A. Mey.	EBee EPPr LRHS NBir SRGP WCru XLum
- 'Dark Side of the Moon' **new**	EBee
- 'Genyell'	EBee EPPr WCra
- 'Georgia Blue'	WCru
- 'Turco'	EBee EPPr NLar WCra
§ ***pogonanthum***	CHid GLog NBir
polyanthes	EWes NChi
§ ***potentilloides***	GCal NBir SRGP WMoo
pratense	CArn CBre CHab CMac CNec CWld EBee ECtt ELan EPPr GJos GMaP MHer MLHP MNHC NCot NMir SCob SPer SPlb SPoG SRGP SRms SWat WCot WMoo WPnP WSFF WWEG XLum
- 'Akaton'	NLar
- 'Algera Double'	GBin
- 'Bittersweet'	EPPr
- Black Beauty = 'Nodbeauty'PBR	CAby CBcs CExl CSBt CWCL CWGN EBee ECtt EPfP EWes IPot LRHS MGos MPnt NCGa NLar NPri SMrm SPer SPoG SRkn SRot SWat WFar WHoo
- 'Blue Lagoon'	EBee EPPr MAsh WCra
* - 'Blue Skies'	LSou WFar
- 'Cluden Sapphire'	EBee EPPr GQue MWhi NEoE NHol WCru
§ - 'Double Jewel' (d)	CMos CWCL CWGN EBee EPfP IPot LLHF LRHS MAsh MAvo MBNS MBri NLar WBor WCra WFar WPtf
- 'Else Lacey' (d)	CDes EBee
- 'Flore Pleno'	see *G. pratense* 'Plenum Violaceum'
I - 'Himalayanum'	NLar
- 'Hocus Pocus'	CBod CWGN ECtt ELan EWoo LRHS MAsh MAvo MBNS MBri MSCN NBro NLar NSti SCob WCAu WCra
- 'Ilja'	EBee
- 'Janet's Special'	WHoo
- 'Midnight Blues'	CMos CWGN EBee GBin MAsh NCGa NSti SMrm WCra
- Midnight Reiter strain	CBct CExl CSpe CWGN ECtt ELan GBuc IBoy IFoB LRHS MAvo MBel MLHP NBro NChi NGdn NLar NSbr SDys SGSe SPhx SWat SWvt WCra WCru WFar
- 'Milk Cow Blues'	EBee
- 'Mrs Kendall Clark' ♀H7	Widely available
- 'New Dimension'	CBcs CBod CUse EBee ELan MAsh MBri NSti WHoo
- 'Okey Dokey'	EBee
- 'Pink Splash'	CBcs EPPr LSou WMoo WPtf
- 'Plenum Caeruleum' (d)	CMHG ECtt EPPr GCra MRav NBid NEgg NLar SWat WSHC
§ - 'Plenum Violaceum' (d) ♀H7	Widely available
- var. ***pratense*** f. ***albiflorum***	CElw CSam EPPr EPfP EWoo GCra GMaP IFro LRHS MLHP MNrw NBid NOrc SGbt SMrm SPer WMnd WMoo WPtf
- - - 'Galactic'	CBod CLAP CMea ECtt EPPr LSun MHol NBir NCot NLar NPCo SPhx WCot WCra WCru WMoo WPGP WPnP
- - - 'Laura'PBR (d)	CBod CExl EBee EPfP EWes LSou NSti SCob SKHP WCra
- - - 'Plenum Album' (d)	CDes CLAP CUse EBee ECtt ELan EPPr EPfP EWes GBin LLHF LRHS MBel MNrw MRav NEgg NGdn NLar SGbt SPer SPoG SWvt WBor WCot WCra WFar WPnP WWEG
- - - 'Silver Queen'	CAby CNec EBee ECtt EPPr GQue LRHS LSou NBir NCGa SRGP WCra WGwG WMoo WPGP
- 'Purple Heron'	CDes
* - 'Purple-haze'	CPla CTca WMoo WTou
- 'Rectum Album'	see *G. clarkei* 'Kashmir White'
- 'Robin's Grey Beard'	EBee
§ - 'Rose Queen'	EPPr NBir SGbt SRGP WCru
- 'Roseum'	see *G. pratense* 'Rose Queen'
- 'Splish-splash'	see *G. pratense* 'Striatum'
- 'Stanton Mill'	NBid
- var. ***stewartianum***	LRHS MRav
- - 'Elizabeth Yeo'	CAby CBod CLAP CNec ECtt EPPr EWoo MAsh NCGa NLar NWad SPoG WCra WCru
- - 'Raina'	EBee
§ - 'Striatum'	Widely available
- 'Striatum' dwarf	WCru
- variegated, white-flowered (v)	WCot
§ - Victor Reiter Junior strain	CSpe ELan LEdu MLHP MMHG MNFA NBir NGdn SPoG SRot WCot
- 'Wisley Blue'	EPPr SRGP WCra WHal
- 'Yorkshire Queen'	EBee EPPr NGdn NSti WCru WPtf
'Prelude'	CBre CElw EBee ELon EPPr NBir NCot NEoE NLar SRGP WPtf
procurrens	CBre CElw CTri EPPr GAbr GCal GCra WBor WBrk WCru WMoo WPtf
§ ***psilostemon*** ♀H7	Widely available
- 'Bressingham Flair'	CCon CKno CLAP EPfP GBuc GCra LRHS MRav NBid NChi NLar SRms WCra WCru WFar WMoo WPnP
- 'Coton Goliath'	EPPr EWes NCot
- 'Jason Bloom'	EPPr LRHS
- 'Madelon'	CElw MAvo NCot NLar
- 'Moorland Jack'	WMoo
'Midnight Star'	EWes WFar
pulchrum	CFil CSpe EBee EWes SRGP WPGP
punctatum hort.	see *G.* × *monacense* var. *monacense* 'Muldoon'
- 'Variegatum'	see *G. phaeum* 'Variegatum'
'Purple Rain'	EBee EPPr
pylzowianum	NBid NRya SBch WMoo
pyrenaicum	GAbr NCot NSti WTou
- f. ***albiflorum***	EPPr GAbr IFro MNrw NBir SRGP WBrk WCot WCra WFar WTou
- 'Barney Brighteye'	SRGP
- 'Bill Wallis'	Widely available
- 'Bright Eyes'	LLWP NCot
- 'Isparta'	EPPr IFro LPla MNrw NCot SHar SPhx SRGP WBrk WTou
- 'Summer Sky'	CBod GBin SPav SRGP
- 'Summer Snow'	CBod CCon
'Rainbow'PBR	EWoo MBNS WCra
Rambling Robin Group	CSpe ECre EHoe EPri EWes LLHF
'Ray's Pink'	CPla
rectum	EPPr NBre NLar WCru
- 'Album'	see *G. clarkei* 'Kashmir White'

	Name	Suppliers
	'Red Admiral'	CNec ECtt EPPr GBin GBuc GCal LAst MAvo MCot MWhi NCot NLar NSti SRGP WCot WCra WFar WGwG WHoo WPtf
	'Red Propellers'	CElw
	reflexum	CFis EPPr EPfP LRHS WCru
	- 'Katara Pass'	EPPr
	refractoides	WCot
	refractum	CExl
	regelii	EPPr WCru WMoo WPtf
	renardii ♀[H5]	Widely available
	- 'Beldo'	MAvo
	- blue-flowered	see *G. renardii* 'Whiteknights'
	- 'Rothbury Hills'	EBee EPPr
	- 'Sarah Comish'	EBee
	- 'Tcschelda'	CBod CMHG EAEE ECha ECtt EPPr EShb GBuc NBir NLar SMrm SRms WCra WMoo WPtf
§	- 'Whiteknights'	EBee NBir WCru
	- 'Zetterlund'	CBod CFis CMos EAEE EBee ELan EPPr EPfP EPri EWTr LRHS NEgg NSoo NSti WCra WMnd WMoo WPtf
§	***reuteri***	CHid CPla NLos SRGP WCru WOut
	'Richard Nutt'	EBee
	richardsonii	CBod CSpe EBee EPPr GCal LRHS MCot NBir NDov NWad SRGP WCra WCru WPtf
	- pink-flowered	MAvo
	- white-flowered	NChi
	× ***riversleaianum*** 'Russell Prichard' ♀[H4]	Widely available
§	***rivulare***	GLog NLar
	robertianum	CArn ENfk EPPr LLHF MHer SRms WSFF
§	- 'Album'	CBod EPPr SHar SRGP SRms WHer
	- f. ***bernettii***	see *G. robertianum* 'Album'
	- 'Celtic White'	CBre EPPr GCal IFro MMuc SEND SPav SRGP
	robustum	EPri MGos NBir NBro SKHP SPav SPlb SRGP WHrl WKif
	'Rosetta'[PBR]	CUse GBin NCGa NDov NLar
	'Rosie Crûg'	SWvt
	rosthornii	WCru
	'Rothbury Red'	EBee NChi SBch
§	Rozanne = 'Gerwat'[PBR] ♀[H7]	Widely available
	rubescens	see *G. yeoi*
	rubifolium	WCru
	ruprechtii (Grossh.) Woronow	EPPr MNrw SRGP
	Sabani Blue = 'Bremigo'[PBR]	CAbP CBod CLAP CMac CSpe EBee ECtt EPPr EWes EWoo LPla MHol NLar NSti SMHy SPer WCot WCra WSHC
	'Salome'	CAby CBcs CBod CLAP CMos EBee ECtt ELan GAbr LBMP MCot NBir NSti SMrm SPoG SRms SRot SWat SWvt WCot WCra WGwG WHoo WMoo WPnP WWEG
	'Sandrine'[PBR]	CBcs CLAP CWCL CWGN EBee EPfP GBin IMou IPot LLHF LRHS LSou MHol MNrw NDov NPCo NPri NSti SGol SMrm SPoG SRms WCot WCra WHil WPnP
	sanguineum	Widely available
	- Alan Bloom = 'Bloger'[PBR]	EBee EPPr LRHS WCra
	- 'Album'	Widely available
	- 'Alpenglow'	EBee EPPr SRGP WBrk WCra
	- 'Ankum's Pride' ♀[H7]	CElw EPPr EPfP EPla EWoo LRHS LSou MNFA MTis NCGa NDov NGdn NHar NLar NSti SBch SRGP SWat WBrk WCra WCru WMoo WPnP WPtf
	- 'Apfelblüte'	ELon EPPr GJos IPot NLar WCAu WCra
	- 'Aviemore' ♀[H7]	CElw CFis EPPr GCal
	- 'Barnsley'	CElw CPrp EPPr NBro NEoE WCra WHrl
	- 'Belle of Herterton'	CElw EPPr MAvo NBid NEoE WBrk WCra WCru
	- 'Bloody Graham'	EPPr LRHS MAvo MNFA WBrk WCra WMoo
	- 'Canon Miles'	CElw ECtt EPPr IPot LRHS NLar SRGP. SRms WCra
	- 'Catforth Carnival'	EBee EPPr MAvo
	- 'Cedric Morris'	CElw ECha ELon EPPr GCra MAvo MNFA NBid SBch SRGP WBrk WCra WCru
	- 'Compactum'	WCra WMoo XLum
	- 'Connie Hansen' **new**	WCra
§	- 'Droplet'	SRGP
	- 'Elsbeth'	CElw CNec CPrp EBee ECha ECtt ELan EPPr EPla EWes GCal LRHS MSpe NGdn NLar SMrm SPoG SRGP WBrk WCra WCru WFar WHal WMoo WPnP WWEG XLum
	- 'Feu d'Automne'	EBee EPPr WCra
	- 'Fran's Star'	see *G.* × *oxonianum* 'Fran's Star'
	- 'Glenluce'	CElw CUse ECtt EPPr EPfP EPla EShb GBuc GCal LRHS MRav MSpe NChi NDov NLar NOrc NWad SRGP SRms SWat WBrk WCra WHal WMnd
	- 'Hampshire Purple'	see *G. sanguineum* 'New Hampshire Purple'
	- 'Holden'	CElw EBee EPPr WBrk
	- 'Inverness'	EBee EPPr XLum
	- 'Joanna'	CFis MAvo WCra
	- 'John Elsley'	CPrp EAEE EBee ECtt EHoe EPPr LAst LLWP LRHS LSou MAsh MNFA MSpe MWhi NBro NGdn SRGP SWat WCra WMnd WPnP
	- 'John Innes'	EPPr
	- 'Jubilee Pink'	GCal WCru
	- 'Kristin Jacob'	EPPr
	- var. ***lancastrense***	see *G. sanguineum* var. *striatum*
	- 'Leeds Variety'	see *G. sanguineum* 'Rod Leeds'
§	- 'Little Bead' ♀[H5]	ECho NWad WBrk WCra XLum
	- 'Max Frei'	Widely available
	- 'Minutum'	see *G. sanguineum* 'Droplet'
	- 'Nanum'	see *G. sanguineum* 'Little Bead'
§	- 'New Hampshire Purple'	CLAP CPrp EBee ECtt EPPr EPfP GLog IPot LAst LRHS MAvo MNFA NBro NGdn NLar NSti WCra
	- 'Nyewood'	CNec EAEE EBee ECGP ECtt EPPr EPla EWll LRHS MSpe SEND SRGP WBrk WCra WCru
I	- 'Plenum' (d)	EPPr
	- 'Prado'	XLum
	- var. ***prostratum*** (Cav.) Pers.	see *G. sanguineum* var. *striatum*
	- 'Purple Flame'	see *G. sanguineum* 'New Hampshire Purple'
§	- 'Rod Leeds'	CFis CLAP EBee MNFA SRGP WFar
	- 'Sara'	MAvo
§	- 'Shepherd's Delight'	EPPr

– 'Shepherd's Warning' misapplied	see *G. sanguineum* 'Shepherd's Delight'
– 'Shepherd's Warning' 🏆[H7]	CTri ECtt GCal MMuc NBir NLar SEND SRGP SWat WCru WHoo WIce
– 'Shooting Star'	NCot
– 'South Nutfield'	CElw
§ – var. ***striatum*** 🏆[H5]	Widely available
– – deep pink-flowered	CSBt MSwo SWvt
– – 'Mottisfont'	SBch
– – 'Reginald Farrer'	WCru
– – 'Splendens' 🏆[H7]	EBee EPPr EPot GCal LRHS NBid NCot WCru
– 'Tirol'	EBee
– 'Vision Light Pink'	CBod CNec EPPr WCra
– 'Vision Violet'	CBod CNec CSpe EBee EPPr IFoB LSqH MAvo MSpe SWvt WBrk WCra XLum
– 'Westacre Poppet'	EWes WCra
'Sanne'	CBod CUse EPPr EWoo MBri MHol NLar SMrm STPC WCot WCra WPGP
saxatile	EBee EPPr
'Scapa Flow'	EBee EPPr GCal MAvo WHea
schlechteri	EWes WKif
I ***sessiliflorum*** subsp. ***novae-zelandiae*** 'Nigricans'	CFis ECha ECho ELan GAbr GKev MHer SBch SRGP WFar
§ – – 'Porters Pass'	CUse ECho EHoe EWes SBch SPlb WFar WHoo
– – red-leaved	see *G. sessiliflorum* subsp. *novae-zelandiae* 'Porters Pass'
shikokianum	EBee NLar SRGP WCra WHrl
– var. ***kaimontanum***	WCru
– var. ***quelpaertense***	CDes CFis EBee MAvo WPtf
– – 'Crûg's Cloak'	WCru
– var. ***yoshiianum*** B&SWJ 6147	WCru
'Shocking Blue'	EPPr NLar NSti WCra
'Shouting Star'	see *G.* 'Kanahitobanawa'
'Silva'	CElw ECtt EPPr MNFA MRav SWat WCru
* 'Silver Shadow'	SPhx
'Simonside' **new**	EBee
§ ***sinense***	CCon CExl ECtt GBuc GCal LRHS MCot MNrw NGdn SRGP WCra WGwG XLum
'Sirak' 🏆[H7]	Widely available
soboliferum	ELan EPPr NBir NLar SPer SRGP WCra WCru WMoo WPtf
– Cally strain	CDes EBee EPPr GCal MAvo
– var. ***kiusianum***	CElw
– 'Rothbury Star' **new**	EBee
– 'Starman'	CBod CMea CMos CUse EBee ECtt EPPr EPfP EWoo MBri MSwo NCGa NLar SKHP STPC WCra WMoo
'Solitaire'	CDes CFil EBee WCot
'Southcombe Star'	see *G.* × *oxonianum* f. *thurstonianum* 'Southcombe Star'
'Southease Celestial'	SMHy
'Spinners'	CAby CElw CHid CMac CSam CWCL EBee ECtt EPPr EPfP EPla GCal GMaP LRHS MAvo MNFA MRav MWhi NBid NBir NGdn NLar NSti SMrm SPer SWat WCra WCru WMnd WMoo
stapfianum var. ***roseum***	see *G. orientalitibeticum*
'Stephanie'	CDes CElw CNec EPPr EPfP EPla EWes GBuc LRHS MAsh MAvo MBNS MNFA MNrw MRav MSpe NChi NCot NGdn NLar NSti WCAu WCra WPnP WPtf
'Storm Chaser'	CBod CLAP CSpe EBee GBin LBMP LRHS NSti
'Strawberry Frost'	LLHF
subcaulescens 🏆[H4]	Widely available
– 'Giuseppii' 🏆[H5]	CExl EAEE ECtt ELon EPot GAbr GBuc LRHS LSou MHer MRav NPri SMrm SRGP SRot SWvt WCra
– 'Splendens' 🏆[H5]	CSpe CTri EAEE ECtt EPPr GBuc GCrg LAst LRHS LSou MAsh MHer NEgg NPri NSla SRms SWat WCra WFar WGwG
'Sue Crûg'	EBee ECtt ELan EPfP GCra LAst LLWP LRHS LSou MNFA MWhi NEgg NSti SBch SPer SRGP WCra WCru WMoo
'Sue's Sister'	WCru
'Summer Cloud'	EPPr MNFA SRGP WOut
Summer Skies = 'Gernic'[PBR] (d)	Widely available
suzukii B&SWJ 016	CExl WCru
'Sweet Heidy'[PBR]	CBod EBee ECtt EPPr EPfP LBMP LLHF MSwo NLar NSti SPoG WBor WCAu WCra WFar
sylvaticum	NBid NGdn WFar WMoo WShi
– 'Afrodite'	EPPr
– f. ***albiflorum***	CBre ELan EWoo NSti WCru
– – 'Cyril's Superb White'	EBee
– 'Album' 🏆[H7]	Widely available
– 'Amanda'	EBee EPPr
– 'Amy Doncaster'	Widely available
– 'Angulatum'	CElw EPPr MNFA WMoo WPtf
– 'Birch Lilac'	CElw CLAP EBee EPPr EPri GBuc GCal LRHS NLar WCAu WCra WMoo
– 'Caeruleum'	GCal
– 'Coquetdale Lilac'	EBee EPPr
– 'Greek Fire'	EBee EPPr
– 'Ice Blue'	EBee EPPr MNFA NChi
– 'Immaculée'	EPPr MRav
– 'Kanzlersgrund'	CElw EPPr
– 'Lilac Time'	EPPr
– 'Mayflower' 🏆[H7]	Widely available
– 'Meran'	EPPr
– 'Mrs Connie Wilson' **new**	EBee EPPr
– 'Nikita'	CLAP EPPr
– f. ***roseum***	CFis EPPr NLar WPtf
– – 'Baker's Pink'	CLAP EBee EPPr GCra MNFA MNrw MRav NBir SBch SRGP WCru WMoo WPtf
– subsp. ***sylvaticum*** var. ***wanneri***	EPPr WCru
§ 'Tanya Rendall'[PBR]	CMHG CSam CUse EBee ECtt ELan ELon EPPr GBin IPot LRHS MBri MHol NDov NLar SPer SRms WCot WCra WFar WPnP
'Terre Franche'	EPPr NLar WCra WWEG
§ ***thunbergii***	CCon CHid EWes EWll LSou NLar SRGP WMoo WPnP XLum
– 'Jester's Jacket' (v)	CPla EPPr LRHS MGos MLHP MNrw SRGP WFar WMoo WOut
– pink-flowered	SRGP
– white-flowered	EPPr SRGP
thurstonianum	see *G.* × *oxonianum* f. *thurstonianum*
'Tinpenny Mauve'	MAvo WCra WHoo

'Tiny Monster'	CFis CMos CNec CUse EAJP EBee ECtt EPPr EWes GBin GQue IBoy IKil LPla MAvo MNFA MNrw MTis MWhi NDov NGdn NLar NSti SPhx SPoG WCra WPtf XLum
transbaicalicum	CFis EPPr XLum
traversii var. ***elegans***	ECho LRHS
tuberosum	CElw CHid ECha ECho ELan EPfP IMou MRav NBir NBro NCot NGdn NSbr SKHP SPhx WCra
- subsp. ***linearifolium***	EPPr
- pink-flowered	IFro
- 'Richard Hobbs'	EPPr
'Ushguli Grijs'	see *G. ibericum* Cav. 'Ushguli Grijs'
'Verguld Saffier'PBR	see *G.* Blue Sunrise
versicolor	CMac CMea EBee EPPr EPfP EPla GAbr MBri MHer MMuc NCot NLar SEND SRms WCra WHea WMoo
- 'Kingston'	see *G.* × *oxonianum* 'Kingston'
§ - 'Snow White'	EPPr MNrw SRGP WCru WMoo
- 'White Lady'	see *G. versicolor* 'Snow White'
'Victor Reiter'	see *G. pratense* Victor Reiter Junior strain
violareum	see *Pelargonium* 'Splendide'
viscosissimum	SRGP WMnd
wallichianum	CFis CMac CPou EBee IFro NBir NChi NSti WMoo
§ - 'Buxton's Variety'	Widely available
- 'Chris'	EWes SRGP
- 'Crystal Lake'PBR	CHel CWGN EBee ECtt EPfP EWoo IPot LAst MAvo MBNS NBir NSti SCob SMrm WCra WFar WHil WPtf
- 'Havana Blues'	CBod CUse EBee EWoo GBin LRHS MAvo MBri MHol MTis NSti STPC WCot WCra WFar WPtf
- magenta-flowered	GBuc
- pale blue-flowered	CElw
- 'Pink Buxton'	EWes NLar
- pink-flowered	CLAP GBuc GCal WCru
- 'Rise and Shine'PBR	EBee EWoo STPC
- 'Rosetta'	IMou
- 'Rosie'	SRGP
- 'Syabru'	CMea MNrw SMHy WMoo
- 'Sylvia's Surprise'PBR	CLAP IMou SCob
'Wednesday's Child'	WFar
'White Doves' **new**	NDov
wilfordii misapplied	see *G. thunbergii*
Wisley hybrid	see *G.* 'Khan'
wlassovianum	Widely available
- 'Blue Star'	MRav NEoE SRGP WFar
§ ***yeoi***	CSpe NBir NBro NSti SEND SRGP WCru WOut
yesoense	EBee IFro NBir NSti SRGP
- var. ***nipponicum***	WCru
yoshinoi misapplied	see *G. thunbergii*
yunnanense misapplied	see *G. pogonanthum*
yunnanense ambig.	CCon

Gerbera (*Asteraceae*)

(Everlast Series) Everlast Carmine = 'Amgerbcar'	ELon EUJe LSou MBNS
- Everlast Honey	MBNS
- Everlast Pink = 'Amgerbpink'	LSou MBNS
- Everlast Yellow	LSou
(Garvinea Series) 'Fleurie'PBR	LAst LRHS MBNS WHil
- Garvinea Crista = 'Garcrista'PBR **new**	LRHS
- Garvinea Cindy = 'Garcindy'PBR **new**	LSou
- Garvinea Jilly	LRHS SPoG
- Garvinea Lisa = 'Garlisa'PBR	WHlf
- Garvinea Nikki = 'Garnikki'PBR **new**	LRHS SPoG
- Garvinea Orangina = 'Orangina'PBR	LAst LRHS WHlf
- Garvinea Pam = 'Pam'PBR	LRHS SPoG
- Garvinea Rachel = 'Garrachel'PBR	MHol MNrw MPie WCot WHlf
- Garvinea Sunny	see *G.* 'Sunny'
- Garvinea Sylvana = 'Garsylvana'PBR	CAbP MHol MPie WCot
- Garvinea Valerie = 'Garvalerie'	LRHS WHlf
- Garvinea Vivian = 'Garvivian' **new**	LRHS
'Spider Lemon' **new**	WHlf
'Spider Orange' **new**	WHlf
'Spider Pink' **new**	WHlf
'Spider Red' **new**	WHlf
'Spider Salmon' **new**	WHlf
§ 'Sunny'PBR (Garvinea Series)	LRHS SPoG WHlf

Gesneria (*Gesneriaceae*)

cardinalis	see *Sinningia cardinalis*

Gethyllis (*Amaryllidaceae*)

afra 'Paarl'	ECho
barkerae	ECho
- 'Nardouwsberg'	ECho
- subsp. ***paucifolius***	ECho
britteniana 'Rietputs'	ECho
ciliaris	ECho
- 'Porterville'	ECho
grandiflora	ECho
gregoriana	ECho
hallii 'Komiesberg'	ECho
linearis 'Piketburg'	ECho
oligophylla 'Moedverloor'	ECho
transkarooica 'Waboomsberg'	ECho
verticillata	ECho
- 'Pikenierskloof'	ECho
villosa	ECho

Gethyum (*Alliaceae*)

atropurpureum	WCot

Geum ✿ (*Rosaceae*)

'Abendsonne'	CDes CElw EBee MAvo MHer MSpe NEoE WOut WWEG
'Alabama Slammer' (Cocktails Series) **new**	GBin SCob
alpinum	see *G. montanum*
'Apricot Beauty'	CWCL
'Apricot Delight'	LLHF NEoE
'Bachelfe' **new**	SBri
'Beech House Apricot'	CElw CLAP CTal EAJP ECtt EPri GCra LRHS MAvo MLHP MNFA MNrw MRav NChi NEoE NHol SBri SPoG WMoo WPnP WWEG
'Bell Bank'	Widely available
'Birkhead's Creamy Lemon'	CElw EBee NBir
'Blazing Sunset' (d)	Widely available
'Blood Orange'	MAvo NEoE

'Borisii'	Widely available
'Bremner's Gold'	NEoE SBri
'Bremner's Nectarine'	CElw MNrw MSpe NChi NEoE SHar WWEG
'Broomrigg Beauty'	NEoE
'Brown Sugar' **new**	NEoE
bulgaricum	CElw EBee MRav NBir NEoE NLar NRya WWEG XLum
'Butterscotch'	EBee
calthifolium	EPPr NBro
'Cantamos' **new**	NEoE
capense	CTal NBre NEoE SPlb
'Carlotta' **new**	WWEG
'Cherry Bomb' **new**	NEoE
§ ***chiloense***	LEdu
- 'Farncombe'	NCot
- 'Red Dragon'	CBre CWCL ELon LLHF MMuc SEND SGSe SWvt WOut WWEG
'Chipchase'	CElw MAvo NChi NEoE SHar WHoo WWEG
coccineum misapplied	see *G. chiloense*
coccineum ambig.	NCGa
coccineum Sibth. & Sm.	GLog
- 'Ann'	EPri MSpe
- 'Cooky'	CElw EAJP EPfP GJos LBMP LRHS LSqH MMuc NEoE NGBl NLar SBri SHil SPhx SPoG SRms SWvt WFar WRHF WWEG
- 'Eos'	CDes CElw CSpe CWCL EBee ECtt ELon EPPr EWes GAbr GQue LEdu MAsh MAvo MBri MHol MNrw MPnt MRav MSpe NEoE NGdn NLar NPri SPoG SRms WGwG WHrl WMoo WWEG
- 'Koi'	EBee NEoE NPri SPad WMoo
- 'Queen of Orange'	CBod CBre CElw GBin GJos LAst NEoE SRms SRot
- 'Werner Arends'	CElw CMHG GAbr GCal LRHS MAvo MBri MNrw MRav SBri WFar WMoo WWEG
'Copper Pennies'	CElw NEoE WWEG
'Coppertone'	CElw CLAP CPla CWCL ELan EPri LSun MRav NBir NBro NCGa NChi NRya XEll
'Cotton Candy'	NEoE WWEG
'Country Rock Star'	NEoE
'Cream Crackers'	NEoE
'Cumbrian Candy' **new**	NEoE
'Cumbrian Cheddar' **new**	NEoE
'Cumbrian Cream' **new**	NEoE
'Custard Pie'	NEoE WWEG
'Custard Tart' **new**	NEoE
'Dawn'	NEoE SBri WWEG
'Deano's Delight'	NEoE WWEG
'Diamond White' **new**	WWEG
'Diana'	MAvo MNrw NEoE NLar WWEG
'Dingle Apricot'	CElw ECtt GAbr GBin MNrw MRav NBir SBri WWEG
'Dolly North' (d)	CCon CElw EBee EPyc EWoo GAbr MArl MCot MNrw MRav MSpe MTis NBro NGdn SHar WCAu WHal WWEG
'Double Sunrise' (d) **new**	MAsh
'Dusky Yellow' **new**	WWEG
'East of Eden' **new**	NEoE
'Eden Valley Angel'	NEoE WWEG
'Eden Valley Elf' **new**	NEoE
'El Wano'	NEoE
'Elworthy Amber'	CElw WOut
'Emory Quinn'	NEoE WWEG
'Fancy Frills'	CElw ECtt MAvo WHoo WWEG
'Farmer John Cross'	CAby CBre CElw CLAP EBee ECtt ELon EPri GJos LPla MAvo MNrw MSpe MTis NCGa NCot NLar SBri WHal WMoo WOut WWEG WWtn
fauriei × ***kamtschatica***	EBee
'Feuermeer'	CElw MAvo NEoE NLar
'Fire Opal' (d) ♀H7	CDes CElw CWCL EAJP LPla MAvo MNrw NBir NEoE SBri WMoo WWEG
'Fire Storm'	CMea CMos CWGN ECtt GAbr GBin IKil MAvo MBel MNrw MPnt MTis NLar NPCo WCot
'Fireball'	ECtt EShb LRHS LSou MAsh NLar
'Flame'	NEoE SBri WWEG
'Flames of Passion' PBR	Widely available
'Flower of Darkness' **new**	NEoE
'Fresh Woods'	WWEG
'Georgeham'	CPla
'Georgenberg'	Widely available
'Glencoe'	CElw
'Golden Joy'	LLHF MAvo WHoo WWEG
'Hannay's'	MAvo MNrw MSpe NEoE SBri SHar SPtp WWEG
'Harvest Moon' **new**	NEoE
'Herterton Lemon' **new**	CElw
'Herterton Primrose'	CCon CDes CElw CLAP CWCL ECtt EPPr GBuc GCal LLHF LLWG MAvo MSpe NCGa NSti SBri SBrt WHal WHoo WOut WWEG
'Hilltop Beacon' (d)	CElw LLHF MAvo NEoE SBri WHoo WPnn
* ***hybridum luteum***	NSti SBri
× ***intermedium***	CBre EPPr MAvo NEoE NGdn NLar SBri WMoo WWEG
- 'Diane'	MSpe NChi SBri
- 'Hofrennydd'	NWad
'Jolly Roger'	EBee NEoE NWad WWEG
'Karlskaer'	CBod CCon CElw CWCL ECtt EPri EWes EWoo GBin GBuc GQue LRHS LSun MBel MCot MNrw MSpe NGdn NLar SBri SMrm SPtp WCAu WFar WGwG WMoo WPtf WWEG WWtn
'Kath Inman'	SBri WWEG
'Lady Stratheden' (d) ♀H7	Widely available
'Lemon Delight'	CDes CElw
'Lemon Drops'	Widely available
'Lionel Cox'	CElw CPla CPrp CWCL ECtt ELan EPPr GCal GCra GMaP LAst LBMP MBNS MCot MNFA MRav NBir NBro NChi NGdn NLar SRGP SRms WFar WWEG
'Lipstick Sunset'	NEoE
'Lisanne'	CElw CSam IPot MAsh MAvo MHer MSpe NCGa NDov SBri SMHy SPtp WWEG
'Little Lottie'	NEoE
'Little Twister'	NEoE WWEG
macrophyllum	EBee
'Maddy Prior' **new**	NEoE
magellanicum	EWes NBre NLar SBri
'Magic Toybox'	NEoE WWEG
'Mai Tai'	CBod CElw CMos CWCL EBee ECtt EWes GBin IBoy LBuc LLHF MAvo MTis NEoE NLar SPad WCAu WWEG

	'Mandarin' (d)	CCse CDes GAbr GCal SBri
	'Mango'	NDov
	'Mango Lassi'	GBin NEoE WCAu
	'Marmalade'	ECtt EPri GAbr GJos LLWG MAvo MNrw MRav MSpe NCGa NEoE NLar SMHy WCAu WFar WHrl WKif WMoo WOut WWEG
	'McClure's Magic'	NEoE
§	***montanum*** ♀H5	EBee ECho EDAr GBin GCra GLog LRHS MMuc NBir NBro NPri NRya NSla SEND SRms WWEG XLum
	'Moonlight Serenade'	EBee MAvo NEoE WWEG
	'Moorland Sorbet'	NEoE SBri WMoo WWEG
	'Morning Sun' **new**	SBri
	'Mrs J. Bradshaw' (d) ♀H7	Widely available
	'Mrs W. Moore'	CBre CDes CElw CLAP CWCL EBee ECtt EPPr EShb GAbr GJos MHer MNrw MRav MSpe NBir NChi NEoE NLar NSbr SBri SRGP WHoo WMoo WWEG
	'Nordek'	CBod CElw CMos ECtt GAbr GBuc GCal GQue LAst LRHS MNFA MNrw MRav NEgg SBri SPoG WWEG
	'Norwell Yellow Lamp'	MAvo
	'Octavie'	SBri WWEG
	'Orangeman'	MNrw
	parviflorum	NBre NBro
	'Peachy Proud'	NEoE WWEG
	'Pear Drops'	NEoE
	pentapetalum	see *Sieversia pentapetala*
	'Pink Frills'	CAby CElw CWCL ECtt EPPr EPri EWes GAbr GBin GBuc GQue LLWG LPla MAvo MPnt MRav MSpe MTis NCGa NLar SGbt SMHy SPtp WCAu WWEG
	'Poco'	EBee MAvo NEoE
	'Pomelos'	SBri
	'Present'	ECtt NBre NCGa NChi NEoE SBri WWEG
	'Primrose'	GAbr GJos GQue NEoE NGdn NLar SBri
	'Primrose Cottage' **new**	EBee
	'Prince of Orange' (d)	CElw GAbr LRHS MNrw MRav NBre NHol SBri WFar WHrl WWEG
	'Prinses Juliana'	Widely available
	pyrenaicum	EBee NBre NCGa
	quellyon	see *G. chiloense*
I	'Rearsby Hybrid'	CElw LLHF MRav NEoE SPlb WHoo WWEG
	'Red Wings' (d)	EPPr GBin GBuc GCal GMaP GQue LRHS MCot MRav NBir NCGa NSoo SBri SHar SMHy WGwG WWEG
§	***reptans***	GBin
	rhodopeum	EBee
	'Rijnstroom'	EPPr MNrw SBri SHar WCAu
	rivale	CArn CBAq CBen CHab CWld EHon EPfP MCot MHer MHol MMuc MNHC MWts NBro NMir NPer SPlb SRms SWat WFar WMAq WMoo WOut WWEG
	- 'Album'	Widely available
	- 'Apricot'	SBri
	- 'Barbra Lawton'	MSpe SBri WWEG
	- 'Cream Drop'	CElw GJos LLWG MCot MSpe NCGa NChi NEoE SBri SHar SMrm WWEG
	- 'Elfenbein' **new**	WWEG
	- subsp. ***islandicum***	SBrt
	- 'Leonard's Double' (d)	WWEG
	- 'Leonard's Variety'	Widely available
	- 'Marika'	CAby CHid EBee EPri NCGa SMrm SRGP WMoo WWEG WWtn
	- 'Marmalade'	CAby CBre CElw CWCL EBee IPot MPnt NChi NEoE SBri WPtf WWEG
	- 'Snowflake'	CElw GJos MAvo MSpe NChi NEoE WWEG
	'Rubin'	EBee ECtt EPPr EPyc GCra IPot NBro NDov SBri WCAu
	'Rusty Young'	NEoE
	'Savanna Sunset'	NEoE WWEG
	'Sigiswang'	CElw EWes GJos MNrw MRav NEoE SBri SMrm WCAu WWEG
	'Spider Muffin'	NEoE WWEG
	'Stacey's Sunrise'	MAvo NEoE SBri
	'Star of Bethlehem'	NEoE WWEG
I	'Starker's Magnificum'	WCot WWEG
	'Strawberries and Cream'	NEoE
	'Sundrud Star'	NEoE
	'Sunrise' (d)	EDAr LRHS SHil
	'Sweet Angel Dar'	NEoE WWEG
	'Tangerine'	EPri GJos MRav MSpe NEoE WWEG
	'Tango Dream'	NEoE WWEG
	'Tequila Sunrise'	ECtt MTis SCob
	'Tinkerbell'	NEoE
	'Tinpenny Orange'	CElw NEoE WHoo WWEG
	× ***tirolense***	EBee NBre NCGa NEoE
	'Totally Tangerine'PBR	CSpe CWCL EBee ECtt EPfP EWTr GBin LBuc LRHS LSou MBri MCot MTis SCob SDys SHar SHil SPoG WCAu
	'Trevor's Lemon'	MAvo
	triflorum	CElw EShb EWes GEdr LEdu MHer MNrw WOut
	- var. ***campanulatum***	CCon GJos NEoE WWEG
	'Turbango'	NEoE
	'Turnpike Troubadour'	NEoE
	urbanum	CArn ENfk GJos SWat WHer WHfH WMoo
	'Wallace's Peach'	WWEG

Gevuina (*Proteaceae*)

avellana	CBcs CHEx WPGP

Gilia ✿ (*Polemoniaceae*)

achilleifolia	SPhx
tricolor	NPol

Gillenia (*Rosaceae*)

stipulata	CLAP GBin LEdu MNrw SHar SPhx
trifoliata ♀H7	Widely available
- 'Pink Profusion'	STPC

Ginkgo (*Ginkgoaceae*)

	biloba	Widely available
	- B&SWJ 8753	WCru
	- 'Anny's Dwarf'	MAsh NLar SBig
	- 'Autumn Gold' (m) ♀H6	CBcs CDul CEnd CMCN EBee ECrN EPla LAst LLHF MBlu MGos MPkF NLar SBig SLim
	- 'Barabits' Fastigiata'	ESwi ETwe SMad
I	- 'Barabits Nana'	SBig
	- 'Beijing Gold'	IVic MBlu MPkF NLar SBig WPGP
	- 'Broom with Tubes'	SMad
	- 'California Sunset'	MBlu SBig
	- 'Chase Manhattan'	MPkF NLar

- 'Chi-chi'	MPkF SBig
- 'Chotek'	SBig
- 'Chris' Dwarf'	NLar
- 'David' **new**	SBig
- 'Eastern Star' (f)	CAgr
- 'Elsie'	SBig
- 'Everton Broom'	NLar NPCo SBig
- 'Fairmount' (m)	MBlu SBig
- 'Fastigiata' (m)	CMCN EBee EPfP ESwi MBlu MGos SBig
- 'Globosa'	MBlu SBig
- 'Gnome'	ESwi MGos MPkF
- 'Golden Dragon' **new**	MBlu
- 'Golden Globe'	ESwi MPkF SBig
- 'Gresham'	MPkF
- 'Horizontalis'	MBlu SBig
- 'Jade Butterflies' ♀H6	MBlu MPkF NLar SBig SLim
- 'Jehosaphat'	NLar SBig
- 'Jerry Vercade'	MPkF
- 'King of Dongting' (f)	CAgr ESwi MBlu SBig
- 'Lakeview' (m)	MPkF SBig
- 'Long March' **new**	CAgr
- 'Mariken' ♀H6	ELan EPfP ESwi MPkF NLar SBig SLim SLon SPoG
- 'Mayfield' (m)	NLar SBig
- 'McFarland' **new**	CAgr
- 'Menhir'	EBee ELan EPfP MPkF
- 'Montezuma'	SBig
- 'Obelisk'	NLar
- Ohazuki Group (f)	CAgr SBig
- Pendula Group	CAco CEnd CMCN EBee ESwi MAsh MBlu MNHC MPkF NPCo SBig SGol
- 'Pendula Gruga'	SBig
- 'Pixie'	SBig
- 'Princeton Sentry' (m) ♀H6	EBee EPla IVic LLHF NLar SBig SMad
- 'Robbie's Twist'	MPkF SBig
- 'Santa Cruz'	SBig
- 'Saratoga' (m) ♀H6	CAgr CEnd CJun CMCN EBee EPfP ESwi MBlu MBri MPkF NLar SBig SLim SMad SSpi
- 'Shangri-La' (m)	MBlu
- 'Sinclair'	MPkF
- 'Survivor'	SMad
- 'Tit'	CEnd CMCN EPfP ESwi NLar SBig
- 'Tremonia'	CMCN EPfP MBlu MPkF SBig
- 'Troll' ♀H6	CDoC LRHS MAsh MBlu SBig SCoo SLim SMad
- 'Tubifolia'	CMCN ESwi ETwe MBlu MPkF NLar SBig SLim
- 'Umbrella'	SBig
- Variegata Group (v)	CBcs CJun ESwi MGos MPkF NLar SBig
- 'W.B.'	MPkF SBig
- 'Weeping Wonder' (f)	SBig

ginseng see *Panax ginseng*

Gladiolus (*Iridaceae*)

sp.	EAJP MNrw
acuminatus	WCot
'Ajax' **new**	WPhe
alatus	ECho NRog WPhe
- 'Rawsonville'	ECho
'Alba' (N)	WPhe
'Amanda Mahy' (N)	GKev LAma NRog WPhe
'Amsterdam' (G)	WPhe
angustus L.	CDes CTal NRog WPhe
antakiensis	CPou
'Antica' (L)	WPhe
'Astarte' **new**	WPhe
'Atom' (S/P)	CAvo CBro ECho GKev LAma NRog WPhe
aureus	WCot WPhe
'Bangladesh' PBR **new**	WPhe
'Beautiful Angel'	WPhe
'Black Star'	EPfP ERCP SPer
'Black Surprise' **new**	WPhe
'Blue Frost' (L)	ERCP SDeJ WPhe
'Blue Mountain' **new**	WPhe
'Bonfire' (G)	WPhe
'Boone'	GBin SMrm
'Break of Dawn'	SDeJ
brevifolius 'Somerset West'	ECho
- 'Villiersdorp'	ECho
'Brown Sugar' **new**	WPhe
'Buggy' (S) **new**	CSut
byzantinus	see *G. communis* subsp. *byzantinus*
caeruleus	WCot WPhe
- 'Saldanha'	ECho
callianthus	see *G. murielae*
'Cardinal'	WPhe
cardinalis	EWoo GCal IBlr LEdu SKHP WCru WPhe
carinatus	CDes ECho NRog WCot
carinatus* × *huttonii 'Purple Spray'	WCot
carinatus* × *orchidiflorus	WCot
'Carine' (N)	EAJP GKev NRog SDeJ WPhe
carmineus	ECho WCot
carneus	ECho EPot GCal NRog SDeJ WPhe
caryophyllaceus	ECho
'Charm' (N/Tub)	CBro GKev LEdu NRog SDeJ WPhe
'Charming Beauty' (Tub)	ECho GKev LAma LRHS NRog SDeJ WPhe
'Charming Lady' (Tub)	ECho GKev LAma NRog WPhe
'Cindy' (B)	ECho WPhe
citrinus	see *G. trichonemifolius*
'Claudia' (N)	GKev WPhe
'Columbine' (P)	SDeJ WPhe
× ***colvillii***	CMea CPne IBlr WPhe
- 'Albus'	ERCP GKev
- 'The Bride'	CAvo CBro CHel EBee GKev ITim LAma LEdu SBod SDeJ WPhe
§ ***communis*** subsp. ***byzantinus*** ♀H5	CAvo CBcs CBro CHel CTal CTca ECha ECho ELan EPfP EPot ERCP EWoo GKev LEdu LRHS LSun MWat NBir NSti SBod SDeJ SEND SPer SRms WCot WHoo WKif WPhe WShi
'Coral Lace' (L)	SDeJ WPhe
'Côte d'Azur' (G)	WPhe
crassifolius	ECho
'Cream Perfection' (L)	SDeJ WPhe
cunonius	CTal WHil
§ ***dalenii***	CExl CPou CSde ECho GCal IBlr LEdu WCot WPhe
- 'Apricot Delight' (v)	IBlr
- 'Boone' **new**	WCot
- 'Citrone Spectrum' (v)	IBlr
- subsp. ***dalenii***	CPrp IBlr
- green-flowered	CDes IBlr
- 'Guardsman' (v)	IBlr
* - f. ***rubra***	IBlr

'David Hills' (*papilio* hybrid)	CDes CMea NCGa WCot WHal
'Debbieanne' **new**	WPhe
'Decadent' **new**	WPhe
densifolius	ECho
'Dion' (M)	WPhe
'Dixon' (L)	WPhe
'Domenica' **new**	WPhe
'Dusted Red' **new**	GKev
ecklonii	ECho
- 'Mount Thomas'	ECho
'Elegance' (G)	WPhe
'Elvira' (N)	CSut ECho GKev LAma NRog WPhe
'Emerald Spring' (S)	WCot
'Esta Bonita' (G)	WPhe
'Extasy'[PBR] (L)	WPhe
'Farondole'	SDeJ
'Felicita' (L)	WPhe
'Fidelio' (L)	SDeJ
'Finishing Touch'[PBR] (L)	WPhe
flanaganii	CBro CDes CExl CMea CPBP CSpe ECho GCal GEdr GKev LLHF NSla SChr WAbe WCot WPhe
- JCA 261.000	SKHP
'Flevo Cosmic' (Min)	WPhe
'Flevo Dancer' (S)	WPhe
'Flevo Eclips'[PBR] (G)	WPhe
'Flevo Laguna' (S) **new**	CAvo
'Flevo Smile' (S)	WPhe
floribundus hort.	ECho
floribundus Jacq.	NRog
- subsp. ***fasciatus***	WPhe
'Fortarosa' **new**	WPhe
fourcadei	ECho
'Frizzled Coral Lace' (E) **new**	CSut
× ***gandavensis*** hort.	GBin WPhe
garnieri misapplied	see *G.* 'Spinners'
geardii	WCot
'Good Luck' (N)	CBro
gracilis	ECho WCot WPhe
grandis	see *G. liliaceus*
'Green Star' (L)	ERCP SDeJ WPhe
griseus **new**	NRog
gueinzii 'Mossel Bay'	ECho
'Halley' (N)	ECho GKev LAma NRog WPhe
'Hansnett' **new**	WCot
'Happy Weekend' (L)	SDeJ
hirsutus	ECho
'Holland Pearl' (B)	ERCP SDeJ WPhe
huttonii	CDes ECho NRog WCot
huttonii* × *liliaceus	CDes WPhe
huttonii* × *tristis	CPou WPhe
huttonii* × *tristis var. ***concolor***	CDes WCot
hyalinus	WCot
'Ice Cream'	SPer
illyricus	ECho GCal WShi
imbricatus	ECho MHer
'Imperialis' **new**	IBlr
'Impressive' (N)	CBro GKev LAma NRog SDeJ WPhe
inflatus	ECho WPhe
- 'Ceres'	ECho
'Internet' **new**	WPhe
involutus 'Mossel Bay'	ECho
§ ***italicus***	CHid ELan EPfP GCal GKev SKHP XLum
'Jacksonville Gold' (L)	SDeJ
'Jester' (L)	SDeJ WPhe
'Kazimir' **new**	WPhe
'Kings Lynn' **new**	WPhe
'Kissy Ruffle' (L) **new**	ERCP
kotschyanus	ECho
'Lady Lucille' (M)	WPhe
'Las Vegas'	GKev NRog WPhe
'Lavy Linda' (L)	WPhe
'Lemon Drop' (S)	WPhe
leptosiphon 'Molenaars River'	ECho
§ ***liliaceus***	ECho NRog WCot
- 'Caledon'	ECho
longicollis	ECho
'Lucifer'[PBR]	WPhe
'Mademoiselle de Paris'	ERCP WPhe
'Magma'	WPhe
'Mamma Mia' **new**	WPhe
'Marj S' (L)	WPhe
'Marvinka' (M) **new**	CSut
'Match Point' (L)	SDeJ
meliusculus	ECho NRog
'Mexico'	CSut SDeJ WPhe
'Millennium' (L)	WPhe
miniatus	CDes NRog WCot WPhe
'Mirella' (N)	CAvo GKev LAma NRog WPhe
'Mon Amour'[PBR]	SDeJ WPhe
mortonius	GCal
'Mr Chris' (S)	WPhe
'Mrs Rowley' (P)	SMrm
§ ***murielae*** ♀[H3]	CAby CAvo CBod CBro CMea CWld EAJP ECho EPfP ERCP EWll GKev LRHS MCot MPie NChi SCoo SDeJ SHil SPer SPlb SRms WBor WHal WPhe
natalensis	see *G. dalenii*
'Nathalie' (N)	GKev NRog SDeJ WPhe
'Nori' (M)	ERCP WPhe
'Nova Lux' (L)	SDeJ WPhe
'Nymph' (N)	CAvo CHel EAJP GKev LAma LEdu LSun NRog SDeJ WPhe
'Oasis'[PBR] (G)	WPhe
ochroleucus	WHil
'Odysee' **new**	WPhe
'Old Spice' (L) **new**	ERCP
§ ***oppositiflorus***	CDes IBlr LEdu SChr SMrm SPlb
- subsp. ***salmoneus***	see *G. oppositiflorus*
'Orange King' **new**	WPhe
orchidiflorus	ECho
'Oscar' (G)	ERCP
'Pandora' **new**	WPhe
papilio	Widely available
§ - Purpureoauratus Group	CBro IBlr SRms WSHC
- yellow-flowered	CMea SMad
'Passos'[PBR]	ERCP
'Peach Blossom' (N)	IBlr WCot
'Peach Melba' (L)	WPhe
'Perseus' (P/Min)	ERCP WPhe
'Peter Pears' (L)	SDeJ WPhe
Pilbeam hybrids	WCot
'Platini' **new**	WPhe
'Plum Tart' (L)	CBro ERCP SMrm WPhe
'Pop Art'	SDeJ
primulinus	see *G. dalenii*
'Prins Claus' (N)	CBro CTca GKev LAma NRog WPhe
'Prinses Margaret Rose' (Min)	SDeJ WPhe
priorii 'Dasberg'	ECho
'Priscilla' (L)	MLHP SDeJ WPhe

pritzelli 'Quaggasfontein'	ECho
'Purple Flora'	ERCP WPhe
purpureoauratus	see *G. papilio* Purpureoauratus Group
quadrangularis	ECho
recurvus	ECho
'Red Shadow' **new**	WPhe
'Robinetta' (*recurvus* hybrid) ♀H3	CWCL ECho LAma LRHS NRog SDeJ WPhe
'Roma' (L)	WPhe
'Rosario' **new**	WPhe
'Rotary' **new**	WPhe
'Roxy' **new**	WPhe
'Ruby' (*papilio* hybrid)	CAby CAvo CBro CDes CExl CMea CPou CPrp CSde CTal CTca ECha EPri GKev IMou LEdu MHer NChi SMad WAul WCot WHoo WPhe
'Ruth Ann'	WPhe
Sancerre (B/L)	EPfP
saundersii	GCal
scullyi 'Ceres Karoo'	ECho NRog
segetum	see *G. italicus*
sericeovillosus	IBlr
'Solferino' **new**	WPhe
'Solveiga' (L/E)	WPhe
'Sophie'PBR	WPhe
'Spic and Span' (L)	SDeJ WPhe
§ 'Spinners'	CDes IBlr WCot
splendens	CDes NRog WCot WHil WPGP
- 'Roggeveld'	ECho
'Stiena' (L)	WPhe
'Sweet Blue' **new**	WPhe
'Terry' (G)	WPhe
'Thalia' **new**	WPhe
'That's Love' (L)	SDeJ
'Trader Horn' (G)	SDeJ WPhe
§ ***trichonemifolius***	ECho
tristis	CAvo CBro CDes CElw CPne CPou CPrp ECho ELan ELon EWoo NRog WHil WPGP WPhe
- var. ***concolor***	CPou CPrp WCot
undulatus	CDes EBee ECho NRog WCot WPhe
uysiae	ECho
- 'Gannaga'	ECho
vandermerwei	ECho
'Velvet Eyes' (M)	SDeJ WPhe
venustus	ECho NRog
'Video' (L)	WPhe
'Violetta' (M)	SDeJ SMrm WPhe
virescens	NRog
- 'Ceres'	ECho
'Volcano' **new**	GKev
watsonioides	SKHP WCot
watsonius	NRog
'White Prosperity' (L)	CSut ERCP SDeJ
'Yellow Gem'	SDeJ
'Zizane' **new**	CSut

Glandularia see *Verbena*

Glaucidium (*Ranunculaceae*)

palmatum ♀H5	CExl EFEx EWld GBuc GEdr GKev NSla WCru WHal
- 'Album'	see *G. palmatum* var. *leucanthum*
§ - var. ***leucanthum***	EFEx GEdr

Glaucium (*Papaveraceae*)

§ ***corniculatum***	CAbP CCon CSpe LRHS SPhx
flavum	CArn CCon CSpe EBee ECha ELan LRHS MHer MMuc SEND SMrm SPav XSen
- ***aurantiacum***	see *G. flavum* f. *fulvum*
§ - f. ***fulvum***	ECha EWTr LRHS MMuc SDix SEND SMrm WCot XSen
- orange-flowered	see *G. flavum* f. *fulvum*
- red-flowered	see *G. corniculatum*
phoenicium	see *G. corniculatum*

Glaucosciadium (*Apiaceae*)

cordifolium **new**	WCot

Glebionis (*Asteraceae*)

coronaria	MNHC
§ ***segetum***	CHab

Glechoma (*Lamiaceae*)

hederacea	CArn GPoy MHer NMir WHer
- 'Barry Yinger Variegated' (v)	EBee
§ - 'Variegata' (v)	SPer XLum

Gleditsia (*Caesalpiniaceae*)

caspia	CArn LEdu
japonica	NLar
koraiensis	LEdu
- B&SWJ 12569 **new**	WCru
triacanthos	CAco CDul IDee LEdu SPlb
- 'Calhoun'	CAgr
- 'Emerald Cascade'	CBcs CEnd EBee
- 'Goofy'	SMad
- f. ***inermis*** Spectrum = 'Speczam'	LRHS MAsh MBri WHar
- 'Millwood'	CAgr
- 'Rubylace'	CBcs CCVT CDul CEnd CLnd CMCN CSBt EBee ECrN ELan EPfP EPla EWTr IVic LAst MBlu MBri MGos MRav MSwo NLar NPri SCob SGol SKHP SLim SPer WHar
- 'Sunburst'	Widely available

Globba ✿ (*Zingiberaceae*)

marantina	LAma
racemosa var. ***hookeri*** HWJCM 471	WCru
winitii 'Mount Everest'	LAma

Globularia (*Plantaginaceae*)

albiflora	EPot
bellidifolia	see *G. meridionalis*
cordifolia ♀H5	ECho EDAr EPot GCrg GEdr GKev LRHS NBir NSla WCot XSen
- 'Alba'	NHar
incanescens	XSen
§ ***meridionalis***	CBod ECho EPot EWes EWld GKev GMaP MWat SIgm
- 'Blue Bonnets'	NHar
- 'Hort's Variety'	NSla WAbe
nana	see *G. repens*
nudicaulis	ECho GEdr GKev IMou
punctata	CCon SRms XSen
pygmaea	see *G. meridionalis*
§ ***repens***	CPBP ECho EPot LLHF NHar SIgm WAbe
stygia	XSen
trichosantha	GEdr SRms XSen
valentina	GEdr GKev
vulgaris	XSen

Gloriosa (*Colchicaceae*)

	lutea	see *G. superba* 'Lutea'
	rothschildiana	see *G. superba* 'Rothschildiana'
	superba ♀H1c	ECho ERCP GKev SDeJ
	- 'Carsonii'	ECho ERCP GKev LAma SDeJ
	- 'Greenii'	ECho ERCP GKev LAma SDeJ
§	- 'Lutea'	ECho GKev LAma SDeJ
§	- 'Rothschildiana'	CBcs ECho GKev LAma SDeJ SRms WCot
	- 'Rothschildiana Orange' **new**	GKev
	- 'Rothschildiana Salmon' **new**	GKev
	- 'Simplex'	CLak
	- 'Sparkling Jip' **new**	GKev
	- 'Sparkling Orange' **new**	GKev
	- 'Sparkling Striped' **new**	GKev
	- 'Verschuurii'	CLak

Gloxinia (*Gesneriaceae*)

sp.	EABi
nematanthodes	SBrt
sylvatica 'Bolivian Sunset'	WDib

Glumicalyx (*Scrophulariaceae*)

flanaganii	SBrt

Glyceria (*Poaceae*)

	aquatica variegata	see *G. maxima* var. *variegata*
	maxima	MMuc MSKA NPer SEND SPlb
§	- var. ***variegata*** (v)	CBAq CWat ECha EHoe EHon ELan EPla EShb EWay GCra GMaP IBoy LRHS MMuc MWhi NGdn NOrc NWsh SCob SEND SMrm SPer SRms SVic SWat WMAq WMoo WWEG XLum
	notata	SVic
	spectabilis 'Variegata'	see *G. maxima* var. *variegata*

Glycyrrhiza (*Papilionaceae*)

§	***glabra***	CArn CBod CCCN CHby EBee ELau ENfk GPoy MHer MNHC NLar SDix SRms WHfH WJek
	glandulifera	see *G. glabra*
	uralensis	CArn EBee ELau GPoy MHer NLar SPhx
	yunnanensis	CSpe LPla

Glyptostrobus (*Cupressaceae*)

pensilis	CExl CFil IDee SLim WPGP

Gmelina (*Lamiaceae*)

hystrix	CCCN

Gnaphalium (*Asteraceae*)

'Fairy Gold'	see *Helichrysum thianschanicum* 'Goldkind'
trinerve	see *Anaphalis trinervis*

Godetia see *Clarkia*

Gomphocarpus ✿ (*Apocynaceae*)

§	***fruticosus***	SVen
§	***physocarpus***	CArn

Gomphostigma (*Scrophulariaceae*)

virgatum	CAbP CExl CFis CSpe EPPr ETwe EWld IDee ITim LLWG LSou MHol MNFA MPie SMad SMrm SPlb WCFE WCot WRHF
- 'White Candy'	ETwe NLar SVen

Gomphrena (*Amaranthaceae*)

globosa	CCCN

Goniolimon (*Plumbaginaceae*)

§	***incanum***	SMrm
	- 'Blue Diamond'	LSun WCot
	speciosum	LLHF
§	***tataricum*** var. ***angustifolium***	SRms

Goodia (*Papilionaceae*)

lotifolia	CCCN

Goodyera (*Orchidaceae*)

biflora	EFEx
pubescens	EFEx
schlechtendaliana	EFEx

gooseberry see *Ribes uva-crispa*

Gordonia (*Theaceae*)

axillaris	see *Polyspora axillaris*

Gorgonidium (*Araceae*)

intermedium **new**	WCot

granadilla see *Passiflora quadrangularis*

granadilla, purple see *Passiflora edulis*

granadilla, sweet see *Passiflora ligularis*

granadilla, yellow see *Passiflora laurifolia*

grape see *Vitis*

grapefruit see *Citrus* × *aurantium* Grapefruit Group

Graptopetalum (*Crassulaceae*)

	filiferum	CDoC EUJe SPlb
§	***paraguayense***	CDoC SEND SVen

× *Graptoveria* (*Crassulaceae*)

'Caerulescens'	CDoC
'Ghostly' **new**	WCot
'Mrs Richards'	CSuc
'Titubans'	CDoC

Gratiola (*Plantaginaceae*)

officinalis	CArn CBAq EHon LLWG LRHS MHer MSKA

Greenovia (*Crassulaceae*)

	aizoon	CSuc
§	***aurea***	CSuc SPlb
	diplocycla 'Gigantea'	SPlb

Grevillea (*Proteaceae*)

alpina 'Olympic Flame'	CBcs CCCN CDoC CExl CHel CSBt CTsd LEdu LRHS LSou MGos MMuc MOWG SCoo SEND SPoG SVen WBor WGrn
aquifolium	MOWG

banksii 'Canberra Hybrid'	see *G.* 'Canberra Gem'
- var. ***forsteri***	SPlb
barklyana	MOWG
'Bronze Rambler'	MOWG
§ 'Canberra Gem' ♀H4	Widely available
'Clearview David'	CCCN LRHS MMuc MOWG SEND SLim SSpi SVen
'Cranbrook Yellow'	EPfP
crithmifolia	SPlb
'Evelyn's Coronet'	MOWG
iaspicula	MOWG
johnsonii	CMac MOWG
juniperina	CBcs CCCN CExl CMac EPfP ETwe SLim SVen
- prostrate, yellow-flowered	MOWG
- f. ***sulphurea***	CCCN CExl CHel CTsd ELon EPfP MGil MMuc MOWG SBod SEND SEle SPer SPlb SPoG WSHC
lanigera	EUJe
I - 'Lutea'	MOWG
- 'Mount Tamboritha'	CBcs CCCN CDoC CExl CMac CSde EBee ECou EPfP IDee LRHS SEle SLim SPoG SVen
- prostrate	MAsh MOWG WGrn WPat
leucopteris	SPlb
'Long John'	MOWG
'Mason's Hybrid'	MOWG
olivacea 'Apricot Glow'	MOWG
paniculata	SPlb
'Pink Lady'	CCCN ECou ELon EPfP LRHS MOWG
'Poorinda Constance'	MOWG
'Red Dragon' (v)	LRHS
'Red Hooks'	MOWG
rhyolitica	MOWG
robusta ♀H1c	MOWG SPlb SSta
'Robyn Gordon'	MOWG
'Rondeau'	CCCN
rosmarinifolia ♀H4	CBcs CCCN CDoC CExl CMac CSBt CTri ELan EPfP GKin MOWG MWat NSoo SArc SBod SCoo SIgm SLim SLon SPer SPlb SPoG SSta WFar WGwG
- 'Desert Flame'	CExl
- 'Jenkinsii'	CCCN CExl CMac CSBt EBee EPfP EUJe IDee LSou MOWG SEle SLim
'Scarlet Sprite'	MOWG
§ × ***semperflorens***	CSde LRHS MOWG SPlb WGrn
'Splendour'	MOWG
thelemanniana Spriggs' form	MOWG
thyrsoides	GGal
tolminsis	see *G.* × *semperflorens*
victoriae	CCCN CDoC CJun CTsd EBee EPfP IVic LRHS MOWG SCoo SEle WCot WPGP
- 'Mount Annan'	MOWG
- subsp. ***victoriae***	CExl
- yellow-flowered	LRHS
williamsonii	LRHS SCoo WPat

Grewia (*Malvaceae*)

biloba	ETwe
occidentalis	CDoC MOWG

Greyia (*Melianthaceae*)

sutherlandii	MOWG SPlb

Grindelia (*Asteraceae*)

§ ***camporum***	CCon IMou SPlb
chiloensis	CAbb
- F&W 9390	WCot
integrifolia	XLum
robusta	see *G. camporum*
squarrosa	WHil
stricta	CArn

Griselinia ✿ (*Griseliniaceae*)

littoralis ♀H4	Widely available
- 'Bantry Bay' (v)	CAbP CCCN CDoC CSde CTsd EHoe ELan ESwi LRHS MAsh NWad SLim SPer SPoG SWvt WFar
- 'Brodick Gold'	CExl ELon GKin
- 'Dixon's Cream' (v)	CBcs CCCN CDul CMac CSBt EBee EPfP LRHS SGol SLim SLon SPoG SVen
- Green Horizon = 'Whenuapai'PBR	CDoC LBuc SLim SPer STPC
- 'Green Jewel' (v)	CCCN ESwi
- 'Variegata' (v) ♀H4	Widely available
ruscifolia	LEdu
scandens	CCCN

guava, common see *Psidium guajava*

guava, purple or strawberry see *Psidium littorale* var. *longipes*

Guichenotia (*Sterculiaceae*)

macrantha	SPlb

Gunnera ✿ (*Gunneraceae*)

chilensis	see *G. tinctoria*
cordifolia	LLWG
densiflora	GEdr LLWG
dentata	CPla
flavida	CPla LLWG
hamiltonii	CPla ECha GAbr LLWG NBir
killipiana B&SWJ 9009	WCru
magellanica	Widely available
- 'Osorno'	MMoz
manicata ♀H4	Widely available
monoica	LLWG
aff. ***monoica*** purple-leaved	CPne
perpensa	CBcs CCCN CDes EBee GKev IMou LLWG
prorepens	CExl CMac CPla ECha EPot GKev LLWG NBir
scabra	see *G. tinctoria*
§ ***tinctoria*** ♀H4	CCCN CExl CHEx CHel CMac ECha ELan EPfP EWoo GBin IBoy IVic LRHS LSun MMuc NCot NLar SDix SEND SWat SWvt WFar WPGP

Guzmania (*Bromeliaceae*)

'Tempo'PBR **new**	LAir
'Torch'PBR **new**	LAir

Gymnadenia (*Orchidaceae*)

conopsea	ECho EFEx

Gymnocarpium (*Woodsiaceae*)

dryopteris ♀H5	CLAP EFer EFtx EShb EWld GKev GMaP ISha MMoz NLar SGSe WAbe WFib WOut WShi
- PAB 1757	LEdu
- 'Plumosum' ♀H7	CBty CKel CLAP EFtx EPfP ERod GEdr LEdu LRHS NHar NLar WFib WHal WMoo WWEG

oyamense ♀H5	EFtx SKHP
robertianum	EFer EWld

Gymnocladus (*Caesalpiniaceae*)

chinensis	WPGP
dioica	CBcs CDul CLnd CMCN EBee EBtc ELan EPfP EUJe LEdu LRHS MBlu MBri SMad SPer SSpi WPGP

Gymnocoronis (*Asteraceae*)

spilanthoides	LLWG

Gymnospermium (*Berberidaceae*)

§ ***albertii***	ECho
altaicum	ECho

Gynandriris see *Moraea*

Gynerium (*Poaceae*)

argenteum	see *Cortaderia selloana*

Gynostemma (*Cucurbitaceae*)

pentaphyllum	CAgr
- B&SWJ 570	WCru

Gypsophila (*Caryophyllaceae*)

aretioides	ECho EPot LRHS
§ - 'Caucasica'	ECho EPot LLHF
- 'Compacta'	see *G. aretioides* 'Caucasica'
cerastioides	CMea CTri ECho ECtt EDAr EPfP EPot GBin GCrg LBMP LRHS LSun MMuc NGdn NLar SEND SPlb SRms SWvt WAbe WHoo WIce XLum
- 'Rosy Stripe' **new**	GAbr
- silver variegated (v)	MHol NOrc
dubia	see *G. repens* 'Dubia'
elegans **new**	SVic
fastigiata 'Silverstar'	LRHS LSou
'Festival' (Festival Series) (d)	SGbt
gracilescens	see *G. tenuifolia*
'Jolien' (v)	ELan WIce
muralis 'Garden Bride'	SWvt
- 'Gypsy Deep Rose'	EPfP LRHS
- 'Gypsy Pink' (d)	EPfP SWvt
nana 'Compacta'	ECho
'Pacific Rose'	MRav
pacifica	LRHS NLar
paniculata	EPfP GKev MHol MRav SMrm SRms XLum
- 'Bristol Fairy' (d)	CSBt ECha ELan EPfP EWoo GMaP LRHS MJak NLar SCob SHar SPoG SWvt WFar WWEG XLum
- 'Compacta Plena' (d)	CBod ECtt ELan EPfP GMaP MRav NGdn SRms
- double white-flowered (d)	XLum
- 'Flamingo' (d)	CBcs ECha LRHS NLar SHar SWvt XLum
- 'Magic Golan' (d)	COtt
- 'Pacific Pink'	EBee
- 'Perfect Alba' **new**	LRHS
- 'Perfekta'	CBcs SPer
§ - 'Schneeflocke' (d)	CBod EPfP GMaP LRHS MBel MWat NLar SHar SRms WWEG
- Snowflake	see *G. paniculata* 'Schneeflocke'
- Summer Sparkles = 'Esm Chispa'^PBR	NPri
§ ***petraea***	NSla
'Pink Festival' (Festival Series) (d)	ECtt GBee LRHS SPoG WFar
repens ♀H5	ECtt EWTr GBin GJos MAsh MWat SBch SCob SPlb SWvt WFar XLum
- 'Dorothy Teacher'	CMea CTal ECho ECtt MAsh SBch
§ - 'Dubia'	ECha ECho ECtt EPot MAsh MHer MMuc NLar SEND SRms
- 'Fratensis'	ECho ECtt LLHF WIce
- Pink Beauty	see *G. repens* 'Rosa Schönheit'
§ - 'Rosa Schönheit'	ECha ECtt EPot NDov SPer XLum
- 'Rosea'	CTri EBee ECho ECtt EDAr EPfP GJos GMaP ITim LBMP MHol MMuc MWat NGdn SCob SEND SPoG SRms SWvt WFar WHoo WIce XLum
- 'Silver Carpet' (v)	EBee
- white-flowered	CMea ECho ELan EPfP NGdn SWvt
§ 'Rosenschleier' (d) ♀H6	CBod CMea EBee ECha ECtt ELan EPfP LBMP MBel MCot MRav NDov NGdn SBch SRms SRot SWvt WHoo WSHC WWEG XLum
I 'Rosenschleier Variegata' (v)	EBee WWEG
'Rosy Veil'	see *G.* 'Rosenschleier'
§ ***tenuifolia***	ECho EPot GMaP MWat
transylvanica	see *G. petraea*
Veil of Roses	see *G.* 'Rosenschleier'
'White Festival'^PBR (Festival Series) (d)	COtt LRHS SPoG

Haberlea (*Gesneriaceae*)

ferdinandi-coburgii	CLAP ECho
- 'Connie Davidson'	GEdr GKev
rhodopensis ♀H5	CElw EBee ECho EPPr GEdr MWat NSla SRms WAbe WPGP WThu XLum
- 'Virginalis'	CElw CLAP ECho GKev NSla WAbe WThu

Hablitzia (*Chenopodiaceae*)

tamnoides	CAgr LEdu MCoo

Habranthus (*Amaryllidaceae*)

'Amazing Jumbo' **new**	NRog
andersonii	see *H. tubispathus*
brachyandrus	CTal GCal NRog SRms
caeruleus **new**	NRog
gracilifolius	ECho NRog
howardii	ECho
magnoi **new**	NRog
martinezii ♀H2	CPBP CTal ECho NRog
mexicanus	ECho
§ ***robustus*** ♀H2	CAby CCCN CExl CTal ECho EPot GKev LAma NRog WPGP
- 'Russell Manning'	NRog
'Snow White' **new**	GKev
§ ***tubispathus*** ♀H2	CTal ECho GCal GKev NRog WCot WHil
- var. ***roseus*** **new**	NRog

Hacquetia (*Apiaceae*)

epipactis ♀H5	Widely available
§ - 'Thor' (v)	EBee ECha ECho EWes GEdr LLHF NBir NChi SIgm WPGP
- 'Variegata'	see *H. epipactis* 'Thor'

Haemanthus (*Amaryllidaceae*)

	albiflos ♀H2	CHEx CPne CPrp CTca ECho EOHP EShb GKev LAma SRms WCot
	amarylloides subsp. ***polyanthes***	ECho
	barkerae	ECho
	carneus	ECho WCot
	coccineus ♀H2	CLak ECho WCot
	crispus	ECho
	humilis	ECho
	- subsp. ***hirsutus***	WCot
	kalbreyeri	see *Scadoxus multiflorus* subsp. *multiflorus*
	katherinae	see *Scadoxus multiflorus* subsp. *katherinae*
	lanceifolius	ECho
	natalensis	see *Scadoxus puniceus*
	pauculifolius	ECho
	pubescens subsp. ***leipoldtii***	ECho
	sanguineus	ECho

Hakea (*Proteaceae*)

§	***drupacea***	CTre
	epiglottis	ECou
	laurina	SPlb
§	***lissosperma***	CDoC ECou EPfP SPlb WPGP
	nodosa	CCCN
	oleifolia new	CTre
	platysperma	SPlb
§	***salicifolia***	CBcs CCCN ETwe NPri SPlb WCot
	saligna	see *H. salicifolia*
	sericea misapplied	see *H. lissosperma*
	sericea Schrad. & J.C.Wendl.	WCot
	- pink-flowered	SPlb WCot
	suaveolens	see *H. drupacea*
	victoriae	SPlb

Hakonechloa ✿ (*Poaceae*)

	macra ♀H7	CFil CKno CMac CPla CSam EAEE ECha EHoe ELan EPPr EPla EShb EWoo GBin GCal LEdu LRHS MAvo MBel MMoz NDov NOak NPol SCob SMad SPhx SPoG WPGP WSHC
§	- 'Alboaurea' (v) ♀H7	CBcs CExl CKno COtt CTsd CWGN ELan EPfP LAst LRHS MGos MMuc NPla SEND SHil
	- 'Albovariegata' (v)	CKno EPPr GCal LEdu SCob
§	- 'All Gold'	CBod CExl CFil CKno EBee ECha ECtt EPPr EShb EWes GQue IBoy IKil ITim LBMP LEdu LRHS MAsh MBri MGos SMad SPad SPoG WCot WPGP
	- 'Aureola' ♀H7	Widely available
	- 'Mediovariegata' (v)	EBee ECha EPPr EPla WPGP
	- 'Naomi' (v)	EBee LRHS MBri SPoG
	- 'Nicolas'	CExl CKno CSam EBee ECtt EHoe ELan ELon EPfP EWes GBin LEdu LLHF LPla LRHS LSou MBel MBri MSCN NSbr NSti SCob SPoG
	- 'Ogon'	see *H. macra* 'All Gold'
	- 'Samurai' (v)	CKno LRHS
	- 'Stripe It Rich' (v)	CWCL ECtt ESwi EWes SGol WGrn
	- 'Variegata'	see *H. macra* 'Alboaurea'

Halesia (*Styracaceae*)

§	***carolina***	CAgr CBcs CDoC CDul CEnd CHab CJun CMCN CTho ECrN ELan EPfP GKin IDee IVic LRHS MBlu MBri MCoo MGos MLHP NLar NWea SKHP SPer WHar
	- Monticola Group	CAco CBcs CCVT CDul CMCN EBee ELan EPfP IVic LRHS MMuc NLar SEND SPer SSpi SWvt WHar WMou
I	- - 'Variegata' (v)	MBlu NLar SSta
	- 'Uconn Wedding Bells'	CJun MBlu SKHP
	- Vestita Group ♀H5	CDoC CJun CTho EPfP LRHS MAsh MBlu MGos MRav NLar SPer SSpi SSta
	- - 'Rosea'	CJun EPfP MBlu NLar SKHP
	diptera	MBlu SKHP
	- Magniflora Group	CJun EPfP MBlu MBri
	tetraptera	see *H. carolina*

× *Halimiocistus* (*Cistaceae*)

	algarvensis	see *Halimium ocymoides*
§	'Ingwersenii' ♀H4	CBcs CDoC ECho EDAr ELan EWes SPer SPoG SRms XLum
	revolii misapplied	see × *H. sahucii*
§	***sahucii*** ♀H4	CBcs CBod CDoC CSBt CTri ECha ELan EPfP EUJe LBMP LRHS MAsh MBNS MBri MMuc MRav MSwo NPri SCob SPer SPoG SRms SWvt WHea XLum
	- Ice Dancer = 'Ebhals'PBR (v)	CDoC EBee EPfP LAst MAsh SCob SPer SWvt
	'Susan'	see *Halimium* 'Susan'
§	***wintonensis*** ♀H4	CBcs CDoC ELan EPfP LRHS MAsh MMuc SCob SLon SPer SRms WHar WSHC
§	- 'Merrist Wood Cream' ♀H4	CBcs CBod CDoC CMac COtt CSBt EBee ELan EPfP LAst MAsh MGil MMuc MSwo NBir SEle SLim SPer SPoG SWvt WSHC

Halimium (*Cistaceae*)

§	***calycinum***	CBod CDoC ELan EPfP IVic LRHS MAsh MBri MMuc SCoo SEND SHil SLim SPer SPoG SWvt WAbe WCFE
	commutatum	see *H. calycinum*
	formosum	see *H. lasianthum* subsp. *formosum*
	halimifolium misapplied	see *H.* × *pauanum*
§	***lasianthum***	CBcs CMac CSBt ELan EPfP LRHS MRav SLim
	- 'Concolor' ♀H4	LRHS MAsh MSwo SWvt
§	- subsp. ***formosum***	MMuc
	- - 'Sandling' ♀H4	ELan EPfP LRHS MAsh MMuc SLon SPoG SRms
	libanotis misapplied	see *H. calycinum*
§	***ocymoides***	CBcs CDoC ELan EPfP IVic LRHS MSwo WHar WKif
§	× ***pauanum***	LRHS MMuc
§	'Susan' ♀H4	CDoC EBee ELan GKev LBrs LRHS MMHG MMuc SCoo SLim SPer WAbe
§	***umbellatum***	CBod EPfP SPer
	wintonense	see × *Halimiocistus wintonensis*

Halimodendron (*Papilionaceae*)

	halodendron	CArn CDul MBlu SPer

Halleria (*Stilbaceae*)

	lucida	CCCN SEle SPlb SVen

Halocarpus (*Podocarpaceae*)

§	***bidwillii***	CDoC

Haloragis (*Haloragaceae*)

erecta	SPlb SVen XLum
- 'Rubra'	WCot
- 'Wellington Bronze'	CBod CExl CHel CSpe ECou EHoe EUJe GEdr LEdu MLHP SPtp WHer WMoo XLum

Hamamelis ✿ (*Hamamelidaceae*)

'Amethyst'	CJun NLar SGol
'Brevipetala'	CEnd CJun
'Danny'	CJun
'Dishi'	CJun
'Doerak'	CJun NLar
'Fire Blaze'	CJun MBlu NLar
× ***intermedia***	CDul
- 'Advent'	CJun NLar
- 'Angelly' ♀H5	CEnd CJun MBlu NLar SPoG
- 'Anne' **new**	LRHS NLar
- 'Aphrodite' ♀H5	CDoC CJun CRos EPfP LRHS MAsh MBlu MBri MGos MMuc MRav NCGa NLar SCob SHil SPer
- 'Arnhem'	NLar
- 'Arnold Promise' ♀H5	Widely available
- 'Aurora' ♀H5	CJun CRos EPfP LRHS MBlu MBri MGos MMuc NLar SHil SPoG
- 'Barmstedt Gold' ♀H5	CJun CRos EPfP LRHS MAsh MGos SCob SHil SPoG WPat
- 'Bernstein'	CJun
- 'Birgit'	NLar
- 'Carmine Red'	CJun CMac MGos
- 'Copper Beauty'	see *H.* × *intermedia* 'Jelena'
- 'Cyrille'	MMuc NLar
- 'Diane' ♀H5	Widely available
§ - 'Feuerzauber'	CEnd CMac CSBt CTri LBuc MGos NLar SCob SPer SWvt
- Fire Cracker	see *H.* × *intermedia* 'Feuerzauber'
- 'Foxy Lady'	CRos LRHS MAsh SPoG
- 'Frederic' ♀H5	CJun EPfP LRHS MAsh
- 'Georges' **new**	NLar
- 'Gimborn's Perfume'	NLar
- 'Gingerbread'	CJun EPfP LLHF LRHS MAsh
- 'Glowing Embers'	CJun LRHS MAsh
- 'Harlow Carr'	LRHS MAsh
- 'Harry' ♀H5	CJun CRos LRHS MAsh
- 'Heinrich Bruns'	CJun
§ - 'Jelena' ♀H5	Widely available
- 'John'	LRHS MAsh
- 'Limelight'	CJun MBlu NLar
- 'Livia'	CJun CRos EPfP LRHS MAsh NLar SCoo SHil SPoG SSpi
- Magic Fire	see *H.* × *intermedia* 'Feuerzauber'
- 'Moonlight'	CJun
- 'Nina'	EPfP LRHS MAsh MGos
- 'Ninotchka'	CJun
- 'Old Copper'	NLar
- 'Orange Beauty'	CBcs CRos LRHS MBlu MGos MMuc SCoo SGol SHil WPGP
- 'Orange Peel'	CJun CRos EPfP LLHF LRHS MAsh NLar SHil WPat
- 'Ostergold'	CJun NLar
- 'Pallida' ♀H5	Widely available
- 'Primavera'	CJun CLnd IArd LRHS MGos NPCo
- 'Ripe Corn'	CJun EPfP LRHS MAsh
- 'Robert' ♀H5	CJun CRos EPfP LRHS MAsh SHil SPoG WPat
- 'Rubin' ♀H5	CJun CRos EPfP GKin LRHS MAsh MBri MGos NLar SCoo SHil SPer SPoG
- 'Rubinstar'	CJun
- 'Ruby Glow'	CBcs CMac CWGN MGos NLar NPCo NWea SCoo SLim SPer SWvt
- 'Savill Starlight'	CJun
- 'Spanish Spider'	CJun MBlu NLar
- 'Strawberries and Cream'	CJun MAsh NLar
- 'Sunburst'	CJun CRos LRHS MBlu NLar SGol SHil
- 'Twilight'	CJun NLar
- 'Vesna' ♀H5	CJun CMac CRos EPfP LRHS MAsh MBlu NLar SCoo SHil SPoG
- 'Westerstede'	CJun EPfP IArd MGos NHol NLar NPla NWea SCob SCoo SEWo SGol SLim
- 'Wiero'	CJun
- 'Zitronenjette'	CJun
japonica 'Pendula'	CJun MBlu NLar
- 'Zuccariniana'	NLar
mollis	CBcs CCVT CDul CEnd CHab CHel CMac CNWT CSBt CTri CWSG ELan EPfP GKin LRHS MBlu MBri MGos MJak MRav MSwo NEgg NWea SCob SGol SLim SPer SRms SWvt
- 'Boskoop'	CJun GKin NLar
- 'Coombe Wood'	CJun LRHS MGos
- 'Emily'	LRHS MAsh
- 'Goldcrest'	CJun
- 'Imperialis'	CJun LRHS MAsh
- 'Iwado'	CJun
- 'Jermyns Gold' ♀H5	CJun LRHS MAsh SHil SPoG
- 'Kort's Yellow'	CJun
- var. ***pallida***	SEWo SWvt
- 'Wisley Supreme' ♀H5	CJun ELan EPfP LLHF LRHS MAsh SGol SHil SPoG
'Rochester'	CJun NLar
vernalis 'Lombarts' Weeping'	NLar
- purple-flowered	MBlu
- 'Quasimodo' **new**	NLar
- 'Sandra'	CMCN ELan EPfP LRHS MAsh MBlu MGos MRav NLar SLon SPer
virginiana	CAco CAgr GPoy IDee MMuc NWea
- 'Mohonk Red'	CJun
'Yamina'	NLar

Hamelia (*Rubiaceae*)

patens	CCCN

Hanabusaya (*Campanulaceae*)

§ ***asiatica***	NCGa NChi SBrt WHil

Haplocarpha (*Asteraceae*)

rueppellii	SRms SRot

Haplopappus (*Asteraceae*)

coronopifolius	see *H. glutinosus*
§ ***glutinosus***	ECha ECho ECtt EDAr EPot GEdr MMuc NLar SEND SPlb SRms
prunelloides var. ***mustersii*** F&W 9384	WCot
'Purple Carpet'	EBee
rehderi	MWat

Hardenbergia (*Papilionaceae*)

comptoniana ♀H3	CExl WCot
violacea ♀H3	CCCN CHel CHll CRHN ELan IDee MHer MMuc SEND SLim SPer WCot

- f. ***alba*** CHll ECou
- - 'White Crystal' SPer
- - 'White Wanderer' CCCN
- dwarf ECou
- 'Happy Wanderer' CCCN MOWG SChF
- f. ***rosea*** CCCN

Harpephyllum (*Anacardiaceae*)

caffrum (F) XBlo

Hastingsia (*Asparagaceae*)

alba WSHC

hazelnut see *Corylus*

Haworthia ✿ (*Asphodelaceae*)

attenuata EShb
'Black Major' **new** LToo
'Black Prince' EPfP EShb SBch
'Chocolate' **new** LToo
* ***conigra*** **new** LToo
cooperii var. ***pilifera*** **new** LToo
cymbiformis EPfP
fasciata EPfP SEND
glabrata var. ***concolor*** EPfP EShb
'Kermit' **new** LToo
mirabilis LToo
var. ***sublineata*** **new**
- var. ***triebneriana*** **new** LToo
pumila ♀H2 SEND
radula EPfP
tesselata see *H. venosa* subsp. *tesselata*
truncata ♀H2 **new** LToo
§ ***venosa*** SEND
subsp. ***tesselata*** ♀H2

Hebe ✿ (*Plantaginaceae*)

albicans ♀H4 CBcs CMac ELan EPfP GKin LAst LPot LRHS MAsh MBri MGos MJak MRav NPri NWea SCob SCoo SHil SLim SPer SPoG SRms SWvt WHar XLum
- prostrate see *H. albicans* 'Snow Cover'
* - 'Snow Carpet' CCCN LRHS
§ - 'Snow Cover' EWes LRHS
- 'Snow Drift' see *H. albicans* 'Snow Cover'
- 'Snow Mound' SHea
§ 'Alicia Amherst' LRHS SHea
'Amanda Cook' (v) NPer SGol SPoG
'Amethyst' SHea
§ 'Amy' ELon GGal LRHS NPer SHea SPer SWvt
× ***andersonii*** LRHS SHea
§ - 'Andersonii Variegata' (v) LRHS SRms
- 'Argenteovariegata' see *H.* × *andersonii* 'Andersonii Variegata'
'Andressa Paula' CCCN LRHS
'Anna' EPfP
anomala misapplied see *H.* 'Imposter'
anomala (Armstr.) Cockayne LRHS SHea
§ ***armstrongii*** ECho SCob SEND
'Arthur' ECou
'Autumn Glory' CAco CSBt CTsd ELan EPfP LAst LRHS MAsh MBri MGos MJak MRav MSwo NBir NPri SCob SGol SLim SPer SPlb SPoG SVen SWvt XLum
'Autumn Joy' SWvt
azurea see *H. venustula*
'Azurens' see *H.* 'Maori Gem'
'Baby Blush'PBR CSBt LRHS SLim
'Baby Boo' (v) LRHS SLon
'Baby Marie' CAbP CSBt EBee ECho ELan EPfP GKin LBMP LBuc LRHS MBri MSwo NLar NPer SCob SCoo SLim SPoG SRGP SRms SRot SWvt
'Beatrice' SHea
'Beverley Hills'PBR CSBt LRHS SCob
'Bicolor Wand' CCCN CTsd LRHS SHea
bishopiana EPfP SCob
'Black Beauty' EPfP LBMP LBuc LRHS MJak
'Black Knight' SLim
'Black Panther' ELon LSou NSoo
'Blue Clouds' ♀H4 EBee EPfP LAst LLHF LRHS MBri MSwo SCob SPer WCFE
Blue Elegance = 'Lowgeko'PBR (Garden Beauty Series) LRHS NPri SLim SPoG
§ 'Blue Gem' LBuc SCob SLim
'Blue Shamrock' SWvt
Blue Star = 'Vergeer 1'PBR EPfP LBuc LRHS MBri NLar SLon SPoG SRms
'Bluebell' SHea
'Blush Wand' SHea
bollonsii SHea
'Boscawenii' ECre SHea WHer
§ 'Bowles's Hybrid' CCCN LRHS MRav MSwo SCob SEND SHea SRms
brachysiphon CTri SCob SEND SHea SPer SRms SVen
'Bracken Hill' SHea
brevifolia LRHS SLim
breviracemosa SHea
Bronze Glow = 'Lowglo' (Garden Beauty Series) LBuc LRHS
'Bronzy Baby'PBR (v) SPoG
buchananii ECho MHer NPer SIgm
§ - 'Fenwickii' ECho WHoo
- 'Minima' ECho
- 'Minor' Hort. NZ ECho GBin GCrg NBir
buxifolia misapplied see *H. odora*
buxifolia (Benth.) Andersen CMac ELan MMuc NWea SEND
'C.P. Raffill' SHea
§ 'Caledonia' ♀H4 CCCN CSBt EPfP LBMP LRHS MAsh MBri MGos NPer NPri SCob SCoo SHea SLim SPoG SRms SWvt WHoo XLum
'Candy' SHea
§ ***canterburiensis*** EAEE ECou
'Carl Teschner' see *H.* 'Youngii'
'Carnea' SHea
'Carnea Variegata' (v) EPfP EShb LRHS SLim SPer SRms WOut
carnosula NBir SPer
catarractae see *Parahebe catarractae*
'Celine' EBee EPfP LBuc LRHS SRGP
'Champagne' CCCN EBee EPfP LAst LPot LRHS MBlu MBri MWat NLar NSoo SCob SCoo SLim SRms XLum
Champion = 'Champseiont'PBR EAEE EBee LRHS MSwo SCoo
'Charming White' CChe EAEE EPla LRHS SCob
chathamica ECou LRHS
cheesemanii WAbe
'Christabel' LRHS

	Name	Suppliers
	'Clear Skies'[PBR]	CSBt ECou LBuc LRHS SLim SRms
	'Colwall'	ECho
	'Conwy Knight'	SRms WAbe
	corriganii	SHea
	corstorphinensis	LRHS SHea
	'County Park'	ECou EWes
	'Cranleighensis'	CTsd SHea
	cupressoides	CFis LRHS MSCN
	- 'Boughton Dome'	CTri ECho EPfP MHer WAbe WCFE WHoo WOld
	darwiniana	see *H. glaucophylla*
	'Dazzler' (v)	CAbP
	decumbens	EWes
	'Denise'	LRHS
	'Diamond'	LRHS SLon SRms
	dieffenbachii	SHea
	diosmifolia	CDoC EPfP LRHS SHea SLim
	- 'Wairua Beauty'	SLim
	divaricata	SHea
	'Dorothy Peach'	see *H.* 'Watson's Pink'
	'E.B.Anderson'	see *H.* 'Caledonia'
	'Eclipse'	LAst
	'Edington'	SHea SPer WCFE
	'Ellie'	LRHS
	elliptica	ECou SHea
	- 'Anatoki'	SHea
	- 'Charleston'	SHea
	- 'Kapiti'	ECou
	- 'Variegata'	see *H.* 'Silver Queen'
	'Emerald Dome'	see *H.* 'Emerald Gem'
§	'Emerald Gem' ♀H4	CAco CMac CTri EAEE ECho EPfP EShb LBMP LRHS MAsh MBri MGos MHer MJak MMuc MSwo MWat NLar SCob SEND SHil SPer SPlb SPoG WFar WHar
	'Emerald Green'	see *H.* 'Emerald Gem'
	epacridea	EWes
§	'Eveline'	CSBt CTri LRHS MJak NBir SLim SPer
	evenosa	SHea
	'Eversley Seedling'	see *H.* 'Bowles's Hybrid'
	'Fairfieldii'	WPat WSHC
	'First Light'[PBR]	LRHS NPri SCob SGol SRms
	'Fragrant Jewel'	CAbP LRHS SEND SLim SPhx
	×***franciscana***	SBod SHea
	- 'Blue Gem' ambig.	CTsd ELan EPfP LRHS MRav NBir NPer SCob SEND SGol SPer SPlb SPoG SRms
	- 'Foreness Pink' **new**	SEND
	- 'Lavender Queen'	LRHS SHea
	- lime variegated (v) **new**	SEND
	- 'Purple Tips' misapplied	see *H. speciosa* 'Variegata'
	- 'Variegata'	see *H.* 'Silver Queen'
I	- 'White Gem'	SRms
	- yellow variegated (v)	SPer
	'Frozen Flame' (v)	ELan LBuc LRHS SPoG
	'Galway Bay' **new**	LSou
	Garden Beauty Blue = 'Cliv'[PBR] (Garden Beauty Series)	LBuc LRHS SLim SRms
	Garden Beauty Pink = 'Lowink' (Garden Beauty Series)	SLim SRms
	Garden Beauty Purple = 'Nold'[PBR] (Garden Beauty Series)	LBuc LRHS SLim
	'Garden Elegance Blush'	LRHS
	'Garden Elegance Pink'	NPri SLim
	'Garden Elegance Purple'	SLim SPoG
	'Garden Elegance Rose'	SLim
	'Gauntlettii'	see *H.* 'Eveline'
	'Gibby'	LRHS
§	***glaucophylla***	SHea
	- 'Clarence'	ECou
	- 'Joan Hunwick'	LRHS SHea
I	- 'Variegata' (v)	CTri EPfP LBuc NBir SCoo SLim SPer
	'Gnome'	LRHS
	'Goethe'	SEND
	'Gold Beauty' (v)	SRms
	'Golden Nugget'	LRHS
	'Goldrush'[PBR] (v)	SPoG
	gracillima	SCob SEle SHea
	'Gran's Favourite'	LRHS
	'Great Orme' ♀H4	CDul ECou ELan EPfP GBin GGal LAst LRHS MAsh MGos MJak MMuc MRav MSCN MSwo NPer SBod SEND SLim SPer SPlb SPoG SRms SWvt WAbe WSFF
	'Green Globe'	see *H.* 'Emerald Gem'
	'Greensleeves'	LRHS
	'Grethe'	SPoG
	'Hadspen Pink'	LRHS
	'Hagley Park'	LRHS
§	'Hartii'	EPfP LRHS MRav SLim
	'Headfortii'	SHea
	'Heartbreaker'[PBR] (v)	ELan LAst LBuc LRHS MAsh MGos MJak MWat NLar NPri SCob SCoo SLim SPoG SWvt
	HebeDonna Diana = 'Zenia'[PBR]	ELan
	'Heidi'	SHea
	'Hielan Lassie'	LRHS SHea
	'Highdown Pink'	SHea
	'Highdownensis'	LRHS
	'Hinderwell'	NPer
	hulkeana	LRHS LSou MHer WKif
§	'Imposter'	SRms
	'Inspiration'	LRHS SHea
	'James Stirling'	see *H. ochracea* 'James Stirling'
	'Jane Holden'	LRHS
	'Joanna'	ECou
	'John Collier' **new**	SEND
§	'Johny Day'	LRHS
	'Judy'	LRHS
	'Karna'	LPot
	'Karo Golden Esk'	EAEE EPfP
	'Killiney Variety'	SHea
	'Kirkii'	EPfP EPla LAst MSwo NLar SCob SHea XLum
	'Knightshayes'	see *H.* 'Caledonia'
	'La Favorite'	CTsd SHea
	'La Séduisante'	CTri ECou LRHS SEND SHea SRms
	'Lady Ann'[PBR] (v)	CSBt EPfP LBuc LRHS LSou MWat NLar NPri SPoG
	'Lady Ardilaun'	see *H.* 'Amy'
	laevis	see *H. venustula*
	laingii	GCrg
	latifolia	see *H.* 'Blue Gem'
	'Lavender Spray'	see *H.* 'Hartii'
	leiophylla	SHea SVen
	Leopard = 'Lowand' (Garden Beauty Series)	LBuc
	'Lewisii'	SHea
	'Lilac Wand'	CTsd SHea
	'Linda'	SEND

	Name	Suppliers
	'Lindsayi'	ECou LRHS SHea
§	'Loganioides'	EPla
	lyallii	see *Parahebe lyallii*
	lycopodioides 'Aurea'	see *H. armstrongii*
	'Lynash'	LRHS
	mackenii	see *H.* 'Emerald Gem'
	macrantha ΨH4	CBod GBin LRHS SDix SPer SRms WAbe
	macrocarpa	LRHS
	- var. ***latisepala***	LBuc LRHS SLim
	- var. ***macrocarpa***	SLim
	'Magic Summer'	LBuc LRHS MBri SPoG
§	'Maori Gem'	MRav
	'Margery Fish'	see *H.* 'Primley Gem'
	'Margret'[PBR] ΨH4	CSBt EPfP LAst LBMP LRHS MAsh MBrN MBri MGos NPri NSoo SCob SCoo SHea SLim SPoG SRGP SRms
	'Marie Antoinette'	LRHS
	'Marilyn Monroe'[PBR]	LRHS
	'Marjorie'	CDul CMac EAEE ELan EPfP EPla GBin LAst LRHS MJak MSwo NLar NPer NWea SCob SPer SPoG SRms SWvt
	'Mauve Queen'	LRHS
	'McKean'	see *H.* 'Emerald Gem'
	'Megan'	ECou
	'Mette'	EAEE
	Midnight Sky = 'Lowten'[PBR] (Garden Beauty Series)	LBuc LRHS NPri SCoo SLim SPoG
	'Midsummer Beauty' ΨH4	CWCL ECrN EPfP EPla LAst LRHS MBri MGos MJak MMuc MRav NBir SCob SEND SHea SLim SPer SPlb SPoG SRms SWvt WOut WSFF XLum
	'Milmont Emerald'	see *H.* 'Emerald Gem'
	'Miss Fittall'	SHea
§	'Mohawk'[PBR]	LBuc
*	'Moppets Hardy'	SPer
	'Mrs E.Tennant'	SHea
§	'Mrs Winder' ΨH4	Widely available
	'Nantyderry'	LRHS SHea
§	'Neil's Choice' ΨH4	ECou ELon LRHS SHea
	'Neopolitan'	LBuc LRHS SPoG
	'New Zealand'	XLum
	'Nicola's Blush' ΨH4	CDul CSBt ECou ELon EPfP EShb LAst LRHS MCot MMuc MRav MWat NBir NCot NLar SCob SEND SGol SPer SPoG SRGP SRms SWvt WKif
	ochracea	LRHS
§	- 'James Stirling' ΨH4	CBcs CMac CSBt ECho ELan EPfP EShb GKin LRHS MAsh MGos MJak MSwo NLar NPri NWad SCob SCoo SLim SPer SPlb SPoG SWvt WFar WHar
	'Oddity'	LRHS
§	***odora***	CSde ECou MJak SCob SEND
	- 'New Zealand Gold'	LRHS MAsh MMuc SCoo SEND SHil
	- 'Summer Frost'	CSde LRHS
	'Oratia Beauty' ΨH4	LRHS MMuc MRav NLar SCob SEND SLim
	parviflora misapplied	see *H.* 'Bowles's Hybrid'
	parviflora (Vahl) Cockayne & Allan var. ***angustifolia***	see *H. stenophylla*
	- 'Holdsworth'	CBod LRHS
	- 'Palmerston'	SHea
	'Pascal' ΨH4	ELan EPfP LRHS MAsh MBri MGos SCoo SLim SLon SPer SPoG SRms SWvt

	Name	Suppliers
	Pastel Elegance = 'Lowjap'[PBR] (Garden Beauty Series)	SLim
	'Patti Dossett'	see *H. speciosa* 'Patti Dossett'
	pauciramosa	GCal SRms
	'Pearl of Paradise'[PBR]	LBuc SPoG
	perfoliata	see *Parahebe perfoliata*
	'Perry's Rubyleaf'	NPer
	'Petra's Pink'	CCCN LRHS SLim
	'Pewter Dome' ΨH4	CMac CSBt ECou EHoe EPfP LRHS MGos MRav SCob SDix SHea SPer SRms SWvt
	pimeleoides	SCob
	- 'Glauca'	NPer SGol
	- 'Glaucocaerulea'	ECou
	- 'Quicksilver' ΨH4	CSBt CTri ECou ELan EPfP LAst LRHS MGos MMuc MRav NBir NPer SCob SCoo SLim SPer SRms WHar
	pinguifolia	SPlb
	- 'Dobson'	LRHS
	- 'Pagei' ΨH5	Widely available
	- 'Sutherlandii'	CBcs CDoC EAEE ECho EPla LRHS MGos MJak NSoo NWea SCob SCoo SHea SWvt WFar
	'Pink Elegance'	LRHS
	'Pink Elephant' (v) ΨH4	LBMP LBuc LRHS MAsh MJak MWat NLar NPri SLim SPoG
	'Pink Fantasy'	LRHS
	'Pink Goddess'	EPfP LRHS SRGP
	'Pink Lady'[PBR]	SGol SPoG
	'Pink Paradise'[PBR]	CAbP ELan EPfP LBuc LRHS MJak SPoG SRms
	'Pink Payne'	see *H.* 'Eveline'
	'Pink Pixie'	LBuc MAsh MBri SCoo SRms
	'Pink Wand'	CTsd SHea
	poppelwellii	GBin
	'Porlock Purple'	see *Parahebe catarractae* 'Delight'
§	'Primley Gem'	CFis LRHS
I	'Prostrata'	CSBt
	'Purple Emperor'	see *H.* 'Neil's Choice'
	'Purple Paradise'[PBR]	EBee MBri MJak SPoG
	'Purple Picture'	ELon
	'Purple Pixie'[PBR]	see *H.* 'Mohawk'
	'Purple Princess'	LRHS SGol
	'Purple Queen'	EPfP EShb LRHS MJak NPCo SPoG
	Purple Shamrock = 'Neprock'[PBR] (v)	EPfP LAst LBuc LRHS MAsh MBri MGos MWat NEgg NLar SCoo SLim SPer SPoG SRms SWvt
	'Purple Tips' misapplied	see *H. speciosa* 'Variegata'
	'Rachel'	LRHS SLon
§	***rakaiensis*** ΨH4	Widely available
	- 'Golden Dome'	see *H. rakaiensis*
	raoulii	SRms WAbe
	Raspberry Ripple = 'Tullyraspb'[PBR]	LBuc
	'Raven'	LRHS
	recurva	CSam CTri LPot LRHS MCot SCob SHea SRms
	- 'Boughton Silver' ΨH5	LRHS MMuc SLim
	'Red Edge' ΨH4	Widely available
	'Red Rum'	LBuc
	'Red Ruth'	see *H.* 'Eveline'
	'Reine des Blanches'	SHea
	'Rhubarb and Custard' **new**	LBuc LRHS
	rigidula	LRHS MMuc SEND
	'Ronda'	ECou
	'Rosie'[PBR]	CSBt LBuc LRHS SCoo SPer SWvt
	'Royal Blue'	LRHS SLim

	'Royal Purple'	see *H.* 'Alicia Amherst'
	salicifolia	CCCN CMac CTca ECou ELan EPfP LAst LRHS MGos MJak MRav NWad SCob SEND SHea SPer SPlb SRms XLum
	- pale blue-flowered **new**	SEND
	'Sandra Joy'	LRHS
	'Sapphire' ♀H4	ECou EPfP LRHS MAsh MJak NPri SCob SCoo SHea SLim SRms SWvt
	'Sarana'	LRHS
	selaginoides hort.	see *H.* 'Loganioides'
	'Shiraz'	LRHS
	'Silver Dollar' (v)	CAbP CCCN CMac CSBt ELan LRHS MMuc NEgg NWad SLim SPer SPoG SRms
§	'Silver Queen' (v) ♀H3	CMac CSBt ELan EShb GBin LRHS MAsh MJak NLar NPer SCob SEND SPer SPoG SRms WOut
	'Silver Swallow'	LRHS
	'Simon Délaux'	LRHS SEND SPer
I	'Southlandii'	MWhi SGol
	'Sparkling Sapphires'	LBuc LRHS
	speciosa	SHea
	- 'Johny Day'	see *H.* 'Johny Day'
§	- 'Patti Dossett'	LRHS
	- 'Rangatira'	ECou
§	- 'Variegata' (v)	LRHS NPer NSoo
	'Spender's Seedling' misapplied	see *H. stenophylla*
	'Spender's Seedling' ambig.	MCot MMuc
	'Spender's Seedling' Hort.	ECou LRHS MRav SEND SHea SPoG SRms
	'Spring Glory'	LRHS
§	***stenophylla***	EShb GGal LRHS NLar SArc SDix SPer SPlb
	stricta	ECou LRHS SEND
	- var. ***egmontiana***	LRHS
	- var. ***macroura***	SHea
	- var. ***stricta***	SHea
	subalpina	CSBt SHea
	'Summer Blue'	LRHS MBlu MRav
	'Super Red'	CSBt EAEE MBri SLim SPoG
	'Sweet Kim' (v)	CMac LBuc LRHS MBri SLim SPoG
	'Tina'	ECou
	'Tom Marshall'	see *H. canterburiensis*
	topiaria ♀H4	CAbP CSBt CSam EPfP GCal LRHS MBrN MMuc MRav MSwo NBir NWad SBod SCob SCoo SEND SEle SGbt SPer SPoG WAbe WHoo WRHF
	- 'Doctor Favier'	LRHS SRms
	townsonii	ECou LRHS SCob
	traversii	ECou SHea SRms
	'Tricolor'	see *H. speciosa* 'Variegata'
	'Twisty'	LRHS
	'Valentino'PBR	CSBt SCoo SLim
	'Veitchii'	see *H.* 'Alicia Amherst'
§	***venustula***	ECou LRHS MMuc
	- 'Patricia Davies'	ECou
	vernicosa ♀H4	CDul EAEE EPfP LRHS MGos MHer NWad SCoo SEle SPer SPlb SRot SVen SWvt WAbe
	'Violet Wand'	LRHS SHea
	'Vogue'	LRHS
	'Waikiki'	see *H.* 'Mrs Winder'
§	'Warley'	LRHS
	'Warleyensis'	see *H.* 'Warley'
§	'Watson's Pink'	LRHS SHea SPer WKif WSHC
	'White Gem' (*brachysiphon* hybrid) ♀H4	LRHS NPer SEND SHea SPer
	'White Heather'	EPfP LRHS NBir SHea
	'White Paradise'PBR	SPoG
	'Wild Romance'	LBuc LRHS
	'Willcoxii'	see *H. buchananii* 'Fenwickii'
	'Wingletye' ♀H4	CCCN ECou LRHS
	'Winter Glow'	CCCN LRHS SCoo
	'Wiri Blush'	LRHS SLim SWvt
	'Wiri Charm'	CAbP CBcs CMac CSBt EBee EPfP LRHS MGos MSwo SCob SEND SHea SLim
	'Wiri Cloud' ♀H4	CBcs CMac EPfP LRHS MGos MMuc MSwo SCob SEND SEle SRms
	'Wiri Dawn' ♀H4	ELan EPfP EWes LBuc LRHS SLim SRms SWvt
	'Wiri Desire'	CCCN LRHS
	'Wiri Image'	CBcs CSBt EAEE EPfP LRHS MRav SEND
	'Wiri Joy'	LRHS SGol
	'Wiri Mist'	CBcs ELan LRHS MJak SCob
	'Wiri Prince'	LRHS
	'Wiri Splash'	EPfP LRHS SEND SGol
	'Wiri Vision'	CSBt LRHS SEND
	'Wiri Vogue'	LRHS SLim
§	'Youngii' ♀H4	CSBt CTri ELan EPfP GKin LAst LBMP LPot LRHS MAsh MHer MJak MLHP MMuc MRav MWat NBir NPri SEND SGol SLim SPer SPlb SPoG SRms SWvt WCFE WHoo WSHC

Hechtia (*Bromeliaceae*)

	sp.	WCot

Hedeoma (*Lamiaceae*)

	ciliolata	WAbe
	hyssopifolia	SPhx

Hedera ✿ (*Araliaceae*)

	sp.	SCob
§	***algeriensis***	CDoC SArc WFib
	- 'Bellecour'	WFib XLum
§	- 'Gloire de Marengo' (v) ♀H5	CBcs CDul CMac CTri EBee ELan EPfP GCra GKin LAst LBMP LRHS MAsh MBri MGos MJak MSwo NPri SCob SDix SEND SEWo SGol SLim SPer SPoG SWvt WFib WMoo
	- 'Gloire de Marengo' arborescent (v)	SPer
	- 'Marginomaculata' (v)	CDoC EPfP EShb LRHS MAsh SMad SPoG WFib
	- 'Montgomery'	EAEE LRHS
	- 'Ravensholst' ♀H4	CMac EShb MRav SCob SGol WFib
§	***azorica***	EShb WFib
	- 'Pico'	WFib
	canariensis misapplied	see *H. algeriensis*
	- var. ***azorica***	see *H. azorica*
	- 'Cantabrian'	see *H. maroccana* 'Spanish Canary'
	- 'Variegata'	see *H. algeriensis* 'Gloire de Marengo'
	chinensis	see *H. sinensis* var. *sinensis*
	- typica	see *H. sinensis* var. *sinensis*
§	***colchica***	CDul ECrN NWea SPer WCFE WFib
	- 'Arborescens'	see *H. colchica* 'Dendroides'
	- 'Batumi'	MBNS WFib
§	- 'Dendroides'	NWea
	- 'Dentata' ♀H5	CHEx MRav MWhi SGol WFar WFib
	- 'Dentata Aurea'	see *H. colchica* 'Dentata Variegata'
§	- 'Dentata Variegata' (v) ♀H5	Widely available
	- 'My Heart'	see *H. colchica*

	- 'Paddy's Pride'	see *H. colchica* 'Sulphur Heart'
§	- 'Sulphur Heart' (v) 🏆H5	Widely available
	- 'Variegata'	see *H. colchica* 'Dentata Variegata'
	cristata	see *H. helix* 'Parsley Crested'
§	***cypria***	CDoC WFib
	helix	CArn CCVT CMac CTri NWea SCob WSFF XLum
	- 'Adam' (v)	MBri WFib
	- 'Amberwaves'	MBri WFib
	- 'Angularis Aurea' 🏆H5	EPfP NBir WFib
	- 'Anita'	GBin WFib
§	- 'Anna Marie' (v)	CMac MBri SRms WFib
	- 'Anne Borch'	see *H. helix* 'Anna Marie'
	- 'Arborescens'	WSFF XLum
	- 'Ardingly' (v)	MWhi WFib
	- 'Atropurpurea'	ELan EPPr GBin MMuc WFib
	- var. ***baltica***	WFib
	- 'Barabits' Silver' (v)	EPla
	- 'Bill Archer'	GBin WFib
	- 'Bird's Foot'	see *H. helix* 'Pedata'
	- 'Boskoop'	WFib
	- 'Bredon'	MRav
	- 'Brimstone' (v)	WFib
§	- 'Brokamp'	WFib
	- 'Buttercup' 🏆H5	CBcs CDul CMac CTri EHoe ELan EPfP LAst LRHS MAsh MBri MGos MJak MWhi NBid NLar SLim SPoG SRms SWvt WCFE WFib
	- 'Caecilia' (v) 🏆H5	EPfP MSwo SWvt WFib
	- 'Caenwoodiana'	see *H. helix* 'Pedata'
	- 'Caenwoodiana Aurea'	WFib
	- 'Calico' (v)	WFib
	- 'Calypso'	WFib
	- 'Carolina Crinkle'	MWhi
	- 'Cathedral Wall'	WFib
§	- 'Cavendishii' (v)	SRms WFib
§	- 'Ceridwen' (v) 🏆H5	CSde MBri SPlb WFib
	- 'Cheeky'	WFib
	- 'Cheltenham Blizzard' (v)	CNat
	- 'Chester' (v)	LRHS WFib
	- 'Chicago'	WFib
	- 'Chicago Variegated' (v)	WFib
	- 'Chrysophylla'	MSwo
	- 'Clotted Cream' (v)	CMac ECGP ECrN ELon LBMP LRHS MAsh SPoG WFib
	- 'Cockle Shell'	WFib
	- 'Colin'	GBin
§	- 'Congesta' 🏆H5	CMac GCra MLHP NBir SRms WFib
	- 'Conglomerata'	CBcs ELan EPla MMoz NBir SRms WFib
	- 'Conglomerata Erecta'	see *H. helix* 'Erecta'
	- 'Courage'	WFib
	- 'Crenata'	WFib
	- 'Crispa'	MRav
	- 'Cristata'	see *H. helix* 'Parsley Crested'
	- 'Curleylocks'	see *H. helix* 'Manda's Crested'
	- 'Curley-Q'	see *H. helix* 'Dragon Claw'
	- 'Curvaceous' (v)	WFib
	- 'Cyprus'	see *H. cypria*
§	- 'Dealbata' (v)	CMac WFib
	- 'Deltoidea'	see *H. hibernica* 'Deltoidea'
	- 'Discolor'	see *H. helix* 'Minor Marmorata', *H. helix* 'Dealbata'
§	- 'Donerailensis'	MBlu WFib
	- 'Don's Papillon'	CNat
§	- 'Dragon Claw'	WFib
	- 'Duckfoot' 🏆H5	CDoC EShb MWhi WCot WFib
	- 'Eileen' (v)	WFib
	- 'Elfenbein' (v)	WFib
§	- 'Erecta'	CDul CTca EPPr EPfP GCal IDee LAst LRHS MBlu MGos NHol NWad SHil SPer SPlb WCFE WFib XLum
	- 'Ester' (v)	LAst SRGP WHar
§	- 'Eva' (v)	WFib
	- 'Fantasia' (v)	MBri WFib
	- 'Feenfinger'	WFib
	- 'Filigran'	WFib
	- 'Flashback' (v)	WFib
	- 'Flavescens'	WFib
	- 'Fluffy Ruffles'	WFib
I	- 'Francis Ivy'	WFib
	- 'Frosty' (v)	WFib
	- 'Garland'	WFib
	- 'Gavotte'	WFib
	- 'Gilded Hawke'	WFib
	- 'Glache' (v)	MRav WFib
	- 'Glacier' (v) 🏆H5	CBcs CDoC CDul CTri ELan EPfP LBMP LPal LRHS MAsh MBri MGos MJak MMuc MRav MSwo MWhi NBro NHol NWea SCob SEND SLim SPer SPoG SRms SWvt WFib
	- 'Glymii'	EBee ELan WFib
	- 'Gold Harald'	see *H. helix* 'Goldchild'
	- 'Gold Ripple'	NLar SEND
§	- 'Goldchild' (v) 🏆H5	CBcs CDoC CMac EBee ELon EPfP EShb LAst LRHS MAsh MGos MJak MMuc MRav MSwo MWat NBir NHol SCob SLim SPer SPoG SWvt WFib WHar
	- 'Golden Ann'	see *H. helix* 'Ceridwen'
*	- 'Golden Arrow'	LRHS MAsh
	- 'Golden Curl' (v)	CMac EPfP LRHS
	- 'Golden Ester'	see *H. helix* 'Ceridwen'
	- 'Golden Girl'	WFib
	- 'Golden Ingot' (v) 🏆H5	ELan MWhi WFib
	- 'Golden Jytte' (v)	WFib
	- 'Golden Kolibri'	see *H. helix* 'Midas Touch'
	- 'Golden Mathilde' (v)	GBin
	- 'Goldfinch'	MBri WFib
	- 'Goldfinger'	MBri WFib
	- 'Goldheart'	see *H. helix* 'Oro di Bogliasco'
	- 'Goldstern' (v)	MRav MWhi WFib
	- 'Gracilis'	see *H. hibernica* 'Gracilis'
	- 'Green Finger'	see *H. helix* 'Très Coupé'
	- 'Green Ripple'	CBcs CTri EAEE ELan EPfP LRHS MBlu MGos MJak MMuc MSwo MWht NBro SCob SEND SLim SPer SPlb SRms SWvt WFib
	- 'Greenman'	WFib
	- 'Halebob'	MBri WFib
	- 'Hamilton'	see *H. hibernica* 'Hamilton'
	- 'Harald' (v)	CTri EBee WFib
	- 'Harry Wood'	see *H. helix* 'Modern Times'
*	- 'Hazel' (v)	WFib
	- 'Heise' (v)	WFib
	- 'Heise Denmark' (v)	WFib
	- 'Helvig'	see *H. helix* 'White Knight'
	- 'Henrietta'	WFib
	- 'Hispanica'	see *H. iberica*
	- 'Hite's Miniature'	see *H. helix* 'Merion Beauty'
	- 'Holly'	see *H. helix* 'Parsley Crested'
	- 'Hullavington'	CNat
	- 'Humpty Dumpty'	CExl
	- 'Imp'	see *H. helix* 'Brokamp'
	- 'Ivalace'	CBcs EAEE EPfP EShb MGos MSwo MWhi SRms WFib XLum

	Plant	Suppliers
	- 'Jake'	MBri WFib
	- 'Jasper'	WFib
	- 'Jersey Doris' (v)	WFib
	- 'Jerusalem'	see *H. helix* 'Schäfer Three'
	- 'Jester's Gold'	EPfP MBri
	- 'Jubilee' (v)	WFib
	- 'Kaleidoscope'	WFib
	- 'Kevin'	WFib
	- 'Kolibri' (v)	CDoC EPfP LAst MBri WFib
§	- 'Königer's Auslese'	WFib
	- 'Lalla Rookh'	MRav WFib WRHF
	- 'Leo Swicegood'	MWhi WFib
	- 'Light Fingers'	ELon EPfP LRHS WFib
	- 'Little Diamond' (v)	CDoC CMac CTri ELan LRHS MBri SLon SWvt WFib WHrl
	- 'Little Luzii'	WFib
	- 'Liz'	see *H. helix* 'Eva'
	- 'Luzii' (v)	WFib
	- 'Maculata'	see *H. helix* 'Minor Marmorata'
§	- 'Manda's Crested' ♀H5	ELan NLar WFib
	- 'Maple Leaf' ♀H5	EShb WFib
	- 'Maple Queen'	MBri
	- 'Marginata Elegantissima'	see *H. helix* 'Tricolor'
	- 'Marginata Minor'	see *H. helix* 'Cavendishii'
I	- 'Marmorata' Fibrex	WFib
	- 'Mathilde' (v)	WFib
	- 'Melanie'	SRGP WFib
	- 'Meon'	WFib
§	- 'Merion Beauty'	WFib
§	- 'Midas Touch' (v) ♀H5	EPPr EPfP MBri WFib
	- 'Mini Ester' (v)	MBri
	- 'Mini Heron'	MBri
	- 'Minima' misapplied	see *H. helix* 'Spetchley'
	- 'Minima' Hibberd	see *H. helix* 'Donerailensis'
	- 'Minima' M.Young	see *H. helix* 'Congesta'
§	- 'Minor Marmorata' (v)	XLum
	- 'Mint Kolibri'	EHoe MBri
	- 'Minty' (v)	WFib
	- 'Misty' (v)	WFib
§	- 'Modern Times'	LPal
	- 'Needlepoint'	XLum
	- 'Niagara Falls'	LRHS
	- 'Nigra Aurea' (v)	WFib
	- 'Obovata'	WFib
	- 'Oro di Bogliasco' (v)	CDul CMac CTri EBee ECrN EPfP LRHS MAsh MBri MJak MMuc MRav MSwo NLar NWad NWea SCob SEND SLim SPer SPlb SRms SWvt WFar WFib
	- 'Ovata'	WFib
§	- 'Parsley Crested' ♀H5	EPfP NBid SGol WFib
	- 'Patent Leather'	WFib
	- 'Pedata'	CDul MSwo WFib
	- 'Perkeo'	WFib
	- 'Peter' (v)	WFib
	- 'Pink 'n' Curly'	WCot WFib
	- 'Pink 'n' Very Curly'	WCot
§	- 'Pittsburgh'	WFib
	- 'Plume d'Or'	WFib
§	- f. ***poetarum***	MBlu WCot WFib
	- - 'Poetica Arborea'	SDix
	- 'Poetica'	see *H. helix* f. *poetarum*
	- 'Raleigh Delight' (v)	WCot
	- 'Ray's Supreme'	see *H. helix* 'Pittsburgh'
	- subsp. ***rhizomatifera***	WFib
	- 'Richard John'	WFib
	- 'Ritterkreuz'	WFib
	- 'Romanze' (v)	WFib
	- 'Russelliana'	WFib
	- 'Sagittifolia' misapplied	see *H. helix* 'Königer's Auslese'
	- 'Sagittifolia' Hibberd	see *H. hibernica* 'Sagittifolia'
	- 'Sagittifolia' ambig.	ECrN LRHS MAsh MBlu
	- 'Sagittifolia Variegata' (v)	MBri WFib WRHF
	- 'Saint Agnes'	LRHS
	- 'Sally' (v)	WFib
	- 'Salt and Pepper'	see *H. helix* 'Minor Marmorata'
§	- 'Schäfer Three' (v)	WFib
	- 'Seabreeze'	WFib
	- 'Shamrock' ♀H5	EPfP WFib
	- 'Shannon'	WFib
	- 'Silver Ferny'	WFib
	- 'Silver King' (v)	WFib
	- 'Silver Queen'	see *H. helix* 'Tricolor'
§	- 'Spetchley' ♀H5	CMac GCal GEdr GKev MAsh MRav MWhi NLar NPer NWad WCot WFib WHrl
	- 'Splashes'	WFib
	- 'Sunrise'	WFib
	- 'Suzanne'	see *H. nepalensis* 'Suzanne'
	- 'Tanja'	WFib
	- 'Teardrop'	WFib
	- 'Telecurl'	WFib
	- 'Temptation' (v)	WFib
	- 'Tenerife' (v)	WFib
	- 'Topazolite' (v)	WFib
§	- 'Très Coupé'	CDoC LRHS MMuc SArc SEND
§	- 'Tricolor' (v)	CMac CTri EPfP WCFE WFib
	- 'Trinity' (v)	WFib
	- 'Tripod'	WFib
	- 'Triton'	EPfP WFib
	- 'Troll'	WFib
	- 'Ursula' (v)	WFib
	- 'Very Merry'	WFib
*	- 'Vitifolium'	WFib
§	- 'White Knight' (v) ♀H5	WFib
	- 'White Mein Herz' (v)	WFib
	- 'White Ripple' (v)	WFib
	- 'Williamsiana' (v)	WFib
	- 'Winter Purple Vein'	CNat
	- 'Woerneri'	NLar WFib
	- 'Woodsii'	see *H. helix* 'Modern Times'
	- 'Yellow Ripple'	EShb MBri WFib
	- 'Zebra' (v)	WFib
	hibernica	CCVT CDul CSBt CSde EAEE EPfP LBuc LPal LRHS MJak MRav MSwo MWhi NWea SCob SEWo SGol SPer SWvt WFib
	- 'Anna Marie'	see *H. helix* 'Anna Marie'
I	- 'Arbori Compact'	EPfP WBor
	- 'Betty Allen'	WFib
§	- 'Deltoidea' ♀H5	MWht WCFE WFib
I	- 'Digitata Crûg Gold'	WCot WCru
	- 'Ebony'	WFib
	- 'Glengariff'	WFib
§	- 'Gracilis'	WFib
§	- 'Hamilton'	WFib
	- 'Helena' (v)	CNec
	- 'Lobata Major'	SRms
	- 'Maculata' (v)	WSHC
	- 'Palmata'	WFib
	- 'Rona'	WFib
§	- 'Sagittifolia'	CTri EPfP
	- 'Sulphurea' (v)	WFib
	- 'Variegata' (v)	WFib
§	***iberica***	WFib
	maderensis	WFib
	maroccana 'Morocco'	WFib

§ - 'Spanish Canary' WFib
nepalensis WFib
- 'Marble Dragon' see *H. sinensis* var. *sinensis* 'Marble Dragon'
§ - 'Suzanne' WFib
pastuchovii CDoC EShb WFib
- from Troödos, Cyprus see *H. cypria*
- 'Ann Ala' ♀H5 CDoC CFil GBin MBlu WCot WFib WGwG
- 'Lagocetti' WFib
§ ***rhombea*** WCot WFib
- 'Eastern Dawn' WFib
- 'Japonica' see *H. rhombea*
- var. ***rhombea*** 'Variegata' (v) WFib
§ ***sinensis*** var. ***sinensis*** WFib
- - KWJ 12345 WCru
§ - - 'Marble Dragon' WFib

Hedychium ✿ (*Zingiberaceae*)

'Anne Bishop' NLos SEND
aurantiacum CBcs CBct CCCN CHEx CTsd GKev LAma LEdu SBig XLum
brevicaule B&SWJ 7171 WCru
'C.P. Raffill' see *H.* × *moorei* 'Raffillii'
chrysoleucum CCCN
* 'Clarkei' CTsd
coccineum CDTJ CTsd EUJe GKev IKil LPal MNrw SBig XLum
- B&SWJ 5238 WCru
- var. ***angustifolium*** CFil WPGP
- - 'Disney' CDTJ
- - 'Shillong Orange Ghost' **new** LEdu
coronarium ♀H1c CAbb CAvo CBct CCCN CDTJ CExl CFil CHll CTsd EUJe GKev IKil LLWG MMuc NLos SBig SPer WPGP XBlo XLum
- B&SWJ 3745 WCru
- 'Gold Spot' CBct CCCN CTsd EUJe GKev NLos SKHP
- var. ***urophyllum*** IBlr
- - HWJ 604 WCru
densiflorum CAbb CCCN CDTJ CExl CHEx CHll CTsd ECha EUJe GKev IBlr LEdu NLos SDix SSpi WCot WCru WPGP XLum
- EN 562 CExl CFil
- LS&H 17393 CExl CFil WPGP
- Sch 582 CDes
- 'Assam Orange' CAvo CCCN CDes CDoC CExl CHEx CPne CSam CTsd EBee GCal IBlr LEdu LRHS MNrw SBig SChr SDix SEND SMad SPlb WCru WPGP
- pale-flowered **new** GCal
- 'Sorung' CExl CFil LEdu SChr WPGP
- 'Stephen' CAvo CBct CCCN CCon CDTJ CDes CExl CFil CHEx EUJe LEdu LRHS MNrw SChr SPlb WPGP
'Devon Cream' CCCN CDTJ CExl CHll LRHS SChr
'Doctor Moy' (v) CDTJ EUJe
'Elizabeth' CCon
ellipticum CAbb CCCN CDTJ CTsd EUJe GCal GKev LAma NLos SBig XLum
- B&SWJ 8354 WCru
'Filigree' CExl
§ ***flavescens*** CBct CCCN CDTJ CTsd EBee EUJe GKev LAma NLos SChr
flavum misapplied see *H. flavescens*
flavum Roxb. CAbb CBcs XLum
forrestii misapplied see *H.* 'Helen Dillon'
gardnerianum ♀H2 CAbb CCon CExl CHEx CHll CPne CTsd EUJe GKev IDee IKil LAma LEdu LPal LRHS MNrw NLos NSoo SArc SChr SDeJ SPer WCru WPGP XLum
'Gold Flame' EBee
gracile EUJe NLos WCru
greenii CBcs CBct CCCN CCon CHEx CHll CPne CTsd EUJe GKev LEdu LPal MNrw NLos NSoo SBig SDix SPlb WBor WCru XLum
griffithianum CCCN CTsd EBee GKev IKil SBig XLum
- white-flowered CCCN
'Hardy Exotics 1' CHEx
§ 'Helen Dillon' CCCN CDes CExl EUJe GCal IBlr MNrw SArc SPlb WCru WPGP
'Luna Moth' CFil NLos WPGP
luteum CTsd
maximum CFil NLos SChr SKHP WPGP
- B&SWJ 8261A WCru
- HWJ 810 WCru
§ × ***moorei*** 'Raffillii' MNrw SBig WCru
'Orange Glow' **new** CPne
'Pink Princess' CBct
'Pink V' CCon NLos
'Pradhan' CCon
'Samsheri' CCCN CHll SChr
spicatum CAbb CAvo CCCN CCon CDTJ CExl CHEx CTsd EUJe EWld GCal GKev GPoy IBlr LEdu MNrw NLos WPGP
- B&SWJ 7231 WCru
- BWJ 8116 from Sichuan, China WCru
- CC 1705 CExl
- P. Bon. 57188 CExl CFil WPGP
- from Ciaojiang **new** SBrt
- from Salween Valley, China CExl
- 'Himalayan Lipstick' GKev
- 'Huani' **new** LEdu
- 'Liberty' WCru
- 'Singalila' WCru
'St Martin's' CCCN
stenopetalum B&SWJ 7155 WCru
'Tahitian Flame' (v) EUJe
'Tai Pink Princess' (Tai Series) CTsd
'Tara' ♀H4 CAbb CAvo CBct CDes CDoC CExl CHEx CHll CPne CSam EBee EUJe IBlr LEdu LRHS MNrw SArc SChr SPlb SPoG WCru WPGP
thyrsiforme CTsd EUJe GKev NSoo SBig WCru XLum
villosum CDTJ
- var. ***tenuiflorum*** KWJ 12305 **new** WCru
wardii CExl CFil CTsd EUJe WPGP
× ***wilkeanum*** SPer
yunnanense CCon CDes CHll LEdu SBig SBrt WPGP
- B&SWJ 9717 WCru
- BWJ 7900 WCru
- L 633 CExl IBlr
- from Cally Gardens GCal

Hedysarum (*Papilionaceae*)

	coronarium	CSpe ELan WKif
	hedysaroides	IKil SPhx
	multijugum	MBlu WSHC
	tauricum	SPhx

Heimia (*Lythraceae*)

	salicifolia	CArn IMou

Helenium ✿ (*Asteraceae*)

	'Adios'	MAvo
	'Amber' **new**	ECtt MSpe
	autumnale	CBod CExl CSBt CTri LPot MLHP MMuc NChi SWvt WFar WHar WMoo WPtf XLum
	- 'All Gold'	SWvt
I	- 'Cupreum'	SBch
§	- Helena Series	SWvt
§	- - 'Helena Gold'	EPfP NBre
	- - 'Helena Rote Töne'	CBod CNec EAJP EPfP LBMP LRHS LSun MWhi
	- - 'Helena Yellow' **new**	LRHS
	'Baronin Linden'	MAvo MSpe
	'Baudirektor Linne' ♀H7	CSam LEdu LRHS MSpe MTis
	'Beatrice'	MSpe
	'Biedermeier'	CWCL ECtt LRHS MSpe WCAu
	bigelovii	XLum
	'Blanche Royale'	MSpe
	'Blütentisch' misapplied	see *H.* 'Riverton Beauty'
	'Blütentisch' Foerster ♀H7	CHVG CMea CPrp GMaP LRHS MAvo MTis NCGa NLar WMnd WWEG
	'Bressingham Gold'	LRHS MNrw MSpe WHrl
	'Bruno'	CAby ELon LRHS MArl MSpe SMrm
	'Butterpat' ♀H7	ECtt GCra GMaP LRHS MArl MRav NSti WWEG
	'Can Can'	ECtt ELon LSou MAsh MAvo MBri MSpe MTis NGdn SPer WFar
	'Chelsey'	CPrp CTsd ECtt ELan EPfP GQue LRHS LSou MBri MNrw MRav MSpe NLar NSti WBor WHil
	'Chipperfield Orange'	CElw CSam EBee ECtt GMaP MArl MSpe NGdn WOld WWEG
	'Coppelia'	LRHS MTis NBir NGdn
	Copper Spray	see *H.* 'Kupfersprudel'
	'Crimson Beauty'	LRHS
	Dark Beauty	see *H.* 'Dunkle Pracht'
	'Dauerbrenner'	LEdu MAvo MSpe MTis
	'Die Blonde'	MAvo SMHy
	'Doktor Hartmann' **new**	MSpe
	'Double Trouble'PBR	CMos COtt EBee ECtt IBoy IKil LLHF LRHS MAsh MBNS MBri MSpe NGdn NPri SGbt SPer SPoG WCAu WCot WFar
§	'Dunkle Pracht' ♀H7	CHVG CSam EBee ECtt MPie MSpe NLar NPri WCot WFar WOld WWEG
	'El Dorado'	CSam ECtt EWoo MAsh MAvo MSpe MTis SHar WCot WFar
	'Fata Morgana'	CBod ECtt LLHF MTis NBre
	'Feuersiegel' ♀H7	CSam ECtt LRHS MSpe WOld
	'Fiesta'	ECtt MAvo MBri MSpe NDov
	'Flammendes Käthchen'	CSam EBee EHoe LRHS MAvo NCGa NDov SHar SMrm SPhx
	'Flammenrad'	CAby CSam EBee MSpe
	'Flammenspiel'	ECtt LRHS MCot MNrw MSpe NLar
	flexuosum	SPhx
	'Françoise'	CSam
	'Gartensonne' ♀H7	CSam MSpe SMrm WWEG
	'Gay-go-round'	CSam MSpe
	'Gelbe Waltraut'	MSpe
	Gold Fox	see *H.* 'Goldfuchs'
	'Gold Intoxication'	see *H.* 'Goldrausch'
	Golden Youth	see *H.* 'Goldene Jugend'
§	'Goldene Jugend'	CMea ELan MSpe MTis WCot WWEG
§	'Goldfuchs'	CWCL MSpe WCot
	'Goldkogel'	EBee MSpe
§	'Goldlackzwerg'	LRHS MSpe MTis
§	'Goldrausch'	CAby CSam CWCL EBee ECtt EPfP GCra LSou MSpe MTis MWat NGdn NSti WFar WMoo WOld WWEG
	'Goldreif'	MSpe
	'Goldriese'	MSpe
	'Hartmut Rieger'	CSam MSpe
	'Helena' misapplied	see *H. autumnale* 'Helena Gold'
	'Helena' Foerster	MSpe
	'Herbstgold'	MSpe
	hoopesii	see *Hymenoxys hoopesii*
	'Hot Lava' **new**	ECtt MAsh MBel MSpe SCob
	'Hot Luv' **new**	MSpe
	'Indianersommer'	CElw CSam ECtt GMaP LRHS MSpe NDov NLar NOrc SGSe SPer SPtp WWEG
	'Jam Tarts'	WCot
	'Julisamt'	LEdu
	'July Sun'	NBir
	'Kanaria'	CAby CHVG CPrp EBee ECtt EWll GBin GKev GQue LRHS MAvo MRav MSpe MTis NDov NEgg NLar SMrm WHil WMnd
	'Karneol' ♀H7	CSam MSpe
	'Kleine Aprikose'	MSpe MTis
	'Kleiner Fuchs'	MHer MSpe NLar WWEG
	'Kokarde'	CSam MAvo MSpe WWEG
	'Königstiger'	CSam ECtt GBin LRHS LSou MNrw MSpe MTis NDov SMrm WFar
	'Kugelsonne'	CSam MSpe NBre
§	'Kupfersprudel'	MAvo MSpe MTis
	'Kupferziegel'	CSam MSpe MTis
	'Kupferzwerg'	CWCL ELan IPot MSpe NBre NDov SPhx
	'Lambada'	EBee IPot MSpe MTis
	'Louise Beacock'	MSpe
	'Loysder Wieck'	EBee ECtt EPfP LRHS MAvo MSpe MTis NGdn SHil WWEG
	'Luc'	MAvo MSpe MTis WCot
§	'Mahagoni'	CSam LEdu MSpe
	'Mahogany'	see *H.* 'Goldlackzwerg'
	Mahogany	see *H.* 'Mahagoni'
	'Mardi Gras'	CMac ECtt LRHS LSou MBel MBri MSpe MTis NCGa SLon SPoG
	'Margot'	CAby CSam CWCL MSpe MTis NBre
	'Marion Nickig'	CSam MSpe MTis
	'Meranti'	CMea MAvo WCot
	'Mien Ruys'	MSpe
	'Moerheim Beauty' ♀H7	Widely available
	'Moth'	MSpe NPCo
	'Oldenburg'	MSpe
	'Patsy'	MSpe
	Pipsqueak = 'Blopip'	LLHF LRHS NBre SPoG
	'Potter's Wheel'	MSpe WCot WWEG
	puberulum	CBod LRHS NBir
	'Puck'	MSpe
	'Pumilum Magnificum'	CWCL ELan EPfP GQue IBoy LEdu LRHS MSpe MTis SMad WFar WPGP XLum

	'Ragamuffin'	CSam MSpe MTis WCot
	'Rauchtopas'	CAby CSam EBee GQue IPot LSou MAvo MSpe MTis NCGa NDov SDix SMrm WHoo WPGP
	Red and Gold	see *H.* 'Rotgold' Foerster
	'Red Army'	CAby CHVG CPrp CSam ELan ELon IPot LEdu LRHS LSou MAvo MBri MNrw MSpe MTis NCGa NGdn NLar SWvt
	'Red Glory'	MSpe
	'Red Jewel'	Widely available
	'Ring of Fire' 🏆H7	MSpe SMHy
§	'Riverton Beauty'	CSam ECtt LLHF MNrw MSpe WCot WHoo
	'Riverton Gem'	CSam ECtt LLHF MNrw MSpe NChi WHoo
	'Rotgold' misapplied	see *H. autumnale* Helena Series
§	'Rotgold' Foerster	CBod ECtt NChi SRms WMoo
	'Rouge Foncé' **new**	WCot
	'Rubinzwerg' 🏆H7	Widely available
	'Ruby Charm' **new**	ECtt MAsh MSpe SMrm WFar
§	'Ruby Thuesday'	CAby CMos CTsd ECtt ELan EPfP IBoy IKil IPot LLHF LRHS MAvo MBNS MBel MNrw MSpe MTis NGdn NHol NLar NSti SCob SMad SPoG SWvt WCAu
	'Ruby Tuesday'	see *H.* 'Ruby Thuesday'
	'Sahin's Early Flowerer' 🏆H7	Widely available
	'Samtjuwel'	MSpe MTis
	'Schokoladenkönigin'	MSpe
	'Septemberfuchs'	LEdu LPla MCot MTis NDov SPhx WWEG
	'Septembergold'	MSpe
	'Sonnenwunder'	CSam MLHP MSpe NBre
	'Sophie zur Linden'	MSpe MTis WCot
	'Sunshine'	MSpe
	'Sunshine Superman'	MSpe
	'The Bishop'	EBee ECtt ELon EPfP GCra LAst LBMP LRHS MBri MRav MSpe NHol NPCo NPri NSoo SCob SGbt SGol SPer SWvt WFar WMnd
	'Tie Dye'	EBee MSpe SMrm SPoG WFar
	'Tijuana Brass'	ECtt NLar
	'Tip Top'	EAJP
	'Tura'	MSpe
	'Two Faced Fan'	MSpe MTis
	'Vicky'	MAvo MSpe
	'Vivace'	LEdu MAvo MSpe WCot
	'Wagon Wheel'	MSpe WCot WWEG
	'Waldhorn'	MSpe MTis
	'Waltraut' 🏆H7	Widely available
	'Wesergold' 🏆H7	EBee LLHF LRHS LSou MAvo MHer MSpe NDov NLar
	'Westerstede'	MSpe MTis
	'Wonnadonga'	GBin MSpe MTis
	'Wyndley'	CBcs CHVG CMea CSam ECtt EHoe ELan EPfP GMaP LRHS LSou MAsh MBri MHer MRav MSpe MTis NGdn NLar NPri NSti SCob SGSe SMrm SPer WCAu WFar WHoo WMnd WWEG
	'Zimbelstern'	CCse ECtt ELon IPot MAvo MCot MPie MSpe MTis NLar SPhx WCot WFar WPGP WWEG

Helianthella (*Asteraceae*)

§	***quinquenervis***	EBee GCal LLHF MHer NLar SMad SPer

Helianthemum (*Cistaceae*)

	sp.	SCob SVic
	'Alice Howorth'	WIce
	alpestre serpyllifolium	see *H. nummularium* subsp. *glabrum*
	'Amabile Plenum' (d)	GAbr GCal
	'Amy Baring' 🏆H4	CTri ECho ECtt GAbr GCrg LRHS NWad
	'Annabel' (d)	ECho ECtt GAbr LRHS NSla
	apenninum	EWTr LLHF SRms XLum
	'Apricot'	CTri ECtt
	'Apricot Blush'	WAbe
	'Baby Buttercup'	CMea GAbr
	'Beech Park Red'	CTri EPot GCrg MHer WAbe WHoo WIce WKif
	'Ben Afflick'	ECho ECtt LRHS SRms
	'Ben Alder'	ECtt GAbr MHer
	'Ben Dearg'	CMea ECho ECtt SRms
	'Ben Fhada'	CBcs CMea CTal CTri ECho ECtt ELan ELon EPfP GAbr GCrg GJos GMaP LBMP LBee LRHS MAsh MHer MLHP NEgg SEND SPoG SRGP SRms WAbe XLum
	'Ben Heckla'	CTal ECho ECtt GAbr LRHS MAsh SRms XLum
	'Ben Hope'	CTri ECho ECtt ELan EPfP EWoo MJak SGol SRGP SRms XLum
§	'Ben Ledi'	CBcs CTal ECho ECtt ELan ELon EPfP GAbr GCrg GMaP MAsh MHer MSCN NHol NSla SEND SGbt SPoG SRms SRot WAbe
	'Ben Lomond'	ECho GAbr
	'Ben More'	CBcs CHel CMea CTal ECho ECtt ELan EPfP GAbr GJos GMaP LRHS MAsh MRav MSwo NBir SEND SIgm SPoG SRGP SRms SRot WHoo WIce
	'Ben Nevis'	CTri ECho ECtt GAbr SRms
	'Ben Vane'	ECho ECtt LRHS
	'Boughton Double Primrose' (d)	ECho ECtt WAbe WHoo WSHC
	'Broughty Beacon'	ECtt
	'Broughty Sunset'	ECtt GAbr NBir
	'Bunbury'	ECtt ELon GAbr GCrg GJos LRHS MWat NBir SDix SPoG SRms WIce WRHF
	canum subsp. ***balcanicum***	WAbe
	'Captivation'	ECtt GAbr NHol
	'Cerise Queen' (d)	CTal CTri ECha ECho ECtt EPfP GAbr GKev LAst LBMP MCot MSwo SDix SEND SRms WHoo XSen
	chamaecistus	see *H. nummularium*
	'Cheviot'	GAbr NBir SBch WHoo WSHC XLum
I	'Chloe's Variegata' (v)	EWes
	'Chocolate Blotch'	ECho GCra LRHS NWad SEND SRms
	'Cornish Cream'	ECtt GAbr LBee NHol SRms
	cupreum	ECtt GAbr
	'David'	NHol
	'David Ritchie'	WHoo
	'Diana'	CMea SBch
	double apricot-flowered (d)	GAbr
	double primrose-flowered (d)	GAbr
	'Dunwich'	GGal
	'Everton Ruby'	see *H.* 'Ben Ledi'
	'Fairy'	ELan EPfP GAbr LLHF

§	'Fire Dragon' 🏆H4	CMea CTal ECho ECtt ELan EPfP EWoo GAbr GCrg GMaP GQue LRHS NBir SGbt SIgm SRms WAbe WRHF XLum XSen
	'Fireball'	see *H.* 'Mrs C.W. Earle'
	'Firegold' (v)	WAbe
	'Georgeham'	CMea CSam CTal ECtt ELon GAbr GCrg NBir NHol SRms WHoo WRHF XLum
§	'Golden Queen'	ECho ECtt EPfP GAbr LAst MAsh MCot MSwo WRHF
	'Hampstead Orange'	CTri
	'Hartswood Ruby'	GMaP MBNS SRms
	'Henfield Brilliant' 🏆H4	CExl CHVG CSam CSpe CTal ECho ECtt ELan EPfP EWoo GAbr GCrg GEdr LRHS MRav NBir NHol NSla SDix SIgm SMad SRms WHoo XLum
	'Highdown'	GAbr SRms
	'Highdown Apricot'	ECho ECtt GCrg GJos LLHF LRHS SPoG SRms
	'Honeymoon'	ECtt EPfP GAbr NWad
	hymettium	ITim
	'Jeanie' (d)	ECho
	'Jubilee' (d) 🏆H4	CHVG CTal CTri ECho ECtt ELan ELon EPfP GAbr GJos MAsh MBNS NBir NChi NHol SPoG SRms WHil WKif
	'Karen's Silver'	WAbe
	'Kathleen Druce' (d)	CTal ECho ECtt EWes GAbr NWad WHoo
	'Kathleen Mary'	CMea
	'Lawrenson's Pink'	CTal ECho ECtt GAbr GCrg LPot LRHS MLHP SRGP SRms
	'Lemon Queen'	GCrg
	'Lucy Elizabeth'	ECtt
	lunulatum	CMea ECho LLHF LRHS NWad WAbe
	'Magnificum'	MWat
	'Mead Sunset' **new**	CMea
§	'Mrs C.W. Earle' (d) 🏆H4	CTri ECho ECtt ELan EPfP GCra LRHS MBNS MWat NSla SRms
	'Mrs Clay'	see *H.* 'Fire Dragon'
	'Mrs Hays'	ECtt
	'Mrs Lake'	GAbr
	'Mrs Moules'	SRms
	mutabile	SPhx SPlb
	'New Moon' **new**	CTal
§	***nummularium***	ECho ENfk GPoy MHer MNHC NMir WAbe WIce WSFF XSen
§	- subsp. ***glabrum***	GAbr
§	- subsp. ***tomentosum***	GAbr MWat
	oelandicum	NSla NWad SRms WAbe
	- subsp. ***piloselloides***	WAbe
	'Old Gold'	CTal ECtt GAbr SRms WAbe
	'Orange Phoenix' (d)	ECtt EPfP MBNS NWad
	'Ovum Supreme'	GAbr NHol
	'Pink Angel' (d)	CTal ECtt ELon GCrg MBNS WAbe
	'Praecox'	CMea CTri ECho ECtt GAbr SRms WHoo
	'Prima Donna'	ELan EPfP NBir
	'Prostrate Orange'	SRms
	'Raspberry Ripple'	ECho ECtt ELan EPfP EPot EWTr GCrg LRHS SPoG SRms
	'Razzle Dazzle' (v)	ECtt ELon LLHF SLon SRms
	'Red Dragon'	EPot GCrg MLHP WAbe
	'Red Orient'	see *H.* 'Supreme'
	'Regenbogen' (d)	GCal SEND
§	'Rhodanthe Carneum' 🏆H4	Widely available
† §	'Rosakönigin'	ECtt GAbr MHer NHol WAbe WRHF
	'Rose of Leeswood' (d)	CMea CTri ECtt LBee NEgg SPoG SRms WHoo WKif WSHC XLum
	Rose Queen	see *H.* 'Rosakönigin'
	'Roxburgh Gold'	SRms
	'Ruth'	SEND
	'Saint John's College Yellow'	CSam ECho LRHS
	'Salmon Queen'	ECho ECtt GAbr LRHS SEND SRms
*	***scardicum***	CMea
	serpyllifolium	see *H. nummularium* subsp. *glabrum*
	'Shot Silk'	CTal ECtt EWes SRms
	'Snow Queen'	see *H.* 'The Bride'
	'Sterntaler'	GAbr LLHF SRms
	'Sudbury Gem'	CTri ECha ECho ECtt LRHS SEND SGol
	'Sulphur Moon'	ECho LLHF LRHS
	'Sulphureum Plenum' (d)	SGol
	'Sunbeam'	ECho ECtt SRms
§	'Supreme'	ECho ELan EPfP EWes SEND SRms XLum XSen
	'Tangerine'	ECtt
§	'The Bride' 🏆H4	CBcs CMea CSpe CTal ECha ECho ECtt ELan EPfP GJos GMaP LAst LRHS MAsh MHer MRav NPri SDix SIgm SPer SPoG SRms SRot WAbe WHoo WKif XLum
	'Tigrinum Plenum' (d)	ECho EWes
	'Tomato Red'	NSla SEND XLum
	tomentosum	see *H. nummularium* subsp. *tomentosum*
	umbellatum	see *Halimium umbellatum*
	'Voltaire'	CTal ECtt GAbr LLHF NWad XLum
	'Watergate Rose'	MWat NBir
	'Welsh Flame'	ECtt NHol WAbe
	'Whenday'	CMea
	'Wisley Pink'	see *H.* 'Rhodanthe Carneum'
	'Wisley Primrose' 🏆H4	Widely available
	'Wisley Rose'	LRHS
	'Wisley White'	CTri ECha ECho ECtt ELan EPfP GAbr
	'Wisley Yellow'	ECtt ELan
	'Yellow Queen'	see *H.* 'Golden Queen'

Helianthus (*Asteraceae*)

sp.	SVic
atrorubens	MRav MSpe NBro
'Bitter Chocolate'	MAvo MSpe NLar WBor
'Capenoch Star' 🏆H7	CElw CPrp ECtt GMaP IBoy LEdu LRHS MBri MRav MSpe MTis NBro NLar SDix SMrm SWvt WWEG
'Capenoch Supreme'	ECtt LRHS
'Carine'	MLHP MNrw MTis NLar WCot
'Cosmic Whisper'	MPie
decapetalus Morning Sun	see *H.* 'Morgensonne'
'Dorian Roxburgh'	MAvo MTis
'Double Whammy' (d) **new**	ECtt
giganteus	SHar
- 'Sheila's Sunshine'	CBre CElw EWes GBin LRHS NDov SHar SMHy WOld WWEG
grosseserratus	MPie
'Gullick's Variety' 🏆H7	CBre ECtt LLWP NBro NChi NLar SPhx SWvt WOld WWEG XLum
'Happy Days'	CBre CElw ECtt ELon EWes LBMP LSou MPie MSpe MTis NCGa NSti WCot WHoo WMoo WWEG
'Hazel's Gold'	LRHS

	hirsutus	EBee
	× ***kellermanii***	EBee MTis SPhx
§	× ***laetiflorus***	MWhi NLar NOrc
	- 'Daniel Dewar' **new**	MMuc
§	'Lemon Queen' ♀H7	Widely available
	'Limelight'	see *H.* 'Lemon Queen'
	'Loddon Gold' ♀H7	ECtt ELan EPfP LRHS MBel MRav MSCN MSpe MTis NBir NWsh SMrm SRGP SWvt WBor WCot WWEG
§	***maximiliani***	ELan ELon MMuc SPhx SPtp
	microcephalus	CSam EBee ELon MMuc NDov WPtf
	- 'JS Straffe Prairie Gast'	EBee
	'Miss Mellish' ♀H7	EBee GCal LEdu MSCN MSpe WBrk WCot WHoo WWEG
	mollis	CSam SBrt SPav SPhx
	'Monarch' ♀H4	CMea CSam EBee GBee MAvo MBel MMuc MRav MSpe NCGa NLar WCot WHal WHil WOld WWEG
§	'Morgensonne'	MTis MWat WBor WCot
	× ***multiflorus*** 'Meteor'	LRHS NBre WCot WWEG
	'O Sole Mio'	WCot
	occidentalis	SMad
	orgyalis	see *H. salicifolius*
	petiolaris **new**	COtt
	quinquenervis	see *Helianthella quinquenervis*
	rigidus misapplied	see *H.* × *laetiflorus*
§	***salicifolius***	Widely available
	- 'Low Down'PBR	ECtt SWvt
	- 'Table Mountain'PBR	CSpe GBin LRHS MAvo NLar SWvt WCot
	scaberrimus	see *H.* × *laetiflorus*
	'Soleil d'Or'	ECtt EWll MSpe WHal
	strumosus	WCot
	'Triomphe de Gand'	MTis MWat NDov
	tuberosus	CArn EBee GPoy SVic
	- 'Fuseau'	SVic
	- 'Garnet'	LEdu
	- 'Sugarball'	LEdu

Helichrysum (*Asteraceae*)

	from Drakensberg Mountains, South Africa	GAbr
	adenocarpum	SPlb
	alveolatum	see *H. splendidum*
	amorginum 'Pink Bud' **new**	MMuc
	- Ruby Cluster = 'Blorub'PBR	EPfP LRHS
	angustifolium from Crete	see *H. microphyllum* (Willd.) Cambess.
§	***arwae***	WAbe
	bellidioides	see *Anaphalioides bellidioides*
	bracteatum	see *Xerochrysum bracteatum*
	'Coco'	see *Xerochrysum bracteatum* 'Coco'
	confertum	SPlb
	coralloides	see *Ozothamnus coralloides*
	'County Park Silver'	see *Ozothamnus* 'County Park Silver'
	'Dargan Hill Monarch'	see *Xerochrysum bracteatum* 'Dargan Hill Monarch'
	'Elmstead'	see *H. stoechas* 'White Barn'
	frigidum	WAbe
	hookeri	see *Ozothamnus hookeri*
§	***hypoleucum***	SDix
	'Icicles'	GBin
	italicum	CAco CArn CUse ECha ECrN ENfk EPfP EPla GBin GMaP GPoy LPot MHer MMuc MNHC NPri SEND SPoG SRms SVen WHer WHfH WJek XLum
	- 'Dartington'	CBod ENfk GBin WJek
	- 'Korma'PBR	EBee ECGP EHoe ELan EPfP GBin LRHS LSou MAsh MGos NPri SLon SPoG SRms WJek
	- subsp. ***microphyllum***	see *H. microphyllum* (Willd.) Cambess.
	- 'Nanum'	see *H. microphyllum* (Willd.) Cambess.
§	- subsp. ***serotinum***	CBcs ECrN EHoe EPfP GPoy LRHS MAsh MRav SLim SPer SRms SWvt WRHF XSen
	lanatum	see *H. thianschanicum*
	ledifolium	see *Ozothamnus ledifolius*
	marginatum misapplied	see *H. milfordiae*
	marginatum DC.	GKev
	microphyllum ambig.	MMuc SPer SRms
§	***microphyllum*** (Willd.) Cambess.	ENfk MNHC SEND WJek
§	***milfordiae*** ♀H4	EPot NSla NWad SRms WAbe
	orientale	EPot XSen
	pagophilum	EPot WAbe
	petiolare ♀H3	EBak ECtt LAst MCot SPer SPoG WHea
	- 'Aureum'	see *H. petiolare* 'Limelight'
	- 'Goring Silver' ♀H3	SPoG
§	- 'Limelight' ♀H3	ECtt LAst MCot NPri SPer SPoG
	- 'Variegatum' (v) ♀H3	ECtt LAst MCot NPri SPoG
	plicatum	WCot
	populifolium misapplied	see *H. hypoleucum*
	rosmarinifolium	see *Ozothamnus rosmarinifolius*
§	'Schwefellicht'	EBee ECha EPfP MLHP MRav SPer WKif WSHC WWEG
	selago	see *Ozothamnus selago*
	serotinum	see *H. italicum* subsp. *serotinum*
	sessilioides	EPot WAbe
§	***sibthorpii***	WAbe
§	***splendidum*** ♀H5	EPfP LRHS NBro SKHP SLon XSen
	stoechas	CArn
§	- 'White Barn'	CSpe WCot XLum
	Sulphur Light	see *H.* 'Schwefellicht'
§	***thianschanicum***	LRHS SRms XLum XSen
	- Golden Baby	see *H. thianschanicum* 'Goldkind'
§	- 'Goldkind'	NBir XLum
	trilineatum misapplied	see *H. splendidum*
	tumidum	see *Ozothamnus selago* var. *tumidus*
	virgineum	see *H. sibthorpii*
	witbergense	GKev WAbe
	woodii	see *H. arwae*

Helicodiceros (*Araceae*)

§	***muscivorus***	CHid EBee WCot

Heliconia ✿ (*Heliconiaceae*)

	caribaea 'Burgundy'	see *H. caribaea* 'Purpurea'
§	- 'Purpurea'	XBlo
	'Golden Torch'	XBlo
	indica 'Spectabilis'	XBlo
	latispatha 'Orange Gyro'	XBlo
*	- 'Red Gyro'	XBlo
	metallica	XBlo
	psittacorum	CCCN
	rostrata	CCCN XBlo
	schiedeana	CHll

Helictotrichon (*Poaceae*)

	pratense	CHab EHoe
§	***sempervirens*** ♀H7	Widely available

I	- 'Pendulum'	EBee GBin MAvo MSpe
	- 'Saphirsprudel'	CCse EBee EPfP LRHS SHil WCot WPGP WWEG

Heliophila (*Brassicaceae*)

	coronopifolia	CSpe

Heliopsis (*Asteraceae*)

	Golden Plume	see *H. helianthoides* var. *scabra* 'Goldgefieder'
	helianthoides	LRHS MLHP NBre WFar WWtn
	- 'Limelight'	see *Helianthus* 'Lemon Queen'
	- Loraine Sunshine = 'Helhan'PBR (v)	CWGN IKil LBMP LSou MBri MPie SMad SPer SPoG WCot WFar
	- var. ***scabra***	LRHS NHol SRot WMnd XLum
	- - 'Asahi'	CBod ECtt ELan GMaP NLar NPri WHoo
	- - Ballerina	see *H. helianthoides* var. *scabra* 'Spitzentänzerin'
	- - 'Benzinggold' ♀H5	LSou MRav SMrm
	- - 'Bressingham Doubloon' (d)	ECtt
	- - Golden Plume	see *H. helianthoides* var. *scabra* 'Goldgefieder'
§	- - 'Goldgefieder' ♀H5	EBee NBre WFar
	- - 'Patula'	EBee ECtt
	- - 'Prairie Sunset'PBR	ECtt MBri MSCN MTis
§	- - 'Sommersonne'	CSBt ECtt EPfP EWll LRHS MSpe MWhi NGBl NLar NPer SMrm SPer SRms WMnd
§	- - 'Spitzentänzerin' ♀H5	ECtt
	- - 'Summer Nights'	CBod EBee EPfP LBMP LSou MBri MNrw MPie MRav MSpe MWat SMrm SPhx WCot WWEG
	- - Summer Sun	see *H. helianthoides* var. *scabra* 'Sommersonne'
	- - 'Sunburst' (v)	SPav
	- - 'Venus'	ECtt EWll LRHS LSou NLar WHoo
	- - 'Waterperry Gold' **new**	MWat
	- 'Summer Pink'	SPoG
	- 'Tuscan Sun'PBR	EBee ECtt LRHS NPri WHil

Heliotropium ✿ (*Boraginaceae*)

§	***amplexicaule***	SDys
	anchusifolium	see *H. amplexicaule*
§	***arborescens***	CArn ENfk EPfP EShb MCot MHom
	- 'Chatsworth' ♀H1c	CAby CCCN CSpe ECre ECtt MHom
	- 'Dame Alice de Hales'	ECtt MHom
	- 'Gatton Park'	MHom
	- 'Lord Roberts'	ECtt MHom
	- 'Marine'	CSam NPri
	- 'Mary Fox'	MHom
	- 'Mrs J.W. Lowther'	MHom
	- pale lilac-flowered	CSam
	- 'President Garfield'	MHom
	- 'Princess Marina' ♀H1c	EPfP LAst NLar
	- 'Reva'	ECtt MHom
	- 'The Queen'	ECtt
	- 'The Speaker'	MHom
	- 'White Lady'	CCCN CSpe ECtt MHom
	- 'White Queen'	ECtt MHom
	- 'Woodcote'	MHom
	'Butterfly Kisses'	EPfP LBuc
	peruvianum	see *H. arborescens*

Helipterum see *Syncarpha*

Helleborus ✿ (*Ranunculaceae*)

	abschasicus	see *H. orientalis* Lam. subsp. *abchasicus*
	'Angel Glow'	LRHS SCob WHil
§	***argutifolius*** ♀H5	Widely available
	- mottled-leaved	see *H. argutifolius* 'Pacific Frost'
§	- 'Pacific Frost' (v)	CPla MMHG
	- 'Red Riding Hood'	LRHS
	- 'Silver Lace'	CCon EAEE ELan EPfP EPla GKev IBoy LRHS MBel MHol MWat NBir NLar NWad SKHP SPer SPoG SPtp WMoo
	atrorubens misapplied	see *H. orientalis* Lam. subsp. *abchasicus* Early Purple Group
	atrorubens ambig.	MAsh SCob
	atrorubens Waldst. & Kit.	MRav
	- WM 9805 from Croatia	GBuc
	× ***ballardiae***	CLAP
	- 'Candy Love'PBR	CRos EBee GBin LRHS MAsh MBri MHol NLar SCob SHil WCot
	'Blue Moon'	IBoy
	bocconei	GCal MAsh
	colchicus	see *H. orientalis* Lam. subsp. *abchasicus*
	corsicus	see *H. argutifolius*
	- 'Marble' (v)	CSpe
	croaticus	MAsh
	cyclophyllus	GKev MAsh SCob SPer
	dumetorum	GBuc GCal
	- WM 9627 from Croatia	GBuc
§	× ***ericsmithii***	CDes CExl CLAP CMHG CMil CSpe ECha ELon EPfP GAbr GBuc GMaP LAst LLHF LRHS LSou LSun MAsh MNFA NBir NGdn NLar SCob WHoo WPGP
	- 'Bob's Best'	CEnd CExl CHel CHid CLAP ECtt ESwi GBin LBMP LPla LRHS MBNS MHol MNrw NWad SEND SHar SKHP SMrm SPer SWvt WCot WRHF
	- 'HGC Silvermoon'PBR	IBoy LRHS NLar
	- 'Pirouette'PBR	CLAP EPfP LRHS MAsh MBri SCob
	- 'Ruby Glow'	LRHS MAsh MWat SCob WHil
	- 'Snow Love'PBR	CRos LBuc LRHS MAsh MBri NLar SCob SHil WCot
	- 'Winter Moonbeam'PBR	CLAP CSpe EPfP LBuc LRHS MBri MCot NCGa SCob SKHP SLon SPoG WCot WHil
	- 'Winter Sunshine'PBR	CLAP EPfP LBuc LRHS MBri MWat SCob SKHP SPoG WHil
	foetidus ♀H7	Widely available
	- from Italy	IFoB
	- 'Chedglow'	CNat
	- 'Gold Bullion'	CBod CPla ECtt GBuc MAsh
	- 'Green Giant'	SEND
	- 'Harvington Pewter'	CLAP LRHS
	- 'Miss Jekyll'	SVic
	- 'Pewter'	CLAP
	- 'Ruth'	EWoo MAsh SCob
	- 'Sienna'	SCob
	- sweet-scented	MHom
	- 'Vogezen' **new**	SCob
	- Wester Flisk Group	CExl ECtt EPfP GBuc IFoB LRHS MAsh MRav NHol NPer SCob WCot WHar WPGP WWEG
	- Wilgenbroek selection **new**	SCob

- 'Yellow Wilgenbroek' **new**	LRHS SCob
Gold Collection	see *Helloborus* with names starting HGC
'Golden Sunrise' (Winter Jewels Series)	CBod MPnt NCGa SMrm
'Harlequin Gem' (Winter Jewels Series) (d)	MPnt
HGC Cinnamon Snow = 'Coseh 700'PBR	ESwi LRHS NLar
'HGC Jericho'PBR	IVic
HGC Pink Frost = 'Coseh 710'PBR	LRHS
× ***hybridus***	Widely available
- anemone-centred	CHid CLAP GBin IFoB LHel MNrw WFar
- 'Apple Blossom'	IFoB WFar
- 'Apricot Blush' (Winter Jewels Series)	CWGN NCGa SMrm
- apricot-flowered	CLAP CTal EPfP GBuc IFoB WFar
- 'Ashwood Elegance Pearl' **new**	MAsh
- 'Ashwood Elegance Snow' **new**	MAsh
- 'Ashwood Fascination' **new**	MAsh
- Ashwood Garden hybrids	ELan EPPr EPfP LRHS MAsh MRav SLon SRms
- - anemone-centred	MAsh
- - double-flowered (d)	MAsh
- 'Ashwood Glade' **new**	MAsh
- 'Ashwood Meadow' **new**	MAsh
- 'Ashwood Peach Cocktail' **new**	MAsh
- Ballard's Group	CLAP IBoy LRHS MWat SPer WFar WPnP
- best greens	IFoB
- 'Black Beauty'	IFoB
- 'Black Diamond' (Winter Jewels Series) **new**	NCGa SMrm
- 'Black Knight'	IFoB
- black-flowered	CLAP GBuc GMaP IFoB NChi WFar
- 'Blue Lady' (Lady Series)	CBcs CBod EPfP GAbr GBin IFoB LRHS MBNS MGos NGdn SMrm SPer
- 'Blue Metallic Lady' (Lady Series)	CBod CExl EAEE EPfP GKev IBoy IFoB LAst MBNS MHol NEgg NGdn SMrm SPer
- Bradfield hybrids	MCot
- - anemone-centred	MCot
- - double-flowered (d)	MCot
- - picotee	MCot
- Caborn hybrids	LLWP
- 'Cherry Blossom' (Winter Jewels Series)	CBod CWGN MPnt NCGa
- 'Cherry Frost' **new**	MAsh
- 'Clare's Purple'	CBod EWTr
- 'Cosmos'	CTal MBNS
- cream-flowered	CLAP IFro WFar
- dark picotee **new**	WFar
- dark purple-flowered	IFoB LHel WFar
- dark red-flowered	CLAP GBuc IFoB LHel NChi WFar
- dark-flowered	WFar
- double (d)	CLAP CSpe GBuc IFoB MNrw WFar
- - black-flowered (d)	CExl IFoB WFar
- - pink-flowered (d)	IFoB LHel WFar
- - dark purple-flowered **new**	WFar
- - green-flowered (d)	IFoB LHel WFar
- - purple-flowered (d)	LHel WFar
- - red-flowered (d)	CExl WFar
- - white-flowered (d)	CExl IFoB LHel WFar
- - yellow picotee (d) **new**	WCot
- - yellow-flowered (d)	CExl IFoB IFro LHel WFar
- 'Double Ellen Picotee' (d)	CWGN GBin SMrm WHlf
- 'Double Ellen Red' (d)	GBin LRHS WHlf
- 'Double Ellen White' (d)	CWGN GBin LRHS SMrm WHlf
- Double Ladies, mixed (d)	GAbr WCot
- 'Double Vision' (d)	EPPr
- Elizabeth Town anemone-centred	IFro
- - double-centred (d)	IFro
- - picotee-centred	IFro
- - red-centred	IFro
- 'Emerald Queen' (Queen Series)	ELan GBin GQue
- 'Enchantment' **new**	MAsh
- Farmyard anemone-centred	WFar
- - apricot	WFar
- - black	WFar
- - cream	WFar
- - cream, spotted	WFar
- - dark pink	WFar
- - double apricot (d)	WFar
- - - black (d)	WFar
- - - cream (d)	WFar
- - - - spotted (d)	WFar
- - - pink (d)	WFar
- - - - spotted (d)	WFar
- - - primrose (d)	WFar
- - - - spotted (d)	WFar
- - - red (d)	WFar
- - - slate-grey (d)	WFar
- - - white (d)	WFar
- - - - spotted (d)	WFar
- - green	WFar
- - - spotted	WFar
- - picotee	WFar
- - pink	WFar
- - pink spotted	WFar
- - plum	WFar
- - primrose	WFar
- - - dark-eyed	WFar
- - - spotted	WFar
- - red	WFar
- - slate spotted	WFar
- - slate-grey	WFar
- - white	WFar
- - - dark-eyed	WFar
- - - splash	WFar
- - - spotted	WFar
- 'Farmyard Appleblossom'	WFar
- 'Farmyard Woodland'	WFar
- Field of Blooms hybrids	IFoB
- - anemone-centred	IFoB
- - double-flowered (d)	IFoB
- - picotee	IFoB
- 'Gala Queen' (Queen Series)	ELon
- 'Golden Discovery' mixed (d) **new**	CBod
- 'Golden Lotus' (d)	CWGN MPnt
- 'Green Ripple'	WFar
- green-flowered	WFar
- 'Harvington Apricots'	CRos LRHS NBir NLar NPri SKHP SLon SPoG
- Harvington double chocolate (d)	CHel CLAP LRHS NPri SPoG

--- dark purple (d) CHel LRHS NPri
--- pink (d) CLAP CRos LRHS NPri SKHP SLon SPoG
---- speckled (d) CHel LRHS NPri SPoG
--- purple (d) CHel CLAP LRHS NBir NLar NPri SKHP SPoG
--- purple cascade (d) **new** SPoG
--- red (d) CHel CLAP CRos LRHS NBir NLar NPri SLon SPoG
--- speckled (d) CHel NPri
--- white (d) CLAP CRos LRHS NBir NLar NPri SKHP SLon SPoG
--- yellow (d) CHel CLAP LRHS NBir NLar NPri SKHP SLon SPoG
---- speckled (d) CHel SPoG
--- apricot (d) CHel LRHS NPri
--- lime-green (d) CLAP LRHS NPri
-- dusky **new** SPoG
-- picotee CHel CLAP LRHS NBir NLar NPri SKHP SLon SPoG
-- pink CHel CRos LRHS NLar NPri SLon SPoG
--- speckled CHel NLar NPri SLon SPoG
-- red CHel CRos LRHS MHer NLar NPri SLon SPoG
-- speckled CHel MHer NPri SLon
-- white CHel CRos LRHS MHer NLar NPri SKHP SLon SPoG
--- speckled NPri SKHP SLon SPoG
-- yellow CHel CRos LRHS MHer NLar NPri SKHP SLon SPoG
--- speckled CHel CRos LRHS MHer NLar NPri SLon SPoG
- 'Harvington Shades of the Night' CHel LRHS MHer NLar NPri SKHP SLon SPoG
- 'Harvington Smokey Blues' CHel NPri SKHP SLon SPoG
- 'Harvington Smokey Double' (d) NPri
- 'Helen Ballard' SVic
- Hillier hybrids, anemone-centred CRos
--- spotted pink **new** SHil
--- yellow **new** LRHS SHil
-- burgundy CBod LRHS MBri SHil
-- clear white CRos LRHS SHil
-- double pink (d) CRos LRHS
--- white (d) **new** LRHS
-- pink and white LRHS
-- slate CRos LRHS SHil
-- spotted, double yellow (d) LRHS SHil
--- double-pink (d) LRHS SHil
--- green LRHS
--- pink CRos LRHS MBri
--- white CRos LRHS MBri
-- yellow CRos MBri
- 'Ice Queen' (Queen Series) ELan
- 'Kingston Cardinal' **new** MAsh
- 'Lady in Red' IBoy
- Lady Series IFoB NSum
- large, pink-flowered IFoB IFro
- maroon-flowered WFar
- mauve freckled, double (d) IFro WFar
- 'Mrs Betty Ranicar' (d) CBro EPfP IFoB LRHS MBri SCob
- nearly black-flowered WFar
- 'Onyx Odyssey' CBod CSpe CWGN MPnt NCGa
- 'Orion' CTal
- 'Pale Picotee' GBuc
- pale pink-flowered GBuc WFar
- 'Pamina' IFoB
§ - Party Dress Group (d) CBod CHid ELan ELon GBin IFoB LEdu LRHS NLar SCob WBor WFar
-- 'Party Dress Pink' (d) CBod CWCL
-- 'Party Dress Primrose' (d) **new** CBod
- 'Pebworth White' CTal
- 'Philip Ballard' CTal
- 'Phoebe' **new** MAsh
- 'Phoenix' **new** MAsh
- Picotee Group NLar WFar
- 'Picotee' CLAP GBuc IFoB LHel WCru WFar
- 'Picotee' double-flowered (d) CWCL LHel WFar
- pink freckled, double (d) IFro WFar
- 'Pink Lady' (Lady Series) CBcs CBod GQue IFoB NEgg NGdn NPri SPer
- 'Pink Upstart' IFoB
- pink-flowered CLAP GBuc LHel MBNS SDeJ WHoo
- pink-red-flowered LHel WFar
- plum-flowered CLAP GBuc MMuc SEND
- 'Pluto' CTal WFar
- 'Primrose Picotee' **new** WFar
- primrose-flowered CBod CLAP ECGP ELan EWTr GBuc MCot MMuc
- 'Purity' **new** MAsh
- purple-flowered CLAP SGSe WFar WHoo
- (Queen Series) 'Queen of Hearts' ELan
-- 'Queen of Spades' ELan SMad
-- 'Queen of the Night' CBod CBro CExl CLAP ELan EPfP IBal
- 'Red Lady' (Lady Series) CBcs CBod CExl EAEE EPfP EPla EPot GAbr IBal IFoB LRHS MBNS NEgg NHol NOrc SMrm SPer
- 'Red Spotted' EPfP
- 'Red Upstart' IFoB
- red-flowered CBod GBuc WFar
- red and purple **new** CBod
- 'Sirius' **new** CTal
- slaty blue-flowered CBod CLAP GBuc IFoB LEdu LHel SEND
- slaty purple-flowered GBuc SEND
- 'Smokey Blue' IFoB LRHS
- smokey purple-flowered ELan MAsh MMuc SGbt
- 'Speckled Draco' CExl
§ - spotted CLAP EPfP GBuc GMaP IFoB NEgg WCot WFar WHoo
-- cream CBod CLAP IFoB NBir WFar
-- double, pink (d) LHel WFar
--- white (d) IFoB LHel WFar
--- yellow (d) IFoB WFar
-- green CLAP WFar
-- ivory CLAP WFar
-- light purple WFar
-- pink CLAP IFro LHel LRHS MBNS NBir SEND SHil WFar WHoo
-- primrose CLAP ELan SGbt WFar
-- white CBod GBuc IFro LHel MMuc NBir SEND SHil WBor WFar
-- yellow LHel SHil WFar WHlf
- 'Spotted Lady' CBod GBin
- 'Stained Glass' **new** MAsh
- Sunshine selections IBal
- 'Swirling Skirts' GBin
- 'Titania' CTal
- 'Tricastin' CBro IBoy

- 'Tutu'[PBR]	EPfP LBuc LRHS MBri SCob SPer SPoG SRms WHil
- 'Ushba'	CLAP IFoB
- 'Warbler' **new**	MAsh
- Washfield double-flowered (d)	CSpe EPfP LBrs LEdu SPer SRkn WRHF
- - white (d)	IFoB
- 'White Lady' (Lady Series)	CBcs CBod CExl EPot IFoB MBNS NEgg NPri SMrm SPer
- 'White Lady Spotted' (Lady Series)	CBod CHVG ELon EPfP GBin GQue LRHS MHol NEgg NHol SPer
- white-flowered	GBuc IFoB LHel SEND WCFE WFar WHoo
- white-veined	WFar
- Wilgenbroek hybrids anemone-centred, red **new**	SCob
- - - white freckled **new**	SCob
- - apricot **new**	SCob
- - aubergine with white edge **new**	SCob
- - black **new**	SCob
- - dark **new**	SCob
- - double, picotee (d) **new**	SCob
- - - red (d) **new**	SCob
- - - slaty blue (d) **new**	SCob
- - - white (d) **new**	SCob
- - - - spotted (d) **new**	SCob
- - green **new**	SCob
- - picotee **new**	SCob
- - red **new**	SCob
- - slaty blue **new**	SCob
- - spotted, apricot **new**	SCob
- - - aubergine **new**	SCob
- - - pink **new**	SCob
- - - red **new**	SCob
- - - yellow **new**	SCob
- - white **new**	SCob
- - - with pink edge **new**	SCob
- yellow freckled, double (d)	IFro
- 'Yellow Lady' (Lady Series)	CBcs CBod CBro CCon EPla EPot LRHS MBNS NEgg SMrm SPer
- yellow-flowered	GMaP IFoB LHel SEND WFar WHoo
- Zodiac Group	EPla MBNS
§ 'Ivory Prince'[PBR]	EPfP LBuc LRHS MAsh SPoG
'Jade Star' (Winter Jewels Series)	CBod MPnt
'Kiwi Black Velvet'	IBal
liguricus	MAsh
lividus	CAby CBro CLAP EBee ECho EPfP EWes IFoB LRHS NBir SDeJ SKHP SRms SWat
- subsp. ***corsicus***	see *H. argutifolius*
- 'Purple Rose' **new**	LRHS
- 'Silver Edge'	EPfP
- 'White Marble'	LRHS MAsh SKHP
'Moonshine'[PBR]	CLAP EBee ELon MHol NHol NLar NWad SLon
multifidus	EPPr IFoB NBir
- subsp. ***hercegovinus***	SCob
- subsp. ***istriacus***	CBro MAsh WCot
- subsp. ***multifidus***	MAsh
niger	Widely available
- Ashwood marble leaf	MAsh
- Ashwood strain	CLAP MAsh
- Blackthorn Group	CLAP NLar
- 'David'	IVic
- 'Double Fashion'[PBR]	EBee EPfP LRHS SCob
- double-flowered (d)	CHel MAsh
- 'Eifelturm'	IVic
- Harvington hybrids (d)	CLAP LRHS MAsh MHer NPri SPoG
- - double-flowered	SPoG
- 'HGC Jacob'[PBR]	IVic LBuc LRHS SRms
- 'HGC Josef Lemper'[PBR]	IVic LRHS NLar SRms
- 'HGC Joshua'[PBR]	IVic
- 'Ivory Prince'[PBR]	see *H.* 'Ivory Prince'
- marbled leaves **new**	SCob
- 'Marion' (d)	IFoB
- 'Maximus'	CLAP EWes
- pink-flowered	MAsh
- 'Potter's Wheel'	CLAP LRHS NBir SCob
- 'Praecox'	EWes LRHS
- 'Schneeball'	IVic
- Sunset Group	SCob
- 'White Christmas'	LRHS
- 'Wilgenbroek Select' **new**	SCob
× ***nigercors***	CSpe ECha ECtt GBin GMaP LPla MAsh MCot SCob WPGP
- double-flowered (d)	GBin LSou
- 'Emma'[PBR] **new**	LSun SCob WCot
- 'HGC Green Corsican'[PBR]	EBee LRHS
- 'Morning's Pride'[PBR]	EBee LRHS
- 'Pink Beauty'	LBuc NLar SCob
× ***nigristern***	see *H.* × *ericsmithii*
odorus	GCal IFoB MAsh SCob SPer XLum
orientalis misapplied	see *H.* × *hybridus*
orientalis ambig.	CBod CTsd ECho LAst MSCN MWat NPri SCob WCAu WHar WPtf
orientalis Lam.	CBcs EWes LPal LRHS LSun MJak MSwo XLum
§ - subsp. ***abchasicus*** (A. Braun) B. Mathew	MAsh
§ - - Early Purple Group	CTri GCal MRav SRms
- subsp. ***guttatus*** misapplied	see *H.* × *hybridus* spotted
- subsp. ***guttatus*** (A. Braun & Sauer) B. Matthew	NChi SRkn
'Pink Beauty'[PBR]	EPfP LRHS MBri NLar SLon SPoG
purpurascens	EPPr GBuc GMaP IFoB LBuc LRHS MAsh MRav MWat NBir XEll
(Rodney Davey Marbled Group) 'Anna's Red'	LBuc MAsh MBri WCot
- 'Penny's Pink'	CBcs LBuc MAsh MBri SCob SPoG WCot WHil
'Silver Dollar'	CBod EBee EPfP EWes LRHS MAsh SHil SPer SPoG
'Snow White'	MAsh
× ***sternii***	CBcs CHel CSpe CTri CWCL ELan EPfP EWTr GMaP IFro LRHS MCot MMoz MNrw MWat NEgg NLar SCob SPer SPoG WBrk WMoo WWtn
- Aberconwy strain	CLAP
- Ashwood strain	MAsh NLar
- 'Beatrice le Blanc'	MAsh
- Blackthorn Group	CBod ELon EPfP EUJe EWTr IFoB LRHS MCot MRav SWvt
- Blackthorn dwarf strain	CLAP
- Boughton Group	MRav
- 'Boughton Beauty'	CLAP ELan GBuc MAsh SCob
- pewter-flowered	CSpe ECho
- 'Tom' **new**	SCob
- 'Wilgenbroek' **new**	SCob
thibetanus	CCon CExl CLAP ECho EFEx EWes LAma MAsh

torquatus	CBro CTal GBuc MAsh
– from Montenegro WM 9106	GBuc
– Caborn hybrids	LLWP
– 'Dido' (d)	CExl WFar
– hybrids	CTal IFoB
– Party Dress Group	see *H.* × *hybridus* Party Dress Group
'Verboom Beauty'	LRHS
vesicarius	MAsh
viridis	GCal GPoy IFoB LRHS MAsh MHer SCob SRms XLum
– subsp. ***occidentalis***	CBro
Walberton's Rosemary = 'Walhero'PBR	EPfP LRHS MAsh SHar SPoG
'Washfield Queen' (Queen Series)	CBod CWCL
'White Beauty'PBR	EPfP LBuc LRHS MBri NCGa NLar SCob SPoG WHil

Helonias (*Melanthiaceae*)

bullata	EBee

Heloniopsis (*Melanthiaceae*)

acutifolia	CDes
– B&SWJ 218	WCru
– B&SWJ 6817	WCru
– B&SWJ 6836	WCru
japonica	see *H. orientalis*
§ ***kawanoi***	CDes EBee SKHP WCot WCru
koreana B&SWJ 4173	WCru
leucantha B&SWJ 11148	WCru
§ ***orientalis***	CBro CLAP CTal ECho GBuc GCal LLHF WCot WCru
– B&SWJ 6278	WCru
– B&SWJ 6327	WCru
– B&SWJ 6380 from Japan	WCru
– from Japan	EBee
– from Korea	EPfP SChF SKHP
– var. ***breviscapa***	CHel EBee EPfP LEdu SChF SMad WCru
– – B&SWJ 5635	WCru
– – B&SWJ 5873	WCru
– – B&SWJ 5938	WCru
– – 'A-so'	LEdu WCru
– var. ***flavida*** B&SWJ 11400	CTal WCru
– variegated (v)	WCru
– var. ***yakusimensis***	see *H. kawanoi*
tubiflora B&SWJ 822	WCot WCru
– 'Temple Blue'	CDes CLAP WCru
umbellata	CTal EBee EPfP SKHP SMad WMoo WSHC
– B&SWJ 1839	CLAP WCru
– B&SWJ 3732	WCru
– B&SWJ 6836	WCru
– B&SWJ 6846	WCru
– B&SWJ 7117	WCru

Helwingia (*Helwingiaceae*)

chinensis	ESwi ETwe EWld NLar SBrt SSpi WBor WPGP
– broad-leaved **new**	WPGP
– narrow-leaved **new**	ESwi
himalaica	CExl CFil ESwi ETwe WPGP
– broad-leaved **new**	WPGP
– narrow-leaved **new**	WPGP
japonica	CHGN EFEx
– broad-leaved **new**	WPGP
– narrow-leaved **new**	WPGP

Helxine see *Soleirolia*

Hemerocallis ✿ (*Hemerocallidaceae*)

'A Quack in Time' **new**	CFwr
'A Special Lady'	EStr
'Aabaa'	EWoo
'Aabachee'	CBgR
'Above the Clouds'	EWoo
'Absolute Treasure'	CFwr
'Absolute Zero'	SPol
'Adah'	SDay
'Adamas'	CFwr
'Addie Branch Smith'	SDay
'Adeline Goldner'	CFwr
'Admiral's Braid'	EWoo
'Adorable Tiger'	CFwr
'Adoration'	SPer
'Africa'	SPol
'Africa Nightbeacon' **new**	EStr
'African Chant'	ELan
'Age of Miracles'	SPol
'Ageless Beauty'	EStr
'Agnes Elpers' **new**	WAul
'Ahoya'	CBgR SPol
'Airs and Graces'	SDay
'Alabama Jubilee'	WNHG
'Alabama Wildfire'	CFwr
'Alakazam'	EWoo
'Alan'	ECtt LRHS MRav
'Alaqua'	CCon GBuc MBNS
'Alberene'	CFwr
'Alec Allen'	SDay
'Alexander the Great'	WHrl
'Alien Encounter'	SPol
'All American Baby'	CWat MBNS MSpe SPol
'All American Eagle'	SPol
'All American Magic'	SPol
'All American Plum'	CWCL EPfP IBoy MBNS MSpe SPol WAul WHrl
'All American Tiger'	SDay
'All American Windmill'	CBgR CFwr EWoo
'All Creation Sings' **new**	CFwr
'All Fired Up'	SDay SPol
'All I Want for Christmas'	CFwr
'Allegiance'	WNHG
'Alli Sheldon' **new**	ECha
'Almost Paradise'	SPol
'Alpine Mist'	SDay
'Alpine Rhapsody'	SPol
'Alternate Universe'	CFwr
altissima	CHEx LPla MNrw SDix SPhx XSen
'Always Afternoon' ♀H6	CBgR CKel EStr EWoo GBuc MBNS MNrw SPol WCAu WHrl WWEG XSen
'Amadeus'	CUse GBuc SCob
'Amazon Amethyst'	WCAu
'Ambassador'	CBgR
'Amber Classic'	ELon
'American Freedom'	EWoo
'American Revolution'	CBgR CBod CPar ELon EStr EWoo GBin IPot MBNS MBel MGos MHol MNFA MWat MWhi NChi SDys SPol WAul WCot WHrl WMoo WPnP XLum XSen
'America's Most Wanted' **new**	EStr
'Amersham'	MNFA
'Amerstone Amethyst Jewel'	SPol

Cultivar	Suppliers
'Amethyst Island' **new**	CFwr
'Amethyst Squid'	EWoo
'Among Us'	CFwr
'Amy'	WWEG
'Anatomically Correct'	EWoo
'Andrew Christian'	SPol
'Android'	CFwr
'Andy Candy'	CFwr
'Angel Artistry'	SDay
'Angel Rodgers'	EStr
'Aniakchak'	EWoo
'Anna Warner'	ELon MMuc SEND
'Annabelle's Ghost'	CBgR SPol
'Annie Welch'	ELon EPfP EPla MBNS NBre
'Answering Angels'	CFwr
'Antarctica'	SPol
'Antique Rose'	CKel SDay
'Anzac'	CTsd ECha ECtt EPla EStr IBoy LRHS MBNS MBel MNHC NGdn SGol SWvt WMoo
'Apache Bandana'	EWoo
'Apache Beacon'	EWoo
'Apollo'	XSen
'Apollodorus'	SDay
'Apple Court Chablis'	SPol
'Apple Court Champagne'	SPol
'Apple Court Damson'	SPol
'Apple Court Ruby'	SPol
'Apple Of My Eye'	EWoo
'Apple Swirl'	CFwr EStr SPol
'Apple Tart'	SDay
'Applique'	CFwr
'Après Moi'	MBNS NLar
'Apricot Beauty' (d)	CPrp MBNS NSoo SGol
'Apricot Velvet' **new**	CBgR
'Apricotta'	WCot WPnP
'Apron Strings'	CFwr
'Arachnephobia'	EWoo
'Arctic Snow' ♀H6	CBgR CBro CMac ECrc ECtt ELon EStr EWoo LRHS MBNS MNrw SCob SPol WAul WPnP
'Armed and Dangerous'	CFwr
'Arms to Heaven'	EWoo
'Arpeggio'	EStr
'Arriba'	MNFA NBro
'Arthur Moore'	SDay
'As You Wish' **new**	CFwr
'Asian Artistry'	WNHG
'Asiatic Pheasant'	SPol
'Asterisk' ♀H6	SDay
'Astolat' **new**	EBee
'Astral Voyager'	CFwr
'Aten'	CBgR SDay
'Athlone'	EWoo
'Atlanta Cover Girl'	SDay
'Atlanta Fringe Benefit'	SDay
'August Frost' ♀H6	SDay SPol
'August Morn'	CBgR
'Aunt Wimp'	EWoo
'Authur Vincent'	SPol
'Autumn Jewels'	EWoo SPol
'Autumn Minaret'	EWoo
'Autumn Prince'	EWoo
'Autumn Red'	CBcs CBgR EPla EStr GKin MBNS MMuc MNrw NBir SEND SPol WCot
'Ava Michelle'	SDay
'Avant Garde'	EStr SPol WCAu
'Avon Crystal Rose'	WNHG

Cultivar	Suppliers
'Awesome Blossom'	LSou MBNS MNrw SMrm WHrl
'Awesome Candy'	EWoo
'Aztec Firebird'	CFwr EStr EWoo
'Aztec Furnace'	CBro SDay
'Baby Blues'	SDay SPol
'Baby Darling'	SDay
'Baby Red Eyes'	WFar
'Baby Talk'	CCon
'Baja'	MNFA WFar
'Bakabana'	MSCN
'Bald Eagle'	MNrw WWEG
'Bali Hai'	MBNS SRms WHrl
'Bam'	EStr
'Bama Belle' **new**	CFwr
'Bamboo Blackie'	CBgR EWoo SPol XSen
'Banana Cream Beauty'	SDeJ
'Banbury Cinnamon'	MBNS MSpe
'Bangkok Belle'	CWat
'Banned in Boston'	EWoo
'Barbara Dittmer'	SPol
'Barbara Mitchell'	EWoo GBuc MBNS SDay SDeJ WCAu XSen
'Barbaresco'	SPol
'Barbarian Princess' **new**	CFwr
'Barbary Corsair'	SDay
'Bark At Me'	CFwr
'Barnegat Orange Twister'	CFwr
'Barney Barnes'	CFwr
'Baronet's Badge'	SPol
'Baroni'	ECha SMrm
'Baroody' **new**	EStr
'Bat Signal'	CFwr EWoo SPol
'Bathsheba'	SPol
'Battle Hymn'	WCAu
'Beagle Bess'	CFwr
'Beaming Blessings'	CFwr
'Beat the Barons'	MSpe SPol
'Beautiful Edgings'	EStr SPol
'Beauty to Behold' ♀H6	SDay
'Becky Lynn'	ECtt MBNS
'Bed of Roses'	MNFA
'Before Night Falls'	CFwr
'Bela Lugosi'	CAbP CBgR CMac CWat ECrc ELon EPfP EStr EWoo GQue LRHS LSun MBNS MCot MNrw MWat MWhi NBro NEgg SPad SPer SPol WCAu WCot WHrl WNHG
'Believe It'	WNHG
'Bella Isabella' **new**	CFwr
'Ben Adams'	SDay
'Ben Webster'	CFwr
'Benchmark'	WHrl
'Bengal Bay'	EWoo
'Bengal Fire'	WNHG
'Berlin Lavender' **new**	MNFA
'Berlin Lemon'	MNFA
'Berlin Lemon Crepe' **new**	MNFA
'Berlin Multi' **new**	MNFA
'Berlin Oxblood'	WAul
'Berlin Red'	CAby CBod CWCL ECha ELon EStr GBee GKin LBMP MNFA MNrw MSpe SDay WFar
'Berlin Red Star' **new**	MNFA
'Berlin Red Velvet'	MNFA
'Berlin Tallboy'	WAul
'Berlin Watermelon'	MBNS
'Berliner Ring' **new**	MNFA
'Bernard Thompson'	MNFA

'Berry Blitz' **new** EStr
'Berrylicious' EPfP
'Bertie Ferris' EStr EWoo NLar SDay
'Beside Myself' **new** CFwr
'Bess Ross' CMHG MNFA XSen
'Bess Vestal' MWat
'Best Kept Secret' EWoo SPol
'Bette Davis Eyes' CBgR CWat SDay SPol
'Better Yet' (d) **new** CFwr
'Betty Warren Woods' SDay
'Betty Woods' (d) SDay
'Betty's Pick' EWoo
'Beware the Wizard' CFwr
'Beyond 2000' CFwr
'Big Apple' SDay SPol
'Big Bird' EWoo MBNS SDay
'Big City Eye' MBNS
'Big Edge Fred' **new** EStr
'Big Golden' WWEG
'Big Kiss' (d) SPol
'Big Ross' CFwr
'Big Smile' CWGN MBNS MNrw NBro NSoo SDeJ WFar
'Big Snowbird' CFwr
'Big Success' (d) **new** EStr
'Big Time Happy' LRHS MBNS SPoG STPC
'Big World' CBgR EStr
'Bigcabin Neon Beacon' CFwr
'Bill Norris' SDay SPol
'Bird Bath Pink' SPol
'Birdwing Butterfly' SPol
'Bite the Bullet' CFwr
'Bitsy' ELon SCob WCot WMnd WWEG
'Black Ambrosia' EStr SPol
'Black Arrowhead' CFwr EStr SPol
'Black Emanuelle' CExl IKil LAst MBNS MNrw NLar
'Black Eye' SDay WNHG
'Black Eyed Stella' CKel MBNS WCot
'Black Eyed Susan' ECtt EStr MBNS MSpe
'Black Falcon Ritual' CFwr
'Black Friar' EWoo
'Black Ice' CFwr EWoo SPol
'Black Knight' EWoo NLar SRms
'Black Magic' CBod CBro CTri CWat ELan EPfP EStr GKin GMaP LRHS MHer MRav MWhi NBir NEgg NGdn SGSe SMrm WHer WHrl WMoo
'Black Plush' EStr EWoo SPol
'Black Prince' CBgR CCon EStr EWll EWoo IBoy MBNS NBre NBro WAul
'Black Stockings' EBee EStr EWes IPot MBri MWhi SCob SDeJ
'Blackberries and Cream' **new** EStr
'Blackberry Candy' CHel CSam EAEE ECtt EStr GKin MBNS MNrw MSpe NHol NWad SDay WCAu
'Blackberry Sherbert' WFar
'Blackeye Belle' EWoo
'Blessed Again' SDay
'Blessing' EStr SPol
'Blizzard Bay' **new** SPol
'Blonde Ambition' (d) CFwr
'Blonde is Beautiful' SDay
'Blue Beat' CFwr
'Blue Happiness' SDay
'Blue Sheen' CBgR CCon CMac ECtt GMaP MBNS WFar WMoo
'Blueberry Candy' ECtt EStr IBoy MBNS
'Blueberry Cream' CWCL ELon EStr MBNS MMHG MNrw MSpe
'Blueberry Frost' CBgR
'Blueberry Sundae' CWat EBee ELon NSoo SGol
'Blue-eyed Butterfly' SPol
'Blushing Angel' SDay
'Blushing Belle' MBNS NBro NEgg
'Blutorange' CFwr
'Bobby Martin' CFwr
'Bobby's Lavender Eyes' **new** EStr
'Bobo Anne' CWat EStr
'Body Rub' **new** CFwr
'Bogie and Becall' SPol
'Bold Courtier' CBgR
'Bold Encounter' CFwr
'Bold One' CMHG SPol
'Bold Ruler' SPol
'Bonanza' Widely available
'Boney Maroney' CBgR CFwr EWoo
'Bonnie Boy' XLum XSen
'Bonnie Holley' CFwr
'Boogie my Woogie Baby' CFwr EWoo
'Booroobin Magic' EStr EWoo
'Border Baby' ECtt
'Border Lord' EStr EWoo
'Both Sides Now' ECtt
'Boulderbrook Serenity' SDay
'Bourbon Kings' EStr MBNS MSpe SDeJ WHrl WWtn
'Bradley Bernard' SPol
'Braided Edgings' CFwr
'Brand New Lover' SDay
'Brass Buckles' see *H.* 'Puddin'
'Brasstown' SPol
'Brazilian Orange' XSen
'Breed Apart' SPol
'Brenda Newbold' SDay SPol
'Brer Rabbit's Baby' EWoo
'Bridge of Dreams' CFwr
'Bridget' ELan
'Bright Beacon' SDay SPol
'Bright Island' XSen
'Bright Side' CBgR
'Bright Spangles' MSpe SDay WAul
'Brilliant Circle' ECtt
'Bring It On' CFwr
'Broadway Bold Eyes' SPol
'Broadway Valentine' XSen
'Brocaded Gown' ELan SDay
'Brother Cal' **new** CFwr
'Brown Billows' EWoo
'Brown Exotica' CFwr
'Brown Witch' EWoo
'Brown-Eyed Girl' SPol
'Bruce' **new** EStr
'Bruno Müller' MNFA
'Brushed with Bronze' SPol
'Brutus' WHrl
'Bubbly' SDay
'Bud Producer' CBgR SPol
'Buenos Aires' XSen
'Buffys Doll' MBNS SDay
'Bugs Ear' SDay
'Bug's Hug' EStr
'Bumble Bee' CWat ECtt MBNS NBre SDay
'Bumble Bee Boogie' CFwr
'Bunny Puff' **new** EStr

Cultivar	Suppliers
'Burgundy Baroness' **new**	EStr
'Burlesque'	SDay SPol WCot
'Burning Daylight' ♀H6	CBgR EBee ECtt EPfP EStr LRHS MNFA MNrw MRav MWat NEgg SCob SGol SPer SRms WAul WCAu WCFE WCot WFar WPtf
'Bus Stop'	SPol
'Buster Ruster' **new**	CFwr
'Buttercup Parade'	EStr
'Butterfly Charm'	CWat SDay
'Butterpat'	SDay
'Butterscotch'	WFar
'Butterscotch Ruffles'	SDay
'Buzz Bomb'	CWat ECGP ECrc ECtt GBee GKin LRHS MBNS MCot MNFA NEgg NGdn SPer WCAu WFar WWEG
'By Myself'	XSen
'Cabbage Flower'	SDay XSen
'Cabriolet'	XSen
'Cajun Christmas'	CFwr
'Cake Plate' **new**	CFwr
'Calico Spider'	SPol XSen
'California Sunshine'	SPol
'Call Girl'	SDay
'Calypso'	EWoo
'Camden Ballerina'	SDay
'Camden Gold Dollar'	SDay
'Camelot Green'	WNHG
'Cameroons'	SPol
'Canadian Border Patrol'	CWCL EStr IPot MBNS MNrw NLar SPer SPol WHrl
'Canary Glow'	CTri IBoy SMrm
'Canary Wings'	CBgR
'Candid Colors'	CFwr
'Candide'	SDay
'Candied Popcorn Perfection'	CFwr
'Candy Cane Dreams'	CFwr
'Candy Gram' **new**	EStr
'Cantique'	SDay SPol
'Capernaum Cocktail'	SPol
'Capulina'	EWoo
'Cara Mia'	CBgR EStr MBNS NBir SPol
'Caramba'	CBgR
'Caribbean Jack Dolan'	EWoo
'Carlotta'	SDay
'Carmen Marie'	XSen
'Carnival in Mexico'	CFwr
'Carnival Mask'	CFwr
'Carolicolossal'	ELon SDay SPol
'Carolina Cranberry'	ELan
'Carolina Dynamite' **new**	CFwr
'Carolina Low Country'	CFwr
'Carolina Red Bug'	CFwr
'Caroline Taylor'	WHrl
'Carousel Princess' **new**	LRHS
'Carrick Wildon'	CFwr EBee
'Carrot'	SDay
'Cartwheels'	ECha EPfP EPla EShb EStr GBuc GKin GMaP LRHS MBNS MBel MRav MSpe NBro SBch SPer WCAu WMoo
'Carved Initials' **new**	CFwr
'Carved Pumpkin Pie'	CFwr
'Casa des Juan'	CFwr
'Castile'	SDay
'Castle Pinkney'	CFwr
'Castle Strawberry Delight'	SPol
'Catapult Sam'	CFwr
'Catch a Falling Star'	CFwr
'Catherine Neal'	SDay SPol
'Catherine Woodbery'	Widely available
'Cathy Cute Legs'	CFwr
'Cathy's Sunset'	CKel CSam ECtt EPla GKin LRHS MBNS MSpe MWat NBro NGdn NWad SRGP
'Cat's Cradle'	SDay
'Cause for Pause' **new**	EStr
'Caviar'	SDay
'Cayenne' ♀H6	SPol
'Cedar Waxwing'	MNrw
'Celery Plate' **new**	CFwr
'Celestial City'	SDay
'Celtic Christmas'	CFwr SPol
'Cenla Crepe Myrtle'	EWoo
'Cerulean Star'	EWoo SPol
'Challenger'	EWoo
'Chamonix'	XSen
'Chance Encounter'	MBNS NHol SPol WCAu
'Chang Dynasty'	CFwr
'Changing Latitudes'	SPol WHrl
'Charlene Moore'	SPol
'Charles Johnston'	CBgR CKel CPrp EPfP EWoo MBNS SDay
'Charlie Pierce Memorial'	SPol
'Charon the Ferryman'	CFwr
'Chartreuse Magic'	CMHG EPla
'Chartwell'	EWoo
'Chasing the Sun'	CFwr
'Château Lafite'	SPol
'Checkerboard Curls' **new**	CFwr
'Cheerful Note'	WNHG
'Cherokee Mary' (d) **new**	EStr
'Cherokee Patterns'	SPol
'Cherokee Vision'	CFwr
'Cherry Candy'	MSpe
'Cherry Cheeks'	CCon ECtt ELan ELon EPla EStr LRHS MBNS MHol MNrw MRav SPol WCAu WCot WMoo WWEG WWtn
'Cherry Eyed Pumpkin' ♀H6	EWoo SDay SPol WCAu
'Cherry Kiss'	IVic
'Cherry Lace'	XSen
'Cherry Ripe'	MNFA
'Cherry Smash Cupcake' (d) **new**	CFwr
'Cherry Tiger'	MBNS
'Cherry Valentine'	CBcs MBNS MSpe
'Chesapeake Crablegs'	CFwr
'Chesières Lunar Moth'	CBgR ELon SPol
'Chester Cyclone'	SDay
'Chevron Spider'	EStr
'Chicago Antique Tapestry'	SDay
'Chicago Apache'	CCon EBee ELon EPfP EWoo MBNS MNFA NBir SBch SPer SPol WWEG
'Chicago Aztec'	ELon
'Chicago Blackout'	CBod CCon CWat ECtt MSpe WAul WCot
'Chicago Cardinal'	EStr
'Chicago Cattleya'	CCon
'Chicago Cherry'	WNHG
'Chicago Fire'	EBee EPfP MBNS SDay
'Chicago Firecracker'	XLum XSen
'Chicago Heirloom'	CCon MBNS WCAu
'Chicago Jewel'	CCon ELon NSti
'Chicago Knobby'	EBee EStr MBNS MNrw SDay

'Chicago Knockout' CCon ELan EPfP EWoo SPer WAul WWEG
'Chicago Mist' WNHG
'Chicago Peach' NBir WCAu
'Chicago Picotee Lace' WWEG
'Chicago Picotee Memories' EBee MBNS MSpe
'Chicago Picotee Promise' WNHG
'Chicago Princess' EWoo
'Chicago Queen' SDay WMnd WNHG
'Chicago Rainbow' CBgR MBNS
'Chicago Royal Crown' EAEE ECtt
'Chicago Royal Robe' CWCL CWat ELon EWll MBNS NBid SPer SRms SWat WCot WWtn
'Chicago Silver' CCon MBNS WAul
'Chicago Star' WNHG
'Chicago Sugarplum' SDay
'Chicago Sunrise' CBgR EPla GMaP IBoy LRHS MBNS MRav NGdn NOrc SPol SWvt WCot WWEG
'Chief Four Fingers' EWoo
'Chief Sequoia' EStr
'Children's Festival' CMac ECtt EStr GMaP LRHS MBNS MRav MSpe NLar SGSe SWvt WMoo
'China Bride' EStr EWoo SCob SPol
'Chinese Coral' EWoo
'Chinese Imp' NLar SDay
'Chireno' **new** EStr
'Chocolate Candy' CWGN EBee EPfP IPot MBNS
'Choctaw Chick' CFwr
'Chokecherry Mountain' EStr EWoo
'Chorus Line' EStr SDay SPol WNHG
'Chorus Line Kid' SPol
'Christina's Pink Parasol' **new** EStr
'Christine Lynn' WNHG
'Christine Walser-Hite' **new** CFwr
'Christmas Is' CBgR CMac CWGN EBee ECtt ELon EStr GBin GKin LPot LRHS LSou MBNS MBel MNrw MSpe NCGa NHol SDay SPol WAul WCot WHrl WWEG XSen
'Church and Wellesley' (d) **new** CFwr
'Ciara Marie' **new** CFwr
'Ciarra Vonnie' SDay
'Cimarron Knight' CBgR EWoo SPol WCAu
'Cinderella Sue' **new** CFwr
'Cindy's Eye' WCot
'Circle of Beauty' SPol
citrina ♀H6 CBgR CExl CHid CMac EBee EWoo GQue IBoy IMou LRHS MCot WCot WHrl WRHF XLum XSen
citrina × (× ***ochroleuca***) SMHy WCot
'Civil Law' SDay
'Civil Rights' SDay
'Classic Caper' WNHG
'Claudine' ELon
'Cleo' EWoo
'Cleopatra' ELon EWoo SDay SPol
'Clothed in Glory' EStr EWoo MBNS WCot WWEG
'Coach's Hot Lips' **new** CFwr
'Coburg Fright Wig' EWoo
'Cocktail Party' MBri
'Colonel Joe' EWoo
'Color Stick' **new** EStr
'Comanche Eyes' SDay
'Comet Flash' SPol
'Coming Up Roses' ELon
'Concorde Nelson' CFwr
'Condilla' (d) ♀H6 SPol
'Connie Abel' CFwr
'Connie Can't Have It' CFwr
'Conspicua' CBgR SMHy SPol
'Contessa' CBro GBin LRHS SPer
'Cool and Crepy' **new** EStr
'Cool It' CKel MBNS MPie NLar SCob SDeJ WHrl
'Cool Jazz' SDay SPol
'Cool Summer Breeze' SPol
'Copper Dawn' NChi SPol
'Copper Windmill' CBgR SDay SPol
'Copperhead' EStr SPol
'Copperhead Road' **new** CFwr
'Coral Crab' EWoo
'Coral Eye Shadow' EWoo
'Coral Mist' ECrc MBNS NBre
'Coral Sparkler' WNHG
'Coral Spider' SPol
'Corky' Widely available
'Corolla Light' **new** CFwr
'Corryton Pink' SPol
'Cosmic Hummingbird' SDay
'Cosmopolitan' MBNS
'Country Club' EBee GMaP MBNS SPol WCAu WWEG
'Country Melody' SDay
'Court Magician' EWoo
'Court Troubadour' ELon SPol
'Coyote Moon' SDay
'Craig Green' CFwr
'Cranberry Baby' SDay WHoo WNHG
'Cranberry Coulis' CWat MBNS
'Crawleycrow' XSen
'Crazy Crane' CFwr
'Crazy Ivan' CFwr
'Crazy Larry' EStr
'Crazy Pierre' EWoo SPol WHrl XSen
'Cream Drop' COtt CPrp ECtt EPPr GBuc GMaP IBoy LRHS MCot MHer MRav NBro NGdn NLar NSti SCob WAul WCot WHrl WMoo
'Creation' CFwr EWoo
'Cricket Call' CFwr
'Crimson Flood' EWoo
'Crimson Icon' SDay
'Crimson Pirate' CBgR CBod CBre CMac ECrc ELon EPfP EStr EWoo GKev GLog IBoy MBNS MSpe NBir NEoE NOrc SCob SPer SPlb SPol SWat WCAu WHar WHrl WMoo WWEG WWtn XLum
'Crintonic Shadowlands' SPol
'Cripple Creek' CFwr EWoo
'Croesus' SRms
'Crooked House' CFwr
'Crystal Cupid' XSen
'Crystal Pinot' ELon
'Cupid's Gold' SDay
'Curls' CBgR MBNS SDay
'Curly Brick Road' SPol
'Curly Cinnamon Windmill' ♀H6 SDay SPol
'Curly Rosy Posy' SDay
'Custard Candy' ♀H6 CWCL CWGN ECtt EStr EWoo GKin MBNS MSpe NHol WCAu WNHG
'Cute As Can Be' EStr

'Cynthia Mary' ECtt GKin MBNS NBro SRGP
'Cypriana' EBee XSen
'D.R. McKeithan' CFwr
'Daily Dollar' LRHS MBNS MSpe NGdn
'Dainty Pink' WWtn
'Dallas Spider Time' MNFA SDay
'Dallas Star' SPol WHrl
'Dan Mahony' MBNS NSoo
'Dan Tau' CKel
'Dance Among the Stars' CFwr
'Dance Ballerina Dance' EBee SDay
'Dancing Crab' CBgR EWoo SPol
'Dancing Dwarf' SDay
'Dancing Lions' SDay
'Dancing Shiva' SDay SPol
'Dancing Summerbird' ELon SPol
'Dancing with Julie' CFwr
'Daring Deception' CCon CKel ECtt ELon EPfP EStr IPot MBNS MNrw SCob SPad WCAu
'Daring Dilemma' EStr SPol
'Daring Reflection' MSpe SDay
'Darius' WNHG
'Dark and Handsome' MBNS
'Dark Avenger' MBNS
'Dark Elf' SDay
'Dark Monkey' CFwr
'Date Book' EWoo
'David Holman' WNHG
'David Kirchhoff' NSoo
'Davidson Update' WNHG
'Dazzling Spider' CFwr
'Dean Corey' **new** CFwr
'Debary Canary' EWoo
'Debussy' EStr EWoo
'Decatur Ballerina' WNHG
'Decatur Captivation' WNHG
'Decatur Dictator' WNHG
'Decatur Elevator' EWoo
'Decatur Imp' WHrl
'Decatur Jewel' WNHG
'Decatur Rhythm' WNHG
'Decatur Supreme' WNHG
'Decatur Treasure Chest' WNHG
'Deep in My Heart' CFwr
'Delicate Design' SPol
'Delightful David' (d) CFwr
'Delightsome' SDay
'Deloris Gould' **new** SDay
'Demetrius' CWat EStr
'Derrick Cane' SPol
'Desdemona' SPol XLum
'Desert Dreams' WCot
'Desert Icicle' EWoo SPol
'Designer Gown' SDay
'Designer Jeans' SPol
'Destination Y' XSen
'Destined to See' CBcs CBro CCon CPar ECtt ELon EStr IPot LRHS LSou MBNS MNrw NBir NBro NEgg SPer SPol WCot WHrl
'Devil's Footprint' SDay SPol
'Devon Cream' SPer
'Devonshire' EStr SDay
'Dewberry Candy' ELon
'Diabolique' EWoo
'Diamond Dust' CKel ECtt GBee LRHS MBNS NLar SPer
'Diamonds and Ringlets' **new** CFwr
'Diana Grenfell' **new** CBgR
'Dick Kitchingman' CBgR SPol
'Dido' CTri
'Dipped in Ink' SPol
'Distant Star' EWoo
'Distinctive Elegance' CFwr
'Divertissment' CBgR ELon EWoo SDay WHrl
'Dixie Rooster' CFwr
'Dizzy Miss Lizzy' CFwr
'Do the Twist' EWoo
'Do You Know Doris' SDay
'Doc Holliday' **new** EStr
'Dominic' CBgR CPar EPla EWoo IBoy MSpe SPol WCot WMoo
'Don Stevens' WHrl
'Don't Know Jack' CFwr
'Don't Mess with Me' CFwr
'Dooty Owl' **new** CFwr
'Dorcas' **new** WCAu
'Dorethe Louise' CBgR SDay SPol
'Dorothy McDade' EWoo MNrw
'Dot Paul' ELan
'Double Action' (d) SDay SPol
'Double Bold One' (d) SPol
'Double Charm' (d) XSen
'Double Coffee' (d) SPol
'Double Corsage' (d) SPol
'Double Cream' (d) WCot
'Double Cutie' (d) EStr NLar SDay SRms
'Double Delicious' (d) WCot
'Double Doubloon' (d) XLum
'Double Dream' (d) EStr WHrl
'Double Firecracker' (d) CWat EBee MBNS NBro NLar XSen
'Double Flash Splash' (d) **new** SDay
'Double Glitter' (d) XSen
'Double Oh Seven' (d) ELon SPol
'Double Passion' (d) MBNS
'Double Pompon' (d) EStr
'Double Pop Art' (d) XSen
'Double Red Royal' (d) EPfP XSen
'Double River Wye' (d) CBgR CCon CWat ECtt EShb EStr GBin IBoy LRHS MBNS MHer MNrw NGdn SPol SWat WAul WBrk WCot WHoo WHrl WMnd WWEG
'Dowager Queen' WNHG
'Dragon Dreams' SPol
'Dragon Fire Breath' CFwr
'Dragon Heart' EWoo
'Dragon King' SPol
'Dragon Lore' MBNS
'Dragon's Eye' CWat EWoo MSpe SDay SPol
'Dragon's Orb' CKel SDay
'Dream Baby' NBre
'Dream Candy' **new** CFwr
'Dream Catcher' CFwr EWoo
'Dream Keeper' EWoo
'Dresden Doll' EBee SPer
'Droopy Drawers' SPol
'Druid's Chant' EWoo
'Duke of Durham' EWoo MBNS MSpe
'Duke of Earl' **new** CBgR
dumortieri CBro EBee ECha ELan MCoo MCot MRav NBid NBir NSti SEND SPer WCot WHrl WWEG WWtn XSen
- B&SWJ 1283 WCru
'Dumpy' **new** EStr
'Dune Buggy' XSen

'Dune Needlepoint'	SPol WHrl
'Duplex' (d)	XSen
'Dutch Art' **new**	SDay
'Dutch Beauty'	EPla
'Dutch Gold'	MNrw NBro
'Earl of Warwick'	CBgR SPol
'Earlianna'	SPol
'Early Days' **new**	WCAu
'Earnest Yearwood'	SDay
'Earth Angel'	SPol
'Earth Fire'	SDay
'Easter Star' **new**	CFwr
'Easy Ned'	ELon EWoo SDay SPol
'Easy Street'	SDay
'Eat Our Wake Pintaheads'	CFwr
'Ed Kirchhoff'	XLum
'Ed Murray'	EStr MNFA WAul WCAu
'Edgar Brown'	MBNS SPol WCot
'Edge Ahead'	CMac ECtt EStr GKin LRHS MBNS NHol WCAu WHrl
'Edge of Darkness'	CKel CWGN EPfP MBNS NBro NLar NSti
'Edge of Frenzy'	CFwr
'Edge of Heaven'	EStr
'Edith Vaughan' **new**	EStr
'Edna Selman' **new**	CFwr
'Edna Spalding'	LRHS SDay
'Eenie Allegro'	CBro ECtt MBNS SPer WMnd
'Eenie Fanfare'	MBNS NBir WWEG
'Eenie Weenie'	CBro ECtt ELon EPla GKev IBoy LRHS MBNS NBro SRms WOut WWEG WWtn
'Eenie Weenie Non-stop'	ECha EPPr
'Eggplant Ecstasy'	CFwr
'Eggplant Electricity'	EWoo
'Eggplant Escapade' ♀H6	CBgR MSpe SPol
'Egyptian Ibis'	EStr EWoo SPol WMnd WNHG
'Egyptian Queen'	CBgR
'Eight Miles High' **new**	EStr
'Eighteen Karat' **new**	EStr
'Einstein' **new**	CFwr
'El Desperado'	CBgR CPar CSam ECtt ELon EPfP EWoo GBin GBuc IPot LRHS LSun MBNS MHol MLHP MNrw MSpe NEgg SPav WCAu WCFE WCot WWEG
'El Glorioso'	CWat
'Elaine Strutt'	MBNS MNFA MNrw SDay SWvt WCot
'Eleanor Marcotte'	SDay
'Electric Marmalade Magic' **new**	EStr
'Elegant Candy' ♀H6	CBgR CKel CMac EWoo MBNS WCAu
I 'Elegantissima'	SPol
'Eleonor'	EBee EPfP MBNS
'Elfin Daydream'	SPol
'Elf's Cap'	SDay
'Elijah Sain'	SPol
'Elizabeth Anne Hudson'	SDay
'Elizabeth Salter'	CWCL MBNS NLar SPol
'Elmore James'	EWoo
'Eloquent Cay'	CFwr
'Eloquent Silence' **new**	SDay
'Elva White Grow'	SDay
'Elves' Watermark'	SPol
'Emerald Eye'	SDay
'Emerald Lady'	SPol
'Emily Anne'	SPol
'Emily's Fiery Horse'	CFwr
'Emperor's Choice'	SDay
'Emperor's Dragon'	EStr SDay
'Enchanted April'	SPol
'Enchanted Forest' **new**	EStr
'Enchanter's Spell'	SDay
'Energizer Ty Howard' **new**	CFwr
'English Cameo'	SPol
'Enigma Variations'	SPol
'Entransette'	SDay
'Entrapment'	CBod ECtt EStr IBoy MBNS SDeJ
'Envoyé Spécial'	XSen
'Envy Me'	SPol
'Erica Nichole Gonzales'	SDay
'Erin Prairie'	SPol
'Etched Eyes'	EWoo MSpe SPol
'Eternal Blessing'	SPol
'Eternity Road'	EStr
'Ethel Buccola'	CFwr
'Etruscan Tomb'	SPol
'Euro-mazing'	CFwr
'Evelyn Claar'	CMac
'Evelyn Kloeris'	CFwr
'Evelyn Lela Stout'	SDay
'Even Stephen'	SPol
'Evening Gown'	SPol
'Evening Solitude' **new**	WCAu
'Ever So Ruffled'	SDay
'Exotic Candy' **new**	SPol
'Exotic Dancer'	CFwr
'Exotic Design'	CFwr
'Exotic Love'	SDay
'Exotic Treasure'	CFwr
'Exploded Pumpkin' **new**	EBee
'Eye Catching'	EWoo
'Eye of Round'	CFwr
'Eye on America'	EBee EStr WCAu
'Eyes Right Jones'	CFwr
'Eyes Wide Shut'	CFwr
'Eye-yi-yi'	SPol
'Ezekiel'	SPol XSen
'Fabergé'	SDay
'Fairest Love'	EBee MBNS MNrw
'Fairest of Them'	CBgR
'Fairy Charm'	SDay
'Fairy Firecracker' **new**	SPol
'Fairy Frosting'	SDay
'Fairy Summerbird'	SPol
'Fairy Tale Pink'	EStr MNFA SDay SPol
'Fairy Wings'	EStr SPer
'Faith Nabor'	SPol
'Falcon'	SPol
'Fall Farewell'	WNHG
'Fandango'	LPla SPer
'Fantasia'	EWoo
'Fantasy Finish' **new**	WCAu
'Farmer's Daughter'	CBgR EWoo
'Fashion Police'	CFwr
'Fat Lady Sings'	SPol
'Father's Day Gift'	CFwr
'Feather Down'	SPol
'Fellow'	SPol
'Femme Fatale'	SDay
'Femme Osage'	SDay
'Feria'	XSen
'Festive Art'	SPol
'Fiestaville' **new**	EStr

'Final Touch'	CBgR EAEE EBee EStr MBNS NBro SGol SHar SPol
'Finders Keepers' **new**	EStr
'Finlandia'	MNFA
'Fire and Fog'	CHel EStr MBNS
'Fire and Wind'	CFwr
'Fire Dance'	ELon
'Fire from Heaven'	WHrl
'Fire Tree'	CBgR ELon EStr SPol
'Fireborn'	CFwr
'Firestorm'	EWoo SPol
'First Formal'	SMrm SPer
'First Knight'	SDay
'Fitzasaurus'	CFwr
'Flaming Firebird' **new**	EStr
'Flaming Frolic' **new**	SPol
'Flaming Sword'	WBrk WRHF
flava	see *H. lilioasphodelus*
'Florida Sunshine' (d)	XSen
'Florissant Miss' **new**	EStr
'Flower Basket' (d) **new**	EStr
'Flower Pavilion'	SDay SPol
'Floyd Cove'	SDay
'Fly Catcher'	CBgR
'Flyaway Home'	SPol
'Flying Frisbee'	CFwr
'Flying Saucer'	EWoo
'Fol de Rol'	EWoo
'Fooled Me' ♀H6	EBee ECtt EStr MBNS MBri MSpe SDay SPad SPol
'Foolscap'	EWoo
'For the Good Times'	CFwr EWoo
'Forbidden Desires' **new**	EStr
'Forbidden Dreams'	EWoo
'Forestlake Ragamuffin'	SPol
'Forgotten Dreams'	EBee MBNS MSpe
forrestii	CExl
'Forsooth' **new**	CBgR
'Forsyth Ace of Hearts'	CBgR
'Forsyth Evening Glow' **new**	EStr
'Forsyth Flamboyant' **new**	CFwr
'Forsyth Frostbound'	SPol
'Forsyth Lemon Drop'	SDay
'Forsyth Myra Dolores' **new**	CFwr
'Forsyth White Sentinel'	CFwr
'Forsyth Wrinkles and Crinkles' **new**	CFwr
'Forty Second Street'	CCon CFwr MBNS
'Fox Ears'	EWoo
'Fox Hunter'	CFwr
'Foxhaven Enigma'	CFwr
'Fragrant Pastel Cheers'	SDay
'Fragrant Treasure'	ERCP
'Frances Busby'	CFwr
'Frances Fay'	SPol
'Frances Joiner'	EWoo
'Francis of Assisi'	EWoo
'Francois Verhaert'	EWoo
'Frank Gladney'	MNFA SPol XSen
'Frank Smith'	WCAu
'Frans Hals'	Widely available
'Fred Ham'	XSen
'Fred Manning'	CFwr
'Free Wheelin''	CWGN EPfP EStr MBri MSCN NSoo
'French Cavalier'	CFwr
'French Connection'	SDay

'French Lingerie' **new**	EStr
'French Porcelain'	MSpe SDay
'French Twist'	CFwr
'Fresh Air'	MNrw
'Frilly Bliss'	CFwr
'Fritz Schroer'	CBgR
'Frosted Encore'	SDay
'Frosted Pink Ice'	SPol
'Frosted Vintage Ruffles'	CHel EBee EStr MBri
'Frosty White'	SDay
'Fuchsia Beauty'	SPol
'Fuchsia Cockatoo' **new**	CFwr
'Fuchsia Four'	SPol
'Full Grown' **new**	EStr
fulva	CTri ELan EPla LPot MMuc NBir SCob SEND SPol SRms WBrk WHrl XSen
- B&SWJ 8647	WCru
- 'Flore Pleno' (d)	CAvo CMHG CMac COtt ECtt EHon ELan EPla MHer MRav NBir NBro NGdn NSti SMad SPav SPer SRms SWat WBrk WMoo WWEG XSen
- 'Green Kwanso' (d)	CBgR CExl ECGP ECha ITim MMHG MMoz WPnP
- var. ***kwanso*** B&SWJ 6328	WCru
- 'Kwanso' ambig. (d)	NOrc
- var. ***littorea***	CMac EPla XLum XSen
- var. ***rosea***	SPol WCot XSen
§ - 'Variegated Kwanso' (d/v)	CBro CRow EBee EWoo GCra MRav NBir SMad WBor WCot WHer WHoo WHrl
- yellow variegated (v) **new**	WCot
'Fun Fling'	SPol
'Funky Fuchsia'	SPol
'Future Whispers' **new**	CFwr
'Gadsden Firefly'	CFwr
'Gadsden Goliath'	CFwr SPol
'Gadsden Light'	SDay SPol
'Gala Greetings'	XSen
'Galaxy Ranger' **new**	CFwr
'Gale Storm'	WNHG
'Ganz Rot' **new**	MNFA
'Garden Crawler'	CBgR
'Garden Portrait'	EWoo SDay SPol
'Gay Music'	MBNS
'Gay Octopus'	CBgR SPol
'Gay Rapture'	SPer
'Gay Troubadour'	EWoo
'Gemini Jack' (d)	CFwr
'Geneva Chainsaw'	CFwr
'Geneva Firetruck'	CFwr
'Gentle Country Breeze'	SDay SPol
'Gentle Rose'	SDay
'Gentle Shepherd'	Widely available
'George Cunningham'	ECtt ELan EStr LRHS MRav NBir SPol
'George David'	WHrl
'Georgette Belden'	ECGP ECtt GKin LRHS MBNS MSpe MWat NHol SPol WWEG
'Georgia Cream' (d)	NLar
'Gerard Deschenes'	CFwr
'German Ballerina'	SPol
'Get All Excited'	SPol
'Giant Moon'	CBgR CMHG ECtt ELan EPla LRHS MBNS SRms WHal
'Giant on the Mountain'	CFwr
'Giddy Go Round'	EWoo SPol
'Gilded by Grace'	CFwr
'Ginger Twist' **new**	CFwr

'Gingerbread Man'	MSpe
'Girouette'	XSen
'Give Me Eight'	SPol
'Glacier Bay'	CBgR CWat EWoo MBNS
'Gladys Campbell' (d) **new**	CFwr
'Glass Menagerie'	CFwr
'Gleeman Song' **new**	CBgR
'Glittering Treasure'	XLum
'Glowing Heart'	SDay
'Go Seminoles'	CFwr
'Going Bananas'[PBR]	WCot
'Gold Elephant'	SDay
'Gold Imperial'	NBre
'Golden Bell'	NGdn
'Golden Chance'	WCAu
'Golden Change'	CFwr
'Golden Chimes'	Widely available
'Golden Ginkgo'	MSpe
'Golden Marvel'	EWoo
'Golden Prize'	EPla EWoo GQue NGdn SDay WCot XSen
'Golden Scroll'	SDay
Golden Zebra = 'Malja'[PBR] (v)	CWGN ELan EPfP IBoy MAvo MBNS MRav NLar NSti SRms WCot
'Golliwog'	CBgR EStr
'Graal'	XSen
'Grace and Favour'	SPol
'Grace and Grandeur'	EWoo
'Graceful Eye'	SDay
'Graceland'	SDay
'Grand Masterpiece'	NGdn SDay
'Grand Palais'	SDay
'Grandma Kissed Me'	SPol
'Grandma's Smile'	CFwr
'Granite City Towhead'	CFwr ELon
'Granny Coot'	EStr
'Grape Arbor'	WNHG
'Grape Harvest'	WNHG
'Grape Magic'	MSpe WCot
'Grape Twizzler'	CFwr
'Grape Velvet'	CSpe EStr EWoo MNFA NSti SBch SPol SRms WCAu WMnd WWEG WWtn
'Green Canary'	SPol
'Green Dolphin Street'	SDay SPol
'Green Dragon'	SPol
'Green Eyed Lady'	SDay
'Green Eyes Wink'	MHol MLHP
'Green Flutter'	CBgR EBee EStr EWoo GCal GQue IMou LPla MBNS MBri MNFA NBir NGdn NSti SPhx SPol WCot WWEG
'Green Goddess'	XLum
'Green Gold'	CMHG
'Green Mystique'	EBee MBri
'Green Nautilus'	EStr
'Green Puff'	NBir SDay
'Green Spider'	CBgR SDay
'Green Warrior'	CFwr EWoo
'Green Widow'	EWoo SDay
'Grey Witch' ♀H6	SPol
'Greywoods Nautical Nellie'	CFwr
'Grumbly'	ELan WPnP
'Guadalajara' (d)	CFwr
'Guardian Angel'	WCFE
'Gypsy Cranberry'	SPol
'Gypsy Prince'	MNFA
'Hail Mary'	SDay
'Halloween Costume'	CFwr
'Halloween Harvest'	CFwr
'Hamlet'	SDay WNHG
'Happy Hopi'	EStr
'Happy Returns'	CBgR CHel CHid CSBt CTri ECha ELan EPfP EPla EStr EWoo GBin GBuc LPot LRHS MBNS MBel MSpe NGdn NHol SGol SRGP SRms WCAu WWEG XLum
'Harbor Blue'	SDay
'Harrods'	EStr
'Harry Barras'	XLum
'Hawaiian Nights'	EWoo
'Hawk'	ELon SDay SPol
'Heady Wine'	EStr SDay
'Heartbreak Ridge' **new**	CFwr
'Heart's Glee'	XSen
'Heat of the Moment'	CFwr
'Heat Wave'	CFwr
'Heavenly Angel Ice'	CFwr EStr
'Heavenly Beginnings'	CFwr
'Heavenly Curls'	SPol
'Heavenly Dragon Fire'	CFwr
'Heavenly Final Destiny' **new**	CFwr
'Heavenly Fire Arrow'	CFwr
'Heavenly Flight of Angels'	CFwr EStr
'Heavenly Starfire'	CFwr EWoo SPol
'Heavenly Treasure'	SPol
'Heidi Eidelweiss'	CExl
'Heirloom Lace'	SDay
'Helena Seabird' **new**	EStr
'Helix'	CFwr
'Helle Berlinerin'	MNFA SDay SPol
'Hello Screamer'	CFwr
'Helter Skelter'	SDay SPol
'Hen's Teeth' **new**	CFwr
'Her Majesty's Wizard'	CBgR ELan ELon EWoo IMou MBNS SPol
'Heron's Cove'	EWoo
'Hesperus'	EWoo
'Hexagon'	EStr
'Hey There'	SDay
'High Tor'	GQui MNFA SPol WHrl
'Highland Lord' (d)	EBee MBNS SDay WCAu XSen
'Hillbilly Heart'	CFwr
'Hint of Blue'	SPol
'Hippie Chic'	CFwr
'Holiday Delight'	MBNS
'Holiday Mood'	ELan
'Holly Dancer' ♀H6	EWoo SPol
'Honey Jubilee'	SPol
'Honey Redhead'	SPol
'Hope Diamond'	SDay
'Hornby Castle'	CBro LRHS
'Hot Chocolate'[PBR]	EBee SRGP
'Hot Town'	ELan
'Hot Wheels'	CBgR
'Hot Wire'	SDay
'Hotter than the Fourth of July'	CFwr
'Houdini'	MSpe WMnd
'House Music'	XSen
'House of Bluelights'	SPol
'House of Orange'	SPol
'Howlin' Wolf'	CFwr
I 'How's the Weather up There?'	EWoo

'Hubbles Buddy'	EWoo
'Humdinger'	WCot
'Hunker Down'	CFwr
'Hyperion'	CBgR CBod CMac CPrp CTri EBee ECha ECtt EPfP EShb EStr EWoo GKin LAst LEdu LRHS MHol MMuc MNFA MRav MSpe NBid NGdn SEND SPer SPoG SWvt WCot WWEG WWtn
'I Luv Lucy'	CFwr
'Ice Carnival'	CKel EBee ELon EPfP MBNS NGdn NLar NOrc SCob SPol SWvt
'Ice Castles'	CTri SDay
'Icecap'	CBgR WMoo
'Icy Lemon'	EStr
'Ida Duke Miles'	SDay
'Iditarod'	EStr
'Igor'	CFwr
'Illini Jackpot'	SDay
'Imperator'	EPla
'Impromptu'	SDay
'In Depth' (d)	EWoo MBNS NBro NLar WCot WHrl
'In Excess'	CFwr
'In Search of Angels'	CFwr
'In Strawberry Time'	WNHG
'Inca Secret' **new**	EStr
'Indian Fandango'	EWoo
'Indian Fires'	CFwr
'Indian Giver'	SPol
'Indian Paintbrush'	ELon EWoo MSpe NBir SPol
'Indigo Moon'	SPol XSen
'Inimitable'	CFwr
'Inky Fingers'	SDay SPol
'Inner View'	ECtt ELon EWoo MBNS NLar SDay WMnd
'Innocent Blush' **new**	EStr
'Instant Zéro'	XSen
'Intelligent Design' **new**	CFwr
'Intertwined Entity' **new**	CFwr
'Invitation to Immortality'	EStr EWoo
'Iowa Greenery'	SPol
'Iridescent Jewel'	SDay
'Irish Elf'	EBee ELon SDay SHar
'Irish Handshake'	CFwr
'Iron Gate Glacier'	EBee EStr MBNS MNFA XLum
'Irresistible Charm'	EPfP
'Isaac'	EStr
'Isle of Dreams'	SPol
'Isleworth'	EWoo
'Isolde'	CBgR MSpe
'Itsy Bitsy Spider'	CBgR CFwr EWoo
'Ivelyn Brown'	SDay SPol
'Ivory Cloud' (d) **new**	EStr
'Ivory Coast'	SDay
'Jabo' **new**	SPol
'Jack Sprat'	CFwr
'Jake Russell'	MBNS MNFA
'Jam All Night'	CFwr
'Jamaican Jammin''	SPol
'Jamaican Magic'	CFwr
'James Clark'	EWoo
'James Marsh'	CBgR EWes EWoo GBin MBNS MNFA MNrw MSpe NSti WCAu WCot WMnd
'Jammin' with Jane'	CFwr
'Janet Gordon'	SPol
'Janice Brown'	CKel CUse CWCL EStr EWoo LAst LSou MBNS MNFA MSpe NHol NLar SDay SPol WHrl

'Jan's Twister'	MNrw SPol WHrl
'Jason Salter'	EStr SDay WAul
'Jay Turman'	SDay
'Jazz at the Wool Club'	CFwr
'Jean'	SDay
'Jean Swann'	EStr MBNS NSoo
'Jedi Dot Pierce'	MNFA
'Jellyfish Jealousy' ♀H6	EWoo
'Jenny Wren'	EPPr EPla EWoo MBNS NBro SRGP WAul WWEG
'Jersey Jim'	SPol
'Jersey Spider'	EWoo SDay SPol
'Jerusalem'	SDay
'Jesse James'	SPol
'Jeu de Piste'	XSen
'Jeune Tom'	CBgR
'Jewel Case'	WNHG
'Joan Senior'	Widely available
'Jockey Club' (d)	ECtt EStr MBNS WHrl
'Joe Marinello'	SPol
'Johanna Klein Strack'	CFwr
'John Benoot'	CFwr
'Johnny Come Lately'	EStr SPol
'Joie de Vivre'	EWoo
'Jolly Red Giant'	EWoo
'Jolyene Nichole'	SDay
'Jordan'	SWvt
'Josephine Marina' **new**	EStr
'Journey to Oz'	EWoo
'Journey's End'	SDay
'Joyful Participation' **new**	EStr
'Judah'	SPol
'Judge Roy Bean'	EWoo MSpe SPol
'Julie Newmar' ♀H6	IPot
'Jumping Jack Flash'	CFwr
'June Explosion' **new**	CFwr
'June Melody'	WNHG
'June Rose' **new**	EStr
'Jungle Beauty'	CBgR SPol
'Just Kiss Me'	SPol
'Just My Size' **new**	EBee
'Justin Brent'	XSen
'Justin George'	SDay SPol
'Justin June'	WHrl
'Kachina Firecracker'	CFwr EWoo
'Kalahari Jewel'	CFwr
'Kamadeva'	CFwr
'Kansas Kitten'	EWoo
'Karateake'	CFwr
'Karen's Curls' ♀H6	EWoo SPol
'Kasia'	WHrl
'Katahdin'	EWoo
'Kate Carpenter'	SDay SPol
'Katherine Harris'	CFwr
'Kathleen Salter'	EWoo
'Kathryn June Wood'	EWoo
'Kathy Macartney'	CFwr EWoo
'Kathy's Cat Spooky'	CFwr
'Katie Elizabeth Miller'	SDay
'Kecia'	MNFA
'Keene'	EWoo
'Kelly's Girl'	SPol
'Kempion'	CBgR
'Kenyan Sun'	EWoo
'Kevin Michael Coyne'	SPol
'Key to my Heart'	CBgR
'Key West'	CFwr
'Killarney Castle'	CFwr

'Kindly Light'	EWoo MNFA SPol
'King Kahuna' (d) **new**	CFwr
'King's Throne'	WNHG
'Kipling' **new**	CFwr
'Kisses for Cinderella'	CFwr
'Klaatu Barada Nikto'	CFwr
'Knights in White Satin'	SPol
'Kokopelli'	CFwr
'Kristal Sunset' **new**	CFwr
'Kwanso Flore Pleno'	see *H. fulva* 'Green Kwanso'
'Kwanso Flore Pleno Variegata'	see *H. fulva* 'Variegated Kwanso'
'La Fenice' **new**	EStr
'La Peche'	SDay
'Lacy Doily'	EStr LLHF MBri WCAu
'Lacy Marionette'	ELon EWoo SDay SPol
'Lady Betty Fretz' **new**	EBee
'Lady Blue Eyes' **new**	EStr
'Lady Cynthia'	CKel
'Lady Fingers'	CBgR MNFA SDay SPol WCAu
'Lady Liz'	MNFA SPol
'Lady Mischief'	SDay
'Lady Neva' ♀H6	CBgR ELon EWoo SDay
'Lady Tiger'	WNHG
'Ladybug's Two Moons' (d) **new**	EStr
'Ladykin'	ELon SDay SPol
'Lake Effect'	EWoo
'Lake Norman Spider'	EWoo SPol
'Lamar' **new**	CFwr
'Land of Cotton'	XSen
'Land of Enchantment'	CFwr
'Lark Song'	LRHS WHrl
'Last Song'	CFwr
'Laughing Feather'	CFwr EWoo
'Laughton Tower'	SMHy
'Laura Lambert'	SPol
'Lauradell'	SDay
'Laurena'	SPol
'Lavender Blue Baby'	EPfP LRHS
'Lavender Cascades' **new**	CFwr
'Lavender Deal'	MNrw WNHG
'Lavender Light'	EWoo
'Lavender Lion' **new**	EStr
'Lavender Memories'	SDay
'Lavender Plicata'	SPol
'Lavender Showstopper'	WCAu
'Lavender Silver Cords'	SPol
'Lavender Spider'	CBgR MSpe SPol
'Lavender Tonic'	SPol
'Lavender Tutu' **new**	EStr
'Layers of Gold' (d)	XSen
'Ledgewood's Cinnamon Lace'	CFwr
'Ledgewood's Firecracker' **new**	CFwr
'Lee Reinke'	SPol
'Legs Limmer'	CFwr EWoo
'Leila Mantle' **new**	CBgR
'Lemon Bells'	CWat EAEE ECGP ECha EPfP EStr EWll EWoo GKev GKin GMaP LEdu LRHS MBNS NBro NCGa NSoo SDay SHar WCAu
'Lemon Custard' **new**	EStr
'Lemon Dessert'	ELon
'Lemon Fellow'	EWoo
'Lemon Fringed Pastel' **new**	CFwr
'Lemon Madeline'	EStr EWoo
'Lemon Meringue Twist'	EWoo
'Lemon Mint'	ELon
'Lemonora'	SDay
'Lenox'	SDay
'Leonard Bernstein'	EWoo SPol
'Leslie Renee'	CFwr
'Let it Rip'	EWoo SPol
'Let Loose'	CFwr
'Lexington Avenue'	SPol
'Licorice Candy'	SPol
'Licorice Twist'	CFwr
'Lies and Lipstick'	CFwr
'Life on Mars' **new**	EStr
'Light of the World' **new**	CFwr
'Light the Way'	ECha GBin
'Light Years Away'	ELon MBNS MNrw NBro
'Lilac Lady' **new**	EStr
'Lilac Wine'	SCob
§ ***lilioasphodelus***	Widely available
– 'Rowden Golden Jubilee' (v)	CRow
'Lilly Dache'	EWoo
'Lilting Belle'	SPol
'Lilting Lady'	SDay SPol
'Lilting Lavender'	ELon SPol WCAu WCot
'Lime Frost' ♀H6	CBgR SPol
'Lime Painted Lady'	CBgR
'Limetree' **new**	CBgR
'Limited Edition'	EWoo
'Lin Wright'	EWoo
'Linda'	MRav
'Linda Agin'	EWoo
'Lines of Splendor'	EWoo WCAu
'Lipstick' **new**	EStr
'Little Bee'	NBre
'Little Big Man'	SDay
'Little Bugger'	ELon NLar WWEG
'Little Bumble Bee'	CCon LRHS MBNS WWEG WWtn
'Little Business'	MBNS MNFA SDay SPol
'Little Cadet'	XLum
'Little Carpet'	MBNS
'Little Dart'	ECha
'Little Deeke'	MNFA SDay WHrl
'Little Dream Red'	SDay
'Little Fantastic'	LRHS SDay WWtn
'Little Fat Cat'	EStr
'Little Fat Dazzler'	ELon SDay SPol
'Little Fellow'	EStr MBNS
'Little Grapette'	CPrp CUse ELon EPfP ERCP GCra GQue LPla MBNS MNFA MSpe NLar NSti WAul WWEG
'Little Greenie'	SDay
'Little Gypsy Vagabond'	CBgR CWat SDay SPol
'Little Heavenly Angel'	SPol
'Little Judy'	SPol
'Little Kiki'	SDay
'Little Lassie'	CBgR
'Little Maggie'	SDay SPol
'Little Men'	WCAu
'Little Miss Manners'	EStr NLar
'Little Missy'	CBgR CWat MBNS WHoo WNHG
'Little Monica'	SDay
'Little Music Maker' (d) **new**	EStr
'Little Rainbow'	WWEG
'Little Red Hen'	CSam ECGP GKin LRHS MBNS MSpe NBir NBro NEgg NGdn
'Little Show Stopper'	EWoo MBNS NBro NLar
'Little Showoff'	SDay

'Little Swain'	SDay
'Little Sweet Sue'	MNFA
'Little Sweet Talk'	ELon
'Little Tawny'	ELon LRHS
'Little Toddler'	SDay
'Little Violet Lace'	SDay
'Little Wart'	CBgR SDay WHrl
'Little Wine Cup'	CBod CMHG CMac COtt CSam CWat ECrc ECtt ELon EPfP EPla GKin GMaP LBMP LRHS MNFA MRav MWat MWhi NBir NEgg NGdn NOrc SEND SPer SPol SRms WAul WMoo WWEG
'Little Women'	MBNS SDay
'Little Zinger'	SDay
'Littlest Angel'	SDay
'Littlest Clown'	SDay
'Living in Amsterdam'	EBee EStr
'Liz Schreiner'	CFwr
'Lizard's Purple Fashion'	CFwr
'Lobo Lucy'	ELon EStr
'Lochinvar'	CSam GBuc MRav
'Loco Bo' **new**	EStr
'Lois Burns'	EWoo SDay SPol
'Lonesome Dove'	SPol
'Long John Silver'	ELon EStr
'Long Legged Lap Dancer'	CFwr
'Long Stocking'	EStr EWoo SPol WCot
'Longfield's Anwar'	EWoo
'Longfield's Bandit'	EWoo
'Longfield's Beauty'	EWoo MBNS MSpe
'Longfield's Glory'	MBNS MSpe NBre
'Longfield's Maxim' (d)	EStr MBNS SDeJ
'Longfield's Pride'	ECho EStr IBoy MBNS SRms WBor
'Longfield's Purple Eye'	NLar
'Longfield's Tropica'	MBNS
'Longfield's Twins'	MBNS WCot
longituba AIK 284	WCot
- B&SWJ 4576	WCru
'Look at Me'	ELan
'Look Lucky'	CFwr
'Loose as a Goose'	CFwr
'Loose Reins'	CFwr
'Lord Camden'	MNFA
'Lori Goldston'	EWoo MBNS
'Lorita Wadsworth'	CFwr
'Loth Lorien'	CFwr
'Lotus Position' **new**	EBee
'Louie the Lip' **new**	CFwr
'Louis Burnes'	SPol
'Louis McHargue'	SDay
'Louise Lemly'	CFwr
'Love Glow'	CCon
'Love Those Eyes' **new**	EStr
'Lovin Up a Storm' **new**	CFwr
'Lowcountry Gem' **new**	EStr
'Lucille Ball' **new**	EStr
'Lucille Lennington'	WNHG
'Lucretius'	MNFA
'Lullaby Baby'	CWat ELan GCal MBNS NLar SDay SPol
'Luna'	SPol
'Lunar Sea' **new**	EStr
'Luscious Honeydew'	WNHG
'Lusty Lealand'	MBNS MNFA SDay
'Luxury Lace'	CPrp CWat EBee ECtt ELan EPfP EPla GBin GKin LRHS MSpe NBir NGdn NHol NWad SPer SPol WCAu WHrl WMoo WPnP WWtn XLum XSen
'Lynn Hall'	EMil MBNS NLar
'Lyric Opera'	SDay
'Mabel Fuller'	CBgR MRav SPer WHrl
'Macbeth'	EStr MBNS
'Mad Max'	EStr EWoo MSpe SPol
'Made from Scratch'	CFwr
'Madeline Nettles Eyes' **new**	EBee
'Madge Cayse'	CFwr
'Maestro Puccini'	SDay
'Maggie Fynboe'	CBgR SPol
'Magic Amethyst'	CBgR
'Magic Attraction'	CFwr
'Magic Carpet Ride'	SPol
'Magic Lace'	EWoo
'Magic Masquerade'	SDay
'Magnificent Eyes'	SPol
'Magnificent Rainbow'	CBcs
'Mahogany Magic' ♀H6	EStr
'Malachite Prism'	CWGN
'Malaysian Monarch'	EStr WMnd WNHG
'Malaysian Spice'	WNHG
'Maleny Celestial Magic' **new**	EStr
'Maleny Chantilly Lace'	EStr
'Maleny Debutante'	EStr
'Maleny Emperor'	EStr
'Maleny Flamingo'	EStr
'Maleny Mite'	EWoo
'Maleny Piecrust'	EWoo
'Maleny Tapestry'	MSpe
'Maleny Think Big'	EWoo
'Maleny Vivacious' **new**	EStr
'Mallard'	CAby CBgR CWat ECGP ECtt LLWP LRHS MBNS MNFA MRav NBir SPer SWat WCot
'Mama Joe' **new**	EStr
'Mambo Maid'	XSen
'Man on Fire'	MBNS WNHG
'Manchurian Apricot'	SDay
'Mandalay Bay Music'	EWoo
'Mansfield Plantation' **new**	CFwr
'Marble Faun'	SDay
'Marcus Perry' **new**	CBod
'Margaret McWhorter'	SPol
'Margaret Perry'	CPrp ECrc MNrw
'Margaret Seawright' **new**	EStr
'Margo Reed Indeed'	SPol
'Marietta Charmer'	SDay SPol
'Marilyn Siwik'	EWoo
'Marion Caldwell'	SPol
'Marion Vaughn'	ECtt ELan EPfP EWoo GBuc GKin GMaP LBMP MBel MLHP MNFA MSpe NSti SDix SPer SRGP SSpi SWvt WCAu WCot WHar WHoo WPtf WWEG
'Mariska'	EWoo SDay WNHG
'Marked by Lydia'	CFwr ELon SPol
'Marmalade' **new**	EBee EPfP
'Marse Connell'	MSpe
'Martha Adams'	SDay
'Martie Everest'	EWoo
'Martina Verhaert'	CWGN EBee
'Mary Alice Stokes' **new**	EStr
'Mary Ethel Anderson'	EStr EWoo
'Mary Todd'	EBee MBNS WMnd XSen
'Mary's Gold' ♀H6	SDay SPol

'Masquerade Show' CFwr
'Mata Hari' SDay SPol
'Matisse' SPol
'Mauna Loa' CSBt GQue MBNS MNFA MNrw NLar NOrc SDeJ SWvt WAul WCAu WCot
'May May' CBgR SPol
'Maya Cha Cha' **new** CFwr
'Meadow Mist' CBgR ELon WWtn
'Meadow Sprite' SDay WCot
'Meadowsweet' **new** EStr
'Medicine Feather' EWoo
'Medusa's Glance' EWoo
'Meerkat Manor' **new** CFwr
'Megatrend' CFwr
'Mema's Dingbat' CFwr
'Mephistopheles' EWoo
'Merry Moppet' EWoo
'Metaphor' SDay XSen
'Michele Coe' ECtt GKin LPla MBNS MNFA NBro NEgg NGdn SRGP WHrl WMoo
'Mico' ELon
middendorffii CMac EBee GMaP LPla MCoo NSti WHrl WThu
'Midnight Dynamite' MBNS
'Midnight Love' EWoo
'Midnight Magic' EWoo
'Midnight Mantis' SPol
'Midnight Raider' EWoo
'Mighty Highty Tighty' CFwr
'Mighty Mogul' MNFA
'Mikado' CBgR CMac
'Milady Greensleeves' EWoo SDay SPol WHrl
'Milanese Mango' EStr EWoo
'Mildred Mitchell' CBgR CUse CWat ELon EStr MBNS NLar SPol
'Millie Schlumpf' SPol
'Mimosa Umbrella' SPol
'Ming Lo' SDay
'Ming Porcelain' EStr SPol WCAu
'Mini Pearl' CHel ELon EStr EWTr LRHS MBNS SDay SPer
'Mini Stella' CBro ECtt GJos MBNS NOrc NSoo SDay
miniature hybrids SRms
'Minnie Wildfire' SPol
minor CBro EBee EDAr EPPr GKev LRHS SRms XSen
- B&SWJ 8841 WCru
'Minstrel's Fire' CFwr
'Miracle Maid' WNHG
'Miss Jessie' EWoo MNFA SPol WHrl
'Missenden' CBgR MNFA MNrw
'Missouri Beauty' IBoy MBNS SPol SWvt
'Missouri Memories' SPol
'Misty Twisty' CFwr
'Moment in the Sun' CFwr
'Moment of Truth' EAEE NBre
'Monica Marie' SDay
'Mont Royal Demitasse' ELon SPol
'Montserrat's Revenge' **new** EStr
'Moon Witch' SDay SPol
'Moonlight Masquerade' ♀H6 CBgR CWat ECtt GBuc MMuc NLar SRms WOut
'Moonlight Mist' SDay SPol
'Moonlight Orchid' **new** WHrl
'Moonlit Caress' CBgR EBee MBNS NBro
'Moonlit Crystal' EStr SPol
'Moonlit Masquerade' ♀H6 CPar CWGN EStr EWoo GBin MBNS MBel MNrw MSpe SBch SEND SHar SPer SPol WCAu WHrl
'Moonlit Summerbird' SDay SPol
'Moontraveller' WCot
'Moose Man' **new** CFwr
'Mormon Spider' EStr SPol
'Morning Dawn' WWEG
'Morning Sun' MBNS WCot
'Morocco' SPol
'Morocco Red' CBro CCse CTri ELan WWEG
'Morrie Otte' SPol
'Mosel' SDay
'Moses' Fire' ECtt EPfP EStr MBNS NLar
'Mossy Glade' CBgR
'Mount Echo Sunrise' EWoo
'Mount Joy' SPer
'Mountain Laurel' ECGP ECtt ELon GKin LRHS MBNS MRav NEgg SPol
'Moussaka' **new** WFar
'Move Over Moon' EStr
'Moving Forward' CFwr
'Mrs David Hall' CCse SMrm
'Mrs Hugh Johnson' GCra WHrl
* 'Mrs Lester' SDay
'Muddy Waters' CFwr
'Muffet's Little Friend' SPol
'Mulberry Frosted Edge' EWoo
multiflora MNFA XSen
'Muscle Man' EStr XSen
'Music of the Master' (d) CFwr
'My Belle' SDay
'My Darling Clementine' SDay
'My Friend Floyd' CFwr
'My Heart Belongs to Daddy' CFwr
'My Hope' SPol
'My Melinda' SDay
'Mynelle's Starfish' CPar SPol WHrl
'Nabis' **new** SDay
'Nacogdoches Lady' SWvt
nana CCon GKev
'Nanuq' ELon
'Naomi Ruth' EStr MBNS MSpe
'Nashville' CBro ELan WHrl
'Nashville Lights' CBgR EStr SPol
'Nathan Sommers' EWoo
'Natural Veil' SPol
'Nature's Crown' (d) **new** CFwr
'Navajo Princess' CWat EBee MBNS MNrw SPol
'Neal Berrey' SDay
'Ned Cricket' **new** CFwr
'Ned's Elena' **new** CFwr
'Nefertiti' CBgR ELon MBNS NBir SPer WAul WCAu
'Neon Rose' GKin MWat
'Neon Yellow' **new** EStr
'Never Ending Fantasy' **new** EStr
'Never Get Away' EStr
'New Direction' CFwr EWoo
'Neyron Rose' EPla GBuc GKin GQue LRHS MBNS MCot NEgg NGdn WCAu WMoo WWtn XLum
'Nick's Faith' WHrl
'Nicole Ashley Scott' **new** EStr
'Nicole Joyce' SPol
'Night Beacon' CBgR ECho ECtt ELon EStr EWes EWoo GBuc GKin LPot MBNS

MNFA MNrw MPie MSpe NLar SCob SDay SDeJ SPol WCAu WHrl
'Night Embers' ECtt EWTr EWoo NLar
'Night Raider' CBgR SDay
'Night Wings' EWoo
'Nile Crane' CBgR CUse ELon EStr MBNS MNrw SDay SPer WAul
'Nile Plum' EStr EWoo SDay SPol
'Ninja Throwing Star' CFwr
'Ninth Millennium' CFwr
'Nob Hill' CCse ELon EPla SPol WHrl XLum
'Nona's Garnet Spider' ELon SPol
'Noonday Dreams' CFwr
'Nordic Night' CBgR SDay SPol
'North Wind Dancer' ♀H6 EWoo
'Northbrook Star' MNFA
'Norton Beauté' WCot
'Norton Eyed Seedling' WNHG
'Norton Orange' MNFA
'Nosferatu' SPol
'Not Forgotten' WNHG
'Nouveau Riche' SPol
'Nova' CPrp ELon SDay
'Novarlis' CFwr
'Nuclear Meltdown' EWoo
'Nuka' XLum
'Nutmeg Elf' CBgR EWoo SDay SPol
'Nuttin Bugs Me' CFwr
'Oakes Love' MNrw
'Ocean Rain' EStr SDay SPol
'Octopus Hugs' EStr SPol
'Official Curse' SPol
'Ojo de Dios' EWoo
'Oklahoma Kicking Bird' SDay
'Olallie Lad' **new** EStr
'Old Tangiers' ♀H6 EStr EWoo
'Old Time Memories' CFwr
'Olive Bailey Langdon' EStr SDay SPol WCot
'Oliver Billingslea' EWoo
'Olly Olly Oxen Free' CFwr
'Oloroso' **new** CBgR
'Olympic Gold' XSen
'On and On' GQue MBNS NCGa
'On Pointe' CFwr EWoo
'On Silken Thread' SPol
'On the Border' CFwr
'On the Fringe' **new** CFwr
'On the Web' CFwr
'One Fire' XSen
'Oodles' WHrl
'Open Hearth' SPol WHrl
'Open my Eyes' EStr EWoo
'Orange Clown' CFwr
'Orange Dream' SDay
'Orange Exotica' CBgR EStr
'Orange Pausback' **new** MNFA
'Orange Prelude' XSen
'Orange Splash' CFwr
'Orange UFO' **new** MNFA
'Orange Velvet' SPol
'Orangeman' misapplied EPla LRHS MBNS NGdn
'Orchid Beauty' MLHP WMoo
'Orchid Candy' EWoo MBNS NBir SPol
'Orchid Corsage' ELon SPol
'Orchid Lady Slipper' EWoo
'Orchid Moonrise' EWoo
'Oriental Ruby' SDay
'Orion's Band' EWoo
'Orphée' XSen
'Ostrich Plume' SDay
'Ouachita Beauty' CBgR SPol
'Our Diane' **new** EWTr
'Our Kirsten' SDay
'Out of Darkness' EWoo
'Outrageous' CBgR SPol WNHG
'Outrageous Ramona' WNHG
'Over the Top' MBNS
'Paige's Pinata' EBee MBNS
'Painted Lady' MNFA
'Painted Peach' SPol
'Painted Pink' SDay
'Painting the Roses Red' CFwr
'Palace Garden Beauty' EWoo
'Palace Guard' MNFA
'Pale Moon Windmill' CFwr
'Pandora's Box' CExl CMHG CTri CUse CWat EAJP ECtt ELan EPfP EStr LRHS MBNS MMuc MNFA MNrw MWat NBir NGdn NLar SDay SDeJ SEND SPol SWvt WBor WCAu WHoo WMoo WWEG
'Panic in Detroit' CFwr
'Pantherette' SPol
'Paper Butterfly' SDay SPol
'Papoose' XLum
'Parade of Peacocks' CBgR
'Pardon Me' CBro CMHG CPrp CUse CWld ELan ELon EStr EWoo GKin GMaP LRHS MBNS MBel MNFA MSpe NCGa NGdn SDeJ SPol SRGP SWvt WAul WBor WCAu
'Pardon Me Boy' SPol
'Parfait' CBgR EStr EWoo SPol
'Parson's Robe' **new** SDay
'Passion for Red' SDay
'Pastel Ballerina' SDay
'Pastel Classic' SPol
'Pastilline' SPol
'Pat Mercer' SDay XSen
'Patchwork Puzzle' EWoo SPol
'Patricia' MBNS
'Patricia Fay' XSen
'Patricia Gentzel Wright' EWoo
'Patricia Snider Memorial' CFwr
'Patriotic Flavor' **new** EStr
'Patsy Bickers' EWoo
'Patsy Jane' **new** SPol
'Patterns' SPol
'Pawn of Prophecy' SDay
'Peace be Still' EWoo
'Peach Float' EWoo
'Peach Jubilee' SPol
'Peach Magnolia' (d) **new** EStr
'Peach Yum Yum' CFwr
'Peacock Curls' EWoo
'Peacock Maiden' EWoo SDay SPol WHrl XSen
'Pear Ornament' SDay
'Pearl Lewis' EStr SPol
'Pearl Sherwood' EWoo
'Penelope Vestey' CBgR EStr GBuc MBNS MNFA NBir SDay SPol SRGP
'Penny Pinsley' (d) **new** CFwr
'Penny's Worth' LEdu LRHS MBNS NOrc WAul WCot WHoo XLum
'Perfect Pie' **new** WCAu
'Perfect Pleasure' MBNS

'Persian Melon Plus'	WCAu
'Persian Ruby'	SPol
'Persian Shrine'	SPol
'Persimmone'	SPol
'Persimmons Cinnamon and Marmalade'	CFwr
'Petite Ballerina'	SDay
'Photon Torpedo' **new**	CFwr
'Phyllis Cantini'	SPol
'Piano Man'	MBNS WAul WNHG
'Piccadilly Princess'	SDay
'Picket Fences'	CFwr
'Picotee Rippled Ruffles'	CFwr
'Pinebelt Darkeyes'	CFwr
'Pink Ambrosia'	EWoo
'Pink Attempt' **new**	MNFA
'Pink Ballerina'	WWtn
'Pink Charm'	CBen CHel CMac ECha ECtt EPPr EPla GKin GMaP LRHS MBNS NBro SPol
'Pink Circle'	SDay
'Pink Cotton Candy'	EWoo SDay SPol
'Pink Damask' ♀H6	Widely available
'Pink Dazzler'	WNHG
'Pink Dream'	CBgR MBNS NBir NBre SPol
'Pink Flirt'	SDay
'Pink Grace'	SPol
'Pink Lady'	MNrw MRav SRms
'Pink Monday'	SDay WNHG
'Pink Pajamas'	CFwr
'Pink Prelude'	GBee MBNS MSpe MWat NBro
'Pink Puff'	MBNS NBir NBre NLar
'Pink Rain Dance'	SPol
'Pink Scintillation' **new**	SDay
'Pink Slumber Fifteen' **new**	WCAu
'Pink Spider'	SDay
'Pink Stripes' **new**	CFwr
'Pink Sundae'	WHrl
'Pink Super Spider'	EWoo SDay SPol
'Pink Whip Tips'	CFwr
'Pink Windmill'	ELon EWoo SPol
'Pinocchio'	SMHy
'Piping Rock'	CFwr
'Piquante'	SCob
'Pirate Treasure'	MBNS
'Pirate's Patch'	EWoo SPol WCot
'Pixie Parasol'	WMnd WNHG
'Pixie Pipestone'	SPol
'Pixie Princess' **new**	EStr
'Pizza'	SDay
'Planet Golden Orange Ruffy'	CFwr
'Planet Sunshine'	CFwr
'Plum Beauty'	NLar
'Plum Candy'	EWoo
'Plumburst'	EPfP
'Poetic Dance'	EWoo
'Point of Honor'	EWoo
'Pojo'	EStr SDay
'Pony'	CWat SDay SPol
'Possum in a Sack' **new**	CBgR
'Prague Spring'	MNFA MSpe SDay SPol WCAu WHrl
'Prairie Belle'	MBNS NLar SPol
'Prairie Blue Eyes'	ECtt EStr IBoy MBNS NPri SPlb SPol WCAu WCot WHrl WMnd WWEG WWtn
'Prairie Charmer'	MMuc SEND WHrl
'Precious d'Oro'	EBee GQue
'Pretty Miss'	EAEE ECtt EWTr
'Preview Party'	WNHG
'Primal Scream' ♀H6	EStr SPol WCot
'Primrose Mascotte'	NBir
'Prince of Purple'	ELon
'Prince Redbird'	SDay
'Princess Blue Eyes'	SPol
'Princess Lilli'	MBNS
'Princeton Eye Glow'	MSpe SDay
'Prissy Frills'	SPol
'Prize Picotee Deluxe'	SPol
'Prize Picotee Elite'	SDay SPol
'Promising Future'	CFwr
'Protocol'	MSpe SDay SPol
'Proud Mary'	SDay
'Ptarmigan'	CBgR
§ 'Puddin'	CWat SDay
'Pueblo Dancer' **new**	EStr
'Pueblo Dreamer'	CFwr EWoo
'Puff the Magic Dragon'	CFwr
'Pug Yarborough'	SPol
'Pumpkin Kid'	SDay SPol
'Pumpkin Pie Spice'	SPol
'Pumpkin Prince'	CFwr EStr
'Pumpkins Gone Wild'	CFwr
'Punxsutawney Phil'	CFwr
'Puppet Show'	SDay
'Pure and Simple'	ELon SPol
'Purple Arachne'	SPol
'Purple Bicolor'	WHrl
'Purple Grasshopper'	EWoo
'Purple Many Faces'	SPol
'Purple Oddity'	EWoo SPol
'Purple Pauper'	WCAu
'Purple Pinwheel'	EWoo SPol
'Purple Rain'	CWat MBNS MNFA SDay SPol SWvt
'Purple Rain Dance'	SPol
'Purple Sombrero'	CFwr
'Purple Waters'	EStr MBNS NOrc SPol WPnP
'Purpleicious'	NLar SMrm
'Pyewacket'	SDay
'Pygmy Plum'	SDay XSen
'Queen Empress'	WNHG
'Queen Kathleen' **new**	CFwr
'Queen Lily'	WNHG
'Queen of Can Do'	CFwr
'Queen of May'	MNrw WCot
'Quick Results'	SDay
'Quietly Awesome' **new**	SDay
'Quilt Patch'	EStr SPol
'Quinn Buck'	SDay
'Ra Hansen'	SDay
'Rachael My Love' (d)	XSen
'Racing Stripes'	CFwr
'Radiant'	CBcs
'Radiant Greetings'	MNFA XSen
'Radiant Moonbeam' ♀H6	CBgR
'Radiation Biohazard'	CFwr SPol
'Raging Tiger'	WHrl
'Rags to Riches'	CFwr
'Rainbow Candy'	CWGN LLHF MBNS SPad
'Rainbow Drive'	CFwr
'Rainbow Gold'	XSen
'Rainbow Serpent'	CFwr
'Raining Violets'	EWoo
'Rajah'	CBgR CMac EStr MBNS MSpe NBro SCob WHrl
'Randall Moore'	SPol

'Rander's Pride'	EWoo
'Raspberry Butterflies'	EWoo
'Raspberry Candy'	CBro GCra IBoy MBNS MNrw NBro NOrc SRms WHrl
'Raspberry Fields Forever' **new**	EStr
'Raspberry Griffin' **new**	CFwr
'Raspberry Masquerade'	CFwr
'Raspberry Pixie'	SDay SPol
'Raspberry Wine'	ECha
'Raven Woodsong'	EWoo
'Real Wind'	CFwr SPol
'Red Admiral'	LRHS
'Red Butterfly'	SPol
'Red Eyed Fantasy'	CFwr
'Red Eyed Shocker'	CFwr
'Red Hill'	EWoo
'Red Precious' ♀H6	MNFA MNrw SMHy WCot
'Red Rain'	EWoo WHrl XSen
'Red Resplendence'	EWoo
'Red Ribbons'	ELon EWoo MNFA SDay SPol
'Red Ruby'	ERCP
'Red Rum'	CBgR LRHS MNFA MSpe NBro WMoo
'Red Squirrel'	CFwr
'Red Suspenders'	ECtt MBNS
'Red Tallboy' **new**	MNFA
'Red Twister'	ELon SDay SPol
'Red Volunteer'	EPla EStr SDay SPol
'Red Vortex'	EStr
'Redheaded Hussy'	CFwr
'Redneck Red' **new**	CFwr
'Reflections in Time'	EWoo
'Regal Giant'	EStr EWoo
'Regency Dandy'	SDay SPol XSen
'Regency Heights' **new**	EStr
'Reigning Sunshine' **new**	CFwr
'Renee'	MNrw
'Return Trip'	SPol
'Revolute'	SDay
'Rhode Island Red'	CFwr
'Ribbonette'	EBee EStr MBNS MSpe WCAu
'Ricky Rose'	SDay XSen
'Rigamarole'	SPol
'Riley Barron'	SDay
'River Wye'	MWat
'Roaring Jellyfish'	CFwr
'Robespierre'	SDay
'Rock Candy' **new**	CFwr
'Rock Solid'	CFwr
'Rocket City'	ELan EStr SPol WNHG
'Rocky Mountain Pals'	CFwr
'Rococo'	SDay
'Rodeo Sweetheart'	CFwr
'Roger Grounds'	CBgR SPol
'Roll Up Candy'	CFwr
'Rolling Hill'	CFwr
'Rolling Raven'	CFwr
'Roman Toga'	CBgR
'Romanian Rendevous'	CFwr
'Romantic Returns' **new**	EPla
* 'Romantic Rose'	ELon MBNS NLar WHrl
'Ron Rousseau'	SPol
'Root Beer'	WHrl
'Rose Claire'	LPla
'Rose Corsage'	EWoo
'Rose Emily'	CBgR SDay SPol
'Rose Festival'	WCAu
'Rose Fever'	EWoo
'Rose for Charlotte' **new**	SPol
'Rose Victorious' **new**	CFwr
'Roseate Spoonbill'	EWoo
'Roses in Snow'	IBoy MBNS SPol
'Roswitha'	CWat SPol
'Rosy Lights'	EWoo SPol
'Rosy Polyphemus' **new**	EStr
'Rosy Returns'	EPfP LRHS MBNS NLar WHoo
'Rotes Rathaus' **new**	MNFA
'Round Midnight'	SPol
'Royal Bird' **new**	EStr
'Royal Braid'	MBNS NLar SPer WCot
'Royal Butterfly' **new**	CFwr
'Royal Celebration'	WCot
'Royal Elk'	EWoo
'Royal Emperor'	CFwr
'Royal Eventide'	CFwr XSen
'Royal Flycatcher' **new**	CFwr
'Royal Heritage'	SDay
'Royal Hunter'	CFwr
'Royal Robe'	CTri
'Royal Russian Rendezvous'	CFwr
'Royal Saracen'	SDay
'Royal Thornbird'	CBgR
'Royal Trophy'	WNHG
'Royalty'	GCra
'Ruby Moon'	CFwr
'Ruby Sentinel'	SDay
'Ruby Spider' ♀H6	ELon EWoo SDay SPol
'Ruby Storm'	CFwr
'Rue Madelaine'	SPol
'Ruffled Apricot'	CKel MBNS MNFA SDay WNHG
'Ruffled Carousel'	WNHG
'Ruffled Ivory' **new**	SDay
'Rumble Seat Romance'	WNHG
'Rundblick' **new**	MNFA
'Russian Ragtime'	EStr
'Russian Rhapsody' ♀H6	CKel SDay SPol
'Ruth Oliver' **new**	EStr
'Sabie'	EStr
'Sabine Baur'	CWat EStr IPot LRHS MBNS MNrw NLar WFar
'Sabra Salina'	EWoo SDay
'Sacred Drummer' **new**	SDay
'Saffron Glow'	SDay
'Sahara Sand Storm' **new**	EStr
'Saintly'	EWoo MSpe
'Sallie Brown' **new**	EStr
'Salmon Pagoda'	EWoo
'Salmon Sheen'	SDay SPer
'Sammy'	SDay
'Sammy Russell'	Widely available
'Samuel Bell'	EWoo
'San Luis Halloween'	CFwr
'Sandra Walker'	WWtn
'Sanford Code Red'	CFwr
'Sanford Star Search'	CFwr
'Santa's Little Helper'	CFwr
'Santiago'	SPol
'Saratoga Pinwheel'	SPol
'Satin Glass'	EBee LRHS MNFA
'Satin Glow'	ECha MLHP
'Scapes from Hell'	EWoo
'Scarlet Butterfly'	SPol
'Scarlet Flame'	ECha WMoo
'Scarlet Orbit'	EWoo SDay SPol
'Scarlet Pimpernel'	CFwr

'Scarlet Prince'	WNHG
'Scarlet Ribbons'	SPol
'Scatterbrain'	CKel SPol
'Schnickel Fritz'	EBee
'School Girl'	LRHS
'School Girl Figure' **new**	WCAu
'Scorpio'	CBgR SPol WHrl
'Scout's Honor' (d)	CFwr
'Screaming Demon'	SPol
'Sea Siren'	CWat
'Sea Swept Dreams'	SDay
'Seabiscuit'	CFwr
'Seal of Approval'	EBee
'Sebastian'	MNFA
'Secret Splendor'	SPol
'Secretary's Sand'	EWoo
'Selma Longlegs' ♀H6	EStr MSpe SPol
'Seminole Blood'	SPol
'Seminole Princess'	CFwr
'Seminole Wind'	EWoo SPol
'Semiramide'	CBgR
'Sentinel Solar Burst' (d)	CFwr
'Serena Lady' **new**	SDay
'Serena Sunburst' ♀H6	SPol
'Serenade'	EWoo
'Serene Madonna'	CCon GBin
'Serenity Bay'	CFwr
'Serenity Morgan'	CBgR MBNS
'Serge Rigaud'	WHrl
'Sergeant Major'	EStr EWoo
'Shadowed Pink'	WNHG
'Shady Lady'	SDay SPol
'Shake the Mountains'	CFwr
'Shaman'	SDay SPol
'Shangri La Truffle'	CFwr
'She Devil'	CFwr
'Shelly Victoria'	SDay
'Sherry Lane Carr'	EStr SDay SPol
'Sherwood Gladiator'	WNHG
'Shibui Splendor'	SPol
'Shimek September Morning'	EStr SPol
* 'Shocker'	EWoo
'Shogun'	MBNS
'Shotgun'	SPol
'Shuffle the Deck'	CFwr EWoo
'Sidewinder Oh Seven'	CFwr
'Signature Truffle' (d) **new**	CFwr
'Sigudilla'	WNHG
'Silken Fairy'	CBgR SDay WWtn
'Silken Touch'	CBgR SPol
'Siloam Amazing Grace'	SDay
'Siloam Angel Blush'	SDay
'Siloam Baby Doll'	SDay
'Siloam Baby Talk'	ELon GBuc NBir SDay WAul WMoo WPnP
'Siloam Bertie Ferris'	MBNS
'Siloam Bo Peep'	SDay
'Siloam Button Box'	MBNS WHrl
'Siloam Bye Lo'	EWoo SDay
'Siloam Cinderella'	SDay SPol
'Siloam David Kirchhoff'	EBee MBNS SDay XSen
'Siloam Doodlebug'	CBgR CWat
'Siloam Double Classic' (d)	EStr SPol
'Siloam Dream Baby'	ELon MBNS MSpe
'Siloam Ethel Smith'	SDay SPol
'Siloam Fairy Tale'	CWat SDay
'Siloam Flower Girl'	SDay
'Siloam French Doll'	MBNS NLar
'Siloam French Marble'	SDay
'Siloam Frosted Mint'	SPol
'Siloam Gold Coin'	SDay
'Siloam Grace Stamile'	CCon MBNS SDay
'Siloam Helpmate'	WNHG
'Siloam Jim Cooper'	MSpe
'Siloam Joan Senior'	MBNS
'Siloam John Yonski'	SDay
'Siloam June Bug'	CBgR ELan WCot
'Siloam Justine Lee'	MBNS
'Siloam Little Angel'	SPol
'Siloam Little Girl'	CWat ECtt SDay
'Siloam Mama'	SDay
'Siloam Merle Kent'	EWoo SDay SPol WAul
'Siloam Nugget'	CUse
'Siloam Orchid Jewel'	SDay
'Siloam Paul Watts'	SPol
'Siloam Peewee'	LRHS
'Siloam Pink Glow'	SDay SWat
'Siloam Plum Tree'	SPol
'Siloam Pocket Size'	SDay
'Siloam Queen's Toy'	SPol
'Siloam Red Toy'	SMHy
'Siloam Ribbon Candy'	SDay WNHG
'Siloam Rose Dawn'	SPol
'Siloam Rose Queen'	SDay
'Siloam Royal Prince'	SDay
'Siloam Show Girl'	CWGN EWoo GKin MBNS NLar
'Siloam Spizz'	SDay
'Siloam Tee Tiny'	WAul WWtn
'Siloam Tiny Mite'	SDay WHrl
'Siloam Tom Thumb'	CBgR MBNS
'Siloam Ury Winniford'	CBro CMac EMil MBNS MSpe NLar WHoo WPnP
'Siloam Virginia Henson'	EWoo WWEG WWtn
'Silver Ice'	SDay SPol
'Silver Lance'	SDay SPol
'Silver Quasar'	SDay SPol
'Silver Trumpet'	WWEG
'Silver Veil'	SDay
'Simmering Elephants'	CFwr
'Simmons Overture' **new**	ECtt
'Simplicity in Motion'	CFwr
'Simply Divine'	CFwr
'Sinbad Sailor'	NLar
'Singing in the Sunshine'	EWoo
'Sink Into Your Eyes' **new**	WHrl
'Sir Blackstem'	ELon GCal SDay
'Sir Knight'	SPol
'Sir Modred' ♀H6	SPol WNHG
'Sixth Sense'	ELon MBNS WHrl
'Skeezix' (d)	CFwr
'Skeleton Man' **new**	CFwr
'Skinny Dipping'	CFwr
'Skinwalker'	EWoo
'Slapstick'	ELon SDay SPol
'Sleepy' **new**	ECha
'Slender Lady'	CFwr ELon SDay XSen
'Small Town'	EWoo
'Small World Tornado'	EWoo
'Smith Brothers'	SPol
'Smoke Scream'	CFwr
'Smokestack Lightning'	CFwr
'Smoky Mountain Autumn'	EWoo SPol
'Smooch Hollow' **new**	CBgR EStr
'Smuggler's Gold'	ECtt
'Smuggler's Temptation'	SPol

Cultivar	Suppliers
'Snappy Rhythm'	MNFA
'Snowed In'	EWoo
'Snowy Apparition'	EBee ECrc ECtt GKin LRHS MBNS MNFA MWhi NWad SPol SWvt WCAu
'Snowy Eyes'	CHid GKin MBNS SWat WHrl
'So Excited'	SDay
'So Lovely'	EWoo XLum
'So Many Stars'	CFwr
'Soft Cashmere'	XLum
'Soho Style' **new**	CFwr
'Solano Bull's Eye'	MLHP
'Solid Scarlet'	CWld
'Sombrero Way'	SDay
'Someone Special'	SDay SPol
'Somerset Fandango' **new**	CBgR
'Song In My Heart'	EWoo
'Song Sparrow'	CBro
'Soraya Seline'	CBgR
'Sorcerer's Song'	SDay
'South Seas'	EStr
'Southern Prize'	SDay
'Sovereign Queen'	WNHG
'Spacecoast Color Scheme'	CFwr
'Spacecoast Cranberry Kid'	CFwr
'Spacecoast Dragon Prince'	EWoo
'Spacecoast Freaky Tiki' **new**	EStr
'Spacecoast Peach Fringe'	CFwr
'Spacecoast Royal Ransom'	CFwr
'Spacecoast Scrambled'	CBcs EPfP MBNS NLar
'Spacecoast Starburst'	CBcs EStr MBNS NBro WCot
'Spanish Fandango'	SPol
'Spanish Glow'	SPol
'Spice Hunter'	CFwr
'Spider Breeder'	CBgR ELon
'Spider Man' ♀H6	ELon MNFA MSpe SDay SPol WCAu XSen
'Spider Miracle'	SDay SPol
'Spider Red'	CWGN EWoo
'Spider Web'	EStr
'Spilled Milk'	SPol
'Spindazzle'	CBgR SPol
'Spinne in Lachs'	MNFA SPol
'Spirit of Sapelo'	EWoo
'Spock's Ears'	CFwr
'Spock's Sun'	CFwr
'Spooner'	CBgR
'Spring Willow Song'	SDay
'Square Dancer's Curtsy'	CFwr
'Squash Dolly'	EWoo
'Stafford' ♀H6	Widely available
'Staghorn Sumac'	GKin LEdu MBNS NHol WCAu
'Star Asterisk'	CFwr SPol
'Star of Fantasy'	CFwr EStr
'Star of India'	SPol
'Star Twister'	CFwr
'Stargate Corridor'	SPol
'Starling'	CPar MNFA WWEG WWtn
'Starman's Gift' **new**	EStr
'Starman's Quest'	SPol
'Stars and Stripes'	MNFA
'Starstruck'	WNHG
'Startle'	ELon MBNS MNrw WCAu WCot WHrl
'Startling Creation'	CFwr
'Statuesque'	EWoo
'Stella de Oro'	Widely available
'Stella in Red'	EPfP
'Stinnette'	WCot
'Stippled Starlight'	CFwr
'Stoke Poges'	CBgR CBro EBee ELon EPPr EPfP EPla EWTr GBin LAst LBMP LPot LRHS MBNS MNFA MSpe NPri SPer SWat WHrl WWEG
'Stone Beacon'	CFwr
'Stone Island'	CFwr
'Stoplight'	CBgR ELon SDay SPol WHrl
'Storm of the Century'	EStr MNrw
'Storm Over Toledo'	CFwr
'Strasbourg'	CMac
'Strawberry Candy' ♀H6	CBgR CHel CMac CSBt ECtt ELon EPfP EStr EWll EWoo IBoy MBNS MSpe NGdn NLar SCob SPer WAul WCAu WHoo WHrl WMoo WWEG
'Strawberry Fields Forever'	EStr EWoo MBNS MBri NLar SPol
'Strawberry Swirl'	EStr MNFA
I 'Streaker' B. Brown (v)	XSen
'Street Urchin'	SPol
'Streets of Heaven'	EWoo
'Strikingly Dramatic'	CFwr
'String Bikini' **new**	EStr
'String Theory'	CFwr
'Strutter's Ball'	CBod EWoo LPla MBNS MNFA NGdn SPer SPol SWat WAul WCAu WHrl WMnd
'Stu's Old Pink Spider'	CBgR
'Suburban Golden Eagle' **new**	EStr
'Sugar Cookie'	EWoo SDay SPol
'Summer Dragon'	EStr MBNS
'Summer Fireworks'	EWoo
'Summer Interlude'	WMoo
'Summer Wine'	Widely available
'Sunday Gloves'	SPol WNHG
'Sunday Morning'	EStr SDay
'Sungold Candy'	EStr
'Sunray Brilliance'	EWoo
'Sunset Lagoon' **new**	EStr SPol
'Sunshine Junkie' **new**	CFwr
'Super Purple'	CKel
'Superlative'	SPol
'Susan Weber'	EStr SPol
'Suzie Wong'	MNFA
'Suzy Cream Cheese'	CFwr SPol
'Svengali'	SDay SPol
'Swallow Tail Kite'	SPol
'Swashbuckler Bay Boy'	CFwr
'Sweet Charlotte'	SPol
'Sweet Country Luvin'' **new**	EStr
'Sweet Hot Chocolate'	LRHS MBNS
'Sweet Pea'	EStr SDay
'Sweet Sugar Candy'	ECtt EWoo SDeJ
'Swirling Spider'	CBgR EWoo SPol
'Tail Feathers'	CFwr
'Taj Mahal'	ELon EWoo
'Tammy Faye Eyes'	CFwr
'Tang'	CHid MBNS WCAu
'Tangerine Tango'	EWoo
'Tangerine Twist' **new**	SPol
'Tango Noturno'	SPol
'Tani'	SDay
'Taos' **new**	EStr
'Tarantula'	ELon SPol
'Taruga'	EWoo SDay
'Tasmania'	SPer

'Tchao Pantin' XSen
'Teacup Fingers' CFwr
'Technical Knockout' EWoo
'Techny Peach Lace' SPol
'Techny Spider' SPol
'Tejas' CElw ELon SPer
'Témoin' XSen
'Tennessee Flycatcher' EStr EWoo SPol
'Tennessee Williams' SPol
'Tennyson' CFwr
'Tequila Mockingbird' CFwr
'Tet Set' WNHG
'Tetraploid Stella de Oro' SDay
'Tetrina's Daughter' CBgR LRHS SGSe
'Texas Sunlight' CHel
'Thanks a Bunch' SPol
'The Band Played On' CFwr
'The Tingler' CFwr EWoo
'Thelma Perry' LEdu
'Thin Man' CFwr
'Think Pink' **new** EBee EPfP
'Third Witch' CFwr EWoo
'Thomas Tew' CFwr
'Three Diamonds' SPol
'Three Times a Lady' **new** CFwr
'Thrill Ride' **new** SPol
'Thumbelina' ECha WMoo XLum
§ ***thunbergii*** ECha EPla GCal MCoo
- 'Ovation' MBNS
'Thundering Ovation' CWGN
'Thy True Love' SDay
'Tierra Del Fuego' **new** EStr
'Tiger Prince' **new** CFwr
'Tiger Swirl' CFwr
'Tigereye Spider' EWoo
'Tigerland' CFwr
'Tigerling' EWoo SPol
'Tigger' SPol
'Time Lord' SDay XSen
'Time to Believe' SPol
'Time Window' **new** EStr
'Tiny Talisman' SDay
'Tiny Temptress' SDay
'Tis Midnight' WNHG
'Titanic Tower' CFwr
'Tom Collins' SDay
'Tom Wise' SPol
'Tomorrow's Song' SPol
'Tone Poem' WNHG
'Tonia Gay' SDay SPol
'Toodleloo Kangaroo' EWoo
'Tooth' **new** EStr
'Toothpick' EWoo SPol WHrl
'Tootsie' SDay
'Tootsie Rose' SDay SPol
'Top Honors' SPol
'Topaz Gem' SPol
'Topguns Aleah Kaye' CFwr
'Topguns Anita Causey' (d) CFwr
'Topguns Bandit's Bandana' CFwr
'Topguns Butterball' (d) CFwr
'Topguns Cactus Jack' CFwr
'Topguns Cherokee Dancer' CFwr
'Topguns Cherry Limeade' CFwr
'Topguns Citrine Dream' (d) CFwr
'Topguns Copper Butterflies' (d) CFwr
'Topguns Dragonfly Sunset' (d) CFwr
'Topguns Dream Catcher' (d) CFwr
'Topguns Eye Popper' CFwr
'Topguns Grim Reaper' CFwr
'Topguns Harlequin Ruffles' CFwr
'Topguns Jennifer Hankins' CFwr
'Topguns Lemon Ruffles' CFwr
'Topguns Linda Farris' (d) CFwr
'Topguns Molten Lava' (d) CFwr
'Topguns Okie Twister' CFwr
'Topguns Orange Fizz' (d) CFwr
'Topguns Orange Marmalade' CFwr
'Topguns Pawnee Princess' CFwr
'Topguns Pinwheel' CFwr
'Topguns Rising Sun' (d) CFwr
'Topguns Ruffled Amazement' (d) CFwr
'Topguns Stop 'n' Go' CFwr
'Topguns Tilt-A-Whirl' CFwr
'Torpoint' CBgR GBee MBNS MRav NEgg
'Towhead' MRav SDay WCot
'Toyland' EPfP MBNS NBir NGdn NLar SPol
'Trahlyta' CBgR EWoo SDay SPol WHrl
'Treasure of Love' EWoo
'Tremor' EStr
'Trevi Fountain' EWoo
'Trond' SDay
'Tropical Breeze' CFwr
'Tropical Depression' CFwr EWoo
'Tropical Toy' SDay
'Troubled Sleep' EWoo
'Truchas Sunrise' CFwr EWoo
'True Gertrude Demarest' WHrl
'True North' CFwr
'True Pink Beauty' EWoo
'Truffle Heritage' CFwr
'Tune the Harp' EStr SPol
'Tuolumne Fairy Tale' SPol
'Turkey Lurkey' CFwr
'Turkish Tapestry' **new** CBgR
'Turkish Turban' SDay SPol
'Tuscawilla Blackout' MSpe SPol XSen
'Tuscawilla Tigress' EStr GKin IKil MBNS MNrw MSpe SPol WAul WHrl
'Tutti Frutti Truffle' CFwr
'Tuxedo' SPol
'Twenty Third Psalm' WHal
'Twiggy' CFwr MSpe
'Twilight Secrets' MBNS SGol
'Twilight Swan' WNHG
'Twirling Wings' CFwr
'Twist and Shout' CFwr
'Twist and Spin' CFwr
'Twist of Lemon' CFwr EWoo SDay
'Twisted Mint Julep' CFwr
'Twister Time' CFwr
'Two Faces of Love' SPol
'Two Part Harmony' CFwr
'Tylwyth Teg' CFwr SPol
'Ulla Wilsch' **new** MNFA
'Ultimate Destiny' CWat
'Unchartered Waters' MBNS
'Unforgetable Fire' EWoo
'Unique Purple' SPol

'Uniquely Different'	SPol
'Valiant'	EWoo MBNS WHrl
'Valley Monster'	SPol
'Vanilla Candy'	MSpe
'Vanilla Fluff'	EStr
'Variegated Woottens' (v)	EWoo
'Varsity'	CExl CWat LRHS NBir SPer
'Veins of Truth'	CBgR EBee
'Velvet Eyes' **new**	EStr
'Velvet Onyx' (d)	CFwr
'Velvet Ribbons'	CFwr
'Velvet Shadows'	CBgR
'Vendetta'	WNHG
'Venusian Heat'	CFwr
'Venusian Mirage' **new**	EStr
'Venus's Fire'	CFwr
'Vera Biaglow'	MSpe SPol
'Very Berry Ice'	SPol
'Vespers'	CAbP WPnP
vespertina	see *H. thunbergii*
'Veuve Joyeuse'	XSen
'Vicountess Byng'	WWtn
'Victoria Aden'	CBro
'Victoria Elizabeth Barnes'	WNHG
'Victorian Lace'	EWoo
'Victorian Ribbons'	SPol
'Victorian Violet'	SDay
'Video'	SDay
'Vintage Bordeaux'	ELan
'Vintage Burgundy'	CBgR WNHG
'Violent Thunder'	CFwr
'Violet Hour'	EStr SDay
'Viracocha'	WMnd WNHG
'Virgil Earp'	CFwr
'Virgin's Blush'	SPer
'Vohann'	SDay
'Volcano Queen'	CFwr
'Walking on Sunshine'	WCot
'Walnut Hill'	EStr
'Walt Disney'	GKin
'War Paint'	SDay
'Warrior Victorious'	CFwr
'Watch Tower'	CBgR
'Watchyl Christmas Widow'	CFwr
'Watchyl Dancing Spider'	SPol
'Water Bird' **new**	EStr
'Water Witch'	CWat SDay
'Watermelon Man'	CBgR EWoo
'Watership Down'	EWoo
'Watson Park Tempest'	CFwr
'Wayside Green Imp'	MNrw
'We Love'	EWoo
'Weaver's Art'	SPol
'Web Browser'	CFwr
'Web Dancer'	SPol
'Wee Willie Wonka'	WNHG
'Wekiwa'	EWoo
'Welchkins'	SDay WAul
'Welfo White Diamond'	SPol
'Westward Wind'	EWoo
'Whammer Jammer'	CFwr
'What a Day for a Daydream'	CFwr
'Whichford'	CAby CBgR CBod CBro CSam ECha ECrc ECtt ELan EPfP EPla EWoo GBuc GCal GKin LRHS MBNS MNFA MSpe SPhx WCAu WGwG WHrl WPtf
'Whirling Fury'	ELon EWoo
'White Coral'	EAEE LRHS MBNS MNFA NBro WCAu
'White Edged Madonna'	SBch WHrl
'White Temptation'	CCon EPfP IBoy NGdn NOrc WAul WHoo WMnd WNHG WWEG XSen
'White Tie Affair'	EWoo
'White Zone'	EWoo
'Whooperee'	SDay
'Whoopie' **new**	CHid
'Wideyed'	EPla XLum
'Wild about Sherry'	CFwr SPol
'Wild and Wonderful'	EPfP EStr EWoo MBri
'Wild Child'	CFwr
'Wild Horses'	CWGN EPfP EWes LRHS MNrw NLar SCob SMad SPad SPol WHrl
'Wild Mustang'	EStr MBNS MSpe
'Wild Rose Fandango'	CFwr EWoo
'Wild Winter Wine'	CFwr
'Wildest Dreams'	EWoo
'Willy Nilly' **new**	SPol
'Wilson Spider'	SDay SPol
'Wind Beneath My Sails'	EWoo
'Wind Frills'	SDay SPol XSen
'Wind Master' **new**	CFwr
'Wind Song'	ELon
'Windmill Yellow'	EWoo SDay
'Window Dressing'	EWoo
'Winds of Love'	EWoo
'Wine Delight'	SDay
'Wine Merchant'	MNFA
'Wineberry Candy'	EStr EWoo MBNS NLar SDay
'Winged Migration'	CFwr EWoo
'Wings on High'	EWoo
'Winnie the Pooh'	SDay
'Winsome Lady'	ECGP ECha ECtt GKin MBNS WHrl
'Wisest of Wizards'	EStr MBNS MNrw SPol WHrl
'Wishing Well'	WCot
'Witch Hazel'	WCAu WWtn
'Witch Stitchery'	SDay
'Witches Brew'	CBgR
'Witches Wink'	EWoo
'Witch's Stick'	CFwr
'Without Warning'	CBgR
'Woodside Ruby'	WNHG
'Written on the Wind'	CFwr
'Wyoming Wildfire'	CBgR
'Xia Xiang'	EWoo
'Xochimilco'	WNHG
'Ya Ya Girl'	EWoo
'Yabba Dabba Doo'	MNrw SPol
'Yazoo Green Octopus'	EWoo
'Yazoo Wild Violet' **new**	EStr
'Yellow Angel'	ELon SPol WCot
'Yellow Finch'	CFwr
'Yellow Lollipop'	SDay
'Yellow Rain'	WCot
'Yellow Ribbon'	SPol
'Yellow Submarine'	EPfP MBNS
'Yesterday Memories'	SDay
yezoensis	EBtc
'Yo-rick Yost'	CFwr
'You Angel You'	MBNS MSpe
'Young Cha' **new**	MNFA
'Yuma'	WNHG
'Zagora'	EStr WCAu
'Zampa'	CBgR SDay
'Zara'	SPer

'Zenobia'	EStr
'Zuni Thunderbird'	EWoo

Hepatica ✿ (*Ranunculaceae*)

acutiloba	CBro ECho EPot GBuc GEdr GKev MMoz NBir XEll
- blue-flowered	MAsh
- white-flowered	MAsh
americana	ECho ELan GKev MAsh NBir
angulosa	see *H. transsilvanica*
(Forest Series) 'Forest Pink'	ELan XEll
- 'Forest Purple'	XEll
- 'Forest Red'	ELan GEdr XEll
- 'Forest White'	ELan XEll
henryi	EBee ECho GEdr GKev MAsh NLar NSla
insularis	GBuc MAsh
maxima	ECho GBuc GEdr MAsh
× ***media*** 'Ballardii'	GBuc GEdr IBlr LLHF
- 'Harvington Beauty'	CLAP GEdr IBlr IFoB MAsh MHom NBir
- 'Millstream Merlin'	GEdr
'Miyoshino'	GEdr
§ ***nobilis*** ♀H5	CBro CPBP CWCL ECho EPfP EPot GBBs GCra GEdr GKev GMaP IBlr ITim LRHS MAsh MBel MCot MHer NBir NCGa NSum SRms WAbe WCot WHoo WPnP XLum
- var. ***asiatica***	MAsh
- - pink-flowered **new**	MAsh
- - purple-flowered **new**	MAsh
- - white-flowered **new**	MAsh
- blue-flowered	ECho IFoB MAsh NSla WAbe
- 'Cobalt'	CLAP ECho GEdr NSla
- compact evergreen **new**	MAsh
- 'Cremar'	GEdr MAsh
- dark-blue-flowered	CLAP
- dwarf white-flowered	IFoB
- 'Elkofener Heidi' **new**	GEdr
- var. ***japonica***	EPfP EWes IFoB MAsh NBir NSla
- - 'Akabuku'	GEdr
- - 'Akafuku' **new**	GEdr
- - 'Akane' (1)	GEdr
- - 'Akanezora' (6/d)	GEdr
- - 'Akebono' (9/d)	GEdr
- - 'Anjyu' (9/d)	GEdr
- - 'Asahi' (7/d)	GEdr
- - 'Asahizuru' (6/d)	GEdr
- - 'Benikanzan'	GEdr
- - 'Benikujyaku' **new**	GEdr
- - 'Benioiran'	GEdr
- - 'Beniokesa' (d) **new**	GEdr
- - 'Benishinjyu' **new**	GEdr
- - 'Benisuzume' (1)	GEdr
- - 'Benitaiko' (9/d)	GEdr
- - 'Bojyou' (5A/d)	GEdr
- - 'Daishihou' (9/d) **new**	GEdr
- - 'Dewa' (9/d)	GEdr
- - 'Echigobijin'	GEdr
- - 'Fukujyu'	GEdr
- - 'Getsurin' (5A/d)	GEdr
- - 'Gosho-zakura' (5A/d)	GEdr
- - 'Gyousei' (1)	GBuc GEdr
- - 'Hakuji' **new**	GEdr
- - 'Hakurin' (6/d)	GEdr
- - 'Hakusetsu' (9/d)	GEdr
- - 'Haruka' (2)	GEdr
- - 'Harukaze' (5A/d)	GEdr
- - 'Haruno-awajuki' (9/d)	GEdr
- - 'Hatsune'	GEdr
- - Herashibe Group (5/d)	GBuc
- - 'Hohobeni' (9/d)	GEdr
- - 'Hokutosei' (7/d)	GEdr
- - 'Hosyun' **new**	GEdr
- - 'Houkan' (9/d)	GEdr
- - 'Isaribi' (1)	GEdr
- - 'Junissen' (6/d)	GEdr
- - 'Kagura' (5A/d)	GEdr
- - 'Kasumino'	GEdr
- - 'Kiko' (9/d)	GEdr
- - 'Kimon' (9/d)	GEdr
- - 'Koshi-no-maboroshi'	GEdr
- - 'Kougyoku' (9/d)	GEdr
- - 'Kousei' (9/d)	GEdr
- - 'Kuetsu' (9/d)	GEdr
- - 'Kuukai' (8/d)	GEdr
- - f. ***magna***	MAsh
- - - 'Murasaki-shikibu' (9/d)	GEdr
- - - 'Seizan'	GEdr
- - - 'Taeka'	GEdr
- - 'Manazuru' (9/d)	GEdr
- - 'Miwaku' (1)	GEdr
- - 'Miyuki' (9/d)	GEdr
- - 'Murasaki-sakama' (9/d)	GEdr
- - 'Odoriko' (9/d)	GEdr
- - 'Okina' (9/d)	GEdr
- - 'Ō-murasaki' (1)	GEdr
- - 'Orihime' (9/d)	GEdr
- - 'Reeka' (1)	GEdr
- - 'Ryokurei' (5A/d)	GEdr
- - 'Ryokusetsu' (9/d)	GEdr
- - 'Ryokuun' (9/d)	GEdr
- - 'Ryougetsu' (1)	GEdr LLHF
- - 'Sadobeni' (1)	GEdr
- - 'Saichou' (7/d)	GEdr
- - Sandan Group (7/d)	GEdr
- - 'Sawanemidori' (6/d)	GEdr
- - 'Sayaka' (1)	GEdr
- - 'Seikai' (5A/d-8d)	GEdr
- - 'Senhime' (9/d)	GEdr
- - 'Setsudo' (d)	GEdr
- - 'Shihou' (9/d)	GEdr
- - 'Shikouden' (9/d)	GEdr
- - 'Shikouryuu' (9/d)	GEdr
- - 'Shirayuki' (9/d)	GEdr
- - 'Shirin' (d)	GEdr
- - 'Shiun' (9/d)	GEdr
- - 'Shoujyouno-homare' (9/d)	GEdr
- - 'Sougetsu' (6/d)	GEdr
- - 'Soushyunka' (9/d) **new**	GEdr
- - 'Subaru' (9/d)	GEdr
- - 'Suien' (9/d)	GEdr
- - 'Syoujyouno-Homare' (9/d) **new**	GEdr
- - 'Tae' (5A/d)	GEdr
- - 'Taeka' (9/d)	GEdr
- - 'Takumi' (9/d)	GEdr
- - 'Tamahime' (8/d)	GEdr
- - 'Tamakujyaku' (6/d)	GEdr
- - 'Tamamushi' (9/d)	GEdr
- - 'Tamao' (1)	GEdr
- - 'Tamasaburou' (1)	GEdr
- - 'Tenjinbai' (1)	GEdr
- - 'Tennyonomai' (6A/d) **new**	GEdr

- - 'Tenzan' (7) **new**	GEdr
- - 'Toki' (9/d)	GEdr
- - 'Touen' (d) **new**	GEdr
- - 'Touhou' (9/d)	GEdr
- - 'Touryoku' (9/d)	GEdr
- - 'Toyama-chiyoiwai'	GEdr
- - 'Unabara' (9/d) **new**	GEdr
- - 'Usugesyou' (9/d)	GEdr
- - 'Utyuu' (1) **new**	GEdr
- - 'Wakakusa' (9/d)	GEdr
- - 'Yaegoromo' **new**	GEdr
- - 'Yahiko'	GEdr
- - 'Yahikomuasaki'	GEdr
- - 'Yamahibiki' (9/d) **new**	GEdr
- - 'Yukishino'	GEdr
- - 'Yuunagi' **new**	GEdr
- - 'Yuunami' (1)	GEdr
- - 'Yuzuru' (9/d)	GEdr
- large, pale blue-flowered	NSla
- 'Lilac Picotee'	NSla
- mottled leaf	ECho
- patterned leaf	NSla
- pink-flowered	CLAP ECho MAsh WCot
- var. ***pubescens***	MAsh
* - var. ***pyrenaica***	GBuc LEdu MAsh NSla WThu
* - - 'Apple Blossom'	GBuc NBir WAbe
- 'Pyrenean Marbles'	CLAP GBin
- red-flowered	ECho
- var. ***rubra***	CLAP ECho NSla
- 'Rubra Plena' (d)	CWCL GEdr NHar NSla
- violet-flowered	MAsh
- white-flowered	CLAP ECho MAsh
'Noubeni'	GEdr
'Oboroyo'	GEdr
'Sakaya'	GEdr
× ***schlyteri*** 'Ashwood Hybrids' **new**	MAsh
§ ***transsilvanica*** ♀H5	CBro CLAP ECho EPot GAbr GBin MAsh MCot MMoz SMrm WCot WThu
- 'Ada Scott'	GEdr
- 'Blue Eyes'	ECho EPot GEdr GKev NCGa
- 'Blue Jewel'	CCon CLAP CWCL ECho ELan EPot GEdr GKev MCot MHol NCGa WCot WPnP
- blue-flowered	IBlr IFoB MAsh
- 'Buis'	CLAP ECha ECho GEdr IFoB MHom NLar WPnP
- 'Eisvogel'	ECho GEdr
- 'Elison Spence' (d)	GEdr IBlr LLHF MCot
- 'Lilacina'	GEdr MAsh NSla
- 'Loddon Blue'	GEdr IBlr
- pink-flowered	ECho MAsh
- 'Sieben Bergen'	IBlr
- white-flowered	ECho MAsh
triloba	see *H. nobilis*
'Umezono'	GEdr
'Wakana'	GEdr
yamatutai	GBuc GEdr GKev NLar
aff. ***yamatutai***	MAsh

Heptacodium (*Caprifoliaceae*)

jasminoides	see *H. miconioides*
§ ***miconioides*** ♀H5	Widely available

Heptapleurum see *Schefflera*

Heptaptera (*Apiaceae*)

triquetra W&B BG A-2 **new**	WCot

Heracleum (*Apiaceae*)

lehmannianum	WCot
sphondylium	WSFF
- 'You're so Vein' **new**	CNat
stevenii **new**	WCot

Herbertia (*Iridaceae*)

§ ***lahue***	CDes ECho
platensis hort. ex L. H. Bailey	GKev

Hereroa (*Aizoaceae*)

glenensis	CTal ECho EDAr LRHS SPlb

Hermannia (*Malvaceae*)

flammea	SPlb
stricta	CPBP SDys WAbe

Hermodactylus see *Iris*

Herniaria (*Caryophyllaceae*)

glabra	CArn GPoy WHfH

Hertia see *Othonna*

Hesperaloe (*Asparagaceae*)

F&M 311.1	WPGP
malacophylla **new**	CFil
'Mamulique'	WCot
'New Blue'	WCot
parviflora	EBee LEdu SBig SPlb XSen
- creamy yellow-flowered	WCot

Hesperantha ✿ (*Iridaceae*)

§ ***baurii***	CTre ECho GBuc GLin LLHF WAbe WThu
coccinea	Widely available
- from Giants Castle	CTca
- f. ***alba***	Widely available
- 'Ballyrogan Giant'	CCon CPrp CTca GBuc IBlr WFar WHer WPGP
- 'Big Moma'	CPrp
- 'Cardinal'	NHol WMoo
- 'Countesse de Vere'	EBee
- 'Elburton Glow'	WFar
- 'Fenland Daybreak'	Widely available
- 'Good White'	NBir NCGa
- 'Hilary Gould'	CMea CPrp GBuc WHal
- 'Jack Frost'	EBee WMoo
- 'Jennifer' ♀H4	CBro CPrp CTca CTri EBee ELon EPfP GAbr GBin GBuc LPot LRHS LSou MCot MMuc MRav NCGa NLar SRms SWvt WFar WMoo XLum
- late-flowering	NCot
- 'Maiden's Blush'	ELan LRHS LSou MCot NLar SRms WFar
§ - 'Major' ♀H4	Widely available
- 'Marietta'	NWad
- 'Mollie Gould'	CPrp CTca ECtt ELon EPla GBuc GCra LLWG LSou MAvo MHer MMHG NCGa NHol SCoo SRms WMoo
- 'Mrs Hegarty'	Widely available
- 'November Cheer'	CMac CPrp IBlr NBir NLar WWEG XLum
- 'Oregon Sunset'	CPrp

- 'Pallida' CPrp CSam ELan MLHP MRav NBir WFar
- 'Pink Marg' CPrp
- 'Pink Princess' see *H. coccinea* 'Wilfred H. Bryant'
- pink-flowered **new** MBel
- 'Professor Barnard' CCCN CHel CSpe CTca EBee ECho ECtt ELon EPfP EPri GAbr MBNS NBir SRot WMoo
- 'Red Arrow' EWes
- 'Red Dragon' GBuc LLHF NHol
I - 'Rosea' SDeJ
- 'Salmon Charm' ECtt GBuc LRHS WFar WMoo
- 'Silver Pink' IBlr
- 'Snow Maiden' CBod CElw CHel CWCL EBee LRHS
- 'Strawberry' EBee
§ - 'Sunrise' ♀H4 Widely available
- 'Tambara' CCse CPou CPrp CSam GAbr GBuc XLum
- 'Viscountess Byng' CBcs CHel CTca CTri CWCL EBee EPau NBir SPer WWEG
§ - 'Wilfred H. Bryant' ♀H4 Widely available
- 'Zeal Salmon' CCon CElw CPou ECha GAbr NBir NCGa SMHy

cucullata ECho NRog
falcata ECho
grandiflora ECho
huttonii ECho LLHF MHer MSCN NBir
mossii see *H. baurii*
oligantha 'Kamiesberg' CDes ECho
pauciflora ECho

Hesperis (*Brassicaceae*)

matronalis Widely available
- ***alba*** see *H. matronalis* var. *albiflora*
§ - var. ***albiflora*** CSpe CTri CUse CWld ELau EPfP EWoo LRHS MCot MMuc MNHC NGdn SIde SPer SPoG SWat WBrk WMoo
- - 'Alba Plena' (d) CAbP ELan ELon IBoy LRHS MCot MHol MNrw NBir NPCo NPri WHer
- - 'Edith Harriet' (d/v) WCot
- 'Cally Dwarf' (d) GCal
- 'Lilacina' SWat
nivea **new** LEdu

× *Hesperotropsis* see × *Cuprocyparis*

Hessea (*Amaryllidaceae*)

breviflora ECho
incana 'Pendoornhoek' ECho
mathewsii ECho
pulcherrima ECho
speciosa ECho
stellaris ECho

Heteromeles (*Rosaceae*)

arbutifolia see *H. salicifolia*
§ ***salicifolia*** ETwe LEdu

Heteromorpha (*Apiaceae*)

arborescens CExl SPlb SVen

Heteropolygonatum (*Convallariaceae*)

roseolum CAby

Heterotheca (*Asteraceae*)

mariana see *Chrysopsis mariana*
subaxillaris **new** WCot
§ ***villosa*** EPPr
- 'Golden Sunshine' CPrp

Heuchera ✿ (*Saxifragaceae*)

'Alan Davidson' MPnt
'Alison' MPnt
'Amber Waves'PBR CExl CNor ELan EPfP LRHS MJak MPnt NBir SCob SGol SPtp SRGP SWvt
§ ***americana*** EAEE EPla LRHS MNFA MRav NBir SHeu SWvt
- var. ***americana*** MPnt
- Dale's strain CUse EHoe IFoB LSun MPnt NLar SHeu SPlb SWvt WPnP WRHF WWtn
- 'Garnet' **new** EPla
- 'Harry Hay' CDes EBee EPPr LPla MPnt SHeu WPGP WSHC
- 'Ring of Fire' EPla MPnt NPri SHeu SWvt
'Amethyst Myst' CLAP ECtt EPfP LRHS MPnt NPla SGol SHeu SLim SPer
'Apple Crisp' ECtt LBMP LSou MAsh MPnt SCob SHeu SWvt WGor WNPC
'Apple Souffle' MPnt
'Autumn Haze'PBR MPnt SHeu
'Autumn Leaves' CAbP CBod CLAP CUse ECtt ELan ELon ESwi EWll EWoo LBMP LRHS LSou MPnt MWhi NPCo NPri SHeu SMrm SPoG SRot SWvt WBrk WCot
'Baby's Breath' ECho MPnt
'Bardot' MPnt
'Beaujolais'PBR CAbP CBod CLAP CUse ECtt ESwi LRHS LSou MBNS MBri MNrw MPnt NBir SHeu WCot
'Beauty Colour' CAbP CLAP CRos ECha ECtt ELan ELon EPfP GMaP LRHS MBri MJak MRav NGdn NWad SHeu SHil SWvt
'Belle Notte' ECtt MAsh MPnt SHeu WNPC
'Berry Marmalade' ECtt GBin LSou MAsh MPnt NWad SHeu SWvt WGor WHar WNPC
'Berry Smoothie'PBR Widely available
(Big Top Series) 'Big Top Burgundy' **new** NSir
- 'Big Top Gold' CBod MNrw
'Binoche' EBee ECtt LRHS MAsh MPnt SCob SHeu SHil
'Birkin' LRHS MPnt SHeu
'Blackberry Crisp' EBee ECtt LSou MAsh MPnt SHeu WNPC
'Blackberry Jam' CHel CLAP CSpe CUse ECha ECtt ELan ELon ESwi GBin LAst LBMP LRHS MAsh MGos MPnt NBir NHol NSti SHeu SWvt
'Blackbird' CLAP MPnt MWat SHeu SWvt WMnd
'Blackout' CAbP ECtt ESwi MAsh MMuc MNrw MPnt NLar SHeu WNPC WWEG
'Blondie' (Little Cutie Series) **new** MPnt SHeu WCot
'Blood Red' CLAP LSou MPnt SHeu SLim
'Blood Vein' MPnt SHeu
'Blushing Down' **new** MPnt
'Bouquet' MPnt
bracteata MPnt XLum
'Bressingham Glow' MPnt SHeu
Bressingham hybrids GJos IFoB MLHP NBir SPer SRms
'Bressingham Spire' MPnt

'Bronze Beauty'	CMil CUse ECtt MPnt SHeu WBrk WCot
'Brown Sugar'	ECtt MPnt SHeu WNPC
'Brownfinch'	LPla MPnt SHeu SMHy
'Brownies'	CAbP CBod CLAP ECtt ESwi LPla MBNS MPie MPnt SHeu WCot WPtf WWtn
'Burgundy Frost'	MPnt
'Café Olé'	ECtt MAsh MPnt NLar SHeu WHer WNPC
'Cajun Fire'	CWGN ECtt LBMP MAsh MPnt SCob SHeu WNPC
'Can-can' ♀H6	CTri ECtt ELon EPfP EWoo ITim LRHS MNrw MPnt NBir NGdn NLar NPri SCob SHeu SHil SPer SRot SWvt WWEG
'Canyon Duet'	MBNS MPnt SHeu
'Cappuccino'	EAEE EBee ELan EPfP EPla IBoy MPnt MRav SCob SGol SHeu SWvt
'Caramel'PBR	Widely available
'Carmen'	MPnt
'Cascade Dawn'	CLAP CWCL EBee ECtt EPfP MPnt NBir SWvt WNPC
'Champagne Bubbles'	MLHP MPnt SHeu
Charles Bloom = 'Chablo'	LRHS MPnt
'Chatterbox'	MPnt SHeu
'Checkers'	see *H.* 'Quilter's Joy'
'Cherries Jubilee'PBR	CAbP CLAP ELon EPfP GMaP MPnt SLim WNPC
'Cherry Cola'	CBcs EBee ECtt EPfP LBMP LRHS LSou MAsh MPnt MTis NLar NSti SBod SCob SDys SHeu WGor WNPC
'Chiqui'	MPnt SMHy
chlorantha	MPnt
- 'Burnt Sienna'	GCal
'Chocolate Ruffles'PBR	Widely available
'Chocolate Veil'	MPnt WWEG
'Christa'	MPnt SHeu
'Cinnabar Silver'PBR	CLAP ECtt LRHS MPnt NBir SCob SHeu WNPC
'Circus'	MAsh MPnt SHeu
'Citronelle'	CBod CUse CWGN ECtt EPfP ITim MBNS MPnt NPCo SHeu SPer SWvt WCot
'City Lights'	SHeu
'Coco' (Little Cutie Series) **new**	LSou MPnt SHeu
'Color Dream'PBR	MPnt SHeu
coral bells	see *H. sanguinea*
'Coral Bouquet'	MPnt SHeu
'Coral Cloud'	MPnt
'Corallion'	MPnt
Crème Brûlée = 'Tnheu041' (Dolce Series)	Widely available
'Crème Caramel'	CExl IFoB MPnt SHar
'Creole Nights'	MAsh MPnt SHeu WNPC
'Crimson Curls'	CLAP ECtt EPfP LBuc LRHS LSou MAsh MPnt MWat SCob SHeu SRms SWvt
'Crispy Curly'	MPnt SHeu
cylindrica	EPfP LLWP MLHP MPnt SHeu WWEG
- var. ***alpina***	GKev LLHF
- 'Cream'	MPnt
- 'Francis'	MPnt
- 'Greenfinch'	CFis ELan GKev GMaP LRHS MPnt MRav NBir SHeu SWat SWvt WHea WMnd XLum
- 'Hyperion'	LRHS MPnt
'Damask'	MPnt
'Dark Beauty'PBR	CLAP ECtt ELon LBMP LRHS MBNS NLar NPri SCob SHeu SRot WNPC
'Dark Mystery'	MAsh
'Dark Secret'PBR	EBee MPnt SHeu
'David'	MPnt SHeu WBrk
'Delta Dawn'	CMos LAst LBMP LSou MAsh MAvo MPnt SCob SHeu SWvt WNPC
'Dennis Davidson'	see *H.* 'Huntsman'
Ebony and Ivory = 'E and I'PBR	CAbP CBcs CLAP CRos EBee ECtt EHoe EShb GKev GMaP LBMP LRHS MBri MCot MGos MPnt NBir SCob SHil SRms SRot SWvt
'Eden's Aurora'	MPnt
'Eden's Mystery'	NLar
'Electra'PBR	CLAP CMea CWCL ECtt ELon ESwi EUJe LRHS LSou MBNS MBri MPnt NDov NPri SCob SHeu SMrm SRot SWvt WBor WHlf
'Electric Lime'	CLAP ECtt EHoe ELan ESwi GBin MPnt NLar NPri SHeu WNPC
elegans NNS 05-372	WCot
'Elworthy Rusty'	CElw
'Emperor's Cloak'	GLog LEdu SHeu SPad SWvt WMoo
'Encore'PBR	ECtt MNrw MPnt SHeu
'Fairy Dance' **new**	MPnt
'Fantasia'	SHeu
'Fire Alarm'	CMos ECtt MPnt SHeu WNPC
'Fire Chief'PBR	CHel CLAP CWCL CWGN EAEE EBee ECtt EPfP EPla ESwi EWoo GBin LBMP LRHS LSou MAsh MPnt NBir NHol NLar NPri NWad SHeu SMrm SPer SPoG SRkn SRot SWvt
'Firebird'	LRHS MPnt NBir
Firefly	see *H.* 'Leuchtkäfer'
'Fireworks'PBR ♀H6	CAbP CBod CRos ECtt LRHS MBNS MPnt MRav NLar NPri SHil SLim SPer SRot
'Florist's Choice'	MNFA SHeu
'French Quarter'	MPnt SHeu
'Frost' (Little Cutie Series) **new**	MPnt SHeu
'Frosted Violet'PBR	see *H.* 'Frosted Violet Dream'
§ 'Frosted Violet Dream'PBR	CLAP ECtt LSou MPnt NCGa SCob SHeu SWvt WNPC
'Galaxy' (Little Cutie Series) **new**	CWGN MPnt SHeu
'Gauguin' (Master Painters Series) **new**	MPnt SHeu
'Georgia Peach'PBR	Widely available
'Georgia Plum'	ECtt MPnt SHeu WNPC
'Ginger Ale'PBR	Widely available
'Ginger Peach'	CLAP ECtt LSou MPnt NDov SCob SHeu WNPC
'Ginger Snap' (Little Cutie Series) **new**	LSou MPnt SHeu
glabra	MPnt
glauca	see *H. americana*
'Gloire d'Orléans'	MPnt XLum
'Gotham'	ECtt MAsh MPnt SHeu WNPC
'Green Ivory'	EAEE MPnt SHeu XLum
'Green Sashay'	MPnt SHeu
'Green Spice'	CLAP EAEE EBee ECtt EHoe ELan ELon EPfP ESwi EUJe LRHS MBri MPnt NBir NCGa NDov NHol NPla NPri NWad SCob SHeu SPer SPoG SRkn SWvt WGwG

	grossulariifolia	GMaP
	'Guardian Angel'	CLAP MPnt SHeu SRGP
	'Gypsy Dancer'PBR (Dancer Series)	CLAP EBee MPnt SHeu WNPC
	'Hailstorm' (v)	MPnt
	hallii	CPBP MPnt
	Harvest Burgundy = 'Balheubur' **new**	MPnt
	Harvest Silver = 'Balheusil' **new**	MPnt
	'Havana'PBR	LSou MPnt SHeu
	'Helen Dillon' (v)	EPla GMaP LAst MPnt NBir SPoG SRGP SWvt WGwG WWEG
	'Hercules'PBR	ECtt MPnt SHeu
	hispida	MPnt
	'Hollywood'PBR	CHel CMea EBee ECtt ELon EPfP ESwi LAst LBMP MBri MGos MPnt NBir NHol NLar NPri NWad SCob SHeu SMrm SPoG SRot
§	'Huntsman'	MPnt MRav
	'Jade Gloss'PBR	CLAP CRos EPfP GBin LRHS MBri MPnt SHeu SWvt WNPC WWEG
	'June Bride'	MPnt
	'Kadastra'	MPnt SHeu
	'Kassandra'PBR	EBee ECtt MPnt SCob SGol SHeu STPC SWvt
	Key Lime Pie = 'Tnheu042'PBR (Dolce Series)	CBcs CBod CExl CRos CWGN ECtt EPfP GMaP LRHS MBri MGos NBir NBro NHol NPla SCob SHeu SPer SRms SRot SWvt WBor
	Kira Series	MPnt
	'Lady in Red'	NBre
	'Lady Romney'	XLum
	'Lemon Chiffon'PBR	ECtt MPnt SHeu
§	'Leuchtkäfer'	CWat ECtt EPfP EPla GMaP LAst LPot LRHS MBel MHer MMuc MPnt MRav MWat MWhi NBir NMir NOrc SGol SPer SPlb SRms WGwG WMnd WMoo WPtf WWEG XLum
	Licorice = 'Tnheu044'PBR (Dolce Series)	CBod CRos ECtt ELon ESwi EUJe EWll GBin LRHS MAsh MBNS MBri MGos MPnt NBir NLar NPri SHeu SHil SLim SPoG SRot SWvt WHoo WWEG
	'Lime Marmalade'	CLAP CRos CUse CWGN ECtt ELan ELon EPfP EPla ESwi LBMP LRHS LSou MAsh MBNS MBri MGos MPnt NDov NHol NLar NPri NWad SCob SHeu SHil SMrm SPad SPoG SRot
	'Lime Rickey'PBR	CBcs CMea CUse CWGN ECtt EPfP EUJe LBrs LRHS MBri MGos MJak MNrw NBir NSoo NSti SGol SHeu SPer SRGP SWvt WCot WHer
	'Lipstick'PBR	CWGN ELon MPnt NDov SHeu SWvt WNPC
	'Little Tinker'	MPnt
	'Lune Rousse'	MPnt SHeu
	'Magic Wand' ♀H6	CAbP ELon MBNS SHeu
	'Magnum'	CUse CWGN EBee ECtt ESwi IBoy MPnt SHeu WCot WRHF
	'Mahogany'PBR	CLAP ELon EPfP EUJe GBin LRHS LSou MJak MPnt NBir NPri SCob SHeu SLim SWvt WHoo
	'Malachite'	MPnt SHeu
	'Mango' **new**	MPnt
	'Marmalade'PBR	Widely available
	'Mars'	EPfP LRHS MPnt SHeu
	'Mary Rose'	MPnt

	'Melting Fire'	CBod GJos LRHS MAsh MPnt SGol SHeu WHar WNPC
	'Mercury'	SHeu
	'Metallic Shimmer' (Fox Series)	MPnt
	'Metallica'	NGBl SHeu WMoo
	micans	see *H. rubescens*
	micrantha	GCal MLHP MNFA MPnt SHeu SRms
	- var. ***diversifolia*** misapplied	see *H. villosa*
	- 'Martha's Compact'	MPnt WCot
§	- 'Ruffles'	ECha MPnt
	'Midas Touch'	CLAP CWGN EBee LBMP LSou MPnt NLar SHeu WNPC
	'Midnight Bayou'	EBee ECtt ELan ELon EPfP ESwi EWll GBin LRHS MBri MPnt NLar NPer NPri SHeu SRot SWvt WNPC
	'Midnight Rose'	Widely available
	'Midnight Rose Select'	MPnt NWad
	'Milan'PBR	CBod ECtt MPnt SHeu WNPC
	'Mini Mouse'	MPnt SHeu
	'Mint Frost'PBR	ECtt ELan EPfP LPot LRHS MPnt NBir SHeu SWvt
	'Mint Julep'PBR	CWGN ECtt MBri MPnt SHeu WNPC
	'Miracle'PBR	CLAP CMos ECtt EPfP EWoo MPnt SHeu WNPC
	'Mocha'PBR	CBod CLAP ECtt MNrw MPnt SHeu SWvt WCot
	'Molly Bush' ♀H6	EBee MBri MPnt MWhi SHeu
	'Mother of Pearl'	MPnt
	'Muscat'	ECtt MPnt SHeu
	'Mysteria'PBR	LBMP LSou MPnt SHeu WNPC
	'Mystic Angel'	MPnt SHeu
	'Neptune'	ECtt EPla EWTr LRHS MPnt SHeu WGwG
	'Oakington Jewel'	MPnt
	'Obsidian'PBR	Widely available
	'Orange Blush' **new**	MAsh
	'Orphée'	MPnt
	'Paprika'	CUse ECtt MPnt SHeu WCot WNPC
	'Paris'PBR	CLAP CRos CUse ECtt EPfP GBin LRHS LSou MAsh MBri MGos MPnt NDov NHol NPri SHeu SHil SPoG WNPC WWEG
	parishii NNS 93384	MPnt
	parvifolia var. ***nivalis***	MPnt
	- var. ***utahensis***	MPnt
	'Peach Crisp'	CMos CWGN ECtt LBMP LSou SHeu SRkn WNPC
	'Peach Flambé'PBR	Widely available
	'Peach Pie'	MPnt
	'Peachy Keen'	SHeu
	'Pear Crisp'	CWGN ECtt LBMP LSou MPnt SHeu WNPC
	'Penelope'	MPnt
	'Peppermint' (Little Cutie Series) **new**	MPnt SHeu
	'Peppermint Spice'PBR (21st Century Collection Series)	MPnt SGol SHeu
	'Persian Carpet'	CHEx GMaP LRHS MPnt NBir SHeu SWvt WPtf
	(Petite Series) 'Petite Marbled Burgundy'	ECtt EHoe LLHF MPnt NDov SHeu SWvt
	- 'Petite Pearl Fairy'	CAbP EHoe ELan MPnt SHeu SWvt
	- 'Petite Pink Bouquet'	EHoe MPnt SHeu

'Pewter Moon'	CBcs ELan GMaP MGos MPnt NBir SHeu XLum
'Pewter Veil'	MPnt SHeu WMnd
'Phoebe's Blush' (Fox Series) **new**	MPnt
'Picasso' (Master Painters Series) **new**	MPnt SHeu
pilosissima	XLum
'Pinot Bianco'	MAsh MPnt SHeu
'Pinot Gris'PBR	CLAP CSpe CUse CWGN ECtt ESwi LRHS LSou MAsh MNrw MPnt SHeu WCot WNPC
'Pinot Noir'	MPnt SHeu WOut
'Pistache'	CAbP ECtt LBMP MPie MPnt SHeu WCot
§ 'Pluie de Feu'	CCon EPPr GBuc LRHS MAvo MPnt MRav XLum
'Plum Pudding'PBR	Widely available
'Plum Royale'PBR	CLAP CRos CUse CWGN ELon EPfP LBMP LBrs LRHS LSou MAvo MBri MCot MGos MPnt MSCN MTis NLar NPCo NPri NSti NWad SHeu SHil SPer SRkn SWvt WWEG
'Pretty Perinne'	EBee MPnt SHeu
'Pretty Polly'	MPnt
'Prince'	ELan LRHS MBNS MBel MPnt SHeu SPoG SWvt WPtf
'Prince of Silver'	CBod LRHS MPnt MWhi SHeu
pringlei	see *H. rubescens*
pubescens	ECho MPnt SHeu XLum
- 'Alba'	MPnt
pulchella	CPBP EDAr GCal LLHF MHer MPnt MWat NLar SHeu SRms
'Purple Petticoats' ♀H6	CBcs ELan EPfP GBin LRHS LSou MLHP MNFA MPnt NPri SBod SHeu SLim SPoG SRot
'Quick Silver'	LRHS MNFA MPnt NBir SHeu SWvt
§ 'Quilter's Joy'	MPnt
'Rachel'	CAbP EAEE EBee ELan EPfP EPla GBuc GMaP IFoB LRHS MPnt MRav NBir NGdn SRGP SWvt XLum
Rain of Fire	see *H.* 'Pluie de Feu'
'Raspberry' (Fox Series)	MPnt
'Raspberry Ice'PBR	MPnt SHeu
'Raspberry Regal' ♀H6	ECtt MPnt MRav NBir SHeu SWvt WCot WSHC
'Rave On'PBR	CAbP CHVG CRos CWGN EBee ECtt ELan ELon GBin LRHS LSou MBel MBri MPnt NEgg NHol NLar NPri NWad SBod SCob SHeu SHil SPer SRkn SRot SWvt WHoo
'Red Dress'	MPnt SHeu
'Red Spangles'	LRHS MPnt NBir SHeu WWEG
'Regina' ♀H6	CAbP ECtt EPfP MPnt SHeu SWvt
'Renoir' (Master Painters Series) **new**	MPnt SHeu
'Rhapsody'	LRHS
richardsonii	MNrw MPnt XLum
'Rickard'	MPnt
'Rio'	ECtt LSou MPnt SCob SHeu WNPC
'Robert'	MPnt
'Root Beer'	CMos ECtt EPfP LRHS LSou MPnt NDov SHeu SRkn WNPC
Rosemary Bloom = 'Heuros'PBR	EBee LRHS SHeu
§ ***rubescens***	CAbP ECho NBro WThu
'Ruffles'	see *H. micrantha* 'Ruffles'
'Sanbrot'	MPnt
§ ***sanguinea***	CMac CSBt IMou MPnt MRav NBir
- 'Alba'	CSpe EPPr LPla MPnt SMHy
- 'Geisha's Fan'	CHid ECtt MPnt SHeu SWvt WNPC
- 'Monet' (v)	EBee MLHP MPnt SHeu
- 'Ruby Bells'	CBod CMea EPPr LRHS MAsh MPnt MSpe NLar SHeu WHoo
- 'Sioux Falls'	CUse SHeu
- 'Snow Storm' (v)	ELan MPnt SHeu SPlb WMnd WNPC
- 'Splendens'	MPnt XLum
- 'Taff's Joy' (v)	MPnt
- 'White Cloud' (v)	EBee EPfP EPla EShb LRHS MPnt NBre NDov SHeu SRms WGwG XLum
'Sashay' ♀H6	CLAP ELon IBoy LSou MHol MPnt NLar NSoo SBod SGol SHeu WNPC
'Saturn'	MPnt SHeu SWvt WNPC
'Schneewittchen'	MPnt MRav
'Scintillation' ♀H6	MPnt
'Shanghai'PBR	CMos ECtt EPfP EPla GBin LRHS LSou MAsh MPnt MWhi NCGa NWad SHeu SWvt WNPC
'Shenandoah Mountain'	MPnt
'Silver Blush' **new**	MAsh MSCN
'Silver Heart' **new**	MPnt
'Silver Indiana'	MPnt SHeu
'Silver Light'PBR	EPfP MPnt SHeu
'Silver Lode'PBR	MPnt SHeu
'Silver Scrolls'PBR	Widely available
'Silver Shadows'	MBrN MPnt SHeu
'Silver Streak'	see × *Heucherella* 'Silver Streak'
'Sioux Falls'	CFis MPnt
'Slater's Pink' (Fox Series) **new**	MPnt
'Snow Angel'	CUse CWGN ECtt LBMP LSou MAsh MPnt SHeu SPer SPoG WCot WRHF
'Snowfire' (v)	MPnt SHeu
'Southern Comfort'PBR	CBod CLAP CWGN ECtt ESwi LBrs LRHS MBNS MPnt NDov NHol NLar NPer NPri SGol SHeu SLim SPoG SRot SWvt WCot
'Sparkler'	MPnt
'Sparkling Burgundy'	ECtt ELon LPal LRHS MPnt NDov NPri SHeu SWvt
'Spellbound'	CWGN EBee ECtt LBMP MAsh MPnt SCob SHeu SPoG SRkn WNPC
'Starry Night'	MPnt
'Steel City'	MPnt SHeu
'Stormy Seas'	CBod EAEE EBee ELan EPfP EPla GCra LRHS MLHP MPnt MRav NBir SCob SHeu SPer SWvt WPtf
'Strawberries and Cream' (v)	MPnt SHeu
'Strawberry Candy'PBR	CWGN ELon GBin GJos LAst MBNS MPnt NBir NLar NWad SHeu SLim SRkn WNPC WWtn
'Strawberry Swirl'	CElw EPfP GMaP MGos MPnt MRav NBir NLar SCob SHar SHeu SWvt WNPC
'Sugar Berry' (Little Cutie Series) **new**	LSou MPnt SCob SHeu
Sugar Frosting = 'Pwheu0104'PBR	CRos EHoe GBin LRHS MBri MGos MPnt NHol NPri SHeu SHil SRot SWvt
'Sugar Plum'PBR	CAby CSpe ECtt ELon EPfP EUJe LBMP LRHS MBNS MPnt NPri SHeu SRot WCot WHoo WNPC
'Sweet Berry' **new**	MPnt
'Sweet Tart' (Little Cutie Series) **new**	LSou MPnt SHeu

'Swirling Fantasy'PBR	COtt EShb GJos LSou MPnt MSCN SHeu
'Tangerine Wave' (Fox Series)	MPnt
'Tara'	ECtt MPnt SHeu
'Thomas' (Fox Series) **new**	MPnt
'Tiramisu'PBR	CAbP CLAP CMea CUse CWCL CWGN ECtt ESwi IBoy ITim LBMP LRHS MBNS MJak MPnt NBir NSti SHeu SPoG SWvt
'Tresahor White' **new**	MPnt
'Van Gogh' (Master Painters Series)	ECtt MPnt SHeu
'Vanilla Spice'	MPnt SHeu
'Veil of Passion'	NBre
'Velvet Night'	EPfP LSou MJak MPnt NBir SHeu SPlb WMnd WWEG
'Venus'	CUse CWGN ECtt LBMP LPal LRHS LSun MBNS MBel MMuc MNrw MPie MPnt NGdn NSti SHeu SPer WBrk WCot WHoo
'Vesuvius'	MPnt SHeu WNPC
'Vienna' (City Series)	MPnt SHeu WNPC
§ ***villosa***	CSam MPnt MRav SVic XLum
- 'Autumn Bride'	MPnt SHeu
- Bressingham Bronze = 'Absi'PBR	EAEE EPla LRHS MPnt SHeu
- 'Chantilly'	MPnt SHeu
- var. ***macrorhiza***	EShb LBMP MPnt NBre XLum
- 'Palace Purple'	Widely available
- 'Palace Purple Select'	CMac CTri CUse CWat LAst LSun MCot MJak SLim SWvt WHar
- Purpurea Group **new**	EPla
'Virginale'	MPnt
'Vulcano'	CUse EBee ECtt LSou MAsh WBrk WCot
'Walnut' (Fox Series) **new**	MPnt
'White Marble'	MPnt SHar
'White Spires'	LRHS MPnt SHar SHeu
'White Swirls'	MPnt
'William How'	MPnt
'Winter Red'	EPla LRHS MPnt SHeu
'Zabeliana'	MPnt

× *Heucherella* ✿ (*Saxifragaceae*)

'Alabama Sunrise'PBR	CHid CLAP CMHG ECtt ELan ESwi GBin LRHS MBri MPkF MPnt NPer NPri SGol SHeu SPoG SRot SWvt WBor
alba 'Bridget Bloom'	ECha ELan EPfP GMaP LPot LRHS MNFA MPnt MRav NOrc NPCo SHeu SPer SRms XLum
§ - 'Rosalie'	ECha EWoo LRHS MPnt MRav NBir NBro SHeu SPlb WSHC
'Art Deco'	SHeu
'Berry Fizz'	MPkF MPnt SHeu STPC SWvt WNPC
'Birthday Cake'	MPnt SHeu
'Blue Ridge' **new**	MPnt
'Brass Lantern'PBR	CBod CMos CSpe CWCL CWGN ECtt EPfP GBin LRHS LSou MAsh MBel MBri MPnt NCGa NHol NPri NWad SCob SHeu SRot STPC SWvt WNPC
'Burnished Bronze'PBR	CBod ECtt ELon EPfP GBin LRHS LSou MBri MPkF MPnt NBro NLar NPla NWad SHeu SPer SRot SWvt
'Buttered Rum' **new**	SHeu
'Chocolate Lace'PBR	MPnt SHeu
'Cinnamon Bear'	MPnt SHeu
'Citrus Shock'	MPnt SHeu
'Cracked Ice' **new**	SHeu
'Dayglow Pink'PBR	CLAP ECtt EShb GBin GMaP MPkF MPnt NBro NLar SCob SHeu WBor WNPC
'Fan Dancer'	CLAP MPnt SHeu
'Freefolk Stars'	SHar
Gold Strike = 'Hertn041'PBR	CLAP ECtt LRHS MBNS MPnt SHeu
'Golden Zebra'PBR	CBod CLAP CWGN EBee ECtt ELan LBrs LRHS MAvo MBNS MBri MNrw MPkF MPnt MWhi NSoo SHeu SWvt WCot
'Great Smokies'	ECtt MPnt SHeu
'Gunsmoke'PBR	CLAP ECtt GBin LBMP LSou MBri MPkF MPnt NCGa NWad SCob SHeu SWvt WGor WNPC
'Heart of Darkness'PBR	MPnt SHeu
'Kimono'PBR ♀H6	Widely available
'Ninja'	see *Tiarella* 'Ninja'
'Party Time'PBR	SHeu
Pink Whispers = 'Hertn042'PBR	LPot MPnt SHeu
'Quicksilver'	CBcs GMaP MBri MPnt SHeu SWvt
'Redstone Falls'PBR	CWCL CWGN ECtt LBMP LSou MPnt NCGa NLar NPri NWad SHeu SPer SPoG STPC SWvt WCot WGor WNPC
'Ring of Fire'	SWvt
§ 'Silver Streak'	MPnt NBro SHeu SWvt
'Solar Eclipse'	CMos ECtt IBoy LSou MAsh MAvo MHol MPkF MPnt NCGa NLar SHeu SPer SPoG SWvt WCot WGor WNPC
'Solar Power'PBR	CBod CWGN ECtt LRHS LSou MPnt NLar NWad SHeu SHil SWvt WNPC
'Stoplight'PBR	Widely available
'Sunrise Falls' (Falls Series)	CWGN MAsh MPkF MPnt NWad SHeu SPer SWvt WCot WGor WNPC
'Sunspot'PBR (v)	CLAP EAEE EPfP MGos NBro NSti SGol SHeu WHer
'Sweet Tea'PBR	Widely available
'Tapestry'PBR	Widely available
tiarelloides ♀H6	CMac EPfP LRHS
§ 'Viking Ship'	CUse EAEE ECtt LRHS MPnt MTPN NBir SHeu
'Yellowstone Falls'PBR	CWCL CWGN LBMP LSou MPnt NWad SHeu SPoG SRot STPC SWvt WGor WNPC WWFP

Hexastylis see *Asarum*

Hibanobambusa (*Poaceae*)

tranquillans	CEnt EPla ERod MBrN MMoz MMuc MWht SEND
- 'Shiroshima' (v)	CAbb CBod CDTJ CDoC CEnt EPfP EPla ERod EUJe LPal MBrN MBri MJak MMoz MMuc MWhi MWht SBig SEND

Hibbertia (*Dilleniaceae*)

aspera	CAbb CBcs CCCN CRHN CTsd EBee ECre IVic LRHS MOWG WCFE WSHC
§ ***cuneiformis***	CCCN
procumbens	WAbe
§ ***scandens*** ♀H1c	CBcs CCCN CHII CRHN ECou ELan MOWG

'Spring Sunshine'	CHel ESwi ETwe SEle
tetrandra	see *H. cuneiformis*
volubilis	see *H. scandens*

Hibiscus ✿ (*Malvaceae*)

coccineus	SBrt SMad SPlb
- white-flowered	SBrt
coccineus × moscheutos	SBrt
'Eruption' new	EPfP
'Fireball'PBR	EUJe SPoG
huegelii	see *Alyogyne huegelii*
'Kopper King'PBR	EUJe MBNS SMad SPoG
leopoldii	SRms
militaris	SBrt
moscheutos	CArn EBee SBrt SMad SVic XLum
- 'Galaxy'	XLum
- 'Robert Fleming'PBR	EUJe
mutabilis ♀H1b	LEdu MOWG
paramutabilis	EWes SMad
'Resi'	EPla LRHS
rosa-sinensis	EBak MOWG SPre
- 'Arcadian Spring'	MOWG
- 'Big Tango'	MOWG
- 'Blues Man'	MOWG
- 'Byron Metts'	MOWG
- 'Cajun Cocktail'	see *H. rosa-sinensis* 'Jambalaya'
- 'Candy Floss' (d)	MOWG
- 'Carmen Keene'	MOWG
- 'Cloud Nine'PBR	MOWG
- 'Cockatoo'	MOWG
- 'Courier Mail'	MOWG
- 'Dorothy Brady'	MOWG
- 'Enid Lewis' (d)	MOWG
- 'Erin Rachael'	MOWG
- 'Expo'	MOWG
- 'Gwen Mary'	MOWG
- 'Holly's Pride'	MOWG
- 'Hot Bikini'	MOWG
§ - 'Jambalaya'	MOWG
- 'June's Joy'	MOWG
- 'Key West Thunderhead' (d)	MOWG
- 'Lady Bug'	MOWG
- 'Lady Flo'	MOWG
- 'Lemon Chiffon'	MOWG
- 'Linda Pear' (d)	MOWG
- 'Madame Dupont'	MOWG
- 'Mrs Andreasen' (d)	MOWG
- 'Rhinestone'	MOWG
- 'Soft Shoulders'	MOWG
- 'Spanish Lady'	MOWG
- 'Sprinkle Rain'	MOWG
- 'Tarantella'	MOWG
- 'The Path'	MOWG
- 'Vermillion Queen'	MOWG
- 'Weekend'	MOWG
- 'White Swan'	MOWG
schizopetalus ♀H1b	MOWG
sinosyriacus 'Lilac Queen'	CExl LRHS SKHP WPGP
- 'Ruby Glow'	CExl LRHS SKHP WPGP
syriacus	LPal
- 'Aphrodite'	LRHS MAsh
- 'Ardens' (d)	CEnd SPer SPoG
- Blue Bird	see *H. syriacus* 'Oiseau Bleu'
- Blue Chiffon = 'Notwood3'PBR ♀H5	CSBt LRHS MBri MGos SPoG
- China Chiffon = 'Bricutts'	LRHS MAsh MBri MGos MMuc SEND SHil SPoG
- 'Diana' ♀H5	EBee EPfP LRHS MAsh MGos MRav SCoo SKHP SLon
- 'Dorothy Crane'	LRHS SKHP
- 'Duc de Brabant' (d)	CSBt ELon EPfP MBlu SPer
- 'Elegantissimus'	see *H. syriacus* 'Lady Stanley'
- 'Hamabo' ♀H5	CDul CSBt CTri EBee ELan ELon EPfP LAst LRHS MBri MGos MMuc MWat NLar NPri SCoo SEND SGol SHil SLim SPer SPoG SWvt WHar
- 'Helene'	ELan MBlu
- 'Jeanne d'Arc' (d)	SGol
§ - 'Lady Stanley' (d)	CMac CSBt LSou SCoo SPer
- Lavender Chiffon = 'Notwoodone'PBR ♀H5	CSBt EBee ELan ELon EPfP EWes LRHS MBri MGos MMuc SCoo SEND SHil SPer SPoG
- 'Leopoldii'	SKHP
- 'Marina'	EPfP LSou MBlu MRav SGol
- 'Mauve Queen'	SSta
- 'Meehanii' misapplied	see *H. syriacus* 'Purpureus Variegatus'
- 'Meehanii' (v) ♀H5	CEnd EMil EPfP LRHS SCoo SKHP SPoG
- 'Monstrosus'	NLar
§ - 'Oiseau Bleu' ♀H5	Widely available
- Pink Chiffon	LRHS SLon
- Pink Giant = 'Flogi'	CMac ELan EPfP LRHS MGos MWat SPad SPer
- 'Pinky Spot' new	LRHS
- Purple Ruffles = 'Sanchoyo' (d)	EPfP LRHS MBri SHil SPoG
§ - 'Purpureus Variegatus' (v)	CMac LRHS SPoG
- 'Red Heart' ♀H5	CAco CDul CEnd CMac CSBt CTri ELan EPfP LRHS MAsh MBri MGos MMuc NLar SEND SHil SKHP SLim SPad SPer SPoG SRms SWvt WCFE
- Rosalbane = 'Minrosa'	SGol
- Russian Violet = 'Floru'	CEnd ELan EPfP LRHS SKHP
- 'Shintaeyang'	MBri
- 'Speciosus'	SPer SPoG
- 'Totus Albus'	CMac
- Ultramarine = 'Minultra'PBR	EPfP LRHS SKHP
- 'Variegatus'	see *H. syriacus* 'Purpureus Variegatus'
- 'Violet Clair Double' (d)	CMac
- White Chiffon = 'Notwoodtwo'PBR (d) ♀H5	CSBt ELan EPfP EWes LRHS MAsh MBri MGos MRav SCoo SHil SPer SPoG
- 'William R. Smith' ♀H5	ELan LRHS MBri MSwo SPer
- 'Woodbridge' ♀H5	CBcs CEnd CMac CSBt CTri ELan EPfP EShb LRHS LSou MAsh MBri MGos MMuc MSwo NLar NPri SCob SEND SGol SHil SKHP SLim SPer SPlb SPoG SRms SSpi SWvt
trionum	CSpe WKif
- 'Sunny Day'	ELan

hickory, shagbark see *Carya ovata*

Hieracium (*Asteraceae*)

aurantiacum	see *Pilosella aurantiaca*
brunneocroceum	see *Pilosella aurantiaca* subsp. *carpathicola*
§ ***lanatum***	ECho NBir
maculatum	see *H. spilophaeum*
pilosella	see *Pilosella officinarum*
scullyi	EPPr
§ ***spilophaeum***	EHoe MMuc NBid NPer NSti WOut

- 'Blue Leaf'	WCot
umbellatum	WOut
villosum	CPBP ECho EHoe NBro WHer
welwitschii	see *H. lanatum*

Hierochloe (*Poaceae*)

odorata	CBod ELon EPPr GPoy MBNS XLum

hildaberry see *Rubus* 'Hildaberry'

Himalayacalamus (*Poaceae*)

asper	CDTJ ERod
§ ***falconeri***	CEnt SDix
§ - 'Damarapa'	CEnt EPfP MMoz
§ ***hookerianus***	CExl EPfP IMou
- 'Himalaya Blue'	CDTJ
porcatus	WPGP

× *Hippeasprekelia* (*Amaryllidaceae*)

sp.	CDes
'Durga Pradhan'	WCot
'Red Beauty'	WCot
'Red Star'	CCCN

Hippeastrum ✿ (*Amaryllidaceae*)

× ***acramannii*** ♀H2	CDes GCal WCot
advenum	see *Rhodophiala advena*
'Alfresco'PBR	LAma
'Amputo'	LAma
'Apple Blossom' ♀H2	LAma SDeJ
'Baby Star'	SDeJ
'Benfica' ♀H2	CSpe
bifidum	see *Rhodophiala bifida*
'Black Beauty'	LAma
'Blossom Peacock' (d)	LAma
'Bolero'	LAma
'Charisma' ♀H2	SDeJ
'Chico' ♀H2	LAma
'Christmas Gift'	LAma
'Dancing Queen'	LAma
'Double Record' (d)	SDeJ
'Emerald'	LAma
'Fairytale'	SDeJ
'Ferrari'	LAma
'Flaming Peacock'	LAma
gracile 'Pamela'	LAma
'Grandeur'	LAma
'Green Goddess'	LAma
'Inca'	LAma
× ***johnsonii*** hort. ♀H2	CExl WCot
'La Paz'	LAma
'Lady Jane'	SDeJ
'Lemon Lime'	LAma
'Liberty'	SDeJ
'Lima'	LAma
'Misty'	LAma
'Mont Blanc'	SDeJ
'Mrs Garfield'	LAma
'Naughty Lady'	LAma
papilio ♀H1c	LAma MMHG SDeJ
'Picotee'	LAma SDeJ
'Pink Floyd'	LAma
puniceum	LAma
'Red Lion' ♀H2	LAma
'Red Peacock' (d)	LAma SDeJ
'Rembrandt van Rijn'	LAma
'Rilona'	LAma SDeJ
'Rosario'	LAma
'Royal Velvet'	LAma
'Ruby Meyer'	LAma
'San Antonio Rose'	WCot
'Santiago'	LAma
striatum	WCot
'Sweet Surrender'	LAma
'Toughie'	CTal EBee LLHF
vittatum	LAma
'White Dazzler'	LAma
yungacense 'Kiara'	XTur

Hippocrepis (*Papilionaceae*)

§ ***comosa***	EDAr SPhx SSpi
§ ***emerus***	CBcs CCCN CExl CMHG ELan EPfP MGil MGos MMuc NLar SEND SVen WSHC

Hippophae (*Elaeagnaceae*)

rhamnoides	CArn CBcs CCVT CDul CHab CLnd CMac CSpe CTri CUse ECrN EHoe ELan EPfP EPom LBuc LEdu LRHS MBlu MCoo MMuc NHed NWea SCob SEND SEWo SGol SPlb
- (m)	EPom
- 'Askola' (f)	CAgr
- 'Dorana' (f)	CAgr CUse
- 'Frugna' (f)	CAgr NLar
- 'Hergo' (f)	CAgr MCoo NLar
- 'Hikul' (m)	CAgr CUse NLar
- 'Juliet' (f)	CAgr
- 'Leikora' (f) ♀H7	CAgr ELan IVic MBlu MCoo MGos NLar SPer
- 'Orange Energy' (f/F)	CAgr CUse EPfP MCoo NSoo
- 'Pollmix' (m) ♀H7	CAgr ELan EPfP IVic MBlu MCoo MGos NLar NSoo SPer
- 'Pollmix 3' (m)	MCoo
- 'Sirola' (f)	CAgr MCoo
salicifolia	CAgr
- GWJ 9221	WCru

Hippuris (*Plantaginaceae*)

vulgaris	CBAq CBen CWat EHon EWay MSKA NPer WMAq XLum

Hirpicium (*Asteraceae*)

armerioides	SPlb

Hohenbergia (*Bromeliaceae*)

correia-araujii new	LAir

Hoheria ✿ (*Malvaceae*)

'Ace of Spades'	CAbb CMHG EBee EPfP EWTr LRHS SKHP SPer SWvt WPGP
§ ***angustifolia***	ECou EPfP SVen WPGP
angustifolia* × *sexstylosa	WPGP
'Borde Hill'	CAbb CDul CJun CMHG CMac CTho EBee ECou EPfP EWoo IVic LRHS MAsh SKHP SLim SPer SSpi SWvt WPGP
'County Park'	ECou
glabrata	CMac ECou EPfP GGGa GGal IDee NBir SKHP WPGP
'Glory of Amlwch' ♀H4	CAbb CBcs CDoC CDul CJun CSam CTho ECou ELan EPfP GGGa GQui LRHS SChF SEND SKHP SPer SSpi SWvt WPGP
'Hill House'	CHll

§ ***lyallii*** ♀H4	CCCN CDoC CDul CExl CTho ECou ELan GCra IDee LRHS SPer SSpi SVen
- 'Chalk Hills'	ECou
- 'Swale Stream'	ECou
microphylla	see *H. angustifolia*
populnea	CBcs CCCN CTsd
- 'Alba Variegata' (v) ♀H3	ECou
- 'Holbrook'	CSam
- 'Moonlight'	CHGN
- 'Purple Shadow'	ECou
- 'Variegata' (v)	ECou
'Purple Delta'	ECou
sexstylosa	CAbb CDul CHEx CHid CMHG CTho CTri ECou ELan EPfP ETwe LRHS MGos NEgg SDix SKHP SPer SVen SWvt
- 'Crataegifolia'	CAbb CHel EBee EWTr NLar NSoo
- 'Pendula'	CBcs CMac
- 'Stardust' ♀H4	Widely available

Holboellia (*Lardizabalaceae*)

angustifolia	NLar WCru
- HWJK 2419 **new**	WCru
- subsp. ***linearifolia*** BWJ 8004	WCru
- subsp. ***obtusa*** DJHC 506	WCru
brachyandra HWJ 1023	WCru
aff. ***chapaensis*** B&SWJ 7250	WCru
coriacea	CBcs CCCN CHEx CHll CRHN CSPN CSde ELan EPfP EShb LRHS MGos MRav NLar SArc SEND SKHP SPer WCFE WCru
- B&SWJ 2818	WCru
fargesii	LRHS SKHP WCot WCru
latifolia	CBcs CCCN CHll CMac CTri EBee ELan EPfP GCal LEdu LRHS NLar SAdn SEND SEle SHil SKHP SLim SPer SPoG SWvt WBor WCot WCru WPGP
- HWJCM 008	WCru
- HWJK 2014	WCru
- SF 95134	EPfP
- dark-flowered HWJK 2213	WCru
- pale-flowered HWJK 2213C **new**	WCru

Holcus (*Poaceae*)

lanatus	WSFF
mollis 'Albovariegatus' (v)	CWCL ECha EHoe ELan EPPr EPfP GMaP LBMP MWhi NBid NBro NPer NSti SPlb SRms WCot WWEG XLum
- 'Jackdaw's Cream' (v)	EPPr
- 'White Fog' (v)	CBod EAJP EBee EPPr MMuc NWad

Holmskioldia (*Lamiaceae*)

* ***lutea***	CCCN
sanguinea	CCCN

Holodiscus (*Rosaceae*)

discolor	CBcs CDul CWld ELan EPfP EWes GCal IDee LEdu LRHS MBlu MBri MMuc MRav NLar SCoo SHil SKHP SLon SMad SPer SPlb SSpi WBor
- var. ***ariifolius***	CDul

Homalocladium (*Polygonaceae*)

§ ***platycladum***	EShb LEdu

Homeria (*Iridaceae*)

breyniana var. ***aurantiaca***	see *Moraea collina*

Homoglossum see *Gladiolus*

Hordeum (*Poaceae*)

chilense	EBee
jubatum	CKno CSpe CWCL EAJP EHoe EWes MSCN MWhi NChi NGdn SEND SMrm SPhx
- 'Early Pink'	NDov
secalinum	CHab

Horminum (*Lamiaceae*)

pyrenaicum	ECho MMuc SEND SRms WMoo WPtf
- dark-flowered	ECho GCal
- 'Roseum'	EBee

Hornungia (*Brassicaceae*)

alpina	XLum

horseradish see *Armoracia rusticana*

Hosta ✿ (*Asparagaceae*)

AGSJ 302	CDes WCot WPGP
'A Many-Splendored Thing'	EMic IBal NSue
'Abba Dabba Do' (v)	ECtt ELon EMic EPla IBal LBuc LPla NEgg NPCo NSue
'Abba Showtime'	IBal
'Abby' (v)	EMic IBal WWEG
'Abiqua Ariel'	EMic
'Abiqua Blue Crinkles'	EMic IBal NBir
'Abiqua Blue Edger'	EMic IBal
'Abiqua Drinking Gourd' ♀H7	EMic GMaP IBal IFoB MHom NMyG NPCo NSue WWEG
'Abiqua Elephant Ears'	IBal
'Abiqua Ground Cover'	IBal
'Abiqua Moonbeam' (v)	CCon EMic IBal MSwo NGdn
'Abiqua Recluse'	EMic IBal
'Abiqua Trumpet'	EMic IBal NGdn NLar NNor
'Abraham Lincoln'	IBal
'Ada Reed'	IBal
'Adorable'	IBal
aequinoctiiantha	IBal
'Aksarben'	EMic
'Alakazaam' (v)	EMic IBal NSue
'Alan Titchmarsh'	IBal
albomarginata	see *H.* 'Paxton's Original' (*sieboldii*)
§ 'Albomarginata' (*fortunei*) (v)	CBcs CMac GKev IFoB LRHS MNrw NBir NGdn SPoG SWvt
'Alex Summers'	EMic IBal NMyG WFar
'All That Jazz' (v)	EMic IBal
'Allan P. McConnell' (v)	EMic GCra IBal LRHS MHom NSue WHal WWEG
'Allegan Emperor' (v)	IBal
'Allegan Fog' (v) ♀H7	EMic IBal IFoB LRHS NSue
'Alligator Shoes' (v) ♀H7	EMic IBal
'Alpine Aire'	EMic IBal
'Alpine Dream'	IBal
'Alvatine Taylor' (v)	EMic IBal LAst NGdn NSue
'Amanuma'	EMic IBal MHom
'Amazing Grace' (v)	EMic IBal
'Amber Tiara'	EMic IBal
'American Dream' (v)	EMic EPla IBal LRHS
'American Gothic' (v)	IBal

'American Great Expectations' (v)	IFoB
'American Halo'	EMic IBal NLar NPCo NSti
'American Hero' (v)	EMic
'American Icon'	EMic IBal
'American Sweetheart'[PBR]	EMic IBal
'Americana' (v)	EMic IBal
'Amethyst Gem'	IBal
'Amy Elizabeth' (v)	EMic IBal
'Andorian'	IBal NSue
'Andrew' **new**	NSue
'Angel Feathers' (v)	IBal
'Anglo Saxon' (v)	IBal
'Ann Kulpa' (v)	EMic IBal NGdn
'Annabel Lee' **new**	IBal
'Anne' (v)	IBal LRHS NSue
'Ansly' (v)	IBal
'Antioch' (*fortunei*) (v)	EMic EPla GLog IBal MRav NLar NSue
'Aoba Tsugaru'	IBal
'Aoki' (*fortunei*)	EMic IBal
'Aphrodite' (*plantaginea*) (d)	EPfP GAbr IBal LSou MBNS NGdn NLar WCot WWEG
'Apollo'	NNor
'Apple Green'	EMic GKev IBal
'Apple Pie'	IBal
'Aqua Velva'	IBal
'Arc de Triomphe'	EMic IBal
'Arctic Blast'	EMic IBal
'Argentea Variegata' (*undulata*)	see *H. undulata* var. *undulata*
'Aristocrat' (Tardiana Group) (v)	EBee EMic IBal LRHS MBri NGdn NPCo NSue WFar
'Asian Pearl' (v)	IBal
'Aspen Gold' (*tokudama* hybrid)	EMic
'Astral Bliss' **new**	IBal
'Atlantis'[PBR] (v) ♀H7	EMic IBal NGdn NSue
'Atomic Elvis' **new**	IBal
'August Beauty'	EMic IBal
'August Moon'	Widely available
'Aureafolia'	see *H.* 'Starker Yellow Leaf'
'Aureoalba' (*fortunei*)	see *H.* 'Spinners'
'Aureomaculata' (*fortunei*)	see *H. fortunei* var. *albopicta*
'Aureomarginata' ambig. (v)	SCoo
'Aureomarginata' (*montana*) (v) ♀H7	CMac EHoe ELan EMic GCal GMaP IBal MMuc NEgg NGdn NLar WFar
'Aureomarginata' (*rohdeifolia*) (v)	EMic
§ 'Aureomarginata' (*ventricosa*) (v) ♀H7	EMic IBal MWat NGdn WFar
'Aureostriata' (*tardiva*)	see *H.* 'Inaho'
'Austin Dickinson' (v)	ECtt EMic IBal LBuc LRHS NEgg
'Autumn Frost' (v) **new**	IBal
'Avalanche'	IBal
'Avocado'	ELon EMic EWTr IBal NSue
'Azure Snow'	IBal
'Azuretini'	IBal
'Babbling Brook'	IBal
'Baby Blue' (Tardiana Group)	EMic
'Baby Blue Eyes'	IBal NSue
'Baby Bunting' ♀H7	EMic IBal IFoB NBro NEoE NLar NNor NSue
'Baby Doll' (v)	IBal
'Bailey's Cream' (v)	IBal
'Bali-Hai'	IBal
'Ballerina'	IBal NSue
'Banana Muffins'	IBal
'Band of Gold'	EMic IBal
'Banyai's Dancing Girl'	EMic IBal
'Barbara Ann' (v) ♀H7	EBee EMic IBal MHom NGdn NMyG WWEG
'Barbara May'	IBal
'Barbara White'	IBal
'Barney Fife'	IBal
'Battle Star' (v)	EMic IBal
'Beach Boy' (v) **new**	IBal NSue
'Bea's Colossus'	IBal
'Beauty Little Blue'	IBal NSue
'Beauty Substance'	EMic IBal NNor
'Beckoning'	IBal NSue
'Bedazzled' (v) **new**	IBal
'Bedford Blue'	EMic IBal
'Bedford Rise and Shine' (v)	EMic EPla IBal
'Bedford Wakey-Wakey'	IBal
'Behemoth' **new**	IBal
'Bell Bottom Blues'	IBal
bella	see *H. crassifolia*
'Bells of Edinburgh'	IBal
'Bennie McRae'	IBal
'Best of Twenty' **new**	IBal
'Betcher's Blue'	EMic IBal
'Betsy King'	CMac MRav
'Bette Davis Eyes'	IBal
'Betty'	IBal
'Biddy's Blue'	IBal
'Big Boy' (*montana*)	IBal LRHS NSue
'Big Daddy' (*sieboldiana* hybrid) (v) ♀H7	Widely available
'Big John' (*sieboldiana*)	IBal
'Big Mama'	EMic IBal MBNS MNrw NGdn NLar NSue
'Big Top'	IBal
'Bigfoot'	IBal
'Biggie'	IBal
'Bill Brinka' (v)	EMic LRHS
'Birchwood Blue Beauty'	IBal
'Birchwood Gem'	IBal
§ 'Birchwood Parky's Gold'	EBee ECtt EMic EPfP GMaP IBal LBMP MBNS NGdn NHol NNor SCob
'Birchwood Ruffled Queen'	EMic IBal
'Bitsy Gold'	EMic
'Bix Blues'	IBal
'Bizarre'	EMic IBal
'Black Beauty'	IBal
'Black Hills'	EMic IBal
'Black Pearl'	IBal
'Blackfoot'	EMic IBal
'Blackjack' (*sieboldiana*)	IBal WFar
'Blaue Venus'	IBal
'Blaze of Glory'	IBal
'Blazing Saddles' (v)	EMic IBal MBNS
'Blonde Elf'	EMic IBal MPnt NEgg NGdn NHol NNor WWEG
'Blue Angel' misapplied	see *H. sieboldiana* var. *elegans*
'Blue Angel' (*sieboldiana*) ♀H7	Widely available
'Blue Arrow' ♀H7	EPla IBal LRHS NNor NSue
'Blue Baron'	EMic IBal
'Blue Beard'	IBal
'Blue Belle' (Tardiana Group)	EMic IBal NEoE NGdn WWEG
'Blue Blush' (Tardiana Group)	EMic IBal NGdn

'Blue Boy'	EMic EWes IBal NNor
'Blue Cadet'	CMac COtt EBee EHoe EMic EPla EShb GQue IBoy IFoB LRHS MLHP MWhi NBir NGdn NLar NSue NWad SMrm SPoG WFar WMnd WWEG
'Blue Canoe'	EMic IBal
'Blue Cascade'	EMic IBal
'Blue Chip'	EMic IBal
'Blue Circle'[PBR]	IBal
'Blue Clown'	IBal
'Blue Cup' (*sieboldiana*)	EMic MRav SRms
'Blue Danube' (Tardiana Group)	EMic IBal MHom NPCo
'Blue Diamond' (Tardiana Group)	EMic LRHS NNor WFar WWEG
'Blue Dimples' (Tardiana Group)	ECtt EMic IBal
'Blue Dolphin' **new**	IBal
'Blue Edger'	EMic IBal NBir
'Blue Eyes'	NSue
'Blue Flame'	EMic IBal
'Blue Frost'	IBal
'Blue Haired Lady'	IBal
'Blue Hawaii'	EMic IBal
'Blue Heart' (*sieboldiana*)	ECha EMic IBal
'Blue Impression'	EMic
'Blue Ivory' (v)	CBcs EBee ECtt IBal LRHS MAsh NSue SGol
'Blue Jay' (Tardiana Group)	EMic
'Blue Lady'	EMic IBal
'Blue Lollipop'	NSue
'Blue Mammoth' (*sieboldiana*)	EMic IBal NPCo NSue WWEG
'Blue Maui'	EMic IBal
'Blue Monday'	EMic IBal
'Blue Moon' (Tardiana Group)	EMic GKev IBal MJak NGdn NLar NNor
'Blue Mountains'	IBal LBuc
'Blue Mouse Ears' ♀H7	CBod ECha ECtt EMic EPfP GBin GEdr IBal IBoy LLWG LRHS MBNS MBri MHom MPnt NBro NGdn NHar NHol NLar NMyG NNor NSla NSue SPoG WCot WFar WPtf WWEG
'Blue River' (v)	EMic IBal
'Blue Seer' (*sieboldiana*)	EMic
'Blue Shadows' (*tokudama*) (v)	EMic ESwi IBal NLar WFar
'Blue Skies' (Tardiana Group)	IBal MHom
'Blue Splendor' (Tardiana Group)	IBal
'Blue Umbrellas' (*sieboldiana* hybrid)	ELan EMic EPfP GMaP IBal LRHS MHom NGdn NLar NNor
'Blue Vision'	EMic IBal MWhi
'Blue Wedgwood' (Tardiana Group)	ELan EMic GQue IBal LRHS MGos NGdn WWEG
'Blue Wonder'	IBal
'Blue Wu' **new**	IBal
'Blueberry à la Mode'	EMic IBal
'Blueberry Cobbler' **new**	IBal
'Blueberry Muffin'	EMic NSue
'Blueberry Tart'	IBal
'Bluetooth'	IBal
'Bob Deane' (v)	EMic IBal
'Bob Olson' (v)	IBal
'Bobbie Sue' (v)	IBal
'Bobcat' **new**	IBal
'Bogie and Bacall' (v)	IBal
'Bold Edger' (v)	EMic IBal
'Bold Intrigue' (v)	IBal
'Bold Ribbons' (v)	EMic GAbr
'Bolt out of the Blue'	EMic
'Bonanza'	EMic
'Boracay' **new**	IBal
'Border Bandit' (v)	IBal
'Border Favorite'	EMic
§ 'Borwick Beauty' (*sieboldiana*) (v)	ELon EMic IBal LSou NGdn SPer WWEG
'Bottom Line' (v)	IBal
'Bountiful'	EMic IBal
'Boyz Toy'	EMic IBal NSue
'Brandywine'	IBal
'Brave Amherst' (v)	IBal
'Brenda's Beauty' (v)	EMic IBal NMyG
'Bressingham Blue'	CAby EBee ECtt EMic GQue IBal LRHS MRav NNor SPer SWvt WFar WMnd
'Bridal Veil'	EMic IBal
'Bridegroom'	EMic IBal
'Bridgeville'	IBal
'Brigham Blue'	IBal
'Bright Glow' (Tardiana Group)	EMic IBal
'Bright Lights' (*tokudama*) (v)	EMic IBal NGdn WFar
'Brim Cup' (v)	CAby CBod EBee ECtt ELon GAbr GBuc IBal LAst LSou MBNS NBro NGdn NMyG NNor NOrc NSir SMrm SPer WWEG
'Brooke'	EMic IBal NMyG WWEG
'Brother Ronald' (Tardiana Group)	EMic IBal NPCo
'Brother Stefan'	EMic IBal
'Brutus'	IBal
'Bubba'	IBal
'Buckshaw Blue'	IBal NBir NEoE NGdn WHrl
'Bulletproof'	IBal
'Bunchoko'	IBal NNor
'Burke's Dwarf'	IBal
'Cadillac' (v)	EMic
* 'Caerula' (*ventricosa*)	IFoB
'Cally Atom'	GCal IBal
'Cally Colossus'	GCal IBal
I 'Cally Strain' (*nigrescens*)	MHer
'Cally White' (*nigrescens*)	GCal
'Calypso' (v)	EMic EPla IBal WWEG
'Camelot' (Tardiana Group)	IBal LRHS NGdn
'Cameo'	EMic NSue
'Camouflage'	EMic IBal
'Canadian Blue'	EMic IBal MWhi
'Candy Dish'	IBal NSue
'Candy Hearts'	CSam EMic IBal MHom NNor
capitata	NNor
- B&SWJ 588	WCru
'Captain Kirk' (v) ♀H7	EMic IBal NGdn NMyG NSue
'Captain's Adventure' (v)	EMic NGdn NSue WFar
caput-avis	see *H. kikutii* var. *caput-avis*
'Carder Blue'	EMic
'Carnival' (v)	EMic IBal IFoB LRHS NEgg NGdn NPCo
'Carol' (*fortunei*) (v)	EMic IBal MBel NEgg NGdn NLar NMyG NNor
'Carolina Blue'	IBal
'Carousel' (v)	IBal

'Cascades' (v)	EMic IBal NGdn
'Cathedral Windows' (v) ♀H7	EMic IBal NSue
'Catherine'	ELon IBal NSue WFar
'Cat's Eyes' (*venusta*) (v)	EMic IBal NNor NSue
'Cavalcade' (v)	EMic
'Celebration' (v)	ELan EMic IBal WWEG
'Celestial'	IBal
'Celtic Dancer'	EMic IBal
'Celtic Uplands'	EMic
'Center of Attention'	EMic IBal NGdn
'Centerfold' **new**	NSue
'Cha Cha Cha'	IBal
'Chain Lightning' (v)	EMic IBal
'Challenger'	EMic
'Chameleon' (v)	EMic
'Change of Tradition' (*lancifolia*) (v)	EMic
'Chantilly Lace' (v)	EMic EPla WWEG
'Chariots of Fire' (v)	IBal
'Chartreuse Waves'	IBal
'Chartreuse Wiggles' (*sieboldii*)	IBal NSue
'Cheatin' Heart'	EMic IBal NMyG NSue WWEG
'Chelsea Babe' (*fortunei*) (v)	IBal
'Cherish' ♀H7	IBal NGdn NSue
'Cherry Berry' (v)	CBod CWGN EMic EPfP GBin IBal IFoB LRHS MBNS MHol MNrw MPie NBro NEgg NEoE NGdn NLar NPCo NWad SCob SHar SPoG WFar WWEG
'Cherry Tart'	EMic IBal NSue
'Cherub' (v)	EMic IBal LRHS
'Chesapeake Bay'	EMic IBal NSue
'Chesterland Gold'	IBal
'Childhood Sweetheart' (v) **new**	IBal
'China Girl'	EMic
'Chinese Gold'	IBal
'Chinese Sunrise' (v) ♀H7	CWCL EMic EPla GBin IBal MHom NNor SRms
'Chiquita'	IBal
'Chi-town Classic' (v)	IBal
'Chodai Ginba'	IBal
§ 'Chōkō-nishiki' (*montana*) (v)	EMic IBal LRHS NGdn NNor
'Choo Choo Train'	EMic
'Chopsticks'	EMic
'Christmas Candy'PBR	EMic EPla GAbr IBal LRHS MBri
'Christmas Charm' (v) **new**	IBal
'Christmas Cookies'	IBal
'Christmas Pageant' (v)	EMic IBal
'Christmas Song' (v) **new**	EWTr
'Christmas Tree' (v) ♀H7	CBod EBee EMic EPla IBal IFoB LPla LRHS NEgg NGdn NPCo NSue WMoo WWEG
'Cinderella'	EMic IBal
'Cinnamon Sticks'	IBal
'Citation' (v)	IBal
'City Lights'	ECtt EMic NEgg
'City Slicker' (v)	IBal
'Claudia'	IBal
clausa	EMic
- var. ***normalis***	GQui IBal NBir NGdn NLar
'Clear Fork River Valley'	EMic IBal
'Clifford's Forest Fire'	ECtt EMic IBal LRHS NLar WFar
'Clifford's Stingray' (v)	EMic IBal NSue
'Climax' (v) ♀H7	EMic IBal IBoy NSue
'Cloudburst'	EMic IBal
'Clovelly'	EMic IBal
'Clown's Collar' (v)	EMic IBal
'Coal Miner'	EMic IBal
'Coconut Custard'	EMic NSue
'Cody'	IBal
'Cold Heart'	EMic IBal
'Collector's Banner'	IBal
'Collector's Choice'	IBal
'Color Festival' (v)	EMic IBal NSue
'Color Glory'	see *H.* 'Borwick Beauty'
'Colossal'	EMic IBal
'Columbus Circle' (v)	EMic IBal
'Con Te Partiro' (v) **new**	NSue
'Confused Angel' (v)	IBal
'Cookie Crumbs' (v)	EMic EPla IBal NSue
'Cool Hand Luke' (*tokudama*) (v)	IBal
'Coquette' (v)	EMic GAbr IBal
'Corkscrew'	EMic NSue
'Corn Belt' (v)	EMic IBal
'Corn Muffins'	EMic
'Cotillion' (v)	EMic IBal NSue
'Count Your Blessings' (v)	EMic IBal
'Country Mouse' (v)	EMic IBal NSue
'County Park'	EMic IBal
'Cowrie' (v)	IBal
'Cracker Crumbs' (v) ♀H7	EMic GEdr GKev IBal MHom NHar NMyG NNor NSla NSue WWEG
'Craig's Temptation'	IBal
'Cranberry Wine' **new**	IBal
§ ***crassifolia***	EMic LRHS XLum
'Cream Cheese' (v)	IBal
'Cream Delight' (*undulata*)	see *H. undulata* var. *undulata*
'Crepe Soul' (v)	IBal
'Crepe Suzette' (v)	IBal NNor
'Crested Reef'	EMic
'Crested Surf' (v)	EMic EPla IBal
'Crinoline Petticoats'	IBal
§ ***crispula*** (v)	EMic EPfP IBal MCot MHom MRav NChi
'Crown Prince' (v)	IBal NGdn
'Crown Royalty'	EMic
§ 'Crowned Imperial' (*fortunei*) (v)	EMic
'Crumples' (*sieboldiana*)	IBal
'Crusader' (v) ♀H7	ELon EMic IBal LRHS WFar WWEG
'Crystal Chimes'	IBal
'Crystal Dixie'	EMic IBal NSue
'Cumulonimbus'	IBal
'Curlew' (Tardiana Group)	IBal
'Curls'	EMic IBal
'Curly Fries'	EMic
'Curtain Call'	IBal
'Cutting Edge'	EMic IBal
'Cuyahoga' (v)	IBal
'Dab a Green'	IBal
'Daisy Doolittle' (v)	EMic IBal
'Dance with Me' (v)	EMic IBal
'Dancing in the Rain' (v)	CWGN EMic EPla LLWG MBri NBro NSue WFar
'Dancing Mouse' (v)	IBal NSue
'Dancing Queen'	IBal
'Dark Shadows'	EBee EMic NGdn NSti WFar
'Dark Star' (v)	EMic EPla IBal NGdn NSue
'Dawn'	EMic IBal
'Dawn's Early Light'	EMic IBal
'Dax'	IBal
'Daybreak' ♀H7	EMic IBal MBri NBro

'Day's End' (v)	EMic IBal
'Deane's Dream'	EMic IBal NSue
decorata	EMic
'Deep Blue Sea' 🏆[H7]	EMic IBal
'Deep Pockets'	IBal
'Dee's Golden Jewel'	EMic
'Déjà Blu' (v)	EMic IBal
'Deliverance'	IBal NSue
'Delta Dawn' (v)	EMic IBal NGdn
'Delta Desire'	IBal
'Desert Mouse'[PBR] (v)	IBal NSue
'Designer Genes'	EMic IBal NSue
'Devon Blue' (Tardiana Group)	IBal NNor
'Devon Desire' (*montana*)	IBal NLar
'Devon Discovery'	IBal
'Devon Giant'	EMic NNor
'Devon Gold'	EMic GAbr IBal
'Devon Green' 🏆[H7]	CRos EAEE ELan EMic EWoo GBin IBal IPot LRHS MBel MHom MMuc NBro NEgg NEoE NGdn NLar NMyG NPCo NRya NSue SEND WAul WFar WHal WHoo WWEG
'Devon Mist'	IBal NNor
'Devon Tor'	IBal
'Dew Drop' (v)	EMic WWEG
'Dewed Steel'	IBal
'Diamond Tiara' (v)	EMic EPla IBal LRHS NBir NGdn WWEG WWtn
'Diana Remembered'	EMic IBal NGdn
'Dick Ward'	EMic IBal
'Dilithium Crystal'	IBal NSue
'Dillie Perkeo'	IBal
'Dilys'	EMic MNrw
'Dimple'	EMic
'Dinky Donna' (v)	EMic IBal NSue
'Dinner Jacket'	ELan IBal LRHS
'Dixie Chick' (v)	EMic IBal NNor NSue
'Dixie Chickadee' (v)	EMic
'Dixieland Heat'	IBal
'Doctor Fu Manchu'	IBal
'Domaine de Courson'	EMic EPla IBal NSue WFar
'Don Stevens' (v)	IBal
'Dorothy'	EMic
'Dorset Blue' (Tardiana Group)	EMic IBal LRHS
'Dorset Charm' (Tardiana Group)	EMic EPla
'Dorset Flair' (Tardiana Group)	EMic IBal
'Doubled Up'	IBal
'Doubloons'	EMic NMyG
'Dragon Tails' 🏆[H7]	EMic IBal NHar NMyG NSue
'Dragon Warrior' (v) **new**	IBal
'Dream Queen' (v)	ECtt EMic IBal SPoG
'Dream Weaver' (v) 🏆[H7]	ELon EMic IBal IFoB IPot LRHS MHom MNrw NBro NGdn NPCo NSue SPer WFar WWEG
'Dress Blues'	CMac EMic IBal
'Drummer Boy'	EMic IBal WWEG
'Duke of Cornwall' (v)	IBal
'DuPage Delight' (*sieboldiana*) (v)	EMic IBal NGdn NLar
'Dust Devil' (*fortunei*) (v)	IBal
'Dusty Waters' **new**	IBal
'Early Times' **new**	IBal
'Earth Angel'[PBR] (v) 🏆[H7]	EMic IBal NGdn NSue
'Ebony Towers'	EMic

'Edge of Night'	EMic IBal
'Edwin Bibby'	EMic
'El Capitan' (v)	EMic IBal IFoB LRHS
'El Niño'[PBR] (Tardiana Group) (v) 🏆[H7]	CWGN EMic IBal LRHS MHom MNrw NBro NGdn SPoG WFar WWEG
§ 'Elata'	EMic
'Elatior' (*nigrescens*)	EMic IBal
'Elbridge Gerry' (v)	IBal
'Eldorado'	see *H.* 'Frances Williams'
'Eleanor Lachman' (v)	EMic IBal
'Eleanor Roosevelt'	IBal
'Electrocution' (v)	NSue
'Elegans'	see *H. sieboldiana* var. *elegans*
'Elisabeth'	EMic IBal
'Elizabeth Campbell' (*fortunei*) (v)	EMic
'Elkheart Lake'	EMic IBal
'Ellen'	EMic
'Ellerbroek' (*fortunei*) (v)	EMic IBal
'Elsley Runner'	EPla IBal NSue WWEG
'Elvis Lives'	EMic EPla IBal NEgg NEoE NGdn NLar NMyG NNor NSue
'Emerald Carpet'	IBal
'Emerald Crown'	IBal
'Emerald Necklace' (v)	EMic IBal
'Emerald Ruff Cut'	EMic IBal
'Emerald Tiara' (v)	EMic IBal LRHS MLHP NLar SHil WWEG
'Emeralds and Rubies'	EMic IBal NSue
'Emily Dickinson' (v)	CBod EMic IBal LRHS NNor WWEG
'Empress Wu'[PBR]	CAby CUse EBee EMic ESwi EUJe GAbr GBin IBal IBoy ITim LSun MHol NGdn NSue SPoG WCot
'Encore'	IBal
'English Sunrise' (Tardiana Group)	IBal
'Enterprise' (v)	EBee EMic IBal NGdn NSue
'Eola Sapphire'	EMic IBal
'Eos'	NLar
'Eric Smith' (Tardiana Group)	EMic IBal MHom SHar WFar
'Eric Smith Gold'	GKev
'Eric's Gold'	IBal
'Erie Magic' (v)	IBal
'Eskimo Pie' (v)	EMic MBri NGdn NSue WFar
'Essence of Summer'	EMic EPfP IBal
'Eternal Flame'	EMic IBal
'Evelyn McCafferty' (*tokudama* hybrid)	IBal
'Eventide' (v)	IBal
'Everlasting Love' (v)	IBal
'Excitation'	EMic
'Exotic Presentation' (v)	EMic
'Extasy' (v)	EMic IBal NGdn NSue
'Eye Candy' (v)	IBal
'Eye Catcher'	EMic
'Eye Declare' (v)	IBal
'Faith'	EMic
'Faithful Heart' (v)	IBal NSue
'Fall Emerald'	EMic
'Fan Dance' (v)	EMic IBal
'Fantabulous' (v)	IBal
'Fantasy Island' (v)	EMic IBal
'Fat Boy'	IBal
'Fatal Attraction'	IBal
'Feather Boa'	EMic IBal IFoB LRHS NHar NSue WWEG

	Name	Suppliers
	'Fenman's Fascination'	EMic
	'Fiesta' (v)	IBal
	'Final Summation' (v)	EMic IBal NSue
	'Finlandia'	IBal
	'Fire and Ice' (v) 🏆H7	Widely available
	'Fire Island' 🏆H7	CMea EBee ECtt ELan EMic EPfP EPla GBin IBal LRHS MHom MNrw NGdn NSue SPoG
	'Fire Opal' (v) **new**	IBal
	'Fireworks' (v) 🏆H7	EMic EPfP GBin IBal LRHS MBNS MBri NBro NGdn NSue
	'First Frost' (v) 🏆H7	EBee EMic IBal LRHS MAsh MBri NGdn NMyG NSue WWEG
	'First Love' (*montana*)	EMic
	'First Mate' (v)	EMic IBal NSue
	'Five O'Clock Shadow' (v)	IBal
	'Five O'Clock Somewhere' (v)	IBal
	'Fleet Week'	EMic
	'Flemish Angel' (v)	IBal NSue
	'Flemish Gold'	IBal
	'Flemish Sky'	EMic IBal IFoB MBri NGdn
	'Floradora'	EMic IBal NSue
	'Flower Power'	IBal NNor
	'Fluted Fountain'	EMic
	'Fool's Gold' (*fortunei*)	EMic IBal
	'Forest Fireworks' (v)	IBal
	'Forest Shadows'	IBal
	'Formal Attire' (*sieboldiana* hybrid) (v) 🏆H7	EMic IBal LRHS
	'Forncett Frances' (v)	IBal
	'Fortis'	see *H. undulata* var. *erromena*
	fortunei	EMic NNor WFar
§	- var. ***albopicta*** (v)	CSam ECha EHoe ELan EMic EPfP EUJe GMaP IFoB LEdu LPot LRHS MRav NEgg NGdn NLar NMyG NNor SPer SRms WBrk WHoo WMnd WWEG
	- - f. ***aurea***	CMac ECha EHoe EMic MMuc NEgg NLar SEND SRms WFar WHal
	- - - dwarf	EMic
	- - f. ***viridis***	NNor
§	- var. ***aureomarginata*** (v) 🏆H7	CSam CTri ECha EHoe ELan ELon EMic EPfP EPla EShb GMaP IBal LBMP LPot LRHS MLHP MMuc MSwo NGdn NLar NNor SEND SPer SPlb SPoG WFar WMnd WWEG
	- var. ***gigantea***	see *H. montana*
	- var. ***hyacinthina***	EMic EPfP LRHS MRav NGdn NLar WFar XLum
	- - variegated	see *H.* 'Crowned Imperial'
	- var. ***rugosa***	EMic
	- var. ***stenantha***	EMic
	'Fountain of Youth' (*kikutii*)	IBal
	'Fourteen Carats'	EMic IBal
	'Fourth of July'	NSue
	'Fragrant Blue'	EMic IBal LRHS NBro NGdn NSue SPoG XLum
	'Fragrant Blue Ribbons' (v)	EMic
	'Fragrant Bouquet' (v) 🏆H7	ECtt ELan EMic IBal LAst LRHS NGdn NHol NLar NMyG NPCo NSue SEND WFar WWEG
	'Fragrant Dream'	EBee EMic IBal NLar WWEG
	'Fragrant Fire'	EMic IBal
	'Fragrant Gold'	EMic
	'Fragrant King'	IBal
	'Fragrant Queen' PBR (v)	EMic IBal NSue
	'Fragrant Star'	EMic IBal
	'Fragrant Surprise' (v)	IBal
	'Fran Godfrey'	EMic IBal NMyG
	'Francee' (*fortunei*) (v) 🏆H7	Widely available
§	'Frances Williams' (*sieboldiana*) (v) 🏆H7	Widely available
	'Frances Williams Improved' (*sieboldiana*) (v)	EPfP EPla GBuc IFoB MWat
	'Francheska' (v)	EMic IBal
	'Fresh' (v)	EMic IBal
	'Fried Bananas'	EMic IBal WWEG
	'Fried Green Tomatoes'	EMic IBal NLar NNor
	'Friends' (v)	EMic
	'Fringe Benefit' (v)	EMic GAbr WWEG
	'Frost Giant' (v)	IBal
	'Frosted Dimples'	EMic IBal
	'Frosted Frolic' (v)	EMic IBal
	'Frosted Jade' (v) 🏆H7	EBee EMic EPfP IBal MMuc NLar NPCo
	'Frosted June'	EMic IBal
	'Frosted Mouse Ears' PBR	EMic IBal MAsh NSue
	'Frozen Margarita'	EMic IBal
	'Frühlingsgold' (v)	IBal
	'Fruit Punch'	EMic IFoB
	'Fujibotan' (v)	EMic IBal IFoB
	'Fulda'	EMic IBal
	'Funky Monkey'	EMic
	'Funny Mouse' (v) **new**	IBal NSue
	'Gaiety' (v)	EMic IBal
	'Gaijin' (v)	IBal NSue
	'Garden Party' (v)	IBal
	'Garnet Prince'	IBal
	'Gay Blade' (v)	IBal
	'Gay Feather' (v)	EMic IFoB
	'Gay Search' (v)	EPla IBal
	'Geisha' (v)	IBal LBMP LRHS NEoE NGdn NNor NSue WWEG
	'Geisha Satin Ripples'	IBal
	'Gemini Moon' (v)	IBal
	'Gene's Joy'	IBal
	'Gentle Giant'	IBal
	'Gentle Spirit' (v)	IBal
	'George M. Dallas' (v)	IBal
	'George Smith' (*sieboldiana*)	EMic IBal
	'Ghost Spirit'	IBal NSue WFar
	'Ghostmaster' (v)	EMic IBal
	'Gig Harbor'	IBal
	'Gigantea' (*sieboldiana*)	see *H.* 'Elata'
	'Gilt by Association'	IBal
	'Gilt Edge' (*sieboldiana*) (v)	EMic WWEG
	'Gingee'	IBal
	'Ginko Craig' (v) 🏆H7	CMac ECha EHoe ELan EMic EPfP GKev GMaP IBal IFoB LRHS MRav MWhi NBir NGdn NLar NNor NPCo NSti SPer SPoG WFar WMnd
	'Ginrei'	IBal
	'Ginsu Knife' (v)	EMic IBal
	'Glad Rags' (v)	IBal
	'Glad Tidings'	IBal
	'Glamour'	EMic IBal
	'Glass Hearts'	EMic IBal
	glauca	see *H. sieboldiana* var. *elegans*
	'Glitter'	EMic IBal
	'Glockenspiel'	EMic IBal
I	'Gloriosa' (*fortunei*) (v)	IBal IFoB LRHS NSue WFar
	'Glory'	IBal
	'Glory Hallelujah'	EMic
	'Goblin'	EMic
	'Goddess of Athena' (*decorata*) (v)	IBal

'Gold Drop' (*venusta* hybrid)	EMic NHol WWEG
'Gold Edger'	CBcs CBod CMac EBee EHoe ELan EMic EPfP GCal GKev GMaP IBal LRHS MMuc MRav NBir NGdn NLar NNor NSti SEND WFar WWEG
'Gold Edger Surprise' (v)	EMic
'Gold Flush' (*ventricosa*)	EMic
§ 'Gold Haze' (*fortunei*)	EMic EPla IBal MHom NBir NMyG WWEG
'Gold Leaf' (*fortunei*)	IBal
'Gold Pressed Latinum'	IBal
'Gold Regal'	EBee EMic EPla GBin IBal IFoB MHom NMyG WFar WMnd
'Gold Rush'	NMyG
'Gold Standard' (*fortunei*) (v) ♀H7	Widely available
'Goldbrook' (v)	EMic IBal
'Goldbrook Galleon'	IBal
'Goldbrook Gaynor'	IBal
'Goldbrook Genie'	IBal
'Goldbrook Glamour' (v)	IBal
'Goldbrook Gleam' (v)	IBal
'Goldbrook Glimmer' (Tardiana Group) (v)	IBal LRHS
'Goldbrook Glory'	EMic IBal
'Goldbrook Gold'	IBal
'Goldbrook Good Gracious' (v)	IBal
'Goldbrook Gratis' (v)	IBal
'Goldbrook Grayling'	EMic IBal NSue
'Goldbrook Grebe'	IBal
'Goldbrook Greenheart'	IBal
'Golden Age'	see *H.* 'Gold Haze'
'Golden Fountain'	EMic
'Golden Gate'	IBal
'Golden Goal'	IBal
'Golden Guernsey' (v)	EMic
'Golden Isle'	EMic IBal
'Golden Meadows'[PBR] (*sieboldiana*)	ECtt EMic IBal NGdn NSue SGol SMrm WFar
'Golden Medallion' (*tokudama*)	ECtt EMic IBal LRHS NEgg NGdn WFar
'Golden Nakaiana'	see *H.* 'Birchwood Parky's Gold'
'Golden' (*nakaiana*)	see *H.* 'Birchwood Parky's Gold'
'Golden Oriole'	EMic IBal NNor WWEG
'Golden Prayers' (*tokudama*)	EBee ECtt EHoe ELan MRav NBir NBro NEgg NGdn NLar WFar WHal WSHC
'Golden Scepter'	CBod EMic EPla IBal LRHS NNor WFar
'Golden Sculpture' (*sieboldiana*)	EMic
'Golden Spades'	NSue
'Golden Spider'	EMic WWEG
'Golden Sunburst' (*sieboldiana*)	NEgg NGdn NLar WFar XLum
'Golden Tiara' (v) ♀H7	Widely available
'Golden Tusk'	IBal
'Golden Waffles'	EMic NEgg
'Gone Fishin'' (v)	IBal
'Goober'	IBal
'Good as Gold'	EMic IBal
'Goodness Gracious' (v) **new**	IBal
'Gorgeous George'	IBal
'Gosan Leather Strap'	IBal
'Gosan' (*takahashii*)	IBal
gracillima	IBal NRya WWEG
'Granary Gold' (*fortunei*)	MHom
'Grand Canyon'	EMic
'Grand Finale'	IBal
'Grand Marquee' (v)	EMic IBal NGdn NLar SGol WFar WWEG
'Grand Master'	IBal
'Grand Prize' (v)	IBal
'Grand Rapids'	EMic IBal
'Grand Slam'	EMic IBal
'Grand Tiara' (v)	EMic EPla IBal NGdn
'Grand Total'	IBal
'Grant Park'	IBal
'Grape Fizz'	IBal
'Gray Cole' (*sieboldiana*)	EMic IBal
'Great Arrival'	EMic IBal
'Great Escape'[PBR] (v)	EBee EMic IBal LLWG MAvo
'Great Expectations' (*sieboldiana*) (v)	CHid CMac CNor EMic EPfP GAbr IBal IBoy IFoB IVic LRHS MBNS MHer MNrw MWhi NBro NGdn NNor NSti SMrm SPoG WWEG
'Great Lakes Gold'	IBal
'Green Acres' (*montana*)	EMic IBal LEdu WFar
'Green Angel' (*sieboldiana*)	IBal
'Green Eyes' (*sieboldii*) (v)	EMic IBal NSue
'Green Fountain' (*kikutii*)	EMic IBal WWEG
'Green Gold' (*fortunei*) (v)	EMic
'Green Lama'	IBal
'Green Mouse Ears'	EMic IBal MAsh NMyG NSue
'Green Piecrust'	NNor
'Green Sheen'	EMic
'Green Velveteen'	IBal
'Green with Envy' (v) ♀H7	EMic IBal LLHF NNor NSue WWEG
'Greensleeves' (v)	IBal
'Grey Ghost'	EMic IBal
'Grey Goose' (Tardiana Group)	EMic
'Ground Master' (v)	CMac EBee ECtt ELan EPfP GCra GMaP IBal IFoB MRav NBro NGdn NLar NNor NSti WFar WMoo WWEG
'Ground Sulphur'	EMic IBal
'Grover Cleveland'	IBal
'Grünherz'	IBal
'Grunspecht' (Tardiana Group)	IBal
'Guacamole' (v) ♀H7	CAby CBcs ECha ECtt ELon EMic EPfP IBal LRHS NGdn NLar NNor SBod SPoG WWEG
'Guardian Angel' (*sieboldiana*) ♀H7	EMic IBal NLar NSue
'Gum Drop'	EMic NNor
'Gun Metal Blue'	IBal
'Gunther's Rim' (v) **new**	IBal
'Gypsy Rose' ♀H7	IBal NGdn NMyG NSue WFar
'Hacksaw'	EMic IBal NSue
'Hadspen Blue' (Tardiana Group) ♀H7	CSBt CWCL EBee ELan EMic EPfP GBin GMaP IBal IBoy LRHS MBrN MGos MRav NBir NBro NEgg NGdn NHol NNor NPCo SHil SPer SPoG WMnd WWEG
'Hadspen Hawk' (Tardiana Group)	IBal
'Hadspen Heron' (Tardiana Group)	EMic MHom MWat XLum
'Hadspen Honey' **new**	LRHS
'Hadspen Nymphaea'	IBal
'Hadspen Rainbow'	EMic IBal
'Hadspen Samphire'	EMic IBal LRHS MHom NBir NBro NMyG

Name	Suppliers
'Hadspen White' (*fortunei*)	EMic IBal NLar
'Haku-chu-han' (*sieboldii*) (v)	IBal
'Hakujima' (*sieboldii*)	IBal NSue
'Hakumuo' (v)	IBal
§ 'Halcyon' (Tardiana Group) ♀[H7]	Widely available
'Halcyon Gold'	SGol
'Half and Half'	EMic IBal
'Hampshire County' (v)	EMic IBal
'Hands Up' (v) **new**	IBal NSue
'Hanky Panky' (v)	EMic IBal LRHS NGdn NSti NSue WFar
'Hannibal Hamlin' (v)	IBal
'Happily Ever After' (v)	IBal
'Happiness' (Tardiana Group)	EHoe EMic IBal MHom MRav
'Happy Camper' (v)	IBal
'Happy Hearts'	EMic
'Happy Valley' (v)	IBal
'Harmony' (Tardiana Group)	EMic
'Harpoon' (v)	EMic
'Harriette Ward'	IBal
'Harry van de Laar'	EMic IBal
'Harry van Trier'	EMic GBin
'Hart's Tongue'	IBal
'Harvest Delight'	EMic
'Harvest Glow'	IBal
'Hawkeye' (v)	IBal
'Hazel'	EMic IBal
'Heart Ache'	IBal
'Heart and Soul' (v)	EMic IBal
'Heart Broken'	IBal
'Heart of Chan'	IBal
'Heart Throb'	EMic
'Heartbeat' (v)	IBal
'Heartleaf'	EMic
'Heart's Content' (v)	IBal
'Heartsong' (v)	EMic IBal LRHS NMyG
'Heat Wave'[PBR] (v)	EMic IBal
'Heavenly Beginnings' (v)	IBal
'Heavy Duty' **new**	IBal
'Heideturm'	EPla IBal
'Helen Doriot' (*sieboldiana*)	EMic
'Helen Field Fischer' (*fortunei*)	IBal NLar
helonioides f. ***albopicta*** misapplied	see *H. rohdeifolia*
'Herifu' (v)	EMic
'Hertha' (v)	EMic
'Hidden Cove' (v)	EPla IBal NSue
'Hidden Treasure' (v)	IBal
'Hideout' (v)	IBal
'High Kicker'	IBal
'High Society' (v)	CBcs ELan EMic EPfP IBal IFoB MHom MNrw NGdn NNor NSue
'Hi-ho Silver' (v)	EMic IBal NSue WWEG
'Hilda Wassman' (v)	IBal
'Hillbilly Blues' (v)	NSue
'Hippodrome' (v)	EMic IBal
'Hirao Elite'	EMic IBal
'Hirao Majesty'	IBal
'Hirao Supreme'	EMic IBal
'His Honor' (v)	EMic IBal
'Holly's Dazzler'	IBal
'Hollywood Lights' (v)	EMic EPfP IBal NGdn
'Holstein'	see *H.* (Tardiana Group) 'Halcyon'
'Holy Molé' (v)	EMic IBal
'Holy Mouse Ears'[PBR]	EMic IBal NSue
'Honey Moon'	IBal NNor
'Honeybells'	CBcs CMac CTri EBee ECha ELan EMic EPfP IBal LEdu MCot MRav NBid NGdn NNor NSti SPer WFar WWEG XLum
'Honeysong' (v)	EMic IBal NNor
'Hoosier Dome'	EMic
'Hoosier Harmony' (v)	EMic
'Hope' (v)	IBal
'Hotcakes'	IBal
'Hotspur' (v)	EMic
'Hush Puppie'	EMic IBal NSue
'Hyacintha Variegata' (*fortunei*) (v)	CMac NNor
'Hydon Gleam'	EMic IBal
'Hydon Sunset'	CNor EBee ECtt EMic EPla GCra GEdr IBal LRHS NBir NLar NNor NRya NSti NSue WHal WMnd WWEG
hypoleuca	EMic IBal
'Hyuga-urajiro' (v)	EMic IBal
'Ice Age Trail' (v)	IBal
'Ice Cream' (*cathayana*) (v)	IBal NGdn
'Ice Cube' (v) **new**	NSue
'Ice Prancer'	EMic
'Iced Lemon' (v)	EMic IBal NNor NSue
'Illicit Affair'	EMic IBal NSue
'Imp' (v)	EMic IBal
§ 'Inaho'	LRHS NSue
'Inca Gold'	IBal NSue
'Independence' (v)	EBee EMic EPla IBal MBri NBro NMyG NSue SPoG WFar
'Independence Day' (v)	EMic
'Inniswood' (v)	CWCL ECtt EMic IBal LRHS MBNS NBro NGdn NLar NSti WFar WMnd WWEG
'Invincible'	CBod ECtt EMic IBal LAst NBid NEgg NGdn NLar NMyG NNor WWEG
'Invincible Spirit'	IBal
'Iona' (*fortunei*)	EMic IBal NNor
'Irische See' (Tardiana Group)	IBal
'Irish Eyes' (v)	EMic IBal
'Irish Luck'	EMic NSue
'Iron Gate Delight' (v)	NNor
'Iron Gate Special' (v)	EMic
'Iron Gate Supreme' (v)	EMic
'Island Charm' (v) ♀[H7]	EMic IBal LRHS NHar NLar NMyG
'Ivory Coast' (v)	EMic IBal
'Ivory Necklace' (v)	IBal
'Iwa Yara Moto'	IBal
'Jack of Diamonds'	IBal
'Jade Cascade'	EMic GBin IBal NBir NEgg NLar WHal WWEG
'Jade Scepter' (*nakaiana*)	EMic
'Janet Day' (v)	EMic IBal
'Janet' (*fortunei*) (v)	EMic IBal NGdn NNor NPCo
'Jason and Katie' (v) **new**	IBal
'Jaws'	EMic IBal NSue
'Jaz'	IBal
'Jennifer Bailey' (v)	IBal
'Jerry Landwehr'	IBal
'Jewel of the Nile' (v)	EMic IBal
'Jim Mathews'	IBal
'Jimmy Crack Corn'	EMic IBal NGdn NPCo

	'Jingle Bells'	IBal
	'John Wargo'	IBal
	'Johnny Angel'	EMic
	'Joker' (*fortunei*) (v)	NNor
	'Jolly Green Giant' (*sieboldiana* hybrid)	EMic
	jonesii	EMic
	'Joseph'	IBal
	'Josephine' (v)	NNor
	'Journeyman'	EMic IBal
	'Journey's End' (v)	EMic IBal
	'Joyce Trott' (v)	EMic
	'Joyful' (v)	IBal
	'Jubilee' (v)	EMic IBal
	'Judy Rocco'	IBal
	'Juha' (v)	EMic
	'Jules'	IBal
	'Julia' (v)	EMic IBal
	'Julie Morss'	EMic GMaP IBal MHom NEgg WWEG
	'June'[PBR] (Tardiana Group) (v) ♀H7	Widely available
	'June Fever'[PBR] (Tardiana Group)	EMic ESwi IBal LLWG MBri NBro NGdn NLar NSue WFar
	'Jurassic Park'	EBee EMic GBin IBal LLWG MNrw NLar
	'Just June' (Tardiana Group) (v)	MAsh
	'Just So' (v)	EMic IBal
	'Justine'	EMic IBal NSue
	'Kabitan'	see *H. sieboldii* var. *sieboldii* f. *kabitan*
	'Kabuki'	IBal
	'Kalamazoo' (v)	EMic IBal
	'Kaleidochrome' (v)	IBal
	'Karin'	EMic IBal
	'Katherine Lewis' (Tardiana Group) (v)	ECtt EMic IBal LRHS NHol
	'Kath's Gold'	EMic
	'Katie Q' (v)	EMic IBal
	'Katsuragawa-beni' (v)	EMic IBal
	'Kelsey'	EMic
	'Kenzie' (v)	EMic
	'Key Lime Pie'	EMic IBal
	'Key West'	EMic
	'Kifukurin' (*kikutii*)	see *H.* 'Kifukurin-hyuga'
	'Kifukurin' (*venusta*) (v)	EMic
§	'Kifukurin-hyuga' (v)	IBal
	'Kifukurin-ko-mame' (*gracillima*) (v)	EMic NSue
	'Kifukurin-otome' (*venusta*) (v) **new**	NSue
	'Kifukurin-ubatake' (*pulchella*) (v)	EMic IBal
	kikutii	EMic IBal IMou LRHS
§	- var. ***caput-avis***	EMic
§	- var. ***yakusimensis***	IBal SMad
	'Ki-nakafu-otome' (*venusta*)	IBal
	'Kinbotan' (v)	EMic
	'Kinbuchi Tachi' (*rectifolia*) (v)	IBal
	'King James'	IBal
	'King of Spades'	IBal
	'King Tut'	EMic
	'Kingfisher' (Tardiana Group)	LRHS
§	'Kirishima'	EMic NSla NSue
	'Kisuji'	see *H.* 'Mediopicta'

	'Kitty Cat'	EMic IBal NSue
	'Kiwi Black Magic'	IBal
	'Kiwi Blue Baby'	EMic IBal
	'Kiwi Blue Ruffles'	IBal
	'Kiwi Blue Sky'	IBal
	'Kiwi Canoe'	IBal
	'Kiwi Cream Edge' (v)	EMic
	'Kiwi Forest'	IBal
	'Kiwi Full Monty' (v)	EBee EMic IBal LRHS MSCN NSue
	'Kiwi Gold Rush'	IBal
	'Kiwi Hippo'	IBal
	'Kiwi Jordan'	IBal
	'Kiwi Kaniere Gold'	IBal
	'Kiwi Minnie Gold'	IBal
	'Kiwi Parasol'	IBal
	'Kiwi Skyscraper'	IBal
	'Kiwi Sunshine'	IBal
	'Klopping Variegated' (v)	EMic
	'Knight's Journey'	IBal
	'Knockout' (v)	MBNS MNrw MRav NBro NEgg NGdn NLar NMyG NNor
	'Komodo Dragon'	EMic IBal SKHP
	'Konkubine'	EMic
	'Korean Snow'	IBal
I	'Koreana Variegated' (*undulata*)	EMic
	'Koriyama' (*sieboldiana*) (v)	EMic IBal
	'Krossa Cream Edge' (*sieboldii*) (v)	IBal
	'Krossa Regal' ♀H7	Widely available
	'Krugerrand'	IBal
	'La Donna'	IBal
	'Lacy Belle' (v)	CSBt EBee EMic EPfP IBal NBro NEoE NGdn NSue WRHF
	'Lady Godiva'	IBal
	'Lady Guineverre'	EMic IBal
	'Lady Helen'	EMic
	'Lady in Red'	IBal
	'Lady Isobel Barnett' (v) ♀H7	IBal
	laevigata	IBal NSue
	'Lake Hitchock'	IBal
	'Lake Huron'	IBal
	'Lake Superior' **new**	IBal
	'Lakeside Alex Andra' (v)	IBal
	'Lakeside April Snow' (v)	EMic IBal
	'Lakeside Baby Face' (v)	EMic IBal NSue
	'Lakeside Banana Bay' (v)	IBal
	'Lakeside Beach Bum' **new**	IBal NSue
	'Lakeside Beach Captain' (v)	EMic
	'Lakeside Black Satin'	EMic WFar
	'Lakeside Blue Cherub'	EMic IBal
	'Lakeside Breaking News' (v)	EMic IBal
	'Lakeside Butter Ball'	IBal
	'Lakeside Cha Cha' (v)	EMic IBal LRHS MWhi
	'Lakeside Cindy Cee' (v)	IBal
	'Lakeside Coal Miner'	EMic IBal NGdn
	'Lakeside Color Blue'	IBal
	'Lakeside Contender'	IBal
	'Lakeside Cupcake' (v)	EMic IBal LRHS
	'Lakeside Cupid's Cup' (v)	IBal
	'Lakeside Dividing Line' (v)	IBal
	'Lakeside Doodad' (v)	IBal
	'Lakeside Down Sized' (v)	EMic IBal NSue
	'Lakeside Dragonfly' (v)	EBee EMic EPfP IBal LLWG LRHS NMyG NSue WFar
	'Lakeside Elfin Fire'	EMic

'Lakeside Fancy Pants' (v)	IBal
'Lakeside Feather Light' (v)	IBal
'Lakeside Foaming Sea'	IBal
'Lakeside Full Tide'	IBal
'Lakeside Hazy Morn' (v)	IBal
'Lakeside Hoola Hoop' (v)	IBal
'Lakeside Iron Man'	IBal
'Lakeside Jazzy Jane' (v)	IBal
'Lakeside Kaleidoscope'	EMic IBal NGdn
'Lakeside Keepsake' (v)	IBal
'Lakeside Legal Tender'	IBal
'Lakeside Lime Time'	IBal
'Lakeside Little Gem'	IBal NSue
'Lakeside Little Tuft' (v)	EMic IBal MBri NMyG NSue
'Lakeside Lollipop'	EMic IBal
'Lakeside Looking Glass'	EMic
'Lakeside Love Affaire'	EMic IBal WFar
'Lakeside Maestro'	NLar
'Lakeside Maverick'	IBal
'Lakeside Meadow Ice' (v)	IBal
'Lakeside Meter Maid' (v)	IBal
'Lakeside Midnight Miss'	IBal
'Lakeside Miss Muffett' (v)	IBal
'Lakeside Missy Little' (v)	IBal
'Lakeside Neat Petite'	IBal NSue
'Lakeside Ninita' (v)	EMic EPla IBal LRHS NSue
'Lakeside Old Smokey'	IBal
'Lakeside Paisley Print' (v)	IBal NSue
'Lakeside Pebbles'	IBal
'Lakeside Premier'	EMic
'Lakeside Prophecy'	IBal
'Lakeside Prophecy Fulfilled' (v)	IBal
'Lakeside Rhapsody' (v)	EMic IBal
'Lakeside Ring Master' (v)	IBal
'Lakeside Ripples'	IBal
'Lakeside Rocky Top' (v)	IBal
'Lakeside Roy El' (v)	IBal
'Lakeside Sassy Sally'	IBal
'Lakeside Scamp' (v)	EMic NSue
'Lakeside Shadows' (v)	IBal
'Lakeside Shoremaster' (v)	IBal
'Lakeside Slick Chick' (v)	IBal
'Lakeside Sophistication' (v)	IBal
'Lakeside Sparkle Plenty' (v)	IBal
'Lakeside Spellbinder' (v)	IBal LRHS
'Lakeside Spruce Goose' (v)	EMic IBal
'Lakeside Storm Watch'	EMic IBal NSue
'Lakeside Symphony' (v)	EMic
'Lakeside Tee Ki' (v)	IBal
'Lakeside Whizzit' (v)	IBal
'Lakeside Zesty Zeno' (v)	IBal
'Lakeside Zinger' (v)	EMic IBal NSue
lancifolia	CMac EBee ELan EMic GMaP IBal MRav NGdn NSti SBod SRms WKif WSHC WThu
'Last Dance' (v)	IBal
'Laura Lanier'	EMic
'Laura Z'	IBal
'Lavender Doll'	IBal
'Leading Lady' ♀H7	IBal
'Leather Sheen'	EMic
'Leatherneck'	IBal
'Lederhosen'	EMic
'Lemon Delight'	EMic EPla IBal LRHS NNor NSue WWEG
'Lemon Frost'	EMic IBal
'Lemon Juice'	EBee NMyG
'Lemon Lime'	EMic IBal MHom MNrw NEoE NNor NPCo NSue WWEG
'Lemon Twist'	IBal
'Lemonade'	GBin IBal
'Leola Fraim' (v)	EMic IBal LRHS
'Let Me Entertain You'	EMic
'Leviathan'	EMic
'Lewis and Clark'	IBal
'Libby'	EMic IBal
'Liberty'PBR (v) ♀H7	CWGN EMic EPfP IBal LRHS MBri NBro NGdn NNor NSue WFar
'Li'l Abner' (v)	IBal
* ***lilacina***	WFar
'Lily Blue Eyes'	EMic
'Lime Fizz'	EMic IBal NSue
'Lime Shag' (*sieboldii* f. *spathulata*)	IBal NSue
'Limey Lisa'	EMic EPla IBal NSue WWEG
'Linda Sue' (v)	IBal
'Lionheart' (v)	EMic IBal
'Little Aurora' (*tokudama* hybrid)	EMic IBal NSue WFar WWEG
'Little Bit'	NSue
'Little Black Scape'	EMic IBal MHom NEgg NEoE NGdn NLar
'Little Blue' (*ventricosa*)	EMic
'Little Bo Beep' (v)	IBal NSue WWEG
'Little Boy'	IBal
'Little Caesar' (v)	EMic IBal NGdn NSue
'Little Devil'	EMic IBal NSue
'Little Doll' (v)	IBal
'Little Jay' (v)	EMic IBal NSue
'Little Maddie'	EMic NSue
'Little Miss Magic'	IBal
'Little Razor'	IBal
'Little Red Joy'	EMic EPla IBal NSue
'Little Red Rooster'	EMic IBal NGdn NMyG NNor NSue WFar WWEG
'Little Stiffy'	EMic NSue
'Little Sunspot' (v)	EMic IBal NHar NSue
'Little Treasure' (v)	EMic IBal NSue
'Little White Lines' (v)	EMic EPla GKev IBal NSue
'Little Willie' (v)	NSue
'Little Wonder' (v) ♀H7	EMic NSue WWEG
'Living Water'	EMic
'Lizard Lick'	IBal NSue
'Lollapalooza' (v)	IBal
'London Fog' (v)	IBal NSue
'Lonesome Dove' (v)	EMic
longipes B&SWJ 10806	WCru
longissima var. ***brevifolia*** **new**	NSue
'Lost World' **new**	IBal
'Lothar the Giant'	IBal
'Love Pat' ♀H7	CCon ECtt EMic EPfP GAbr IBal LRHS MRav NGdn NLar NNor NSue WCAu
'Loyalist'PBR (v)	EMic IBal NGdn NLar SPoG WFar WWEG
'Lucky Mouse'PBR (v)	IBal NSue
'Lucy Vitols' (v)	EMic IBal
'Lullabye'	EMic
'Lunar Eclipse' (v)	CHid EMic NEgg WWEG
'Machete'	IBal
'Mack the Knife'	EMic IBal
'Maekawa'	EMic IBal
'Magic Fire'PBR (v)	EMic EPfP EPla IBal MNrw

'Magic Island'	IBal NSue
'Majesty'	EMic EPla IBal MBri NGdn
'Major Tom' **new**	IBal
'Malabar' (v)	EMic IBal
'Mama Mia' (v)	EMic EPfP IBal LRHS MBNS NBro NGdn NHol NWad
'Manhattan'	EMic
'Maraschino Cherry'	EMic IBal NEgg NGdn
'Mardi Gras' (v)	EMic IBal
'Marge' (*sieboldiana* hybrid)	EMic
'Margie's Angel' (v)	NSue
'Margin of Error' (v)	IBal
'Marginata Alba' misapplied	see *H.* 'Albomarginata' (*fortunei*), *H. crispula*
'Marginata Alba' ambig. (v)	NNor
'Marilyn'	EMic IBal
'Marilyn Monroe'	EMic IBal NSue
'Marmalade on Toast'	EMic
'Marquis' (*nakaiana* hybrid)	IBal
'Marrakech'	EMic IBal NSue
'Mary Joe'	EMic
'Mary Marie Ann' (*fortunei*) (v)	EMic IBal
'Masquerade' (v)	EMic LLHF NHar NRya NSue SMHy WFar WHal WThu
'Maui Buttercups'	EMic
'May'	EMic IBal
'Maya' (*fortunei*) (v)	EMic IBal
'Medieval Age' (v)	IBal
§ 'Mediopicta' (*sieboldii*)	EMic IBal
'Mediovariegata' (*undulata*)	see *H. undulata* var. *undulata*
'Medusa' (v)	EMic IBal NGdn NSue
'Memories of Dorothy'	EMic IBal
'Mesa Fringe' (*montana*)	EMic IBal NLar
'Midas Touch'	NEgg NLar NNor
'Middle Ridge'	EMic
'Midnight at the Oasis' (v)	EMic IBal
'Midnight Ride'	IBal
'Midwest Gold'	MHom
'Midwest Magic' (v)	EMic IBal NLar
'Mighty Mite'	NSue
'Mighty Mouse' (v)	IBal
'Mikawa-no-yuki'	IBal
'Mike Shadrack' (v)	EMic IBal
'Miki'	IBal
'Mildred Seaver' (v)	EMic IBal LRHS MHom
'Millennium'	EMic IBal
'Minnie Bell' (v)	IBal
'Minnie Klopping'	EMic
§ ***minor***	EBee GEdr ITim NSue WCot WFar XLum
- B&SWJ 1209 from Korea	WCru
- B&SWJ 8775 from Korea	WCru
- B&SWJ 11103 from Japan	WCru
- from Korea	IBal
minor f. ***alba*** misapplied	see *H. sieboldii* var. *alba*
'Minor' (*ventricosa*)	see *H. minor* Maekawa
'Mint Julep' (v)	IBal
'Minuet' (v)	IBal
'Minuta' (*venusta*)	NSue
'Minuteman' (*fortunei*) (v) ♀[H7]	CCon ECtt EMic EPfP EPla EWoo GBin IBal LRHS MBNS MMuc MWat NGdn NLar NMyG NNor NOrc NSir SEND WFar WWEG
'Miss Linda Smith'	EMic IBal
'Miss Ruby'	EMic IBal
'Miss Saigon' (v)	IBal
'Miss Tokyo' (v)	EMic IBal
'Mississippi Delta'	EMic
'Mister Watson'	EMic IBal
'Misty Waters' (*sieboldiana*)	EMic
'Moerheim' (*fortunei*) (v)	EMic EPla IBal LRHS WHal WWEG
'Mohegan'	EMic
montana	EMic
- B&SWJ 4796	WCru
- B&SWJ 5585	WCru
- 'Hida-no-hana' (v)	IBal
- f. ***macrophylla***	IBal
'Moody Blues' (Tardiana Group)	EMic
'Moon Lily'	EMic
'Moon River' (v)	EMic IBal
'Moon Split' (v)	EMic EPfP NGdn
'Moonbeam'	EShb
'Moongate Flying Saucer'	EMic
'Moonlight' (*fortunei*) (v)	EMic GMaP IBal LRHS NNor NPCo
'Moonlight Sonata'	EMic EPla IBal
'Moonstruck'[PBR] (v)	ECtt EMic IBal
'Morning Light'[PBR]	ECtt EMic EPfP GBin IBal LBMP LLWG MAvo MBNS MBri NBro NGdn NLar NMyG SRkn WFar
'Morning Star' (v)	EMic IBal MAvo NSue
'Moscow Blue'	EMic
'Moulin Rouge' **new**	IBal
'Mount Everest'	EMic IBal
'Mount Fuji' (*montana*)	IBal
'Mount Kirishima' (*sieboldii*)	see *H.* 'Kirishima'
'Mount Tom' (v)	EMic IBal
'Mountain Snow' (*montana*) (v)	EMic LRHS
'Mourning Dove' (v)	EMic IBal
'Mouse Trap' (v)	IBal NSue
'Mr Big'	IBal NGdn WCot
'Mrs Minky'	EBee EMic LRHS
'Muffie' (v)	EMic
'Munchkin' (*sieboldii*)	LLHF NSue
'My Claire' (v)	IBal
'My Cup of Tea'	IBal
'My Friend Nancy' (v)	IBal
'Mystic Star'	IBal
nakaiana	EBee EMic IBal
'Nakaimo'	IBal
'Nana' (*ventricosa*)	see *H. minor* Maekawa
'Nancy'	EMic
§ 'Nancy Lindsay' (*fortunei*)	CTri EMic IBal NGdn NLar
'Nancy Minks'	EMic IBal
'Neat and Tidy'	IBal
'Neat Splash' (v)	CWCL NBir WWEG
'Neelix'	IBal
'Nemesis' (v)	IBal
'Neptune'	EMic IBal NSue
'Niagara Falls' ♀[H7]	CCon EMic IBal NGdn NPCo NSue
'Nicola'	EMic IBal MHom NSue
'Night before Christmas' (v) ♀[H7]	CCon CHid EMic IBal LRHS MNrw NBro NEgg NGdn NHol NMyG NNor NPCo WHoo WWEG
'Night Life'	EMic IBal
nigrescens	EMic EPla GGal IBal LRHS NChi NPCo
'Niko' (v)	IBal
'Nippers' **new**	NSue
'Nokogiryama'	EMic
'None Lovelier' (v)	EMic IBal
'Nor'easter' (v)	IBal
'North Hills' (*fortunei*) (v)	EMic IBal MHom NBir NGdn SWvt WFar WWEG

'Northern Exposure' (*sieboldiana*) (v)	CCon EMic NGdn NLar SPoG
'Northern Halo' (*sieboldiana*) (v)	EMic
'Norwalk Chartreuse'	IBal
'Nutty Professor' (v)	IBal
'Oberon'	NSue
'Obscura Marginata' (*fortunei*)	see *H. fortunei* var. *aureomarginata*
'Obsession'	IBal
'Ocean Isle' (v)	IBal
'October Sky'	EMic
'Oder'	IBal
'Ogon Tachi' (*rectifolia*) (v)	EMic IBal
'Ogon-chirifu-hime'	IBal
'Ogon-hime-tokudama'	IBal
'Ogon-koba'	IBal
'Oh Cindy' (v)	EMic IBal
'O'Harra'	EMic NSue
'Old Faithful'	EMic IBal LRHS
'Old Glory'[PBR] (v)	ECtt EMic IBal
'Olga's Shiny Leaf'	EMic
'Olive Bailey Langdon' (*sieboldiana*) (v)	EMic IBal
'Olive Branch' (v)	EMic IBal
'Olympic Edger'	EMic IBal
'Olympic Glacier' (v)	EMic IBal
'Olympic Gold Medal'	EMic IBal
'Olympic Silver Medal'	EMic IBal
'Olympic Sunrise' (v)	EMic IBal
'Olympic Twilight'	EMic IBal
'On Stage'	see *H.* 'Chōkō-nishiki'
'On the Border' (v)	IBal
'One Man's Treasure' ♀H7	EMic IBal MBel NGdn NPCo
'Ooh La La' (v)	IBal
'Ophir'	EMic IBal
opipara	NPCo
'Ops' (v)	EMic IBal NSue
'Orange Crush' (v)	IBal
'Orange Marmalade' (v) ♀H7	ECtt EMic GBin IBal LRHS MWat NGdn NSue SCob SGol SPoG
'Oriana' (*fortunei*)	EMic
'Orion's Belt' (v)	IBal
'Oxheart'	EMic IBal
'Oze' (v)	EMic IBal NSue
pachyscapa	EMic
'Pacific Blue Edger'	CCon EMic LRHS NGdn NNor WAul WFar WWEG
'Painted Lady' (*sieboldii*) (v)	GKev
'Pamela Lee' (v)	IBal NGdn NMyG NSue
'Pandora's Box' (v)	GEdr LRHS NHar NSue WCot
'Paradigm' (v)	EBee EMic IBal LRHS NGdn
'Paradise Backstage' (v)	EMic IBal
'Paradise Beach'	EMic IBal
'Paradise Blue Sky'	IBal
'Paradise Expectations' (*sieboldiana*) (v)	EMic IBal
'Paradise Glory'	EMic IBal
'Paradise Gold Line' (*ventricosa*) (v)	IBal
'Paradise Island'[PBR] (*sieboldiana*) (v)	EMic EPfP IBal NGdn NSue
'Paradise Joyce'[PBR]	EMic IBal NLar NNor NPCo WWEG
'Paradise Ocean'	EMic
'Paradise on Fire' (v)	EMic IBal
'Paradise Parade' (v)	IBal
'Paradise Passion' (v)	IBal
'Paradise Power'[PBR]	EMic
'Paradise Puppet' (*venusta*) ♀H7	EMic EPla GKev IBal NNor NSue WWEG
'Paradise Red Delight' (*pycnophylla*)	EMic IBal
'Paradise Sandstorm'	IBal
'Paradise Standard' (d)	EMic IBal
'Paradise Sunset'	EMic IBal NSue
'Paradise Sunshine'	EMic IBal
'Paradise Surprise' (v)	IBal
'Paradise Tritone' (v)	EMic
'Parhelion'	EMic
'Parky's Prize' (v)	IBal
'Pastures Green'	IBal
'Pastures New'	EMic EPla MHom NPCo WWEG
'Pathfinder' (v)	EMic IBal
'Patricia'	EMic
'Patrician' (v)	EMic IBal
'Patriot' (v) ♀H7	Widely available
'Patriot's Fire' (v)	IBal LRHS
'Patriot's Green Pride'	IBal
'Paul's Glory' (v) ♀H7	EMic EPfP GLog GMaP IBal LRHS MBri NBir NGdn NMyG NNor NSue SPoG WFar WWEG
§ 'Paxton's Original' (*sieboldii*) (v)	IFoB WWEG
'Peace' (v)	EMic IBal LRHS
'Peacock Strut'	IBal
'Peanut'	IBal NSue
'Pearl Lake'	EMic IBal MHom NBir NEgg NGdn NHol NLar NMyG NNor SRGP
'Peedee Absinth'	EMic
'Pelham Blue Tump'	EMic
'Peppermint Ice' (v)	EMic IBal NGdn
'Percy'	EMic
'Permanent Wave'	IBal
'Perry's True Blue'	EMic IBal
'Peter Pan'	EMic IBal NPCo
'Pete's Dark Satellite'	EMic IBal NSue
'Pewterware'	EMic IBal
'Phantom'	IBal
'Philadelphia'	EMic IBal
'Phoenix'	EMic IBal NLar
'Photo Finish' (v)	EMic IBal
'Phyllis Campbell' (*fortunei*)	see *H.* 'Sharmon'
'Picta' (*fortunei*)	see *H. fortunei* var. *albopicta*
'Piecrust Power'	IBal
'Piedmont Gold'	CBod CHid EHoe EMic GBin IBal LRHS
'Pilgrim' (v)	EMic EPla IBal LRHS MMuc NBro NGdn NPCo SEND WFar
'Pineapple Poll'	EMic NNor NSue WWEG
'Pineapple Upside Down Cake' (v)	EMic IBal NBro NLar NSue
'Pinky'	IBal
'Pistache' (v)	EMic IBal NSue
'Pixie Vamp' (v)	EMic IBal
'Pizzazz' (v)	EMic IBal LRHS MHom NGdn NHol NLar WFar WWEG
plantaginea	EMic IBal LEdu LPla LRHS SSpi WFar WWtn
- var. ***grandiflora***	see *H. plantaginea* var. *japonica*
§ - var. ***japonica*** ♀H7	CAby CAvo EBee ECha IBal LRHS MNrw MRav SMad WCFE WFar WPGP WWEG
'Platinum Tiara' (v)	EMic IBal MWat NBir
'Plug Nickel'	EMic IBal
'Poker' **new**	IBal
'Polar Moon' (v)	IBal

'Pole Cat' (v)	IBal
'Pooh Bear' (v)	EMic IBal NSue
'Popcorn'	EMic IBal NSue
'Popo' ♀H7	EMic IBal NSue
'Porter' (*venusta*)	IBal
'Pot of Gold'	EMic
'Potomac Pride'	EMic LRHS NPCo
'Powder Blue' (v)	IBal
'Prairie Moon'	NSue
'Prairie Sky'	EMic IBal MBri NGdn NLar WFar
'Praying Hands' (v) ♀H7	EBee ECha ECtt ELan EMic EPfP GBin GEdr GKev IBal IBoy IFoB IPot LBMP LRHS LSou MBNS NMyG NPCo NSue SCob SPoG WFar WWEG
'Prestige and Promise' (v)	IBal
'Pretty Flamingo'	EMic IBal
'Prima Donna'	EMic
'Prince of Wales'	EMic IBal LRHS LSqu NNor SPoG
'Princess Anastasia' (v)	IBal
'Private Dancer' **new**	IBal
'Proud Sentry'	EMic NSue
'Punky' (v)	EMic IBal
'Purple Boots'	EMic IBal
'Purple Dwarf'	EMic IBal NLar WCru WHal WWEG
'Purple Glory'	EMic
'Purple Haze'	EMic IBal LRHS NGdn NSue SHar WCot
'Purple Heart'	EBee ECtt GBin IBal NMyG NSti NSue NWad SHar WCot WNPC
'Purple Lady Finger'	IBal WWEG
'Purple Passion'	EMic IBal NSue
'Purple Profusion'	EMic IBal
'Quarter Note' (v)	IBal
'Queen Josephine' (v)	EMic EPfP IBal LRHS MBNS MHom NGdn NPCo SRGP WFar
'Queen of the Seas'	EMic IBal NSue
'Quill'	EMic NSue
'Quilting Bee'	EMic IBal
'Radiant Edger' (v)	EMic GCra IBal LRHS NHol NSue WWEG
'Radio Waves'	EMic
'Rain Dancer'	EMic IBal
'Rain Forest'	EMic IBal
'Rainbow's End' (v)	IBal NSue
'Rainforest Sunrise' (v)	ELon EMic IBal LSou NGdn NSue
'Rascal' (v)	EMic EPla
'Raspberries and Cream' (v)	IBal
'Raspberry Sorbet'	EMic IBal NSue
'Raspberry Sundae' (v)	CMil CWGN EBee IBal NSue SCob WNPC
rectifolia	NNor
'Red Cadet'	EMic IBal
'Red Dog'	EMic NSue
'Red Dragon'	IBal
'Red Hot Flash' (v)	EMic IBal
'Red Hot Poker'	IBal
'Red Neck Heaven' (*kikutii* var. *caput-avis*)	IBal
'Red October'	ECtt EMic EPfP EUJe EWoo GAbr IBal IBoy LBMP LEdu LPal LRHS LSou MBNS MHol MPie NGdn NLar NPCo NSue SMad SPoG WCot WFar WWEG
'Red Salamander'	EMic IBal
'Red Sox'	IBal
'Red Stepper'	EMic IBal
'Red Tubes' (*venusta*)	IBal
'Regal Rhubarb'	EMic IBal
'Regal Splendor' (v) ♀H7	ELan ELon EMic IBal LRHS MHom NBro NGdn NNor NSue WFar WHoo WMnd
'Regal Supreme' (v)	EMic IBal
'Reginald Kaye'	EMic
'Rembrandt Blue'	EMic IBal
'Remember Me' PBR ♀H7	CWCL ELan ELon GBin IBal MBNS MBri MPnt NGdn NHol NLar NMyG NNor NPCo NSue NWad WFar WWEG
'Reptilian'	EMic IBal
'Resonance' (v)	NGdn NLar
'Restless Sea'	EMic
'Reverend Mac' **new**	IBal
'Reversed' (*sieboldiana*) (v)	EMic IBal LRHS NBro NGdn NNor WFar WHal
'Revolution' PBR (v) ♀H7	EMic IBal LRHS NBro NEgg NGdn NLar NSue SPoG WFar WWEG
'Rhapsody' (*fortunei*) (v)	EMic
'Rhein' (*tardiana*)	IBal
'Rheingold' (v)	IBal
'Rhinestone Cowboy' (v)	IBal
'Rhino Hide' (v) **new**	IBal NSue
'Rhythm and Blues'	IBal NSue
'Rich Uncle'	IBal
'Richland Gold' (*fortunei*)	EMic
'Rim Rock'	EMic
'Ringtail'	EMic IBal
'Ripple Effect' (v) **new**	NSue
'Rippled Honey'	ELan EMic IBal NEoE NMyG
'Rippling Waves'	EMic
'Riptide'	NGdn
'Risa'	IBal
'Risky Business' PBR (v)	CWGN EBee EMic IBal NSue SMrm
'Robert Frost' (v)	EMic IBal
'Robin Hood'	EMic IBal
'Robin of Loxley'	EMic IBal
'Robusta' (*fortunei*)	see *H. sieboldiana* var. *elegans*
'Robyn's Choice' (v)	IBal
'Rock and Roll'	EMic
'Rock Island Line' (v)	EMic IBal NSue
'Rock Princess'	IBal LLHF
§ ***rohdeifolia*** (v) B&SWJ 10862 **new**	WCru
- f. ***albopicta***	ELan
'Roller Coaster Ride'	IBal NSue
'Ron Damant'	IBal
'Rootin'-Tootin'' (v)	IBal
'Roseann Walter' (v)	EMic IBal
'Rosedale Golden Goose'	EMic
'Rosedale Knox'	IBal
'Rosedale Lost Dutchman'	IBal
'Rosedale Melody of Summer' (v)	IBal
'Rosedale Misty Magic' (v)	IBal
'Rosedale Richie Valens'	IBal
'Rosemoor'	IBal
'Roxsanne'	EMic
'Roy Klehm' (v)	EMic IBal
'Royal Charm'	IBal
'Royal Flush' (v)	IBal
'Royal Golden Jubilee'	EMic IBal
§ 'Royal Standard' ♀H7	Widely available
'Royal Tapestry' (v)	IBal
'Royal Tiara' (*nakaiana*) (v)	IBal
'Royalty'	IBal
'Rufus Rider' **new**	IBal

	Name	Suppliers
	rupifraga	IBal
	'Rusty Bee'	IBal
	'Ryan's Big One'	EBee IBal
§	'Sagae' (v) ♀H7	EMic IBal LRHS MBri MHom MNrw NGdn NNor SDix WAul WFar WWEG
	'Saint Elmo's Fire' (v)	EMic IBal LRHS
	'Saint Paul'	EMic IBal MNrw NSue
	'Saishu-jima' (*sieboldii* f. *spathulata*)	EMic GEdr WCru
	'Saishu-yahato-sito' (v)	IBal
	'Salute' (Tardiana Group)	EMic
	'Samurai' (*sieboldiana*) (v)	EMic IBal MRav NBir NBro NGdn NLar NNor NPCo NSue
	'Sandhill Crane' (v)	IBal
	'Sarah Kennedy' (v)	IBal
	'Sara's Sensation' (v)	IBal
	'Satisfaction' (v) ♀H7	EMic IBal
	'Savannah'	IBal
	'Sazanami' (*crispula*)	see *H. crispula*
	'Scallion Pancakes'	EMic
	'Scarlet Ribbons' (v) **new**	IBal
	'Schwan'	GBin
	'Scooter' (v)	IBal
	'Sea Current' **new**	IBal
	'Sea Dream' (v)	EMic LRHS NEgg NGdn NNor NPCo
	'Sea Fire'	IBal NGdn
	'Sea Gulf Stream'	EMic
	'Sea Lotus Leaf'	EMic LLWP NLar NNor
	'Sea Monster'	IBal
	'Sea Sapphire'	IBal
	'Sea Thunder' (v)	EMic IBal NGdn
	'Sea Yellow Sunrise'	EMic IBal
	'Searing Flame' (v) **new**	IBal
	'Second Wind' (*fortunei*) (v)	EMic NMyG
	'Secret Ambition'[PBR] (v)	EMic IBal
	'Secret Love'	EMic IBal
	'Seducer' (v)	EMic IBal
	'See Saw' (*undulata*)	EMic IBal
	'Semperaurea' (*sieboldiana*)	IBal
	'September Sun' (v)	EMic IBal LRHS NNor
	'Serena' (Tardiana Group)	IBal
	'Serendipity'	EMic GAbr IBal MHom
	'Shade Beauty' (v)	IBal
	'Shade Fanfare' (v)	ECtt EHoe ELan ELon EMic EPfP EPla IBal LAst LPla LRHS MBNS MRav MWhi NBir NGdn NLar NSti SPer WFar WMnd WWEG
	'Shade Finale' (v)	IBal
	'Shade Master'	EMic
	'Shade Parade' (v)	EMic IBal
§	'Sharmon' (*fortunei*) (v)	ELon EMic MBNS NEgg NLar NPCo
	'Sharp Dressed Man'	EMic IBal NGdn
	'Shazaam'	EMic IBal
	'Sheila West'	EMic IBal
	'Shelleys' (v)	IBal
	'Sherborne Profusion' (Tardiana Group)	EMic IBal
	'Sherborne Songbird' (Tardiana Group)	IBal
	'Sherborne Swallow' (Tardiana Group)	IBal
	'Sherborne Swan' (Tardiana Group)	IBal
	'Sherborne Swift' (Tardiana Group)	EMic EPla IBal LRHS
	'Shimmy Shake'	EMic
	'Shining Tot' ♀H7	LLHF
	'Shiny Penny' (v)	EMic IBal NSue WWEG
	'Shirley Levy'	IBal
	'Shirley Vaughn' (v)	IBal
	'Shogun' (v)	IBal
	'Showboat' (v)	EMic IBal
	sieboldiana	CMac CSBt ECha ELan EMic GCra GMaP LBMP LLWP MRav MSwo NChi SPlb SRms WMoo WWEG XLum
§	- var. ***elegans*** ♀H7	Widely available
	- var. ***mira***	EMic
	- var. ***sieboldiana***	NGdn
	sieboldiana* × *venusta	NGdn
	sieboldii	GBin MRav
§	- var. ***alba***	IBal
§	- var. ***sieboldii*** f. ***kabitan*** (v)	EMic IBal NGdn NHar WWEG
	- - f. ***shiro-kabitan*** (v)	EMic LRHS
	- f. ***spathulata***	EMic
	'Silberpfeil'	EMic NSue
	'Silver Bay' ♀H7	EMic
	'Silver Crown'	see *H.* 'Albomarginata'
	'Silver Lance' (v)	EMic IBal
	'Silver Lode' (v)	IBal
	'Silver Moon'	EMic
	'Silver Shadow' (v)	CHid EMic GBin IBal NBir NGdn NNor NWad WHoo
	'Silver Spray' (v)	IBal
	'Silver Star' (v)	IBal
	'Silver Threads and Gold Needles' (v)	IBal NSue
	'Silverado' (v)	IBal
	'Silvery Slugproof' (Tardiana Group)	LRHS WWEG
	'Singin' the Blues'	IBal
	'Singing in the Rain' (v)	IBal
	'Sitting Pretty' (v)	IBal
	'Sky Dancer'	EMic IBal MBri NSue
	'Sleeping Beauty'	CWGN EMic EPla IBal NGdn NMyG
	'Slick Willie'	EMic
	'Slim and Trim'	EMic IBal NSue
	'Small Parts'	EMic IBal NSue
	'Small Sum'	IBal
	'Smoke Signals' **new**	IBal
	'Smooth Sailing' (v)	IBal
	'Snow Boy' (v) **new**	IBal
	'Snow Cap' (v)	ECtt EMic IBal NEoE NGdn NLar NMyG NNor SPoG WFar WWEG
	'Snow Crust' (v)	EMic
	'Snow Flakes' (*sieboldii*)	CMac NBro NEoE NGdn NLar WFar WWEG
	'Snow Mouse' (v)	EMic IBal NSue
	'Snow White' (*undulata*) (v)	IBal
	'Snowbound' (v)	IBal
	'Snowden' ♀H7	ECha EMic GMaP IBal LRHS MWat NBir NGdn NNor SSpi WCru WWEG
	'Snowy Lake' (v)	IBal
	'So Sweet' (v)	EBee ECtt EHoe ELan EMic EPfP EPla EWoo GBin IBal LRHS LSun MHom MSwo NBro NGdn NHol NMyG NNor SHil SPad SPoG WFar WWEG
	'Solar Flare'	EMic
	'Something Blue'	EMic
	'Something Different' (*fortunei*) (v)	IBal
	'Something Else'	EMic

Name	Suppliers
'Southern Gold'	EMic
'Space Odyssey' **new**	IBal
'Sparkling Burgundy'	EMic EPla LRHS NSue
'Sparky' (v)	IBal
'Spartacus' (v)	EMic IBal NSue
'Spartan Arrow'	NSue
'Spartan Glory' (v)	IBal
'Special Blend' (v) **new**	IBal
'Special Gift'	EMic WWEG
'Spellbound' (v)	IBal
'Spilt Milk' (*tokudama*) (v) ♀H7	EBee EMic IBal LRHS SPoG WHoo
§ 'Spinners' (*fortunei*) (v)	ECha EMic NNor
'Spock's Ears'	IBal
'Spring Break' (v)	EMic
'Spring Fling'	EMic IBal
'Spritzer' (v)	EMic MNrw NSue
'Squash Casserole'	IBal NSue
'Stained Glass' ♀H7	CAby CBcs ECtt ELon EMic EPfP IBal LRHS NGdn NNor NPCo NSue WFar WRHF
'Stand by Me' (v)	EMic IBal NSue
'Star Kissed'	IBal
'Starburst' stable (v)	IBal
'Stardust'	IBal
'Stargate'	IBal
§ 'Starker Yellow Leaf'	EMic
'Starship' (v)	EMic IBal
'Steffi' (v)	IBal
'Step Sister'	EMic IBal
'Stepping Out' (v)	EMic IBal
'Stetson' (v)	EMic IBal
'Stiletto' (v)	CCon EHoe ELon EMic GAbr GCra GEdr GKev IBal LBMP LRHS MBNS MHom MNrw NBro NEoE NGdn NLar NMyG NNor NSue SPoG SWvt WSHC WWEG
'Stirfry'	EMic
'Stitch in Time' (v)	IBal
'Stonewall'	IBal
'Strawberry Surprise' (v)	EMic IBal
'Striker' (v)	IBal NSue
'Striptease' (*fortunei*) (v) ♀H7	CMac EMic EPfP IBal LRHS MBNS MBri MNrw NGdn NHol NLar NPCo NSue WFar WWEG
'Sugar and Cream' (v)	EMic EPla IBal LRHS NGdn NNor
'Sugar and Spice' (v)	EMic IBal
'Sugar Daddy'	EMic
'Sultana' (v)	EMic IBal WWEG
'Sum and Substance' ♀H7	Widely available
'Sum and Subtle' (v)	EMic IBal
'Sum Cup-o-Joe' (v)	EMic
'Sum it Up' (v)	EMic
'Sum of All' (v)	NSue
'Summer Breeze' (v)	EMic IBal NGdn NSue
'Summer Fragrance'	EBee ECtt EMic GBin IBal LRHS
'Summer Lovin'' (v)	IBal
'Summer Music' (v) ♀H7	CWCL EMic IBal WWEG
'Summer Serenade' (v)	EMic IBal NGdn
'Summer Squall'	IBal
'Sun Catcher'	EMic
'Sun Power'	EBee ELon EMic LRHS MBNS MBri NBro NGdn NLar NSti SMrm
'Sun Worshipper'	IBal
'Sunlight Child'	IBal NSue
'Sunny Smiles' (v)	EMic
'Sunshine Glory'	EMic IBal
'Super Nova' (v)	EMic IBal

Name	Suppliers
'Super Sagae'	EMic IBal WFar
'Surprised by Joy' (v)	EMic IBal NNor NSue WWEG
'Susy'	IBal
'Sutter's Mill'	IBal
'Suzuki Thumbnail'	EMic
'Swamp Thing' (v)	IBal
'Sweet Bo Beep'	IBal LRHS
'Sweet Bouquet'	EMic
'Sweet Home Chicago' (v)	EBee EMic IBal
'Sweet Innocence' (v)	EMic IBal
'Sweet Marjorie'	IBal
'Sweet Sunshine'	EMic
'Sweet Susan'	EMic LPla MBNS SPer SWvt
'Sweet Tater Pie'	EMic IBal
'Sweetheart'	EMic
'Sweetie' (v)	EMic IBal LRHS NSue WWEG
'Sweetness'	IBal
'Swirling Hearts'	IBal NSue
'T. Rex'	ELon EMic IBal WFar
'Tall Boy'	GBin IBal NBir NNor
'Tamborine' (v)	IBal LRHS
'Tango'	EMic IBal
'Tappen Zee' (v)	EMic IBal
Tardiana Group	MHom NGdn
tardiflora	CExl CFil IBal WPGP
'Tattle Tails'	EMic IBal NSue
'Tattoo'PBR (v)	CWGN EMic MBNS MNrw NLar WWEG
'Tea and Crumpets' (v)	IBal
'Tea at Betty's' ♀H7	IBal
'Teacher's Pride' **new**	IBal
'Tears of Joy'	NSue
'Teaspoon'	EMic IBal NNor NSue
'Teatime' (v)	EMic IBal
'Teeny-weeny Bikini' (v)	EMic IBal NSue
'Templar Gold'	IBal
'Temptation'	EMic
'Tequila Sunrise'	IBal
'Terpsichore'	EMic
'Terracotta'	MCri
'Terry Wogan'	IBal NNor
'Tet-a-Poo'	IBal
'The King' (v)	IBal
'The Leading Edge' (v)	IBal
'The Queen' (v)	IBal
'The Razor's Edge'	IBal
'The Right One' (v)	IBal
'The Shining'	IBal
'The Twister'	IBal
'Theo's Blue'	EMic IBal
'Thomas Hogg'	see *H. undulata* var. *albomarginata*
'Thumb Nail'	EMic IBal NNor
'Thumbelina'	EMic IBal NGdn
'Thunderbolt'PBR (*sieboldiana*)	EMic IBal MBNS NGdn NLar WFar
tibae	IBal
'Tick Tock' (v)	EMic IBal NSue
'Tickle Me Pink'	EMic IBal NSue
'Tidewater'	IBal
'Time Tunnel' (*sieboldiana*) (v)	EMic IBal
'Timeless Beauty' (v)	LLWG WFar
'Tiny Tears'	GAbr IFoB NSue
'Titanic'PBR	EMic IBal
'Titanium' **new**	IBal
tokudama	EMic IBal LRHS MHom NBir NGdn NNor NSti WFar XLum
§ - f. ***aureo-nebulosa*** (v)	EMic IBal NGdn SRms WMnd

- f. ***flavocircinalis*** (v) ♀H7	EBee ELon EMic EPfP GMaP IBal NBro WFar WHoo WMnd
'Tokudama Blue'	IBoy
'Toledo'	IBal
'Tom Schmid' (v)	EMic IBal LBMP LRHS MWat NMyG NSue
'Tom Thumb'	EMic IBal NSue
'Topaz'	IBal
'Topscore'	NNor
'Torchlight' (v) ♀H7	EMic IBal LRHS MHom NSue
tortifrons	EMic
'Tortilla Chip'	IBal NSue
'Tot Tot'	EMic IBal NSue
'Touch of Class'PBR (v) ♀H7	ECtt EMic GBin IBal LRHS NGdn NHol NMyG NNor NSue WFar WWEG
'Touchstone' (v)	SWvt WWEG
'Toy Soldier'	EMic IBal NGdn NSue
'Tranquility' (v)	EMic
'Tremors'	EMic
'Trill'	IBal
'Trixi' (v)	IBal
'Tropical Dancer'	EMic IBal
'True Blue'	EBee ECtt EMic IBal WWEG
'Tsugaru Komachi'	EMic
'Tsugaru Komachi Kifukurin' (v)	IBal
'Turnabout' (v)	IBal
'Turning Point'	IBal
'Twiggie'	EMic
'Twilight' (*fortunei*) (v)	CAby ECtt ELon EMic EShb IBal LRHS MBNS NGdn NLar NPCo SWvt WHar WWEG
'Twilight Time'	IBal LRHS
'Twinkle Toes'	EMic IBal
'Twist of Lime' (v)	EMic GKev IBal LRHS NGdn NNor NPCo NSue WWEG
'Twitter' **new**	IBal
'UFO'	EMic IBal NSue
'Ultramarine'	IBal
'Ultraviolet Light'	IBal
'Ulysses S. Grant'	IBal
'Unchained Melody'	IBal
undulata	NNor WFar
§ - var. ***albomarginata***	CBcs CMac CSam EMic EPfP EPla GMaP IBoy LRHS MRav MWat NBid NBir NGdn SCob SPer SRms SWvt WFar WMnd WWEG XLum
§ - var. ***erromena***	EMic GMaP LRHS NNor WHrl XLum
§ - var. ***undulata*** (v) ♀H7	CBod COtt EBee GMaP IBal LPot LRHS MCot MRav MSwo NEgg NGdn NLar NNor SCob SPer WWEG
- var. ***univittata*** (v)	ECha EMic GKev LAst MHom MWhi NBir NEoE WFar WMoo
'Unforgettable'	EMic IBal
'Upper Crust' (v)	IBal
'Uprising' (v) **new**	IBal
'Urajiro' (*hypoleuca*)	IBal
'Urajiro-hachijo' (*longipes* var. *latifolia*)	IBal
'Valentine Lace'	EMic GKev IBal
'Valley's Chute the Chute'	EMic IBal
'Valley's Glacier' (v)	EMic IBal WFar
'Valley's Vanilla Sticks'	EMic IBal
'Van Wade' (v)	EMic IBal
'Vanilla Cream' (*cathayana*)	EMic IBal
'Variegata' (*gracillima*)	see *H.* 'Vera Verde'

'Variegata' (*tokudama*)	see *H. tokudama* f. ***aureo-nebulosa***
'Variegata' (*undulata*)	see *H. undulata* var. ***undulata***
'Variegata' (*ventricosa*)	see *H.* 'Aureomarginata' (*ventricosa*)
'Variegated' (*fluctuans*)	see *H.* 'Sagae'
'Velvet Moon' (v)	EMic IBal
ventricosa ♀H7	CMac EMic GMaP IBal MWhi NGdn WFar XLum
- BWJ 8160 from Sichuan	WCru
- var. ***aureomaculata***	EMic NBir NNor NSti WFar
'Venus' (d)	CAby ECtt EMic IBal LRHS MHol NGdn WCot WFar
'Venus Star'	EMic
venusta ♀H7	CCon CDes EBee ECho EMic GCra GEdr IBal LRHS MHer MRav NBid NBir NNor NRya NSti SRot WWEG
- B&SWJ 4389	WCru
- 'Kin Botan' (v)	GEdr
- ***yakusimensis***	see *H. kikutii* var. ***yakusimensis***
§ 'Vera Verde' (v)	GCra GQui NBir NSue
'Verdi Valentine'	IBal
'Verkade's No 1'	IBal
'Verna Jean' (v)	EMic IBal LRHS
'Veronica Lake' (v)	EMic IBal LRHS NNor NSue WHal
'Victory' ♀H7	EMic IBal
'Viking Ship'	EMic
'Vilmoriniana'	EMic
'Vim and Vigor'	EMic IBal
'Vina'	IBal
'Viridis Marginata'	see *H. sieboldii* var. ***sieboldii*** f. ***kabitan***
'Vulcan' (v)	EMic IBal
'Wagtail' (Tardiana Group)	EMic IBal
'Wahoo' (*tokudama*) (v)	IBal
'War Paint' ♀H7	EMic NSue WFar
'Warwick Ballerina'	IBal
'Warwick Comet' (v)	IBal
'Warwick Curtsey' (v)	EMic IBal
'Warwick Edge' (v)	EMic IBal NPCo
'Warwick Essence'	EMic IBal
'Warwick Sheen'	IBal
'Waukon Glass'	EMic IBal
'Waukon Thin Ice'	EMic IBal
'Waukon Water'	EMic IBal
'Waving Winds' (v)	IBal
'Waving Wuffles'	EMic
'Wayside Blue'	EMic
'Wayside Perfection'	see *H.* 'Royal Standard'
'Weihenstephan' (*sieboldii*)	EMic IBal
'Well Shaked' (v)	IBal
'Wheaton Blue'	EMic LRHS
'Whirligig' (v)	EMic
'Whirling Dervish' (v)	IBal
'Whirlwind' (*fortunei*) (v) ♀H7	EBee EMic GBin GQue IBal LBMP LRHS MBri MNrw MRav NBro NEgg NGdn NMyG NNor NOrc NSue SPad SPtp WAul WBor WFar WMnd WWEG
'Whirlwind Tour' (v)	IBal
'Whiskey Sour'	IBal
'White Bikini' (v)	IBal NSue
'White Ceiling'	IBal
'White Christmas' (*fortunei*) (v)	NGdn
'White Christmas' (*undulata*) (v)	EMic
'White Dove' (v)	EMic IBal
'White Edger'	EMic
'White Elephant' (v)	IBal

'White Fairy' (*plantaginea*) (d)	EMic
'White Feather' (*undulata*)	CHid CWGN EBee ELan ELon EPfP LRHS MNrw NBir NGdn NLar NMyG NNor SMad SPoG WFar
'White Knight'	IBal
'White On' (*montana*)	EMic
'White Triumphator' (*rectifolia*)	EMic GBin IBal
'White Trumpets'	EMic
'White Vision'	IBal
'Wide Brim' (v) ♀H7	Widely available
'Wiggle Worms' (v)	IBal
'William Lachman' (v)	NLar
'Wily Willy'	IBal
'Wind River Gold'	EMic IBal
'Windsor Gold'	see *H.* 'Nancy Lindsay'
'Winfield Blue'	EMic IBal
'Winfield Gold'	EMic
'Winfield Mist' (v)	IBal
'Winsome' (v)	IBal
'Winter Lightning' (v)	NNor
'Winter Snow' (v)	EMic IBal NGdn NSue
'Winter Warrior' (v)	EMic IBal
'Wogon' (*sieboldii*)	EMic GKev GMaP ITim NSti
'Wogon's Boy'	EMic LRHS WWEG
'Wolverine' (v) ♀H7	EBee ECtt EHoe EMic GAbr LRHS LSou MHom NGdn NSbr NSue SPoG SWvt WCot WFar WWEG
'Woodland Elf' (v)	IBal
'Woolly Mammoth' (v)	IBal
'Woop Woop' (v)	EMic IBal NSue
'World Cup'	IBal
'Worldly Treasure'	IBal
'Wrinkles and Crinkles'	EMic
'Wylde Green Cream'	EMic IBal NGdn
'Xanadu' (v)	IBal
'X-rated' (v)	IBal
'X-ray' (v)	NSue
'Yakushima-mizu' (*gracillima*)	EMic IBal NMyG
* ***yakushimana***	NHar
'Yankee Blue'	IBal
'Yellow Boa'	EMic IBal NSue
'Yellow Edge' (*fortunei*)	see *H. fortunei* var. *aureomarginata*
'Yellow Edge' (*sieboldiana*)	see *H.* 'Frances Williams'
'Yellow Polka Dot Bikini' (v)	NSue
'Yellow River' (v)	EMic IBal LRHS NGdn NNor NSue
'Yellow Splash' (v)	EMic LRHS MHom NNor
'Yellow Splash Rim' (v)	EMic
'Yellow Splashed Edged' (v)	EMic
'Yesterday's Memories' (v)	EMic
'Yin' (v)	EMic IBal
yingeri	WPGP WSHC
- B&SWJ 546	LEdu WCru
'Yucca Ducka Do' (v)	IBal
'Zager Blue'	EMic
'Zager Green'	EMic
'Zager White Edge' (*fortunei*) (v)	EMic IBal
'Zebra Stripes' (v)	IBal
'Zion's Hope'	EMic
'Zodiac' (*fortunei*) (v)	IBal
'Zounds'	EBee ECtt EMic EPfP EShb GKev IBal LRHS MRav NGdn NLar NSti NSue SRms WFar WWEG

Hottonia (*Primulaceae*)

palustris	EHon MSKA MWts NPer SWat

Houstonia (*Rubiaceae*)

caerulea L.	ECho
- var. ***alba***	SPlb
- 'Millard's Variety'	WIce
michauxii 'Fred Mullard'	EWes GCrg

Houttuynia (*Saururaceae*)

cordata	CBAq CBod COtt EWTr GKev GPoy LEdu LPot SDix SWat WFar WWEG XLum
§ - 'Boo-Boo' (v)	CMac EPfP EPla NBro SMrm WWEG
§ - 'Chameleon' (v)	Widely available
- 'Fantasy'	EBee LLWG
- 'Flame' (v)	CHel CMac EBee EPla LBMP MBri SHil SMrm WFar WWEG
- 'Flore Pleno' (d)	CBAq CBen CMac CRow CWat ECha EHon EPfP EPla MRav MSCN NBir NPer SPer SPlb SRms SWat WHrl WPnP XLum
- 'Joker's Gold'	CMac EBee ECtt ELan EPPr EPfP EPla SMrm WFar
- 'Pied Piper'	CDoC CWCL ELan NBir SGol SPad SPtp
- 'Tequila Sunrise'	CHEx
- 'Terry Clarke'	see *H. cordata* 'Boo-Boo'
- 'Tricolor'	see *H. cordata* 'Chameleon'
- Variegata Group (v)	CBAq NBro

Hovea (*Papilionaceae*)

celsii	see *H. elliptica*
§ ***elliptica***	SPlb
montana	SPlb

Hovenia (*Rhamnaceae*)

dulcis	CAgr CBcs EPfP ETwe LEdu NLar
- B&SWJ 11024	WCru
- NJM 11.003 **new**	WPGP

Howea (*Arecaceae*)

§ ***belmoreana*** ♀H1b	XBlo
§ ***forsteriana*** ♀H1b	CCCN LPal NPla XBlo

Hoya (*Apocynaceae*)

§ ***australis***	CBcs
bella	see *H. lanceolata* subsp. *bella*
carnosa ♀H2	CBcs EBak EOHP WWFP
- 'Compacta Regalis' (v)	NPer
- 'Krinkle 8'	NPer
- 'Tricolor' (v)	NPer
* ***compacta*** 'Tricolor'	NPer
darwinii misapplied	see *H. australis*
lacunosa	CCCN
§ ***lanceolata***	CBcs EShb
subsp. ***bella*** ♀H1c	
linearis	EShb

huckleberry, garden see *Solanum scabrum*

Hugueninia (*Brassicaceae*)

alpina	see *H. tanacetifolia*
§ ***tanacetifolia***	WOut

Humata (*Davalliaceae*)

tyermannii	CMen EFtx EShb ISha SPlb WFib

Humea see *Calomeria*

elegans	see *Calomeria amaranthoides*

Humulus ✿ (*Cannabaceae*)

japonicus 'Variegatus' (v)	SGol
lupulus	CArn CBcs CUse EPfP GPoy NLar NMir SCob SIde WHer
- 'Aureus' ♀H6	Widely available
- 'Aureus' (f)	CHel CRHN ELon GCal GKev SPoG WBor WCot WWFP
* - ***compactus***	GPoy
- 'Fuggle'	CAgr GPoy SDea
- 'Golden Tassels' (f)	CSPN EAEE ECrN ELon LBrs LRHS MCoo MGos MJak MMuc MNHC NLar NPri SEND SGol SPer SPoG
- (Goldings Group) 'Cobbs'	SDea
- - 'Mathons'	CAgr SDea
- 'Hallertauer'	SDea
- 'Prima Donna'	CAgr CMac MCoo NLar SCoo SPer SPoG SWvt
- 'Taff's Variegated' (v)	EWes WSHC
- 'Wye Challenger'	CAgr GPoy MHer
- 'Wye Northdown'	CAgr SDea

Hunnemannia (*Papaveraceae*)

fumariifolia	CSpe XSen

Huodendron (*Styracaceae*)

tibeticum	CFil

Hutchinsia see *Pritzelago*

rotundifolia	see *Thlaspi cepaeifolium* subsp. *rotundifolium*

Hyacinthella (*Asparagaceae*)

acutiloba	ECho
dalmatica	ECho
glabrescens	WCot
heldreichii	ECho
leucophaea	ECho
millingenii	ECho
pallens	ECho

Hyacinthoides (*Asparagaceae*)

aristidis	ECho WCot
§ ***hispanica***	ECho LRHS NBir SEND WCot
- 'Alba'	ECho LRHS
- subsp. ***algeriensis***	WCot
- 'Dainty Maid'	ECho WCot
- 'Miss World'	WCot
- 'Queen of the Pinks'	WCot
- 'Rosea'	ECho
- 'White City'	ECho WCot
§ ***italica*** ♀H4	ECho WShi
mauritanica	ECho
§ ***non-scripta***	CAvo CBro CHab CTca CTri CWld ECho EPot GKev LAma LPot LRHS MCot MHer MMuc NBir NPri SDeJ SEND SPer SRms SVic WHer WShi XLum
- 'Alba'	CAvo ECho MMuc NBir SEND
- 'Backkum's Blue'	NMin
- 'Bracteata'	CNat
- cleistogamous	CNat
- long-bracteate, white-flowered **new**	CDes
- 'Rosea'	ECho
- 'Stuart Williams'	CAvo
§ ***vincentina***	WCot

Hyacinthus ✿ (*Asparagaceae*)

amethystinus	see *Brimeura amethystina*
azureus	see *Muscari azureum*
comosus 'Plumosus'	see *Muscari comosum* 'Plumosum'
orientalis 'Aiolos'	SDeJ SPer
- 'Amethyst'	LAma
- 'Amsterdam'	LAma
- 'Anastasia'	CAvo
- 'Anna Liza'	MBri SDeJ
- 'Anna Marie' ♀H4	CBro LAma MBri SDeJ
- 'Apricot Passion'	SDeJ
- 'Blue Eyes' **new**	SDeJ
- 'Blue Festival' ♀H4	SDeJ
- 'Blue Giant'	LAma SDeJ
- 'Blue Jacket' ♀H4	CBro LAma MBri SDeJ
- 'Blue Magic'	SDeJ
- 'Blue Pearl' PBR	SDeJ
- 'Blue Star'	LAma
- 'Carnegie'	CAvo CBro EPfP ERCP LAma MJak
- 'Chestnut Flower' (d)	SDeJ
- 'China Pink'	LRHS SDeJ SPer
- 'City of Haarlem' ♀H4	CBro EPfP LAma LRHS MBri MJak SDeJ
- 'Crystal Palace' (d)	LAma SDeJ
- 'Delft Blue' ♀H4	CAvo CBro EPfP LAma LRHS MBri MJak SDeJ SPer
- 'Fondant'	LAma LRHS SDeJ
- 'General Köhler' (d)	LAma SDeJ
- 'Gipsy Princess'	LAma
- 'Gipsy Queen' ♀H4	EPfP LAma MBri SDeJ WCot
- 'Hollyhock' (d) ♀H4	ERCP LAma SDeJ
- 'Jan Bos' ♀H4	LAma LRHS MBri SDeJ
- 'Lady Derby'	SDeJ
- 'L'Innocence' ♀H4	CAvo CBro
- 'Miss Saigon' ♀H4	ERCP SDeJ
- multi-flowered	ERCP SDeJ
- 'Odysseus'	LAma SDeJ
- 'Ostara' ♀H4	LAma MBri
- 'Paul Hermann' ♀H4	SDeJ
- 'Peter Stuyvesant'	EPfP ERCP LAma SDeJ
- 'Pink Festival' ♀H4	SDeJ
- 'Pink Pearl'	EPfP LAma LRHS MBri SDeJ
- 'Pink Royal' (d)	LAma
- 'Red Magic'	SDeJ
- 'Rosette' (d)	LAma SDeJ
- 'Splendid Cornelia'	ERCP SDeJ
- 'White Festival' ♀H4	SDeJ
- 'White Pearl'	LAma LRHS MBri SDeJ
- 'Woodstock'	CAvo CBro EPfP ERCP LAma SDeJ SPer

Hydrangea ✿ (*Hydrangeaceae*)

sp.	CAco
angustipetala	see *H. scandens* subsp. *chinensis* f. *angustipetala*
anomala subsp. ***anomala*** BWJ 8052 from China	WCru
- - HWJK 2065 from Nepal	WCru
§ - - 'Winter Glow'	CJun ESwi MTPN WCot WCru WFar
- subsp. ***glabra*** B&SWJ 6804	WCru
- - 'Crûg Coral'	WCru
§ - subsp. ***petiolaris*** ♀H5	Widely available
- - B&SWJ 5996 from Yakushima	WCru

	- - B&SWJ 6337	WCru
	- - from Yakushima	CFil
§	- - var. ***cordifolia***	NBro NLar
	- - - B&SWJ 6081	WCru
	- - - B&SWJ 11487	WCru
§	- - - 'Brookside Littleleaf'	GKin IDee NBro NLar WFar
	- - dwarf	see *H. anomala* subsp. *petiolaris* var. *cordifolia*
	- - 'Early Light' (v) new	SGbt
	- - 'Firefly' (v)	WPat
	- - var. ***megaphylla*** B&SWJ 4400	WCru
	- - - B&SWJ 8497 new	WCru
*	- - var. ***minor*** B&SWJ 5991	GEdr WCru
	- - 'Mirranda'	CBcs CRHN ELan EPfP ESwi GCal NBro NLar SGol SPoG SWvt WBor WGrn
§	- - var. ***ovalifolia***	CMil CRHN ESwi EWTr GQui LRHS
	- - - B&SWJ 8799	WCru
	- - - B&SWJ 8846	WCru
	- - 'Silver Lining' new	EPfP SPoG
	- - 'Summer Snow' (v) new	LRHS
	- - var. ***tiliifolia***	see *H. anomala* subsp. *petiolaris* var. *ovalifolia*
	- - 'Yakushima'	WCru
	- subsp. ***quelpartensis***	see *H. anomala* subsp. *petiolaris* var. *ovalifolia*
	- Semiola = 'Inovalaur'PBR	EPfP ESwi EWTr LLHF LRHS SGol SKHP SLim SPoG WPGP
	- 'Winter Surprise'	see *H. anomala* subsp. *anomala* 'Winter Glow'
§	***arborescens***	CArn CExl MRav WPGP
	- 'Annabelle' ♀H6	Widely available
	- 'Bounty'	MAsh WPat
§	- subsp. ***discolor***	LEdu WPat
	- - 'Sterilis'	CFil GBin GGGa SHyH WPGP WPat
	- Endless Summer Bella Anna = 'Piiha-I' (Endless Summer Series)	LBuc MBri NSoo
	- 'Grandiflora'	CBcs EPfP IBoy NBro NEgg WPGP
	- 'Hayes Starburst'PBR	CDoC CMil CWGN EBee GGGa LEdu LLHF LRHS SHyH SKHP SPoG SSpi SWvt WPGP WPat
	- 'Hills of Snow'	IVic NLar
	- Incrediball = 'Abetwo'	CBcs CRos ELan EPfP LRHS LSqu MBlu NLar SLon SPoG
§	- Invincibelle Spirit = 'Ncha1'	CBcs CDoC CRos ELan EPfP GBin LLHF LRHS LSqu MBlu SCob SGol SHyH SLon SPer SPoG SWvt
	- 'Invincible Spirit'	see *H. arborescens* Invincibelle Spirit
	- 'Picadilly'	NLar
	- 'Pink Annabelle'	see *H. arborescens* Invincibelle Spirit
	- 'Pink Pincushion'	CJun NBro NLar
	- 'Puffed Green'	NLar
	- subsp. ***radiata***	ETwe LRHS MRav WCru WPGP
	- - 'Samantha'	EPfP LLHF LRHS WPGP
	- 'Ryan Gainey'	EUJe LEdu MPkF
	- 'Vasterival'	NLar
	- 'Visitation' new	ETwe
	- White Dome = 'Dardom'PBR	NBro
	aspera	CMac CTri EUJe SHyH SLon SSpi SSta WCru WKif WPGP
	- HWJCM 452	WCru
	- from Gongshan, China	CExl CFil CMil WPGP
	- 'Anthony Bullivant' ♀H5	CDul IArd IDee LRHS MAsh MBri NLar SHyH SKHP SWvt WPat
	- 'Bellevue'	IVic WPGP
	- Farrell form	CFil
	- 'Hot Chocolate' new	CMil SCob SPoG WCot WGrn WHlf
	- Kawakamii Group	CExl CHEx CMil CSpe ESwi LRHS NLar SGol SKHP SWvt WCru WPGP WPat
	- - B&SWJ 3456	WCru
	- - B&SWJ 3527	WCru
	- - B&SWJ 6702	WCru
	- - B&SWJ 6714	WCru
	- - B&SWJ 6827	WCru
	- - B&SWJ 6996	WCru
	- - B&SWJ 7101	WCru
	- (Kawakamii Group) 'August Abundance'	WCru
	- - 'Formosa'	WCru
	- - 'Maurice Mason'	CExl CFil
	- - 'September Splendour'	WCru
	- Kawakamii Group × ***involucrata***	CFil WPGP
	- 'Macrophylla' ♀H5	CFil EPfP EWTr GCal GKin IVic MBri MGos MRav NLar SHil SHyH SPer SWvt WCru WPGP
	- 'Mauvette'	CMil ECre EPfP GKin LRHS MBlu MBri NBro NLar SCob SGol SHyH SPer WCru
	- 'Peter Chappell' ♀H5	CExl CMac CMil LRHS NLar SHyH SWvt WPat
	- 'Pink Cloud'	CFil
§	- subsp. ***robusta***	CExl WPGP
	- - GWJ 9430	WCru
	- - WWJ 11888	WCru
	- 'Rocklon'	CMil ESwi ETwe NLar WCru
	- 'Rosthornii'	see *H. aspera* subsp. *robusta*
	- 'Sam MacDonald'	CExl LRHS NLar SKHP SSpi WPGP WPat
§	- subsp. ***sargentiana***	Widely available
	- - 'La Fosse'	WPGP
	- - large-leaved	CExl CFil WCru
	- 'Spinners'	NLar
	- subsp. ***strigosa***	CDul CExl EPfP LRHS SHyH SSpi SWvt WCru WPGP
	- - B&SWJ 8201	WCru
	- - HWJ 653	WCru
	- - HWJ 737	WCru
	- - KWJ 12151 from northern Vietnam new	WCru
	- - from Gong Shan, China	CExl
	- aff. subsp. ***strigosa***	CFil
	- 'Taiwan Pink'	EPfP IArd NLar
	- 'The Ditch'	ESwi ETwe NLar
	- 'Trelissick Blue Skies'	CFil
	- 'Velvet and Lace' ♀H5	CJun LRHS MBri MGos NLar SHil
§	- Villosa Group	Widely available
	- - 'Trelissick'	CFil
	asterolasia B&SWJ 10481	WCru
	cinerea	see *H. arborescens* subsp. *discolor*
	'Dark Angel'	LRHS
	davidii B&SWJ 11692 new	WCru
	- B&SWJ 11717 new	WCru
	- f. ***purpurascens*** KWJ 12233B new	WCru
	'Garden House Glory'	CExl CFil WPGP
	glabrifolia	see *H. scandens* subsp. *chinensis*
	glandulosa B&SWJ 4031	WCru
	'Glyn Church'	EBee WPGP
	aff. ***gracilis*** B&SWJ 3942	WCru
§	***heteromalla***	CMHG GGGa GGal NBro WPGP

- B&SWJ 2142 from India WCru
- B&SWJ 2602 from Sikkim WCru
- BWJ 7657 from China WCru
- GWJ 9337 from Sikkim WCru
- HWJ 526 from Vietnam **new** WCru
- HWJ 938 from Vietnam WCru
- HWJCM 180 WCru
- HWJK 2127 from Nepal WCru
- KR 9913 from India **new** WPGP
- SBEC GGGa
- Bretschneideri Group EBee EPfP GKin GQui SHyH WCru
- 'Fan Si Pan' WCru
- 'June Pink' **new** NLar
- 'Long White' **new** NLar
- 'Morrey's Form' NLar WCru WPGP
- 'Nepal Beauty' EPfP ESwi ETwe EUJe IVic NLar SGol WPGP
- 'Snowcap' EPfP GQui IArd LRHS NLar SHyH SKHP WPGP
- f. ***xanthoneura*** NJM 11.009 **new** WPGP
- - 'Wilsonii' WCru WKif
- 'Yalung Ridge' WCru

hirta B&SWJ 5000 WCru
- B&SWJ 11022 WCru

indochinensis CExl ESwi
- B&SWJ 8307 WCru
- WWJ 11609 **new** WCru

integerrima see *H. serratifolia*

integrifolia B&SWJ 022 WCru
- B&SWJ 6967 NLar WCru

involucrata LLHF LRHS MMHG SBrt SHil SHyH
- B&SWJ 4790 WCru
- dwarf CExl CFil WCru
- 'Hortensis' (d) CMil MRav NLar SMad SSpi WCru WKif WPGP WSHC
- 'Mihara-kokonoe' WPGP
- 'Multiplex' WCru
- 'Oshima' WPGP
- 'Plena' (d) EBee LRHS MRav NLar WCru WPGP
- 'Plenissima' (d) **new** WCru
- 'Sterilis' CMil WCru
- 'Tokada Yama' CMil NLar
- 'Viridescens' ♀H4 LLHF LRHS NLar SHyH WCru WPGP
- 'Yohraku-tama' ♀H4 CFil NLar WPGP
- 'Yokudanka' (d) CMil GQui NLar WPGP
- 'Yoraku' (d) **new** WCru

kawagoeana WCru
var. ***grosseserrata*** B&SWJ 11500

lingii B&SWJ 11790 WCru

lobbii see *H. scandens* subsp. *chinensis*

longifolia B&SWJ 6883 WCru
- CWJ 12413 WCru

longipes CExl CMil GQui WCru WPGP
- var. ***fulvescens*** B&SWJ 8188 WCru
- var. ***longipes*** CExl CFil
- - NJM 11.052 **new** WPGP

luteovenosa WCru
- B&SWJ 5647 WCru
- B&SWJ 5929 WCru
- B&SWJ 6220 WCru
- B&SWJ 6317 WCru

macrophylla (H) GGal LRHS
- 'AB Green Shadow'PBR (H) COtt ETwe MAsh MMHG SPoG
- 'Adria' (H) COtt MBri MWat NLar SHyH
- 'Aduarda' see *H. macrophylla* 'Mousmée'
- 'All Summer Beauty' (H) CDoC ELon GBin GGGa MAsh SHyH
- Alpen Glow see *H. macrophylla* 'Alpenglühen'

§ - 'Alpenglühen' (H) CBcs CExl CSBt IVic LRHS MBri SHyH SLim
- 'Altona' (H) ♀H5 CBcs EPfP GGGa IArd LRHS MAsh MBri MGos MRav NBir NLar SPer
- 'Ami Pasquier' (H) CBcs CDoC CMac CSBt CSde CTri CTsd ELan EPfP GGal IVic LRHS MAsh MBri MMuc MRav MSwo NEgg SCob SCoo SEND SHyH SLim SSpi SWvt
- 'Amor' (H) **new** SCob

* - 'Aureomarginata' (v) SHyH WCot
- 'Ave Maria' (H) GGGa MAsh

§ - 'Ayesha' (H) Widely available
- 'Bachstelze' (Teller Series) (L) IVic MAsh WPGP
- 'Bavaria' (H) GKin WFar
- 'Beauté Vendômoise' (L) CMil LRHS NLar SHyH SSpi WPGP
- 'Bela'PBR (H) COtt LRHS SCob
- 'Benelux' (H) CBcs
- 'Bicolor' see *H. macrophylla* 'Harlequin'
- 'Black Steel Zambia' (H) EPfP LBuc MBri NPri SLon
- 'Black Steel Zaza' (H) **new** LBuc
- 'Black Steel Zebra' (H) EPfP LBuc NPri SLon

§ - 'Blauer Prinz' (H) SHyH

§ - 'Bläuling' (Teller Series) (L) ♀H5 CDoC EPfP GKin LRHS MBri SCob SLim WHar

§ - 'Blaumeise' (Teller Series) (L) ♀H5 CDoC CFil CMHG COtt EAEE ELon EPfP GGGa LRHS MAsh MBri MGos MRav MWat SCoo SHyH SLim SLon SPoG SSpi SWvt WFar WPGP
- 'Blue Bonnet' (H) CDul EPfP LRHS MRav SHyH SPer
- Blue Butterfly see *H. macrophylla* 'Bläuling'
- Blue Prince see *H. macrophylla* 'Blauer Prinz'
- Blue Sky see *H. macrophylla* 'Blaumeise'
- Blue Tit see *H. macrophylla* 'Blaumeise'
- 'Blue Wave' see *H. macrophylla* 'Mariesii Perfecta'
- Bluebird see *H. macrophylla* 'Bläuling'
- 'Bluebird' misapplied see *H. serrata* 'Bluebird'

§ - 'Blushing Bride'PBR (H) ELan MAsh MBri NPri SLon SPoG
- 'Bodensee' (H) MBri MGos MMuc MWat SEND SHyH
- 'Bouquet Rose' (H) ECtt MJak MMuc NLar SEND SHyH
- 'Brestenburg' (H) MAsh
- 'Brügg' (H) LRHS MAsh SHyH SLim SPer WPGP
- 'Camilla'PBR (H) **new** WFar
- 'Camino' (L) **new** EPfP
- Cardinal see *H. macrophylla* 'Kardinal' (Teller Series)

§ - 'Cardinal Red' (H) ECre NPri WFar
- 'Cendrillon' (H) CMil LLHF LRHS STPC
- 'Coco Blanc' (H/d) **new** SCob
- Color Fantasy (H) MBrN
- 'Cordata' see *H. arborescens*
- 'Dandenong' (L) GQui
- 'Dart's Romance' (L) SHyH
- 'Deutschland' (H) CTri MBri
- 'Doctor Jean Varnier' (L) EMil EPfP SHyH
- Dolce Gipsy = 'Dolgip'PBR (L) EPfP ESwi ETwe LRHS SHil
- Dolce Kiss = 'Dolkis'PBR (L) CDoC EPfP ETwe LRHS SHil
- 'Domotoi' see *H. macrophylla* 'Setsuka-yae'
- 'Doris' (H) **new** SCob
- Dragonfly see *H. macrophylla* 'Libelle'

	Name	Suppliers
	- Early Blue = 'Hba 202911'PBR (H) **new**	COtt LRHS
§	- 'Early Sensation' (Forever & Ever Series) (H)	CMac GKin LBuc LLHF
	- 'Eldorado' (H)	SHyH
	- Endless Summer = 'Bailmer' (H)	ELan EPfP LBuc MAsh MGos NPri SPoG
	- Endless Summer Blushing BridePBR	see *H. macrophylla* 'Blushing Bride'
	- Endless Summer Twist-n-Shout = 'Piihm-I' (L)	EPfP MBri
§	- 'Enziandom' (H)	CBcs CExl CFil CSBt GGal MAsh WPGP
	- Eternity = 'Youmetwo'PBR (H/d)	WCot
	- 'Etoile Violette' (L)	ESwi LRHS
	- 'Europa' (H) ℽH5	CBcs CExl LRHS SHyH
§	- 'Fasan' (Teller Series) (L)	MAsh NBro SDix WHar
	- Firelight	see *H. macrophylla* 'Leuchtfeuer'
	- Fireworks	see *H. macrophylla* 'Hanabi'
	- Fireworks Blue	see *H. macrophylla* 'Jōgasaki'
	- Fireworks Pink	see *H. macrophylla* 'Jōgasaki'
	- Fireworks White	see *H. macrophylla* 'Hanabi'
	- Forever & Ever Together = 'Rie 05' (Forever & Ever Series) (H/d) **new**	SMDP
	- Forever and Ever	see *H. macrophylla* 'Early Sensation'
	- 'Forever Pink' (H)	GGGa MAsh MWat NLar
§	- 'Frau Fujiyo' (Lady Series) (H)	CExl
§	- 'Frau Katsuko' (Lady Series) (H)	SPer
§	- 'Frau Mariko' (Lady Series) (H)	MRav
§	- 'Frau Taiko' (Lady Series) (H)	SPer
	- 'Freudenstein' (H)	ESwi
	- 'Frillibet' (H)	CAbP MRav NLar
	- 'Ganku Bo Chokens' (H)	WCot
	- 'Gartenbaudirektor Kühnert' (H)	SHyH
§	- 'Générale Vicomtesse de Vibraye' (H) ℽH5	CBcs CDoC CDul CEnd CSde CTri ELan ELon EPfP GGal LRHS MAsh SCob SHyH SLim SPer SPoG SSpi
	- Gentian Dome	see *H. macrophylla* 'Enziandom'
	- 'Geoffrey Chadbund'	see *H. macrophylla* 'Möwe'
	- 'Gerda Steiniger' (H)	SHyH
	- 'Gertrud Glahn' (H)	SHyH
	- 'Gimpel' (Teller Series) (L)	MAsh
	- 'Glowing Embers' (H)	IArd
	- Goldrush = 'Nehyosh' (L/v)	CDul EBee LRHS NHol SLim WCot
	- 'Goliath' (H)	ELon EPfP
§	- 'Grant's Choice' (L)	NBro
	- Great Star = 'Blanc Bleu' (L)	ECrN EPfP EPla LRHS SLim WFar
	- 'Hamburg' (H)	CBcs CTri ECtt EPfP MGos SCob SDix SHyH SLim WFar
§	- 'Hanabi' (L/d) ℽH5	CAbP CBcs CDoC CEnd ECre GGal LRHS MBlu NLar SHyH
§	- 'Harlequin' (H)	CMac GGGa WCot
	- 'Harry's Red' (H)	MAsh
	- 'Hatsu-shime' (L)	NLar
	- 'Heinrich Seidel' (H)	CBcs CTri WMoo
	- 'Hobella'PBR (Hovaria Series) (L)	CBcs WFar
	- 'Holehird Purple' (H)	MAsh
	- Hot Red = 'Hba 206901'PBR (H) **new**	LRHS
	- 'Izu-no-hana' (L/d)	CAbb CBcs CFil CHel CMil ELon ESwi GBin MBlu NLar SBod SHyH WBor WPGP
	- 'James Grant'	see *H. macrophylla* 'Grant's Choice'
	- 'Jofloma' (H)	ESwi NLar
§	- 'Jōgasaki' (L/d)	CBcs CExl CLAP CMil LRHS MAsh MBlu NLar SDys SHyH WPGP
	- 'Joseph Banks' (H)	CBcs CTri SHyH
	- 'Kardinal'	see *H. macrophylla* 'Cardinal Red' (H)
§	- 'Kardinal' (Teller Series) (L) ℽH5	MAsh MWat SCob SGol
	- 'King George' (H)	CBcs CDoC CDul CSBt EBee EPfP LRHS MGos MMuc MSCN NEgg NHol SAdn SCob SGol SHyH SLim SPer SPoG SWvt WFar WMoo
§	- 'Klaveren' (L) ℽH5	CMil GGGa MAsh NBro
	- 'Kluis Superba' (H)	CBcs CTri GGal SHyH
	- 'La France' (H)	CTri IVic LRHS SCob SHyH SLim
	- 'Lady Fujiyo'	see *H. macrophylla* 'Frau Fujiyo'
	- 'Lady in Red' (L)	CMil EPfP LRHS SPoG
	- Lady Katsuko	see *H. macrophylla* 'Frau Katsuko'
	- 'Lady Mariko'	see *H. macrophylla* 'Frau Mariko'
	- 'Lady Taiko Blue'	see *H. macrophylla* 'Frau Taiko'
	- 'Lady Taiko Pink'	see *H. macrophylla* 'Frau Taiko'
	- 'Lanarth White' (L) ℽH5	CBcs CDoC CDul CExl CFil CHel CSBt CTri EAEE ECre ELan EPfP LBMP LRHS MAsh MMuc MSwo NLar SEND SGol SHyH SLim SPer SRms SSpi SWvt WBor WKif WPGP WPat
	- 'Lemon Wave' (L/v)	NLar
§	- 'Leuchtfeuer' (H)	ELon LRHS MBri MWat SHyH WMoo
§	- 'Libelle' (Teller Series) (L) ℽH5	CBcs CDoC CMil ELon EPfP LRHS MGos MRav MWat NLar SCob SGol SHyH SLim SPer SSpi
	- 'Lilacina'	see *H. macrophylla* 'Mariesii Lilacina'
	- 'Love You Kiss'PBR (Hovaria Series) (L) ℽH5	CBcs CMil COtt LRHS NLar SCoo SPoG SRGP STPC WCot
§	- 'Maculata' (L/v)	GQui WGwG
	- 'Madame A. Riverain' (H)	EPfP NLar SHyH
	- 'Madame Emile Mouillère' (H) ℽH5	Widely available
	- Magical Harmony = 'Hortmahar'PBR (H) **new**	NLar
	- Magical Jade = 'Hortmaja'PBR (H)	EPfP MBlu WCot
	- 'Maréchal Foch' (H)	CTri GGal NLar
	- 'Mariesii' (L)	CMHG CTri ELan GGal LRHS MSwo NLar SHyH SPer
§	- 'Mariesii Grandiflora' (L)	EPfP GGal LRHS MMuc NBro SEND SHyH SPer SRms WMoo
§	- 'Mariesii Lilacina' (L) ℽH5	EPfP MMuc SEND SHyH SLon SPer SSpi WMoo
§	- 'Mariesii Perfecta' (L)	Widely available
	- 'Masja' (H)	CBcs ELon GKin IArd IVic LAst MAsh MGos MMuc MRav MSwo NBro NLar SCob SEND SGol SHyH SLim WBor WMoo
	- 'Mathilde Gütges' (H)	CDoC GGal
	- 'Max Löbner' (H)	SHyH
	- 'Merveille' (H) **new**	NBro

	Name	Suppliers
	- 'Merveille Sanguine' (H)	Widely available
	- 'Messalina' (L)	MWat SCob SHyH
	- 'Mirai'PBR (H)	CBcs CDoC CMil ELan ESwi SHyH WCot WPGP
	- 'Miss Belgium' (H)	CMac CTri GKin MAsh
§	- 'Mousmée' (L)	IArd SHyH SSpi
	- 'Mousseline' (H)	CFil CMil MAsh
§	- 'Möwe' (Teller Series) (L) 🏆H5	CBcs CDoC CEnd CExl CMil ECtt ELon EPfP GBin GGal MAsh MBri MMuc MNHC SCob SCoo SDix SEND SGol SHyH SLim SPer SRms SSpi SSta WPat
	- 'Mrs W.J. Hepburn' (H)	CSBt SHyH SPer
§	- 'Nachtigall' (Teller Series) (L) 🏆H5	GGal IVic MAsh WPGP WPat
	- 'Nanping'PBR (Sturdy Series) (L)	EPfP
	- 'Niedersachsen' (H)	CDoC CTri MRav SHyH
	- Nightingale	see *H. macrophylla* 'Nachtigall'
	- 'Nigra' (H)	CBcs CExl CFil CHel CMac CTsd ELan ELon EPfP GBin IFoB LRHS MAsh MGos MMuc MNHC MRav MSCN NBro NLar SAdn SDix SEND SHyH SLim SPer WGrn WGwG WPGP WPat
	- 'Nikko Blue' (H)	CBcs EPfP GKin LRHS MBri MJak NLar SHyH
	- Nizza = 'Ranice'PBR (City-line Series) (H) **new**	SCob
	- var. ***normalis*** (L)	CExl
§	- 'Nymphe' (H)	MBri MWat SCob SHyH
	- 'Oregon Pride' (H)	CFil GGGa MAsh WFar WPGP
	- 'Otaksa' (H)	NLar
	- 'Papagei' (Teller Series) (L)	SPer
	- 'Parzifal' (H) 🏆H5	CDul
	- Passion = 'Youmefour' (L) **new**	WCot
	- 'Pax'	see *H. macrophylla* 'Nymphe'
	- 'Pfau' (Teller Series) (L) 🏆H5	CHel CMil ELon GBin MAsh SHyH
	- Pheasant	see *H. macrophylla* 'Fasan'
	- 'Pia' (H)	CDoC CExl CMac CMil CPla EShb LBMP LRHS MBri MGos MRav SHyH SMad SPer SRms WBor WGrn
	- Pigeon	see *H. macrophylla* 'Taube'
	- 'Pirate's Gold' (v)	EHoe WHar WMoo
	- 'Prinses Beatrix' (H)	SHyH
	- 'Quadricolor' (L/v) 🏆H5	CExl CHll CMac CMil CTsd EHoe GCal GGal MAsh MGos MRav SAdn SDix SHyH SLim SMDP SPer SPlb SRms WCot WSHC
	- 'Queen Elizabeth' (H)	GKin
	- 'R.F. Felton' (H)	CBcs SHyH
	- 'Red Baron'	see *H. macrophylla* 'Schöne Bautznerin'
	- 'Red Red' (H)	MAsh
	- Redbreast	see *H. macrophylla* 'Rotkehlchen'
	- 'Regula' (H)	SHyH
	- 'Renate Steiniger' (H)	CDoC LRHS MBri MGos MMuc MRav SCob SEND SHyH SLim WMoo
	- 'Romance'	MWat SCob WCot
	- 'Rosea'	MCri
	- 'Rosita' (H)	COtt MAsh MBri MWat NBir SCob
	- 'Rotdrossel' (Teller Series) (L)	GBin
§	- 'Rotkehlchen' (Teller Series) (L)	CDoC EPfP NLar SLim SPlb SWvt
	- 'Rotschwanz' (Teller Series) (L) 🏆H5	CFil CMil ESwi GBin LLHF LRHS MAsh SHyH WPGP WPat
	- 'Sabrina'PBR (H)	CBcs CMil LLHF LRHS MAsh MWat SCob SHyH SRkn
	- 'Saint Claire' (H)	CBcs
	- 'Salsa'	CMil LLHF MAsh MBri SHyH
	- 'Sandra' (Dutch Ladies Series) (L)	CBcs CMil MAsh STPC
	- 'Schneeball' (H)	MAsh MBri MWat SCob SHyH
§	- 'Schöne Bautznerin'	COtt LRHS MBri MWat SAdn SHyH SLim
	- 'Sea Foam' (L)	EPla NLar
	- 'Selina'	CBcs CDoC EPfP LAst LBuc LLHF LRHS MAsh MBri SCoo
	- 'Selma'PBR (Dutch Ladies Series) (L)	CBcs MBri SGol
§	- 'Setsuka-yae' (L/d)	CMil
	- 'Shakira' (H)	LLHF
	- 'Sheila' (Dutch Ladies Series) (L)	CBcs EPfP MBri
	- 'Shin-ozaki' (H)	NLar
	- 'Sibilla' (H)	MJak SPlb
	- 'Sindarella'	MBri
	- Sister Therese	see *H. macrophylla* 'Soeur Thérèse'
	- 'Sita' (L) **new**	SHyH
§	- 'Soeur Thérèse' (H)	CBcs EPfP MAsh MMuc MWat NLar SEND SGol SWvt WGwG
	- subsp. ***stylosa*** **new**	WCru
	- - f. ***indochinensis*** **new**	ETwe
	- 'Sumida-no-hanabi' (L/d)	WPGP
*	- 'Sunset' (L)	CBcs
	- 'Superba' (H) **new**	SCob
	- 'Sweet Fantasy' (Hovaria Series) (H)	ELan EPfP
§	- 'Taube' (Teller Series) (L)	CBcs CDoC CExl CMHG EPfP GGal GQui MAsh MGos SCoo SHyH SLim SWvt
	- 'Teller Pink'	see *H. macrophylla* 'Taube'
	- 'Teller Red'	see *H. macrophylla* 'Rotkehlchen'
	- Teller variegated	see *H. macrophylla* 'Tricolor'
	- Teller Weiss	see *H. macrophylla* 'Libelle'
	- var. ***thunbergii***	see *H. serrata* var. *thunbergii*
	- 'Tivoli' (H)	SCob WFar
	- 'Tokyo Delight' (L) 🏆H5	CExl CMac CTsd LRHS MAsh SDys SHyH WPGP
§	- 'Tricolor' (L/v)	CBcs CDoC CDul CTri EBee ELan ELon ESwi LAst LRHS MGos SHyH SLon SPer WFar WMoo
	- 'Variegata'	see *H. macrophylla* 'Maculata'
	- 'Veitchii' (L) 🏆H5	CBcs CDul CExl CMHG CMil CSBt ECre EPfP EWTr GGal LPot LRHS MGos MRav MSwo SDix SHyH SPer SSpi WPGP
	- 'Vicomte de Vibraye'	see *H. macrophylla* 'Générale Vicomtesse de Vibraye'
	- 'Westfalen' (H) 🏆H5	CMac IArd SDix
I	- 'White Lace' (L)	GKin
	- 'White Wave'	see *H. macrophylla* 'Mariesii Grandiflora'
	- 'Yola' (H)	NBro SMDP
	- 'Zaunkoenig' (L)	MAsh
	- 'Zebra'PBR (H)	ELan ESwi LBuc LSun MGos SCob SMDP WCot
	- 'Zhuni Hito' (L)	NLar
	- 'Zorro'PBR (L) 🏆H5	CBcs CDoC CMil EPfP ESwi GGGa GKin LRHS MAsh MCri MGos SCob SCoo SLim SLon SPer SPoG SSpi WCot

Plant	Suppliers
- 'Zsasa' (H)	EPfP
- 'Zulu' (H)	ELan
aff. ***mangshanensis*** BWJ 8120	WCru
paniculata	CMCN
- B&SWJ 3556 from Taiwan	WCru WFar
- B&SWJ 5413 from Japan	WCru
- B&SWJ 8894 from Japan	WCru
- from Taiwan	SKHP
- 'Ammarin'	GQui LLHF WPat
- Angel's Blush	see *H. paniculata* 'Ruby'
- 'Big Ben' ♀H5	CMil EPfP GGGa GQui LRHS NLar SHyH SKHP
- Bobo = 'Ilvobo' **new**	MPkF SCob
- 'Bombshell'PBR	ESwi NLar
- 'Brussels Lace'	CAbP CAbb CDul CLAP CMil EPfP EWTr GBin LEdu LRHS MAsh MRav NLar SCob SGol SHyH SLon SPoG SSta WPat
- 'Burgundy Lace'	CBcs CLAP MBlu NLar
- 'Chantilly Lace'	CMHG CMil EMil LRHS SCob SHyH
- Dart's Little Dot = 'Darlido'PBR	GBin IVic LLHF NLar SLim WFar WPGP WPat
- 'Dharuma'	GKin LLHF LRHS SGol
- Diamant Rouge = 'Rendia'	MPkF SGol
- 'Dolly'	GQui LRHS
- Early Sensation = 'Bulk'PBR	EShb ESwi EThi GBin GKin LRHS MSwo NSoo SHyH SKHP SMDP SSpi WFar WGrn WMoo
- 'Everest'	CAbP CLAP CMil EPfP LRHS MAsh SHyH WPat
- 'Floribunda'	ELan EPfP LRHS SHyH WFar WPGP
- 'Grandiflora'	CBcs CDoC CDul CExl CMac CSBt CTri ELan EPfP EUJe GBin GKin LAst LRHS MGos MJak MRav MSwo NLar NPer SCob SGol SHyH SLim SPer SSta SWvt WHar WMoo WPGP
- 'Great Escape'	NLar
- 'Greenspire'	EPfP LRHS MAsh MBlu MRav SHyH WFar WPat
- 'Harry's Souvenir'	NLar
- 'Kyushu'	Widely available
- 'Last Post'	GQui
- 'Levana' **new**	CMil SHyH
- 'Limelight'PBR ♀H5	Widely available
- Magical Candle = 'Bokraflame'PBR	EPPr EPfP WCot
- Magical Fire = 'Bokraplume'PBR	NLar SCob
- 'Mathilde'	NLar
- Mega Mindy = 'Ilvomindy'PBR	ESwi SCob SKHP
- 'Mega Pearl'	NLar
- 'Melody'	NLar
- 'Mount Aso'	EWld GQui NBro WPGP
- 'October Bride'	CEnd GQui NLar WPGP
- 'Papillon'	WPGP WPat
- 'Pee Wee'	LLHF NLar
- 'Phantom' ♀H5	Widely available
- 'Pink Beauty'PBR (H)	CTri
- Pink Diamond = 'Interhydia' ♀H5	Widely available
- 'Pink Jewel'	LLHF WPat
- 'Pink Lady'	NBro SCob SHyH
- Pinky-Winky = 'Dvppinky'PBR ♀H5	CDul CRos CWGN ECrN EPfP ESwi GBin GKin GQui IArd IVic LBuc LLHF LRHS MBlu MPkF NLar SCob SGol SHil SHyH SKHP SLim SLon SPoG SSpi SSta
- 'Praecox'	GQui MRav WCru
- Prim'White = 'Dolprim'	CDoC LRHS
- 'Rosy Morn'	LRHS
§ - 'Ruby'	CBcs IArd NLar
- 'Silver Dollar' ♀H5	CDoC CMil EPfP ESwi LRHS MBri SCob SHyH SWvt WFar
- Sundae Fraise = 'Rensun'	CDoC CMil CWGN EPfP EShb GGGa LRHS LSqu MAsh MPkF SGol SHil WGrn
- 'Tardiva'	CBcs EPfP GGal GKin GQui LRHS MGos MRav NBro SCob SDix SHyH SPer SRms SWvt WFar WPGP WPat
- 'Tender Rose'	NLar
- 'Unique'	CBcs CDoC CDul EAEE ELan EPfP GQui LRHS MAsh MMuc MRav MSwo NBro NLar SCob SCoo SGol SHil SHyH SPer SSpi SSta WBor WCru WFar WHar WPGP WPat
- Vanille Fraise = 'Renhy'PBR	Widely available
- 'White Goliath'	GQui IArd NLar
- 'White Lace'	NLar
- 'White Lady'	CBcs
- 'White Moth'	CAbP CBcs EBee GGGa LLHF LRHS NBro NLar SAdn SHyH WPat
- 'Wim's Red'PBR	CMil ELan ESwi MMHG NLar SCob SGol SPoG
- 'Yuan-Yang'	WCru
peruviana × ***seemanii***	CEnd GKin IArd IDee SSta
peruviana × ***serratifolia***	WPGP
petiolaris	see *H. anomala* subsp. *petiolaris*
'Preziosa' ♀H4	Widely available
quercifolia	Widely available
- 'Alice'	CJun EBee ELan EMil EPfP ESwi ETwe LRHS MAsh NLar SGol SHyH SSpi WPGP
- 'Alison'	SGol
I - 'Amethyst' Dirr	CJun ETwe NLar SGol
- 'Applause'	LRHS NLar
- 'Back Porch'	GBin MBri NLar SGol
- 'Burgundy'	CBcs CJun CMil EBee EPfP ESwi GBin IArd IDee IVic LRHS NLar SGol WPGP
- 'Flore Pleno'	see *H. quercifolia* Snowflake
- 'Harmony'	CJun CMil EBee ELan EPfP ESwi ETwe IArd LRHS MBri NLar SHil SHyH SKHP SSta WPGP WPat
- 'Ice Crystal'	CMil IVic NLar SGol SHyH WHar WPGP
- 'Lady Anne'	EPfP WPGP
- 'Little Honey'PBR	CMil ETwe NLar SGol SSpi
- Little Honey = 'Brihon'	CAbP IVic LRHS MAsh MPkF SPoG
- 'Pee Wee'	CAbP CBcs CDoC CJun ELan LRHS MAsh MPkF SGol SHyH SKHP SLon SMDP SPoG SSta SWvt WPGP
- 'Sike's Dwarf'	CJun IVic MPkF MRav NLar SGol WCot WPat
- 'Snow Giant'	CJun
- Snow Queen = 'Flemygea' ♀H5	Widely available
- 'Snowdrift'	CJun CMil
§ - Snowflake = 'Brido' (d) ♀H5	CAbP CBcs CDoC CDul CEnd CMac CMil CSde CWGN ELan EPfP LRHS MAsh MGos MRav NLar SHyH SKHP SLon SPer SPoG SSpi SSta WCFE WPGP WPat

Name	Suppliers
- 'Stardust'	MMHG
- 'Tennessee Clone'	CJun ESwi LRHS NLar SHyH SKHP
sargentiana	see *H. aspera* subsp. *sargentiana*
scandens	CFil NBro
- B&SWJ 5448	WCru
- B&SWJ 5481	WCru
- B&SWJ 5496	WCru
- B&SWJ 5523	WCru
- B&SWJ 5602	WCru
- B&SWJ 5725 **new**	WCru
- B&SWJ 5893	WCru
- B&SWJ 6159	WCru
- B&SWJ 6317	WCru
§ - subsp. ***chinensis***	CExl
- - B&SWJ 1488	WCru
- - B&SWJ 3214	WCru
- - B&SWJ 3410 from Taiwan	WCru
- - B&SWJ 3420	WCru
- - B&SWJ 3423	WCru
- - B&SWJ 3487	WCru
- - B&SWJ 3869	WCru
- - BWJ 8000 from Sichuan	WCru
- - BWJ 8035 **new**	WCru
§ - - f. ***angustipetala*** B&SWJ 3454	WCru
- - - B&SWJ 3553	WCru
- - - B&SWJ 3667	WCru
- - - B&SWJ 3733	WCru
- - - B&SWJ 3814	WCru
- - - B&SWJ 6038 from Yakushima	WCru
- - - B&SWJ 6041 from Yakushima	WCru
- - - B&SWJ 6056 from Yakushima	WCru
- - - B&SWJ 6787	WCru
- - - B&SWJ 6802	WCru
- - - B&SWJ 7121	WCru
- - - B&SWJ 7128	WCru
- - - 'Mon-long-shou' **new**	SCob WCru
- - f. ***formosana*** B&SWJ 1488	WCru
- - - B&SWJ 3271	WCru
- - - B&SWJ 3869 from the Philippines **new**	WCru
- - - B&SWJ 7058	NLar WCru
- - - B&SWJ 7097	NLar WCru
- - f. ***macrosepala*** B&SWJ 3423	ESwi WCru
- - - B&SWJ 3476	WCru
- - - CWJ 12441	WCru
- - f. ***obovatifolia*** B&SWJ 3487b	WCru
- - - B&SWJ 3683	WCru
- - - B&SWJ 7121	WCru
- subsp. ***liukiuensis***	WCru
- - B&SWJ 6022	WCru
- - B&SWJ 11471	WCru
- 'Splash' (v)	CMil
seemannii	Widely available
- 'Roger Grounds' (v)	WCot
aff. ***seemannii***	GKin
serrata	CExl CTri WKif
- B&SWJ 6184	WCru
- B&SWJ 6241	WCru
- PAB 4757 **new**	LEdu
- 'Acuminata'	see *H. serrata* 'Bluebird'
- 'Aigaku' (L)	CExl CFil CMil

Name	Suppliers
- 'Aka Beni-yama'	CLAP GQui
- 'Akabe-yama'	NBro NLar
- 'Akishino-temari'	WPGP
- (Amacha Group) 'Amagi-amacha' (L)	CMil GQui NBro NLar
- - 'Ō-amacha' (L)	CMil GQui WPGP
- 'Amagyana' (L)	CExl
- subsp. ***angustata***	WCru
- 'Ao-yama'	WPGP
- Avelroz = 'Dolmyf'^{PBR}	EPfP LRHS
- 'Belladonna'	GQui NBro
- 'Belle Deckle'	see *H. serrata* 'Blue Deckle'
- 'Beni-gaku' (L)	CExl CFil CLAP CMil ECre LRHS MAsh NBro NLar SHyH
- 'Beni-temari'	NBro
- 'Beni-yama' (L) 🏆^{H5}	CFil CMil GQui
- 'Besshi-temari'	CFil
- 'Blue Billow' (L)	NBro NLar
§ - 'Blue Deckle' (L)	CAbb CMHG CMac GGal MAsh MBri MGos MRav NBro SDys
§ - 'Bluebird' (L) 🏆^{H5}	Widely available
- 'Cap Sizun'	WPGP
- 'Chiba Cherry-lips'	ESwi WCru
- 'Chiri-san Sue' (d)	CFil WCru
- 'Crûg Bicolor' (L) **new**	WCru
- 'Crûg Cobalt'	ESwi WCru
- 'Diadem' (L) 🏆^{H5}	CAbb CDoC CExl CLAP CMil EPfP GQui LRHS NBro SHyH
- dwarf white-flowered (L)	WCru
- 'Forget Me Not'	GQui MBri NBro
- 'Fuji Snowstorm' (v)	CMil
- 'Fuji Waterfall'	see *H. serrata* 'Fuji-no-taki'
§ - 'Fuji-no-taki' (L/d) 🏆^{H5}	CAbP CMil ELon ESwi ETwe LLHF NCGa NLar WPGP WWFP
- 'Golden Showers' (L)	NBro
- 'Golden Sunlight'^{PBR} (L)	CDoC SGol SWvt
- 'Graciosa' (L)	LLHF WPat
- 'Grayswood' (L) 🏆^{H5}	CBcs CDul CExl CHel CLAP CMac CSBt EPfP GGal GQui LRHS MAsh MRav NBro SDix SGol SHyH SLim SPer SSpi WBor WKif WPGP
- 'Hakucho' (L/d)	NBro WPGP
- 'Hallasan' misapplied	see *H. serrata* 'Maiko', 'Spreading Beauty'
- 'Hallasan' ambig.	CMil
- 'Hallasan' R. & J. de Belder (L)	CMil WPGP
- 'Hime-benigaku' (L)	CMil MAsh WFar
- 'Impératrice Eugénie' (L)	GQui NLar
- 'Intermedia' (L)	CExl NBro
- 'Isusai-jaku' (L)	GQui
- 'Kiyosumi' (L) 🏆^{H5}	CDoC CEnd CExl CFil CLAP CMil ECre ELon EPfP GGal GQui NBir NLar SBrt SHyH WBor WCot WCru WPGP WPat
- 'Klaveren'	see *H. macrophylla* 'Klaveren'
- 'Kurenai' (L)	CMil NBro NLar WPGP
- 'Kurohime' (L)	CMil NBro WPGP
- 'Macrosepala' (L)	CDoC SHyH WPGP
§ - 'Maiko' (L)	IArd
- 'Midori' (L)	CExl SHyH
- 'Mikata Yae'	CMil WPGP
- 'Miranda' (L) 🏆^{H5}	CDoC CExl CLAP CMil CSam EPfP LRHS MAsh NBro NLar SDys SHyH SSpi WFar
- 'Miyama-yae-murasaki' (L/d) 🏆^{H5}	CAbP CExl CFil CLAP CMil CSpe ESwi WPGP
- 'Momo-beni-yama'	CMil NBro

	- 'Mont Aso'	CMil
	- 'Niji' (L)	WPGP
	- 'Odoriko-amacha'	EBee WPGP
	- 'Otsu-hime'	NLar
	- 'Panachée' (L/v) new	SHyH
	- 'Pretty Maiden'	see *H. serrata* 'Shichidanka'
§	- 'Prolifera' (L/d)	CMil LLHF WPat
	- 'Pulchella'	see *H. serrata* 'Prolifera'
	- 'Ramis Pictis' (L)	CBcs GQui NBro NLar SHyH
	- 'Rosalba' (L) ♀H5	CExl CLAP ECre GGal IVic NBro WSHC
	- 'Santiago'PBR (L)	CDoC EPfP WCot
	- 'Sapphirine' (L)	GQui
	- 'Sekka'	WPGP
§	- 'Shichidanka' (L/d)	CFil CLAP EBee EPfP LLHF LRHS NBro WPat
	- 'Shichidanka-nishiki' (L/d/v)	CDoC CExl CLAP ECre ESwi GQui SHyH WBor
	- 'Shinonome' (L/d)	CExl CMil GQui
	- 'Shirofuji' (L/d) ♀H5	CFil CLAP CMil EWld LLHF MAsh WPGP WPat
	- 'Shiro-gaku' (L)	MAsh NBro NLar
	- 'Shiro-maiko'	WPGP
	- 'Shirotae' (L/d)	CExl CFil CMil WPGP
	- 'Shōjō' ♀H5	CMil NBro WPGP WPat
§	- 'Spreading Beauty' (L)	CMil WPGP
	- 'Suzukayama-yama'	WPGP
§	- var. ***thunbergii*** (L)	GQui
*	- - 'Plena' (L/d)	GQui WCru
	- 'Tiara' (L) ♀H5	CAbb CDoC CDul CExl CFil CLAP CMil EPfP GGGa GGal IVic LRHS MAsh NBir NBro NLar SDix SDys SHyH SLim WPGP WPat
	- 'Tosa-no-akatsuki'	CFil
	- Tuff Stuff = 'Mak20' (L) new	LRHS
	- 'Veerle' (L)	NBro NLar
	- 'Woodlander' (L)	WPat
	- 'Yae-no-amacha' (L/d)	CBcs CExl NBro NLar
	- subsp. ***yezoensis***	CMil GQui NLar
	- - 'Hime-gaku'	CMil
§	***serratifolia***	CExl CHEx EPfP EPla IArd IDee SSpi SSta WPGP
	- HCM 98056	WCru
	sikokiana	CLAP
	- B&SWJ 5035	WCru
	- B&SWJ 5855	WCru
	- B&SWJ 11174	WCru
	- B&SWJ 11381	WCru
	'Silver Slipper'	see *H. macrophylla* 'Ayesha'
	tiliifolia	see *H. anomala* subsp. *petiolaris* var. *ovalifolia*
	villosa	see *H. aspera* Villosa Group
	xanthoneura	see *H. heteromalla*
	'Zambia'	WCot
	aff. ***zhewanensis*** MF 93117 new	WCru

Hydrastis (*Ranunculaceae*)

canadensis	CArn GPoy LEdu

Hydrocharis (*Hydrocharitaceae*)

morsus-ranae	CBAq CBen CHab CRow CWat EHon EWay MSKA MWts NPer SWat WPnP

Hydrocleys (*Alismataceae*)

nymphoides	LLWG XBlo

Hydrocotyle (*Araliaceae*)

asiatica	see *Centella asiatica*
sibthorpioides 'Crystal Confetti' (v)	LLWG
vulgaris	CWat

Hydrophyllum (*Boraginaceae*)

canadense	IMou
'Spring Silver'	SKHP
virginianum	LEdu WHal

Hylomecon (*Papaveraceae*)

	hylomeconoides	EWld WCru
§	***japonica***	CAby CLAP EBee ECho ELan EWld GBBs GCra GEdr GKev IMou LEdu LRHS NBir NRya NSbr WCru WThu

Hylotelephium see *Sedum*

Hymenanthera see *Melicytus*

Hymenocallis (*Amaryllidaceae*)

	'Advance'	ECho LAma
§	***caroliniana***	ECho
	× ***festalis*** ♀H1c	CCCN ECho LAma SDeJ SPav
	- 'Zwanenburg'	ECho
	harrisiana	CCCN CTca ECho SDeJ
§	***longipetala***	ECho
	occidentalis	see *H. caroliniana*
	'Sulphur Queen' ♀H1c	ECho SDeJ SPav

Hymenolepis (*Asteraceae*)

parviflora	see *Athanasia parviflora*

Hymenosporum (*Pittosporaceae*)

flavum	EShb EUJe MOWG

Hymenoxys (*Asteraceae*)

	grandiflora	see *Tetraneuris grandiflora*
§	***hoopesii***	CBod CMac COtt EBee ELan EPfP GMaP LRHS MPie NBir NLar NPri SPer SPoG SRms WCot WFar WHar WMnd WWEG XLum

Hyophorbe (*Arecaceae*)

lagenicaulis	LPal
verschaffeltii	LPal

Hyoscyamus (*Solanaceae*)

niger	CArn GPoy MNHC

Hypericum ✿ (*Hypericaceae*)

	CC 4131	CExl
	CC 4544	CExl
	aegypticum	ECho MHer SBrt SIgm SPlb WAbe WThu
	androsaemum	CArn ECha ELan GAbr MHer MMuc MSwo NPer SEND WFar WHfH WMoo WOut
§	- 'Albury Purple'	ELan EShb NLar WMoo XLum
	- 'Autumn Blaze'	CBcs MBri
§	- 'Dart's Golden Penny'	SPer
	- 'Excellent Flair'	MBri NLar
	- 'Golden Flair'	MMuc
§	- f. ***variegatum*** 'Mrs Gladis Brabazon' (v)	EShb NBir WCot
	athoum	WAbe WIce WThu

avicularifolium var. ***uniflorum*** new	NSla
balearicum	SBrt WAbe XSen
bellum	EBee GCal SLon
buckleyi	WAbe
calycinum	CBcs CBod CDul CMac COtt CTri EBee ECrN ELan ELon EPfP LAst LBuc LSun MGos MRav MWat NWea SCob SEND SGol SPer SWvt WFar WMoo XLum
- 'Brigadoon' ♀H5	LRHS MAsh SGol
- 'Senior'	LAst
cerastioides	CTri ECho EDAr EWes GCrg MMuc NGdn SIgm SRms WAbe XSen
coris	EWes SRms WAbe
cuneatum	see *H. pallens*
× ***cyathiflorum*** 'Gold Cup'	CMac LRHS MAsh
× ***dummeri*** 'Peter Dummer'	EAEE MBri NLar
'Eastleigh Gold'	CMac
elatum	see *H.* × *inodorum*
'Elite Baby Green'	EPfP
'Elite Mayor'	EPfP
'Elite Sweet Lion'	EPfP
elodes	CBAq CWat LLWG MSKA
forrestii ♀H5	MMuc SEND
fragile misapplied	see *H. olympicum* f. *minus*
'Gemo'	SLim
'Gold Penny'	see *H. androsaemum* 'Dart's Golden Penny'
Golden Beacon = 'Wilhyp'PBR ♀H5	CBod CEnd CSpe CUse ESwi GAbr LRHS LSou LSun MNrw NEgg NLar NWad SEND SPad WCot WRHF
grandiflorum	see *H. kouytchense*
grandifolium	EDAr
henryi L 753	SRms
- subsp. ***hancockii*** NJM 10.092	WPGP
'Hidcote' ♀H5	Widely available
'Hidcote Variegated' (v)	LRHS MAsh SLim SRms
hirsutum	CHab NMir
(Hypearls Series) Hypearls Annelies	LRHS
- Hypearls Ella	LRHS
- Hypearls Jacqueline	LRHS
§ × ***inodorum***	WCot
- 'Albury Purple'	see *H. androsaemum* 'Albury Purple'
- 'Autumn Surprise'PBR	NEgg NWad
- 'Dream'	NLar
- 'Elstead'	ECtt ELan EPfP MRav MWat NLar NWad NWea
- Magical Cherry = 'Kolmcherrip'PBR	ELan EPfP NSoo SCob
- Magical Limelight = 'Kolmalimeli'	ELan NSoo
- Magical Sunshine = 'Kolmasun' new	LRHS
- Magical White Fall = 'Kolmwhifa'PBR new	SCob
- Magical White = 'Kolmawhi'PBR	ELan EPfP SPoG
- 'Rheingold'	MAsh
- 'Ysella'	MRav
japonicum	ECho
kalmianum	SBrt WCot
kamtschaticum	XLum
§ ***kouytchense*** ♀H5	CDul EPfP EWes GQui LRHS MAsh MMuc MRav SEND SPoG SWvt WCot WPat
lancasteri	EPfP LRHS SPoG
leschenaultii misapplied	see *H.* 'Rowallane'
'Little Misstery' new	SPoG
maclarenii	EWes
Magical Beauty = 'Kolmbeau'PBR	ELon EPfP LRHS MJak NLar NSoo SCob SPoG WCot
Magical Red = 'Kolmred'PBR	EPfP MJak NLar NSoo SCob SPoG
Miracle Attraction = 'Alldiablo'PBR new	LRHS SHil
Miracle Fantasy = 'Hymirfan'	NLar
Miracle Summer = 'Hymirsum'	EPfP LRHS NLar SHil
Miracle Wonder = 'Hymirwon'	LRHS NLar SHil
× ***moserianum*** ♀H5	CDul CMac EAEE EPfP LRHS MGos MJak NPer SCob SHil SLon SPer SRms WFar
- 'Daybreak'	LRHS MAsh SPoG WRHF
§ - 'Tricolor' (v)	Widely available
- 'Variegatum'	see *H.* × *moserianum* 'Tricolor'
'Mrs Brabazon'	see *H. androsaemum* f. *variegatum* 'Mrs Gladis Brabazon'
nummularium	WAbe
oblongifolium	CExl
olympicum ♀H5	CArn CTri EBee ECha ECho ELan GJos LRHS MAsh MMuc MWat SCob SEND SPer SRms SWvt WIce WSHC XLum XSen
- 'Grandiflorum'	see *H. olympicum* f. *uniflorum*
§ - f. ***minus***	CTri ECho ECtt NGdn SPlb SRms WHrl
§ - - 'Sulphureum'	CBod ECho ELon EWTr EWes LRHS MLHP NBir SPer SRms SWvt WCFE
- - 'Variegatum' (v)	EWes NBir SPoG SWvt
§ - f. ***uniflorum***	ECho NBro NRya
- - 'Citrinum' ♀H5	CMea CSpe ECha ECtt EPfP GBuc MRav MWat NBro NLar SEND SIgm SRot WAbe WCot WHoo WKif
orientale	EWes GLog
§ ***pallens***	ECho WAbe
perforatum	CArn CBod CHab CHby CUse ENfk EPfP GPoy MHer MNHC NMir SEND SIde SRms WHer WHfH WJek WMoo WSFF
polyphyllum	see *H. olympicum* f. *minus*
- 'Citrinum'	see *H. olympicum* f. *minus* 'Sulphureum'
- 'Grandiflorum'	see *H. olympicum* f. *uniflorum*
prolificum	MMHG WCFE
quadrangulum L.	see *H. tetrapterum*
reptans misapplied	see *H. olympicum* f. *minus*
reptans Hook.f. & Thomson ex Dyer	CMea EWes SBrt
revolutum PAB 3861 new	LEdu
§ 'Rowallane' ♀H4	CTri GCal LRHS SDix SSpi SWvt
subsessile	CExl
'Sungold'	see *H. kouytchense*
'Sweet Lion'	CMac
§ ***tetrapterum***	CArn CWld LLWG
trichocaulon	ECho EWes
uralum	SLim
- HWJ 520	WCru
xylosteifolium	SLon

Hypocalyptus (*Papilionaceae*)

sophoroides SPlb

Hypochaeris (*Asteraceae*)

radicata CHab NMir

Hypocyrta see *Nematanthus*

Hypoestes (*Acanthaceae*)

aristata CExl EShb SVen

Hypolepis (*Dennstaedtiaceae*)

millefolium EFtx

Hypoxis (*Hypoxidaceae*)

hemerocallidea WCot
- 'Bloemfontein' ECho
hirsuta CCCN ECho GKev
hygrometrica ECho ECou IBal WThu
krebsii ECho
obtusa 'Harrismith' ECho
parvula XLum
§ - var. **albiflora** 'Hebron Farm Biscuit' CBro CCCN CTal ECho EWes GEdr NWad WAbe WFar
- pink-flowered GKev
rigidula 'Harrismith' ECho
villosa ECho

Hypoxis × *Rhodohypoxis* see × *Rhodoxis*

H. parvula × **R. baurii** see × *Rhodoxis hybrida*

Hypsela (*Campanulaceae*)

longiflora see *H. reniformis*
§ **reniformis** ECho GCrg ITim LLWG MSCN

Hyssopus ✿ (*Lamiaceae*)

from Georgia EWes
officinalis Widely available
- f. **albus** ECha ELau ENfk EPfP GPoy MHer MNHC SPer SPlb SRms WHfH WJek XLum XSen
- subsp. **aristatus** CArn CBod EBee ELau ELon ENfk EPfP GPoy IMou MHer MNHC SPoG WHoo WJek XLum XSen
- 'Roseus' CWld ECha ELau ENfk EPfP GPoy MHer MHol MNHC SIde SPer SPoG WJek XLum XSen

Hystrix (*Poaceae*)

patula CKno EBee EHoe EPPr EShb GCal LLWP MBel MMoz MNrw SPlb XLum

I

Iberis (*Brassicaceae*)

Absolutely Amethyst ='Ib2401' CBct ECtt ELon GBin LRHS MCot MHol NPri SMrm WIce
candolleana see *I. pruitii* Candolleana Group
commutata see *I. sempervirens*
gibraltarica CPne ECho SRms
- 'Betty Swainson' ♀H4 SBch SPhx WAbe
jordanii see *I. pruitii*
'Masterpiece' ECtt LRHS WHlf
'Pink Ice' new ECtt WHlf
§ **pruitii** CTal WAbe
§ - Candolleana Group ECho
saxatilis ECho ITim LRHS WThu
semperflorens WCFE
§ **sempervirens** CHVG CMea CTri ECho ELan EPfP GMaP IFoB LAst MAsh MCot MWat NBro NOrc NSoo SEND SRms WCFE WHar
- 'Compacta' ECho
- 'Elfenreigen' GCal
- 'Fischbeck' SRot
- 'Golden Candy' CTri EHoe GEdr SPoG WCot
- 'Little Gem' see *I. sempervirens* 'Weisser Zwerg'
- 'Pygmaea' CTal ECho
- Schneeflocke see *I. sempervirens* 'Snowflake'
- 'Snow Cushion' ECho EPfP LSun WHoo
§ - 'Snowflake' ♀H5 ECho EPfP EPot GBin IFoB LPal MBel MHer MWat NPri NRya SPer SPoG SWvt WIce WRHF XLum
- 'Snowstorm' new NSir
- 'Tahoe' LPot
§ - 'Weisser Zwerg' CMea ECha ECho ECtt ELan GCrg GMaP MHer MRav SRms WThu
umbellata ECrN

Ichthyoselmis (*Papaveraceae*)

§ **macrantha** EPfP GCra IMou MNrw WCru WPGP

Idesia (*Salicaceae*)

polycarpa CBcs CDul CMCN EBtc EPfP IVic NLar WPGP
- CWJ 12837 WCru

Ilex ✿ (*Aquifoliaceae*)

§ × **altaclerensis** 'Belgica Aurea' (f/v) ♀H6 CBcs CDoC CJun CTho EPfP MBri MSwo NHol
- 'Camelliifolia' (f) ♀H6 CBcs CTho ELan MBlu NPCo SGol
- 'Camelliifolia Variegata' (f/v) CMac
- 'Golden King' (f/v) ♀H6 Widely available
- 'Hendersonii' (f) NPCo
- 'Hodginsii' (m) CTri NWea
- 'James G. Esson' (f) CRos LRHS SHil
- 'Lawsoniana' (f/v) ♀H6 CDoC CDul CJun CMac CRos CSBt CTri EHoe ELan EPfP LRHS MAsh MBlu MJak MMuc NEgg NHol NLar NPCo NWea SEND SGol SHil SLim SLon SPer SPoG SRms WHar WPat
- 'Maderensis' (m) CBcs
- 'Purple Shaft' (f) CMCN MRav
- 'Ripley Gold' (f/v) CLnd CMac LRHS MAsh MBri MRav NWea
- 'Silver Sentinel' see *I.* × *altaclerensis* 'Belgica Aurea'
- 'Wilsonii' (f) NLar NPCo NWea
aquifolium ♀H6 Widely available
- 'Alaska' (f) CCVT CDoC CDul CJun CMCN CRos EPfP LBuc LRHS MAsh MBri NHed NLar NSoo NWea SGol SHil SWvt WFar
- 'Amber' (f) ♀H6 CTri NLar NPCo NWea
- 'Angustifolia' (f) CJun WCFE
- 'Angustifolia' (m or f) EPfP MAsh
- 'Angustimarginata Aurea' (m/v) NPCo
§ - 'Argentea Marginata' (f/v) ♀H6 Widely available

	Name	Suppliers
§	- 'Argentea Marginata Pendula' (f/v)	CDoC CMac CTri ELan EPfP LRHS MAsh NWea SPer SRms WFar WPat
	- 'Argentea Pendula'	see *I. aquifolium* 'Argentea Marginata Pendula'
	- 'Argentea Variegata'	see *I. aquifolium* 'Argentea Marginata'
	- 'Atlas' (m)	CBcs CDoC LBuc SWvt
	- 'Aurea Marginata' (f/v)	CLnd CMac EPfP EPla LBuc MGos NPCo NWea SCob SEWo WCFE WHar WPat
	- 'Aurea Marginata Pendula' (f/v)	CDoC WPat
	- 'Aurea Regina'	see *I. aquifolium* 'Golden Queen'
	- 'Aureovariegata Pendula'	see *I. aquifolium* 'Weeping Golden Milkmaid'
	- 'Aurifodina' (f)	CJun NPCo
	- 'Bacciflava' (f)	CBcs CDoC CDul CJun CMac CTho CTri EBee ELan ELon EPfP IArd MBlu MGos MRav NEgg NLar NPCo NWea SLim SPer SRms SWvt WCFE WFar
	- 'Crassifolia' (f)	IArd SMad
	- 'Elegantissima' (m/v)	CJun SCoo
	- 'Fastigiata Sartori'	NLar
	- 'Ferox' (m)	CJun ELan EPfP LRHS NLar
	- 'Ferox Argentea' (m/v) ♀H6	Widely available
	- 'Ferox Aurea' (m/v)	CDoC CJun ELan ELon EPfP LRHS MAsh NEgg NPCo SPoG
§	- 'Flavescens' (f)	MBlu NPCo
	- 'Fructu Luteo' (f)	WHar
	- 'Gold Flash' (f/v)	LRHS NLar
	- 'Golden Milkboy' (m/v)	CLnd CMac ELan EPfP SGol WPat
§	- 'Golden Queen' (m/v) ♀H6	CDoC CMac IArd MGos NBir NPCo SRms WPat
	- 'Golden Tears' (f/v)	CJun
	- 'Golden van Tol' (f/v)	CBcs CDoC CSBt CTri ECrN ELan ELon EPfP LRHS MAsh MBlu MGos MSwo NLar NPCo SCoo SGol SRms WFar WMoo
	- 'Green Minaret'	IVic
	- 'Handsworth New Silver' (f/v) ♀H6	Widely available
	- 'Harpune' (f)	IArd
§	- 'Hascombensis'	CDoC NWea
	- 'Hastata' (m)	IArd IDee
	- 'J.C. van Tol' (f) ♀H6	Widely available
	- 'Latispina' (f)	CJun
	- 'Lichtenthalii' (f)	IArd IVic NPCo
	- 'Madame Briot' (f/v) ♀H6	Widely available
	- 'Marijo'	CRos LRHS SHil
	- moonlight holly	see *I. aquifolium* 'Flavescens'
	- 'Myrtifolia' (f)	NPCo SWvt
	- 'Myrtifolia' (m)	CMac ELan EPfP GCal MGos NLar NPCo SMad WMoo
	- 'Myrtifolia Aurea' (m/v)	NWea SWvt
	- 'Myrtifolia Aurea Maculata' (m/v)	CDoC CJun CTri ELan LRHS MAsh MBri MRav NPCo NWea SPoG SWvt WPat
	- 'Northern Lights' (v)	EPfP LRHS MSwo
	- 'Pendula' (f)	MRav NWea
	- 'Pendula Mediopicta'	see *I. aquifolium* 'Weeping Golden Milkmaid'
	- 'Pyramidalis' (f) ♀H6	CDoC CDul CMac CTri ELan LRHS MAsh MBri MGos NLar NPCo NWea SCob SGol SHil SPer SRms WFar WMoo
	- 'Pyramidalis Aureomarginata' (f/v)	CDoC NLar
	- 'Pyramidalis Fructu Luteo' (f) ♀H6	MAsh MBri
	- 'Recurva' (m)	CMac
	- 'Rubricaulis Aurea' (f/v)	NLar NPCo
	- 'Scotica' (f)	NWea
	- Siberia = 'Limsi'PBR (f)	IVic NLar
	- 'Silver King'	see *I. aquifolium* 'Silver Queen'
	- 'Silver Milkboy' (f/v)	ELan MBlu WFar
	- 'Silver Milkmaid' (f/v)	CDoC CJun LRHS MJak NSoo SLim SWvt WMoo
§	- 'Silver Queen' (m/v) ♀H6	Widely available
	- 'Silver Sentinel'	see *I.* × *altaclerensis* 'Belgica Aurea'
	- 'Silver van Tol' (f/v)	CDoC CJun CLnd CWSG EBee ELan EPfP MAsh NLar NPCo NPer
	- 'Somerset Cream' (f/v)	CJun CTri
	- 'Sterntaler'	IVic
§	- 'Weeping Golden Milkmaid' (f/v)	WPat
	- 'White Cream' (m/v)	IVic
	- 'Wichtel'	IVic
	- 'Yellow Star' (f/v)	IVic
	× ***aquipernyi*** Dragon Lady = 'Meschick' (f) ♀H6	CDoC CJun NPCo
	× ***attenuata*** 'Sunny Foster' (f/v)	CDoC EPfP
	× ***beanii*** **new**	CJun
§	***bioritsensis***	CMCN CTri
	'Brilliant' (f)	NPCo
	cassine L. non Walt.	CMCN
	'Clusterberry' (f)	NPCo
	colchica	CMCN
	cornuta	EPfP
	- B&SWJ 8756	WCru
	- 'Anicet Delcambre' (f)	CJun
	- 'Burfordii' (f)	NLar
§	- 'Dazzler' (f)	CJun
	- 'Ira S. Nelson' (f/v)	CJun IArd IDee
	- 'O. Spring' (f/v)	CJun
	crenata	CAco CMCN CTal CTri EPfP GCra MGos NHol NWea SArc SCob STrG SVic WFar
*	- 'Akagi'	WFar
	- 'Aureovariegata'	see *I. crenata* 'Variegata'
	- 'Convexa' (f) ♀H6	CDul CTal EAEE EPfP MAsh MRav NPCo NWea SCob SPer WMoo WPat
	- 'Convexed Gold' (f/v)	LRHS MBri NSoo NWad WFar
	- Dark Green = 'Icoprins11'PBR **new**	NWea SVic
	- 'Dwarf Pagoda' (f)	IVic
	- 'Fastigiata' (f) ♀H6	CAco CDoC EPfP LRHS MAsh MBri MGos NLar SBod SPer SPoG
	- Fastigiata Group upright	SCob
	- - 'Sky Pencil' (f)	CMCN
	- 'Fructu Luteo'	see *I. crenata* f. *watanabeana*
*	- 'Glory Gem' (f)	CBcs
	- 'Golden Gem' (f/v) ♀H6	CDoC CMac CRos CSBt CTri ELan ELon EPfP IVic LRHS MAsh MGos MSwo NSoo NWea SCoo SGol SHil SPer SPoG SWvt WFar WPat WThu
	- 'Golden Rock'PBR	EBee
*	- 'Green Hedge' ♀H6	EPfP LBuc
	- 'Helleri' (f)	WPat
	- 'Ivory Tower' (f)	NPCo
	- 'Kinme' **new**	LPal
	- 'Korean Gem'	CTal
	- 'Luteovariegata'	see *I. crenata* 'Variegata'
	- 'Mariesii' (f)	CMac MBlu
	- 'Midas Touch' (m/v) **new**	CTal

I	- 'Pyramidalis' (f)	MRav NWea
	- 'Robert Culpepper' (m) new	CTal
§	- 'Shiro-fukurin' (f/v)	CMCN ELan EPfP LRHS SLon
	- 'Snowflake'	see *I. crenata* 'Shiro-fukurin'
	- 'Stokes' (m)	MSwo NLar
	- 'Twiggy' (f) new	CTal
§	- 'Variegata' (v)	CMCN CMac EPfP LRHS
§	- f. ***watanabeana*** (f)	WGwG
	'Dazzler'	see *I. cornuta* 'Dazzler'
	dimorphophylla	CMac
	dipyrena	ESwi
	'Doctor Kassab' (f)	CMCN
	'Elegance' (f)	MBlu WFar
	'Good Taste' (f)	WFar
	hascombensis	see *I. aquifolium* 'Hascombensis'
	'Indian Chief' (f)	CJun NPCo
	× ***koehneana***	CDul
	- 'Chestnut Leaf' (f) 🏆[H5]	CDoC CJun CLnd CMCN EBtc EWTr MRav NLar NPCo NSoo SSta WFar WGrn
	laevigata	CMCN
	latifolia	CHEx CJun CMCN NLar
	'Lydia Morris' (f)	CSam
	'Mary Nell' (f)	CJun
	× ***meserveae***	NSoo
	- Blue Angel = 'Conang' (f)	CAco CBcs CDoC CDul CMac EBee ELan EPfP IFoB LRHS MBri MRav NLar NPCo NWea SPer SPoG SRms WFar
	- Blue Bunny = 'Meseal' (f)	IVic
	- 'Blue Girl' (f)	CTri
	- Blue Maid = 'Mesid' (f)	NLar NPCo STrG
	- Blue Prince = 'Conablu' (m) 🏆[H6]	CAco CBcs CDoC CLnd CMCN CMac ELan LBuc LRHS MBlu MJak MMuc NHol NLar NSoo NWea SCob SLim SPer SPoG WFar
	- Blue Princess = 'Conapri' (f) 🏆[H6]	CBcs CMCN CMac ELan EPfP LBuc LRHS MBlu MJak MRav NLar NPCo NPri NWea SCob SCoo SLim SPer SPoG WFar
	- Castle Spire = 'Hachfee'[PBR]	EBee NLar WFar
	- Castle Wall = 'Hecken Star'[PBR]	EBee IVic WFar
	- 'Heckenpracht'[PBR]	EBee IVic WFar
	- Little Rascal = 'Mondo' (m) new	LRHS
	myrtifolia	MAsh MRav NHol
	'Nellie R. Stevens' (f)	CAco CCVT CDoC CJun EBee ECrN EPfP EPla NLar NWea SCob SEWo
	opaca	CMCN
	perado subsp. ***azorica***	CFil WPGP
	- - B&SWJ 12526	WCru
	- subsp. ***perado***	CBcs NPCo
	- subsp. ***platyphylla***	CBcs CMCN MBlu SArc
	pernyi	CDoC CJun CMCN CMac CTri LRHS MAsh MJak SLon
	- var. ***veitchii***	see *I. bioritsensis*
	rotunda	LEdu
	'September Gem' (f)	CJun CMCN NPCo
	serrata	CMac CMen
	- 'Koshobai'	CMen
	- 'Leucocarpa'	CMen
	suaveolens	CMCN
	sugerokii var. ***brevipedunculata*** B&SWJ 10856 new	WCru
	triflora var. ***kanehirae***	CDul NLar
	verticillata	CMCN EBee LRHS WFar
	- (f)	CBcs EBtc ELon EPfP MMHG NLar NWea
	- (m)	EBtc ELon EPfP MMHG NLar NWea
	- f. ***chrysocarpa*** (f)	NLar
	- 'Maryland Beauty' (f)	CJun NLar
	- 'Southern Gentleman' (m)	CJun MBlu NLar
	- 'Winter Gold' (f)	CJun MBlu
	- 'Winter Red' (f)	CJun CMCN MBlu
	vomitoria	CMCN EBtc
	'William Cowgill' (f) new	CJun
	yunnanensis	GQui IArd

Iliamna see *Sphaeralcea*

Illicium (*Schisandraceae*)

anisatum	CBcs CDoC CExl CFil CMac EBee EPfP NLar WPGP WPat WSHC
floridanum	CBcs CPne EPfP GKin LEdu SSpi WPat
- f. ***album***	EPfP
- 'Halley's Comet'	CExl CFil
aff. ***griffithii***	WCru
- WWJ 11974 new	WCru
henryi	CDoC CExl EPfP IVic NLar SSpi WPGP WSHC
aff. ***henryi***	CBcs
lanceolatum	CExl CFil
- KWJ 12245	WCru
majus	CFil
- WWJ 11919	WCru
aff. ***majus***	WCru
- WWJ 12017 new	WCru
mexicanum	CExl CFil
oligandrum	CExl NLar
parviflorum	CFil
simonsii	CExl CFil IVic MBlu WPGP
- BWJ 8024	WCru
'Woodland Ruby'	NLar WPGP

Ilysanthes see *Lindernia*

Impatiens ✿ (*Balsaminaceae*)

CC 4980	CExl
DJHC 98415	WCru WPGP
apiculata	EBee GCal
arguta	CCon CDes CExl CLAP CSam CSpe EShb GCal MPie SBrt WPGP
- 'Alba'	CExl CSpe
auricoma × ***bicaudata***	MPie WDib
balfourii	CPla
bicaudata	CSpe
congolensis	CCCN
'Emei Dawn'	CExl GCal WCru
ernstii new	CExl
flanaganae	CCon CFil WPGP
forrestii	CDes CLAP
gomphophylla	CCon CFil
keilii	WDib
kerriae B&SWJ 7219	WCru
kilimanjari subsp. ***kilimanjari***	CCon CDoC CSpe GCal MPie WCot
kilimanjari × ***pseudoviola***	CDoC CSpe MPie WDib
langbianensis HWJ 1054	WCru
(LaTina Series) LaTina Appleblossom = 'Kleni10120'	LAst

- LaTina Electric Purple = 'Kleni10119'PBR	LAst
- LaTina Red Orange = 'Kleni10123'	LAst
'Linda's White'	WCot
'Little Brother Montgomery' new	CHll
macrophylla B&SWJ 10157	WCru
namchabarwensis	CDes CSpe WPGP
niamniamensis 🏆H1b	CHll EBak EShb WDib
- 'Congo Cockatoo'	CDTJ CDoC NPer SRms
- 'Golden Cockatoo' (v)	CDTJ CDoC CHll EBak EShb
noli-tangere	WSFF
omeiana	CAby CCCN CCon CDes CDoC CHEx CHel CLAP CPom CSam CSpe EBee EPPr ESwi EUJe EWld GCal GEdr IGor LEdu MNrw MSCN NLar SBch WCot WCru WFar WPGP WPtf WSHC
- DJH C98492 new	CDes WCru
- 'Ice Storm'	CAby CDes CHEx CLAP EBee GCal GEdr LEdu NLar WCru WPGP
- variegated (v)	GEdr
parasitica	WDib
platypetala B&SWJ 9722	WCru
puberula	CCon CDoC CSam
- HWJK 2063	CDes EBee SBrt WCru WPGP
repens 🏆H1c	WDib
rothii	CCon CDes CSpe GCal
scabrida	CPla CSpe
§ 'Secret Love'	CCCN WDib
sodenii 🏆H1c	CDTJ CHll CSpe EShb GCal SBHP WDib
stenantha	CCon CDes
(Sunpatiens Series) Sunpatiens Spreading Variegated Salmon = 'Sakimp005' (v)	LSou
- Sunpatiens Spreading Variegated White = 'Sakimp018'PBR (v)	LSou
tinctoria	CAby CCon CDoC CExl CFil CHEx CHel CHll CPom CSpe GCal GCra SDix
- from Cherangani, Kenya	GCal
- subsp. ***tinctoria***	IFro
tuberosa	WDib
ugandensis	GCal
uniflora	CCon EBee GCal SBrt WPGP
Velvetea	see *I.* 'Secret Love'
walleriana DeZire Series	NPri
- - 'DeZire Lavender Splash'	LAst
- (Musica Series) 'Musica Bicolor Cherry' (d)	LAst
- - 'Musica Pink Aroma' (d)	LAst
- - 'Musica Salmon' (d)	LAst

Imperata (*Poaceae*)

cylindrica	CMen XLum
- 'Red Baron'	see *I. cylindrica* 'Rubra'
§ - 'Rubra'	Widely available

Incarvillea (*Bignoniaceae*)

arguta	GKev LLHF SGSe XLum
brevipes	see *I. mairei*
compacta	EBee GKev LLHF
- BWJ 7620	WCru
delavayi	Widely available
- SDR 4711	GKev
- 'Alba'	see *I. delavayi* 'Snowtop'
- 'Bees' Pink'	CAby CBod CMos EPfP GBuc LRHS NLar
§ - 'Snowtop'	CAby CBct CBod CHel COtt EBee ELan EPfP EPot GMaP IBoy LRHS NBir NLar NSoo SDeJ SGSe SGol SPer SWvt WWEG
cf. ***delavayi***	WBor
forrestii	GKev
grandiflora	EBee GKev
himalayensis 'Frank Ludlow'	GKev
lutea	EBee GKev
§ ***mairei***	CTsd ECho GKev LRHS NLar
- SDR 1812	GKev
- var. ***mairei***	EPot GBuc
- - f. ***multifoliata***	see *I. zhongdianensis*
olgae	EBee EPfP
sinensis 'Cheron'	CHel
§ ***zhongdianensis***	CFis CPBP EBee ECho EPot GKev LLHF SPhx
- ACE 1600	GBuc
- BWJ 7692	WCru
- BWJ 7978	WCru
- white-flowered	GKev

Indigofera (*Papilionaceae*)

amblyantha	CBcs CCCN CExl CWSG EPfP LRHS MAsh MBlu MBri MNHC NLar SEND SKHP SPlb SSpi WSHC
aff. ***amblyantha*** new	LSou
balfouriana BWJ 7851	WCru
cassioides	WCru
dielsiana	CCCN EBee ELan EPfP LRHS WPGP
'Dosua'	SEND
gerardiana	see *I. heterantha*
hancockii	CExl SKHP WPGP WSHC
hebepetala	CHid EBee EPfP SBrt SKHP WPGP WSHC
§ ***heterantha*** 🏆H5	Widely available
heterophylla	CCCN
himalayensis	CExl CMHG EBee SKHP
- Yu 10941	CExl WPGP
- 'Silk Road'	CCCN ELan EPfP LRHS MBlu MBri MGos NLar SHil SKHP WSHC
howellii	CExl CHid CMHG SChF SKHP WCru WPGP
howellii × ***pendula***	WSHC
kirilowii	EPfP IVic LRHS NLar SKHP WPGP WSHC
- var. ***alba*** new	EPfP
pendula	CCCN CExl CHel CMHG CSpe CWGN EPfP LRHS MOWG SKHP SPoG SSpi WKif WPGP WSHC
- B&SWJ 7741	WCru
potaninii	CBcs CExl CHel CMac EPfP LRHS MOWG WHer
pseudotinctoria	CCCN EPfP SRms
aff. ***pseudotinctoria***	CCCN
subverticillata	WSHC
szechuensis	SKHP
tinctoria	CArn CCCN

Indocalamus (*Poaceae*)

latifolius	EPPr EPla ERod EUJe MMoz MMuc MWht

- 'Hopei' EPla
longiauritus EPla
solidus see *Bonia solida*
§ **tessellatus** ♀H4 CAbb CBod CDoC CEnt CHEx ELon EPla ERod GCal IDee LPal MBri MMoz MWht NGdn SEND SMad WMoo WPGP
- f. **hamadae** EPla ERod MMoz MWht

Indosasa (*Poaceae*)

gigantea ERod

Inula (*Asteraceae*)

acaulis WCot
barbata GCal
conyzae WHer
dysenterica see *Pulicaria dysenterica*
ensifolia CBcs EBee ELan EPfP GJos LRHS MNFA MNHC NBro XLum
- 'Compacta' ECho GCal
- 'Gold Star' CMac EBee ECho MBNS MRav NBid NBir SPoG
'Finnish Feathers' **new** EBee
glandulosa see *I. orientalis*
helenium CArn CBod CHab CHby CUse ELau ENfk GAbr GPoy IBoy LEdu MHer NBid NBir NLar NMir SPoG SRms WGwG WHer WHfH WJek WMoo
hirta XLum
hookeri CBre CMea CSam ECha ELan GBin GCal GJos GMaP IFro LEdu LLWG MBel MHol MLHP MMuc MNFA NBid NChi NDov NPer NSti SDix SEND WBrk WHil WWEG WWtn
- GWJ 9033 WCru
macrocephala misapplied see *I. royleana*
magnifica Widely available
- 'Sonnenstrahl' ♀H7 GQue LEdu NLar SEND SPhx
oculus-christi EBee EWes NBre WCot WMoo
§ **orientalis** EBee EPfP GAbr GJos LSun MBri NGBl NLar NSoo SGSe SPad SPer SRms WJek XLum
racemosa CTca EBee EPPr EPla EWes GBin GCal LRHS MNrw SMrm SPlb WBor
- 'Sonnenspeer' GBin NBid NLar
§ **royleana** GCal MNrw MRav
salicina EBee

Inulanthera (*Asteraceae*)

calva **new** WCot

Iochroma (*Solanaceae*)

§ **australe** ♀H3 CCCN CExl CHll CNor CSpe EWld MOWG SPlb SPtp SVen
§ - 'Andean Snow' CHll EShb MNai
§ - 'Bill Evans' EShb MNai
- purple-flowered **new** MNai
- 'Rubin' **new** MNai
- violet-flowered **new** MNai
cyaneum CCCN CDoC CHll MOWG
- purple-flowered CCCN CHll
gesnerioides 'Coccineum' CCCN CDoC CHll WCot
§ **grandiflorum** CCCN CDoC CHll SEND
warscewiczii see *I. grandiflorum*

Ipheion (*Alliaceae*)

'Alberto Castillo' ♀H4 CAby CAvo CBro CDes CHid CMea CPom ECho ELan ELon EPot ERCP EWes GBuc GKev LAma LLHF LRHS MNrw NMin SDeJ SDys SPhx WCot WHil WHoo WPGP WWFP
dialystemon ECho EPot LLHF WAbe
- JCA 2420010 WPGP
'Jessie' CAby CBro CDes CMea CPom CPrp EBee ECha ECho EPot ERCP GBuc LAma LLHF LRHS MNrw NMin WCot WHil
'Rolf Fiedler' ♀H3 CAvo CBro CPom CPrp CTri EBee ECho ELan EPPr EPfP EPot ERCP EWes GBuc GKev LAma LRHS LSun MNrw SBch SDeJ SMrm WHoo
sellowianum CAby CDes WCot
sessile CDes EBee ECho
'Tessa'PBR ECho ERCP LLHF
§ **uniflorum** CBro CTri ECha ECho ITim LAma MMoz MNrw SBch SEND SGSe SRms WBrk WCot XLum
- f. **album** CBro CPom CPrp EBee ECha ECho EPPr EPot EWes GKev LEdu LRHS MNrw WCot WHal WHil
- 'Charlotte Bishop' CAvo CBro CCon CDes CMea CPne CPom CPrp EBee ECha ECho ELon EPPr EPot ERCP EWes GBuc GKev LAma LLHF LRHS MNrw NBir NMin NRya SDeJ SMrm WCot WHoo
- 'Froyle Mill' ♀H5 CBro CMea CPom CPrp ECho ELon EPPr EPot ERCP EWes GKev LLWP LRHS MNrw SBch SDeJ WCot WHoo WWFP
- subsp. **tandiliense** CDes EBee
- 'Wisley Blue' ♀H5 CBro CCon CExl CMea CPom CPrp CTri ECha ECho ELan ELon EPPr EPfP EPot ERCP GBuc GKev LAma LLWP LRHS MRav NRya SDeJ SMrm SRms WCot WHea WHoo

Ipomoea (*Convolvulaceae*)

acuminata see *I. indica*
alba CCCN EShb
batatas 'Blackie' EShb ESwi
- (Bright Ideas Series) Bright Ideas Black **new** NPri
- - Bright Ideas Lime = 'Fripalligr' **new** NPri
- 'Margarita' EShb ESwi
- (Sweet Caroline Series) 'Sweet Caroline Bronze'PBR ESwi EUJe
- - 'Sweet Caroline Purple'PBR EUJe
- - 'Sweet Caroline Sweetheart Light Green'PBR ESwi
- - 'Sweet Caroline Sweetheart Purple'PBR CSpe ESwi
carnea CCCN
coccinea var. **hederifolia** see *I. hederifolia*
§ **hederifolia** CCCN
× **imperialis** 'Sunrise Serenade' CCCN
§ **indica** ♀H1c CCCN CHEx CHVG CHll CRHN CSam EShb MOWG SPer
learii see *I. indica*
§ **lobata** CSpe LSou
mauritiana **new** CCCN

	'Milky Way'	CCCN
	muellerii	CCCN
	× ***multifida***	CSpe
	purpurea 'Grandpa Otts'	CWCL
	- 'Kniola's Black Night'	CSpe
	quamoclit	CSpe
	versicolor	see *I. lobata*

Iresine (*Amaranthaceae*)

	Blazin' Lime	see *I.* 'Lime'
	Blazin' Rose	see *I.* 'Rose'
	herbstii ♀H1c	EShb EUJe
§	'Lime'	EUJe
§	'Rose'	EUJe

Iris ✿ (*Iridaceae*)

	'Abbey Chant' (IB)	CIri WCAu XSen
	'Abbondanza' (TB) new	WCAu
	'About Town' (TB)	WCAu
	'Acoma' (TB)	WCAu
	'Action Front' (TB)	CWld EAEE ECGP EIri EPfP ESgI EWoo LRHS MGos MLHP SDeJ SHil WCAu WGwG WWEG
	'Actress' (TB)	CKel CMac CWld EAEE EBee EPfP LBuc LRHS MGos SHil WGwG
	acutiloba subsp. ***lineolata***	CTal
	'Adobe Rose' (TB)	SIri XSen
	'Adventuress' (TB)	XSen
	'Afternoon Delight' (TB)	EWoo WCAu
	'Afternoon in Rio' (TB)	WCAu
	'Again and Again' (TB)	EWoo
	'Agatha Christie' (IB)	WCAu
	'Age of Innocence' (TB)	WCAu
	'Aglow Again' (MTB)	SDys
	'Agnes James' (CH)	CBro
	'Agua Fresca' (TB/v)	WCAu
	'Ahwahnee Princess' (SDB)	EWoo
	'Aichi-no-kagayaki' (SpH)	CBod EBee WCot WHil XLum
	'Alabaster Unicorn' (TB)	ESgI
	albicans ♀H5	CMea CTal ECho LEdu
	- 'Blue Pygmy'	CAby CTal
	albomarginata	ECho
	'Alcazar' (TB)	SWat WMnd WWEG
	'Aldo Ratti' (TB)	ESgI
	'Alene's New Love' (SDB)	EWoo
	'Alene's Other Love' (SDB)	WCAu
	'Alenette' (TB)	WCAu
	'Alice Harding' (TB)	ESgI
	'Alida' (Reticulata)	CBro ECho EPot ERCP GKev LAma LLHF SDeJ
	'Alizes' (TB) ♀H7	CPar ESgI LRHS WCAu XSen
	'All Night Long' (TB)	EWoo
	'Allegiance' (TB)	WCAu
	'Amadora' (TB)	CKel EIri
	'Amazing Grace' (TB)	EWoo
	'Ambassadeur' (TB)	EWoo
	'Amber Beauty' (Dut)	GKev
	'Amber Queen' (DB)	CAby CTal ECtt ELan NBir SDeJ SPer
	'Ambroisie' (TB) ♀H7	ESgI EWoo
	'Amelia Bedeila' (IB)	SIri
	'American Patriot' (IB)	CKel WCAu
	'Amethyst Dancer' (TB)	WCAu
	'Amethyst Flame' (TB)	ECho SRms WCAu
	'Amherst Blue' (IB)	EIri SIri
	'Amherst Bluebeard' (SDB)	ESgI
	'Amherst Caper' (SDB)	EIri ESgI
	'Amherst Glacier' (IB)	WCAu
	'Amherst Jester' (BB)	SIri
	'Amherst Purple Ribbon' (SDB)	WCAu
	'Amigo' (TB)	EWoo
	'Amphora' (SDB)	CBro LBuc
	'Amy Remy' (TB)	CIri
	'Ancient Echoes' (TB)	ESgI
	'Andalou' (TB) ♀H7	CWCL EWoo XSen
	'Angel Unawares' (TB)	WCAu
	'Angel Wings' (TB) new	CIri
	'Angel's Tears'	see *I. histrioides* 'Angel's Tears'
	'Angel's Touch' (TB)	ESgI
	anglica	see *I. latifolia*
	'Ann Dasch' (Sib)	WAul WWEG
	'Annabel Jane' (TB)	CHid CKel ELon WCAu
	'Anne Elizabeth' (SDB)	CBro
	'Annemarie Troeger' (Sib) ♀H7	ELon SMrm
	'Annick' (Sib)	EBee LRHS
	'Annikins' (IB)	CKel
	'Anniversary' (Sib)	WWEG
	'Anniversary Celebration' (TB)	CKel
	'Announcement' (TB)	CIri
	'Antarctique' (IB)	ESgI
	'Antigone' (TB)	EWoo
	'Antiope' (Rc)	GKev
	'Anvil of Darkness' (TB)	EWoo
	'Aphrodisiac' (TB)	XSen
	aphylla	GBin SBrt WThu
	- 'Slick'	SDys
	'Apollo' (Dut)	CAvo
	'Appledore' (SDB)	CBro
	'Appointer' (SpH)	NChi WWtn
	'Apricorange' (TB)	CKel WCot
	'Apricot Blaze' (TB)	ESgI
	'Apricot Drops' (MTB) ♀H7	ESgI WCAu
	'Apricot Frosty' (BB)	WCAu XSen
	'Apricot Silk' (IB)	CCCN IBoy WWEG
	'Apricot Topping' (BB)	WCAu
	'Arab Chief' (TB)	CKel
	'Arabi Pasha' (TB)	WCAu
*	'Arabic Night' (IB)	WCAu
	'Archie Owen' (Spuria)	WCAu
	'Arcobaleno' (TB)	CIri
	'Arctic Age' (TB)	WCAu
	'Arctic Fancy' (IB)	CKel
	'Arctic Fox' (TB) new	WCAu
	'Arctic Sunrise' (TB)	ESgI
	'Arctic Wind' (IB)	WCAu
	'Argus Pheasant' (TB)	ESgI WCAu
	'Arms Wide Open' (TB)	CIri
	'Around Midnight' (TB)	LRHS WCAu
	'Arpège' (TB)	XSen
	'Art Deco' (TB)	SIri XSen
	'Art School Angel' (TB)	CIri
	'As de Coeur' (TB)	XSen
	'As You Were' (TB)	CIri
	'Ascension Crown' (TB)	ESgI
	'Ask Alma' (IB)	ESgI XSen
	'Astrid Cayeux' (TB)	ESgI
	'Astro Flash' (TB)	ESgI
	'Astrology' (TB)	WCAu
	'Athaenos' (IB)	CIri
	'Atlantic Crossing' (Sib)	SIri WAul
	'Atlantic Sky' (TB)	ESgI
	'Attention Please' (TB)	CKel ELan WWEG

attica	CBro CPBP ECho GEdr LLHF NRya WThu
– lemon-flowered	WThu
'Attitude' (IB) **new**	WCAu
§ ***aucheri*** 𝒀H4	ECho EPot GKev LLHF NMin
– 'Snow Princess'	ECho
– 'Snow White'	ECho
'Aunt Josephine' (TB)	ESgI
'Aurean' (IB)	CKel
'Austrian Sky' (SDB)	CAby CMac ECtt LRHS NSoo SDeJ WAul WCot
'Autumn Apricot' (TB)	EWoo
'Autumn Circus' (TB)	EWoo WCAu
'Autumn Echo' (TB)	ESgI XSen
'Autumn Embers' (SDB)	WCAu
'Autumn Encore' (TB)	EWoo MHer
'Autumn Leaves' (TB)	WCAu
'Autumn Princess' (Dut) **new**	GKev
'Autumn Riesling' (TB)	WCAu
'Autumn Tryst' (TB)	ESgI EWoo WCAu
'Avalon Sunset' (TB)	EIri
'Awesome Blossom' (TB)	ESgI
'Az Ap' (IB)	ELon WCAu WHil
babadagica	WAbe
'Babbling Brook' (TB)	XSen
'Baby Bengal' (BB)	XSen
'Baby Blessed' (SDB)	CBro WCAu
'Baby Prince' (SDB)	ESgI
'Baby Sister' (Sib)	CMHG EBee EWoo GBin GBuc LRHS NBro SRGP SWat
'Bach Toccata' (MTB)	SDys
'Back in Black' (TB)	CKel WCAu
'Badlands' (TB)	WCAu
'Bal Masqué' (TB)	ESgI XSen
'Ballistic' (SDB)	WCAu
'Ballyhoo' (TB)	WCAu XSen
'Baltic Star' (TB)	EWoo WCAu
'Banbury Beauty' (CH) 𝒀H7	MAvo
'Banbury Melody' (CH)	MAvo
'Banbury Ruffles' (SDB)	ESgI LRHS WCAu
'Bandera Waltz' (TB)	WCAu
'Bang' (TB)	CKel
'Bangles' (MTB) 𝒀H7	SDys WCAu
'Banish Misfortune' (Sib)	WAul
'Banker Dave' (TB)	CIri
'Bar de Nuit' (TB)	ESgI EWoo
'Barbara My Love' (TB)	WCAu
barbatula BWJ 7663	WCru
'Baria' (SDB)	CTal
'Baroque Prelude' (TB)	CKel WCAu
'Batik' (BB)	SIri WCot XSen
'Battlestar Atlantis' (TB)	CIri
'Bayberry Candle' (TB)	CIri WCAu
'Be Mine' (TB)	CIri
'Be My Baby' (BB)	WCAu
'Beach Girl' (TB)	EWoo
'Bedtime Story' (IB)	SWat WWEG XSen
'Bee's Knees' (SDB) 𝒀H7	SIri
'Before the Storm' (TB)	CKel ELon ESgI GBin LRHS WCAu XSen
'Beguine' (TB)	ESgI
'Being Busy' (SDB)	ESgI
'Bel Azur' (IB)	ESgI LRHS
'Bel Esprit' (TB)	WCAu
'Belgian Princess' (TB)	WCAu
'Belise' (Spuria) 𝒀H7	WCot
'Belle de Nuit' (TB)	EWoo
'Ben a Factor' (MTB)	ESgI
'Benbow' (TB) **new**	WMil
'Benton Arundel' (TB)	EMal EWoo
'Benton Bluejohn' (TB)	EMal
'Benton Caramel' (TB)	EMal EWoo
'Benton Cordelia' (TB)	EMal EWoo
'Benton Daphne' (TB)	EMal
'Benton Dierdre' (TB)	ELon EMal EWoo MNHC SRms
'Benton Evora' (TB)	EMal
'Benton Farewell' (TB) **new**	EWoo
'Benton Lorna' (TB)	EMal
'Benton Nigel' (TB)	EMal EWoo WCAu
'Benton Olive' (TB)	EMal EWoo
'Benton Opal' (TB)	EMal
'Benton Pearl' (TB)	EMal
'Benton Primrose' (TB)	EMal EWoo
'Benton Sheila' (TB)	ECha ELon
'Benton Susan' (TB)	EMal EWoo
'Beotie' (TB)	EWoo
'Bering Sea' (IB)	WCAu
'Berkeley Gold' (TB)	CKel CSBt ECtt ELan EWes LRHS NOrc SCob SDeJ SPer SWat WGwG WWEG
'Berlin Bluebird' (Sib)	SMHy
'Berlin Purple Wine' (Sib)	EPri IMou
'Berlin Ruffles' (Sib) 𝒀H7	EWes EWoo WAul
'Berlin Sky' (Sib)	ESgI EWes
'Berlin Tiger' (SpH) 𝒀H7	CRow EBee EPPr EPla LLWG MSCN MWts NLar SCob SGol WHil
'Bermuda Triangle' (BB)	SDys
'Best Bet' (TB)	ESgI EWoo WCAu
'Bethany Claire' (TB)	ESgI WCAu
'Betty Cooper' (Spuria)	WCAu
'Betty Simon' (TB)	CWCL EWoo XSen
'Beverly Sills' (TB)	EAEE EPfP EWoo GBin LSou MRav SCob SDeJ SRGP WCAu WGwG XSen
'Bewilderbeast' (TB)	XSen
'Beyond Dreams' (TB) **new**	CIri
'Bianco' (TB)	WCAu WHil
'Bibury' (SDB) 𝒀H7	WCAu
'Bickley Cape' (Sib)	WWEG
'Big Blue' (Sib) **new**	WFar
'Big Dipper' (TB)	ECtt
'Big Squeeze' (TB)	WCAu
biglumis	see *I. lactea*
biliottii	CBro
'Bishop's Robe' (TB)	ESgI
'Black as Night' (TB)	XSen
'Black Beauty' (Dut)	EPfP
'Black Beauty' (TB)	MWat SPer
'Black Cherry Delight' (SDB)	ESgI
'Black Dragon' (TB)	CCCN CHid NLar SHar XSen
'Black Flag' (TB)	XSen
'Black Gamecock' (La)	CBod CCon CWCL EBee ECtt ELan MBNS MNrw MSCN MWat MWts NBro NLar SKHP SMrm WMAq
'Black Hope' (TB)	CIri EWoo
'Black Knight' (TB)	MRav NLar WKif
'Black Magic' (IB)	EWoo
'Black Night' (IB)	SRGP WWEG
'Black Prince' (IB) **new**	SCob
'Black Stallion' (MDB)	ESgI
'Black Swan' (TB)	CKel CMac CWCL ECha ECtt ELan EPfP ESgI EShb EUJe EWoo GCal LAst LRHS MAvo MNrw SCob SPer SPoG WCot WHil XSen

	Name	Suppliers
	'Black Taffeta' (TB)	CKel
	'Black Tie Affair' (TB)	EAEE EPfP ESgI EWoo MAsh MSpe WCAu XSen
	'Blackbeard' (BB) 🏆H7	CKel WCAu
	'Blackberry Tease' (TB)	WCAu
	'Blackberry Towers' (TB)	ESgI
	'Blackcurrant' (IB)	WCAu
	'Blackout' (TB)	ESgI EWoo
	'Blast' (IB)	CKel
	'Blatant' (TB)	ESgI EWoo WCAu XSen
	'Blazing Light' (TB)	XSen
	'Blenheim Royal' (TB)	ESgI WCAu XSen
	'Blessed Again' (IB)	EBee
	'Blitzen' (IB)	WCAu
	'Blue Admiral' (TB)	GBin
	'Blue Boy' (IB)	EWoo
	'Blue Burgee' (Sib)	ECha
I	'Blue Butterfly' (Sib)	CBod EBee EPfP LAst MNrw NGdn
	'Blue Denim' (SDB)	ECho ECtt EPfP GCal GMaP MRav NBir NLar WBor WCAu WCot WWEG
	'Blue Eyed Blond' (IB)	MNrw
	'Blue Eyed Brunette' (TB)	WCAu
	'Blue Giant' (Dut) **new**	LLWG
	'Blue Gown' (TB)	EWoo
	'Blue Hendred' (SDB)	NBir WCAu
	'Blue King' (Sib)	CHid ELan EPfP GBin GKev GMaP MRav NBro NGdn SCob SMrm SPer WMnd WMoo WWEG
	'Blue Lamp' (TB)	CKel
	'Blue Line' (SDB)	CDes
	'Blue Meadow Fly' (Sino-Sib)	LLHF
	'Blue Mere' (Sib)	MCot
	'Blue Moon' (Sib)	ELon GBuc GQue IMou MJak SMrm WFar
	'Blue Mystery' (J)	LLHF
	'Blue Note Blues' (TB)	WCAu
	'Blue Note' (Reticulata)	CBro ECho ERCP LLHF NMin
	'Blue Pigmy' (SDB)	CBod CTal CWat ECtt EPfP LRHS MWat NLar SDeJ SPer
	'Blue Pools' (SDB)	NBir
	'Blue Reverie' (Sib)	ELon EPPr ESgI
	'Blue Rhythm' (TB)	CAby CKel ELan ELon EPfP EWoo GMaP LRHS MNHC MRav SCoo SDeJ SPer WCAu WMnd WWEG
	'Blue Sapphire' (TB)	ESgI WCAu
	'Blue Sceptre' (Sib)	IBlr
	'Blue Shimmer' (TB)	CSBt EBee ECha ELan EPfP ESgI EWoo LRHS LSou SDeJ SPer SWat WCAu WGwG WWEG
	'Blue Staccato' (TB)	WCAu XSen
	'Blue Suede Shoes' (TB)	ESgI EWoo XSen
	'Bluebeard's Ghost' (SDB) 🏆H7	WCAu
	'Bluebird Wine' (TB)	WCAu
	'Blue-eyed Susan' (TB) **new**	CIri
	'Bob Nichol' (TB)	CKel
	'Bob's Fancy'	SDeJ
	'Bockingford' (MTB)	SIri
	'Bohemia Sekt' (TB)	CKel
	'Bohemian' (TB)	CWCL
	'Bold Encounter' (TB)	WCAu
	'Bold Pretender' (La)	ECtt ELan EPfP LLWG MBNS MSCN NLar SKHP WHil
	'Bold Print' (IB)	EAEE ELon IPot LRHS MGos SHil SPoG WCAu WWEG
	'Bollinger'	see *I.* 'Hornpipe'
	'Bonnie Davenport' (TB)	CIri
I	'Bonny' (MDB)	CBro
	'Boo' (SDB)	CPBP WCAu XSen
	'Border Happy' (TB)	WCAu
	'Bottled Sunshine' (IB)	LRHS
	'Bound for Glory' (La) **new**	LLWG
	'Bournemouth Ball Gown' (Sib)	WAul
	'Bournemouth Beauty' (Sib) 🏆H7	WAul
	'Bouzy Bouzy' (TB)	ESgI XSen
	'Bracknell' (Sib)	WAul
	bracteata	EBee GBuc
	- NNS 04-223	GBuc
	'Braithwaite' (TB)	CAby CKel CWGN ECGP ELan EPfP ESgI EWoo LRHS MSpe NSoo SDeJ SPer SRms SWat WCAu WGwG
	'Brandaris' (TB)	ESgI
	'Brannigan' (SDB)	CBro NBir NSti
	'Brasero' (TB)	CWCL EWoo
	'Brash and Bold' (AB)	WCAu
	'Brasilia' (TB)	NBir
	'Brassie' (SDB)	CBro MBNS WHil WWEG XSen
	'Brave New World' (TB) 🏆H7	CIri
	'Breakers' (TB) 🏆H7	CKel EWoo WCAu
	'Breezy Blue' (SDB)	WCAu
	'Brenchley' (IB) **new**	SIri
	'Bridal Icing' (TB)	WCAu
	'Bridal Jig' (Sib)	EBee
	'Bride's Blush' (TB)	CIri
	'Bride's Halo' (TB)	WCAu XSen
	'Bright Button' (SDB)	CKel ESgI EWoo
	'Bright Fire' (TB)	EIri
	'Bright Vision' (SDB)	ESgI
	'Bright White' (MDB)	CBro CKel ECho
	'Bright Yellow' (DB)	MRav
	'Brighteyes' (IB)	SRms
	'Brindisi' (TB)	XSen
	'Brise de Mer' (TB)	XSen
	'Bristo Magic' (TB)	XSen
	'Bristol Gem' (TB)	XSen
	'Broad Shoulders' (TB)	WCAu
	'Broadleigh Angela' (CH)	CBro
	'Broadleigh Ann' (CH)	CBro
	'Broadleigh Carolyn' (CH) 🏆H5	CBro CElw
	'Broadleigh Clare' (CH)	CBro
	'Broadleigh Dorothy' (CH)	CBro
	'Broadleigh Eleanor' (CH)	CBro
	'Broadleigh Elizabeth' (CH)	CBro
	'Broadleigh Emily' (CH)	CBro
	'Broadleigh Fenella' (CH)	CBro
	'Broadleigh Jean' (CH)	CBro
	'Broadleigh Joan' (CH)	CBro
	'Broadleigh Lavinia' (CH)	CBro MRav
	'Broadleigh Mitre' (CH)	CBro CElw
	'Broadleigh Nancy' (CH)	CBro
	'Broadleigh Peacock' (CH)	CBro CElw MAvo WSHC
	'Broadleigh Penny' (CH)	CBro
	'Broadleigh Rose' (CH)	CBro CElw EPri EPyc MBrN MRav WSHC
	'Broadway Baby' (IB)	ESgI SIri
	'Broken Link' (BB) **new**	CIri
	'Bronzaire' (IB)	CKel EIri WCAu WGwG
	'Bronze Beauty' (Dut)	ERCP GKev SBod
	'Bronze Beauty' (TB)	SDeJ
	'Bronze Beauty' van Tubergen (*boogiana* hybrid)	NBir SDeJ

	Name	Suppliers
	'Brother Carl' (TB)	XSen
	'Brown Chocolate' (TB)	WCAu
	'Brown Lasso' (BB) ♀H7	WCAu
	'Bruce' (TB)	WCAu
	'Brummit's Mauve' (TB)	WCAu
	'Bruno' (TB)	NLar WMil
	'Brussels' (TB)	ESgI
	bucharica misapplied	see *I. orchioides* Carrière
	bucharica ambig.	CHel ECho ELon LSun MNrw SDeJ WBor
§	***bucharica*** Foster ♀H5	CBro ECho EPfP EPot GKev LAma
	- 'Princess'	ECho
*	- 'Top Gold'	ECho
	bucharica* × *orchioides	ECho
	'Buckwheat' (TB)	EWoo SIri
	'Buisson de Roses' (TB)	XSen
	bulleyana	ECho GEdr GKev MMuc SRms
	- BWJ 7912	WCru
	- from Dali, Yunnan, China	SBrt
	- black-flowered	CExl GKev
	- - SDR 1792	EBee
	'Bumble Boogie' (MTB)	WCAu
	'Bumblebee Deelite' (MTB) ♀H7	CJun CKel WCAu
	'Burgermeister' (TB)	XSen
	'Burgundy Party' (TB)	XSen
	'Burka' (TB)	ESgI
	'Burnt Toffee' (TB)	ESgI XSen
	'Burst' (TB)	CKel WCAu
	'Buto' (TB)	EWoo
	'Butter and Sugar' (Sib) ♀H7	Widely available
	'Butter Pecan' (IB)	WCAu
	'Buttercup Bower' (TB)	WCAu
	'Buttermere' (TB)	SRms
	'Butterpat' (IB)	ESgI
	'Butterscotch Carpet' (SDB)	WCAu
	'Butterscotch Kiss' (TB)	CAby CKel CMac ECGP ELan EPfP GMaP LRHS MBNS MGos MRav NBir NLar SHil SPer
	'Buzzword' (SDB)	WCAu
	'Bye Bye Blues' (TB)	ESgI XSen
	'Byzantine Purple' (TB)	EWoo
	'Cabaret Royale' (TB)	ESgI XSen
	'Cable Car' (TB)	CKel CWCL ESgI EWoo WCAu
	'Cache of Gold' (SDB)	EWoo
	'Caesar' (Sib)	CRow EWoo SDys SRms
	'Caesar's Brother' (Sib)	CCon CHid ELan EPfP EWoo GAbr GBin GBuc LRHS MGos MNFA MSpe NHol NLar SHil SPer SWat WCAu WFar WHoo WWEG
	'Cajun Rhythm' (TB)	XSen
	'Calico Cat' (IB) **new**	WCAu
	'Caliente' (TB)	EWoo MRav MWhi WCAu XSen
	'California Dreamin'' (TB)	CIri
	'California Gold' (TB)	WWEG
	'California Style' (IB)	XSen
§	Californian hybrids	CElw CMac CPBP EPot GCra NBir WCot
	'Calligrapher' (IB)	WCAu
	'Calm Stream' (TB)	WCAu
	'Calypso Mood' (TB)	XSen
	'Cambridge' (Sib) ♀H7	CAby CAvo EHoe EIri GBuc IMou LRHS MLHP MNFA MWat NGdn SWat WAul WCAu WFar WHoo
	'Cameliard' (TB)	EWoo
	'Camelot Rose' (TB)	WCAu XSen
	'Cameo Blush' (BB)	XSen
	'Cameo Wine' (TB)	ESgI MNrw XSen
	'Cameroun' (TB)	ESgI EWoo
	'Campbellii'	see *I. lutescens* 'Campbellii'
	canadensis	see *I. hookeri*
	'Canadian Kisses' (SDB)	ESgI
	'Canadian Streaker' (TB/v)	WCot
	'Canary Bird' (TB)	ESgI
	'Candy Rock' (IB)	CIri EWoo WCAu
	'Cannington Apricot' (IB)	CKel
	'Cannington Bluebird' (TB)	WCAu
	'Cannington Ochre' (SDB)	CBro
	'Canonbury Belle' (Sib)	WAul
	'Can't Touch This' (TB)	WCAu
	'Cantab' (Reticulata)	CBro ECho EPot ERCP GBin GKev LAma LRHS SDeJ
	'Caprice' (TB)	EWoo
	'Capricious Candles' (TB)	CIri
	'Captain Indigo' (IB)	ESgI WCAu
	'Captive Sun' (SDB)	CTal EAEE EPfP LRHS NSoo SIri
	'Caramba' (TB)	WCAu
	'Caramel' (TB)	XSen
	'Cardinal' (TB) **new**	WMil
	'Careless Sally' (Sib)	WAul WCAu
	'Caribbean Dream' (TB)	XSen
	'Carnaby' (TB)	CBod CKel ESgI EShb IPot LRHS MRav MSpe SDeJ WCAu XSen
	'Carnival Ride' (TB)	WCAu
	'Carnival Song' (TB)	WCAu
	'Carnival Time' (TB)	CKel CMac CWGN EBee ECtt LRHS MCot MSpe SPer WHoo XSen
	'Carol Lee' (TB)	EBee
	'Carolina' (Reticulata) **new**	ERCP
	'Carolina Gold' (TB)	XSen
*	'Caronte' (IB)	ESgI
	'Carriage Trade' (TB)	LRHS
	'Casbah' (TB)	XSen
	'Cascade Rhythm' (TB)	WCAu
	'Cascade Springs' (TB)	XSen
	'Cascade Sprite' (SDB)	SRms
	'Casual Joy' (TB)	CIri
	'Catalyst' (TB)	XSen
	'Cat's Eye' (SDB)	ESgI SIri
	'Catwalk Idol' (La) **new**	LLWG
	caucasica	CMac
	'Cayenne Capers' (TB)	ESgI
*	'Cedric Morris'	EWes
	'Cee Jay' (IB) ♀H7	EWoo
	'Cee Tee'	EWoo XSen
	'Celebration Song' (TB)	ESgI SIri WCAu XSen
	'Celestial Glory' (TB)	XSen
	'Cerdagne' (TB)	XSen
	'Chalkhill' (SDB)	WCAu
	chamaeiris	see *I. lutescens* subsp. *lutescens*
	'Champagne Elegance' (TB)	EIri EPri NBir WCAu XSen
	'Champagne Encore' (IB)	EWoo LSun
	'Champagne Frost' (TB)	XSen
	'Champagne Music' (TB)	WCAu
	'Champagne Waltz' (TB)	XSen
	'Chandler's Choice' (Sib)	EWes
	'Change of Pace' (TB)	ESgI WCAu XSen
	'Chanted' (SDB)	EWoo WCAu XSen
	'Chantilly' (TB)	CHid EAJP EBee ELan EPfP EWoo LRHS MRav NBir NGdn NLar SPer SWat
	'Chapeau' (TB)	ESgI WCAu
	'Charmaine' (TB)	XSen
	'Chartreuse Bounty' (Sib)	EPri EWes NLar NSti
	'Chasing Rainbows' (TB)	SDys WCAu

	Name	Suppliers
	'Château d'Auvers-sur-Oise' (TB)	SIri
	'Cheap Frills' (TB)	WCAu
	'Cherie' (TB)	WCAu
	'Cherished' (TB)	WWEG
	'Cherished One' (La) **new**	LLWG
	'Cherokee Heritage' (TB) **new**	WCAu
	'Cherry Blossom Special' (TB)	CIri
	'Cherry Garden' (SDB)	Widely available
	'Cherry Twist' (La) **new**	LLWG
	'Cherrywood' (SDB)	CBro
	'Cherub's Smile' (TB)	XSen
	'Cheryl Ann O'Leary' (TB)	CIri
	'Chickee' (MTB) ♀H7	CKel
	'Chicken Little' (MDB)	CBro
	'Chief Moses' (TB)	WCAu
I	'Chieftain' (SDB)	MRav
	'Childhood Sweetheart' (La) **new**	LLWG
	'Chilled Wine' (Sib)	ELon
	'China Dragon' (TB)	SWat XSen
	'Chinese Coral' (TB)	XSen
	'Chinese Treasure' (TB)	XSen
	'Chinook Winds' (TB)	ESgI
	'Chivalry' (TB)	ESgI
	'Chorus Girl' (TB)	CKel
	'Christine Mullins' (Sib)	WBor
	'Christmas Angel' (TB)	WCAu
	chrysographes ♀H7	CBro CHid CMac CTsd CWCL EHoe EPfP EPri EWll EWoo GJos IBoy IKil LAst LRHS MBel MHer MLHP MMuc MRav NPri NSti SCob SRot
I	- 'Black Beauty'	CCon ECho EPfP EWoo
	- 'Black Gold'	EPri MHol
I	- 'Black Knight'	CCse CExl ELon EPfP GBuc GCal GCra ITim MCot NChi NLar SWat WMnd
I	- 'Black Velvet'	GEdr
	- black-flowered	CBod CDes CExl CFil EBee ELan GAbr GBin GBuc GCal GKev GKin LRHS MNrw MSCN MWhi NGdn NSoo SCob SPer SPoG WCot WCru WFar WGwG WMoo WPGP WPnP WSHC WWEG
	- dark-flowered	CHel GKev MSCN WFar
	- 'Goldvein'	CMac
	- hybrid **new**	WFar
	- 'Inshriach'	IMou LEdu
	- 'Kew Black'	CExl ECho GKev LEdu NBir WHer WWEG
	- 'Kilmurry Black'	IKil
	- 'Mandarin Purple'	GCal MBri SWat
§	- 'Rubella'	GCra
	- 'Rubra'	see *I. chrysographes* 'Rubella'
	- yellow-flowered	WFar
	chrysographes* × *forrestii	GBin NBir
	'Chubby Cheeks' (SDB)	CKel WCAu
	'Church Stoke' (SDB)	WCAu
	'Cimarron Rose' (SDB)	ESgI
	'Cimarron Strip' (TB)	EPfP WWEG XSen
	'Cimarron Trail' (TB)	WCAu
	'Circle of Light' (TB)	WCAu
	'Circle Round' (Sib)	CSpe
	'Circus Stripes' (TB)	XSen
	'Cirrus Veil' (SDB)	WCAu
	'Citoyen' (TB)	XSen
	'Citronnade' (TB)	ESgI
	'City' (SDB) **new**	SIri
	'City of Paradise' (TB)	ESgI
	'Clairette' (Reticulata)	ECho EPot LAma MWat NMin SDeJ
	'Clara Garland' (IB)	WCAu
	'Clarence' (TB)	ESgI EWoo XSen
	clarkei	CHel CPrp ECho GBin GEdr
	- B&SWJ 2122	WCru
	- CC 2751	CExl
	- SDR 3819	GKev
	'Classic Look' (TB)	ESgI
	'Classic Navy' (BB)	ESgI
	'Clear Choice' (TB)	WCAu
	'Clear Morning Sky' (TB)	EPot GKev
	'Clearwater River' (TB)	WCAu
	'Clee Hills' (Sib)	WAul
	'Cleedownton' (Sib)	WAul
	'Clematis' (TB) **new**	WMil
	'Cleo' (TB)	NSti
	'Cleo Murrell' (TB)	ESgI EWoo
	'Cleve Dodge' (Sib)	EPri ESgI EWoo SIri XLum
	'Cliffs of Dover' (TB)	CKel EIri ESgI EWoo GCal MCot SCob SRms
	'Close Shave' (TB)	CIri
	'Cloudcap' (TB)	SRms
	'Clown Around' (TB)	CIri
	'Clownerie' (TB)	EWoo
	'Clyde Redmond' (La) ♀H5	WMAq
	'Coalignition' (TB)	EWoo WCAu
	'Codicil' (TB)	EIri EWoo XSen
	'Coffee Boy' (SDB) **new**	CBro
	colchica **new**	LEdu
	'Colette Thurillet' (TB)	WCAu XSen
*	'Colin's Pale Blue' (Sib)	SMHy
	collettii	ECho
	'Color Carnival' (TB)	ESgI
	'Color Me Blue' (TB)	WCAu
	'Color Splash' (TB)	XSen
	'Colorific' (La)	EBee NLar WHil
	'Colortart' (TB)	XSen
	'Come to Me' (TB)	CIri
	'Coming Up Roses' (TB)	XSen
	'Con Fuoco' (TB)	XSen
	'Concertina' (IB)	CIri EWoo WCAu
	'Concord Crush' (Sib) **new**	LLWG SMrm
	confusa	CHEx CPla CPne EUJe GGal SArc SBig SEND SGSe SMad XSen
§	- 'Martyn Rix'	CAbb CAby CBct CDes CHEx CHel CHid CMac CPou ELon EPfP GCal IDee IGor LRHS MLHP MMoz SBrt SEND SGSe WGwG WHer
	confusa* × *japonica **new**	WWFP
	'Conjuration' (TB)	EWoo SIri WCAu
	'Connection' (TB)	WCAu
	'Constant Wattez' (IB)	CKel ESgI NLar
	'Constantine Bay' (TB)	ESgI
	'Consummation' (MTB)	SGol
	'Contrast in Styles' (Sib)	CBod EPri LSou MSCN WBor WFar
	'Cool Spring' (Sib)	MSpe
	'Copatonic' (TB)	ESgI WCAu
	'Copper Capers' (TB)	ESgI
	'Copper Classic' (TB)	ELon ESgI SEND WCAu
	'Coquet Waters' (Sib)	NBid WAul
	'Coquetterie' (TB)	EWoo
	'Coral Point' (TB)	WCAu
	'Coral Sunset' (TB)	WCAu XSen

'Cordoba' (TB)	WCAu XSen
'Coronation Anthem' (Sib)	EPri EWoo WAul
'Côte d'Or' (TB)	XSen
'County Town Red' (TB)	SIri
'Coup de Soleil' (TB)	EWoo
'Cozy Calico' (TB)	WCAu
'Cracklin Burgundy' (TB)	XSen
'Craithie' (TB)	EMal
'Cranapple' (BB) ♀H7	ESgI
'Cranberry Ice' (TB)	ELon EWoo XSen
'Cranberry Sauce' (TB)	SIri WCAu
'Cranbrook' (IB) ♀H7	SIri
'Cream Beauty' (Dut)	GKev SBod SDeJ
'Cream Pixie' (SDB)	WCAu
'Creative Artistry' (La) **new**	LLWG
cretensis	see *I. unguicularis* subsp. *cretensis*
'Crimson King' (IB)	EWoo
'Crimson Snow' (TB)	WCAu
'Crinoline' (TB)	XSen
'Crispette' (TB)	WCAu
cristata	GEdr NHar NLar SRms
- 'Alba'	EBee GCal GEdr NHar WThu
crocea ♀H7	GKev
'Croftway Lemon' (TB)	ELon
'Cross Current' (TB)	WCAu
'Crowned Heads' (TB)	WCAu XSen
'Crushed Ice' (La) **new**	LLWG
'Crushed Velvet' (TB)	WCAu
'Crystal Fountain' (TB)	CIri
'Crystal Gazer' (TB)	ESgI
'Crystal Glitters' (TB)	ESgI
'Crystal Phoenix'	CRow
'Cumulus' (TB)	EWoo SIri
cuniculiformis	ECho WCot
'Cup Race' (TB)	WCAu XSen
'Cupid's Arrow' (TB)	WCAu
'Curlew' (IB)	WCAu
'Cutie' (IB)	ESgI EWoo WCAu
'Cyanea' (DB)	ECho
'Cyclamint' (La) **new**	LLWG
cycloglossa	ECho EPot GKev WCot
'Dainty Lace' (La) **new**	LLWG
'Dakota Smoke' (TB)	EWoo
'Dale Dennis' (DB)	XSen
'Dance Away' (TB)	ESgI
'Dance Ballerina Dance' (Sib)	CCon CHid CWCL EBee EPfP EPri LLWG MRav NLar SMrm WFar
'Dance for Joy' (TB)	XSen
'Dance the Night Away' (TB)	WCAu
'Dancer's Veil' (TB)	CBod CKel CMac EBee ECtt ELon ESgI LRHS MRav SPer WCAu
'Dancing Bunnies' (SDB)	WCAu
'Dancing Gypsy'	WCAu
'Dancing Lilacs' (MTB)	ESgI
'Dancing Nanou' (Sib)	EBee ECtt SWat
danfordiae	CAby CBro ECho EPfP EPot GKev LAma LRHS SDeJ SPer
'Dangerous Mood' (TB)	EWoo
'Dante's Inferno' (TB)	EWoo
'Dardanus' (Rc)	ECho EPot ERCP GKev LLHF SDeJ WCot
'Dark Avenger' (IB)	CIri
'Dark Crystal' (SDB)	ESgI EWoo
'Dark Desire' (Sib)	MRav
'Dark Spark' (SDB)	WCAu
'Dark Vader' (SDB)	ESgI WCAu
'Darkness' (IB)	SIri
'Darkside' (TB)	XSen
'Darts' (IB) **new**	CIri
'Dash Away' (SDB)	ESgI SIri
'Dashing' (TB)	EWoo
'Dauber's Delight'	CIri
'Dauber's Surprise' (TB)	CIri
'Daughter of Stars' (TB)	ESgI
'Dauntless' (TB)	ESgI
'Dawn of Fall' (TB)	ESgI
'Dawn Waltz' (Sib)	EBee LLWG WFar
'Dawning' (TB) ♀H7	ESgI EWoo
'Dazzle Time' (TB)	CIri
'Dazzling' (IB)	WCAu
'Dazzling Gold' (TB)	ESgI WCAu XSen
'Dear Delight' (Sib)	LLHF LLWG NLar WBor WFar
'Dear Dianne' (Sib)	CHid
'Death by Chocolate' (SDB)	ESgI
'Decadence' (TB)	WCAu
§ ***decora***	CTal
'Deep Black' (TB)	CAby CKel CPar CWGN CWld EAJP EBee ELan EPfP ESgI EUJe GBin GMaP IPot LRHS MBNS MCot MRav MWat NLar NOrc NWad SDeJ SPer SPoG SWat WCAu WGwG WWEG
'Deep Pacific' (TB)	WCAu
'Deft Touch' (TB)	XSen
delavayi ♀H7	ECho EWes GMaP WRHF
- SDR 50	CExl GKev
- 'Didcot'	LRHS
'Delicate Lady' (IB) ♀H7	CKel
'Delirium' (IB)	WCAu
'Delta Blues' (TB)	EWoo SIri
'Delta Butterfly' (La)	WMAq
'Demi-Deuil' (TB)	EWoo
'Demon' (SDB)	CJun XSen
'Demure Illini' (Sib)	MNrw
'Denys Humphry' (TB)	WCAu
'Derwentwater' (TB)	SRms WCAu
I 'Desert Dream' (Sino-Sib)	GAbr
'Desert Echo' (TB)	MHer XSen
'Desert Song' (TB)	CKel WCAu
'Devil David' (TB)	CIri
'Devil May Care' (IB)	ESgI
'Devilry' (SDB)	EWoo
'Devil's Spoon' (TB)	CIri
'Devonshire Cream' (TB)	CIri WCAu
'Devoted' (SDB)	WCAu
'Dewful' (Sib)	EBee WFar
'Diabolique' (TB) ♀H7	XSen
'Diamond Ring' (TB)	SDys
§ ***dichotoma***	EWes SBrt
'Dinky Circus' (MDB)	CPBP
'Dinky Doodle' (SDB)	WCAu
'Disco Jewel' (MTB)	ESgI
'Discovered Treasure' (TB)	WCAu
'Distant Music' (La) **new**	LLWG
'Ditzy' (SDB)	SIri
'Diversion' (TB)	ESgI
'Dixie Darling' (TB)	ESgI XSen
'Dixie Pixie' (SDB)	WCAu
'Doctor No' (TB)	CIri
'Dogrose' (TB)	EWoo
'Doll Ribbons' (MTB)	EPfP
'Dolly Madison' (TB)	ESgI
§ ***domestica***	CArn CBro CHll ELan EPfP EWld SPav SPlb SRms WSHC
- B&SWJ 8692B	WCru
- 'Crûg Colossal'	WCru

Plant	Suppliers
– 'Freckle Face'	CWCL LSou
'Dominion' (TB) **new**	WMil
'Don Juan' (TB)	EWoo
'Dorcas Lives Again' (TB)	WHil
'Dotted Swiss' (TB)	XSen
'Double Bubble' (TB)	EWoo
'Double Byte' (SDB)	XSen
'Double Click' (TB)	EWoo
'Double Espoir' (TB)	XSen
'Double Lament' (SDB)	CBro
'Double Mini'	EWoo
'Double Shot' (TB)	EWoo
'Double Standards' (Sib)	EBee EPri WHil
'Double Vision' (TB)	EWoo XSen
douglasiana	ECho GCal GKev
– 'Cape Ferrelo'	SKHP
'Dover Beach' (TB)	SIri
'Dover Castle' (BB) ♀H7 **new**	SIri
'Draco' (TB)	ESgI XSen
'Drake Carne' (TB)	CKel
'Drama Queen' (TB)	CIri
'Dream Indigo' (IB)	EWoo WCAu XSen
'Dreaming Green' (Sib)	EBee
'Dreaming Orange' (Sib)	ECtt EPri
'Dreaming Spires' (Sib)	ESgI SIri
'Dreaming Yellow' (Sib)	CBre CMHG CSam EAEE ECha EHon EPfP EPla EPri EShb GBuc GKin LEdu LRHS MLHP MMuc MRav NGdn SPer WAul WMoo
'Dreamsicle' (TB)	EWoo
'Dresden Candleglow' (IB)	WCAu
'Dualtone' (TB)	CKel
'Dude Ranch' (TB)	WCAu
'Duded Up' (TB) **new**	CIri
'Duke of Bedford' (TB) **new**	WMil
'Dunkler Wein' (Sib)	EBee EWes
'Dunlin' (MDB)	CBro CTal ECho NBir
'Dural White Butterfly' (La)	CBod CHid
'Durham Dream' (TB)	CIri
'Dusky Challenger' (TB)	CKel ESgI EWoo WCAu XSen
'Dusky Evening' (TB)	XSen
'Dutch Chocolate' (TB)	CKel ESgI EWes EWoo WCAu XSen
dykesii	WWtn
'Dynamite' (TB)	ESgI EWoo XSen
'Dyonisos' (TB)	SIri
'Eagle's Flight' (TB)	XSen
'Earl of Essex' (TB)	WCAu XSen
'Early Frost' (IB)	CKel
'Early Light' (TB) ♀H7	ESgI LPot WCAu
'East Indies' (TB)	WCAu
'Easter' (SDB)	SIri
'Eastertime' (TB)	ESgI EWoo
'Eastman Winds' (La) **new**	LLWG
'Easy' (MTB)	EIri SIri
'Ebony Echo' (TB)	EWoo
'Echo de France' (TB)	ESgI EWoo XSen
'Eden's Paradise Blue' (Sib) **new**	EBee ELon
'Edge of Winter' (TB)	CKel SIri XSen
'Edith Wolford' (TB)	CCCN CWCL EBee ESgI MMHG NSoo SCob SGol SHar SRGP XSen
'Edna Grace' (La) **new**	LLWG
'Ed's Blue' (DB)	ELan
'Edward' (Reticulata)	CBro ECho EPfP EPot GKev LAma LRHS NMin SDeJ
'Edward of Windsor' (TB)	ELan GMaP LRHS NLar SCob SRGP WMnd
'Ego' (Sib)	CAvo CHid ECha ELon EPfP EPri EWoo GBuc MGos SGSe SWat WMoo
'Egyptian' (TB)	EWoo
'Eileen Louise' (TB) ♀H7	WCAu
'El Tovar' (TB)	EWoo
'Eldorado' (TB)	EWoo
'Eleanor Clare' (IB)	CKel
'Eleanor Roosevelt' (IB)	EWoo
'Eleanor's Pride' (TB)	CKel ESgI WCAu
'Electrique' (TB)	WCAu
elegantissima	see *I. iberica* subsp. *elegantissima*
'Elizabeth Arden' (TB)	CKel
'Elizabeth of England' (TB)	EWoo GKev LBuc MLHP WWEG
'Elizabeth Poldark' (TB)	ESgI XSen
'Ellenbank Sapphire' (Sib)	GBin
'Ellesmere' (Sib)	EBee NGdn WAul
'Elsa Sass' (TB)	ESgI
'Elsie Petty' (IB)	SIri
'Elvinhall'	CBro
'Emperor' (Sib)	CRow CWat NSti SWat
'Encre Bleue' (IB)	ESgI
'Endless Love' (TB)	EIri
'English Charm' (TB)	ESgI WCAu XSen
'English Cottage' (TB)	ELon GBin GCal LBuc MWat NLar WCAu WSHC XSen
'Ennerdale' (TB)	SRms
'Enriched' (MTB) ♀H7	SIri WCAu
§ ***ensata***	CBcs CBro CHEx CHel ELan EPfP GKev LRHS MHer MJak MLHP MMuc MNrw NLar SEND SPlb SRms SWat WWtn
– 'Activity'	CRow SHar WFar WWEG
– 'Agrippine'	SKHP
– 'Alba'	ECha
– 'Alpine Majesty' ♀H7	CIri
– 'Apollo'	CRow
– 'Asian Warrior'	WFar
– 'August Emperor'	MBel
– 'Azuma-kagami'	CCon EBee ELan EPfP MNrw
– 'Azure'	EBee WFar WMoo
– 'Barnhawk Sybil'	SKHP
– 'Barr Purple East' ♀H7	CRow
– 'Blue Beauty'	GAbr
I – 'Blue King'	NHol
I – 'Blue Peter'	CBen CRow
– 'Blue Prince'	CBen
– 'Butterflies in Flight'	CRow
– 'Caprician Butterfly' ♀H7	EPfP NLar
– 'Carnival Prince'	CCon WFar WMoo
– 'Cascade Crest'	SWat WFar
– 'Center of Interest'	NBir
* – 'Charm'	LRHS
– 'Chitose-no-tomo'	CRow
– 'Crepe Paper'	WFar
– 'Cry of Rejoice'	EBee ECho ECtt SGol SWat
– 'Crystal Halo' ♀H7	CIri EBee LSun
– 'Dace'	GBin
– 'Dancing Waves'	CRow
I – 'Darling'	CPrp CRow ECho EPfP SWat WFar WMoo WWEG
– 'Diamant'	GBin
– 'Dramatic Moment'	GBuc WFar WWEG
I – 'Dresden China'	CRow
– 'Eden's Blush'	EBee MLHP
– 'Eden's Charm'	EPfP GBin
– 'Eden's Paintbrush'	EPfP SPer
– 'Eden's Picasso'	CCon
– 'Eden's Purple Glory'	CHid GBin WCot

	– 'Eden's Starship'	CCon
	– 'Electric Rays'	EBee WFar
I	– 'Emotion'	CMac EBee WFar
	– 'Flying Tiger' ♀H7	CIri
I	– 'Fortune'	CBod GBin IKil MSCN MWat SMrm
	– 'Freckled Geisha'	CIri EBee ELon EPfP IPot NBir SGol SPoG WFar
	– 'Frilled Enchantment' ♀H7	IPot WFar
I	– 'Galatea'	CExl CHel EBee LEdu WFar
*	– 'Gipsy'	CMac EBee
	– 'Gold Bound'	SKHP
	– 'Gracieuse'	ELan GBin LRHS NLar SWat WCot WWEG
	– 'Gusto'	CMHG EBee ELon EPfP EWTr IPot MBri MNrw SMrm SWat WBor WFar
	– 'Hercule'	CExl CHel CHid CRow GAbr NBir
	– Higo white	SPer
	– 'Hokkaido'	CRow
	– 'Hoshi-akari'	WBor WFar
	– 'Hue and Cry' ♀H7	CIri
	– hybrids	CHel EHon
	– 'Imperial Velvet'	WFar
*	– 'Innocence'	NLar SWat WFar WMoo
	– 'Iso-no-nami'	CDes EBee WFar
*	– 'Jitsugetsu'	CCon NLar
	– 'Jeweled Kimono' **new**	LSun
	– 'Jocasta'	EPfP MBri WFar
*	– 'Jodlesong'	WFar
	– 'Kalamazoo'	WFar
	– 'Katy Mendez' ♀H7	IPot LLWG NLar
*	– 'Kiyo-zuru'	EPfP
	– 'Kogesho'	EBee EPfP GBuc MNrw NLar
	– 'Koh Dom'	SPer
	– 'Kongo San'	NLar WFar
	– 'Kuma-funjin'	CExl CHel CRow EBee
	– 'Kumo-no-obi'	CExl CHel CMHG EBee GBin GBuc LRHS MCot NHol SPtp SWat WFar
	– 'Lace Ruff'	CMHG MBri
	– 'Lady in Waiting'	CHel CMHG EBee ECtt EPfP MBri NLar NWad
	– 'Landscape at Dawn'	CRow
	– 'Laughing Lion'	ECtt EWoo IKil WFar WMoo WWEG
	– 'Light at Dawn'	CMHG MBel WMoo
	– 'Lilac Blotch'	SPer
I	– 'Loyalty'	CExl ECho EWoo LRHS SHar WFar
I	– 'Mandarin'	CRow
	– 'Momogasumi' **new**	LLWG
	– 'Momozomo'	LLHF
§	– 'Moonlight Waves'	CExl CHid CMHG CPrp CRow EAEE EBee ELan EPfP GBuc GCra GKin GMaP LRHS MCot MRav MWts NGdn NHol SMrm SWat WFar
	– 'Oase'	ECtt
	– 'Ocean Mist'	CHid EBee ECtt GBuc IKil
	– 'Oku-banri'	CExl CHEx CHel EBee WFar
	– 'Oriental Eyes'	NGdn NLar
	– pale mauve-flowered	NBir
	– 'Pin Stripe'	CDes EBee LSun NLar SWat WMoo
	– 'Pink Frost'	CPrp CRow EBee ELan EPfP LBMP LRHS WFar
	– 'Pinkerton'	CIri
	– 'Pleasant Earlybird'	WFar
	– 'Pleasant Journey'	ECtt
	– 'Prairie Frost'	EBee NLar
	– 'Prairie Noble'	EBee
	– purple-flowered	SPer
	– 'Queen's Tiara'	ELon LLWG
	– 'Rakka-no-utage'	EBee NLar
	– 'Ranpo'	CRow
I	– 'Reveille'	EBee SWat
	– 'Rivulets of Wine'	CIri
§	– 'Rose Queen' ♀H7	CBAq CExl CMac CPrp CRow CSam ECha EHon ELan EPfP GBin GBuc GCra GKin GMaP LRHS MCot MRav NBir NGdn NHol SMrm SPer WFar WMoo XLum
	– 'Rowden'	CRow
	– 'Rowden Amir'	CRow
	– 'Rowden Autocrat'	CRow
	– 'Rowden Begum'	CRow
	– 'Rowden Caliph'	CRow
	– 'Rowden Consul'	CRow
	– 'Rowden Dauphin'	CRow
	– 'Rowden Dictator'	CRow
	– 'Rowden Empress'	CRow
	– 'Rowden King'	CRow
	– 'Rowden Knight'	CRow
	– 'Rowden Mikado'	CRow
	– 'Rowden Naib'	CRow
	– 'Rowden Nuncio'	CRow
	– 'Rowden Pasha'	CRow
	– 'Rowden Prince'	CRow
	– 'Rowden Queen'	CRow
	– 'Rowden Shah'	CRow
	– 'Rowden Sirdar'	CRow
	– 'Rowden Sultan'	CRow
I	– 'Royal Banner'	EBee ECtt EWoo LRHS SHar WFar WWEG
	– 'Royal Crown'	ECho XLum
I	– 'Ruby King'	LEdu LRHS
	– 'Ruffled Dimity'	CBcs EBee IPot
	– 'Sandsation'	CIri
	– 'Sapphire Star'	CKel
I	– 'Sensation'	CWCL ECho ECtt EWoo GBin IKil MWts NLar SMrm SWat WWEG
	– 'Snowy Hills'	XLum
	– 'Sorcerer's Triumph'	WFar
	– var. ***spontanea***	SWat
	– – B&SWJ 1103	WCru
	– – B&SWJ 8699	WCru
	– 'Stippled Ripples'	IPot MWts
	– 'Strut and Flourish'	EWoo
	– 'Sylvia's Masquerade'	CHel
	– 'Taketori-hime' (v)	XLum
	– 'The Great Mogul' ♀H7	CRow
	– 'Umi-kaze'	NLar
	– 'Variegata' (v) ♀H7	Widely available
	– 'Velvety Queen'	CPrp ECtt
I	– 'White Ladies'	CSBt EWoo LRHS SWat WWEG
I	– 'White Pearl'	CRow
	– white-flowered	WFar
	– 'Wine Ruffles'	CHel CMHG SMrm
	– 'Yako-no-tama'	CRow WMoo
	– 'Yamato Hime'	NLar
	– 'Yedo-yeman'	EBee IMou WFar
*	– 'Yu Nagi'	SPer
	'Épée Violette' (TB)	ESgI
	'Epicenter' (TB)	XSen
	'Eramosa Miss' (BB)	WCAu
	'Eramosa Skies' (SDB)	WCAu
	'Erect' (IB)	CKel
	'Eric the Red' (Sib)	EWoo
	'Erste Sahne' (Sib)	GBin
	'Eternal Bliss' (TB)	SIri
	'Evadne' (TB) **new**	WMil
	'Evening Drama' (TB)	WCAu

'Evening Gown' (TB)	XSen
'Ever After' (TB)	EWoo XSen
'Ever Again' (Sib)	EWoo
'Everything Plus' (TB)	ESgI XSen
'Ewen' (Sib)	CHid CPou CRow EWoo GBin GKin GLog GMaP LEdu MNrw NGdn SGSe SMrm SWat WAul WCot WFar WWEG
'Exotic Isle' (TB)	ESgI XSen
'Expose' (TB) **new**	WCAu
'Extra' (BB)	CPBP LLHF
'Extra Dazzle' (La)	LLWG
'Extra Innings' (TB)	EWoo
'Eye Magic' (IB)	CKel XSen
'Eye of Tiger'	see *I.* 'Tigereye'
'Eye Shadow' (SDB)	WCAu
'Eyebright' (SDB) 🏆H7	CBro
'Fabiola' (Reticulata) **new**	ERCP
'Fabuleux' (TB)	SIri
'Faenelia Hicks' (La)	WMAq
'Falconeer' (TB)	CIri
'Fall Empire' (TB)	EWoo
'Fall Enterprise' (TB)	CIri
'Fall Fiesta' (TB)	XSen
'Fancy Brass' (TB)	SIri
'Fancy Dress' (TB)	SIri
'Fancy Woman' (TB)	WCAu
'Fanfaron' (TB)	ESgI XSen
'Farleigh Damson' (SDB)	SIri
'Fashion Holiday' (IB)	SIri
'Fashion Lady' (MDB)	CBro ECho
'Fathom' (IB)	WCAu
'Feminine Charm' (TB)	MRav WCAu
'Festive Skirt' (TB)	CKel WCAu
'Feu du Ciel' (TB) 🏆H7	ESgI EWoo XSen
'Few Are Chosen' (La) **new**	LLWG
'Fierce Fire' (IB) 🏆H7	CKel
'Fiesta Time' (TB)	CWCL XSen
'Filibuster' (TB)	WCAu
filifolia var. ***latifolia***	NMin
'Film Festival' (TB)	ESgI
'Finalist' (TB)	WCAu XSen
'Firebeard' (TB)	CIri
'Firebreather' (TB)	MAsh
'Firebug' (IB)	ESgI XSen
'Firecracker' (TB)	MRav WCAu
'First Interstate' (TB)	CWCL ESgI XSen
'First Movement' (TB)	ESgI
'First Violet' (TB)	ESgI
'Fit the Bill' (TB)	EWoo
'Five Star Admiral' (TB)	XSen
'Flaming Dragon' (TB)	XSen
'Flaming Victory' (TB)	XSen
'Flammenschwert' (TB)	WCAu
flavescens	ESgI EWoo WCAu XSen
'Fleece of White' (BB)	WCAu
'Fleur Collette Louise' (La)	CIri
'Flight of Butterflies' (Sib)	Widely available
'Flight of Fantasy' (La)	CKel
'Flirting Again' (SDB) 🏆H7	SIri
'Floorshow' (TB)	XSen
'Flopsy' (TB)	CIri
§ 'Florentina' (IB/TB) 🏆H7	CArn CBro CHby EBee ECGP ESgI EWoo GCal GPoy MNHC MRav NBid NBir SEND WCAu WHer WHfH XSen
'Florentine Silk' (TB)	WCAu
'Floridor' (TB)	EWoo
'Fluffy Pillows' (TB)	CIri
'Flumadiddle' (IB)	CBro WCFE
'Flûte Enchantée' (TB)	CIri XSen
'Focus' (TB)	XSen
foetidissima 🏆H5	Widely available
- 'Aurea'	EBee WCot
- ***chinensis***	see *I. foetidissima* var. *citrina*
§ - var. ***citrina***	CBre CCon ECGP EPfP EPla EPri EWld GAbr GCal GCra LEdu NLar SChr WCot WGwG
- 'Fructu Albo'	GBin NSti
- var. ***lutescens***	CHid EPPr
- 'Variegata' (v) 🏆H5	CElw EPfP EWoo MSCN NBir NPer
- yellow-seeded	GCal
'Fogbound' (TB)	WCAu
'Foggy Dew' (TB)	EAEE LRHS
'Fondation Van Gogh' (TB)	XSen
'Foolish Fancy' (TB)	SIri
'Footloose' (TB)	SIri XSen
'For Mary' (TB)	CIri
'Fordwich' (SDB) **new**	SIri
'Forecasting Rain' (SDB) **new**	SIri
'Foreign Legion' (TB)	WCAu
'Foreigner' (TB)	WCAu
'Forest Light' (SDB)	CBro ESgI
'Forever Blue' (SDB)	WCAu
'Forever Gold' (TB)	EWoo XSen
'Forge Fire' (TB)	ESgI
formosana	ECho
- B&SWJ 3076	WCru
'Forrest Hills' (TB)	CBod EPfP LRHS
forrestii 🏆H7	CAby CAvo CBro CCon CExl CHid CMac ECho EHoe EWoo GAbr GBin GCal GCra GKev GLog ITim LRHS MHer MMuc NBir NBro SPtp SRot WAbe
- SDR 5802	GKev
'Fort Apache' (TB)	EWes EWoo
'Fortunata' (TB)	XSen
'Fortunate Son'	EWoo WCAu
'Fortune Teller' (TB)	CKel
'Fourfold Blue' (SpH)	GBin
'Fourfold Lavender' (Sib)	EWes
'Fourfold White' (Sib)	ESgI
'Foxy Lady' (TB)	EWoo
'Framboise' (TB)	XSen
'Frances Iva' (TB)	EWoo
'Francheville' (TB)	EWoo
'Francina' (TB) **new**	WMil
'Frank Elder' (Reticulata)	ECho EPot ERCP GKev LAma LLHF LRHS SDeJ WAbe
'Frans Hals' (Dut)	MMHG
'Freedom Flight' (TB)	CIri
'French Can Can' (TB)	EWoo SIri
'French Horn' (TB)	CIri
'French Rose' (TB)	WCAu
'Fresno Calypso' (TB)	ESgI WCAu XSen
'Frison-roche' (TB)	CWCL
'Frisounette' (TB)	ESgI
'Fritillary Flight' (IB) 🏆H7	CKel
'From this Moment' (La) **new**	LLWG
'Frontier Lady' (TB)	CIri
'Frontier Marshall' (TB)	XSen
'Frost and Flame' (TB)	EBee ECGP ECtt ELan EWoo GBin LRHS MRav NBir NLar SDeJ SPer SPoG SWat WGwG
'Frost Echo' (TB)	EWoo

'Frosted Angel' (SDB)	CBro
'Frosted Biscuit' (TB) ♀H7	CKel
'Frosted Velvet' (MTB)	WCAu
'Frosty Crown' (SDB)	CDes
'Frosty Jewels' (TB)	XSen
'Frosty Moonscape' (TB)	CIri
'Fruit Cocktail' (IB)	XSen
'Full Sun' (Spuria)	EWoo
fulva ♀H5	CRow CSpe EBee EPri GBin GCal LPot MMHG MWts NBir NBro NSti SBrt WBor WCot
- 'Marvell Gold' (La)	CRow EBee
× ***fulvala*** ♀H5	CCon EWes GBin NBir NSti
- 'Violacea'	LRHS
'Furnaceman' (SDB)	CBro CTal
'Futuriste' (TB)	SIri
'Fuzzy' (MDB)	EPot
'Gai Luron' (TB)	WWEG
'Gallant Moment' (TB)	ECtt EWoo SIri XSen
'Galleon Gold' (SDB)	CKel
'Galway' (IB)	SIri XSen
'Game Plan' (TB)	WCAu
'Gandalf the Grey' (TB)	ESgI
'Gelbe Mantel' (Sino-Sib)	CHid GBin GKin MSpe NBir NSti
'Gemstone Walls' (TB)	ESgI
'Gentius' (TB)	WMnd
'George' (Reticulata) ♀H7	CAby CAvo CBro ECho EPfP EPot ERCP GKev LAma LRHS NMin WBor WBrk WCot WHoo
'Gerald Darby'	see *I.* × *robusta* 'Gerald Darby'
'Germaine Perthuis' (TB)	EWoo
§ ***germanica***	MMuc SEND WCAu WCot
- var. ***florentina***	see *I.* 'Florentina'
§ - 'Nepalensis'	WCAu
- 'The King'	see *I. germanica* 'Nepalensis'
'Gertrude' (TB)	EWoo
'Ghost Train' (TB)	EWoo SIri
'Giacatollo' (TB) **new**	CIri
'Gingerbread Castle' (TB)	WCAu
'Gingerbread Man' (SDB)	CBro CMea CTal EBee ESgI EWoo MBrN WCAu
'Gingersnap' (TB)	EWoo
'Glacier Gold' (TB)	XSen
'Glad Rags' (TB)	XSen
'Gladiator's Gift' (La) **new**	LLWG
'Gladys Austin' (TB)	XSen
'Glowing Embers' (TB)	ESgI
'Gnu' (TB)	XSen
'Go Between' (TB)	WCAu
'Goddess of Green' (IB)	EWoo
'Godfrey Owen' (TB)	CKel WCAu
'Godsend' (TB)	CIri
'Going Green' (TB)	CIri
'Going Home' (TB) ♀H7	SIri
'Going My Way' (TB)	ESgI EWoo LSou SIri WCAu WWEG XSen
'Gold Burst' (TB)	XSen
'Gold Country' (TB)	XSen
'Gold of Autumn' (TB)	CKel
'Goldberry' (IB)	WCAu
'Golden Alien' (TB)	CIri
'Golden Alps' (TB)	SRms WCAu
'Golden Beauty'	GKev SDeJ
'Golden Child' (SDB)	XSen
'Golden Crimping' (Sib)	EWoo
'Golden Ducat' (Spuria)	CIri
'Golden Edge' (Sib)	EWoo GQue LLWG MBel MSCN MWts NLar WFar WHil

'Golden Encore' (TB)	CKel WCAu
'Golden Forest' (TB)	GBin
'Golden Immortal' (TB)	EWoo
'Golden Panther' (TB)	WCAu
'Golden Sunrise' **new**	LBuc
'Golden Violet' (SDB)	ESgI
goniocarpa	WAbe
'Good Looking' (TB)	ESgI WCAu
'Good Show' (TB)	ESgI EWoo WCAu XSen
'Good Vibrations' (TB)	SIri XSen
'Goodbye Heart' (TB)	EWoo
'Gordon' (Reticulata)	CAvo CBro ECho EPfP EPot ERCP GKev LAma LRHS
gormanii	see *I. tenax*
'Gossip' (SDB)	CBro
'Got the Melody' (TB)	EWoo WCAu
'Goudhurst' (SDB) **new**	SIri
'Gracchus' (TB)	EWoo WCAu
gracilipes	GEdr SBrt
- 'Alba'	GEdr
gracilipes* × *lacustris	GEdr WAbe
graeberiana	ECho EPot GKev SDeJ
- yellow fall	ECho
graminea ♀H7	CAvo CBro CHid CMac CRow ECho ELan EPfP EPla EPri IFro LLWP LRHS MLHP NBir NSti WCot XEll
- var. ***pseudocyperus***	GCal SDys
graminifolia	see *I. kerneriana*
'Granaat' (Sib)	EBee
'Granada Gold' (TB)	SRms XSen
'Grand Circle' (TB)	EWoo
'Grand Illusion' (Spuria)	EWoo
'Grand Waltz' (TB)	XSen
'Grape Adventure' (TB)	LBuc
'Grapelet' (MDB)	CPBP WCAu
'Great Gatsby' (TB)	CKel
'Great Lakes' (TB)	ESgI
'Grecian Skies' (TB)	ESgI
'Green Eyed Lady' (TB)	ESgI
'Green Ice' (TB)	LRHS MRav
'Green Prophecy' (TB)	CKel
'Green Spot' (SDB) ♀H7	CBod CBro CKel CTal EAEE ECha ECho ECtt ELan GBuc LAst LRHS MNrw MRav NBir NLar SDeJ SPer WAul WCAu
'Greenstuff' (SDB)	CTal
grey-flowered (Sib)	ELon
'Gringo' (TB)	WCAu
'Grooving' (BB)	ESgI
'Guatemala' (TB)	WCAu
'Gudrun' (TB)	EWoo
'Gull's Wing' (Sib)	EWTr LLWG NLar NSti SMrm
'Gurkha's Dance' (SDB)	SIri
'Gypsy Beauty' (Dut)	CAvo EPfP GKev MWat SDeJ
'Gypsy Jewels' (TB)	CKel ESgI XSen
'Gypsy Romance' (TB) ♀H7	EIri ESgI SIri WCAu
'Gypsy Tart' (SDB)	SIri
'Habit' (TB)	EWoo WCAu
'Hakuna Matata' (AB)	SDys
'Halloween Halo' (TB)	WCAu
halophila	see *I. spuria* subsp. *halophila*
'Happenstance' (TB)	EWoo WCAu
'Happy Mood' (IB)	WCAu
'Harbor Blue' (TB)	CKel CTsd EWoo MWat SWat WCAu WWEG
'Harlow Gold' (IB)	ESgI
'Harmonium' (IB)	WCAu
'Harmony' ambig.	SCob SPer

	'Harmony' (Reticulata)	CAby CAvo CBro ECho EPfP EPot GKev LAma LRHS MBri SDeJ WBrk
	'Harpswell Hallelujah' (Sib)	EBee EWoo SBch
	'Harpswell Happiness' (Sib) ♀H7	CPrp EBee EPfP EPri GBin GCra MLHP MNFA SBch SWat WAul WMoo
	'Harpswell Haze' (Sib)	ECha
	'Harriette Halloway' (TB)	CBod CWGN ECGP EPfP EShb EWoo LRHS NLar SHar SRGP WCot
	hartwegii	ECho
	'Harvest King' (TB)	XSen
	'Harvest of Memories' (TB)	CKel ESgI EWoo WWEG
	'Haut les Voiles' (TB)	CWCL
	'Haute Couture' (TB)	XSen
	'Haviland' (TB)	XSen
	'Headcorn' (MTB) ♀H7	SIri
	'Headline Banner' (BB)	EWoo WCAu
	'Headlines' (TB)	WCAu
	'Headway' (Spuria)	WCAu
	'Heartbeat Away' (TB)	CIri
	'Heartbreak Point' (TB)	EWoo
	'Heart's Radiance' (MTB)	SDys
	'Heather Carpet' (SDB)	WCAu
	'Heather Sky' (TB)	CIri
	'Heavenly Blue' (Sib)	LSun MWat SPer
	'Heavenly Days' (TB)	WCAu
	'Heavenly Horns' (TB) **new**	CIri
	'Heaven's Edge' (TB)	WCAu
	'Helen Astor' (Sib)	CPrp CRow CTri MRav SWat WWEG
	'Helen Collingwood' (TB)	ESgI EWoo
	'Helen Dawn' (TB) ♀H7	SIri
	'Helen McGregor' (TB)	CKel
	'Helen Proctor' (IB)	ESgI WCot XSen
	'Helen Traubel' (TB)	WCAu
	'Helena Terry' (TB)	ESgI
	'Helene C.' (TB)	EWoo XSen
	'Helge' (IB)	ECho SWat
	'Heliotrope Bouquet' (Sib)	EWoo
	'Hellcat' (IB)	EWoo WCAu
	'Hello Darkness' (TB) ♀H7	ESgI EWoo WCAu WCot XSen
	'Hell's Fire' (TB)	ELon EWoo WCAu
	'Hemstitched' (TB)	EWoo MAsh WCAu
	'Her Majesty' (TB)	EWoo
	'Hercules' (Reticulata)	ECho LAma NMin
	'Here Comes The Night' (TB) **new**	WCAu
	'Hever Castle' (Kent Castles Series) (BB)	SIri
	'Hi' (IB)	CIri
	'High Barbaree' (TB)	EWoo
	'High Blue Sky' (TB)	WCAu
	'High Command' (TB)	CKel WCAu
	'High Impact' (TB)	CIri EWoo
	'High Peak'	WCAu
	'Highline Amethyst' (Spuria)	EPri
	'Hildegarde' (Dut)	SDeJ
	'Himmel von Komi' (Sib)	GBin
	'His Royal Highness'	WCAu
	'Hissy-Fit' (IB)	CKel
	histrio	ECho EPot
	- subsp. ***aintabensis***	ECho GKev
	histrioides	ECho
§	- 'Angel's Tears' (Reticulata)	CAvo ECho GKev NMin
	- 'Halkis' (Reticulata)	EPot ERCP GKev LAma NMin SDeJ
	- 'Lady Beatrix Stanley'	CAvo CBro ECho EPfP EPot ERCP GKev LAma LLHF NMin SBch WBrk WHoo
*	- 'Major'	CDes ECho GKev LAma
	- var. ***sophenensis***	ECho
	'Hoar Edge' (Sib)	NChi WAul
	'Hocus Pocus' (SDB)	CBod CHel CPBP CTal CWGN EAEE ECho EPfP EWoo GBuc IGor LRHS NSoo WAul
	'Hohe Warte' (Sib) ♀H7	GBin WAul
	'Höhenflug' (Sib)	GBin
	'Holden Clough' (SpH) ♀H7	CExl CHel CPrp ELan EPfP GBin GCra GMaP LEdu MMuc MNrw MRav MSpe NBir NChi NGdn NSti SEND WFar WHer WSHC WWEG
	'Holden's Child'	CWat
	'Holidaze' (IB) ♀H7 **new**	EIri
	'Hollywood Nights' (TB)	EWoo
	'Holy Night' (TB)	CKel
	'Honey Behold' (SDB)	CKel
	'Honey Glazed' (IB)	ESgI WCAu
	'Honey Mocha Lotta' (Spuria)	EWoo
	'Honeylove' (SDB)	SDys
	'Honeymoon Suite' (TB)	EWoo
	'Honeyplic' (IB) ♀H7	ESgI SIri
	'Honington' (SDB)	WCAu
	'Honky Tonk Blues' (TB)	ESgI
	'Honky Tonk Hussy' (BB)	WCAu
	'Honorabile' (MTB)	ESgI WCAu
	hoogiana ♀H4	ECho EPot GKev
	- 'Purpurea'	ECho
§	***hookeri***	CFis CPBP CPrp CTal ECho ELan EPfP GBin GKev GMaP MGos SBrt SGSe WIce WThu
	- SDR 2202	GKev
	hookeriana	LBuc LRHS
	'Hoptoit' (TB)	CIri
	'Horizon Bleu' (TB)	EWoo
	'Horned Rosyred' (TB)	EWoo
§	'Hornpipe' (TB)	WCAu
	'Hortensia Rose' (TB)	SIri
	'Hot Gossip' (TB)	WCAu
	'Hot to Trot' (TB)	ESgI
	'Hottentot' (SDB) **new**	WCAu
	'Howard Weed' (TB)	MNrw
	'Hubbard' (Sib)	EPri LLWG MBel MNrw WFar
	'Huckleberry Fudge' (TB)	XSen
	'Hugh Miller' (TB)	WCAu
	'Hula Hands' (IB)	CIri
	'Hula Moon' (TB)	ESgI
	'Hypnotizer' (TB) **new**	CIri
	hyrcana	ECho
	'I Feel Good' (TB)	WCAu
	'I Repeat' (TB)	XSen
	'I Seek You' (TB)	ESgI
	iberica	ECho
§	- subsp. ***elegantissima***	ECho
	'Ice and Indigo' (SDB)	WCAu
	'Ice Cave' (TB)	WCAu
	'Ice Dancer' (TB) ♀H7	CKel
	'Ice Etching' (SDB)	WCAu
	'Ice for Brice' (TB) **new**	CIri
	'Ice Wings' (BB)	WCAu
	'Ida' (Reticulata)	ECho LAma
	'Idol' (TB)	EWoo
	'Ila Crawford' (Spuria) ♀H7	XSen
	'Illini Charm' (Sib)	CHid EBee WFar WMoo
	illyrica	see *I. pallida*
	'I'm Back' (TB)	WCAu
	'Immortality' (TB)	CKel CWGN ESgI LRHS SCob WCAu WWEG XSen

	Name	Suppliers
	'Imperative' (IB)	EWoo SIri
I	'Imperial Velvet' (Sib)	EWoo WFar
	'Impersonator' (TB)	CIri
	'Impetuous' (BB) ♀H7	CKel
	'Imprimis' (TB)	EWoo XSen
	'In a Flash' (IB)	WCAu
	'In Love' (TB)	XSen
	'In Town' (TB)	EWoo XSen
	'In Your Dreams' (TB)	CIri
	'Incentive' (TB)	EWoo
	'Incognito Too' (TB)	CIri
*	'Incoscente' (TB)	ESgI
	'Indeed' (IB)	ESgI
	'Indian Chief' (TB)	CCCN CWCL EPfP ESgI EWoo IBoy MCot MRav WCAu WWEG
	'Indian Hills' (TB)	EWoo
	'Indian Idyll' (IB)	CKel
	'Indian Jewel' (SDB)	ECho
	'Indiana Sunset' (TB)	CKel
	'Indigo Flight' (IB)	CKel
	'Indigo Princess' (TB)	EWoo XSen
	'Inferno' (TB)	EWoo
	'Infinity Ring' (IB)	WCAu
	'Innocent Devil' (TB)	CIri
	'Innocent Heart' (IB) ♀H7	WCAu
	'Innocent Pink' (TB)	ESgI
	innominata	ECho EPot GKev LRHS NBir NBro SRms WWEG
	– yellow-flowered	NRya
	'Inscription' (SDB)	ECho
	'Inside Track' (TB) **new**	WCAu
	'Inspired' (TB) **new**	WCAu
	'Instant Hit' (TB)	WCAu
	'Intermediary' (IB)	WCAu
	'Interpol' (TB)	ESgI EWoo XSen
	'Invicta Daybreak' (IB)	SIri
	'Invicta Garnet' (SDB)	SIri
	'Invicta Gold' (SDB)	SIri
	'Invicta Reprieve' (IB) **new**	SIri
	'Irish Chant' (SDB)	WCAu
	'Irish Doll' (MDB)	WCAu
	'Irish Harp' (SDB)	ESgI
	'Irish Tune' (TB)	ESgI
	'Iron Eagle' (TB)	CIri
	'Isabelle' (Sib)	XSen
	'Island Sun' (SDB)	SIri
	'Island Sunset' (TB)	ESgI SIri
	'Isoline' (TB)	ESgI
	'It Happens' (TB) **new**	WCAu
	'Italian Ice' (TB)	EIri
	'Italian Velvet' (TB)	WCAu
	'Ivory Queen' (Sib)	EWoo
	'J.S. Dijt' (Reticulata)	CAvo CBro ECho EPot ERCP GKev LAma LRHS MBri MGos SDeJ
	'Jack Attack' (La)	CPrp LAst MSCN SMrm SPoG WMoo
	'Jacquessiana'	WCAu
	'Jac-y-do' (Sib)	EWes
	'Jade Mist' (SDB)	ECho
	'Jaguar Blue' (TB)	EWoo WCAu
	'Jane Phillips' (TB) ♀H7	Widely available
	'Jane Taylor' (SDB)	CBro
	'Janet Lane' (BB)	CKel
	'Japanesque' (MTB) **new**	CIri
	japonica ♀H4	CExl CHEx ECho NLar NPer SPlb XLum XSen
	– B&SWJ 8921	WCru
	– 'Bourne Graceful'	CExl
	– 'Ledger'	CAby CAvo CExl CHll CMac CPrp ECha MRav SEND SGSe SMad
	– 'Monty'	WWFP
	– f. ***pallescens***	SGSe
I	– 'Purple Heart'	CAvo
	– 'Rudolph Spring'	EBee GCal WWFP
I	– 'Snowflake'	CAvo
§	– 'Variegata' (v) ♀H4	CAby CBro CHEx CPrp CTsd ECha ECho ELan EPla ESwi MHer NPer NSti SArc SEND SMad WHil WWFP XSen
	'Jasper Gem' (MDB)	ECho
	'Jazz Festival' (TB)	EWoo SIri WCAu XSen
	'Jazzed Up' (TB)	XSen
	'Je l'Adore' (TB)	EWoo
	'Jean Cayeux' (TB)	ESgI
	'Jean Guymer' (TB)	ESgI
	'Jeanne Price' (TB)	ESgI EWoo WCAu
	'Jelly Belly' (SDB)	EWoo
	'Jennifer Rebecca' (TB) **new**	WCAu
	'Jeremy Brian' (SDB)	WCAu
	'Jeremy Jets On' (TB)	CIri
	'Jesse's Song' (TB)	ESgI WCAu XSen
	'Jet Black' (TB)	EWoo
	'Jet-Setter' (TB)	CIri
	'Jeunesse' (TB)	ESgI
	'Jewel Baby' (SDB)	CBro CKel
	'Jewel Bright' (SDB)	WCAu
	'Jeweler's Art' (SDB)	ESgI EWoo
	'Jewelled Crown' (Sib)	EBee WFar
	'Jiansada' (SDB)	CBro
	'Jigsaw' (TB)	ESgI XSen
	'Jitterbug' (TB)	WCAu
	'Joanna' (TB)	NLar WWEG
	'John' (IB)	CKel
	'Joli Coeur' (TB)	EWoo
	'Joyce' (Reticulata)	CBro ECho EPfP EPot GKev LAma LRHS MBri SDeJ
	'Joyful Skies' (TB) **new**	WCAu
	'Jubilant Spirit' (Spuria)	EWes
	'Jubilation' (TB)	EWoo
	'Jubilee Gem' (TB)	CKel WCAu
	'Judy Mogil' (TB)	CIri
	'Juliet' (TB)	ESgI
	'Jump for Joy' (TB) **new**	CIri
	'Jump Start' (IB)	EWoo WCAu
	'Jumping Jupiter' (TB)	CIri
	'June Prom' (IB)	EAEE LRHS SRGP WCAu
	'Jungle Fires' (TB)	WCAu
	'Jungle Shadows' (BB)	ESgI EWoo MRav NBir WCAu
	'Jurassic Park' (TB)	ESgI EWoo WCAu XSen
	'Just Before Midnight'	LRHS NPri
	'Just Jennifer' (BB)	WCAu
	kaempferi	see *I. ensata*
	'Kahuna' (IB) **new**	WCAu
	'Katharine Hodgkin' (Reticulata) ♀H7	CAvo CBro CTca CWCL EBee ECha ECho EPfP EPot ERCP GAbr GKev LAma LRHS MNrw MRav MWat NBir NHar NLar SDeJ WAbe WBrk WCot WFar WHoo WSHC
	'Katharine Hodgkin' dark-flowered	EPot NMin
	'Kathleen Mary' (Sib)	WAul
	'Katie-Koo' (IB) ♀H7	CKel
	'Katy Petts' (SDB)	ESgI WCAu
	'Keep the Peace' (TB)	WCAu
	'Keeping up Appearances' (TB)	WCAu

	'Kelway Renaissance' (TB)	CKel
	'Kent Arrival' (Sib)	SIri
	'Kent Blackguard' (IB)	SIri
	'Kent Compote' (IB)	SIri
	'Kent Pride' (TB)	CAby CBod CKel COtt CSBt EAEE ECha ECtt EPfP ESgI EWoo GBin LRHS LSun MCot MNrw MRav MSpe MWhi SCob SPer SPoG SWat WCAu
	Kenta No Se129 (Sib)	EPri
	'Kentish Icon' (SDB)	SIri
	'Kentish Lad' (IB) **new**	SIri
	'Kentucky Bluegrass' (SDB)	WCAu
	'Kentucky Derby' (TB)	XSen
§	***kerneriana*** 🏆H4	EHoe GBuc NBir
	'Kęstutis Genys' (Sib) **new**	WAul
	'Kharput' (IB)	EWoo
	'Kildonan' (TB)	WCAu
	'King of Kings' (Sib)	WFar
	'Kingfisher' (Sib)	WAul
	'King's Jester' (TB)	EWoo
	'Kinshizen' (SpH)	CIri
	'Kirkstone' (TB)	WCAu
	kirkwoodii	ECho
	'Kiss of Summer' (TB) 🏆H7	ESgI SDys
	'Kissing Circle' (TB)	ESgI EWoo
	'Kita-no-seiza' (Sib)	CIri EBee
	'Kiwi Slices' (SDB)	CWat ESgI
	'Knick Knack' (MDB)	CBro CPBP CTal ECho ELan EPfP GMaP MRav SDeJ SPoG
	korolkowii	CTal ECho
	'La Meije' (TB)	SIri
	'La Senda' (Spuria)	WCot
	'Lace Legacy' (TB)	EWoo
	'Laced Cotton' (TB)	WCAu XSen
§	***lactea***	SBrt XEll XSen
	lacustris	CBro WAbe XSen
	'Lacy Snowflake' (TB)	LRHS
	'Lad'	WCAu
	'Lady Belle' (MTB)	ESgI
	'Lady Byng' (TB) **new**	WMil
	'Lady Essex' (TB)	EWoo WCAu
	'Lady Friend' (TB)	WCAu XSen
	'Lady Gale' (IB)	CKel
	'Lady in Red' (SDB)	ESgI WCAu
	'Lady Mohr' (AB)	WCAu
	'Lady Phyllis' (MTB)	CIri
	'Lady R' (SDB)	ECho
	'Lady Vanessa' (Sib)	CPou EBee ELon EPPr MRav NSti SMrm
	laevigata	CBAq CRow ECho EHon ELan EPfP EWay ITim MRav NBro NPer SWat WFar WMAq WMoo WShi WWEG
	- var. ***alba***	CBAq CRow ECho SWat WAbe WMoo
	- 'Albopurpurea'	SGSe
	- 'Atropurpurea'	CRow
	- 'Colchesterensis'	CRow CWat EPri EWay NGdn NPer SWat WMAq WMoo
I	- 'Dorothy'	NGdn
	- 'Dorothy Robinson'	LRHS SWat
	- 'Elegant'	see *I. laevigata* 'Weymouth Elegant'
I	- 'Elegante'	EWay
*	- 'Elgar'	WMAq
	- 'Liam Johns'	CRow
	- 'Midnight'	see *I. laevigata* 'Weymouth Midnight'
	- 'Monstrosa'	CDes EWay
	- 'Plena' (d)	CRow
	- 'Rashomon'	CRow
	- 'Richard Greaney'	CRow EWay
	- 'Rose Queen'	see *I. ensata* 'Rose Queen'
	- 'Shirasagi'	CRow
I	- 'Snowdrift'	CBAq CRow CWat EHon EWay LRHS NBir NGdn NLar NPer SWat WFar WMAq WMoo
	- 'Variegata' (v) 🏆H7	CBen CRow CWat EAEE ECha ECho EHoe ELon EPfP EWay LLWG MWts NBro NGdn NPer SWat WMAq WMoo WWtn
	- 'Violet Garth'	EWay
	- 'Weymouth'	see *I. laevigata* 'Weymouth Blue'
§	- 'Weymouth Blue'	CBen CRow EWay
§	- 'Weymouth Elegant'	CRow
§	- 'Weymouth Midnight'	CRow SWat
	- 'Weymouth Purity'	EWay
§	'Lake Niklas' (Sib)	EBee ELon GBin MHol NCGa
	'Lamia' (TB)	CIri
	'Langport Chapter' (IB)	CKel ESgI
	'Langport Chief' (IB)	CKel
	'Langport Claret' (IB)	CKel ESgI
	'Langport Curlew' (IB)	CKel ESgI
	'Langport Duchess' (IB)	ESgI
	'Langport Fairy' (IB)	CKel
	'Langport Flame' (IB)	CKel ESgI
*	'Langport Hope' (IB)	CKel
	'Langport Jane' (IB)	CKel
	'Langport Lady' (IB)	CKel
	'Langport Lord' (IB)	ESgI
	'Langport Minstrel' (IB)	CKel ESgI
	'Langport Pearl' (IB)	CKel
	'Langport Pinnacle' (IB)	CKel
	'Langport Smoke' (IB)	CKel
	'Langport Star' (IB)	CKel ESgI
	'Langport Storm' (IB)	CKel ECGP EPfP LRHS MRav SDeJ
	'Langport Sun' (IB)	ESgI
	'Langport Sylvia' (IB)	CKel
	'Langport Violet' (IB)	CKel ESgI
	'Langport Vista' (IB)	CKel
	'Langport Wren' (IB) 🏆H7	CAby CBro CKel EPfP EPri ESgI EShb GBuc GCal LAst MBri MWhi NBir NGdn WAul WPtf WWEG
	'Langthorns Pink' (Sib)	CCse ELan MRav WAul
	'Lark Rise' (TB) 🏆H7	CKel
	'Larry Gaulter' (TB)	WCAu
	'Las Vegas' (TB)	WCAu
	'Last Hurrah' (TB)	EWoo
	'Late Liftoff' (TB)	CIri
§	***latifolia***	GKev MMuc NMin SEND WShi
	- 'Duchess of York'	EBee ECho GKev
	- 'Isabella'	GKev SDeJ WCot
	- 'King of the Blues'	CAvo EBee ECho GKev SDeJ
	- 'Mansfield'	ECho
	- 'Montblanc'	CAvo GKev SDeJ
	- 'Queen of the Blues' (Eng)	ECho SDeJ
	- wild-collected	GCal
	'Latin Lark' (TB)	ESgI
	'Latin Rock' (TB)	WCAu
	'Latino' (IB)	WCAu
	'Laura Jean' (TB)	EWoo
	'Laura Louise' (La)	LLWG SKHP
	'Laurenbuhl' (Sib)	CExl
	'Lava Moonscape' (TB)	CIri
	'Lavanesque' (TB)	WCAu
	'Lavender Bounty' (Sib)	CHid
	'Lavender Light' (Sib)	WAul

	Name	Suppliers
	lazica ♀H5	CBct CBro CHel CHll CMac CPrp CRow EPPr EPfP EPot EWoo GBin GKev IBlr LRHS MRav NBir NCGa NSti SBrt SEND SPlb WCot WGwG WHil WSHC
	- 'Joy Bishop'	CJun
*	- 'Richard Nutt'	CJun ELon
	- 'Turkish Blue'	CPrp IBlr
	'Legato' (TB)	ESgI
	'Lemon Brocade' (TB)	EWoo WCAu
	'Lemon Flare' (SDB)	EIri MRav SRms
	'Lemon Ice' (TB)	CAby CBod CKel EAEE ECha EPfP GBin LRHS MSpe SDeJ SPer WHoo
	'Lemon Lyric' (TB)	ESgI
	'Lemon on Ice' (SDB)	WCAu
	'Lemon Pop' (IB)	WCAu
	'Lemon Puff' (MDB)	CBro LLHF WCAu
	'Lemon Tree' (TB)	WCAu
	'Lemon Whip' (IB)	EWoo
	'Lena' (SDB)	CBro
	'Lenna M' (SDB)	CKel ECho
	'Lenora Pearl' (BB)	XSen
	'Lent A. Williamson' (TB)	GMaP WWEG
	'Lenten Prayer' (TB)	SIri WCAu
	'Lenzschnee' (TB)	EWoo
	'Leprechaun's Delight' (SDB)	CKel
	'Leprechaun's Purse' (SDB)	WCAu
	'Let's Elope' (IB)	ESgI WCAu
	'Licorice Stick' (TB)	XSen
	'Light Beam' (TB)	XSen
	'Light Cavalry' (IB)	ESgI EWoo
	'Light Laughter' (IB)	WCAu
	'Light Rebuff' (TB)	EWoo
	'Lilac Times'	EWoo
	'Lilli-white' (SDB)	CAby CHel CKel CWat ELan EPfP GEdr LRHS MBNS MRav SPoG WCAu WWEG
	'Lilting' (TB)	XSen
	'Limbo' (SpH)	CRow
	'Lime Fizz' (TB)	XSen
	'Limeheart' (Sib)	CPou LLHF
	'Limelight' (TB)	SRms
	'Linda Mary' (Sib)	EWoo
	'Linda's Child' (TB)	WCAu
	'Line Dancing' (Spuria)	CIri
	'Lingering Love' (TB)	WCAu
	'Little Big Horn' (IB)	CIri
	'Little Black Belt' (SDB)	EWoo LRHS
	'Little Blackfoot' (SDB)	CDes ESgI WCAu WCot
	'Little Blue-eyes' (SDB)	ESgI WCAu
	'Little Bluets' (SDB)	ESgI
	'Little Dandy' (SDB)	ECho
	'Little Dogie' (SDB)	ECho
	'Little Dream' (SDB)	WCAu
	'Little Firecracker' (SDB)	WCAu
	'Little Paul' (MTB)	ESgI
	'Little Rosy Wings' (SDB)	CBro CPBP
	'Little Shadow' (IB)	MRav SRms WWEG
	'Little Sheba' (AB)	WCAu
	'Little Showoff' (SDB)	ESgI
	'Little Tilgates' (CH)	WCot
	'Little Twinkle Star' (Sib)	NEoE
	'Living Waters' (TB)	ESgI
	'Local Color' (TB)	ESgI EWoo SIri XSen
	'Local Hero' (IB)	WCAu
	'Lodore' (TB)	SRms
	'Logo' (IB)	WCAu
	'Lohengrin' (TB)	EWoo
	'Lollipop' (SDB)	ESgI SIri
	'London Pride' (TB)	EWoo
	longipetala	EPPr EWes NBir
	'Looking Forward' (TB)	ESgI
	'Loop the Loop' (TB)	CMac CTsd EWoo NSoo SGol SPoG SWat
	'Loose Valley' (MTB) ♀H7	SIri
	'Lord Warden' (TB)	CBod CKel ECtt EPfP LRHS WCAu WGwG
	'Lorilee' (TB)	ESgI WCAu
	'Lost in Space' (BB)	CIri
	'Lothario' (TB)	WCAu
	'Lottie Lou' (TB)	SIri
	'Lotus Land' (TB)	WCAu
	'Louisa's Song' (TB)	WCAu
	louisiana 'Festival's Acadian' (La)	LLWG
	- 'Highland Mist' (La)	LLWG
	- 'Honey Stars' (La)	LLWG
	- 'Hopelessly Devoted' (La)	LLWG
	- 'Just Imagine' (La)	LLWG
	- 'Swirling Waters' (La)	LLWG
	'Louvois' (TB)	ESgI EWoo NLar
	'Love the Sun' (TB)	ESgI XSen
	'Lovely Again' (TB)	LRHS MRav WCAu
	'Lovely Dawn' (TB)	WCAu
	'Lovely Leilani' (TB)	ESgI
	'Lovely Señorita' (TB)	WCAu
	'Lover's Charm' (TB)	WCAu
	'Love's Tune' (IB)	EAEE EBee LRHS SRGP SWat
	'Low Ho Silver' (IB)	WCAu
	'Loyalist' (TB)	CPar EWoo SIri
	'Lucy's Gift' (MTB) ♀H7	SRGP
	'Lugano' (TB)	ESgI EWoo
	'Lula Marguerite' (TB)	EWoo
	'Luli-Ann' (SDB)	CKel
	'Lullaby of Spring' (TB)	CKel
	'Lullingstone Castle' (Kent Castles Series) (IB)	SIri
	'Lumarco' (TB)	EWoo
	'Lumière d'Automne' (TB)	ESgI XSen
	'Lure of Gold' (IB)	WCAu
	'Lurline' (TB) **new**	WMil
	lutescens ♀H7	ECho GCra WAbe WCot
§	- 'Campbellii'	ECho
§	- subsp. ***lutescens***	XSen
	maackii	GEdr
	'Mabel Coday' (Sib)	EPri EWoo
	'Madame Lynn' (Spuria)	EWoo
	'Madeira Belle' (TB)	CAby CKel EAEE ESgI LRHS WCAu WGwG
	'Madeleine Frances' (SDB)	SIri
	'Magharee' (TB)	ESgI
	'Magic Man' (TB)	XSen
	'Magical Encounter' (TB)	EWoo
	magnifica ♀H5	ECho ELon
	- 'Agalik'	ECho GKev
	- 'Alba'	ECho
	'Maid of Orange' (BB)	WCAu
	'Maisie Lowe' (TB)	ESgI EWoo
	'Majestic Ruler' (TB)	WCAu
	'Making Eyes' (SDB)	WCAu
	'Man About Town' (TB)	WCAu
	'Mandarin Purple' (Sino-Sib)	EBee NPCo
	mandshurica	CPBP
	'Mango Entree' (TB)	WCAu

'Mango Smoothy' (BB) ESgI
'Marden Meadow' (MTB) new SIri
'Margrave' (TB) EWoo XSen
'Marguérite' (Reticulata/v) ECho WCAu
'Marilyn Holmes' (Sib) GBin GLog GQue WCot
'Mariposa Autumn' (TB) EWoo SIri
'Marmalade Skies' (BB) WCAu
'Marshmallow Frosting' (Sib) WFar
'Martyn Rix' see *I. confusa* 'Martyn Rix'
'Mary Constance' (IB) ♀H7 CKel
'Mary Frances' (TB) ESgI WCAu XSen
'Mary Geddes' (TB) EWoo
'Mary McIlroy' (SDB) ♀H7 CBro CKel
'Master Touch' (TB) ELon XSen
'Masterwork' (TB) CIri
'Material Girl' (TB) new WCAu
'Matinata' (TB) CKel EWoo XSen
'Matt McNames' (TB) EWoo
'Maui Moonlight' (IB) ♀H7 CKel ESgI EWoo NLar WCAu
'May Melody' (TB) WCAu
'Maya Mint' (MDB) LLHF
'Meadow Court' (SDB) CBro CKel CTal WCAu WWEG
'Medallion' (Spuria) EWoo
'Media Luz' (Spuria) WCAu
'Medici Prince' (TB) EWoo
'Medway Valley' (MTB) ♀H7 SIri WCAu
'Megglethorp' (IB) WCAu
'Meg's Mantle' (TB) CKel
'Melbreak' (TB) ESgI
mellita see *I. suaveolens*
'Melon Honey' (SDB) CKel EBee ELon WCAu
'Melted Butter' (TB) WCAu
§ 'Melton Red Flare' (Sib) EBee EPPr LRHS LSou MBNS MSpe SDys SMrm WWEG
'Memphis Memory' (Sib) ELan ELon GCra MHol MNrw NLar SPer WWEG
'Men in Black' (TB) EWoo WCAu
'Menton' (SDB) CKel
'Mer du Sud' (TB) ♀H7 EIri ESgI EWoo LRHS LSun XSen
* 'Merebrook Blue Lagoon' (La) WMAq
'Merebrook Jemma J' (La) WMAq
* 'Merebrook Lemon Maid' (La) WMAq
'Merebrook Purpla' (La) WMAq
'Merebrook Rum 'n' Raisin' (La) WMAq
* 'Merebrook Rusty Red' (La) WMAq
* 'Merebrook Snowflake' (La) WMAq
'Merebrook Sunnyside Up' (La) WMAq
'Merebrook Symphony' (La) WMAq
'Merit' (MTB) WCAu
'Merry Dance' (SDB) CKel
'Mescal' (TB) WCAu
mesopotamica see *I. germanica*
'Messire Pierre' (BB) CIri
'Messy Jessi' (TB) CIri
'Metaphor' (TB) WCAu
'Mezza Cartuccia' (IB) ESgI
'Miami Beach' (TB) WCAu
'Midas Mite' (MDB) LLHF
I 'Midnight Blue' (MDB) CBro
'Midnight Caller' (TB) ESgI EWoo XSen
'Midnight Majesty' (TB) EWoo
'Midnight Mango' see *I.* 'Midnight Web'
'Midnight Oil' (TB) EWoo WCAu
'Midnight Thunder' (TB) new CIri
'Midnight Treat' (TB) WCAu
§ 'Midnight Web' (IB) ♀H7 CKel
'Midsummer Night's Dream' (IB) ESgI EWoo
'Mighty Mouse' EWoo
milesii ♀H3 CExl NBir SBrt WSHC
– CC 6839 GKev
'Millennium Sunrise' (TB) WCAu
'Ming' (IB) WCAu
'Mini Big Horn' (IB) CIri
'Mini-Agnes' (SDB) CBro
'Minisa' (TB) ESgI
'Miss Nellie' (BB) CKel
'Missouri Streams' (Spuria) EWoo
missouriensis CMac
'Mist Arising' (TB) CIri
'Mister Roberts' (SDB) ESgI
'Mistress of Camelot' (TB) SDys
'Mme Chéreau' (TB) ESgI EWoo
'Mon Prince' (BB) new CIri
'Monsieur-Monsieur' (TB) ESgI
Monspur Group WCot
'Moon Journey' (TB) EWoo
'Moon Silk' (Sib) ECtt ELon EPri GBuc LLHF SCob WCot WFar
'Moon Sparkle' (IB) CKel
'Moonlight Cascade' (La) new LLWG
'Moonlight Waves' see *I. ensata* 'Moonlight Waves'
'Moonlit' CIri
'Moonlit Water' (TB) new WCAu
'Moonlit Waves' (TB) CKel
'Morwell' (TB) new WMil
'Morwenna' (TB) ♀H7 ESgI
'Mother Earth' (TB) ESgI
'Mountain Lake' (Sib) EPfP EShb GBin LRHS SHar SPtp SWat WCot WFar WPtf
'Mountain Violet' (TB) new EWoo
'Mrs Horace Darwin' (TB) CCon EWoo SWat WMnd
'Mrs Nate Rudolph' (SDB) WCAu
'Mrs Rowe' (Sib) CCse CPou CRow EIri EPri GBuc LLWP MRav MWat SWat WAul WFar
'Mrs Tait' (Spuria) NChi
'Mrs Valerie West' (TB) new WMil
'Muggles' (SDB) SIri
'Mukaddam' (TB) CIri
'Murder Mystery' (TB) WCAu
'Murmuring Morn' (TB) WCAu
'Music' (SDB) SIri
'Must Unite' (TB) WCAu
'My Kayla' (SDB) ESgI
'My Love' (Sib) GBin IMou WAul
'My Seedling' (MDB) CBro
'Myra' (SDB) XSen
'Mysterieux' (TB) SIri
'Mystic' (TB) new WMil
'Mystic Beauty' (Dut) GKev
'Mystic Dragon' (TB) CIri SDys
'Naivasha' (TB) CKel
'Nancy Hardy' (MDB) CBro
'Naples' (TB) WCAu
narcissiflora WCot
'Nassak' (TB) EWoo
'Natascha' (Reticulata) ECho EPfP EPot LAma NMin SDeJ

	'Natchez Trace' (TB)	EPri WCot XSen
	'Navajo Code' (TB)	CIri
	'Navajo Jewel' (TB)	ESgI EWoo WCAu XSen
	'Navy Brass' (Sib)	EPri WAul
	'Needlecraft' (TB)	XSen
	'Needlepoint' (TB)	ESgI
	'Negro Modelo' (SDB)	WCAu
	'Neige de Mai' (TB)	ESgI
*	'Nel Jupe' (TB)	LRHS NLar
	nepalensis	see *I. decora*
	nertschinskia	see *I. sanguinea*
	'Neutron' (SDB)	WCAu
	'Neutron Dance' (TB)	WCAu
	'New Argument' (J)	LLHF
	'New Centurion' (TB)	EWoo XSen
	'New Face' (TB)	WCAu
	'New Flame' (TB)	ESgI
	'New Idea' (MTB)	CBro ESgI WCAu
	'New Leaf' (TB)	WCAu
	'New Snow' (TB)	WCAu
	'Next in Line'	EWoo
	'Nibelungen' (TB)	CBro CJun ESgI MNrw WCAu XSen
	'Night Breeze' (Sib)	EPri SIri
	'Night Edition' (TB)	ESgI EWoo XSen
	'Night Game' (TB)	EWoo XSen
	'Night Owl' (TB)	CKel ELan ELon ESgI LBuc MHer SPoG
	'Night Ruler' (TB)	EWoo WCAu
	'Nights of Gladness' (TB)	ESgI
	'No Down Payment' (TB)	WCAu
	'Noble Lady' (TB)	CIri
	'Noctambule' (TB)	EWoo
	'Noon Siesta' (TB)	ESgI
	'Nordica' (TB)	ESgI
§	× ***norrisii***	EBee EWes
	- 'Butterfly Magic'	EBee
	- 'Dazzler'	MBel NSbr
	- 'Heart of Darkness'	EBee
	'North Downs' (BB)	SIri
	'Northern Jewel' (IB)	SIri
	'Northumberland Piper' (TB) **new**	SIri
	'Nottingham Lace' (Sib)	GBin LLHF SWat
	'Now This' (Spuria)	EWoo
	'Oasis Fuzzy Wuzzy' (TB)	CIri
	'Oasis Sydney' (TB)	CIri
	'Oban' (Sib)	ESgI GBuc MNFA
	'Obsidian' (TB)	WCAu
	'Ochre Doll' (SDB)	CBro CKel CTal
	ochroleuca	see *I. orientalis* Mill.
	'O'Cool' (IB)	CKel
	'Octave' (AB)	WCAu
	'October' (TB)	ESgI
	'October Storm' (IB)	CIri EWoo
	'Oh Jamaica' (TB)	WCAu XSen
	'Oh So Cool' (MTB)	ESgI
	'Oklahoma' (TB)	EWoo
	'Oktoberfest' (TB)	XSen
	'Ola Kalá' (TB)	EAEE EWll GMaP LRHS MCot MGos MWat NLar SHil SPer WCAu XSen
	'Old Black Magic' (TB)	ESgI EWoo XSen
	'Old Flame' (TB)	XSen
	'Olympiad' (TB)	ESgI XSen
	'Olympic Challenge' (TB)	ESgI MRav WCAu
	'Olympic Torch' (TB)	WCAu
	'Ominous Stranger' (TB)	ESgI WCAu
	'Once Again' (TB)	EWoo XSen
	'One Desire' (TB)	XSen
	'Opal Sunset' (La) **new**	LLWG
	'Open Arms' (TB) **new**	CIri
	'Open Sky' (SDB)	EWoo LRHS SIri XSen
	'Opposing Forces' (TB)	WCAu
	'Orageux' (IB)	CWCL SIri
	'Orange Caper' (SDB)	CBod CMac CTal EAEE ECtt EPfP ESgI GBuc LRHS MRav MWat NSoo
	'Orange Harvest' (TB)	ESgI XSen
	'Orange Order' (TB)	WCAu
	'Orchardist' (TB)	CKel
	'Orchidarium' (TB)	CKel
	'Orchidea Selvaggia' (TB)	ESgI
	orchioides misapplied	see *I. bucharica* Foster
§	***orchioides*** Carrière	CAby ECho
	- 'Urungachsai'	EPot
	'Oregon Skies' (TB)	ESgI EWoo
	'Oreo' (TB)	WCAu
	'Oriental Baby' (IB)	CKel
	'Oriental Beauty' (Dut)	CAvo GKev
	'Oriental Beauty' (TB)	SDeJ
	orientalis Thunb.	see *I. sanguinea*
	orientalis ambig.	CAvo EWes MNrw
§	***orientalis*** Mill. ♀H7	CCon GBin GCal WCru XSen
	'Orinoco Flow' (BB) ♀H7	CKel ESgI WCAu
	'Orloff' (TB)	ESgI
	'Oro Antico' (TB)	CIri
	'Orville Fay' (Sib)	WBor WCot WFar
	'Osay Canuc' (TB)	CIri
	'Osborne's Grey' (Sib) **new**	WAul
	'Ostrogoth' (TB)	CIri
	'Ottawa' (Sib)	CPou CRow CWat LPot LRHS MMuc SEND SWat WFar
	'Oulo' (TB)	ESgI XSen
	'Our House' (TB)	ESgI
	'Out Yonder' (TB)	WCAu
	'Outrage' (SDB)	CIri
	'Outset' (Sib)	ELon WWEG
	'Over Easy' (SDB)	CKel
	'Overjoyed' (TB)	XSen
	'O'What' (SDB)	ESgI
	'Ozark Maid' (MTB)	SDys
	Pacific Coast hybrids	see *I.* Californian hybrids
	'Pacific Mist' (TB)	WCAu
	'Pacific Panorama' (TB)	XSen
	'Pagan Dance' (TB)	EWoo WCAu
	'Pagan Goddess' (TB)	EWoo
	'Pagan Pink' (TB)	XSen
	'Pagan Princess' (TB)	WCAu
I	'Pageant' (Sib)	WCot
	'Paint It Black' (TB)	EWoo XSen
	'Pale Shades' (IB)	CBro CKel
§	***pallida***	CMac ESgI EWoo GMaP MRav MWat SCob SEND SRms WCAu WMnd XSen
§	- 'Argentea Variegata' (TB/v)	Widely available
	- 'Aurea'	see *I. pallida* 'Variegata' Hort.
	- 'Aurea Variegata'	see *I. pallida* 'Variegata' Hort.
	- subsp. ***cengialtii***	XSen
	- var. ***dalmatica***	see *I. pallida* subsp. *pallida*
§	- subsp. ***pallida***	CArn CExl CKel EAEE ECha ELan EPfP GCal LRHS SDix SHar SPer
	- 'Variegata' misapplied	see *I. pallida* 'Argentea Variegata'
§	- 'Variegata' Hort. (v) ♀H7	CBcs CBro CMac CWat EAJP ECha ELan EPfP ESgI LRHS MAsh MBri MRav MWat NSti SDix SPer SPlb SRot SWvt WAbe WWEG XSen
	'Palm Springs' (IB)	LLHF NMin
	'Palomino' (TB)	WCAu

'Pane e Vino' (TB)	ESgI
'Pansy Purple' (Sib)	WHil
'Panther' (SDB)	WCAu
'Papillon' (Sib)	CAby CTri ECtt ELan ELon EPri EWoo LRHS MBel MNFA MWat NBir NBro NGdn NSti SCob SDeJ SPer SWat WAul WFar WWEG
'Paradise' (TB)	CKel
paradoxa	ECho
'Paricutin' (SDB)	CBro
'Paris Lights' (TB)	XSen
'Parisian Dawn' (TB)	WCAu
'Parisien' (TB)	CWCL EIri
'Parts Plus' (IB)	CIri
'Party Dress' (TB)	CKel CMac EBee ELan EPfP LRHS MRav MWhi NBir NGdn NLar NWad SPer SPoG SRms SWat WGwG
'Party's Over' (TB) **new**	WCAu
'Pastel Accent' (La) **new**	LLWG
'Pastel Charm' (SDB)	WMnd
'Patina' (TB)	EIri EWoo LRHS WCAu
'Patterdale' (TB)	NBir WCAu
'Paul Black' (TB) 🏆H7	CIri WCAu
'Pauline' (Reticulata)	CAvo CBro ECho EPfP ERCP GKev LAma LRHS MWat
'Pause' (SDB)	WCAu
'Pay the Price' (TB) **new**	WCAu
'Peaceful Waters' (TB)	XSen
'Peach Eyes' (SDB)	CBro CKel CTal
'Peach Picotee' (TB)	ESgI XSen
'Peachy Face' (IB)	ESgI XSen
'Pearl Queen' (Sib)	MCot WFar
'Pearls of Autumn' (TB)	WCAu
'Pearly Dawn' (TB)	ECtt SRGP SWat WWEG
* 'Pêche Melba' (TB)	XSen
'Peg Edwards' (Sib)	EWoo
'Pelion Hills'	LBuc LRHS
'Penny a Pinch' (TB)	WWEG
'Pepita' (SDB)	EWoo
'Percheron' (Sib)	EBee EPri ESgI EWoo SIri
'Peresh' (AB) **new**	CTal
'Perfect Interlude' (TB)	EIri XSen
'Perfect Vision' (Sib) 🏆H7	CIri
'Performer' (MTB)	EIri
'Perky' (MDB)	CPBP
'Perry's Blue' (Sib)	CBcs CMac CSBt EBee EHon EPfP EPri GKin GMaP IKil LRHS MBel MGos MRav MSpe NBir NBro NGdn NPer SPer SRms SWat WFar WMnd WWtn
I 'Perry's Favourite' (Sib)	CRow
'Persan' (TB)	EWoo
'Persian Berry' (TB)	WCAu XSen
'Persimmon' misapplied	see *I.* 'Tycoon'
'Persimmon' ambig. (Sib)	CAby CCon CHid ECtt GCra GKin LRHS SHil SPtp SWat WFar WMoo WPtf
'Petal Pushers' (TB)	CIri
'Peter Hewitt' (Sib) 🏆H7	EPri WAul
'Pétillant' (TB)	EWoo
'Petite Monet' (MTB)	ESgI
'Petite Polka' (SDB) **new**	NLar
'Pharaoh's Daughter' (IB)	EWoo SIri
'Phil Keen' (TB) 🏆H7	CKel
'Picadee'	CDes EBee EPfP
'Picasso Moon' (TB)	WCAu
'Pigeon' (SDB)	XSen
'Pilot' (SDB)	WCAu
'Pinewood Charmer' (CH)	CElw
'Pinewood Sunshine' (CH)	MAvo
'Pink Attraction' (TB)	ESgI XSen
'Pink Bubbles' (BB)	WCAu XSen
'Pink Charm' (TB)	COtt EAEE EPfP LRHS SDeJ SPlb SPoG
'Pink Confetti' (TB)	EWoo XSen
'Pink Haze' (Sib)	CRow EBee EPfP ESgI GBin WWEG
'Pink Horizon' (TB)	MAvo XSen
'Pink Invasion' (TB)	WCAu
'Pink Kitten' (IB)	WCAu WGwG XSen
'Pink Lavender' (TB)	ELon
'Pink Parchment' (BB)	CKel
'Pink Pele' (IB)	ESgI
'Pink Pinafore' (TB)	EWoo
'Pink Pussycat' (TB)	WCAu
'Pink Quartz' (TB)	ESgI
'Pink Reprise' (BB)	EWoo LSun
'Pink Swan' (TB)	XSen
'Pink Taffeta' (TB)	EWoo XSen
'Pinnacle' (TB)	CKel GCal LBuc SWat
'Pioneer' (TB) **new**	WMil
'Pipes of Pan' (TB)	ESgI MRav WCAu
'Pirate Prince' (Sib)	NPer
'Pirate's Quest' (TB)	ESgI EWoo XSen
'Piroska' (TB)	ESgI XSen
* 'Piu Blue' (TB)	ESgI
'Pixie' (DB)	GKev
'Pixie' (Reticulata) 🏆H7	ECho ELan EPot LAma NMin SDeJ SMrm
planifolia	ECho
'Pleasures of May' (Sib)	EBee ELon WBor
'Pledge Allegiance' (TB)	ESgI EWoo WCAu
plicata	WCAu
'Plickadee' (SDB)	CBro
'Plissée' (Sib) 🏆H7	GBin
'Plum Lucky' (SDB)	SIri
'Plum Twist' (SDB)	WCAu
'Plum Wine' (SDB)	CKel
'Poem of Ecstasy' (TB)	WCAu
'Pogo' (SDB)	CHel CMac ECho ECtt ELan EPfP EPot EShb GBuc GMaP LRHS MRav NBir NSoo SDeJ SRms
'Pokemon' (MDB)	CIri
'Polvere di Stelle' (TB)	ESgI
'Port of Call' (Spuria)	EWoo
'Potpourri Rose' (La) **new**	LLWG
'Pounsley Purple' (Sib)	CPou EPri
'Powder Blue Cadillac' (TB)	CKel WCAu
'Power Point' (TB)	CIri WCAu
'Praetorian Guard' (TB)	CIri
'Prairie Sunset' (TB)	EWoo
'Prairie Thunder' (AB)	WCAu
'Precious Heather' (TB)	CKel
'Presby's Crown Jewel' (TB)	WCAu
'Presence' (TB)	SIri
'Pretender' (TB)	WCAu
'Pretty Please' (TB)	ESgI
'Primrose Cream' (Sib)	WCot
'Primrose Drift' (TB)	ESgI
'Prince Indigo' (TB)	MRav
'Prince of Burgundy' (IB)	WCAu
'Princess Beatrice' (TB)	WCAu
'Princess Bride' (BB) 🏆H7	WCAu
'Princess Leia' (La) **new**	LLWG
'Princess Osra' (TB) **new**	WMil
'Princess Sabra' (TB)	CKel

'Princesse Caroline de Monaco' (TB) ESgI EWoo
prismatica GKev
'Professor Blaauw' (Dut) ♀^{H5} CAvo
'Progressive Attitude' (TB) EPri
'Props' (SDB) **new** CIri
'Prosper Laugier' (IB) SEND
'Prospero' (TB) **new** EWoo
'Protocol' (IB) CKel
'Proud Tradition' (TB) ESgI SIri WCAu XSen
'Provençal' (TB) CKel CPar CWCL ESgI EWoo WCAu XSen
'Prudy' (BB) ♀^{H7} CKel
'Prussian Blue' (Sib) ♀^{H7} GBin SMHy WSHC
pseudacorus Widely available
- from Japan B&SWJ 5018 WCru
- from Korea CRow
- 'Alba' CPrp GCal MRav MSKA MWts NGdn SWat
- var. ***bastardii*** CBen CRow CWat ECha ELon EPfP LLWG MSKA NPer SLon SPer SWat WBrk WFar WMoo WPnP WWtn XLum
- 'Beuron' CRow
- 'Come in Spinner' LLWG
- cream-flowered NBir SWat
- 'Crème de la Crème' ELon EWoo GBin GQue LLWG MWts NLar NSti WFar
- 'Esk' GCal
- 'Flore Pleno' (d) CBen CPrp CRow ECho GCra LLWG MSKA NLar NPer WBrk WCot WFar WPnP WWEG WWtn
I - 'Golden Fleece' SPer
- 'Golden Queen' CRow EWay LLWG
- 'Ilgengold' CRow
- 'Ivory' CRow LLWG
- 'Krill' CIri EBee LLWG WHil
- 'Mandchurica' XBlo
* - ***nana*** CRow
- 'Roy Davidson' ♀^{H7} CBro CPrp CRow GBin GCal IBlr NLar WCot WFar WHil
- 'Spartacus' **new** EBee
* - 'Sulphur Queen' NLar WCot WWEG
- 'Sun Cascade' CRow GBin
- 'Tiger Brother' CBro LLWG WBrk
- 'Tiggah' CRow
- 'Turnipseed' WCot
- 'Variegata' (v) ♀^{H7} Widely available
'Pulse Rate' (SDB) CBro
pumila EPot ITim LRHS MCot MWat
- f. ***atroviolacea*** CKel GEdr IGor WAbe
* - 'Gelber Mantel' NBir WFar
- 'Violacea' (DB) SRms
'Pumpin' Iron' (SDB) ♀^{H7} CKel ESgI
'Punchline' (TB) CWCL
'Punk' (MDB) CIri
'Pure and Simple' (TB) WCAu
'Pure As Gold' (TB) CWCL ESgI EWoo WCot XSen
'Purple Gem' (Reticulata) ECho EPfP EPot GKev LAma LRHS
'Purple People Eater' (TB) CIri
'Purple Pepper' (TB) WCAu
'Purple Ritz' (TB) WCAu
'Purple Sensation' (Dut) ECho SDeJ
'Purple Study' (MTB) WCAu
'Purr for Mints' (TB) CIri
'Pussycat Pink' (SDB) ESgI WCAu
'Quaker Lady' (TB) ESgI EWoo SIri WCAu
'Qualified' (TB) CIri
'Quantum Leap' (TB) CIri
'Quark' (SDB) CBro CKel
'Quechee' (TB) CKel COtt CWCL EAEE EAJP EBee EPfP ESgI EWoo GMaP IPot LBuc LRHS MCot MNrw MRav MSpe MWat NLar NSoo NWad SCob SDeJ SPer SWat WGwG
'Queen in Calico' (TB) ESgI WCAu
'Queen Jeanne' (La) **new** LLWG
'Queen of Angels' (TB) WCAu
'Queen of Hearts' (TB) XSen
'Queen of May' (TB) EWoo
'Queen's Prize' (SDB) SIri
'Quito' (TB) WCAu
'Rabbit's Foot' (SDB) SIri
'Radiant Apogee' (TB) EIri
'Radiant Burst' (IB) SIri
'Rain Dance' (SDB) ♀^{H7} ESgI
Rainbow Grand Mixture SDeJ
'Rainbow Rim' (SDB) ESgI
'Rainbow Selection' (TB) **new** CIri
'Rajah' (TB) CAby CBod CKel ELan EPfP EWoo GMaP LRHS MLHP MRav NOrc NSoo SDeJ SPer SPoG WMnd
'Rameses' (TB) ESgI EWoo WCAu
'Rancho Rose' (TB) XSen
'Rapture in Blue' (TB) EWoo
'Rare Edition' (IB) CKel EWoo NBir XSen
'Rare Quality' (TB) XSen
'Rare Treat' (TB) XSen
'Raspberry Acres' (IB) MRav WCAu
'Raspberry Blush' (IB) ♀^{H7} CAby CKel CPar EIri EPfP GBin LBMP LRHS LSou MRav SWat WAul WGwG WHoo WWFP XSen
'Razoo' (SDB) CKel
'Re La Blanche' (TB) SIri
'Reach for the Sky' (TB) CIri
'Real Coquette' (SDB) EWoo SIri
'Rebecca Perret' (TB) WCAu
'Rebus' (SDB) SIri
'Red Canyon Glow' (TB) CIri
'Red Dazzler' (La) CIri
'Red Echo' (La) CIri
'Red Flare' (TB) **new** WFar
'Red Flash' (TB) ESgI
'Red Hawk' (TB) EWoo
'Red Heart' (SDB) ESgI MRav WWEG XSen
'Red Orchid' (IB) ELan ESgI LRHS SRms WCAu
'Red Revival' (TB) MRav WCAu
'Red Rum' (TB) CKel EWes
'Red Zinger' (IB) ESgI EWoo LRHS LSun MWat
'Redelta' (TB) XSen
'Redondo' (IB) EWoo
'Reflets Safran' (TB) SIri XSen
'Regal Surprise' (SpH) ♀^{H7} CRow LLWG
'Regality' (Sib) CWCL EBee MHer MMuc
'Regards' (SDB) CBro XSen
'Regency Belle' (Sib) ♀^{H7} EWoo SIri
'Regency Buck' (Sib) EWoo SBch WCot
§ ***reichenbachii*** EPot WAbe
'Reincarnation' (TB) CIri EWoo
'Remembering Vic' (Spuria) EWoo
'Renewal' (TB) EWoo
'Renown' (TB) EWoo
'Repartee' (TB) XSen
'Replicator' (SDB) EWoo

	Name	Suppliers
	reticulata	ECho ELan EPfP LRHS SDeJ SEND SPer
	- var. ***bakeriana***	ECho LLHF NMin
*	- 'Violet Queen'	ECho
	'Return to Elegance' (TB)	WCAu
	'Réussite' (TB)	EWoo
	'Reversi' (TB)	CIri
	'Rhages' (TB)	EWoo
	'Rhapsody' (Reticulata)	ECho SDeJ
	'Rheinfels' (TB)	EWoo
	'Rheingauperle' (TB)	ESgI EWoo
	'Rhythm' (TB)	CIri
	'Rich and Rare' (La) **new**	LLWG
	'Rigamarole' (Sib) **new**	LLWG MSCN
	'Rigmarole' (Sib) **new**	WFar
	'Rikugi-sakura' (Sib)	EBee EPri GBin LLHF NLar WCot
	'Ringo' (TB)	CKel EWoo MRav
	'Rings of Saturn' (TB)	CIri
	'Rio Rojo' (TB)	WCAu
	'Rip City' (TB)	ESgI EWoo
	'Rising Moon' (TB)	EWoo SIri
	'Ritz' (SDB)	EAJP GEdr WWEG
	'Rive Gauche' (TB)	ESgI
	'River Avon' (TB)	WCAu
	'Riverbuds' (SDB)	SIri WCAu
	'Riverdance' (Sib)	EWoo
	'Roanoke's Choice' (Sib)	CBro CElw EBee ELon EWes GAbr GBin NCGa WFar
	'Roaring Jelly' (Sib)	EPri EWes NLar WCot
	'Rob Cornell' (TB)	ESgI
	'Robe d'Été' (TB)	CWCL
§	× ***robusta*** 'Dark Aura' ♀H7	MAvo MSCN WCot
§	- 'Gerald Darby'	Widely available
	- 'Mountain Brook'	CRow LLWG
*	- 'Purple Fan'	LLWG
	'Rochester Castle' (Kent Castles Series) (IB)	SIri
§	'Rocket' (TB)	EPfP GMaP LBuc LRHS MCot MRav MSpe NBir SDeJ SPer
	'Rocket Master' (TB)	ESgI
	'Rocket Randy' (TB)	CIri
	'Roku Oji' (Sib)	CIri
	'Roman Carnival' (TB)	EWoo
	'Romance' (TB)	EWoo
	'Romano' (Dut)	GKev
	'Romantic Evening' (TB)	EIri EWoo WCAu XSen
	'Romney Marsh' (IB)	SIri
	'Romola' (TB) **new**	WMil
	'Rosace' (Sib)	EWoo
	'Rosalie Figge' (TB)	ESgI EWoo WCAu WCot
	'Rose Queen'	see *I. ensata* 'Rose Queen'
	'Rose Violet' (TB)	WCAu
	'Rose-Marie' (TB)	EWoo
	'Rosemohr' (TB)	EWoo
	rosenbachiana	ECho
*	- 'Harangon'	ECho
	'Roseplic' (TB)	LRHS
	'Rosette Wine' (TB)	ESgI WCAu
	'Rosselline' (Sib)	WAul
	'Rosy Veil' (TB)	ESgI EWoo
	'Rosy Wings' (TB)	ECho ESgI EWoo
	'Roucoulade' (TB)	SIri
	'Rouge Gorge' (TB)	SIri
	'Rowden Aurelius' (Sib)	WAul
	'Rowden Starlight'	CRow CWat LLWG
I	'Royal Blue' (Sib)	EBee ECha SWat
	'Royal Crusader' (TB)	CCse EWoo WCAu XSen
	'Royal Elegance' (TB)	SIri
	'Royal Intrigue' (TB)	SIri
	'Royal Satin' (TB)	CHid
	'Royal Snowcap' (TB)	WCAu
	'Royal Summer' (TB)	EWoo
	'Rubacuori' (TB)	ESgI EWoo
	'Rubistar' (TB)	EWoo
	'Ruby Chimes' (IB)	ESgI WCAu
	'Ruby Contrast' (TB)	WCAu
	'Ruby Eruption' (SDB)	EIri WCAu
	'Ruby Mine' (TB)	WCAu
	'Ruby Morn' (TB)	WCAu
	'Ruby Wine' (Sib)	CCon EPri LEdu
	rudskyi	see *I. variegata*
	'Ruffled Velvet' (Sib) ♀H7	CBcs CElw CHid CKel ECho ECtt ELan EPfP EPri EWoo GBin GLog IMou IPot LRHS MBri MCot MRav MSpe NLar SCob SGSe SPer SWat WAul WFar WWEG
	'Ruffles Plus' (Sib)	EPri MBel
	'Russet Crown' (TB)	CKel
	'Rustic Cedar' (TB)	ESgI WCAu
	'Rustler' (TB)	WCAu
	'Rusty Beauty' (Dut)	GKev SDeJ
	'Rusty Magnificence' (TB)	EWoo
	'Ruth Black' (TB)	WCAu
	'Ruth Rowlands' (TB)	ESgI EWoo
	ruthenica	ECho WCot
	- var. ***nana***	CExl GEdr GKev
	'Sable' (TB)	ELan EPfP ESgI EWoo GMaP LRHS MCot MRav MWat MWhi NLar NOrc SCob SDeJ SEND SPer WAul WCAu WGwG WWEG
	'Sable Night' (TB)	CKel ESgI
	'Safari Sunset' (TB)	WCAu
	'Sailor' (IB)	WCAu
	'Saint Crispin' (TB)	EBee EPfP GCra GMaP LRHS MRav SPer SPoG WGwG
	'Salamander Crossing' (Sib) ♀H7	WAul WCAu
	'Sally Jane' (TB)	WCAu
	'Salmon Sunset' (Spuria)	EWoo
	'Salonique' (TB)	ESgI MMHG NLar WCAu
	'Saltwood' (SDB)	CBro ESgI
	'Saltwood Castle' (Kent Castles Series) (IB)	SIri
	'Salzburg Echo' (TB) **new**	WCAu
	'Sam Carne' (TB)	WCAu
	'Samarcande' (TB)	ESgI
	× ***sambucina***	XSen
	'San Diego' (TB)	ESgI
	'San Francisco' (TB)	ESgI EWoo
	'San Gabriel' (TB)	EWoo
	'Sandling Sunset' (TB)	SIri
	'Sandy Caper' (IB)	WCAu
	'Sangone' (IB)	ESgI MNrw
	'Sangreal' (IB)	LRHS
§	***sanguinea*** ♀H7	CMCN
	- 'Nana Alba'	GBin
§	- 'Snow Queen'	Widely available
	'Sapphire Beauty' (Dut)	GKev SDeJ
	'Sapphire Gem' (SDB)	CKel ESgI EWoo WCAu
	'Sapphire Hills' (TB)	LRHS WCAu XSen
	'Sarah Taylor' (SDB) ♀H7	ECho EWoo WCAu
	sari	ECho
	'Sasha Borisovich' (TB)	ESgI
	'Sass with Class' (SDB)	CKel
	'Satin Gown' (TB)	WCAu
	'Saturn' (TB)	WCAu

'Satyre' (SDB) **new**	CIri
'Savoir Faire' (Sib)	ECha
'Scottish Warrior' (TB)	CIri
'Scramble' (Sib)	CAby NPCo WCot
'Scribe' (MDB)	CBro NBir WCAu
'Sea Double' (TB)	WWEG
'Sea Fret' (SDB)	CBro
'Sea of Joy' (TB)	XSen
'Sea Shadows' (Sib)	EPri ESgI NBir
'Sea Wisp' (La)	NBro SKHP
'Seafire' (SDB)	WCAu
'Seakist' (TB)	WCAu
'Season Ticket' (IB)	XSen
'Seastone' (SDB)	WCAu
'Second Look' (TB)	XSen
'Second Wind' (TB)	EWoo WCAu
'Secret Decree' (La) **new**	LLWG
'Secret Melody' (TB)	XSen
'Secret Service' (TB)	CIri
'Self Evident' (MDB)	LLHF
'Semola' (SDB)	ESgI
'Senlac' (TB)	NLar WMil WMnd
'Señor Frog' (SDB)	ESgI
serbica	see *I. reichenbachii*
'Serene Moment' (TB)	SIri
'Serenity Prayer' (SDB)	WCAu
setosa ♀H7	CBro CMac CTri CWCL ECho EWld GCra GKev LEdu LRHS MNrw NCGa WOld
- ***alba***	NLar
- var. ***arctica***	GBuc GKev LEdu MHer
I - 'Baby Blue'	EPfP LRHS MBNS NPri
- subsp. ***canadensis***	see *I. hookeri*
- dark violet-flowered	EPri
- var. ***nana***	see *I. hookeri*
'Seven Hills' (TB)	ESgI
'Shadow Cast' (IB)	WCAu
'Shaker's Prayer' (Sib) ♀H7	CPrp EWes LSun MBrN
'Shakespeare's Sonnet' (SDB)	ESgI
'Shall We Dance' (Sib) ♀H7	CIri EWes
'Shampoo' (IB)	SIri WCAu
'Shawano' (TB)	EWoo
'Sheila Ann Germaney' (Reticulata)	CBro EBee ECho EPot ERCP GKev LAma LLHF LRHS NMin NWad SBch WRHF
'Shelby Lynne' (TB)	CIri
'Shelford Giant' (Spuria) ♀H7	CIri NEgg
'Sherbet Lemon' (IB) ♀H7	CBod CKel WCAu
'Shifnal'	WCAu
'Shirley Chandler' (IB) ♀H7	SIri
'Shirley Pope' (Sib) ♀H7	EWes GBin GBuc LRHS MNFA NCGa NSti WFar WMoo WWEG
'Shirley's Choice' (Sib)	EBee EPri SIri
'Short Distance' (IB)	EWoo SIri
'Showdown' (Sib)	ECtt GMaP LRHS SWat WWEG
'Shrawley' (Sib)	EWoo WAul
shrevei	see *I. virginica* var. *shrevei*
'Shurton Brook' (TB)	CKel
'Shurton Inn' (TB)	CKel WCAu
sibirica	CAvo CMHG CTsd CWat EHon GAbr GBBs GKev LLWP MCot MLHP MMuc NChi SCob SEND SPlb SRot WBrk WCFE WFar WHer WMoo WShi
- PAB 6119 **new**	LEdu
- 'Niklas Sea'	see *I.* 'Lake Niklas'
- 'Redflare'	see *I.* 'Melton Red Flare'
- 'Snow Queen'	see *I. sanguinea* 'Snow Queen'
'Sibirica Alba'	ECha EPfP EPri GBBs IBoy LLWP SWat WBrk WFar
sichuanensis	CExl SPlb
sieboldii	see *I. sanguinea*
'Sierra Blue' (TB)	ESgI EWoo
'Sierra Grande' (TB)	SIri XSen
'Sierra Nevada' (Spuria)	XSen
'Sign of Leo' (TB)	EWoo XSen
'Silence in Heaven' (Spuria)	CIri
'Silkirim' (TB)	CKel
'Silver Edge' (Sib) ♀H7	Widely available
'Silver Shower' (TB)	EWoo
'Silverado' (TB)	CKel ESgI EWoo GBin LRHS WCAu
'Silvery Beauty' (Dut)	GKev NBir SDeJ
sindjarensis	see *I. aucheri*
'Sing to Me' (TB)	WCAu
'Sinister Desire' (IB)	EWoo SIri
sintenisii ♀H5	CBro CPBP ECho SBrt XSen
'Sir Michael' (TB)	ESgI EWoo
'Siva Siva' (TB)	MRav
'Sixteen Candles' (IB)	EWoo
'Sixtine C' (TB)	SIri
'Skating Party' (TB)	CKel ESgI XSen
'Sky Beauty' (Dut)	GKev SBod SDeJ
'Sky Hooks' (TB)	XSen
'Sky Tracery' (MTB)	SDys
'Sky Wings' (Sib)	CRow ECha EWoo GQue MArl WMoo
'Skydancer' (SDB)	WCAu
'Skyfire' (TB)	EBee ESgI WWEG
'Skylark's Song' (TB)	EIri EWoo
'Small Sky' (SDB)	CBro
'Smart' (SDB)	WCAu
'Smart Aleck' (TB)	ESgI
'Smart Girl' (TB)	CKel EIri
'Smart Move' (TB)	CWCL ESgI
'Smiling Faces' (TB)	WCAu
'Smith Named Keith' (TB)	CIri
'Smitten Kitten' (IB)	WCAu
'Smokey Dream' (TB)	CKel
'Smokey Salmon' (TB)	CKel
'Smooth' (SDB)	SDys
'Snow Plum' (IB)	SIri
'Snow Prince' (Sib)	EPri
'Snow Season' (SDB)	ESgI
'Snow Shoes' (TB)	CIri
'Snow Tracery' (TB)	EBee LRHS
'Snow Troll' (SDB)	WCAu
'Snowcone' (IB)	EWoo LSun
'Snowcrest' (Sib)	CBre MRav MSpe
'Snowmound' (TB)	CCCN CKel ESgI EWoo WCAu
'Snowy Owl' (TB)	CKel WCAu
'Snugglebug' (SDB)	CTal EWoo WCAu
'Soaring Kite' (TB)	WCAu
'Social Event' (TB)	ESgI XSen
'Social Graces' (TB)	WCAu
'Soft Blue' (Sib) ♀H7	EPri WAul
'Soft Rain' (TB)	CIri
'Soft Return'	EWoo
'Solar Fire' (TB)	CIri
'Solar Fusion' (Spuria)	EWoo
'Solid Mahogany' (TB)	MRav
'Soligo' (MDB)	ESgI
'Solo Flight' (TB)	SDys
'Somerset Blue' (TB)	CKel
'Somerset Cider' (TB)	SIri

	Name	Suppliers
	'Somerton Dance' (SDB)	CKel
	'Song of Norway' (TB)	EIri EWoo XSen
	'Sonoran Sands' (IB)	SDys
	'Sopra il Vulcano' (BB)	ESgI EWoo
	'Sordid Lives' (TB)	WCAu
	'Sostenique' (TB)	ESgI
	'Southcombe White' (Sib)	CRow WWEG
	'Souvenir de Madame Gaudichau' (TB)	ESgI
	'Sparkling Rose' (Sib)	Widely available
	'Sparkling Waters' (TB)	ESgI
	'Sparkplug' (SDB)	ESgI
	'Spartan' (TB)	CKel
	'Special Feature' (TB)	CIri
	'Speck So' (MTB)	WCAu
	'Speckled Hen' (La) **new**	LLWG
I	'Speckles' (Sib) **new**	EPPr
	'Spellbreaker' (TB)	EWoo SIri
	'Spice Lord' (TB)	WCAu
	'Spiced Custard' (TB)	CKel EIri ESgI EWoo WCAu
	'Spiced Tiger' (TB)	ESgI
	'Spicy Cajun' (La)	WHil
	'Spinning Wheel' (TB)	SIri
	'Spirit of Memphis' (TB)	XSen
	'Splashacata' (TB)	WCAu XSen
	'Splashdown' (Sino-Sib)	SWat
	'Splat' (IB)	CIri
	'Spot of Tea' (MDB)	LLHF
	'Spreckles' (TB)	ESgI
	'Spree' (SDB)	WCAu
	'Spring Blush' (MTB) ♀H7	SIri
	'Spring Festival' (TB)	WCAu
	'Spring Kiss' (TB)	SIri
	'Spring Madness' (TB)	WCAu
	'Spring Time' (Reticulata)	ECho GKev LAma SDeJ
	'Spun Gold' (TB)	EWoo
	spuria	CMac CPou WCot
§	- subsp. ***halophila***	GBin GKev
	- subsp. ***notha*** CC 725	WCot
	- subsp. ***ochroleuca***	see *I. orientalis* Mill.
	'Spy' (BB)	WCAu
	'Square Dance Skirt' (TB)	SDys
	'St Louis Blues' (TB)	ESgI XSen
	'Stairway to Heaven' (TB)	ESgI WCAu
	'Stapleford' (SDB)	CBro
	'Staplehurst' (MTB) ♀H7	SIri
	'Star Cluster' (Sib)	WFar
	'Star Shine' (TB)	CKel ESgI WCAu
	'Starcrest' (TB)	EWoo
	'Stardate' (SDB)	CKel
	'Starheart' (IB)	WCAu
	'Starlette Rose' (TB)	EWoo
	'Starring' (TB)	EWoo
	'Starship' (TB)	XSen
	'Starwoman' (IB) ♀H7	SDys WCAu
	'Staten Island' (TB)	ESgI SEND SRms WCAu
	'Steffie' (MTB)	WCAu
	'Stella Polaris' (TB)	ELon
	'Stellar Lights' (TB)	EIri EWoo WCAu
	'Stephen Wilcox' (Sib)	CIri EPri WAul
	'Stepping Out' (TB) ♀H7	CKel CMac CPar EAEE EPfP ESgI GBin IPot LRHS SCob SDeJ WCAu
	'Steve' (Sib)	CPar EWes SWat
	'Steve Varner' (Sib)	EPri EWoo IMou
	'Stinger' (SDB) ♀H7	CIri
	'Stingray' (TB)	ESgI
	'Stitch in Time' (TB)	EIri EWoo WCAu
	'Stockholm' (SDB)	CKel
	stolonifera	ECho
	- 'Zwanenburg Beauty'	ECho
	'Stop the Music' (TB)	XSen
	'Storm Center' (TB)	EWoo
	'Stormy Circle' (SDB)	WCAu
	'Storrington' (TB)	EMal EWoo
	'Strange Brew' (TB)	WCAu
	'Strathmore' (TB)	EMal EWoo
	'Strawberry Fair' (Sib) ♀H7	CIri WCAu
	'Strictly Jazz' (TB)	WCAu
	'Strike it Rich' (TB)	ESgI
	'Striking' (TB)	EWoo
	'Strozzapreti' (TB)	ESgI
	'Study In Black' (TB)	XSen
	'Stylish Socialite' (La) **new**	LLWG
	stylosa	see *I. unguicularis*
§	***suaveolens***	CPBP CPou ECho GEdr NWad
	- var. ***flavescens***	see *I. suaveolens* yellow-flowered
§	- purple-flowered	ECho GEdr
	- var. ***violacea***	see *I. suaveolens* purple-flowered
§	- yellow-flowered	ECho EPot GKev
	'Subtle'	WCAu
	'Succès Fou' (TB)	EWoo SIri
	'Sugar' (IB)	NSti WCAu
	'Sugar Magnolia' (TB)	EWoo
	'Sugarplum Treat' (La) **new**	LLWG
	'Sultan's Palace' (TB)	CKel EBee ECho ESgI EWoo LPot LRHS MAvo WCAu XSen
	'Summer Holidays' (TB)	XSen
	'Summer Revels' (Sib)	EPri EWTr
	'Summer Sky' (Sib)	CBre CSpe GBin LEdu MSCN NCGa SWat WAul WCot WWEG
	'Summer's Smile' (TB)	EWoo
	'Summertime Blues' (TB)	EWoo
	'Sun Ada Beach' (TB)	CIri
	'Sunblaze' (TB)	WCAu
	'Sunny Dawn' (IB)	CKel
	'Sunny Disposition' (TB)	XSen
	'Sunny Side Up'	ECho
	'Sunnyside Delight' (TB)	WCAu
	'Sunset Skies' (TB)	CWCL
	'Super Model' (TB) **new**	WCAu
	'Superba' (Sib)	WWtn
	'Superstition' (TB) ♀H7	CKel EIri ELan ESgI EWes EWoo LAst LRHS LSun MRav SCob WCAu WCot XSen
	'Supreme Sultan' (TB)	CKel CWCL ESgI EWoo WCAu XSen
	'Surprise Caller' (La) **new**	LLWG
	'Susan Bliss' (TB)	CKel ELan EPfP ESgI EWoo WCAu WMil
	'Susan Gillespie' (IB)	CKel
	'Susannah Fullerton' (La) **new**	LLWG
	'Suspect' (AB)	WCAu
	'Suspicion' (TB)	CIri
	'Sutton Valence' (Sib)	SIri
	'Swain' (TB)	ESgI
	'Swan Ballet' (TB)	ESgI
	'Swank' (Sib)	WAul
	'Swazi Princess' (TB)	ELon ESgI
	'Sweet Kate' (SDB)	WCAu
	'Sweet Lavender' (TB) **new**	WMil
	'Sweet Lena' (TB)	ESgI
	'Sweet Musette' (TB)	WCAu
	'Sweet Surrender' (Sib)	EPri
	'Sweeter than Wine' (TB)	EWoo MRav
	'Swingtown' (TB)	EWoo WCAu
	'Swiss Majesty' (TB)	WCAu

'Swizzle' (IB)	XSen
'Sybil' (TB)	GBin GCra
'Sylvan' (TB)	XSen
'Sylvia Murray' (TB)	WCAu
'Symphony' (Dut)	ECho NBir SDeJ
'Symphony of Light' (TB) new	CIri
'Syncopation' (TB)	ESgI WCAu XSen
'Tabac Blond' (TB)	EWoo
'Tact' (IB)	SIri
'Take Me Away' (TB)	SDys
'Tall Chief' (TB)	WCAu
'Tamberg' (Sib)	EBee EWoo
'Tamerlan' (TB)	EWoo
'Tan Tingo' (IB)	WCAu XSen
'Tanex'	ECho
'Tangerine Sky' (TB)	EWoo WCAu
'Tangfu' (IB)	ESgI
'Tantara' (SDB)	XSen
'Tantrum' (IB)	WCAu XSen
'Tanz Nochmal' (Sib)	GBin
'Tanzanian Tangerine' (TB)	WCAu
'Tarn Hows' (TB)	ESgI SRms WCAu
'Teal Velvet' (Sib)	ECha EPfP EPri EWoo GLog LRHS MCot SCob WFar
'Tealwood' (Sib)	CIri
'Teapot Tempest' (BB)	WCAu
'Teasaucer Hill' (MTB) ♀H7	SIri
tectorum	CCse GKev SChr SDix WCot XLum XSen
- BWJ 8191	WCru
- 'Alba'	WThu XSen
- 'Cruella'	EPfP
- 'Variegata' misapplied	see *I. japonica* 'Variegata'
- 'Variegata' (v)	CBod SGSe
'Tell Fibs' (SDB)	CBro CKel
'Temper Tantrum' (Sib)	CPrp LRHS MBNS
'Temple Gold' (TB)	CKel NPer
'Temple Meads' (IB)	ESgI WCAu
'Templecloud' (IB) ♀H7	CKel
'Tempting Fate' (TB)	WCAu
§ ***tenax***	ECho GBuc LRHS
'Tennison Ridge' (TB)	WCAu
'Teverlae' (Sib)	EBee LRHS
'Thaïs' (TB)	ESgI
'The Black Douglas' (TB)	EWoo
'The Citadel' (TB)	ELon
'The Red Douglas' (TB)	ESgI
'The Rocket'	see *I.* 'Rocket'
'Theatre' (TB)	ESgI
'Theodolinda' (TB)	EWoo
'Think Spring' (MTB)	WCAu
'Third Charm' (SDB)	CBro
'Third World' (SDB)	CBro
'This and That' (IB)	WCAu
'Thornbird' (TB) ♀H7	CIri EIri ESgI EWoo WCAu
'Three Cherries' (MDB)	CBro ECho SIri
'Thriller' (TB)	ESgI EWoo WCAu XSen
thunbergii	see *I. sanguinea*
'Thunder Echo' (TB)	ESgI SIri
'Thundering Hills' (TB)	CKel
'Tickety Boo' (SDB)	CIri
'Tickle the Ivories' (IB)	CIri
§ 'Tigereye' (Dut)	EPot ERCP GKev SDeJ
tigridia	CExl
'Time to Shine' (SDB)	WCAu
'Time Traveler' (TB)	CIri
'Time Zone' (TB)	WCAu
'Tinkerbell' (SDB)	CAby CPBP CTal EBee EPfP GMaP LRHS NBir NGdn SDeJ
'Tishomingo'	EWoo
'Titan's Glory' (TB) ♀H7	CKel ESgI EWoo LEdu MRav WCot WHoo
'To the Point' (TB)	CIri
'Toasted Watermelon' (TB)	WCAu
'Tollong'	IKil IMou
'Tom Johnson' (TB) ♀H7	EWoo
'Tom Tit' (TB)	WCAu WMil
'Toni Lynn' (MDB)	ECho
'Toots' (SDB)	ECho
'Top Flight' (TB)	CKel ELan LRHS SPer SRms
'Top Gun' (TB)	ESgI
'Topolino' (TB)	CKel
'Torchlight' (TB)	SEND
'Torero' (TB)	EWoo SIri
'Toro Blanco' (IB)	CIri
'Total Eclipse' (TB)	SRms
'Totally Cool' (SDB)	SIri
'Toy Clown' (SDB)	EWoo
'Trails West' (TB)	EWoo
'Trajectory' (SDB)	WCAu
'Trapel' (TB)	ESgI
'Trencavel' (TB)	ESgI
'Trenwith' (TB)	ESgI
'Triffid' (TB)	CIri
'Trillion' (TB)	CIri
'Trim the Velvet' (Sib)	WAul
'Triple Whammy' (TB)	ESgI XSen
'Tripod' (IB)	CIri
'Tristram' (TB) new	WMil
'Tropic Night' (Sib)	Widely available
'True Charm' (TB)	EWoo
tuberosa	CAby CArn CAvo CBro CDes CHid CTri CWCL ECGP ECha ECho ERCP GKev LAma MHer NMin SDeJ WCot
- BS 348	WCot
- MS 76	WCot
- MS 729	WCot
- MS 731	WCot
- MS 821	CDes WCot
- MS 964	WCot
- PB	WCot
'Tulip Festival' (TB)	EBee SGol
'Tumultueux' (TB)	EWoo
'Tut's Gold' (TB)	ESgI WCAu
'Tuxedo' (TB)	XSen
'Twilight Tango' (La) new	LLWG
'Two Sided Coin' (TB)	WCAu
§ 'Tycoon' (Sib)	EShb EWoo GQue LRHS SMrm SPer
'Tyland Blue' (TB)	SIri
typhifolia	SBrt
'Tyrian Dream' (IB)	WCAu
'UFO' (TB)	CIri
'Ultimate' (SDB)	CIri
'Undercurrent' (TB) new	WCAu
'Unfinished Business' (TB)	WCAu
§ ***unguicularis***	Widely available
- 'Abington Purple'	CAvo CJun EIri
- 'Alba'	CAvo CExl EWoo XSen
* - 'Bob Thompson'	CAvo
§ - subsp. ***cretensis***	ECho EPot GKev SKHP XSen
- 'Diana Clare'	CJun
- 'Kilbroney Marble'	EPri
- 'Marondera'	CAvo CJun
- 'Mary Barnard' ♀H5	CAvo CBro CJun CPou CTca ECGP ECho EWoo LRHS MAvo NBir WHoo

	Name	Suppliers
	- 'Oxford Dwarf'	ECho LLHF
	- 'Stavendale Tiger' **new**	MAvo
§	- 'Walter Butt'	CAvo CJun ECGP EWoo MAvo NBir
	'Unicorn' (TB)	CIri
	'Vague à l'Ame' (TB)	ESgI EWoo
	'Val de Loire'	EWoo
	'Valda' (Sib)	EBee ELon
	'Valerie Joyce'	WCAu
	'Vamp' (IB)	CKel EWoo XSen
	'Vanilla Skies' (TB)	WCAu
	'Vanity' (TB)	XSen
	'Vanity's Child' (TB)	WCAu XSen
§	***variegata*** ♀H7	IGor XSen
	'Vegas Heat' (BB)	CIri
	'Velvet Dusk' (TB)	EWoo
	'Velvet King' (TB)	ESgI
	'Velvet Purple'	XBlo
	'Venita Faye' (TB)	WCAu
	'Vera' (Rc)	GKev
	'Verity Blamey' (TB)	CKel
	verna	EPot
	versicolor	CArn CBAq CBen CRow GBin GKev GMaP GPoy MGos MMuc MNHC MWts SEND SPlb SRms SWat WBrk WFar WMAq WMoo WPnP WShi WWtn
	- 'Algonquin'	CRow LLWG
	- 'Between the Lines'	CRow LLWG
	- 'China West Lake'	CRow LLWG
	- 'Claret Cup'	CPou WWEG
	- 'Dottie's Double'	CRow
*	- 'Georgia Bay'	CRow
	- 'Kermesina'	CPrp CRow CWat ECha ELan ESgI GBuc LLWG MGos MWts NPer NSti SRms SWat WFar WMAq WMoo WPnP
	- 'Mint Fresh'	LLWG
	- 'Mysterious Monique'	CCse CDes CWat LLWG
	- 'Party Line'	SIri
	- purple-flowered	EWay
	- 'Rosea'	CRow EWay
	- 'Rowden Allegro'	CRow
	- 'Rowden Aria'	CRow
	- 'Rowden Cadenza'	CRow EWay LLWG
	- 'Rowden Calypso'	CRow
	- 'Rowden Cantata'	CRow LLWG
	- 'Rowden Concerto'	CRow LLWG
	- 'Rowden Descant'	CRow
	- 'Rowden Harmony'	CRow
	- 'Rowden Jingle'	CRow
	- 'Rowden Lullaby'	CRow
	- 'Rowden Lyric'	CRow
	- 'Rowden Mazurka'	CRow
	- 'Rowden Melody'	CRow LLWG
	- 'Rowden Minuet'	CRow
	- 'Rowden Nocturne'	CRow
	- 'Rowden Pastorale'	CRow LLWG
	- 'Rowden Refrain'	CRow
	- 'Rowden Rondo'	CRow
	- 'Rowden Sonata'	CRow LLWG
	- 'Rowden Symphony'	CRow
	- 'Rowden Waltz'	CRow
	- 'Silvington'	CRow
	- 'Whodunit'	CRow
	'Vi Luihn' (Sib)	ECha WMoo
	'Vibrant' (TB)	WCAu
	'Vibrations' (TB)	ESgI WCAu
	vicaria	ECho GKev
	'Victoria Falls' (TB)	ESgI EWoo WCAu

	Name	Suppliers
	'Victorian Secret' (Sib)	EBee ELon
	'Viel Schnee' (Sib)	GBin
	'Vigilante' (TB)	EWoo
	'Vin Nouveau' (TB)	XSen
	'Vinho Verde' (IB)	CKel
	'Vino Rosso' (SDB)	ESgI
	'Violet Beauty' (Reticulata)	ECho ERCP GKev LAma
	'Violet Classic' (TB)	WCAu
	'Violet Fusion' (Spuria)	EWoo
	'Violet Harmony' (TB)	ESgI
	'Violet Icing' (TB)	CKel
	'Violet Rings' (TB)	WCAu
	'Violet Skies' (Sib)	GBin
	'Viper' (IB)	CIri EWoo
	virginica	LLWG
	- 'De Luxe'	see *I.* × *robusta* 'Dark Aura'
	- 'Lavender Lustre'	LLWG
	- 'Orchid Purple'	LLWG
	- 'Pale Lavender'	LLWG
	- 'Pink Perfection'	LLWG
	- 'Pond Crown Point'	CRow
	- 'Pond Lilac Dream'	CRow
*	- 'Purple Fan'	CRow
§	- var. ***shrevei***	LLWG
	- 'Slightly Daft'	LLWG
	'Vision in Pink' (TB)	WCAu
	'Visual Intrigue' (TB)	EWoo
	'Visual Treat' (Sib)	EWoo SIri
	'Vitafire' (TB)	ESgI EWoo LRHS
	'Vitality' (IB)	ELon ESgI
	'Viva Mexico' (TB)	EWoo
	'Vizier' (TB)	WCAu
	'Voilà' (IB)	CMea ESgI
	'Volts' (SDB)	XSen
	'Volute' (TB)	ESgI
	'Voyage' (SDB)	EWoo XSen
	'Wabash' (TB)	WCAu XSen
	'Wall Street Blues' (Sib)	EWoo
	'Walmer Castle' (Kent Castles Series) (IB)	SIri
	'Walter Butt'	see *I. unguicularis* 'Walter Butt'
	'War Chief' (TB)	ESgI MRav WCAu
	'War Sails' (TB)	EWoo SIri WCAu
	warleyensis	ECho
	'Warrior King' (TB)	EWoo
	'Waters Of Miraba' (BB)	EWoo
	wattii	CExl GCal IKil WCot
	'Way to Go' (TB)	CIri
	'Wealden Butterfly' (Sib) ♀H7	SIri WAul
	'Wealden Carousel' (Sib)	SIri WAul
	'Wealden Mystery' (Sib)	EPri SIri WAul
	'Wealden Skies' (Sib)	SIri WAul
	'Wealden Spires' (Sib) **new**	WAul
	'Wealden Summer' (Sib) **new**	WAul
	'Wearing Rubies' (TB)	ESgI WCAu
	'Webelos' (SDB)	MRav
	'Webmaster' (SDB)	SIri
	'Wedding Vow' (TB)	CKel EIri
	'Welch's Reward' (MTB)	CKel ESgI
	'Welcome Discovery' (TB)	WCAu
	'Welcome Return' (Sib)	CElw EBee GQue LRHS MBNS MMuc NLar SEND SWat WMoo
	'Welfenfürstin' (Sib)	GBin
	'Welfenprinz' (Sib) ♀H7	WAul
	'Well Suited' (SDB)	EWoo WCAu
	'Wench' (TB)	EWoo WCAu

	'Westar' (SDB)	CKel EIri
	'Westpointer' (TB)	CIri
	'What Again' (SDB)	XSen
	'Whispering Spirits' (TB)	WCAu
	'White Caucasus' (Reticulata)	EPot
	'White City' (TB)	CKel EAEE EPfP ESgI EWoo GMaP LRHS MCot MRav MWat MWhi NPer SCob SDeJ SPer SRms SWat WCAu WMnd
	'White Excelsior' (Dut)	ECho
	'White Gem' (SDB)	ESgI EWoo
	'White Knight' (TB)	EBee ELan EPfP ESgI WMnd
I	'White Queen' (Sib)	ESgI SWat
	'White Reprise' (TB)	ESgI XSen
I	'White Swan' (Sib)	EPri
	'White Swirl' (Sib)	Widely available
	'White Triangles' (Sib)	EWoo
	'White Umbrella' (La) new	LLWG
	'White van Vliet' (Dut)	SDeJ
	'White Wine' (MTB)	WCAu
	'White-Wave' (TB)	XBlo
	'Widow's Veil' (SDB)	ESgI
	'Wild Echo' (TB)	CKel
	'Wild Jasmine' (TB)	WCAu
	'Wild Ruby' (SDB)	CKel
	'Wild West' (TB)	CKel
	'Wild Wings' (TB)	EWoo LRHS MCot SGbt WCAu
	willmottiana	ECho
	- 'Alba'	ECho
	wilsonii ♀H7	CExl CHel EBee GBin GKev SBrt WCot
	'Windjammer Seas' (TB)	SDys
	'Winemaster' (TB)	EWoo SIri
	'Winesap' (TB)	ESgI EWoo
	'Winged Angel' (IB)	CIri
	'Wings of Peace' (TB)	CIri
	'Winning Edge' (TB)	WCAu
	winogradowii ♀H7	CBro ECho EPot ERCP GKev LAma LLHF LRHS WAbe XEll
	'Winter Olympics' (TB)	CKel EAEE EPfP LRHS MRav SPer WGwG
	'Winter Pearl' (IB)	EWoo
	'Wintry Sky' (TB)	WCAu
	'Wise' (SDB)	WCAu
	'Wish Upon a Star' (SDB)	WCAu
	'Wishful Thinking' (TB)	SIri
	'Wisteria Sachet' (IB)	WCAu
	'Witch's Wand' (TB)	ESgI EWoo
	'Wizard's Return' (SDB)	SIri
	'Wonders Never Cease' (TB)	WCAu
	'Wondrous' (TB)	ESgI
	'World Premier' (TB)	WCAu
	'Wrangler' (IB)	EWoo SIri
	xiphioides	see *I. latifolia*
	'Yankee Consul' (Sib)	EPri
	'Yaquina Blue' (TB)	WCAu
	'Yellow Flirt' (MTB)	WCAu
	'Yes' (TB)	CJun ESgI
	'Yippy Skippy' (SDB)	WCAu
	'Yosemite Nights' (TB)	EWoo
	'Yosemite Star' (TB)	EWoo
	'Youth Dew' (TB)	EWoo
	'Yvonne Pelletier' (TB)	WCAu
	'Zakopane' (Sib)	EBee EWes WAul
	'Zandria' (TB)	WCAu
	'Zantha' (TB)	XSen
	zenaidae	ECho
	'Zero' (SDB)	CKel
	'Zweites Hundert' (Sib)	WFar

Isatis (*Brassicaceae*)

	glauca	CFis
	tinctoria	CArn CBod CHab CHby CUse ENfk EOHP GJos GPoy MHer MNHC SIde SPav SRms WHfH WJek

Ismelia (*Asteraceae*)

	carinata 'Sunset' new	LRHS

Ismene see *Hymenocallis*

Isodon (*Lamiaceae*)

	calycinus	SPlb
	longitubus	SBrt
	- B&SWJ 11027	WCru
	rubescens	IMou

Isolepis (*Cyperaceae*)

§	***cernua***	CBen COtt CWat EShb MSKA MWts NOak SCoo SHDw SPad WMAq

Isoloma see *Kohleria*

Isomeris see *Cleome*

Isoplexis see *Digitalis*

Isopogon (*Proteaceae*)

	anemonifolius	SPlb
	anethifolius	SPlb

Isopyrum (*Ranunculaceae*)

	dicarpon	see *Dichocarpum dicarpon*
	nipponicum	WCot WCru WPGP
	stoloniferum	WCru
	thalictroides	EBee EPot GEdr LLHF SDys WCot

Isotoma (*Campanulaceae*)

	sp.	SWvt
§	***axillaris***	CSpe NPer SCoo SPer SPoG WHea
	- 'Fairy Carpet'	LRHS SBod SRms
	fluviatilis	NLar

Itea (*Iteaceae*)

	chinensis	CExl
	ilicifolia ♀H5	Widely available
*	- 'Rubrifolia'	ELan LRHS SLon SPoG
	japonica 'Beppu'	SSpi
	virginica	CAbP CBcs CMCN ELon ESwi MRav SLim SLon
§	- 'Henry's Garnet' ♀H5	CAbP CDoC CEnd CJun CMCN CMac COtt CSBt ECrN EPfP EWTr GBin IDee LAst LEdu LRHS MBri MGos MWat NLar NSoo SCob SEle SHil SLim SPer SPoG SRGP SSpi SWvt
	- Little Henry = 'Sprich' PBR	CHGN CMac CSBt EBee EPfP IVic LRHS NLar SCob
	- 'Long Spire'	CJun NLar
	- 'Merlot'	CJun MBlu NLar
	- 'Sarah Eve'	CJun CMCN NLar SRGP
	- 'Saturnalia'	NLar
	- Swarthmore form	see *I. virginica* 'Henry's Garnet'
	yunnanensis	CExl MBlu NLar SSpi WSHC

Itoa (*Salicaceae*)

	orientalis	SVen

Ixeris (*Asteraceae*)

stolonifera	XLum

Ixia (*Iridaceae*)

aurea 'Saldanha'	ECho
'Blue Bird'	CCon ECho LAma NRog SDeJ
capillaris 'Citrusdal'	ECho
'Castor'	ECho GKev NRog
curta	ECho
dubia	ECho
flexuosa	ECho WHil
'Gemini'	ECho
'Giant'	CTca ECho GKev SDeJ WHil
'Hogarth'	ECho GKev IFro LAma NRog WHil
'Holland Glory'	ECho NRog
latifolia var. ***latifolia***	ECho
longituba 'Citrusdal'	ECho
lutea	ECho
'Mabel'	ECho GKev NRog WCot
maculata	ECho
marginifolia from Komsberg	ECho
'Marquette'	ECho GKev
metelerkampiae	ECho
- 'Goudini'	ECho
mixed	SDeJ
monadelpha	ECho
orientalis	ECho
paniculata	ECho
- 'Eos'	GKev
'Panorama'	ECho GKev NRog
polystachya	ECho
- var. ***longistylis***	ECho
- var. ***lutea***	ECho
pumilio	WCot
purpureorosea 'Saldanha'	ECho
rapunculoides	ECho
- var. ***rigida***	ECho
- var. ***subpendula***	ECho
'Rose Emperor'	ECho GKev LAma NRog SBod SDeJ
scillaris var. ***subundulata***	ECho
'Spotlight'	ECho GKev NRog WHil
thomasiae	WCot
trifolia	ECho
'Venus'	CCon CTca ECho GKev LAma NRog SDeJ WHil
versicolor	ECho
viridiflora	CDes ECho NRog WCot
- var. ***minor***	ECho WCot
'Vulcan'	ECho NRog WHil
'Yellow Emperor'	CTca ECho GKev NRog SDeJ

Ixiolirion (*Ixioliriaceae*)

montanum	ECho
pallasii	see *I. tataricum*
§ ***tataricum***	EBee ECho LAma MCot SDeJ
- Ledebourii Group	CAvo

J

Jaborosa (*Solanaceae*)

integrifolia	CCon CExl EBee LEdu SBrt WCot WPGP XLum

Jacaranda (*Bignoniaceae*)

acutifolia misapplied	see *J. mimosifolia*
§ ***mimosifolia*** ♀H1c	CBcs CCCN EShb SPlb

Jacobinia see *Justicia*

Jamesbrittenia (*Scrophulariaceae*)

stellata	SPlb

Jamesia (*Hydrangeaceae*)

americana	CBcs CJun ESwi ETwe NLar WCru WSHC

Jasione (*Campanulaceae*)

§ ***heldreichii***	NBir SRms
jankae	see *J. heldreichii*
§ ***laevis***	ECho EPfP GAbr LRHS SRms
§ - 'Blaulicht'	CBod CMHG ECha EPfP EPla GEdr LRHS MBNS MHol NEgg NLar SBod SPlb WMoo
- Blue Light	see *J. laevis* 'Blaulicht'
montana	ECho MNHC WPnn
perennis	see *J. laevis*

Jasminum ✿ (*Oleaceae*)

CC 4728	CExl
adenophyllum	CTyn MOWG
affine	see *J. officinale* f. *affine*
angulare ♀H2	CExl CRHN CTyn MOWG
azoricum ♀H2	CCCN CDoC CHll CRHN CTyn EPfP EShb GCal MOWG SEle SPre
beesianum	Widely available
bignoniaceum	CTyn WSHC
blinii	see *J. polyanthum*
dispermum	CRHN
diversifolium	see *J. subhumile*
farreri	see *J. humile* f. *farreri*
§ ***floridum***	EWes
fruticans	CMac ELon EPla LRHS SBrt SEND WCru XLum
- RCB UA 22	WCot
giraldii misapplied	see *J. humile* f. *farreri*
giraldii Diels	see *J. floridum*
grandiflorum misapplied	see *J. officinale* f. *affine*
grandiflorum L.	IDee
- 'De Grasse' ♀H2	CRHN CTyn EShb MOWG
heterophyllum	see *J. subhumile*
humile	CExl MGil SEND WKif
§ - f. ***farreri***	CTyn MBri
- var. ***glabrum***	see *J. humile* f. *wallichianum*
§ - 'Revolutum' ♀H5	CBcs CDul CHel CMac COtt CRHN CSBt CTyn EBee ECrN ELan EPfP EShb GCal LAst LRHS MGos MRav NLar SEND SGbt SLon SPoG SRms SWvt WHar WSHC
§ - f. ***wallichianum***	CTyn
- - B&SWJ 2559	WCru
- - PAB 2534	LEdu
§ ***laurifolium*** f. ***nitidum*** ♀H2	CTyn MOWG
§ ***mesnyi*** ♀H3	CCCN CExl CHll CMac CRHN CSde CTri CTyn EBak ELan EPfP EWTr LRHS MOWG SEND SPer SVen WSHC
multiflorum	CCCN MOWG
multipartitum	CTyn
- bushy	CSpe CTyn

	nitidum	see *J. laurifolium* f. *nitidum*
§	***nudiflorum*** ♀H5	Widely available
	- 'Argenteum'	see *J. nudiflorum* 'Mystique'
	- 'Aureum'	CTyn ELan LBMP LRHS MAsh MBNS MRav NLar NSti SPer SRms
*	- 'Compactum'	MAsh
§	- 'Mystique' (v)	ELan LRHS MRav SLon
	odoratissimum	MOWG
	officinale	Widely available
	- CC 1709	WMoo
§	- f. ***affine***	CArn CBcs CCCN COtt CRHN CSPN CTri CTyn CWCL ELan EPfP LAst LRHS MAsh MRav SCoo SDix SLim SRms WHar WPat
§	- 'Argenteovariegatum' (v) ♀H5	CBcs CDul CHel COtt CTyn CWGN EHoe ELan EPfP LRHS MAsh MBri MGos MHer MRav MWat NPri SEND SLim SPer SWvt WCFE WHar WPat WSHC
	- 'Aureovariegatum'	see *J. officinale* 'Aureum'
§	- 'Aureum' (v)	CBcs CDoC CMac CTyn CWCL CWSG EBee ECtt ELan EPfP IBoy LRHS MAsh MBri MHer NBir SCoo SLim SLon SPer SRms WPat
	- 'Clotted Cream'PBR	see *J. officinale* 'Devon Cream'
	- 'Crûg's Collection'	CTyn WCru
§	- 'Devon Cream'PBR	Widely available
	- Fiona Sunrise = 'Frojas'PBR ♀H5	Widely available
	- 'Grandiflorum'	see *J. officinale* f. *affine*
	- 'Inverleith' ♀H5	CCCN CDoC CHel CMac CTyn CWCL CWSG EBee ELan EPfP IArd LAst LBMP LRHS MAsh MBNS MBri MGos MRav SCoo SHil SLim SMad SPad SPer SPoG WGrn WSHC
	- 'Variegatum'	see *J. officinale* 'Argenteovariegatum'
	parkeri	CBcs CCCN CJun CMac CTri CTyn EBee ECho ELon EPfP GCal GMaP LRHS MBNS NLar WPat XEll
	- 'Bychan'	WAbe
§	***polyanthum*** ♀H2	CArn CBcs CChe CExl COtt CRHN CSBt CSde CTri CTyn EBak ELan EPfP IDee MBri MOWG SEND SLim SPer SPre SRms WHar
	- dark-red-leaved	CExl CHel EBee WPGP
	- 'Greenholm' (v)	CTyn
	primulinum	see *J. mesnyi*
	reevesii hort.	see *J. humile* 'Revolutum'
	sambac ♀H2	CArn CCCN CDoC CHll CRHN CTyn ELan MOWG SPre
	- 'Grand Duke of Tuscany' (d)	MOWG SPre
	- 'Maid of Orleans' (d)	EShb SPre
	sieboldianum	see *J. nudiflorum*
§	***simplicifolium*** subsp. ***suavissimum***	CHll CRHN
	stenalobium	CTyn MOWG
	× ***stephanense***	Widely available
	suavissimum	see *J. simplicifolium* subsp. *suavissimum*
§	***subhumile***	MOWG

Jatropha (*Euphorbiaceae*)

	cinerea	SPlb
	integerrima	CCCN
	multifida	SPlb

Jeffersonia (*Berberidaceae*)

	diphylla	CArn CBro CLAP EBee ECho EPPr EPri GBin GKev LAma LEdu LRHS MMoz MNrw NBir NChi WAbe WCru WThu
	dubia	CCon CLAP ECho EPot EWes LEdu LLHF LRHS MNrw NBir NHar NSla WAbe WCru WThu XEll
	- from Korea **new**	GKev
	- 'Alba'	WThu

jostaberry see *Ribes* × *culverwellii*

Jovellana (*Calceolariaceae*)

	punctata	CCCN CDoC CExl CMac EBee GCal IBlr SPlb
	- var. ***coerulea***	IBlr
	sinclairii	CExl CHll SMrm
	violacea ♀H2	CAbP CAbb CBcs CCCN CDoC CExl CHel CMac CPne CSde CTsd EPfP GCal IBlr IDee IMou IVic LRHS SArc SEle SMad SVen WPGP WSHC

Jovibarba ✿ (*Crassulaceae*)

§	***allionii***	CBod CMea CTri CWil EDAr EPot LBMP MHer MSCN WHal WHoo
	- 'Oki'	ECho LRHS SRms
	allionii × ***hirta***	CTal CWil MSCN SDys SFgr
§	***arenaria***	GAbr XLum
	- from Passo di Monte Croce Carnico, Italy	CWil
	'Autumn Fires'	MSCN
*	***echiniformis***	XLum
	'Emerald Spring'	SFgr
§	***heuffelii***	ECho LRHS XLum
	- 'Aiolos'	NHol
	- 'Almkroon'	NHol
	- 'Angel Wings'	CWil WHoo
	- 'Aquarius'	CWil
	- 'Be Mine'	CWil
	- 'Beacon Hill'	CWil
	- 'Belcore'	CWil XLum
	- 'Benjamin'	CWil
	- 'Bermuda'	CWil
	- 'Big Red'	NHol
	- 'Blaze'	CWil
	- 'Bolero' **new**	CWil
	- 'Brandaris'	SDys
	- 'Brocade'	MSCN NHol
	- 'Bronze Ingot'	CWil WCot
§	- 'Cherry Glow'	CWil
I	- 'Compacta'	CWil
	- 'Copper King'	CWil
	- 'Cover Girl'	CWil
	- 'Elmo's Fire'	CWil
	- 'Eos Moment' **new**	CWil
	- 'Fan Joy'	CWil
	- 'Fandango'	CWil MHom
	- 'Geronimo'	CWil NHol
	- 'Giuseppi Spiny'	MHom SPlb
	- var. ***glabra***	WHoo
	- - from Anaba Kanak, Bulgaria	CWil MHom NHol
	- - from Anthoborio, southern Caparthians	CWil
	- - from Haila, Montenegro/Kosovo	CWil SFgr
	- - from Jakupica, Macedonia	CWil
	- - from Ljuboten, Balkans	CWil

	– – from Ošljak, Albania	CWil
	– – from Pasina Glava, Macedonia	CWil
	– – from Rhodope, Bulgaria	CWil MHom
	– – from Treska Gorge, Macedonia	CWil
	– 'Gladiator'	CWil
	– 'Gold Rand'	NHol
	– 'Grand Slam'	CWil
	– 'Green Land'	CWil
	– 'Greenstone'	CWil MHom NHol
	– 'Harmony'	CWil NHol
	– 'Henry Correvon'	CWil
	– 'Hot Lips'	CWil
	– 'Idylle'	CWil
	– 'Ikaros'	NHol
	– 'Inferno'	CWil MHom
	– 'Ithaca'	NHol
	– 'Iuno'	CWil NHol
	– 'Jade'	CWil
I	– 'Jovi King'	CWil
	– 'King Sunny'	CWil
	– var. ***kopaonikensis***	CWil MHom
	– 'Lorelei' **new**	CWil
	– 'Lucky Bell'	CWil
	– 'Mary Ann'	MHom
	– 'Miller's Violet'	CWil
	– 'Mink'	CWil
	– 'Minuta'	CWil
	– 'Movie Star' **new**	CWil
	– 'Mystique'	CWil WHoo
	– 'Nannette'	CWil
	– 'Orion'	CTal CWil XLum
	– var. ***patens***	CWil
	– 'Pelister'	CWil
	– 'Pink Skies'	CWil
	– 'Pink Star'	CWil
	– 'Prisma'	CWil
	– 'Purple Haze'	XLum
	– 'Purple Heide' **new**	CWil
	– 'Red Rose'	CWil
	– 'Serenade'	CWil
	– 'Silex' **new**	CWil
	– 'Springael's Choice'	CWil
	– 'Sundancer'	CWil
	– 'Sungold'	NHol
	– 'Suntan'	CWil
	– 'Sylvan Memory'	CWil
	– 'Tan'	CWil
	– 'Tancredi'	CWil
	– 'Torrid Zone'	MBrN
	– 'Tuxedo'	CWil
	– 'Vesta'	CWil
	– 'Violet'	CWil SDys
	– 'Wotan'	CWil
	– 'Yodelheuff' **new**	CWil
§	***hirta***	CWil EDAr EUJe GAbr SFgr XLum
	– from Wintergraben, Austria	SPlb
	– 'Belansky Tatra'	CWil
§	– subsp. ***borealis***	CWil ESem
	– subsp. ***glabrescens*** from High Tatra, Slovakia/Poland	XLum
I	– 'Glauca'	SFgr
	– 'Hedgehog'	SFgr
	– var. ***neilreichii***	ECho LRHS MHom
	– 'Purpurea'	XLum
	– 'Rax'	SFgr
	preissiana	SFgr
§	***sobolifera***	CHEx EDAr GKev SFgr SPlb WHal XLum
	– 'Bronze Globe'	SFgr
	– 'Green Globe'	CTal ECho LRHS SDys SFgr
	– 'Miss Lorraine'	SFgr XLum

Jubaea (*Arecaceae*)

§	***chilensis***	CBcs CPHo LPal SBig SPlb WHor
	spectabilis	see *J. chilensis*

Juglans ✿ (*Juglandaceae*)

§	***ailanthifolia***	CBcs CMCN
	– B&SWJ 11026	WCru
	– var. ***cordiformis*** 'Brock' (F)	CAgr
	– – 'Campbell Cw3' (F)	CAgr
	– – 'Fodermaier' seedling	CAgr
	– – 'Rhodes' (F)	CAgr
	ailanthifolia × ***cinerea***	see *J.* × *bixbyi*
§	× ***bixbyi***	CAgr
	cinerea (F)	CBcs
	– 'Beckwith' (F)	CAgr
	– 'Booth' seedlings (F)	CAgr
	– 'Craxezy' (F)	CAgr
	– 'Kenworthy' seedling	CAgr
	– 'Myjoy' (F)	CAgr
	hindsii	EBtc
	mandshurica (F)	CBcs
	– B&SWJ 12550 from Korea **new**	WCru
	– BWJ 8097 from China	WCru
	– RWJ 9905 from Taiwan	WCru
	microcarpa	CMCN
	nigra (F) ♀H6	CAco CBcs CCVT CDul CHab CLnd CMCN CMac COtt CSBt CTho EBee ECrN ELan EPfP EPla GTwe LAst LRHS MAsh MBri MGos NWea SDea SEND SGol SPer WMou
	– 'Bicentennial' (F)	CAgr
	– 'Emma Kay' (F)	CAgr
	– 'Laciniata'	EPfP ERea GBin MBlu WPat
	– 'Purpurea'	ERea
	– 'Thomas' (F)	CAgr
	– 'Weschke' (F)	CAgr
	regia (F)	Widely available
	– 'Axel' (F)	CAgr
	– 'Broadview' (F) ♀H6	CAgr CDul CEnd CLnd CSBt CTho ELan EPla EPom ERea GQue GTwe IVic LBuc LRHS MBlu MBri MCoo MGos NOra NWea SCoo SDea SEWo SKee SPer SPoG SVic WHar
	– 'Buccaneer' (F) ♀H6	CAgr CDul CLnd CTho EPom GTwe NOra SDea SKee WHar
	– 'Chandler' (F)	CAgr
	– 'Corne du Périgord' (F)	CAgr
	– 'Excelsior of Taynton' (F)	CAgr CDul MCoo
	– 'Ferjean' (F)	CAgr
	– 'Fernette' PBR (F)	CAgr NOra WHar
	– 'Fernor' (F)	CAgr WHar
	– 'Franquette' (F)	CAgr GTwe MCoo NOra SPer WHar
	– 'Hansen' (F)	CAgr
	– 'Hartley' (F)	CAgr
	– 'Laciniata' ♀H6	CMCN WPat
	– 'Lara' (F)	CAgr GTwe NOra
	– 'Mayette' (F)	CAgr
	– 'Meylannaise' (F)	CAgr
	– number 16 (F)	CAgr WHar
	– 'Parisienne' (F)	CAgr SGol
	– 'Plovdivski' (F)	CAgr WHar

	- 'Proslavski' (F)	CAgr CDul WHar
	- 'Purpurea'	CMCN MBlu
	- 'Rita' (F)	CAgr LBuc
	- 'Ronde de Montignac' (F)	CAgr
	- 'Soleze' (F)	CAgr
	sieboldiana	see *J. ailanthifolia*

jujube see *Ziziphus jujuba*

Juncus (*Juncaceae*)

	from Crete new	SEND
	articulatus	LLWG XLum
	bulbosus	CNat
	capitatus new	WWEG
	conglomeratus	LLWG
	'Curly Gold Strike' (v)	LRHS MSKA
§	***decipiens*** 'Curly-wurly'	CBAq EPfP EPla LRHS NWad SWat
	- 'Spiralis'	see *J. decipiens* 'Curly-wurly'
	effusus	CBen CWat EHon MSKA NPer SWat WMAq XLum
	- 'Carman's Japanese'	CKno NSti
	- 'Gold Strike' (v)	EPPr LLWG
§	- f. ***spiralis***	CBAq CBen CRow CSpe CWat EHoe EHon ELan EPfP GKev GMaP LRHS MAsh MBri MJak NBir NOak NWsh SLim SPlb SPoG SVic WMAq XLum
§	- - 'Unicorn'[PBR]	EBee LBMP SPoG
	ensifolius	CBAq CBen CKno CRow CWat EBee EHoe EWay EWes MMHG MSKA MWts NPer NSti
	filiformis 'Spiralis'	GAbr LPot WWEG
	inflexus	CBen CWat EHon MMuc MSKA SEND SWat XLum
	- 'Afro'	CBod EBee MMuc NBro NOak NWsh SEND SPlb WWEG
	pallidus	EPPr GCal
	patens 'Carman's Gray'	CKno CWCL EPPr EPla GCal GQue LRHS MMoz NNor NOak NWad NWsh WMoo WWEG
	- 'Elk Blue'	CKno
	subnodulosus	LLWG
	'Swarm of Hedgehogs' new	WWEG
	'Unicorn'[PBR]	see *J. effusus* f. *spiralis* 'Unicorn'
	xiphioides	EHoe

Junellia (*Verbenaceae*)

	azorelloides	WAbe
§	***micrantha***	WAbe
	odonnellii	WAbe

Juniperus ✿ (*Cupressaceae*)

	chinensis	CMen
	- 'Aurea' 𝕐H6	CBcs CMac EHul
§	- 'Blaauw' 𝕐H6	CDoC CMac CMen EHul SGol
	- 'Blue Alps' 𝕐H6	CAco EHul LRHS MBri MGos MMuc NEgg SCob SCoo SEND SGol SLim
	- 'Densa Spartan'	see *J. chinensis* 'Spartan'
	- 'Echiniformis'	CKen
	- 'Expansa Aureospicata' (v)	CDoC EHul EPfP SEND
§	- 'Expansa Variegata' (v)	CDoC EHul EPfP SLim
	- 'Ferngold'	CDoC
	- 'Itoigawa'	CMen
§	- 'Kaizuka' 𝕐H6	EHul SGol
	- 'Kaizuka Variegata'	see *J. chinensis* 'Variegated Kaizuka'
	- 'Kuriwao Gold'	see *J.* × *pfitzeriana* 'Kuriwao Gold'
	- 'Obelisk'	EHul
	- 'Oblonga'	CDoC EHul
§	- 'Parsonsii'	WCFE
	- 'Plumosa Aurea' 𝕐H6	EHul
	- 'Plumosa Aureovariegata' (v)	CKen
	- 'Pyramidalis' 𝕐H6	CDoC EHul EPfP EPla MAsh MBri NPri SCoo
	- 'San José'	CMen EHul MAsh
§	- var. ***sargentii***	CMen
	- 'Shimpaku'	CKen CMen NLar
§	- 'Spartan'	EHul
	- 'Stricta'	CAco CSBt EHul LBee MGos SGol SLim
	- 'Sulphur Spray'	see *J.* × *pfitzeriana* 'Sulphur Spray'
	- 'Torulosa'	see *J. chinensis* 'Kaizuka'
§	- 'Variegated Kaizuka' (v)	EHul SCoo
	communis	CAco CArn CDul CHab EHul GPoy NWea SIde WAbe
	- (f)	SIde
	- 'Arnold'	CDul
	- 'Arnold Sentinel'	CKen
	- 'Barton'	NLar NWad
	- 'Barton Gem'	NWad
	- 'Brien'	CDoC CKen
	- 'Brynhyfryd Gold'	CKen SLim
	- 'Compressa' 𝕐H7	CBcs CDoC CKen CMac CSBt CTri EHul EPfP EPla EPot GEdr LAst LBee LRHS MAsh MBri MGos MJak NEgg NHol NWea SBod SLim SPer SPoG WIce WPat
§	- 'Constance Franklin' (v)	EHul
	- 'Corielagan'	CKen NLar
	- 'Cracovia'	CKen
	- var. ***depressa***	GPoy SEND SGol
	- 'Depressa Aurea'	CKen CSBt EHul LBee
	- 'Depressed Star'	EHul EPla MGos SPoG
	- 'Derrynane'	EHul
	- 'Effusa'	CKen
	- 'Gelb'	see *J. communis* 'Schneverdingen Goldmachangel'
	- 'Gold Cone'	CKen EHul ELan EPfP EPla EUJe LBee MAsh MBri MGos NLar SLim SPoG
	- 'Golden Showers'	see *J. communis* 'Schneverdingen Goldmachangel'
	- 'Goldschatz'	CKen EPla LAst NLar SLim SPoG
	- 'Green Carpet' 𝕐H7	CAco CDoC CKen EHul ELan EPfP EPla GKin LBuc LRHS MAsh MBri MGos NLar SCoo SLim SPoG WCFE
	- 'Haverbeck'	CKen
	- 'Hibernica' 𝕐H7	CDul CSBt EHul ELan EPfP LAst MGos MJak NLar NWea SLim SPer SPoG
	- 'Hibernica Aurea'	CMac
	- 'Hibernica Variegata'	see *J. communis* 'Constance Franklin'
	- 'Hornibrookii'	EHul NWea SRms
	- 'Horstmann'	NLar
I	- 'Horstmann's Pendula'	CDoC
	- 'Kenwith Castle'	CKen
	- 'Meyer'	GKin
	- 'Pyramidalis'	SPlb
	- 'Rakete'	IVic
	- 'Repanda' 𝕐H7	CAco CBcs CDoC CMac CSBt EAEE EHul EPfP EPla LAst MAsh MBri MGos NWea SCoo SGol SLim SPer SPoG
§	- 'Schneverdingen Goldmachangel'	EPla IBoy MAsh MBri MGos NLar SLim
	- 'Sentinel'	CDoC EHul SLim WCFE WMou
	- 'Sieben Steinhauser'	CKen NLar
	- 'Silver Mist'	CKen
	- 'Spotty Spreader' (v)	SLim
	- Suecica Group	EHul MGos NWea
	- - 'Suecica Aurea'	EHul

	- 'Zeal'	CKen
	conferta	see *J. rigida* subsp. *conferta*
	- var. ***maritima***	see *J. taxifolia*
	davurica	EHul
	- 'Expansa'	see *J. chinensis* 'Parsonsii'
	- 'Expansa Albopicta'	see *J. chinensis* 'Expansa Variegata'
	- 'Expansa Variegata'	see *J. chinensis* 'Expansa Variegata'
	- 'Leningrad'	LPot NLar
	foetidissima	CMen
	× ***gracilis*** 'Blaauw'	see *J. chinensis* 'Blaauw'
	'Grey Owl' ♀H7	CAco EHul ELan EPfP MMuc NWea SEND SGol SLim
	horizontalis	NWea
§	- 'Andorra Compact'	NLar
I	- 'Andorra Variegata' (v)	SCoo
	- 'Bar Harbor'	CMac EHul
§	- 'Blue Chip'	EHul ELan EPfP LBee MGos MJak NBir SCoo SLim SPer SPoG
	- 'Blue Moon'	see *J. horizontalis* 'Blue Chip'
	- 'Blue Rug'	see *J. horizontalis* 'Wiltonii'
	- 'Douglasii'	EHul
	- 'Emerald Spreader'	EHul ELan
	- Glauca Group	EHul NWea
	- 'Golden Carpet' ♀H7	ELan EPfP LBuc MGos NLar
	- 'Golden Spreader'	CDoC
	- 'Grey Pearl'	CKen EHul
	- 'Hughes'	CAco EHul LBee MBri MRav NWea
	- Icee Blue = 'Monber' ♀H7	CKen EPla GKin LRHS MAsh MBri NLar SLim SPoG
	- 'Jade River'	CAco EHul
	- 'Limeglow' ♀H7	CDoC CKen ELan EPfP EPla LAst MGos NLar SCoo SLim SPoG
	- 'Mother Lode'	CKen
	- 'Neumann'	CKen
	- 'Pancake' **new**	NLar
	- 'Plumosa Compacta'	see *J. horizontalis* 'Andorra Compact'
	- 'Prince of Wales'	EHul EPla MAsh MGos
	- 'Prostrata'	IBoy
	- 'Turquoise Spreader'	CSBt EHul MBri NWea SGol
	- 'Villa Marie'	CKen
§	- 'Wiltonii'	CDul EHul MGos NWea
	- 'Winter Blue'	LBee SLim
	- 'Youngstown'	EPla MBri SEND
	- 'Yukon Belle'	CKen
	× ***media***	see *J.* × *pfitzeriana*
§	× ***pfitzeriana***	CDul CMac SCob SGol
	- 'Arctic'	NLar
	- 'Armstrongii'	EHul
	- 'Blaauw'	see *J. chinensis* 'Blaauw'
	- 'Blue and Gold' (v)	CKen EHul SPoG
	- 'Blue Cloud'	see *J. virginiana* 'Blue Cloud'
§	- 'Carbery Gold' ♀H7	CBcs CDoC CDul CMac CSBt EHul EPla GKin LBee LRHS MAsh MBri MGos SCoo SLim SPoG
	- 'Gold Coast'	CDoC CKen CSBt EHul EPfP EPla LBee MBri MGos SGol SLim
	- Gold Sovereign = 'Blound'PBR	LBee MAsh MGos
	- 'Gold Star'	MBri
*	- 'Golden Joy'	SPoG
	- 'Goldkissen'	MGos
	- 'King of Spring'	SLim
§	- 'Kuriwao Gold'	CMac EHul GKin MBri MGos MMuc MRav NPri SCoo SEND SGol SPoG
	- 'Mint Julep'	CSBt EHul MGos MJak SCob SCoo SGol SLim
	- 'Old Gold' ♀H7	CDul EHul EPfP EPla GKin LBee MBri MGos MJak MMuc NEgg NPri NWea SCoo SEND SGol SLim SPlb WCFE WHar
	- 'Old Gold Carbery'	see *J.* × *pfitzeriana* 'Carbery Gold'
	- 'Pfitzeriana'	see *J.* × *pfitzeriana* 'Wilhelm Pfitzer'
	- 'Pfitzeriana Aurea'	CMac EHul EPfP MGos NWea SCob SGol
	- 'Pfitzeriana Compacta'	EHul
	- 'Pfitzeriana Glauca'	CAco EHul
§	- 'Sulphur Spray' ♀H7	CDul EHul MAsh MMuc SEND SGol SLim WCFE
§	- 'Wilhelm Pfitzer'	EHul EPfP NWea
§	***pingii*** 'Glassell'	CDoC MAsh NLar
	- 'Hulsdonk Yellow'PBR	MAsh NLar SPoG
§	- var. ***wilsonii***	CDoC CKen NLar
	procera	WPGP
	procumbens	NLar
	'Kishiogima' **new**	
	- 'Nana' ♀H7	CDoC CKen CMac CSBt EHul EPfP EPla LAst LBee LRHS MAsh MBri MGos MJak NEgg NHol NLar SCoo SGol SLim SPoG WCFE
	recurva	CDoC
	- 'Castlewellan'	CDoC NLar WHor
	- var. ***coxii***	CDoC CMac EHul NHol NLar SMad WCFE
§	- 'Densa'	CDoC CKen
	- 'Nana'	see *J. recurva* 'Densa'
	rigida	CMen
§	- subsp. ***conferta***	CMac MBri MGos SEND SGol
	- - 'All Gold' ♀H6	NLar SLim SPoG
*	- - 'Blue Ice'	CKen
	- - 'Blue Pacific'	CAco EHul MMuc NLar SGol SPoG
	- - 'Blue Tosho'	CDul NLar
	- - 'Emerald Sea'	EHul
	- - 'Schlager' ♀H6	MGos SLim SPoG
	- - 'Silver Mist'	CKen
	sabina	CArn NWea
§	- 'Blaue Donau'	EHul
	- Blue Danube	see *J. sabina* 'Blaue Donau'
	- 'Broadmoor'	EHul
	- 'Knap Hill'	see *J.* × *pfitzeriana* 'Wilhelm Pfitzer'
	- 'Mountaineer'	see *J. scopulorum* 'Mountaineer'
	- 'Rockery Gem'	EHul SLim
	- 'Skandia'	CKen
	- 'Tamariscifolia'	CBcs CDul EHul GKin LBee MAsh MGos MJak MMuc NWea SEND SGol SLim SPer SPoG WCFE
	- 'Variegata' (v)	EHul
	sargentii	see *J. chinensis* var. *sargentii*
	scopulorum 'Blue Arrow' ♀H7	CDoC CDul CKen CSBt CTho ELan EPfP EPla GKin IBoy LAst LBee MAsh MBri MGos MJak NEgg NHol NLar NSoo NWea SCoo SGol SLim SPer SPoG WHar WMou
	- 'Blue Banff'	CKen
	- 'Blue Heaven'	EHul
	- 'Blue Pyramid'	EHul
	- 'Moonglow'	EHul
§	- 'Mountaineer'	EHul
	- 'Silver Star' (v)	EHul
	- 'Skyrocket'	CBcs CCVT CDul CMac CSBt ECrN EHul EPfP GGal LAst MGos MJak MRav NWea SCob SEND SGol SPlb WCFE WHar WMou
	- 'Springbank'	EHul WCFE
	- 'Wichita Blue'	EHul EPfP IVic
§	***squamata*** CC 6278 **new**	GKev

	- 'Blue Carpet' ♀H7	CBcs CDoC CDul CKen CMac CSBt EHul EPfP EPla LAst LBuc LRHS MAsh MBri MGos MJak NEgg NHol NLar NPri NWea SCob SEND SGol SLim SPer SPoG WCFE WHar
	- 'Blue Star' ♀H7	CDoC CJun CKen CMac CSBt EHul ELan EPfP EPla EPot LAst LBee LRHS MAsh MBri MGos MJak NEgg NHol NLar NPri NWad NWea SGol SLim SPer SPoG WCFE
	- 'Blue Star Variegated'	see *J. squamata* 'Golden Flame'
	- 'Blue Swede'	see *J. squamata* 'Hunnetorp'
	- 'Chinese Silver'	EHul
	- 'Dream Joy'	CKen NLar NWad
	- var. ***fargesii***	see *J. squamata*
	- 'Filborna'	CKen LBee
	- 'Floreant' **new**	SLim
	- 'Glassell'	see *J. pingii* 'Glassell'
§	- 'Golden Flame' (v)	CKen
	- 'Holger' ♀H7	CDoC CDul CMac EHul EPfP EPla LAst LBee MAsh MBri MGos MJak NHol NLar SCoo SGol SLim SPoG WGor
§	- 'Hunnetorp'	MGos
	- 'Loderi'	see *J. pingii* var. *wilsonii*
	- 'Meyeri'	EHul MGos NWea SGol
	- 'Wilsonii'	see *J. pingii* var. *wilsonii*
§	***taxifolia***	CSBt
	virginiana	NWea
§	- 'Blue Cloud'	EHul SLim
	- 'Burkii'	EHul
	- 'Frosty Morn'	CKen EHul
	- 'Glauca'	EHul NWea
	- 'Golden Spring'	CKen
	- 'Helle'	see *J. chinensis* 'Spartan'
	- 'Hetzii'	EHul NLar NWea
	- 'Hillspire'	EHul
	- Silver Spreader = 'Mona'	CKen EHul
	- 'Sulphur Spray'	see *J.* × *pfitzeriana* 'Sulphur Spray'

Justicia (*Acanthaceae*)

	americana	LLWG
	aurea	EShb
§	***brandegeeana*** ♀H1b	CCCN MOWG
	- 'Lutea'	see *J. brandegeeana* 'Yellow Queen'
	- variegated (v)	EShb
§	- 'Yellow Queen'	EShb
	- yellow-flowered	EShb
§	***carnea***	CHll EBak EShb GCal MOWG WCot
	- 'Alba'	CCCN EShb
	- dark-leaved	CHll EShb WCot
	- 'Radiant'	SMad
	guttata	see *J. brandegeeana*
	'Penrhosiensis'	EShb
	pohliana	see *J. carnea*
	rizzinii ♀H1b	CBcs CCCN CHll SRot
	spicigera	EShb
	suberecta	see *Dicliptera sericea*

K

Kadsura (*Schisandraceae*)

coccinea B&SWJ 11793	WCru
heteroclita WWJ 11947 **new**	WCru
japonica	CBcs
- B&SWJ 1027	WCru
- from Japan	EPfP WSHC
- - B&SWJ 11109	WCru
- from Korea B&SWJ 4463	WCru
- 'Fukurin' (v)	NLar
- 'Variegata' (v)	CCCN EBee EPfP LRHS SEND WSHC
- white fruit	CBcs NLar

Kaempferia ✿ (*Zingiberaceae*)

rotunda	CCCN LAma

Kageneckia (*Rosaceae*)

oblonga	SPlb

Kalanchoe (*Crassulaceae*)

	beharensis ♀H1b	CCCN CDTJ EShb EUJe WCot
	- 'Fang' ♀H1b	CDTJ
	- 'Rusty'	CDTJ CSpe
§	***delagoensis***	CCCN EShb
	fedtschenkoi	EShb
	- 'Variegata' (v) **new**	WCot
	humilis	WCot
	laciniata	EShb
	orgyalis	EShb
	pinnata	EShb
	pubescens	EShb
	pumila ♀H1b	EShb SBch
	serrata **new**	EShb
	sexangularis	EShb
	'Tessa' ♀H1b	CDes WCot
	thyrsiflora 'Bronze Sculpture'	CAbb CHel EUJe
	tomentosa ♀H1b	EShb WCot
	tubiflora	see *K. delagoensis*

Kalimeris (*Asteraceae*)

§	***incisa***	MMuc MRav WBor
	- 'Alba'	ECha NLar WFar XLum
	- 'Blue Star'	ECha ECtt MSpe NLar WFar WPtf WSHC
	- 'Charlotte'	EWes MSpe NBre NDov
	- 'Madiva'	CSam EBee IMou LPla NDov
	- 'Nana Blue'	NDov
	integrifolia	MMuc
	'Mon Jardin'	WCot
§	***mongolica***	CAby CDes CMac ECGP ECha LPla MMuc SDix WFar WSHC
	- 'Antonia'	NDov WCot
	pinnatifida 'Hortensis'	ECtt
§	***yomena*** 'Shogun' (v)	CBod CPrp ECha ECtt EHoe ELan EPfP EPla LEdu MNrw MSpe NBir NLar NSti SMrm SPer WFar WWEG
	- 'Variegata'	see *K. yomena* 'Shogun'

Kalmia ✿ (*Ericaceae*)

	angustifolia ♀H4	SRms
	- f. ***rubra*** ♀H6	CBcs CDoC CDul EBee ELan EPfP IDee LRHS MAsh NLar NPri NSoo SPer
I	- 'Rubra Nana'	CMac
	latifolia	CBcs ELan EPfP LRHS LSou MGil MJak NPri NWea SPer SWvt
	- 'Bandeau'	GGGa
	- 'Bullseye'	LRHS NLar SPoG
	- 'Carousel'	CBcs CCCN NLar
	- 'Clementine Churchill'	CMac
	- 'Eskimo'	GGGa

- 'Freckles' ♀H6 EPfP MPkF NPCo SPoG
- 'Fresca' NPCo
- 'Galaxy' GGGa IVic LRHS
- 'Ginkona' GGGa
- 'Kaleidoscope' GGGa IVic MGos
- 'Minuet' CBcs CCCN CEnd EPfP GGGa IVic LRHS MLea NLar NPCo SLim SPoG SWvt
- 'Mitternacht' GGGa
- 'Moyland' GGGa
- f. ***myrtifolia*** LRHS
- - 'Elf' IVic LRHS MAsh MGos NLar SLim
- 'Nani' GGGa
- 'Nipmuck' MPkF
- 'Olympic Fire' ♀H6 CBcs CEnd GBin GGGa IVic LRHS NLar SLim SWvt
- 'Olympic Wedding' NLar SPoG
- 'Ostbo Red' CBcs CDoC CDul CEnd CMac EPfP GBin IVic LRHS MLea NPCo SPoG SSpi SWvt
- 'Peppermint' GGGa IVic SLim
- 'Pink Charm' ♀H6 IVic
- 'Pink Frost' NPCo
- 'Pinkobello' GGGa
- 'Pinwheel' LRHS NLar SLim SPoG
- 'Quinnipiac' MJak
- 'Sarah' LRHS MLea NPCo

§ ***microphylla*** WAbe
polifolia CBcs MJak NHar NSoo SPer WThu
- 'Glauca' see *K. microphylla*
- f. ***leucantha*** NHar WThu

× *Kalmiothamnus* (*Ericaceae*)

'Haytor' WAbe
ornithomma 'Cosdon' WAbe
'Sindelberg' WAbe

Kalopanax (*Araliaceae*)

pictus see *K. septemlobus*
§ ***septemlobus*** CBcs CDul ELan EPfP EUJe GBin LEdu MMuc NLar SEND SPtp
- var. ***magnificus*** B&SWJ 10900 WCru
- f. ***maximowiczii*** EPfP IVic MBlu NLar WCot

Keckiella (*Plantaginaceae*)

§ ***antirrhinoides*** SBrt
§ ***cordifolia*** SBrt

Keiskea (*Lamiaceae*)

japonica SBrt
- pink-flowered new SBrt

Kelleria (*Thymelaeaceae*)

dieffenbachii WThu

Kelseya (*Rosaceae*)

uniflora WAbe

Kennedia (*Papilionaceae*)

coccinea CCCN SVen
macrophylla CRHN
nigricans CCCN MOWG
prostrata SBrt SPlb
rubicunda CCCN CRHN MOWG

Kentia (*Arecaceae*)

belmoreana see *Howea belmoreana*
forsteriana see *Howea forsteriana*

Kentranthus see *Centranthus*

Kerria (*Rosaceae*)

japonica misapplied single see *K. japonica* 'Simplex'
japonica (L.) DC. (d) see *K. japonica* 'Pleniflora'
- 'Albescens' WCot
- 'Golden Guinea' ♀H5 CExl CMac ECtt ELan EPfP GGal IFro LRHS MAsh MGos MMuc MNrw MRav SCob SCoo SHil SPer SRms SWvt WFar
§ - 'Picta' (v) CDul CMac CTsd EBee ELan LRHS MGos MRav MSwo SCob SGol SLim SLon SPer SPoG SRms WFar WSHC
§ - 'Pleniflora' (d) ♀H5 Widely available
§ - 'Simplex' CExl CMac GGal NWea
- 'Variegata' see *K. japonica* 'Picta'

Khadia (*Aizoaceae*)

acutipetala CCCN

Kiggelaria (*Flacourtiaceae*)

africana new SVen

Kirengeshoma (*Hydrangeaceae*)

palmata Widely available
- Koreana Group ♀H7 Widely available

Kitaibela (*Malvaceae*)

vitifolia CExl CSpe ELan ETwe EWoo MPie NBid NPCo SEND SGSe SPav SPlb

Kitchingia see *Kalanchoe*

kiwi fruit see *Actinidia deliciosa*

Kleinia (*Asteraceae*)

articulata see *Senecio articulatus*
grantii CSpe WCot
repens see *Senecio serpens*

Knautia (*Caprifoliaceae*)

§ ***arvensis*** CArn CHab CWld EPfP EWoo LRHS MHer MNHC NLar NMir SEND SGSe SPer SPhx WHer WMoo WOut WSFF
- 'Rachael' CElw
- white-flowered SPhx
dipsacifolia SHar
'Jardin d'en Face' CBod EPfP LRHS
§ ***macedonica*** Widely available
- 'Crimson Cushion' CSpe ECtt LSou
- 'Mars Midget' CBod CExl CHll COtt CSpe EBee ELan ELon EPfP GQue IBoy LAst LBMP LRHS LSou MGos MLHP MSpe NLar NPri SCob SPad SPhx SPoG SWvt WFar WHoo WSHC
- Melton pastels CBod CExl COtt EBee ELan EPfP GJos IBoy LRHS MCot MGos NLar NPer SPer SPoG SRot SWat SWvt WFar
- pink-flowered CSam
- 'Red Knight' CBod EPfP LPal LRHS MBNS MCot MSCN SGSe SHil WCAu
- short ECtt
- tall, pale-flowered SPhx
- 'Thunder and Lightning' (v) CBct CBod CMea CWGN EBee ECtt EWes IBoy IKil LBMP LBuc LSou

	MAvo MHol MNrw MPie MRav NLar SPad SPer SPoG WCot WHil WWEG
sarajevensis	MAvo

Knightia (*Proteaceae*)

excelsa	CBcs

Kniphofia ✿ (*Asphodelaceae*)

'Ada'	ELon EWes SGSe
albescens	NLos SPlb XLum
'Alcazar'	CBcs CPrp ECtt ELon EPfP IBoy LPal MAvo MBri MHer NSoo SCob SGSe SPer SRkn SWvt WCAu WCFE WFar WMnd WWEG
'Ample Dwarf'	ECtt WCot
'Amsterdam'	MWat SHar
angustifolia	SPlb
'Apricot'	LRHS
'Apricot Souffle'	EPri SGSe WCot
'Atlanta'	LRHS SGSe
'Aurora'	XLum
'Barton Fever' 🏆H6	WCot
baurii	CExl SPlb
'Bees' Jubilee'	MAvo MNrw NChi
'Bees' Lemon'	Widely available
§ 'Bees' Sunset' 🏆H5	CAvo CDes CSam EBee ECha ECtt EPla GCra LPla LRHS MAvo MBel MNFA MNrw MSpe MWat NLar SGSe SMHy SWvt WAul WCot WWEG
'Bees' Yellow'	SBch
'Bitter Chocolate'	WCot
'Border Ballet'	CRos LBMP LRHS NBir NGdn NLar SWat WFar XLum
brachystachya	ELon GCal SPlb
'Bressingham Comet'	CRos ECtt LEdu LRHS MAvo NBir NCGa SHil WWEG
Bressingham Sunbeam = 'Bresun'	EBee ECtt LRHS NBir WWEG
'Bressingham Yellow'	ECtt
'Brimstone' Bloom 🏆H5	CElw CPrp ECtt EPPr EPfP EPla GBin LEdu LRHS MSpe NBir NPri SGSe SPtp SRkn SWvt WFar WGwG WMnd WWEG
bruceae	EPri SVen
'Buttercup' 🏆H5	CAvo WSHC
'Butterfly'	EBee
'Candlelight'	CCse EBee ECtt EPri MAvo SGSe WSHC
'Candlemass'	CTca
caulescens	Widely available
- 'Coral Breakers'	CExl CPrp CTca ECtt ELon GAbr GCal LRHS MAvo MHol MNFA NEgg NLos SDix SKHP SMad SPer SPoG WCot
- 'John May'	CAby CBod EBee ECtt ESwi GAbr LRHS MAvo MSCN SCob SMad WCot
- short	ECha
- 'Tiny Girl' **new**	ECtt
'Chichi'	MAvo WCot
'Christmas Cheer'	CDes
citrina	CCon GCra GLog IBoy LAst MBrN NGBl NLar NPri WCot WHar WHil XLum
'C.M. Prichard' misapplied	see *K. rooperi*
'C.M. Prichard' Prichard	WCot
'Cobra'	ECtt GBin GMaP LRHS MTis WAul WCot WHil
'Coral Flame' 🏆H5	EBee LRHS
'Coral Sceptre'	LPla WCot
'Creamsicle' (Popsicle Series)	ECtt WCot
'Dingaan'	CAbb EBee ECtt MBel MNrw MTis NBir NLar WCot
'Dorset Sentry'	CAbb CAby EBee ECtt ELon EPfP EWoo LRHS MBel MGos MNrw NBir NEgg NLar NOrc SGSe SKHP SMad SMrm WCot WFar WWEG
drepanophylla	MHer
'Drummore Apricot'	CMHG EAEE ECha ECtt ELan EPfP EWTr GBin GBuc IBoy LRHS MAvo MSpe NBir NEgg SPtp WCot WFar WGwG
'Early Buttercup'	CTca WFar
'Elvira'PBR **new**	ECtt
'Ember Glow' (Glow Series)	ECtt
ensifolia	CTca ECtt NGdn SVen WMnd XLum
'Erecta'	CTal
'Ernest Mitchell'	WCot
Express hybrids	XLum
'Fairyland'	NGBl
'Fiery Fred' 🏆H6	CPrp EBee ECGP ECtt ELon EPla GQue LRHS SBod SGSe SPtp WCot
'Fire Glow' **new**	CMos NCGa
'First Sunrise'PBR	ECtt LRHS MBri
'Flamenco'	ELon EWll LRHS NGdn NSir WRHF
'Flaming Torch'	ECtt
'Florence Bedecked'	WCot
foliosa Hochst.	LEdu
'Frances Victoria'	WCot
galpinii misapplied	see *K. triangularis* subsp. *triangularis*
galpinii Baker 🏆H4	MAvo
'Gilt Bronze'	WCot
'Gladness'	MAvo NBir SGSe WCot WWEG
'Gloire d'Orléans'	XLum
'Goldelse'	EBee LRHS NBir
'Goldfinch'	CCse CSam SGSe
gracilis	LEdu
'Grandiflora'	CMac MWhi WHar
'Green and Cream'	MAvo
'Green Goddess'	SGSe
'Green Jade'	Widely available
'H.E. Beale'	WCot
'Hen and Chickens'	EBee ECtt ESwi MTis SMad WCot
hirsuta	CCon EBee LRHS NLos WSHC
- JCA 3.461.900	SKHP
- 'Fire Dance'	CSde EPla LRHS LSun
- 'Traffic Lights'	WHar
'Ice Queen'	CAvo CCon EBee ECha ECtt ELon EPPr EPri EWoo GBin IPot MAvo MHer MNrw MRav MSpe MTis NChi NLar NSoo SEND SGSe SGol SMad SRms SWvt WCot WWEG
ichopensis	LEdu NLos SVen WPGP
'Innocence' 🏆H4	EPfP LRHS
'Jane Henry'	CDes EBee LEdu
'Jenny Bloom'	COtt CPrp CRos ECtt ELan ELon EPfP EWTr EWoo GBin GBuc GCal GMaP LAst LEdu LRHS MRav MWat NLar NSti SMrm SPtp WAul WCot WFar WWEG
'Jess's Delight'	WCot
'John Benary'	CPrp CRos EAEE EBee ECtt EPla GBin GLog GMaP IKil LLWG LRHS MAvo MBel MSpe NBir NEgg NGdn NLar SEND SMrm SPer SPtp WCot WGwG WKif

	Name	Suppliers
	'Jonathan' ♀H5	WCot
	laxiflora	EPri NLos WPGP
	'Lemon Popsicle' (Popsicle Series) new	LAst SCob
	'Light of the World'	see *K. triangularis* subsp. *triangularis* 'Light of the World'
	linearifolia	CExl CPrp EBee GCra NLos SPlb WCot XLum
	'Little Elf'	XLum
	'Little Maid'	Widely available
	'Little Red Rooster' new	EAEE
	littoralis	SGSe
	'Lord Roberts'	GCal MRav SGSe SMad WCot WPGP
	'Luna'	WCot
	macowanii	see *K. triangularis* subsp. *triangularis*
	'Maid of Orleans'	ELon
	'Mango Popsicle' (Popsicle Series)	CAbb ECtt LSou MBri NLar WCot WHlf
	'Mermaiden'	CCon CMHG CRos ECtt MAvo MNrw WCot
	'Minister Verschuur'	EBee ECtt GQue LRHS MBri
	'Modesta'	WSHC
	'Moonstone' ♀H5	CHVG ECtt GBin LLHF LLWG LPla LRHS LSun MNrw NSti WCot
	'Mount Etna'	WCot
	multiflora	CTca NLos
	- cream-flowered new	NLos
	- 'November Glory'	WCot
	- yellow/orange-flowered new	NLos
	'Nancy's Red'	Widely available
	nelsonii Mast.	see *K. triangularis* subsp. *triangularis*
	'New England'	EBee
§	'Nobilis' ♀H6	Widely available
	northiae ♀H4	CExl CHid CTca CTsd EBee ELan ELon EPri EUJe EWes GCal LEdu LRHS LSun MNrw NLos SArc SDix SEND SGSe SMad SPlb WCot WCru WPGP XLum
	- JCA 3.462.600	WCot
	'Old Court Seedling'	GGal SGSe
	'Orange Vanilla Popsicle' (Popsicle Series) new	CMos ECtt SCob SPad
§	'Painted Lady'	CSam CSde CTca CTri EBee ECtt GMaP LAst MAvo MHol MNrw NLar SMHy WCot
	'Papaya Popsicle' (Popsicle) Series	CWGN ECtt LSou MBri SCob
	parviflora	XLum
	pauciflora	WCot
	'Penny Rockets' ♀H6 new	LRHS
	'Percy's Pride'	Widely available
	'Pfitzeri'	SRms
	'Pineapple Popsicle' (Popsicle Series)	CAbb CWGN ECtt MBri NLar WHlf
	× ***praecox***	NLos SGSe
	'Primrose Upward' ♀H6	WCot
I	'Primulina' Bloom	EBee LRHS
	'Prince Igor' misapplied	see *K.* 'Nobilis'
	'Prince Igor' Prichard	ECtt MLHP NBir SGSe
	pumila	LLHF
	'Red Rocket'PBR	EBee EWoo IBoy MBri MNrw WCot
	'Rich Echoes' ♀H5	CAvo CWGN ECGP ECtt ELon ESwi GBin LEdu LLHF MAvo MHol MTis WCot WRHF
	ritualis	CExl SKHP WWEG
§	***rooperi*** ♀H5	Widely available
I	- 'Torchlight'	CPne
	'Rosea Superba'	EBee
	'Royal Castle'	CExl GMaP LRHS NBir NGdn NOrc SEND WFar WWEG XLum
	'Royal Standard' ♀H5	CBcs CBod CMac COtt CPrp ECtt ELan ELon EPfP EPla LRHS MBri NLar SCob SMrm SPer SPoG SPtp SWvt WFar WHil WMnd WWEG
	rufa Baker	LEdu MAvo
	'Safranvogel' ♀H4	EBee ECtt SGSe SMad WCot
	'Samuel's Sensation' misapplied	see *K.* 'Painted Lady'
	'Samuel's Sensation' Samuel ♀H5	CCon EBee ECtt LRHS LSun NLar SGSe SRGP WCot WWEG
	sarmentosa	CExl NLos SGSe SPlb SVen WCot XLum
	'Saturn'	MAvo
	'Scorched Corn'	MAvo MSpe WCot
	'Sherbet Lemon'	MNrw WCot
	'Shining Sceptre'	see *K.* 'Bees' Sunset'
	'Son of Notung'	IBlr
	'Springtime'	WCot
	'Star of Baden-Baden'	EBee IBlr NBir SEND SMad WCot WWEG
	Stark's early perpetual-flowering hybrids	XLum
	'Strawberries and Cream'	CBcs CMac CTsd CWCL EBee ECha ECtt ELon EWld GQue LAst LRHS SBod SGbt SHar SPer SWvt
	stricta	XLum
	'Sunningdale Yellow' ♀H6	CCse EAEE ECha ECtt GMaP MAvo MLHP SMHy SRms WWEG
	'Tawny King' ♀H5	Widely available
	'Tetbury Torch'PBR	CExl CMos CPrp CWGN EAEE EBee ECtt EPla GBin GQue LRHS MAvo MCot NLar SGSe SMrm SPtp WAul WWEG
	thomsonii	CExl GCal NGdn
	- 'Kichocheo'	GCal WCot
	- var. ***snowdenii*** misapplied	see *K. thomsonii* var. *thomsonii*
	- var. ***snowdenii*** ambig.	CCon CExl CPne WPGP XLum
§	- var. ***thomsonii*** (C.H.Wright) Marais	SMHy
	- - 'Stern's Trip' ♀H4	CDes
	'Timothy' ♀H5	Widely available
	'Toffee Nosed' ♀H5	Widely available
	'Torchbearer'	WCot
	'Torchlight' Wallace	SGSe
	triangularis	CBod EPla WFar XLum
§	- subsp. ***triangularis***	CBod CBro EPfP GBuc GCal LAst LRHS SPer SRms SVen SWat WCot WWEG XLum
§	- - 'Light of the World'	CAby CBcs CBod CTca EAEE ECtt GBin LAst LEdu MBel MHer NBir NLar SGSe SPer SPtp SWvt WCot WFar WGrn WWEG
	'Tuckii'	SRms
	typhoides	NBir NLos SPlb
	tysonii	SPlb XLum
	- subsp. ***tysonii*** new	NLos
	uvaria	CBod CPrp EBee LPal LRHS MJak NBir NLos NSoo SCob SPer SRms SVic WMnd XLum XSen
	'Vanilla'	CCon EWoo LRHS NLar SEND SGSe WWEG
	'Vesta'	EBee LRHS

'Victoria' Prichard SGSe
'Vincent Lepage' EBee NLar
'Wol's Red Seedling' CAby CBro CSam ECtt ELon EUJe EWoo GAbr GBin MCot MNFA MNrw NGdn NLar NSti SBch SEND SPoG WCot WGrn WHoo
'Wrexham Buttercup' ♀H6 CSam EBee ECtt ELan EPfP GAbr GMaP GQue LRHS LSun MCot MNrw NPri SCob SEND SGSe SMrm WCot WHal WHoo WWEG
'Yellow Cheer' WCot
'Yellow Hammer' CSam ECha SEND WHil
Slieve Donard

Knowltonia (*Ranunculaceae*)

filia CExl

Kochia see *Bassia*

Koeleria (*Poaceae*)

cristata misapplied see *K. macrantha*
glauca ECha EHoe EPPr EPfP EPla EShb GMaP LRHS MBNS MJak MWat MWhi NBro NGdn NWsh SCob SLim SMrm SPlb SWvt WFar WWEG
§ ***macrantha*** NLar XLum
pyramidata SMea XLum
vallesiana EHoe SMea
- 'Mountain Breeze' EPPr

Koelreuteria (*Sapindaceae*)

paniculata Widely available
- 'Coral Sun'PBR ♀H5 CExl CMHG ELan EPfP EPla EUJe LRHS MBlu MBri NLar SChF SPoG WCot WPat
- 'Fastigiata' CDul EBee EPfP EPla MBlu MBri SCoo WHar
- 'Rosseels' NLar
- 'September' EPfP

Kohleria (*Gesneriaceae*)

'Ampallang' WDib
'An's Nagging Macaws' WDib
'Brazil Gem' WDib
'Cybele' EABi WDib
'Dark Velvet' WDib
eriantha ♀H1c WDib
'Hcy's Jardin de Monet' **new** WDib
'Heartland's Blackberry Butterfly' WDib
hirsuta WDib
'Jester' ♀H1c EABi WDib
'Manchu' WDib
'Marquis de Sade' EABi
'Red Ryder' EABi
'Roundelay' **new** WDib
'Ruby Red' WDib
'Ryssiten' **new** EABi
'Silver Feather' WDib
§ 'Sunrise' WDib
'Sunshine' see *K.* 'Sunrise'
'Texas Rainbow' WDib
warscewiczii ♀H1c WDib

Kolkwitzia (*Caprifoliaceae*)

amabilis CExl CSBt CTri ECGP ELan EPfP NPCo NWea SGol SPlb SRms WCFE WHar WMoo WRHF

- Dream Catcher CMac EPfP MGos MRav NEoE NLar
= 'Maradco' WPat
- 'Pink Cloud' ♀H5 Widely available

Kosteletzkya (*Malvaceae*)

virginica MHol SPhx

kumquat see *Citrus japonica*

Kunzea (*Myrtaceae*)

ambigua EBee ECou MOWG SPlb
- pink-flowered ECou
- prostrate ECou
'Badja Carpet' SEle
baxteri CTre ECou MOWG
ericifolia SPlb
§ ***ericoides*** CTsd ECou
- 'Auckland' ECou
parvifolia SEle SPlb
pauciflora SPlb

L

Lablab (*Papilionaceae*)

§ ***purpureus*** LSou SHDw
- 'Ruby Moon' CSpe

+ *Laburnocytisus* (*Papilionaceae*)

'Adamii' CDul CMac EBee ECrN ELan EPfP EPla GBin IVic LAst MGos MPkF NLar SMad SPer

Laburnum ✿ (*Papilionaceae*)

alpinum NWea SPlb
§ - 'Pendulum' CAco CCVT CDul CLnd ELan EPla IDee MAsh MGos MRav SGol SLim SPer SPoG
§ ***anagyroides*** CAco CDul MMuc NWea SEND SRms
'Famous Walk' see *L.* × *watereri* 'Vossii'
vulgare see *L. anagyroides*
× ***watereri*** IBoy
§ - 'Vossii' ♀H6 Widely available

Lachenalia (*Asparagaceae*)

alba 'Nieuwoudtville' ECho
algoensis ECho
§ ***aloides*** CDoC CTal ECho GKev NRog SDeJ
- var. ***aurea*** ♀H2 ECho NRog SBch WCot
I - var. ***luteola*** ECho
- 'Nelsonii' ECho WCot
- 'Pearsonii' ECho GKev NRog
- var. ***quadricolor*** ♀H2 CPrp CTsd ECho NRog WCot
- var. ***vanzyliae*** ♀H2 NRog WCot
angelica 'Agterkop' ECho
anguinea ECho
arbuthnotiae 'Somerset West' ECho
attenuata ECho
bachmanii NRog
barkeriana ECho
bolusii ECho
§ ***bulbifera*** ♀H2 ECho WCot
- 'George' ♀H2 CTal ECho WCot
capensis ECho

carnosa	ECho
cernua 'Goudini'	ECho
comptonii	ECho
congesta 'Roggeveld'	ECho
contaminata ♀H2	CPrp ECho NRog WCot
doleritica	ECho
elegans	ECho
- var. ***membranacea***	ECho
- var. ***suaveolens***	ECho NRog
fistulosa	ECho
- 'Klein Drakenstein'	ECho
framesii	ECho
'Fransie' (African Beauty Series)	ECho
gillettii	ECho
glaucophylla	ECho
hirta	ECho
juncifolia	ECho NRog
- var. ***juncifolia***	ECho
kliprandensis new	NRog
- 'Kliprand'	ECho
* ***komsbergensis***	WCot
lactosa	ECho
latimerae	ECho
leipoldtii	ECho
'Lemon Ripple' (v)	WCot
liliiflora	CTal ECho NRog
longibracteata	ECho
longituba ♀H3	WCot
marginata	ECho
mathewsii	ECho NRog
maximilianii 'Cederberg'	ECho
mediana	ECho NRog
montana	ECho
muirii 'Bredasdorp'	ECho
multifolia	ECho
mutabilis	ECho WCot
'Namakwa' (African Beauty Series)	ECho NRog
namaquensis	ECho NRog
namibiensis	ECho
nardoubergensis	ECho
neilii	ECho
nervosa	ECho WCot
obscura	ECho WCot
orchioides var. ***glaucina***	CDes ECho NRog WCot
orthopetala	CDes ECho GKev NRog
pallida	ECho NRog
peersii 'Betty's Bay'	ECho
pendula	see *L. bulbifera*
polyphylla	ECho
polypodantha 'Varsputs'	ECho
purpureocoerulea 'Darling'	ECho
pusilla	ECho WCot
pustulata ♀H2	ECho NRog WCot
- blue-flowered	ECho GKev NRog
- 'Meerlust'	ECho
- yellow-flowered	ECho NRog
reflexa	ECho NRog
'Robijn' (African Beauty Series)	ECho
'Rolina' (African Beauty Series)	ECho
'Romaud' (African Beauty Series)	ECho NRog WCot
'Romelia' (African Beauty Series)	ECho WCot
'Ronina' (African Beauty Series)	CPrp ECho GKev NRog WCot
'Rosabeth' (African Beauty Series)	ECho NRog WCot
rosea	ECho NRog
rubida	CDes ECho WCot
'Rupert' (African Beauty Series) ♀H2	ECho GKev NRog WCot
salteri 'Elim'	ECho
splendida	ECho
stayneri	CLak
thomasiae	ECho
trichophylla	ECho
tricolor	see *L. aloides*
unicolor	ECho NRog WCot
unifolia	ECho NRog
variegata 'Mamre'	ECho
violacea	ECho WCot
- var. ***glauca***	ECho
viridiflora ♀H2	ECho NRog WCot
xerophila	ECho
youngii 'Humansdorp'	ECho
zebrina	ECho
- f. ***densiflora*** 'Tanqua'	ECho
zeyheri	ECho NRog WCot

Lactuca (*Asteraceae*)

alpina	see *Cicerbita alpina*
intricata	SIgm
perennis	CPom EPPr NLar WHer
virosa	CArn

Lagarostrobos (*Podocarpaceae*)

§ ***franklinii***	CBcs CDoC IDee WPGP
- 'Fota' (f)	WThu
- 'Picton Castle' (m)	WThu

Lagenaria (*Cucurbitaceae*)

siceraria 'Speckled Swan' new	SVic

Lagerstroemia (*Lythraceae*)

indica ♀H1c	CAco CBod CCCN CDul EPfP SEND SPlb SSpi SVen WSHC
- B&SWJ 12660	WCru
§ - 'Baton Rouge'	MGos
- 'Beverly'	see *L. indica* 'Baton Rouge'
- 'Cordon Bleu'	MGos
- Petite Pinkie = 'Monkie'	IDee
- 'Red Imperator'	CBcs SEND
- 'Rosea'	CBcs SEND
subcostata CWJ 12352	WCru
'Tuskegee' new	WPGP

Lagunaria (*Malvaceae*)

patersonii	CHll WPGP

Lagurus (*Poaceae*)

ovatus	CKno MJak SAdn

Lallemantia (*Lamiaceae*)

canescens	GEdr

Lamiastrum see *Lamium*

Lamium ✿ (*Lamiaceae*)

album	CArn CHab MWat NMir
- 'Friday' (v)	NBir WHer WWEG
armenum	WAbe

flexuosum EPPr
§ ***galeobdolon*** CArn CTri EPla EShb MHer SRms WHer WWtn
§ - 'Florentinum' (v) CMac EBee ECha ELan MMuc MRav SPer WWEG
- 'Hermann's Pride' CBod EBee EHoe ELan ELon EPfP EPla GMaP LBMP LRHS NBir NMir SMrm SPer SRms SWvt WAul WHoo WMoo WWEG XLum
- 'Kirkcudbright Dwarf' EBee EPPr EWes GBin NBre XLum
§ - 'Silberteppich' ECha MRav XLum
- 'Silver Angel' XLum
- Silver Carpet see *L. galeobdolon* 'Silberteppich'
- 'Variegatum' see *L. galeobdolon* 'Florentinum'
garganicum subsp. ***garganicum*** CCse CPom EWes LPla
- subsp. ***pictum*** see *L. garganicum* subsp. *striatum*
- subsp. ***reniforme*** see *L. garganicum* subsp. *striatum*
§ - subsp. ***striatum*** WAbe
(Lami Series) 'Lami Blush' **new** LRHS
- 'Lami Pink' **new** LRHS
luteum see *L. galeobdolon*
maculatum MCot MMuc NChi SRms WWtn
- 'Album' ELan EPfP EPla LRHS SHar SPer SRms WWtn
- 'Anne Greenaway' (v) CBod EWes MBri
§ - 'Aureum' CBod ECtt EHoe ELan SMrm SWvt XLum
- 'Beacon Silver' CMac COtt EBee ECha ECtt ELan EPfP LPot LRHS MGos MHer MLHP MSCN MWhi NBir SCob SPer SPlb SPoG SRGP SRms SWvt WHar WWEG XLum
- 'Brightstone Pearl' EBee EWes EWld
- 'Cannon's Gold' ECtt ELan EWes LPot SWvt WHil WMoo WWEG
- 'Chequers' ambig. EBee ELan EPla SPer
- 'Elisabeth de Haas' (v) EWes NBre
- 'Forncett Lustre' EWes
- 'Ghost' ECtt EPPr LBuc
- 'Gold Leaf' see *L. maculatum* 'Aureum'
- Golden Anniversary = 'Dellam'PBR (v) ECtt ELan LAst NBro SWvt
- 'Golden Nuggets' see *L. maculatum* 'Aureum'
- 'Golden Wedding' SRms
- 'Ickwell Beauty' (v) EBee WHil WWEG
- 'Margery Fish' SRms
- 'Moonglow' EBee
- 'Orchid Frost' CHid EBee ECtt EHoe ELon EPla EWll GQue LRHS
- Pink Chablis = 'Checkin'PBR CBod ELon LRHS MHol NLar
- 'Pink Nancy' MWat SMrm SWvt
- 'Pink Pearls' CSBt NLar SHar SMrm WHil WMoo WWEG
- 'Pink Pewter' EBee ECha ECtt EHoe ELan EPfP EPla EShb EWoo GMaP LRHS NLar SCob SPer SPlb SPoG WWEG
- 'Purple Winter' EPPr
- 'Red Nancy' CBod CFis ELan ELon LRHS MBri SWvt XLum
§ - 'Roseum' EBee ELan EPla MBri MCot MRav MWat NChi SPer WMoo XLum
- 'Shell Pink' see *L. maculatum* 'Roseum'
- 'Silver Shield' EWes
- 'Sterling Silver' CSam
- 'White Nancy' Widely available
- 'Wootton Pink' MHer NBir NLar SWvt
'Marshmallow' LBuc
orvala Widely available
- 'Album' CExl CLAP EBee ELan EPPr GBin LEdu LRHS NBir NLar SHar SMrm WHer
- pink-flowered CSpe
- 'Silva' CExl CLAP EPfP GBin LEdu LRHS WCot WSHC
purpureum CArn
sandrasicum WAbe

Lampranthus (*Aizoaceae*)

aberdeenensis see *Delosperma aberdeenense*
aurantiacus CBcs CHEx
'Bagdad' CHEx
blandus CBcs CCCN
'Blousey Pink' CHEx SVen
§ ***brownii*** CBcs CCCN ECho ELan EPfP LRHS SPlb WPnn
deltoides see *Oscularia deltoides*
edulis see *Carpobrotus edulis*
glaucus SEND
multiradiatus SEND
oscularis see *Oscularia deltoides*
'Pink' EUJe SPlb WPnn
purple-flowered EUJe SPlb
roseus CCCN CHEx ECho LRHS
'Salmon Pink' SPlb WPnn
'Shanklin' SPlb SVen
spectabilis CBcs CCCN CTri SArc WPnn
- orange-flowered CAbb EUJe SBod
- purple-flowered SPlb
- 'Tresco Apricot' CCCN ECho
- 'Tresco Brilliant' CCCN CHEx CHVG ELon MSCN SEND WPnn
- 'Tresco Fire' CAbb CCCN CDoC CExl ELon SPlb SVen
- 'Tresco Orange' CCCN WPnn
- 'Tresco Peach' CCCN CHEx
- 'Tresco Purple' CHEx CWCL
- 'Tresco Red' CCCN CHEx ELon EUJe SEND WPnn
- white-flowered CHEx SPlb SVen WPnn
- yellow-flowered SVen WPnn
stipulaceus SPlb
'Sugar Pink' CHEx

Lamprocapnos (*Papaveraceae*)

§ ***spectabilis*** ♀H7 Widely available
- 'Alba' ♀H7 Widely available
- 'Gold Heart'PBR CAby CBcs CBod CWCL CWGN EBee ECha ECtt EPfP ESwi IBoy ITim LBMP LRHS MBri MGos MHol MMHG MRav NLar NPri NSti SCob SGol SPoG WCot WFar WHil
- 'Valentine' CAby CBcs CBct CBod CBro CWCL ECtt ESwi GBin IBoy LBMP LPla LRHS MAsh MAvo MBel MBri MHol MPie MPro NDov NLar SCob SGol SHar SPoG STPC WCot
- 'White Heart' **new** GJos

Lamprothyrsus (*Poaceae*)

hieronymi CDPR 3096 EPPr
- RCB RA K2-2 CDes MAvo WCot WPGP

Lanaria (*Lanariaceae*)

lanata CLak

Lancea (*Phrymaceae*)

tibetica CPBP

Lantana ✿ (*Verbenaceae*)

'Calippo Tutti Frutti' ESwi EUJe LSou
camara CArn ELan EShb MSCN
- (Lucky Series) Lucky Peach = 'Balucpea' new SPoG
- - Lucky Pure Gold = 'Balucpure'PBR new SPoG
- - Lucky Red Flame = 'Balandimfla' LAst SPoG
- - Lucky Sunrise Rose = 'Balandrise'PBR LAst SPoG
- - Lucky White = 'Balucwite'PBR SPoG
- 'Mine d'Or' EUJe
- orange-flowered CCCN
- pink-flowered CCCN
- red-flowered CCCN
- white-flowered CCCN
'Miss Huff' new EBee
§ ***montevidensis*** CSam
sellowiana see *L. montevidensis*
'Spreading Sunset' MOWG

Lapageria ✿ (*Philesiaceae*)

rosea ♀H3 CBcs CCCN CExl CFil CPne CRHN CTsd EPfP SAdn SChF SWvt WPGP
- var. ***albiflora*** ♀H3 CPne CRHN SChF
- 'Flesh Pink' CExl CRHN

Lapeirousia (*Iridaceae*)

anceps ECho
corymbosa ECho
cruenta see *Freesia laxa*
divaricata ECho
fabricii 'Grey's Pass' ECho
fastigiata ECho
jacquinii 'Gilberg' ECho
laxa see *Freesia laxa*
montana 'Danielskuil' ECho
plicata 'Nieuwoudtville' ECho
pyramidalis 'Worcester' ECho

Lapiedra (*Amaryllidaceae*)

martinezii ECho

Lapsana (*Asteraceae*)

communis 'Inky' CNat

Larix ✿ (*Pinaceae*)

decidua CAco CBcs CCVT CDul CMen ECrN ELan EPfP MGos MMuc NEgg NWea SEND SPlb WHar WMou
- 'Corley' CKen
§ - var. ***decidua*** MJak
- 'Globus' SLim
- 'Horstmann Recurved' NLar NPCo SLim
- 'Krejci' NLar
- 'Little Bogle' CKen MAsh MBlu MGos NLar NPCo
- 'Nukwitz' new NLar
- 'Oberförster Karsten' CKen NLar
- 'Pendula' CBcs CMen
- 'Puli' ♀H7 CEnd MAsh MBlu NHol NLar SLim SPer SPoG
- 'Roman' new NLar
- 'Schwarzenburg' SLim
× ***eurolepis*** see *L.* × *marschlinsii*
europaea DC. see *L. decidua* var. *decidua*
gmelinii var. ***gmelinii*** CMen
- 'Tharandt' CKen SLim
§ ***kaempferi*** CAco CCVT CDul CLnd CMen ELan EPfP LBuc LPal NPCo NWea SCoo SEWo WMou
- 'Bambino' CKen
- 'Bingman' CKen
- 'Blue Ball' CKen NLar SLim
- 'Blue Dwarf' ♀H7 MAsh MBri MGos SLim
- 'Blue Rabbit' CKen NPCo
- 'Cruwys Morchard' CKen
- 'Cupido' SLim
- 'Diana' CEnd CKen CMen MAsh MGos NHol NLar NPCo SLim
- 'Elizabeth Rehder' CKen
- 'Grant Haddow' CKen
- 'Grey Green Dwarf' MAsh
- 'Grey Pearl' CKen MAsh NLar
- 'Hanna's Broom' SLim
- 'Hobbit' CKen
- 'Jakobsen' NLar
* - 'Jakobsen's Pyramid' CMen MAsh MGos
- 'Lobby Dosser' CMen NPCo
I - 'Nana' ♀H7 CKen CMen NHol NPCo SLim
I - 'Nana Prostrata' CKen
- 'Paper Lanterns' new NLar
- 'Pendula' CAco CEnd EBee EPfP SPoG
- 'Stiff Weeping' ♀H7 MGos MPkF NLar NPCo SLim
- 'Varley' CKen
- 'Wehlen' CKen
- 'Wolterdingen' CKen NLar SLim
laricina 'Arethusa Bog' CKen
- 'Bear Swamp' CKen SLim
- 'Bingman' CKen
- 'Hartwig Pine' CKen
- 'Newport Beauty' CKen
- 'Stubby' SLim
leptolepis see *L. kaempferi*
§ × ***marschlinsii*** CCVT MMuc NWea SEND
- 'Domino' CKen CMen NPCo SLim
- 'Gail' CKen
- 'Julie' CKen
- 'Snapewood Broom' SLim

Laser (*Apiaceae*)

trilobum NDov SPhx
- PAB 3382 LEdu

Laserpitium (*Apiaceae*)

latifolium EBee
§ ***siler*** CArn CSpe IMou MAvo NDov SMHy SPhx SPlb WSHC

Lasiagrostis see *Stipa*

Lasiospermum (*Asteraceae*)

bipinnatum SPlb

Lastreopsis (*Dryopteridaceae*)

hispida ESwi

Latania (*Arecaceae*)

loddigesii LPal

Lathraea (*Orobanchaceae*)

clandestina CAvo

Lathyrus ✿ (*Papilionaceae*)

	'Adorabel' **new**	MPet
§	***articulatus***	CSpe
§	***aureus***	CHid CLAP CPom CSpe GBin GBuc GCal GJos IFro MCot MHer MNrw NBid NBir NChi SBrt SKHP WAul WHal WHea WHil WWEG
	- 'Cally Variegated' (v)	GCal
	chilensis	LLHF
	chloranthus	SPav
	cirrhosus	EBee
	clymenum articulatus	see *L. articulatus*
	cyaneus misapplied	see *L. vernus*
	davidii	EWes LLHF SBrt WCot WSHC
	'Endeavour' **new**	MPet
	'Erewhon' **new**	CHid WHlf
	fremontii hort.	see *L. laxiflorus*
	grandiflorus ♀H7	CTri CUse EBee ECGP NChi NLar SDix SWat WCot
	heterophyllus	EBee SGSe
	incurvus	MPet SPhx
	inermis	see *L. laxiflorus*
	japonicus	GJos SPhx WCot
	subsp. ***maritimus***	
	latifolius ♀H7	CArn CRHN CSde ECrN EPfP LAst MBel MHol MWat MWhi NPer SPoG SRms SVic WBor WBrk WHer XLum
§	- 'Albus' ♀H7	CFlo CTri ELan SGSe SPav SRms WCot WKif XLum
	- 'Appleblossom' **new**	WCot
	- 'Blushing Bride'	CSpe WCot
	- deep pink-flowered	MHer
	- Pink Pearl	see *L. latifolius* 'Rosa Perle'
	- 'Red Pearl'	CBcs CFlo EBee ELan EPfP GAbr LBuc LRHS MBri MLHP MNHC MWat NLar NPri SEND SPav SPer SPlb SPoG SWvt WCot
§	- 'Rosa Perle' ♀H7	CBcs CFlo CTri EBee ECha LRHS MAvo MBri MLHP MNHC MRav NBir NLar NPer NPri SGSe SPer SWvt WMoo WWEG XLum
	- Weisse Perle	see *L. latifolius* 'White Pearl'
	- 'White Pearl' misapplied	see *L. latifolius* 'Albus'
§	- 'White Pearl' ♀H7	CBcs EBee ECha EPfP GAbr LRHS MAvo MBri MHer MLHP MRav NBir NLar NPer SPer SPoG SWvt XLum
§	***laxiflorus***	CDes CPom EBee MCot MMuc SEND WMoo WSHC
	linifolius	EBee NLar WCot WHfH
	montanus	GPoy
	nervosus	CSpe MCot SRms
	neurolobus	CPom
	niger	CFis CSpe CWCL EBee EWld GJos LEdu LSou MCot MHer MMHG WWEG
	nissolia	WSFF
	odoratus	SVic
	- 'Anniversary'	MCot
	- 'Beth Chatto'	MCot
	- 'Betty Maiden'	MCot
	- 'Blue Medley'	MCot
	- 'Burnished Bronze'	MCot
	- 'Charlie's Angel' ♀H2	MCot
	- 'Cupani'	SPhx
	- 'Dancing Queen'	MPet
	- 'Dark Passion'	MCot
	- 'Dawn'	MCot
	- 'Ethel Grace'	MCot
	- 'Evening Glow' ♀H2	MCot
	- 'First Lady' **new**	MPet
I	- 'Fragrantissima' (mixed) **new**	CHid
	- 'George Priestley'	MCot
	- 'Honey Pink'	MCot
	- 'Honeymoon' **new**	MCot
	- 'Jilly' ♀H2	MCot
	- 'Lord Nelson'	SPhx
	- 'Lucinda Jane'	MPet
	- 'Mammoth Mixed'	MPet
	- 'Marion'	MCot
	- 'Marti Caine' **new**	MCot
	- 'Matucana'	CSpe MWat
	- 'Midnight'	SPhx
	- 'Milly'	MCot
	- 'Misty Mountain'	MCot
	- 'Mollie Rilstone'	MCot
	- 'Mrs Bernard Jones' ♀H2	MCot
	- 'Mrs Collier'	SPhx
	- 'Promise'	MCot
	- 'Restormel'	MCot
	- 'Richard and Judy'	MCot
	- 'Tutankhamun's Pea'	WHfH
	- 'Wedding Day' ♀H2	MCot
	- 'White Frills'	SPhx
	- Winter Elegance Series	MPet
	odoratus* × *belinensis 'Erewhon'	MPet
	odoratus* × *belinensis 'Navy'	MPet
	palustris	LLWG SPlb
	pisiformis	EBee
	polyphyllus	MPet WCot
	pratensis	CHab EBee NMir WSFF
	pubescens	MPet
	roseus	EBee GCal WHea WSHC
	rotundifolius ♀H7	CHid GLog NSti SPhx WHoo WSHC
	- 'Tillyperone' ♀H7	EBee SPhx
	sativus	CHid CSpe ELan MCot
	- f. ***albus***	CHid CSpe
	splendens	SBrt
	subandinus	SPlb
	sylvestris	EBee GJos WBrk
	transsylvanicus	CPom EBee GBin SPhx
	tuberosus	CArn CHid EBee WCot WSHC
	'Tubro'	EBee
	venetus	EBee EWes GCal MNrw WSHC
§	***vernus*** ♀H5	Widely available
	- 'Albiflorus'	MNrw XEll
	- 'Alboroseus' ♀H5	CLAP CPla ELan EPfP GBuc GCal GCra IFro MNFA MNrw NBir NChi NLar SPhx SPoG SWat SWvt WCot WHoo
	- var. ***albus***	CLAP CMea CPom MNrw WCot
	- ***aurantiacus***	see *L. aureus*
	- 'Caeruleus'	CLAP ECGP MNFA WHoo
*	- 'Cyaneus'	SHar SWat WCot
	- 'Dama Emily' **new**	SHar
	- 'Dama Violetta' **new**	SHar
I	- 'Filifolius'	CSpe MMuc
	- 'Flaccidus'	CAby CFis MNFA MNrw SBrt WCot WKif
*	- 'Gracilis'	EBee LEdu NLar SHar
I	- 'Gracilis Alboroseus' **new**	SHar
	- 'Indigo Eyes'	CDes
	- 'Little Elf' **new**	SHar
	- 'Madelaine'	WCot

I	- 'Pendulus' **new**	SHar
	- purple-flowered	LRHS MMuc SEND
	- 'Rainbow'	CLAP EPfP LRHS MMHG
	- 'Rosenelfe'	CMea GBuc LBMP LEdu MHer SHar SMrm SPhx SPoG WCot WHal WHil WSHC
	- f. ***roseus***	ECha LRHS MMuc MRav NBir SEND SRms WBrk WCot
	- 'Spring Melody'	EBee MRav SHar WCot
	- 'Subtle Hints'	SHar WCot
	- 'Winter Blush' **new**	SHar

Laurelia (*Atherospermataceae*)

§	***sempervirens***	CBcs WPGP
	serrata	see *L. sempervirens*

Laureliopsis (*Atherospermataceae*)

	philippiana	IArd NLar WPGP

Laurentia see *Isotoma*

Laurus (*Lauraceae*)

§	***azorica***	CBcs
	canariensis	see *L. azorica*
	nobilis ♀H4	Widely available
	- f. ***angustifolia*** ♀H4	CMac CTsd IDee LRHS MBlu MHer MRav NLar SArc SCob SEND SPoG
	- 'Aurea' ♀H4	CBcs CDul CMac EBee ELan ELon EPfP LRHS MGos MHer MMuc NLar SCob SEND SLim SLon SMad SPer SPoG SWvt WMoo
	- 'Crispa'	MRav
	- variegated (v)	CMac SRms

Lavandula ✿ (*Lamiaceae*)

	'After Midnight'	see *L.* 'Avonview'
	'Alba'	see *L. angustifolia* 'Alba', *L.* × *intermedia* 'Alba'
	'Alba' ambig.	SIde SPer
	'Alexandra'PBR	MWat
§	***angustifolia***	CArn CCVT CUse CWSG EBee ELau ENfk EPfP GPoy LBuc LRHS MAsh MGos MHer MHol MWat NGdn NLar NPer NPri SDow SLim SPlb SPoG SVic XLum XSen
	- 'Alba' misapplied	see *L. angustifolia* 'Blue Mountain White'
§	- 'Alba'	ELan EPfP EPla EWoo GPoy GQue LBuc LRHS MHer MRav MSwo SCob SLon SPlb SVen WGwG WJek XSen
	- 'Alba Nana'	see *L. angustifolia* 'Nana Alba'
	- 'Arctic Snow'	CBcs CUse EPfP LRHS MBri MHer MSwo MWat NGdn NPri SDow SFai SHil SPoG SRms WLav
	- Aromatico Blue = 'Lablusa'PBR	LRHS
	- Aromatico Silver = 'Lasila'	LRHS
	- 'Ashdown Forest'	ENfk GQue LRHS MHer MLHP MNHC SAdn SBch SCob SDow SFai SPer SRms WHoo WJek WLav XSen
	- 'Babelle'	XSen
	- 'Backhouse Purple'	SDow XSen
	- 'Beechwood Blue' ♀H5	SCob SDow WLav
	- 'Belle Hélène'	XSen
	- 'Betty's Blue'	SDow XSen
	- Blue Cushion = 'Lavandula Schola'PBR	MAsh SFai SPoG WLav
	- Blue Ice = 'Dow3'PBR	ENfk EPla MNHC MWat NDov NLar NWad SDow SFai SGol SLim SRms WLav
	- 'Blue Lance'	MHol
	- 'Blue Mountain'	XSen
§	- 'Blue Mountain White'	SDow SHil WLav XSen
	- 'Blue Rider'	EAEE EPla LRHS NGdn WGwG WLav
	- Blue Scent = 'Syngablusc'	LRHS
§	- 'Bowles's Early'	WGwG XSen
	- 'Bowles's Grey'	see *L. angustifolia* 'Bowles's Early'
	- 'Bowles's Variety'	see *L. angustifolia* 'Bowles's Early'
	- 'Cedar Blue'	ELan ENfk MHer SDow SHDw SRms WGwG WJek WLav XSen
	- 'Coconut Ice'	WLav XSen
	- 'Compacta'	SDow WLav XSen
	- 'Dursley White' **new**	WLav
	- 'Dwarf Blue'	CBod EPfP SRms WFar XSen
	- 'Elizabeth'	CWCL SCob SDow SFai SPoG WLav XSen
	- 'Ellagance Ice'	CBod CUse CWSG LRHS SRms
	- 'Ellagance Purple'	CBod CUse LRHS SHil SRms
	- 'Ellagance Sky'	CUse LBMP LBuc LRHS SHil SRms
	- 'Folgate' ♀H5	CArn ECtt ENfk EPfP MHer MNHC NGdn SDow SGol SRms WHoo WJek WLav WMnd XSen
	- Garden Beauty = 'Lowmar'PBR (v)	LBuc LRHS NPri SPoG
	- Granny's Bouquet = 'Lavang38'	XSen
	- 'Havana' **new**	GBin
§	- 'Hidcote' ♀H5	Widely available
	- 'Hidcote Pink'	CUse CWCL LSou MHer MNHC MRav NGdn SCob SDow SPer SRms SWat WMnd XSen
	- 'Hidcote Superior'	LBMP LSun NGdn
	- 'Imperial Gem' ♀H5	Widely available
	- 'Jean Davis'	see *L. angustifolia* 'Rosea'
	- 'Lady'	LRHS NPer
	- 'Lady Ann'	CWCL SDow WLav XSen
	- 'Lavenite Petite'PBR	LBMP LLHF LRHS NLar SDow SFai SPoG WLav
	- Little Lady = 'Batlad' ♀H5	CMea CUse EBee ECtt EPla EWTr LAst LBMP LRHS MAsh MBri MSwo NLar SFai SGol SRms SWvt WHoo WLav
	- Little Lottie = 'Clarmo' ♀H5	CWCL GQue MHer SDow SWvt WLav XSen
	- 'Loddon Blue'	EPfP GQue LRHS MAsh SDow SFai SHil SRms WLav XSen
§	- 'Loddon Pink'	ELan EPfP GMaP LRHS MAsh MBri MMuc MNHC MRav NGdn SEND SFai SHil SRms WLav XSen
	- 'Luberon'	XSen
	- 'Lullaby Blue'	SDow XSen
	- 'Lumières des Alpes'	XSen
	- 'Maillette'	NGdn SDow WLav XSen
	- 'Matheronne'	XSen
	- 'Melissa' **new**	XSen
	- Melissa Lilac = 'Dow4'PBR	CBcs CSBt CUse ENfk EPla EWTr LBMP LRHS MBri MGos MHer MNHC NLar NWad SDow SFai SHil SRkn SRms WLav
	- 'Middachten'	XSen
	- 'Miss Dawnderry' **new**	SDow
	- 'Miss Donnington'	see *L. angustifolia* 'Bowles's Early'
	- 'Miss Katherine'PBR ♀H5	CWCL ECtt EPfP LRHS MAsh NLar SDow SPoG WLav
	- Miss Muffet = 'Scholmis' ♀H5	LLHF SBch SDow SRms WLav XSen

	Name	Suppliers
	– 'Mont Ventoux'	XSen
	– 'Montagne de Lure'	XSen
	– 'Munstead'	Widely available
§	– 'Nana Alba' 🏆^{H5}	CArn ECha ELan ENfk EPfP GMaP GPoy LRHS MAsh MHer MWat SBch SDow SPer SRms SWvt WHoo WJek XSen
	– 'Nana Atropurpurea'	SDow XSen
	– 'Nikita'	XSen
	– 'No 9'	SDow XSen
	– 'Pacific Blue'	LRHS MBri SHil XSen
	– 'Perle de Rosée'	XSen
	– 'Peter Pan'	ECtt EPla GBuc LRHS MHer NGdn NWad SBch SDow WLav XSen
	– 'Princess Blue'	LRHS MAsh MWat WLav XSen
§	– 'Rosea'	Widely available
	– 'Royal Purple'	CBcs EWes GQue LSou MWat NGdn SDow SFai SWvt WLav XSen
	– 'Royal Velvet'	SDow XSen
	– 'Saint Jean'	SDow XSen
	– 'Siesta'	SFai XSen
	– 'Silver Blue'	XSen
	– 'Silver Mist'	CBod CMea EPfP LRHS SRms WHer
	– 'Sophie'	SFai
	– 'Thumbelina Leigh'^{PBR}	LBMP SDow SFai
	– 'Twickel Purple'	CBcs CWCL EBee ELan ENfk EPfP EPla LBMP LRHS MNHC NGdn SBod SCob SDow SFai SPer SRms SWat SWvt WGwG WLav XSen
	– 'Walberton's Silver Edge'	see *L.* × *intermedia* Walberton's Silver Edge
	aristibracteata	MHer WLav
§	'Avonview'	MHer SDow WHoo WLav
	'Ballerina' 🏆^{H4}	CWCL LRHS SDow
§	'Bee Brilliant'^{PBR}	ENfk WLav
§	'Bee Cool'^{PBR}	ENfk MHer WLav
§	'Bee Happy'	CWCL ENfk NBir WJek WLav
§	'Bee Pretty'	ENfk
	'Bella Zealand' (Bella Series) **new**	LRHS
	'Blue Star'	CUse EPfP MNHC NGdn NSir SHil
	'Bowers Beauty'	LRHS
	buchii var. ***buchii***	SDow SVen WLav
	'Bulls Cross'	WLav
	canariensis	MHer SDow SVen WLav
	× ***chaytoriae*** 'Gorgeous'	SDow
	– 'Joan Head'	XSen
	– 'Molton Silver' **new**	XSen
	– 'Richard Gray' 🏆^{H4}	CArn MHer MNHC SDow SIgm SLim SRms WLav WMnd XSen
§	– 'Sawyers' 🏆^{H4}	CBod CEnd CWSG ELau EPfP EPla EWTr GMaP LRHS MBri MCot MHer MNHC MRav MWat NBir NEgg NPer SDow SEND SFai SHil SLim SPer SPhx SPoG SRms WJek XSen
	– 'Silver Sands'	EPfP LBMP LRHS LSou SFai SPoG
	× ***christiana***	CArn LRHS NLar NPri SDow SFai SHDw SVen WJek WLav
	'Coco Deep White on Rose' (Coco Series) **new**	LRHS
	'Cornard Blue'	see *L.* × *chaytoriae* 'Sawyers'
	Crème Brûlée = 'Lavsts10' **new**	LRHS
	dentata	CUse ELan ENfk GPoy MNHC SBod SEND SRms WJek XSen
§	– var. ***candicans***	MHer MNHC SDow SRms WJek WLav XSen
	– var. ***dentata*** 'Dusky Maiden'	LRHS SDow WLav
	– – 'Ploughman's Blue'	SVen
	– – f. ***rosea***	SDow
	– – 'Royal Crown' 🏆^{H3}	MHer WLav
	– – Serenity = 'Lavden123'^{PBR}	LRHS
	– 'Harmony' **new**	LRHS
	– silver-leaved	see *L. dentata* var. *candicans*
	'Devonshire Compact'	CSBt CTsd CUse SRms WJek
	'Devonshire Compact White'	CUse LRHS
	'Fathead'	CBcs CWCL EBee ECtt ELan EPfP LRHS LSou MGos MHer MNHC MWat NBir NGdn NLar NPri SCob SCoo SDow SFai SGol SLim SPoG WJek WLav
	'Flaming Purple'	SDow XSen
	× ***ginginsii*** 'Goodwin Creek Grey' 🏆^{H4}	MHer SDow SGol SRms WGwG WLav XSen
	'Hazel'	EPfP LRHS
	'Heavenly Blue'	EPfP
	'Helmsdale'^{PBR}	CEnd CSBt CWCL CWSG ELan EPfP GAbr GBin GMaP IKil LRHS LSou MAsh MHer MRav MWat NGdn NLar SCob SCoo SFai SGol SLim SPer WJek
	heterophylla misapplied	see *L.* × *heterophylla* Viv. Gaston Allard Group
§	× ***heterophylla*** Viv. Gaston Allard Group	WLav
	– – 'African Pride'	SVen
	'Hidcote Blue'	see *L. angustifolia* 'Hidcote'
§	× ***intermedia***	CAco
	– 'Abrialii'	SDow XSen
§	– 'Alba' 🏆^{H5}	CMea EPfP MHer MMuc MNHC SCob SEND SVen WKif XSen
	– 'Arabian Night'	see *L.* × *intermedia* 'Impress Purple', 'Sussex'
	– 'Arabian Night' ambig.	SRms
§	– Dutch Group	CSBt ENfk EPfP EPla LRHS MNHC MRav MSwo MWat SCoo SDow SFai SLim SPer SPoG SRms SWat XSen
	– 'Edelweiss'	CBod CSBt ENfk EPfP LRHS MNHC MRav NEgg NGdn SCob SDow SFai SGol SPer SPoG SRms SWvt WLav XSen
	– 'Fragrant Memories'	EPfP SDow SIde WLav XSen
	– 'Fred Boutin'	SGol
*	– 'Futura'	XSen
	– Goldburg = 'Burgoldeen' (v)	MBri MWat
	– 'Grappenhall' misapplied	see *L.* × *intermedia* 'Pale Pretender'
	– 'Grey Hedge'	WLav
	– 'Gros Bleu'	SDow WLav XSen
	– 'Grosse Séguret' **new**	LRHS
	– 'Grosso'	CArn CCVT CSBt EAEE ECrN ELan ENfk EPfP GMaP MHer MMuc MNHC NLar SCob SCoo SDow SEND SFai SGol SPer SRms SWvt WHfH WJek WLav XSen
	– 'Hidcote Giant' 🏆^{H5}	CArn EPfP EWTr GCal LRHS MBri NPer SDow SHil WKif WLav XSen
§	– 'Impress Purple'	SDow WLav XSen
	– 'Jaubert'	XSen
	– 'Julien'	XSen
	– 'Lullingstone Castle'	ENfk SDow SRms WJek WLav
	– 'Nizza'	XSen

- 'Old English' misapplied see *L.* × *intermedia* 'Seal'
- 'Old English' CBod ENfk SDow
- Old English Group CArn ELau MMuc MNHC SEND WHoo WJek WLav XSen
- 'Olympia' **new** SDow
§ - 'Pale Pretender' CBod CSBt GQue MHer MRav MSwo SDow SPer SRms WJek XSen
- 'Provence' SDow XSen
§ - 'Seal' CArn ENfk GMaP MNHC SCob SDow SRms WJek XSen
- 'Sumian' XSen
- 'Super' XSen
§ - 'Sussex' ♀H5 CBod CFis EPfP LBuc LRHS SDow WLav XSen
- 'Twickel Purple' ECtt ELan EPla EWes NLar SGol SWat WJek
§ - Walberton's Silver Edge = 'Walvera' (v) CSBt EPfP LBuc LRHS MBri MGos MWat SCoo SDow SFai SPoG SRms XSen
'Jamboree' WLav
'Jean Davis' see *L. angustifolia* 'Rosea'
lanata ♀H3 CArn ECha GPoy SRms WJek WLav
§ ***latifolia*** CArn XSen
'Loddon Pink' see *L. angustifolia* 'Loddon Pink'
'Madrid Blue' see *L.* 'Bee Happy'
'Madrid Pink' see *L.* 'Bee Pretty'
'Madrid Purple'[PBR] see *L.* 'Bee Brilliant'
'Madrid White'[PBR] see *L.* 'Bee Cool'
'Marshwood'[PBR] CTri SLim
minutolii SDow
multifida MHer WLav
officinalis see *L. angustifolia*
Passionné = 'Lavsts 08'[PBR] ♀H4 CWSG WLav
pedunculata CUse XSen
- subsp. ***lusitanica*** SHil
§ - subsp. ***pedunculata*** CUse ECha ECrN ECtt EPfP LAst LPot LRHS MAsh MGos MHer MJak MMuc MNHC MSwo MWat NGdn NWea SCob SDow SEND SFai SGol SLim SPer SPoG SRms SWat WJek
- - 'James Compton' ♀H3 ECha LRHS MAsh NGdn
- - 'Wine' CBcs
- subsp. ***sampaiana*** 'Purple Emperor' EPfP LRHS MBri SHil WLav
pinnata CUse ENfk EPfP LRHS MHer MNHC SDow
'Pretty Polly' ♀H4 CAbP CBcs EPfP LRHS SDow SFai SRkn WLav
'Pukehou' EPfP SCoo SDow WLav
'Regal Splendour'[PBR] CSBt CUse CWCL ECtt ELan EPfP LRHS MAsh MBri MGos MHer MNHC NPri SCob SCoo SDow SFai SGol SHil SLim SPoG SRms WLav
Rocky Road = 'Fair09'[PBR] CUse NGdn SFai WLav
'Rosea' see *L. angustifolia* 'Rosea'
rotundifolia SDow WHil
'Roxlea Park' CWCL
'Saint Brelade' EPfP LRHS
'Silver Edge' see *L.* × *intermedia* Walberton's Silver Edge
Silver Sands = 'Fair 14' EWoo
'Somerset Mist' WLav
spica nom. rejic. see *L. angustifolia*, *L. latifolia*, *L.* × *intermedia*
- 'Hidcote Purple' see *L. angustifolia* 'Hidcote'
stoechas CArn CBcs CBod CDul CMea CSBt CUse ECha ELan ELau EPfP GMaP GPoy LBMP LPal LRHS MBri MNHC MRav MSwo SCob SDow SFai SIgm SPer SPlb SWvt WHar WMnd
- var. ***albiflora*** see *L. stoechas* subsp. *stoechas* f. *leucantha*
- 'Anouk'[PBR] EBee ELan EPfP LRHS NGdn SPoG
- 'Antibes' (Provençal Series) LBMP LRHS SRms
- 'Avignon' (Provençal Series) SRms
- (Bella Series) 'Bella Lavender' **new** SHil
- - 'Bella Peach' **new** SHil
- - Bella Rose = 'Belros' LRHS SHil
- - Bella Rouge = 'Belrou' LRHS
- blue-flowered **new** LRHS
- 'Bouquet of Roses' **new** LRHS SHil
- 'Boysenberry Ruffles'[PBR] (Ruffles Series) LRHS
- Castilliano Violet **new** CBod
- (Coco Series) 'Coco Deep Pink' SHil
- - 'Coco Deep White on Blue' SHil
- 'Dark Royalty'[PBR] **new** ELan
- deep purple-flowered **new** LRHS
- deep rose-flowered **new** LRHS
- 'Early Summer'[PBR] **new** LRHS
- 'Lace' WLav
- Lilac Wings = 'Prolil'[PBR] EPfP LLHF LRHS MBri NLar SCoo SFai SHil WLav
- (Little Bee Series) Little Bee Deep Purple = 'Florvendula Deep Purple' LRHS
- - Little Bee Deep Rose LRHS
- - Little Bee Lilac = 'Florvendula Lilac' LRHS
- subsp. ***luisieri*** 'Tickled Pink'[PBR] CWCL
- 'Night of Passion' LRHS SDow
- 'Papillon' see *L. pedunculata* subsp. *pedunculata*
- subsp. ***pedunculata*** see *L. pedunculata* subsp. *pedunculata*
- 'Purley' SRms
- 'Raspberry Ruffles' (Ruffles Series) MWat
- Ruffles Series ENfk
- 'Silver Anouk'[PBR] CBod EPfP LRHS
§ - subsp. ***stoechas*** f. ***leucantha*** CWCL EPfP LRHS MSwo MWat SCob SDow SHil
- - - 'Snowman' CBcs CSBt EPfP LRHS MAsh MHer MWat SCoo SFai SLim SPoG SWvt
- - 'Provençal' LRHS MBri MGos SCoo SHil
- - 'Purple Wings' EPfP LRHS LSou MAsh MGos SFai SLim
- - f. ***rosea*** WHil
- - - 'Kew Red' CBcs CTri CWCL ECrN ENfk LBMP LRHS MGos MHer MNHC SDow SFai SLim SRms SWvt WGwG WHar WJek WLav
- 'Sugarberry Ruffles'[PBR] (Ruffles Series) ENfk
- 'Victory' LRHS MBri MGos SHil SPoG
- 'With Love'[PBR] SDow
Tiara = 'Fair 10'[PBR] CSBt CUse CWSG ENfk LRHS MBri MGos MWat NLar NPri SCoo SDow SFai SHil SLim SRms WLav
'Van Gogh' SDow

vera misapplied	see *L.* × *intermedia* Dutch Group
vera DC.	see *L. angustifolia*
viridis	CArn CPla ELan ELau EPfP LRHS MHer NPer SDow SRms WAbe WJek WLav
'Whero Iti'	SDow XSen
'Willow Vale' ♀H3	EPfP LBMP LBuc LRHS MAsh MHer SDow SFai SRms SWvt WJek

Lavatera (*Malvaceae*)

arborea	CArn SChr SEND WHer
- 'Rosea'	see *L.* × *clementii* 'Rosea'
- 'Variegata' (v)	ELan NPer SDix SEND WCot
bicolor	see *L. maritima*
cachemiriana	NBir NPer SPhx
Chamallow = 'Inovera' PBR	EPfP LBuc LRHS SPoG
× ***clementii*** 'Barnsley'	Widely available
- 'Barnsley Baby'	EBee LBMP LBuc LRHS MBri MSCN MWat NGdn NLar NPer NPri SHil SPer SRkn SWvt
- 'Blushing Bride'	CDoC EPfP LRHS MBri MGos NLar SEND SPer SWvt
- 'Bredon Springs' ♀H5	CDoC CDul COtt CSBt CWSG ECha ELon EPfP LRHS MAsh MGos MMuc MSwo MWat NGdn NLar SEND SGol SLim SPer SWvt WHar
- 'Burgundy Wine' ♀H5	CBcs COtt EBee ELan EPfP EUJe LBMP LRHS MAsh MBri MGos MJak MSwo MWat NBir NEgg NGdn NLar NPer NPri SGbt SHil SLim SLon SPer SPoG SWvt WFar WHar
- 'Candy Floss' ♀H5	LBuc LRHS MAsh NBir NLar NPer SGol
- 'Kew Rose'	CDoC COtt LRHS MMuc MSwo NPer SEND SLim SRms XLum
- 'Lavender Lady'	NPer SEND
- 'Lisanne'	LRHS MSwo SGol
- 'Mary Hope' ♀H5	EPfP LRHS MAsh MBri MGos SEle SHil SWvt
- Memories = 'Stelav'	LRHS NLar
- 'Pavlova'	CExl
§ - 'Rosea' ♀H5	CAco CBcs CDul CMac CNec CWSG EBee ECrN EPfP LAst LBMP LRHS MAsh MGos MWat NBir NEgg NHol NPri NSoo SCob SGbt SGol SHil SLon SPer SPoG SWvt WHar
§ - 'Wembdon Variegated' (v)	NPer
'Frederique' **new**	CMac LRHS SWvt
'Magenta Magic' **new**	SPoG
§ ***maritima*** ♀H3	CAbP CDoC CExl CMac CNec CSde ELan EPfP LRHS NPri SEND SRkn SWvt WFar WKif WSHC
- 'Princesse de Lignes'	XLum
olbia	SPlb SRms WFar XSen
- 'Eye Catcher'	COtt CSBt IVic LRHS MSwo NLar SPer WHar
- 'Lilac Lady'	EBee ECha ECrN ELan LRHS MGos NSoo SLim SPer WFar WHar WKif
§ - 'Pink Frills'	SWvt WCot WFar
'Peppermint Ice'	see *L. thuringiaca* 'Ice Cool'
'Pink Frills'	see *L. olbia* 'Pink Frills'
'Rosea'	see *L.* × *clementii* 'Rosea'
'Sweet Dreams' PBR	LSou NLar NSoo
thuringiaca	GCal NNor
- 'First Light'	GCal MPie MSpe SPhx
§ - 'Ice Cool'	SCob SWvt WKif
- Red Rum = 'Rigrum' PBR ♀H5	CMac COtt CSBt EPfP LBuc LLHF MGos MHol NEgg NLar NPri SCob SEND SHar SLim SPoG SWvt WFar
'Variegata'	see *L.* × *clementii* 'Wembdon Variegated'
'White Angel' PBR	GBin NLar
'White Satin' PBR	LBuc LRHS NHol NLar

Lecanthus (*Urticaceae*)

peduncularis	CHEx

Ledebouria (*Asparagaceae*)

adlamii	see *L. cooperi*
concolor misapplied	see *L. socialis*
§ ***cooperi***	CTal ECho EPri GKev LEdu LRHS SBch WBor WPGP
ovalifolia	ECho
§ ***socialis***	ECho LEdu LToo MCot SBch
violacea	see *L. socialis*

Ledum see *Rhododendron*

Leiophyllum (*Ericaceae*)

buxifolium ♀H5	EPfP NLar WThu
- subsp. ***hugeri***	GBin
- 'Maryfield'	WAbe

Lembotropis see *Cytisus*

Lemna (*Araceae*)

gibba	NPer
minor	CWat MSKA NPer SWat
polyrrhiza	see *Spirodela polyrrhiza*
trisulca	CWat EHon EWay MSKA NPer SWat

lemon see *Citrus* × *limon*

lemon, rough see *Citrus* × *taitensis*

lemon balm see *Melissa officinalis*

lemon grass see *Cymbopogon citratus*

lemon verbena see *Aloysia citrodora*

lemonquat see *Citrus* × *japonica* × *C.* × *limon*

Leonotis (*Lamiaceae*)

leonitis	see *L. ocymifolia*
leonurus	CBcs CCCN CDTJ CHGN CHll ECre EShb EWes LRHS MNrw SLim SLon SMad SMrm SPlb SPoG XLum
- var. ***albiflora***	CCCN
nepetifolia	CHll
- var. ***nepetifolia*** 'Staircase'	CCCN NGBl SPav
§ ***ocymifolia***	CCCN CExl LSou
- var. ***raineriana***	CHll CSpe

Leontice (*Berberidaceae*)

albertii	see *Gymnospermium albertii*

Leontochir (*Alstroemeriaceae*)

ovallei	CCCN

Leontodon (*Asteraceae*)

autumnalis	CHab NMir
hispidus	CHab NMir
§ ***rigens***	CSpe CTal MHer MMuc NBid NBir SDix SMrm WMoo
- B&SWJ 12527	WCru

- 'Girandole'	see *L. rigens*

Leontopodium (Asteraceae)

alpinum	CTri ECho EPfP EWTr GAbr GKev LRHS MAsh MWat SPlb SPoG SRms XLum
- 'Everest'	EDAr
- 'Matterhorn' new	GEdr
- 'Mignon'	ECho EWes GMaP WAbe
coreanum	GKev
§ ***ochroleucum*** var. ***campestre***	NLar
palibinianum	see *L. ochroleucum* var. *campestre*
pusillum	WAbe
souliei	EPot SRot XLum

Leonurus (Lamiaceae)

artemisia	see *L. japonicus*
cardiaca	CArn CBod GPoy MHer MNHC SIde SRms WHfH XSen
- 'Crispa'	SMad
§ ***japonicus***	CArn SHar
- pink-flowered new	GCal
- white-flowered new	GCal
macranthus	EFEx
- var. ***alba***	EFEx
sibiricus misapplied	see *L. japonicus*
sibiricus L.	CArn GCal
turkestanicus	EBee

Leopoldia (Asparagaceae)

comosa	see *Muscari comosum*
spreitzenhoferi	see *Muscari spreitzenhoferi*
tenuiflora	see *Muscari tenuiflorum*

Lepechinia (Lamiaceae)

bella	CSpe SDys
chamaedryoides	CExl CHll CSpe
fragans	SBrt
hastata	CCse CFil CSpe SBHP SBrt WJek WOut
salviae	MMuc

Lepidium (Brassicaceae)

campestre	CArn CHab
latifolium	CArn ENfk LEdu

Lepidothamnus (Podocarpaceae)

§ ***laxifolius***	WThu

Lepidozamia (Zamiaceae)

peroffskyana	CBrP

Leptinella (Asteraceae)

'County Park'	ECou EDAr
dendyi	EWes GEdr MHer NSla WIce
dioica	GBin
hispida	see *Cotula hispida* (DC.) Harv.
§ ***minor***	WMoo
§ ***potentillina***	CTal CTri ECha ECho ECou EHoe GBin GEdr MBNS MSCN NLar SRms WMoo XLum
§ ***pyrethrifolia***	ECho EDAr GEdr
§ ***squalida***	ECha ECho GBin MWat NLar NSti WMoo
§ - 'Platt's Black'	CBcs CTal EBee ECha ECho ECou EDAr EHoe EShb EWes GAbr GBin GCrg GKev IBoy LEdu MSCN NLar SBch SMad SWvt WFar WMoo WWFP XLum

Leptocodon (Campanulaceae)

gracilis	CSpe EWld
- HWJK 2155	WCru

Leptospermum ✿ (Myrtaceae)

citratum	see *L. petersonii*
'Copper Glow'	ECou
'Copper Sheen'	CBcs
'County Park Blush'	ECou
cunninghamii	see *L. myrtifolium*
'Electric Red' (Galaxy Series)	CAbb CEnd EBee LRHS SEle SLim
ericoides	see *Kunzea ericoides*
flavescens misapplied	see *L. glaucescens*
flavescens Sm.	see *L. polygalifolium*
§ ***glaucescens***	SPlb
§ ***grandiflorum***	ELan EPfP MMuc SSpi SVen WSHC
grandifolium ♀H4	ECou
'Havering Hardy'	ECou
humifusum	see *L. rupestre*
juniperinum	SPlb
'Karo Pearl Star'	CBcs
'Karo Silver Ice' new	CBcs
'Karo Spectrobay'	CBcs
laevigatum	SVen
- 'Yarrum'	ECou
§ ***lanigerum***	CExl CMHG CTri CTsd ECou EPfP SPlb SVen
- 'Cunninghamii'	see *L. myrtifolium*
- 'Wellington'	ECou
liversidgei	CChe ECou SPlb
minutifolium	ECou
morrisonii	ECou
§ ***myrtifolium***	CMac CTri ECou EWes
- 'Newnes Forest'	ECou
nitidum	SPlb
obovatum	CTsd GGal
§ ***petersonii***	CArn ECou MHer MOWG
phylicoides	see *Kunzea ericoides*
'Pink Surprise'	ECou MOWG
§ ***polygalifolium***	CBcs SPlb
prostratum	see *L. rupestre*
pubescens	see *L. lanigerum*
'Red Cascade'	SWvt
rodwayanum	see *L. grandiflorum*
rotundifolium	ECou SPlb
§ ***rupestre***	CDoC CSde CTri ECou SPlb SVen WSHC
rupestre* × *scoparium	ECou
scoparium	CArn CHel CTsd ECou GPoy MNHC SPlb SVen WHfH WJek
- 'Adrianne'	EPfP LRHS MRav
- 'Appleblossom' ♀H3	CEnd EPfP SEle SGol SLim
- 'Autumn Glory'	SLim
- 'Blossom' (d)	CBcs CMac MOWG
- 'Burgundy Queen' (d)	CBcs CMac CSBt EUJe
- 'Chapmanii'	CMHG WPGP
- 'Coral Candy'	CBcs CEnd MMuc
- 'County Park Pink'	ECou
- 'Crimson Glory' (d)	CSBt
- 'Elizabeth Jane'	MMuc SEND WFar
- 'Essex'	ECou
- 'Fred's Red'	MHer
- 'Gaiety Girl' (d)	CSBt
- var. ***incanum*** 'Keatleyi' ♀H3	MOWG

- 'Jubilee' (d)	CMac
- 'Kerry'	CAbP
- 'Lady Bird'	ECou
- 'Leonard Wilson' (d)	CTri
- 'Martini'	CAbb CBcs CDoC CMac CSBt EBee EPfP LRHS MMuc SEND
- (Nanum Group) 'Kea'	CBcs MHer MRav
- - 'Kiwi' ♀H3	CAbP CAbb CBcs CCCN CDoC CHel CSBt CSde ECou ELon EPfP EUJe EWes LRHS MAsh MMuc SEND SEle SLim SLon WFar
- - 'Nanum'	ECou
- - 'Tui'	CMac CSBt
- 'Nichollsii' ♀H3	SVen WSHC
- 'Nichollsii Nanum' ♀H3	WAbe WPat WThu
- 'Pink Cascade'	CBcs CMac CTri SLim
- 'Pink Damask'	IVic SLim SWvt
- 'Pink Frills'	ECou
- var. ***prostratum*** misapplied	see *L. rupestre*
- 'Red Damask' (d) ♀H3	Widely available
- 'Red Falls'	CExl ECou
* - 'Ruby Wedding'	ELan EPfP LRHS MAsh SLon SPoG
- 'Snow Flurry'	CBcs EPfP LRHS SGol SLim SVen
- 'Sunraysia'	CHel
- 'Wingletye'	ECou
- 'Winter Cheer' (d)	EPfP LRHS SGol
- 'Wiri Donna' new	CSde
- 'Wiri Joan' (d)	CBcs CHel
- 'Wiri Linda'	CAbb CBcs CMac
- 'Zeehan'	ECou
sericeum	MNHC MOWG
'Silver Sheen' ♀H3	CAbb CDoC CEnd CHel CSde EBee ECou ECre ELan EPfP LRHS MAsh NLar SEle SPer SPlb SPoG SVen WPGP WPat
'Snow Column'	ECou
turbinatum 'Thunder Cloud'	ECou
'Wellington Dwarf'	ECou

Lespedeza (*Papilionaceae*)

bicolor	CCCN CSpe EBee LRHS MMuc SEND SKHP WCFE WFar WSHC
buergeri	EPfP LRHS MMHG NLar WSHC
japonica	SPlb
thunbergii ♀H5	CBcs CDul CHll CSde CSpe EBee ELan EPfP EPri IDee IVic LRHS MAsh MBlu MGil MGos MOWG SBod SLon SMad SPer SPoG SSta WCFE WPGP WSHC
- 'Avalanche'	NLar
- 'Gibraltar' new	WPGP
- 'Summer Beauty'	CBcs LRHS MGos
- subsp. ***thunbergii*** 'Albiflora'	ELan LRHS WPGP
- - 'Edo-shibori'	NLar WPGP
- - 'White Fountain'	EPfP LRHS SChF SKHP SPoG
tiliifolia	see *Desmodium elegans*

Lesquerella (*Brassicaceae*)

arctica new	WCFE
intermedia new	SIgm

Leucadendron (*Proteaceae*)

argenteum	CCCN CHEx CTre SPlb
daphnoides	SPlb
discolor	SPlb
eucalyptifolium	SPlb
gandogeri	CTre
'Inca Gold' ♀H1c	CTre MOWG
laureolum	CCCN CTre
'Safari Sunset' ♀H1c	CCCN CDoC CTre MPkF
'Safari Sunshine'	CTre
salicifolium	SPlb
salignum	CCCN
- 'Fireglow'	CDoC
sessile new	CTre
strobilinum	CDoC

Leucaena (*Mimosaceae*)

leucocephala	SPlb

Leucanthemella (*Asteraceae*)

§ ***serotina*** ♀H7	Widely available
- 'Herbststern'	IMou NLar

Leucanthemopsis (*Asteraceae*)

§ ***alpina***	ECho NSla
hosmariensis	see *Rhodanthemum hosmariense*

Leucanthemum ✿ (*Asteraceae*)

'Angel'	ELon NPri WGrn
atlanticum	see *Rhodanthemum atlanticum*
catananche	see *Rhodanthemum catananche*
graminifolium	EPfP LRHS
hosmariense	see *Rhodanthemum hosmariense*
mawii	see *Rhodanthemum gayanum*
maximum misapplied	see *L.* × *superbum*
§ ***maximum*** (Ramond) DC.	NBro NPer
- ***uliginosum***	see *Leucanthemella serotina*
nipponicum	see *Nipponanthemum nipponicum*
'Osiris Neige'	ECtt MAvo
'Real Galaxy'	LBuc LRHS
'Sante'	NPri NSir
'Sunshine Peach'	ECho SRot
§ × ***superbum***	CMac GAbr IBoy MHer MLHP MMuc SEND WBrk
- 'Aglaia' (d)	Widely available
- 'Alaska'	CAni CExl COtt CTsd EAEE EBee EPfP IBoy LAst LRHS LSun MCot NLar SCob SPer SWvt WWEG XLum
- 'Amelia'	EBee LRHS NBre NLar SRGP
- 'Andernach'	CAni
- 'Anita Allen' (d)	CAni CElw EBee ECtt WCot WWEG
- 'Anna Camilla'	CAni
- 'Antwerp Star'	NBre NLar WBrk
- 'Banana Cream'	CMos CWGN ECtt LAst LRHS MAsh MHol NPri SPoG STPC
- 'Banwell'	CAni
- 'Barbara Bush' (v/d)	NBir SWvt
§ - 'Beauté Nivelloise'	CAni CBod CElw CHVG CWCL EBee ECtt EPfP GBin LRHS MAvo NLar SHil SMrm SPoG SRms SWat WWEG
- 'Becky'	CCse CElw CMac EBee ECha ELan ELon EWes GBin LLHF LRHS LSou NEoE NLar SRGP WCAu WWEG
- 'Bishopstone'	CAni EBee ECtt ELan LBMP LEdu LLHF MSpe NCGa SMrm WWEG
- 'Bridal Bouquet' new	ECtt
- 'Brightside'	EBee ELan ELon GQue LRHS MWat WFar WMoo
- Broadway Lights = 'Leumayel'PBR	EBee EPfP EWoo GBin IBoy IPot LBMP LPot LRHS MAsh MBri MRav NBir NPri SCob SHil SPoG WCAu WCFE WFar WGrn WHil WWEG

	Name	Suppliers
	- 'Christine Hagemann'	CAni CElw EBee ECtt EWes GBin IPot MAvo MRav NLar SHar WCFE WCot WWEG
	- 'Cobham Gold' (d)	CAni CWCL NBre NOrc
	- 'Coconut Ice'	WWEG
	- 'Colwall'	CAni WWEG
	- 'Crazy Daisy'	CAni CBod CChe CTri EAJP ECtt LRHS NLar SMrm SRot SWvt WFar
	- 'Devon Mist'	CAni
	- 'Droitwich Beauty'	CAni ECtt LLHF MAvo WCFE WHoo WWEG
	- 'Duchess of Abercorn'	CAni
	- 'Dwarf Snow Lady'	LSun NBre NLar
	- 'Easton Lady'	CAni
	- 'Eclipse'	CAni MAvo WWEG
	- 'Edgebrook Giant'	CAni WBrk WWEG
	- 'Edward VII'	CAni
	- 'Eisstern'	EBee LEdu MAvo NCGa SHar
	- 'Elworthy Sparkler'	CElw MAvo WBrk WWEG
	- 'Engelina'PBR	EBee NLar
	- 'Esther Read' (d)	CBod CPrp EBee ECtt ELan EPfP GBin GMaP LRHS MBri NBro NEgg NLar SPer SRGP SRms SWat SWvt WCot WMnd WWEG
§	- 'Everest'	CAni SRms WWEG
	- 'Exhibition'	WWEG
	- 'Fiona Coghill' (d)	CAni CElw CHVG CWGN EAEE ECtt EPfP EPla GBin GBuc IBoy IKil LBMP LRHS LSou MBri MNrw MSpe NBir NEgg NGdn NLar NPCo WCot WFar WHoo WWEG
	- 'Firnglanz'	CAni GBin MAvo WWEG
	- 'Flore Pleno' (d)	SPlb
	- 'Freak!' **new**	CKno GBin LSun MBri NPri SHar
	- 'Goldfinch' **new**	CMos
	- 'Goldrausch'PBR	Widely available
	- 'Gruppenstolz'	CAni
	- 'H. Seibert'	CAni MArl MAvo WWEG
	- 'Harry'	CAni
	- 'Highland White Dream'PBR	IKil LRHS
	- 'Horace Read' (d)	CAni CElw ECtt NBir SBch SWvt WWEG
	- 'Jennifer Read'	CAni CPrp MAvo WCFE WWEG
§	- 'John Murray' (d)	CAni EWes NBir NWsh SMrm WCot WWEG
	- 'Lacrosse'	EBee LRHS MBri SCob SHil
	- 'Laspider'	EBee LRHS SRot
	- 'Little Miss Muffet'	CSBt CWGN EBee ECtt EPla LAst LLHF LRHS LSou MBNS NCGa NWad WWEG
	- 'Little Princess'	see *L.* × *superbum* 'Silberprinzesschen'
	- 'Majestic'	CAni
	- 'Manhattan'	CAni CCse EBee EWes GBin
	- 'Margaretchen'	CAni MAvo WWEG
	- 'Marion Bilsland'	CAni MAvo MSpe NChi WBrk
	- 'Marion Collyer'	CAni
	- 'Mayfield Giant'	CAni CTri
	- 'Mount Everest'	see *L.* × *superbum* 'Everest'
	- 'Octopus'	CAni WBrk
	- 'Old Court'	see *L.* × *superbum* 'Beauté Nivelloise'
	- 'Paladin'PBR	EBee ECtt GBin IPot LRHS SHar
	- 'Phyllis Smith'	CAni CBod CPrp EBee ECtt ELan MAvo MCot MHer MPie MRav MSCN MSpe NCGa NGdn SGSe SMad SMrm SPer WBrk WCAu WCot WMoo WWEG
	- 'Polaris'	EBee NBre WMoo XLum
	- 'Rags and Tatters'	CAni EBee ECtt EWes WWEG
	- 'Real Glory' **new**	ECtt
	- 'Real Neat' **new**	ECtt SCob
	- 'Schwabengruss'	CAni
	- 'Shaggy'	see *L.* × *superbum* 'Beauté Nivelloise'
§	- 'Silberprinzesschen'	CAni CSBt ELon EPfP GJos GMaP LPot LRHS LSqH NPri SPlb SRms WHar WMoo WRHF WWEG XLum
	- 'Silver Spoon'	EPfP LRHS
	- 'Snehurka'	CAni LLHF LRHS LSou MAvo WCot WWEG
	- 'Snow Lady'	CChe EAJP EBee LRHS NPer NPri SRms WFar
	- 'Snowcap'	CHid ECha EPfP EPla LRHS MBri MRav SPer SPoG SWvt
	- 'Snowdrift'	CAni NBre NLar WBrk WCot WFar WMoo WWEG
	- 'Snowstorm'	MAvo
§	- 'Sonnenschein'	CHVG CPrp EBee ECha ECtt ELan EPfP EPla GMaP LRHS LSou MArl MBri MCot MHer MRav MSpe NBir NChi NEgg NGdn NSti SMrm SPer SRms SWat WWEG
	- 'Starburst' (d)	EBee ELan LRHS SRms
	- 'Stina'	EBee MAvo WWEG
	- 'Summer Snowball'	see *L.* × *superbum* 'John Murray'
	- 'Sunny Killin'	CAni
	- 'Sunny Side Up'PBR	CBod CHVG CWCL EBee ECtt LRHS MBri NLar NPri SCob SMrm SRot WAul WFar WWEG
	- Sunshine	see *L.* × *superbum* 'Sonnenschein'
	- 'T.E. Killin' (d) ♀H4	CBod EAEE EBee ECha ECtt ELan EPfP EPla GBin GBuc LRHS LSou MRav MWat SPoG SPtp WCot WFar WHoo WPtf WWEG
	- 'Victorian Secret'	ECtt GBin IPot LBuc LRHS MAsh NLar NPri SCob WHil WMoo WWEG
	- 'White Iceberg' (d)	CAni
	- White Mountain = 'Gfleuwhmtn'PBR	NPri STPC
	- 'White Tutu'	MAvo
	- 'Wirral Pride'	CAni ELon EPfP WBrk WMnd WWEG
	- 'Wirral Supreme' (d) ♀H5	CAni CBcs CPrp CSBt CTsd ELan ELon EPfP GAbr GBBs GMaP IBoy LRHS LSun MBri MNrw MRav MWat NBir NPri SCob SMrm SPer SRms SWat SWvt WBrk WFar WMnd WWEG
	'Tizi-n-Test'	see *Rhodanthemum catananche* 'Tizi-n-Test'
§	***vulgare***	CArn CBod CHab CMac CWld ENfk EPfP EShb GJos MHer MNHC MWat NMir SEND SIde SPhx WFar WHer WJek WMoo WOut WSFF WShi XLum
	- 'Filigran'	EBee LRHS WFar
§	- 'Maikönigin'	NLar WHrl XLum
	- May Queen	see *L. vulgare* 'Maikönigin'
	- 'Sunny'	CBre EWes

Leucocoryne (*Alliaceae*)

Name	Suppliers
alliacea	ECho
'Andes' ♀H3	CCCN ECho GKev NRog
'Caravelle'	ECho

coronata	SPlb
'Dione'	ECho GKev NRog SDeJ
'Double Fantasy' new	NRog
hybrids	ECho
ixioides	ECho
* - ***alba***	ECho NRog
- 'Blue Ocean'	ECho GKev NRog SDeJ
pauciflora new	NRog
purpurea ♀H3	ECho NRog
'Spotlight'	ECho GKev NRog
'Sunny Stripe'	ECho GKev
vittata new	NRog
'White Dream'	ECho GKev NRog SDeJ

Leucogenes (*Asteraceae*)

grandiceps	NSla WAbe
leontopodium	EPot NSla WAbe WIce WThu
tarahaoa	WAbe

Leucogenes × *Raoulia* see × *Leucoraoulia*

Leucojum ✿ (*Amaryllidaceae*)

aestivum	CBcs CTri EBee ECGP ECho EPfP GCal LAma MCot MSCN NChi NEgg NHol SDeJ SEND SRms WBor WCot WFar WHea WRHF WShi
- 'Gravetye Giant' ♀H7	Widely available
- var. ***pulchellum***	CElw
autumnale	see *Acis autumnalis*
roseum	see *Acis rosea*
tingitanum	see *Acis tingitana*
trichophyllum	see *Acis trichophylla*
valentinum	see *Acis valentina*
vernum ♀H5	CAvo CBro CExl CHid COtt ECho ELan EPfP EPot ERCP GBuc GCal GKev LAma LRHS MNrw NBir NHol NPol NRya NWad SDeJ SRms WCot WHer WHil WShi
- var. ***carpathicum***	CLAP ECho
- var. ***vagneri***	CLAP ECha IGor SDys

Leucophysalis (*Solanaceae*)

sinense BWJ 8093	WCru

Leucophyta (*Asteraceae*)

brownii 'Challenge'	EDAr
- 'Silver Sand'	LAst LSou

Leucopogon (*Ericaceae*)

§ ***colensoi***	EBee GKev WThu
ericoides	GKev
§ ***fraseri***	ECou NHar WThu
§ ***parviflorus***	ECou

× *Leucoraoulia* (*Asteraceae*)

§ ***loganii***	WAbe

Leucosceptrum (*Lamiaceae*)

canum	CExl
- GWJ 9424	WCru
japonicum B&SWJ 10804	WCru
- B&SWJ 10981	WCru
stellipilum var. ***formosanum***	IMou
- - B&SWJ 1926	WCru
- - RWJ 9907	SBrt WCru
- var. ***tosaense*** B&SWJ 8892	WCru

Leucospermum (*Proteaceae*)

conocarpodendron 'Mardi Gras Ribbons'	EBee
cordifolium	CTre
glabrum	SPlb
'Scarlet Ribbon'	CCCN

Leucothoe (*Ericaceae*)

axillaris 'Curly Red'PBR	CDoC CRos CWSG EBee ELan EPfP IVic LRHS MGos MJak MPkF NLar NSoo SHil SLim SLon SPoG SWvt
- Twisting Red = 'Opstal20'PBR new	MBlu
Carinella = 'Zebekot'	CRos EBee EPfP LRHS NLar SHil SPoG
davisiae	NLar
§ ***fontanesiana***	CMac GGal GKev
- 'Makijaz'PBR (v) new	CRos EPfP LRHS SHil
- 'Rainbow' (v)	CBcs CDoC CDul CMac CNec CRos ELan EPfP LPal LRHS LSou MAsh MGos NLar NPri SGbt SGol SHil SLim SPad SPer SPoG SRms SSta SWvt WFar WHar WHil WMoo
- 'Rollissonii' ♀H6	MRav SRms
- Whitewater = 'Howw'PBR (v)	CRos LRHS MPkF NLar NPri SHil
keiskei 'Royal Ruby'	CRos LRHS LSou MGos MJak MPkF NEgg NLar NSoo NWad SGbt SGol SHil SLim SPoG WFar WMoo
Lovita = 'Zebonard'	MBri MRav NLar SCoo
Red Lips = 'Lipsbolwi'PBR	CDoC EPfP IVic
Scarletta = 'Zeblid' ♀H6	Widely available
walteri	see *L. fontanesiana*

Leuzea (*Asteraceae*)

centaureoides	see *Stemmacantha centaureoides*

Levisticum (*Apiaceae*)

officinale	CArn CBod CHby CUse ELau ENfk EPfP GAbr GPoy LEdu MHer MMuc MNHC NPri SDix SEND SIde SPlb SRms SVic SWat WHer WHfH WJek

Lewisia ✿ (*Portulacaceae*)

'Archangel'	NRya
Ashwood Carousel hybrids	CTri ECho MAsh NHar NRya
Birch strain	CBcs ECho ELan
brachycalyx ♀H4	CPBP ECho EWes LLHF NHar
brachycalyx × ***cotyledon***	LLHF
cantelovii	CWCL MAsh
columbiana	CTal ECho ECou MAsh
- 'Alba'	NRya NSla
- 'Rosea'	GKev MAsh
- subsp. ***rupicola***	ITim LLHF MAsh NSla
- subsp. ***wallowensis***	MAsh
congdonii	MAsh
cotyledon ♀H4	CWCL ECho GAbr GKev GMaP ITim LLHF LRHS NSla WIce
- f. ***alba***	CWCL
- - 'Snowstorm'	LLHF
- 'Ashwood Ruby'	MAsh
- Ashwood strain	ECho EPfP EWes LRHS MAsh SRms WOld
- 'Brannan Bar'	MAsh
- 'Bright Eyes'	GKev
- var. ***cotyledon***	LLHF
- double-flowered (d)	GKev

– 'Fransi'	NLar
– var. ***howellii***	LLHF
– hybrid	ECho EPot LRHS NRya SPoG
– 'John's Special'	MAsh
– magenta-flowered	CWCL ECho
– orange-flowered **new**	CWCL
§ – 'Regenbogen'	ECho
– rose-pink flowered **new**	CWCL
– salmon-flowered **new**	CWCL
– Sunset Group ♀H4	CHel ECho EPfP GCrg LAst MHer NLar WHar
– 'White Splendour'	MAsh
'George Henley'	ECho EPot EWes LLHF MAsh NRya WAbe
leeana	MAsh
'Little Mango'	EDAr NSla
'Little Peach'	CPBP CWCL ECho ECtt EDAr EPot GBin GKev MAsh NSla
'Little Plum'	CMea CPBP ECho ECtt EDAr GCrg LBMP LRHS MAsh NLar NRya NSla WHoo
§ ***longipetala***	ECho
§ ***nevadensis***	CPne ECho EDAr EPot GCrg ITim LRHS NRya
– ***bernardina***	see *L. nevadensis*
– 'Rosea'	ECho NRya NSla
oppositifolia	MAsh
'Pinkie'	EPot MAsh
pygmaea	CWCL ECho EWes ITim LRHS MAsh MHer NBir NRya NSla XLum
– subsp. ***longipetala***	see *L. longipetala*
pygmaea* × *rediviva	LLHF
Rainbow mixture	see *L. cotyledon* 'Regenbogen'
'Rawreth'	ECho LLHF WAbe
rediviva	CPBP EWes LLHF
serrata	MAsh SIgm
'Trevosia'	MAsh
tweedyi ♀H4	EAEE ECho EPot LRHS MAsh NRya SIgm WAbe WThu
– 'Alba'	LLHF MAsh WAbe
– 'Elliott's Variety'	MAsh
– 'Lovedream' **new**	ECho
– 'Rosea'	EAEE ECho EPot LRHS MAsh WAbe

Leycesteria (*Caprifoliaceae*)

crocothyrsos	CBcs CHEx EBee ELan NLar
formosa	Widely available
– brown-stemmed	IFoB
– from Longstock	SLon
– 'Gold Leaf'	MGos MHer WFar WHil
– Golden Lanterns = 'Notbruce'PBR ♀H4	CBcs CDoC CMac COtt CSBt EBee ELan EPfP EPla LBMP LBuc LRHS LSou MAsh MBri MGos MMHG MMuc MPkF MSwo NEgg NLar SCoo SHil SLim SPer SPoG SWvt WMoo
– 'Golden Pheasant' (v)	EHoe
– 'Lydia'	LRHS
– 'Purple Rain'	EWes GBin LRHS MBri MGos NLar SHil SLim

Leymus (*Poaceae*)

from Falkland Islands	EPPr
§ ***arenarius***	Widely available
cinereus	WCot
hispidus	see *Elymus hispidus*

Lhotzkya see *Calytrix*

Liatris (*Asteraceae*)

aspera	NSbr SPhx
cylindracea	SPhx
elegans	EBee EPfP NBre NSbr SPlb
ligulistylis	EBee LEdu NSbr SPhx
mucronata	NLar NSbr
pycnostachya	EBee NDov NLar NSbr SRms
§ ***spicata***	Widely available
– 'Alba'	CBod CMac COtt CSBt CSpe EAJP ECha ELan EPfP GKev LAst LEdu MNFA MNrw MSCN NGdn NLar NPri NSoo SCob SPer SPlb XLum
– ***callilepis***	see *L. spicata*
– 'Floristan Violett'	CBod CTri EBee EPfP EPla GMaP LBMP LRHS MBel MHer MJak MSpe MWhi NEgg NLar NSbr SCob SCoo SPlb SPoG SWvt WFar WGwG WMnd WMoo WWEG WWtn XLum
– 'Floristan Weiss'	CExl CTri EPPr EPfP EPla ERCP GKev GMaP LRHS LSun MBel MHer MRav MWat MWhi NCGa NDov NLar SDeJ SMrm SPoG SWvt WFar WGwG WHil WMnd WMoo WWEG WWtn
– Goblin	see *L. spicata* 'Kobold'
§ – 'Kobold'	Widely available
squarrosa	SPhx

Libanotis see *Seseli*

montana	see *Seseli libanotis*

Libertia ✿ (*Iridaceae*)

'Amazing Grace'	CDes EBee GCal
'Ballyrogan Blue'	CDes
* ***breunioides***	CExl WPGP
caerulescens	CBod CCCN CExl CHel CMac CSde CTsd EAJP ECho EPfP EWll LRHS NBir NCGa SMad SPer SPtp WMoo WSHC
chilensis	see *L. formosa*
elegans	CExl EBee
§ ***formosa***	CBcs CBod CBro CElw CExl CHel CHid COtt CTri ECho ELan GCal GCra GGal GKev LRHS NChi NSti SArc SCob SEND SPer SPtp SRms SWvt WHer
– brown-stemmed	IFoB
grandiflora ♀H3	Widely available
'Highlander'	ELon LRHS MHol
ixioides	CBcs ECha ECho ECou LEdu SPtp WPGP WRHF
– 'Goldfinger' (v)	Widely available
– hybrid	SDix
– 'Tricolor'	CHel CSde ECha MRav WMoo
ixioides* × *peregrinans	LPal
'Nelson Dwarf'	GCal
paniculata	CExl
peregrinans	CAbb CBod CExl CHel CKno CSpe EBee ECha ECho ECou EHoe ELan EPri GBuc GCal IBoy IFro LEdu LRHS MRav NBir SDix SEND SKHP SPtp SRkn SWvt WGrn WPGP WPat
– 'Gold Leaf'	CBcs CCCN CJun CSpe CTri CTsd EPfP EUJe GBuc LAst LRHS SMad SWvt
– 'Gold Stripe'	CUse SPad SWvt
* ***procera***	CCon CSpe EBee EPfP IVic LEdu LRHS SKHP SPtp WKif WPGP WSHC

pulchella	CSde
'Red Devil'	MHol
sessiliflora	CExl NBir
- RB 94073	SMad
'Taupo Blaze'	CBcs CMac EBee LRHS MRav SKHP SLon
'Taupo Sunset'PBR	CBod CCCN CExl ELon EPfP EUJe EWes LAst LPal LRHS MBNS MPkF NOak NSoo SKHP SWvt
tricococca HCM 98.089	WPGP

Libocedrus (*Cupressaceae*)

chilensis	see *Austrocedrus chilensis*
decurrens	see *Calocedrus decurrens*

Libonia see *Justicia*

Ligularia ✿ (*Asteraceae*)

amplexicaulis CC 6829	GKev
'Britt Marie Crawford'PBR ♀H6	Widely available
calthifolia	EBee
clivorum	see *L. dentata*
§ ***dentata***	CRow ECtt GGal NBro NLar SRms SWat
- 'Dark Beauty'	MWhi
- dark-leaved	WWEG
- 'Desdemona'	Widely available
- 'Enkelrig'	EBee
- 'Midnight Lady'	CBod EAJP ELan LAst MHol MMuc NLar SPad WWEG
- 'Orange Princess'	NPer
- 'Osiris Fantaisie' (v)	CAbP CExl CMos ECtt EWes GBee LLHF MAsh MAvo MBel MHol MNrw MWts NLar NMyG NSti SMad SPoG WBor WCot WFar WPnP WWEG
- 'Othello'	CBod CHel COtt CRow EBee ECtt EHon EPfP LRHS MAsh NBid NEgg NGdn NLar NWad SCob SWat SWvt WWEG
- 'Sommergold'	ECha WFar
- 'Twilight'	CBct ECtt MBNS
dictyoneura new	GKev
§ ***fischeri***	ECha LEdu NBre SGSe WWtn
- B&SWJ 2570	WCru
- B&SWJ 4381	WCru
- B&SWJ 4478	WCru
- B&SWJ 5653	WCru
- B&SWJ 8802	WCru
- var. ***megalorhiza*** 'Cheju Charmer'	ELon WCru WWEG
'Franz Marc'	GCal
'Gold Torch'	CBct ECtt NLar
§ 'Gregynog Gold' ♀H6	ECha ECtt ELan GAbr GMaP LRHS MRav MWhi NBro NLar NOrc SPer WWEG WWtn
× ***hessei***	GMaP LRHS MMuc NLar SWat WWtn
hodgsonii	CKno EPPr LEdu LRHS MRav
- B&SWJ 10855	WCru
intermedia B&SWJ 606a	WCru
japonica	CLAP ECha GCra LEdu LRHS MWhi NLar WCot WWtn
- B&SWJ 2883	WCru
- 'Rising Sun'	CExl NLar WCru
'Laternchen'PBR	ECtt GBin IBal MWts
'Little Rocket'PBR	CBct CBod CExl CHel ECtt EPfP LLWG MBNS MPie MWts NBro NGdn NLar SCob WFar WHil
'Osiris Café Noir'	CAbb EBee ECtt MBri NLar WFar
'Osiris Pistache' (v)	EBee ECtt
× ***palmatiloba***	see *L.* × *yoshizoeana* 'Palmatiloba'
§ ***przewalskii***	Widely available
- SSSE 176 new	WCot
- 'Dragon's Breath'	ECtt
- 'Light Fingered'	NBre
sibirica	CSam CUse MMuc NLar SEND WMoo WWEG
- B&SWJ 4383	WCru
- B&SWJ 5841	WCru
- var. ***speciosa***	see *L. fischeri*
smithii	see *Senecio smithii*
speciosa	see *L. fischeri*
stenocephala	EBee NBro NLar SCob SHar SWat WWtn XLum
'Sungold'	CMac CSam ECtt LRHS NGdn
tangutica	see *Sinacalia tangutica*
'The Rocket' ♀H5	Widely available
tussilaginea	see *Farfugium japonicum*
- 'Aureo-maculata'	see *Farfugium japonicum* 'Aureomaculatum'
veitchiana	CBod CCon CRow CSam EPfP GCal GKev LRHS SWat WWtn
vorobievii	GCal NLar
'Weihenstephan'	GCal
wilsoniana	ECtt LLWG LRHS MMuc MRav SEND SWat WFar WWEG WWtn
§ × ***yoshizoeana*** 'Palmatiloba'	CHEx ELan ELon EPla EWes GBee GCal LEdu LRHS MRav SPhx SWat WFar WWEG WWtn
'Zepter'	CBct CHel ECtt EUJe GBuc GCal GQue LRHS MBNS MMuc MWhi NEgg NHol NLar NWad SEND WCot WWEG WWtn

Ligusticum (*Apiaceae*)

lucidum	CMCN EBee EPfP IVic LEdu SPhx WBor WFar WPGP
- 'Curley Whirley'	SPoG
porteri	CArn
§ ***scoticum***	CArn CHid EBee EShb EWes GPoy LEdu MHer NChi SGSe SRms WHrl WJek WOut WPtf

Ligustrum ✿ (*Oleaceae*)

§ ***delavayanum***	CAco EBtc EPfP SArc STrG WPGP
- B&L 12083	CExl
ibota	EBtc NLar
- Musli = 'Muster' (v)	LRHS SHil WCot
ionandrum	see *L. delavayanum*
japonicum	ECrN LRHS SEND SGol SPer
- 'Coriaceum'	see *L. japonicum* 'Rotundifolium'
* - 'Coriaceum Aureum'	LRHS
- Green Century = 'Melgreen'PBR new	GBin LRHS
- 'Korea Dwarf' new	NLar
- 'Macrophyllum'	EPfP
§ - 'Rotundifolium'	CAbP CBcs CDoC CDul CExl CHEx EBee ELan EPfP IVic LBMP LRHS MAsh MRav NLar SMad SPer SPoG WCFE WCot WFar
§ - 'Silver Star' (v)	NLar SEND SGol SLon
§ - 'Texanum'	CDoC ECrN EPfP NLar WCFE
- 'Texanum Argenteum'	see *L. japonicum* 'Silver Star'
- 'Variegatum' (v)	SGol
lucidum ♀H5	CCVT CDoC CDul CSBt CSde CTri ELan EWTr GCal IDee LAst LPla

	MMuc MRav NLar NWea SArc SCob SEND SGol SPer SWvt
- Guiz 296	CExl
- 'Curly Wurly' **new**	LRHS
- 'Excelsum Superbum' (v) 🏆H5	CCVT CJun CMac ECrN ELan EPfP LRHS SGol SSpi WCot
- 'Golden Wax'	CJun MRav SSpi
- 'Tricolor' (v) 🏆H5	CJun ELan EPfP LRHS MAsh SPoG SSpi SWvt
ovalifolium	Widely available
§ - 'Argenteum' (v)	CBcs CCVT CDoC CDul CMac COtt CTri ECrN EHoe EPla EShb MMuc MRav MWat NEgg SEND SGol SLim SPer SPoG SWvt
- 'Aureomarginatum'	see *L. ovalifolium* 'Aureum'
§ - 'Aureum' (v) 🏆H5	Widely available
- 'Lemon and Lime' (v)	CBod CDoC COtt EHoe EPfP LRHS SCob SCoo SHil SWvt WCot WRHF
- 'Variegatum'	see *L. ovalifolium* 'Argenteum'
quihoui	EBee ECre ELan EPfP GKin IDee LRHS NLar SDix SEND SKHP SLon SMad SPer SSpi
sempervirens	EBee EPfP
sinense	CMCN GLin MRav
- 'Multiflorum'	WFar
- 'Pendulum'	LRHS
- 'Variegatum' (v)	CJun MRav SPer
- 'Wimbei'	WPat
strongylophyllum	CDoC CExl
texanum	see *L. japonicum* 'Texanum'
tschonoskii	NLar
undulatum 'Lemon Lime and Clippers'	EShb LRHS MAsh MBNS NLar NPri SDix SLim
'Vicaryi'	CDul CJun ELan EPfP LRHS MGos NEoE SCob SGol SHil SPer WFar
vulgare	CArn CBcs CBod CCVT CDul CHab CMac CTri ECrN EPfP LBuc MMuc MSwo NHed NWea SCob SEND SEWo SWvt WMou WSFF
- 'Aureovariegatum' (v)	CNat
- 'Lodense'	EBtc

Lilium ✿ (*Liliaceae*)

'Abbeville's Pride' (Ia/b) **new**	SDeJ
'Acapulco' (VII-/d)	LAma MCri NGdn SDeJ
'Adonis' (Ic/d) **new**	GEdr
African Queen Group (VI-/a) 🏆H6	ERCP GKev LAma LSun SCoo SPer SRms
- 'African Queen' (VIb-c/a)	CBro CHel MCri SDeJ
'Altari' (VIIIa-b/b)	MCri SDeJ
amabile var. ***luteum*** (IXc/d)	MCri
'Ambergate'	SDeJ
'Anastasia' (VIIIb-c/b-d)	GKev LAma SDeJ
'Annemarie's Dream' (Ia/c)	GKev SDeJ
'Apeldoorn' (Ia/b)	MCri NNor
'Aphrodite' (Ia-b/b)	CSut
Apollo (Ia-b)	see *L.* 'Blizzard'
'Arabian Knight' (IIc/d)	GKev SDeJ
'Arena' (VIIa/b)	MCri SCoo
'Ariadne' (Ic-d)	CDes
Asiatic hybrids (I)	NGdn
'Aubade' (VII a/b) **new**	CSut
auratum (IXb/c)	ECho EFEx EPfP GBuc
- 'Gold Band'	see *L. auratum* var. *platyphyllum*
- 'Golden Ray'	GBuc
§ - var. ***platyphyllum*** (IXb/c)	MCri NNor SDeJ
- - B&SWJ 4824	WCru
- - B&SWJ 5041	WCru
- var. ***virginale*** (IXb/c)	MCri SDeJ
'Avignon' (Ia/b)	MCri
'Barbara North' (Ic/d)	GEdr
'Barbaresco' (VIIa-b/b)	SCoo
'Barcelona' (Ia/b-c)	NNor
'Belgrado'[PBR] (VIIa/b-c)	SDeJ
'Belladonna'[PBR] (VIIIb-a/b)	SDeJ
'Belle Epoque' (VIIb/b-c)	SDeJ
'Bergamo' (VIIb/b)	SCoo SDeJ
'Black Beauty' (VIIIb-c/d)	EPfP GBin GKev LAma MCri NNor SDeJ
'Black Bird' (Ia/b)	MAsh
'Black Dragon'	see *L. leucanthum* var. *centifolium* 'Black Dragon'
'Black Tie' (VIIa-b/b)	MCri
§ 'Blizzard' (Ia-b) 🏆H6	LAma NNor SDeJ
'Bonbini' (VIIIa-b/b) **new**	LRHS
'Boogie Woogie' (VIIIa-b/b)	SDeJ
'Bracelet' (VIIIa-b/b)	SDeJ
Brasilia = 'Zora' (VII)	SDeJ
Bright Pixie = 'Ceb Bright' (Ia/b)	CBod MAsh NSoo SDeJ
'Bright Star' (VIb-c/c)	LAma MCri
brownii (IXb-c/a)	ECho MCri
bulbiferum (IXa/b)	EBee ECho GKev
- var. ***croceum*** (IXa/b)	XEll
'Burgundy Splash' (Ia-b/b)	LAma
'Butter Pixie'[PBR] (Ia/b)	CBod NNor SDeJ
§ ***canadense*** (IXc/a)	GBuc GEdr LAma WCru XEll
- var. ***coccineum*** (IXc/a)	GBuc
- var. ***flavum***	see *L. canadense*
'Cancun' (Ia/b-c)	SDeJ
candidum (IXb/a) 🏆H5	CArn CAvo CBcs CBro CTca CWCL EBee ECha ECho ELan ERCP GKev LAma LSun MAvo MCri MHer NLar NRog SDeJ SEND SRms
'Capuchino' (Ia-b/c)	CBod MCri
carniolicum	see *L. pyrenaicum* subsp. *carniolicum*
'Casa Blanca' (VIIb/b-c) 🏆H6	CAvo CBro EPfP GKev LAma LSun MCri NBir NLar NNor SCoo SDeJ
'Cecil' (VIIIa/b)	GKev SDeJ
'Centerfold' (Ia-b/b)	NNor
cernuum (IXc/d)	EBee ECho GKev LAma MCri SDeJ
* - 'Album'	ECho SDeJ
§ 'Chocolate Canary' (Ic/-)	SDeJ
Citronella Group (Ic/d)	ECho SDeJ
'Claude Shride' (IIc/d)	GKev SDeJ
'Cocktail Twins' (Ia/b)	SDeJ
'Coldplay' (VIIa-b/b-c) **new**	LBuc LRHS
columbianum (IXc/d)	ECho WHal
- B&SWJ 9564	WCru
'Con Amore' (VIIb/b)	SCoo
'Conca d'Or'[PBR] (VIIIb/b)	LAma LRHS SDeJ
'Connecticut King' (Ia/b)	MCri
'Corina' (Ia/b)	NNor
'Côte d'Azur' (Ia/b-c)	NNor
'Creation' (VIa/b)	SDeJ
'Crimson Pixie' (Ia/b)	CBod CBro SDeJ
× ***dalhansonii*** (IIc/d)	CAby SPhx
§ - 'Marhan' (IIc/d)	ECho GBuc
- 'Mrs R.O. Backhouse' (IIc/d)	ECho GEdr SDeJ
- 'Sutton Court' (II)	GBuc
dauricum var. ***alpinum*** (IX)	MCri

	Name	Suppliers
	davidii (IXc/d)	CExl EBee ECho GBuc LAma MCri MMoz SDeJ WBor WCru
	- var. ***unicolor***	GBuc
§	- var. ***willmottiae*** (IXc/d)	MCri WCru
	'Debby' (VIII a-b/b-c) **new**	CSut
	'Diabora' (Ia/b)	GBuc
	'Dimension' (Ia/b-c)	LAma
	'Disco' (Ia)	SDeJ
	distichum (IXb-c/d)	WCot
	- B&SWJ 794	WCru
	- B&SWJ 4465	WCru
	'Dizzy' (VIIa-b/b-c)	CSut MCri NNor SDeJ
	duchartrei (IXc/d)	CAby CExl ECho GKev LAma NSla WAbe WCru
	'Electric' (Ia/b-c)	MCri NNor
	'Electric Yellow'	see *L.* 'Yellow Electric'
	'Elodie'PBR (Ia/b)	CAvo CSut GKev LAma
	'Elusive' (VIIIb/b-d)	SDeJ
	'Enchantment' (Ia/b)	SDeJ
	'Expression' (VII)	SDeJ
	'Eyeliner'PBR (VIIIa/b)	CSut LAma
	'Fangio' (VIIIa/b)	NNor
	fargesii (IXc/d)	CExl GKev
	'Fata Morgana' (Ia/b) ♀H6	CSut LAma NNor SCoo SDeJ
	'Fire King' (Ib/d)	LAma MCri SCoo SDeJ SRms
	'Fopapo'	SDeJ
	'Forever Susan' (Ia/b)	SDeJ
	formosanum (IXb/a)	CPne MCri
	- var. ***formosanum*** (IXb/a) B&SWJ 1589 **new**	WCru
	- var. ***pricei*** (IXb/a)	EAJP EBee ECho EDAr ELan EPot GBin GKev LRHS MHer NSla SHil WIce
	- - 'Snow Queen' (Vb/a)	SDeJ
	- short, from high altitude (IX b/a) RWJ 10005 **new**	WCru
	'Friso' (VIIIb/b) **new**	CBro GKev
	'Garden Party' (VIIb/b) ♀H6	GKev SDeJ
	'Gay Lights' (II)	WCot
	'Gironde' (Ia/b)	SDeJ
	'Glossy Wings' (VIIIa-b/b)	NNor
	'Gluhwein'PBR (VIIIa-b/b) **new**	LRHS
	Golden Splendor Group (VIb-c/a) ♀H6	GKev LAma MCri SCoo SDeJ
	'Golden Stone' (VIIIa-b/b)	GKev SDeJ
	'Gran Paradiso' (Ia/b)	MCri SRms
	'Grand Cru' (Ia/b) ♀H6	MCri NNor SDeJ
	grayi (IXc/a)	GBuc
	Green Magic Group (VI-/a)	NNor
	'Hannah North' (Ic/d)	GEdr
	hansonii (IXb-c/d)	CWCL EBee ECha ECho GBuc GKev LAma MCri SDeJ
	- B&SWJ 4309 **new**	WCru
	- B&SWJ 4756 from Aomori, Japan	WCru
	- B&SWJ 8506	WCru
	- B&SWJ 8528	WCru
	henryi (IXc/d) ♀H6	CBro EBee ECho GKev LAma MCri NLar NNor SDeJ WCru
	'Hit Parade' (VII)	SDeJ
	× ***hollandicum*** (Ia/b)	MCri
	'Honeymoon' (VIIIa-b/b)	SDeJ
	'Ibarra' (Ia/b)	MCri
	'Ice Pixie' (Ia/b)	SDeJ
	'Inuvik' (Ia/b) **new**	CBod MAsh
	'Ivory Pixie' (Ia/b)	CBod SDeJ
	japonicum (IXb/a)	EFEx
	'Jo's Choice'	SDeJ
	'Josephine' (VIIa/b)	SDeJ
	'Journey's End' (VIIb/c)	LAma
	'Joy'	see *L.* 'Le Rêve'
	'Karen North' (Ic/d)	GEdr
	'King Pete' (Ib/b-c)	SDeJ
	'Kingdom'PBR (VIIIa/b-c)	SDeJ
	'Lady Alice' (VI-/d)	GKev SDeJ
	'Lake Tulare' (IVc/c-d)	GEdr
§	***lancifolium*** (IXc/d)	CArn CHid CPne EPot EWld GBin WBrk XLum
	- B&SWJ 4352	WCru
	- var. ***flaviflorum*** (IXc/d)	CBro EBee GBuc IBoy MCri SDeJ
	- 'Flore Pleno' (IXc/d)	CSut EPPr GCal GKev LRHS MHer MMHG NBir NNor SDeJ SMrm WCot WCru WHil XLum
*	- var. ***forrestii*** (IX)	MCri
	- var. ***fortunei*** (IXc/d)	GCal SDix
	- - B&SWJ 539	WCru
	- pink-flowered	SDeJ
	- 'Splendens' (IXc/d) ♀H6	CBro EBee ECGP ECho EPfP GKev MCri NBid NNor SDeJ SPhx
	'Landini'PBR (Ia/b)	CAby CBod CSut SDeJ
	'Lankon' (VIIIc/a) **new**	ERCP
	lankongense (IXc/d)	CWCL ECho EPot GBin GBuc GGGa GKev LAma MCri WCru
	- BWJ 7554 **new**	WCru
	- BWJ 7691	WCru
	'Latvia' (Ia/b)	MCri SDeJ
	'Lazy Lady'	see *L.* 'Chocolate Canary'
§	'Le Rêve' (VIIa-b/b) ♀H6	MCri NNor SDeJ
	leichtlinii (IXc/d)	CAby CAvo CBro EBee ECGP ECho EPot GBin GKev IMou LLHF MCri SDeJ
	- B&SWJ 4519	WCru
	- 'Iwashimiza' (IXc/d)	MCri
	leucanthum (IXb-c/a)	LAma
	- var. ***centifolium*** (IXb-c/a)	MCri WCru
	- - BWJ 8130	WCru
§	- - 'Black Dragon' (IXb-c/a)	MCri
	lijiangense (IXc/d)	GKev MCri
I	'Linda' (Ia/b)	SDeJ
	'Little John' (VIIa-b/b)	SDeJ
	'Little Kiss' (Ia/d)	SDeJ
	Lollypop = 'Holebibi' (Ia/b)	CBod CSut GBuc NNor SCoo
	longiflorum (IXb/a) ♀H2	EBee ECho MCri SCoo XLum
	- B&SWJ 11376	WCru
	- 'Rose'	SDeJ
§	- 'White American' (Vb/a)	CBro ECho EWoo
	- 'White Heaven'PBR (Vb/a)	EPfP GKev SPer
	lophophorum (IXc/b)	EPot GKev LAma
	'Lovely Girl' (VII-/b)	SDeJ
	'Luxor' (Ia/b)	MCri NBir
	mackliniae (IXc/a) ♀H5	CWCL ECho EWes GBuc GCal GCra GGGa GKev NBir WAbe WHal WPGP
	- from Nagaland, India	GGGa
	- deep pink-flowered	GGGa
	'Magic Star'PBR (VII a-b/b) **new**	CSut
	'Manitoba Morning' (IIc/c) **new**	GKev
	'Mapira' (I) **new**	CHid
	'Marco Polo' ambig.	SCoo SDeJ
	'Marhan'	see *L.* × *dalhansonii* 'Marhan'
	'Marie North' (Ic/d)	GEdr
	martagon (IXc/d) ♀H7	CAvo CBro CCon CTca CWCL EBee ECha ECho ELan EPot ERCP ETwe

		GBuc GEdr GKev GPoy LAma LRHS NBir NChi NLar SDeJ SRms WAbe WCot WPnP WShi WWFP
	- var. ***albiflorum*** (IXc/d)	GBuc GKev
	- var. ***album*** (IXc/d) ♀H7	CAvo CBro CWCL ECho ELan EPot GBin GKev LAma NBir NChi SDeJ WShi
	- var. ***cattaniae*** (IXc/d)	GBuc GEdr MCri WCot
	- var. ***hirsutum*** (IXc/d) **new**	GEdr
*	- var. ***rubrum***	CBro CWCL
	'Maru' (VIIa/b) **new**	LBuc LRHS
	medeoloides (IXc/d)	ECho EFEx GBuc
	- B&SWJ 4184 **new**	WCru
	- B&SWJ 4363 **new**	WCru
	'Mediterrannee' (VIIb/d)	NNor
	michiganense (IXc/d)	GBuc
	'Miss Feya' (VIIIb/c)	LAma SDeJ
	'Miss France' (VIIb/b-c)	SDeJ
I	'Miss Lily'	SDeJ
	'Miss Lucy'PBR (VIIa-b/b-c)	CHid LAma SDeJ
	'Miss Rio' (VII)	SCoo
	'Mister Job' (VIIIa/c)	GKev SDeJ
	'Mona Lisa' (VIIb/b-c)	GKev LAma LRHS MCri NGdn NLar NNor SDeJ
	monadelphum (IXc/d)	ECho GKev LAma SDeJ
	'Mont Blanc' (Ia/b-c)	SDeJ
	'Monte Negro' (Ia/b)	MCri
	'Montezuma'PBR (VIIa-b/b)	SDeJ
	'Montreux' (Ia/b-c)	SDeJ
	'Mount Duckling' (Ia-b/b)	CBod
	'Muscadet'PBR (VIIa-b/b)	GKev LAma NGdn SDeJ
§	***nanum*** (IXc/b)	ECho LAma WAbe WHal
	nepalense (IXc/a)	CAby CBcs CBro CCon CExl CHid CTca EBee ECho EPot ERCP GBin GBuc GEdr GKev LAma MCri SDeJ WAbe WCot WCru XLum
	- B&SWJ 2985	WCru
	'Nerone' (Ia/b)	CHid NNor
	'Netty's Pride' (Ia/b-c)	CAvo CBro CHid ERCP GBuc GKev MCri SDeJ SPer WCot
	'New Wave' (Ia/b)	SDeJ
	'New Yellow'	LRHS
	'Night Flyer' (Ib-c/b-c)	SDeJ
	nobilissimum (IXa-b/a)	EFEx
	'Nove Cento' (Ia/b) ♀H6	MCri SDeJ
	Odeon Group (VI-/a)	MCri
	'Olivia' (Ia)	LAma MCri
	Olympic Group (VI-/a)	MCri
	'Orange County' (Ia/b)	SDeJ
	'Orange Electric' (Ia/b)	GKev SDeJ
	'Orange Marmalade' (IIb/c-d)	GKev SDeJ
	'Orange Pixie' (Ia/b)	CBod MAsh MCri NNor SCoo
	'Orange Twinkle' (Ib-c/b)	SDeJ
	'Orania'PBR (VIIIb/b)	SDeJ
	oriental hybrids (VII)	SDeJ
*	Oriental Superb Group	NGdn
§	***oxypetalum*** (IXb-c/b)	ECho
	- var. ***insigne*** (IXb-c/b)	ECho EPot GBin GBuc WAbe WHal
	Painted Pixie = 'Ceb Paint' (Ia/b)	CBod
	papilliferum (IXc/d)	LAma
	pardalinum (IXc/d)	CAvo CBro CWCL EBee ECho GKev WCru WHal
	- var. ***giganteum*** (IXc/d) ♀H6	EPfP MCri MNrw
	- subsp. ***pardalinum*** (IX)	GBuc
§	- subsp. ***vollmeri*** (IXc/d)	GBuc WCru

§	- subsp. ***wigginsii*** (IXc/d)	MCri WCru
	× ***parkmanii*** 'Rosy Dimple' (VIIa/b)	SDeJ
	parryi (IXb-c/a)	EBee WHal
	parvum (IXa-b/a)	ECho GBuc
	'Patricia's Pride' (Ia-b/b-c)	MCri SDeJ
	'Peach Butterflies' (Ic/d)	SDeJ
	'Peach Dwarf' (Ia/b-c)	SDeJ
	'Peach Pixie' (Ia/b)	NBir SCoo
	'Pearl Jennifer' (Ib-a/c)	SDeJ
	'Pearl Jessica' (Ib-c/b-c)	SDeJ
	'Pearl Loraine' (Ib-c/b-c)	CAvo SDeJ
	'Pearl Sonja'	SDeJ
	'Pearl Stacey' (Ib-c/c)	GKev SDeJ
	'Peggy North' (Ic/d)	GEdr
	'Penthouse' (VIIa/b) **new**	LRHS
	philippinense (IXa-b/a)	EWoo GKev LAma MCri WPGP
	'Pimento' (VIIa/b)	CBod SDeJ
	'Pink Flavour' (Ic/c)	GKev SDeJ
	'Pink Heart'	LBuc LRHS
	Pink Perfection Group (VIb/a) ♀H6	CBro ERCP GKev LAma MCri NNor SCoo SDeJ SPer
	'Pink Pixie'PBR (Ia/b)	CBod NNor NSoo SDeJ
	'Pink Tiger' (VIIIb/c)	MCri NNor
	poilanei HWJ 681	WCru
	- WWJ 11679	WCru
	polyphyllum (IXc/d)	GLin
	pomponium (IXc/d)	EBee
	primulinum (IX)	GKev
	- var. ***ochraceum*** (IXc/a)	GKev LAma MCri WCru
	aff. ***primulinum*** var. ***ochraceum*** KWJ 12064 (IXc/a) **new**	WCru
	'Proud Bride' (VIIa/b) **new**	MAsh
§	***pumilum*** (IXc/d) ♀H6	EBee ECho EPot GKev LAma MCri SDeJ
	'Purple Prince' (VIIIa-b/a-b)	SDeJ
	pyrenaicum (IXc/d)	CAby ECho GBuc IBlr MCri WShi
§	- subsp. ***carniolicum*** (IXc/d)	MCri
	'Red Carpet' (Ia/b)	MCri NNor SDeJ
	'Red County' (Ia/c-b)	SDeJ
	'Red Electric' (Ia/b)	SDeJ
	'Red Flavour' (Ic/b-c) **new**	GKev SBod
	'Red Hot' (VIIIc-d/b)	SDeJ
	'Red Twinkle'	SDeJ
	'Red Velvet' (Ic/d)	CAvo SDeJ
	regale (IXb/a) ♀H6	CAvo CBro CCon CHel CTca CWCL EBee ECha ELan EPfP EPot ERCP GKev LAma MCri NLar NNor SDeJ SPer WCot
	- 'Album' (IXb/a)	CAvo EBee ERCP GKev IMou LAma LRHS MCri NLar NNor SCoo SDeJ WCot
§	- 'Royal Gold' (IXb/a)	MCri
	'Reinesse' (Ia/b)	SDeJ
	'Robert Swanson' (VIIIb-c/b)	GKev LAma SDeJ
	'Robina' (VIIIa-b/b-c)	WCot
	'Roma' (Ia/b)	NBir
	'Rosefire' (Ia/b)	NNor
	'Rosella's Dream' (Ia/b)	GKev SDeJ
	'Rosemary North' (Ic/d)	CDes
	'Rosselini'	SDeJ
	rosthornii (IXc/d)	CExl EBee GKev LAma WCru
	'Royal Fantasy' (VIIIa-b/b)	NNor
	'Royal Gold'	see *L. regale* 'Royal Gold'
	rubellum (IXb/a)	EFEx GEdr

* 'Rubina' MCri
sachalinense (IXa/b) RBS 0235 EPPr
'Salinas' (VIIa/b) SDeJ
'Salmon Tiger' SBod SDeJ
'Salmon Twinkle' (Ib-c/c) SDeJ
sargentiae (IXb-c/a) GCal MCri WCot WCru
'Satisfaction' (VIIIa-b/-) SDeJ
'Scarlet Delight' (VIIb-c/c-d) GKev SDeJ
'Scheherazade' (VIIIc/d) LAma MCri SDeJ
'Set Point' (VIIb/b) SDeJ
'Silly Girl' (Ia/-) NNor
'Smoky Mountain' (VIIIc/d) GKev SDeJ
'Souvenir'[PBR] (VIIa-b/b) CSut NGdn
'Spark' (Ia-b/b) NNor
speciosum (IXb-c/d) B&SWJ 4847 WCru
\- B&SWJ 4924 WCru
\- var. ***album*** (IXb-c/d) ECho GKev LEdu MCri NBir SDeJ
\- var. ***gloriosoides*** (IXb-c/d) GKev LAma
\- var. ***rubrum*** (IXb-c/d) ECha ECho EPfP GKev LAma MCri NBir SDeJ SPer SRms
§ - - 'Uchida' (IXb-c/d) CExl MCri SDeJ
Sphinx = 'Holecaca' (Ia/c-d) CBod NNor WCot
'Spring Pink' (Ia/-) ERCP GKev SDeJ
'Staccato' (Ia/c) MCri
'Stainless Steel' (Ia/b) SDeJ
'Star Gazer' (VIIa/c) CBod CBro GKev LAma LRHS MCri NNor SCoo SDeJ
'Starfighter' (VIIa-b/c) CBod CSut GKev MCri SDeJ
'Sterling Star' (Ia/b) MCri NNor
Stones = 'Holebobo' (Ia/b) NNor
'Sulphur King' WCot
sulphureum (IXb-c/a) LAma MCri
'Sun Ray' (Ia/b) MCri
'Sunny Morning' (IIc/c) **new** GKev
superbum (IXc/d) EBee GBuc GKev LAma WCru WPGP
* 'Sutter's Gold' (I) MCri
'Sweet Lord' (Ia/b) NSoo SBod SDeJ
'Sweet Surrender' (Ib-c/c-d) GKev MCri NNor SDeJ
'Tailor Made' (Ia/b) GKev SBod SDeJ
taliense (IXc/d) ECho LAma MCri WCru
'Tarragona'[PBR] (VIIIb/b) SDeJ
tenuifolium see *L. pumilum*
Tiger Babies Group (VIIIb-c/c-d) CAvo
tigrinum see *L. lancifolium*
'Tom Pouce' (VIIa/b) MCri SDeJ
'Toronto' (Ia-b/b) SDeJ
'Toscane' (Ia/b-c) SDeJ
'Touch' (VIIb/-) MCri
Triumphator = 'Zanlophator'[PBR] (VIIIb/a-b) GKev MCri NNor SDeJ
tsingtauense (IXa/c) EBee GKev MCri SDeJ
\- B&SWJ 4263 WCru
\- B&SWJ 4698 WCru
\- B&SWJ 519 WCru
'Uchida Kanoka' see *L. speciosum* var. *rubrum* 'Uchida'
'Urandi' (VIIIc/b) SDeJ
'Val Di Sole'[PBR] (Ia/b) SDeJ
'Venezuela'[PBR] (VIIa-b/b-c) NLar SDeJ
'Venture' (Ia/b) NNor
'Vico Queen' (VI-/a) **new** GKev
'Visaversa' (VIIIa-b/b) SDeJ
'Vivaldi' (Ia/b) SDeJ
vollmeri see *L. pardalinum* subsp. *vollmeri*
wallichianum (IXb/a) ECho EPot GKev LAma SDeJ XLum
wardii (IXc/d) CExl
'White American' see *L. longiflorum* 'White American'
'White Paradise' (V) SCoo
'White Present' (Vb/a) SDeJ
'White Twinkle' (Ia-b/b) SDeJ
wigginsii see *L. pardalinum* subsp. *wigginsii*
willmottiae see *L. davidii* var. *willmottiae*
wilsonii var. ***luteum*** MCri
'Wine Electric' (Ia/c) SDeJ
'Wine Flavour' (Ib/b) **new** GKev
xanthellum var. ***luteum*** (IXb-c/d) CDes WCru
§ 'Yellow Electric' (Ia/b) MCri SDeJ
'Yellow Eye' SDeJ
'Yeti' (Ia/b) SDeJ
'Zulu' **new** LRHS

lime see *Citrus* × *aurantiifolia*

lime, djeruk see *Citrus amblycarpa*

lime, Philippine see *Citrus* × *microcarpa*

limequat see *Citrus* × *floridana*

Limnanthes (*Limnanthaceae*)

douglasii ♀H7 CArn EPfP MNHC
\- subsp. ***rosea*** CSpe

Limonium (*Plumbaginaceae*)

bellidifolium CMea EDAr MWat NSla
binervosum SEND
'Blauer Diamant' EWoo
chilwellii EBee EPla MWat
cosyrense CMea MHer WAbe
dregeanum WThu
dumosum see *Goniolimon tataricum* var. *angustifolium*
gmelinii SPlb
* - subsp. ***hungaricum*** XLum
latifolium see *L. platyphyllum*
perezii CCon
§ ***platyphyllum*** CBod CChe CCon COtt EPfP EPla EWoo GMaP LAst LRHS LSun MBel MHer MMuc MWat SBod SCob SEND SMHy SPer SRms WBor WHar WHoo
\- 'Robert Butler' EPla GCal GQue MRav
\- 'Violetta' CBod EBee ELan EPfP EPla LAst MBel SPer SPoG WAul WHoo
sinuatum SVic
speciosum see *Goniolimon incanum*
vulgare WHer

Linaria (*Plantaginaceae*)

aeruginea CPBP
\- 'Neon Lights' CSpe EDAr NGdn SPoG
\- subsp. ***nevadensis*** 'Gemstones' SBch
alpina CSpe GJos NRya NSla SRms
anticaria 'Antique Silver' CExl LSou MRav WPtf
Blue Lace = 'Yalin' LSou

Name	Suppliers
cymbalaria	see *Cymbalaria muralis*
§ ***dalmatica***	EBee ECGP ELan EPPr IFro MPie NBid SBch SEND SPhx WCot WHea WMoo
dalmatica × purpurea	WCot
× ***dominii*** 'Carnforth'	SHar WWEG
- 'Yuppie Surprise'	CHid NBir
'Florence Lily Sophia Brown' new	WCot
genistifolia subsp. ***dalmatica***	see *L. dalmatica*
'Globosa Alba'	see *Cymbalaria muralis* 'Globosa Alba'
hepaticifolia	see *Cymbalaria hepaticifolia*
'Lemon Mousse' new	WCot
* ***lobata alba***	ECho SPlb
origanifolia	see *Chaenorhinum origanifolium*
pallida	see *Cymbalaria pallida*
'Peachy'	CSpe MCot MHol MTis SPoG WCot WRHF
pilosa	see *Cymbalaria pilosa*
purpurea	CTri EHoe ELan EPfP IFoB MHer MLHP MNHC NBro NPer NPol NPri NWad SEND SPhx SRms WCot WFar WMoo WSFF XLum
- 'Alba'	see *L. purpurea* 'Springside White'
- 'Brown's White Strain'	CBre CSpe EBee EPPr IBoy LRHS MHol SPad WCot
- 'Canon Came'	CNat
- 'Canon Went'	CBre CSpe CTri EBee EHoe ELan EPfP EWoo GJos LBMP LRHS MMuc MNHC MSpe NBir NBro NPol SGbt SHil SPer SPhx SRms SWvt WCAu WFar WKif WMoo WWEG
- 'Freefolk Piccolo'	SHar
- pink-flowered	CSpe
- 'Radcliffe Innocence'	see *L. purpurea* 'Springside White'
§ - 'Springside White'	GJos LBMP LRHS NBir NGdn SBch SPer SPhx WFar WWEG XLum
repens	WCot WHer
× ***sepium***	WCot
triornithophora	CCon LBMP MHol MSpe SPlb WKif WMoo
- 'Pink Budgies'	LSou
- purple-flowered	WMoo
- 'Rosea'	CSpe
vulgaris	CArn CHab CWld EPfP MHer MLHP MNHC NMir WHer WHfH WJek
- f. ***peloria***	CPBP

Lindelofia (*Boraginaceae*)

Name	Suppliers
anchusoides misapplied	see *L. longiflora*
anchusoides (Lindl.) Lehm.	EPPr NBid
§ ***longiflora***	EBee GCal GCra GMaP LPla WHea WSHC

Lindera (*Lauraceae*)

Name	Suppliers
angustifolia FMWJ 13156 new	WCru
benzoin	CBcs EPfP LRHS MBlu NLar
erythrocarpa	EPfP
- B&SWJ 6271	WCru
- B&SWJ 8730	WCru
megaphylla	CBcs CHEx
metcalfiana var. ***dictyophylla*** KWJ 12312 new	WCru
obtusiloba 🏆^{H5}	CAbP MBlu
- B&SWJ 8723	WCru
- B&SWJ 11054	WCru
- B&SWJ 12555 from Korea new	WCru
praecox	EPfP
- B&SWJ 10802	WCru
- B&SWJ 10953 from north Japan	WCru
- B&SWJ 11125 from south Japan	WCru
reflexa	NLar
sericea B&SWJ 11123	WCru
- B&SWJ 11141	WCru
- var. ***lancea*** B&SWJ 11071	WCru
- - B&SWJ 11118	WCru
strychnifolia	EPfP
tonkinensis FMWJ 13123 new	WCru
triloba B&SWJ 5570	WCru
- B&SWJ 11121	WCru
- B&SWJ 11466	WCru
umbellata B&SWJ 10881	WCru
- var. ***membranacea*** B&SWJ 6227	WCru
- - B&SWJ 10837	WCru

Lindernia (*Linderniaceae*)

Name	Suppliers
grandiflora	ESwi LLWG

Linnaea (*Caprifoliaceae*)

Name	Suppliers
borealis	CExl EPot NSla WAbe XEll
- subsp. ***americana***	NHar WAbe

Linum (*Linaceae*)

Name	Suppliers
alexeenkoanum	XSen
anatolicum	XSen
arboreum 🏆^{H4}	GKev LLHF NBir
bienne	WCot
boissieri new	LLHF
campanulatum	WThu
flavum	GKev XSen
- 'Compactum'	CMea EBee ECho LLHF SRms
'Gemmell's Hybrid' 🏆^{H4}	ECho EWes GKev ITim NBir WAbe WThu
grandiflorum 'Rubrum'	CSpe
hirsutum	XSen
hypericifolium new	MNHC
monogynum	ECou LLHF
§ - var. ***diffusum***	ECou
- 'Nelson'	see *L. monogynum* var. *diffusum*
narbonense	CCse EWld SIgm SPhx
- 'Heavenly Blue'	NCGa
§ ***perenne***	CArn CBod ECha ELan ENfk EPfP GMaP LSun MHer MMuc MNHC NLar SCob SIde SPer SPoG WJek WSHC WWEG
- 'Album'	EBee ECha ELan EPfP NLar WJek
- subsp. ***alpinum*** 'Alice Blue'	WAbe
§ - 'Blau Saphir'	GQue NHol NLar
- Blue Sapphire	see *L. perenne* 'Blau Saphir'
- 'Himmelszelt'	NLar
- subsp. ***lewisii***	NBir
- 'Nanum Diamond'	NLar
- 'Nanum Sapphire'	see *L. perenne* 'Blau Saphir'
sibiricum	see *L. perenne*
suffruticosum subsp. ***salsoloides***	SBrt

– subsp. ***salsoloides*** 'Nanum'	WThu
tenuifolium	SPhx
uninerve	WAbe
usitatissimum	MHer SIde
– 'Blue Dress'	CSpe SPhx

Lippia (*Verbenaceae*)

sp.	SWvt
canescens	see *Phyla nodiflora* var. *canescens*
chamaedrifolia	see *Verbena peruviana*
citriodora	see *Aloysia citrodora*
dulcis	CArn ENfk EOHP
nodiflora	see *Phyla nodiflora*
repens	see *Phyla nodiflora*

Liquidambar ✿ (*Hamamelidaceae*)

acalycina	CDul CJun EBee EBtc ELan EPfP EPla MGos NLar SBir SCoo SGol SLim SSta WPGP WPat
– 'Burgundy Flush' [H6]	CJun NLar SBir SSta
– 'Spinners'	LMil LRHS SBir SSpi
formosana	CDul CMCN CMac IArd LAst MSnd SBir SGol SSta WPGP
– 'Afterglow'	CJun NLar
– 'Ellen'	CJun NLar
– Monticola Group	CJun SLim SSta
orientalis	CDul CJun CLnd CMCN EBtc EPfP LLHF NPCo SBir SSta WPat
– 'M. Foster'	NLar
styraciflua	Widely available
– 'Andrew Hewson'	CAbP CJun CLnd EBee EPfP IVic LRHS MAsh MBlu NLar SBir SSta WPat
– 'Anja'	CJun MBlu SBir SSta WPat
– 'Anneke'	CJun SBir SSta
– 'Aurea'	see *L. styraciflua* 'Variegata' Overeynder
– 'Aurea Variegata'	see *L. styraciflua* 'Variegata' Overeynder
– 'Aurora'	CJun SBir
– 'Burgundy'	CJun CLnd LLHF MBlu SBir SSta WPat
I – 'Corky'	SSta
– 'Elstead Mill'	CAbP
– 'Emerald Sentinel'	SSta
– 'Festeri'	CEnd SBir SSta WPat
– 'Festival'	CJun CLnd EUJe MBlu
– 'Frosty' (v)	CJun SBir SSta
– 'Globe'	see *L. styraciflua* 'Gum Ball'
– 'Gold Beacon'	MPkF
– 'Golden Treasure' (v)	CDul CJun CLnd CMCN LRHS MBri MGos SBir SGol SReu SSta
– 'Goldmember'	CJun SSta
– 'Granary Sunset'	SBir SSta
§ – 'Gum Ball'	CEnd CJun CLnd CMCN EBee ELon EPfP EPla EWes LLHF MGos NLar NPCo SBir SCob SLim SMad SSta SWvt WPat
– Happidaze = 'Hapdell'	CJun NLar SBir WPat
– 'Jennifer Carol'	CJun NLar SBir SSta
– 'Kia'	CAbP CEnd CJun LLHF SBir WPat
– 'Kirsten'	CJun
– 'Lane Roberts' [H6]	CDoC CDul CLnd CMCN CMHG CMac CSBt CTho EBee ELan EPfP EPla IArd LEdu MAsh MBlu MBri MGos NLar SBir SCob SCoo SEWo SPer SPoG SSta SWvt WCFE WPat
– 'Lynn'	SBir SSta
– 'Manon' (v)	CEnd CJun SPoG
– 'Midwest Sunset'	CJun MBlu SBir WPat
– 'Moonbeam' (v)	CEnd CJun NLar SBir SCob SLim SSta WPat
– 'Moraine'	CJun
– 'Naree'	CJun NLar SSta WPat
– 'Nina'	SSta
– 'Nyewood'	SBir
– 'Oconee'	CEnd EPfP LEdu LLHF MAsh NLar SSta WPat
– 'Paarl' (v)	CJun CLnd NLar SGol
– 'Palo Alto' [H6]	CEnd CJun LLHF LRHS MAsh MBlu SBir SCoo SLim SSta WPGP WPat
– 'Parasol'	CAbP CEnd CJun CLnd EBtc SBir SSta
– 'Pendula'	CJun CLnd MBlu SBir SSta
– 'Penwood' [H6]	CJun NLar SBir SSta WPat
– 'Red Sunset'	SSta
– 'Rotundiloba'	CJun CLnd CMCN EPfP LLHF LRHS MAsh MBlu SSta WPGP WPat
– 'Savill Torch'	SBir SSta
– 'Schock's Gold'	CJun MAsh SSta WPat
§ – 'Silver King' (v)	CDul CJun CLnd CMCN CMac EBee EPla LRHS MGos MPkF NLar NPCo SCoo SGol SHil SLim SPer SPoG SReu SSta WPat
– 'Simone'	SBir SGol SSta
– 'Slender Silhouette' [H6]	CAbP CDoC CDul CJun CLnd EBee EPfP EPla EUJe GKin LLHF LRHS MAsh MBlu MBri NLar SBir SCoo SGol SLim SMad SPoG SSpi SSta WHor WMou WPat
– 'Stared'	CDul CEnd CJun CLnd EBee EBtc EPfP GQue LEdu LRHS MBlu MBri NLar SBir SCoo SLim SSta WPGP WPat
– 'Thea'	CAbP CJun CLnd EBee EPfP LRHS MAsh MBlu SBir SSta
– 'Variegata' misapplied	see *L. styraciflua* 'Silver King'
§ – 'Variegata' Overeynder (v)	CJun CLnd CMac EBee ELan LRHS MAsh SBir SLim SPer SSta
– 'White Star' (v)	CJun
– 'Woorby Rose'	NLar SBir
– 'Worplesdon' [H6]	Widely available

Liriodendron (*Magnoliaceae*)

'Chapel Hill'	MBlu NLar WPat
chinense [H6]	CBcs CDul CMCN EBee EPfP MBlu SGol WPGP
chinense × ***tulipifera***	WPGP
'Doc Deforce's Delight'	MBlu MBri NLar
tulipifera [H6]	Widely available
– 'Ardis'	NLar
– 'Aureomarginatum' (v) [H6]	Widely available
– 'Fastigiatum'	CDoC CDul CEnd CLnd CMCN CTho EBee ECrN ELan EPfP EPla MAsh MBlu MBri NLar SGol SPer WPat
– 'Glen Gold'	CEnd MBlu NLar
– 'Heltorf'	NLar
– 'Integrifolium'	NLar
– 'Purgatory'	MBlu
– 'Roodhaan'	ETwe NLar
– 'Rotundiloba' **new**	MBlu
– 'Snow Bird' (v) **new**	EBee

Liriope ✿ (*Asparagaceae*)

'Big Blue'	see *L. muscari* 'Big Blue'
§ ***exiliflora***	CLAP WWEG
– 'Ariaka-janshige' (v)	LRHS WWEG

	- Silvery Sunproof misapplied	see *L. spicata* 'Gin-ryu', *L. muscari* 'Variegata'
§	***gigantea***	CLAP EPPr SCob
	graminifolia misapplied	see *L. muscari*
	hyacinthifolia	see *Reineckea carnea*
	koreana	EBee EPPr GCal WWEG
	- B&SWJ 8821	WCru
	'Majestic'	CBct CLAP MHer WHoo
	'Minnow'	WCot
	minor	CMac
§	***muscari*** ♀H5	Widely available
	- B&SWJ 561	WCru
	- 'Alba'	see *L. muscari* 'Monroe White'
	- Amethyst = 'Liptp'	NPri
§	- 'Big Blue'	CAbb CBct CBod CDul CExl CHel CLAP CMac EAEE EBee ECtt ELan ELon EPPr EPfP EPri EShb EWoo GBin LPal LRHS MRav MSwo NLar SCob SGol SWvt WMoo WWEG
	- 'Christmas Tree'	EPPr WHoo WMoo WWEG
	- 'Evergreen Giant'	see *L. gigantea*
	- 'Gold-banded' (v)	CBct CLAP EPPr EPfP LRHS SCob WCot WHil WWEG
	- 'Goldfinger'	CExl EBee SMad WWEG
	- 'Ingwersen'	CExl EBee ECho ELon EPPr EPfP EWoo SCob WWEG XLum
	- Isabella = 'Lirf'	EBee EPPr
	- 'John Burch' (v)	CBct CExl CLAP ELon LAst NLar NOak SMad WGrn WWEG
	- 'Lilac Wonder'	EPPr LRHS SCob
	- 'Majestic' misapplied	see *L. exiliflora*
	- 'Moneymaker'	EPPr GBin GKev LAst LRHS SCob XEll
§	- 'Monroe White'	CBct CBro CExl CLAP CMac EBee ECha ELan EPPr EPfP EShb EWoo LAst LEdu LRHS MRav NBid NLar NOak SCob SPer SPoG SWvt WWEG
	- 'Okina' (v)	CDes CHel CKno EBee ELon LBMP LLHF LRHS MNrw MSCN NLar NSti SMad SPer WCot WRHF
	- 'Pee Dee Ingot'	EShb
	- 'Purple Passion' **new**	SCob
	- 'Royal Purple'	CBct CBod CLAP EBee ECtt ELon EPPr EWoo LRHS MAsh MBri NLar SCob SPer WGrn WWEG
	- 'Silver Ribbon'	CBro CLAP EPfP MGos WWEG
	- 'Super Blue'	EPPr
	- 'Superba'	WCot
§	- 'Variegata' (v)	CBod CCon CDes CExl CLAP EBee ECho ELan EPPr EWes LAst LBMP LEdu LPal LRHS MAsh MAvo NBir SPer SPoG SWvt WWEG
	- variegated, white-flowered (v)	ECho
	- 'Webster Wideleaf'	EBee WCot WWEG
	platyphylla	see *L. muscari*
	Pure Blonde = 'Lirblonde' **new**	CBct ESwi
	spicata	EBee ECho EWoo LRHS WWEG XLum
	- 'Alba'	ECho LRHS MRav
§	- 'Gin-ryu' (v)	CBct CExl CLAP CMac EAEE ELan ELon EPPr EPfP EShb EWes LEdu LPal LPot MRav SCob SGol SMad SPer WCot WWEG XLum
	- 'Silver Dragon'	see *L. spicata* 'Gin-ryu'
	- 'Small Green'	WWEG

Listera (*Orchidaceae*)

	ovata	WHer

Litchi (*Sapindaceae*)

	chinensis	CCCN

Lithocarpus ✿ (*Fagaceae*)

	densiflorus var. ***echinoides***	CMCN
	edulis	CExl CFil CHEx EBee SArc SKHP
§	***glaber***	CFil

Lithodora (*Boraginaceae*)

§	***diffusa***	ECho SGol SRot
	- 'Alba'	CTri ECho NCGa SPer SPoG
	- 'Cambridge Blue'	SPer
	- 'Compacta'	EWes WAbe
§	- 'Grace Ward' ♀H5	CBod ECtt EPfP GMaP LLHF MMuc NSir NWad WAbe
§	- 'Heavenly Blue' ♀H5	Widely available
	- 'Inverleith'	ECho
	- 'Pete's Favourite'	ECtt NWad WAbe WHil WRHF
	- 'Picos'	CMea ECho EPot GCrg NLar NSla NWad SIgm WAbe WThu
	- 'Star'PBR	CHel CHid CMHG ELon EPfP LRHS NLar SCoo SPer SPoG SRot SWvt WFar WIce
	- 'White Star' **new**	WIce
	fruticosa	CArn
	× ***intermedia***	see *Moltkia* × *intermedia*
§	***oleifolia*** ♀H4	ECho EPot LLHF LRHS MWat NBir WHil
	rosmarinifolia	WCFE
	zahnii	ECho EPot LLHF LRHS SVen
	- 'Azure-ness'	CPBP MCot SChF WAbe
	- compact **new**	SIgm

Lithophragma (*Saxifragaceae*)

	heterophyllum	EBee
	parviflorum	EWes

Lithospermum (*Boraginaceae*)

	diffusum	see *Lithodora diffusa*
	doerfleri	see *Moltkia doerfleri*
	'Grace Ward'	see *Lithodora diffusa* 'Grace Ward'
	'Heavenly Blue'	see *Lithodora diffusa* 'Heavenly Blue'
	officinale	CArn GPoy NMir WHfH
	oleifolium	see *Lithodora oleifolia*
	purpureocaeruleum	see *Buglossoides purpurocaerulea*

Litsea (*Lauraceae*)

	cubeba FMWJ 13011 **new**	WCru
	glauca	see *Neolitsea sericea*
	japonica	SVen

Littonia (*Colchicaceae*)

	modesta	CPne CRHN ECho

Livistona (*Arecaceae*)

	chinensis ♀H1c	CPHo LPal SBig
	decora	LPal
	jenkinsiana	NLos

Loasa (*Loasaceae*)

	sp.	CArn
	triphylla var. ***volcanica***	EWes WSHC

Lobelia ✿ (*Campanulaceae*)

	bridgesii	CDTJ CExl CFil EWes GCal LRHS WKif WMoo
§	***cardinalis*** ♀H3	CArn CBAq CHEx CMac CUse EHon ELon GMaP NGBl NLar NPer SPlb SRms SWat SWvt WFar WHil WMAq
	- 'Bee's Flame'	CBod CCon CNor CPrp CWGN EAEE ECtt EPla GBuc IKil LRHS MAsh MRav MSpe NEgg NGdn SPtp WWtn
§	- 'Elmfeuer'	CMHG CWCL ECtt EHoe EWoo IBoy NLar NPri SPlb SPoG SWvt XLum
	- subsp. ***graminea*** var. ***multiflora***	CCon
	- 'Illumination'	ELon
§	- 'Queen Victoria' ♀H3	Widely available
	- 'Russian Princess' misapplied	CWCL EPfP IBoy LRHS MAsh MHol NGdn SPoG SWvt WFar WHar WWEG
	chinensis	LLWG
	'Cinnabar Deep Red'	see *L.* × *speciosa* 'Fan Tiefrot'
	'Cinnabar Rose'	see *L.* × *speciosa* 'Fan Zinnoberrosa'
	Compliment Blue	see *L.* × *speciosa* 'Kompliment Blau'
	Compliment Deep Red	see *L.* × *speciosa* 'Kompliment Tiefrot'
	Compliment Purple	see *L.* × *speciosa* 'Kompliment Purpur'
	Compliment Scarlet	see *L.* × *speciosa* 'Kompliment Scharlach'
	'Compton Pink'	CBod EWes LBuc MCot SCob
	Elizabeth Strangman selection	NDov
	erinus Big Blue = 'Weslobigblue'[PBR]	LAst
	- Blue Star = 'Wesstar'[PBR]	LSou
	- 'Crystal Palace'	NPri
	- (Fountain Series) 'Fountain Blue'	NPri
	- - 'Fountain White'	NPri
	- Hot Tiger = 'Wesloti'[PBR]	LAst
	- 'Kathleen Mallard' (d)	CCCN SWvt
	- Purple Star = 'Wespurstar'[PBR]	LSou
	- 'Richardii'	see *L. richardsonii* hort.
	- Riviera Series	NPri
	- 'Sapphire'	NPri
	- Super Star = 'Weslosu'[PBR] (Star Series)	LAst LSou
	excelsa	MTPN SBrt
	- B&SWJ 9513	WCru
	Fan Deep Red	see *L.* × *speciosa* 'Fan Tiefrot'
	Fan Deep Rose	see *L.* × *speciosa* 'Fan Orchidrosa'
	Fan Salmon	see *L.* × *speciosa* 'Fan Lachs'
	'Flamingo'	see *L.* × *speciosa* 'Pink Flamingo'
	fulgens	see *L. cardinalis*
	- Saint Elmo's Fire	see *L. cardinalis* 'Elmfeuer'
	× ***gerardii***	see *L.* × *speciosa*
	gibberoa	CDTJ CHEx
	'Gladys Lindley'	LRHS
	'Hadspen Purple'[PBR]	see *L.* × *speciosa* 'Hadspen Purple'
	inflata	CArn GPoy
	laxiflora	CFis CHll
	- B&SWJ 9064	WCru
	- var. ***angustifolia***	CAby CDTJ CHEx CPrp CSam EWld GCal MSpe SMHy SMrm SRms
	linnaeoides	SPlb
	'Lipstick'	WWEG
§	***montana***	EWld GLin WCot
	- B&SWJ 8220	WCru
	pedunculata	see *Pratia pedunculata*
	'Periwinkle Blue'	LAst
	'Pink Passion'	LRHS
	polyphylla	SBrt
	'Queen Victoria'	see *L. cardinalis* 'Queen Victoria'
§	***richardsonii*** hort.	SWvt WOth
	sessilifolia	CExl LLWG
	- B&SWJ 8875	WCru
	siphilitica	Widely available
	- 'Alba'	CSam EBee EPfP GCal LRHS SBch SPoG SRms SWat SWvt WBor WHrl WMoo WShi
	- blue-flowered	CSpe NCGa SGSe SMrm SWat SWvt
	- 'Rosea'	MNrw
§	× ***speciosa***	IKil SVic SWat WBor WMoo XLum
	- 'Butterfly Blue'	CNor SGbt SPad
	- 'Butterfly Rose'	SRot
	- 'Cherry Ripe'	CPrp GCra LLHF
	- 'Dark Crusader'	CCon ECtt ELan EPfP LRHS NHol SWat WMnd
	- Fan Series	MRav
	- - 'Fan Blau'	CBod ELan EPfP LPot LRHS MCot MHol NSir SCob SMrm WWEG
	- - 'Fan Burgundy'	CBod EPfP EWoo LRHS MHer NGdn NLar SCob
§	- - 'Fan Lachs'	CBod CWCL EPfP LRHS MHer SMrm
§	- - 'Fan Orchidrosa' ♀H5	CHEx EPfP LRHS NGdn SGSe SRot
	- - 'Fan Scharlach' ♀H5	EPfP LRHS NLar SPoG SRot SWvt WOut
§	- - 'Fan Tiefrot' ♀H5	LRHS SRms SWvt WOut
§	- - 'Fan Zinnoberrosa' ♀H5	SRms SRot SWvt WMoo
	- 'Grape Knee-high'	GCra LLHF WWEG
§	- 'Hadspen Purple'[PBR]	CHel CMHG CMac CSpe CWGN EBee ECtt ELan EPfP IPot LRHS MAsh MBri MCot MRav NCGa NDov SGSe SHar SRms SWat SWvt
	- 'Kimbridge Beet'	CMac SGSe
§	- (Kompliment Series) 'Kompliment Blau'	SWvt
§	- - 'Kompliment Purpur'	MMuc MNrw SWvt
§	- - 'Kompliment Scharlach' ♀H5	CWat EPfP MNrw NPer SWvt
§	- - 'Kompliment Tiefrot'	EPfP MMuc MNrw SMrm SWvt
	- 'Monet Moment'	EBee ECtt EWes SPoG SWvt
	- 'Pauline'	ECtt
	- 'Pink Elephant' ♀H3	ECtt GCra SHar WCFE WFar WWEG
§	- 'Pink Flamingo'	MBri SHar SPer WMoo WShi
	- 'Red Velvet'	WOut
	- 'Ruby Slippers'	EBee EPfP WWEG
	- 'Russian Princess' purple-flowered	CCon ECtt EHoe ELan EPla EWoo LAst LSou MBel MBri MCot MHer MPie MSpe MWat NCGa NDov NHol SPer SPtp WFar WMnd
	- 'Sparkling Burgundy'	LRHS
	- 'Sparkling Ruby'	CHel EPfP IKil LBuc MCot SWvt
	- 'Tania'	Widely available
§	- 'Vedrariensis'	CBod CMac CSpe ECtt ELan EPfP GBuc LRHS MBel MCot MHer MMuc MNrw SEND SMrm SPer SPoG SRms SWvt WCFE WFar WHoo WMnd XLum
	- 'Will Scarlet'	LRHS
	spicata	SBrt
	'Tania's Sister'	WCot WGrn WOut
	treadwellii	see *Pratia angulata* 'Treadwellii'
	tupa	Widely available

- JCA 12527 | IBlr
- Archibald's form | CExl GCra WPGP
- dark orange-flowered | SGSe
urens | CFil
valida | SWvt
- 'True Blue' | CWGN SWvt
vedrariensis | see *L.* × *speciosa* 'Vedrariensis'
villosa | SGSe
wollastonii | SPlb

Lobularia (*Brassicaceae*)

maritima Easter Bonnet Series | NPri
- 'Snow Crystals' | NPri
Snow Princess = 'Inlbusnopr'PBR | NPri

Loeselia (*Polemoniaceae*)

mexicana | CHll

loganberry see *Rubus* × *loganobaccus*

Lomandra (*Asparagaceae*)

filiformis Savanna Blue = 'Lmf500' | CKno ESwi LSou NOak
hystrix | SPlb
longifolia | ECou GCal LEdu SPlb
- 'Kulnura' | ECou
- Tanika = 'Lm300'PBR | ESwi NOak

Lomaria see *Blechnum*

Lomatia (*Proteaceae*)

dentata | LRHS MGil MRav
ferruginea | CBcs CDoC CExl CHel CSde CTsd EPfP GGal MGil SArc SChF SKHP WCru WPGP
fraseri | EBee EPfP LRHS NLar SSpi
hirsuta | MGil SKHP
longifolia | see *L. myricoides*
§ ***myricoides*** | CBcs CCCN CExl CTsd ELan EPfP LRHS MAsh MBri NLar SArc SKHP SLon SPer SSpi
silaifolia | LRHS SPoG
tinctoria | CBcs CDoC CExl CHel CTsd EPfP IDee LRHS MAsh NLar SSpi

Lomatium (*Apiaceae*)

columbianum | SIgm
grayi | SPhx
utriculatum | SIgm

Lonicera ✿ (*Caprifoliaceae*)

sp. | CMen
KR 291 | ELon
§ ***acuminata*** | CCon LRHS
- B&SWJ 3480 | WCru
- B&SWJ 6743 | WCru
- B&SWJ 6815 | WCru
- var. ***acuminata*** new | WCot
aff. ***acuminata*** NJM 11.033 new | WPGP
alberti | CDul EBee EPfP MBNS NLar SEND
alpigena | GJos
alseuosmoides | CDul EBee GBin LEdu LRHS NLar SEND SKHP SLon SPoG WCru WPGP WSHC
× ***americana*** misapplied | see *L.* × *italica*
§ × ***americana*** (Miller) K. Koch | CBcs CFlo CRHN EPfP LEdu MBri MMuc MSwo MWhi NLar NWea SEND SKHP SLim SRms WBor
§ × ***brownii*** 'Dropmore Scarlet' | Widely available
- 'Fuchsioides' misapplied | see *L.* × *brownii* 'Dropmore Scarlet'
- 'Fuchsioides' K. Koch | WSHC
caerulea | EPom MRav SVic WHar
- var. ***altaica*** | LEdu
- 'Atut' new | NLar
- 'Balalaika' new | CAgr
- 'Duet' new | NLar
- var. ***edulis*** | CAgr EWTr LBuc LEdu MCoo SDea
- - 'Blue Moon' | CAgr
- 'Eisbar' new | CAgr
- 'Kalinka' new | CAgr
- var. ***kamtschatica*** | CAgr EPom NLar
- - 'Fialka'PBR new | NLar
- - 'Morena'PBR | EPom GGGa
- - 'Nimfa' | GGGa
- 'Kirke' | GBin NLar
* - var. ***longifolia*** | NLar
§ ***caprifolium*** | CAco CDoC CFlo CRHN ECrN ELan EPfP LRHS NLar SPer WCot
- 'Anna Fletcher' | CRHN CSPN WCFE
- 'Cornish Cream' | SGol
- f. ***pauciflora*** | see *L.* × *italica*
- 'Spring Bouquet' | LRHS
chaetocarpa | CEnd MRav WSHC
'Clavey's Dwarf' | EPPr GKin LLHF
crassifolia | NLar SBrt WSHC
- 'Little Honey' | EPPr MBNS MMHG MPie MRav NLar WCot
deflexicalyx | EPfP NLar
demissa | EPfP
'Early Cream' | see *L. caprifolium*
'Elegant' | LBuc SCob
elisae | CAbP CJun CMac EPfP EWTr IArd IDee IMou MMuc NLar WSHC
etrusca | CCon MRav
- 'Donald Waterer' | CFlo CRHN EPfP LRHS NLar WFar
- 'Michael Rosse' | ELan IArd LRHS MBNS SKHP
- 'Superba' ♀H5 | CFlo CRHN EBee ELan EPfP LRHS NLar SEND SLim SPer WSHC
'Fire Cracker' | NLar SLon
flexuosa | see *L. japonica* var. *repens*
fragrantissima | Widely available
giraldii misapplied | see *L. acuminata*
giraldii Rehder | SLim
glabrata | NLar SCoo SLim
- B&SWJ 2150 | WCru
glaucescens | WPat
'Golden Trumpet' | CWGN LRHS
grata | see *L.* × *americana* (Miller) K. Koch
× ***heckrottii*** | CDoC CSBt NLar
- 'Gold Flame' ambig. | CFlo COtt CWld GKin NLar SCob
- 'Gold Flame' hort. ♀H5 | CDul CMac EBee ELan EPfP LBMP LBuc LRHS MAsh MBri MRav SEND SLim SPer SPoG SRms WFar WMoo WSHC
§ ***henryi*** | CBcs CDoC CDul CMac CRHN EPfP EWTr GKin IBoy LAst LRHS MAsh MGos MJak MSwo MWhi SCob SEND SLim SPer SPlb WFar WMoo WSHC
- B&SWJ 8109 | WCru
- 'Copper Beauty'PBR | CBcs CCon CEnd CMac COtt CWCL ECrN EPPr EUJe GKin IBoy

Name	Suppliers
	LBMP LBuc LRHS LSou MAsh MGos MJak MRav MWat NLar NPri NWad SGol SLon SPoG WCot WHar WPGP
- var. ***subcoriacea***	see *L. henryi*
hildebrandiana ♀H2	CCCN CDoC CExl CFil CHel CHll CRHN MOWG NLar SKHP
hispidula	SBrt
'Honey Baby'PBR	ELon EPfP ETwe LLHF LRHS NHol NWad
implexa	CMCN
insularis	see *L. morrowii*
involucrata	CExl CHll CMCN CMHG EPPr MBNS MBlu MMuc NChi SEND SPer WCFE
- var. ***ledebourii***	CBcs CDul ELan EPfP EWTr LAst LLHF LRHS MGil MMHG MRav NLar SKHP
- - 'Vian'	NLar
- 'Orange Dwarf'	SKHP
× ***americana*** ambig.	see *L.* × *italica*
§ × ***italica***	CRHN CSam CTri EBee ECrN LRHS MAsh MBNS MJak MSwo NPer SCoo SKHP SPer
§ - Harlequin = 'Sherlite'PBR (v)	CMac CSPN EHoe EPfP LRHS MJak SLim SPlb SRms SWvt
japonica	CMen IBoy WFar
§ - 'Aureoreticulata' (v) ♀H5	CDul CMac ECrN EHoe ELan EPfP EShb LRHS MGos MJak MRav MWhi NPer SGol SPer SRms WFar
- 'Cream Cascade'	COtt EWoo LRHS MSwo NLar SCoo SGol
- 'Dart's Acumen'	CRHN
- 'Dart's World'	COtt CWld MBri NLar
- 'Halliana'	Widely available
- 'Hall's Prolific' ♀H5	CDoC CDul CSBt ECrN ELan EPfP EWTr LBMP LBrs LBuc LRHS MAsh MBlu MBri MGos MRav MSwo MWat SCob SGol SLim SPad SPoG SWvt WFar WHar
§ - 'Horwood Gem' (v)	ECtt NLar SCoo SLim
- 'Maskerade' (v)	LLHF NBro NLar
- 'Mint Crisp'PBR (v)	CDul CMac COtt CSBt CSPN CWGN ECrN ECtt ELan EPfP EShb LAst LRHS LSou MBlu MBri MGos MJak NLar SGol SLim SLon SPad SPer SPoG SWvt WHar
- 'Peter Adams'	see *L. japonica* 'Horwood Gem'
- 'Princess Kate' **new**	ELan MBri NLar
- 'Red World'	WPat
§ - var. ***repens*** ♀H5	CDul CMac COtt CSBt CTri CWSG ECrN ECtt ELan EPfP LAst LRHS MBri MRav MSwo MWat NLar SCoo SGol SLim SLon SPad SPer SRms WMoo
- 'Variegata'	see *L. japonica* 'Aureoreticulata'
korolkowii	CFil CJun EPPr MBNS NBir NLar SEND WCFE WSHC
- 'Blue Velvet'	CAgr GBin MCoo NLar
- var. ***zabelii*** misapplied	see *L. tatarica* 'Zabelii'
- var. ***zabelii*** (Rehder) Rehder	ELan
lanceolata BWJ 7935	WCru
maackii	CHll CJun CMCN EPPr EPfP GJos MMHG MRav NLar WCFE
- f. ***podocarpa***	MMuc NLar
* ***macgregorii***	CMCN
macrantha B&SWJ 11687	WCru
- WWJ 11606	WCru
'Mandarin' ♀H5	CDoC CRHN ELan LRHS MBlu NLar SCoo SGol SLim SWvt WPat WSHC
maximowiczii var. ***sachalinensis***	NLar
§ ***morrowii***	CMCN
myrtillus	NLar
nitida	CAco CBcs CCVT CDul CMac CMen COtt CSBt CTri ECrN EPfP LAst NHed NWea SArc SCob SEWo SGol SPer WHar
- 'Baggesen's Gold' ♀H5	Widely available
- Edmée Gold = 'Briloni'	MAsh
- 'Ernest Wilson'	EPPr
- 'Fertilis'	SPer
- 'Lemon Beauty' (v)	CBcs CDoC CMac EBee ECrN EHoe EPPr EPfP EShb LAst LRHS MAsh MBNS MGos MSCN MWhi NBir NLar NWad SCob SGol SHil SPer SPoG SWvt WFar WHar WMoo
- 'Lemon Queen'	ELan MBri MMuc MSwo SEND
§ - 'Maigrün'	CBcs CCVT CDul EAEE EPfP EPla EShb LRHS MSwo NEoE SCob SHil SPer SWvt WFar
- Maygreen	see *L. nitida* 'Maigrün'
- 'Red Tips'	EHoe EShb GKin SCob SCoo WMoo
- 'Silver Beauty' (v)	CDul CMac ECrN EHoe EPla LAst LBMP MGos MSwo SCob SPer SPlb SRms SWvt WFar WMoo
- 'Tidy Tips'	EPPr NSoo
- 'Twiggy' (v)	CDoC CSBt EAEE EDAr EHoe LBuc LRHS MAsh NHol STPC WGrn
periclymenum	CArn CCVT CTri CWld ECrN GJos GPoy MHer MLHP MRav NMir NWea SCob SPlb WPnn WSFF
- 'Belgica' misapplied	see *L.* × *italica*
- 'Belgica'	Widely available
- 'Belgica Select' **new**	EWoo
- Caprilia Imperial = 'Inov86'PBR	LRHS
- Chic et Choc = 'Inov205' **new**	WCot
- 'Florida'	see *L. periclymenum* 'Serotina'
- 'Fragrant Cloud'	LBuc
- 'Graham Thomas' ♀H5	Widely available
- 'Harlequin'PBR	see *L.* × *italica* Harlequin
- 'Heaven Scent'	CFlo LBuc NLar WFar WPnn
- 'Honeybush'	CDoC CJun CSPN CWGN ETwe LBMP MAsh MGos NHol NWad SLim WFar WMoo
- 'La Gasnérie'	SLim
- 'Munster'	WSHC
- 'Red Gables'	CRHN ELon MBNS MBri MGos NLar SCoo SLim WCot WHlf WKif WPat
- 'Scentsation'PBR	CFlo CMac CSBt CWCL CWGN ELan EPfP EUJe LBMP LRHS MAsh MBri NCGa NLar SCoo SLon SPoG
- 'Serotina' ♀H5	Widely available
- 'Sweet Sue'	CCon CFlo COtt CRHN CSPN CSpe ELan ELon EPfP EWTr GBin LRHS MAsh MBNS MBri MGos MLHP MSwo NEgg SCoo SPoG SWvt WFar WMoo
pileata	Widely available
- 'Moss Green'	CBod EShb
- 'Silver Lining' (v)	WCFE
pilosa Willd. F&M 207	CFil WPGP
- F&M 256	CFil WPGP

× ***purpusii***	CHll CMac CRHN CTri EBee ECrN MBNS MLHP SCob SPer SRms WCFE WFar WSHC
- 'Spring Romance'	CMac
- 'Winter Beauty' ♀H5	Widely available
ramosissima	NLar
reticulata 'Silver'	NLar
saccata	EPfP
sempervirens	CRHN CSBt MBNS MRav WHar WSHC
- 'Cedar Lane'	LRHS
- 'Dropmore Scarlet'	see *L.* × *brownii* 'Dropmore Scarlet'
- 'Leo'	CWGN
- f. ***sulphurea***	WSHC
- - 'John Clayton'	EPfP LRHS SKHP
setifera 'Daphnis'	CJun
similis var. ***delavayi*** ♀H5	CFlo COtt CRHN CSPN CSde CWGN ELan EPfP LBMP LRHS MAsh MBri MRav NEgg NSoo SDix SEND SRms WCru WSHC
'Simonet'	CWCL NLar
splendida	WSHC
standishii	CTri WFar
- 'Budapest'	ELon EPfP LEdu LLHF LRHS MAsh MBlu MBri MRav NLar SPoG WFar WPat
subaequalis	CFil CRHN
- Og 93.329	CExl SKHP WPGP WSHC
Sweet Isabel = 'Genbel'PBR	EPfP LRHS SKHP
syringantha	CArn CDoC CHel CRHN CWld ECrN ELan EPfP EWTr LAst LEdu MMuc MNrw MRav MWhi NEgg NEoE NLar NSoo SEND SEle SPer WBor WCFE WFar WSHC
- 'Grandiflora'	GQui
tatarica	CHll CMCN MRav
- 'Alba'	CJun EPPr EWTr
- 'Arnold Red'	CBcs ELan EPPr EPfP MBlu MHer NLar SEND WBor
- 'Hack's Red'	CMCN ELon EPPr EPfP LEdu LRHS NSoo SCoo SKHP SMDP SPer SPoG SVen SWvt WGrn
- 'Rosea'	EPPr
§ - 'Zabelii'	MNrw
× ***tellmanniana*** ♀H5	CBcs CDoC CDul CExl CHel CMac CRHN CWCL ECtt ELan EPfP LRHS MAsh MBlu MBri MGos MJak MSwo MWat NEgg SCob SEND SLim SPer SPoG SRms WMoo WSHC
- 'Joan Sayers'	SCoo SLim WCFE
- 'Pharaoh's Trumpet'	EPfP LRHS SLon
thibetica	MBlu
tomentella B&SWJ 2654 new	WCru
tragophylla ♀H5	CDoC CSBt ELan EWTr IDee LEdu LRHS MBNS MRav NLar SCoo SEND SLim SPer SWvt WPat WSHC
- 'Maurice Foster'	ELan SMDP WSHC
webbiana	ELan
xylosteum	CArn EBtc EPPr NLar SSta

Lophomyrtus ✿ (*Myrtaceae*)

§ ***bullata*** ♀H2	CDTJ SPer
× ***ralphii*** 'Black Pearl'	CWSG EShb LRHS MBri MPkF NSoo SCoo SEle SHil SLim SPoG SRkn WFar
- 'Gloriosa' (v)	EPfP
- 'Kathryn'	CBcs CDoC COtt CSde CTsd ELan LRHS MPkF NLar SPoG SRGP
- 'Krinkly'	SVen
- 'Little Star' (v)	CBcs COtt CSde LRHS SEle WPat
- Logan's form (v)	CBcs EBee LRHS MGil NLar
- 'Magic Dragon'PBR (v)	EBee LRHS MBri SEle SHil SPoG
- 'Multicolor' (v)	CBcs LRHS NPri SLim SVen
- 'Pixie'	CBcs COtt CSde EPfP GKin LRHS MAsh SEle SLim SPoG SVen WPat
- 'Purpurea'	MPkF
- 'Red Dragon'	CAbP CBcs CMac LRHS LSou MAsh SLim WFar WPat
- 'Wild Cherry'	COtt EBee LRHS

Lophosoria (*Dicksoniaceae*)

quadripinnata	CBty CCon CDTJ NLos SBig WPGP

Lophospermum (*Plantaginaceae*)

'Cream Delight'	CCCN
§ ***erubescens*** ♀H2	CRHN SBch
- 'Bridal Bouquet'	CPla
Lofos Summer Cream = 'Sunasashiro'	LAst
Lofos Wine Red = 'Sunasaro'	LAst MCot
§ 'Magic Dragon'	CPla SEND SLim WBor WHil
§ 'Red Dragon'	CCCN CPla SBch
§ ***scandens***	CCCN
'Wine Red'	EShb LAst

loquat see *Eriobotrya japonica*

Loropetalum (*Hamamelidaceae*)

chinense 'Ming Dynasty'	CAbP MAsh SSta WAbe WFar
- 'Rose Blush'	SSpi
- var. ***rubrum***	CExl
- - 'Blush'	CBcs SEle SGol
- - 'Burgundy'	MPkF
- - 'Daybreak's Flame'	CBcs LRHS MGil MPkF SGol SSta WCot
- - 'Fire Dance'	CAbP CBcs CCCN CDoC CExl CSde CTsd ELon EPfP EUJe LRHS MAsh MGos MPkF SEle SPad SPoG SRkn SSpi SWvt WFar WHlf WPat
- - 'Fire Glow'	LRHS SHil
- - 'Pipa's Red'	MPkF
- 'Snowdance'	CAbP
- 'Tang Dynasty'	ESwi WFar

Lotononis (*Papilionaceae*)

galpinii new	SBrt

Lotus (*Papilionaceae*)

berthelotii	CCCN CDTJ ECtt EOHP LPot MCot
- deep red-flowered ♀H1c	SWvt
berthelotii × ***maculatus*** ♀H1c	CCCN MSCN
corniculatus	CArn CHab CWld GJos MCoo MHer MMuc MNHC NMir SEND SIde WSFF
germanicus	SPhx
'Gold Flash'	LAst
hirsutus ♀H4	CArn CBod CChe CExl CHEx ECha EHoe ELan EPfP LBMP LPot LRHS MAsh MBri MCot MRav SEND SIgm SLon SPer SPhx SPlb SPoG SRms SWvt WIce XLum XSen
- 'Brimstone' (v)	LRHS MRav SPer SPoG SWvt XSen
* - var. *italica* new	CBcs EPla
- Little Boy Blue = 'Lisbob'PBR	CSBt EPfP LBMP LRHS LSqu SSpi
- 'Lois'	LRHS SPoG
jacobaeus	MCot

	maculatus	EOHP MOWG
	maritimus	CPom SRot
	pedunculatus	CHab MCoo NMir WSFF
	pentaphyllus	CArn XSen
	tetragonolobus	SPhx SVic

lovage see *Levisticum officinale*

Loxostigma (*Gesneriaceae*)

	kurzii GWJ 9342	WCru

Luetkea (*Rosaceae*)

	pectinata	GCrg GEdr

Luffa (*Cucurbitaceae*)

	aegyptiaca	SVic

Luma ✿ (*Myrtaceae*)

§	***apiculata*** ♀H4	Widely available
§	- 'Glanleam Gold' (v)	Widely available
	- 'Nana'	LEdu WJek
	- 'Penlee'	SRms WJek
	- 'Rainbow's Gold' (v) **new**	EShb
	- 'Saint Hilary' (v)	EPfP LRHS SRms WJek
	- 'Variegata' (v)	CTri SLim WFar
§	***chequen***	CBcs CBod CSde CSpe EShb IDee LEdu MHer NLar SRms WJek WMoo

Lunaria (*Brassicaceae*)

§	***annua***	CArn CWCL EWoo LSun MNHC SIde SWat WCot WJek WSFF
	- var. ***albiflora*** ♀H7	MMuc NBir SEND SWat WCot WTou
I	- - 'Alba Variegata' (v) ♀H7	CSpe LBMP WBor WBrk
	- 'Chedglow'	CNat LEdu
	- 'Corfu Blue'	CDes CPom CSpe EBee SPtp WCot WWFP
	- 'Munstead Purple' ♀H7	CSpe
	- 'Nettleton'	CNat
	- purple-leaved	CMea
	- 'Ruth' **new**	CNat LEdu
	- 'Variegata' (v)	NBir SWat WCot WHer
	- violet-flowered	NBir
	biennis	see *L. annua*
	rediviva ♀H7	CSpe EBee ECGP ECha EPPr EPla GAbr GBin GCal GCra IBlr IFro LEdu LPla LRHS MMuc MWat NBid NChi NPer NSti SEND WCot WFar WHer WHil WPGP
	- 'Partway White'	CMil WCot

Lunathyrium (*Woodsiaceae*)

	petersenii **new**	CBty ISha
	pycnosorum	ISha

Lupinus ✿ (*Papilionaceae*)

	'African Sunset'	CWCL
	albus	CArn
	'Animal'	CWCL
	arboreus ♀H4	Widely available
	- blue and white-flowered	SCob WFar
	- 'Blue Boy'	ELan LRHS SWvt
	- blue-flowered	CWCL CWld EShb LRHS MCot SPer SPhx SPlb SWvt WFar
	- 'Chelsea Blue'	EPfP LRHS
	- cream-flowered	SCob
	- 'Rhubarb and Custard'	CWCL
	- 'Snow Queen'	CWCL LRHS MGos SPoG SWvt
	- 'Sulphur Yellow'	SWvt
	- white-flowered	CSpe CWld MCot SPlb
	- yellow and blue-flowered	IBoy NBir SRkn WFar
	- yellow-flowered	CWld ELan EWTr GKev MLHP SPhx SWvt WWEG
	arcticus	CSpe EBee
	Band of Nobles Series	COtt MLHP
	'Beefeater'	CWCL GBin LBuc LLHF LRHS MBri NPri
	'Bishop's Tipple'	EWes
	'Blossom'[PBR]	CWCL CWGN GBin LLHF LRHS MBri NPri SPoG
	'Blue Streak'	CWCL
	'Bruiser'	CWCL
	'Camelot Blue'	EPfP
	'Cashmere Cream'	CWCL MBri
	'Chameleon'	CWCL LBuc LRHS MBri
	chamissonis	CHll CPla CSpe CWCL ELan EWes LRHS NLar SMrm SPer
	'Chandelier' (Band of Nobles Series)	Widely available
	'Desert Sun'	CWCL MBri
	Dwarf Gallery hybrids	IBoy WRHF
	'Dwarf Lulu'	see *L.* 'Lulu'
	'Everest'	CWCL
	Gallery Series	CSBt GAbr IBoy NSir SCoo SPlb WFar
	- 'Gallery Blue'	CBod ECtt ELan EPfP IBoy MWat NLar NPri SCoo SMrm SPer SPoG WFar
	- 'Gallery Pink'	CBod ELan EPfP IBoy LRHS NLar NPri SCoo SMrm SPer SPoG WFar
	- 'Gallery Red'	CBod ECtt ELan EPfP IBoy LRHS MWat NLar NPri SCoo SMrm SPer SPoG WFar
	- 'Gallery Rose'	IBoy SPoG WFar
	- 'Gallery White'	CBod ELan EPfP IBoy LBMP LRHS MWat NLar NPri SCoo SPer SPoG WFar
	- 'Gallery Yellow'	CBod ECtt ELan EPfP IBoy LBMP LRHS LSun NLar NPri SPer SPoG WFar
	'Gladiator'	CWCL ECtt EWes GBin LLHF LRHS LSou MBri MNrw NPri SPoG
	'Heathcliffe Blue'	WOut
	'Imperial Robe'	CWCL
	'Inspiration'	CWCL MBri
	'Judy Harper'	ECtt GBin LRHS
	'Jupiter'	CWCL
	'King Canute'	CWCL
	'Le Gentilhomme' (Band of Nobles Series)	MCot
	'Lindy Lou'	CWCL
§	'Lulu'	EPfP IBoy LRHS MWat SGbt SPer SPoG SWvt WHar WMoo
	'Manhattan Lights'[PBR]	CWCL CWGN EWes EWoo GBin IPot LLHF LRHS MBri NPri SPoG
	'Masterpiece'[PBR]	CWCL EWoo GBin IPot LLHF LRHS LSou MBri NPri
	Minarette Group	CTri LRHS MNrw SRms
	montanus	CHid
	'Morello Cherry'	CWCL GJos SHar
	'Mrs Perkins'	SMrm
	'My Castle' (Band of Nobles Series)	CBcs COtt CSBt CTri ECtt ELan EPfP GMaP IBoy LRHS MAsh MBri MGos MJak MWat NGBl NLar NPri SGbt SHil SMrm SPer SPoG SWvt WFar WHar WHil WMoo
	'Neptune'	CWCL
	'Noble Maiden' (Band of Nobles Series)	Widely available

nootkatensis GLog SDix WThu
'Pam Ayres' ECtt GBin LRHS
'Pen and Ink' CWCL
perennis SEND
'Persian Slipper'PBR CEnd CWCL CWGN ECtt EWes EWoo GBin IPot LBuc LLHF LRHS MBri NPri SPoG
'Polar Princess' CWCL ECtt EWes GBin IPot LRHS MBri SWat
'Purple Swirl' CWCL ECtt MBri
'Rachel de Thame' **new** CWCL
'Red Arrow' CWCL
'Red Rum'PBR CEnd CWCL CWGN EWoo GBin LBuc LRHS MBri MNrw NPri SPoG
'Redhead' CWCL
'Rote Flamme' CPrp ELon EWes LSun SCob
Russell hybrids CBod CSBt EPfP IBoy LAst MHer MMuc SEND SPlb SRms SVic SWvt WFar
'Saffron'PBR CEnd CWCL EWoo GBin LBuc LRHS MBri NPri
'Salmon Star'PBR CWCL GBin LRHS MBri MNrw NPri SPoG
'Sand Pink' EWes
'Silver Fleece' CHid SEND
'Sparky' CWCL
'Tequila Flame' CWCL GBin LBuc LLHF LRHS MBri NPri SPoG
'Terracotta' CWCL GBin LRHS LSou
texensis CSpe
'The Chatelaine' (Band of Nobles Series) Widely available
'The Governor' (Band of Nobles Series) Widely available
'The Page' (Band of Nobles Series) CAby CBcs COtt CWld ELan ELon EPfP EWoo IBoy LRHS MAsh MBri MCot MNHC MWat NLar NPri SCob SMrm SPer SPoG SWvt WFar WHar WMoo
'Thundercloud' CDes EBee SMrm
'Towering Inferno' CEnd CWCL ECtt EWes GBin LBuc LRHS MBri NPri SPoG
'Tutti Frutti' GJos IBoy WHar
variicolor SIgm SMHy
Woodfield hybrids COtt GAbr LRHS

Luzula (*Juncaceae*)

alpinopilosa EPPr GBin
× ***borreri*** EPPr
- 'Botany Bay' (v) EPPr GBin
'Engel' EBee EPPr EWes
forsteri IMou
luzuloides EPPr WPtf
- 'Schneehäschen' GBin GCal NWsh WSHC
maxima see *L. sylvatica*
nivalis GAbr
nivea Widely available
pedemontana EPPr SMea
pilosa EBee GCal
- 'Igel' CKno LEdu NBid SCob SMad
purpureosplendens LEdu NOak
§ ***sylvatica*** CHEx CRow ELan EPPr EPla EWoo LPal LRHS MMoz MMuc MRav NBro NMir NOrc SCob SEND SPer WHer WShi WWEG XLum
- from Tatra Mountains, Slovakia EPPr
- 'A. Rutherford' see *L. sylvatica* 'Taggart's Cream'
- 'Aurea' CHEx CKno ECha ELon EPPr EPla EWoo LAst LBMP LRHS MJak MMoz MRav NBid NOak NSti NWsh SEND SGSe WCot WFar WGrn WMoo WPat WPtf
- 'Aureomarginata' see *L. sylvatica* 'Marginata'
I - 'Auslese' EPPr EPfP WMoo
- 'Bromel' EPPr SGSe
- 'Hohe Tatra' CBod CElw CSpe EHoe EPPr EWes GMaP LEdu MBNS MWhi NBro NGdn NOak SCob SPoG WPnP WWEG
§ - 'Marginata' (v) Widely available
- 'Mariusz' EPPr
* - f. ***nova*** ELon EPPr
- 'Solar Flair' MWhi
- 'Starmaker' **new** CBod
§ - 'Taggart's Cream' (v) EBee EHoe EPla LRHS NBid NHol WMoo WWEG
- 'Tauernpass' EHoe EPPr EPla GCal
- 'Thierry's Cream' (v) **new** WCot
- 'Wäldler' EPPr
ulophylla ECou GCrg GEdr WThu

Luzuriaga (*Luzuriagaceae*)

polyphylla CTal
- HCM 98202 WCru
radicans CCCN ECou GEdr IMou WCru WSHC
- RH 0602 WCru

Lychnis (*Caryophyllaceae*)

alpina CMac ECho EDAr GKev NGdn WFar XLum
- compact ITim
- 'Rosea' NBir
- 'Snow Flurry' EDAr GKev
§ × ***arkwrightii*** ECha ELan LRHS
- 'Orange Zwerg' ELon MBNS SGbt
- 'Vesuvius' CBcs CMac EAEE EBee ELon EPla LRHS MWat NBir NSoo SPer SRms WGwG WMnd XLum
chalcedonica ♀H7 Widely available
- var. ***albiflora*** EPfP MBel NBro SMrm WHrl WMoo
- - 'Snow White' SGSe
- 'Carnea' EBee LRHS MBNS NGdn SMrm SPhx WWEG
- 'Dusky Salmon' WOut
- 'Flore Pleno' (d) EShb GCal NChi WCot
- 'Morgenrot' MBel
- 'Pinkie' NLar NWad SGSe
- 'Rauhreif' NBre NLar SPhx
- 'Rosea' EPfP NBir WHrl WMoo
* - 'Salmonea' NBir SRms
cognata CTal GEdr IMou
- B&SWJ 4234 WCru
§ ***coronaria*** ♀H7 Widely available
- MESE 356 SPhx
- 'Abbotswood Rose' see *L.* × *walkeri* 'Abbotswood Rose'
- 'Alba' ♀H7 Widely available
- 'Angel's Blush' NBir NLar SPav SRkn WTou
- Atrosanguinea Group CBod CBre EPfP EPla EWTr GMaP IBlr LRHS MBel MHol MRav MSCN MSpe NEgg NGdn NPri NSti NWad SPer WGwG
- 'Blood Red' CSpe LRHS
- 'Cerise' MArl NBir
- Gardeners' World = 'Blych' (d) CBod CDes CElw CSpe CUse EBee ECtt EWes GBin LRHS LSou LSun

	MBNS MBel MHol MPie MTis NSti SMrm SPer WBrk WCot
- 'Hutchinson's Cream' (v)	NBir
- Oculata Group	CBod CElw CSpe EAJP EBee ECGP ELan EPfP LEdu LPot SMrm SPav SPlb WFar WKif WMoo WRHF
§ ***coronata*** var. ***sieboldii***	SBrt
dioica	see *Silene dioica*
flos-cuculi	CArn CBAq CBod CHab CPom CSam CWat CWld ECho EHon GJos LEdu LLWG MHer MMuc MNHC NLar NMir SEND SPhx WFar WHer WMAq WMoo WOut WPnP WSFF WWFP XLum
- var. ***albiflora***	CBAq CBre CElw CSam CWld EWoo MSKA NBro NLar WHer WMnd WMoo WWFP
- var. ***congesta***	WAbe
- Jenny = 'Lychjen'[PBR] (d)	CChe CWCL EBee ECtt ELan GBin GQue LBMP LEdu LLWG LRHS LSun MBNS MBel MHol MNrw MPie MTis MWat NSti SCob SMad SPad SPoG SRkn WBor WCot WGrn WHer WMnd
- 'Little Robin'	LLWG
- 'Nana'	ECho EDAr MSKA NGdn NLar
- 'White Robin'	Widely available
flos-jovis ♀H5	ECha EPfP GJos LRHS MBel NBir NLar SGSe SRms WMoo XLum
- 'Hort's Variety'	EBee LRHS NBir NSti
- 'Minor'	see *L. flos-jovis* 'Nana'
§ - 'Nana'	MSCN SBch WAbe
- 'Peggy'	EBee LRHS NBre NGdn NLar
fulgens	NBre
× ***haageana***	NLar SRms
- 'Lumina Bronze Leaf Red'	LRHS SMrm
'Hill Grounds'	CDes CElw WCot WSHC
lagascae	see *Petrocoptis pyrenaica* subsp. *glaucifolia*
miqueliana	WMoo
'Molten Lava'	ELan EPfP LRHS NLar SGSe WHar
sieboldii 'Matsu Moto'	SGSe
'Terry's Pink'	NCGa
§ ***viscaria***	CArn CWld ECha GCra GJos NPCo WFar WMoo
- 'Alba'	ECha NBre NBro XLum
- ***alpina***	see *L. viscaria*
§ - subsp. ***atropurpurea***	CFis EBee EWes LRHS LSou MPie SRms WHrl WPtf
- 'Feuer'	EBee EWes GJos LRHS NGBl NLar SPhx WMoo
- 'Firebird'	EWes
- 'Plena' (d)	NBir SRkn
- 'Schnee'	GJos LRHS NLar
- 'Snowbird'	CTsd
- 'Splendens'	LPot WFar XLum
- 'Splendens Plena' (d) ♀H5	NBro XLum
§ × ***walkeri*** 'Abbotswood Rose' ♀H7	IBlr
wilfordii	SHar
§ ***yunnanensis***	EBee NBid SGSe SPhx WPtf XLum
- ***alba***	see *L. yunnanensis*

Lycianthes (*Solanaceae*)

biflora FMWJ 13059 new	WCru
§ ***rantonnetii***	CCCN CHll ELan EPfP EUJe IDee MOWG NSoo SEND SPoG WBor
- 'Variegatum' (v)	CHll MSCN WCot

Lycium (*Solanaceae*)

afrum	SVen
barbarum	CAgr CBcs CCCN EBee EPom EWes IDee LBuc LEdu LRHS MCoo NLar SDea SEND SPre SVic SWvt WHar
- 'Big Lifeberry'	CAgr CUse LEdu MCoo
- 'Number 1 Lifeberry'	CAgr
- 'Sweet Lifeberry'	CAgr LEdu
chinense	CArn CUse IBoy

Lycopodium (*Lycopodiaceae*)

clavatum	GPoy

Lycopsis see *Anchusa*

Lycopus (*Lamiaceae*)

americanus	CArn
europaeus	CArn CHab EBee ELau GPoy LLWG WGwG

Lycoris (*Amaryllidaceae*)

albiflora	ECho NRog
aurea	CCon EBee ECho GKev NRog SDeJ
caldwellii new	NRog
chinensis	NRog
haywardii	NRog
houdyshelii new	NRog
incarnata	ECho
longituba	NRog
radiata	CCCN CCon EBee ECho GKev SDeJ
rosea new	NRog
sanguinea	NRog
sprengeri	EBee NRog

Lygodium (*Lygodiaceae*)

japonicum	ISha WFib

Lyonia (*Ericaceae*)

mariana	NLar
ovalifolia new	CPne
villosa	CPne

Lyonothamnus (*Rosaceae*)

floribundus subsp. ***aspleniifolius***	CCCN CDoC CExl EUJe SArc WPGP

Lysichiton (*Araceae*)

sp.	GGal
americanus ♀H7	Widely available
camtschatcensis ♀H7	CBcs CBen CFwr CLAP CRow CTsd CWat ECha EHon EPfP EUJe GBin GBuc LLWG LRHS MWts NLar NOrc NPer SMad SPer SSpi SWat SWvt WPnP WShi XLum
× ***hortensis***	ECha

Lysiloma (*Mimosaceae*)

watsonii	SPlb

Lysimachia (*Primulaceae*)

albescens	CExl GEdr SPad XLum
§ ***atropurpurea***	CSpe EAJP EBee ELan EPfP EShb GJos LRHS SPer WMnd WWEG
- 'Beaujolais'	CExl GJos IBoy LPot LRHS MNHC MPie NPri SCob SDix SMrm SPoG WHil
- 'Geronimo'	CSpe

barystachys ♀H7	CPrp CSam LPla MBel MRav SHar WCot WFar WWEG XLum
- 'Huntingbrook'	CDes MAvo WPGP WWtn
Candela = 'Innlyscand'	CMos CSpe ECtt EPla GBin LSou MHol NPri SPoG WCot WHil WMoo
candida	WCot
ciliata	CMHG CMac ECha EHoe ELan GMaP LRHS MNrw NBir NGdn NLar SWat WCot WWtn
§ - 'Firecracker' ♀H7	Widely available
- 'Purpurea'	see *L. ciliata* 'Firecracker'
clethroides ♀H7	Widely available
- 'Geisha' (v)	EBee WCot
- 'Lady Jane'	CCon MNrw SRms
§ ***congestiflora***	NPer
- 'Golden Falls'	CTsd
- 'Midnight Sun'[PBR]	ECtt LAst
- 'Outback Sunset'[PBR] (v)	ECtt LAst
- 'Persian Carpet'	WCot
- 'Persian Chocolate'	WCot WFar
ephemerum ♀H6	Widely available
fortunei	EBee MWat XLum
lichiangensis	CExl EBee GKev IMou LRHS NBir WMoo
lyssii	see *L. congestiflora*
minoricensis	SWat XLum
nemorum	CWld IMou
- 'Lola Playle'[PBR] **new**	WCot
- 'Pale Star'	CBre EBee
nummularia	CBAq CSBt CTri CWat ECtt EHon EPfP GPoy MJak MMuc NBir SGol SWat WBrk WHfH
- 'Aurea' ♀H5	Widely available
paridiformis	CExl
var. ***stenophylla***	
- - DJHC 704	EBee
punctata misapplied	see *L. verticillaris*
punctata L.	CBAq CRow CSBt ECha EHon EPfP GMaP MHer MMuc MRav MWat NBro NMir NPer NSoo SCob SEND SPer SPlb SRms SWat WBrk WFar WMAq WMoo
§ - 'Alexander' (v)	Widely available
- 'Gaulthier Brousse'	WCot WWEG
- Golden Alexander = 'Walgoldalex'[PBR] (v)	CBod CExl ELon LBMP LRHS MBNS MBel NHol NLar NPri SHil SPoG WMoo
- 'Golden Glory' (v)	WCot
- 'Hometown Hero'	EBee
- 'Ivy Maclean' (v)	SWvt WWEG
- 'Variegata'	see *L. punctata* 'Alexander'
- ***verticillata***	see *L. verticillaris*
'Purpurea'	see *L. atropurpurea*
pyramidalis	WWEG
Snow Candles = 'L9902'	EBee
thyrsiflora	CBAq CWat EBee EHon EWay NPer SWat WCot WMAq
§ ***verticillaris***	CTri WCot
vulgaris	CArn CHab LLWG MSKA WJek WMoo
- subsp. ***davurica***	WCot
- - B&SWJ 8632	WCru

Lysionotus (*Gesneriaceae*)

gamosepalus B&SWJ 7241	WCru
aff. ***kwangsiensis*** HWJ 643	WCru
'Lavender Lady'	EBee MAsh NCGa
pauciflorus	CDes WAbe WSHC
- B&SWJ 303	WCru
- B&SWJ 335	WCru
- HWJ 811 from Vietnam **new**	WCru
- dwarf B&SWJ 189 **new**	WCru
serratus HWJK 2426	WCru

Lythrum (*Lythraceae*)

alatum	NDov
anceps	NBre NLar
'Rose Dream' **new**	NWad
salicaria	CArn CBAq CBen CHab CKno CWat CWld EHon ENfk GAbr GJos MCot MHer MLHP MMuc MNHC MWts NBro SEND SPlb SRms SWat WBrk WHer WJek WMoo WPnP WSFF WShi XLum
- 'Augenweide'	XLum
- 'Blush' ♀H7	Widely available
§ - 'Feuerkerze' ♀H7	Widely available
- Firecandle	see *L. salicaria* 'Feuerkerze'
- 'Happy'	ELon SMrm
- 'Lady Sackville'	EBee ECtt ELon EPPr GMaP IKil IPot MCot MTis NLar WSHC WWEG
- 'Little Robert'	ECtt IBoy LBMP
- 'Morden Pink'	CBod EBee MMuc NLar SEND SPhx
- 'Prichard's Variety'	CKno EBee WPGP
- 'Red Beauty' **new**	LSun
- 'Robert'	Widely available
- 'Robin'	ECtt GJos LLHF LRHS MAsh MBri NPri SGbt SRot SWvt
- 'Rose'	ELan NBir SWvt
- 'Swirl'	ECtt EPfP IKil LLWG MTis NLar SHar SMrm WHoo
- 'The Beacon'	EBee NLar SGSe SPad SRms
- Ulverscroft form	WHil
- 'Zigeunerblut'	CElw CKno CMHG ELon EPPr GQue IPot MRav NLar SPhx SWat WHil
virgatum	CMHG SMHy SPhx WCFE WMoo WOut WSHC
- 'Dropmore Purple'	CBod CSam EBee ECtt ELon EPPr EPfP EPla GMaP GQue IPot LAst LLWG LRHS MBri MCot MRav MSpe NDov NEgg NPri SPer SPhx SPoG WCAu WCFE WFar WHar WSHC XLum
- 'Helene'	IMou
- 'Rose Queen'	SMHy
- 'Rosy Gem'	COtt EBee EPfP GJos GMaP IBoy LAst LRHS MWat MWhi NBro SGSe SRms SWvt WHar WWEG
- 'The Rocket'	CAby CBod CSam CTri EPPr EPfP EPla EShb GBee GQue LAst LRHS MPie MRav NBro NDov SPer SWvt WFar WPnP

Lytocaryum (*Arecaceae*)

§ ***weddellianum*** ♀H1b	LPal

M

Maackia (*Papilionaceae*)

amurensis	CBcs CDul CHGN CMCN ELan EPfP IVic LRHS NLar
hupehensis	MBlu NLar

mace, English see *Achillea ageratum*

Macfadyena (*Bignoniaceae*)

	uncata	MOWG
§	***unguis-cati*** 🏆^{H2}	CCCN CRHN

Machaerina (*Cyperaceae*)

	rubiginosa 'Variegata' (v)	EWay LLWG

Machilus see *Persea*

Mackaya (*Acanthaceae*)

§	***bella*** 🏆^{H1b}	CHll EShb

Macleaya (*Papaveraceae*)

	cordata misapplied	see *M.* × *kewensis*
§	***cordata*** (Willd.) R. Br. 🏆^{H6}	EBee ELan EWTr LRHS LSun MBri MHol NBir NOrc SPer SPlb SRms WCAu WCot WMoo XLum
§	× ***kewensis***	EBee SCob
	- 'Flamingo' 🏆^{H6}	CExl CHel EBee ECha ECtt GBuc GQue LRHS MBNS MNFA SWvt WHoo WWEG
§	***microcarpa***	MHol SWat WWEG
	- 'Kelway's Coral Plume' 🏆^{H6}	CBcs CBod CExl CKno CMac EBee ECtt ELan EPfP EWoo GMaP LPal LRHS MAvo MGos MLHP MRav MWat NBid NBro NEgg NLar NPri SPer SPoG SWvt WBor WCot WMnd WWEG
	- 'Spetchley Ruby'	CExl EBee MRav SPhx WCot WWEG XLum

Maclura (*Moraceae*)

pomifera	CArn CBcs ETwe IVic LEdu NLar SPlb
- 'Naughty Boy' **new**	NLar
- 'Pretty Woman'	NLar
tricuspidata B&SWJ 12755 **new**	WCru

Macrodiervilla see *Weigela*

Macropiper (*Piperaceae*)

§	***excelsum***	CHEx ECou

Macrozamia (*Zamiaceae*)

	communis	CBrP LPal
	diplomera	CBrP
	dyeri	see *M. riedlei*
	lucida	CBrP
	moorei	CBrP
§	***riedlei***	CBrP

Maddenia (*Rosaceae*)

hypocleuca	NLar

Maesa (*Primulaceae*)

japonica	CExl
- CWJ 12371	WCru
montana	CExl

Magnolia ✿ (*Magnoliaceae*)

	acuminata	CBcs CDul CMCN EPfP
	- 'Blue Opal'	CBcs CJun
*	- 'Kinju'	CEnd CJun MBri NLar
	- 'Koban Dori'	CBcs CJun
	- 'Moegi Dori'	NLar
	- 'Patriot'	CMCN SKHP
	- 'Patriot' × (× ***brooklynensis*** 'Yellow Bird')	CJun MAsh
	- 'Seiju'	CJun
§	- var. ***subcordata***	NLar
	- - 'Miss Honeybee'	CBcs CJun
	- - 'Mister Yellowjacket'	CJun
	acuminata × 'Elizabeth'	ERea SEWo
	'Advance'	CBcs CJun NLar
	'Albatross'	CBcs CDoC CEnd ERea WPGP
	'Alex'	CJun
	'Alixeed'	CJun
	'Amber'	CJun
	'Ambrosia'	CJun
	amoena	CTho
	'Angelica'	CJun
	'Anilou'	CJun
	'Ann'	CExl
	'Anna'	CJun
	'Anne Rosse'	SKHP WPGP
	'Anticipation'	CEnd CJun CMHG
	'Apollo'	CBcs CDoC CJun IVic SKHP WPGP
	'Apricot Brandy' **new**	NLar
	'Archangel'	CJun
	ashei	see *M. macrophylla* subsp. *ashei*
	'Asian Artistry'	CJun
	'Athene' 🏆^{H5}	CBcs CDoC CEnd CJun CMHG IVic LRHS WPGP
	'Atlas'	CBcs CDoC CEnd CJun CTho ERea WPGP
	'Aurora'	CBcs CDoC CJun
	'Banana Split'	CBcs CJun LMil NLar
	'Betty'	CBcs CDoC CDul CLnd CMac ELon EPfP EShb LRHS LSou MBlu MGos MMuc NLar NPCo NPla SKHP SLim SSta
	'Big Dude'	CBcs CDoC CEnd CJun EPfP LRHS
	biondii	CBcs CLnd NLar
	'Black Beauty'	CBcs CJun LRHS
	Black Tulip = 'Jurmag1'^{PBR}	CBcs ELan EPfP ERea IVic LBuc LRHS MAsh MBri NLar NSoo SCoo SKHP SLon WHor
	'Blushing Belle'	CJun
	'Brenda'	CJun
	'Brixton Belle' **new**	CBcs WPGP
	× ***brooklynensis*** 'Evamaria'	CTho NLar
	- 'Golden Joy'	CDoC CJun MPkF
	- 'Hattie Carthan'	CBcs CJun
	- 'Woodsman'	CBcs MBri NLar
	- 'Yellow Bird'	CBcs CDoC CDul CEnd CJun CMCN CMHG CTho EPfP ETwe GKin IArd LMil LRHS MAsh MBlu MBri MGos NLar SHil SKHP SPoG
	'Butterbowl'	CJun
	'Butterflies'	CBcs CDoC CDul CJun CTho CTsd ELan ELon EPfP GBin LRHS MBlu MBri MGos NLar SGol SKHP SSta WFar
	'Caerhays Belle' 🏆^{H5}	CBcs CJun IVic LRHS MBri SKHP SSta WPGP
	'Caerhays New Purple'	CLnd
	'Caerhays Surprise' 🏆^{H5}	CBcs CEnd CJun SKHP WPGP
	campbellii	CAco CMCN ELan EPfP LRHS SKHP
	- Alba Group	CBcs WPGP
	- - 'Sir Harold Hillier'	CJun
	- 'Ambrose Congreve'	WPGP
	- 'Betty Jessel'	CBcs CJun CMHG WPGP
	- 'Darjeeling' 🏆^{H4}	CBcs CDoC CJun IVic LRHS SKHP WPGP

- 'John Gallagher'	SKHP
- 'Lamellan Pink'	CTho
- 'Lamellan White'	CTho
- subsp. ***mollicomata***	EPfP
- - 'Lanarth'	CBcs CJun LRHS WPGP
- 'Queen Caroline'	WPGP
- (Raffillii Group) 'Charles Raffill'	CBcs CDoC CDul CTho ELan EPfP IDee LRHS MGos WHor WMou WPGP
- - 'Kew's Surprise'	CBcs CDoC CJun WPGP
- 'Sidbury'	CBcs MBri
campbellii* × *sprengeri	WPGP
'Candy Cane'	CBcs CJun
'Carlos'	CBcs CJun
cathcartii B&SWJ 11802	WCru
- HWJ 874	WCru
cavaleriei var. ***platypetala***	CExl
'Cecil Nice'	CBcs CDoC
Chameleon	see *M.* 'Chang Hua'
§ 'Chang Hua'	CJun
chapensis	CBcs SKHP
'Charles Coates'	CJun EPfP NLar WPGP
chevalieri B&SWJ 11802	WCru
- DJHV 06037	WCru
- HWJ 533	WCru
- HWJ 621	WCru
China Town = 'Jing Ning'	CJun
'Columnar Pink'	LRHS NLar
'Coral Lake'	CJun SKHP
cordata	see *M. acuminata* var. *subcordata*
'Crystal Chalice'	CJun
'Cup Cake'	CJun
'Curly Locks'	CJun
cylindrica misapplied	see *M.* 'Pegasus'
cylindrica ambig.	CBcs CMCN
cylindrica E.H.Wilson	EPfP
- 'Bjuv'	CJun
'Daphne' ♀H6	CBcs CDul CJun CMHG EPfP IVic LMil LRHS MAsh MBri NLar SKHP WPGP
'Darrell Dean'	CJun ERea
'David Clulow' ♀H5	CBcs CJun ERea SKHP WPGP
dawsoniana	CBcs CTho EBee EPfP
- 'Barbara Cook'	CJun
- 'Chyverton Red'	CBcs WPGP
- 'Valley Splendour'	CJun
'Daybreak' ♀H6	CBcs CJun LRHS MBlu MBri MRav SGol SSta WPGP
dealbata	see *M. macrophylla* subsp. *dealbata*
'Deborah'	CJun
decidua	CBcs SKHP
delavayi	CBcs CBrP CDul CFil CHEx CMCN EBee EPfP EUJe IArd LRHS SArc SBig WPGP
§ ***denudata*** ♀H6	CBcs CDul CMCN CTho EPfP GKin IArd LMil LRHS MBlu MGos SEWo SSpi SSta
- 'Double Diamond'	CJun
- 'Forrest's Pink'	CBcs LRHS
- Fragrant Cloud = 'Dan Xin'	CJun WHar
- 'Gere'	CBcs CJun
- 'Ghost Ship'	CJun
- late-flowered	see *M. denudata* 'Sleeping Beauty'
- 'Rubiflora'	SSta
§ - 'Sleeping Beauty'	ERea
- Yellow River = 'Fei Huang'	CBcs CEnd CJun IDee LRHS MBri MJak NLar

doltsopa	CBcs CCCN CExl CHEx CTsd SKHP SSta WPGP
- 'Silver Cloud'	CBcs CDoC CExl
'Early Rose'	CJun GGGa
'Eleanor May'	CJun
'Elegance'	CJun
'Elisa Odenwald'	CJun
'Elizabeth' ♀H6	CBcs CDoC CJun CMCN CTho ELan EPfP ERea GGGa IArd LAst LMil LRHS MAsh MBlu MBri MGos NLar SKHP SPoG SWvt
§ ***ernestii***	CExl NLar WPGP
'Eskimo'	CJun SKHP SSpi
'Eternal Flames' **new**	NLar
'F.J. Williams'	CBcs
Fairy Blush = 'Micjur01'	EPfP LRHS NSoo
'Felicity'	CJun
Felix Jury = 'Jurmag2' PBR	ELan EPfP ERea LRHS SPoG SSta
figo	CBcs CCCN CDoC CExl CFil EBee ELan EPfP LRHS MMuc SKHP SSta WPGP
- var. ***crassipes***	CBcs
figo* × *laevifolia	SKHP
'Fireglow'	CJun CTho
'Flamingo'	CJun
floribunda NJM 09.179	WPGP
- WWJ 11874	WCru
- WWJ 11996	WCru
- WWJ 12003	WCru
- WWJ 12011	WCru
aff. ***floribunda*** var. ***tonkinensis*** DJHV 06 105	WCru
fordiana	CExl
§ ***foveolata***	CBcs
- B&SWJ 11749	WCru
- WWJ 11929	WCru
- WWJ 11955	WCru
'Frank Gladney'	CJun CTho
'Frank's Masterpiece'	CJun IArd SKHP
fraseri	SKHP
- var. ***pyramidata***	SKHP
'Full Eclipse'	NLar
'Galaxy' ♀H6	CBcs CDoC CDul CEnd CJun CMHG CMac ELon EPfP ERea GGGa GKin LMil LRHS MAsh MBri MGos MMuc NLar SEWo SPoG SSta
garrettii **new**	CPne
'Genie' PBR	CBcs CDoC LRHS NLar SCob
'George Henry Kern' ♀H6	CAco CBcs CDoC CDul CTho EPfP IArd IDee LRHS MBri MGos MMuc NEgg NLar NPCo SEND SHil
'Gladys Carlson'	CJun
globosa	CBcs CExl
'Gold Crown'	CBcs CJun LMil
'Gold Cup'	CBcs
'Gold Star' ♀H6	CBcs CDoC CDul CEnd CJun CMHG CTho EPfP LMil MGos NLar SKHP SSpi
'Golden Endeavour'	CBcs CJun
'Golden Gala'	CJun
'Golden Gift'	CJun LRHS MAsh SSpi WPGP
'Golden Pond'	CJun
'Golden Rain'	CJun
'Golden Sun'	CBcs CJun IArd
'Goldfinch'	CJun
I × ***gotoburgensis*** Chollipo clone	WPGP

I	– clone 2	CJun
	grandiflora	CMCN EBee EPfP ESwi LEdu LRHS MGos MMuc MRav NEgg NLar NSoo SArc SCob SEWo
	– 'Blanchard'	CBcs CJun EUJe NLar
	– 'Bracken's Brown Beauty'	CMCN
	– 'Charles Dickens'	CJun
	– 'Edith Bogue'	CJun EUJe GKin LMil LRHS NEgg NLar NPCo
	– 'Exmouth'	Widely available
	– 'Ferruginea'	CBcs CJun EPfP NLar SGol
	– 'Flore Pleno' (d)	SGol
	– 'François Treyve'	EPfP LRHS
	– 'Galissonnière'	CAco CBcs CCVT EAEE EPfP EWTr LPal LRHS MGos SCob SEND SGol SKHP SSpi SWvt WPGP
I	– 'Galissonnière Nana'	LPal
	– 'Goliath'	CBcs CDul CHEx ELan EPfP LRHS SEND SEWo SKHP SPer SSpi WPGP
	– 'Harold Poole'	CJun
	– 'Kay Parris' 🏆H5	CJun EPfP LRHS SKHP SPoG SSpi
	– 'Little Gem'	CBcs CDoC CJun ELan EPfP EUJe LRHS MGos SGol SSpi
	– 'Mainstreet'	CJun
	– 'Monlia'	CJun
	– 'Nannetensis'	CJun LRHS MBri
	– 'Overton'	CJun
	– 'Russet'	CJun
	– 'Saint Mary'	CJun
	– 'Samuel Sommer'	CJun SSpi
	– 'Symmes Select'	CJun
	– 'Treyvei'	CJun
	– 'Victoria' 🏆H5	CDoC CDul CJun CTho ELan ELon EPfP EWTr LMil LRHS MAsh MBlu MGos NLar SPer SPoG SReu SSpi SSta WPGP
	'Green Bee'	CBcs CJun
	'Green Mist'	CJun LMil LRHS SSpi
	'Hawk'	WPGP
	'Heaven Scent' 🏆H5	CAco CBcs CDoC CDul CMCN CMHG CTho CTsd ELan EPfP EPla ERea GGGa LMil LRHS MAsh MBlu MBri MGos MRav MSwo NLar NWea SGol SHil SPer SSta WFar WHar
	'Helen Fogg'	CJun
	heptapeta	see *M. denudata*
	'Honey Flower'	CJun
	'Honey Liz'	CBcs LMil SKHP
§	'Hong Yun'	CJun
	'Hot Flash'	CBcs CJun NLar
	'Hot Lips'	CJun
	hypoleuca	see *M. obovata* Thunb.
	'Ian's Red'	CBcs CJun IVic LRHS MBri WPGP
§	***insignis***	CBcs CExl CHEx LEdu SKHP WPGP
	insignis × 'Silk Road' **new**	WPGP
	insignis × ***yuyuanensis*** **new**	WPGP
	'Iolanthe'	CBcs CDoC CEnd CJun CMCN CMHG CTho ELan EPfP ERea IVic MAsh MBri MGos WPGP
	'Iufer'	CJun
	'J.C. Williams'	CBcs CDoC CJun CTho IVic WPGP
	'Jack Fogg'	ETwe MPkF SKHP
	'Jane'	CDoC CJun CMac ELan EPfP LMil LRHS MAsh MGos MRav
	'Janet' **new**	SKHP
	'Jersey Belle'	CBcs CJun
	'Joe McDaniel'	CBcs CJun ERea IArd NLar SKHP
	'John Congreve'	WPGP
	'Joli Pompom'	CBcs CJun
	'Judy'	CBcs
	'Judy Zuk'	CBcs ERea LMil NLar SKHP
	× ***kewensis*** 'Wada's Memory'	see *M. salicifolia* 'Wada's Memory'
	kobus	CBcs CCVT CDul CLnd CMCN CTho CTsd EPfP ERea GKin IArd MBlu NLar NWea SCob SEWo WMou
	– B&SWJ 12751 **new**	WCru
	– 'Esveld Select'	CJun
	– 'Janaki Ammal'	CJun
§	– 'Norman Gould'	CDoC CJun CMCN EPfP MBri NPla
	– 'Octopus'	CJun
	– pink-flowered	CBcs CJun
	– 'White Elegance'	CJun
	– 'Wisley Star'	SSta
§	***laevifolia***	CExl CHel CHid CTho EBee EPfP SChF SKHP WPGP
	– 'Cascade' **new**	SKHP
	– 'Dali Velvet'	CExl
	– 'Gail's Favourite'	EPfP LMil LRHS MAsh SKHP SPoG SSpi
	– 'Mini Mouse'	LRHS SKHP SPoG
	– 'Velvet and Cream'	IVic
	– 'Willow Leaf'	SKHP
	'Laura Saylor'	CJun
	'Leda'	CJun ERea MBri NLar SSta
	'Legacy'	CJun SKHP WPGP
	'Legend'	CJun EPfP
	'Lennarth Jonsson'	CJun
§	***liliiflora***	GKin
	– 'Darkest Purple'	CJun
§	– 'Nigra' 🏆H6	Widely available
	– 'Raven'	SKHP WPGP
*	'Limelight'	CJun EPfP SSpi WPGP
	× ***loebneri*** 'Ballerina'	CBcs CDoC NLar
	– 'Donna' 🏆H6	CJun EPfP LMil LRHS MAsh SKHP SSta
	– 'Encore'	CJun
	– 'Leonard Messel' 🏆H6	Widely available
	– 'Lesley Jane'	CJun
	– 'Mag's Pirouette' 🏆H6	CBcs CJun EPfP LLHF LMil LRHS MMuc SSpi
	– 'Merrill' 🏆H6	CBcs CJun CLnd CMCN CMHG CMac CTho ELan EPfP ERea LMil LRHS MAsh MGos MMuc MRav NLar NPCo SEND SGol SHil SKHP SPer SReu SSpi SSta
	– 'Neil McEacharn'	CJun
	– 'Pink Cloud'	CJun
	– 'Powder Puff'	CJun
	– 'Raspberry Fun'	CJun IArd
	– 'Snowdrift'	CJun
	– 'Star Bright'	CJun
	– 'White Stardust'	CJun
	– 'Wildcat' 🏆H6	CBcs CJun NLar SKHP
	– 'Willow Wood'	CJun
	'Lois' 🏆H6	CBcs CJun EPfP ERea GGGa LMil LRHS MBri SKHP SPoG SSpi WPGP
	'Lombardy Rose'	NLar
	lotungensis	NLar
	'Lotus'	CBcs CJun LMil
	'Lucy Carlson'	CJun
	macclurei	CBcs
	macrophylla	CBcs CBrP CFil CMac EPfP IArd IDee LRHS MBlu MPkF NLar SArc SKHP WPGP

	Name	Suppliers
§	- subsp. ***ashei***	CBcs CFil CMCN SKHP WPGP
	- subsp. ***ashei* × *virginiana***	CJun
§	- subsp. ***dealbata***	CFil
	macrophylla* × *macrophylla subsp. ***ashei***	SKHP
	macrophylla* × *sieboldii	CJun
	'Mag's Pirouette'	EBee MBri SKHP SLim
	'Malin'	CJun
	'Manchu Fan'	CBcs CJun EMil EPfP ETwe IArd IVic LRHS SKHP SLim SSpi WPGP
§	'March Til Frost'	CBcs CJun NLar SKHP WPGP
	'Margaret Helen'	CBcs CDoC CJun CMHG
	'Marj Gossler'	CJun
	'Marjorie Congreve'	WPGP
	'Mark Jury'	CBcs SKHP WPGP
	martinii	CBcs SKHP
	'Mary Bee'	SKHP
	'Mary Nell'	CJun
	'Maryland'	CJun EPfP GGGa SKHP SSpi
	maudiae	CBcs CDoC CExl EPfP IDee NLar SKHP SSpi WPGP
	'Maxine Merrill'	CJun IDee
	'May to Frost'	see *M.* 'March Til Frost'
	'Mazeppa' **new**	WPGP
	'Milky Way' ♀H5	CBcs CDoC CJun CMHG CTho EPfP LMil MGos SKHP WPGP
	'Mister Yellowjacket' **new**	CJun
	'Moondance'	CJun
	'Morning Calm'	SKHP
	'Nimbus'	CJun SKHP SSpi WPGP
	nitida	CBcs CExl CFil
	obovata Diels	see *M. officinalis*
§	***obovata*** Thunb.	CBcs CDul CJun CMCN CTho EPfP IDee MGos NLar NWea SBig SSpi WMou WPGP
	- B&SWJ 12626 **new**	WCru
	obovata* × *sargentiana var. ***robusta*** **new**	WPGP
§	***officinalis***	CBcs EPfP NLar
	- var. ***biloba***	CBcs MBlu NLar WPGP
	'Old Port'	CBcs
	'Olivia'	CJun
	'Orchid'	LRHS
	'Paul Cook'	CBcs
	'Peachy'	CBcs CJun LRHS MBri
§	'Pegasus' ♀H6	CBcs CEnd CJun LMil LRHS SKHP SSpi SSta
	'Peppermint Stick'	CBcs
	'Peter Dummer'	LMil SSta
	'Peter Smithers'	CJun
	'Petit Chicon'	CBcs
	'Phelan Bright'	CJun
	'Phillip Tregunna'	CBcs CMHG CTho SKHP WPGP
	'Phil's Masterpiece'	CJun
	'Pickard's Garnet'	CBcs
	'Pickard's Stardust'	EPfP
	'Pickard's Sundew'	see *M.* 'Sundew'
	'Piet van Veen'	CJun
	'Pink Delight'	CJun
	'Pink Goblet'	LRHS
	'Pink Surprise'	CJun
	'Pinkie'	CJun EMil
	'Porcelain Dove'	CBcs CJun SKHP WPGP
	'Princess Margaret'	CBcs CDoC CJun MBri
	'Pristine' **new**	EPfP LMil
	× ***proctoriana***	CAbP CBcs CDoC LMil LRHS SChF SKHP WPGP
	- Gloster form	NLar
	- 'Robert's Dream'	CJun LRHS MAsh SSta
	- 'Slavin's No 44'	CJun
	'Purple Globe'	CJun EBee SKHP WPGP
	'Purple Platter'	CBcs
	'Purple Sensation'	CBcs CJun
	quinquepeta	see *M. liliiflora*
	'Randy'	CBcs
	'Raspberry Ice'	CBcs CDoC CMHG CMac CTho EPfP LMil LRHS MAsh SPoG SRms WFar
	'Raspberry Swirl'	SSta
	'Rebecca's Perfume' **new**	MBri
	'Red as Red'	CBcs CDoC
	'Red Baron'	CJun
	'Red Lion'	CBcs CJun
	'Ricki'	CAco CJun EMil MBlu
	'Roseanne'	CJun
	rostrata	CBcs CExl CFil GLin SKHP WPGP
	'Rouged Alabaster'	CBcs CDoC
	'Royal Crown'	CBcs CDoC EPfP IDee LRHS MRav NPCo
	'Ruby'	CJun NLar
	salicifolia	CBcs CMCN SSpi
	- var. ***concolor***	CJun
	- 'Jermyns'	CJun
	- 'Louisa Fete'	CJun
*	- 'Rosea'	CJun
	- upright	WPGP
	- 'Van Veen'	CJun
§	- 'Wada's Memory' ♀H6	CDoC CDul CExl CHid CJun CMCN CTho ELan EPfP ERea LMil LRHS MAsh MBlu MBri MMuc SKHP SSpi SSta WFar
	- 'Windsor Beauty'	CJun ERea SSta
	sapaensis FMWJ 13330 **new**	WCru
	- NJM 09.168	WPGP
	'Sara Koe'	MBri
	sargentiana	CBcs SSta
	- 'Broadleas'	CJun
	- var. ***robusta***	CBcs CLnd CMCN ELan EPfP NLar
	- - 'Blood Moon'	CJun WPGP
	- - 'Multipetal'	WPGP
	- - 'Trengwainton Glory'	ERea
	'Satisfaction'	CBcs CJun NLar
	'Sayonara' ♀H5	CBcs CJun ERea LRHS MBri SSpi
	'Schmetterling'	see *M.* × *soulangeana* 'Pickard's Schmetterling'
	'Serene'	CBcs CEnd CJun CMHG EPfP LMil LRHS MBri WPGP
	Shirazz = 'Vulden' **new**	CBcs CDoC CJun MBri NLar SKHP WPGP
	sieboldii	CAco CBcs CDul CJun CMCN CMac CTho ELan EPfP GKin LRHS MBlu MBri MGos MRav NLar SHil SKHP SPer WPGP
	- B&SWJ 4127	WCru
	- 'Colossus' ♀H6	CJun IArd IDee MBlu SKHP
	- 'Genesis'	CJun
	- 'Genesis' × ***tripetala***	CJun
	- 'Genesis' × ***virginiana***	CJun
	- 'Michiko Renge' (d)	CJun
	- 'Min Pyong-gal'	CJun
	- 'Pride of Norway'	CJun

	- subsp. ***sieboldii*** B&SWJ 12553 from Korea **new**	WCru
	- subsp. ***sinensis***	CBcs CDoC CJun CMCN CTho ELan EPfP NLar WPGP
I	- - 'Grandiflora'	CJun
	'Sir Harold Hillier'	CBcs WPGP
	'Sleeping Beauty'	SKHP
	'Snow Goose'	CJun
	'Solar Flair'	CBcs CJun IArd LRHS MBri NLar SKHP
	× ***soulangeana***	Widely available
	- 'Alba Superba'	CAco CBcs CDoC CTri EMil EPfP GBin LMil LRHS MBlu MBri MMuc MRav NLar SLim WFar
	- 'Alexandrina'	EPfP MBlu NLar
	- 'André Leroy'	EPfP
	- 'Brozzonii' ♀H5	CBcs CDoC CMac EPfP GCra IArd LMil LRHS MMuc NPCo SSta
	- 'Burgundy'	CBcs CDoC
	- 'Cleopatra' **new**	CBcs
	- 'Fukuju'	CJun
	- 'Lennei'	CBcs CDoC CMCN CMac CSBt CTho EPfP IArd LAst LRHS MGos MMuc MRav NLar SHil SRms WFar
	- 'Lennei Alba'	CDoC CMCN CMac ELan IArd MBlu MBri WFar
	- 'Nigra'	see *M. liliiflora* 'Nigra'
	- 'Pickard's Opal'	CMCN
	- 'Pickard's Ruby'	CBcs LRHS MBri
§	- 'Pickard's Schmetterling' ♀H5	CBcs CDoC EPfP LMil LRHS MAsh MBri
	- 'Pickard's Snow Queen'	CJun
	- 'Pickard's Sundew'	see *M.* 'Sundew'
	- 'Picture'	CDoC CMac CTri
	- Red Lucky	see *M.* 'Hong Yun'
	- 'Rubra' misapplied	see *M.* × *soulangeana* 'Rustica Rubra'
§	- 'Rustica Rubra'	CBcs CDoC CDul CLnd CMCN CMac CTri ELan EPfP LMil LRHS MAsh MBri SGol SRms SSpi WFar
	- 'San José'	CJun LMil LRHS MAsh NLar
	- 'Speciosa'	SSta
	- 'Superba'	CMac
	- 'Verbanica'	EPfP LMil LRHS MAsh
	'Spectrum' ♀H6	CBcs CDoC CEnd CJun EPfP ERea GKin IArd IDee LMil LRHS MGos NLar SKHP SSpi SSta
	sprengeri var. ***diva***	CBcs CEnd CExl MBri NLar SKHP WPGP
	- - 'Burncoose' ♀H6	CBcs CDoC
	- - 'Copeland Court' ♀H6	CBcs CJun WPGP
	- - 'Dark Diva'	CJun
	- - 'Diva'	GGal LMil WPGP
	- - 'Eric Savill' ♀H6	CBcs CJun ERea IVic SKHP WPGP
	- - 'Lanhydrock'	CJun LRHS SKHP SSta WPGP
	- - 'Westonbirt'	WPGP
	- var. ***elongata***	SKHP
	- 'Marwood Spring'	CMHG ERea MBri SKHP SSta WPGP
	'Spring Rite'	CJun SKHP
	'Star Wars' ♀H5	CBcs CCVT CDoC CDul CEnd CExl CJun CLnd CTho CTsd ELan EPfP ERea GGGa GKin LMil LRHS MAsh MBri MGos SKHP SPoG SSpi SSta WPGP
	'Stellar Acclaim'	CBcs CJun LMil
	stellata	Widely available
	- 'Centennial' ♀H6	CDoC CJun CTho NLar
	- 'Chrysanthemumiflora'	CJun ERea SKHP
	- 'Dawn'	CJun
	- 'Jane Platt' ♀H6	CBcs CJun ELan EPfP LMil LRHS MGos SKHP SPoG SSta WPGP
	- f. ***keiskei***	CBcs CEnd CJun MGos NHol SKHP
	- 'Kikuzaki'	CJun
	- 'King Rose'	CBcs CDoC CJun CTsd EPfP LRHS MAsh
	- 'Massey'	CJun
	- 'Norman Gould'	see *M. kobus* 'Norman Gould'
	- 'Rosea'	CDul CJun CLnd CMCN CTho ELan ELon LMil MGos MRav MSwo NEgg NLar NSoo SCob SKHP
	- 'Rosea Massey'	CJun WFar
	- 'Royal Star' ♀H6	Widely available
	- 'Scented Silver'	CJun LRHS MAsh SKHP
	- 'Shi-banchi Rosea'	CJun
	- 'Two Stones'	SKHP
	- 'Water Lily'	CBcs CJun CMCN CTho ELan ELon EPfP LMil LRHS MAsh MBlu MGos MMuc NLar NPCo SHil SKHP SPer SSta WFar WPGP
	- 'Wisley Stardust'	LRHS
	'Summer Solstice'	CBcs CJun MBri
	'Sun Ray'	CBcs CJun
	'Sunburst'	CBcs CJun SRms
	'Sundance'	CBcs CJun IArd MBlu MBri NLar
§	'Sundew'	CBcs CDoC EPfP ERea
	'Sunrise'	CBcs MBri
	'Sunsation'	CBcs CDoC CJun LRHS MBri SSta
	'Sunspire'	CJun NLar
	'Suntown'	CJun
	'Susan' ♀H6	Widely available
	'Susanna van Veen'	CDoC CEnd CJun MBri WPGP
	'Swedish Star'	CJun
	'Sweet Merlot'	CBcs CDoC CJun
	'Sweet Valentine'	CBcs CJun
	'Sweetheart' ♀H5	CBcs CJun
	'Sybille' **new**	CMCN
	'Theodora'	MBri
	× ***thompsoniana***	CBcs CMCN NLar
	- 'Olmenhof'	IArd
	'Thousand Butterflies'	CBcs CJun
	'Tina Durio'	CBcs LRHS MBri SKHP
	'Todd Gresham'	CJun
	'Todd's Forty Niner'	CBcs CJun
	'Touch of Pink'	CBcs
	'Tranquility'	CBcs CJun SKHP
	'Treve Holman'	CBcs
	'Trewidden Belle'	CEnd
	tripetala	CBcs CExl CLnd CMCN CTho ELan EPfP MBlu NLar SBig SKHP SSpi SSta WPGP
	- 'Bloomfield'	CJun
	- 'Petite'	SKHP
	'Ultimate Yellow'	CJun NLar
	× ***veitchii***	CBcs EPfP
	- 'Columbus'	CJun SKHP WPGP
	- 'Peter Veitch'	CTho
	virginiana	CBcs CJun CMCN EPfP IDee NLar SBig SKHP SSpi WPGP
	- 'Aiken County'	SKHP
	- var. ***australis*** 'Green Shadow'	SGol
	- - 'Satellite'	CJun NLar
	- 'Havener'	SKHP
	- 'Henry Hicks'	CJun
	- 'Moonglow'	CJun EPfP MBlu WPGP
	- 'Pink Halo'	CJun

'Vulcan'	CBcs CDoC CEnd CJun ELan EPfP MBri SCoo SPoG
× ***watsonii***	see *M.* × *wieseneri*
'White Mystery'	CJun
§ × ***wieseneri***	CBcs CJun CMCN CMHG EPfP ERea MBlu MBri SKHP WPGP
- 'Aashild Kalleberg'	CBcs CJun SKHP SSpi
- 'Lupo Osti'	SKHP
wilsonii ♀H6	CBcs CDoC CDul CExl CJun CMCN CTho CTri ELan EPfP GGGa IArd IDee ITim LRHS MBlu MBri MGos MMuc NLar SBrt SEND SKHP WMou WPGP WSHC
- 'Gwen Baker'	CEnd CJun
'Yaeko'	CBcs CJun
'Yellow Fever'	CBcs CJun CTho WPGP
'Yellow Garland'	CJun
'Yellow Lantern' ♀H6	CAbP CBcs CDoC CEnd CJun EPfP EWTr GGGa LMil LRHS MAsh MBlu MMuc SPoG SSta WPGP
'Yellow Sea'	CJun SKHP
Yuchelia No. 1	CBcs
yunnanensis	CCCN CDoC MPkF
yuyuanensis	CBcs
zenii	CBcs CMCN
- 'Pink Parchment'	CJun

× *Mahoberberis* (*Berberidaceae*)

aquisargentii	CMac EBee EMil EPfP GCal IVic LRHS MMuc MRav NLar SCob SEND SKHP WFar
'Dart's Desire'	ETwe NLar
miethkeana	SRms

Mahonia ✿ (*Berberidaceae*)

§ ***aquifolium***	CAco CAgr CBcs CDul EAEE ECrN MGos MMuc MRav NWea SCob SEND SGol SPer SPlb SWvt WHar
- 'Apollo' ♀H5	CBcs CSBt ELan ELon EPfP LAst LRHS MAsh MGos MJak MRav NLar SCob SCoo SPer SPoG SWvt WFar
- 'Atropurpurea'	CMac CSBt ELan EPfP LRHS MRav NLar SPer
- 'Cosmo Crawl'	CRos LRHS MBri SHil
- 'Fascicularis'	see *M.* × *wagneri* 'Pinnacle'
- 'Green Ripple'	EPfP NLar
- 'Mirena'	NLar
- 'Orange Flame'	NLar
- 'Smaragd'	CDoC CMac ELan EPfP LRHS MBlu MGos MRav NLar SCob WHar
- 'Versicolor'	EPla MBlu
bealei	see *M. japonica* Bealei Group
bodinieri	WPGP
'Bokrafoot'PBR	EPfP LLHF LRHS MAsh SLon
chochoco	CExl CFil SKHP
conferta	CFil
confusa × ***gracilipes*** new	SKHP
eurybracteata	CDoC CExl CFil CHEx CLAP EBee LLHF LRHS SKHP WPGP
- subsp. ***ganpinensis*** 'Soft Caress' new	EPfP LRHS NLar SCob SPoG
eutriphylla	see *M. trifolia*
fortunei	CBcs IDee
- 'Winter Prince'	NLar
fremontii	SBrt
gracilipes	CExl CFil CHEx EPfP EWes GCal MBlu NLar SBrt SKHP SLon SMad WCru WHar WPGP WWFP
gracilis	CFil
japonica ♀H5	Widely available
§ - Bealei Group	CAco CBcs CDul CRos CSBt EBee ELan ELon EPfP LRHS MAsh MGos MRav MSwo NLar NPer NPla SCob SCoo SGol SKHP SLim SWvt
- 'Gold Dust'	CMac NLar
- 'Hiemalis'	see *M. japonica* 'Hivernant'
§ - 'Hivernant'	EAEE MBri NWea
lanceolata	CFil WPGP
leschenaultii B&SWJ 9535	WCru
× ***lindsayae***	CFil WPGP
- 'Cantab' ♀H4	CFil NLar WPGP
lomariifolia	see *M. oiwakensis* subsp. *lomariifolia*
longibracteata	GKin
× ***media*** 'Arthur Menzies'	NLar
- 'Buckland' ♀H4	CDul CMac EPfP MBri NLar SCob SDix SPer SRms WPat
- 'Charity'	Widely available
- 'Lionel Fortescue' ♀H4	CBcs CMac CRos CSBt EBee ELan EPfP GKin LAst LRHS MAsh MRav NEgg SCob SDix SKHP SPer SPoG SSpi SWvt
- 'Maharajah'	IArd
- 'Winter Sun' ♀H4	Widely available
moranensis	CExl CFil
- T 292	WPGP
napaulensis	CFil
nervosa	CBcs CMac EPfP MBlu NLar SKHP WCru WPGP
- B&SWJ 9562	WCru
nevinii new	SBrt
nitens	CBcs WPGP
- 'Cabaret'PBR ♀H4	CRos EBee EPfP EPla LBuc LLHF LRHS MAsh MBlu MBri SCob SHil SPoG WPGP
oiwakensis	NLar WPGP
- B&SWJ 371	WCru
- B&SWJ 3660	WCru
§ - subsp. ***lomariifolia*** ♀H4	CExl CFil CHEx EBee EPfP EWes LRHS SArc SKHP
pallida	CExl CFil SKHP WPGP
- from Tamazunchale, Mexico	CFil
- from Zimapan, Mexico	CFil
'Pan's Peculiar' new	WPGP
pinnata misapplied	see *M.* × *wagneri* 'Pinnacle'
- 'Ken S. Howard'	NLar WPGP
repens	EPla GCal NLar
× ***savilliana***	CFil EPla NLar WPGP
siamensis	CFil
Sioux = 'Bokrasio'PBR	LLHF LRHS MAsh SPoG
§ ***trifolia***	CFil GCal SKHP
trifoliolata var. ***glauca***	CEnd CJun SKHP
× ***wagneri*** 'Aldenhamensis' new	NLar
- 'Fireflame'	GCal
- 'Hastings Elegant'	NLar
- 'Moseri'	NLar WPat
§ - 'Pinnacle' ♀H5	ELan EPfP IDee LRHS MAsh NLar SPer SPoG SWvt
- 'Sunset'	GKin MBlu NLar
- 'Undulata'	LRHS MBlu SPer SRms

Maianthemum (*Asparagaceae*)

amoenum B&SWJ 10390	WCru
atropurpureum	WCru
bicolor	CDes CTal LEdu SWat

	bifolium	CAvo CBct CCon CHid CTal ECho GCra GLog GMaP LEdu MAvo MMoz MNrw NBro SRms WCru WPtf WWEG XLum
§	- subsp. ***kamtschaticum***	CAvo CLAP ECha EPPr LEdu MAvo NLar NRya WCot WWEG
	- - B&SWJ 4360	WCru
	- - CD&R 2300	WCru
*	- - var. ***minimum***	EBee GCal LEdu WCru
*	- - var. ***pumilum***	CDes LEdu
	canadense	EAJP EBee ECho EPot GBuc GCal GKev LEdu MNrw NBid WCru
	chasmanthum	see *M. bifolium* subsp. *kamtschaticum*
	comaltepecense B&SWJ 10215	WCru
	dilatatum	see *M. bifolium* subsp. *kamtschaticum*
	flexuosum	LEdu
	- B&SWJ 9069	WCru
	- B&SWJ 9079	WCru
	- B&SWJ 9150	WCru
	aff. ***flexuosum*** B&SWJ 9026	WCru
	- B&SWJ 9055	WCru
	formosanum B&SWJ 349	EPPr WCru
	forrestii	WCru
	fuscum	GEdr WCru
	- PAB 7749 **new**	LEdu
	- var. ***cordatum***	WCru
	gigas B&SWJ 10470	WCru
	henryi	ECho GEdr LEdu WCru
	- BWJ 7616 **new**	WCru
	japonicum	CTal LEdu
	- B&SWJ 1179	WCru
	- B&SWJ 4714	WCru
	- B&SWJ 7306 **new**	WCru
	oleraceum	CBct CExl EBee GEdr GKev LEdu MMoz
	- B&SWJ 2148	WCru
	- purple-flowered	GEdr
	paniculatum	EBee LEdu
	- B&SWJ 9137	WCru
	- B&SWJ 9140	WCru
	- purple-flowered B&SWJ 9139	WCru
	pendent, B&SWJ 10305 from Guatemala	WCru
	purpureum	GEdr GKev
	- G-W&P 150	EPPr
	racemosum ♀H7	Widely available
	- subsp. ***amplexicaule***	CAvo GCal
	- - 'Emily Moody'	CBct CDes CExl CPou EBee EPPr EPfP SKHP WPGP
	- dwarf	ECho
	- 'Major' **new**	LRHS
	aff. ***salvinii*** B&SWJ 9000	WCru
	- B&SWJ 9088	WCru
	- B&SWJ 10402	WCru
	scilloideum B&SWJ 10407	WCru
*	- var. ***roseum*** B&SWJ 10335	WCru
	stellatum	CBct CCon CSam CTal EBee ECha ECho EPPr EPfP EPot GBin GBuc GCal GEdr LEdu LRHS MBel NChi NLar SMrm SPoG WCru WPnP
	szechuanicum	WCru
	tatsienense	CBct CExl GEdr LEdu WCru

Maihuenia (*Cactaceae*)

	poeppigii	SPlb
	- F&W 9670	WCot

Maireana (*Amaranthaceae*)

	georgei	SPlb

Mallotus (*Euphorbiaceae*)

	japonicus	WPGP

Malus ✿ (*Rosaceae*)

§	'Adirondack' ♀H6	CLnd EBee EPfP EPla LRHS MAsh MBri MMuc NOra SCoo SEND SLim SLon SPoG WJas
	'Admiration'	see *M.* 'Adirondack'
	× ***adstringens*** 'Hopa'	CDul CLnd
	- 'Simcoe'	EBee
	'Aldenhamensis'	see *M.* × *purpurea* 'Aldenhamensis'
	'Amberina'	CLnd
	× ***atrosanguinea*** 'Gorgeous'	CDul CLnd CMac CNWT COtt CTho EBee ECrN EPfP GTwe LBuc LRHS MAsh MBri MGos MRav MSwo NOra NWea SCoo SEWo SKee SLim SPer WJas WMou
	baccata	CDul CLnd CMCN CTho GTwe MMuc NWea SCoo SEND SPlb
	- 'Dolgo'	EPom NOra SKee WHar
	- var. ***mandshurica***	CTho
	aff. ***baccata***	NWea
§	***bhutanica***	CDul CLnd SCrf
	- 'Mandarin'	MBri SCoo
	brevipes	CLnd LRHS SCoo
	- 'Wedding Bouquet' ♀H6	EBee ERea LBuc MAsh MBri NLar NOra SPer WMou
	'Butterball' ♀H6	CDoC CDul CLnd CNWT CTho CTsd EPfP ERea GQue LAst NOra NWea SCoo SLim SVic WHar WJas WMou
	'Candymint Sargent'	CLnd
	'Cave Hill'	CLnd
	'Cheal's Scarlet'	CHab
*	'Cheal's Weeping'	CAco CMac EWTr LAst NEgg
	Coccinella = 'Courtarou'	LRHS SGol
	'Comtessa de Paris' ♀H6	CLnd EBee EPfP LRHS MAsh MBlu
	'Coralburst'	MAsh MBri
	coronaria var. ***dasycalyx*** 'Charlottae' (d)	CDul CLnd SPer
	- 'Elk River'	EPfP LRHS MAsh SCoo
	'Cowichan'	CLnd ECrN
	'Crimson Brilliant'	CLnd
	'Crittenden'	MAsh MRav SLim
	'Dartmouth'	CDul CHab CLnd CSBt CTri NPCo SFam
*	'Directeur Moerlands'	CCVT CDoC ECrN EPfP IArd LAst SEND SPer
	domestica 'Acklam Russet' (D)	CHab SKee
	- 'Acme' (D)	ECrN SDea
	- 'Adams's Pearmain' (D)	CDoC CHab CLnd CTho CTri ECrN ERea GTwe LRHS MAsh MCoo NOra SDea SFam SKee WHar
	- 'Admiral' PBR (D)	ECrN ERea
	- 'Akane' (D)	SDea
	- 'Alfriston' (C)	CAgr CHab SKee
§	- 'Alkmene' (D) ♀H6	CAgr ECrN NOra SDea SKee
	- 'All Doer' (C/D/Cider)	CTho
	- 'Allen's Everlasting' (D)	SDea SKee

- 'Allington Pippin' (D)	CHab CSBt CTho CTri ECrN IArd LRHS MGos NOra SDea SFam SKee WHar
- Ambassy = 'Dalil'PBR (D)	EBee
- 'American Mother'	see *M. domestica* 'Mother'
- 'Ananas Reinette' (D)	CHab ECrN SKee
- 'Anna Boelens' (D)	SDea
- 'Annie Elizabeth' (C)	CAgr CCAT CHab CTho ECrN GTwe IArd LAst LRHS MCoo MGos NOra SDea SFam SKee SVic WHar WJas
- 'Anniversary' (D)	SDea
- 'Api' (D)	GQue NOra SKee WHar
- 'Api Noir' (D)	SKee
- 'Ard Cairn Russet' (D)	ECrN IArd SDea SKee
- 'Arkansas' (D)	SKee
- 'Aromatic Russet' (D)	SKee
- 'Arthur Turner' (C) ♀H6	CCVT CHab CLnd CTri ECrN EPom EWTr GTwe IArd LAst LBuc MWat NOra SCrf SDea SFam SKee WHar WJas
- 'Ashmead's Kernel' (D) ♀H6	Widely available
- 'Ashton Bitter' (Cider)	CCAT CHab CTho CTri GTwe
- 'Ashton Brown Jersey' (Cider)	CCAT
- 'Askham Pippin' (F)	MCoo
- 'Autumn Pearmain' (D)	SDea WHar
- 'Baker's Delicious' (D)	EBee ECrN ERea SDea SKee WHar
- 'Ballerina Flamenco' (D)	MAsh NOra
- 'Ball's Bittersweet' (Cider)	CCAT CTho
- 'Ballyfatten' (C)	IArd
- 'Ballyvaughan Seedling' (D)	IArd
- 'Balsam'	see *M. domestica* 'Green Balsam'
- 'Banana Pippin' (F)	CEnd
- 'Banns' (D)	ECrN ERea
- 'Bardsey' (D)	CAgr CHab EPom NOra SKee WGwG WHar
- 'Barnack Beauty' (D)	CHab CTho CTri LEdu NOra SKee
- 'Barnack Orange' (D)	SKee
- 'Baron Ward' (C)	CHab
- 'Baumann's Reinette' (D)	SKee
- 'Baxter's Pearmain' (D)	ECrN SDea SKee
- 'Beauty of Bath' (D)	CAgr CCAT CCVT CDoC CDul CHab CLnd CTho CTri ECrN ELan EPom GTwd GTwe LAst LBuc LRHS MRav NOra SDea SFam SKee SPer WHar WJas
- 'Beauty of Hants' (C/D)	ECrN SKee
- 'Beauty of Kent' (C)	SDea SKee
- 'Beauty of Moray' (C)	GTwd SKee
- 'Beauty of Stoke' (C)	SKee
- 'Bedwyn Beauty' (C)	CTho
- 'Beeley Pippin' (D)	SDea SKee
- 'Bell Apple' (Cider/C)	CCAT CTho
- 'Bella Bionda Patrizia' (D) **new**	CSut
- 'Belle de Boskoop' (C/D) ♀H6	CAgr CCAT CHab ECrN GTwe MCoo NOra SDea SKee
- 'Belledge Pippin' (C/D) **new**	SKee
- 'Belvoir Seedling' (C/D)	SKee
- 'Bembridge Beauty' (F)	CHab SDea
- 'Benenden Early' (D)	SKee
- 'Ben's Red' (D)	CAgr CCAT CDoC CEnd CTho
- 'Bess Pool' (D)	CCAT CHab MCoo SDea SFam
- 'Bewley Down Pippin'	see *M. domestica* 'Crimson King' (Cider/C)
- 'Bickington Grey' (Cider)	CCAT CTho
- 'Billy Down Pippin' (F)	CTho
- 'Bismarck' (C)	CCAT SKee
- 'Black Dabinett' (Cider)	CCAT CEnd CTho LRHS
- 'Black Tom Putt' (C/D)	CTho
- 'Black Vallis' (Cider)	CCAT
- 'Blenheim Orange' (C/D) ♀H6	Widely available
- 'Blood of the Boyne' (D)	IArd
- 'Bloody Ploughman' (D)	CHab ECrN GBin GQue GTwd GTwe MWat SKee SLon WHar
- 'Blue Pearmain' (D)	SDea
- 'Blue Sweet' (Cider)	CTho
- BoleroPBR	see *M. domestica* 'Tuscan'
- 'Boston Russet'	see *M. domestica* 'Roxbury Russet'
- 'Bountiful' (C)	CAgr CDoC CDul CLnd CMac CSBt CTri ECrN EPom GTwd GTwe IArd LRHS MAsh MBri NOra SDea SKee SPoG WHar
- 'Box Apple' (D)	CDoC
- 'Braddick's Nonpareil' (D)	SKee
- 'Bradley's Beauty' (C/D)	NWea
- 'Braeburn' (D)	CAgr CDul CLnd CSBt CSut CTri ECrN EPom ERea LAst LBuc LEdu LRHS MWat NOra SCrf SDea SEND SEWo SFam SFrt SKee SPer WHar WJas
- 'Braeburn Hillwell' (D)	EPom NOra
- 'Braintree Seedling' (D)	EBee ECrN SKee
- 'Bramley's Seedling' (C) ♀H6	Widely available
- 'Bramley's Seedling' clone 20 (F)	CDoC CTsd ERea MAsh MBri MWat NLar NOra SCoo SDea SKee SLim SPer SPoG WHar
- 'Bramshott Rectory' (D/C)	SKee
- 'Bread Fruit' (C/D)	CDoC CEnd CTho
- 'Breakwell's Seedling' (Cider)	CCAT CTho
- 'Bridgwater Pippin' (C)	CCAT CTho
- 'Bright Future' (D)	EPom LBuc MCoo NOra
- 'Brith Mawr' (C) **new**	WGwG
- 'Broad-eyed Pippin' (C)	SKee
- 'Broadholm Beauty' (C)	EPom MAsh WHar
- 'Brookes's' (D)	WHar
- 'Brown Crofton' (D)	IArd
- 'Brown Snout' (Cider)	CCAT CTho SFrt
- 'Brownlee's Russet' (D)	CAgr CHab CTho CTri GTwd GTwe MCoo NEgg NOra NWea SDea SFam SKee WHar
- 'Brown's Apple' (Cider)	CAgr CCAT CHab ECrN GTwe NOra SFrt
- 'Broxwood Foxwhelp' (Cider)	CCAT SFrt
- 'Burn's Seedling' (D)	CTho SKee
- 'Burrowhill Early' (Cider)	CTho
- 'Bushey Grove' (C)	SDea SKee
- 'Buttery Do' (F)	CCAT CTho
- 'Cadbury' (F)	CCAT
- 'Calville Blanc d'Hiver' (D)	NOra SKee
- 'Cambusnethan Pippin' (D)	GTwd SKee
- 'Camelot' (Cider/C)	CCAT
- 'Cap of Liberty' (Cider)	CCAT
§ - 'Captain Broad' (Cider/D)	CCAT CDoC CEnd CTho
- 'Captain Kidd' (D)	EPom NOra SKee WHar
- 'Carlisle Codlin' (C)	NWea SDea
- 'Caroline' (D)	ECrN ERea

	Cultivar	Suppliers
	- 'Catherine' (C)	ECrN
	- 'Catshead' (C)	CAgr CHab CTri CTsd ECrN IArd NOra SDea SKee WHar
	- 'Cellini' (C)	NOra SDea SKee
	- 'Chacewater Longstem' (F)	CDoC
	- 'Charles Ross' (C/D) ♀H6	Widely available
	- 'Charlotte'[PBR] (C)	SDea SKee
	- 'Chaxhill Red' (Cider/D)	CCAT CTho
	- 'Cheddar Cross' (D)	CAgr CCVT CTri ECrN
	- 'Chelmsford Wonder' (C)	ECrN
	- 'Chisel Jersey' (Cider)	CAgr CCAT CTri NOra SFrt SKee
	- 'Chivers Delight' (D)	CAgr CSBt EBee ECrN EPom ERea GTwe LRHS MCoo NOra SDea SKee WHar WJas
	- 'Chorister Boy' (D)	CTho
	- 'Christmas Pearmain' (D)	CAgr CTho ECrN GTwe SDea SFam SKee
	- 'Christmas Pippin' (D)	CDoC EBee EPom GQue LBuc LRHS MCoo MWat NOra
	- 'Cider Lady's Finger' (Cider)	SKee
	- 'Cissy' (D)	WGwG
	- 'Claygate Pearmain' (D) ♀H6	CAgr CDoC CHab CTho CTri ECrN GTwe LRHS MCoo NOra SDea SFam SKee SVic WHar
	- 'Clopton Red' (D)	ECrN
	- 'Clydeside' (C)	GTwd
	- 'Coat Jersey' (Cider)	CCAT
	- 'Cobra' (F)	CAgr CDoC LBuc LRHS MAsh MBri MCoo SKee WHar WJas
	- 'Cockle Pippin' (D)	CAgr CTho SDea
	- 'Cockpit' (C)	CHab NWea
	- 'Coeur de Boeuf' (C/D)	SKee
	- 'Coleman's Seedling' (Cider)	CTho
	- 'Collogett Pippin' (C/Cider)	CCAT CDoC CEnd CTho
	- 'Colonel Vaughan' (C/D)	SKee
	- 'Cornish Aromatic' (D)	CAgr CDoC CTho CTri CTsd GTwe LRHS NOra SCrf SDea SFam SKee WHar
	- 'Cornish Gilliflower' (D)	CAgr CCAT CDoC CDul CEnd CHab CTho EBee ECrN LRHS MCoo NOra SDea SFam SKee WHar
	- 'Cornish Honeypin' (D)	CEnd CTho
	- 'Cornish Longstem' (D)	CAgr CDoC CEnd CTho
	- 'Cornish Mother' (D)	CDoC CEnd CTho CTsd
	- 'Cornish Pine' (D)	CDoC CEnd CTho SDea
	- 'Coronation' (D)	CHab SDea
	- 'Corse Hill' (D)	CCAT CTho
	- 'Costard' (C)	CCAT CHab SKee
	- 'Cottenham Seedling' (C)	SKee
	- 'Coul Blush' (D)	GTwd SKee
	- 'Court of Wick' (D)	CAgr CCAT CHab CTho CTri ECrN GTwd NOra SKee SVic WHar
	- 'Court Pendu Plat' (D)	CAgr CCAT CHab CTho GQue GTwd LEdu MAsh MWat NOra NWea SDea SFam SKee WHar WJas
	- 'Court Royal' (Cider)	CCAT
	- 'Cox Cymraeg' (D)	WGwG
	- 'Cox's Orange Pippin' (D)	Widely available
	- 'Cox's Pomona' (C)	SDea SKee WHar
	- 'Cox's Rouge de Flandres' (D)	SKee
	- 'Cox's Selfing' (D)	CDoC CDul CLnd CMac CTri CWSG EPfP GTwe LBuc MAsh MBri MGos MNHC NLar SCrf SDea SKee SPer SPoG WHar WJas
	- 'Crawley Beauty' (C)	CAgr CHab GTwe SDea SFam SKee WHar
	- 'Crawley Reinette' (D)	CHab SKee
	- 'Crimson Beauty of Bath' (D)	CAgr
	- 'Crimson Bramley' (C)	CCAT IArd LAst
	- 'Crimson Cox' (D)	SDea
§	- 'Crimson King' (Cider/C)	CAgr CCAT SFrt
	- 'Crimson King' (D)	CAgr CHab CTri
	- 'Crimson Peasgood' (C)	ECrN SKee
	- 'Crimson Queening' (D)	SKee WHar
	- 'Crimson Victoria' (Cider)	CTho
	- Crispin	see *M. domestica* 'Mutsu'
	- 'Croen Mochyn' (D)	WGwG
§	- 'Crowngold' (D)	EPom
	- 'Cutler Grieve' (D)	GTwd SDea
	- Cybèle = 'Delrouval' (D)	LRHS
	- 'Dabinett' (Cider)	CAgr CCAT CHab CTho CTri GTwe LAst LBuc NOra SCrf SDea SFrt SKee WHar
	- 'D'Arcy Spice' (D)	CAgr CCAT CDoC ECrN EPfP ERea GQue MCoo MWat NOra SDea SFam SFrt SKee WHar
	- 'Deacon's Blushing Beauty' (C/D)	SDea
	- 'Deacon's Millennium' (D)	SDea
	- 'Decio' (D)	SKee
	- Delbarestivale = 'Delcorf' (red) (D) ♀H6	LRHS
	- 'Devon Crimson Queen' (D)	CDoC CTho
	- 'Devonshire Buckland' (C)	CEnd CTho
	- 'Devonshire Crimson Queen' (D)	SDea
	- 'Devonshire Quarrenden' (D)	CAgr CCAT CDoC CDul CHab CTho CTsd GTwd NOra SDea SFam SKee SVic WHar
	- 'Dewdney's Seedling' (C)	SKee
	- 'Diamond' (D)	WGwG
	- 'Discovery' (D) ♀H6	Widely available
	- 'Doctor Harvey' (C)	ECrN ERea SFam
	- 'Doctor Kidd's Orange Red'	see *M. domestica* 'Kidd's Orange Red'
	- 'Domino' (C)	MCoo
	- 'Don's Delight' (C)	CTho
	- 'Dove' (Cider)	CCAT
	- 'Downton Pippin' (D)	CHab WHar
	- 'Dredge's Fame' (D)	CTho
	- 'Duchess of Oldenburg' (C)	NOra SKee
	- 'Duchess's Favourite' (D)	SKee
	- 'Duck's Bill' (D)	SKee
	- 'Dufflin' (Cider)	CCAT CTho
	- 'Duke of Cornwall' (C)	CDoC CTho
	- 'Duke of Devonshire' (D)	CCAT CSBt CTho CTri SDea SFam SKee
	- 'Dumeller's Seedling'	see *M. domestica* 'Dummellor's Seedling'
§	- 'Dummellor's Seedling' (C) ♀H6	CCAT CHab CTri MCoo MGos NOra SDea SKee WHar
	- 'Dunkerton Late Sweet' (Cider)	CCAT CCVT CHab CTho LBuc
	- 'Dunn's Seedling' (D)	SDea
§	- 'Dutch Mignonne' (D)	SKee
	- 'Dymock Red' (Cider)	CCAT
	- 'Early Blenheim' (D/C)	CCAT CEnd CTho
	- 'Early Bower' (D)	CEnd
	- 'Early Julyan' (C)	GTwd SKee

	- 'Early Victoria'	see *M. domestica* 'Emneth Early'
	- Early Windsor	see *M. domestica* 'Alkmene'
	- 'Early Worcester'	see *M. domestica* 'Tydeman's Early Worcester'
	- 'East Lothian Pippin' (C)	GTwd
	- 'Ecklinville' (C)	SDea SKee
	- 'Edith Hopwood' (D)	ECrN
	- 'Edward VII' (C) ♀H6	CCAT CHab GTwe MAsh NOra SCrf SDea SFam SKee WHar
	- 'Egremont Russet' (D) ♀H6	Widely available
	- 'Ellis' Bitter' (Cider)	CCAT CTho GTwe LBuc SKee SVic
	- 'Ellison's Orange' (D) ♀H6	CAgr CCAT CDul CHab CMac CSBt CTri ECrN EPfP EPom GTwd GTwe LAst LBuc MMuc MWat NOra NWea SDea SEND SFam SFrt SKee SLon SPer SVic WHar WJas
	- 'Elstar' (D) ♀H6	CCVT CLnd ECrN EPom GTwe LAst NOra SDea SKee WHar
	- 'Elton Beauty' (D)	SDea SKee
§	- 'Emneth Early' (C) ♀H6	CAgr CHab ECrN GTwe SDea SFam SKee WJas
	- 'Empire' (D)	NOra SKee
	- 'Encore' (C)	SDea
	- 'Endsleigh Beauty' (D)	CEnd
	- 'English Codlin' (C)	CTho CTri ERea
	- 'Epicure'	see *M. domestica* 'Laxton's Epicure'
	- 'Ernie's Russet' (D)	SDea
	- 'Eros' (D)	ECrN
	- 'Esopus Spitzenburg' (D)	SKee
	- 'Essex Pippin' (D)	ECrN
	- 'Evening Gold' (C)	SDea
	- 'Eve's Delight' (D)	SDea
	- 'Excelsior' (C)	ECrN
	- 'Exeter Cross' (D)	CSBt ECrN SDea SFam
	- 'Fair Maid of Devon' (Cider)	CAgr CCAT CDul CEnd CTho
	- 'Fair Maid of Taunton' (D)	CCAT
	- 'Fairfield' (D)	CTho
	- 'Falstaff'[PBR] (D) ♀H6	CAgr CDul ECrN EPfP EPom GTwe MGos NOra SCoo SDea SKee SPer WHar
	- 'Fameuse' (D)	NOra
	- 'Farmer's Glory' (D)	CAgr CCAT CTho
	- 'Fiesta'[PBR] (D) ♀H6	Widely available
	- 'Fillbarrel' (Cider)	CCAT CHab
	- 'Fillingham Pippin' (C)	CHab
	- 'Firmgold' (D)	SDea
	- 'Flame' (D)	ECrN
	- 'Flamenco'[PBR]	see *M. domestica* 'Obelisk'
§	- 'Flower of Kent' (C)	CHab EPom MAsh NOra NWea SCrf SDea SKee
	- 'Flower of the Town' (D)	CHab
	- 'Forfar'	see *M. domestica* 'Dutch Mignonne'
	- 'Forge' (D)	CAgr CHab SDea SKee
	- 'Fortune'	see *M. domestica* 'Laxton's Fortune'
	- 'Four Square' (F)	CCAT
	- 'Foxwhelp' (Cider)	CHab MGos NWea SKee
	- 'Francis' (D)	ECrN
	- 'Frederick' (Cider)	CCAT CTho
	- 'French Crab' (C)	SDea
	- 'Freyberg' (D)	NOra SKee
	- 'Fuji' (D)	NOra SDea SKee
	- 'Gala' (D)	CSBt EBee EPom LAst LRHS NOra SCoo SCrf SDea SFam SKee SLim WHar
	- 'Galaxy'[PBR] (D)	NOra
	- 'Galloway Pippin' (C)	GTwd GTwe SKee
	- 'Gascoyne's Scarlet' (C/D)	CCAT SDea SFam SKee WHar
	- 'Gavin' (D)	CAgr SDea SKee
	- 'Genesis II' (C/D)	SDea
	- 'Genet Moyle' (C/Cider)	CTri MCoo WHar
	- 'George Carpenter' (D)	SDea
	- 'George Cave' (D)	CDul CTho ECrN GTwe IArd MCoo NOra SDea SEND SFam SFrt SKee WHar WJas
	- 'George Neal' (C) ♀H6	CAgr SDea SFam
	- 'Gibbon's Russet' (D)	IArd
	- 'Gilliflower of Gloucester' (D)	CTho
	- 'Gin' (Cider)	CCAT
	- 'Gladstone' (D)	CAgr CCAT CTho EBee GTwd NOra SKee WHar
	- 'Glansevin' (D)	WGwG
§	- 'Glass Apple' (C/D)	CCAT CEnd CTho
	- 'Gloria Mundi' (C)	SDea SKee
	- 'Gloster '69' (D)	SDea
	- 'Gloucester Royal' (D)	CTho
	- 'Gloucester Underleaf' (D)	CTho
	- 'Golden Ball' (Cider)	CCAT CTho
	- 'Golden Bittersweet' (D)	CAgr CTho
	- 'Golden Delicious' (D) ♀H6	CCVT CDul CMac CSBt EBee ECrN ELan EPfP EPom LAst LBuc LRHS MJak MMuc NOra SCrf SDea SEND SEWo SKee SVic WHar
	- 'Golden Glow' (C)	SDea
	- 'Golden Harvey' (D)	CAgr
	- 'Golden Jubilee' (F)	CEnd
	- 'Golden Knob' (D)	CCAT CTho CTri SKee
	- 'Golden Noble' (C) ♀H6	CAgr CCAT CDul CTho CTri ECrN ERea GTwe IArd MCoo NOra SDea SFam SKee
	- 'Golden Nugget' (D)	CAgr SKee
	- 'Golden Pippin' (C)	CAgr NOra SKee WHar
	- 'Golden Reinette' (D)	SFam SKee
	- 'Golden Russet' (D)	CAgr ECrN NOra SDea SKee WHar
	- 'Golden Spire' (C)	CHab MCoo NOra SDea SKee WHar
	- 'Goring' (Cider)	CTho
	- 'Grand Sultan' (D)	CCAT
	- 'Grandpa Ailes' (D)	CTho
	- 'Grandpa Buxton' (C)	CHab
	- 'Granny Smith' (D)	CBcs CDul ECrN LAst NOra SCrf SDea SKee SPer SVic WHar
	- 'Gravenstein' (D)	CHab NOra SDea SFam SKee
§	- 'Green Balsam' (D)	CHab CTri
	- 'Green Roland' (C/D)	ECrN
	- 'Greensleeves'[PBR] (D) ♀H6	CAgr CDul CMac CSBt CTri EBee ECrN EPfP EPom GTwd GTwe LAst MAsh MGos MMuc NOra SDea SEND SKee SLim SPer WHar WJas
	- 'Greenup's Pippin' (D)	CHab
	- 'Grenadier' (C) ♀H6	CAgr CDoC CHab CLnd CSBt CTri ECrN EPom GTwe MGos MJak MMuc MWat NLar NOra NWea SDea SEND SFam SKee SLon SPer WHar WJas
	- 'Guillevic' (Cider) **new**	CHab
	- 'Gwell Na Mil' (D)	WGwG
	- 'Halstow Natural' (Cider)	CAgr CTho
	- 'Hambledon Deux Ans' (C)	SDea SFam SKee
	- 'Hangy Down' (Cider)	CCAT CTho
	- 'Harling Hero' (D)	ECrN
	- Harmonie = 'Delorina' (F)	LRHS
§	- 'Harry Master's Jersey' (Cider)	CAgr CCAT CTho CTri MWat NOra SDea SKee WHar

	Cultivar	Suppliers
	– 'Harvester' (D)	CTho
	– 'Harvey' (C)	SDea
	– 'Hawthornden' (C)	CHab GTwd GTwe SKee
	– 'Hector MacDonald' (C)	GTwd SKee
	– 'Herefordshire Redstreak' (Cider)	CAgr CDul LAst LBuc NOra WHar
	– 'Herefordshire Russet'[PBR] (D)	CDoC EBee EPom ERea LBuc LRHS MAsh MBri MCoo MWat NLar NOra SKee SLim SPer WHar WJas
	– 'Herring's Pippin' (C/D)	CTri SDea SKee
	– 'High View Pippin' (D)	SKee
	– 'Histon Favourite' (D)	SKee
	– 'Hoary Morning' (C)	CCAT CTho ECrN SDea SKee
	– 'Hocking's Green' (C/D)	CAgr CCAT CEnd CTho CTsd
	– 'Holland Pippin' (C)	WHar
	– 'Hollow Core' (C)	CAgr CTho
	– 'Holstein' (D)	CTho NOra SDea SKee WHar
	– 'Honey Pippin' (D)	ECrN
	– 'Honey String' (F)	CCAT
§	– 'Honeygold' (D)	CEnd
	– 'Hood's Supreme' (D)	GTwd
	– 'Horneburger Pfannkuchen' (C)	SKee
	– 'Horsford Prolific' (D)	ECrN
	– 'Horsham Russet' (D)	SKee
	– 'Houblon' (D)	SKee
	– 'Hounslow Wonder' (C)	MWat
	– 'Howgate Wonder' (C)	CAgr CCVT CDul CHab CLnd CSBt EBee ECrN EPom GTwd GTwe LAst LBuc MAsh MMuc MWat NOra SCrf SDea SEND SFam SFrt SKee SPer SVic WHar WJas
	– 'Hubbard's Pearmain' (D)	ECrN
	– 'Hunter's Majestic' (D/C)	ECrN
	– 'Hunt's Duke of Gloucester' (D)	CTho
	– 'Idared' (D) ♀H6	ECrN NOra SDea SKee SVic WHar
	– 'Improved Dove' (Cider)	CCAT
	– 'Improved Keswick' (C/D)	CCAT CDoC CEnd CTho
	– 'Improved Lambrook Pippin' (Cider)	CCAT CTho CTri
	– 'Improved Redstreak' (Cider)	CTho
	– 'Ingrid Marie' (D)	NWea SDea SKee
	– 'Irish Peach' (D)	CAgr CHab CTri ECrN ERea GTwe IArd MCoo NOra SDea SFam SKee WHar
	– 'Isaac Newton's Tree'	see *M. domestica* 'Flower of Kent'
	– 'Isle of Wight Pippin' (D)	SDea
	– 'Isle of Wight Russet' (D)	SDea
	– 'Jackson's'	see *M. domestica* 'Crimson King' (Cider/C)
	– 'James Grieve' (D) ♀H6	Widely available
	– 'Jerseymac' (D)	SDea
	– 'Jester' (D)	ECrN SDea
	– 'Joaneting' (D)	CAgr CHab
	– 'John Broad'	see *M. domestica* 'Captain Broad'
	– 'John Standish' (D)	CAgr CCAT CTri ERea SDea
	– 'John Toucher's'	see *M. domestica* 'Crimson King' (Cider/C)
	– 'Johnny Andrews' (Cider)	CAgr CTho
	– 'Johnny Voun' (D)	CEnd CTho
	– 'Jonagold' (D) ♀H6	CLnd CTri ECrN ELan EPom GTwe IArd NLar NOra SCrf SDea SFam SKee SPer
	– 'Jonagold Crowngold'	see *M. domestica* 'Crowngold'
§	– 'Jonagored'[PBR] (D)	NOra SDea WHar
	– 'Jonathan' (D)	NOra SDea SKee
	– 'Jordan's Weeping' (C)	SDea
	– 'Josephine' (D)	SDea
	– 'Jubilee'	see *M. domestica* 'Royal Jubilee'
	– 'Julie's Late Golden' (F)	CTri
	– 'Jumbo' (C/D)	MAsh MBri MCoo SKee WHar WJas
	– 'Jupiter'[PBR] (D) ♀H6	CAgr CSBt CTri ECrN GTwe MJak MRav NOra SDea SKee SLon WHar WJas
	– 'Kapai Red Jonathan' (D)	SDea
	– 'Karmijn de Sonnaville' (D)	NOra SDea SKee
§	– 'Katja' (D)	Widely available
	– Katy	see *M. domestica* 'Katja'
	– 'Kent' (D)	ECrN SDea SKee
	– 'Kentish Fillbasket' (C)	SKee
	– 'Kerry Pippin' (D)	IArd SKee
	– 'Keswick Codlin' (C)	CHab CTho ECrN ERea GQue GTwd GTwe MBri MCoo NEgg NLar NOra NWea SDea SKee WHar WJas
§	– 'Kidd's Orange Red' (D) ♀H6	CAgr CCAT CDul CLnd CMac CTri ECrN EPfP EPom GTwe LBuc LRHS MWat NOra SCrf SDea SEND SFam SFrt SKee SLon WHar
	– 'Kilkenny Pearmain' (D)	IArd
	– 'Kill Boy' (F)	CTho
	– 'Killerton Sharp' (Cider)	CTho
	– 'Killerton Sweet' (Cider)	CTho
	– 'King Byerd' (C/D)	CCAT CDoC CEnd CTho
	– 'King Coffee' (D)	WHar
	– 'King George V' (D)	SKee
	– 'King Luscious' (D)	SDea
§	– 'King of the Pippins' (D) ♀H6	CCAT CHab CLnd CTho CTri ECrN GTwe MCoo NOra SCrf SDea SFam SKee SVic WHar
	– 'King of Tompkins County' (D)	SFam
	– 'King Russet' (D) ♀H6	SDea
	– 'King's Acre Pippin' (D)	NOra SDea SFam WHar
	– 'Kingston Bitter' (Cider)	CTho
	– 'Kingston Black' (Cider/C)	CAgr CCAT CDul CEnd CHab CTho CTri GTwe LBuc MGos NOra SDea SFrt SKee
	– 'Kirton Fair' (D)	CTho
	– 'Knobby Russet' (D)	SKee
	– 'Lady Henniker' (C)	CCAT CDul CEnd CHab CTho EBee ECrN GTwd SDea SKee WHar
	– 'Lady Hollendale' (D)	SKee
	– 'Lady Lambourne' (C/D)	CHab
	– 'Lady of the Wemyss' (C)	GTwd SKee
	– 'Lady Sudeley' (D)	CCAT CDoC CEnd CHab CTho GTwd SDea SKee
	– 'Lady's Finger' (C/D)	CDoC CEnd
	– 'Lady's Finger of Lancaster' (C/D)	CHab SKee
	– 'Lady's Finger of Offaly' (D)	IArd SDea
	– 'Lake's Kernel' (D)	CTho
	– 'Lambourne Pippin' (F) **new**	CTho
	– 'Lamb's Seedling' (D)	SKee
	– 'Lane's Prince Albert' (C) ♀H6	CAgr CCAT CHab CLnd CSBt ECrN EPfP GTwe IArd MGos MRav MWat NOra NWea SCoo SCrf SDea SFam SKee SVic WHar WJas
	– 'Langley Pippin' (D)	SDea
§	– 'Langworthy' (Cider)	CCAT CTho
	– 'Lass o' Gowrie' (C)	GTwd SKee
§	– 'Laxton's Epicure' (D) ♀H6	CAgr CDul CHab ECrN GTwe LAst SDea SFam SKee WHar

Variety	Suppliers
§ - 'Laxton's Fortune' (D) ♀H6	CCAT CDul CHab CMac CSBt CTri ECrN GTwd GTwe IArd LAst NOra SCrf SDea SFam SKee WHar WJas
- 'Laxton's Pearmain' (D)	MCoo SFam
- 'Laxton's Royalty' (D)	SDea
§ - 'Laxton's Superb' (D)	Widely available
- 'Leathercoat Russet' (D)	CAgr CDoC CTri SKee
- 'Lemon Pippin' (C)	EBee ECrN ELan NOra SDea SKee WHar
- 'Lemon Pippin of Gloucestershire' (D)	CTho
- 'Lemon Queen' (D) **new**	GTwd
- 'Liberty' (D)	SDea SKee
- 'Liddel's Seedling' (C/D) **new**	GTwd
- 'Limberland' (C)	CTho
- 'Limelight' (D)	CDoC EBee ERea GTwd LRHS MAsh MBri MCoo MWat NLar NOra SCoo SKee WHar
- 'Link Wonder' (F)	CEnd
- 'Lodi' (C)	SDea
- 'London Pearmain' (D)	ECrN
- 'London Pippin' (C)	CAgr CTho
- 'Longkeeper' (D)	CAgr CDoC CEnd CTho LRHS
- 'Longney Russet' (Cider/D)	CCAT
- 'Longstem' (Cider)	CTho
- 'Lord Burghley' (D)	SDea SKee
- 'Lord Derby' (C)	CAgr CCAT CDoC CDul CHab CMac CTho ECrN EPom GTwe MRav NOra SDea SEND SFam SKee SPer SVic WHar
- 'Lord Grosvenor' (C)	SKee WHar
- 'Lord Hindlip' (D)	CHab NOra SDea SFam
- 'Lord Lambourne' (D) ♀H6	CAgr CCAT CDoC CDul CHab CLnd CMac CSBt CTri ECrN EPfP EPom GTwd GTwe LAst LRHS MAsh MCoo MGos MWat NOra SCrf SDea SFam SKee SLon SPer WHar WJas
- 'Lord of the Isles' (Cider)	CAgr CCAT CDoC
- 'Lord Rosebery' (D)	GTwd SKee
- 'Lord Stradbroke' (C)	ECrN SKee
- 'Lord Suffield' (C)	CTri ECrN SKee
- 'Lough Tree of Wexford' (D)	IArd
- 'Lucombe's Pine' (D)	CAgr CCAT CEnd CTho CTsd ECrN SVic
- 'Lucombe's Seedling' (D)	CTho
- 'Lynn's Pippin' (D)	ECrN
- 'Mabbott's Pearmain' (D)	SDea
- 'Machen' (D)	WGwG
- 'Maclean's Favourite' (D)	ECrN
- 'Madresfield Court' (D)	SDea
- 'Maggie' (D) **new**	GTwd
- 'Maggie Sinclair' (D)	GTwd
- 'Maidstone Favourite' (D)	SKee
- 'Major' (Cider)	CAgr CCAT LRHS SFrt
- 'Maldon Wonder' (D)	ECrN
- Malini Dulcessa (D)	CSut
- Malini Fresco (D)	CSut
- Malini Lu 72/06 (D) **new**	CSut
- 'Malling Kent' (D)	SDea SFam SFrt
- Maloni Lilly (D)	CSut
- Maloni Sally (D)	CSut
- 'Maltster' (D)	MCoo
- 'Manaccan Primrose' (C/D)	CDoC CEnd
- 'Margil' (D)	SDea SFam WHar
- 'Markham Pippin' (D)	MCoo
- 'Maxton' (D)	ECrN
- 'May Queen' (D)	SDea SFam
- 'Maypole'[PBR] (D)	SDea
- 'McIntosh' (D)	NOra SKee
- 'Mead's Broading' (C)	SKee
- 'Médaille d'Or' (Cider)	CCAT SFrt SKee
- 'Melba' (D)	SKee
- 'Melon' (D)	SDea
- 'Melrose' (D)	ECrN
- 'Merchant Apple' (D)	CCAT CTho CTri
- 'Mère de Ménage' (C)	SFam WHar
- 'Meridian'[PBR] (D)	CAgr CDoC EBee ECrN MCoo MWat NOra SDea
- 'Merton Knave' (D)	SDea SFam
- 'Merton Russet' (D)	SDea
- 'Merton Worcester' (D)	ECrN SDea SKee
- 'Michaelmas Red' (D)	GTwe SKee
- 'Michelin' (Cider)	CAgr CCAT CTri GTwe LBuc MGos NOra SDea SKee WHar
- Miel d'Or	see *M. domestica* 'Honeygold'
- 'Miller's Seedling' (D)	NOra SKee
- 'Millicent Barnes' (D)	SDea
- 'Mollie's Delicious' (D)	SKee
- 'Monarch' (C)	CAgr CTri ECrN EPom GTwd GTwe SDea SFam SKee
- 'Montfort' (D)	ECrN
- 'Morgan's Sweet' (C/Cider)	CCAT CEnd CHab CTho CTri NOra SDea SKee
- 'Moss's Seedling' (D)	SDea
§ - 'Mother' (D) ♀H6	CAgr CCAT CEnd CTri ECrN GTwe SDea SKee
- 'Mrs Phillimore' (D)	SKee
§ - 'Mutsu' (C/D)	CTri ECrN MRav NOra SDea SEND SKee SPer
- 'Mylor Pike' (D) **new**	CEnd
- 'Nancy Jackson' (C)	CHab
- 'Nanny' (D)	SKee
- 'Nant Gwrtheyrn' (D)	WGwG
- 'Nettlestone Pippin' (D)	SDea
- 'Newton Wonder' (C) ♀H6	CAgr CCAT CDoC CDul CHab CLnd CSBt CTho CTri ECrN EPom ERea GTwe IArd LAst MCoo MGos NOra SCrf SDea SFam SFrt SKee WHar WJas
- 'Newtown Pippin' (D)	SDea
- 'Nine Square' (D)	CTho
- 'Nittany Red' (D)	SDea
- 'No Pip' (C)	CTho
- 'Nolan Pippin' (D)	ECrN
- 'Nonpareil' (D)	SKee WHar
- 'Norfolk Beauty' (C)	ECrN ERea SKee
- 'Norfolk Beefing' (C)	CHab ECrN ERea SDea SFam SKee
- 'Norfolk Royal' (D)	CDoC ECrN ERea GTwe NOra SDea SKee
- 'Norfolk Royal Russet' (D)	ECrN ERea GTwd LRHS NOra SFrt SKee
- 'Norfolk Winter Coleman' (C)	ERea
- 'Northcott Superb' (D)	CTho
- 'Northern Greening' (C)	SKee WHar
§ - 'Northwood' (Cider)	CCAT CTho
- 'Nutmeg Pippin' (D)	ECrN SDea SFam
- Nuvar Cheerfull Gold (D)	SKee
- Nuvar Freckles (D)	SKee
- Nuvar Golden Elf (D)	SKee
- Nuvar Golden Hills (D)	SKee
- Nuvar Home Farm (D)	SKee

- Nuvar Melody (D)	SKee
- 'Oaken Pin' (D)	CCAT CDoC CEnd CTho
§ - 'Obelisk'^{PBR} (D)	SDea SKee
- 'Old Pearmain' (D)	SDea SKee WHar
- 'Old Somerset Russet' (D)	CCAT CTho
- 'Onibury Pippin' (D)	WHar
- 'Opalescent' (D)	CEnd SKee
- 'Orkney Apple' (F)	SKee
- 'Orleans Reinette' (D)	CAgr CCAT CLnd CTho CTri ECrN GTwe IArd LBuc LRHS MWat NOra SCrf SDea SFam SFrt WHar WJas
- 'Oslin' (D)	GTwd SKee
- 'Otava'^{PBR} (C/D)	SKee
- 'Owen Thomas' (D)	CTri
- 'Paignton Marigold' (Cider)	CCAT CTho
- 'Palmer's Rosey' (D)	SKee
- Paradis Myra (D)	CSut
- 'Pascoe's Pippin' (C/D)	CTho
- 'Payhembury' (C/Cider)	CAgr CTho CTri
- 'Peacemaker' (D)	SKee
- 'Pear Apple' (D)	CAgr CCAT CDoC CEnd CTho
- 'Pearl' (D)	SDea SKee
- 'Peasgood's Nonsuch' (C) ♀^{H6}	CAgr CCAT CDoC CHab ECrN ERea GTwd GTwe IArd LRHS MAsh NOra SCrf SDea SFam SFrt SKee SLon
- 'Pendragon' (D)	CEnd CTho
- 'Penhallow Pippin' (D)	CDoC CTho
- 'Pennard Bitter' (Cider)	CCAT
- 'Peter Lock' (C/D)	CAgr CCAT CEnd CTho
- 'Peter's Pippin' (D)	SDea
- 'Peter's Seedling' (D)	SDea
- 'Pethyre' (Cider)	CCVT
- 'Pickering's Seedling' (D)	SKee
- 'Pig Aderyn' (C)	CHab WGwG
- 'Pig y Colomen' (C)	WGwG
- 'Pig's Nose Pippin' (D)	CEnd
- 'Pig's Nose Pippin' Type III (D)	CAgr CCAT CTho
- 'Pig's Snout' (Cider/C/D)	CCAT CEnd CTho
- 'Pine Apple Russet of Devon' (D) **new**	CEnd
- 'Pineapple Russet' (C/D)	CAgr ERea MAsh
- 'Pinova'^{PBR} (D)	CAgr EPom MCoo WHar
- 'Pitmaston Pine Apple' (D)	CCAT CDul CHab CTho CTri ECrN ERea GTwd IArd LAst LRHS MCoo MWat NOra SDea SFam SFrt SKee SLon WHar
- 'Pixie' (D) ♀^{H6}	CDoC EPom GTwe MWat NOra SDea SFam SKee SLon WHar
- 'Plum Vite' (D)	CAgr CTho CTri
- 'Plymouth Cross' (D)	SKee
- 'Plympton Pippin' (C)	CDoC CEnd CTho CTri
- Polka = 'Trajan'^{PBR} (D)	SDea SKee
- 'Polly' (C/D)	CDoC
- 'Polly Whitehair' (C/D)	CTho SDea
- 'Poltimore Seedling' (D)	CTho
- 'Pomeroy of Somerset' (D)	CCAT CHab CTho CTri
- 'Ponsford' (C)	CAgr CCAT CTho SKee
- 'Port Allen Russet' (C/D)	GTwd
- 'Port Wine'	see *M. domestica* 'Harry Master's Jersey'
- 'Porter's Perfection' (Cider)	CCAT NOra
- 'Prince Charles' (D)	SKee
- 'Princesse' (F)	CLnd ECrN SDea
- 'Profit' (F)	CCAT CTho
- 'Quarry Apple' (C)	CTho
- 'Queen' (C)	CAgr CTho ECrN SKee WHar
- 'Queen Caroline' (C)	SKee
- 'Queen Cox' (D)	CLnd CSut CTri EBee ECrN EPom ERea NOra SDea SKee SLon SWvt WHar
- 'Queenie' (D)	CCAT
- 'Queens' (D)	CEnd CTho
- 'Quench' (Cider/D)	CTho
- 'Rafzubin'	see *M. domestica* Rubinette
- 'Rajka'^{PBR} (D)	CDoC GQue NOra SKee
- 'Red Alkmene'	see *M. domestica* 'Red Windsor'
- 'Red Belle de Boskoop' (D)	CAgr
- 'Red Bramley' (C)	ECrN
- 'Red Charles Ross' (C/D)	SDea
- 'Red Delicious' (D)	NOra SCrf SKee
- 'Red Devil' (D)	CAgr CLnd CMac CTri CWSG ECrN EPom GTwd GTwe LAst LRHS MAsh MBri MRav MWat NLar NOra NPri SCoo SDea SEWo SKee SLim SLon WHar WJas
- 'Red Ellison' (D)	CTho CTri ECrN ERea GTwe SDea
- 'Red Elstar' (D)	IArd
- 'Red Falstaff'^{PBR} (D)	CAgr CCVT CDoC CDul CMac CTri EBee ECrN EPfP ERea GKin LBuc LRHS MAsh MBri MCoo MWat NLar NOra SFrt SKee SLim SLon SPer SPoG WHar
- 'Red Fuji' (D)	SDea
- 'Red Jersey' (Cider)	CCAT
- 'Red Joaneting' (D)	SKee WHar
- 'Red Jonagold'^{PBR}	see *M. domestica* 'Jonagored'
- 'Red Jonathan' (D)	SDea
- 'Red Miller's seedling' (D)	ECrN SCrf SDea
- 'Red Pixie' (D)	GQue LRHS MCoo
- 'Red Rattler' (D)	CTho CTri
- 'Red Roller' (D)	CTho
- 'Red Ruby' (F)	CTho
- 'Red Sauce' (C)	SKee
- 'Red Victoria' (C)	GTwe
§ - 'Red Windsor' (D)	CDoC CDul CLnd CMac EBee EPom ERea LBuc LRHS MBri MWat NLar NOra SCoo SKee SLim SPoG WHar WJas
- 'Redcoat Grieve' (D)	SDea
- Redlove Era (C/D)	CSut
- Redlove Sirena (C/D)	CSut
- 'Redsleeves' (D)	CAgr CLnd ECrN GTwd GTwe IArd NOra SDea
- 'Redstrake' (Cider)	CCAT
- Regali = 'Delkistar'^{PBR} (D)	LRHS
- 'Reine des Reinettes'	see *M. domestica* 'King of the Pippins'
- 'Reinette Descardre' (D)	SVic
- 'Reinette d'Obry' (Cider)	CCAT
- 'Reinette Rouge Etoilée' (D)	SDea
- 'Reverend Greeves' (C)	SDea
- 'Reverend McCormick' (D)	CTho
- 'Reverend W. Wilks' (C)	CAgr CDoC CHab CSBt CTri EBee ECrN GTwd LAst LRHS MAsh MBri NOra SDea SFam SFrt SKee WHar WJas
- 'Rhode Island Greening' (C/D) **new**	SKee
- 'Ribston Pippin' (D) ♀^{H6}	CCAT CTho CTri ECrN ERea GTwe LBuc LRHS MCoo MRav MWat NOra NWea SCrf SDea SFam SFrt SKee SLon WHar WJas
- 'Rival' (D)	CAgr SDea

	Name	Suppliers
	- 'Rivers' Nonsuch' (D)	CHab
	- 'Rock' (C) **new**	GTwd
	- 'Rome Beauty' (D)	SDea
	- 'Rosemary Russet' (D) 🏆H6	CAgr CCAT CDoC CHab CTho EBee ERea GTwd GTwe LRHS MCoo NOra SDea SFam SFrt SKee SLon WHar
	- 'Rosette' (D)	EPom LBuc LRHS MAsh NOra
	- 'Ross Nonpareil' (D)	CAgr IArd SDea SKee WHar
	- 'Rosy Blenheim' (D)	ECrN
	- 'Rough Pippin' (D)	CEnd
	- 'Roundway Magnum Bonum' (C/D)	CAgr CTho SDea
§	- 'Roxbury Russet' (D)	SKee
	- 'Royal Gala' (D) 🏆H6	CMac ECrN EPom LBuc MRav SDea SLon
§	- 'Royal Jubilee' (C)	CCAT
	- 'Royal Russet' (C)	CEnd ECrN SDea
	- 'Royal Somerset' (C/Cider)	CCAT CTho CTri
§	- Rubinette = 'Rafzubin' (D)	ECrN NOra SDea SKee
	- Rubinette Rosso = 'Rafzubex'PBR (D)	NOra
	- 'Rubinola'PBR (D)	SKee
	- 'Ruby' Thorrington (D)	ECrN
	- 'Saint Cecilia' (D)	CHab SDea WGwG
§	- 'Saint Edmund's Pippin' (D) 🏆H6	CHab CTho ECrN ELan EPfP ERea GTwd GTwe MCoo NOra SCrf SDea SFam SFrt SKee
	- 'Saint Edmund's Russet'	see *M. domestica* 'Saint Edmund's Pippin'
	- 'Saint Everard' (D)	SKee
	- 'Saint Magdalen' (D)	SKee
	- 'Sam Young' (D)	CAgr IArd SKee
	- 'Sandlands' (D)	SDea
	- 'Sandringham' (C)	ECrN
	- 'Sanspareil' (D)	CAgr
	- 'Santana' (D)	MBri NOra
	- 'Saturn' (D)	CAgr CCVT CDoC CTri NOra SDea SKee WHar
	- 'Saw Pits' (D)	CAgr CEnd
	- 'Scarlet Crofton' (D)	IArd
	- 'Scarlet Nonpareil' (D)	SDea
	- 'Scotch Bridget' (C)	CHab GBin GQue GTwd LRHS NBid NOra SCoo SKee WHar
	- 'Scotch Dumpling' (C)	EBee GBin GKin GQue GTwd GTwe MCoo NOra SKee WHar
	- 'Scrumptious'PBR (D) 🏆H6	CAgr CCVT CDoC CDul CMac CSBt CTri EMil EPfP EPom GKin LBuc LRHS MAsh MBri MWat NLar NOra NPri NWea SCoo SEWo SKee SLim SLon SPer SPoG WHar WJas
	- 'Sercombe's Natural' (Cider)	CCAT CTho
	- 'Severn Bank' (C)	CCAT CTho
	- 'Sheep's Nose' (C)	CCAT CHab CTho IArd SDea
	- 'Shenandoah' (C)	SKee
	- 'Sidney Strake' (C)	CAgr CEnd
	- 'Sir Isaac Newton's'	see *M. domestica* 'Flower of Kent'
	- 'Sir John Thornycroft' (D)	SDea
	- 'Sisson's Worksop Newtown' (D)	MCoo SKee
	- 'Slack Ma Girdle' (Cider)	CCAT CTho
	- 'Smart's Prince Arthur' (C)	CHab SDea
	- 'Snell's Glass Apple'	see *M. domestica* 'Glass Apple'
	- 'Somerset Lasting' (C)	CTri
	- 'Somerset Redstreak' (Cider)	CAgr CCAT CHab CTho CTri GTwe NOra WHar
	- 'Sops in Wine' (Cider/D)	CCAT CTho CTsd ECrN NOra SVic
	- 'Sour Bay' (Cider)	CAgr CTho
	- 'Sour Natural'	see *M. domestica* 'Langworthy'
	- 'Spartan' (D)	Widely available
	- 'Spencer' (D)	CTri ECrN SKee
	- 'Spotted Dick' (Cider)	CTho
	- 'Stable Jersey' (Cider)	CCAT
	- 'Stamford Pippin' (D)	SDea
	- 'Stanway Seedling' (C)	ECrN
	- 'Star of Devon' (D)	CEnd SDea
	- 'Stark' (D)	SDea
	- 'Starking' (D)	ECrN
	- 'Stark's Earliest' (D)	SVic
	- 'Stembridge Cluster' (Cider)	CCAT
	- 'Stembridge Jersey' (Cider)	CCAT
	- 'Steyne Seedling' (D)	SDea
	- 'Stirling Castle' (C)	CAgr GBin GQue NOra SKee
	- 'Stobo Castle' (C)	GTwd SKee
	- 'Stockbearer' (C)	CTho
	- 'Stoke Edith Pippin' (D)	WHar
	- 'Stoke Red' (Cider)	CCAT CTho NOra SFrt SKee
	- 'Storey's Seedling' (D) **new**	SKee
	- 'Strawberry Pippin' (D)	CTho
	- 'Striped Beefing' (C)	ECrN ERea
	- 'Sturmer Pippin' (D)	CCAT CSBt CTri ECrN GTwe MWat NOra SCrf SDea SFam SKee WHar
*	- 'Sugar Apple' (F)	CTho
	- 'Sugar Bush' (C/D)	CTho
	- 'Sugar Loaf'	see *M. domestica* 'Sugar Apple'
	- 'Summerred' (D)	ECrN
	- 'Sunburn' (D)	ECrN
	- 'Sunlight'PBR (F)	MWat
	- 'Sunnydale' (D/C)	SDea
	- 'Sunrise'PBR (D)	NOra SKee WHar
	- 'Sunset' (D) 🏆H6	Widely available
	- 'Suntan' (D) 🏆H6	CCAT CDoC ECrN LAst MWat NOra SDea SKee
	- 'Superb'	see *M. domestica* 'Laxton's Superb'
	- 'Sussex Mother' (C/D)	CHab
	- 'Swaar' (D)	SKee
	- 'Sweet Alford' (Cider)	CCAT CTho
	- 'Sweet Bay' (Cider)	CAgr CTho
	- 'Sweet Cleave' (Cider)	CTho
	- 'Sweet Coppin' (Cider)	CCAT CTho CTri
	- 'Sweet Lilibet'	see *M. domestica* 'Red Windsor'
	- 'Sweet Society' (D)	MAsh MCoo NOra SKee WHar WJas
	- 'Tale Sweet' (Cider)	CCAT CTho
	- 'Tamar Beauty' (D)	CEnd
	- 'Tan Harvey' (Cider)	CCAT CEnd CTho
	- 'Taunton Cross' (D)	CAgr
	- 'Taunton Fair Maid' (Cider)	CCAT CTho
	- 'Taylor's' (Cider)	CAgr CCAT SDea
	- 'Ten Commandments' (Cider/D)	CCAT SDea
	- Tentation = 'Delblush'PBR (D)	SDea
	- 'Tewkesbury Baron' (D)	CTho
	- 'The Rattler' (Cider)	CDoC CEnd
	- 'Thomas Jeffrey' (D)	GTwd
	- 'Thomas Rivers' (C)	SDea
	- 'Thorle Pippin' (D)	GTwd SKee
	- 'Thurso' (D) **new**	GTwd
	- 'Tidicombe Seedling' (D)	CTho
	- 'Tom Putt' (C)	CAgr CCAT CCVT CDul CHab CTho CTri ECrN GTwe LBuc NOra SDea SKee WHar WJas

Plant	Suppliers
- 'Tommy Knight' (D)	CAgr CCAT CDoC CEnd CTho
- 'Topaz'PBR (D)	CDoC SKee
- 'Totnes Apple' (D)	CTho
- 'Tower of Glamis' (C)	CHab GBin GQue GTwd GTwe SKee
- Town Farm Number 59 (Cider)	CTho
- 'Tregonna King' (C/D)	CCAT CDoC CTho CTsd
- 'Tremlett's Bitter' (Cider)	CAgr CCAT CHab CTho NOra SDea SKee SVic
- 'Trwyn Mochyn' (C)	WGwG
§ - 'Tuscan'PBR (D)	MCoo SDea SKee
§ - 'Tydeman's Early Worcester' (D)	CAgr CDul CHab CLnd ECrN GTwe SDea SKee SVic
- 'Tydeman's Late Orange' (D)	CDoC CHab CTri ECrN EMil GTwe IArd LAst LRHS MCoo NOra NWea SDea SFam SFrt SKee WHar
- 'Uncle John's Cooker' (C)	IArd
- 'Upton Pyne' (C/D)	CCAT CDoC CTho SDea
- 'Vallis Apple' (Cider)	CCAT CTho
- 'Veitch's Perfection' (C/D)	CTho
- 'Veitch's Prolific' (F)	CDoC
- 'Venus Pippin' (C/D)	CEnd
- 'Vicar of Beighton' (D)	ECrN SKee
- 'Vicary's Late Keeper' (C)	CTho
- 'Vickey's Delight' (D)	NWea SDea
- 'Vileberie' (Cider)	CCAT
- 'Vista-bella' (D)	ECrN SDea
- 'Wagener' (D)	ECrN SDea SKee
- 'Waltham Abbey Seedling' (C)	ECrN
- Waltz = 'Telamon'PBR (D)	SDea
- 'Wanstall Pippin' (D)	SKee
- 'Warden' (D) **new**	GTwd
- 'Warner's King' (C) ♀H6	CTho CTri NOra SDea SKee WHar
- 'Warrior' (F)	CCAT CTho
- 'Wealthy' (D)	SDea
- 'Weight' (C) **new**	GTwd
- 'Wellington' (C)	see *M. domestica* 'Dummellor's Seedling'
- 'Wellington' (Cider)	CAgr CTho
- 'Welsh Russet' (D)	SDea
- 'Wern' (C)	WGwG
- 'Werrington Wonder' (F) **new**	CEnd
- 'West View Seedling' (D)	ECrN
- 'White Alphington' (Cider)	CTho
- 'White Close Pippin' (Cider)	CTho
- 'White Jersey' (Cider)	CCAT
- 'White Melrose' (C)	GBin GQue GTwd GTwe SDea SKee
- 'White Quarrenden' (D)	SKee
- 'White Transparent' (C/D)	SDea SKee
- 'Whitpot Sweet' (Cider)	CEnd
- 'Wick White Styre' (Cider)	CTho
- 'William Crump' (D)	CCAT CDul CHab CTho ECrN NOra SDea SFam SKee WHar
- 'Willoughby' (D)	MCoo
- 'Winston' (D) ♀H6	CAgr CCAT CCVT CMac CSBt CTri ECrN MCoo NWea SDea SFam SVic WHar
- 'Winter Banana' (D)	CHab ECrN GQue LEdu MCoo NOra SDea SKee SVic WHar
- 'Winter Gem' (D)	CAgr CCVT CDul CLnd ECrN EPom ERea LAst LBuc NOra SDea SKee WHar WJas
- 'Winter Lawrence' (D)	CTho
- 'Winter Lemon' (C/D)	SKee
- 'Winter Peach' (D/C)	CAgr CDoC CTho ECrN
- 'Winter Pearmain' (D)	WHar
- 'Winter Quarrenden' (D)	SDea SKee
- 'Winter Queening' (D/C)	SDea
- 'Winter Red' (F) **new**	CEnd
- 'Winter Stubbard' (C)	CTho
- 'Wintergreen' (C)	CDoC
- 'Woodbine'	see *M. domestica* 'Northwood'
- 'Woodford' (C)	ECrN SKee
- 'Woolbrook Pippin' (D)	CAgr CEnd CTho
- 'Woolbrook Russet' (C)	CEnd CTho ECrN
- 'Worcester Pearmain' (D) ♀H6	Widely available
- 'Wormsley Pippin' (D)	ECrN
- 'Wyatt's Seedling'	see *M. domestica* 'Langworthy'
- 'Wyken Pippin' (D)	CCAT ECrN SDea SFam SKee
- 'Yarlington Mill' (Cider)	CAgr CCAT CHab CTho CTri NOra SDea SFrt SKee SVic
- 'Yellow Ingestrie' (D)	CHab ERea LRHS MCoo NOra SFam SKee WHar
- 'Yellow Styre' (Cider)	CTho
- 'Yorkshire Greening' (C)	CHab NOra SKee WHar
- 'Zabergäu Renette' (D)	NOra SKee
'Donald Wyman'	CLnd EPfP MAsh NLar SCoo
'Echtermeyer'	see *M.* × *gloriosa* 'Oekonomierat Echtermeyer'
'Elise Rathke'	CLnd
'Evelyn'	CLnd
§ 'Evereste' ♀H6	Widely available
florentina	CTho EPfP SBrt
- 'Rosemoor'	CLnd EBee
- 'Skopje'	EPfP WMou
floribunda ♀H6	Widely available
fusca	CLnd
'Gardener's Gold'	CEnd CTho
§ × ***gloriosa*** 'Oekonomierat Echtermeyer'	SDea SGol
'Golden Gem'	CLnd EPfP GQue MAsh NOra SEWo SLim
'Golden Hornet'	see *M.* × *zumi* 'Golden Hornet'
'Harry Baker'	CCVT CDul CEnd CLnd COtt ECrN EMil EPfP EPom ERea LRHS MAsh MBlu MBri SCoo SEWo SLim WHar WJas WMou
× ***hartwigii***	CLnd
'Hillieri'	see *M.* × *scheideckeri* 'Hillieri'
'Honeycrisp'PBR	NOra WHar
hupehensis ♀H6	CDul CEnd CLnd CMCN CSBt CTho EBee EPfP EPla IMou MBlu MGos MRav NWea SCrf SDix SFam SPer WMou
'Hyde Hall Spire'	SCoo
'Indian Magic'	CLnd EBee LRHS MAsh MBri NLar NOra
'Indian Summer'	CLnd
Jelly King = 'Mattfru' ♀H6	CLnd EBee ECrN EPom LRHS MAsh MBri MWat NLar NOra SPoG WHCr WHar WMou
'John Downie' (C)	Widely available
'Kaido'	see *M.* × *micromalus*
kansuensis	CLnd
'Kemp'	SDea
'Lady Northcliffe'	CDul CLnd SFam
'Laura' ♀H6	CDul CLnd COtt EPfP EPom ERea LRHS MAsh MBri NLar NOra SCoo SKee SLim SLon SPoG WHar WJas
'Lisa'	CLnd
'Louisa'	CLnd LRHS NOra NWea SCoo SGol

Name	Suppliers
× ***magdeburgensis***	CCVT CDul CLnd CSBt
'Mary Potter'	CLnd
§ × ***micromalus***	CLnd NLar
× ***moerlandsii***	CLnd
- 'Liset'	CDul CEnd CLnd CSBt CTsd EBee ECrN MRav NEgg NLar NOra SCoo SFam WFar
§ - 'Profusion'	CBcs CDul COtt CTri EBee ELan EPla EWTr LAst MGos MJak MMuc MRav MSwo MWat NOra NPri NWea SCob SCrf SEND SGol SPer SWvt WJas
- 'Profusion Improved'	CEnd CSBt CWSG LRHS MWat NOra SCoo SWvt WHar
'Mokum'	CLnd
'Molten Lava'	CLnd MAsh
niedzwetzkyana	CLnd CTho
Nuvar Marble	MBri SKee
orthocarpa	CLnd
Perpetu	see *M.* 'Evereste'
'Pink Glow'	CLnd CSBt EPom ERea MBlu MWat NLar SCoo SEWo SLim SPer WHar WMou
'Pink Perfection'	CDoC CEnd COtt NPri NWea
'Pond Red'	CLnd
'Prairifire'	CDul CLnd LRHS MAsh MBri SCoo SLim SLon SPoG WMou
prattii	CLnd CTho EPfP
- 'Pourpre Noir'	CLnd
'Princeton Cardinal' ♀H6	CLnd CMac EPfP MAsh MBri SCoo SLim SPoG
'Professor Sprenger'	see *M.* × *zumi* 'Professor Sprenger'
'Profusion'	see *M.* × *moerlandsii* 'Profusion'
prunifolia	MBlu
- var. ***rinkii***	CLnd
pumila 'Montreal Beauty'	CLnd WJas
'Purple Prince'	CLnd
§ × ***purpurea*** 'Aldenhamensis'	CLnd SDea WHar
- 'Eleyi'	CLnd CNWT LAst NWea
- 'Lemoinei'	CDul CLnd
- 'Neville Copeman'	CCVT CDoC CDul CLnd EPom EWTr WJas WMou
- 'Pendula'	see *M.* × *gloriosa* 'Oekonomierat Echtermeyer'
'R.J. Fulcher'	CLnd CTho
'Ralph Shay'	CLnd
'Red Ace'	CDul
'Red Barron'	CLnd
'Red Glow'	CDul CLnd MAsh WJas
'Red Jade'	see *M.* × *scheideckeri* 'Red Jade'
Red Obelisk = 'Dvp Obel'	CLnd LBuc LRHS MBri SCoo SPoG
'Red Peacock'	CLnd
'Robinson'	CLnd
§ × ***robusta***	CLnd GTwe NWea SLon
- 'Red Sentinel' ♀H6	Widely available
- 'Red Siberian'	SDea SPer
- 'Yellow Siberian'	CLnd
'Rosehip'	MAsh MBri NOra
'Royal Beauty'	CDoC CDul CLnd EPfP EPla EWTr LAst LRHS MAsh MBri MGos MJak MSwo NOra NPri SCoo SCrf SLon SPer WHar WMou
'Royalty'	CBcs CDul CLnd COtt CSBt EBee ECrN ELan GTwe LAst LBuc LRHS MGos MRav MSwo MWat NEgg NOra NPla SCob SCrf SEND SEWo SGol SPer WHar WJas
'Rudolph'	CCVT CDul CLnd CNWT EBee ECrN EPla GKin LBuc MAsh MGos SCoo SEWo SLim SPer SPoG WJas WMou
'Ruth Ann'	CLnd
sargentii	CDul CTho LRHS NOra NWea SFam
- 'Tina'	CLnd MAsh
'Satin Cloud'	CLnd
§ × ***scheideckeri*** 'Hillieri'	CDul CLnd MBlu SFam
§ - 'Red Jade'	CDul CLnd CMac COtt CTri EBee ELan LAst LRHS MGos MRav MSwo MWat NWea SPer WHar WJas
Siberian crab	see *M.* × *robusta*
sieboldii	see *M. toringo*
- 'Wooster'	CLnd
sieversii	CDul CLnd
sikkimensis B&SWJ 2431	WCru
'Silver Drift'	CLnd
'Snowcloud'	CDul CLnd ECrN MAsh SLim SPer
'Snowdrift'	CLnd
spectabilis	CLnd
'Street Parade'	CLnd
× ***sublobata***	CLnd
Sugar Tyme = 'Sutyzam'	CLnd
'Sun Rival' ♀H6	CCVT CDoC CDul CEnd CLnd CMac COtt CSBt EPfP EPla LRHS MAsh MBlu MBri MRav NOra NSoo SCoo SEWo SLim SPoG WHar WJas
sylvestris	CAco CCVT CDul CHab CLnd ECrN EPfP LBuc MJak MMuc MRav NHed NLar NWea SEND SEWo SPer SPre WMou
Tickled Pink = 'Baya Marisa' (C/D) **new**	EPom NOra
§ ***toringo***	CLnd COtt CTho ECrN EPfP LEdu MBri NOra WSHC
I - var. ***arborescens***	CLnd CTho
- 'Browers'	CNWT
- 'Scarlett' ♀H6	CLnd EPfP IArd LRHS MBri NLar NOra NWea SCoo SEWo SLim SPoG WHar WMou
- 'Wintergold'	MMuc
toringoides	see *M. bhutanica*
transitoria ♀H6	CDoC CDul CEnd CLnd CTho EBee ECrN ELan EPfP GKin LRHS MAsh MBlu MBri MRav NLar NWea SCoo SFam SLau WMou WPGP
- 'Thornhayes Tansy'	CDul CTho EBee SLim SPoG
trilobata	CDul CLnd CTho EBee ELan EPfP EPla GKin MBlu MGos MMuc SCoo SEND
- 'Guardsman'	EPfP LRHS MBlu MBri SSpi WMou
tschonoskii	CDoC CDul CLnd CMCN CMac COtt CSBt CTri ELan EPfP GTwe LAst MBlu MBri MGos MJak MMuc NPri NWea SEND SPer SWvt WJas WMou
'Van Eseltine'	CLnd CMac CSBt EBee ECrN EPfP MAsh MWat SFam WHar WJas
'Veitch's Scarlet'	CDul CHab CLnd CSBt LEdu SFam
'Virginia Crab' **new**	SKee
Weeping Candied Apple = 'Weepcanzam'	CLnd
'White Angel'	CLnd
'White Star'	CCVT CDoC CDul CLnd CSBt EBee ECrN LRHS SLon
'Winter Gold'	CDul LAst SCrf SGol
'Wisley Crab'	CLnd LAst SDea SFam SKee SLon WMou

yunnanensis	EPfP
- var. ***veitchii***	CTho
× ***zumi*** var. ***calocarpa***	CLnd
§ - 'Golden Hornet'	Widely available
§ - 'Professor Sprenger'	CLnd CSam EPfP MBri SCoo

Malva (*Malvaceae*)

alcea var. ***fastigiata***	CMac EBee ECGP LRHS NBro SRms
bicolor	see *Lavatera maritima*
moschata	CArn CBcs CBod EAJP EBee ECha ELan ENfk EPfP GAbr GJos GPoy MHer MMuc MNHC NLar NMir NWad SIde SPer SPhx SPlb SWat WHar WHer WJek WMoo WOut
- f. ***alba*** ♀H5	CArn CBcs CBod CSpe ECha ELan EPfP GAbr GJos GMaP LEdu LRHS MHer MMuc MNHC MSpe NBir NBro NGBl NLar SPer SPhx SPoG SWvt WBrk WGwG WKif WMnd WMoo
- 'Appleblossom'	CBod ELon EWTr SEND WTou
- 'Romney Marsh'	see *Althaea officinalis* 'Romney Marsh'
- 'Rosea'	EPfP GMaP LAst LRHS NPer SPoG SWvt WHar
- 'White Perfection'	ELon
pusilla	CCCN
sylvestris	CArn CBod NBro SRms SWat WHfH WJek WMoo
- 'Blue Fountain'[PBR]	WKif
- 'Brave Heart'	SPav SWvt
- Marina = 'Dema'[PBR]	NLar
- var. ***mauritiana***	CBod MSpe NPer WMoo
- - 'Mystic Merlin'	SPav
- - 'Primley Blue'	ECtt ELan EPfP GMaP MCot MRav NPer
- - 'Zebrina'	CBod EPfP MSpe NGBl NPer SWvt WMoo
- 'Minety Blue'	CNat
- 'Perry's Blue'	NPer
- 'Windsor Castle'	MPie

Malvaviscus (*Malvaceae*)

arboreus	CHll

mandarin see *Citrus reticulata* Mandarin Group

mandarin, Cleopatra see *Citrus reticulata*

Mandevilla (*Apocynaceae*)

sp.	CHel
§ × ***amabilis***	CCCN
- 'Alice du Pont' ♀H1c	CCCN CMan ELan EShb MOWG SPre
× ***amoena***	see *M.* × *amabilis*
'Audrey'[PBR] (Vogue Series)	CHel CSpe CWGN
boliviensis ♀H1c	CCCN CMan CRHN MOWG
'Ginger' (Vogue Series) **new**	CWGN
§ ***laxa*** ♀H1c	CCCN CHGN CHll CMan CRHN CSpe EBee ELan LRHS MOWG SVen WHrl WSHC
(Rio Series) Rio Deep Red = 'Fisrix Dered'[PBR]	CCCN
- Rio Pink = 'Fisrix Pinka'[PBR]	CCCN
- Rio White = 'Fisrix Whit'[PBR] **new**	CMan
'Ruby' (Vogue Series) **new**	CWGN
sanderi	CCCN EShb SPre
- 'Pink of Hint' **new**	CMan
- 'Rosea'	CCCN
splendens ♀H1c	CCCN CHll CMan MOWG
suaveolens	see *M. laxa*
Sundaville Series	CCCN
- Sundaville Cosmos Crimson King = 'Sunmandecrikin'[PBR] **new**	CMan
- Sundaville Cosmos Pink = 'Sunmandecos'[PBR] **new**	CMan
- Sundaville Cosmos White = 'Sunmandeho'[PBR] **new**	CMan
- Sundaville Cream Pink = 'Sunparapibra'[PBR] **new**	CMan
- Sundaville Dark Red = 'Sunparabeni'[PBR] **new**	CMan
- Sundaville Pink = 'Sunmandecripi'[PBR]	LAst LSou
- Sundaville Pretty Red = 'Sunmanderemi'[PBR] **new**	CMan
- Sundaville Pretty Rose = 'Sunparaprero'[PBR] **new**	CMan
- Sundaville Red = 'Sunmandecrim'[PBR]	LAst LSou
- Sundaville Red Star = 'Sunparasuji'[PBR] **new**	CMan

Mandragora (*Solanaceae*)

autumnalis	CDes
§ ***officinarum***	CArn CCon GCal GPoy SBrt SMad WCot

Manettia (*Rubiaceae*)

inflata	see *M. luteorubra*
§ ***luteorubra***	CCCN

Manfreda see *Agave*

× *Mangave* see *Agave*

Mangifera (*Anacardiaceae*)

indica (F)	CCCN SPre
- 'Osteen' (F)	NPla
- 'Tommy Atkins' (F)	NPla

Manglietia see *Magnolia*

yunnanensis	see *Magnolia insignis*

mango see *Mangifera indica*

Manihot (*Euphorbiaceae*)

carthaginensis	SPlb

Mantisalca (*Asteraceae*)

salmantica	WCot

Mantisia (*Zingiberaceae*)

saltatoria	WCot
- PAB 4208	LEdu

Maranta (*Marantaceae*)

leuconeura var. ***erythroneura*** ♀H1b	XBlo
- var. ***kerchoveana*** ♀H1b	XBlo

Marchantia (*Marchantiaceae*)

polymorpha	CArn

Mariscus see *Cyperus*

marjoram, pot see *Origanum onites*

marjoram, sweet see *Origanum majorana*

marjoram, wild, or oregano see *Origanum vulgare*

Marrubium (*Lamiaceae*)

§	***bourgaei*** var. ***bourgaei*** 'All Hallows Green'	ECha ECtt LRHS MRav NEgg XSen
	candidissimum	see *M. incanum*
*	***cylleneum*** 'Velvetissimum'	WCot XSen
§	***incanum***	WCot XSen
	lutescens	XSen
	supinum	CArn WHea
	vulgare	CArn CBod ENfk GPoy MHer MNHC SIde SRms WHfH WJek

Marsdenia (*Asclepiadaceae*)

	formosana CWJ 12354	WCru
	oreophila	CRHN

Marshallia (*Asteraceae*)

	grandiflora	CDes
	trinerva	ELon

Marsilea (*Marsileaceae*)

	mutica	EWay
	quadrifolia	CBAq EWay
	- variegated (v)	LLWG

Mascarena see *Hyophorbe*

Massonia (*Asparagaceae*)

	depressa ♀H2	ECho NRog
	- 'Branvlei Dam'	ECho
	- 'Reitfontein Gamoep'	ECho
	echinata	CAbP ECho LSou NRog WCot
	aff. ***echinata***	ECho
	jasminiflora	ECho
	pustulata ♀H2	ECho EUJe NRog WCot
	pygmaea subsp. ***kamiesbergensis***	ECho
	- subsp. ***pygmaea***	ECho

Mathiasella (*Apiaceae*)

	bupleuroides	CFis CHid LSou
	- 'Green Dream'	CAbP CAby CAvo CBcs CBre CMea CSpe EBee ECtt EWoo GBin LEdu LRHS MBel MNrw NCGa NSti SDix SLon SMrm SPoG WCot

Matricaria (*Asteraceae*)

	chamomilla	see *M. recutita*
	parthenium	see *Tanacetum parthenium*
§	***recutita***	CArn GPoy MNHC
	- 'Bodegold'	WHfH
	tchihatchewii	XSen
	'White Star'	EPfP

Matteuccia (*Onocleaceae*)

	orientalis ♀H5	CBty CDTJ CDes CKel CLAP CTal CWCL ECha EFer EPfP ERod GCal GMaP LEdu LPal LRHS MMuc NBid NLar NMyG NOrc SEND WMoo WPnP XLum
	pensylvanica	CLAP MMoz
	struthiopteris ♀H4	Widely available
*	- 'Depauperata'	CLAP
	- 'Jumbo'	CBty CCCN CLAP ISha LRHS
	- 'The King'	WCot

Matthiola (*Brassicaceae*)

	from Jersey **new**	CPne
	fruticulosa 'Alba'	CAby CDes EPfP LEdu WBor WPGP
	- subsp. ***perennis***	NSti WHal
	incana	EBee LRHS MArl SPad SVic WKif
	- ***alba***	CHid CWld ECha ELan GBBs LRHS LSou NCGa SEND SPav WCot WRHF
	- 'Legacy' (mixed)	NPri
	- 'Pillow Talk'	SPhx
	- purple-flowered	CWld SEND
	scapifera	CPBP
	white-flowered perennial	CArn CSpe CUse NPer

Maurandya (*Plantaginaceae*)

§	***barclayana***	WHea WHil
	erubescens	see *Lophospermum erubescens*
	lophantha	see *Lophospermum scandens*
	lophospermum	see *Lophospermum scandens*
	'Magic Dragon'	see *Lophospermum* 'Magic Dragon'
	'Red Dragon'	see *Lophospermum* 'Red Dragon'

Maytenus (*Celastraceae*)

	boaria	CBcs CMCN EPfP GGal IArd IDee LEdu MGos NLar SArc SEND WPat WSHC
	disticha (Hook.f.) Urb.	LEdu
	magellanica	WPGP

Mazus (*Phrymaceae*)

	miquelii	EBee
	reptans	CCon ECho ECtt EPot GEdr MSKA NLar NPer NSbr WRHF XLum
	- B&SWJ	CExl
	- 'Albus'	CCon ECho ECtt LLWG MSKA NLar SPlb
	- 'Blue'	LLWG

Mecardonia (*Plantaginaceae*)

	'Goldflake'	CCCN
	'Sundona Early Yellow'	LAst

Meconopsis ✿ (*Papaveraceae*)

	aculeata	GCra
	- CC 5248 **new**	GKev
	- CC 7193 **new**	GKev
§	***baileyi***	CBcs CBod CSBt CTri CTsd CWCL EBee ELan EPau EPfP GBuc GCra GEdr GGGa GKin IBoy ITim LRHS MBri NBir NEgg NLar NSum SPoG WFar WMoo
*	- var. ***alba***	CBod EBee ELan GBin GCra GGGa GKev IMou LRHS NSum
	- 'Hensol Violet'	CPne GBuc GCra GEdr GGGa NSum
	- violet-flowered	ITim
	Ballyrogan form	GEdr
	× ***beamishii***	GKev
	betonicifolia misapplied	see *M. baileyi*
	cambrica	CCCN CExl CMac CTri EBee ELan EPfP EWoo MMuc NPCo WBrk WCot WFar WHer
	- 'Anne Greenaway' (d)	WCot

- var. ***aurantiaca***	WCot
- double-flowered (d)	WCot
- - orange-flowered (d)	NBir WCot
§ - 'Frances Perry'	GCal WCot
- 'Muriel Brown' (d)	GCal WCot
- 'Rubra'	see *M. cambrica* 'Frances Perry'
chelidoniifolia	GCra NBid WCru
× ***cookei***	GKev NSum
- 'Old Rose'	CWCL GBin GBuc GEdr GGGa GMaP NHar NLar
'Evelyn' **new**	GEdr
Fertile Blue Group	EBee ITim
- 'Blue Ice'	see *M.* (Fertile Blue Group) 'Lingholm'
- 'Cally Lingholm'	GCal
- 'Lingholm'	Widely available
- 'Louise' **new**	GEdr
- 'Mop-head'	GEdr GMaP
§ George Sherriff Group	GCal GCra MArl NBir
- 'Ascreavie'	GBuc GEdr GKev GMaP
- 'Barney's Blue'	GEdr GMaP
- 'Branklyn' ambig.	CExl GEdr WPGP
- 'Dalemain'	GBuc GEdr GMaP
- 'Huntfield'	GBin GEdr GGGa GKev GMaP
- 'Jimmy Bayne'	GBin GEdr GGGa GMaP
- 'Susan's Reward'	GEdr GMaP
grandis misapplied	see *M.* George Sherriff Group
grandis ambig.	CPla GLin NPCo
- GS 600	see *M.* George Sherriff Group
- Balruddery form	GEdr
horridula	GCra GGGa MMuc
- var. ***racemosa***	see *M. racemosa* var. *racemosa*
- Rudis Group	GKev
(Infertile Blue Group) 'Bobby Masterton'	GCra GEdr GMaP
- 'Bryan Conway' **new**	GEdr
- 'Crarae'	GEdr GGGa
- 'Crewdson Hybrid'	GBuc GCal GEdr GMaP
- 'Dawyck'	see *M.* (Infertile Blue Group) 'Slieve Donard'
- 'Mrs Jebb'	GBuc GCra GEdr GMaP
- 'P.C. Abildgaard' **new**	GMaP
§ - 'Slieve Donard' ♀H5	GBuc GCal GCra GEdr GGGa GKev GKin GMaP LRHS
integrifolia	CCCN GBin
'Inverewe' **new**	GEdr
'Keillour'	GEdr
'Marit'	GEdr
napaulensis misapplied	EBee GCra GKev ITim NLar
- pink-flowered	NGdn
- from Solukhumbu, Nepal	GCra
nudicaulis	see *Papaver nudicaule*
paniculata	CPne EBee GGGa WPGP
- from Bhutan	GCra
- from Ghunsa, Nepal	CLAP
- ginger foliage	CHid
pseudointegrifolia	GEdr GGGa
punicea	GGGa GKev
quintuplinervia ♀H5	CLAP GBin GCra GEdr NHar NSla
- 'Kaye's Compact'	GEdr
§ ***racemosa*** var. ***racemosa***	GAbr
regia hybrids	GGGa
× ***sheldonii*** misapplied (fertile)	see *M.* Fertile Blue Group
× ***sheldonii*** misapplied (sterile)	see *M.* Infertile Blue Group
× ***sheldonii*** ambig.	CBcs CWCL GAbr MSCN NBir NLar NPer
simplicifolia	GGGa
'Stewart Annand'	GEdr GMaP
superba	EBee GGGa
villosa	GCra GGGa GLin
wallichii misapplied	see *M. wallichii* Hook.
wallichii ambig.	GLin
§ ***wallichii*** Hook.	GGGa
'Willie Duncan'	GEdr GMaP
wilsonii	GLin
subsp. ***orientalis*** **new**	

Medicago (*Papilionaceae*)

arborea	CArn SEND SPlb
lupulina	CHab
sativa	WHer WSFF

Medinilla (*Melastomataceae*)

magnifica ♀H1a	CCCN

medlar see *Mespilus germanica*

Meehania (*Lamiaceae*)

cordata	CDes EBee
urticifolia	EPPr GCal GEdr WSHC
- B&SWJ 1210	WCru
- 'Japanblau'	IMou
- 'Wandering Minstrel' (v)	WCot

Megacarpaea (*Brassicaceae*)

polyandra	WCot

Megaskepasma (*Acanthaceae*)

erythrochlamys	SVen

Melaleuca (*Myrtaceae*)

acerosa	ECou
acuminata	ECou SPlb
alternifolia	CArn CBcs CCCN CTsd ECou EOHP EShb GPoy IDee MHer MOWG SEND SPlb SVen
armillaris	CCCN CDoC ECou IDee SEND SPlb
blaeriifolia	ECou
cuticularis	SPlb
decussata	ECou SPlb
§ ***diosmatifolia***	CBcs CExl
elliptica	MOWG
ericifolia	CTri CTsd SEND SPlb
erubescens	see *M. diosmatifolia*
fulgens	ECou MOWG SPlb
- apricot-flowered	MOWG
* - 'Hot Pink'	MOWG
- purple-flowered	MOWG
gibbosa	CExl CHel EBee ECou ELan IVic LRHS LSou MOWG SEND SVen WSHC
hypericifolia	CDoC CExl MOWG SPlb
incana	MOWG
lateritia	ECou MOWG
linariifolia	CCCN ECou SPlb
nesophila	SPlb
pentagona var. ***subulifolia***	ECou
pulchella	MOWG
pungens	SPlb
pustulata	ECou SVen
spathulata	ECou
squamea	CTsd SEND SPlb
* ***squarmania***	MOWG
squarrosa	CExl ECou IDee MOWG SPlb SVen

tamariscina	ECou
thymifolia	ECou MOWG SPlb
trichophylla	SPlb
wilsonii	ECou IDee

Melandrium (*Caryophyllaceae*)

rubrum	see *Silene dioica*

Melanoselinum (*Apiaceae*)

§ ***decipiens***	CAbb CArn CSpe IMou LEdu LRHS SPhx WCru WJek WPGP

Melasphaerula (*Iridaceae*)

graminea	see *M. ramosa*
§ ***ramosa***	ECho NRog

Melia (*Meliaceae*)

§ ***azedarach***	CArn CBcs CCCN EPfP EShb GPoy SEND SPlb
- B&SWJ 7039	WCru
- var. ***japonica***	see *M. azedarach*

Melianthus (*Melianthaceae*)

comosus	CDTJ ELan EPri ESwi EWTr EWes NLar NLos NSoo SCoo SPlb
dregeanus	NLos
subsp. ***insignis*** new	
major ♀H3	Widely available
minor	CHid
pectinatus	NLos
villosus	CCon CHGN EWes NLos SPlb WPGP

Melica (*Poaceae*)

altissima 'Alba'	MLHP
- 'Atropurpurea'	CBod ECha EHoe EPPr EPla LEdu LLWP LRHS MMoz MNrw MWat MWhi NBid SEND SPlb WHea WMoo WPtf WWEG
californica	EPPr
ciliata	EHoe EPPr EPfP MMoz MWhi NDov WWEG XLum
nutans	EAJP EBee EHoe EPPr EPla EShb GMaP MAsh NOak NWsh SMHy SMrm WCot
persica	EPPr MAvo
transsilvanica 'Atropurpurea'	MMuc SPer
- 'Red Spire'	MBNS MWhi SGol SHDw SMea WMoo XLum
uniflora	IMou MBel NOak
- f. ***albida***	ECha EHoe GCal LLWP MAvo MRav NDov NOak SMHy WCot WSHC
- 'Variegata' (v)	CBre ECGP ECha EHoe EPla GCal MAvo MMoz NOak WCot WMoo WWEG

Melicytus (*Violaceae*)

alpinus	ECou WThu
angustifolius	ECou
crassifolius	ECou WSHC
dentatus new	ECou
obovatus	ECou NLar
ramiflorus	CHEx ECou

Melilotus (*Papilionaceae*)

officinalis	CArn CHab GPoy SIde WHer
- subsp. ***albus***	CArn

Meliosma (*Sabiaceae*)

cuneifolia	CBcs CExl WPGP
dilleniifolia new	IDee
- subsp. ***flexuosa***	CBcs
- subsp. ***tenuis***	CBcs CExl
oldhamii	CExl
simplicifolia	CBcs CExl
subsp. ***pungens***	
tenuis	CExl
veitchiorum	CBcs CExl NLar WPGP

Melissa ✿ (*Lamiaceae*)

officinalis	CArn CBod CHab CPbn CTri CUse ELau ENfk GJos GMaP GPoy LEdu LPot MBri MHer MNHC NBir SEND SIde SPlb SRms SVic WBor WHfH WJek XLum
- 'All Gold'	CArn CBre CPbn CUse ECha EHoe ELan ELau ENfk LSun MNHC NBid SPer SPoG SRms
§ - 'Aurea' (v)	CArn CBod CExl CUse ELan ELau GCra GMaP GPoy MBri MHer MNHC MRav NBid NBir NBro NPri SEND SIde SPer SPoG SRms WHea WJek WMnd WMoo XLum
* - 'Compacta'	CPbn GPoy
- 'Lime Balm'	CPbn
- 'Quedlinburger Niederliegende'	CArn CPbn
- 'Variegata' misapplied	see *M. officinalis* 'Aurea'

Melittis (*Lamiaceae*)

melissophyllum	CAby CArn CLAP CMea CPom CSpe ELon IMou LEdu LRHS LSou MHol MNrw MPie MPnt MRav MSCN SHar WCot WOut
- subsp. ***albida***	MBri WCot
- 'Apple Blossom'	CDes
- pink-flowered	CLAP LEdu WBor WCot WPtf
- 'Royal Velvet Distinction'PBR	CBod CSpe EBee LBMP LRHS MAvo MBri MRav NDov SGSe SHar SHil SPad SPoG WCot WHil WPtf

Melliodendron (*Styracaceae*)

xylocarpum	CExl

Menispermum (*Menispermaceae*)

canadense	CTri GPoy
dauricum	NLar

Mentha ✿ (*Lamiaceae*)

sp.	CHab
from Jamaica	CArn
angustifolia Corb.	see *M.* × *villosa*
angustifolia Host	see *M. arvensis*
angustifolia ambig.	CPbn
aquatica	CArn CBAq CBen CHab CPbn CRow CWat EHon GPoy LEdu MHer MNHC MWts NMir NPer NPol SIde SPlb SRms SVic SWat WHer WMAq WMoo WPnP WSFF XLum
§ - var. ***crispa***	CPbn
- krause minze	see *M. aquatica* var. *crispa*
- 'Mandeliensis'	CPbn
§ ***arvensis***	CArn CPbn MHer SIde
- 'Banana'	CPbn ENfk LEdu MHer MNHC NPri SIde SRms WJek

	Name	Suppliers
	- var. ***piperascens***	LEdu MHer SIde WJek
§	- - 'Sayakaze'	CArn ELau
	- var. ***villosa***	CPbn
	asiatica	CPbn ELau MHer
	'Berries and Cream'	CBod ENfk LEdu SRms WJek
	'Betty's Slovakian'	CPbn
	Bowles's mint	see *M.* × *villosa* var. *alopecuroides* Bowles's mint
*	***brevifolia***	CPbn
	cervina	CArn CBAq CBen CPbn CWat EHon LEdu MHer MSKA MWts SIde SRms SWat WJek XLum
*	- ***alba***	CBAq CPbn ENfk LLWG MHer MSKA MWts WMAq
I	'Chocolate Peppermint'	ENfk GAbr LEdu LLWG NBir NLar NPri
	citrata	see *M.* × *piperita* f. *citrata*
	'Clarissa's Millennium'	CPbn
	cordifolia	see *M.* × *villosa*
	corsica	see *M. requienii*
	crispa L. (1753)	see *M. spicata* var. *crispa*
	crispa L. (1763)	see *M. aquatica* var. *crispa*
	crispa ambig. × (× ***piperita***)	CArn CPbn
	cucumber mint	CPbn
	'Dionysus'	CPbn
	× ***dumetorum***	CPbn
	- wine mint	CPbn
	'Eau de Cologne'	see *M.* × *piperita* f. *citrata*
	eucalyptus mint	CPbn MHer
	gattefossei	CArn
	× ***gentilis***	see *M.* × *gracilis*
§	× ***gracilis***	CArn CPbn ELau ENfk GAbr NLar NPri SIde
	- 'Aurea'	see *M.* × *gracilis* 'Variegata'
§	- 'Variegata' (v)	CPbn CUse ECha ELau GPoy LEdu MCot MHer MNHC NPri SPlb SRms WHer WJek XLum
	haplocalyx	CArn ELau
	'Herbert McHale'	LEdu
*	'Hillary's Sweet Lemon'	CPbn ELau ENfk MHer SIde
	'Julia's Sweet Citrus'	CPbn MHer
*	***lacerata***	SIde
	lavender mint	ELau GPoy LEdu MHer MNHC WJek
§	***longifolia***	CPbn ELau ENfk LEdu MMuc SEND SPlb WHer
	- Buddleia Mint Group	CArn CPbn EBee ELau ENfk GAbr LEdu MHer MRav NSti SIde WJek XLum
	- - variegated (v)	CBod LEdu WJek
	- dwarf	CPbn
	- 'Habek'	EOHP
	- subsp. ***schimperi***	LEdu WJek
	- silver-leaved	CArn CPbn ELau GAbr LEdu MHer MNHC SEND WJek
*	- 'Variegata' (v)	CPbn GAbr
	Nile Valley mint	CArn ELau LEdu SHDw SIde SRms WJek
	× ***piperita***	CArn CHby CPbn CUse CWld ECha EHoe ELau GJos GPoy MBri MHer MNHC NPri SPlb
	- 'Black Mitcham'	CArn CPbn XLum
	- black peppermint	CHby CPbn ENfk EPfP GAbr LEdu LLWG MMuc MNHC NBir NLar SEND SRms WJek
§	- f. ***citrata***	CArn CHby CPbn CTri ECha ELau GJos GMaP GPoy LEdu LLWG MBri MHer MMuc MNHC MRav NBir NLar NPri SEND SHDw SIde SPlb SVic WJek
	- - from Portugal	CPbn
*	- - 'Basil'	CPbn ELau GAbr GLog LEdu MHer MNHC MRav NPri SHDw SIde SRms WGwG WJek XLum
	- - 'Bergamot'	CPbn XLum
	- - 'Chocolate'	CArn CBod CPbn ELau ENfk EPfP GJos LEdu MHer MNHC NPer SHDw SIde SPlb SRms WJek XLum
	- - 'Grapefruit'	CBod CPbn CWld GLog LSou MHer MNHC NWad SRms WJek
	- - 'Lemon'	CPbn ELau ENfk GAbr GPoy LEdu MBri MHer MNHC NPer SHDw SIde SRms WJek
	- - 'Lime'	CPbn ENfk GAbr GLog LEdu MHer SHDw SIde SPlb SRms WJek
	- - 'Orange'	CPbn ENfk LEdu MHer MMuc MNHC NPer SEND SRms WHil WJek
	- - 'Reverchonii'	CPbn
	- - 'Swiss Ricola'	MHer
	- 'Crispa'	NPol
	- 'Logee's' (v)	CPbn
	- 'Milly Mitcham'	CPbn
	- f. ***officinalis***	CPbn ELau SIde
	- var. ***ouweneellii*** Belgian mint	CPbn
	- 'Persephone'	CPbn
	- 'Reine Rouge'	CPbn
	- 'Swiss'	LEdu MNHC NLar NPri WJek
I	- Swiss mint	CArn CPbn ENfk NPri
*	- white-flowered	CArn CPbn
	'Polynesian Mint'	CPbn
	pulegium	CArn CHby CPbn CTri CUse ELau ENfk GPoy LLWG MHer MMuc MNHC MSKA NPri SEND SIde SPlb SRms SVic WHer WHfH WJek
	- 'Upright'	CArn CPbn ENfk GPoy MHer SHDw SIde WJek
§	***requienii***	CArn CPbn CPrp CTri ECho ELau ENfk GAbr GCal GPoy LEdu MBri MHer MNHC NBir NRya NWad SDix SIde SPlb SRms WGwG WHfH WJek
	rotundifolia misapplied	see *M. suaveolens*
	rotundifolia (L.) Huds.	see *M.* × *villosa*
	rubra var. ***raripila***	see *M.* × *smithiana*
	'Russian' curled leaf	CPbn
	'Russian' plain leaf	CPbn
	'Sayakaze'	see *M. arvensis* var. *piperascens* 'Sayakaze'
§	× ***smithiana***	CArn CPbn ELau ENfk GPoy LEdu MHer MNHC MRav NBir NPri SRms WJek
	- 'Capel Ulo' (v)	ELau
	'South of France'	CPbn
§	***spicata***	CArn CHby CPbn CTri CTsd CUse ELau ENfk GJos GPoy LPot MBri MCot MHer MJak MMuc MNHC NPol NPri SEND SPlb SRms WHer WJek XLum
	- Algerian fruity	CPbn LEdu
	- 'Austrian'	CPbn
*	- 'Brundall'	CPbn ELau SIde
	- 'Canaries'	CPbn
*	- var. ***crispa***	CArn CPbn ECha ELau ENfk LEdu LPot MHer MMuc MNHC NRya SIde SPlb SRms WJek
	- - 'Moroccan'	CArn CPbn CPrp CUse ELau ENfk GAbr GJos GLog GPoy LEdu MHer

	MNHC NLar NPri SEND SHDw SIde SRms WJek
- - 'Persian'	CPbn
- 'Crispula'	GAbr XLum
- 'Guernsey'	CPbn SHDw SIde SRms
- 'Irish'	CPbn
- 'Kentucky Colonel'	CPbn LEdu
- 'Mexican'	CArn CPbn
- 'Newbourne'	CPbn ELau
- 'Pharaoh'	CArn CPbn
- 'Rhodos'	CPbn
- 'Russian'	CArn LEdu MHer SIde
- 'Small Dole' (v)	SHDw
- 'Spanish'	LEdu NLar SRms
- 'Spanish Furry'	CPbn MHer
- 'Spanish Pointed'	CPbn ELau WJek
- 'Tashkent'	CArn CHby CPbn ELau ENfk LEdu MHer MNHC SHDw SIde SRms WGwG WHer WJek
- subsp. ***tomentosa***	CPbn
* - 'Variegata' (v)	CPbn SHDw
- 'Verte Blanche'	CPbn
§ ***suaveolens***	CAgr CArn CHby CPbn ELau ENfk GJos GMaP GPoy MBri MHer MLHP MNHC SIde SPlb SRms SVic WJek WSFF
* - 'Grapefruit'	LEdu
- 'Jokka'	CPbn
* - 'Mobillei'	CPbn
* - 'Pineapple'	ENfk GLog LBuc WJek
- subsp. ***timija***	CPbn ELau LEdu MHer WJek
- 'Variegata' (v)	CArn CPbn CPrp CTri ECha EHoe ELau GJos GMaP GPoy LEdu MBri MCot MHer MMuc MNHC MRav NChi NPri SEND SIde SPlb SRms WHer XLum
'Sweet Pear'	MHer
sylvestris L.	see *M. longifolia*
* ***verona***	CPbn
× ***verticillata***	WJek
§ × ***villosa***	CArn CPbn MMuc SEND
§ - var. ***alopecuroides*** Bowles's mint	CBre CPbn CPrp ELau GPoy LEdu MHer MNHC NBir NLar NSti SWat WHer WJek
- 'Jack Green'	LEdu
viridis	see *M. spicata*

Menyanthes (*Menyanthaceae*)

trifoliata	CBAq CBen CRow CWat EHon EWay GPoy LLWG MMuc MSKA MWts NPer WHal WMAq WSFF WWtn XLum

Menziesia (*Ericaceae*)

alba	see *Daboecia cantabrica* f. *alba*
ciliicalyx 'Honshu Blue'	GGGa
- 'Judith'	WAbe
- ***lasiophylla***	see *M. ciliicalyx* var. *purpurea*
- 'Plum Drops'	GGGa
§ - var. ***purpurea***	GGGa
- 'Slieve Donard'	CMac
- 'Ylva'	GGGa
ferruginea	GLin IVic
'Spring Morning'	CPne WAbe

Mercurialis (*Euphorbiaceae*)

perennis	GPoy WHer WHfH WSFF WShi

Merendera (*Colchicaceae*)

attica	ECho NRog
eichleri	see *M. trigyna*
filifolia	ECho NRog
§ ***montana***	ECho GKev NRog
- 'Norman Barratt' new	WCot
pyrenaica	see *M. montana*
raddeana	see *M. trigyna*
sobolifera	NRog WCot
§ ***trigyna***	ECho NRog

Mertensia (*Boraginaceae*)

ciliata	CCse SWat
franciscana	GCal
lanceolata	GKev
§ ***maritima***	CCon CSpe CWCL CWld ECho EWes EWld GBee GKev GPoy LEdu LRHS NBir NLar SMrm SPlb WHoo WWEG
- subsp. ***asiatica***	see *M. maritima*
pterocarpa	see *M. sibirica*
pulmonarioides	see *M. virginica*
§ ***sibirica***	CSpe MMuc SPlb
§ ***virginica*** ♀H4	CBro CCon CHel CLAP CWCL EBee ECho ECtt ELan EPfP IFro LAma LEdu LRHS MBel MMoz MNrw NBir NLar NPri SRms WFar WHlf

Merwilla (*Asparagaceae*)

§ ***plumbea***	GKev WCot

Merxmuellera see *Rytidosperma*

cincta	see *Danthonia cincta*

Mesembryanthemum (*Aizoaceae*)

'Basutoland'	see *Delosperma nubigenum*
brownii	see *Lampranthus brownii*

Mespilus ✿ (*Rosaceae*)

germanica (F)	CBcs CDul CHab CLnd CMCN CTri EBee ECrN ELan EPla EWTr IDee NLar SLon WFar WMou
- var. ***apyrena*** (F) new	ERea
- 'Bredase Reus' (F)	SKee
- 'Dutch' (F)	SDea SFam SKee
- 'Iranian' (F)	SKee
- 'Large Russian' (F)	CAgr
- 'Macrocarpa' (F)	SKee
- 'Monstrous' (F)	SDea
- 'Nottingham' (F) ♀H6	Widely available
- 'Royal' (F)	CAgr ERea LRHS MBri MCoo NOra SCoo SKee WHar
- 'Westerveld' (F)	CLnd SKee

Metapanax (*Araliaceae*)

davidii	CFil SLon
delavayi	SBig

Metarungia (*Acanthaceae*)

galpinii	WHil

Metasequoia ✿ (*Cupressaceae*)

glyptostroboides ♀H7	Widely available
- 'All Bronze'	NLar
- 'Chubby' PBR	NLar
- 'Fastigiata'	see *M. glyptostroboides* 'National'
- 'Gold Rush' ♀H7	CBcs CCVT CDoC CDul CEnd CMen CTri EBee ELan EPfP EPla

	EUJe IArd MAsh MBlu MBri MGos NEgg NLar NPCo SCoo SEWo SLim SPer SPoG SWvt WHar
- 'Golden Dawn'	NLar
- 'Hamlet's Broom'	SLim
- 'Little Creamy'	NLar
- 'Little Giant'	MBlu
- 'Matthaei Broom'	SLim
- 'McCracken's White' (v)	NLar SLim
- 'Miss Grace'	MAsh NLar SLim
§ - 'National'	MBlu
- 'Ōgon'	SGol
- 'Royal Air'	NLar WBor
- 'Schirrmann's Nordlicht'	SLim
- 'Sheridan Spire'	CEnd MBlu
- 'Waasland'	MBlu
- 'White Spot' (v)	EPla MBlu SLim

Metrosideros (*Myrtaceae*)

carminea	CCCN CTsd
§ ***excelsa***	CHII CTsd ECou ECre ESwi SArc
- 'Aurea'	ECou
- 'Parnell'	CBcs CCCN
- 'Vibrance'	CCCN
kermadecensis	ECou
- 'Red and Gold'	CDoC
- 'Twisty' (v)	CBcs
- 'Variegata' (v)	CBcs CDoC ECou ETwe
lucida	see *M. umbellata*
Moonlight = 'Lowmoo'	LSou SLim
robusta	CBcs CCCN CHEx SPlb
- ***aureovariegata***	CCCN EShb
§ 'Springfire'	CCCN
× ***subtomentosa*** 'Mistral'	ECou
'Thomasii'	see *M.* 'Springfire'
tomentosa	see *M. excelsa*
§ ***umbellata***	CBcs CCCN CDoC CHEx CTsd ECou
- Gold Nugget = 'Lownug'	LSou SLim
villosa 'Tahiti'	CBcs

Meum (*Apiaceae*)

from Bulgaria	CSpe
athamanticum	CArn CSpe EBee GCal GPoy LEdu LPla MAvo MNFA MRav SPhx

Michauxia (*Campanulaceae*)

campanuloides	CSpe
tchihatchewii	CDTJ CSpe NGBl

Michelia see *Magnolia*

fulgens	see *Magnolia foveolata*
wilsonii	see *Magnolia ernestii*
yunnanensis	see *Magnolia laevifolia*

Microbiota (*Cupressaceae*)

decussata ♀H5	CBcs CDoC CMac CSBt ECho EHul EPla LBee LRHS MBri MGos MMuc NHol NWea SEND
- 'Gold Spot'	CDoC
- 'Jakobsen'	CDoC CKen
- 'Trompenburg'	CKen

Microcachrys (*Podocarpaceae*)

tetragona	CDoC ECou EHul IArd WThu

Microcoelum see *Lytocaryum*

Microlepia (*Dennstaedtiaceae*)

strigosa	CBty CCCN CLAP ISha LRHS WWEG
- 'MacFaddeniae' new	CBty ISha

Micromeria (*Lamiaceae*)

sp.	CUse SRms
corsica	see *Acinos corsicus*
croatica	CPBP
fruticosa	WJek
graeca	CArn
juliana	XLum
rupestris	see *M. thymifolia*
§ ***thymifolia***	SPlb

Microseris (*Asteraceae*)

ringens hort.	see *Leontodon rigens*

Microsorum (*Polypodiaceae*)

diversifolium	see *Phymatosorus diversifolius*

Microtropis (*Celastraceae*)

petelotii HWJ 719	WCru

Mikania (*Asteraceae*)

araucana	LSou

Milium (*Poaceae*)

effusum 'Aureum' ♀H7	Widely available
- 'Yaffle' (v)	CBod CBre CKno EBee EPPr EPla EShb LEdu MWat WCot WPnP WWEG

Millettia (*Papilionaceae*)

japonica 'Hime Fuji'	NLar
murasaki-natsu-fuji	see *M. reticulata*
§ ***reticulata***	CExl WPat

Mimetes (*Proteaceae*)

chrysanthus	SPlb

Mimosa (*Mimosaceae*)

pudica ♀H1c	CCCN CDTJ SPlb

Mimulus (*Phrymaceae*)

sp.	SVic
'Andean Nymph'	see *M. naiandinus*
§ ***aurantiacus*** ♀H2	CMac CSpe CTri EBak ECtt LPot MGil NPer SBch SPlb
× ***bartonianus***	see *M.* × *harrisonii*
× ***burnetii***	ECho SRms
cardinalis ♀H1c	EBee ELan EPfP EWes EWld MNrw MSKA NBir WMoo
- 'Red Dragon'	CBod CFis
cardinalis × ***lewisii*** new	EWes
cupreus 'Whitecroft Scarlet' ♀H5	ECho GCrg SRms
'Eleanor'	ECtt
glutinosus	see *M. aurantiacus*
- ***atrosanguineus***	see *M. puniceus*
- ***luteus***	see *M. aurantiacus*
§ ***guttatus***	NMir NPer SRms WMoo WPnP
§ × ***harrisonii***	EWes LSou
'Highland Orange'	ECho EPfP MAsh SPlb SPoG
'Highland Pink'	ECho EPfP MAsh SPlb SPoG
'Highland Red' ♀H5	ECho ECtt EPfP GAbr GKev GMaP MAsh NPri SPlb SPoG SRms WIce

	'Highland Yellow'	ECho ECtt GKev GMaP SPlb SPoG WIce
	hose-in-hose (d)	NPer
	langsdorffii	see *M. guttatus*
	lewisii 𝕐H1c	CHll EWes MNrw SRms
	'Lothian Fire'	CWat
	luteus	CBAq CBen CWat EHon GAbr LLWG NPer SPlb WBrk WMAq XLum
	- 'Variegatus' ambig. (v)	NPer
	Magic Series	NPri
*	'Major Bees'	MJak
	'Malibu Orange'	EPfP
	moschatus	CBAq EBee LLWG
§	***naiandinus*** 𝕐H4	EWes GCrg GKev SPlb
	'Orange Glow'	LLWG MJak WHal
	orange hose-in-hose (d)	NBir
§	'Orkney Gold' (d)	ECtt
	'Popacatapetl'	CSpe
	primuloides	ECho EWes GCrg LLWG SPlb
§	***puniceus***	CTri SHil SRkn
	'Queen's Prize'	LLWG
	ringens	CBAq CBen CWat EHon MSKA NBir NPer SPlb SRms WMAq WMoo
	'Threave Variegated' (v)	EBee
	'Vortex'	LSou
	'Wisley Red'	ECho SRms
	yellow hose-in-hose	see *M.* 'Orkney Gold'

Mina see *Ipomoea*

mint, apple see *Mentha suaveolens*

mint, Bowles's see *M.* × *villosa* var. *alopecuroides*

mint, curly see *M. spicata* var. *crispa*

mint, eau-de-Cologne see *M.* × *piperita* f. *citrata*

mint, ginger see *M.* × *gracilis*

mint, horse or long-leaved see *M. longifolia*

mint (pennyroyal) see *M. pulegium*

mint (peppermint) see *M.* × *piperita*

mint, round-leaved see *M. suaveolens*

mint (spearmint) see *M. spicata*

Minuartia (*Caryophyllaceae*)

	capillacea	ECho
	laricifolia	XSen
	parnassica	see *M. stellata*
§	***stellata***	EPot
§	***verna***	ECho EDAr
	- subsp. ***caespitosa***	CTri ECho
	- - 'Aurea'	see *Sagina subulata* var. *glabrata* 'Aurea'

Mirabilis (*Nyctaginaceae*)

	dichotoma	EShb
	jalapa	CArn CExl CSpe EPfP LAma LEdu SEND SRms
	- 'Buttermilk'	CCCN
	- red-flowered	SGSe
	longiflora	EShb SBrt
	multiflora	SBrt

Miscanthus ✿ (*Poaceae*)

	capensis	SPlb
	chejuensis B&SWJ 8803	WCru
	'Dronning Ingrid'	CKno EPPr GBin IMou XLum
	'Elfin'	CKno
	flavidus B&SWJ 6749	WCru
	floridulus misapplied	see *M.* × *giganteus*
	floridulus ambig.	CCon MMuc MNrw SCob SEND SPlb XLum
	floridulus (Labill.) Warb. ex K. Schum. & Lauterb. HWJ 522	WCru
§	× ***giganteus***	CBod CKno CSpe EHoe ELon EPPr EUJe GCal GQue IBoy MAsh MMoz MNrw MWat NLos NWsh SCob SDix SDys SGSe SMad SVic WCot WPGP WWEG
	- 'Gilt Edge' (v)	CKno EPPr
	- 'Gotemba' (v)	EBee EPPr EWes NWsh
	nepalensis	CAby CElw CExl CKno CSam CSde CWCL ECha ECre EHoe EUJe EWes EWoo GCal LEdu LRHS LSun MAvo MNrw NDov NLos NOak NWsh SDix SGSe SMrm WPGP
	- NJM 09.141	WPGP
	- 'Shikola'	WCru
	oligostachyus	IMou SDys
§	- 'Afrika'	CDes CKno EPPr GBin IMou MAvo MNrw WPGP XLum
I	- 'Nanus Variegatus' (v)	CKno EHoe LEdu WCot WPGP WWEG
§	'Purpurascens'	CBod CKno CWCL ECha EHoe EPPr EPla IBoy LBMP LPla LPot LRHS MMoz MNrw NOak SCob SGSe SGol SPer WCot WMoo
	sacchariflorus misapplied	see *M.* × *giganteus*
	sacchariflorus ambig.	CBcs CDul CHEx CKno ECha ELan EPfP EPla LRHS MBrN NGdn SPer WMoo XLum
	sacchariflorus (Maxim.) Hack.	LEdu MMuc MWhi WWEG
	sinensis	CHEx CTri LEdu NOak WFar WHar WMoo WWEG XSen
	- from Yakushima, Japan	LAst SGSe
	- 'Abundance'	CKno EPfP LRHS LSqu MMuc
	- 'Adagio'	CBod CKno CPrp CSde EAEE EHoe ELon EPPr EPla EWoo GBin GQue LRHS MBri MWhi NWad NWsh SCob SHDw SMHy SMad SMea WCot XLum
	- 'Afrika'	see *M. oligostachyus* 'Afrika'
	- 'Aldebaran'	EBee IMou
	- 'Andante'	CKno
	- 'Arabesque'	EPPr MMoz WWEG XLum
	- 'Augustfeder'	EPPr SMea WWEG XLum
	- 'Autumn Light'	EPPr MMoz SMea XLum
	- 'Blütenwunder'	EPPr XLum
	- 'Bogenlampe'	GBin
	- 'China' 𝕐H6	CKno CPar EAEE EHoe ELon EPPr EPla EShb EWes GBin LEdu LRHS MAsh MAvo MNrw MSpe NOrc NWsh SDys SHDw SRms SWat WMoo WPGP WWEG XLum
	- 'Cindy'	CKno
	- var. ***condensatus***	LEdu LSou SMHy

- - NJM 11.021 **new**	WPGP
- - 'Cabaret' (v)	CBod CHEx CKno EAEE EHoe ELon EPPr EUJe GMaP LBMP LEdu LRHS NOak NWsh SEND SGSe SHDw WCot WHal WMoo WPGP WWEG XLum
- - 'Central Park'	see *M. sinensis* var. *condensatus* 'Cosmo Revert'
§ - - 'Cosmo Revert'	EPPr LEdu MMoz NWsh
- - 'Cosmopolitan' (v) ♀H5	Widely available
- - 'Emerald Giant'	see *M. sinensis* var. *condensatus* 'Cosmo Revert'
- - 'Laigong' **new**	LEdu
- 'David'	ELon EPPr LEdu MAvo MBNS MSpe NWsh XLum
- 'Dixieland' (v)	CKno ELan ELon EPPr EWes IFoB IMou LEdu NLar WWEG XLum
- 'Dreadlocks'	EPPr MAvo
- 'Emmanuel Lepage'	CKno EPPr XLum
- 'Etincelle'	CKno EWes XLum
- 'Federriese'	GBin
- 'Ferner Osten' ♀H7	Widely available
- 'Flamingo' ♀H6	Widely available
- 'Gearmella'	CBod EPPr NWsh XLum
- 'Gewitterwolke' ♀H6	EPPr EWes NWsh SMHy SMad XLum
- 'Ghana' ♀H6	CKno EBee ELon EPPr GBin GQue IMou MAvo SDys SMHy XLum
- 'Giraffe'	CDTJ CKno EWes LEdu WPGP WWEG XLum
- 'Gnome'	CKno EAEE EHoe EPPr EPla EShb GQue IMou LRHS MAsh MMHG MWhi WWEG
- 'Gold Bar' PBR (v)	CBod CChe CDul CElw CKno CMea COtt CWGN EAEE ECha EHoe ELon EPfP EPla EUJe LRHS LSou MAsh MBNS MGos NGdn NWad SEle SGol SPad SPer SPoG WCot WMoo WWEG
- 'Gold und Silber' ♀H6	XLum
- 'Goldfeder' (v)	XLum
- 'Goliath'	CKno EHoe ELan ELon EPPr GBin GQue LBMP LEdu LRHS MBNS MMoz WWEG XLum
- 'Gracillimus'	Widely available
- 'Gracillimus Nanus'	CKno
- 'Graziella'	CBod CEnd CKno CSam CWCL EHoe EPPr EPfP EPla LBMP LRHS MMoz MWhi NGdn NOak NOrc SHil SPer SRms WBor WPGP XLum XSen
- 'Grosse Fontäne' ♀H6	CCon EHoe ELan EPPr LEdu LRHS MWhi NWsh SGSe SMHy SMad WCot WMoo WWEG XLum
- 'Gutenberg Gold'	XLum
- 'Haiku'	CKno EBee EPPr LEdu XLum
- 'Helga Reich'	EWes WWEG
- 'Hercules'	EBee EPPr MAvo MMoz XLum
- 'Hermann Müssel'	CKno EBee EPPr EWes GBin GQue IMou LEdu LPla LRHS NOak SMHy SMea WWEG XLum
§ - 'Hinjo' (v)	CDul ECha EHoe ELon EPPr EPla GBin GBuc GQue LRHS LSou MMoz MSpe NGdn NLar NWsh WCot WPGP WWEG
- hybrids	SGol
I - 'Jubilaris' (v)	EPPr EWes GBin WWEG
- 'Juli'	EBee EPPr LRHS MMoz WWEG XLum
- 'Kaskade' ♀H6	CKno CPar CPrp EHoe EPPr LEdu LRHS MMoz MMuc NDov NLar WMoo WWEG XLum
- 'Kirk Alexander' (v)	EPPr
- 'Kleine Fontäne' ♀H6	Widely available
- 'Kleine Silberspinne' ♀H6	CKno CPrp CSam CWCL EHoe EPPr EPfP EPla EWoo GCal GMaP LEdu LPal LRHS MAsh MGos MJak MMuc MSpe MTis MWhi NGdn NLar NWsh SEND SPer WHoo WMoo WWEG XLum
- 'Korea' **new**	EPPr
- 'Krater'	EBee EHoe EPPr LPla LRHS MBrN SDys SGSe SMea SWat WWEG
- 'Kupferberg'	XLum
- 'Largo'	XLum
§ - 'Little Kitten'	CKno LEdu SGSe SMad SMea WMoo WPGP WWEG
- Little Nicky	see *M. sinensis* 'Hinjo'
- 'Little Zebra' PBR (v)	EBee EPfP EUJe GMaP NOak SCob SEle SMad SRms
- 'Malepartus'	Widely available
- 'Memory' **new**	EPPr
- 'Moonlight'	GBin
- 'Morning Light' (v) ♀H6	Widely available
- 'Nippon'	CElw CPrp EAEE EHoe EPPr EPla GBin LEdu LPla LRHS MMoz MWhi NBro NGdn NOrc NWsh SCob SDys SPer WPGP WWEG XLum
- 'Nishidake'	EPPr XLum
- 'November Sunset'	EPPr EWes MMoz XLum
- 'Overdam'	IFoB NGdn
- 'Poseidon'	EBee EPPr MAvo NChi SDys SMad WWEG XLum
- 'Positano'	CKno MMoz WPGP XLum
- 'Professor Richard Hansen'	CKno EPPr NWsh SMHy XLum
- 'Pünktchen' (v)	CWCL EAEE ECha EHoe EPPr GBin LEdu LRHS MAsh MSpe NOak SCob SHDw SMHy SMad SRms WMoo WWEG XLum
- 'Purple Fall'	CPar CSpe IPot LRHS LSou MAvo MBri MNrw STPC
- var. ***purpurascens*** misapplied	see *M.* 'Purpurascens'
- 'Red Chief'	EPPr EWes GQue IMou MAvo
- 'Red Meister'	CKno CRos EPfP LRHS MAsh
- 'Red Star'	SRms
- 'Rigoletto' (v)	EPPr
- 'Roland'	CKno EHoe EPPr GBin XLum
- 'Roterpfeil'	EPPr
- 'Rotfeder'	EPPr
- 'Rotfuchs'	EBee LLWP LPla MAvo XLum
- 'Rotsilber'	CBod CKno CPrp CSpe ECha EHoe EPPr EPla GBin GMaP IArd LRHS MMuc MWhi NOak SBod WHoo WMoo WWEG XLum
- 'Russia'	NWsh
- 'Samurai'	EPPr GMaP GQue MAvo MNrw XLum
- 'Sarabande' ♀H6	EHoe EPPr GQue SMHy WMoo XLum
- 'Septemberrot' ♀H6	CKno CPrp CWCL EPPr LEdu MMuc SEND
§ - 'Silberfeder' ♀H6	Widely available
- 'Silberpfeil' (v)	NWsh
- 'Silberspinne'	CCse EBee EPPr EPla GBin LEdu LRHS MWat SCob SMHy SMea SPlb XLum
- 'Silberturm'	EPPr LPla XLum

- Silver Feather see *M. sinensis* 'Silberfeder'
- 'Silver Sceptre' MAvo SMHy
- 'Silver Stripe' EPPr EWoo MAvo
- 'Sioux' EBee EHoe EPPr EPfP EPla EShb GBin GQue LRHS MAvo MBNS MMoz SPer WWEG
- 'Sirene' CCon EAEE EHoe EPPr GQue LRHS MBNS MSpe MWhi XLum
- 'Spätgrün' EPPr XLum
- 'Starlight' CKno
- 'Strictus' (v) ♀H6 Widely available
- 'Super Stripe' (v) EPPr IMou
- 'Tiger Cub' (v) CWCL EPPr EWes SGSe WWEG
- 'Undine' ♀H6 CCon CKno CMea ECha EHoe ELan EPPr EPfP LEdu MBel MBrN MMuc NWsh WMoo XLum
- 'Variegatus' (v) Widely available
- 'Verneigung' GBin
- 'Vorläufer' EPPr GBin
- 'Westacre Wine' EWes
- 'Wetterfahne' LEdu
§ - 'Yaku-jima' CBod CSam ECha EPPr MMuc MWhi SCob SMea WWEG
- 'Yakushima Dwarf' Widely available
- 'Zebrinus' (v) ♀H6 Widely available
- 'Zwergelefant' MAvo MMoz SMHy WWEG XLum
tinctorius 'Nanus Variegatus' misapplied see *M. oligostachyus* 'Nanus Variegatus'
transmorrisonensis CKno EHoe ELan EPPr EUJe LPla LRHS MAvo MBel MMoz NDov NLos NWsh SMHy WCot WWEG XLum
- B&SWJ 3697 WCru
yakushimensis see *M. sinensis* 'Yaku-jima', *M. sinensis* 'Little Kitten'

Mitchella (*Rubiaceae*)

repens EBee EPot GBin LEdu WAbe WCru
undulata B&SWJ 10928 WCru
* - f. ***quelpartensis*** B&SWJ 4402 WCru

Mitella (*Saxifragaceae*)

acerina B&SWJ 11029 EWld WCru
breweri CCon CHid CMac EBee ECha GCal MMoz MRav WBor WMoo WOut WPnP
caulescens ECha NBro
diphylla EPPr
formosana B&SWJ 125 EPPr WCru
furusei var. ***subramosa*** B&SWJ 11097 WCru
× ***inami*** B&SWJ 11122 WCru
japonica B&SWJ 4971 WCru
kiusiana CLAP
- B&SWJ 5888 WCru
makinoi CLAP EWld MMoz
- B&SWJ 4992 CExl WCru
ovalis EBee EPPr
pauciflora B&SWJ 6361 WCru
stylosa B&SWJ 5669 WCru
yoshinagae B&SWJ 4893 CExl CHid EBee EPPr WCru WMoo

Mitraria (*Gesneriaceae*)

coccinea CBcs CCCN CExl CHll CMac CTsd ECho ELan GKev LRHS LSou MBlu NLar SEND SLim SLon SPer SPlb SSpi
- Clark's form EUJe IDee LAst NSoo
- 'Lake Caburgua' CCCN CSpe ELon EWld GCal GGal IArd NLar WHor
- 'Lake Puyehue' CAbb CBcs CCCN CDoC CExl CHel EPfP LRHS SPlb SVen SWvt WSHC WThu

Modiolastrum (*Malvaceae*)

lateritium CHel CHll CRHN CSpe CTri EPri LRHS MAvo NBir SPhx SRms WHal WHar WHil WPGP WSHC XLum

Moehringia (*Caryophyllaceae*)

muscosa WCot

Moenchia (*Caryophyllaceae*)

mantica WCot

Molinia ✿ (*Poaceae*)

altissima see *M. caerulea* subsp. *arundinacea*
'Autumn Charm' CKno
caerulea CKno EPPr LRHS MAsh MBlu NChi
§ - subsp. ***arundinacea*** CKno CSpe CWCL ECha EPPr NLar WPtf WWEG XLum
- - 'Bergfreund' CKno CSam EBee EHoe EPPr GBin MAvo NWsh SMHy
- - 'Black Arrow' NDov
- - 'Breeze' CKno
- - 'Cordoba' CKno EBee EPPr GBin GQue IPot MAvo NDov SMHy SPhx WWEG XLum
- - 'Fontäne' CSam EHoe EPPr GCal GQue LEdu LPla MAsh MAvo NDov NWsh SGSe SPhx
- - 'Karl Foerster' Widely available
- - 'Liebreiz' EPPr
- - 'Skyracer' CChe CKno CPrp CSde EBee EHoe ELan ELon EPPr EUJe GBin GCal GLog GQue LRHS MAsh MAvo MMoz MWhi SMHy SMad SPhx WCot WGrn WMoo WWEG
- - 'Staefa' EHoe
- - 'Tears of Joy' new EPPr
- - 'Transparent' Widely available
- - 'Windsaule' CKno EPPr MAvo SPhx
- - 'Windspiel' Widely available
- - 'Zuneigung' CKno CPrp CSam EPPr LPla LRHS MAvo SPhx
- subsp. ***caerulea*** 'Carmarthen' (v) EHoe EPPr LRHS WWEG
- - 'Claerwen' (v) ECha EPPr MAvo SMHy SPhx WMoo
- - 'Coneyhill Gold' (v) EPPr
- - 'Dark Defender' EPPr NDov SPhx
- - 'Dauerstrahl' CKno EBee EPPr GCal GQue LPla MAsh MAvo MNrw NDov WWEG
- - 'Edith Dudszus' CBod CKno EAEE ECha EHoe ELan ELon EPPr EPla GBin GQue LPla LRHS MAvo MBel MBrN NCGa NDov NGdn NHol NLar NOrc NWsh SCob SMHy SPhx WCot WGrn WMoo WWEG
- - 'Heidebraut' CBod EAEE EBee EHoe EPPr EPla EWoo GBin GMaP GQue IBoy LRHS MBel MBri MRav MSpe NBro NDov NOrc SCob SPhx WMoo WWEG
- - 'Moorflamme' CSam EPPr MAvo MSpe SPhx
- - 'Moorhexe' Widely available

- - 'Overdam'	NDov
- - 'Poul Petersen'	CKno EBee EPPr NDov SPhx WWEG
- - 'Strahlenquelle'	CBod CSam ELan EPPr EPla GCal GQue LPla LRHS MAvo MNFA MSpe MWhi NBro NDov NHol NWsh WCAu WWEG
- - 'Variegata' (v) ℽH7	Widely available
- 'Heidezwerg'	GBin
- 'Showers of Gold'	SPhx
litoralis	see *M. caerulea* subsp. *arundinacea*

Molospermum (*Apiaceae*)

peloponnesiacum	CAby CSpe GBin GCal IMou LEdu MSpe SBrt SMHy SPhx WCru WPGP WPnP WPtf WSHC

Moltkia (*Boraginaceae*)

§ ***doerfleri***	GCal NBir NChi SBrt WSHC
§ × ***intermedia*** ℽH5	CMea SBch SBrt SIgm WAbe WThu
petraea	ECho LLHF LRHS MWat WAbe

Moluccella (*Lamiaceae*)

laevis	SVic
- 'Pixie Bells'	CSpe

Monarda (*Lamiaceae*)

sp.	ENfk
'Adam'	GBuc GCal MSpe NLar SHar WSHC
'Amethyst'	ECtt EWes
'Aquarius'	CAby EPPr EPla EWoo GQue IKil LAst LRHS MSpe WFar XLum
austromontana	see *M. citriodora* subsp. *austromontana*
§ 'Balance'	EBee ECtt GCal LRHS MRav MSpe NBro NDov NGdn NSti SHar SMrm WSHC WWEG XLum
'Beauty of Cobham' ℽH4	Widely available
§ 'Blaustrumpf'	CElw EAJP ECtt ELon EWTr EWes EWoo GBBS GQue LRHS NLar SPer WHea WSHC WWEG XLum
Blue Stocking	see *M.* 'Blaustrumpf'
Bowman	see *M.* 'Sagittarius'
bradburyana	GJos MMuc SBrt SPhx
'Cambridge Scarlet'	Widely available
'Capricorn'	WWEG XLum
citriodora	CUse GPoy NSti SIde SRms SWat
§ - subsp. ***austromontana***	NBir SBch
- - 'Bee's Favourite'	IKil
'Comanche'	EWes
'Croftway Pink'	Widely available
didyma	CArn CBod CNec ENfk EPfP LPot NBro SVic SWat WJek
- 'Alba'	NLar
- 'Coral Reef'	EWes LRHS WWEG
- 'Cranberry Lace'[PBR]	EBee ECtt GBin LRHS MBri MSCN NLar SGol
- 'Duddiscombe'	CSam
- 'Pink Lace'[PBR]	ECtt IBoy LRHS LSou LSun MBri MNrw MSpe NHol NLar SCob
- 'Sugar Lace'[PBR] **new**	MBri NLar
'Earl Grey'	ECtt GAbr MSpe NDov SCoo
'Elsie's Lavender'	EBee EPfP LPla MSpe MTis NDov NLar WWEG
'Elworthy'	CElw WWFP
'Fireball'[PBR]	CBct CWCL EBee ECtt ELon EUJe EWoo LLHF LRHS LSou MHol MNrw NHol NLar NOrc NPri SPad WBor WFar WHil
§ 'Fishes'	CExl CMac EAEE EBee ECtt ELan EPPr EPla EWTr EWes EWoo IKil LAst LEdu LRHS LSou MAvo MMuc MRav MSpe NDov NGdn NLar SGbt SMrm SPoG WPtf WWEG
fistulosa	CArn CHby CMac GJos GPoy MHer MMuc MNHC WJek WMoo XLum
'Gardenview Scarlet' ℽH4	CElw CSam CWCL ECtt EWes GCra GQue IKil LEdu LRHS MBri MCot MMuc MNFA MPie MSpe MWat NDov NHol NLar NSti SMrm SPoG SWvt WHoo WWEG
Gemini	see *M.* 'Twins'
'Gewitterwolke'	CSam MSpe MTis NDov WWEG
'Hartswood Wine'	EBee ECtt EWes SMad SMrm WWEG
'Heidelerche'	EPPr
'Jacob Cline'	EAJP ECtt EPPr EWes GBin IPot LRHS MSpe MTis NBre NCGa SGbt SHar SPhx WBor WWEG XLum
'Kardinal'	GBin LPla LRHS MTis NDov NLar WWEG XLum
Libra	see *M.* 'Balance'
'Loddon Crown'	CWld ECtt ELon GQue LRHS MPro MSpe MTis NHol NLar SHar SIde WFar WSHC WWEG
'Mahogany'	CMos EBee ECtt ELan GBuc GKev GMaP GQue IBoy IKil LPla LRHS MCot MNrw MRav MSpe MTis NSti SCob SPer SPhx SPoG WWEG XLum
'Marshall's Delight' ℽH4	CWCL EAJP EBee ECtt EPla EWes GQue LAst LRHS MRav MSpe NLar SMrm WHoo
'Melissa'	EBee NBre NLar WSHC
menthifolia	GCal SMrm SRms
'Mohawk'	EAEE ECtt EPPr EPfP GQue LRHS MPie MRav MSpe MTis MWat NDov NGdn NOrc SDix WPtf WWEG XLum
'Mrs Perry'	EWes
'Neon'	MSpe MTis NDov SPhx
'On Parade'	CElw CSam CWCL CWld EAEE ECtt EPla LRHS MMHG MSpe MTis NDov NGdn SHar
'Othello'	MTis NDov
'Ou Charm'	EBee EWes GBin NLar SMad SMrm
Panorama Series	SPlb WMoo
- 'Panorama Red Shades'	MNHC WCFE
'Pawnee'	MTis NDov WWEG
Petite Delight = 'Acpetdel'	CBcs ELan LBMP LSou MPkF NLar NPri SMad WWEG XLum
'Petite Wonder'	CBod EBee
'Pink Supreme'[PBR]	CBct ECtt ELon LRHS LSou MBri MHol MSpe NCGa NLar SCoo WHil
'Pink Tourmaline'	MSpe MTis NDov SMrm WWEG
Pisces	see *M.* 'Fishes'
'Poyntzfield Pink'	GPoy LEdu
Prairie Night	see *M.* 'Prärienacht'
§ 'Prärienacht'	CSBt CSam EAJP EBee ECha ELan EPfP LPot LRHS MCot MHer MJak MSpe NBro NGdn NLar NPri NSoo SCob SGol SPer SPlb SRms SWvt WCAu WFar WHar WSHC WWEG XLum
punctata	CArn GJos MMuc MNHC MNrw SGSe SPhx SWat

'Purple Ann'	XLum
'Purple Tower' new	EWes
'Raspberry Wine'	CBod EBee ECtt EPPr LEdu LRHS MSpe
'Ruby Glow'	CSam CWCL LRHS MMHG SMad SMrm
§ 'Sagittarius'	EAEE EBee EPPr EPla GQue LRHS MBNS MMHG MSpe NGdn NSti WWEG
'Saxon Purple'	MTis NDov NLar XLum
§ 'Schneewittchen'	CWCL EBee ECha ECtt ELan EPfP EWTr GBin LRHS MGos MHer MHol MRav MSpe MTis NHol NLar NPri NSoo NSti SCob SCoo SGbt SIde SPer SPoG SWvt WCAu WWEG XLum
'Scorpion'	CWld EBee ECtt ELan EPPr EPfP EPla EWTr GBin LEdu LRHS MRav MSpe NBir NEgg NGdn NLar NOrc SMrm SPhx SWvt WSHC XLum
'Shelley'	ECha
'Sioux'	EWes
'Snow Maiden'	see *M.* 'Schneewittchen'
'Snow Queen'	CBod CMos CWCL EBee ECtt EPPr EPla LRHS MBel MSpe MWat NEoE SMrm
Snow White	see *M.* 'Schneewittchen'
'Squaw' ♀H4	Widely available
'Talud' ♀H4	NDov
§ 'Twins'	CBod CWCL EAJP EPPr GKev LRHS MSpe NLar SWvt WSHC WWEG
'Velvet Queen'	LSou
'Vintage Wine'	CWCL MMuc MSpe NDov
'Violacea'	NHol
'Violet Queen' ♀H4	CBod CWCL EAEE EBee ECtt ELan EPla EWes GQue LEdu LRHS MBel MCot MSpe NEoE SCoo SMrm WPtf WWEG
'Violette'	EBee MSpe
'Westacre Purple'	EBee EPPr EWes

Monardella (*Lamiaceae*)

macrantha subsp. ***hallii***	CPBP
nana subsp. ***arida***	CPBP
odoratissima	MHer

Monochoria (*Pontederiaceae*)

§ ***hastata***	CBAq LLWG MSKA

Monopsis (*Campanulaceae*)

Midnight = 'Yagemon'	LAst

Monstera (*Araceae*)

deliciosa (F) ♀H1b	MBri XBlo
- 'Variegata' (v) ♀H1b	MBri

Montbretia see *Crocosmia*

Montia (*Portulacaceae*)

perfoliata	see *Claytonia perfoliata*
sibirica	see *Claytonia sibirica*

Moraea (*Iridaceae*)

algoensis	WCot
alticola	CPne ECho GCal
§ ***aristata***	ECho NRog WCot
atropunctata	NRog
§ ***bellendenii***	ECho NRog WCot
bifida from Roggeveld	ECho
bipartita	NRog WCot
britteniae	ECho
calcicola	ECho
ciliata	ECho NRog WCot
citrina	ECho
§ ***collina***	ECho GKev NRog
crispa from Roggeveld	ECho
elegans	ECho
fergusoniae from Swellendam	ECho
flaccida	ECho
- from Roggeveld	ECho
fugacissima	ECho
§ ***fugax***	WCot
gawleri	WCot
gigandra	CDes ECho NRog WCot
glaucopsis	see *M. aristata*
huttonii	CCCN CCon CSpe CTca CTre EPri GAbr MHer SBrt SGSe SMad WKif WSHC
- from Eastern Cape	ECho
inclinata from Howick	ECho
incurva	ECho
iridioides	see *Dietes iridioides*
longiaristata from Caledon	ECho
longifolia Sweet	see *M. fugax*
longifolia (Jacq.) Pers.	MHol
loubseri	NRog WCot
lugubris new	NRog
lurida	WCot
- from Bredasdorp	ECho
macrocarpa new	NRog
macronyx from Komsberg	ECho
marlothii	ECho
mediterranea	ECho
neglecta	ECho
ochroleuca	ECho GKev NRog
papilionacea from Gordon's Bay	ECho
pavonia var. ***lutea***	see *M. bellendenii*
polystachya	ECho NRog
reflexa from Calvinia	ECho
robusta	EBee GCal
serpentina	ECho
setifolia	ECho
sisyrinchium	ECho
- purple-flowered	ECho
spathacea	see *M. spathulata*
§ ***spathulata***	CCon CExl CTca EBee ECho GCal GKev LEdu WCot WKif
speciosa from Tanqua	ECho
thomsonii	NRog
tortilis from Nababeep	ECho
tricolor	ECho
tricuspidata	NRog
trifida from Sentinel Peak	ECho
tripetala	NRog
- from Riverlands	ECho
tulbaghensis	NRog
unibracteata from Sentinel Peak	ECho
vegeta	ECho NRog WCot
- brown-flowered new	CDes

versicolor from Paarl	ECho
villosa	ECho NRog WCot

Morella (*Myricaceae*)

californica	CAgr
pensylvanica	CAgr CArn CDul IVic NLar

Moricandia (*Brassicaceae*)

moricandioides	CSpe WCot

Morina (*Caprifoliaceae*)

* ***afghanica***	GAbr
alba	GCra
longifolia	Widely available
persica	EWes SPhx

Morinda (*Rubiaceae*)

umbellata WWJ 11688	WCru

Morisia (*Brassicaceae*)

hypogaea	see *M. monanthos*
§ ***monanthos***	CPla GCrg GEdr LRHS SRot
- 'Fred Hemingway'	ECho ECtt LRHS NSla WAbe WCot

Morus ✿ (*Moraceae*)

alba	CAco CAgr CArn CBcs CCVT CDul CHab CLnd CMCN CTho ECrN ELan EPfP EPla ERea GTwe LBuc MRav SDea SVic WFar
- 'Black Tabor'	CAgr
- 'Chaparral'	LRHS
- 'Issai'	LRHS MGos SHil
- 'Macrophylla'	CMCN MBlu NLar
- 'Pakistan' (F)	ERea
- 'Paradise'	CAgr
- 'Pendula'	CAco CAgr CDoC CDul CEnd CMac CTho CTri ELan IDee MBlu MBri NLar SCoo SLim
- 'Platanifolia'	CLnd MBlu
- 'San Martin'	ERea
- var. ***tatarica***	CAgr LEdu NLar
§ ***bombycis***	CLnd
'Capsrum' (F)	CAgr
'Carmen' (F)	CAgr
'Illinois Everbearing' (F)	CAgr ERea
'Italian' (F)	CAgr
'Ivory' (F)	CAgr
kagayamae	see *M. bombycis*
latifolia 'Spirata'	NLar
nigra (F)	Widely available
§ - 'Chelsea' (F) ♀H6	CAco CDul CEnd CTho CTri ECrN EPfP EPom ERea GQue GTwe IVic LRHS MBri MGos MWat NOra NWea SCoo SEWo SKee SLim SPer SPoG WHar
- 'Jerusalem' (F) ♀H6	CAco CTho EPom LRHS MCoo NOra SKee WHar
- 'King James'	see *M. nigra* 'Chelsea'
- 'Large Black' (F)	EPom
- 'Repsime' (F) **new**	CAgr
- 'Sham Dudu' (F) **new**	CAgr
rubra	CAgr NLar
- 'Nana'	NLar
'Wellington' (F)	CAgr CCVT CEnd CLnd EPla LRHS NOra NPri

Mosla (*Lamiaceae*)

dianthera	EWld GCal MAvo MNrw

Muehlenbeckia (*Polygonaceae*)

astonii	CDoC ECou LRHS WPGP
axillaris misapplied	see *M. complexa*
§ ***axillaris*** Walp.	CBcs CTri ECou SBig XLum
- 'Mount Cook' (f)	ECou
- 'Ohau' (m)	ECou
§ ***complexa***	Widely available
- (f)	ECou
- 'Nana'	see *M. axillaris* Walp.
- small-leaved	EUJe
- 'Spotlight'PBR (v)	EShb
- var. ***trilobata***	CBcs CHEx ECou EPla EShb ESwi EUJe SSta XLum
- 'Ward' (m)	ECou
ephedroides	ECou
* - var. ***muricatula***	ECou
platyclados	see *Homalocladium platycladum*

Muhlenbergia (*Poaceae*)

capillaris	LPal SDix SHDw SMad WCot
- white-flowered	SPhx
dubia	WPGP
dumosa	CKno LEdu SMad WCot
japonica 'Cream Delight' (v)	EHoe
lindheimeri	CBod CKno SDix SMea WCot
mexicana	LEdu SRms
rigens	CKno WPGP XLum

Mukdenia (*Saxifragaceae*)

sp.	CCon
acanthifolia	LEdu
rossii	CAby CLAP CTal ELon EPla GCal IFro LEdu LRHS MBel MNrw NBid NLar NMyG SGSe SHil WCru WOld WPGP WSHC WThu XLum
- from Japan	GCal
- 'Crimson Fans'	see *M. rossii* 'Karasuba'
- dwarf	CDes CLAP CTal GCal MNrw
§ - 'Karasuba'	CBod CLAP CMos CTal CWGN EBee ECtt ELon EPfP EWoo IDee LBMP LEdu LRHS LSou MAvo MMHG MPnt NLar NMyG SPoG SWvt WHil

mulberry see *Morus*

Murraya (*Rutaceae*)

* ***elliptica***	MOWG
exotica	see *M. paniculata*
koenigii	EOHP GPoy SCit SPre SVen WJek
§ ***paniculata***	CArn EShb MOWG

Musa ✿ (*Musaceae*)

from Yunnan, China	see *M. itinerans* 'Yunnan'
§ ***acuminata*** 'Dwarf Cavendish' (AAA Group) (F) ♀H1b	CDoC ELan IDee NPla XBlo
- 'Williams' (AAA Group) (F)	XBlo
- 'Zebrina' ♀H1b	CDTJ LRHS XBlo
basjoo ♀H2	CAbb CAgr CBcs CDoC CHEx CHel CHll CSBt ELan EPfP EUJe IDee LEdu LPal LRHS MGos MMuc NLos NPla NSoo SArc SChr SEND SHil SLim SPer SPlb SPoG
I - 'Rubra'	CCCN ESwi
'Cavendish Super Dwarf'	CBct XBlo

	cavendishii	see *M. acuminata* 'Dwarf Cavendish'
§	***coccinea*** ♀H1b	XBlo
	ensete	see *Ensete ventricosum*
	hookeri	see *M. sikkimensis*
	itinerans var. ***xishuangbannaensis*** 'Mekong Giant'	EUJe
§	- 'Yunnan'	NLos
	lasiocarpa ♀H1c	CDTJ CDoC CHEx CHll ESwi EUJe LRHS MGos NLos NPla SBig SPlb
	nana misapplied	see *M. acuminata* 'Dwarf Cavendish'
	ornata ♀H1b	CCCN XBlo
	× ***paradisiaca*** 'Ney Poovan' (AB Group) (F)	CCCN
§	***sikkimensis*** ♀H1c	CDTJ ELan ESwi EUJe LPal SBig SPlb XBlo
	- 'Red Tiger'	CCCN CDTJ NLos
	uranoscopus misapplied	see *M. coccinea*
	velutina ♀H1b	CCCN CDoC NLos SBig

Muscari ✿ (*Asparagaceae*)

	adilii **new**	NRog
	'Aleyna'	ECho NMin NRog
	ambrosiacum	see *M. muscarimi*
	anatolicum	ECho NRog WCot
	armeniacum ♀H5	CBro CTri EAJP ECho EPfP LPot LRHS MBri MMuc NRog SEND SPer SRms WCot WShi
	- PAB 6748 **new**	LEdu
	- 'Argaei Album'	ECho EPot NRog
	- 'Artist' **new**	NRog
	- 'Atlantic'	ECho EPfP LRHS NRog
	- 'Blue Pearl'	ECho GKev NRog WPnP
	- 'Blue Spike' (d)	CBro ECho EPfP GKev LAma MBri NBir NEgg NRog SDeJ WCot WGwG
	- 'Cantab'	ECho SDeJ XLum
	- 'Christmas Pearl' ♀H4	ECho GKev NRog WCot
	- 'Côte d'Azur'	GKev
	- 'Cupido'	GKev
	- 'Dark Eyes'	ECho EPfP SPer
	- 'Early Giant'	ECho SDeJ
	- 'Fantasy Creation'	ECho EPot NRog SDeJ
	- 'Gül'	CDes WCot
	- 'Heavenly Blue'	ECho
	- 'New Creation'	ECho
	- 'Peppermint'	CTca ECho EPfP ERCP LAma LRHS NMin SPhx WCot WRHF
	- 'Saffier' ♀H5	ECho LAma NRog WCot WHil
	- 'Siberian Tiger' **new**	ERCP
	- 'Valerie Finnis'	CAby CAvo CBre CBro CTca EBee ECho EPPr EPfP EPot ERCP EShb LBMP MBri NLar SDeJ SPer SPhx WBor WBrk WCot WPnP
	aucheri ♀H5	ECho NRya
*	- var. ***bicolor***	WCot
	- 'Blue Magic'	CAvo ECho EPot ERCP LAma NRog SDeJ
	- 'Ocean Magic'	CBro ECho GBin GKev LAma MBri NLar
§	- 'Tubergenianum'	ECho
	- 'White Magic'	CAvo CBro ECho ERCP LAma SDeJ SMrm SPer WCot
§	***azureum*** ♀H5	CAvo CBro CTca ECho ELan EPfP ERCP GMaP LAma LPot NLar NRog SPhx WCot
	- 'Album'	ECho LAma NRog SPhx WCot
	- 'Bling Bling' **new**	ERCP
	'Baby's Breath'	see *M.* 'Jenny Robinson'
	'Big Smile'	GKev NRog WCot
	'Blue Dream'	ECho
	'Blue Eyes'	ECho WCot
	'Blue Star'	ECho GKev
	botryoides	CAvo ECho LAma NRog
	- 'Album'	CAvo CBro CTca CTri ECho EPfP LAma LRHS MBri NRog SDeJ SRms WCot WShi
	bourgaei **new**	WCot
	caucasicum	ECho WCot
	chalusicum	see *M. pseudomuscari*
	commutatum	ECho
§	***comosum***	CArn CBro ECho EPfP ERCP MCot NEgg NRog WCot
	- 'Monstrosum'	see *M. comosum* 'Plumosum'
	- 'Pinard'	ECho
§	- 'Plumosum'	ECho ELan EPfP EPot GKev LAma MBri NRog SDeJ WCot
	dionysicum	ECho
	- HOA 8965	ECho WCot
	discolor	NRog
	grandifolium JCA 689.450	WCot
	inconstrictum	ECho
	'Ivor's Pink'	WCot
§	'Jenny Robinson' ♀H5	ECho IFoB SDys SMad WCot
	latifolium ♀H5	CAby CAvo CBro CTca ECho EPfP ERCP LAma LRHS MBri MWat NEgg NLar NRog SDeJ SGSe SMrm SPhx WBor WCot
*	- 'Blue Angels'	NBir
	macbeathianum	WCot
§	***macrocarpum***	CBro CPom CTal CTca EBee ECha ECho EPot LAma NRog WCot
	- 'Golden Fragrance' PBR	CAvo CBro CExl CHid ECho EPot ERCP GKev IFoB LAma MCot MNrw NMin NRog SDeJ WCot WHil
	- white-flowered	ECho
	mirum	ECho
	moschatum	see *M. muscarimi*
	'Mount Hood'	CBro ECho EPot ERCP SDeJ WBor
§	***muscarimi***	CAvo CBro CTca ECho IFoB LAma NLar NRog SDeJ WCot
	- var. ***flavum***	see *M. macrocarpum*
§	***neglectum***	ECho LAma MMuc NLar NRog SEND WCot WShi
	pallens	ECho NMin NRog WCot
	paradoxum	see *Bellevalia paradoxa*
	parviflorum	ECho WCot
	'Pink Sunrise'	ECho EPfP ERCP
§	***pseudomuscari*** ♀H5	CDes ECho GKev WCot
	racemosum	see *M. neglectum*
	'Rosy Sunrise'	WCot
	'Sky Blue'	ECho WCot
§	***spreitzenhoferi***	NRog
	'Superstar'	ECho
§	***tenuiflorum***	ECho WCot
	aff. ***tenuiflorum*** JCA 0.691.251	WCot
	tubergenianum	see *M. aucheri* 'Tubergenianum'
	'Venus'	WCot
	'White Beauty'	ECho SPhx WBor
	'Winter Amethyst'	WCot

Muscarimia (*Asparagaceae*)

	ambrosiacum	see *Muscari muscarimi*

macrocarpum see *Muscari macrocarpum*

Musella see *Musa*

Mussaenda (*Rubiaceae*)

'Tropic Snow' CCCN

Mutisia (*Asteraceae*)

acerosa new MGil
decurrens MGil
ilicifolia WCot
linearifolia new MGil
oligodon MGil
retusa see *M. spinosa* var. *pulchella*
spinosa MGil
§ - var. **pulchella** GGal

Myoporum (*Scrophulariaceae*)

acuminatum see *M. tenuifolium*
debile see *Eremophila debilis*
laetum CExl IDee SVen
§ **tenuifolium** SPlb SVen

Myosotidium (*Boraginaceae*)

§ **hortensia** CAby CBcs CBct CExl CHel CSpe ECre EPfP EUJe EWTr EWes EWoo GBin GCal IBoy IKil LRHS WBor WCot WPGP
- 'True Blue' CHid
- white-flowered IKil
nobile see *M. hortensia*

Myosotis (*Boraginaceae*)

arvensis SPhx
capitata CHid SPhx
colensoi ECou
'Malmesbury' CNat
My Oh My = 'Myomark'[PBR] CHel LSou NPri
palustris see *M. scorpioides*
pulvinaris CPBP WAbe
pygmaea SDR 7257 GKev
§ **scorpioides** CBAq CBen CHab CWat EHon MMuc MNrw MSKA MWts NMir SCoo SPlb SRms SWat WBrk WMAq WMoo WPnP WRHF XLum
- 'Alba' CBAq MSKA MWts
- 'Ice Pearl' ECha
- Maytime = 'Blaqua' (v) LLWG NBir
- 'Mermaid' CBAq CBen CRow CWat ECha EWay LLWG SDix SWat WPtf
- 'Pinkie' CWat LLWG SWat
- 'Snowflakes' CWat EWay SWat
- variegated (v) MSKA
sylvatica MMuc NMir
- (Sylva Series) SPhx
'Bluesylva' new
- - 'Rosylva' CWCL
- 'Ultramarine' WMoo
- 'Victoria Indigo-blue' (Victoria Series) CWCL
traversii SBch

Myrica (*Myricaceae*)

gale CAgr CSde GPoy IVic MGos NLar SWat WGwG

Myricaria (*Tamaricaceae*)

germanica NLar

Myriophyllum (*Haloragaceae*)

propinquum LLWG
spicatum EHon MSKA MWts WMAq
verticillatum CWat EWay MSKA SCoo

Myrrhis (*Apiaceae*)

odorata CArn CBod CBre CCon CHby CSpe CUse ECha ELau ENfk GPoy IFro LRHS MHer MMuc MNHC NPri SIde SPad SPer SRms SWvt WJek WSFF WWFP
- 'Forncett Chevron' LEdu

Myrsine (*Primulaceae*)

africana CBcs CFil EShb MHer
aquilonia ECou
australis SVen
divaricata ECou SVen

Myrteola (*Myrtaceae*)

§ **nummularia** GAbr ITim NHar WAbe WThu

Myrtus ✿ (*Myrtaceae*)

apiculata see *Luma apiculata*
bullata see *Lophomyrtus bullata*
chequen see *Luma chequen*
communis 🏆^{H4} Widely available
- 'Flore Pleno' (d) EOHP MHer
- 'Jenny Reitenbach' see *M. communis* subsp. *tarentina*
- 'Merion' WJek
- 'Microphylla' see *M. communis* subsp. *tarentina*
- 'Nana' see *M. communis* subsp. *tarentina*
- 'Pyewood Park' SRms WJek
§ - subsp. **tarentina** 🏆^{H4} Widely available
- - 'Compacta' LRHS SLon
- - 'Microphylla Variegata' (v) CBcs EShb LRHS MHer MNHC SPer SRms WHar WJek
I - - 'Variegata' (v) CBod EOHP EPfP SEND
- 'Tricolor' see *M. communis* 'Variegata'
§ - 'Variegata' (v) CArn CMCN CMac CSBt CTri ELan ELon ENfk EPfP EShb LBMP LEdu LRHS MGil MHer MSwo NLar SEND SLon SPer SPoG WCFE WJek WMoo WSHC
'Glanleam Gold' see *Luma apiculata* 'Glanleam Gold'
lechleriana see *Amomyrtus luma*
luma see *Luma apiculata*
nummularia see *Myrteola nummularia*
ugni see *Ugni molinae*

N

Nandina (*Berberidaceae*)

domestica Widely available
- B&SWJ 4923 WCru
- B&SWJ 11113 WCru
- 'Filamentosa' EPfP SCob
- 'Fire Power' Widely available
- Flirt = 'Murasaki' LRHS SCob SPoG
- 'Gulf Stream' LBuc MGos NLar WPat
- 'Harbour Dwarf' CDoC CEnd LRHS NLar WFar
- var. **leucocarpa** CMCN NLar
- 'Nana' see *N. domestica* 'Pygmaea'

- Obsessed	see *N. domestica* 'Seika'
- Plum Passion = 'Monum'	EPfP LRHS MAsh
§ - 'Pygmaea'	CMen SGol
- 'Richmond' ♀H5	CBcs CDul ELan EPfP EPla LAst LRHS MAsh MGos NLar NPri SCob SHil SLim SPer SPoG SRkn SWvt WFar
§ - 'Seika' **new**	EPfP LSou SCob SPoG WCot
- 'Sunset' **new**	NLar
- 'Wood's Dwarf'	CBcs MPkF NLar

Nannorrhops (*Arecaceae*)

ritchiana	LPal SPlb
- blue-leaved	LPal
- green-leaved	LPal

Napaea (*Malvaceae*)

dioica	SPhx WCot

Narcissus ✿ (*Amaryllidaceae*)

'Abba' (4) ♀H6	CFen CQua
'Abbey Road' (5)	CQua NMin
'Aberfoyle' (2) ♀H6	CQua
'Abstract' (11a)	CQua
'Accent' (2)	CQua
'Accomplice' (3)	IRhd
'Achduart' (3)	CQua
'Achentoul' (4)	CQua
'Achnasheen' (3)	CQua
'Acropolis' (4)	CQua SDeJ
'Actaea' (9) ♀H6	CBro CFen CQua CTca MBri SDeJ
'Acumen' (2)	CQua
'Admiration' (8)	CQua
'Adorable Lass' (6)	CQua
'Ad-Rem' (2)	CFen LAma
'Adversane' (3) **new**	CQua
'Advocat' (3)	CQua
'Aflame' (3)	CFen
'African Sunset' (3)	IRhd
'After All' (3)	CFen
'Agnes Mace' (2)	IRhd
'Ahwahnee' (2)	CQua IRhd
'Ainley' (2)	CQua
'Aintree' (3)	CQua
'Aircastle' (3)	CQua
'Airtime' (2)	IRhd
'Albatross' (3)	CQua GCro
'Albus Plenus Odoratus'	see *N. poeticus* 'Plenus' ambig.
'Alex Jones' (2) **new**	CQua
'Alice Knights' (1) **new**	GCro
'All Rounder' (3)	IRhd
'Alpine Glow' (1)	CQua
'Alpine Winter' (1)	IRhd
'Alston' (2)	IRhd
'Alto' (2)	IRhd
'Altruist' (3)	CQua ERCP SDeJ
'Altun Ha' (2)	CQua IRhd
'Altun Ha Gold' (2)	CQua
'Amazing Grace' (2)	IRhd
'Amber Castle' (2)	CQua
'Ambergate' (2)	CQua LAma SDeJ
'Ambergris Caye' (1)	CQua
'American Goldfinch' (7)	CQua
'American Heritage' (1)	CQua IRhd
'American Robin' (6)	CQua
'American Shores' (1)	CQua IRhd
'Amstel' (4)	CQua
'Andalusia' (6)	CQua
'Andrew's Choice' (7) ♀H6	CQua
'Angel' (3)	CQua
'Angel Face' (3)	CQua IRhd
'Angel Wings'	see *N.* 'Celtic Wings'
'Angelito' (3) ♀H6	IRhd
'Angel's Breath' (5) ♀H6	CQua NMin
'Angel's Whisper' (5)	CQua NMin
'Angels Wood' (2)	IRhd
'Angkor' (4)	CQua
'An-gof' (7)	CQua
'Animal Crackers' (2) **new**	CQua
'Ann Sonia' (4)	IRhd
'Anna Panna' (3)	IRhd
'Annequin' (3)	CQua
'Apollo Gold' (10)	CQua ECho NMin
'Apotheose' (4)	CFen SDeJ
'Applins' (2)	IRhd
'Apricot' (1)	CBro GCro
'Apricot Blush' (2)	CQua
'Apricot Whirl' (11a)	CQua
'April Love' (1)	CQua
'April Snow' (2)	CBro
'April Tears' (5)	NMin
'Apropos' (2)	CQua
'Ara' (6)	CQua
'Aranjuez' (2)	CFen CQua
'Aranka' (2)	CQua
'Arctic Gem' (3)	CQua
'Arctic Gold' (1) ♀H6	CQua LAma
'Ard Righ' (1)	GCro
'Ardress' (2)	CQua
'Areley Kings' (2)	CQua
'Argent' (4)	CQua GCro
'Argosy' (1)	CQua
'Arid Plains' (3)	IRhd
'Ariel'^PBR (8)	GKev
'Ark Royal' (1)	CFen
'Arkle' (1) ♀H6	CQua SDeJ
'Arleston' (2)	IRhd
'Armada' (2)	CFen
'Armidale' (3)	IRhd
'Armoury' (4)	CQua
'Arndilly' (2)	CQua
'Arpege' (2)	CQua
'Arran Isle' (2)	IRhd
'Arrowhead' (6)	NMin
'Arthurian' (1)	IRhd
'Articol' (11a)	CQua
'Arwenack' (11a)	CQua
'Asante' (1)	IRhd
'Ashland' (2)	IRhd
'Ashmore' (2)	CQua IRhd
'Ashton Wold' (2)	CQua
'Asila' (2)	IRhd
'Assertion' (2)	IRhd
§ ***assoanus*** (13)	CBro ECho EPot GKev LLHF NMin NSla SPhx
'Astropink' (11a)	CQua
§ ***asturiensis*** (13)	ECho EPot GKev MMuc NMin
- giant	see *N. asturiensis* 'Wavertree'
§ - 'Wavertree' (1)	CQua NMin
'Atholl Palace' (4)	IRhd
'Atlas Gold'	see *N. romieuxii* 'Atlas Gold'
'Atricilla' (11a)	IRhd
'Auchranie' (2)	IRhd
'Audubon' (2)	CQua SDeJ
'Aunt Betty' (1)	CQua IRhd
'Auntie Eileen' (2)	CQua

'Auspicious' (2)	IRhd
'Autumn Habit' (3) **new**	IRhd
'Avalanche' (8) ♀H4	CFen CQua IRhd NMin SDeJ
'Avalanche of Gold' (8)	CQua
'Avalon' (2)	CQua
'Ave' (2)	CQua
'Avril Amour' (1)	IRhd
'Azocor' (1)	IRhd
'Baby Boomer' (7)	LAma NMin
'Baby Moon' (7)	CFen CQua CTca EPfP EPot ERCP GKev LAma MBri NMin SDeJ
'Back Flash' (2)	CQua
'Badanloch' (3)	CQua
'Badbury Rings' (3) ♀H6	CQua IRhd
'Bailey' (2)	IRhd
'Bala' (4)	CQua
'Balalaika' (2)	CQua
'Baldock' (4)	CQua
'Ballydorn' (9)	IRhd
'Ballygowan' (3)	IRhd
'Ballynichol' (3)	CQua
'Ballyrobert' (1)	CQua
'Baltic Shore' (3)	IRhd
'Balvenie' (2)	CQua
'Bandesara' (3)	CQua IRhd
'Bandit' (2)	CQua IRhd
'Banker' (2)	CQua IRhd
'Banstead Village' (2)	CQua
'Bantam' (2) ♀H6	CBro CQua NMin SDeJ
'Barbara Hunt' (7) **new**	CQua
'Barbary Gold' (2)	CQua IRhd
'Barlow' (6)	CQua
'Barnesgold' (1)	IRhd
'Barnham' (1)	CQua
'Barnsdale Wood' (2)	CQua
'Barnum' (1) ♀H6	IRhd
'Barrett Browning' (3)	SDeJ
'Barrii' (3)	CQua
'Barron Lake' (2) **new**	CQua
'Bartley' (6)	CQua
'Bath's Flame' (3)	CAvo CQua GCro WShi
'Bear Springs' (4)	IRhd
'Bear's Gold' (4)	CQua
'Beaulieu' (1)	CQua
'Beautiful Dream' (3)	CQua
'Beauvallon' (4)	SDeJ
'Bebop' (7)	CBro
'Bedruthan' (2)	CQua
'Beersheba' (1)	CQua
'Beige Beauty' (3)	CQua
'Belbroughton' (2)	CQua
'Belcanto' (11a)	CQua SDeJ
'Belfast Lough' (1)	IRhd
'Belisana' (2)	SDeJ
'Bell Rock' (1) ♀H6	CQua
'Bell Song' (7)	CAvo CBro CFen CQua GKev LSou SDeJ WShi
'Bella Estrella' (11a)	ERCP NMin
'Belzone' (2)	CQua
'Ben Aligin' (1)	IRhd
'Ben Hee' (2)	CQua IRhd
'Benbane Head' (9)	CQua
'Berceuse' (2)	CQua IRhd
'Bere Ferrers' (4)	CQua
'Bergerac' (11a)	CQua
'Bernardino' (2)	CQua GCro
'Beryl' (6)	CBro CQua NMin WShi
'Best Friend' (3)	CQua
'Best Seller' (1)	SPer
'Bethal' (3)	CQua
'Bethan-Sîan' (2) **new**	CQua
'Betsy MacDonald' (6)	CQua
'Biffo' (4)	CQua
'Big Mo' (1) **new**	CQua
Biggar Bountiful (2) **new**	GCro
'Bikini Beach' (2)	IRhd
'Bilbo' (6)	CBro CQua
'Billy Graham' (2)	CQua
'Binkie' (2)	CBro CQua SPer
'Birchwood' (3)	CQua IRhd
'Birdsong' (3)	CQua
'Birma' (3)	LAma SDeJ
'Birthday Girl' (2)	IRhd NMin
'Bishops Light' (2)	CQua
'Bittern' (12)	CQua SDeJ
'Blackstone' (2) **new**	CQua
'Blarney' (3)	CQua
'Blisland' (9)	CQua
'Blossom' (4)	CQua
'Blue Danube' (1)	CQua IRhd
'Blushing Maiden' (4)	CQua
'Bob Spotts' (2)	CQua
'Bobbysoxer' (7)	CBro CQua NMin
'Bobolink' (2)	CQua
'Boconnoc' (2)	CQua
'Bodelva' (2)	CQua
'Bodwannick' (2)	CQua
'Bolton' (7)	GCro
'Bombay' (2)	CFen
'Bon Viveur' (11a)	IRhd
'Bonython' (1)	GCro
'Bosbigal' (11a)	CQua
'Boscastle' (7)	CQua
'Boscoppa' (11a)	CQua
'Boslowick' (11a) ♀H6	CQua
'Bosmeor' (2)	CQua
'Bossa Nova' (3)	CQua
'Bossiney' (11a)	CQua
'Bosvale' (11a)	CQua IRhd
'Bosvigo' (11a)	CQua
'Boulder Bay' (2) ♀H6	CQua IRhd
'Bouzouki' (2)	IRhd
'Bowles's Early Sulphur' (1)	CDes CRow
'Boyne Bridge' (1)	IRhd
'Brackenhurst' (2)	CQua SDeJ
'Brahms' (2)	CFen
'Braid Song' (9)	IRhd
'Braid Valley' (9)	IRhd
'Brandaris' (11a)	CQua
'Bravoure' (1) ♀H6	CFen CQua SDeJ
'Brentswood' (8)	CQua
'Brian's Favorite' (2)	CQua IRhd
'Bridal Crown' (4) ♀H6	CFen EPfP LAma LRHS
'Brideshead' (2)	CFen
'Bright Spangles' (8)	IRhd
'Bright Spot' (8)	CQua
'Brilliancy' (3)	CQua GCro
'Brindaleena' (2)	IRhd
'Brindle Pink' (2)	IRhd
'Broadland' (2)	CQua
'Broadway Star' (11b)	LAma SDeJ
'Broadway Village' (2) **new**	CQua
'Brodick' (3)	CQua IRhd
'Bronzewing' (1)	IRhd
'Brooke Ager' (2) ♀H6	CQua IRhd
'Broomhill' (2) ♀H6	CQua

Name	Suppliers
'Broughshane' (1)	CQua
broussonetii (13)	CFil
- from Morocco	WPGP
'Brunswick' (2)	CFen CQua SDeJ
'Bryanston' (2) ♀H6	CQua
'Bryher' (3)	CQua
'Buckshead' (4)	CQua
'Budock Water' (2)	CQua
'Bugle Major' (2)	CQua
bulbocodium (13)	CBro CDes GKev LEdu LRHS SRms
§ - subsp. ***bulbocodium*** (13)	CBro
§ - - var. ***citrinus*** (13)	LRHS SSpi
- - var. ***conspicuus*** (13)	CAby CBro CQua CTca ECho EPot ERCP GKev LAma MPie SDeJ WCot XLum
* - - var. ***filifolius*** (13)	CBro
- - var. ***nivalis*** (13)	ECho EPot WShi
§ - - var. ***tenuifolius*** (13)	EPot
§ - Golden Bells Group (10)	CAvo CHid CQua CTri CWCL ECho EPfP EPot GKev LRHS MBri NHol NMin SDeJ
- 'Ice Warrior' (10)	SKHP
- var. ***mesatlanticus***	see *N. romieuxii* subsp. *romieuxii* var. *mesatlanticus*
- subsp. ***obesus*** (13)	ECho EPot WAbe WCot
§ - - 'Diamond Ring' (10)	CQua ECho EPot LAma NMin
- subsp. ***praecox*** (13)	ECho LRHS
- - var. ***paucinervis*** (13)	ECho
- subsp. ***tananicus***	see *N. cantabricus* subsp. *tananicus*
- subsp. ***vulgaris***	see *N. bulbocodium* subsp. *bulbocodium*
'Bunchie' (5)	CQua
'Bunclody' (2)	CQua
'Bunting' (7) ♀H6	CQua
'Burning Bush' (3)	IRhd
'Burning Ring' (3)	IRhd
'Burravoe' (1)	CQua
'Burt House' (2)	IRhd
'Busselton' (3)	IRhd
'Bute Park' (4)	CQua
'Butter and Eggs' (4)	GCro
'Butterscotch' (2)	CQua
'Cabernet' (2)	IRhd
'Cacatua' (11a)	IRhd
'Cadgwith' (2)	CQua
'Cairngorm' (2)	SDeJ
'Cairntoul' (3)	CQua
'Calamansack' (2)	CQua
'Calgary' (4) **new**	CQua
'California Rose' (4)	IRhd
'Camaraderie' (2)	IRhd
'Camelot' (2) ♀H6	CFen CQua SDeJ SPer
'Cameo Baron' (2) **new**	CQua
'Cameo Frills' (2) **new**	CQua
'Cameo Gem' (1) **new**	CQua
'Cameo King' (2)	CQua
'Cameo Marie' (3)	CQua
'Camilla Duchess of Cornwall' (2)	CFen CQua
'Campernelli' (7)	CQua
'Campernelli Plenus'	see *N.* 'Double Campernelle'
'Campion' (9)	CQua IRhd
'Canaliculatus' (8)	CBro CFen CQua CTri ECho EPfP ERCP GCro GKev LAma LRHS MBri SDeJ SPer
canaliculatus Gussone	see *N. tazetta* subsp. *lacticolor*
canariensis (13) **new**	CQua
'Canary' (7)	CQua
'Canarybird' (8)	CQua WShi
'Canasta' (11a)	CQua
'Candida' (4)	CQua
'Canisp' (2)	CQua
'Cantabile' (9) ♀H6	CQua
cantabricus (13)	CPne CQua ECho EPot
- subsp. ***cantabricus*** (13)	CFil NMin
- - var. ***foliosus*** (13) ♀H4	CFil ECho EPot GKev WAbe
§ - subsp. ***tananicus*** (13)	ECho
'Cantatrice' (1)	CQua
'Canterbury' (5)	CQua
'Canticle' (9)	IRhd
'Capax Plenus'	see *N.* 'Eystettensis'
'Cape Cornwall' (2)	CQua
'Cape Helles' (3)	IRhd
'Cape Point' (2)	IRhd
'Capisco' (3)	CQua
'Carbineer' (2)	CQua SDeJ
'Cardiff' (2)	CFen CQua
'Cargreen' (9)	CQua
'Carib Gipsy' (2) ♀H6	CQua IRhd
'Caribbean Snow' (2)	CQua
'Carlton' (2) ♀H6	CFen CQua EPfP GKev LAma SDeJ
'Carnearny' (3)	CQua
'Carnkeeran' (2)	CQua
'Carnkief' (2)	CQua
'Carnyorth' (11a)	CQua
'Carole Lombard' (3)	CQua
'Carolina Dale' (2)	IRhd
'Carra' (8) **new**	CQua
'Carwinion' (2)	CQua
'Casiah' (2)	CQua
'Cassandra' (9) **new**	GCro
'Cassata' (11a)	LAma NBir SDeJ
'Cassopolis' (2) **new**	CQua
'Castanets' (8)	CQua IRhd
'Casterbridge' (2)	CQua IRhd
'Castle Howard' (1) **new**	CQua
'Castle Rings' (4)	CQua
'Castlerock' (2)	CFen
'Catalyst' (2)	IRhd
'Cataract' (1)	IRhd
'Catistock' (2)	CQua
'Causeway Gem' (6)	IRhd
'Causeway Ringer' (3)	IRhd
'Causeway Sunset' (2)	IRhd
'Causeway Sunshine' (1)	IRhd
'Causeway Torch' (2) **new**	IRhd
'Causeway Winner' (2) **new**	IRhd
'Cavalli King' (4)	CQua
'Cavalryman' (3)	IRhd
'Cawdron' (2)	CQua
'Caye Chapel' (3)	CQua
'Cazique' (6)	CQua
'Ceasefire' (2)	IRhd
'Cedar Hills' (3)	CQua
'Cedric Morris' (1)	CDes CHid CLAP ECha EWoo GBuc WCot
'Celestial Fire' (2)	CQua
'Celtic Gold' (2)	CQua
§ 'Celtic Wings' (5)	IRhd
'Centenary Gold' (2) **new**	CQua
'Centrefold' (3)	CQua
'Cha-cha' (6)	CBro CQua
'Changing Colors' (11a)	CQua SDeJ
'Chanson' (1) ♀H6	CQua IRhd
'Chanterelle' (11a)	LAma SDeJ

'Chantilly' (2)	CQua
'Charity May' (6)	CQua
'Charlbury' (2)	IRhd
'Charleston' (2)	CQua
'Charlie Connor' (1)	CQua
'Chasseur' (2)	IRhd
'Chaste' (1)	CQua IRhd
'Chat' (7)	CQua
'Chateau Impney' (2)	IRhd
'Cheer Leader' (3)	CQua
'Cheerfulness' (4) 🏆H6	CAvo CFen CQua LAma LRHS MBri NPer SDeJ
'Cheesewring' (3)	CQua
'Cheetah' (1)	CQua IRhd
'Chelsea Girl' (2)	CQua IRhd
'Cheltenham' (2)	CQua
'Chérie' (7)	CQua
'Cherish' (2)	CQua
'Cherry Glow' (3)	IRhd
'Cherry Ice' (2) **new**	CQua
'Cherrygardens' (2)	CQua IRhd
'Chesapeake Bay' (1)	CQua
'Chesterton' (9) 🏆H6	CQua
'Chickadee' (6)	CQua
'Chicken Hill' (1)	CQua
'Chickerell' (3)	CQua
'Chief Inspector' (1)	IRhd
'Chiffon' (2)	CFen
'Chiloquin' (1)	CQua
'China Doll' (2)	CQua
'China Gold' (10)	CQua
'Chinchilla' (2)	CQua IRhd
'Chingah' (1)	IRhd
'Chinita' (8)	CQua
'Chipper' (5)	CQua NMin
'Chippewa' (3)	IRhd
'Chit Chat' (7) 🏆H4	CQua EPot LLHF NMin SDeJ
'Chiva' (7)	CBro ECho GKev LLHF NMin
'Chobe River' (1)	CQua IRhd
'Chortle' (3)	IRhd
'Chukar' (4) 🏆H6	IRhd
'Churchfield Bells' (5)	CQua
'Churston Ferrers' (4)	CQua
'Chy Noweth' (2)	CQua
'Cinco de Mayo' (2)	CQua
'Cinder Hill' (2)	IRhd
'Cinnamon Ring' (3) **new**	CQua
'Circle of Friends' (3) **new**	CQua
'Cisticola' (3)	CQua IRhd
citrinus	see *N. bulbocodium* subsp. *bulbocodium* var. *citrinus*
'Citron' (3)	CQua
'Citronita' (3)	CQua
'Clare' (7)	CBro CQua NMin
'Classic Gold' (10) 🏆H6	CQua
'Claverley' (2)	CQua
'Clean Sweep' (3) **new**	IRhd
'Clearbrook' (2)	CQua
'Cloth of Gold' (8) **new**	CQua
'Cloud Nine' (2)	CBro
'Clouded Yellow' (2)	CQua IRhd
'Clouds Hill' (4)	CQua
'Clouds Rest' (2)	IRhd
'Clovelly Ayr' (9)	CQua
'Codlins and Cream'	see *N.* 'Sulphur Phoenix'
'Coker's Frome' (9)	CQua
'Coldbrook' (2)	CQua
'Colin's Joy' (2)	CQua
'Coliseum' (2)	IRhd
'Colleen Bawn' (1)	CQua NMin WShi
'Colley Gate' (3)	CQua
'Colliford' (2)	CQua
'Colorama' (11a)	CQua
'Colorful' (2)	IRhd
'Columbus' (2)	CQua
'Colville' (9)	CQua
'Comal' (1)	CQua
'Come to Good' (2) **new**	CQua
'Commodore Perry' (1) **new**	CQua
'Compressus'	see *N.* × *intermedius* 'Compressus'
'Compton Court' (3)	IRhd
'Conestoga' (2)	CQua IRhd
'Congress' (11a)	CQua
'Conly' (3)	CQua IRhd
'Conowingo' (11a)	CQua
'Conspicuus' ambig. (3)	LAma
'Contralto' (2)	IRhd
'Cool Autumn' (2)	CQua
'Cool Crystal' (3)	CQua
'Cool Evening' (11a)	CQua IRhd
'Cool Pink' (2)	CQua
'Cool River' (11a) **new**	CQua
'Cool Shades' (2)	CQua
'Coolmaghery' (2)	IRhd
'Coombe Creek' (6)	CQua
'Copper Bowl' (2) **new**	GCro
'Copper Nob' (2)	IRhd
'Copper Rings' (3)	CQua
'Copperfield' (2)	CQua
'Cora Ann' (7)	CBro
'Coral Fair' (2)	CQua
'Corbiere' (1)	CQua IRhd
'Corbridge' (2)	CQua
'Corky's Song' (2)	CQua
'Cornet' (6)	CQua
'Cornish Chuckles' (12) 🏆H6	CBro CFen CQua NMin
'Cornish Pride' (2)	CFen
'Cornish Sun' (2)	CQua
'Cornish Vanguard' (2) 🏆H6	CFen CQua
'Cornsilk' (11a)	CQua
'Corofin' (3)	CQua
'Coromandel' (2)	IRhd
'Corozal' (3)	CQua
'Corroboree' (2)	IRhd
'Cosine' (11a)	IRhd
'Cosmic Dance' (2)	IRhd
'Cotehele' (1)	CQua
'Cotinga' (6)	CQua NMin SDeJ
'Countdown' (2)	CQua
'Court Martial' (2)	CFen
'Coverack Glory' (2)	CQua
'Crackington' (4) 🏆H6	CQua IRhd
'Cragford' (8)	MBri SDeJ
'Craig Stiel' (2)	CQua
'Creag Dubh' (2)	CQua
'Creation' (1) **new**	CQua
'Creed' (6)	CQua
'Crenver' (3)	CQua GCro
'Crevenagh' (2)	IRhd
'Crevette' (8) **new**	CQua
'Crewenna' (1)	CQua
'Crill' (7)	CQua
'Crimson Chalice' (3)	CQua IRhd
'Cristobal' (1)	CQua
'Crock of Gold' (1)	CFen

Name	Suppliers
'Croesus' (2)	CQua
'Crofty' (6)	CQua
'Croila' (2)	CQua
'Crown of Gold' (2)	IRhd
'Crowndale' (4)	CQua IRhd
'Crugmeer' (11a)	CQua
'Cryptic' (1)	CQua IRhd
'Crystal Star' (2)	CQua
'Cudden Point' (2)	CQua
'Cul Beag' (3)	CQua
'Culmination' (2)	CQua
'Cultured Pearl' (2)	CQua IRhd
'Cum Laude' (11a)	ERCP SDeJ
'Curlew' (7) ♀H6	CQua GKev SDeJ
'Curly' (2)	SDeJ
'Curlylocks' (7)	NMin
cyclamineus (13) ♀H6	CBro CExl CFil ECho GKev LLHF LRHS SKHP SRms
'Cyclope' (1)	CQua
'Cynosure' (2)	GCro
cypri (13)	CQua
'Cyros' (1)	CQua
'Dailmanach' (2)	CQua IRhd
'Dailmystic' (2)	IRhd
'Dainty Miss' (7)	CQua
'Daisy Schäffer' (2) **new**	GCro
'Dallas' (3)	CFen CQua ECho
'Dalmeny' (2)	CQua
'Dambuster' (4)	IRhd
'Damson' (2)	CQua GCro
'Dan du Plessis' (8)	CFen CQua
'Dancing Queen' (2)	IRhd
'Dardanelles' (2)	IRhd
'Darlow Dale' (2)	IRhd
'Dateline' (3)	CQua IRhd
'David Alexander' (1)	CQua
'David Mills' (2)	CQua
'Dawn Brooker' (2)	CQua
'Dawn Call' (2)	IRhd
'Dawn Run' (2)	CQua IRhd
'Dawn Sky' (2)	CQua
'Daydream' (2)	CQua
'Daymark' (8)	CQua
'Daymer Bay' (1)	CFen
'Dayton Lake' (2)	CQua
'Dear Love' (11a)	IRhd
'Debutante' (2)	CQua
'December Bride' (11a)	CQua
'Decision' (2)	IRhd
'Defence Corps' (1)	IRhd
'Del Rey' (1)	CQua
'De Lacey' (11a) **new**	CQua
'Delia' (6)	IRhd
'Dell Chapel' (3)	CQua
'Delnashaugh' (4)	CQua ERCP LAma NHol SDeJ
'Delos' (3)	CQua
'Delta Flight' (6)	IRhd
'Demand' (2)	CQua
'Demeanour' (3)	IRhd
'Demmo' (2)	CQua IRhd
'Dena' (3)	IRhd
'Denali' (1)	CQua IRhd
'Derek Tangye' (2) **new**	CQua
'Derringer' (7) **new**	CAvo
'Descant' (1)	IRhd
'Desdemona' (2) ♀H6	CQua SDeJ
'Desert Bells' (7)	CQua NMin
'Desert Orchid' (2)	CQua

Name	Suppliers
'Dewy Dell' (3)	IRhd
'Diamond Ring'	see *N. bulbocodium* subsp. *obesus* 'Diamond Ring'
'Dick Wilden' (4)	SDeJ
'Dickcissel' (7) ♀H6	CQua ERCP
'Dignitary' (2)	IRhd
'Dimity' (3)	CQua
'Dimple' (9)	CQua IRhd
'Dinkie' (3)	CBro
'Discreet' (2) **new**	IRhd
'Dispatch Box' (1) ♀H6	IRhd
'Disquiet' (1)	CQua IRhd
'Diversity' (11a)	IRhd
'Doctor David Hough' (1) **new**	CQua
'Doctor Hugh' (3) ♀H6	CQua IRhd
'Doctor Jazz' (2)	CQua IRhd
'Doll Baby' (7)	NMin
'Doombar' (1)	CQua
'Dorchester' (4)	CQua IRhd
'Dorneywood' (1)	IRhd
'Dorothy Yorke' (2) **new**	GCro
§ 'Double Campernelle' (4)	CQua ECho IFro MBri SDeJ WShi
'Double Itzim' (4)	NMin
'Double Mayflower' (4) **new**	CQua
double pheasant eye	see *N. poeticus* 'Plenus' ambig.
double Roman	see *N.* 'Romanus'
'Double White' (4)	CQua
'Doubleday' (4)	IRhd
'Doublet' (4)	CQua
'Doubtful' (3)	CQua
'Dove Song' (2)	IRhd
'Dover Cliffs' (2)	CQua
'Downfield' (4)	IRhd
'Downing College' (2) **new**	CQua
'Downlands' (3)	CQua
'Downpatrick' (1)	CQua
'Dragon Run' (2)	CQua
'Drama Queen' (11a)	IRhd
'Dream Catcher' (2)	IRhd
'Dreamlight' (3)	CQua
'Drumboe' (2)	CQua
dubius (13)	ECho EPot
'Duchess of Westminster' (2)	CQua
'Duiker' (6)	IRhd
'Duke of Windsor' (2)	CFen
'Dulcimer' (9)	CQua
'Dunadry Inn' (4)	IRhd
'Dunkeld' (2)	CQua
'Dunkery' (4)	CQua IRhd
'Dunley Hall' (3)	CQua IRhd
'Dunmurry' (1)	CQua
'Dunskey' (3)	CQua
'Dupli Kate' (4)	IRhd
'Duration' (4) **new**	CQua
'Dusky Lad' (2)	IRhd
'Dusky Maiden' (2)	IRhd
'Dutch Delight' (2)	IRhd
'Dutch Lemon Drops' (5) ♀H6	CMea CQua EPot NMin
'Dutch Master' (1) ♀H6	CFen CQua EPfP LAma LRHS SDeJ SPer
'Early Bride' (2)	CFen CQua
'Early Splendour' (8)	CQua
'Earthlight' (3)	CQua
'Easter Moon' (2)	CQua
'Eastern Dawn' (2)	CFen CQua SDeJ

	Name	Suppliers
	'Eastern Promise' (2)	CQua IRhd
	'Eaton Song' (12) ♀^{H6}	CBro CQua NMin
	'Ebony' (1)	CQua
	'Eddy Canzony' (2)	CFen CQua
	'Eden Gold' (2)	CFen
	'Edenderry' (1)	IRhd
	'Edgbaston' (2)	CQua
	'Edge Grove' (2)	CQua
	'Edgedin Gold' (7)	NMin
	'Editor' (2)	IRhd
	'Edward Buxton' (3)	CFen CQua GCro
	'Edward Hart' (2) **new**	GCro
	'Egard' (11a)	CQua
	'Egmont King' (2)	CQua
	'Eira Hibbert' (3) **new**	CQua
	'Eland' (7)	CQua
	'Elburton' (2)	CQua
	'Electrus' (11a)	IRhd
	'Elegance' (2)	CAvo CQua
	elegans (13)	ECho EPot
	'Elegant Queen' (2)	IRhd
	'Elf' (2)	CQua
	'Elfin Gold' (6)	CQua
	'Elizabeth Ann' (6)	CQua IFro IRhd
	'Elka' (1) ♀^{H6}	CAvo CBro CDes CQua LLHF NMin
	'Ellen' (2)	CQua
	'Elmbridge' (1)	IRhd
	'Elphin' (4)	CQua
	'Elrond' (2)	CQua
	'Elven Lady' (2)	CQua
	'Elvira' (8)	CQua WShi
	'Emcys' (6)	LLHF NMin
	'Emerald City' (3)	IRhd
	'Emerald Pink' (3)	CQua
	'Emily' (2)	NMin
	'Eminent' (3)	CQua
	'Emperor' (1)	CQua
	'Empress' (1) **new**	GCro
	'Empress of Ireland' (1)	IRhd
	'English Caye' (1)	CQua IRhd
	'Ensemble' (4)	CQua
	'Epona' (3)	CQua
	'Erin' (3)	CQua
	'Erlicheer' (4)	CQua SDeJ
	'Escapee' (2)	IRhd
	'Estrella' (3)	CQua
	'Ethereal Beauty' (2)	IRhd
	'Ethos' (1)	IRhd
§	***eugeniae*** (13)	CFil
	'Euryalus' (1)	CQua
	'Evangeline' (3)	GCro
	'Eve Robertson' (2)	CQua
	'Evelyn Roberts' (11a)	CQua
	'Evening' (2)	CQua
	'Everready' (1) **new**	CQua
	'Evesham' (3)	CQua IRhd
	'Eyeglass' (3)	CQua IRhd
	'Eyelet' (3)	CQua IRhd
	'Eype' (4)	IRhd
	'Eyrie' (3)	CQua IRhd
§	'Eystettensis' (4)	CBro IBlr
	'Fair Prospect' (2)	CQua
	'Fair William' (2)	CQua
	'Fairgreen' (3)	CFen
	'Fairlawns' (3)	CQua
	'Fairmile' (3)	CQua
	'Fairy Chimes' (5)	CQua
	'Fairy Footsteps' (3)	CQua
	'Fairy Island' (3)	CQua
	'Fairy Magic' (2)	IRhd
	'Fairy Tale' (3)	CQua
I	'Faith' (1)	SDeJ
	'Falconet' (8) ♀^{H6}	CQua SDeJ SPer
	'Falstaff' (2)	CQua
	'Far Country' (2)	CQua
	'Farro' (1)	IRhd
I	'Fashion' (11b)	CQua
	'Fashion Model' (2)	IRhd
	'Fastidious' (2)	CQua
	'February Gold' (6) ♀^{H6}	CAvo CBro CQua CTri EPfP EPot ERCP GKev LAma LRHS MBri MMuc NBir SDeJ SEND SPer SRms WShi
	'February Silver' (1)	CBro EPot ERCP LAma SDeJ
	'Feeling Lucky' (2)	CQua
	'Felindre' (9)	CFen CQua
	'Feline Queen' (1)	IRhd
	'Feock' (3)	CQua
	'Ferial Wendy' (2)	CFen
	fernandesii (13)	ECho NMin WAbe WCot WThu
	- var. ***cordubensis*** (13)	CFil ECho
	- var. ***cordubensis*** × ***jonquilla*** (13)	NMin
	'Ferndown' (3)	CQua IRhd
	'Ferral' (4)	IRhd
	'Fertile Crescent' (7)	CQua
	'Ffitch's Ffolly' (2)	CQua
	'Fiery Maiden' (2)	CFen
	'Filoli' (1)	CQua
	'Filskit' (2) **new**	CQua
	'Finchcocks' (2)	CQua
	'Fine Gold' (1)	CQua
	'Fine Romance' (2)	CQua IRhd
	'Finland' (2)	CFen CQua
	'Fiona Linford' (3)	IRhd
	'Fiona MacKillop' (2)	IRhd
	'Fire-Blade' (2) **new**	CQua
	'Firebrand' (3)	CQua
	'Firefighter' (3)	IRhd
	'Firehills' (2)	IRhd
	'Firetail' (3)	EPot WShi
	'First Born' (6)	CQua NMin
	'First Formal' (3)	CQua
	'First Hope' (6)	CFen CQua
	'Flambards Village' (4)	CQua
	'Fletching' (1)	IRhd
	'Flirt' (6)	CQua
	'Flomay' (7)	NMin
	'Florida Manor' (3)	IRhd
	'Flower Record' (2)	LAma
	'Flusher' (2)	CQua
	'Flycatcher' (7)	CQua
	'Flying Colours' (4)	IRhd
	'Flying High' (3)	CQua
	'Foff's Way' (1)	CQua
	'Foresight' (1)	CQua
	'Forge Mill' (2)	CQua
	'Forged Gold' (2)	IRhd
	'Fort Mitchell' (1)	CQua
	'Fortescue' (4)	IRhd
	'Fortissimo' (2)	SDeJ SPer
	'Fortune' (2)	CQua GCro LAma MBri SDeJ
	'Fossie' (4)	CQua
	'Foundling' (6)	CQua
	'Fowey' (3)	CFen
	'Foxfire' (2)	CQua

'Foxhunter' (2)	CQua
'Fragrant Breeze' (2)	SDeJ
'Fragrant Rose' (2)	CQua EPfP ERCP IRhd
'Frances Delight' (11a)	CQua
'Francolin' (1)	IRhd
'Frank' (9)	IRhd
'Frank Miles' (2)	CQua GCro
'Freedom Rings' (2)	CQua
'Freedom Stars' (11a) ♀^{H6}	IRhd
'Fresco' (11a)	IRhd
'Fresh Lime' (1)	CQua
'Fresno' (3)	IRhd
'Frigid' (3)	CQua
'Front Royal' (2)	CQua
'Frosted Pink' (2)	IRhd
'Frostkist' (6)	CBro CQua
'Frosty Morn' (5)	NMin
'Frozen Jade' (1)	CQua IRhd
'Fruit Cup' (7)	CQua SDeJ
'Fuco' (1)	CQua NMin
'Full House' (4)	SDeJ
'Fulwell' (4)	CQua
'Furbelow' (4)	CQua
'Furnace Creek' (2)	IRhd
'Fynbos' (3)	IRhd
'Gabriella Rose' (4)	CQua
gaditanus (13)	CBro
gaditanus × ***rupicola*** subsp. ***watieri*** (13)	ECho
'Gambas' (1) **new**	CQua
'Gamebird' (1)	IRhd
'Ganilly' (2)	CFen
'Garden News' (3)	IRhd
'Garden Opera' (7) ♀^{H6}	CFen CQua
'Garden Treasure' (2)	IRhd
'Gatecrasher' (1)	IRhd
'Gay Cavalier' (4)	CQua
'Gay Kybo' (4) ♀^{H6}	CQua
'Gay Song' (4)	CQua
'Gay Time' (4)	CFen SDeJ
gayi (13)	CQua WShi
'Geevor' (4)	CQua
'Gellymill' (2)	CQua
'Gem of Antrim' (2) **new**	CQua
'Gemini Girl' (2)	CQua
'Gentle Giant' (2)	SDeJ
'Geometrics' (2)	IRhd
'George Leak' (2)	CFen
'Georgia Moon' (2)	CFen
'Georgie Girl' (6)	IRhd
'Geranium' (8) ♀^{H6}	CBro CFen CQua EPfP ERCP LAma SDeJ SPer WShi
'Gerry Smith' (2)	CQua
'Gettysburg' (2)	CQua
'Gigantic Star' (2)	CQua SDeJ
'Gillan' (11a)	CQua
'Gin and Lime' (1)	CQua
'Gipsy Moon' (2)	CQua
'Gipsy Queen' (1)	CBro CQua EPot LLHF NMin WShi
'Gironde' (11)	CQua
'Glacier' (1)	CQua
'Glapthorne' (2) **new**	CQua
'Glasnevin' (2)	CQua IRhd
'Glasney' (3) **new**	CQua
'Glen Clova' (2)	CQua
'Glen Lake' (2)	IRhd
'Glendermott' (2)	CQua
'Glenside' (2)	CQua

'Glissando' (2)	CQua IRhd
'Gloriosus' (8)	CQua
'Glover's Reef' (1)	CQua
'Glowing Phoenix' (4)	CQua GCro
'Glowing Red' (4)	CQua
'Goblet' (1)	SDeJ
'Goff's Caye' (2)	CQua IRhd
'Golant' (2)	CQua
'Gold Bond' (2)	CQua IRhd
'Gold Cache' (11a)	CQua
'Gold Charm' (2)	CQua
'Gold Convention' (2) ♀^{H6}	CQua IRhd
'Gold Ingot' (2) ♀^{H6}	IRhd
'Gold Medallion' (1)	CQua
'Gold Top' (2)	CQua
'Golden Amber' (2)	CQua
'Golden Anniversary' (2)	CFen CQua
'Golden Aura' (2) ♀^{H6}	CQua
'Golden Bear' (4)	CQua
'Golden Bells'	see *N. bulbocodium* Golden Bells Group
'Golden Cheer' (2)	CFen CQua
'Golden Dawn' (8) ♀^{H4}	CFen CQua EPfP
'Golden Ducat' (4)	CFen CQua LAma MBri NBir SDeJ
'Golden Echo' (7)	EPfP
'Golden Flute' (2)	IRhd
'Golden Gamble' (11a)	IRhd
'Golden Halo' (2)	CQua
'Golden Harvest' (1)	CQua LAma NPer
'Golden Incense' (7)	CQua
'Golden Jewel' (2) ♀^{H6}	CQua
'Golden Joy' (2)	CQua
'Golden Lady' (1)	CQua
'Golden Lion' (1)	CFen CQua
'Golden Marvel' (1)	CQua
'Golden Mary' (3)	GCro
'Golden Orbit' (4)	CQua
'Golden Peak' (1)	IRhd
'Golden Phoenix' (4)	CQua WShi
'Golden Rain' (4)	CQua
'Golden Rapture' (1)	CQua
'Golden Sheen' (2)	CQua
'Golden Splash' (11a)	IRhd
'Golden Spur' (1)	CQua GCro LAma
'Golden Torch' (2)	CQua
'Golden Twins' (7)	CQua
'Golden Vale' (1)	CQua
'Goldfinger' (1) ♀^{H6}	CQua IRhd
'Goldhanger' (2)	CQua IRhd
'Golitha Falls' (2)	CQua
'Good Fella' (2)	CQua
'Good Intentions' (2) **new**	IRhd
'Good Measure' (2)	CQua
'Good Success' (11a) **new**	CQua
'Goonbell' (2)	CQua
'Goose Green' (3)	GKev
'Gorran' (3)	CQua
'Gossmoor' (4)	CQua
'Grace Note' (3)	CQua
'Graduation' (2)	IRhd
'Grand Monarque'	see *N. tazetta* subsp. *lacticolor* 'Grand Monarque'
'Grand Opening' (4)	IRhd
'Grand Primo Citronière' (8)	CQua
'Grand Prospect' (2)	CQua
'Grand Soleil d'Or' (8)	CQua LAma SDeJ
'Grandis' (1) **new**	GCro

'Great Expectations' (2)	CQua
'Great Warley' (2)	GCro
'Greatwood' (1)	CQua
'Greek Surprise' (4)	IRhd
'Green Chartreuse' (2)	CQua
'Green Envy' (3) **new**	CQua
'Green Island' (2)	CFen SDeJ
'Green Lawns' (9)	CQua
'Green Lodge' (9)	IRhd
'Green Pearl' (3)	NMin
'Greenodd' (3)	CQua
'Greenpark' (9)	IRhd
'Grenoble' (2)	CQua
'Gresham' (4)	CQua
'Gribben Head' (4)	CQua
'Groundkeeper' (3)	IRhd
'Guiding Spirit' (4)	CQua
'Gull' (2)	CQua
'Gulliver' (3)	CQua GCro
'Gunwalloe' (11a)	CQua
'Guy Wilson' (2)	CQua
'Gwawr' (2) **new**	CQua
'Gwenllian' (3) **new**	CQua
'Gwennap' (1)	CQua
'Gwinear' (2)	CQua
'Habit' (1)	IRhd
'Hacienda' (1)	CQua
'Half Moon Caye' (2)	CQua
'Halley's Comet' (3)	CQua IRhd
'Halloon' (3)	CQua
'Halzephron' (2)	CQua
'Hambledon' (2) 𝕐H6	CQua
'Hampton Court' (2)	CQua IRhd
'Hanky Panky' (11a) **new**	CQua
'Hanley Swan' (1)	IRhd
'Happy Dreams' (2)	IRhd
'Happy Fellow' (2)	CQua
'Happy Valley' (2)	IRhd
'Harbour View' (2)	IRhd
'Harmony Bells' (5)	CQua NMin
'Harp Music' (2)	IRhd
'Harpers Ferry' (1)	CQua
'Hartlebury' (3)	CQua
'Havelock' (2)	GCro
'Hawangi' (3)	IRhd
'Hawera' (5) 𝕐H6	CAvo CBro CFen CQua CTca CTri EPfP EPot ERCP GKev LAma LPot LRHS MBri SDeJ SPer WShi
'Heamoor' (4) 𝕐H6	CQua
hedraeanthus (13)	ECho
'Helford Dawn' (2)	CQua
'Helford Sunset' (2)	CQua
'Helios' (2)	CQua GCro
hellenicus	see *N. poeticus* var. *hellenicus*
henriquesii	see *N. jonquilla* var. *henriquesii*
'Henry Irving' (1)	CQua GCro
'Hero' (1)	CQua
'Heslington' (3)	CQua
'Hexameter' (9)	CQua
'Hexworthy' (3)	CQua
'Hibernian' (4)	IRhd
'High Life' (2)	CFen
'High Society' (2) 𝕐H6	CQua SDeJ
'Highfield Beauty' (8) 𝕐H6	CQua
'Highgrove' (1)	CQua
'Highlite' (2)	CQua
'Hihitahi' (2)	CQua
'Hilda's Pink' (2)	CQua

'Hill Head' (9)	IRhd
'Hillstar' (7) 𝕐H6	CQua NMin SDeJ
hispanicus (13)	CQua ECho
'Hocus Pocus' (3)	IRhd
'Holland's Glory' (4)	GCro
'Holly Berry' (2)	CFen
'Hollypark' (3)	IRhd
'Hollywood' (2)	CFen
'Holme Fen' (2)	CQua IRhd
'Home Fires' (2)	CFen CQua
'Homestead' (2) 𝕐H6	IRhd
'Honey Pink' (2)	CQua
'Honeybird' (1)	CQua
'Honeybourne' (2) **new**	CQua
'Honeyorange' (2)	CQua IRhd
'Hoopoe' (8) 𝕐H6	CQua GKev
'Hope House' (2)	IRhd
'Horace' (9)	CQua GCro
'Horn of Plenty' (5)	CQua
'Hornpipe' (1)	IRhd
'Hors d'Oeuvre' (1)	CBro
'Hospodar' (2)	CQua GCro
'Hot Affair' (2)	IRhd
'Hot Gossip' (2)	CFen CQua
'Hotspur' (2)	CQua
Howick Beauty (2)	GCro
Howick's Half Nelson (2) **new**	GCro
'Hugh Town' (8)	CQua
'Hugus' (7)	CQua
'Hullabaloo' (2)	IRhd
humilis misapplied	see *N. pseudonarcissus* subsp. *pseudonarcissus* var. *humilis*
'Hummingbird' (6)	EPot NMin
'Hunting Caye' (2)	CQua
'Huntley Down' (1)	CQua
'Hyperbole' (2)	IRhd
'Ice Chimes' (5)	CQua
'Ice Dancer' (2)	CQua IRhd
'Ice Diamond' (4)	CQua
'Ice Emerald' (3)	IRhd
'Ice Follies' (2) 𝕐H6	CFen CQua EPfP GKev LAma MBri NBir SDeJ SPer
'Ice King' (4)	LRHS NBir SDeJ
'Ice Wings' (5) 𝕐H6	CAvo CBro CFen CQua ECho EPot NMin SDeJ WShi
'Idless' (1)	CQua
'Idol' (7)	CQua ECho EPot NMin
'Immaculate' (2)	CQua
'Impeccable' (2)	IRhd
'Inara' (4)	CQua
'Inca' (6)	CQua
'Inchbonnie' (2)	CQua
× ***incomparabilis*** (13)	MMuc SEND
'Independence Day' (4)	CQua
'Indian Maid' (7) 𝕐H6	CQua IRhd
'Indian Ruler' (2)	CFen
'Indora' (4)	CQua
'Inglescombe' (4)	GCro
'Inner Glow' (2)	IRhd
'Innisidgen' (8)	CQua
'Innovator' (4)	CQua IRhd
'Innuendo' (2)	IRhd
'Inny River' (1)	IRhd
'Interim' (2)	CFen CQua SDeJ
× ***intermedius*** (13)	CBro CQua NMin WAbe
§ – 'Compressus' (8)	CBro CQua
'Intrigue' (7) 𝕐H6	CQua

Name	Suppliers
'Invercassley' (3)	CQua
'Inverpolly' (2)	CQua
'Irene Copeland' (4)	CQua GCro
'Irish Affair' (2) **new**	CQua
'Irish Fire' (2)	CQua
'Irish Light' (2)	CQua
'Irish Minstrel' (2) ♀H6	CFen CQua
'Irish Mist' (2)	CQua
'Irish Rum' (2)	CQua
'Irish Trip' (7)	IRhd
'Irish Wedding' (2)	CQua
'Isabella Alice' (1) **new**	CQua
'Isambard' (4)	CQua
'Island Pride' (8)	CQua
'Ita' (2)	IRhd
'Itsy Bitsy Splitsy' (11a)	IRhd
'Itzim' (6) ♀H6	CBro CQua SBod SDeJ
'Jabberwocky' (11a) **new**	CQua
jacetanus (13)	NMin
'Jack Snipe' (6) ♀H6	CAvo CBro CQua ECho EPfP EPot ERCP GKev LAma MBri MMuc NHol SDeJ SEND WShi XEll
'Jack Wood' (11a)	CQua IRhd
'Jackadee' (2)	CQua IRhd
'Jacob Maurer' (6)	CQua
'Jake' (3)	IRhd
'Jamage' (8)	CQua
'Jamaica Inn' (4)	CQua
'Jamboree' (2)	CQua
'Jammin' (3)	IRhd
'Janelle' (3)	CQua
'Janet's Gold' (2)	IRhd
'Jantje' (11a)	CQua
'Jauno' (1)	IRhd
'Javelin' (2)	CQua
'Jeanine' (2)	CQua
'Jeannie Tangye' (2) **new**	CQua
'Jenny' (6) ♀H6	CBro CMea CQua ECho ERCP GKev LAma MBri MCot NBir SDeJ SPhx WShi
'Jenny Out' (7) ♀H6	CFen
'Jersey Lace' (2)	CQua
'Jersey Roundabout' (4)	CQua
'Jersey Star' (4)	CQua
'Jersey Torch' (4)	CQua
'Jetfire' (6) ♀H6	CQua ECho EPfP EPot ERCP GKev LAma LPot LRHS LSou MBri NHol SDeJ SPer WShi
'Jim Lad' (2)	ECho
'Jimmy Noone' (1)	CQua
'Jodi' (11b)	IRhd
'Jodi's Sister' (11a)	IRhd
'Johanna' (5)	CBro
'John Daniel' (4)	CQua
'John Dickens' (2)	CQua
'John Evelyn' (2)	GCro
'John Lanyon' (3)	CQua
'John Philip Sousa' (2)	CQua
'Johnny Dodds' (1)	CQua
'John's Delight' (3)	CQua
'Joke Fulmer' (2)	CFen
'Jolly Good' (2)	IRhd
jonquilla (13)	CBro CQua ECho EPot GKev LAma NMin WShi
- 'Flore Pleno' (4)	ECho
§ - var. ***henriquesii*** (13)	CFil CQua ECho GKev NMin
'Joppa' (7)	CQua
'Joy Bishop'	see *N. romieuxii* 'Joy Bishop'
'Joybell' (6)	CQua
'Juanita' (2)	CFen NPer SDeJ
'Jules Verne' (2)	CQua
'Julia Jane'	see *N. romieuxii* 'Julia Jane'
'Juliet Firstbrook' (2)	CQua
'Jumblie' (12) ♀H6	CBro EPfP EPot LAma LRHS MBri SDeJ
'Jumbo Gold' (1)	CTri
juncifolius Req. ex Lag.	see *N. assoanus*
'June Allyson' (2)	CFen
'June Lake' (2)	CQua IRhd
'Kabani' (9)	CQua
'Kaka Point' (2)	IRhd
'Kalimna' (1)	CQua
'Kamau' (9)	IRhd
'Kamms' (1)	CQua
'Kamura' (2)	CQua
'Kaputi Pride' (1) **new**	CQua
'Kate' (1)	IRhd
'Kate Davies' (2)	CQua
'Katherine Jenkins' (7)	CQua
'Kathy A' (5)	IRhd
'Kathy's Clown' (6)	CQua
'Katie Heath' (5)	EPfP ERCP MBri SDeJ
'Katrina Rea' (6)	CQua
'Kaydee' (6) ♀H6	CQua IFro IRhd SDeJ
'Kea' (6)	CQua
'Keats' (4)	CQua NMin
'Kebaya' (2)	CQua
'Kedron' (7)	ERCP
'Kelly Bray' (1)	CQua
'Kenellis' (10)	EPot
'Kernow' (2)	CQua
'Kidling' (7)	CQua EPot NMin
'Killara' (8)	CQua
'Killearnan' (9)	CQua
'Killigrew' (2)	CQua
'Killivose' (3)	CQua
'Kilmood' (2)	CQua
'Kilrea' (2) **new**	CQua
'Kiltonga' (2)	IRhd
'Kilworth' (2)	CQua
'Kimmeridge' (3)	CQua
'King Alfred' (1)	CQua EPfP SDeJ SEND SPer
'King Size' (11a)	CQua
'Kinglet' (7)	CQua
'King's Grove' (1)	CQua
'Kings Pipe' (2)	CQua
'Kingscourt' (1)	CFen CQua
'Kingsleigh' (1)	IRhd
'Kingsmill Lake' (2)	CQua
'Kirklington' (2)	CQua
'Kit Hill' (7)	CQua
'Kitten' (6)	CQua
'Kiwi Magic' (4)	CQua IRhd
'Kiwi Sunset' (4)	CQua IRhd
'Knight of Saint John' (2)	CFen
'Knightsbridge' (1)	CQua
'Knowing Look' (3)	IRhd
'Kokopelli' (7) ♀H6	CBro CQua NMin SDeJ
'Koomooloo' (2)	CQua
'Korora Bay' (1)	IRhd
'Koukouli' (3) **new**	CQua
'La Belle' (7)	LLHF SDeJ
'La Riante' (3)	GCro
'La Vella' (2)	CQua
'Ladies' Choice' (7)	IRhd
'Lady Alice' (7)	CQua

'Lady Ann' (2)	IRhd
'Lady Be Good' (2)	CQua IRhd
'Lady Diana' (2)	CQua IRhd
'Lady Emily' (2)	CQua
'Lady Eve' (11a)	IRhd
'Lady Godiva' (3)	GCro
'Lady Hilaria' (2)	CQua
'Lady Margaret Boscawen' (2)	CQua GCro
'Lady Marina Cowdray' (1)	CFen
'Lady Moore' (3)	GCro
'Lady Sainsbury' (2)	CFen
'Lady Serena' (9)	CQua
'Lady's Favorite' (7)	IRhd
'Lake District' (2)	IRhd
'Lake Tahoe' (2)	IRhd
'Lalique' (3)	CQua
'Lamanva' (2)	CQua
'Lamlash' (2)	IRhd
'Lanarth' (7)	GCro
'Lancaster' (3)	CFen CQua
'Landewednack Lady' (4)	CQua
'Langarth' (11a)	CQua
'Lapwing' (5)	IRhd
'Larkelly' (6)	CQua
'Larkhill' (2)	CQua
'Larkwhistle' (6)	LAma SDeJ
'Las Vegas' (1)	EPfP SDeJ
'Latchley' (2)	CQua
'Latchley Meadows' (2)	CQua
'Laughing Bird Caye' (1) **new**	CQua
'Laurelbank' (2)	IRhd
'Lauren' (3)	IRhd
'Laurens Koster' (8)	CQua
'Lava Flow' (3)	IRhd
'Lavender Lass' (6)	CQua
'Lavender Mist' (2)	CQua
'Lazy River' (1)	CQua
'Lee Moor' (1)	CQua
'Leedsii' (3) **new**	CQua
'Lemma' (3)	IRhd
'Lemon Beauty' (11b)	CQua SDeJ
'Lemon Cocktail' (1) **new**	IRhd
'Lemon Drizzle' (2)	CQua
'Lemon Drops' (5)	ECho ERCP SDeJ SPhx
'Lemon Haze' (2)	CQua
'Lemon Silk' (6)	CBro CQua ECho
'Lemon Snow' (2)	IRhd
'Lemonade' (3)	CQua
'Lennymore' (2)	CQua IRhd
'Lewis George' (1)	CQua
'Lezant' (3) **new**	CQua
'Libby' (2)	IRhd
'Liberty Bells' (5)	CQua ECho LAma MBri
'Liebeslied' (3)	CQua
'Life' (7)	CQua
'Lifeline' (1)	IRhd
'Lighthouse' (3)	CQua
'Lighthouse Reef' (1)	CQua IRhd
'Lilac Charm' (6)	CQua IRhd
'Lilac Hue' (6)	CBro
'Lilac Mist' (2)	CQua IRhd
'Lilliput' ambig.	CQua
'Lilly-May Bostock' (6)	CQua
'Lima's Green Goddess' (8)	IRhd
'Lima's Shooting Stars' (12)	IRhd
'Limbo' (2)	CQua
'Limehurst' (2)	CQua
'Limequilla' (7)	CQua IRhd
'Limpopo' (3)	IRhd
'Lindsay Joy' (2)	CQua
'Lintie' (7)	CQua
'Lisburn' (3)	IRhd
'Lisnamulligan' (3)	IRhd
'Little Alice' (4)	IRhd
'Little Beauty' (1)	CBro CQua LAma NMin
'Little Dancer' (1)	CBro CQua
'Little Dorr' (4)	IRhd
'Little Flik' (12)	CQua ECho NMin
'Little Jewel' (3)	CQua
'Little Karoo' (3)	IRhd
'Little Meg' (7)	CQua
'Little Rosie' (2)	IRhd
'Little Rusky' (7)	CBro CQua NMin
'Little Sentry' (7)	CBro CQua NMin
'Little Soldier' (10)	CQua NMin
'Little Spell' (1)	ECho
'Little Tyke' (2)	CQua
'Little Witch' (6)	CAvo CBro CQua GCro GKev LAma SDeJ SPhx WShi
'Littlefield' (7)	CQua
'Livelands' (1)	CQua
'Liverpool Festival' (2)	CQua
'Lizard Beacon' (2) **new**	CQua
'Lobularis'	see *N. lobularis* (Haw.) Schult. & Schult. f.
lobularis misapplied	see *N. nanus*
§ ***lobularis*** (Haw.) Schult. & Schult. f.	CAby CAvo CBro CQua CTca CTri ECho EPot ERCP GKev MBri SDeJ SPer WBor
'Loch Alsh' (3)	CQua IRhd
'Loch Assynt' (3)	CQua
'Loch Brora' (2)	CQua
'Loch Coire' (3)	CQua
'Loch Fada' (2)	CQua
'Loch Fyne' (2) **new**	GCro
'Loch Hope' (2)	CQua
'Loch Leven' (2)	CQua
'Loch Loyal' (2)	CQua
'Loch Lundie' (2)	CQua
'Loch Maberry' (2)	CQua
'Loch Naver' (2)	CQua
'Loch Owskeich' (2)	CFen CQua
'Logan Rock' (7)	CQua
'Longitude' (1)	IRhd
'Lord Grey' (1) **new**	GCro
'Lorikeet' (1)	CQua
'Lothario' (2)	LAma MBri
'Lough Gowna' (1)	IRhd
'Louise de Coligny' (2)	ERCP
'Love Call' (11a)	CQua
'Loveday' (2)	CFen
'Loveny' (2)	CQua
'Lowdham' (2) **new**	CQua
'Lowin' (1)	CFen
'Lubaantun' (1)	CQua
'Lucciola Inn' (3) **new**	CQua
'Lucie Nottingham' (4) **new**	CQua
'Lucifer' (2)	CAvo CQua WShi
'Lucky Chance' (11a)	IRhd
'Lunar Orbit' (4) **new**	CQua
'Lundy Light' (2)	CQua
'Lutana' (2)	IRhd
'Lyme Bay' (1)	IRhd
'Lynher' (2)	CQua

'Lyrebird' (3)	CQua
'Lyric' (9)	CQua
'Lysander' (2)	CFen CQua
'Madam Speaker' (4)	CQua
'Madame Plemp' (1)	GCro
'Madison' (4)	CQua
'Magic Moment' (3)	CQua
'Magician' (2)	CQua
'Magna Carta' (2)	CQua IRhd
'Magnet' (1)	LAma NPer
'Magnificence' (1)	CFen CQua GCro
'Majestic Gold' (1)	CQua
'Majestic Star' (1)	CQua
'Maker's Mark' (1)	CQua
'Mako' (1) **new**	CQua
'Mallee' (11a) ♀H6	IRhd
'Malpas' (3)	CQua
'Malvern City' (1)	CFen CQua
'Mamma Mia' (4)	IRhd
'Manaccan' (1)	CQua
'Mangaweka' (6)	CQua
'Manly' (4) ♀H6	CQua ERCP
'Mantle' (2)	CQua
'Marabou' (4)	CQua
'Margaret Herbert' (7)	CQua
'Maria Pia' (11a)	IRhd
'Marie Curie Diamond' (7) ♀H6	CFen CQua
'Marie-José' (11b)	IRhd
'Marieke' (1)	LAma SDeJ
'Marilyn Anne' (2)	CQua
'Marjorie Hine' (2)	CQua
'Marjorie Treveal' (4)	CQua
'Marlborough' (2)	CQua
'Marlborough Freya' (2)	CQua
'Marshfire' (2)	CQua
'Martha Washington' (8)	CQua
'Martinette' (8)	CFen CQua CTca SDeJ
'Martinsville' (8)	CQua
'Mary Copeland' (4)	CQua
'Mary Kate' (2)	CQua
'Mary Lou' (6)	IRhd
'Mary Plumstead' (5)	NMin
'Mary Rosina' (4)	CQua
'Mary Veronica' (3)	CQua
'Marzo' (7)	IRhd
'Masked Light' (2)	CFen
'Matador' (8)	CFen CQua IRhd
'Matangi' (1) **new**	CQua
'Mawla' (1)	CQua
'Max' (11a)	CQua
'Maximus Superbus' (1)	CQua
'May Queen' (2) **new**	CQua
'Maya Dynasty' (2)	CQua
'Mayor's Choice' (11a)	CQua
'Maywood' (11a)	CQua
'Mazzard' (4)	CQua
'Media Girl' (2)	IRhd
× ***medioluteus*** (13)	CBro CQua GCro NMin
'Medusa' (8)	CQua GCro
'Melancholy' (1)	CQua
'Melbury' (2)	CQua
'Meldrum' (1)	CQua
'Melen' (2)	CFen
'Memento' (1)	CQua
'Menabilly' (4)	CQua
'Mên-an-Tol' (2)	CQua
'Menehay' (11a) ♀H6	CQua
'Mer d'Or' (1)	IRhd
'Mereworth' (2)	CQua
'Merlin' (3) ♀H6	CFen CQua LAma SDeJ
'Merry Bells' (5)	CQua
'Merrymeet' (4)	CQua
'Mersing' (3)	CQua
'Merthan' (9)	CQua
'Michaels Gold' (2)	CQua
'Midas Touch' (1)	CQua
'Midget'	see *N. nanus* 'Midget'
'Midnight' (3)	IRhd
Midtown Aerolite (2)	GCro
Midtown Alfie (1)	GCro
Midtown Autocrat (2)	GCro
Midtown Beauty (2) **new**	GCro
Midtown Brigadier (2)	GCro
Midtown Noble (1)	GCro
Midtown Torch (2)	GCro
Midtown Twink (4) **new**	GCro
'Mike Pollock' (8)	CFen CQua
'Milan' (9)	CQua
'Millennium Sunrise' (2)	CQua
'Millennium Sunset' (2)	CQua
'Milly's Magic' (2)	CQua
Minicycla Group (6)	ECho
minimus misapplied	see *N. asturiensis*
'Minnow' (8) ♀H4	CAvo CBro CFen CHid CQua ECho EPfP EPot ERCP GKev LAma LPot LRHS MBri NBir SDeJ SPer
minor (13)	CBro CQua ECha ECho EPot GCro NMin WShi
- 'Douglasbank' (1)	EPot LLHF NMin
- 'Little Gem' (1) ♀H6	CBro CQua CTri LAma SDeJ SPhx
- var. ***pumilus*** 'Plenus'	see *N.* 'Rip van Winkle'
- Ulster form (13)	IBlr
'Mint Julep' (3) ♀H6	SDeJ
'Minute Waltz' (6)	CQua
'Mirar' (2)	CQua
'Misquote' (1)	CQua
'Miss Klein' (7)	LLHF NMin
'Miss Muffit' (1)	CQua
'Miss Primm' (2)	IRhd
'Mission Bells' (5) ♀H6	CQua IRhd NMin
'Mission Impossible' (11a)	CQua
'Mist of Avalon' (4)	CQua
'Misty Glen' (2) ♀H6	CQua EPfP SDeJ
'Mite' (6) ♀H6	CAvo CBro CQua ECho EPot LAma LLHF NMin
'Mithrel' (11a)	CQua
'Mitimoto' (10) **new**	ECho
'Mitylene' (2)	GCro
'Mitzy' (6)	LLHF NMin
'Modern Art' (2)	CQua SDeJ
'Mondragon' (11a)	CQua
'Mongleath' (2)	CQua
'Monks Wood' (1)	CQua
'Monksilver' (3)	CQua
'Montclair' (2)	CQua
'Montego' (3)	CQua
'Monterrico' (4)	CFen
'Montroig' (2)	IRhd
'Moon Dream' (1)	CQua
'Moon Ranger' (3)	CQua
'Moon Shadow' (3)	CQua IRhd
'Moon Valley' (2)	IRhd
'Moonstruck' (1)	CQua
'Morab' (1)	CQua
'Moralee' (4)	IRhd

'Morval' (2)	CQua
moschatus (13) ♀H6	CBro CQua ECho EPot GCro NMin WShi
'Mount Fuji' (2)	CQua
'Mount Hood' (1) ♀H6	EPfP GKev LAma LRHS NBir SDeJ SPer
'Movie Star' (2)	IRhd
'Mowser' (7)	CQua
'Mr Sweet' (2) **new**	CQua
'Mrs Langtry' (2)	WShi
'Mrs R.O. Backhouse' (2)	CQua WShi
'Mullion' (3)	CQua
'Mulroy Bay' (1)	CQua IRhd
'Murlough' (9)	CQua
'Muscadet' (2)	CFen CQua
'My Story' (4) ♀H6	SDeJ
'My Sunshine' (2)	CQua
'My Sweetheart' (3)	CQua
'My Word' (2)	CFen
'Mystic' (3)	CQua
'Nacre' (2)	IRhd
'Naivasha' (2)	IRhd
'Namraj' (2)	CQua
'Nancegollan' (7)	CBro CQua
'Nangiles' (4)	CQua
'Nanpee' (7)	CQua
'Nanpusker' (2)	CFen
'Nansidwell' (2)	CQua
'Nanstallon' (1)	CQua
§ ***nanus*** (13)	CQua CWCL ECho GBuc
§ - 'Midget' (1)	CBro CQua ECho ERCP GKev LAma SKHP
'Nare Celebration' (2)	CFen
'Narrative' (2)	IRhd
'Navarre' Buckland (2)	CFil
'Nederburg' (1)	IRhd
'Nelly' ambig.	CQua
Nelsonii Group late-flowering clone (2)	GCro
'Neon' (2) **new**	LRHS
'Neon Light' (2)	CQua
'Nessa' (7)	CQua
'Nether Barr' (2)	CQua
nevadensis (13)	SKHP
'New Hope' (3)	CQua
'New Life' (3)	CQua
'New Paris' (2)	CQua
'New Penny' (3)	CQua IRhd
'New World' (2)	CQua
'New-Baby' (7)	CQua NMin SDeJ
'Newcastle' (1)	CQua
'Newcomer' (3)	CQua
'Nickelodeon' (8) **new**	CQua
'Night Music' (4)	CQua IRhd
'Nightcap' (1)	CQua
'Niphetos' (2) **new**	GCro
'Nirvana' (7)	CBro
'Niveth' (5)	CFen CQua GCro
§ ***nobilis*** (13)	CQua EPot
- var. ***leonensis*** (13)	CFil
- var. ***nobilis*** (13)	NMin
'Nonchalant' (3)	CQua IRhd
'Norma Jean' (2)	CQua
'North Liberty' (2)	CQua
'North Rim' (2)	CQua
'Noss Mayo' (6)	CQua
'Notre Dame' (2) ♀H6	CQua IRhd
'Nouvelle' (3)	CQua
'Nuage' (2)	CFen
'Numen Rose' (2)	IRhd
Nylon Group (10)	CBro ECho EPot EPri
- yellow-flowered (10)	ECho
'Nynja' (2) **new**	CQua
'Oakwood Sprite' (1)	NMin
'Obdam' (4)	SDeJ
'Obsession' (2)	CQua
obvallaris (13) ♀H6	CAvo CBro CFen CQua CTca ECho EPfP EPot ERCP GKev MBri MMuc NMin SDeJ SPer SPhx WHer WShi
'Ocarino' (4)	CFen CQua
'Ocean Blue' (2)	IRhd
'Odd Job' (12)	CQua
× ***odorus*** (13)	WShi
- 'Plenus' (4)	ERCP
'Ohau Lights' (1)	CQua
'Ohau Splendour' (1) **new**	CQua
old pheasant's eye	see *N. poeticus* var. *recurvus*
'Oliver Cromwell' (1) **new**	CQua
'Olympic Medal' (1) **new**	IRhd
'Ombersley' (1)	CQua
'Oops' (2)	IRhd
'Orange Phoenix' (4)	CQua WShi
'Orange Supreme' (2) **new**	CQua
'Orange Tint' (2)	CQua
'Orange Walk' (3)	CQua IRhd
'Orangery' (11a)	LAma SDeJ
'Orbital Pink' (3)	IRhd
'Orchard Place' (3)	CQua
'Oregon Bells' (7)	CQua
'Oregon Pioneer' (2)	IRhd
'Orkney' (2)	CQua
'Ormeau' (2)	CQua
'Ornatus' (9) **new**	GCro
'Ornatus Maximus' (9)	NMin
'Oryx' (7) ♀H6	CQua
'Osceola' (2)	CQua
'Osmington' (2)	CQua
'Ouma' (1)	CQua
'Outline' (2)	IRhd
'Ouzel' (6)	CQua
'Owyhee' (2)	CQua
'Oxford Gold' (10)	CQua
'Oykel' (3)	CQua
'Oz' (12)	LLHF
pachybolbus (13)	CQua ECho NMin
'Pacific Coast' (8) ♀H6	CQua LLHF NMin
'Pacific Mist' (11a)	CQua
'Pacific Rim' (2)	CQua IRhd
'Pacific Waves' (3) **new**	CQua
'Painted Desert' (3)	CQua
'Palace Pink' (2)	IRhd
'Pale Sunlight' (2)	CQua
pallidiflorus (13)	ECha
'Palmares' (11a)	CQua SDeJ
'Pamela Hubble' (2)	CQua
'Pamela Joan' (2)	CQua
'Pampaluna' (11a)	CQua IRhd
'Panache' (1)	CQua
panizzianus (13)	CFil CQua WPGP
'Panorama Pink' (3)	IRhd
'Paper White'	see *N. papyraceus*
'Paper White Grandiflorus' (8)	CQua EPfP MBri SDeJ SPer
'Papillon Blanc' (11b)	ERCP
'Papua' (4)	CFen CQua
§ ***papyraceus*** (13)	CFil CQua NMin

'Paradigm' (4)	IRhd
'Paramour' (4)	IRhd
'Parcpat' (7)	CBro CQua
'Parisienne' (11a)	SDeJ
'Park Springs' (3)	CQua
'Parkdene' (2)	CQua
'Partisan' (2)	IRhd
'Party Time' (2)	IRhd
'Passionale' (2) ♀H6	CQua EPfP LAma NBir
'Pastiche' (2)	CQua
'Pat Brown' (2)	CQua
'Patabundy' (2)	CQua
'Pathos' (3)	IRhd
'Patois' (9)	CBro IRhd
'Patrick Hacket' (1) ♀H6	CQua
'Paula Cottell' (3)	NMin
'Pay Day' (1)	CQua
'Peach Prince' (4)	CQua
'Pearl Wedding' (3)	CQua
'Pearlshell' (11a)	CQua
'Peeping Tom' (6) ♀H6	CBro ECho ERCP LAma SDeJ SRms
'Peggy's Gift' (3)	IRhd
'Pelynt' (3)	CQua
'Pemboa' (1)	CQua
'Pencrebar' (4)	CAvo CQua EPot EShb LAma LRHS NHol NMin SDeJ WShi
'Pend Oreille' (3)	CQua
'Pengarth' (2)	CQua
'Penjerrick' (9)	CQua
'Penkivel' (2) ♀H6	CQua
'Pennance Mill' (2)	CQua
'Pennine Way' (1)	CQua
'Penny Perowne' (7)	CQua
'Pennyfield' (2)	CQua
'Penpol' (7)	CBro CFen CQua
'Penril' (6)	CQua
'Penselwood' (2) **new**	CQua
'Penstraze' (7)	CQua
'Pentewan' (2)	CQua GCro
'Pentille' (1)	CQua
'Pentire' (11a)	CQua
'Penvale' (7)	CQua
'Peppercorn' (6)	CQua
'Pequenita' (7)	NMin
'Percuil' (6)	CQua
'Perdredda' (3)	CQua
perez-chiscanoi (13)	CFil SKHP WPGP
'Perfect Peace' (2) **new**	CQua
'Perimeter' (3)	CQua
'Peripheral Pink' (2)	CQua
'Perky' 1964 (6)	NMin
'Perlax' (11a)	CQua
'Perpetuation' (7)	CQua
'Personable' (2)	CQua
'Petanca' (5)	IRhd
'Petit Four' (4)	LAma SDeJ
'Petrel' (5)	CBro CQua ECho EPot ERCP GKev NMin SDeJ SPhx WShi
'Phantom' (11a)	CQua
'Phil's Gift' (1)	CQua
'Phinda' (2)	IRhd
'Phoenician' (2)	CQua
'Picatou' (3)	IRhd
'Picket Post' (3) **new**	IRhd
'Picoblanco' (2)	CBro CQua NMin
'Pidget' (9) **new**	CQua
'Pigeon' (2)	CQua
'Pineapple Prince' (2) ♀H6	CQua
'Pink Angel' (7)	CQua
'Pink Champagne' (4)	CQua
'Pink Charm' (2)	CQua SDeJ
'Pink China' (2)	CQua
'Pink Clover' (2)	CQua
'Pink Evening' (2)	CQua
'Pink Formal' (11a)	CQua
'Pink Gilt' (2)	IRhd
'Pink Glacier' (11a)	CQua
'Pink Holly' (11a)	CQua
'Pink Ice' (2)	CQua
'Pink Pageant' (4)	CQua IRhd
'Pink Paradise' (4)	CQua IRhd
'Pink Parasol' (1)	SDeJ
'Pink Perry' (2)	IRhd
'Pink Silk' (1)	CQua SDeJ
'Pink Smiles' (2)	CFen
'Pink Step' (7) **new**	CQua
'Pink Surprise' (2)	CQua
'Pink Tango' (11a)	CQua
'Pinza' (2) ♀H6	CQua SDeJ
'Pipe Major' (2)	CQua
'Pipers Barn' (7)	CQua
'Piper's End' (3)	CQua
'Piper's Gold' (1)	CQua
'Pipestone' (2)	CQua
'Pipit' (7)	CAvo CBro CFen CQua ECho EPfP EPot ERCP GKev LAma LPot LRHS MBri NBir NMin SDeJ WShi
'Piraeus' (4)	IRhd
'Pismo Beach' (2)	CQua
'Pitchroy' (2)	CQua
'Pitt's Diamond' (3)	CQua
'Pixie's Sister' (7) ♀H6	CQua LLHF NMin
'Pledge' (1)	NMin
'Plymouth Hoe' (1) **new**	CQua
§ ***poeticus*** var. ***hellenicus*** (13)	CBro CQua GCro IRhd
– old pheasant's eye	see *N. poeticus* var. *recurvus*
– var. ***physaloides*** (13)	CFil CQua ECho
– 'Plenus' misapplied	see *N. poeticus* 'Spalding Double White', *N.* 'Tamar Double White'
§ – 'Plenus' ambig. (4)	CBro CQua ERCP GQui SDeJ WShi
§ – var. ***recurvus*** (13) ♀H6	CAvo CBro CFen CQua CTca ECho EPfP ERCP GKev LAma LRHS MMuc NBir SDeJ SEND SPhx WShi
§ – 'Spalding Double White' (4) **new**	CQua
– white-flowered (13)	SDeJ
'Poet's Dream' (2) **new**	CQua
'Poet's Way' (9)	CQua IRhd
'Pol Crocan' (2)	CQua IRhd
'Pol Dornie' (2)	CQua
'Pol Voulin' (2)	CQua IRhd
'Polar Ice' (3)	CFen CQua ECho LAma SDeJ
'Polar Morn' (3)	CQua
'Polgoon' (2)	CFen
'Polgooth' (2)	CQua
'Polly's Pearl' (8)	CQua
'Polmenor' (2) **new**	CQua
'Polnesk' (7)	GCro
'Polonaise' (2)	CQua
'Polruan' (7)	CQua
'Poltreen' (4)	CQua
'Polwheveral' (2)	CQua
'Pomona' (3)	GCro
'Pooka' (3)	CQua IRhd
'Popeye' (4)	EPfP

'Poppy's Choice' (4) CQua
'Pops Legacy' (1) CQua
'Port Noo' (3) IRhd
'Port Patrick' (3) CQua
'Porthchapel' (7) CQua
'Portloe Bay' (3) CQua
'Portrait' (2) CQua
'Portrush' (3) CQua
'Post Horn' (6) CFen
'Potential' (1) CQua
'Powerstock' (2) IRhd
'Praecox' (9) CBro
'Prairie Fire' (3) CQua IRhd
'Pratincole' (3) IRhd
'Preamble' (1) CQua
I 'Precocious' (2) ♀H6 CQua SDeJ
'Predator' (1) IRhd
'Premiere' (2) CQua IRhd
'Presidential Pink' (2) CQua
'Pretty Baby' (3) CQua
'Pride of Cornwall' (8) CQua
'Primegold' (2) CFen
'Primrose Beauty' (4) CFen CQua
'Princeps' (1) CQua GCro
'Princess Alexandra' (6) CFen
'Princess Diana' (6) CFen
'Princess Zaide' (3) CQua
'Princeton' (3) CQua
'Printal' (11a) SDeJ
'Priorsford' (2) IRhd
'Prism' (2) CQua
'Problem Child' (2) IRhd
'Probus' (1) CQua
'Professor Einstein' (2) EPfP SDeJ
'Prologue' (1) CQua
'Prototype' (6) IRhd
'Proud Fellow' (1) IRhd
'Proverbial Pink' (2) IRhd
'Prussia Cove' (2) CQua
pseudonarcissus (13) CHab CQua CRow GCro MMuc SEND WHer WShi
- subsp. ***eugeniae*** see *N. eugeniae*
- subsp. ***nobilis*** see *N. nobilis*
- subsp. ***pseudonarcissus*** double-flowered (4) CQua
§ - - var. ***humilis*** (13) ECho
'Ptolemy' (1) CFen
'Pueblo' (7) CQua SDeJ WRHF
'Pukenui' (4) CQua
'Pulsar' (2) IRhd
pumilus ambig. (13) CQua ECho LLHF NMin SDeJ
'Punchline' (7) ♀H6 CQua
'Punter' (2) CQua IRhd
'Puppet' (5) CQua
'Purbeck' (3) ♀H6 CQua IRhd
'Quail' (7) ♀H6 CFen CQua CTca EPfP GKev LAma LSou MBri SDeJ
'Quasar' (2) ♀H6 CQua
Queen Anne's double daffodil see *N.* 'Eystettensis'
'Queen Fiona' (1) IRhd
'Queen Juliana' (1) CQua
'Queen Mum' (1) CQua
'Queen of Spain' (5) CAvo CQua NMin
'Queen of the North' (3) GCro
'Queen's Guard' (1) IRhd
'Queensland' (2) CFen
'Quick Step' (7) CQua
'Quiet Day' (2) CQua
'Quiet Hero' (3) IRhd
'Quiet Magic' (2) **new** IRhd
'Quiet Man' (1) IRhd
'Radiant Gem' (8) CQua
radiiflorus (13) EPot
- var. ***poetarum*** (13) CBro CQua
- var. ***radiiflorus*** (13) GCro
'Radjel' (4) CQua
'Raeburn' (9) **new** GCro
'Rainbow' (2) ♀H6 CQua SPer
'Rame Head' (1) CQua
'Rameses' (2) CQua
'Ransom' (4) IRhd
'Rapid Stride' (6) IRhd
'Rapture' (6) ♀H6 CAby CBro CQua ERCP IRhd MBri NMin WShi
'Rashee' (1) CQua
'Raspberry Ring' (2) CQua
'Rathowen Gold' (1) CQua
'Ravenhill' (3) CQua
'Rebekah' (4) CQua
'Recital' (2) CQua
'Red Devon' (2) CFen SDeJ
'Red Era' (3) CQua
'Red Legend' (2) CQua
'Red Lips' (2) CQua
'Red Marvel' (3) CFen
'Red Reed' (1) IRhd
'Red Snapper' (3) **new** CQua
'Red Socks' (6) CQua
'Red Spartan' (2) CQua
'Refrain' (2) CQua
'Regal Bliss' (2) CQua
'Regeneration' (7) **new** NMin
'Reggae' (6) ♀H6 CBro CQua SDeJ
'Rembrandt' (1) CFen CQua
'Rendezvous Caye' (2) CQua
'Renovator' (1) **new** CQua
'Repertoire' (3) IRhd
'Replete' (4) CQua
requienii see *N. assoanus*
'Resistasol' (1) IRhd
'Resolute' (2) GCro
'Reverse Image' (11a) CQua
'Rheban Red' (2) IRhd
'Ribald' (2) IRhd
'Ridgecrest' (3) CQua IRhd
rifanus see *N. romieuxii* subsp. *romieuxii* var. *rifanus*
'Right Stuff' (6) NMin
'Rijnveld's Early Sensation' (1) ♀H6 CAvo CBro CFen CMea CQua ECha ERCP SDeJ
'Rikki' (7) CBro CQua NMin
'Rima' (1) CQua
'Rimmon' (3) CQua
'Rimski' (2) IRhd
'Ring Fence' (3) IRhd
'Ring Flash' (2) IRhd
'Ringhaddy' (3) IRhd
'Ringing Bells' (5) CQua
'Ringleader' (2) CQua
'Ringmaster' (2) CQua
'Ringmer' (3) CQua
'Rio Bravo' (2) IRhd
'Rio Gusto' (2) IRhd
'Rio Lobo' (2) IRhd
'Rio Rondo' (2) CQua IRhd
'Rio Rouge' (2) IRhd

	Name	Suppliers
§	'Rip van Winkle' (4)	CAby CBro CFen CQua CTca EPfP EPot ERCP LAma LRHS MBri NHol SDeJ WShi
	'Rippling Waters' (5)	CQua LAma
	'Rising Star' (7) ♀H6	IRhd
	'Ristin' (1)	CQua
	'Rival' (6)	CQua
	'River Dance' (2)	IRhd
	'River Queen' (2)	CQua IRhd
	'Roberta' (1)	CFen
	'Roberta Watrous' (7)	IRhd
	'Robin Reade' (2) **new**	CQua
	'Rock Creek' (3)	IRhd
	'Rockall' (3)	CQua
	'Rocoza' (2)	IRhd
	'Roger' (6)	CQua
	'Rogue' (2)	CBro
	'Rolling Prairie' (2) **new**	CQua
	'Romance' (2) ♀H6	LAma
§	'Romanus' (4)	CQua
	romieuxii (13) ♀H4	CBro ECho EPri GCal ITim LRHS WCot
	- JCA 805	CFil EPot
	- SF 370	WCot
	- subsp. ***albidus*** (13)	ECho
§	- - var. ***zaianicus*** (13)	ECho
§	- 'Atlas Gold' (10)	ECho EPot
§	- 'Joy Bishop' (10)	ECho
§	- 'Julia Jane' (10)	CQua ECho EPot GKev NMin
§	- subsp. ***romieuxii*** var. ***mesatlanticus*** (13)	ECho
§	- - var. ***rifanus*** (13)	ECho GKev
§	- 'Treble Chance' (10)	EPot
	'Rory's Glen' (2)	CQua
	'Rosannor Gold' (11a)	CQua
	'Roscarrick' (6)	CQua
	'Rose Noble' (2)	CFen
	'Rose of May' (4)	CQua WShi
	'Rose of Tralee' (2)	CQua
	'Rose Royale' (2)	CQua
	'Rose Sheen' (2)	CQua
	'Rose Umber' (2)	IRhd
	'Rose Villa' (2)	CQua
	'Rosemary Pearson' (2) **new**	CQua
	'Rosemerryn' (2)	CQua
	'Rosemoor Gold' (7) ♀H6	CBro CFen CQua
	'Rosemullion' (4)	CQua
	'Rosevine' (3)	CQua
	'Rosy Sunrise' (2)	CQua
	'Rosy Wonder' (2)	CQua
	'Round Oak' (1)	CQua
	'Roxton' (4)	IRhd
	'Royal Armour' (1)	CFen
	'Royal Connection' (8)	CQua
	'Royal Marine' (2)	CQua IRhd
	'Royal Princess' (3)	CQua ERCP
	'Royal Regiment' (2)	CQua
	'Ruby Red' (2)	CQua
	'Ruby Rose' (4)	IRhd
	'Ruby Wedding' (2)	IRhd
	'Rubythroat' (2)	CQua
	'Ruddy Duck' (2)	IRhd
	'Ruddy Rascal' (2)	IRhd
	'Rugulosus' (7)	CBro CQua ECho
*	'Rugulosus Flore Pleno' (d)	ECho
	'Runkerry' (4)	IRhd
	rupicola (13)	CBro CQua CWCL ECho EPot GKev LLHF NMin NSla SPhx WCot
§	- subsp. ***watieri*** (13)	CBro CQua ECho EPot LLHF NMin
	'Rustom Pasha' (2)	CQua GCro
	'Rytha' (2)	CQua
	'Saberwing' (5)	CQua
	'Sabine Hay' (3)	CQua EPot ERCP
	'Sabrosa' (7) ♀H4	CBro CQua LLHF LRHS NMin
	'Sacajawea' (2)	CFen
	'Sacré Coeur' (2)	IRhd
	'Sagana' (9)	CQua
	'Sailboat' (7) ♀H6	CQua EPfP MBri SPer
	'Saint Agnes' (8)	CQua
	'Saint Budock' (1)	CQua
	'Saint Day' (5)	CQua
	'Saint Dilpe' (2)	CQua
	'Saint Keverne' (2) ♀H6	CFen CQua SDeJ
	'Saint Keyne' (8)	CQua
	'Saint Patrick's Day' (2)	CFen CQua LAma SDeJ
	'Saint Peter' (4)	CFen CQua
	'Saint Petroc' (9)	CQua
	'Saint Piran' (7)	CQua
	'Salakee' (2)	CQua
	'Salcey Forest' (1)	CQua
	'Salmon Trout' (2)	CQua
	'Salome' (2) ♀H6	CQua LAma LRHS NBir NPer SDeJ
	'Salute' (2)	CQua
	'Samantha' (4)	CQua
	'Samsara' (3)	IRhd
	'Sandra's Diamond' (3) **new**	CQua
	'Sandycove' (2)	CQua IRhd
	'Sandymount' (2)	CQua
	'Sarah' (2)	CFen
	'Sarah Dear' (2)	CQua
	'Sarah Markillie' (11a)	CQua
	'Sarchedon' (9)	GCro
	'Sargeant's Caye' (1)	CQua IRhd
	'Satchmo' (1)	CQua
	'Satin Blanc' (7)	IRhd
	'Saturn' (3)	CQua
	'Savoir Faire' (2)	IRhd
	'Saxby' (11a) **new**	CQua
	scaberulus (13)	ECho EPot
	'Scarlet Chord' (2)	CQua
	'Scarlet Elegance' (2)	CQua
	'Scarlet Gem' (8)	SDeJ
	'Scarlet Tanager' (2)	IRhd
	'Scarlett O'Hara' (2)	CFen
	'Scented Breeze' (2)	IRhd
	'Scilly Spring' (8)	CAvo
	'Scilly White' (8)	CFen CQua
	'Scorrier' (2)	CQua
	'Scrumpy' (2)	CQua
	'Sea Dream' (3)	CQua
	'Sea Gift' (7)	CBro
	'Sea Green' (9)	CQua
	'Sea Legend' (2)	CQua
	'Sea Moon' (2) **new**	IRhd
	'Sea Princess' (3)	CQua SDeJ
	'Sea Rose' (2) **new**	CQua
	'Sea Shanty' (2)	IRhd
	'Seagull' (3)	CAvo CQua GCro LAma WShi
	'Sealing Wax' (2)	CFen CQua
	'Season's Greetings' (7) **new**	IRhd
	'Segovia' (3) ♀H6	CBro CQua EPot LAma NMin SDeJ
	'Sempre Avanti' (2)	LAma SDeJ
	'Seraglio' (3)	CQua
	'Serena Beach' (4)	IRhd
	'Serena Lodge' (4) ♀H6	CQua IRhd
	serotinus (13)	ECho EPot GKev

'Sextant' (6)	CQua
'Shangani' (2)	IRhd
'Sheelagh Rowan' (2)	CQua IRhd
'Sheer Joy' (6)	CQua
'Shepherd's Hey' (7)	CQua SDeJ
'Sherborne' (4) 🏆H6	CQua
'Sherpa' (1)	CQua IRhd
'Sheskin' (2)	IRhd
'Shindig' (2)	IRhd
'Shining Light' (2)	CQua
'Shockwave' (2)	CQua
'Shortcake' (2)	CQua
'Shrimp Boat' (11a)	IRhd
'Sidley' (3)	CQua IRhd
'Sidney Torch' (2)	CFen
'Signet Ring' (3)	IRhd
'Signorina' (2)	IRhd
'Silent Valley' (1)	CQua IRhd
'Silk Cut' (2)	CQua
'Silkwood' (3)	CQua IRhd
'Silver Bells' (5)	CQua IRhd
'Silver Chimes' (8)	CAvo CBro CFen CQua CTca ECho EPfP LAma NBir SDeJ
'Silver Convention' (1)	CQua
'Silver Crystal' (3)	CQua IRhd
'Silver Hill' (2) **new**	CQua
'Silver Kiwi' (2)	CQua
'Silver Minx' (1)	CQua
'Silver Moon' (2)	CFen
'Silver Plate' (11a)	CQua
'Silver Sabre' (2)	IRhd
'Silver Shell' (11a)	CQua
'Silver Smiles' (7)	SPhx
'Silver Surf' (2)	CQua IRhd
'Silversmith' (2)	CQua
'Silverthorne' (3)	CQua
'Silverwood' (3)	CQua IRhd
'Singing Pub' (3)	IRhd
'Sinopel' (3)	LAma SDeJ
'Sir Samuel' (2)	CQua
'Sir Watkin' (2)	CQua GCro
'Sir Winston Churchill' (4) 🏆H6	CQua EPfP LAma SDeJ SPer
'Sirius' (2)	GCro
'Sissy' (6)	CQua
'Skerry' (2)	CQua
'Skilliwidden' (2) 🏆H6	CQua
'Skookum' (3)	CQua
'Skywalker' (2)	IRhd
'Slieveboy' (1)	CQua
'Slipstream' (6)	IRhd
'Small Fry' (1)	CQua
'Small Talk' (1) 🏆H6	CQua LLHF NMin
'Smokey Bear' (4)	CQua
'Smooth Sails' (3)	CQua
'Snipe' (6)	CAvo CQua NMin WShi
'Snoopie' (6)	CQua
'Snow Bunting' (7)	CBro
'Snowcrest' (3)	CQua
'Snowshill' (2)	CQua
'So Sweet' (3) **new**	CQua
'Soft Focus' (2)	IRhd
'Solar System' (3)	IRhd
'Solar Tan' (3)	CQua
'Soleil d'Or' (8)	CQua
'Solera' (2)	IRhd
'Solferique' (2)	CQua
'Soloist' (2)	IRhd
'Solveig's Song' (12)	WAbe
'Sonata' (9)	CQua
'Songket' (2)	CQua
'Sophie Girl' (2)	CQua
'Sophie's Choice' (4)	CAvo
'Soprano' (2)	CQua IRhd
'Sorcerer' (3)	CQua
'South Street' (2)	CQua
'Southease' (2)	CQua
'Southern Gem' (2)	GCro
'Spaniards Inn' (4)	CQua
'Sparkling Tarts' (8)	CQua
'Sparnon' (11a)	CQua
'Sparrow' (6)	CQua
'Spartan Gold' (2)	IRhd
'Special Envoy' (2)	CQua
'Speenogue' (1)	IRhd
'Spellbinder' (1)	CQua SDeJ
'Spencer Tracy' (2)	CFen CQua
'Sperrin Gold' (1)	IRhd
'Spin Doctor' (3)	IRhd
'Spindletop' (3) 🏆H6	IRhd
'Spirit of Rame' (3)	CQua
'Split Vote' (11a)	IRhd
'Spoirot' (10) 🏆H6	CAby ECho ERCP LEdu SDeJ
'Sportsman' (2)	CQua
'Spring Dawn' (2)	CQua EPfP
'Spring Morn' (2)	CQua IRhd
'Spun Honey' (4)	CQua
'Stadium' (2)	CFen LAma
'Stainless' (2)	SPhx
'Standard Value' (1)	CFen
'Stann Creek' (1)	CQua
'Stanway' (3)	CQua
'Star Glow' (2)	CQua
'Star Quality' (3)	IRhd
'Starfire' (7)	CQua
'State Express' (2)	CQua IRhd
'Statue' (2)	CFen
'Steenbok' (3)	IRhd
'Stella' (2)	GCro WShi
'Stellar Glow' (3)	IRhd
'Stenalees' (6)	CQua
'Step Child' (6)	CQua
'Step Forward' (7)	CQua
'Steren' (7) **new**	CQua
'Steve's Favorite' (2)	CQua
'Stilton' (9)	CQua
'Stinger' (2)	CQua
'Stint' (5) 🏆H6	CQua SDeJ
'Stocken' (7)	CBro CQua ECho EPri NMin WAbe
'Stoke Charity' (2)	CFen CQua
'Stoke Doyle' (2)	CQua
'Stormy Weather' (1)	CQua
'Stratosphere' (7) 🏆H6	CQua NMin SDeJ
'Strines' (2) 🏆H6	CQua
'Suave' (3)	CQua
'Subtle Shades' (2)	IRhd
'Sugar and Spice' (3)	CQua
'Sugar Bird' (2)	IRhd
'Sugar Cups' (8)	CQua
'Sugar Loaf' (4)	CQua
'Sugar Rose' (6) **new**	CQua
'Sugarbush' (7)	WShi
'Suisgill' (4)	CQua
'Sukey' (6)	CQua
§ 'Sulphur Phoenix' (4)	CQua WShi
Sulphur Star (2)	GCro

Name	Suppliers
'Summer Solstice' (3)	IRhd
'Sumo Jewel' (6)	CQua
'Sun Disc' (7) ♀H6	CBro CFen CQua CTri ECho GKev LAma MBri NMin SBod SDeJ WShi
'Sunday Chimes' (5)	CQua
'Sundial' (7)	CBro GKev LAma NMin
'Sunny Girlfriend' (11a) **new**	SDeJ
'Sunnyside Up' (11a) ♀H6	SDeJ
'Sunrise' (3)	CQua
'Sunstroke' (2)	CQua
'Suntory' (3)	CQua
'Suntrap' (2)	IRhd
'Surfside' (6) ♀H6	CQua NMin
'Surprise Packet' (2)	IRhd
'Surrey' (2)	CQua IRhd
'Suzie Dee' (6)	IRhd
'Suzie's Sister' (6)	IRhd
'Suzy' (7) ♀H6	CBro CFen SDeJ
'Swaledale' (2)	CQua
'Swallow' (6)	CQua SDeJ
'Swallow Wing' (6)	IRhd
'Swan of Avon' (1) **new**	CQua
'Swanpool' (3)	CQua
'Sweet Blanche' (7)	CQua
'Sweet Lorraine' (2)	CQua
'Sweet Memory' (2)	CQua
'Sweet Sue' (3)	CQua
'Sweetness' (7) ♀H6	CAvo CBro CFen CQua GCro LAma WShi
'Swift Arrow' (6) ♀H6	CQua
'Swing Wing' (6)	CQua
'Swoop' (6)	SDeJ
'Taffeta' (10)	EPri
'Tahiti' (4) ♀H6	CFen CQua LAma SDeJ
× ***taitii*** (13)	NMin WShi
'Talgarth' (2)	CQua
'Talskiddy' (6) **new**	CQua
§ 'Tamar Double White' (4)	CBro CFil CQua
'Tamar Fire' (4) ♀H6	CQua
'Tamar Lad' (2)	CQua
'Tamar Lass' (3)	CQua
'Tamar Snow' (2)	CQua
'Tamara' (2)	CFen CQua
'Tangent' (2)	CQua
'Tangerine Tango' (4) **new**	IRhd
'Tao' (3) **new**	CQua
'Tarnished Gold' (2)	CQua
'Tasgem' (4)	CQua
'Taslass' (4)	CQua
'Taupere Place' (1) **new**	CQua
tazetta (13)	ECho
§ - subsp. ***lacticolor*** (13)	CFil CQua ERCP SDeJ
§ - - 'Grand Monarque' (8)	CBro CQua
- subsp. ***ochroleucus*** (13)	CQua
* - var. ***odoratus***	CQua NMin
'Teal' (1)	CQua
'Tehidy' (3)	CQua
§ 'Telamonius Plenus' (4)	CBro CQua IGor MMuc SEND WShi
'Temba' (1)	IRhd
'Temple Cloud' (4)	IRhd
'Templeton Bell' (11a) **new**	CQua
'Tenedos' (2)	GCro
tenuifolius	see *N. bulbocodium* subsp. *bulbocodium* var. *tenuifolius*
× ***tenuior*** (13)	NMin
Tequila Sunrise Group (12) **new**	IRhd
'Terminator' (2)	IRhd
'Terracotta' (2)	CQua IRhd
'Terrapin' (3)	IRhd
'Terwegen' (4)	CFen
'Tête-à-tête' (12) ♀H6	CAvo CBro CFen CQua CTca CWCL EPfP EPot ERCP GAbr GKev LAma LPot LRHS LSou MBri MMuc SDeJ SEND SPer
'Texas' (4)	CQua
'Thalia' (5)	CAvo CBro CQua CTca EPfP ERCP GKev IFro LAma LPot LRHS MBri MCot NBir NHol SDeJ SEND SPer SPhx WShi
'The Alliance' (6) ♀H6	CBro CQua
'The Caley' (2)	CQua
'The Grange' (1)	CQua
'The Knave' (6)	CQua
'The Little Gentleman' (6)	NMin
'The Mount' (2)	IRhd
'Thistin' (1)	IRhd
'Thomas Kinkade' (2)	CQua
'Thoresby' (3)	CQua
'Thoughtful' (5)	CBro CQua
'Three Oaks' (1)	CQua
'Three Trees' (1)	IRhd
'Tibet' (2)	CFen CQua
'Tickled Pink' (11a)	IRhd
'Tideford' (2)	CQua
'Tidy Tippet' (2)	IRhd
'Tiercel' (1)	CQua
'Tiffany Jade' (3)	CQua
'Tiger Moth' (6)	CQua
'Timolin' (3)	CQua
'Tinderbox' (2)	IRhd
'Tinhay' (7)	CQua
'Tiritomba' (11a)	CQua
'Titania' (6)	CQua
'Tittle-tattle' (7)	CFen CQua
'Toby' (2)	SDeJ
'Toby the First' (6)	CAvo CQua
'Tommora Gold' (2)	CQua
'Tommy White' (2)	CQua
'Tomphubil' (2) **new**	CQua
'Top Hit' (11a)	CQua
'Topolino' (1) ♀H6	CAvo CBro CFen CQua EPot GKev IFro LAma LRHS
'Topsy Turvy' (4) **new**	CQua
'Toreador' (3)	CFen CQua
'Toretta' (3)	IRhd
'Torianne' (2) ♀H6	CQua
'Torr Head' (9)	IRhd
'Torridon' (2)	CQua
'Toto' (12) ♀H6	CBro CQua ECho ERCP MBri SDeJ SPhx
'Tracey' (6)	CQua IRhd LAma
'Treasure Hunt' (2)	IRhd
'Trebah' (2) ♀H6	CQua
'Trebah Gem' (3) **new**	CQua
'Treble Chance'	see *N. romieuxii* 'Treble Chance'
'Treble Two' (7)	CQua
'Trecara' (3)	CQua
'Trefusis' (1)	CQua
'Treglisson' (2)	CFen
'Trehane' (6)	CQua
'Trelawney Gold' (2)	CFen CQua
'Trelissick' (7)	CQua
'Tremelling' (2)	CFen
'Tremough Dale' (11a)	CQua
'Trena' (6) ♀H6	CQua ERCP NMin

'Trendy Trail' (3)	IRhd
'Trentagh' (3)	IRhd
'Trenwith' (1)	CQua
'Trepolo' (11b)	ERCP
'Tresamble' (5)	CBro CQua GCro LAma MBri SDeJ
'Trevaunance' (6)	CQua
'Treverva' (6)	CQua
'Treviddo' (2)	CQua
'Trevithian' (7)	CBro CQua GCro LAma SDeJ WShi
'Trewarvas' (2)	CQua
'Trewirgie' (6)	CQua
'Tricollet' (11a)	SDeJ
'Trident' (3)	CQua
'Trielfin' (5)	IRhd
'Trigonometry' (11a) 🏆H6	CQua IRhd
'Tripartite' (11a) 🏆H6	CQua IRhd NMin SDeJ
'Triple Crown' (3) 🏆H6	CQua IRhd
'Tristram' (2)	CQua
'Tropic Isle' (4)	CQua
'Tropical Heat' (2)	IRhd
'Trousseau' (1)	CFen CQua
'Troutbeck' (3)	CQua
'Tru' (3)	CQua
'Truculent' (3)	CQua
'Trueblood' (3)	IRhd
'Trumpet Warrior' (1) 🏆H6	CQua IRhd
'Tryst' (2)	CQua
'Tudor Minstrel' (2)	CQua
'Tuesday's Child' (5) 🏆H6	CQua
'Tullyroyal' (2)	CQua
'Tunis' (2)	GCro
'Turncoat' (6)	CQua
'Tutankhamun' (2)	CQua
'Tweety Bird' (6)	EPfP
'Twicer' (2)	IRhd
'Twilight Zone' (2)	IRhd
'Twink' (4)	CQua
'Tyee' (2)	CQua
Tyndrum Flame (3)	GCro
'Tyrian Rose' (2)	CQua
'Tyrone Gold' (1) 🏆H6	CQua IRhd
'Tyrree' (1)	IRhd
'Tywara' (1)	CQua
'Ulster Bank' (3)	CQua
'Ulster Bride' (4)	CQua
'Ultimus' (2)	CQua
'Uncle Bill' (1)	CQua
'Uncle Duncan' (1)	CQua IRhd
'Unique' (4) 🏆H6	CQua LAma SDeJ
'Unsurpassable' (1)	CFen CQua GCro LAma
'Upalong' (12)	CQua
'Upshot' (3)	CQua
'Urchin' (2)	IRhd
'Utiku' (6)	CQua
'Val d'Incles' (3)	CQua IRhd
'Valdrome' (11a)	CQua
'Valinor' (2)	CQua
'Valley Dew' (2)	CQua
'Van Sion'	see *N.* 'Telamonius Plenus'
'Vandalia' (3) **new**	CQua
'Vanellus' (11a) 🏆H6	IRhd
'Vanilla Peach' (11a) **new**	SDeJ
'Vaticaan' (1)	SDeJ
'Velocity' (6) **new**	NMin
'Velvet Spring' (2)	CQua
'Vendell' (3)	IRhd
'Verdant Sparks' (7) **new**	IRhd
'Verdin' (7)	CQua
'Verdoy' (2)	IRhd
'Verger' (3)	LAma MBri SDeJ
'Vernal Prince' (3) 🏆H6	CQua
'Verona' (3) 🏆H6	CQua
'Verran Rose' (2)	IRhd
'Vers Libre' (9)	CQua
'Version' (1)	IRhd
'Vice-President' (2) 🏆H6	CQua
'Vickie Linn' (6)	CQua
'Victoria' (1)	CQua
'Video Kid' (2) **new**	IRhd
'Vigil' (1)	CQua
'Viking' (1) 🏆H6	CQua
'Village Green' (3)	IRhd
'Violetta' (2)	CQua
'Virginia Waters' (3)	CQua
'Viva Diva' (3)	IRhd
'Volare' (2)	CQua
'Volcanic Rim' (3)	IRhd
'Vulcan' (2)	CQua
'W.P. Milner' (1)	CAby CAvo CBro CQua EPfP EPot ERCP LAma MBri MMuc NMin SDeJ SEND SPhx WShi
'Walden Pond' (3)	CQua
'Waldorf Astoria' (4)	CQua IRhd
'Walton' (7)	CQua
'Waltz' (11a) **new**	CQua
'War Dance' (3)	IRhd
'Warbler' (6) 🏆H6	CQua LAma NMin SDeJ
'Warleggan' (2)	CFen
'Warm Day' (2)	IRhd
'Warm Welcome' (2)	IRhd
'Warmington' (3)	CQua
'Warmwell' (3)	IRhd
'Watamu' (3)	IRhd
'Waterperry' (7)	CBro LAma
'Watership Down' (2)	CQua IRhd
'Watersmeet' (4)	CQua
watieri	see *N. rupicola* subsp. *watieri*
'Wave' (4)	CQua
'Wavelength' (3)	IRhd
'Wavertree'	see *N. asturiensis* 'Wavertree'
'Waxwing' (5)	CQua
'Wayward Lad' (3)	IRhd
'Wee Bee' (1)	CQua
'Weena' (2)	CQua
'Welcome' (2)	CFen CQua
'Wells Fargo' (2) **new**	CQua
'Welsh Rugby Union' (1)	CQua
'Welsh Warrior' (1) **new**	CQua
'Wendron' (1)	CFen
'West Post' (3)	IRhd
'Westward' (4)	CQua
'Whang-hi' (6)	CQua
'Wheal Bush' (4)	CQua
'Wheal Coates' (7) 🏆H6	CQua
'Wheal Honey' (1)	CQua
'Wheal Jane' (2)	CQua
'Wheal Kitty' (7)	CQua
'Wheal Rose' (4)	CQua
'Wheatear' (6)	CQua IRhd NMin
'Whetstone' (1)	CQua
'Whipcord' (7) 🏆H6	IRhd
'Whisky Galore' (2)	CQua
'Whisky Mac' (2)	CQua
'White Convention' (1)	IRhd
'White Emperor' (1)	CQua GCro
'White Empress' (1)	CQua

'White Giant' (1)	GKev
'White Lady' (3)	CAvo CQua GCro LAma WShi
'White Lion' (4) ♀H6	CFen CQua LAma SDeJ
'White Marvel' (4)	CQua
'White Medal' (4)	SDeJ
'White Nile' (2)	CQua
'White Star' (1)	IRhd
'White Tea' (2)	CQua IRhd
'White Tie' (3)	CQua
'Whitewell' (2) **new**	GCro
'Wicklow Hills' (3)	CQua
'Widgeon' (2)	CQua
'Wild Honey' (2)	CQua
'Wild Rover' (1)	IRhd
'Will Scarlett' (2)	CQua GCro
willkommii (13)	CBro CDes CQua ECho NMin
'Wimbledon County Girl' (2) ♀H6	CQua
'Wind Song' (2)	CQua
'Winged Victory' (6)	CQua
'Winholm Jenni' (3)	CQua
'Winifred van Graven' (3)	CFen
'Winter Waltz' (6)	CQua
'Wisley' (6) ♀H6	ERCP LRHS
'Witch Hunt' (4)	IRhd
'Woodcock' (6)	CQua
Woodcroft Beauty (2)	GCro
Woodcroft Gold (2) **new**	GCro
'Woodland Prince' (3)	CQua
'Woodland Star' (3)	CQua
'Woodley Vale' (2)	CQua
'Woolsthorpe' (2)	CQua
'World Class' (5)	CQua
'Xit' (3)	CAvo CBro CQua NMin
'Xunantunich' (2)	CQua IRhd
'Yellow Belles' (5)	IRhd
'Yellow Cheerfulness' (4) ♀H6	CQua EPfP LAma MBri SDeJ SPer
'Yellow River' (1) ♀H6	LAma
'Yellow Triumphator' (1)	CFen
'Yellow Xit' (3)	CQua NMin
'Yoley's Pond' (2)	CQua
'York Minster' (1)	CQua
'Young American' (1)	CQua
'Young Blood' (2)	CQua IRhd
'Your Grace' (2)	CQua
'Yummy Mummy' (2) **new**	IRhd
'Yum-Yum' (3)	IRhd
zaianicus	see *N. romieuxii* subsp. *albidus* var. *zaianicus*
'Zekiah' (1)	CQua
'Zion Canyon' (2)	CQua
'Ziva' (8)	CAvo SDeJ
'Zoë's Pink' (3) **new**	CQua
'Zwynner' (2)	IRhd

Nardostachys (*Caprifoliaceae*)

grandiflora	GPoy

Nassauvia (*Asteraceae*)

gaudichaudii	WAbe

Nassella (*Poaceae*)

cernua	WPGP
formicarum (Delile) Barkworth	EBee
poeppigiana	see *Stipa poeppigiana*
pulchra	WPGP
tenuissima	see *Stipa tenuissima*
trichotoma	CAby CKno EHoe EPPr SLim SPer WHal WPGP
- 'Palomino' **new**	LRHS

Nasturtium (*Brassicaceae*)

'Banana Split'	CCCN ELan
officinale	MSKA SVic SWat

Natal plum see *Carissa macrocarpa*

nectarine see *Prunus persica* var. *nectarina*

Nectaroscordum (*Alliaceae*)

§ ***siculum***	CAvo CBre CBro CSpe CTri ECho ELan ERCP GCra GKev LLWP LRHS MBel MCot NBir NChi NDov NSti SDeJ SMrm SPer WBor
§ - subsp. ***bulgaricum***	CAby CBro CTca CWCL EBee ECha EPfP EPot EWTr IBlr LRHS LSun MNrw SPhx WCot XLum
tripedale	CAvo CBro CMea ECho WCot

Neillia (*Rosaceae*)

affinis	CDul CExl EBee EPfP EWTr GCal LLHF LRHS NBid NLar SLon SWvt WPat
longiracemosa	see *N. thibetica*
sinensis	NLar
§ ***thibetica***	Widely available
thyrsiflora PAB 3267	LEdu
- var. ***tunkinensis*** HWJ 505	WCru

Nelumbo (*Nelumbonaceae*)

'Beautiful Dancer'	LLWG
'Carolina Queen'	LLWG
'Emerald Daybreak' (d) **new**	LLWG
'High Noon' **new**	LLWG
nucifera	XBlo
- 'Alba Striata'	LLWG
- 'Chawan Basu'	LLWG
- 'Hindu' **new**	LLWG
'Penelope'	LLWG
'Perry's Giant Sunburst' **new**	LLWG
'Pink 'n' Yellow'	EWay
'Pink Pretty Princess Payton' **new**	LLWG
'Russian Red'	LLWG
'The President'	LLWG
'Wa Ba Sabie' **new**	LLWG
'Wann Shou Hing' **new**	LLWG

Nematanthus (*Gesneriaceae*)

'Apres'	WDib
'Black Magic'	WDib
'Christmas Holly'	WDib
'Freckles'	WDib
§ ***gregarius*** ♀H1c	WDib
§ - 'Golden West' (v)	WDib
- 'Variegatus'	see *N. gregarius* 'Golden West'
'Lemon and Lime'	WDib
radicans	see *N. gregarius*
'Tropicana' ♀H1c	WDib

Nemesia (*Scrophulariaceae*)

§ Amelie = 'Fleurame'PBR	EPfP LBuc SPoG
Berries and Cream = 'Fleurbac'PBR	ECtt EPfP LAst LBuc LSou MCot SPoG
Blue Lagoon = 'Pengoon'PBR (Maritana Series)	LAst SCoo

'Blueberry Ripple'	LSou WGor
'Bluebird'	see *N.* Bluebird = 'Hubbird'
§ Bluebird = 'Hubbird'PBR	CHll
Candy Girl = 'Pencand' (Maritana Series)	SCoo
§ ***denticulata*** ♀H3	CPrp EWoo GBee LRHS MHer NEgg SCoo WHlf
- 'Celebration'PBR	LBuc
- 'Confetti'	see *N. denticulata*
- 'Maggie'	LRHS
'Fleurie Blue'	EPfP LBuc SPoG
'Fragrant Cloud'	LSou
Framboise = 'Fleurfram'	EPfP LBuc SPoG
fruticans Benth.	ELon
Golden Eye = 'Yateye'PBR	MPnt SLon
Honey Girl = 'Penhon' (Maritana Series)	SCoo
Ice Pink = 'Fleuripi'	EPfP LBuc
'Innocence' ♀H3	CPrp SCoo
(Karoo Series) Karoo Blue = 'Innkablue'PBR	SCoo
- Karoo Plum **new**	MAvo
- Karoo Soft Blue = 'Innkarsofb'PBR	CWGN
- Karoo Violet Ice = 'Innemkavic'PBR	NPri
- Karoo White = 'Innkarwhi'PBR	LSou
Lagoon WhitePBR	see *N.* Pure Lagoon
Maritana Sky Lagoon = 'Pensky' (Maritana Series)	SCoo
'Mirabelle'	LBuc SPoG
Myrtille = 'Fleurmyr'	EPfP LBuc SPoG
(Nesia Series) Nesia Dark Blue = 'Dannemes6'	LAst WGor
- Nesia Dark Magenta	LAst
Opal InnocencePBR	see *N.* Amelie
Provençal Dusky Blue = 'Fleurpdblu'PBR	EPfP
Provençal Dusky Pink = 'Fleurpdpnk'PBR	EPfP
§ Pure Lagoon = 'Penpur'PBR	LAst
Raspberries and Cream = 'Fleurrac'	EPfP LBuc MCot SPoG
Sugar Frosted = 'Lowgreg'	LRHS SPoG
'Sugar Plum'	LRHS SLon
(Sunsatia Series) Sunsatia Cherry on Ice	LBuc MAvo NPri SMrm SPoG
- Sunsatia Blackberry = 'Inuppink'PBR	SCoo
- Sunsatia Cassis = 'Inupspink8'PBR	MAvo
- Sunsatia Cranberry = 'Intraired'PBR	SCoo
- Sunsatia Kumquat = 'Intraikum'PBR **new**	MCot
- Sunsatia Lemon = 'Intraigold'PBR	LAst SCoo
- Sunsatia Peach = 'Inupcream'	CWGN SCoo
- Sunsatia Pomelo = 'Innemsunpo'PBR **new**	LBuc NPri
'Sweet Lady'	LAst LSou NPri
sylvatica	CSpe
'Utopia Lavender' (Utopia Series) **new**	EBee
'Vanilla Lady'	ECtt LAst LSou NPri
Vanilla Mist = 'Grega'	LRHS LSou SLon
'Wisley Vanilla'	EPfP LBuc SPoG

Nemophila (*Boraginaceae*)

menziesii 'Penny Black'	CSpe SPer

Neodypsis (*Arecaceae*)

decaryi	see *Dypsis decaryi*

Neolepisorus (*Polypodiaceae*)

lancifolius	CExl

Neolitsea (*Lauraceae*)

glauca	see *N. sericea*
polycarpa B&SWJ 11705 **new**	WCru
- KWJ 12309	WCru
§ ***sericea***	CBcs LEdu SSpi WPGP WSHC

Neomarica ✿ (*Iridaceae*)

caerulea	WCot

Neopanax (*Araliaceae*)

§ ***arboreus***	CDoC CHEx CTsd ECou LEdu SBig
§ ***laetus*** ♀H3	CDoC CHEx IDee LEdu SArc SBig

Neoregelia (*Bromeliaceae*)

'Alpha' **new**	LAir
ampullacea **new**	LAir
- large form **new**	LAir
carolinae	LAir
- Meyendorffii Group **new**	LAir
- - 'Meyendorffii'	XBlo
'Cheers' **new**	LAir
'Chiquita Linda' **new**	LAir NLos
concentrica × 'Pink Polka Dot' **new**	LAir
cruenta **new**	LAir
- 'Bronze' **new**	LAir
- red-leaved **new**	LAir
'Devin's Delight' **new**	LAir
'Dr Oeser' **new**	NLos
dungsiana **new**	LAir
'Fireball' **new**	LAir NLos
'Flandria' **new**	LAir
fluminensis × ***macwilliamsii*** **new**	LAir
'Fool's Gold' **new**	LAir
'Fruit Salad' **new**	LAir
'Hannibal Lector' × 'The Governor's Plea' **new**	XTur
'Hojo Rojo'	XBlo
'Hula Lady' **new**	LAir
'Irazu' **new**	LAir
'Irish Mist' **new**	LAir
'Jalapeno' **new**	LAir
'Kahala Dawn' **new**	LAir
'Lili Marlene' **new**	LAir
lilliputiana **new**	LAir
(***lilliputiana*** × 'Fireball') × ***eltoniana*** **new**	XTur
'Luca' **new**	LAir
'Marconfos'	XBlo
'Michi' **new**	LAir
'Mo Peppa Please' **new**	LAir
'Not Domino' **new**	LAir
pauciflora **new**	LAir

pauciflora* × *wilsoniana new
'Peggy Pollard' new LAir
'Perfection' new LAir
* ***punctatissima*** LAir
var. ***rubra*** new
– var. ***rubra*** × 'Hannibal Lector' new NLos
– var. ***rubra*** × ***tigrina*** new LAir
'Rafa' × 'Betty Head' new LAir
'Red on Green' new NLos
rubrifolia new LAir
'Sara Lee' new LAir
'Sarah Head' new LAir
'Scarlet Charlotte' new NLos
'Shamrock' new LAir
'Spicy' new NLos
'The Auctioneer' new LAir
'Tom Tom' new LAir
'Yellow Devil' new LAir
'Zoë'PBR new LAir
'Zuleica' new LAir NLos

Neoshirakia (*Euphorbiaceae*)

japonica MBlu WPGP WPat
– B&SWJ 8744 WCru

Neottianthe (*Orchidaceae*)

cucullata EFEx

Nepenthes (*Nepenthaceae*)

alata NLos
albomarginata new NLos
aristolochioides* × *spectabilis new NLos
bongso NLos
bongso* × *inermis new NLos
boschiana* × *densiflora new NLos
burbidgeae new NLos
× ***burkei*** new NLos
chaniana* × *veitchii new NLos
***chaniana* × (*clipeata* × *eymae*)** NLos
***clipeata* × (*clipeata* × *eymae*)** NLos
copleandii NLos
densiflora NLos
densiflora* × *spectabilis new NLos
diatas NLos
eymae new NLos
fusca NLos
glabrata NLos
gracillima new NLos
inermis new NLos
inermis* × *singalana new NLos
inermis* × *ventricosa new NLos
'Lady Pauline' ♀H1b new NLos
lowii NLos
maxima NLos
mikei NLos
mira* × *spathulata new NLos
mira* × *spectabilis new NLos
muluensis* × *lowii NLos
ovata NLos
pilosa new NLos
pilosa* × *veitchii new NLos
platychila* × *veitchii new NLos
rajah NLos
ramispina NLos
sanguinea NLos
sibuyanensis* × *spectabilis new NLos
sibuyanensis* × *ventricosa new NLos
singalana NLos
spectabilis NLos
spectabilis* × *talangensis new NLos
talangensis NLos
tobaica NLos
truncata NLos
veitchii new NLos

Nepeta ✿ (*Lamiaceae*)

sp. LAst
from China EWes
amethystina XSen
'Blue Beauty' see *N. sibirica* 'Souvenir d'André Chaudron'
'Blue Dragon' ECtt GBin GQue MAsh MTis NCGa NDov NLar WHoo
bucharica GBuc
* ***buddlejifolium*** MSCN NLar
* – 'Gold Splash' NLar
cataria CArn CBod CTri CWld ELau ENfk GJos GPoy LAst MHer MNHC NBro NLar SIde SVic WHfH WJek WMoo
§ – 'Citriodora' CBod ENfk GPoy SIde SPhx SRms WJek XLum
'Chettle Blue' new MAvo
citriodora Dum. see *N. cataria* 'Citriodora'
clarkei EPPr GMaP MRav MTis SMHy SWat WHrl WMoo
'Dropmore' EBee
§ × ***faassenii*** ♀H7 Widely available
– 'Alba' EBee ECtt ELan EPfP LRHS NLar NRya WJek WWEG XSen
– 'Blauknirps' EPla MAsh NDov
– 'Blue Wonder' LRHS STPC
– 'Kit Cat' CBod CSpe ECtt GBBs GBuc GCal IBoy LPla LRHS MAsh MTis NCGa SBod WCFE WHoo WSHC
– 'Limelight' IBoy WHil
– 'Senior' XLum
glechoma 'Variegata' see *Glechoma hederacea* 'Variegata'
govaniana Widely available
granatensis XSen
grandiflora MPie MRav NBre SIde WHrl
– 'Blue Danube' GBin LPla MTis WWEG XLum
– 'Bramdean' ♀H6 CBod CElw CMea COtt EBee ECtt EPfP EWes GBin LBMP LRHS MCot MRav MTis SPhx WCAu WCot WWEG XLum
– 'Dawn to Dusk' Widely available
– 'Pool Bank' EBee ECtt EWes LPla MAvo MTis SIde SMrm XLum
– 'Wild Cat' EPfP MAvo MTis SPhx
hederacea 'Variegata' see *Glechoma hederacea* 'Variegata'
'Hill Grounds' new WCot
italica SHar WOut
Junior Walker = 'Novanepjun' new CKno
kubanica CSpe EBee IMou LPla SMHy SPhx WCot

'Lamendi'	MTis NDov
latifolia 'Super Cat'	EBee EPfP
§ 'Leeds Castle'	CBod EBee ECGP EPfP EPla LRHS MHer NGdn NSti SHar SPer SWat WHal WHil WWEG
longipes hort.	see *N.* 'Leeds Castle'
macrantha	see *N. sibirica*
'Maurice'	LPla MTis NDov WWEG
melissifolia	SBch
mussinii misapplied	see *N.* × *faassenii*
mussinii Spreng.	see *N. racemosa*
nervosa	CSpe ECha ELan EPfP LAst NBro NLar NSti SBrt SHar SPer SPhx WCot WHar WHea WJek WSHC WWEG
- 'Blue Carpet'	CSpe NEgg
- 'Blue Moon'	CBod CWld EBee EPfP EPla EWes LRHS LSou MBNS MHol MPie NBid SMrm SRms
- 'Forncett Select'	CSam MRav NBre SMrm
- 'Pink Cat'	EPfP LRHS LSou NLar SPhx WFar WWEG
§ ***nuda***	ECha ECrN EWes MRav SBrt SHar SMHy WHil WWEG
- subsp. ***albiflora***	ECha
* - 'Grandiflora'	NBre NLar WMoo
- 'Purple Cat'	EBee EPfP LLHF LSou
- 'Romany Dusk' **new**	LEdu
- 'Snow Cat'	SPhx
pannonica	see *N. nuda*
parnassica	ECtt EWld GLog GQue MBel MCot MHol MMuc MTis NLar SMrm WHrl WMnd WMoo
phyllochlamys	CPBP SRms XSen
Pink Candy	NWad SRms
'Porzellan'	LPla
§ ***prattii***	CBod CSpe MMuc MWat NLar SMrm
'Purple Haze'	NLar
§ ***racemosa*** 🏆H7	CArn CHby CMac CNec CPbn CUse ELau EPfP GJos LRHS LSun MCot MLHP MNHC MSCN SCob SIde WMoo
- RCBAM 3	WCot
- ***alba***	XLum
- 'Amelia'	EBee MHer MPie MSpe MWhi
- 'Grog'	CBod LPla LRHS NLar WWEG
- 'Little Titch'	CBod EBee ECha ECtt EPfP EPla GBuc GCra LRHS MAsh MCot NLar SCob SMrm SPoG SWat WWEG
- 'Senior'	MAsh XSen
- 'Snowflake'	CBcs CHel CMea ECtt ELan ELon EPfP EShb GMaP LRHS MBel MCot MHer MTis NBir NDov NLar SCob SMrm SPer SPoG SWvt WCAu
- 'Superba'	LPla NBre
- 'Toria'	IMou MTis WWEG
- 'Walker's Low' 🏆H7	Widely available
* 'Rae Crug'	EWes
reichenbachiana	see *N. racemosa*
§ ***sibirica***	ECha ELan EPfP LRHS MHer MMuc MSCN NBid NBro NLar NPri SRkn WCot WFar WJek XLum
§ - 'Souvenir d'André Chaudron' 🏆H6	CAby CBod CMHG CSam CWCL EBee ELan EPfP EPla EWTr GBuc GCal GMaP IPot LAst LRHS LSou MCot MRav MTis NLar SCob SPer SPoG WHea WHil WWEG
'Six Hills Giant'	Widely available
'Six Hills Gold' **new**	SCob WHil
stewartiana	LLHF MRav WHil WMoo WWEG
- BWJ 7999	WCru
subsessilis	CBod CMHG ECtt ELan EPfP EPla GMaP IBoy IKil LAst LBMP LRHS MBel MCot MRav MSpe NBid NBir NGdn NLar NSti NWad SPhx SRms WCru WMnd WWEG
- 'Blue Dreams'	ELon MHol MNHC NLar SHar SPhx XLum
- blue-flowered **new**	SMrm
- 'Candy Cat'	CMos EPfP IBoy LPot NBre NLar
- 'Cool Cat'	CMos EBee EPfP NBre NLar
- 'Laufen'	IPot
- Nimbus = 'Yanim'	CBod MPnt
- 'Pink Dreams'	CBod EPfP GBee GJos LRHS MHer SHar XLum
- pink-flowered	ECha SMrm SPhx WWEG
- 'Sweet Dreams'	CBod EPfP MRav MSpe MTis NCGa NLar NSti WMnd XLum
- 'Washfield'	CAby IPot NLar
transcaucasica 'Blue Infinity'	CNor MSCN WHrl WMoo WWEG
tuberosa	CBod CSpe EBee ECha SBch SBrt WCot WMoo WWEG XSen
'Veluwse Wakel'	IMou
yunnanensis	EBee EPPr IPot LPla MPie SMrm WHil WOut WPGP

Nephrolepis (*Lomariopsidaceae*)

cordifolia	NLos
exaltata 'Verona' **new**	WCot
falcata	NLos
- f. ***furcans***	NLos

Nerine ✿ (*Amaryllidaceae*)

'Ada Bryson' **new**	ECho
'Afterglow'	CPne ECho LAma WCot
'Alresford' **new**	ECho
alta	see *N. undulata* Alta Group
'Ancilla'	ECho
'Angelico'	ECho
appendiculata **new**	GKev
'Aries'	WCot
'Atlanta'	ECho
'Audrey Clarke' **new**	CPne
'Aurora'	ECho WCot
'Bach' **new**	ECho
'Baghdad'	ECho WCot
'Belladonna'	GKev WCot
'Bennett-Poë'	WCot
'Berlioz'	ECho WCot
'Beth Chatto' **new**	ECho
'Blanchefleur'	CTal WCot
bowdenii 🏆H5	Widely available
- 'Alba' misapplied	see *N. bowdenii* 'Pallida'
- 'Alba' ambig.	CCon CPrp CTca EBee ECho ELan EPot ERCP SCoo SMHy
- 'Alba'	CAvo CBod CBro CDes ECha EPri GAbr GKev IGor LRHS MNrw SCob SDeJ
- 'Albivetta'	EBee ECho EPri GKev MNrw
- 'Blanca Perla'	EBee GKev WCot
- 'Castlewellan' **new**	IBlr
- 'Codora'	see *N.* 'Codora'
- 'E.B.Anderson'	WCot
- 'Ella K'	CBod ECho EPot EPri ERCP GKev MNrw SPer

	Name	Suppliers
	– 'Eric Smith' **new**	WCot
	– Irish clone	WCot
	– 'Isabel'	CBro CPrp CTsd ECha ECho EPot EPri ERCP EWes GKev WCot WHoo
	– 'John Crisp'	WCot
	– 'Kathleen Pollock' **new**	WCot
	– 'Linda Vista'	WCot
	– 'Manina'	CCse
	– 'Marjorie'	EMal
	– 'Mark Fenwick'	CBro CDes
	– 'Marnie Rogerson'	CBro CPne SMHy
§	– 'Mollie Cowie' (v)	CCse CPrp GCal IBlr WCot WCru WHil
	– 'Mount Stewart'	IBlr WCot
	– 'Nikita'	ECho EPot EPri ERCP GKev LRHS MNrw SDeJ WCot
	– 'Ostara'	CBod CPrp EBee EPot EPri ERCP GKev LRHS MNrw WCot
	– 'Pallida' **new**	LRHS
	– 'Patricia'	EBee EPot EPri GKev MNrw
	– 'Pink Frostwork'	EPri WCot
	– 'Pink Surprise'	CAvo CDes WCot
§	– 'Quinton Wells'	CTca WCot
	– 'Richard Blakeway-Phillips' **new**	WCot
	– 'Rowie'	CPrp EBee EPri ERCP LRHS
	– 'Sheila Owen' **new**	WCot
	– 'Sofie'	EBee GKev
	– 'Stam 63'	GKev
	– 'Stefanie'	CAby CTsd EBee EPri GKev SDeJ
	– Ted Allen No 2 **new**	WCot
	– 'Variegata'	see *N. bowdenii* 'Mollie Cowie'
	– 'Vesta K'	EPri GKev
	– Washfield form	SMHy
	– 'Wellsii'	see *N. bowdenii* 'Quinton Wells'
	'Brahms'	ECho
	'Canasta'	WCot
	'Cardinal'	ECho
	'Caryatid'	WCot
	'Catherine'	CPne WCot
	'Catkin'	CPne WCot
	'Clent Charm'	WCot
§	'Codora'	CCCN ECho EPfP SPer WCot
	'Corlette'	WCot
	corusca 'Major'	see *N. sarniensis* var. *corusca* 'Major'
	'Cranfield'	WCot
	crispa	see *N. undulata* Crispa Group
	'Cynthia Chance'	ECho WCot
	'Daphne'	ECho
	'Diana Oliver'	WCot
	'Doris Vos'	WCot
	'Elspeth'	WCot
	'Evelyn Emmett'	WCot
	'Exbury Red'	WCot
	filamentosa misapplied	see *N. filifolia* Baker
	filamentosa ambig.	CBro CTal ECho
	filifolia misapplied	see *N. masoniorum*
§	***filifolia*** Baker	ECho GKev
	'Firelight' **new**	CPne
	flexuosa	see *N. undulata* Flexuosa Group
	'Fucine'	CDes
	gaberonensis	WAbe
	'Gaiety'	WCot
	'George'	ECho
	'Glacier' **new**	LRHS MNrw
	gracilis	ECho GKev WCot
	'Grania' **new**	ECho
	'Hanley Castle' **new**	ECho
	'Harlequin'	WCot
	'Helena'	ECho
	'Hera'	CBro
	'Hertha Berg'	WCot
*	***hirsuta***	ECho GKev WAbe WCot
	'Hotspur' **new**	ECho
	humilis 🏆H2	ECho WCot
	– Breachiae Group	CTal SBch
	– from Franschhoek, South Africa **new**	CTal
	– (Peersii Group) 'Toorwaterpoort' **new**	CTal
	huttoniae	ECho
	'Iman'	WCot
	'Isobel'	LRHS XEll
	'Janet'	ECho WCot
	'Jenny Wren'	CDes ECho WCot
I	'Judith'	ECho
	'King Leopold'	ECho WCot
	'King of the Belgians'	ECho LAma LRHS
	'Kinn McIntosh'	CDes WCot
	'Koko' **new**	ECho
	'Kola'	CDes
	'Koriba'	ECho
	krigei	ECho GKev WCot
	'Kyle' **new**	WCot
	'Kyrie'	ECho
	'La Reine' **new**	ECho
	'Lady Cynthia Colville'	WCot
	'Lady Downe'	WCot
	'Lady Eleanor Keane'	ECho WCot
	'Lady Havelock-Allen'	WCot
	'Lady Llewellyn'	ECho WCot
	'Lady St Aldwyn'	WCot
	'Lambourne'	WCot
	laticoma	WCot
	'Lavant' **new**	ECho
	'Lawlord'	WCot
	'Leila Hughes'	WCot
	'Lucinda'	CDes WCot
	'Lyndhurst Salmon'	ECho WCot
	'Malvern' **new**	WCot
	'Maria'	WCot
	'Mars'	CTal
§	***masoniorum*** 🏆H2	CTal ECho GKev SBch WAbe
	'Miss E. Cator'	CPne CTal WCot
	'Miss Florence Brown'	WCot
	'Miss Frances Clarke'	WCot
	'Monet'	ECho
	'Mrs C. Goldsmith'	ECho
	'Mrs Cooper'	WCot
	'Mrs Dent Brocklehurst'	WCot
	'Murilla' **new**	ECho
	'Mystic' **new**	ECho
	'Natasha'	ECho
	'Nena'	WCot
	'November Cheer'	ECho LAma
	'Oberon'	CDes WCot
	'Ophelia' **new**	WCot
	'Orange Flame' **new**	ECho
	'Paragon' **new**	ECho
	peersii	WCot
	'Pink Triumph'	CAbP CBcs CTsd EBee ECho EPot ERCP EShb GKev LAma LRHS SDeJ SPer WCot WHoo
	'Plymouth'	CTal ECho
	pudica	CTal SBch

	– pink-flowered	WCot
	pusilla	CLak
	'Quivotina'	WCot
	'Red Pimpernel'	ECho LAma
	'Regina'	WCot
	'Rembrandt'	ECho WCot
	'Rose Princess'	WCot
	'Rushmere Star'	CTal ECho SChr WCot
	'Ruth'	WCot
	'Salmonia'	ECho
	sarniensis ♀H2	CBro CPne ECha ECho EPot EPri GKev SKHP WCot
	– 'Anne Baring' new	ECho
*	– 'Borde Hill White'	WCot
	– var. ***corusca***	CTsd LAma
§	– – 'Major'	ECho SChr WCot
	– var. ***curvifolia*** f. ***fothergillii***	ECho WCot
	– 'Mottistone'	WCot
	– 'Salmon Star' new	LRHS
	– var. ***sarniensis***	GKev
	– 'Shell Pink' new	CTal
	'Sidney Smee'	CTal
	Smee 275	CDes
	'Snowflake'	WCot
	'Stephanie'	CCCN CPne CTca ECho ERCP EShb LAma MNrw WCot WHoo
	'Susan Norris'	WCot
	'Timoshenko'	WCot
	'Tweedledee' new	WCot
	undulata	CAby CCCN CPne CTal CTca ECha ECho EPot EPri GCal GKev LAma LRHS LSou MPie SDeJ SPer
§	– Alta Group	GKev WCot
§	– Crispa Group new	CBod
§	– Flexuosa Group	ECho EWoo MRav
	– – 'Alba' ♀H3	CBro CPne EBee ECha ECho EPri GKev LRHS MRav WAbe WCot
	× ***versicolor*** 'Mansellii'	CBro CDes GKev SKHP
	'Vestal'	EPot
	'Vicky'	WCot
	'Virgo'	ECho LAma
	'White Swan'	ECho
	'Winter Sun'	LRHS
	'Wolsey'	ECho
	'Wombe'	ECho
	'Zeal Giant' ♀H3	CAvo CBro CPne ECho GCal WCot
	'Zeal Grilse'	CDes CPne ECho WCot
	'Zeal Purple Stripe' new	WCot
	'Zeal Salmon'	CDes WCot
	'Zeal Silver Stripe'	CDes
	'Zennor' new	ECho WCot

Nerium (*Apocynaceae*)

	oleander L.	CAbb CArn CBcs CHll CTri EBak ELan EShb SEND SPer SPlb SPoG
	– 'Album'	CTri
	– 'Album Maximum'	CCCN
	– 'Album Plenum' (d)	XSen
*	– 'Atlas'	XSen
	– 'Cavalaire' (d)	XSen
	– 'Commandant Barthélemy' (d)	XSen
	– 'Flavescens Plenum' (d)	EShb XSen
	– 'Hardy Red'	XSen
	– 'Isle of Capri'	CCCN
	– 'Madame Allen' (d)	EShb
	– 'Margaritha'	SEND
*	– 'Maurin des Maures'	CCCN
	– 'Professeur Granel' (d)	EShb
	– 'Provence' (d)	XSen
	– 'Red Beauty'	XSen
	– salmon-flowered	SEND
	– 'Splendens Giganteum' (d)	EShb
	– 'Variegatum' (v) ♀H2	CHll EShb
	– 'Villa Romaine'	XSen
	– white-flowered	SEND

Neviusia (*Rosaceae*)

	alabamensis	CJun NLar

Nicandra (*Solanaceae*)

	physalodes	CArn CHby ELan ENfk GBee NBir SEle WSFF
	– 'Splash of Cream' (v)	CCCN
	– 'Violacea'	CSpe GLog SRms SWvt

Nicotiana (*Solanaceae*)

	alata	CBod CSpe EPfP WSFF
	glauca	CCCN CDTJ CHGN CHll CSpe EUJe SPlb
	'Hopleys'	CSpe
	knightiana	CDTJ CSpe
	langsdorffii ♀H2	CSpe SPav SPhx
	– 'Cream Splash' (v)	CPla
	– 'Hot Chocolate'	CSpe
	'Lime Green'	CSpe ELan
	mutabilis	CSpe SDys SPhx
	'Perfume Deep Purple' (Perfume Series)	CSpe
	suaveolens	CBre SPhx
	sylvestris ♀H2	CBod CDTJ CSpe ELan EPfP LSun SDys SEND SPav SPoG SWvt WTou
	tabacum	CArn
	'Tinkerbell'	CSpe

Nidularium (*Bromeliaceae*)

	correia-araujoi new	NLos
	innocentii	XBlo
	serratum new	LAir

Nierembergia (*Solanaceae*)

§	***repens***	ECho NLar WCot XLum
	rivularis	see *N. repens*

Nigella (*Ranunculaceae*)

	damascena 'Miss Jekyll' ♀H7	CWCL
	– 'Miss Jekyll Alba' ♀H7	CSpe
	– Persian Jewels Group new	SVic
	papillosa 'African Bride'	CSpe
	– 'Midnight'	CSpe

Nigritella see *Gymnadenia*

Nipponanthemum (*Asteraceae*)

§	***nipponicum***	CBod EBee ECho GCal IDee IVic LAst MMuc NLar NSti SRms WHil XLum
	– 'Homa-giku'	NWad

Noccaea see *Thlaspi*

Nolina (*Asparagaceae*)

	bigelovii	WCot XSen
*	***brevifolia***	CFil

durangensis	CFil
- F&M 333	WPGP
lindheimeriana	WCot
longifolia	SChr
microcarpa	XSen
nelsonii	CFil LPal NLos SPlb
- F&M 307	WPGP
parviflora NJM 05.010	WPGP
texana	WCot XSen

Nomocharis (*Liliaceae*)

aperta	CExl CWCL ECho GBin GBuc GCra GGGa GKev GLin LAma WCru
- ACE 2271	EBee
mairei	see *N. pardanthina*
meleagrina	EBee EPot GKev LAma NSoo WAbe
nana	see *Lilium nanum*
oxypetala	see *Lilium oxypetalum*
§ ***pardanthina***	GBuc WAbe
- CLD 1490	GBuc
- f. ***punctulata***	GBuc GGGa
saluenensis	GGGa WAbe

Nonea (*Boraginaceae*)

lutea	LSou NOrc NSti WHal

Nothochelone see *Penstemon*

Nothofagus ✿ (*Nothofagaceae*)

sp.	CAco
§ ***alpina***	CBcs GBin
antarctica ♀H5	CBcs CDul CMCN CNWT CTho EBee ELan EPfP EWTr GKin IVic LPal MAsh MBlu MBri MGos NWea SWvt WHar WSHC
- 'Benmore'	NLar
betuloides	GBin IArd IDee SPlb
cunninghamii	IArd SPlb
dombeyi ♀H5	CBcs CDoC CDul CFil EPfP GBin IArd IVic MBlu SArc SWvt WPGP
fusca	IArd WPGP
glauca	CBcs GBin IVic
menziesii	WPGP
moorei	WPGP
nervosa	see *N. alpina*
nitida	GBin IDee
obliqua	CDul CMCN GAbr IVic SPlb
procera	see *N. alpina*
pumilio	GBin

Notholaena see *Cheilanthes*

Notholirion (*Liliaceae*)

bulbuliferum	EBee ECho GCra
campanulatum	ECho
macrophyllum	EBee ECho
thomsonianum	CTal ECho

Nothoscordum (*Alliaceae*)

sp.	GCal
bivalve	IMou
gracile	CCon
neriniflorum	see *Allium neriniflorum*
ostenii	CDes ECho
strictum	EBee ECho

Nuphar (*Nymphaeaceae*)

advenum	LLWG
japonica	LLWG
- var. ***variegata*** (v)	CRow
lutea	CBAq CBen CHab CRow EHon MSKA SWat
pumila	LLWG

Nuytsia (*Loranthaceae*)

floribunda new	SPlb

Nylandtia (*Polygalaceae*)

spinosa	SPlb

Nymphaea ✿ (*Nymphaeaceae*)

alba (H)	CBen CHab CRow CWat EHon GQue MSKA MWts NBir SVic SWat WMAq WPnP
'Alba Plenissima' (H)	EWay
'Albatros' misapplied	see *N.* 'Hermine'
§ 'Albatros' Latour-Marliac (H)	CBAq CWat LLWG MSKA NPer SWat WPnP
'Albatross'	see *N.* 'Albatros' Latour-Marliac, *N.* 'Hermine'
* 'Albida'	CBAq WMAq XBlo
'Almost Black' (H)	CBAq CBen EWay LLWG MSKA
'Amabilis' (H)	CBen CRow EWay MSKA SWat WMAq
'American Star' (H)	SWat
'Andreana' (H)	EWay LLWG MSKA
'Anna Epple' (H)	LLWG
'Arc-en-ciel' (H)	CBen EWay LLWG SWat WMAq
'Atropurpurea' (H)	CBen EWay LLWG MSKA NPer SWat WMAq
'Attraction' (H)	CBAq CBen CRow EHon EWay MSKA MWts NPer SVic SWat WMAq XBlo XLum
'Augustus McCray' (H)	LLWG
'Aurora' (H)	CBAq CBen CWat GQue MWts SVic SWat WMAq
'Barbara Davies' (H)	EWay LLWG MSKA
'Barbara Dobbins' (H)	CBen EWay LLWG MSKA
'Bateau' (H)	CBen LLWG
'Berit Strawn' (H)	EWay
'Bernice Ikins' (H)	LLWG
'Betsy Sakata' (H)	EWay
'Black Princess' (H)	CBAq CRow EWay LLWG
'Brakeleyi Rosea' (H)	MSKA WMAq
'Burgundy Princess' (H)	CWat EWay LLWG MSKA NPer
candida (H)	CBen MSKA MWts NPer WMAq
'Candidissima' (H)	CBAq CBen SWat
§ ***capensis*** (T/D)	XBlo
'Carolina Sunset' (H)	EWay LLWG
'Caroliniana Nivea' (H)	CBen EHon
'Caroliniana Perfecta' (H)	CBen MSKA SWat
'Celebration' (H)	EWay LLWG
'Charlene Strawn' (H)	EWay LLWG WMAq
'Charles de Meurville' (H)	CBAq CBen CRow LLWG MSKA NPer SVic WMAq WPnP
'Château le Rouge' (H)	CBen LLWG
'Clyde Ikins' (H)	EWay LLWG MSKA
'Colonel A.J. Welch' (H)	CBen EHon MSKA NPer SWat WMAq
'Colorado' (H)	CBen EWay LLWG MSKA NPer
colorata	see *N. capensis*
'Colossea' (H)	CBen CWat MSKA NPer WPnP
'Comanche' (H)	CBen EWay MSKA NPer WMAq
'Conqueror' (H)	CBen LLWG MSKA NPer SVic SWat
'Dallas' (H)	LLWG
§ 'Darwin' (H)	CWat MSKA NPer SLon SWat WMAq WPnP

	× ***daubenyana*** (T/D)	ECho EWay
	'David' (H)	EWay LLWG
	'Debbie June' (H)	LLWG
	'Denver' (H)	EWay LLWG MSKA
	'Ellisiana' (H)	CBAq CBen LLWG MSKA NPer SWat
	'Escarboucle' (H) ♀H7	CBAq CBen CRow CWat EWay LLWG MSKA NPer SVic SWat WMAq WPnP XBlo
§	'Fabiola' (H)	CRow EHon LLWG MSKA NPer WMAq
	'Fiesta' (H)	CBen MSKA
	'Fire Crest' (H)	CBAq CBen GQue LLWG MSKA NPer SVic SWat WMAq
	'Florida Sunset' (H)	EWay
	'Fritz Junge' (H)	CBen
	'Froebelii' (H)	CBen CRow CWat EHon EWay MSKA NPer SWat WMAq
	'Fulva' (H)	LLWG
	'Galatée' (H)	CBen MSKA
	'Geisha Girl' (H)	MSKA
	'Georgia Peach' (H)	EWay LLWG MSKA
	'Gladstoniana' (H) ♀H7	CBen CRow EHon MSKA NPer SWat WMAq
	'Gloire du Temple-sur-Lot' (H)	CBen EWay LLWG NPer SWat WMAq
	'Gloriosa' (H)	CBen LLWG NPer SWat
	'Gold Medal' (H)	CBen EWay LLWG MSKA
	'Gonnère' (H) ♀H7	CBen CRow CWat EHon EWay MSKA MWts NPer SLon SWat WMAq WPnP
	'Graziella' (H)	CBen MSKA WMAq
	'Gypsy' (H)	EWay LLWG
	'Hal Miller' (H)	LLWG
	'Hassell' (H)	LLWG
	'Hazorea Dagan White' (H)	EWay LLWG
	'Helen Fowler' (H)	WMAq
	× ***helvola***	see *N.* 'Pygmaea Helvola'
§	'Hermine' (H)	CBen MSKA MWts NPer SWat WMAq
	'Hidden Violet' (H)	LLWG
§	'Highlight'	EWay LLWG
	'Hilite'	see *N.* 'Highlight'
	'Hollandia' misapplied	see *N.* 'Darwin'
	'Hollandia' ambig.	CBAq
	'Hollandia' Koster (H)	SWat
	'Indiana' (H)	CBen MSKA NPer WMAq
	'Inner Light' (H)	CBen EWay LLWG MSKA
	'J.C.N. Forestier' (H)	CBen
	'James Brydon' (H) ♀H7	CBAq CBen CRow CWat EHon EWay MSKA MWts NPer SLon SVic SWat WMAq WPnP
	'Jean de Lamarsalle' (H)	LLWG MSKA
	'Jerusalem Dawn' (H)	LLWG MSKA
	'Joey Tomocik' (H)	CBAq CBen CWat EWay LLWG MSKA WMAq WPnP
	'Lactea' (H)	CBen LLWG
	'Laura Strawn' (H)	EWay
	'Laydekeri Fulgens' (H)	CBen EWay LLWG MSKA SWat WMAq
	'Laydekeri Lilacea' (H)	CBen CRow SWat WMAq
	'Laydekeri Purpurata' (H)	EWay SWat
	'Laydekeri Rosea' misapplied	see *N.* 'Laydekeri Rosea Prolifera'
§	'Laydekeri Rosea Prolifera' (H)	CBen EWay
	'Lemon Chiffon' (H)	CBen CRow
	'Lemon Mist' (H)	LLWG
	'Lily Pons' (H)	CBen EWay LLWG
	'Liou' (H)	CBen LLWG MSKA
	'Little Sue' (H)	CBAq EWay LLWG MSKA
	'Livingstone' (H)	LLWG
	'Lucida' (H)	CBen MSKA SWat WMAq
	'Madame Bory Latour-Marliac' (H)	CBen
	'Madame Wilfon Gonnère' (H)	CBAq CBen CWat EHon EWay MSKA NPer SVic SWat WMAq
	'Mangkala Ubol' (H) **new**	CBen
	'Marliacea Albida' (H)	CBen CWat EHon EWay LLWG MSKA NPer SWat WMAq WPnP XBlo XLum
	'Marliacea Carnea' (H)	CBen CRow EHon MSKA NPer SWat WMAq
§	'Marliacea Chromatella' (H) ♀H7	CBAq CBen CRow CWat EHon EWay GQue MSKA MWts SVic SWat WMAq XBlo XLum
	'Marliacea Rosea' (H)	CBen MSKA SWat WMAq XBlo XLum
	'Martha' (H)	EWay
	'Mary' (H)	EWay LLWG
	'Masaniello' (H)	CBen CRow EHon MSKA SWat WMAq
	'Maurice Laydeker' (H)	CBen LLWG
	'Maxima'	see *N.* 'Odorata Maxima'
	'Mayla' (H)	CBAq CBen EWay LLWG MSKA NPer
§	'Météor' (H)	CBen EWay MSKA WMAq
	mexicana	LLWG
	'Millennium Pink'	MSKA
	'Moorei' (H)	CBen MSKA SWat WMAq
	'Mrs Richmond' misapplied	see *N.* 'Fabiola'
	'Mrs Richmond' Latour-Marliac (H)	CBen SWat XBlo
	'Munkala Ubon' (H)	LLWG
	'Murillo' (H)	EWay
	'Neptune' (H)	LLWG
	'Newchapel Beauty'	WMAq
	'Newton' (H)	CBen CWat EWay LLWG MSKA SWat WMAq
	'Nigel' (H)	CBAq EWay LLWG MSKA SWat
	'Norma Gedye' (H)	CBen CWat MSKA SWat WMAq
	'Odalisque' (H)	CBen
§	***odorata*** (H)	CBen CRow EHon MSKA WMAq
§	- var. ***minor*** (H)	CBen CRow EWay MSKA SWat WMAq
	- 'Pumila'	see *N. odorata* var. *minor*
	- subsp. ***tuberosa*** (H)	CBen
	'Odorata Alba'	see *N. odorata*
	'Odorata Juliana' (H)	EWay
§	'Odorata Maxima' (H)	WMAq
	'Odorata Sulphurea' (H)	CBAq SWat
§	'Odorata Sulphurea Grandiflora' (H)	CBen CRow SWat XBlo
§	'Odorata Turicensis' (H)	MSKA
	'Odorata William B. Shaw'	see *N.* 'W.B. Shaw'
	'Pam Bennett' (H)	CBen LLWG
	'Pamela' (T/D)	EWay
	'Panama Pacific' (T/D)	XBlo
	'Patio Joe'	EWay LLWG MSKA
	'Paul Hariot' (H)	CWat EWay LLWG MSKA NPer SWat WMAq WPnP
	'Peace Lily' (H)	CBAq EWay LLWG MSKA
	'Peach Glow' (H)	EWay LLWG MSKA
	'Peaches and Cream' (H)	EWay LLWG MSKA
	Pearl of the Pool (H)	SWat
	'Perry's Baby Red' (H)	CBAq CBen CWat EWay LLWG MSKA MWts NPer WMAq

'Perry's Crinkled Pink' (H) CBen
'Perry's Double White' (H) EWay NPer WPnP
'Perry's Double Yellow' (H) LLWG MSKA
'Perry's Dwarf Red' (H) LLWG MSKA
'Perry's Fire Opal' (H) EWay LLWG NPer
'Perry's Orange Sunset' (H) LLWG MSKA
'Perry's Pink' (H) SWat WMAq
'Perry's Red Bicolor' (H) LLWG
'Perry's Red Glow' (H) LLWG MSKA
'Perry's Red Star' (H) EWay MSKA
'Perry's Red Wonder' (H) CBen
'Perry's Viviparous Pink' (H) CBen
'Perry's White Star' (H) LLWG
'Perry's Yellow Sensation' see *N.* 'Yellow Sensation'
'Peter Slocum' (H) CBen EWay SWat
'Phoebus' (H) CBen SWat
'Picciola' (H) LLWG
'Pink Domino' (H) MSKA
'Pink Grapefruit' (H) LLWG XBlo
'Pink Opal' (H) CBen CWat EWay LLWG
'Pink Peony' (H) EWay MSKA
'Pink Pumpkin' (H) EWay LLWG MSKA
'Pink Sensation' (H) CBen EWay LLWG MSKA NPer SLon SWat WMAq
'Pink Sparkle' (H) EWay LLWG
'Pink Starlet' (H) EWay
'Pink Sunrise' (H) EWay MSKA
'Pöstlingberg' (H) LLWG MSKA
'Princess Elizabeth' (H) EHon LLWG
'Pygmaea Alba' see *N. tetragona*
§ 'Pygmaea Helvola' (H) ♀H7 CBen CRow CWat EWay MSKA MWts NPer SLon SVic SWat WMAq WPnP
'Pygmaea Rubis' (H) CRow SWat WMAq
'Pygmaea Rubra' (H) CBen CRow CWat EWay LLWG MSKA MWts NPer SVic WMAq WPnP
'Radiant Red' (H) LLWG
'Ray Davies' (H) CBen LLWG
'Red Paradise' (H) LLWG MSKA
'Red Spider' (H) CWat EWay LLWG MSKA NPer SVic
'Reflected Flame' (H) EWay LLWG
'Rembrandt' misapplied see *N.* 'Météor'
'Rembrandt' Koster (H) CBen
'René Gérard' (H) CBen CWat EHon GQue MSKA MWts NPer SWat WMAq WPnP
'Rosanna Supreme' (H) LLWG SWat
'Rose Arey' (H) CBen EWay LLWG MSKA NPer SVic SWat WMAq
'Rose Magnolia' (H) CWat SWat
'Rosennymphe' (H) CBen MSKA NPer SWat WMAq WPnP
'Rosy Morn' (H) CBen LLWG MSKA
'Seignouretti' (H) LLWG
'Shady Lady' (H) CBAq LLWG MSKA MWts
'Sioux' (H) CBAq CBen MSKA NPer SVic WMAq XBlo
'Sirbangpra' (H) LLWG
'Sirius' (H) CBen LLWG MSKA SWat
'Snow Princess' (H) EWay
'Solfatare' (H) EWay LLWG
'Splendida' (H) WMAq
'Starbright' (H) EWay LLWG
'Starburst' (H) LLWG MSKA
'Steven Strawn' (H) LLWG
'Sultan' (H) MSKA
'Sunny Pink' (H) CBen EWay LLWG MSKA
'Sunrise' see *N.* 'Odorata Sulphurea Grandiflora'
'Tan-khwan' (H) LLWG
§ ***tetragona*** (H) CRow CWat EWay NPer WMAq WPnP
- 'Alba' see *N. tetragona*
'Texas Dawn' (H) CBen CWat EWay LLWG MSKA SLon WMAq
'Thomas O'Brian' (H) LLWG
'Tuberosa Flavescens' see *N.* 'Marliacea Chromatella'
'Tuberosa Richardsonii' (H) CBen EHon MSKA NPer
'Turicensis' see *N.* 'Odorata Turicensis'
'Venusta' (H) EWay
'Vésuve' (H) LLWG MSKA SWat
'Virginalis' (H) CBen LLWG MSKA NPer SWat WMAq
'Virginia' (H) LLWG
§ 'W.B. Shaw' (H) CBAq CBen EHon MSKA NPer SWat WMAq
'Walter Pagels' (H) CBAq EWay LLWG MWts WMAq
'Wanvisa' (H) **new** CBen LLWG
'Weymouth Red' (H) CBen
'White Sultan' (H) CWat LLWG MSKA
'William Doogue' (H) MSKA
'William Falconer' (H) CBen CWat MSKA NPer SWat
'Wow' (H) MSKA
'Yellow Princess' (H) EWay
'Yellow Queen' (H) MSKA
§ 'Yellow Sensation' (H) CBen
'Yul Ling' (H) EWay LLWG
'Zeus' MSKA
'Ziyu' (H) EWay

Nymphoides (*Menyanthaceae*)

indica LLWG XBlo
peltata CBAq CBen CHab CWat EHon EWay MSKA NPer SVic WMAq WPnP XLum

Nyssa ✿ (*Nyssaceae*)

aquatica CBcs
leptophylla NLar SBir WPGP
ogeche SSta
sinensis CAbP CBcs CDul CMCN CMac CTho ELan EPfP IDee LRHS MAsh MBlu MPkF NLar SBir SPer WPat
- 'Jim Russell' ESwi NLar SBir
- Nymans form LRHS SBir
- Savill form SSta
sylvatica Widely available
- 'Autumn Cascades' EBee EPfP EPla LRHS MAsh MBlu NLar SBir SSpi SSta
- var. ***biflora*** SSta
- Bulk's form SSta
- 'Dirr' SSpi
- 'Haymen's Red' see *N. sylvatica* Red Rage
- 'Isabel Grace' EPfP LRHS MAsh SBir SSpi
- 'Jermyns Flame' CAbP EPfP LRHS MAsh NLar SBir
- Jolly = 'Yiping' (v) MPkF
- 'Lakeside Weeper' SBir
- 'Miss Scarlet' (f) NLar SBir SSta
- 'Pendula' SBir
§ - Red Rage = 'Haymanred' EPfP MAsh MPkF NLar SBir
- 'Red Red Wine' EPfP IVic NLar SBir WPGP
- 'Sheffield Park' CAbP LRHS MAsh SBir SLim SPoG
- 'Valley Scorcher' NLar
- 'Wildfire' LRHS MPkF SBir SGol
- 'Windsor' EPfP LRHS MAsh SBir

- 'Wisley Bonfire' (m) CAbP CDoC ELan EPfP LRHS MAsh NLar SBir SPoG SSpi SSta WPGP
ursina CBcs

O

Oakesiella see *Uvularia*

Ochagavia (*Bromeliaceae*)

carnea WCot
- RCB RA S-2 LSou
elegans WCot
§ **litoralis** SArc SMad WCot
* **rosea** CHEx SPlb

Ochna (*Ochnaceae*)

serrulata CCCN

Ocimum (*Lamiaceae*)

'African Blue' CArn CBod CSpe ELau ENfk EOHP GPoy LSou MHer SPoG SRms
§ × **africanum** ENfk MNHC SHDw SIde WJek
- 'Lime' ENfk MNHC
- Pesto Perpetuo = 'Perpetuo'PBR (v) ENfk SRms
- 'Siam Queen' ELau MHer WJek
- 'Spicy Globe' ELau
§ **americanum** WJek
- 'Meng Luk' see *O. americanum*
basilicum CArn ELau GPoy NPri SIde SRms SWat WJek
- 'Anise' see *O. basilicum* 'Horapha'
- 'Ararat' ELau
- **camphorata** see *O. kilimandscharicum*
- 'Cinnamon' ELau ENfk MNHC SHDw WJek
- 'Dark Opal' ENfk MNHC SHDw SRms
- 'Gecofure' ELau
- 'Genovese' ELau MHer MNHC
- 'Genovese Special Select' ELau
- 'Glycyrrhiza' see *O. basilicum* 'Horapha'
- 'Green Ruffles' CUse ELau EPfP WJek
- 'Holy' see *O. tenuiflorum*
§ - 'Horapha' CArn ELau ENfk MHer MNHC SIde WJek
* - 'Horapha Nanum' ENfk WJek
- 'Magic Michael' ELau
- 'Magic Mountain' SPoG
- 'Magic White' SPoG
- 'Mexican' ELau
- 'Mrs Burns' Lemon' ♀1c WJek
- 'Napoletano' CBod ELau ENfk SIde SWat WJek
- 'New Guinea' ELau
- 'Osmin'PBR ELau
- 'Pistou' **new** ELau
- 'Purple Delight' ELau
- var. **purpurascens** SIde
- - 'Purple Ruffles' ENfk EPfP MNHC SIde SWat WJek
- - 'Red Rubin' MHer WJek
- var. **purpurascens** × **kilimandscharicum** CSpe GPoy
- 'Queenette' ELau
- red-leaved ♀H1c **new** CUse
- 'Sweet Genovase' CUse SVic
- 'Thai' see *O. basilicum* 'Horapha'
canum see *O. americanum*
× **citriodorum** see *O.* × *africanum*
gratissimum CArn ELau
§ **kilimandscharicum** ELau GPoy
minimum ELau ENfk MHer MNHC SIde WJek
sanctum see *O. tenuiflorum*
'Spice' ELau ENfk
§ **tenuiflorum** CArn ELau GPoy MNHC SHDw SIde SPre WJek

Odontonema (*Acanthaceae*)

schomburgkianum CCCN
tubaeforme CCCN MOWG

Oemleria (*Rosaceae*)

cerasiformis CBcs CHGN CJun CTri EBtc EPfP EPla LEdu LRHS MMuc NLar WCot WGwG WSHC

Oenanthe (*Apiaceae*)

fistulosa LLWG MSKA
javanica **new** LEdu
- 'Flamingo' (v) CBAq CWat EBee ELan EWay GCal LEdu MSKA MWts NBro WMAq WSHC XLum
lachenalii LLWG SDix
pimpinelloides CHab LLWG

Oenothera ✿ (*Onagraceae*)

§ **acaulis** CSpe MNrw WCot WPGP
§ - 'Aurea' XLum
- 'Lutea' see *O. acaulis* 'Aurea'
'Apricot Delight' CHVG CWld EHoe GJos LRHS SGbt SPad WMnd WMoo
§ **biennis** CArn ELan ENfk GAbr GPoy MHer MNHC NBro SIde SPhx SRms WBrk WHea WHer WJek WSFF
caespitosa GKev
childsii see *O. speciosa*
cinaeus see *O. fruticosa* subsp. *glauca*
'Colin Porter' WMoo
'Copper Canyon' SGSe
'Crown Imperial' CMac LEdu LSou MArl NHol SHar SLon
Crown of Gold = 'Lishal' LLHF
§ **elata** subsp. **hookeri** EWes NBre
erythrosepala see *O. glazioviana*
'Finlay's Fancy' WCru
§ **fruticosa** NLar SPlb XSen
- 'African Sun'PBR SRot
- 'Camel' (v) NEoE WCot WHrl WWEG XLum
- Fireworks see *O. fruticosa* 'Fyrverkeri'
§ - 'Fyrverkeri' CBcs CMea CPrp ECtt ELan GMaP LEdu LRHS MRav NGdn SCob SPer SWvt WWEG XLum
§ - subsp. **glauca** CElw EPfP MHer SMrm SRms WJek
- - 'Erica Robin' (v) CChe ECtt EHoe GBin LPla LRHS LSou MAvo MNrw MRav NEgg NGdn SMad SMrm SRot SWvt WCot WHoo WWEG
- - 'Longest Day' MBrN
- - Solstice see *O. fruticosa* subsp. *glauca* 'Sonnenwende'
§ - - 'Sonnenwende' CBre CElw LRHS NEoE NLar WMoo WWEG XLum
- Highlight see *O. fruticosa* 'Hoheslicht'
§ - 'Hoheslicht' EBee
- 'Lady Brookeborough' MRav
- 'Michelle Ploeger' NBre

Plant	Suppliers
- 'Silberblatt' (v)	EBee
- 'Yellow River'	CElw EBee
- 'Youngii'	EPfP LEdu MMuc SEND WJek WWEG
'Give-me-Sunshine'	SLon
glabra Miller	see *O. biennis*
§ ***glazioviana***	GKev MNHC NBir
hookeri	see *O. elata* subsp. *hookeri*
kunthiana	CBod ECha WMoo
- 'Glowing Magenta'	SPoG
lamarckiana	see *O. glazioviana*
Lemon Drop = 'Innoeno131'^{PBR}	LRHS MPkF
'Lemon Sunset'	EAJP LSou MSpe WMoo
linearis	see *O. fruticosa*
§ ***macrocarpa*** ♀^{H5}	Widely available
- subsp. ***fremontii***	XSen
- - 'Silver Wings'	LRHS SMrm SPhx
- subsp. ***incana***	CMea CSpe SPhx WHoo
- 'Yellow Queen'	GJos
missouriensis	see *O. macrocarpa*
oakesiana	SPhx
odorata misapplied	see *O. stricta*
odorata Hook. & Arn.	see *O. biennis*
odorata Jacquin	XLum
- cream-flowered	CSpe
organensis	CDes EBee MNrw
§ ***perennis***	NEoE SRms WThu XLum
pilosella new	WCot
- 'Yella Fella'	CHVG
pumila	see *O. perennis*
rosea	CMea XLum
serrulata	see *Calylophus serrulatus*
§ ***speciosa***	MMuc SEND SPhx SRms WJek XLum
* - 'Alba'	EBee EWes
- var. ***childsii***	see *O. speciosa*
- 'Pink Petticoats'	ECha LSun NPer
- 'Rosea'	LAst SPlb
- 'Siskiyou'	CBcs CBod EAEE ECtt EPfP EPla EWoo LEdu LRHS MNrw NBro SCob SCoo SMrm SPer SPoG WGwG XLum
- Twilight = 'Turner01'^{PBR} (v)	CAbb LRHS SCob SHar
- 'Woodside White'	SMrm
§ ***stricta***	CMea GCal MNrw
- 'Sulphurea'	CMHG CMea EBee ECGP ELan EWld GCal IFro LRHS MNFA NPer SMrm SPhx WCot
'Summer Sun'	CBod EAEE ECGP EPla MWat SPer
taraxacifolia	see *O. acaulis*
tetragona	see *O. fruticosa* subsp. *glauca*
- var. ***fraseri***	see *O. fruticosa* subsp. *glauca*
versicolor 'Sunset Boulevard'	CSpe CTsd EAJP GCal GJos LRHS MMuc SHar SPer WMoo XLum

Olea (*Oleaceae*)

Plant	Suppliers
europaea (F)	Widely available
- 'Aglandau' (F)	CAgr
- 'Arbequina' (F)	SBig
- 'Bouteillan' (F)	CAgr
- 'Cailletier' (F)	CAgr
- 'Chelsea Physic Garden' (F)	CDoC
§ - 'Cipressino' (F)	ESwi LPal LRHS MGos SBig
- 'El Greco' (F)	CBcs
- 'Fastigiata'	EBee EPla LRHS
- 'Frantoio' (F)	CAgr SBig
- 'Hojiblanca' (F)	EBee SBig
- 'Leccino' (F)	SBig
- 'Maurino' (F)	SBig
- 'Peace'	CDoy
- 'Pendolino' (F)	CAco SBig
- 'Picual' (F)	SBig
- 'Pyramidalis'	see *O. europaea* 'Cipressino'

Olearia ✿ (*Asteraceae*)

Plant	Suppliers
arborescens 'Moondance' (v) new	LRHS
argophylla	CBcs CExl ECou
avicenniifolia	CMac ECou IVic SEND
bullata	ECou
× ***capillaris***	CBcs CDoC EBee ECou
chathamica	IVic
§ ***cheesemanii***	CBcs CDoC CExl GGal LRHS NLar SVen
coriacea	ECou
'County Park'	CWSG ECou
erubescens × ***ilicifolia***	SVen
furfuracea	ECou GLin SEND
glandulosa	ECou
gunniana	see *O. phlogopappa*
× ***haastii***	Widely available
- 'McKenzie'	ECou ELon
'Havering Blush'	ECou
hectorii	ECou
§ 'Henry Travers'	CBcs CCCN CExl EPfP GCal IVic SVen
ilicifolia	CDoC CTsd EPfP IDee IVic LRHS MAsh
insignis	see *Pachystegia insignis*
lacunosa	IDee WHor
lepidophylla	ECou
- silver-leaved	ECou
lirata	ECou
macrodonta ♀^{H4}	Widely available
- 'Major'	CCCN GGal MBri NLar SCob
- 'Minor'	CCCN CMac CSde ELan EPfP GCal GQui IVic SPlb
× ***mollis*** (Kirk) Cockayne	CMac CSde GQui LRHS
- 'Zennorensis' ♀^{H3}	CBcs CCCN CDoC EPfP IDee IVic NLar
nummularifolia	CBcs CBod CCCN CDoC CHll CTri CTsd EBee ECou ELan EPfP EPla GKin IVic LRHS NLar NSoo SEND SPer SVen SWvt
- var. ***cymbifolia***	ECou
odorata	ECou NLar
oleifolia	see *O.* 'Waikariensis'
paniculata	CDoC CMHG CSde CTri CTsd EPfP IDee IVic LRHS NSoo SEND SVen
§ ***phlogopappa***	CTri ECou GLin SVen
- 'Comber's Blue'	CBcs CCCN ELan EPfP GGal GKin IVic LRHS MAsh SLim SPer
§ - 'Comber's Pink'	CBcs CBod CCCN CDoC CExl CHid ELan ELon EPfP EWld GKin LBMP LRHS MMuc MSCN NPer SLim SPer SPoG WGrn WKif WSHC
- 'Rosea'	see *O. phlogopappa* 'Comber's Pink'
I - var. ***subrepanda*** (DC.) J.H.Willis	GGal
ramulosa	CCCN CExl CSde
- 'Blue Stars'	CMac ECou LRHS MBri SLon SRms WGrn
rani misapplied	see *O. cheesemanii*
× ***scilloniensis*** misapplied	see *O. stellulata* DC.

× ***scilloniensis*** ambig.	CBcs ELan EPla EWld MAsh SPoG
× ***scilloniensis*** Dorrien-Smith 🏆H3	CCCN CTsd MMuc MRav SEND
- 'Compacta'	CBcs
- 'Master Michael' 🏆H3	CCCN CDoC CTri ELon EWld IVic LBMP LRHS MOWG NLar SPer SPoG WGrn WPGP WSHC
semidentata misapplied	see *O.* 'Henry Travers'
solandri	CBod CCCN CDoC CMac CSde CTsd ECou EHoe IDee LRHS NLar SDix SEND
- 'Aurea'	CBcs ETwe
'Starburst' **new**	WCot
'Stardust'	LRHS SPlb SVen
stellulata misapplied	see *O. phlogopappa*
§ ***stellulata*** DC.	CExl CMac CSBt ECou EPfP GGal SDix SLim SPer
- 'Michael's Pride'	CBod CExl
- var. ***rugosa***	ECou
traversii	CBcs CBod CCCN CDoC CMHG CSBt CSde EPfP LRHS NWea SEND WHer
- 'Tweedledum' (v)	CBod CCCN CDoC CSde EHoe
- 'Variegata' (v)	CBcs SEND
virgata	CCCN CHEx ECou IDee NLar
- var. ***laxiflora***	WHer
- var. ***lineata***	CSde ECou NLar SEND WHer WSHC
- - 'Dartonii'	CBcs CBod CTsd ECou EPfP GBin LRHS SPlb SVen
§ 'Waikariensis'	CBod CExl CMHG CMac ECou GKin IVic LRHS MAsh SEND SLon WCFE

Oligoneuron see *Solidago*

Oligostachyum (*Poaceae*)

lubricum	see *Semiarundinaria lubrica*
oedogonatum	WPGP

olive see *Olea europaea*

Olsynium (*Iridaceae*)

§ ***douglasii*** 🏆H5	CBro CPom ECho EPot LLHF NRya NSla WWFP
- 'Album'	CWCL EBee ECho ELon EPot GBin LLHF MNrw NHar NRya NSla WWFP
- var. ***inflatum***	EWes
§ ***filifolium***	GAbr
§ ***junceum***	CSpe WPGP
trinerve B&SWJ 10459	WCru

Omphalodes ✿ (*Boraginaceae*)

'Blue Eyes' **new**	MHol MPie WCot
cappadocica 🏆H5	CElw EPfP IFoB LEdu LRHS NBro NPer NSla SRms SWat WBrk
- 'Cherry Ingram' 🏆H5	Widely available
- 'Lilac Mist'	CLAP EBee GBuc LLWP MRav SRms SWvt WWEG
- 'Starry Eyes'	Widely available
§ ***linifolia*** 🏆H3	CSpe GKev MCot SPhx
- ***alba***	see *O. linifolia*
nitida	CSpe EWld IMou LLHF MNrw NSbr WWEG
verna	CBod CHel CMac CTri EBee ECha ECho ELan EPPr EPfP GAbr GEdr GJos GMaP LLWP LRHS MBel MCot MNFA MNrw NChi NPri SCob SPer SPlb SPoG SWat WFar WPGP WWEG
- 'Alba'	Widely available
- 'Elfenauge'	EBee GMaP IMou NBir NLar SMrm WCot WWEG
- ***grandiflora***	WCot

Oncostema see *Scilla*

onion see *Allium cepa*

Onixotis (*Colchicaceae*)

stricta	CLak WCot

Onobrychis (*Papilionaceae*)

viciifolia	CWld

Onoclea (*Onocleaceae*)

sensibilis 🏆H6	Widely available
- copper-leaved	CHEx CJun MMoz WPGP

Ononis (*Papilionaceae*)

cristata **new**	WAbe
repens	CArn
spinosa	IMou MHer SMrm

Onopordum (*Asteraceae*)

acanthium	CArn ECha ELan ENfk GAbr GMaP GPoy LEdu LRHS LSun MHer MWat NBid NChi NGBl SHar SIde SPhx WFar WHea WOut
arabicum	see *O. nervosum*
§ ***nervosum*** 🏆H7	CSpe SEND

Onosma (*Boraginaceae*)

alborosea	CCse ECha ECre ELan GCal GCra SEND WKif
nana	CTal WAbe
rigida	SBrt
tornensis	SBrt

Onychium (*Pteridaceae*)

contiguum	WCot
japonicum	CBty CExl EFer EFtx GQui ISha LRHS MRav WCot

Ophiopogon ✿ (*Asparagaceae*)

BWJ 8244 from Vietnam	WCru
from India	GCal
'Black Dragon'	see *O. planiscapus* 'Nigrescens'
bodinieri	CBct ECho EShb EWes LEdu
- B&L 12505	CLAP EBee EPPr EPla MMoz
caulescens B&SWJ 8230	WCru
- B&SWJ 11813	WCru
aff. ***caulescens*** B&SWJ 11287 **new**	WCru
- HWJ 590	WCru WPGP
chingii	EPPr EWes GCal LEdu WCot
* - 'Crispum'	EBee
clarkei	MMoz
clavatus KWJ 12267	WCru
formosanus B&SWJ 3659	WCru
'Gin-ryu'	see *Liriope spicata* 'Gin-ryu'
graminifolius	see *Liriope muscari*
'Hosoba Kokuryu'	GBin
intermedius	CBct EPPr EShb WCot
- GWJ 9387	WCru

§ - 'Argenteomarginatus' (v) ECho EWes
- 'Variegatus' see *O. intermedius* 'Argenteomarginatus'
§ ***jaburan*** CMac EBee ECho LEdu WMoo WPtf
- 'Variegatus' see *O. jaburan* 'Vittatus'
§ - 'Vittatus' (v) ECho EHoe ELan EWes LEdu MGos MPkF WCot
japonicus CMac CTsd ECho EPPr EPla EShb GPoy LEdu LPal SCob SGol XLum
- B&SWJ 1871 WCru
- 'Albus' CLAP ECho EPri MWat
- 'Compactus' CDoC WPGP
- 'Gyoku-Ryu' EBee GCal
- 'Kigimafukiduma' CExl CMac MRav SGol
- 'Kyoto' EPPr ESwi NOak
- 'Minor' CBct CKno ELon EPPr IGor LBMP LPal NLar SCob WPGP WWEG XLum
- 'Nanus Variegatus' (v) EBee
- 'Nippon' ECho EHoe EPPr NGdn
- 'Silver Dragon' (v) EPPr MBri WCFE
* - 'Tama-ryu Number Two' ECho EPPr
* - 'Variegatus' (v) CDTJ CMac ECho LEdu SPer
aff. ***latifolius*** KWJ 12031 **new** WCru
parviflorus GWJ 9387 WCru
- HWJK 2093 WCru
planiscapus CExl CKno CMHG CUse ECha ECho EPPr EPla NBro SPad SPtp WMoo WWEG
* - 'Albovariegatus' (v) WFar
- 'Black Beard' CKno EAEE EUJe EWTr GBin LRHS MAsh MBri
- f. ***leucanthus*** EPPr WCot
- 'Little Tabby' (v) CDes CFil CLAP CMil EBee ECho EPla MMoz NEoE WCot WGrn WHal WWEG
§ - 'Nigrescens' ♀H5 Widely available
- 'Silver Ribbon' ECho
scaber B&SWJ 1842 WCru
- B&SWJ 3655 WCru
'Spring Gold' EShb
umbraticola **new** EBee

Ophrys (*Orchidaceae*)

apifera WHer

Oplopanax (*Araliaceae*)

horridus CArn
- B&SWJ 9551 WCru
japonicus WCru

Opopanax (*Apiaceae*)

chironium CArn SDix SPhx
- PAB 845 LEdu

Opuntia (*Cactaceae*)

chloritica NNS 99-262 **new** WCot
compressa see *O. humifusa*
engelmannii SChr
erinacea SChr WCot
ficus-indica SPlb WCot
fragilis SChr SKHP XSen
§ ***humifusa*** CDTJ SChr WCot XLum XSen
phaeacantha SChr
§ ***polyacantha*** SChr SPlb
- 'Carmin' XSen
rhodantha see *O. polyacantha*
spinosior XLum

orange, sour or Seville see *Citrus* × *aurantium* Sour Orange Group

orange, sweet see *Citrus* × *aurantium* Sweet Orange Group

Orbexilum (*Papilionaceae*)

pedunculatum var. ***psoralioides*** SBrt SPhx

Orchis (*Orchidaceae*)

anthropophora EFEx
elata see *Dactylorhiza elata*
foliosa see *Dactylorhiza foliosa*
fuchsii see *Dactylorhiza fuchsii*
maculata see *Dactylorhiza maculata*
maderensis see *Dactylorhiza foliosa*
majalis see *Dactylorhiza majalis*
§ ***mascula*** ECho WHer

oregano see *Origanum vulgare*

Oreocharis (*Gesneriaceae*)

aurea B&SWJ 11718 **new** WCru

Oreomyrrhis (*Apiaceae*)

argentea CSpe EBee GKev SDix SPhx

Oreopanax (*Araliaceae*)

floribundus see *O. incisus*
§ ***incisus*** WCru
xalapensis B&SWJ 10444 **new** WCru

Oreopteris (*Thelypteridaceae*)

§ ***limbosperma*** WCot

Origanum ✿ (*Lamiaceae*)

from Kalamata SEND
acutidens XSen
amanum ♀H3 CPBP ECho EPot EWes NBir NSla SBch WAbe
- var. ***album*** ECho NSla WAbe
× ***applii*** ELau
'Barbara Tingey' CTal CWCL ECho EWes ITim MNrw SRms WCFE
'Bristol Cross' CTal ECtt LEdu MHer XSen
'Buckland' CTal ECho ECtt ITim WAbe WSHC
caespitosum see *O. vulgare* 'Nanum'
§ ***calcaratum*** ECho LLHF WAbe XSen
'Carol's Delight' MHer
creticum see *O. vulgare* subsp. *hirtum*
dictamnus CMea ECho GPoy LLHF MHer SIgm WJek XSen
'Dingle Fairy' CPBP CWCL ECho ECtt EPot EWTr EWes MHer MNrw NBir SBch SIde SRot SWvt WMoo XSen
ehrenbergii XSen
'Emma Stanley' WAbe
'Frank Tingey' ECho LLHF
'Gold Splash' EPfP SIde WMoo
'Golden Narrow' **new** EBee LRHS
heracleoticum L. see *O. vulgare* subsp. *hirtum*
'Hot and Spicy' CPbn ENfk LEdu MHer SRms WJek XSen

	'Ingolstadt' (v)	SPhx WCot
	'Jekka's Beauty'	WJek
	'Kent Beauty' ♀H4	CMea CSpe CWCL EBee ECho ECtt ELan EPfP EPot EShb GBuc IMou LRHS LSou MHer MRav NBir SPhx SWvt WAbe WHea WJek WKif WSHC XSen
	'Kent Beauty Variegated' (v)	ECho
	laevigatum ♀H7	ECho ELan EPfP EPot MHer NBro NPer SIde WCot WKif WMoo WSHC XSen
I	- 'Aromaticum'	IMou
	- dwarf **new**	SIgm
	- 'Herrenhausen' ♀H7	Widely available
	- 'Hopleys'	CBod CPrp CTri EAJP EBee ECha ELan EPfP LEdu LRHS MBri MCot MHer MHol MRav MWat NBir NDov SEND SPer SPhx SRms WHea WHoo WSHC XSen
	- 'Purple Charm'	EDAr SRms
	majorana	CArn CHab CPbn CUse ELau ENfk GPoy MHer MNHC SIde SRms SVic SWat WJek
I	- 'Aureum'	GKev
	- Pagoda Bells = 'Lizbell'[PBR]	CBod CWCL MTis SIde SRot WHoo
	'Marchants Seedling'	SMHy SPhx
	microphyllum	CArn
	minutiflorum	ECho LLHF
	'Norton Gold'	CBre ECha ECtt MHer NPer SIde
	'Nymphenburg'	LSou
	onites	CBod CHby CUse ELau ENfk MHer MNHC SIde SPlb SRms WJek
	Overseas Farm hybrid	MHer
	'Rosenkuppel' ♀H7	CBod CMea ECha ECtt ELan EPot MHer MLHP NDov SBch SPer SPhx SPlb SWvt WJek WMoo WPnn WWEG XSen
	'Rotkugel'	WCFE WWEG
	rotundifolium ♀H4	CMea ECho ELan LEdu MHer NBir SBch WThu XSen
	scabrum subsp. ***pulchrum*** 'Newleaze'	SBch
	syriacum	CArn
	tournefortii	see *O. calcaratum*
	vulgare	CArn CHab CPbn CTsd CUse GAbr GJos GMaP GPoy MHer MMuc MNHC NBro NMir NPol NPri SEND SIde SPlb SRms SVic WHer WJek WSFF XLum
	- from Israel	ELau
	- 'Acorn Bank'	CArn CBod CPrp ECtt ELau ENfk EWes LEdu MNHC NLar SIde SPoG SRms WHer WJek
	- var. ***album***	ELau
	- 'Aureum' ♀H6	Widely available
	- 'Aureum Crispum'	CBod CPrp ECha ELau ENfk GPoy NBid SIde SRms SWat WJek
	- 'Compactum'	CArn CBod CMea CPrp CUse EBee ECha ELau ENfk EPot GCal GPoy LEdu MHer MNFA MNHC NBir NSla SIde SPlb SRms SWat WAbe WJek XLum XSen
	- 'Country Cream' (v)	CBod CElw CPbn CPrp EBee ECtt ELau ENfk EPfP EPla EPot EWes LPot LRHS MHer MLHP MNHC NBir NGdn SHDw SPer SPlb SPoG SRms SRot SWat WCFE WMnd WWEG
	- var. ***formosanum*** B&SWJ 3180	WCru
§	- 'Gold Tip' (v)	CBod CMea CUse ELau ENfk MCot MHer MHol MNHC SIde SPlb SRms SWat WHer WJek WWEG
	- 'Golden Shine'	EHoe EWes SIde
§	- subsp. ***hirtum***	CArn CHby CPbn GPoy SPlb WJek
	- - 'Greek'	CBod ELau ENfk LEdu MHer MNHC SRms
§	- 'Nanum'	SRms WJek
	- 'Nyamba'	GPoy
	- 'Pink Mist'	MNrw
	- 'Polyphant' (v)	CBod CPbn CUse LSou NBir SHar SRms WJek XSen
	- 'Thumble's Variety'	CBod CElw CMea CPrp EAEE EBee ECha ECtt EHoe EPfP EPla GCal LRHS MAsh MBri MHer MRav SWat SWvt WCFE WHer WMnd WMoo WWEG XLum XSen
	- 'Tomintoul'	GPoy
	- 'Variegatum'	see *O. vulgare* 'Gold Tip'
	- 'White Charm'	CPbn EBee NWad SIde
	'Z'Attar'	MHer WJek

Orixa (*Rutaceae*)

japonica	CExl NLar WPGP
- 'Variegata' (v)	LRHS NLar

Orlaya (*Apiaceae*)

grandiflora	CBre CCon CSam CSpe LEdu LRHS MCot SBch SPhx WCot WHal

Ornithogalum (*Asparagaceae*)

	algeriense	ECho
	arabicum	CBro CCCN CCon ECho GKev LAma MBri SDeJ SPhx WCot
	arcuatum	WCot
	arianum	ECho
	balansae	see *O. oligophyllum*
	caudatum	see *O. longibracteatum*
	chionophilum	ECho
	dubium ♀H2	ECho ELan
	- hybrids	GKev
	fimbriatum	ECho WCot
	juncifolium **new**	GKev
	lanceolatum	ECho GKev WCot
§	***longibracteatum***	CHEx ECho GKev SChr WHer
	magnum	CAvo CBro CWCL EBee ECho EPot ERCP GBin GBuc GKev MCot MNrw SDeJ WCot
	'Mount Everest'	GKev
	'Mount Fuji'	GKev
	multifolium 'Loeriesfontein'	ECho
	'Namib Gold'	GKev SDeJ
	nanum	see *O. sigmoideum*
	narbonense	ECha ECho EPot GKev WCot
	nutans ♀H4	CAvo CBro CHid CWCL EBee ECho EPot GBin GBuc GCal GKev LAma LRHS MNrw NBir SDeJ SEND
§	***oligophyllum***	ECho EPot MNrw
§	***orthophyllum***	ECho
	ponticum	ECho WCot
	pyramidale	EBee ECho MNrw SPhx
	- short	SMHy
	pyrenaicum	CAvo CSpe ECha GKev WCot WShi XEll
	reverchonii	EBee ECho EPot ERCP

saundersiae	ECho GKev
sibthorpii	see *O. sigmoideum*
§ ***sigmoideum***	EBee GKev
sintenisii	EBee ECho
suaveolens 'Saldanha'	ECho
tenuifolium	see *O. orthophyllum*
- subsp. ***aridum***	ECho
thyrsoides ♀H2	CCCN ECho GBin GKev LAma LRHS SDeJ
ulophyllum	ECho
umbellatum	CAvo CBro CHab CTri ECho GKev GPoy LAma MBri MCot MNrw SDeJ SEND SPer SRms WHil WShi

Ornithoglossum (*Colchicaceae*)

viride	CLak

Orontium (*Araceae*)

aquaticum	CBAq CBen CWat EHon EWay LLWG MSKA MWts NPer SWat WMAq

Orostachys (*Crassulaceae*)

furusei	WHal
iwarenge	CBod
§ ***spinosa***	ECho EDAr EWes GKev LRHS SPlb WAbe WCot

Orthophytum (*Bromeliaceae*)

gurkenii	WCot

Orthrosanthus (*Iridaceae*)

chimboracensis	CCon NLar
- JCA 13743	CPou
laxus	CBod CCon CWCL EAJP ECre EWTr LLHF MAvo NBir SMad WHrl WMoo
multiflorus	CBro CSpe EBee EPri IKil
polystachyus	CAby CTsd LPla SGSe SMrm WSHC

Orychophragmus (*Brassicaceae*)

violaceus	CCCN

Oryzopsis (*Poaceae*)

hymenoides 'Rimrock'	SPhx
lessoniana	see *Anemanthele lessoniana*
miliacea	CSpe EHoe EPPr MMoz SEND SIgm SMHy WCot WHea WPGP WSHC
paradoxa	EPPr

Oscularia (*Aizoaceae*)

§ ***deltoides*** ♀H2	CCCN CHEx SVen

Osmanthus (*Oleaceae*)

armatus	CAbP CBcs CMac EBee EPfP NLar SGol
× ***burkwoodii*** ♀H5	Widely available
§ ***decorus***	CBcs CDoC CHll CMac CTri ELan EPfP MGos MRav NLar NWea SBrt SGol SPer
- 'Angustifolius'	NLar
delavayi ♀H5	Widely available
- 'George Gardner'	CMac
- 'Latifolius'	CExl CJun LRHS MAsh SLon SPoG SWvt
- 'Pearly Gates'	LRHS
forrestii	see *O. yunnanensis*
× ***fortunei***	CDoC CExl CHel EBee EPfP LLHF LRHS SEND SMad WPat
fragrans	CBcs CMCN SLon SWvt
§ ***heterophyllus***	CBcs CDul CMac EBee ECrN ELan EPfP MGos MRav NLar SCob SGol SPer SRms SSta
§ - all gold	ELan EPfP SPoG
- 'Argenteomarginatus'	see *O. heterophyllus* 'Variegatus'
§ - 'Aureomarginatus' (v)	CBcs CDoC CMHG CTsd EHoe ELon GKin SCob SLon SPer WCFE
- 'Aureus' misapplied	see *O. heterophyllus* all gold
- 'Aureus' Rehder	see *O. heterophyllus* 'Aureomarginatus'
§ - 'Goshiki' (v) ♀H5	Widely available
- 'Gulftide'	CDul EPfP LRHS MAsh MGos NLar
- 'Kembu' (v)	NLar
- 'Latifolius Variegatus' (v)	CDoC
- 'Myrtifolius'	CMac NLar
- 'Ōgon'	EPfP
- 'Purple Shaft' ♀H5	CAbP ELan EPfP LRHS MAsh
- 'Purpureus'	CBcs CDoC CDul CHel CMHG CMac EBee ELon GBin MBri MGos MRav MSwo MWat NLar SCob SCoo SEND SGol SLim SLon SPer SSpi WCFE
- 'Rotundifolius'	CBcs CMac NLar
- Tricolor	see *O. heterophyllus* 'Goshiki'
§ - 'Variegatus' (v) ♀H5	CBcs CDoC CDul CMac CSBt EHoe ELan ELon EPfP LAst LBMP LRHS LSou MAsh MGos MRav MSwo NEgg NLar SGbt SGol SHil SLim SPer SPoG SRms SSta SVen WHar
ilicifolius	see *O. heterophyllus*
rigidus	NLar
serrulatus	NLar
suavis	NLar
§ ***yunnanensis*** ♀H5	EPfP MBlu MRav NLar SArc WPGP WPat WSHC

× *Osmarea* see *Osmanthus*

Osmaronia see *Oemleria*

Osmorhiza (*Apiaceae*)

aristata B&SWJ 1607	WCru

Osmunda ✿ (*Osmundaceae*)

sp.	CCCN
asiatica	WCru
cinnamomea ♀H7	CBty CCCN CKel CLAP CWCL EBee EFtx EWes ISha LEdu LRHS MMuc NMyG SEND SGSe
claytoniana	CLAP EBee EFer GLin ISha LRHS WPnP XLum
japonica	CHid CLAP EFtx ISha NCGa
regalis ♀H6	Widely available
- from southern USA	CLAP
- 'Cristata' ♀H6	CBty CLAP ELan EPfP LRHS MMoz MRav NBid NLar SWvt WFib
- 'Purpurascens'	Widely available
- var. ***spectabilis***	CCCN CLAP ISha LRHS
- 'Undulata'	WFib

Osteospermum (*Asteraceae*)

'African Queen'	see *O.* 'Nairobi Purple'
'Astra Outback Purple' (Astra Series)	LAst
Banana Symphony = 'Sekiin47' (Symphony Series)	CBcs CCCN
barberae misapplied	see *O. jucundum*

'Blue Streak'	CCCN CMac
'Buttermilk'	CCCN ELan
'Cannington John'	CCCN
'Cannington Roy'	CBcs CCCN CEnd CMac CSam EBee ECtt ELan EPfP EWoo GAbr GBee LRHS NPri NSir NSoo SPoG
caulescens misapplied	see *O.* 'White Pim'
compact, white-flowered	CHEx
ecklonis	CBcs CCCN CDTJ CHll CTri EPfP NBro NGdn WPnn
- var. ***prostratum***	see *O.* 'White Pim'
Flower Power Double Series (d)	LBuc SPoG
'Giles Gilbey' (v)	CCCN MBNS
'Gold Sparkler' (v)	SEND
'Gweek Variegated' (v)	CCCN
'Helen Dimond'	LRHS
'Hopleys' ♀H3	MHer SEND
'Iced Gem'	LBuc LRHS
'In the Pink'	SHar SPoG WNPC
'Irish'	ECtt EPot IGor LSou SIgm SMrm WIce
§ ***jucundum*** ♀H3	CMea CTri CWCL ECha EWTr MAvo MLHP MMuc NBir NChi NPer SEND SMrm SPlb SRms WCFE WIce WThu
- 'Blackthorn Seedling' ♀H3	CCCN CMea CWGN ECha IVic NGdn
- var. ***compactum***	CBod CHEx CMac CPrp CTsd CWCL ELan ELon EPfP EWoo GLog GMaP LRHS NPer NPri SMrm SPoG SWvt WAbe WHil WHoo WPat
- 'Elliott's Form'	WHoo
- 'Langtrees' ♀H3	SMrm
- 'Nanum'	EDAr
'Keia' (Springstar Series)	CCCN
§ 'Lady Leitrim' ♀H3	CCCN CWCL CWGN EBee ECha ECtt ELan ELon EPfP GCra GLog MGos MSpe NPer NPri SPad SWvt WAbe WPtf
Milk Symphony = 'Seiremi' (Symphony Series)	CCCN CWCL
'Mirach' (Springstar Series)	CWCL
§ 'Nairobi Purple'	CBcs CBod CCCN CHEx CPrp EBee ECtt ELan ELon ESwi LBuc MAvo MHol NPri NSoo SEND SWvt WBor WCot WHil
Nasinga Cream = 'Aknam'PBR (Cape Daisy Series)	CCCN
Orange Symphony = 'Seimora'PBR (Symphony Series)	CBcs CCCN MBNS
'Pale Face'	see *O.* 'Lady Leitrim'
'Peggyi'	see *O.* 'Nairobi Purple'
'Pink Whirls'	CCCN
polygaloides	SPlb
'Port Wine'	see *O.* 'Nairobi Purple'
'Silver Sparkler' (v)	CCCN CDTJ ELan MHer SVen
'Snow Pixie'	CBod CWGN ECtt EDAr ELon EWTr EWoo MHol NPri SWvt
'Sparkler'	CCCN CHEx
'Stardust'PBR	ECtt LBuc LRHS NPer SCoo SPoG
(Sunny Series) 'Sunny Amanda'PBR	SPoG
- 'Sunny Bianca'PBR	SPoG
- 'Sunny Felix'PBR	SPoG
- 'Sunny Mary'PBR	SPoG
I 'Superbum'	CHEx CWCL
I 'Superbum' × 'Lady Leitrim'	CHEx LRHS
'Tauranga'	see *O.* 'Whirlygig'
(Tradewinds Series) Tradewinds Deep Purple = 'Oste Deeppur'PBR	SPoG
- Tradewinds Pearl 10 = 'Tra Whit' **new**	SPoG
'Tresco Peggy'	see *O.* 'Nairobi Purple'
'Tresco Pink'	CCCN
'Tresco Purple'	see *O.* 'Nairobi Purple'
Voltage Yellow = 'Balvoyelo'PBR	WHea
'Weetwood' ♀H3	CCCN CEnd EBee ECtt ELan EPot EWoo GLog LRHS MAvo MHer MLHP SPoG SWvt WAbe WFar
§ 'Whirlygig'	CCCN
§ 'White Pim' ♀H3	CDTJ CHll NPer SDix SEND SMrm
'Wine Purple'	see *O.* 'Nairobi Purple'
'Wisley Pink'	NEgg
Zanzibar Pink Bicolour = 'Akzapib'PBR (Cape Daisy Series)	SPoG
Zanzibar White with Ring = 'Akzawhir'PBR (Cape Daisy Series)	SPoG
'Zaurak' (Springstar Series)	CCCN CWCL
'Zulu' (Cape Daisy Series)	CCCN

Ostrowskia (*Campanulaceae*)

magnifica	EPot

Ostrya (*Betulaceae*)

sp.	CAco
carpinifolia	CBcs CCVT CDul CLnd CMCN CTho EBee ELan EPfP EPla MBlu MBri MMuc NLar NWea SEND SGol SWvt
japonica	CDul CMCN
virginiana	CDul EPfP

Osyris (*Santalaceae*)

alba **new**	CArn

Otatea (*Poaceae*)

aztecorum	ERod

Othonna (*Asteraceae*)

cheirifolia	CCCN CMea CSde EHoe ELan EWes NBir SEND SIgm XLum XSen
coronopifolia	SVen

Othonnopsis see *Othonna*

Ourisia (*Plantaginaceae*)

× ***bitternensis*** 'Cliftonville Crimson'	WAbe
- 'Cliftonville Damask'	WAbe
- 'Cliftonville Ling'	WAbe
- 'Cliftonville Old Rose'	WAbe
- 'Cliftonville Pink'	WAbe
- 'Cliftonville Roset'	WAbe
caespitosa var. ***gracilis***	EPot
coccinea	CCon CTal EWes GAbr GCra GEdr GKev MAvo NBir WHal
'Loch Ewe'	CCon CExl CTal GAbr GKev
macrocarpa	GEdr
macrophylla	NWad
microphylla	WAbe
- 'Hollowcliffe'	WAbe

modesta	GBin
polyantha 'Cliftonville Scarlet'	WAbe
ruelloides	WAbe
'Snowflake' ♀H5	GAbr GEdr GKev IMou NSbr

Oxalis (*Oxalidaceae*)

from Mount Stewart	WMoo
acetosella	GPoy MHer MMHG MMuc NMir NSbr WHer WShi
- var. ***rosea***	IFro IMou
- var. ***subpurpurascens***	IFro WCot
adenodes new	NRog
adenophylla ♀H4	CElw CExl CMea CTri ECho ELan EPot GAbr GEdr GKev GMaP LAma LRHS LSun MJak NEgg NHol NLar SDeJ SPoG SRms
adenophylla × ***enneaphylla***	see *O.* 'Matthew Forrest'
'Anne Christie'	CPBP
anomala	ECho
§ ***articulata***	NPer SEND WCot XLum
- 'Alba'	WCot XLum
- f. ***crassipes*** 'Alba'	WCot
- 'Festival'	EBee ECho GKev
§ - subsp. ***rubra***	EBee GKev SDeJ
'Beatrice Anderson'	ITim
bowiei	EBee ECho EPot WCot
- 'Amarantha'	ECho
brasiliensis	ECho EPot
compressa	NRog
convexula new	NRog
'Dark Eye'	EPot
deppei	see *O. tetraphylla*
§ ***depressa***	CTri ECho EPot EWes GBin GKev LLHF NBir NSla SDeJ SRms
eckloniana	ECho
- var. ***sonderi***	EBee ECho NRog
enneaphylla ♀H4	CElw ECho ELon GBin GEdr LLHF LRHS NRya SBch
- F&W 2715	CPBP
- 'Alba'	CElw CMea CPBP ECho NSla
- subsp. ***ibari***	ECho EPot GEdr GKev ITim NRya NSla
- 'Minutifolia'	LLHF NRya
* - 'Minutifolia Rosea'	CPBP
- 'Rosea'	ECho EPot GKev LLHF NLar NRya NSla SBch
- 'Sheffield Swan'	CPBP ECho GEdr LLHF NHar NSla
- 'Ute'	EPot GEdr
'Fanny'	EBee ECho GKev
flava	CDes ECho NRog
floribunda misapplied	see *O. articulata*
fourcadei	ECho NRog
foveolata new	NRog
griffithii 'Pink Charm'	GEdr
- 'Snowflake'	GEdr MMoz
'Gwen McBride'	CPBP GEdr
hedysaroides misapplied	see *O. spiralis* subsp. *vulcanicola*
hedysaroides Kunth	CCCN
'Hemswell Knight'	CPBP SBch
hirta	EPot SBch
- 'Gothenburg'	EBee ECho EPri NRog
imbricata	ECho LLHF NRog
inops	see *O. depressa*
'Ione Hecker' ♀H4	CMea ECho EPot GCrg GEdr GKev ITim NHar NLar NRya
'Irish Mist' (v)	EBee ECho
* ***karroica***	ECho WCot
§ ***laciniata***	CPBP ECho GKev
- hybrid	GEdr NHar
lactea double-flowered	see *O. magellanica* 'Nelson'
lasiandra	CCCN EBee ECho
loricata	ECho
magellanica	CRow CTri ECho GAbr IMou SPlb WMoo
- 'Flore Pleno'	see *O. magellanica* 'Nelson'
§ - 'Nelson' (d)	EBee ECho ELon GCal MMuc NBir NPer WMoo WPtf
mallobolba 'Citrino'	SBch WAbe
massoniana ♀H2	CDes CSpe ECho EPot WAbe WCot
§ 'Matthew Forrest'	WCot
§ ***megalorrhiza***	CHEx SChr
§ ***melanosticta***	ECho EPot GEdr LLHF NRog SDeJ WCot WIce
monophylla	ECho
namaquana	ECho
obtusa	ECho EPot MPie
- apricot-flowered	CDes WCot
oregana	CHid CMac CRow ECho ELon EWld MMoz SPhx WCot WCru WPGP WSHC
- 'Klamath Ruby'	WSHC
- f. ***smalliana***	EBee EWld GEdr IMou WCru
palmifrons	ECho
perdicaria	ECho EPot EWes LRHS NRog WAbe
polyphylla	EBee ECho
§ ***purpurea***	ECho
- 'Ken Aslet'	see *O. melanosticta*
- yellow-flowered new	ECho
regnellii	see *O. triangularis* subsp. *papilionacea*
'Ridgeway Jewel'	CPBP
'Ridgeway Sapphire'	CPBP
rosea misapplied	see *O. articulata* subsp. *rubra*
semiloba	ECho GCal NCGa
Slack Top hybrids	NSla
'Slack's 53'	NSla
speciosa	see *O. purpurea*
§ ***spiralis*** subsp. ***vulcanicola***	CCCN GCal LSou
- - 'Burgundy'	NPri
- - 'Sunset Velvet'	WCot
- - 'Zinfandel'	WCot
squamata	LLHF
squamoso-radicosa	see *O. laciniata*
* ***stipularis***	ECho LLHF
succulenta Barnéoud	see *O. megalorrhiza*
succulenta ambig.	CHll CTsd
'Sunny'	EBee ECho GKev
'Sweet Sue' new	CPBP
§ ***tetraphylla***	CExl EBee ECho GKev NPer
* - ***alba***	ECho
- 'Iron Cross'	CHEx CHid ECho ELan EPot GAbr GKev LAma MPie NBir SDeJ
'Tina'	CPBP
triangularis	CCCN CExl CHEx CHel ECho EOHP NBir NPer
- 'Birgit'	EBee ECho GKev SDeJ
- Burgundy Wine = 'JR Oxburwi' (Xalis Series)	CWGN NPer
- 'Cupido'	EBee ECho
- 'Marmer' (v) new	EBee GKev
- 'Mijke'	EBee ECho GKev
§ - subsp. ***papilionacea*** ♀H2	ECho GKev LAma

- - 'Atropurpurea'	CSpe SDeJ
- subsp. ***triangularis***	CHid EBee ECho EUJe GKev
tuberosa	GPoy LEdu
- 'Polar Bere'	LEdu
- scarlet-flowered, white-eye new	LEdu
'Ute'	NSla
valdiviensis	GCal NWad
versicolor ♀H2	ECho EPot NBir NRog SDeJ WAbe WCot
virginea new	NRog
I 'Waverley Hybrid'	GBin
zeekoevleyensis	NRog

Oxycoccus see *Vaccinium*

Oxydendrum ✿ (*Ericaceae*)

arboreum	CAbP CBcs CDoC CDul CEnd CMCN EPfP EWTr IDee IVic LRHS MAsh MBlu MBri MMuc NLar NSoo NWea SPer SSpi SSta WBor WHar WPGP

Oxypetalum (*Apocynaceae*)

caeruleum	see *Tweedia caerulea*

Oxyria (*Polygonaceae*)

digyna	GEdr

Oxytropis (*Papilionaceae*)

campestris	EBee
coerulea	CPBP
hailarensis	CPBP
var. ***chankaensis***	
podocarpa	SPlb
purpurea	SPlb
sajanensis	CPBP

Ozothamnus (*Asteraceae*)

antennaria	WSHC
§ ***coralloides***	ECou WAbe WCot WThu
§ 'County Park Silver'	EWes GCrg GEdr GKev
§ ***hookeri***	CDoC MBrN SVen WCFE WJek WPGP WPat
§ ***ledifolius***	CBcs EPfP ETwe LRHS SLon SPer WAbe WPat
§ ***rosmarinifolius***	CBcs CDoC CTsd ELan EPfP LRHS MAsh MSwo SPer SVen WPnn
- 'Kiandra'	ECou
- 'Silver Jubilee'	CBcs CDoC CSBt ECrN ELan EPfP GCal LRHS MGos MNHC MRav MSwo SLim SLon SPer SPlb SRkn
§ ***selago***	ECou WCot
- 'Major'	SPlb
§ - var. ***tumidus***	WThu
'Sussex Silver'	CBcs CDoC
'Threave Seedling'	CBcs CDoC EBee ELan IVic LRHS MAsh SPer

P

Pachyphragma (*Brassicaceae*)

§ ***macrophyllum***	CPom ECGP ECha ELon GCal IBlr IMou LEdu MMuc MNFA MRav NLar NSti WCot WCru WPGP WSHC

Pachyphytum (*Crassulaceae*)

bracteosum	EUJe
glutinicaule RE 477	CDoC

Pachypodium (*Apocynaceae*)

bispinosum	LToo
lamerei ♀H1a	EUJe SPlb
succulentum	LToo

Pachysandra (*Buxaceae*)

axillaris	CLAP EPPr GCal SKHP WCot
- BWJ 8032	WCru
- 'Crûg's Cover'	EWld WCru
procumbens	CLAP EPla IMou NLar SKHP WCot
- 'Angola' (v)	WCot
stylosa	CHEx MRav
terminalis	Widely available
- 'Green Carpet'	Widely available
- 'Green Sheen' ♀H5	ECha EPPr EPfP ESwi EWTr LPal WGrf
- 'Variegata' (v) ♀H5	Widely available

Pachystachys (*Acanthaceae*)

lutea ♀H1b	CCCN

Pachystegia (*Asteraceae*)

§ ***insignis***	CPne LRHS SLim

Pachystima see *Paxistima*

× *Pachyveria* (*Crassulaceae*)

'Mrs Coombes'	CDoC

Paederota (*Plantaginaceae*)

§ ***bonarota***	WAbe
lutea	CDes WAbe

Paeonia ✿ (*Paeoniaceae*)

'Age of Gold' (S)	GBin XGra
'Age of Victoria'	GBin
albiflora	see *P. lactiflora*
'America'	GBin
'Amy Jo' new	WHlf
'Anna Marie' (S)	GBin
anomala	CCon GBin GKev IGor NLar
- var. ***intermedia***	GCal
'Ariadne' (S)	GBin XGra
arietina	see *P. mascula* subsp. *arietina*
'Athena'	GBin WCAu
'Avant Garde'	WCAu
'Baby Whisper' new	GBin
'Bai Xue Ta' (S)	NTPC SPer
banatica	see *P. officinalis* subsp. *banatica*
'Banquet' (S)	GBin
§ 'Bartzella' (d) ♀H5	CKel GBin LRHS NLar WCAu WCot XGra
beresowskii	GKev
'Black Pirate' (S) ♀H5	CKel
'Blaze'	CBod CKel EWoo GMaP LRHS NCGa NSti WCAu XGra
'Border Charm'	GBin XGra
'Boreas' (S)	GBin XGra
'Bravura'	GBin
'Bridal Icing'	GBin WCAu
'Bride's Dream'	GBin
'Brightness' new	XGra
'Brocaded Gown' (S)	GBin
broteroi	SKHP WThu

'Buckeye Belle' (d)	CKel EBee ELan EPfP EWTr EWoo GBin GMaP IBoy LAst LRHS NCGa SCob SHar SMrm SWat WCAu WCot XGra
'Burma Joy'	XGra
'Burma Midnight'	GBin
'Burma Ruby'	GBin WCAu
californica	CCon
'Callie's Memory'	CKel GBin NCGa WCAu
cambessedesii ♀H3	CBro CTal GKev IGor LRHS NBir NSla SSpi WAbe WCot WKif
cambessedesii* × *mlokosewitschii **new**	LRHS
'Cameo Lullaby' **new**	GBin
'Canary Brilliant' PBR	GBin WCAu XGra
'Cardinal's Robe'	GBin
'Carina'	GBin
'Carol'	WCAu
caucasica	see *P. mascula* subsp. *mascula*
'Chalice'	GBin
× ***chamaeleon***	GBin SKHP
'Cheddar Royal'	GBin
'Cherry Ruffles'	GBin
'Cherry Twist' **new**	GBin
'Chocolate Soldier'	CKel GBin WCAu
'Claire de Lune'	CKel GBin LRHS SHar WCAu WCot
'Claudia'	WCAu
'Color Magnet' **new**	WCAu XGra
'Command Performance'	GBin
'Companion of Serenity' (S)	GBin
'Convoy' (d) **new**	WCAu
'Copper Kettle'	CKel GBin
'Cora Louise'	CKel GBin WCAu XGra
'Coral Charm' ♀H7	CKel GBin GMaP IBoy MMHG NCGa NLar SCob SDeJ SKHP WCAu WCot XGra
'Coral Fay'	GBin WCAu
'Coral 'n' Gold'	WCAu
'Coral Scout'	GBin
'Coral Sunset'	CKel CWCL EWTr GBin IBoy NCGa NLar SCob SDeJ WCAu XGra
'Coral Supreme'	GBin
corallina	see *P. mascula* subsp. *mascula*
coriacea var. ***atlantica***	CBro
Crimson Red	see *P. suffruticosa* 'Hu Hong'
'Cutie' **new**	GBin WCAu
'Cytherea'	GBin LRHS WCAu WCot XGra
'Daedalus' (S)	GBin
'Dancing Butterflies'	see *P. lactiflora* 'Zi Yu Nu'
'Daredevil' (S)	GBin
daurica	see *P. mascula* subsp. *triternata*
- subsp. ***coriifolia*** RCB UA 12	WCot
'Dawn Glow'	GBin
decora	see *P. peregrina*
delavayi (S)	CKel CPne CTsd CWCL ELan EPfP ETwe GBin GCal GKev GMaP IGor LRHS MAsh MGos MLHP MMuc NBir NEgg SDix SEND SKHP SPer SPoG SRms SSpi WCAu WCot
- BWJ 7775	WCru
- var. ***angustiloba*** f. ***alba*** (S)	CExl
§ - - f. ***angustiloba*** (S)	GBin GKev SCob SSpi
- - - 'Coffee Cream' (S)	CKel
§ - - f. ***trollioides*** (S)	CExl
§ - var. ***delavayi*** f. ***lutea*** (S)	CCVT CDul EPfP EUJe GBin GKev IBoy IFro LEdu LRHS MAsh MGil MGos MLHP NBir NEgg NPCo NSoo SCob SLon SPoG SRms WHar WHoo
- var. ***lutea***	see *P. delavayi* var. *delavayi* f. *lutea*
- 'Mrs Colville' (S)	GBin GCal
- 'Mrs Sarson' (S)	ELan EWes SWat
- Potaninii Group	see *P. delavayi* var. *angustiloba* f. *angustiloba*
- 'Tapestry' (S)	CSpe
- Trollioides Group	see *P. delavayi* var. *angustiloba* f. *trollioides*
'Diana Parks'	GBin NCGa NLar WCAu XGra
'Don Richardson'	WCAu
Drizzling Rain Cloud	see *P. suffruticosa* 'Shiguregumo'
'Early Bird'	GBin
'Early Daybreak' **new**	GBin
'Early Glow'	GBin WCAu XGra
'Early Scout'	CBod EBee ELon GBin LRHS WCAu WHil XGra
'Early Windflower'	WCAu
'Echt Klasse'	GBin
'Eden's Perfume'	CBod ELon EPfP GBin IKil MBri MSCN NLar
'Eliza Lundy' (d)	GBin WCAu XGra
'Elizabeth Foster'	GBin
'Ellen Cowley'	GBin WCAu
emodi	CAvo CDes CKel GBin LRHS SHar WCAu WCot
'Etched Salmon'	CKel GBin NCGa
'Eventide' **new**	WCAu
'Ezra Pound' (S)	GBin WCAu
'F. Koppius'	CKel
'Fairy Princess'	GBin WCAu XGra
'Feng Dan Bai' (S)	NTPC
'Firelight'	GBin WCAu
'First Arrival'	CKel GBin WCAu
'First Dutch Yellow'	see *P.* 'Garden Treasure'
'Flame'	CKel EBee EPfP IGor MNrw NCGa NLar NSti SDeJ WCAu WCot XGra
'Fragrant Pink Imp' **new**	GBin
'Fuchsia Cuddles'	XGra
§ Gansu Group (S)	CKel GKev NTPC
- 'Bing Xin Zi' (S)	NTPC
- 'Dan Feng Zhan Chi' (S) **new**	NTPC
- 'Fen Die' (S)	NTPC
- 'Fen Guan Yu Zhu' (S) **new**	NTPC
- 'Fen Jin Yu' (S) **new**	NTPC
- 'Hei Feng Die' (S)	NTPC
- 'Hong Lian' (S)	NTPC
- 'Lan Yu San Cai' (S)	NTPC
- 'Lan Zhang Cai Wei' (S)	WKif
- 'Nong Mo Zhong Cai' (S)	WKif
- 'Xiong Mao' (S)	NTPC
- 'Xue Hai Bing Xin' (S)	NTPC
- 'Xue Hai Dan Xin' (S)	NTPC
- 'Xue Lian' (S)	GBin NTPC WKif
- 'Zi Ban Bai' (S)	NTPC
- 'Zi Die Ying Feng' (S)	NTPC
- 'Zi Yan' (S)	NTPC
- 'Zong Ban Bai' (S)	NTPC
Gansu Mudan Group	see *P.* Gansu Group
'Garden Peace'	WCAu
§ 'Garden Treasure'	GBin SDeJ WCAu XGra
'Gold Standard'	GBin
'Golden Bowl'	CKel GBin
'Golden Dream'	see *P.* 'Bartzella'

	Name	Suppliers
	'Golden Isles'	CKel
	'Golden Thunder'	CKel
	'Golden Wings'	GBin
	'Grace Root'	GBin
	'Green Halo' **new**	GBin
	'Happy' **new**	GBin
	'Hei Hua Kui'	see *P. suffruticosa* 'Hei Hua Kui'
	'Henry Bockstace' (d)	GBin NLar WCAu XGra
	'Hephestos' (S)	GBin XGra
	'Heritage'	GBin
	'Hillary'	CKel GBin WCAu
	'Ho-gioku'	GBin
	'Hong Bao Shi' (S)	NTPC
	'Hong Mei Ao Shang' (S) **new**	LBuc
	'Honor'	WCAu
	'Horizon'	GBin WCAu
	humilis	see *P. officinalis* subsp. *microcarpa*
	'Huo Lian Jin Dan' (S)	NTPC
	'Icarus' (S)	GBin XGra
	'Ice Storm' (S)	GBin
	'Illini Belle'	GBin
	'Illini Warrior'	WCAu
	'In the Mood'	GBin
	'Iphigenia' (S)	GBin XGra
	'Isani Gidui'	see *P. lactiflora* 'Isami-jishi'
	japonica misapplied	see *P. lactiflora*
	japonica (Makino) Miyabe & Takeda B&SWJ 10985	WCru
	'Jay Cee'	GBin WCAu
	'Joseph Rock'	see *P. rockii*
	'Joyce Ellen'	GBin NLar
	'Jubilation'	GBin
	'Julia Rose'	CKel GBin NCGa WCAu XGra
	'Kathryn Ann'	GBin
	kavachensis	GCal GKev
	'Kinkaku'	see *P.* × *lemoinei* 'Souvenir de Maxime Cornu'
	'Kinko'	see *P.* × *lemoinei* 'Alice Harding'
	'Kinshi'	see *P.* × *lemoinei* 'Chromatella'
	'Koikagura'	CKel
	'Kokamon'	CKel
	'Kun Shan Ye Guang'	NTPC
§	***lactiflora***	CArn GCal GKev MBel MRav
	- 'Abalone Pearl'	GBin XGra
	- 'Adolphe Rousseau'	CBcs CKel LRHS WCAu
*	- 'Afterglow'	CKel
	- 'Agida'	GBin IGor LRHS MRav
	- 'Agnes Mary Kelway'	CKel
	- ***alba***	MBel WBor
	- 'Albâtre'	CKel
	- 'Albert Crousse'	CBcs CKel GBin MRav NBir SWat WCAu
	- 'Alexander Fleming'	CBod EBee MBNS NBir SMrm SWat WCAu WFar
	- 'Algae Adamson'	CKel
	- 'Alice Harding'	CKel GBin WCAu
	- 'Amabilis' (d) **new**	XGra
	- 'Amalia Olson' (d)	WCAu XGra
	- 'Amibilis'	ELon WCAu
	- 'Angel Cheeks'	CKel EBee GBin NCGa NLar SHar WCAu
	- 'Anna Pavlova'	CKel
	- 'Antwerpen'	LRHS
	- 'Arabian Prince'	CKel
	- 'Argentine'	CKel EBee
	- 'Armistice' (d)	WCAu
	- 'Asa Gray'	CKel

	Name	Suppliers
	- 'Auguste Dessert'	CKel GBin WCAu WCFE
§	- 'Augustin d'Hour'	CKel SHar
	- 'Aureole'	CKel MRav
	- 'Avalanche'	EPfP GBin NLar
	- 'Avalon' (d) **new**	XGra
	- 'Ballerina'	CKel MRav
	- 'Barbara'	CKel GBin WCAu
	- 'Baroness Schröder'	CKel ELan GBin WCAu XGra
	- 'Barrington Belle'	EBee EPfP GBin LRHS WCAu WHoo
	- 'Barrymore'	CKel
	- 'Bayadere' (d)	GBin
	- 'Beacon'	CKel
	- 'Beatrice Kelway'	CKel
	- 'Belle Center'	GBin WCAu
	- 'Bessie' **new**	GBin
	- 'Best Man'	EBee NGdn WCAu
	- 'Bethcar'	CKel
	- 'Better Times'	WCAu
	- 'Bev'	GBin
	- 'Big Ben'	CKel GBin LRHS NLar SHar
	- 'Blaze of Beauty'	CKel
	- 'Blitz Tort' **new**	GBin XGra
	- 'Bluebird'	CKel IBoy
	- 'Blush Queen'	CKel GBin WCAu
	- 'Border Gem'	GBin LRHS MRav
	- 'Bouchela'	NLar NSti
	- 'Boule de Neige'	GBin
	- 'Bouquet Perfect'	GBin WCAu
	- 'Bower of Roses'	CKel
	- 'Bowl of Beauty' ♀H7	Widely available
	- 'Bowl of Cream'	CKel GBin LRHS SWat SWvt WCAu XGra
	- 'Break o' Day'	WCAu
	- 'Bridal Gown'	GBin WCAu
	- 'Bridal Veil'	CKel
	- 'Bridesmaid'	CKel
	- 'Bright Knight'	WCAu
	- 'British Beauty'	CKel
	- 'Brother Chuck' (d) **new**	XGra
	- 'Bunker Hill'	CKel ELon GBin IBoy LRHS NPri SPer SWvt WCAu
	- 'Bu-te'	GBin
	- 'Butter Bowl'	GBin WCAu
	- 'Candeur'	CKel
	- 'Candidissima'	GBin
	- 'Captivation'	CKel
	- 'Carnival'	CKel
	- 'Caroline Allain'	CKel
	- 'Carrara'	GBin
	- 'Cascade'	CKel
	- 'Catherine Fontijn'	CKel GBin WCAu
	- 'Celebrity'	CWCL MSCN
	- 'Charles Burgess'	CKel WCAu
	- 'Charles' White'	CKel GBin NLar SDeJ WCAu
	- 'Charm'	GBin WCAu
	- 'Cheddar Charm'	GBin WCAu
	- 'Cheddar Cheese'	WCot
	- 'Cheddar Supreme'	GBin
	- 'Cherry Hill'	GBin
	- 'Chestine Gowdy'	CKel
	- 'Chief Wapello'	GBin
	- 'Chiffon Clouds' **new**	WCAu
	- 'Chiffon Parfait'	GBin XGra
	- 'Chippewa'	GBin
	- 'Circus Circus'	GBin XGra
	- 'Claire Dubois'	CKel GBin
	- 'Commando' (d) **new**	EBee
	- 'Cora Stubbs'	GBin NCGa SPer WCAu

– 'Cornelia Shaylor'	CKel WCAu
– 'Couronne d'Or'	GBin
– 'Cream Puff'	WCAu
– 'Crimson Glory'	CKel
– 'Crinkles Linens'	GBin
– 'Dairy Anne' **new**	XGra
– 'Daisy Coronet' **new**	XGra
– 'Dawn Crest'	CKel
– 'Dawn Pink' **new**	WCAu
– 'Dayspring'	CKel
– 'Daystar'	MRav
– 'Dayton'	GBin WCAu
– 'Decorative'	CKel
– 'Delachei'	CKel GBin
– 'Dinner Plate'	CKel GBin MBri NCGa SHar SPer WCAu
– 'Do Tell'	CKel CWCL EBee EPfP GBin NCGa NLar SPer WCAu
– 'Docteur H. Barnsby'	CKel
– 'Doctor Alexander Fleming'	CKel GBin LRHS SDeJ SRot SWat SWvt
– 'Don Juan'	CKel
– 'Doreen'	CKel EBee GBin SHar WCAu WHil
– 'Doris Cooper'	WCAu
– 'Dorothy Welsh'	CKel
– 'Dragon'	CKel
– 'Dream Catcher' **new**	GBin
– 'Dresden'	WCAu
– 'Drumline' **new**	SDeJ
– 'Duchesse de Nemours' ♀H7	Widely available
– 'Edulis Superba'	ELan GBin IGor LEdu LRHS MBNS MRav NLar NPer SHar SPer WCAu
– 'Elaine'	MRav
– 'Electric Festival' **new**	GBin
– 'Elizabeth Queen of the Belgians' (d) **new**	XGra
– 'Elizabeth Stone'	CKel
– 'Ella Christine Kelway'	CKel
– 'Elsa Sass'	EBee GBin SHar WCAu XGra
– 'Embraceable Pink' **new**	GBin
– 'Emma Klehm'	CKel GBin WCAu XGra
– 'Emperor of India'	CKel
– 'Emperor's Buttons' **new**	XGra
– 'Enchantment'	CKel
– 'English Princess'	CKel
– 'Ethereal'	CKel
– 'Evelyn Tibbets'	GBin
– 'Evening Glow'	CKel
– 'Evening World'	CKel
– 'Fairy's Petticoat'	CKel GBin WCAu
– 'Fancy Nancy'	GBin
– 'Fashion Show'	CKel
– 'Félix Crousse' ♀H7	CBcs CBod CKel CMac COtt CTri ELan ELon GBin GMaP IBoy LRHS MBNS MGos MRav NBir NLar NPri SDeJ SPer SWat WCAu
– 'Felix Supreme'	GBin XGra
– 'Festiva Maxima' ♀H7	CKel CSBt CTri EBee ELan EPfP EWoo GBin LRHS LSun NBir NEgg NLar NPri SPer SRkn SRot SWat SWvt WCAu WFar WHil
– 'Festiva Supreme'	GBin
– 'Fiesta Posey'	WCAu
– 'Fiona' (d)	WCAu
– 'Firebelle'	WCAu
– 'Florence Ellis'	WCAu
– 'Florence Nicholls'	CKel GBin WCAu XGra

– 'Foxtrot'	GBin XGra
– 'France'	CKel
– 'Fuchsia Dragonfly'	GBin
– 'Fuji-no-mine'	GBin
– 'Garden Lace'	GBin SDeJ WCAu XGra
– 'Gardenia'	CKel EBee GBin IBoy LRHS NLar SDeJ WCAu WCot XGra
– 'Gay Paree'	CKel CWCL GBin IBoy MRav NCGa NLar SCob SHar WCAu
– 'Gayborder June'	CKel
– 'Général Joffre'	MRav
– 'Général MacMahon'	see *P. lactiflora* 'Augustin d'Hour'
– 'General Wolfe'	CKel
– 'Germaine Bigot'	CKel GBin MRav WCAu
– 'Gertrude Allen'	GBin
– 'Gilbert Barthelot'	CKel WCAu
– 'Gladys McArthur'	GBin
– 'Gleam of Light'	CKel
– 'Globe of Light'	CKel GBin
– 'Glory Hallelujah'	WCAu
– 'Go-Daigo'	GBin
– 'Golden Fleece'	WCAu
– 'Goldilocks'	WCAu
– 'Great Sport'	MRav
– 'Green Lotus'	GBin XGra
– 'Guidon'	WCAu
– 'Gypsy Girl'	CKel
– 'Hakodate'	CKel
– 'Hansina Brand' (d)	GBin
– 'Heartbeat'	CKel
– 'Helen Hayes'	WCAu
– 'Henri Potin'	GBin
– 'Her Grace'	CKel
– 'Herbert Oliver'	CKel
– 'Hermione'	CKel GBin WCAu XGra
– 'Hit Parade'	WCAu
– 'Honey Gold'	CKel GBin WCAu
– 'Hot Chocolate'	GBin WCAu XGra
– 'Hyperion'	CKel
– 'Immaculée'	CKel CWCL EBee GBin IBoy IGor LRHS MRav NCGa SCob SPoG XGra
– 'Inspecteur Lavergne'	CKel EBee EPfP GBin IBoy IGor LRHS MGos NGdn SGol SPer WCAu WCot WHil XGra
– 'Instituteur Doriat'	CKel GBin LRHS WCAu
§ – 'Isami-jishi'	GBin
– 'Ivory Inspirations' **new**	XGra
– 'Jacorma'	CCon GBin LRHS
– 'Jacques Doriat'	CKel
– 'Jadwigha'	EBee
– 'James Kelway'	CKel GBin
– 'Jan van Leeuwen'	CKel EBee ELon EPfP GBin GMaP LRHS NCGa SPer WCAu WCot XGra
– 'Jappensha-ikhu'	GBin
– 'Jeanne d'Arc'	CKel
– 'John Howard Wigell'	WCAu
– 'Johnny'	GBin
– 'Joseph Christie' (d)	EBee
– 'Joy of Life'	CKel
– 'Judith Eileen'	GBin
– 'June Morning'	CKel
– 'June Rose'	WCAu
– 'Kakoden'	GBin
– 'Kansas'	CKel CWCL EBee ELan EPfP GBin IBoy LRHS MBri MHol NBir NGdn NLar SPoG WCAu WCot WFar
– 'Karen Gray'	GBin WCAu
– 'Karl Rosenfield'	Widely available

- 'Kathleen Mavoureen' CKel
- 'Kelway's Betty' CKel
- 'Kelway's Brilliant' CKel
- 'Kelway's Circe' CKel
- 'Kelway's Daystar' CKel
- 'Kelway's Exquisite' CKel
- 'Kelway's Glorious' CKel EPfP GBin LRHS MAvo MBNS MRav NLar WCAu
- 'Kelway's Lovely' CKel GBin
- 'Kelway's Lovely Lady' CKel
- 'Kelway's Majestic' CKel MRav
- 'Kelway's Scented Rose' CKel
- 'Kelway's Supreme' CKel SWat
- 'King of England' GBin
- 'Knighthood' CKel
- 'Königswinter' GBin

§ - 'Koningin Wilhelmina' EBee EPfP GBin MNrw
- 'Krinkled White' CKel EBee ELon EPfP EWoo GBBs GBin GMaP LRHS MRav NCGa NLar NSti SDeJ SHar SKHP WCAu WHil XGra
- 'La Belle Hélène' CKel
- 'La Lorraine' CKel
- 'Lady Alexandra Duff' ♀H7 CKel EPfP GBin LRHS MRav NBir NGdn SWvt WCAu WHil XGra
- 'Lady Ley' CKel
- 'Lady Mayoress' CKel
- 'Lady Orchid' EPfP WCAu
- 'Lancaster Imp' GBin WCAu
- 'Langport Triumph' CKel
- 'Largo' WCAu
- 'Laura Dessert' ♀H7 CKel GBin IBoy LRHS NLar SPer WCAu XGra
- 'Laura Shaylor' WCAu
- 'Lavender Lotus' **new** XGra
- 'Lavender Whisper' WCAu
- 'Le Cygne' GBin
- 'L'Éclatante' CKel GBin
- 'Legion of Honor' CKel
- 'Lemon Ice' CKel
- 'Lemon Queen' GBin
- 'L'Étincelante' GBin
- 'Liebchen' WCAu
- 'Lights Out' GBin
- 'Lilac Times' CKel
- 'Lillian Wild' GBin WCAu
- 'Little Medicineman' EBee GBin
- 'Little Pink Lullaby' **new** GBin
- 'Lois Kelsey' GBin WCAu
- 'Lollipop' (d) GBin
- 'Longfellow' CKel GBin
- 'Lord Kitchener' CKel EPfP GBin IGor LRHS
- 'Lorna Doone' CKel
- 'Lotus Queen' GBin NLar WCAu
- 'Louis van Houtte' CKel NEgg XGra
- 'Love's Touch' (d) GBin
- 'Lowell Thomas' WCAu
- 'Lucky' **new** XGra
- 'Lyric' CKel
- 'Ma Petite Cherie' (d) GBin WCAu XGra
- 'Madame Calot' EBee LRHS XGra
- 'Madame Claude Tain' MBri
- 'Madame Ducel' CKel
- 'Madame Emile Debatène' CKel EBee MBNS SMrm WCAu WFar XGra
- 'Madame Gaudichau' WCot
- 'Madelon' CKel
- 'Maestro' GBin
- 'Magenta Glow' **new** XGra
- 'Magenta Moon' WCAu
- 'Magic Orb' CKel
- 'Mandarin's Coat' GBin
- 'Margaret Clark' WCAu
- 'Margaret Truman' CKel EBee WCAu
- 'Marie Lemoine' CKel GBin LRHS WCAu XGra
- 'Marietta Sisson' WCAu
- 'Mary Elizabeth' GBin XGra
- 'Masterpiece' CKel
- 'May Treat' WCAu
- 'Midnight Sun' WCAu
- 'Minnie Shaylor' WCAu
- 'Mischief' MRav WCAu
- 'Miss America' ♀H7 EPfP GBin WCAu XGra
- 'Miss Eckhart' CKel GBin
- 'Miss Mary' EBee
- 'Missie's Blush' GBin
- 'Mister Ed' GBin WCAu
- 'Mistral' CKel
- 'Monsieur Jules Elie' ♀H7 CKel EBee EPfP EWoo GBin IBoy LRHS MBri NGdn NLar SPer WCAu WHoo
- 'Monsieur Martin Cahuzac' CKel GBin LRHS WCAu
- 'Moon of Nippon' LRHS SHar WCAu
- 'Moon River' EPfP GBin SMrm WCAu WHoo
- 'Moonstone' CKel GBin
- 'Morning Kiss' MAvo
- 'Mother's Choice' CKel EWoo GBin NGdn NLar SHar WCAu WCot
- 'Mr G.F. Hemerik' CKel GBin IBoy WCAu XGra
- 'Mrs Edward Harding' CKel WCAu
- 'Mrs Franklin D. Roosevelt' GBin WCAu XGra
- 'Mrs J.V. Edlund' GBin
- 'My Pal Rudy' GBin WCAu
- 'Myrtle Gentry' CKel GBin WCAu
- 'Nancy Nicholls' WCAu
- 'Nancy Nora' SPer WCAu
- 'Nellie Shaylor' (d) **new** WCAu
- 'Neomy Demay' CKel GBin
- 'Neon' GBin LRHS NCGa
- 'Nice Gal' GBin WCAu
- 'Nick Shaylor' GBin WCAu XGra
- 'Nippon Beauty' CKel EBee GBin LRHS MAvo MMHG NCGa NLar SCob SDeJ SKHP WCAu WCot
- 'Nippon Gold' WCAu
- 'Noemie Demay' LRHS
- 'Norma Volz' GBin WCAu XGra
- 'Nymphe' CKel EBee MRav NLar SDeJ WCAu
- 'Orlando Roberts' GBin
- 'Ornament' CKel
- 'Orpen' CKel
- 'Paola' CKel
- 'Paul Bunyan' GBin
- 'Paul M. Wild' CKel NLar XGra

* - 'Pecher' CKel LRHS NLar NPer
- 'Peter Brand' CKel EBee GBin NLar SCob
- 'Petite Elegance' (d) **new** WCAu
- 'Petite Porcelain' GBin XGra
- 'Philippe Rivoire' CKel WCAu
- 'Philomèle' WCAu
- 'Pico' WCAu
- 'Picotee' WCAu
- 'Pillow Cases' WCAu
- 'Pillow Talk' CKel EBee GBin LRHS NLar WCAu
- 'Pink Cameo' WCAu WCot WFar

	– 'Pink Dawn'	CBod EBee EPfP SPer WCAu
	– 'Pink Delight'	GBin WCAu
	– 'Pink Giant'	GBin WCAu
	– 'Pink Jitterburg' **new**	XGra
	– 'Pink Parfait'	GBin NCGa NLar SPer WCAu
	– 'Pink Princess'	GBin WCAu
	– 'Pink Spinners' **new**	XGra
	– 'Plainsman'	GBin
	– 'Pom Pom' (d) **new**	WCAu
	– 'President Franklin D. Roosevelt'	LRHS SWat
	– 'President Lincoln'	WCAu
	– 'Président Poincaré'	CKel MRav SWat
	– 'President Taft'	see *P. lactiflora* 'Reine Hortense'
	– 'President Wilson'	GBin
	– 'Primevère'	CBod CKel GBin LAst NBir NCGa NLar NSti SPer SPoG WCAu WFar
	– 'Princess Bride' **new**	WCAu
	– 'Princess Margaret'	WCAu
	– 'Queen of Sheba'	WCAu
	– 'Queen Victoria'	GBin
	– 'Queen Wilhelmina'	see *P. lactiflora* 'Koningin Wilhelmina'
	– 'Raoul Dessert'	WCAu
	– 'Raspberry Splash' **new**	GBin
	– 'Raspberry Sundae'	CKel ELan ELon GBin LRHS MBri MRav NLar SPer WCAu WCot
	– 'Ray Payton'	GBin
	– 'Red Dwarf'	CKel
	– 'Red Emperor'	WCAu
	– 'Red Sarah Bernhardt'	CKel EPfP SDeJ
§	– 'Reine Hortense'	CKel GBin LRHS MRav
	– 'Renato'	GBin LSun XGra
	– 'Riches and Fame' **new**	LRHS
	– 'Roland' **new**	WCAu
	– 'Rooster Reveille' (d) **new**	XGra
	– 'Ruth Cobb'	WCAu
	– 'Salmon Dream'	CKel GBin
	– 'Sante Fe'	CKel EBee EPfP MSCN NLar WCAu
	– 'Sarah Bernhardt' ♀H7	Widely available
	– 'Schaffe'	GBin
	– 'Sea Shell'	GBin GMaP LRHS WCAu
	– 'Sebastiaan Maas' **new**	EBee
	– 'Serene Pastel'	GBin WCAu
	– 'Shawnee Chief'	GBin
	– 'Shimmering Velvet'	CKel
	– 'Shirley Temple' (d)	CBod CKel EBee ELan EPfP GBin GBuc IBoy IKil LRHS MBNS MBri MGos MJak MRav NBir NGdn NPri SDeJ SPoG WCAu WCot WFar
	– 'Silver Flare'	CKel
	– 'Silver Rose' **new**	GBin
	– 'Sir Ernest Shackleton' (d)	MRav
	– 'Sixteen Candles' **new**	GBin
	– 'Soft Salmon Joy'	GBin WCAu XGra
	– 'Solange'	CKel GBin IKil LRHS NLar SPer WCAu
	– 'Sorbet'	CKel EBee ELon EPfP LRHS NBir NLar NPer SMrm WBor WCAu WFar
	– 'Springfield' (d) **new**	XGra
	– 'Starlight'	CKel EBee GBin LRHS NCGa SHar WCAu WCot
	– 'Strephon'	CKel
	– 'Summer Carnival' **new**	XGra
	– 'Super Gal'	WCAu
	– 'Susie Q' (d) **new**	XGra
	– 'Suzanne Krekler' **new**	WCAu

	– 'Sweet Melody'	GBin
	– 'Sweet Rewards' **new**	GBin
	– 'Sweet Sixteen'	WCAu
	– 'Sword Dance'	CKel GBBs GBin IBoy LRHS SDeJ WCAu XGra
	– 'Tamate-boko'	WCAu
	– 'The Mighty Mo'	GBin WCAu
	– 'The Nymph'	LRHS NBir
	– 'Theatrical' (d) **new**	WCAu
	– 'Thérèse'	WCAu
	– 'Tom Eckhardt'	CKel GBin SPer WCAu
	– 'Top Brass'	CKel GBin MRav NLar WCAu
	– 'Topeka Garnet'	GBin XGra
	– 'Toro-no-maki'	WCAu
	– 'Translucient'	CKel
	– 'Victoire de la Marne'	CKel
	– 'Violet Dawson'	GBin
	– 'Vivid Rose'	WCAu
	– 'Vogue'	CKel EBee GBin LRHS MRav NCGa SWvt WCAu
	– 'W.F. Turner'	CKel
	– 'Walter Faxon'	GBin
	– 'Waltz' **new**	GBin
	– 'West Elkton'	GBin
	– 'Westerner'	GBin
	– 'White Cap'	GBin MMHG NCGa NLar WCAu
	– 'White Grace'	GBin WCAu
	– 'White Ivory'	XGra
	– 'White Rose of Sharon'	CKel
	– 'White Sands'	GBin
	– 'White Sarah Bernhardt'	SMrm SPer
	– 'White Wings'	CBcs CKel CTri ELan EPfP GBin GMaP LRHS NLar NSti SPer SWat SWvt WCAu WCot
	– 'Whitleyi Major' ♀H7	WCot
	– 'Wilbur Wright'	CKel GBin
	– 'Wine Red'	GBin
	– 'Wladyslawa'	GBin LRHS NLar WCot
§	– 'Zi Yu Nu'	EBee LRHS WCAu
	– 'Zuzu'	GBin WCAu
	'Lafayette Escadrille' (S)	WCAu XGra
	× ***lagodechiana***	LEdu
	'Late Windflower'	CKel GBin GCra WCAu
	'Leda' (S)	GBin XGra
	'Legion of Honour'	GBin
	× ***lemoinei*** (S)	WHal
§	– 'Alice Harding' (S)	CKel GBin SPer
§	– 'Chromatella' (S)	CKel
	– 'High Noon' (S) ♀H5	CKel GBin SKHP SWat WCot
	– 'Marchioness' (S)	CKel GBin
§	– 'Souvenir de Maxime Cornu' (S)	CKel SKHP SPer
	'Lemon Dream' PBR	NCGa XGra
	'Lilith' (S)	GBin
	'Little Joe'	WCAu
	'Little Red Gem'	GBin
	lobata 'Fire King'	see *P. peregrina*
	'Lois Arleen'	WCAu
	'Lovebirds'	GBin WCAu
	'Lovely Rose'	GBin WCAu
	ludlowii (S)	Widely available
	lutea	see *P. delavayi* var. *delavayi* f. *lutea*
	'Magenta Gem'	GBin XGra
	'Mai Fleuri'	GBin WCAu
	mairei	CExl GGGa IGor
	'Many Happy Returns'	CKel GBin
	mascula	CBro GEdr GKev IGor IMou LLHF NBir NPCo

§	- subsp. ***arietina***	EBee GKev MWat
	- 'Immaculata'	MHol
§	- subsp. ***mascula***	GKev
§	- subsp. ***russoi***	GKev IGor WThu
	- - 'Picotee'	GBin
	- - 'Reverchoni'	CTal
§	- subsp. ***triternata***	CKel GKev NSla WCot
	'May Apple'	WCAu XGra
	'Merry Mayshine'	GBin XGra
	'Mikuhino-akebono'	CKel SDeJ
	mlokosewitschii ♀H7	CBro CExl CFil CMea CPBP CTal EBee ECha ECho ELan EPPr GBin GEdr GMaP IGor LRHS MNrw NBir NPCo SDix SLon SWvt WAbe WCAu WCot WHoo WKif WPat
	- hybrids	EBee GKev
	mollis	see *P. officinalis* subsp. *villosa*
	'Montezuma'	XGra
	'Moonrise'	WCAu
	'Morning Lilac'	WCAu
	'Murad of Hershey Bar' (S)	GBin XGra
	'My Love'	WCAu XGra
	'Nike' (d) **new**	XGra
	'Normie' (d)	WCAu
	'Nosegay'	WCAu XGra
	'Nova'	CKel GBin
	obovata ♀H5	CCon CKel WCot
	- var. ***alba*** ♀H5	CExl GBin GKev LLHF WAbe
	- var. ***willmottiae***	CExl
	officinalis	CArn GCra GKev MCot
	- 'Alba Plena' (d)	CKel CPou EBee GMaP LRHS MRav NEgg NLar SWvt WCAu WFar
	- 'Anemoniflora Rosea' ♀H7	LRHS SWvt
§	- subsp. ***banatica***	GKev
	- 'China Rose'	GBin
	- subsp. ***humilis***	see *P. officinalis* subsp. *microcarpa*
	- 'Lize van Veen'	GBin
§	- subsp. ***microcarpa***	WCAu
	- 'Mutabilis Plena' (d)	IBlr NLar
	- 'Rosea Plena' (d) ♀H7	CKel EBee ECtt EPfP GMaP LAst LRHS NEgg SCob SPer SWat SWvt WCAu WFar XGra
	- 'Rubra Plena' (d) ♀H7	Widely available
§	- subsp. ***villosa***	CKel ELan LRHS WCAu
	'Old Faithful'	XGra
	'Old Rose Dandy'	GBin
	'Oriental Gold'	CKel EBee
	ostii (S)	CExl CKel GKev SKHP
§	- 'Feng Dan Bai' (S)	CKel GBin
	'Pageant'	GBin XGra
	'Paladin'	GBin
	papaveracea	see *P. suffruticosa*
	paradoxa	see *P. officinalis* subsp. *microcarpa*
	'Paramount'	GBin
	'Pastel Splendor'	CKel GBin NCGa WCAu XGra
	'Paula Fay'	CKel EBee EPfP GBin IMou MBri MRav SDeJ WCAu XGra
	Peony with the Purple Roots	see *P. suffruticosa* 'Shou An Hong'
§	***peregrina***	CBro CKel GKev IGor NLar SKHP SSpi WCot
	- 'Fire King'	CKel GBin NLar
§	- 'Otto Froebel' ♀H7	CKel GBin GCra NLar WCAu WCot
	- 'Sunshine'	see *P. peregrina* 'Otto Froebel'
	'Picotee'	WCAu
	'Pink Hawaiian Coral'	CKel GBin NLar XGra
	'Pink Tea Cup' **new**	XGra
	'Postilion'	GBin
	potaninii	see *P. delavayi* var. *angustiloba* f. *angustiloba*
	'Prairie Charm'	GBin WCAu XGra
	'Prairie Moon'	GBin NLar WCAu
	'Prince Charming'	WCAu
	'Raspberry Charm'	XGra
	'Red Charm'	CKel CWCL EBee EPfP EWoo GBin IBoy LRHS WCAu
	'Red Glory'	GBin
	'Red Magic'	EBee EPfP WFar
	'Red Red Rose'	GBin WCAu XGra
	'Renown' (S)	CKel
	'Requiem'	GBin WCAu
§	***rockii*** (S)	CKel CSpe EWoo GBin NLar WCot
	- hybrid	see *P.* Gansu Group
	- subsp. ***linyanshanii*** (S)	GKev
	'Roman Gold'	CKel GBin
	romanica	see *P. peregrina*
	'Rose Garland'	GBin
	'Rosedale'	XGra
	'Roselette'	GBin WCAu
	'Roselette's Child'	GBin
	'Roy Pehrson's Best Yellow'	GBin
	'Rubyette' **new**	XGra
	'Ruffled Pink Petticoats' (S)	GBin
	russoi	see *P. mascula* subsp. *russoi*
	'Salmon Beauty' (d) **new**	WCAu
	'Salmon Chiffon' **new**	XGra
	'Savage Splendour'	GBin
	'Scarlet Heaven'	CKel GBin
	'Scarlet O'Hara'	CMac EWoo GBin SPer SPoG WCAu XGra
	'Serenade'	WCAu
	'Shimano-fuji'	CKel
	'Shining Light'	GBin NCGa NLar SCob
	'Show Girl'	GBin NCGa WCAu XGra
	'Showanohokori'	CKel
	'Silver Dawn'	GBin
	sinensis	see *P. lactiflora*
	'Singing in the Rain II' **new**	WHlf
	'Sonoma Kaleidoscope'	GBin
	'Soshi'	GBin LRHS NLar SHar
	'Spring Carnival' (S)	GBin XGra
	'Squirt'	GBin
	sterniana	CExl
	steveniana	GKev WCot
§	***suffruticosa*** (S)	ELan GKev MGos SSpi
	- 'Akashigata' (S)	CKel
	- 'Alice Palmer' (S)	CKel
	- 'Bai Yu' (S)	GBin
I	- 'Better Than Peach Blossom' (S)	LRHS
I	- 'Better than Snow Tower' (S)	LRHS
	- Bird of Rimpo	see *P. suffruticosa* 'Rimpo'
*	- 'Black Dragon' (S) **new**	LBuc
	- Black Dragon Brocade	see *P. suffruticosa* 'Kokuryū-nishiki'
	- Black Flower Chief	see *P. suffruticosa* 'Hei Hua Kui'
	- Blue Lotus	see *P. suffruticosa* 'Lan Fu Rong'
	- Brocade of the Naniwa	see *P. suffruticosa* 'Naniwa-nishiki'
	- 'Burgundy Wine' (S)	GBin
	- 'Cardinal Vaughan' (S)	CKel
	- 'Chu Wu' (S)	NTPC
	- Colourful Butterfly	see *P. suffruticosa* 'Hua Hu Die'
	- 'Da Hu Hong' (S)	SPoG
§	- 'Dan Lu Yan' (S)	CBcs SPer
	- 'Dou Lu' (S)	NTPC
	- 'Duchess of Kent' (S)	CKel

- 'Duchess of Marlborough' (S) CKel
- Eternal Camellias see *P. suffruticosa* 'Yachiyo-tsubaki'
- 'Feng Dan Bai' (S) SPer
- Flames in the Furnace see *P. suffruticosa* 'Dan Lu Yan'
- Flight of Cranes see *P. suffruticosa* 'Renkaku'
- Floral Rivalry see *P. suffruticosa* 'Hana-kisoi'
- Fragrant Jade see *P.* 'Xiang Yu'
- 'Frost on Peach Blossom' (S) LRHS
- 'Godaishu' (S) CKel GBin SKHP
- 'Guardian of the Monastry' (S) GBin XGra
- 'Hai Huang' (S) NTPC WKif

§ - 'Hakuo-jisi' (S/d) CKel
§ - 'Hana-kisoi' (S) CKel GBin
- 'Haru-no-akebono' (S) CKel
- 'Hei Hai Sa Jin' (S) NTPC

§ - 'Hei Hua Kui' (S) NTPC
- 'Hinode-sekai' (S/d) GBin

§ - 'Hu Hong' (S) LBuc SPer
§ - 'Hua Hu Die' (S) **new** CBcs
§ - 'Huang Hua Kui' (S) NTPC
- 'Hu's Family Red' (S) LRHS
- Jewel in the Lotus see *P. suffruticosa* 'Tama-fuyo'
- Jewelled Screen see *P. suffruticosa* 'Tama-sudare'
- 'Jin Zhi' NTPC
- 'Jing Ge' (S) NTPC WKif
- 'Jitsugetsu-nishiki' (S) CKel
- 'Joseph Rock' see *P. rockii*
- Kamada Brocade see *P. suffruticosa* 'Kamada-nishiki'

§ - 'Kamada-nishiki' (S) CKel GBin
§ - 'Kaow' (S) CKel
- King of Flowers see *P. suffruticosa* 'Kaow'
- King of White Lions see *P. suffruticosa* 'Hakuo-jisi'
- 'Kinkaku' see *P.* × *lemoinei* 'Souvenir de Maxime Cornu'
- 'Kinshi' see *P.* × *lemoinei* 'Alice Harding'
- 'Kokucho' (S) CKel

§ - 'Kokuryū-nishiki' (S) CKel LRHS SKHP
- 'Koshi-no-yuki' (S) CKel
- 'Lan Bao Shi' (S) GBin NTPC

§ - 'Lan Fu Rong' (S) CBcs
- 'Ma Nao He Hua' (S) **new** NTPC
- 'Ming Xing' (S) NTPC
- 'Mo Sa Jin' (S) NTPC
- 'Montrose' (S) CKel

* - 'Mrs Shirley Fry' (S) CKel
- 'Mrs William Kelway' (S) CKel
- 'Mulberry Purple' (S) **new** CBcs

§ - 'Naniwa-nishiki' (S) CKel
- 'Nigata Akashigata' (S) CKel
- Pride of Taisho see *P. suffruticosa* 'Taisho-no-hokori'
- 'Princess Chiffon' (S) GBin
- 'Reine Elisabeth' (S) CKel

§ - 'Renkaku' (S) CKel SKHP
§ - 'Rimpo' (S) CKel GBin SKHP XGra
§ - 'Shiguregumo' (S) CKel
- 'Shimadaigin' (S) CKel
- 'Shimane-chōjuraku' (S) CKel GBin
- 'Shimane-hakugan' (S) CKel
- 'Shimane-otone-mai' (S/d) GBin
- 'Shimane-seidai' (S) CKel
- 'Shimanishiki' (S) CKel SKHP
- 'Shin Shima Kagayaki' (S) CKel
- 'Shintoyen' (S) CKel

§ - 'Shou An Hong' (S) NTPC
- 'Snow Face Peach' (S) **new** CBcs
- Snow Lotus see *P. suffruticosa* 'Xue Lian'
- Snowy Pagoda see *P. suffruticosa* 'Xue Ta'
- 'Sumi-no-ichi' (S) CKel
- 'Superb' (S) CKel

§ - 'Taisho-no-hokori' (S) CKel
§ - 'Taiyo' (S) CKel SKHP
§ - 'Tama-fuyo' (S) CKel
§ - 'Tama-sudare' (S) CKel GBin XGra
- The Sun see *P. suffruticosa* 'Taiyo'
- 'Toichi Ruby' (S) GBin XGra
- 'White Snow' (S) LRHS
- 'Wu Jin Yao Hui' (S) CBcs
- 'Wu Long Peng Sheng' (S) CKel GBin SPer

§ - 'Xue Lian' (S) CBcs SPer
§ - 'Xue Ta' (S) CBcs CKel LBuc LRHS SPoG
§ - 'Yachiyo-tsubaki' (S) CKel SKHP
- 'Yin Hong Qiao Dui' (S) CKel NTPC SPer
- 'Yoshinogawa' (S) CKel
- 'Yu Ban Bai' (S) NTPC
- 'Yu Pan Sheng Yan' (S) **new** NTPC
- 'Zhao Fen' (S) LRHS NPer NTPC SPoG

'Sugar n' Spice' WCAu
'Sunny Girl' GBin WCAu
'Sunshine' see *P. peregrina* 'Otto Froebel'
'Taiheko' CKel
'Tango' WCAu
'Ten' i' CKel
tenuifolia CAby EBee EPot GBin GCal GKev LRHS NLar SKHP SMad WCAu WCot
- RCB UA 11 WCot
- subsp. ***biebersteiniana*** GKev
- 'Plena' (d) EPot
- 'Rosea' GBin WCAu

'Terpsichore' (S) GBin XGra
'Tria' (S) GBin
turcica GKev
veitchii CKel EPot GCal GKev GMaP IGor NLar SSpi WCot WPGP
- 'Alba' LPla
- pale-flowered GCal
- var. ***woodwardii*** CCon CExl ECho GBin GCra GKev SSpi WCAu WCot WHoo WThu

'Vesuvian' CKel
'Viking Full Moon' GBin
'White Emperor' GBin WCAu
'White Innocence' **new** WCAu
White Phoenix see *P. ostii* 'Feng Dan Bai'
'White Towers' **new** EPfP WFar
'Whopper' **new** GBin XGra
'Wings of the Morning' (S) GBin
wittmanniana CKel GBin GCal GKev NLar WCAu WCot
- PAB 3673 LEdu

§ 'Xiang Yu' (S) SPoG
'Yankee Doodle Dandy' (d) **new** WHlf
§ 'Yao Huang' (S) CBcs GBin SPer
Yao's Yellow see *P.* 'Yao Huang'
'Yellow Crown' CKel GBin NLar
'Yellow Dream' GBin
'Yellow Emperor' CDes GBin
Yellow Flower of Summer see *P. suffruticosa* 'Huang Hua Kui'
'Yellow Gem' GBin
'Yellow Heaven' GBin
'Yokohama' GBin
'Yu Yi Huang' (S) **new** NTPC

I	'Zephyrus' (S)	GBin XGra

Paesia (*Dennstaedtiaceae*)

	scaberula	CDes CLAP NBir WFib

Paliurus (*Rhamnaceae*)

	spina-christi	CArn CBcs

Pallenis (*Asteraceae*)

§	***maritima***	CCCN

Panax (*Araliaceae*)

	ginseng	GPoy
	japonicus	WCru
	- BWJ 7932	WCru

Pancratium (*Amaryllidaceae*)

	illyricum **new**	XEll
	maritimum	CArn EBee ECho GKev NRog SBod SDeJ

Pandorea (*Bignoniaceae*)

	jasminoides ♀H1c	CCCN CDoC CHll CRHN CSpe CTri EBak ECou EShb IDee MOWG
	- 'Alba'	CRHN SPer
§	- 'Charisma' (v)	CCCN CHel CHll EPfP EShb LSou MOWG SEND SLim SPer SPoG
	- 'Lady Di'	CCCN MOWG
	- 'Rosea'	CCCN CHel
	- 'Rosea Superba' ♀H1c	CBcs CHEx CRHN SEND SLim SPer
	- 'Variegata'	see *P. jasminoides* 'Charisma'
	lindleyana	see *Clytostoma calystegioides*
	pandorana	CHll CRHN EBee SLim
	- 'Golden Showers'	CBcs CCCN CDoC CHel CRHN EBee MOWG MRav SEND SLim

Panicum (*Poaceae*)

	amarum 'Dewey Blue'	CKno EPPr MAvo SMHy
	bulbosum	CKno EHoe EPPr EPla
	clandestinum	EHoe EPPr EWes IMou LRHS MMuc MWhi SEND SMea
§	'Fibre Optics'	CSpe
	miliaceum	LRHS
	- 'Purple Majesty'	SPhx
	- 'Violaceum'	CSpe SPhx
	oligosanthes var. ***scribnerianum***	SPhx
	virgatum	CKno LSun MAsh SMrm WMnd WWEG XLum
	- 'Blue Tower'	CKno ELon EPPr SGSe SMea XLum
	- 'Cardinal'	EPPr MAvo
	- 'Cloud Nine'	CKno EPPr LRHS MAvo NOak SGSe SMHy SMrm WHal WRHF WWEG
	- 'Dallas Blues'	CBod CKno EBee ECha EHoe EPPr EPla EShb EWes LAst LRHS MAvo MCot MWhi NOak NSti NWsh SCob SGSe SHDw SMHy SMrm SPer WMoo WPGP WWEG XLum
	- 'Emerald Chief'	LSun MWhi
	- 'Farbende Auslese'	WWEG
	- 'Hänse Herms'	CBod CKno EHoe ELon EPPr LRHS MAvo MWhi SMea WFar WWEG
	- 'Heavy Metal'	Widely available
	- 'Heiliger Hain'	CSpe EPPr MAvo WCot WWEG
I	- 'Kupferhirse'	CKno EPPr
	- 'Nican'	EPPr
	- 'Northwind'	CKno EBee EHoe EPPr LRHS MAvo SCob SHDw SMHy SMad WFar WWEG
	- 'Pathfinder'	SGSe
	- 'Prairie Sky'	CBod CKno CPrp EAEE EBee EHoe ELon EPPr EPla EUJe EWoo GBin LEdu LRHS MAsh MAvo NBro NLar NWsh SCob SDix SGSe SGbt SMHy SMea WMoo WPGP WWEG
	- 'Purple Haze'	EHoe EPPr LRHS WWEG
	- 'Red Cloud'	CKno MAvo SMHy WWEG
	- 'Rehbraun'	CSde EBee EHoe EPPr EPfP LEdu LRHS NOak SGol WWEG XLum
	- 'Rotstrahlbusch'	CKno EBee EHoe EPPr EWoo GMaP LSun MWhi NOak NWsh SPer WCot WMoo WWEG XLum
	- 'Rubrum'	ECha EHoe ELan EPPr MAvo MTis MWat SDix WMoo
	- 'Shenandoah'	Widely available
	- 'Squaw'	CBod CKno CMac CPrp CWCL EAEE EHoe EPPr EPfP EPla EShb EWoo LRHS MAsh MAvo MJak MMuc MTis NOak NOrc NWsh SEND SGSe SMad SPer WCot WFar WMoo WWEG
	- 'Straight Cloud' **new**	EPPr
	- 'Strictum'	EHoe EPPr EWes GQue LEdu LPla LRHS MAvo SCob SMHy SPer SPhx WMoo WWEG
I	- 'Strictum Compactum'	CBod
	- 'Warrior'	CBod CKno CPrp EAEE EHoe ELan ELon EPPr EPfP EPla EWTr GBin LRHS MAsh MAvo MCot MRav MWhi NWsh SCob SGSe SMrm SPer WFar WWEG
	- 'Wood's Variegated' (v)	WCot

Papaver ✿ (*Papaveraceae*)

	aculeatum	CTca
	alboroseum	LLHF LRHS
	'Alpha Centauri' (SPS)	SWat
	alpinum	CSpe LRHS MAsh NGdn SWat
	amurense	SWat
	atlanticum	NBro NGdn SPlb
	- 'Flore Pleno' (d)	CSpe IFro NBro NGdn
	'Aurora' (SPS)	SWat
	'Beyond Red' (SPS)	SWat
	bracteatum	see *P. orientale* var. *bracteatum*
	'Bright Star' (SPS)	CDes GBin SWat
	burseri	SRot
	'Cathay' (SPS)	SWat
	commutatum ♀H5	CSpe ELan SPhx SWat
	- 'Ladybird' ♀H5	SVic WBor
	corona-sancti-stephani	SWat
	'Danish Flag'	NNor
	'Eccentric Silk' (SPS)	SWat
§	'Fire Ball' (d)	ELon GCal IGor NBid NBro SWat WRHF WWEG
	glaucum	SPhx
	'Harlequin' (SPS)	ELon
	'Heartbeat'PBR (SPS)	EBee EPfP IGor IPot LRHS SMrm SWat WFar
	heldreichii	see *P. pilosum* subsp. *spicatum*
	hybridum 'Flore Pleno' (d)	NSti SWat
	'Jacinth' (SPS)	CDes GBin SWat WCot
	lateritium	CHid CPou SRms
	- 'Nanum Flore Pleno'	see *P.* 'Fire Ball'
	'Lauffeuer'	CSam ELon SWat
	'Matador'PBR ♀H7	LBrs LRHS MBel MHol NLar NNor WCot
	'Medallion' (SPS)	CDes EPri GBin LRHS SWat

	microcarpum	LLHF
§	***miyabeanum***	CSpe ECho ELan LRHS MJak SRot
	- ***tatewakii***	see *P. miyabeanum*
	'Moondance'	LRHS
	nanum 'Flore Pleno'	see *P.* 'Fire Ball'
§	***nudicaule***	SVic
	- 'Aurora Borealis'	CSpe
	- Champagne Bubbles Group	CBod NNor SWat
	- var. ***croceum*** 'Flamenco'	NNor
	- Garden Gnome Group	see *P. nudicaule* Gartenzwerg Group
§	- Gartenzwerg Group ♀H7	CSpe EPfP LRHS NGdn SPlb SPoG SRot SWvt WHar WRHF
	- 'Matador'	WRHF
	- orange-flowered **new**	LRHS
	- 'Pacino'	EWll LRHS NLar
	- 'Party Fun' (mixed)	CSpe
	- 'Solar Fire Orange' ♀H7	LRHS
	- 'Summer Breeze Orange' ♀H7	NPri
	- 'Summer Breeze Yellow'	NPri
	- Wonderland Series	NNor
	- - 'Wonderland Orange'	ELan NPri
	- - 'Wonderland Pink Shades'	NPri
	- - 'Wonderland White'	ELan GKev NPri
	- - 'Wonderland Yellow'	ELan NPri
	orientale	CBcs EPfP LPal MJak SRms SVic SWat WHar
	- 'Abu Hassan'	IPot SWat
	- 'Aglaja' ♀H7	CElw CUse CWCL ECtt ELon LRHS MAvo MBel MHol MPie NEgg NGdn NPri NSti SPad SWat WCot
	- 'Aladin'	SWat
	- 'Ali Baba'	GCra SWat
	- 'Alison'	SWat
	- 'Allegro'	CBod CSBt EBee ELon EPfP EWoo GMaP IBoy LRHS LSun MBNS MRav NGdn SCob SPlb SVic SWat SWvt WFar
	- 'Arwide'	SWat
	- 'Aslahan'	ELon MRav SWat
	- 'Atrosanguineum'	SWat
	- 'Avebury Crimson'	MWat SWat
	- 'Baby Kiss'PBR	ECtt SWat WFar
	- 'Ballkleid'	ELon SWat
	- 'Beauty Queen'	ECha MRav NGdn SDix SWat
	- 'Bergermeister Rot'	SWat
	- 'Big Jim'	SWat
	- 'Black and White' ♀H7	ELan EPfP MNrw MPkF MRav NEgg NPri SMrm SWat WCAu
	- 'Blackberry Queen'	SWat
	- 'Blickfang'	SWat
	- 'Bolero'	CBod ECtt ELon EPri NLar SHar
	- 'Bonfire'	ELon GAbr MHol SCob WCAu
	- 'Bonfire Red'	SWat
§	- var. ***bracteatum***	NBir SWat
	- 'Brilliant'	COtt EPfP MWat NGdn SWat WFar WMoo
	- 'Brooklyn' (New York Series)	ECtt LRHS SWat
	- 'Burning Heart'	CWGN ECtt EPri IBoy IPot LRHS MSCN NLar SWat
	- 'Carmen'PBR	CBod ECtt ELon LSun MHol
*	- 'Carneum'	LRHS WWEG
	- 'Carnival'	EBee SWat
	- 'Casino'PBR	GAbr NLar SPer
	- 'Catherina'	SWat
	- 'Cedar Hill'	ECtt EPri EWes GCal MRav SWat
	- 'Cedric Morris' ♀H7	ECha ELan MRav SWat WCot WMnd
	- 'Central Park' (New York Series)	ELon LRHS SWat WCAu WFar
I	- 'Charming' pink-flowered	CAby CMac ECtt MWat SPhx SWat
	- 'Charming' red-flowered	LRHS
	- 'China Boy'	SWat
	- 'Clochard'	CElw ECtt ELon SWat WCot
	- 'Coral Reef'	ELon EPfP MHer MLHP NPri SWat WHar WMoo
	- 'Corrina'	SWat
	- 'Curlilocks'	CBod ECtt ELan ELon EPfP IBoy LRHS MRav MWat SRms SWat SWvt WCAu WCot WFar WWEG
	- 'Derwisch'	ELon SWat
*	- 'Diana'	SWat
	- 'Distinction'	WCot
	- 'Double Pleasure'	ECtt SWat
	- double red shades (d)	NGdn
	- 'Doubloon' (d)	SWat WFar
	- 'Dwarf Allegro Vivace'	LRHS
	- 'Earl Grey'	SWat
	- 'Effendi' ♀H7	CUse CWCL ECtt SWat WCot
	- 'Elam Pink'	SWat WCot
	- 'Erste Zuneigung'	ECha ELon SWat
	- 'Eskimo Pie'	SWat
	- 'Eyecatcher'	ELon NLar NSoo SGol
	- 'Fancy Feathers'PBR	ECtt NLar SWat WHil
	- 'Fatima'	SWat
	- 'Feuerriese'	SWat
	- 'Feuerzwerg'	SWat
	- 'Fiesta'	ELon SWat
	- 'Firefly'PBR	SWat
	- 'Flamenco'	CBcs IBoy SWat WFar
	- 'Flamingo'	ELon IBoy SWat WCAu
*	- 'Flore Pleno' (d)	NGdn
	- 'Forncett Summer'	CPar CUse ECtt ELon LRHS MRav NLar NSoo SPer SWat WCot WWEG
	- 'Frosty' (v)	SHar
	- 'Fruit Punch'	MNHC
	- 'Garden Glory'	ECtt ELon GCra LRHS MArl SWat WCAu
	- 'Glowing Embers'	ECtt SWat
	- 'Glowing Rose'	ELon SWat
	- Goliath Group	ELan ELon LRHS MAvo MRav NBro SCob SDix SRms SWat WFar WMnd
	- - 'Beauty of Livermere'	Widely available
§	- - - clonal	ECtt WCot
	- 'Graue Witwe'	ELon SWat
	- 'Guardsman'	see *P. orientale* (Goliath Group) 'Beauty of Livermere' clonal
	- 'Halima'	SWat
	- 'Harlem' (New York Series)	CElw EBee ELon LAst MSCN SWat
	- 'Harvest Moon' (d)	ECtt NPer SWat WHal WWEG
	- 'Heidi'	SWat
	- 'Hewitt's Old Rose'	WCot
	- 'Hula Hula'	ELon SWat
	- 'Indian Chief'	EPri LRHS MHol MRav NPer SHil SRot WFar
	- 'Inferno'PBR	ECtt
	- 'John III' ♀H7	SPhx SWat
	- 'John Metcalf'	ECtt MRav NSti SWat
	- 'Juliane'	ECha NSti SWat WCot
	- 'Karine' ♀H7	CElw CSam ECha ELan EPPr EPfP IBoy LRHS MAvo NLar SCob SGol SPoG SWat WHoo
	- 'Khedive' (d) ♀H7	EBee IPot SWat

- 'King George' SWat
- 'King Kong' CPar CUse ECtt MHol NLar SWat WCot WFar
- 'Kleine Tänzerin' CSam MBel MHer MRav NSti SWat WCAu WFar
- 'Kollebloem' SWat
- 'Lady Frederick Moore' IGor NBre NLar SWat WWEG
- 'Lady Roscoe' SWat
- 'Ladybird' EPfP LRHS
- 'Laffeuer' SPhx
- 'Lambada' SWat
- 'Lauren's Lilac' ELon SWat
- 'Leuchtfeuer' ♀H7 ECha SWat
- 'Lighthouse' ♀H7 SWat
- 'Lilac Girl' ECha ELon SWat
- 'Little Candyfloss'PBR SWat
- 'Little Patty Plum'PBR NLar
- 'Louvre' (Parisienne Series) ECtt ELon SPoG SWat WCot WFar
- 'Maiden's Blush' ECtt NSti SWat
- 'Manhattan' (New York Series) CElw CSam CSpe ECtt ELon EPfP EWes LRHS MNrw MSCN NSti SGbt SPer SPoG SWat WFar
- 'Marcus Perry' ECtt EWes GMaP LRHS NGdn SGol SPoG SWat
- 'Marlene' CFis ELon IPot LRHS MSCN SWat
- 'Mary Finnan' CTca SWat
- 'Master Richard' SWat
- 'May Queen' (d) ECtt ELon EWes IBlr MRav NLar NSti SWat WCot WFar WPnn
- 'May Sadler' NLar SWat
- 'Midnight' ELon SWat
- 'Miss Piggy'PBR CUse EBee ECtt IKil LLHF NLar NSoo SGbt SPer SWat WCot WFar WHil
- 'Mrs H.G. Stobart' SWat
- 'Mrs Marrow's Plum' see *P. orientale* 'Patty's Plum'
- 'Mrs Perry' CMac CMea COtt CSBt ECtt ELan IFro LRHS MWat NGdn NPer SGbt SPer SRms SWat WBrk WCot WFar WMnd
- 'Nanum Flore Pleno' see *P.* 'Fire Ball'
- 'Noema' SWat
- 'Orange Glow' SWat WMoo
- 'Orangeade Maison' SWat
- 'Oriana' SWat
- 'Oriental' SWat
- 'Pale Face' SWat
- 'Papillon'PBR CBcs CUse LRHS MHol MPie NLar NPri WCot WHar
- 'Paradiso'PBR EPfP NSoo NSti
§ - 'Patty's Plum' Widely available
- 'Perry's White' CBcs COtt CSBt EBee ECtt ELan ELon EPfP EWoo GMaP IBoy LRHS MRav NLar SCob SGol SHil SPer SPoG SRkn SWat SWvt WMnd WWEG
- 'Persepolis' SGol
- 'Peter Pan' ELon SWat
- 'Petticoat' ECtt SWat
- 'Picotée' ECtt ELan ELon LRHS MRav NEgg NLar SPer SPoG SRot SWat SWvt WFar WMoo
- 'Pink Lassie' SWat
- 'Pink Panda' SWat
- 'Pink Pearl'PBR SWat
- 'Pink Ruffles'PBR CBcs ECtt LRHS NLar SGbt SPoG SWat WCot WFar
- 'Pinnacle' EPri SWat WFar
- 'Pizzicato' CBod EPfP LRHS NNor NPer SWat WFar WHar WMoo
- 'Place Pigalle' (Parisienne Series) ECtt EPfP MNrw SPer SPoG SWat
- 'Plum Pudding' **new** CHid
- 'Polka' SWat
- 'Prince of Orange' SWat SWvt
- Princess Victoria Louise see *P. orientale* 'Prinzessin Victoria Louise'
- 'Prinz Eugen' ELon SWat WFar
§ - 'Prinzessin Victoria Louise' COtt EPfP IBoy LAst LRHS MMuc NGdn NLar NNor NPri SEND SWat WBor WBrk WHar
- 'Prospero' SWat
- 'Queen Alexandra' ITim LBMP NGdn NLar
- 'Raspberry Queen' CBod CCon CMac CMea ECtt ELan ELon EPfP EPri GMaP IBoy IGor IPot MArl MBel MRav MWat NChi NLar NSti SWat WCot WHal WHoo WMnd WWEG
- 'Raspberry Ruffles' SWat
- 'Rembrandt' LPal SWat
- 'Rosenpokal' SWat
- 'Roter Zwerg' ECha SWat
- 'Royal Chocolate Distinction' CElw CSpe EBee ECtt ELan ELon EPPr EPfP GBin LRHS MAvo NLar NSti SCob SRot SWat WFar
- 'Royal Wedding' Widely available
- 'Ruffled Patty'PBR CUse ECtt ELon EPfP MHol NSti SGbt SWat
- 'Ruffled Princess of Orange'PBR SWat
* - 'Saffron' SWat
- 'Salmon Glow' (d) SWat WFar WWEG
- 'Salome' SWat
- 'Scarlet King' CMac LRHS SWat
- scarlet-flowered MMuc SEND
- 'Scarlett O'Hara'PBR (d) CPar ECtt EPfP GAbr LLHF MPkF SWat WBor WFar
- 'Showgirl' ELon SWat
* - 'Silberosa' IPot SWat
- 'Sindbad' SWat
- 'Snow Goose' CMea CUse CWGN ECtt ELon ESwi IPot LLHF LRHS LSun MAvo MBel MHol NPri SMad SWat WCot WHoo WKif WRHF
- 'Spätzünder' SWat
- 'Springtime' ELon EWes LAst MRav SWat
- 'Staten Island' (New York Series) SCob
- Stormtorch see *P. orientale* 'Sturmfackel'
§ - 'Sturmfackel' SWat
- 'Suleika' SWat
- 'Sultana' ECha ELon EPri MArl SWat
- 'Sunset'PBR SWat
- 'The Promise' SWat
- 'Tiffany' CMac ECtt ELon NEgg SWat WCot
- 'Trinity' SWat
- 'Türkenlouis' ECGP ECtt ELon GAbr GCra GMaP IBoy IPot LAst LRHS MRav MWat NGdn NLar NSoo SHil SMrm SWat WBrk WCAu WCot WFar WHoo WWEG
- 'Turkish Delight' ELon EWoo GCra LRHS MAvo MBel MRav NBir NSoo SHil SWat SWvt WMnd WWEG
- 'Tutu' SWat
- 'Victoria Dreyfuss' SWat

Name	Suppliers
– 'Viola'	SWat
– 'Violetta'	SWat
– 'Walking Fire'	MNrw
– 'Water Babies'	SWat
– 'Watermelon'	ECtt EWoo NLar SPer SWat
– 'White Ruffles'[PBR]	ECtt IKil SGbt SPoG SWat WCot
– 'Wisley Beacon'	ELon SWat
– 'Wunderkind'	SWat
pilosum	SGSe SWat
§ – subsp. ***spicatum***	CCon CSpe ECha GBin GCal LPla MMuc NBir WHer WMoo
'Rhapsody in Red' (SPS)	SWat
rhoeas	CArn CHab GPoy MNHC NNor SVic WJek
– Angels' Choir Group (d)	NNor SWat
– 'Bridal White'	SPhx
– Mother of Pearl Group	CSpe MCot SPhx SWat
– Shirley Group	CWCL NNor
rupifragum	ECha GAbr WCot WPnn
– 'Double Tangerine Gem'	see *P. rupifragum* 'Flore Pleno'
§ – 'Flore Pleno' (d)	CSpe GBin LAst MMuc NCGa NChi SVic WBrk WMoo
'Serena' (SPS)	SWat
'Shasta' (SPS)	EBee GBin LRHS SWat WFar
'Snow White' (SPS)	CDes SWat
somniferum	CArn ELau ENfk GPoy SVic SWat
– var. ***album***	CArn
– 'Blackcurrant Fizz' (d)	SPhx
– 'Boudoir Babe' (d)	CSpe
– (Laciniatum Group) 'Crimson Feathers'	NNor
– – 'Swansdown' (d)	CSpe
– 'Lauren's Grape'	CSpe SPhx
– Paeoniiflorum Group (d)	SWat
– – 'Black Beauty' (d)	CSpe SDeJ SVic SWat
– – 'Black Paeony' (d)	SPhx
– 'Pink Chiffon'	SWat
– 'Ragged Red' (d)	CSpe
– subsp. ***setigerum***	NNor
– single white-flowered	CSpe
– 'White Cloud' (d)	SWat
'Tequila Sunrise' (SPS)	CDes SWat
'The Falklands' (SPS)	SWat
triniifolium	CSpe GCal MMuc WCot
'Vesuvius' (SPS)	GBin SWat
'Viva' (SPS)	CDes SWat
'Water Melon'	EPri

papaya (pawpaw) see *Carica papaya*

Parabenzoin see *Lindera*

Paracaryum (*Boraginaceae*)

Name	Suppliers
racemosum new	SIgm

Parachampionella see *Strobilanthes*

Paradisea (*Asparagaceae*)

Name	Suppliers
liliastrum ♀H5	CHid EBee ECho EPri GCal IGor NBid NChi WPtf
– 'Major'	ECho
lusitanica	CAvo CDes CHid CMHG CPom CSam CSpe CTca ECho EPri GBin GCal GKev IBlr IBoy LEdu MCot MHol SGSe WPGP

Parahebe (*Plantaginaceae*)

Name	Suppliers
'Angela'	MSCN
× ***bidwillii***	GJos MHer NHar SRms SRot
– 'Kea'	ECho SRot
§ ***catarractae***	CExl CTri EBee ECho EPfP GAbr GCra ITim MLHP MRav MWat NBir NBro SRms WKif
– 'Avalanche' new	LRHS WNPC
– blue-flowered	CDoC SPer WBor
§ – 'Delight' ♀H4	CExl EWes GCal GMaP GQue LRHS MHer NPer SDix SRot
– subsp. ***diffusa***	NPer
– 'Miss Willmott'	SPer SPlb
– 'Porlock'	GKev WHoo
– 'Porlock Purple'	see *P. catarractae* 'Delight'
– 'Rosea'	ECho MAsh SRms
– white-flowered	CSpe MLHP SRms
§ ***formosa***	SPlb SVen
'Greencourt'	see *P. catarractae* 'Delight'
linifolia	CTri
– 'Blue Skies'	EPot
§ ***lyallii***	EBee ECho EPfP GJos GMaP MCot MHer MMuc MRav MSwo MWat NSbr SPlb SRms WKif
– 'Julie-Anne' ♀H4	GCal LRHS
– 'Rosea'	CTri
– 'Snowcap'	CDoC LRHS MRav SPlb
'Mervyn'	CNor CTri
§ ***perfoliata***	CExl CMac CSde EBee ECha ELan EPri GAbr GCal GCra GGal GMaP LEdu LRHS MAsh MCot MMuc MNrw MRav NChi SDix SEND SPer SRms WWFP XLum
'Snow Clouds'	CHel CMea EPfP EWoo SBch SDix SRot

Parakmeria see *Magnolia*

Paramongaia (*Amaryllidaceae*)

Name	Suppliers
weberbaueri	CPne

Paranomus (*Proteaceae*)

Name	Suppliers
reflexus	SPlb

Paraquilegia (*Ranunculaceae*)

Name	Suppliers
§ ***anemonoides***	CExl WAbe
grandiflora	see *P. anemonoides*

Parasenecio (*Asteraceae*)

Name	Suppliers
delphiniifolius B&SWJ 5789	WCru
– B&SWJ 10885	WCru
– B&SWJ 11189	WCru WSHC
– B&SWJ 11415	WCru
farfarifolius	WCru
– var. ***acerinus*** B&SWJ 11549	WCru
– – B&SWJ 11554	WCru
– var. ***bulbifer***	WCru
hastatus var. ***farfarifolius***	see *P. maximowiczianus*
kiusianus B&SWJ 11460	WCru
§ ***maximowiczianus*** B&SWJ 11468	WCru
mortonii GWJ 9419	WCru
– HWJK 2214	WCru
tebakoensis B&SWJ 11167	WCru
– B&SWJ 11536	WCru
aff. ***yatabei*** B&SWJ 11117	WCru

Paraserianthes (*Mimosaceae*)

distachya	see *P. lophantha*
§ ***lophantha*** ♀H2	CExl CHEx EBak SPlb

Parasyringa see *Ligustrum*

Parathelypteris (*Thelypteridaceae*)

§ ***novae-boracensis***	ISha

× *Pardancanda* (*Iridaceae*)

norrisii	see *Iris × norrisii*

Pardanthopsis (*Iridaceae*)

dichotoma	see *Iris dichotoma*

Parietaria (*Urticaceae*)

judaica	CArn GPoy WHer WSFF

Paris ✿ (*Melanthiaceae*)

chinensis	WCru
- B&SWJ 265 from Taiwan	WCru
delavayi	WCru
fargesii	ECho GKev LAma WCru
- var. ***brevipetalata***	WCru
- var. ***petiolata***	WCru
forrestii	WCru
incompleta	CLAP EPot GCal LEdu MAvo WCru
japonica	GKev LAma WCru
lancifolia B&SWJ 3044 from Taiwan	WCru
mairei	WCru
polyphylla	CArn CBct CBro CCon ECho GEdr GKev LAma MAvo MNrw NBid NLar NWad SKHP WCru WPnP WShi
- B&SWJ 2125	WCru
- Forrest 5945	GCal
- HWJCM 475	WCru
- var. ***stenophylla***	CCon EBee GKev LAma WCru
- var. ***yunnanensis***	ECho
* - - ***alba***	GCal
quadrifolia	CLAP CSpe ECho EPfP GCal GKev GPoy LEdu MAvo NLar NMyG SKHP SPhx SSpi WCru WHer WPGP WPnP WShi
- SDR 2828	GKev
tetraphylla	WCru
thibetica	CCon EBee GKev NBid NWad SKHP WCru
- var. ***apetala***	WCru
verticillata	LAma WCru
- 'Ryokutei' (d)	WCru

Parnassia (*Celastraceae*)

SDR 5128	EBee
asarifolia **new**	GKev
grandifolia **new**	GKev
nubicola	GKev
palustris	GKev WHer
- var. ***izuinsularis***	GEdr
- var. ***yakushimensis*** **new**	GEdr

Parochetus (*Papilionaceae*)

§ ***africanus*** ♀H2	CHid ECre
* - 'Blue Gem'	CCCN CSpe
communis misapplied	see *P. africanus*
communis ambig.	CCon CExl MSCN NPer WHil
- from Himalaya	EBee GCra

Paronychia (*Caryophyllaceae*)

sp.	SIgm
§ ***capitata***	CTri SRms WHoo
kapela	SPlb XSen
- 'Binsted Gold' (v)	XLum XSen
§ - subsp. ***serpyllifolia***	GBin XLum
nivea	see *P. capitata*
serpyllifolia	see *P. kapela* subsp. *serpyllifolia*

Parrotia (*Hamamelidaceae*)

persica	Widely available
- 'Biltmore'	CJun NLar SSta
- 'Burgundy'	CJun NLar
- 'Felicie'	CJun EPfP NLar
- 'Globosa'	NLar
- 'Het Plantsoen'	NLar
- 'Jodrell Bank'	CJun MBlu NLar
§ - 'Lamplighter' (v)	CJun
- 'Pendula'	CJun CMCN EPfP MBlu SSta
- 'Persian Carpet'	NLar
- 'Summer Bronze'	LRHS MAsh SBir SSta
- 'Vanessa' ♀H6	CBcs CDoC CJun CLnd CMCN CMac EPfP ETwe EWes GBin GKin IArd LRHS MAsh MBlu MGos NLar SBir SGol SPoG SSta WMou
- 'Variegata'	see *P. persica* 'Lamplighter'
subaequalis	CDul MBri NLar WPGP

Parrotiopsis (*Hamamelidaceae*)

jacquemontiana	CBcs CJun GBin IVic MBlu NLar

parsley see *Petroselinum crispum*

Parsonsia (*Apocynaceae*)

capsularis	ECou
heterophylla	ECou

Parthenium (*Asteraceae*)

integrifolium	CArn GPoy IMou SPhx WCot

Parthenocissus (*Vitaceae*)

§ ***henryana*** ♀H5	Widely available
himalayana	CBcs
- 'Purpurea'	see *P. himalayana* var. *rubrifolia*
§ - var. ***rubrifolia***	CBcs CMac CRHN CWCL ELan EUJe GBin LRHS MMuc MRav SLim SLon SPtp WCru
inserta misapplied	see *P. quinquefolia*
inserta ambig.	CMac CTsd NLar
laetevirens	NLar
§ ***quinquefolia***	Widely available
- var. ***engelmannii***	CBcs LAst LBuc MMuc SCob SPer WCFE
- 'Guy's Garnet'	WCru
- Star Showers = 'Monham' (v)	EBee EPfP NLar
- 'Yellow Wall'PBR **new**	LRHS
semicordata B&SWJ 6551	WCru
striata	see *Cissus striata*
thomsonii	see *Cayratia thomsonii*
§ ***tricuspidata***	CCVT CDul EBee EHoe EPfP IBoy MAsh MGos MMuc SCob SGol
- 'Beverley Brook'	CRHN ELon LRHS MBri NLar SPer SRms
- 'Crûg Compact'	WCru
- 'Fenway Park'	CFlo EBee ELan MRav NLar

– 'Green Spring'	CBcs IArd MGos NLar
– 'Lowii'	CMac EBee EPfP LRHS MBlu MGos MRav NLar SLon
– 'Robusta'	CHEx
§ – 'Veitchii' ♀H5	Widely available

Pasithea (*Hemerocallidaceae*)

caerulea	CAbP CAvo CMea EBee EPri ESwi GAbr MHol NGBl SBrt WCot WPGP

Paspalum (*Poaceae*)

glaucifolium	MNrw
quadrifarium RCB RA S-5	WCot

Passiflora ✿ (*Passifloraceae*)

'Aafue'	CTyn
'Abigail'	CTyn
actinia	CCCN CRHN CTyn SPlb
'Adularia'	CCCN CTyn
alata (F) ♀H1a	CCCN CTyn
– 'Shannon' (F)	CTyn
× ***alatocaerulea***	see *P.* × *belotii*
'Allardii'	CCCN CTyn
amalocarpa	CTyn
ambigua	CCCN
§ 'Amethyst' ♀H3	CCCN CFlo CRHN CSBt CSPN CTyn SArc SPoG
amethystina misapplied	see *P.* 'Amethyst'
§ ***amethystina*** Mikan	CBcs ECre LRHS
ampullacea (F)	CTyn
'Anastasia'	CCCN CTyn
'Andy'	CCCN CTyn
'Anemona'	CCCN CTyn
anfracta	CTyn
'Angelo Blu'	CCCN CTyn
'Annette'	CTyn
'Annika'	CCCN
antioquiensis misapplied	see *P.* × *exoniensis*
antioquiensis ambig.	CBcs CCCN CDoC CHel CSPN MOWG SEND
antioquiensis Karst ♀H2	CHll GGal
apetala	CTyn
'Ariane'	CCCN
× ***atropurpurea***	CCCN CTyn
§ ***aurantia***	CCCN CTyn
'Aurora'	CTyn
banksii	see *P. aurantia*
'Barborea'	CTyn
'Beaky'	CTyn
§ × ***belotii***	CCCN CRHN CTyn
– 'Impératrice Eugénie'	see *P.* × *belotii*
– 'Perfume Passion'PBR **new**	CCCN EShb
'Betty Myles Young'	CCCN CRHN CTyn
biflora ambig.	CTyn
'Blaumilch'	CTyn
'Blue Bird'	CCCN CTyn
'Blue Crown'	CCCN
'Blue Moon'	CCCN CTyn
'Blue Stripper'	CCCN
'Blue Velvet'	CCCN
'Byron Beauty'	CCCN CTyn
'Byte'	CCCN
'Cacita'	CTyn
§ ***caerulea*** ♀H4	Widely available
– 'Chinensis' **new**	CCCN
– 'Clear Sky'PBR	CCCN CFlo CSPN CTyn ELan EPfP LRHS NLar
– 'Constance Eliott' ♀H4	CAgr CBcs CCCN CDoC CFlo CHel CMac COtt CRHN CSBt CSPN CTyn CUse ELan EPfP LBMP LRHS MAsh MBri MHer MOWG MRav NLar NPri SCob SGol SPer SWvt
– 'Pierre Pomié' **new**	CCCN
– ***rubra***	CSBt
– 'White Lightning'	CCCN CFlo CSPN CWSG LRHS LSqu NPri SHil SLim SPoG SWvt
× ***caeruleoracemosa***	see *P.* × *violacea*
× ***caponii***	CCCN
– 'John Innes'	CCCN
capsularis	CTyn
'Celine'	CCCN CTyn
chinensis	see *P. caerulea*
citrifolia	CCCN
citrina	CCCN CTyn MOWG SLim
* ***classica*** × ***coccinea*** **new**	CCCN
colinvauxii	CTyn
× ***colvillii***	CCCN CHll CTyn
conzattiana	CTyn
'Coordination'	CCCN
§ ***coriacea***	CCCN CTyn
'Corry Rooymans'	CTyn
'Crimson Tears'	CCCN CTyn
I 'Curiosa'	CTyn
'Daylight'	CCCN
'Debby'	CCCN CTyn
× ***decaisneana*** (F)	CCCN CTyn
'Divertido'	CCCN
'Eclipse'	CTyn
Eden = 'Hil Pas Eden' ♀H3	CCCN CFlo CSPN CTyn LRHS MBri NLar SCoo SLim SPoG SRkn
edulis (F)	CBcs CCCN CTyn ELau SPre SVic
§ – f. ***edulis*** (F)	CCCN
– f. ***flavicarpa*** (F)	CCCN CTyn
– 'Golden Star'	CTyn
– 'Norfolk' (F)	CCCN CTyn
– 'Parati' (F)	CCCN
eichleriana	CTyn
elegans	CTyn
'Elizabeth' (F)	CCCN
'Empress Eugenie'	see *P.* × *belotii*
'Erik'	CTyn
'Evatoria'	CCCN
'Everywhere'	CTyn
'Excel'	CTyn
§ × ***exoniensis*** ♀H2	CCCN CHll CRHN CSBt CTyn ECre
'Fairylights'	CCCN
'Fantasma'	CCCN
'Fata Confetto'	CCCN
'Fledermouse'	CCCN CTyn
'Flirtation'	CTyn
'Flying V'	CCCN CTyn
foetida	CTyn
gracilis	CTyn
'Grand Duchess'	CCCN
gritensis	CCCN
'Guglielmo Betto' **new**	CCCN
hahnii	CTyn
'Heidi'	CCCN
helleri	CTyn
herbertiana (F)	CTyn
'Hetty Nicolaas'	CCCN
'Hildegard'	CCCN
'Hill House'	CHll
holosericea	CTyn
incarnata (F)	CArn CCCN CTyn GPoy IFro SPlb

	Name	Suppliers
	'Incense' (F) ♀H2	CCCN CTyn SPlb
	'Inspiration'	CCCN CTyn
	'Inverleith'	CTyn
	'Jara' **new**	CCCN
	'Jeanette'	CTyn
	'Jelly Joker'	CCCN CTyn
	jorullensis	CTyn
	'Justine Lyons'	CCCN CRHN CTyn
	kalbreyeri	CTyn
	karwinskii	CCCN
	'Kate Adie'	CTyn
	× ***kewensis***	CCCN CTyn
	- 'Déjà Vu'	CTyn
	'Lady Margaret'	CCCN CTyn
	'Lambiekins'	CCCN CRHN CTyn
§	***ligularis*** (F)	CCCN CTyn
	'Lilac Lady'	see *P.* × *violacea* 'Tresederi'
	'Little Dot Beardshaw'	CTyn
	'Livie'	CCCN
	'Lolly'	CTyn
	lowei	see *P. ligularis*
	lutea	CCCN
	'Luzmarina'	CCCN
	'Manapany' **new**	CCCN
	manicata (F)	CCCN CTyn
	'Maria'	CCCN
	'Marijke' **new**	CCCN
	'Mary Jane'	CCCN
I	***matthewsii*** 'Alba'	CRHN
	'Mavis Mastics'	see *P.* × *violacea* 'Tresederi'
	mayana	see *P. caerulea*
	membranacea (F)	CCCN
	'Michael'	CCCN
	'Minai'	CCCN
	'Mini Lamb'	CCCN CTyn
	mixta (F)	CCCN CTyn SEND
	- clone 2 **new**	CCCN
	- red-flowered	CCCN
	mollissima misapplied	see *P. tarminiana*
	mollissima ambig. (F)	CBcs CCCN CHll CTyn MOWG SPlb
	mollissima (Kunth) L.H. Bailey (F) ♀H2	CRHN
	'Monika Fischer'	CCCN
	morifolia	CTyn
	mucronata	CCCN CTyn
	murucuja	CCCN CTyn
	naviculata	CTyn
	'New Incense'	CCCN CTyn
	'Nightshift'	CCCN
	obtusifolia	see *P. coriacea*
	'Olga'	CTyn
	onychina	see *P. amethystina* Mikan
	organensis	CTyn
	'Oriental Sunset'	CTyn
	'Panda'	CCCN
I	***pardifolia***	CTyn
	'Party Animal' **new**	CCCN
	'Pink Festival'	CCCN
	'Pink Nightmare'	CCCN CTyn
	'Pink Passion' PBR **new**	CCCN EShb
	'Pinky'	CCCN
	× ***piresiae***	CCCN CTyn
	'Poppet' **new**	CCCN
	'Precioso'	CCCN CTyn
	punctata	CTyn
	'Pura Vida'	CCCN
	'Pura Vida 1'	CTyn
	'Pura Vida 2'	CTyn
	'Purple Companion' **new**	CCCN
	'Purple Haze'	CCCN CHel CSPN CTyn LRHS NLar
	'Purple Passion'	see *P. edulis* f. *edulis*
	'Purple Pendulum'	CCCN CTyn
	'Purple Rain'	CCCN CTyn
	quadrangularis (F) ♀H1a	CCCN CHll
	quinquangularis	CCCN CTyn
	racemosa ♀H1b	CCCN CTyn
	- 'Buzios'	CCCN
	'Red Inca'	CCCN
	reflexiflora	CTyn
	reitzii	CCCN
	riparia	CCCN
	rubra	CCCN CTyn SLim
	'Saint Rule'	CTyn
	'Sammie B'	CTyn
	'Sancap'	CTyn
	sanguinolenta	CTyn
	- 'Maria Rosa'	CTyn
	'Sapphire'	CTyn
	serratifolia	CTyn
	sexocellata	see *P. coriacea*
	'Silly Cow' **new**	CCCN
	'Silvie'	CCCN
	'Simply Red'	CCCN CTyn
	'Smythiana'	CTyn
	'Star of Bristol' ♀H2	CSPN CTyn SLim
	'Star of Clevedon'	CTyn
	'Star of Kingston'	CCCN CTyn
	'Star of Surbiton'	CCCN CRHN CTyn
	suberosa	CTyn
	subpeltata	CTyn
	'Sunburst'	CCCN CTyn
	'Surprise'	CCCN CTyn
§	***tarminiana*** (F)	CCCN CRHN CSBt
	- white-flowered	CCCN
	'Temptation'	CCCN CTyn
	tetrandra	CExl
	'Tinalandia'	CTyn
	× ***tresederi***	see *P.* × *violacea* 'Tresederi'
	tricuspis	CTyn
	trifasciata	CCCN
	- 'El Indio'	CTyn
	trisecta	CTyn
	tucumanensis tetraploid	CCCN
	tulae	CCCN CTyn
	umbilicata	CTyn
	'Venus'	CTyn
	venusta **new**	CCCN
§	× ***violacea*** ♀H2	CBcs CCCN CRHN
	- 'Eynsford Gem'	CCCN CTyn
	- 'Lilac Lady'	see *P.* × *violacea* 'Tresederi'
	- 'Sabin'	CCCN CTyn NLar
§	- 'Tresederi'	CCCN WFar
	- 'Twin Star'	CCCN
	- 'Victoria'	CCCN CSBt CTyn EBee EUJe LSou NLar
	vitifolia (F)	CCCN
	- 'Innocentiae' **new**	CCCN
	- 'Scarlet Flame' (F)	CTyn
	'White Queen'	CCCN
	'White Star'	CTyn
	'White Surprise' **new**	CCCN
	'White Wedding'	CCCN CHel CTyn
	'Wilgen Heintje'	CCCN
	'Wilgen K Verhoeff'	CTyn
	'Wilgen Marieke' **new**	CCCN
	'Winterland'	CCCN

passion fruit see *Passiflora*

passion fruit, banana see *Passiflora mollissima* (Kunth) L.H. Bailey

Pastinaca (*Apiaceae*)

sativa	CHab SVic

Patersonia (*Iridaceae*)

occidentalis	LRHS SPlb

Patrinia ✿ (*Caprifoliaceae*)

gibbosa	CSam CSpe CTal MLHP MMHG MMuc NLar SGSe SPhx WMoo WPnP WWFP
- B&SWJ 874	WCru
heterophylla	ITim
HEHEHE 298 **new**	
rupestris B&SWJ 12654	WCru
scabiosifolia	CHll CKno CSpe ECha ECtt GJos MHer MNFA NBir NLar SGSe SPhx WFar WHoo WMoo WPGP
- B&SWJ 8740	WCru
- 'Nagoya'	MNrw
triloba	CPla CPne CSpe CTal ECho GCal GEdr LRHS LSou MMHG WFar WMoo
* - 'Minor'	ECho
- var. ***palmata***	GKev WMoo
villosa	CExl EBee GCal GJos IMou NGdn

Paulownia (*Paulowniaceae*)

catalpifolia	NLar
elongata	NLar
fargesii Osborn	see *P. tomentosa* 'Lilacina'
fortunei	IVic MBlu SPlb
- Fast Blue = 'Minfast' ♀H5	CExl CHGN ESwi ETwe LLHF SGol WHar
kawakamii	EPfP WPGP
- RWJ 9909	WCru
tomentosa ♀H5	Widely available
- 'Coreana'	CHll WCru
§ - 'Lilacina'	CBcs

Pavonia (*Malvaceae*)

multiflora ambig.	CCCN
strictiflora	CCCN
* ***volubilis***	CCCN

pawpaw (false banana) see *Asimina triloba*

pawpaw (papaya) see *Carica papaya*

Paxistima (*Celastraceae*)

canbyi	WThu

peach see *Prunus persica*

pear see *Pyrus communis*

pear, Asian see *Pyrus pyrifolia*

pecan see *Carya illinoinensis*

Peganum (*Nitrariaceae*)

harmala	CArn SBrt

Pelargonium ✿ (*Geraniaceae*)

'A.M. Mayne' (Z/d)	WFib
'Abba' (Z/d)	WFib
abrotanifolium (Sc)	ENfk EWoo MHer SSea SVen WFib WGwG
- broad-leaved	WCot
acetosum	EWoo GCal MHer SMrm SPhx
'Ada Green' (R)	WFib
'Ade's Elf' (Z/St)	NFir
'Ainsdale Beauty' (Z)	WFib
'Ainsdale Duke' (Z)	NFir
album	LAst
alchemilloides	SPhx
var. ***dentatum*** **new**	
'Alde' (Min)	NFir
'Aldwyck' (R) ♀H1c	WFib
'Alex Kitson' (Z)	WFib
'Algenon' (Min/d)	WFib
I 'Alice' (Min)	WFib
'Alice Greenfield' (Z)	NFir
'Allesley Shadow' (Dw/d)	WFib
alpinum	MHer
'Amari' (R)	WFib
'Ambrose' (Min/d)	WFib
Amelit = 'Pacameli'PBR (I/d)	LAst MCot SSea
Ameta = 'Pacmeta'PBR (Z)	LAst SSea
'Amethyst' (R)	SCoo WFib
(Angeleyes Series) Angeleyes Bicolor = 'Pacbicolor'PBR (A)	LAst
- Angeleyes Burgundy = 'Pacburg'PBR (A)	LAst
- Angeleyes Orange = 'Paccrio'PBR (A)	EWoo LAst LSou
- Angeleyes Randy (A)	SSea
'Angelique' (Dw/d)	WFib
'Ann Hoystead' (R) ♀H1c	NFir WFib
'Anna Lisa Pope' (R)	MGbk
'Annsbrook Aquarius' (St)	NFir
'Annsbrook Beauty' (A/C)	NFir WFib
'Annsbrook Jupitor' (Z/St)	NFir
'Annsbrook Mulberry Blotch' (Z/v)	MGbk
Anthony = 'Pacan'PBR (Z/d)	LAst
'Antoine Crozy' (Z × I/d)	WFib
'Apache' (Z/d)	WFib
appendiculatum	CLak MHer
'Apple Betty' (Sc)	EWoo WFib
'Apple Blossom Rosebud' (Z/d) ♀H1c	CHel ECtt EShb LAll MHer SMrm SSea WFib
'Apricot' (Z/St)	LAst
'April Hamilton' (I)	CWCL WFib
'April Showers' (A)	WFib
'Archie Pope' (R)	MGbk
'Arctic Frost'	WFib
§ 'Arctic Star' (Z/St) ♀H1c	CSpe NFir WBrk WFib
'Ardens' ♀H1c	CSpe EUJe EWoo LSou MHer NFir SSea SWvt WCot WFib WWFP
'Ardwick Cinnamon' (Sc)	ENfk EWoo MHer NFir WDib WFib
(Aristo Series) Aristo Apricot = 'Regapri' (R)	LAst
- Aristo Darling = 'Regdar'PBR (R)	LAst
- Aristo Red Velvet = 'Regvel'PBR (R)	LAst
- Aristo Schoko = 'Regschoko' (R)	LAst

	Name	Suppliers
	'Arnside Fringed Aztec' (R)	MHer WFib
	'Ashby' (U/Sc) ♀H1c	CWCL ENfk EWoo MHer NFir SBch SSea
	'Ashfield Jubilee' (Z/C)	NFir
	'Ashfield Monarch' (Z/d) ♀H1c	NFir
	'Ashfield Serenade' (Z) ♀H1c	WFib
	'Askham Fringed Aztec' (R) ♀H1c	MHer WFib
	asperum Ehr. ex Willd.	see *P.* 'Graveolens'
	'Atlantic Burgundy'	CWCL MCot
§	'Atomic Snowflake' (Sc/v)	ENfk MCot MNHC WDib WFib
	'Atrium' (U)	MHer WFib
	'Attar of Roses' (Sc) ♀H1c	CArn CHby CRHN ECtt ENfk EWoo LAll MCot MHer NFir NPri SBch SIde SSea WBrk WFib WGwG
	'Aurora' (Z/d)	LAst
	australe	CSpe EWoo MCot MHer SBch SVen WFib
	'Australian Mystery' (R/Dec) ♀H1c	CSpe NFir WFib
	'Aztec' (R) ♀H1c	NFir WFib
	'Baby Bird's Egg' (Min)	WFib
	'Baby Harry' (Dw/v)	WFib
	Balcon Imperial	see *P.* 'Roi des Balcons Impérial'
	'Balcon Lilas'	see *P.* 'Roi des Balcons Lilas'
	'Balcon Rose'	see *P.* 'Hederinum'
	'Balcon Rouge'	see *P.* 'Roi des Balcons Impérial'
	'Balcon Royale'	see *P.* 'Roi des Balcons Impérial'
	'Balcony Red' (I)	ECtt
	'Ballerina' (R)	see *P.* 'Carisbrooke'
I	'Ballerina' (Min)	WFib
	'Barbara Lambert' (Z/St)	MGbk
§	'Barbe Bleu' (I/d) ♀H1c	NFir WFib
	'Barking' (Min/Z)	NFir
	'Barnston Dale' (Dw/d)	NFir
	'Bath Beauty' (Dw)	CSpe
	'Beatrice Cottington' (I/d)	WFib
	'Beauty of Eastbourne' misapplied	see *P.* 'Lachskönigin'
	'Belinda Adams' (Min/d) ♀H1c	NFir
	'Bell Ernie Oliver' (Z/C/Dw/d) **new**	MGbk
	Belladonna = 'Fisopa' (I/d)	SCoo
	'Bembridge' (Z/St/d)	WFib
	'Ben Franklin' (Z/d/v) ♀H1c	NFir
	'Ben Matt' (R)	WFib
	'Berkswell Bounty' (A)	MGbk
	'Berkswell Gala' (A)	MGbk
	'Berkswell Jester' (A)	LAll
	'Berkswell Lace' (A)	MHer
	'Berkswell Nocturne' (A)	MGbk
	Bernardo = 'Guiber' PBR (I/d)	LAst
	'Beromünster' (Dec)	EWoo MHer NFir WFib
	'Bert Pearce' (R)	WFib
	'Beryl Gibbons' (Z/d)	LAll
	'Beryl Reid' (R)	WFib
	'Bette Shellard' (Z/d/v)	NFir
	'Betty Catchpole' (Z)	EWoo
	betulinum	WFib
	'Big Apple' (Sc)	EWoo
	'Bird Dancer' (Dw/St) ♀H1c	CSpe MHer MNHC NFir SSea WBrk
	(Birdbush Series) 'Birdbush Eleanor' (Z)	WFib
	- 'Birdbush Julie Anne' (Sc)	WDib
	- 'Birdbush Miriam' (Sc)	WDib
	'Birthday Girl' (R)	CWCL WFib
	'Bitter Lemon' (Sc)	ECtt
	'Black Butterfly'	see *P.* 'Brown's Butterfly'
	'Black Knight' (A)	NFir
	'Black Knight' Lea (Dw/d/C) ♀H1c	NFir
	'Black Knight' (R)	CSpe EWoo MHer
	'Black Prince' (R/Dec)	CSpe EWoo NFir WFib
	'Black Velvet' (R)	EWoo MCot
	'Black Vesuvius'	see *P.* 'Red Black Vesuvius'
	'Blackcurrant Yhu' (Dec)	NFir
	'Blackdown Delight' (Z)	NFir
	'Blackdown Romance' (Z) **new**	NFir
	'Blackdown Sensation' (Dw/Z) ♀H1c	NFir
	Blanca = 'Penwei' PBR (Dark Line Series) (Z/d)	LAst LBMP
	Blanche Roche = 'Guitoblanc' (I/d)	LAst LBMP LSou NPri SCoo SSea
§	'Blandfordianum' (Sc)	EWoo MHer
	'Blandfordianum Roseum' (Sc)	EWoo MHer
	'Blazonry' (Z/v)	WFib
	(Blizzard Series) Blizzard Blue = 'Fisrain' PBR (I)	SCoo
	- Blizzard Dark Red = 'Fisblizdark' (I)	CWCL EWoo
	- Blizzard Red = 'Fizzard' (I)	SCoo
	- Blizzard White = 'Fisbliz' PBR	SCoo
	'Blue Beard'	see *P.* 'Barbe Bleu'
	Blue Sybil = 'Pacblusy' PBR (I/d)	LAst LSou
	Blue Wonder = 'Pacbla' PBR (Z/d)	LAst
	'Bob Newing' (Min/St)	WFib
	'Bobberstone' (Z/St)	WFib
	'Bold Appleblossom' (Z)	WFib
	'Bold Carmine' (Z/d)	NFir
	'Bold Carousel' (Z/d)	WFib
	'Bold Cherub' (Z/d)	MGbk
	'Bold Elf' (Z/Min/d)	MGbk
	'Bold Flame' (Z/d)	WFib
	'Bold Gem' (Z/d)	MGbk
	'Bold Limelight' (Z/d)	WFib
	'Bold Minstrel' (Z/d)	MGbk WFib
	'Bold Pixie' (Dw/d)	WFib
	'Bold Princess' (Z/d)	MGbk WFib
	'Bold Special' (Z)	WFib
	'Bold Sunrise' (Z/d)	NFir
	'Bold Sunset' (Z/d) ♀H1c	NFir WFib
	'Bold White' (Z)	NFir
	'Bolero' (U) ♀H1c	LAll NFir WFib
	'Bon Bon' (Min/St)	WFib
	'Bontrosai' PBR (Sc)	MCot
	'Bosham' (R)	WFib
	'Both's Snowflake' (Sc/v)	WDib
	bowkeri	WFib
	'Brackenwood' (Dw/d) ♀H1c	LAll NFir
	Bravo = 'Fisbravo' (Z/d)	WFib
	'Brenda' (Min/d)	WFib
	'Brenda Hyatt' (Dw/d)	WFib
	'Brian West' (Min/St/C)	WFib
	'Brian West Butterfly' (Z/St) ♀H1c	MGbk WFib
	'Bridesmaid' (Dw/d)	NFir

'Brightstone' (Z/d)	WFib
'Brilliant' (Dec)	ENfk WFib
'Brilliantine' (Sc)	ENfk EWoo MHer WFib WGwG
'Brixworth Pearl' (Z)	WFib
'Brook's Purple'	see *P.* 'Royal Purple'
'Brookside Fiesta' (Min/d)	MGbk
'Brookside Flamenco' (Dw/d)	WFib
'Brookside Miranda' (Z/Min/d) **new**	MGbk
'Brookside Primrose' (Min/C/d)	WFib
'Brookside Rosa' (Z/C/Min/d) **new**	MGbk
'Brookside Serenade' (Dw)	WFib
§ 'Brown's Butterfly' (R)	ECtt EWoo WFib
'Brunswick' (Sc)	EWoo MHer SMrm WFib
'Burgundy' (R)	LBMP
'Burns Country' (Dw)	NFir
'Bushfire' (R) ♀H1c	EWoo WFib
Butterfly = 'Fisam'PBR (I)	NFir SCoo
caespitosum **new**	MHer
'Cal'	see *P.* 'Salmon Irene'
Calais = 'Paclai'PBR	LAst
'California Brilliant' (U)	MHer
'Calignon' (Z/St)	WFib
'Camphor Rose' (Sc) ♀H1c	NFir
'Can-can' (I/d)	WFib
Candy Flowers Strawberry Cream = 'Camstra'PBR (Candy Flowers Series) **new**	SMrm
canescens	see *P.* 'Blandfordianum'
'Cape Town' (Dw/z/v)	WFib
capitatum	ENfk MNHC WFib
'Capri' (Sc)	WFib
'Captain Starlight' (A) ♀H1c	EWoo MHer NFir WFib
'Carefree' (U) ♀H1c	NFir WFib
§ 'Carisbrooke' (R) ♀H1c	WFib
'Carlton Princess' (R) **new**	MGbk
'Carmel' (Z)	WFib
carnosum	MHer
'Carol Gibbons' (Z/d) ♀H1c	NFir
'Caroline Schmidt' (Z/d/v)	LAst MCot NFir WBrk WFib
'Carolyn Dean' (St) ♀H1c	NFir
'Carolyn Hardy' (Z/d)	WFib
Cascade Lilac	see *P.* 'Roi des Balcons Lilas'
Cascade Pink	see *P.* 'Hederinum'
'Cathay' (Z/St) ♀H1c	NFir
'Cathy' (R)	NFir
caucalifolium subsp. ***caucalifolium***	MHer
- subsp. ***convolvulifolium***	WFib
'Cézanne' (R)	LAll MCot
'Charity' (Sc) ♀H1c	ENfk MCot MHer NFir WDib WFib
'Charlotte Bronte' (Dw/v)	WFib
'Charmay Cocky' (Z/d)	MGbk
'Chelsea Gem' (Z/d/v) ♀H1c	WFib
'Chelsea Morning' (Z/d)	WFib
'Chelsea Star' (Z/d/v)	MGbk
'Cherry' (Min)	WFib
'Cherry Baby' (Dec)	MHer NFir
'Cherry Orchard' (R)	WFib
'Chew Magna' (R)	WFib
'Chieko' (Min/d)	WFib
'Chinz' (R)	NFir
§ 'Chocolate Peppermint' (Sc)	ENfk EWoo MCot MHer NFir SEND WDib WFib
'Chocolate Tomentosum'	see *P.* 'Chocolate Peppermint'
'Chocolate Twist' (St/C)	LAst
'Chrissie' (R)	WFib
'Cindy' (Dw/d)	WFib
'Citriodorum' (Sc) ♀H1c	MCot MHer WFib
'Citronella' (Sc)	CRHN WFib WGwG
'Claret Rock Unique' (U)	EWoo WFib
'Clatterbridge' (Dw/d) ♀H1c	NFir
'Clorinda' (U/Sc)	CRHN ENfk EWoo MCot MHer MNHC NWad SBch SSea WFib WGwG
'Coddenham' (Dw/d)	WFib
'Cola Bottles'	NPer NPri
§ 'Colonel Baden-Powell' (I/d)	WFib
'Colwell' (Min/d)	MGbk WFib
'Concolor Lace'	see *P.* 'Shottesham Pet'
'Contrast' (Z/C/v)	CWCL SCoo SPoG WFib
'Cook's Peachblossom'	WFib
'Copthorne' (U/Sc) ♀H1c	CRHN EWoo MCot MHer WFib
cordifolium	CRHN WFib
- var. ***rubrocinctum***	NFir
I - 'Valentine'	CSpe
coriandrifolium	see *P. myrrhifolium* var. *coriandrifolium*
'Cornell' (I/d)	WFib
cortusifolium	MHer
'Cottenham Beauty' (A)	NFir
'Cottenham Delight' (A)	NFir
'Cottenham Glamour' (A) ♀H1c	MHer NFir
'Cottenham Jubilee' (A)	MHer
'Cottenham Special' (A)	MGbk
'Cottenham Surprise' (A) ♀H1c	NFir
'Cottenham Wonder' (A) ♀H1c	NFir
cotyledonis	CSpe WFib
'Countess of Scarborough'	see *P.* 'Lady Scarborough'
'Cover Girl' (Z/d)	WFib
'Covina' (R)	WFib
'Cramdon Red' (Dw)	WFib
'Cream 'n' Green' (R/v)	NFir
'Creamery' (d)	WFib
'Creamy Nutmeg' (Sc/v)	ENfk EShb EWoo MHer NFir SEND SSea
'Crimson Unique' (U) ♀H1c	CSpe ENfk EWoo MCot MHer WFib
§ ***crispum*** (Sc)	ENfk GPoy SBch
§ - 'Golden Well Sweep' (Sc/v)	WFib
- 'Major' (Sc)	WFib
- 'Peach Cream' (Sc/v)	ENfk WFib
- 'Variegatum' (Sc/v) ♀H1c	CRHN ENfk GBin GPoy LAll MHer NFir SBch SIde WCot WFib
crithmifolium	MHer
'Crocketta' (I/d/v) ♀H1c	NFir
'Crocodile' (I/C/d) ♀H1c	ECtt MHer MNHC NFir NWad WFib
'Crystal Palace Gem' (Z/v)	WFib
cucullatum	WFib
- 'Flore Pleno' (d)	MHer WFib
- subsp. ***strigifolium***	EWoo
'Cupid' (Min/Dw/d)	WFib
§ 'Czar' (Z/C)	SCoo
'Dainty Maid' (Sc)	CSpe ENfk NFir
'Dale Queen' (Z)	WFib
'Damilola' (Z/St/Min/C)	MGbk
'Dark Gigette' (Min)	NFir
'Dark Red Irene' (Z/d)	WFib
'Dark Secret' (R)	CSpe SMrm WFib

Name	Suppliers
'Dark Venus' (R)	WFib
'Darmsden' (A) ♀H1c	NFir
'Davina' (Min/d)	WFib
'Dawn Star' (Z/St)	NFir
'Deacon Avalon' (Dw/d)	WFib
'Deacon Barbecue' (Z/d)	WFib
'Deacon Bonanza' (Z/d)	WFib
'Deacon Clarion' (Z/d)	WFib
'Deacon Coral Reef' (Z/d)	WFib
'Deacon Fireball' (Z/d)	WFib
'Deacon Gala' (Z/d)	LAll WFib
'Deacon Golden Bonanza' (Z/C/d)	WFib
'Deacon Golden Lilac Mist' (Z/C/d)	WFib
'Deacon Lilac Mist' (Z/d)	WFib
'Deacon Mandarin' (Z/d)	WFib
'Deacon Minuet' (Z/d)	NFir WFib
'Deacon Peacock' (Z/C/d)	WFib
'Deacon Picotee' (Z/d)	WFib
§ 'Deacon Summertime' (Z/d)	WFib
'Deborah Miliken' (Z/d) ♀H1c	NFir WFib
'Decora Lavender'	see *P.* 'Decora Lilas'
§ 'Decora Lilas' (I)	ECtt LAst
'Decora Mauve'	see *P.* 'Decora Lilas'
'Decora Pink'	see *P.* 'Decora Rouge'
'Decora Red'	see *P.* 'Decora Rouge'
§ 'Decora Rose' (I)	ECtt
§ 'Decora Rouge' (I)	ECtt LAst
'Deerwood Darling' (Min/v/d)	WFib
'Deerwood Lavender Lad' (Sc)	ENfk EWoo MHer SSea WDib WFib
'Deerwood Lavender Lass'	MCot MHer
'Deerwood Pink Puff' (St/d)	WFib
'Delightful' (R)	WFib
'Delli' (R) ♀H1c	CWCL MHer NFir NPer SMrm WFib
'Dennis Hunt' (Z/C)	NFir
denticulatum	MHer SSea
§ - 'Filicifolium' (Sc)	CRHN ENfk MCot MHer NFir SSea WFib
Designer Peppermint Twist = 'Baldespep' (Designer Series) (Z)	LAst
'Dibbinsdale' (Z) ♀H1c	NFir
dichondrifolium (Sc)	LAll NFir SSea WFib
dichondrifolium* × *reniforme (Sc)	NFir
'Display' ambig. (Dw/v)	WFib
'Distinction' (Z)	NFir SPoG WFib
'Dodd's Super Double' (Z/d)	SMrm
'Dolly Varden' (Z/v) ♀H1c	NFir WFib
'Donatella Love' (R/Dec)	NFir
'Don's Helen Bainbridge' (Z/C)	NFir
'Don's Mona Noble' (Z/C)	NFir
'Don's Richard A. Costain' (Z/C)	NFir
'Don's Southport' (Z/v)	NFir
'Doreen' (Z/d)	MGbk
'Doris Hancock' (R)	WFib
'Double Pink' (R/d)	WFib
'Dovedale' (Dw/C)	WFib
'Dovepoint' (Dw/2)	NFir
'Downlands' (Z/d)	WFib
'Dream Lover' (Z/St/Dw/d) **new**	MGbk
'Dresden White' (Dw)	WFib
Dresdner Apricot = 'Pacbriap'[PBR] (I/d)	SSea
'Dubai Star' (Z)	MGbk
'Duchess of Devonshire' (U)	WFib
'Duke of Edinburgh'	see *P.* 'Hederinum Variegatum'
'Dunkery Beacon' (R)	WFib
§ 'Dwarf Miriam Baisey' (Min)	LAll
'Dwarf Miriam Read'	see *P.* 'Dwarf Miriam Baisey'
'E. Dabner' (Z/d)	WFib
echinatum	EWoo MHer
- 'Album'	EWoo WFib
'Eden Gem' (Min/d)	WFib
'Edith Stern' (Dw/d)	LAll
'Edmond Lachenal' (Z/d)	WFib
'Eileen Nancy' (Z)	NFir
'Eileen Postle' (R) ♀H1c	WFib
Elbe Silver = 'Pensil' (I) ♀H1c	NFir SCoo
'Elmsett' (Dw/C/d)	LAll NFir WFib
'Els' (1870) **new**	LAll
'Els' (Dw/St)	WBrk
'Elsi' (I × Z/d/v)	WFib
'Elsie Gillam' (St)	WFib
'Embassy' (Min)	WFib
Emilia = 'Pactina'[PBR]	LAst
'Emma Hössle'	see *P.* 'Frau Emma Hössle'
'Emma Jane Read' (Dw/d)	WFib
endlicherianum	MHer SPhx WCot
'Erwarton' (Min/d)	NFir
'Eskay Gold' (A)	WFib
'Eskay Jewel' (A)	WFib
'Eskay Ruby' (A)	MHer
'Eskay Sugar Candy' (A)	WFib
'Eskay Verglo' (A)	WFib
Evening Glow = 'Bergpalais'[PBR]	LAst SSea
'Evka'[PBR] (I/v)	LAst SCoo SSea
exstipulatum	EWoo MHer SSea SVen
'Fair Ellen' (Sc)	MHer WFib
'Fairlee' (DwI)	WFib
'Fairy Lights' (Dw/St)	NFir
'Fairy Orchid' (A)	WFib
'Fandango' (Z/St)	NFir SMrm WFib
'Fanny Eden' (R)	EWoo WFib
'Fantasia' white-flowered (Dw/d) ♀H1c	WFib
'Fareham' (R) ♀H1c	WFib
'Fenton Farm' (Dw/C)	NFir
'Fiat Queen' (Z/d)	WFib
'Fieldings Unique' (U)	EWoo NFir
'Fifth Avenue' (R)	WFib
'Filicifolium'	see *P. denticulatum* 'Filicifolium'
'Fir Trees Audrey B' (St)	NFir
'Fir Trees Betty' (U)	NFir
'Fir Trees Catkins' (A)	NFir
'Fir Trees Echoes of Pink' (A)	EWoo
'Fir Trees Eileen' (St)	NFir SMrm
'Fir Trees Ele' (A/v)	NFir
'Fir Trees Fantail' (Min)	NFir
'Fir Trees Fiesta' (R)	NFir
'Fir Trees Flamingo' (Dw)	NFir
'Fir Trees Jack' (Z/Dw)	NFir

Name	Suppliers
'Fir Trees Janet' (Dw)	NFir
'Fir Trees Jennifer' (R/Dec)	NFir
'Fir Trees John Grainger' (Z/v)	NFir
'Fir Trees Mark' (R/Dec/v)	NFir
'Fir Trees Pink Pom-Pom' (Dw/St/C/d)	NFir
'Fir Trees Ruby Wedding' (C)	NFir
'Fir Trees Silver Wedding' (Z/C/d)	NFir
'Fir Trees Sparkler' (Min/C)	NFir
'Fir Trees Val' (Z)	NFir
'First Blush' (R)	WFib
'First Love' (Z) ♀H1c	NFir
First Yellow = 'Pacyell'PBR	LAst
'Flaming Katy' (Min) ♀H1c	NFir
'Flamingo'	COtt
'Fleurisse' (Z)	WFib
'Floria Moore' (Dec)	EWoo NFir SSea
(Flower Fairy Series) Flower Fairy Berry = 'Sweberry'PBR	LAst SSea
- Flower Fairy Rose = 'Swero'PBR (Z)	LAst LSou SSea
- Flower Fairy Violet = 'Swevio'PBR	SSea
- Flower Fairy White Splash = 'Swewhi'PBR (Z)	LAst LSou
Foxy = 'Pacfox'PBR (Z)	LAst LSou
fragrans	ENfk WDib
Fragrans Group (Sc)	CRHN EWoo GPoy MCot MHer WFib WGwG
§ - 'Fragrans Variegatum' (Sc/v) ♀H1c	NFir WFib
- 'Snowy Nutmeg'	see *P.* (Fragrans Group) 'Fragrans Variegatum'
'Fraiche Beauté' (Z/d)	WFib
'Francis Gibbon' (Z/d)	WFib
'Francis Parmenter' (Min/I/v)	LAst
'Francis Parrett' (Min/d) ♀H1c	WFib
'Frank Hazel' (Dw/Z)	NFir
'Frank Headley' (Z/v) ♀H1c	LAst MCot NPer SCoo SMrm SSea WFib WOld
§ 'Frau Emma Hössle' (Dw/d)	WFib
'Freak of Nature' (Z/v)	MHer NFir WFib
'Frensham' (Sc)	ENfk MHer WFib
'Freshfields Suki' (Dw)	NFir
'Freshwater' (St/C)	WFib
'Friary Wood' (Z/C/d)	NFir WFib
'Friesdorf' (Dw/Fr)	MCot MHer NFir WBrk WFib
'Fringed Aztec' (R) ♀H1c	CWCL NFir WFib
'Frosty' misapplied	see *P.* 'Variegated Kleine Liebling'
'Frosty Petit Pierre'	see *P.* 'Variegated Kleine Liebling'
frutetorum	MHer
fruticosum	EWoo WFib
'Fuji' (R)	NFir
fulgidum	EWoo MCot MHer WFib
'Gabriel' (A)	EWoo
'Galway Star' (Sc/v) ♀H1c	MHer WFib
'Ganther' (Dec)	WFib
'Gareth Mark Pratt' (Z/C)	MGbk
'Garnet Rosebud' (Min/d)	NFir WFib
'Gartendirektor Herman' (Dec) ♀H1c	EWoo NFir WFib
'Gatwig'	LAst
'Gaudy' (Z)	WFib
'Gemini' (Z/St/d) ♀H1c	NFir WFib
'Gemma' (R)	NFir
'Gemstone' (Sc) ♀H1c	ENfk MHer
'Genie' (Z/d)	WFib
'Gentle Georgia' (R)	WFib
'Georgia' (R)	WFib
'Georgia Peach' (R)	WFib
'Georgina Blythe' (R) ♀H1c	WFib
'Gesa'	LAst
gibbosum	CSpe EWoo MHer SSea WFib WHer
'Ginger Frost' (Sc/v)	WFib
'Ginger Rogers' (Z) ♀H1c	NFir
'Glacis'PBR (Quality Series) (Z/d)	LSou SSea
'Gladys Evelyn' (Z/d)	WFib
'Gladys Weller' (Z/d) ♀H1c	NFir WFib
glaucum	see *P. lanceolatum*
'Gloria Griggs' (R) **new**	MGbk
§ ***glutinosum***	WFib
'Goesta' (Z/d)	SSea
Golden Angel	see *P.* 'Sarah Don'
'Golden Brilliantissimum' (Z/v)	WFib
'Golden Chalice' (Min/v)	WFib
'Golden Clorinda' (U/Sc/C)	CRHN SEND
'Golden Ears' (Dw/St/C) ♀H1c	NFir NPer WFib
'Golden Edinburgh' (I/v)	WFib
'Golden Lilac Gem' (I/d)	WFib
'Golden Princess' (Min/C)	WFib
'Golden Square' (Dw/St)	MHer WFib
'Golden Staphs' (Z/St/C)	LAll MHer NFir
'Golden Tears' (MinI/C/d)	ECtt
'Golden Wedding' (Z/d/v)	NFir
'Golden Well Sweep'	see *P. crispum* 'Golden Well Sweep'
'Goldstone Copper' (Min/d)	MGbk
'Gooseberry Leaf'	see *P. grossularioides*
'Gordon Quale' (Z/d)	WFib
'Gosbrook Berry Zest' (A/Sc)	MGbk
'Gosbrook Clifford Taylor' (Min/d)	MGbk
'Gosbrook Ellen Jenkinson' (Z/St/d) **new**	MGbk
'Gosbrook Gillian Martin' (Min/d)	MGbk
'Gosbrook Jacky Tickner' (Z/Dw/d)	MGbk
'Gosbrook Robyn Louise' (Z/St/d)	MGbk
'Gosbrook Ryan David' (Z/Dw/d)	MGbk
'Gosbrook Snowcap' (Z/St/d)	MGbk
'Gosbrook Starstorm' (Z/St/Dw/d) **new**	MGbk
'Grace Thomas' (Sc) ♀H1c	MHer WFib
'Grace Wells' (Min)	WFib
'Grand Slam' (R) ♀H1c	NFir WFib
'Grandad Mac' (Dw/St) ♀H1c	NFir SSea
grandiflorum	EWoo MCot MHer WFib
graveolens L'Hér.	see *P.* 'Graveolens'
graveolens ambig.	SEND
***graveolens** sensu* J.J.A. van der Walt	SBch WFib

	Name	Suppliers
§	'Graveolens' (Sc)	ENfk GPoy MHer SVen WBrk WDib WFib
	'Graveolens Minor' (Sc)	EWoo
	'Great Glemham Lemon' (Sc)	EWoo
	'Green Eyes' (I/d)	MHer
	'Greetings' (Min/v)	WFib
	'Grey Lady Plymouth' (Sc/v)	MCot MHer WFib
	'Grey Sprite' (Min/v)	WFib
§	***grossularioides***	MHer
	- 'Coconut'	EOHP
	'Guernsey Flair' (Z)	LSou
	'Gwen' (Min/v)	NFir
§	'Hannaford Star' (Z/St)	WFib
	'Happy Anniversary' (Dw/C)	NFir
	'Happy Appleblossom' (Z/v/d)	NFir
	'Happy Thought' (Z/v) 🏆H1c	MCot NFir SCoo WFib
	'Harbour Lights' (R)	WFib
	'Harewood Slam' (R)	WFib
	'Harlequin Pretty Girl' (I × Z/d)	WFib
	'Harlequin Rosie O'Day' (I)	WFib
	'Harvard' (I/d)	WFib
	'Hazel' (R)	WFib
	'Hazel Cherry' (R)	WFib
	'Hazel Choice' (R)	NFir
	'Hazel Perfection' (R) 🏆H1c	NFir
	'Hazel Star' (R)	WFib
	'Hazel Stardust' (R)	NFir
§	'Hederinum' (I)	LSou
§	'Hederinum Variegatum' (I/v)	ECtt WFib
	'Helen Christine' (Z/St)	NFir WFib
	'Helena Pope' (R) **new**	MGbk
	'Henry Weller' (A) 🏆H1c	NFir WFib
	'Hermione' (Z/d)	WFib
	'Highfields Attracta' (Z/d)	WFib
	'Highfields Candy Floss' (Z/d)	NFir
	'Highfields Delight' (Z)	WFib
	'Highfields Fancy' (Z/d)	NFir
	'Highfields Festival' (Z/d) 🏆H1c	NFir WFib
	'Highfields Melody' (Z/d)	WFib
	'Highfields Pride' (Z)	WFib
	'Highfields Snowdrift' (Z)	NFir
	'Highfields Symphony' (Z)	WFib
	'Hilbre Island' (Z/C/d)	NFir
	'Hills of Snow' (Z/v)	MHer WFib
	'Hindoo' (R × U) 🏆H1c	CSpe EWoo MCot NFir SBch WFib
	hispidum	MHer
	'Hitcham' (Min/d)	WFib
	'Holbrook' (Dw/C/d)	NFir WFib
	'Holt Beauty'	EWoo
	'Honeywood Suzanne' (Min/Fr)	LAll
	'Hope Valley' (Dw/C/d) 🏆H1c	NFir
	'House and Garden' (R)	NFir
	'Hula' (R × U)	EWoo
	'Hunter's Moon' (Z/C)	NFir
	'Icecrystal'[PBR] (Sweetheart Series) (Z/d)	SSea
	'Icing Sugar' (I/d)	WFib
	ignescens	EWoo NFir
	'Immaculatum' (Z)	WFib
	'Imperial'[PBR] (R)	LAst
	'Imperial Butterfly' (A/Sc) 🏆H1c	CRHN ENfk NFir WFib
	ionidiflorum	CSpe EShb MCot MHer MNHC
	'Irene' (Z/d)	WFib
	'Irene Toyon' (Z)	WFib
	'Islington Peppermint' (Sc)	NFir WFib
	'Ivalo' (Z/d)	WFib
	'Ivory Snow' (Z/d/v)	NFir WFib
	'Jacey' (Z/d)	LAll
	'Jack of Hearts' (I × Z/d)	WFib
	'Jack Wood' (Z/d)	NFir
§	'Jackie' (I/d)	LAll WFib
	'Jackie Davies' (R)	EWoo
	'Jackie Gall'	see *P.* 'Jackie'
	'Jackie Totlis' (Z/St)	WFib
	'Jackpot Wild Rose' (Z/d)	WFib
	'Jake Moss' (Z/d) **new**	MGbk
	'Janet Hofman' (Z/d)	WFib
	'Janet Kerrigan' (Min/d)	WFib
	'Jayne Eyre' (Min/d)	WFib
	'Jean Bart' (I)	LAll
	'Jeanie Hunt' (Z/C/d)	NFir
§	'Jeanne d'Arc' (I/d)	WFib
	'Jer'Rey' (A)	EWoo WFib
	'Jill Brown' (Min/St/C)	MGbk
	'Jips Batty Thomas' (Z/Min/d) **new**	MGbk
	'Jip's Bunjy'	NFir
	'Jip's Desert Poppy' (Z/Min)	WFib
	'Jip's Eleanor Renton' (Dw/d)	WFib
	'Jip's Freda Burgess' (Z/C/d)	NFir
	'Jip's John Morbey' (Z/C/d)	MGbk
	'Jips Little Gaude' (Z/Dw/d) **new**	MGbk
	'Jip's Megan' (Z/C/D) **new**	NFir
	'Jip's Pip' (Z/C/d)	MGbk NFir
	'Jip's Proud Sentinel' (Dw/d)	WFib
	'Jip's Rosy Glow' (Min/d) 🏆H1c	NFir
	'Jip's Timmy' (Z/C/Dw/d)	MGbk
	'Joan Fontaine' (Z)	WFib
	'Joan Morf' (R) 🏆H1c	EWoo NFir WFib
	'Joan of Arc'	see *P.* 'Jeanne d'Arc'
	'John's Pride' (Dw)	NFir
	'Joy' (R) 🏆H1c	CSpe NFir WFib
	'Juliana' (R)	LAst
	'Julie Smith' (R)	WFib
	'Just Bella' (d)	NFir
	'Just Beth' (Z/C/d)	NFir
	'Just Joss' (Dw/d)	NFir
	'Just William' (Min/C/d)	WFib
	'Kamahl' (R)	WFib
	'Karen' (Dw/C)	LAst LSou
	'Karl Hagele' (Z/d)	WFib
	'Karmin Ball'	WFib
	'Karrooense'	see *P. quercifolium*
	'Katie' (R)	EWoo
	'Keepsake' (Min/d)	WFib
	'Keith Vernon' (Z)	NFir
	'Ken Lea Butterfly' (Z/d)	MGbk
	'Kenny's Double' (Z/d)	WFib
	'Kerensa' (Min/d)	WFib
	'Kesgrave' (Min/d)	WFib

	'Kewense' (Z)	EShb
	'Kimono' (R) ♀H1c	NFir
	'King Edmund' (R) ♀H1c	NFir
	'King of Balcon'	see *P.* 'Hederinum'
	'King of Denmark' (Z/d)	WFib
	'King Solomon' (R)	WFib
§	'Kleine Liebling' (Min)	WFib
	'Kyoto' (R)	NFir
	'La France' (I/d) ♀H1c	MCot WFib
	'La Paloma' (R)	WFib
	Laced Red Mini Cascade = 'Achspen' (I) ♀H1c	NFir
§	'Lachskönigin' (I/d)	WFib
	'Lady Ilchester' (Z/d)	WFib
	'Lady Love Song' (R)	NFir WFib
	'Lady Mary' (Sc)	EWoo MHer
	'Lady Mavis Pilkington' (Z/d)	WFib
	'Lady Plymouth' (Sc/v) ♀H1c	CRHN ENfk EPfP EWoo GLog LAll MCot MHer MSCN NFir NWad SEND WFib WGwG
§	'Lady Scarborough' (Sc)	ENfk EWoo MHer WFib
	laevigatum	MHer
	'Lancastrian' (Z/d)	MHer WFib
§	***lanceolatum***	MHer
	'Lara Ballerina' ♀H1c	NFir SBch
	'Lara Beacon'	EWoo
	'Lara Candy Dancer' (Sc) ♀H1c	CRHN WFib
	'Lara Jester' (Sc)	ENfk EWoo WFib
	'Lara Rajah' (R)	EWoo
	'Lara Starshine' (Sc) ♀H1c	ENfk EWoo MHer NFir WFib
	'Lara Waltz' (R/d)	WFib
	'Lass o' Gowrie' (Z/v)	NFir
	'Laurel Hayward' (R)	WFib
	'Lauren Alexandra' (Z/d)	WFib
	'Lavender Grand Slam' (R) ♀H1c	NFir
	'Lavender Lindy' (Sc)	EWoo
	'Lavender Mini Cascade' PBR	see *P.* Lilac Mini Cascade
	'Lavender Sensation' (R)	WFib
	'Lawrenceanum'	WFib
	'L'Élégante' (I/v) ♀H1c	CHel EWoo MCot MHer WFib
	'Lemon Crisp'	see *P. crispum*
	'Lemon Fancy' (Sc) ♀H1c	LAll MHer NFir NWad WDib WFib
	'Lemon Fizz'	ENfk
	'Lemon Kiss' (Sc)	CSpe EWoo
	'Leslie William Burrows'	EWoo
	'Letitia' (A)	ENfk
	Lila Compakt-Cascade	see *P.* 'Decora Lilas'
	Lilac Cascade	see *P.* 'Roi des Balcons Lilas'
	'Lilac Gem' (Min/I/d)	ENfk MCot
§	Lilac Mini Cascade = 'Lilamica' PBR (I) ♀H1c	NFir
	'Lilian Pottinger' (Sc) ♀H1c	CRHN ENfk EWoo MHer NFir SSea
	'Lilian Woodberry' (Z)	WFib
	Lilly = 'Paclill' PBR	LAst
	'Limoneum' (Sc)	ENfk MHer
	'Lipstick' (St)	WFib
	'Lisa Jo' (St/v/Dw/d)	WFib
	'Little Alice' (Dw/d) ♀H1c	NFir WFib
	'Little Fi-fine' (Dw/C)	NFir
	'Little Gem' (Sc)	ENfk MHer WFib
	'Little Jim' (Min/d)	NFir
	'Little Jip' (Z/d/v) ♀H1c	NFir WFib
	'Little Spikey' (St/Min/d)	WFib
	'Lord Baden-Powell'	see *P.* 'Colonel Baden-Powell'
	'Lord Bute' (R) ♀H1c	CSpe ECtt EWoo LAst MCot MHer MSCN NFir NPer SMrm SSea SVen WFib WGwG
	'Lord de Ramsey'	see *P.* 'Tip Top Duet'
	'Lord Roberts' (Z)	WFib
	Lorena = 'Pacdala' PBR (Dark Line Series) (Z/d)	LAst
	'Lotus' (R)	LAst
	'Lotusland' (Dw/St/C) ♀H1c	NFir WFib
I	'Louise' (R) ♀H1c	NFir
	'Love Song' (R/v)	NFir WFib
	'Lucy Gunnett' (Z/d/v) ♀H1c	NFir
	'Lyewood Bonanza' (R)	CWCL WFib
	'Mabel Grey' (Sc) ♀H1c	CRHN CSpe ENfk EWoo MHer MNHC NFir NPer SBch WFib
§	'Madame Auguste Nonin' (U/Sc)	ENfk MHer NFir WFib
	'Madame Butterfly' (Z/d/v)	NFir
	'Madame Crousse' (I/d) ♀H1c	EWoo WFib
	'Madame Layal' (A) ♀H1c	MHer NFir WFib
	'Madame Margot'	see *P.* 'Hederinum Variegatum'
	'Madame Salleron' (Min/v)	LSou
	'Madge Taylor' (R)	NFir
	magenteum	NFir
	'Magic Lantern' (Z/C)	NFir
	'Magnum' (R)	WFib
	'Mangles' Variegated' (Z/v)	WFib
	'Manx Maid' (A)	NFir
	'Maple Leaf' (Sc)	EWoo
	'Maréchal MacMahon' (Z/C)	ENfk
	'Margaret Soley' (R) ♀H1c	WFib
	'Margaret Waite' (R)	WFib
	'Margery Stimpson' (Min/d)	WFib
	'Marie Thomas' (Sc)	SBch
	Marimba = 'Fisrimba' PBR	SCoo
	'Marion Saunders' (Dec)	WFib
	'Mariquita' (R)	WFib
	'Mark' (Dw/d)	WFib
	'Marquis of Bute' (R/v)	NFir
	'Martin Parrett' (Min/d)	WFib
	'Martin Pope' (R) **new**	MGbk
	'Mary Harrison' (Z/d)	WFib
I	'Maureen' Hoddinott (Z/d)	MHer
	'Mauve Beauty' (I/d)	WFib
	(Maverick Series) 'Maverick Appleblossom' (Z)	LAst
	- 'Maverick Orange' (Z)	LAst
	- 'Maverick Red' (Z)	LAst
	- 'Maverick Violet' (Z)	LAst
	- 'Maverick White' (Z)	LAst
	'Maxime Kovalevski' (Z)	WFib
	'Maxine' (Z/C)	NFir
	'May Day' (R)	WFib
	'May Magic' (R)	NFir WFib
	'Meadowside Dark and Dainty' (St)	NFir WFib
	'Meadowside Fancy' (Z/d/C)	LAll
	'Meadowside Harvest' (Z/St/C)	NFir
	'Meadowside Julie Colley' (Dw)	NFir
	'Meadowside Midnight' (St/C)	WFib
	'Medley' (Min/d)	WFib

	Name	Suppliers
	'Megan Hannah' (Dw/c/d)	MGbk NFir
	'Melanie Day' (St) 🏆H1c	NFir
	Melocherry = 'Pacmel'PBR (Tempo Series) (Z/d) **new**	SSea
	'Memento' (Min/d)	WFib
	'Mendip' (R)	WFib
	'Mendip Barbie' (R) 🏆H1c	NFir
	'Mendip Blanche' (R) 🏆H1c	NFir
	'Mendip Lorraine' (R)	NFir
	'Mendip Louise' (R) 🏆H1c	NFir
	'Mendip Sarah' (R)	NFir
	'Meon Maid' (R)	WFib
	'Mere Casino' (Z)	WFib
	'Merry-go-round' (Z/C/v)	MGbk
	'Mexica Tomcat' (I/d)	LAst
	'Mexican Beauty' (I)	WFib
	'Mexicana'	see *P.* 'Rouletta'
	'Mexicanerin'	see *P.* 'Rouletta'
	'Michael' (A) 🏆H1c	MHer NFir
	'Michelle West' (Min)	WFib
	'Milden' (Dw/Z/C) 🏆H1c	NFir
	Millennium Dawn (Dw)	LAll
	'Millfield Gem' (I/d)	WFib
	'Millfield Rose' (I/d)	EWoo LAll
	'Mini-Czech' (Min/St)	ECtt WBrk
	'Minnie' (Z/d/St)	WBrk
	'Minstrel Boy' (R)	EWoo WFib
	'Minx' (Min/d)	WFib
	'Miriam Basey'	see *P.* 'Dwarf Miriam Baisey'
	'Miss Burdett Coutts' (Z/v)	MHer WFib
	'Miss McKinsey' (Z/St/d)	NFir
	'Miss Muffett' (Min/d)	WFib
§	'Miss Stapleton'	EWoo MHer WFib
	'Misterioso' (R)	EWoo WFib
	'Misty Morning' (R)	EWoo WFib
	'Modesty' (Z/d)	WFib
	'Mohawk' (R)	WFib
	'Mole'	see *P.* 'The Mole'
	'Monkwood Rose' (A)	NFir
	'Monkwood Sprite' (R)	SMrm
	'Monsieur Ninon' misapplied	see *P.* 'Madame Auguste Nonin'
§	'Monsieur Ninon' (U)	CRHN WFib
	'Mont Blanc' (Z/v)	WFib
	'Montague Garabaldi Smith' (R)	WFib
	'Moon Maiden' (A)	EWoo WFib
	Moonlight Violino (Moonlight Series) (Z)	LAst
	Morning Sun = 'Pacmorsu'PBR (Green Leaf Series) (Z)	LAst
	'Morval' (Dw/C/d) 🏆H1c	LAll WFib
	'Morwenna' (R)	MHer NFir WCot WFib
	'Mosaic Gay Baby' (Z)	WFib
	'Mosaic Red' (2) **new**	LAll
	'Mr Henry Cox' (Z/v) 🏆H1c	LAll MHer NFir WFib
	'Mr Wren' (Z)	WFib
	'Mrs Cannell' (Z)	WFib
	'Mrs Eve Scott' (Z/d)	MGbk
	'Mrs Farren' (Z/v)	MCot
	'Mrs G.H. Smith' (A) 🏆H1c	NFir WFib
	'Mrs Kingsbury' (U)	WFib
	'Mrs Martin' (I/d)	WFib
	'Mrs May Last' (Z/St/v)	MGbk
	'Mrs McKenzie' (Z/St)	WFib
	'Mrs Parker' (Z/d/v)	NFir WFib
	'Mrs Pat' (Dw/St/C) 🏆H1c	NFir
	'Mrs Pollock' (Z/v)	EUJe LAst MCot NEgg SCoo WBrk WFib
	'Mrs Quilter' (Z/C) 🏆H1c	SMrm WBrk WFib
	'Mrs W.A.R. Clifton' (I/d)	WFib
	mutans	WFib
§	'Mutzel' (I/v)	NFir
	'My Chance' (Dec)	NFir WFib
§	***myrrhifolium*** var. ***coriandrifolium***	MHer NFir WFib
	'Mystery' (U) 🏆H1c	NFir WFib
	'Narina' (I)	SCoo
	'Nellie Nuttall' (Z)	WFib
	Neona = 'Pacneon'PBR (Z) **new**	SSea
	'Nervous Mabel' (Sc) 🏆H1c	MHer WFib
	'New Gypsy' (R)	CWCL
	'New Life' (Z)	NFir
	'Nicola Buck' (R) 🏆H1c	NFir
	'Nicor Star' (Min)	WFib
	'Night' (I)	EWoo
	'Noche' (R)	SMrm
	'Noele Gordon' (Z/d)	WFib
	oblongatum	CDes
	'Occold Profusion' (Dw/d)	NFir
	'Occold Shield' (Dw/C/d) 🏆H1c	NEgg NFir SMrm WBrk WFib
	'Occold Tangerine' (Z)	WFib
	'Occold Volcano' (Dw/C/d)	WFib
	'Octavia Hill' (Z)	LAst
	odoratissimum (Sc) 🏆H1c	ENfk EWoo GPoy MHer NFir SSea WFib
	'Odyssey' (Min)	WFib
	'Old Spice' (Sc/v)	ENfk MCot NFir WFib
	'Oldbury Duet' (A/v) 🏆H1c	LAst MHer NFir
	'Olivia' (R)	WFib
	'Opera House' (R)	WFib
	'Orange Fizz' (Sc) 🏆H1c	EWoo MHer NFir
	'Orange Parfait' (R)	WFib
	'Orangeade' (Dw/d)	WFib
	'Orchid Clorinda' (Sc)	WFib
	'Orion' (Min/d)	WFib
	'Orsett' (Sc) 🏆H1c	GLog
	'Otto's Red' (R)	NFir
	'Our Flynn' (Z/St)	WFib
	'Our Gynette' (Dec)	EWoo
	PAC cultivars	see under selling name
	'Pagoda' (Z/St/d)	MHer WFib
	'Paisley Red' (Z/d)	NFir WFib
	'Pam Tutcher' (St)	NFir
	'Pamela Vaughan' (Z/St)	WFib
	'Pampered Lady' (A)	NFir
	panduriforme	WFib
	papilionaceum	CHEx CRHN EWoo MCot MHer NFir WFib
	'Parisienne' (R)	EWoo WFib
	'Party Dress' (Z/d)	WFib
	'Pat Hannam' (St)	WFib
	'Pat Pope' (R) **new**	MGbk
	'Paton's Unique' (U/Sc) 🏆H1c	CRHN ENfk EWoo MCot MHer NFir SVen WCot WFib
	'Patricia Andrea' (T) 🏆H1c	LAll NFir NPer WFib
	'Paul Crampel' (Z)	EWoo MCot MHer WFib
	'Paul West' (Min/d)	SBch
	'Peace' (Min/C)	WFib
	'Peach Princess' (R)	NFir
	'Peaches and Cream' (R)	WDib
	PELFI cultivars	see under selling name
	peltatum	SPhx WFib

'Penny' (Z/d)	WFib
'Penny Dixon' (R)	NFir
'Penny Lane' (Z)	WFib
'Pensby' (Dw)	NFir
'Penve'PBR (Quality Series) (Z/d)	SSea
'Peppermint Lace' (Sc)	EWoo
'Percy Hunt' (R)	NFir
'Perfect' (Z)	WFib
'Pershore Princess'	WBrk
'Peter Godwin' (R)	WFib
'Peter's Choice' (R)	WFib
'Petit Pierre'	see *P.* 'Kleine Liebling'
'Phyllis Variegated' (U/v)	ENfk EWoo MHer NFir WCot
'Picotee' (Z)	MHer
'Pink Aurore' (U)	WFib
'Pink Bonanza' (R)	NFir WFib
'Pink Capitatum'	see *P.* 'Pink Capricorn'
§ 'Pink Capricorn' (Sc)	CRHN ENfk EWoo LAll WFib
'Pink Cascade'	see *P.* 'Hederinum'
'Pink Champagne' (Sc)	CRHN MHer
'Pink Dolly Varden' (Z/v)	WFib
'Pink Fondant' (Min/d)	WFib
'Pink Gay Baby'	see *P.* 'Sugar Baby'
'Pink Happy Thought' (Z/v)	WFib
'Pink Hindoo' (Dec)	EWoo
'Pink Ice' (Min/d)	NFir
'Pink Mini Cascade'	see *P.* 'Rosa Mini-cascade'
'Pink Needles' (Min/St)	WFib
'Pink Pet' (U)	ECtt NFir
'Pink Rambler' (Z/d)	WFib
'Pink Rosebud' (Z/d)	WFib
'Pippa' (Min/Dw)	NFir
'Playmate' (Min/St)	WFib
'Plum Rambler' (Z/d)	EShb WBrk WFib
'Polka' (U) ♀H1c	EWoo NFir WFib
'Pompeii' (R)	NFir WFib
'Porchfield' (Min/St)	WBrk
(Precision Series) Precision Amethyst **new**	NPri
- Precision Bright Lilac **new**	NPri
- Precision Bright Red **new**	NPri
- Precision Burgundy = 'Balcolbugi'PBR **new**	NPri
- Precision Dark Red **new**	NPri
- Precision Light Pink = 'Klep02060'PBR (I) **new**	NPri
- Precision Pink = 'Balcolink' **new**	NPri
- Precision Red Ice = 'Sil Chris' **new**	NPri
- Precision Rose Lilac **new**	NPri
'Preston Park' (Z/C)	WFib
'Pretty Polly' (Sc)	WFib
'Prim' (Dw/St/d)	WFib
'Prince of Orange' (Sc) ♀H1c	ENfk EWoo GPoy MCot MHer NFir SIde WFib
'Princeanum' (Sc) ♀H1c	WFib
'Princess Abigail' (Dw/d)	NFir
'Princess Alexandra' (Z/d/v)	LAll
'Princess Josephine' (R)	WFib
'Princess of Balcon'	see *P.* 'Roi des Balcons Lilas'
'Princess of Wales' (R)	WFib
'Princess Virginia' (R/v)	WFib
'Priory Coral' (Z/St/v)	MGbk
'Priory Star' (St/Min/d)	WFib
'Proud Sentinel' (Dw)	WFib
pseudoglutinosum	WFib
'Pungent Peppermint' (Sc)	MNHC
'Purple Heart' (Dw/St/C) ♀H1c	NFir
'Purple Rogue' (R)	WFib
Purple Sybil = 'Pacpursyb'PBR	LAst
'Purple Unique' (U/Sc)	ENfk EWoo MCot MHer NFir SVen WFib
'Pygmalion' (Z/d/v)	WFib
'Quantock' (R)	WFib
'Quantock Angelique' (A)	NFir
'Quantock Candy' (A) ♀H1c	EWoo NFir
'Quantock Clare' (A)	NFir
'Quantock Classic' (A)	NFir
'Quantock Darren' (A)	NFir
'Quantock Double Dymond' (A)	NFir
'Quantock Kendy' (A) ♀H1c	NFir
'Quantock Kirsty' (A) ♀H1c	EWoo NFir
'Quantock Louise' (A)	NFir
'Quantock Marjorie' (A) ♀H1c	NFir
'Quantock Matty' (A) ♀H1c	NFir
'Quantock Mr Nunn' (A)	NFir
'Quantock Perfection' (A)	NFir
'Quantock Sally' (A/d)	NFir
'Quantock Star' (A)	NFir
'Quantock Ultimate' (A) ♀H1c	NFir
'Queen of Denmark' (Z/d)	WFib
'Queen of Hearts' (I × Z/d)	WFib
'Queen of the Lemons'	EWoo
quercifolium (Sc)	CRHN GPoy WFib
- variegated (v)	WDib
quinquelobatum	CSpe
radens (Sc)	ENfk WFib
'Rads Star' (Z/St)	NFir
'Radula' (Sc) ♀H1c	ENfk LAll MHer WFib
'Radula Roseum' (Sc)	EWoo WFib
(Rainbow Series) Rainbow Neon = 'Genraineon' (I)	LAst SSea
- Rainbow White = 'Genrawhite' (I) **new**	SSea
'Raspberry Ripple' (A)	NFir
'Ray Bidwell' (Min)	NFir WFib
§ 'Red Black Vesuvius' (Min/C)	WFib
'Red Cactus' (St)	NFir
'Red Cascade' (I) ♀H1c	LAst WFib
'Red Gables'	CSpe
'Red Ice' (Min/d)	NFir
'Red Pandora' (Z) ♀H1c	NFir WFib
'Red Pimpernella'	LAll
'Red Rambler' (Z/d)	WBrk WFib
'Red Robin' (R)	WCot
'Red Silver Cascade'	see *P.* 'Mutzel'
'Red Spider' (Dw/Ca)	WFib
'Red Startel' (Z/St/d)	WFib
'Red Susan Pearce' (R)	WFib
'Red Velvet' (R)	LBMP
'Red Witch' (Dw/St/d)	LAll MHer WBrk WFib
'Redondo' (Dw/d)	EWoo
'Reflections' (Z/d)	WFib
'Reg 'Q'' (Z/C)	NFir

'Regalia Lavendel' (R)	LAst
'Regalia Lilac' (R)	LAst
'Regalia Red' (R)	LAst
'Regina' (Z/d)	WFib
'Rembrandt' (R)	WFib
'Renate Parsley' ♀H1c	CDes MHer NFir WFib
reniforme	GPoy MHer WFib
'Retah's Crystal' (Z/v)	MGbk
'Reverend David Harley' (Z)	NFir
'Richard Gibbs' (Sc)	ENfk MHer
'Richard Key' (Z/d/C)	WFib
'Richard Upward' (Z/d)	MGbk
Ricky = 'Pacric' PBR	LAst
'Rietje van der Lee' (A)	ENfk WFib
'Rigel' (Min/d)	NFir
'Rimey' (St)	NFir
'Rimfire' (R) ♀H1c	CWCL EWoo MHer NFir WFib
'Rio Grande' (I/d)	MHer NFir WFib
'Rober's Lemon Rose' (Sc)	CRHN ENfk MHer SEND WBrk
'Robert Fish' (Z/C)	SCoo
'Robert McElwain' (Z/d)	WFib
'Robin's Unique' (U)	WFib
'Robyn Hannah' (St/d)	MHer NFir
rodneyanum	CDes
'Rogue' (R)	WFib
'Roi des Balcons'	see *P.* 'Hederinum'
§ 'Roi des Balcons Impérial' (I)	SSea
§ 'Roi des Balcons Lilas' (I)	LAst SSea
'Roi des Balcons Rose'	see *P.* 'Hederinum'
'Roller's Echo' (A)	WFib
'Roller's Pioneer' (I/v)	ENfk EWoo
'Roller's Satinique' (U)	MHer
'Rollison's Unique' (U)	MHer WFib
'Romeo' (R)	EWoo
'Rookley' (St/d)	NFir
'Rosa della Sera' (St)	LAll
§ 'Rosa Mini-cascade' (Mini Cascade Series) (I) ♀H1c	NFir
'Rose Bengal' (A)	ENfk
'Rose of Amsterdam' (Min/d)	WFib
'Rose Paton's Unique' (U/Sc)	SMrm
'Rose Pope' (R)	MGbk
'Rose Silver Cascade' (I)	LAll MCot MHer
'Rosebud Supreme' (Z/d)	WFib
'Rosmaroy' (R)	WFib
'Rosy Dawn' (Min/d)	WFib
§ 'Rouletta' (I/d)	LAst WFib
'Royal Ascot' (R)	EWoo NFir SMrm
'Royal Norfolk' (Min/d) ♀H1c	NFir
'Royal Oak' (Sc) ♀H1c	CRHN ENfk MCot MHer MNHC SBch SVen WFib
§ 'Royal Purple' (Z/d)	WFib
'Royal Surprise' (R) ♀H1c	EWoo NFir
'Ruben' (d)	LSou
'Ruben' (Z/d)	LAst
'Ruby' (Min/d)	WFib
'Ruffled Velvet' (R)	EWoo
'Rushmere' (Dw/d)	WFib
'Rushmoor Bondi Blue' (Z/St/Min/d) **new**	MGbk
'Rushmoor Golden Girl' (Z/St/Dw/C/d) **new**	MGbk
'Rushmoor Golden Rosebud' (Z)	MGbk WFib
'Rushmoor Golden Ruffles' (Z/St/Min/C/d)	MGbk
'Rushmoor Jazz' (Z/St/v)	MGbk
'Rushmoor Mrs Eve Scott' (Z/d)	WFib
'Rushmoor Platinum Anniversary' (Z/St/Dw/d) **new**	MGbk
'Rushmoor Rhapsody' (St)	MGbk
'Rushmoor Wind Chimes' (St)	MGbk
Sailing = 'Klesail' PBR **new**	SSea
'Saint Elmo's Fire' (St/Min/d)	MHer WFib
Saint Malo = 'Guisaint' (I)	NFir
'Salmon Beauty' (Dw/d)	WFib
§ 'Salmon Irene' (Z/d)	WFib
Salmon Princess = 'Pacsalpri' PBR	LAst LSou SSea
'Salmon Queen'	see *P.* 'Lachskönigin'
'Samantha' (R)	WFib
'Samantha Stamp' (Dw/C/d)	WFib
Samelia = 'Pensam' PBR (Dark Line Series) (Z/d)	LAst LBMP SSea
'Sancho Panza' (Dec)	CSpe WFib
'Sandra Lorraine' (I/d)	WFib
Sangria Nova = 'Gendana' PBR (Z) **new**	SSea
'Sanguineum'	CSpe
'Sanibel' (Min/d)	MGbk
§ 'Sarah Don' (A/v)	ECtt LAst WFib
'Sarah Hunt' (Min/d) ♀H1c	NFir
'Sassa' PBR (Quality Series) (Z/d)	LAst SSea
'Satsuki' (R) ♀H1c	NFir
Saturn = 'Tingsat' (R) **new**	MGbk
'Scarborough Fair' (A)	NFir
'Scarlet Gem' (Z/St)	WBrk WFib
'Scarlet Pet' (U) ♀H1c	NFir SMrm
'Scarlet Rambler' (Z/d)	EShb SMrm WFib
'Scarlet Unique' (U)	CRHN EWoo MCot SSea WFib
schizopetalum	WFib
'Schottii' ♀H1c	EWoo MHer NFir WFib
'Scilly Robin' (Sc)	WDib
'Scottow Star' (Z/C)	WFib
'Seale Star' (Dw/St/C)	SSea
'Seaview Lilac' (Z/Min/C)	MGbk
'Seaview Silver' (Min/St)	WFib
'Seaview Sparkler' (Z/St)	WFib
'Seeley's Pansy' (A)	EWoo MHer
'Sefton' (R) ♀H1c	WFib
'Sentinel' (R) **new**	NFir
'Shan Hoy' (Dw)	NFir
'Shanks' (Z) ♀H1c	NFir
'Shannon'	EWoo SBch WFib
'Shimmer' (Z/d)	LAll
Shocking Orange = 'Pacshorg' PBR (Quality Series)	LAst
Shocking Pink = 'Pensho' PBR (Quality Series) (Z/d)	LAst
'Shogan' (R)	NFir
§ 'Shottesham Pet' (Sc)	ENfk EWoo MHer MNHC NWad
sidoides ♀H1c	CDes CSpe EWoo GPoy MCot MHer NFir SBch SMHy SMrm SPhx SSea SVen WFib WHer

– black-flowered	CTca SBrt
– 'Sloe Gin Fizz'	CSpe
Sidonia = 'Pensid'[PBR] (Dark Line Series) (Z/d)	LAst
'Sienna' (R)	NFir
'Sil Falko'[PBR] (I)	LSou
'Sil Frauke'[PBR] (Z)	LAst
'Sil Friesia'[PBR] (Z)	LAst
'Sil Hero'[PBR] (Z)	LAst
'Sil Lenja'[PBR] (Z)	LAst
'Sil Linus'[PBR] (Z)	LSou
'Sil Liske'[PBR] (Z)	LAst
'Sil Magnus'[PBR] (Z)	LAst
'Sil Malaika'[PBR] (I)	LSou
'Sil Pia'[PBR] (I)	LAst LSou
'Sil Quirin'[PBR] (I)	LAst
'Sil Raiko'[PBR]	LAst
'Sil Sören'	LAst
'Sil Teske'[PBR] (I)	LAst
'Sil Tomke'[PBR] (I)	LAst LSou
'Sil Wittje'[PBR] (I)	LAst
'Silver Anne' (R/v)	NFir
'Silver Blazon' (Z/Dw/C/v)	MGbk WFib
'Silver Delight' (v/d)	WFib
'Silver Kewense' (Dw/v)	WFib
'Silver Lady' (Z/d/v)	MGbk
'Silver Magic' (Z/C/Dw) **new**	MGbk
'Silver Shadow' (Z/Dw/C/d/v)	MGbk
'Silver Snow' (Min/St/d)	WFib
'Silver Splash' (Z/v)	MGbk
'Silver Wings' (Z/v)	NFir
'Skelly's Pride' (Z)	WFib
'Skies of Italy' (Z/C/d)	WFib
'Sneezy' (Min)	NFir
'Snow Cap' (MinI) ♀H1c	NFir
'Snowbaby' (Min/d)	WFib
'Snowbright' (St/d)	MGbk
'Snowdrift' (I/d)	WFib
'Snowflake' (Min)	see *P.* 'Atomic Snowflake'
'Snowstorm' (Z)	WFib
'Sofie'	see *P.* 'Decora Rose'
'Solferino' (A)	ENfk
Solidor (I/d) ♀H1c	NFir
Solo = 'Guillio' (Z/I)	LAll
'Something Special' (Z/d) ♀H1c	NFir WFib
Sophie Casade	see *P.* 'Decora Rose'
'Sophie Dumaresque' (Z/v) ♀H1c	NFir WFib
'Sophie Emma' (Z)	NFir
'Sophie Marion' (Dw/Z)	MGbk
'South African Sun' (Z/d) ♀H1c	MGbk
'South American Bronze' (R) ♀H1c	SMrm WFib
'Souvenir de Prue'	EWoo
'Spanish Angel' (A) ♀H1c	CWCL MHer NFir WFib
'Spellbound' (R)	WFib
'Spital Dam' (Dw/d)	NFir
'Spitfire' (Z/Ca/d/v)	WFib
§ 'Splendide' ♀H1c	CSpe MHer NFir SWvt WFib
'Spot-on-bonanza' (R) ♀H1c	NFir WFib
'Springfield Black' (R)	LAll MCot
'Springfield Glory' (Z)	MGbk
'Springtime' (Z/d)	WFib
'Stadt Bern' (Z/C)	NFir
× ***stapletoniae***	see *P.* 'Miss Stapleton'
'Star Flecks' (St) ♀H1c	NFir
'Startel Salmon' (Z/St)	MHer
'Stella Ballerina'	SMrm
'Stella Bird Dancer' (Min/St) **new**	LAll
'Stellar Arctic Star'	see *P.* 'Arctic Star'
'Stellar Hannaford Star'	see *P.* 'Hannaford Star'
'Strawberries and Cream' (Z/St)	NFir
'Strawberry Fayre' (Dw/St)	WFib
§ 'Sugar Baby' (DwI)	ECtt MHer WFib
'Summer Cloud' (Z/d)	WFib
'Summertime' (Z/d)	see *P.* 'Deacon Summertime'
'Sun Rocket' (Dw/d)	WFib
'Sundridge Moonlight' (Z/C)	NFir WFib
'Sundridge Surprise' (Z)	WFib
'Sunraysia' (Z/St)	WFib
'Sunset Snow' (R)	WFib
'Sunspot' (Min/C)	NFir
'Sunspot Petit Pierre' (Min/v)	WFib
'Sunstar' (Min/d)	WFib
'Supernova' (Z/St/d)	WFib
'Supreme Lilac' **new**	NPri
'Supreme Red' **new**	NPri
'Supreme White' **new**	NPri
'Surcouf' (I)	WFib
'Susan Payne' (Dw/d)	MHer
'Sussex Gem' (Min/d)	WFib
'Sussex Lace'	see *P.* 'White Mesh'
'Swanland Lace' (I/d/v)	WFib
'Swedish Angel' (A)	WFib
'Sweet Lady Mary' (Sc)	ENfk
'Sweet Mimosa' (Sc) ♀H1c	CRHN ENfk EWoo LAst LPot MCot MHer NFir SBch WFib WGwG
'Sweet Miriam' (Sc)	WDib
'Sweet Sixteen' (R)	WFib
'Sybil Holmes' (I/d)	WFib
'Tamie' (Dw/d)	NFir
tetragonum	CRHN EWoo MHer WFib
'The Boar' (Fr) ♀H1c	EShb EWoo MCot WFib
'The Culm' (A)	WFib
'The Czar'	see *P.* 'Czar'
'The Joker' (I/d)	WFib
'The Kenn-Lad' (A)	EWoo
'The Marchioness of Bute' (R)	MHer NFir WFib
§ 'The Mole' (A)	WFib
'The Tamar' (A)	EWoo MHer
'The Yar' (Z/St)	WFib
'Thomas Earle' (Z)	WFib
'Tilly' (Min)	NFir
'Tinker West' (Z/St/Dw)	WFib
'Tiny Tinker' (Z/St/Min/C/d/v)	MGbk
§ 'Tip Top Duet' (A) ♀H1c	EWoo MHer NFir SMrm WFib
'Tirley Garth' (A)	WFib
'Tomcat'[PBR] (I/d)	LAst
tomentosum (Sc) ♀H1c	CHEx CSpe ENfk EWoo GLog GPoy MCot MHer MNHC NFir NWad WDib WFib WHea
– 'Chocolate'	see *P.* 'Chocolate Peppermint'
Tomgirl = 'Pactomgi'[PBR] (I × Z/d)	LAst
'Topscore' (Z/d)	WFib
'Tornado' (R) ♀H1c	NFir WFib
'Torrento' (Sc)	MHer WFib

'Tortoiseshell' (R)	WFib
'Toscana Okka' (Toscana Series) (I)	LAst LSou
'Tracy' (Min/d)	NFir
transvaalense	NFir
tricolor misapplied	see *P.* 'Splendide'
tricolor Curt.	NFir
tricuspidatum	EWoo WCot
trifidum	EWoo WFib
'Triomphe de Nancy' (Z/d)	WFib
triste	EWoo MCot MHer WCot WFib
'Trudie' (Dw/Fr)	MHer WFib
'Turkish Coffee' (R)	WFib
'Turkish Delight' (Dw/C)	NFir WFib
'Turtle's Surprise' (Z/d/v)	WBrk
'Tweenaway' (Dw)	MGbk NFir
'Tyabb Princess' (R)	EWoo
'Unique Aurore' (U)	MHer
'Unique Mons Ninon'	see *P.* 'Monsieur Ninon'
'Urchin' (Min/St)	NFir WFib
'Ursula Key' (Z/c)	WFib
'Ursula's Choice' (A)	WFib
'Val Merrick' (Dw/St)	WFib
'Valentine' (Z/C)	WFib
'Vancouver Centennial' (Dw/St/C) ♀[H1c]	MCot MHer NEgg NFir SCoo SSea WFib
'Vandersea' (Sc)	EWoo MCot
'Variegated Attar of Roses' (Sc/v)	NWad
'Variegated Clorinda' (Sc/v)	WFib
'Variegated Fragrans'	see *P.* (Fragrans Group) 'Fragrans Variegatum'
§ 'Variegated Kleine Liebling' (Min/v)	WFib
'Variegated Petit Pierre' (Min/v)	MHer WFib
'Vectis Blaze' (I)	EWoo
'Vectis Cascade' (I)	EWoo
'Vectis Dazzler' (Z/St/d)	MGbk
'Vectis Embers' (Z/d/v)	MGbk
'Vectis Finery' (St/d) ♀[H1c]	NFir
'Vectis Glitter' (Z/St) ♀[H1c]	NFir WBrk WFib
'Vectis Pink' (Dw/St)	WFib
'Vectis Purple' (Z/d)	WFib
'Vectis Sparkler' (Dw/St)	NFir
'Vectis Starbright' (Dw/St)	WFib
'Vectis Volcano' (Z/St)	WFib
'Velvet Duet' (A) ♀[H1c]	NFir
'Verona Contreras' (A)	NFir
'Vic Claws' (Dw/St)	NFir
'Vicki' (R)	EWoo
'Vicki Town' (R)	WFib
'Vicky Claire' (R)	EWoo NFir SMrm WFib
Vicky = 'Pacvicky'[PBR] (I)	LAst
Victor = 'Pacvi'[PBR] (Quality Series) (Z/d)	LBMP LSou
Victoria = 'Pacvica'[PBR] (Quality Series) (Z/d)	LAst
Ville de Dresden = 'Pendresd'[PBR] (I)	EWoo
'Ville de Paris'	see *P.* 'Hederinum'
'Vina' (Dw/C/d)	WFib
violareum misapplied	see *P.* 'Splendide'
'Viscossisimum' (Sc)	MHer
viscosum	see *P. glutinosum*
'Vivat Regina' (Z/d)	WFib
'Voodoo' (U) ♀[H1c]	CSpe EWoo MCot MHer NFir SMrm WCot WFib
'Wantirna' (Z/v) ♀[H1c]	NFir
'Warrenorth Coral' (Z/C/d)	WFib
'Warrenorth Pearl' (Z/d)	MGbk
'Warrenorth Platinum' (Z/v/d)	MGbk
'Warrenorth Rubellite' (Z/v)	MGbk
'Warrenorth Thulite' (Z/C)	MGbk
'Washbrook' (Min/d) ♀[H1c]	NFir
'Wedding Royale' (Dw/d)	WFib
'Welling' (Sc)	MHer NFir
'Wendy Jane' (Dw/d)	WFib
'Wendy Read' (Dw/d)	WFib
'Westdale Appleblossom' (Z/C/d)	LAll WFib
'Westside' (Z/d)	WFib
'Westwood' (Z/St)	WFib
'Whisper' (R)	EWoo WFib
'White Bird's Egg' (Z)	WFib
'White Boar' (Fr)	CSpe EShb EWoo NFir WFib
'White Bonanza' (R)	WFib
'White Eggshell' (Min)	WFib
'White Feather' (Z/St)	MHer
'White Glory' (R) ♀[H1c]	NFir
§ 'White Mesh' (I/v)	NFir
'White Unique' (U)	SBch WFib
Wico = 'Guimongol'[PBR] (I/d)	LAst
'Wilhelm Kolle' (Z)	WFib
'Wilhelm Langath' (Z/v)	SCoo WBrk
'Willa' (Dec)	WFib
'Winner' (R)	LAst
'Wolverton' (Z)	WFib
'Wootton's Unique' (U)	CSpe EWoo
'Wychwood' (A/Sc)	EWoo
'Yale' (I/d) ♀[H1c]	WFib
'Yan la Grouch' (Z/C)	WFib
'Yhu' (R)	NFir SMrm WFib
'Yvonne' (Z)	WFib
'Zama' (R)	NFir
'Zinc' (Z/d)	WFib
'Zofia Pope' (R)	MGbk NFir
zonale	WFib
'Zulu King' (R)	WFib
'Zulu Warrior' (R)	WFib

Peliosanthes (*Asparagaceae*)

arisanensis B&SWJ 3639	WCru
caesia B&SWJ 5183	WCru
teta subsp. ***humilis*** RWJ 10044	WCru

Pellaea (*Pteridaceae*)

ovata	SPlb
rotundifolia ♀[H1b]	CBty CLAP ISha LPal LRHS
viridis	WPGP

Pellionia see *Elatostema*

Peltandra (*Araceae*)

alba	see *P. sagittifolia*
§ ***sagittifolia***	CRow
undulata	see *P. virginica* (L.) Schott
§ ***virginica*** (L.) Schott	CRow EWay NPer SWat
- 'Snow Splash' (v)	CRow EWay

Peltaria (*Brassicaceae*)

alliacea	CSpe LEdu WCot
* ***dumulosa***	WCot

Peltiphyllum see *Darmera*

Peltoboykinia (*Saxifragaceae*)

§	***tellimoides***	CLAP EBee GCal GKev NBir WMoo WPnP
	watanabei	CDes CLAP CSpe EBee GEdr IMou LEdu MMoz MSCN NLar WCru WMoo WPGP

Pennantia (*Pennantiaceae*)

baylisiana	ECou
corymbosa	ECou

Pennellianthus see *Penstemon*

Pennisetum ✿ (*Poaceae*)

	× ***advena*** 'Fireworks' PBR (v)	EBee EPfP EUJe LLWG LRHS MAsh SCob SLon SPoG SWvt WCot
§	- 'Rubrum' ♀H2	CBcs CExl CKno CWCL EShb EUJe LPal MAsh MPie NWsh SCoo SHDw SMad SPoG SRot SWvt WCot
§	***alopecuroides***	CAco EAEE ECha EHoe EPfP LRHS LSou MJak MWat NGdn SArc SCob SLim SPer SPlb SWat SWvt WHar WWEG XLum XSen
	- B&SWJ 11434	WCru
	- Autumn Wizard	see *P. alopecuroides* 'Herbstzauber'
	- 'Black Beauty'	CSpe SMHy WWEG
	- 'Cassian's Choice'	CKno EHoe ELon EWes NCGa SHar SMrm WWEG
	- 'Caudatum'	CKno
	- f. ***erythrochaetum*** 'Ferris'	WCru
	- 'Foxtrot'	MAvo
	- 'Gelbstiel'	CKno EPPr LRHS
	- 'Hameln'	Widely available
§	- 'Herbstzauber'	CCon CKno EHoe MAvo NWsh XLum
	- 'Little Bunny'	CKno CSde EBee EHoe ELan ELon EPfP GCal IVic LPal MBri NGdn NLar SCob SMea SWvt WWEG
	- 'Little Honey' (v)	CKno MBNS NLar XLum
	- 'Magic'	CBod ELon EPPr MAvo WWEG
	- 'Moudry'	CExl CKno CSde EAEE EBee EHoe ELon EPfP LPal LRHS MAvo NWsh SHDw XLum
	- 'National Arboretum'	EBee EPPr
	- 'Reborn'	MAvo
	- 'Red Head'	CAbP CKno CMea ELon EUJe EWes GAbr LRHS LSou MAvo MBNS WCot
	- f. ***viridescens***	CKno ELan EPPr EShb LEdu LRHS MRav MWhi SCob SDix SMrm SPhx WWEG XLum
	- 'Weserbergland'	CKno EBee EHoe ELon EPPr WWEG
	- 'Woodside'	CKno CPrp EHoe EPPr LEdu MBNS NWsh SMad XLum
	clandestinum new	EShb
	compressum	see *P. alopecuroides*
	'Fairy Tails'	CKno EPPr EPfP LRHS LSqu MAsh NDov SMHy SPoG
	flaccidum	EPPr
	glaucum 'Purple Baron'	MAsh
	- 'Purple Majesty'	CSpe MNrw SWvt
	incomptum	EHoe XLum
	- purple-flowered	CCon MMoz
	longistylum misapplied	see *P. villosum*
	macrourum	CElw CKno CSam CSde CSpe ECha EHoe ELon EPPr EUJe GCal LEdu LRHS MAvo MNrw MSpe MWhi NDov NWsh SEND SMHy SMad SMrm SPtp WMoo WPGP
	- 'Short Stuff'	CKno
	massaicum 'Red Bunny Tails'	CChe ELon EUJe LRHS
	- 'Red Buttons'	see *P. thunbergii* 'Red Buttons'
	orientale ♀H5	CAby CKno CPrp CSde CSpe EAJP ECha EHoe EPfP EWoo LPal LRHS MNrw MRav NBir NWsh SEND SGSe SPer SPtp SRkn SWvt WCot WHoo WKif WWEG XLum
	- 'Karley Rose' PBR	CKno CPar EHoe EWes EWoo IBoy IPot LRHS MAvo MWhi NDov NOak NWsh SCob SWvt WWEG
I	- 'Robustum'	EPPr MAvo WPGP
	- 'Shogun'	CKno CSam EPPr LRHS SPoG WCot
	- 'Tall Tails'	CBod EHoe EPPr EWes EWoo LRHS MWhi SMea WWEG XLum
	'Paul's Giant'	CKno XLum
	rueppellii	see *P. setaceum*
§	***setaceum*** ♀H6	EPfP NWsh SHDw SWvt
	- 'Emelia Mae'	SHDw
	- 'Rubrum'	see *P.* × *advena* 'Rubrum'
	- 'Sky Rocket' PBR new	MBri
	- 'Summer Samba'	LRHS MBri
	thunbergii	CAby LRHS
§	- 'Red Buttons'	CKno EHoe ELon EPfP EShb LEdu LRHS LSqu MAsh MAvo NOak SDix SHDw SMHy SMea SPhx WHea WHoo
§	***villosum*** ♀H3	CAby CBcs CExl CKno CMac CSpe EAJP ECha EHoe ELan EPPr EPfP EShb LBMP LEdu LRHS MAvo MWat MWhi SEND SGSe SMad SMea SMrm SPer SPhx WWEG XLum XSen
	- 'Cream Falls'	LRHS

pennyroyal see *Mentha pulegium*

Penstemon ✿ (*Plantaginaceae*)

	sp.	SVic
	NJM 09.028	WPGP
	'Abberley'	MBNS
	'Abbotsmerry'	CWCL ECtt EPfP LLHF MBNS MCot NLar SLon
	'Agnes Laing'	MBNS
	albertinus	see *P. humilis*
§	'Alice Hindley' ♀H4	CNec CSpe CTri CWCL ELan EPfP LAst LLWP LRHS MCot MWat NBir SBod SCob SEND SLon SMrm SPer SPoG SRGP SRms SWvt WCFE WCot WHoo WKif WMnd WWEG XLum
	alpinus	EDAr
	ambiguus	CPBP
§	'Andenken an Friedrich Hahn' ♀H5	Widely available
	antirrhinoides	see *Keckiella antirrhinoides*
	'Apple Blossom' misapplied	see *P.* 'Thorn'
	'Apple Blossom' ♀H3	Widely available
	aridus	GEdr
	arizonicus	see *P. whippleanus*
	'Ashton'	MBNS

	Name	Suppliers
	attenuatus* subsp. *militaris	SPlb
	'Audrey Cooper'	CChe CMac MBNS
	'Axe Valley Penny Mitchell'	ECtt
	'Axe Valley Suzie'	CAby
	azureus	CCon GKev
	'Barbara Barker'	see *P.* 'Beech Park'
§	***barbatus***	CTal MAsh SBrt SPer SRms
	- subsp. ***coccineus***	CAby CCon GBin MBNS MNFA XLum
	- 'Iron Maiden'	LRHS SGSe
	- 'Jingle Bells'	EAJP IFro
	- orange-flowered	SPlb
	- 'Peter Catt'	CMea
	- Pinacolada Series	LRHS
	- - 'Pinacolada Blue'	MHol
	- - 'Pinacolada Dark Rose' **new**	LRHS
	- - 'Pinacolada Light Rose' **new**	LRHS
	- - 'Pinacolada Rosy Red' **new**	LRHS
	- - 'Pinacolada White' **new**	LRHS
	- var. ***praecox***	MBNS SRot
	- - f. ***nanus*** 'Rondo'	LRHS
	barrettiae	LLHF
	'Beckford'	CWCL EWTr LLHF MBNS
§	'Beech Park' ♀H3	ELan EPfP EWes MBNS
	'Bisham Seedling'	see *P.* 'White Bedder'
	'Blackbird'	Widely available
	'Blue Spring' misapplied	see *P. heterophyllus* 'Blue Spring'
	'Blueberry Fudge' (Ice Cream Series)	LSou MAvo MTis WCot WNPC
	'Blueberry Taffy'	ECtt
	'Bodnant'	LAst LLHF MBNS WHoo WHrl
	bradburii	see *P. grandiflorus*
	'Bredon'	MBNS
	'Bubblegum' (Ice Cream Series)	CAby LRHS MHol MTis WCot WNPC
	'Burford Purple'	see *P.* 'Burgundy'
	'Burford Seedling'	see *P.* 'Burgundy'
	'Burford White'	see *P.* 'White Bedder'
§	'Burgundy'	CCon CMac CWCL ECtt GMaP LLWP LRHS MHol NBir NPer NPri SPoG SRms XLum
§	***campanulatus***	EPot EWes SBch SRms
	- PC&H 148	SDys
	- ***pulchellus***	see *P. campanulatus*
	- 'Roseus' misapplied	see *P. kunthii*
	'Candy Pink'	see *P.* 'Old Candy Pink'
	cardwellii	EWes
	cardwellii* × *davidsonii	WAbe
	'Castle Forbes'	GMaP MBNS SRms
	'Cathedral Rose'	EPfP
	'Catherine de la Mare'	see *P. heterophyllus* 'Catherine de la Mare'
	'Centra'	MBNS XLum
	'Charles Rudd'	COtt CWCL ECtt ELon EPfP EPla MBNS NLar SBod SEND SRGP SRms SWvt WHrl WRHF
§	'Cherry' ♀H3	ECtt GBee MBNS SHar SPlb WHea WWEG
	'Cherry Ripe' misapplied	see *P.* 'Cherry'
§	'Chester Scarlet' ♀H3	ECtt EWld MBNS SDix WCFE WKif XLum
	'Choirboy'	EWes
	clutei	LLHF
	cobaea	GLog
	comarrhenus	SBrt
	'Comberton'	MBNS
	confertus	CTri EBee ECho EPot MBNS SBrt XLum
	- RCB/MO A-7	WCot
	'Connie's Pink' ♀H4	MBNS SRms WWEG
	cordifolius	see *Keckiella cordifolia*
	'Cottage Garden Red'	see *P.* 'Windsor Red'
§	'Countess of Dalkeith'	ECtt ELan EWes GBin LLWP MCot MRav SHar SPlb SRms SWvt WCFE WCot
	cristatus	see *P. eriantherus*
*	***cyananthus* var. *utahensis***	WCot
	aff. ***cyananthus***	SBrt
	cyaneus	GKev
	'Dark Towers'PBR	CAbb ECtt IPot LRHS NCGa SLon SPoG
	davidsonii	CTal ECho EPot EWes GCrg GEdr NSla WAbe WOld WThu
	- var. ***davidsonii***	WAbe
	- var. ***menziesii***	EPot GCrg GEdr LLHF NHar NSla
	'Microphyllus'	NWad WAbe
	- var. ***praeteritus***	GEdr
	- 'Silverwells' **new**	GEdr
	'Dazzler'	MBNS SWvt
	'Delfts Blue Riding Hood' (Riding Hood Series) **new**	MAsh
	'Devonshire Cream'	CWCL MBNS
	diffusus	see *P. serrulatus*
	digitalis	GCal MBNS
§	- 'Husker Red'	Widely available
	- 'Mystica'	LRHS SPad
	- 'Purpureus'	see *P. digitalis* 'Husker Red'
	- 'Ruby Tuesday'	EWes WPGP
	- white-flowered	EBee
	discolor pale lavender-flowered	NBir
§	'Drinkstone Red'	MBNS SDix SDys
	'Drinkwater Red'	see *P.* 'Drinkstone Red'
	eatonii	GKev
	(Elgar Series) 'Elgar Crown of India'	ELon MHol WCot
	- 'Elgar Enigma'	EBee ELon LLHF MHol WCot
	- 'Elgar Firefly'	ELon EWTr MHol WCot
	- 'Elgar Light of Life'	MHol WCot
	- 'Elgar Nimrod'	EBee ELon MHol WCot
	'Ellenbank Amethyst'	SDys
	'Ellwood Red Phoenix'	MBNS
	'Elmley'	MBNS
§	***eriantherus***	LLHF SPlb
	- dwarf	GKev
	Etna = 'Yatna'	CRos ECtt EPfP LAll LRHS MBNS SRms
	euglaucus	EBee GKev LLHF MMuc
	- NNS 07-397	GKev
§	'Evelyn' ♀H4	CMea CTri ECha ELan EPfP IBoy LRHS MBNS MCot MHer MRav SPer SPoG SRGP SRms SWvt WCot WKif WSHC WWEG XLum
	'Firebird'	see *P.* 'Schoenholzeri'
	'Flame'	MBNS SLon WWEG
	'Flamingo'	CAby CHel CRos CWCL ELon EPfP EWes GBin LAst LRHS MBNS NLar SGbt SHil SMrm SPoG SRms SWvt WHoo WMnd WWEG
§	***fruticosus* var. *scouleri*** ♀H5	MAsh MMuc SEND

- - f. ***albus*** 🏆H5	CSpe WAbe
- - 'Amethyst'	SRms WAbe
Fujiyama = 'Yayama'PBR	CSam CWGN ECtt EPfP LAll LRHS SLon SMrm SPad SRms SWvt
'Garden Red'	see *P.* 'Windsor Red'
'Garnet'	see *P.* 'Andenken an Friedrich Hahn'
gentianoides B&SWJ 10271	WCru
'Geoff Hamilton'	CWCL ECtt MBNS SLon SPoG
'George Elrick'	LLHF WHoo
§ 'George Home' 🏆H3	EWes MBNS SMrm SRms
'George Moon'	SPad
'Gilchrist'	ECtt SLon WRHF
glaber	CMHG CMea EWld GBee LLWP SPlb WKif WSHC
- 'Roundway Snowflake'	SHar SPhx
globosus	SBrt
'Gloire des Quatre Rues'	MBNS XLum
gormanii	GEdr WHil
gracilentus dark blue-flowered from Washoe County, Nevada **new**	SBrt
§ ***grandiflorus***	CCon EBee EPfP
- 'Prairie Snow'	EBee
- 'War Axe'	EDAr
hallii	EWes SBrt
hartwegii 'Albus'	SHar SIgm SRms
- 'Picotee Red'	CWCL LRHS
§ ***heterophyllus***	LRHS MNrw MSCN NBir NGBl SRkn SRms WHea
- 'Blue Eye'	MBrN
- 'Blue Gem'	CElw CTri
§ - 'Blue Spring'	CSpe EPfP LRHS MRav SPoG WAbe
§ - 'Catherine de la Mare' 🏆H4	CKno CWCL EBee ELan EWTr EWoo GBin LRHS MHer MWat NBir NLar NPCo SBch SCob SHar SPer SRGP SWvt WHrl WKif XLum
- 'Electric Blue'	CBod CWCL LRHS SLon SMrm
- 'Heavenly Blue'	CAby CRos CSBt CWCL EBee ECtt EPfP EWoo GMaP LAll LAst LRHS MAvo MBNS MCot MLHP MNHC MSwo MWat NEgg NLar SGbt SHil SPer SPoG SPtp SWat SWvt WHil WHoo
- 'Jeanette'	CMea
- 'Misty Blue Shades'	LRHS
- subsp. ***purdyi***	EPyc
- 'Roundway White'	WCot
- 'True Blue'	see *P. heterophyllus*
- 'Züriblau'	CCon EBee SGSe SPlb
§ 'Hewell Pink Bedder' 🏆H4	CBod EPfP EWoo GBin GBuc LPot LRHS MBNS MBri MRav NCGa NPri SHil SMrm SPtp SRms SWvt WHil WMnd
'Hewitt's Pink'	SLon
hidalgensis	WCot
'Hidcote Pink' 🏆H3	Widely available
'Hidcote Purple'	SHar WHoo XLum
'Hidcote White'	LPot MHer SWvt WWEG
'Hillview Pink'	SLon XLum
'Hillview Red'	MBNS
§ ***hirsutus***	EBee SGSe XLum
- var. ***pygmaeus***	CMea ECho EDAr EWTr GKev MHer NRya SBrt SPlb WHoo WIce
* - - f. ***albus***	EBee ECho WHoo
'Hopleys Variegated' (v)	LRHS MBNS SWvt
§ ***humilis***	SBrt
'James Bowden'	MBNS
Jean Grace = 'Penbow'	CSpe
'Jessica'	CWGN
'John Booth'	MBNS
'John Nash' misapplied	see *P.* 'Alice Hindley'
'John Nash'	SRms
'John Spedan Lewis'	SLon
'Joy'	MBNS
'Juicy Grape' (Ice Cream Series)	LAll LRHS WCot WHil
'June'	see *P.* 'Pennington Gem'
'Kate Gilchrist'	SLon
Kilimanjaro = 'Yajaro'	EPfP LRHS SLon SRms WFar
'King George V'	Widely available
'Knight's Purple'	ECtt MBNS
'Knightwick'	MBNS
§ ***kunthii***	MAsh
§ ***laetus*** subsp. ***roezlii***	ECho EPot GCrg SBrt
'Lane Fox'	WCot
§ 'Le Phare'	MBNS XLum
'Lilac and Burgundy'	MBNS SHar SMrm SRms SWvt WWEG
'Lilac Frost'	LLHF MMuc WMoo
'Lilliput'	ELon GBin SLon SPoG WHil
linarioides 'Marilyn Ross'	ECtt MBNS
'Lord Home'	see *P.* 'George Home'
'Lucinda Gilchrist'	SLon
lyallii	CCon ELan GKev SRms WCot
'Lynette'	MBNS SBch
'Macpenny's Pink'	CMac MBNS
'Madame Golding'	MBNS XLum
'Malvern Springs'	MBNS
'Margery Fish' 🏆H3	CElw CFis ECtt EPyc EWes WWEG
'Martley'	WWEG
'Maurice Gibbs' 🏆H3	CBcs CWCL ECtt EPfP EWTr EWes MBNS MBel SBod SRGP SRms WMnd WWEG
'Melting Candy' (Ice Cream Series)	LRHS MAvo MTis WCot
mensarum	CMea NCGa
× ***mexicanus*** 'Sunburst Amethyst'	SPhx SRms XLum
- 'Sunburst Ruby'	CPla SLon SPhx
'Midnight'	ECtt ELan GBin LPot MBNS MRav MSwo SEND SHar SWvt WCFE WWEG XLum
(Minibird Series) 'Minibird Lilac'	MGos
- 'Minibird Pink'	MGos
- 'Minibird Purple'	MGos
'Modesty'	MBNS SRms
'Mother of Pearl'	CBcs CCon CRos EPfP GBin GMaP LRHS MBNS MCot MSwo MWat SRms SWvt WWEG
'Mrs Miller'	MBNS
'Mrs Morse'	see *P.* 'Chester Scarlet'
'Mrs Oliver'	EWes
§ 'Myddelton Gem'	MWat SRms
'Myddelton Red'	see *P.* 'Myddelton Gem'
newberryi 🏆H5	WIce
- f. ***humilior***	EPot
§ - subsp. ***sonomensis***	NSla SRms WAbe
'Newbury Gem'	MBNS SHar SRGP SWvt
'Oaklea Red'	GBin
§ 'Old Candy Pink'	MBNS SWvt
'Osprey' 🏆H3	CMac CMea CWCL ECtt ELan EPfP EWes GBin LAst LRHS MBNS NBir SMrm SRms SWvt WMnd WWEG

ovatus	CCon CMac CSpe EBee ELan SPhx SRms
'Overbury'	ECtt MBNS SRms
'Papal Purple'	LLWP MAsh MBNS MHer NBir SHar SLon SPhx SRms XLum
parvulus	SBrt
'Patio Bells Pink'	MLHP
'Patio Wine'	MBel
'Peace'	GBin MBNS
§ 'Pennington Gem' ♀H3	ELan MHer NBir SGSe SHar SIgm SRms SWvt
'Pensham Amelia Jane'	CAby CNec COtt CWGN EBee ECtt ELon EPfP LAll LRHS LSou MAsh MBNS MBri MHol NLar NPri SHil SLon SMrm SPer SRkn SRms SWvt WCot WGor WHil
'Pensham Arctic Fox'	ECtt LRHS SLon
'Pensham Arctic Sunset'	SLon WHrl
'Pensham Avonbelle'	MBNS SRms
'Pensham Bilberry Ice'	EPyc MBNS SWvt WMnd
'Pensham Blackberry Ice'	ECtt EPyc LAll LSou MBNS SLon SRms
'Pensham Blueberry Ice'	ECtt EPyc LSou MBNS SWvt
'Pensham Capricorn Moon'	ECtt NLar SRGP
'Pensham Charlotte Louise'	ECtt ELon LAll LRHS MAsh NLar SRms
'Pensham Czar'	CAby CNec COtt ECtt ELon EPfP LAll LRHS LSou LSun MAsh MBNS MBri MCot NCGa NPri SGbt SHil SLon SMrm SPer SPoG SRkn SRms SWvt WHil WHrl
'Pensham Dorothy Wilson'	EPyc LRHS SMrm
'Pensham Edith Biggs'	SMrm
'Pensham Eleanor Young'	COtt ECtt LAll LRHS LSou MBNS SLon SPoG SPtp SRkn SWvt
'Pensham Freshwater Pearl'	SRms WHoo
'Pensham Great Expectations'	ECtt
'Pensham Jessica Mai'	ECtt LRHS LSou SPer SRms SWvt WHil
'Pensham Just Jayne'	ECtt ELon EPfP EPyc LAll LRHS MBNS SLon SRGP SRms SWvt WHoo WMnd XLum
'Pensham Kay Burton'	EPfP EPyc SRGP WMnd
'Pensham Laura'	CAby CNec CSam CWGN ECtt EPfP LAll LRHS LSun MAsh MBNS MBel MBri MHol NLar NPri SHil SLon SMrm SPad SPer SRGP SRkn SWvt WBor WHoo
'Pensham Loganberry Ice'	LSou MBNS SLon
'Pensham Marjorie Lewis'	WMnd
'Pensham Miss Wilson'	SRms
'Pensham Plum Jerkum'	CAby CRos CWGN ECtt ELon EPfP EPyc LAll LRHS LSou MBNS MBri MCot MPie NLar SCob SHil SLon SMrm SPad SPer SRkn SWvt WHoo WMnd
'Pensham Princess'	ECtt WGor
'Pensham Raspberry Ice'	MBNS SLon WMnd
'Pensham Tayberry Ice'	CRos ECtt EPyc MBNS SLon WMnd
'Pensham Victoria Plum'	CElw SHar WHoo
'Pensham Wedding Bells'	SRms
'Pensham Wedding Day'	CMea CWCL EBee EPfP LAll LRHS LSou MBNS MBri MCot NLar NPri SCob SLon SPer SPoG SPtp SRGP WHoo WMnd
'Pensham Westminster Belle'	ECtt
'Pershore Carnival'	SRms WHrl
'Pershore Fanfare'	WHrl
'Pershore Pink Necklace'	CWCL ECtt LRHS SRms SWvt WHlf WRHF WWEG
'Phare'	see *P.* 'Le Phare'
(Phoenix Series) Phoenix Appleblossom 09 = 'Peni Ablos09'	LRHS SHil
- Phoenix Lavender = 'Peni Laver'	LRHS SHil
- Phoenix Magenta 09 = 'Peni Mag09'	LRHS SHil
- Phoenix Red = 'Pheni Reeda'PBR	LRHS SHil
- Phoenix Rose = 'Penharros'PBR **new**	SHil
- Phoenix Violet 09 = 'Peni Vio09'PBR	EPfP LRHS SHil
'Phyllis'	see *P.* 'Evelyn'
pinifolius ♀H4	CCon CMea CTri EBee ECho EDAr ELon EPot EUJe EWTr GCrg GKev LRHS MBel MMuc NHar SPoG WThu XLum XSen
- 'Mersea Yellow'	CCon CMea EBee ECho EDAr EPfP EPot GCrg GEdr GKev LRHS MHer MMuc NHar SLon SPlb SPoG XLum XSen
- 'Wisley Flame' ♀H4	ECho EPfP EPot EWes GCrg GEdr MBNS MHer MSCN MWat SCob SIgm
'Pink Bedder'	see *P.* 'Hewell Pink Bedder', 'Sutton's Pink Bedder'
'Pink Endurance'	MBNS WHal
'Port Wine' ♀H3	CMea CTri ELon EPfP GMaP LPot LRHS MCot MWat NBir SMrm SPoG SWvt WKif WMnd WWEG
'Powis Castle'	EWes
'Precious Gem' **new**	WHlf
'Pretty Petticoat'	IPot LRHS
'Priory Purple'	MBNS WHrl
procerus	MMuc
- var. ***brachyanthus***	GKev
§ - var. ***formosus***	WAbe
§ - 'Roy Davidson' ♀H5	ECho EPot NHar WAbe
- var. ***tolmiei***	EPot GCal GEdr MPie
pubescens	see *P. hirsutus*
pulchellus Greene	see *P. procerus* var. *formosus*
pulchellus Lindl.	see *P. campanulatus*
'Purple and White'	see *P.* 'Countess of Dalkeith'
'Purple Bedder'	CMac COtt EBee EPfP GBin LRHS MBri MWat NBir SHil SPoG SPtp SRkn SRms SWvt XLum
'Purple Passion'	CElw EBee ELan EPfP EWes EWoo LRHS SCob
'Purple Sea'	MAsh
'Purpureus Albus'	see *P.* 'Countess of Dalkeith'
§ ***putus***	SGSe
'Raspberry Ripple' (Ice Cream Series)	LSou
'Raven' ♀H3	CMac COtt CRos CSam CWCL EBee ECtt EHoe EWTr EWoo GBin GCra LAll LAst LLWP LRHS MBel MCot MHer MNHC SCob SEND SRms SWvt WHal WHar WHil WWEG
'Razzle Dazzle'	MBNS SPlb WCot
'Red Emperor'	WWEG
'Red Knight'	GCra MBNS
'Red Riding Hood'PBR	EPfP LRHS

'Red Rocks' GBin LRHS WCot
'Red Sea' MAsh NSir
'Rich Purple' EPyc MBNS SPlb XLum
'Rich Ruby' ♀H3 CAby CWCL ELan EPfP EWes LLWP LRHS NBir SHar SPlb SPtp SRGP SWvt WWEG
richardsonii SBrt
var. ***richardsonii*** new
'Ridgeway Red' MBNS
roezlii Regel see *P. laetus* subsp. *roezlii*
roezlii ambig. MAsh SBrt
'Rosy Blush' MBNS SPlb
'Roy Davidson' see *P. procerus* 'Roy Davidson'
'Royal White' see *P.* 'White Bedder'
'Rubicundus' ♀H4 CHel CWCL ELan EPfP GBBs GBin LRHS MBNS SLon SWvt WBor WHil
'Ruby' misapplied see *P.* 'Schoenholzeri'
'Ruby Candle' new ECtt
'Ruby Field' EPyc
rupicola ♀H5 EPot
- 'Albus' WThu
- 'Conwy Lilac' SRms WAbe
- 'Conwy Rose' GCrg WAbe WThu
'Russian River' EBee ECtt EPfP EWes LRHS MBNS SPlb SWvt XLum
rydbergii GEdr SPlb
'Samsong' WCFE
§ 'Schoenholzeri' ♀H4 Widely available
scouleri see *P. fruticosus* var. *scouleri*
§ ***serrulatus*** EWes SBrt XLum
'Sherbourne Blue' LPot WCot
'Sissinghurst Pink' see *P.* 'Evelyn'
'Six Hills' CMea CTal SDys WAbe WOld
'Skyline' EPfP
smallii CAby EDAr EPPr EPfP EWes LRHS MHer SPhx SRkn WPGP
'Snow Storm' see *P.* 'White Bedder'
'Snowflake' see *P.* 'White Bedder'
sonomensis see *P. newberryi* subsp. *sonomensis*
'Sour Grapes' misapplied see *P.* 'Stapleford Gem'
'Sour Grapes' ambig. CAby CHVG COtt EHoe EPla EWoo IBoy LAll LPot MBel MJak NGdn SCob SHil SMrm WWEG
§ 'Sour Grapes' M. Fish ♀H4 CHel CMac CRos CSpe CWCL EBee ECha ELan EPfP GBin GMaP IBoy LAst LRHS MHer MSwo NLar SEND SHar SPer SPoG SPtp WCot WHea WHil WHoo WKif WMnd WRHF
'Southgate Gem' GBee GKev MBNS MWat SRms SWvt
'Souvenir d'Adrian Regnier' MBNS
'Souvenir d'André Torres' misapplied see *P.* 'Chester Scarlet'
speciosus SBrt
'Spitfire' WCFE
§ 'Stapleford Gem' ♀H3 CBod CWCL ELan GBuc LRHS MBel MRav NPri SHar SMrm SRms SWvt WHar WHoo WMnd WWEG
aff. 'Stapleford Gem' new SLon
'Storm' new WHlf
'Strawberries and Cream' (Ice Cream Series) CWCL ELon LAll LRHS MTis NLar SCob SRkn WCot WHil
strictus CCon EBee EPPr MBNS MNFA SBrt
Stromboli = 'Yaboli' LRHS
subglaber SBrt
§ 'Sutton's Pink Bedder' MBNS
'Sweet Cherry' (Ice Cream Series) ECtt LSou MTis WCot
tall, pink-flowered see *P.* 'Welsh Dawn'
'Taoensis' MBNS
'Ted's Purple' WCFE
teucrioides EPot
'The Juggler' ECtt MBNS SMrm SWvt
§ 'Thorn' COtt ECtt LRHS MWat NBir SPhx SRms SWvt WWEG
'Threave Pink' ECtt LLWP MBNS MRav SEND SHar SMrm SPer SWvt WWEG
'Thundercloud' ECtt
'Torquay Gem' LLHF MBNS
'True Sour Grapes' see *P.* 'Sour Grapes' M. Fish
uintahensis SBrt
utahensis GBee
'Vanilla Plum' (Ice Cream Series) LRHS LSou SRkn WHil
versicolor new SBrt
Vesuvius = 'Yasius' CRos ECtt EPfP LRHS SLon SRms WCAu WFar
virens CTal EBee
virgatus EBee
- 'Blue Buckle' IPot LRHS MHol SPlb
- subsp. ***putus*** see *P. putus*
'Watermelon Taffy' (Taffy Series) new ECtt
§ 'Welsh Dawn' MBNS
§ ***whippleanus*** EDAr MMuc SPlb
§ 'White Bedder' ♀H3 Widely available
'Whitethroat' Sidwell MBNS
I 'Whitethroat' purple-flowered WCot
wilcoxii SBrt
'Willy's Purple' ECtt MBNS
§ 'Windsor Red' CTri ECtt EPfP LRHS MBNS SLon SRms SWvt WCot
'Woodpecker' ECtt MAvo MBNS SRms

Pentaglottis (*Boraginaceae*)

§ ***sempervirens*** CArn EPfP WSFF

Pentapanax see *Aralia*

Pentapterygium see *Agapetes*

Pentas (*Rubiaceae*)

lanceolata CCCN EShb

Penthorum (*Saxifragaceae*)

sedoides LLWG

pepino see *Solanum muricatum*

peppermint see *Mentha* × *piperita*

Pericallis (*Asteraceae*)

aurita CRHN
× ***hybrida*** Senetti Series MGos NPer NPri SPoG
- - Senetti Blue = 'Sunsenebu'PBR SPoG
- - Senetti Blue Bicolor = 'Sunseneribuba'PBR LAst MGos SPoG
- - Senetti Magenta = 'Sunsenere'PBR SPoG
- - Senetti Magenta Bicolor = 'Sunsenereba'PBR LAst MGos SPoG
§ ***lanata*** (L'Hér.) B. Nord. CHII EShb
- Kew form CSpe
steetzii new WCot

Perilla (Lamiaceae)

§ ***frutescens*** var. ***crispa***	CSpe SHDw
- green-leaved	ELau
- var. ***japonica***	GPoy
- var. ***nankinensis***	see *P. frutescens* var. *crispa*
- var. ***purpurascens***	CArn CUse ELau WJek

Periploca (Apocynaceae)

graeca	CBcs CMac EBee EWld SLon
purpurea B&SWJ 7235	WCru
sepium	CExl

Pernettya see *Gaultheria*

mucronata	see *Gaultheria mucronata*

Perovskia (Lamiaceae)

abrotanoides	XLum
atriplicifolia	CArn CMea ELan MGil MHer MNHC NSti WHea WKif WMnd XSen
- 'Blue Shadow'	EWTr LRHS
- Lacey Blue = 'Lisslitt'PBR	EPfP MAsh MBri SCob
'Blue Haze'	GCal LRHS SMHy
'Blue Spire' ♀H5	Widely available
'Filigran'	CWld EBee ELan EPla EUJe GBin GBuc GCal LRHS LSou MGil MWhi SPoG WFar WGrn WHoo WPat XSen
'Hybrida'	GCal LRHS
'Little Spire'PBR	CBod CMac CSBt CSpe EHoe ELon EPfP EWes EWoo GMaP GQue IBoy LRHS LSun MAsh MBel NBid NDov NLar SCob SGol SPer SPoG SRkn WCot WFar WHil

Persea (Lauraceae)

americana	CCCN
indica	CCCN
- B&SWJ 12535 new	WCru
japonica B&SWJ 8410 new	WCru
- B&SWJ 12789	WCru
lingue	CBcs
thunbergii	CBcs CFil CHEx
- B&SWJ 12747 new	WCru

Persicaria (Polygonaceae)

B&SWJ 11268 from Sumatra	WCru
§ ***affinis***	CBcs CBen CSBt EAEE GAbr MWhi NBro SCob SWat WFar WMoo
- 'Darjeeling Red' ♀H5	Widely available
- 'Dimity'	see *P. affinis* 'Superba'
- 'Donald Lowndes' ♀H5	CChe CHVG CMac CTri ELan ELon EPfP EPla GBin GMaP IVic LAst LPot LRHS MCot MHer MNrw MRav MWat NPri SCob SPer SPoG SRms SWat SWvt WFar WMoo WWEG
- 'Kabouter'	GBin IPot NLar WBor
§ - 'Superba' ♀H5	Widely available
alata	see *P. nepalensis*
alpina	CDes EBee ECha EPPr GBin GCal GMaP IPot LEdu LRHS MAvo MNFA MRav NDov SDix SMad SPhx WCot WHil WMoo WWEG WWtn
amphibia	LLWG MSKA SWat XLum
§ ***amplexicaulis***	CBre CKno CPrp CRow CSpe ELan EWes GMaP MBel MCot MHer NOrc WBor WFar WMoo WRHF WWtn XLum
- 'Alba'	Widely available
- 'Anouk'	EBee
- 'Arun Gem'	see *P. amplexicaulis* var. *pendula*
- 'Atrosanguinea'	CKno CMac CRow CTri ECha ELan EPla LRHS MMuc MNFA MRav MSpe MWat NBir NLar SEND SMrm SPer SRms SWat SWvt WFar WOld WWEG XLum
- 'Betty Brandt'	GBin
- 'Blackfield'PBR	CBcs CBct CKno CMos CSpe EBee ECtt ELon EPPr EWes GBin GQue IBoy IKil IPot LRHS MAvo MBNS MSpe NDov NLar SCob STPC WCot
- 'Blush Clent'	WHoo
- 'Clent Charm'	NChi WOut WWEG
- 'Cottesbrooke Gold'	CRow ECtt MAvo
- 'Dikke Floskes'	CRow SPhx WCot
- 'Early Pink Lady'	WMoo
- 'Eastfield' (v)	WCot
- 'Fascination'	WCot
- 'Fat Domino'PBR	CKno EBee GBin GQue IPot MNrw NDov NLar WCAu
- 'Fat White' new	SPhx
- 'Firedance'	CAby CKno EHoe ELon EPPr GQue IPot MSpe NDov SMHy SMrm SPhx SWat WCot WFar
- 'Firetail'	Widely available
- 'Golden Arrow' (v)	CBct LRHS
- 'High Society'	GBin
- 'Inverleith'	CBct CBre CKno CRow EBee ECGP ECha ECtt EPPr EPla GBin GBuc GMaP GQue LBMP LRHS MAvo MBel MHer MMuc MNFA MSpe NBir SPhx WCAu WCot WMoo WOut WPGP WPnP
I - 'Jo and Guido's Form'	CHVG ELon NLar WFar
- 'JS Caliente'PBR	CHVG CKno CMea ECGP ECtt ELon GBin GQue LRHS LSun MHol MSCN NBir SCob WCot WPnP
- 'JS Delgado' new	CMos MNrw
- 'Lisan'	GBin
- Orange Field = 'Orangofield'PBR	CBct CKno EBee ECtt ELon EPPr EWoo GBin GQue LRHS MSpe NDov SCob WCAu
* - var. ***pendula***	EBee GBin GQue NBir WFar WMoo
- - HWJK 2255	WCru
- 'Pink Elephant'	CSam EPPr GBin GQue MAvo MNrw MWhi NDov NLar SCob STPC WWEG
- 'Pink Knot' new	LRHS
- 'Pink Lady'	CRow ECGP MPie
- 'Rosea'	Widely available
- 'Rowden Gem'	CRow WMoo WOut
- 'Rowden Jewel'	CRow
- 'Rowden Rose Quartz'	CRow
- 'Rubie's Pink' new	ECha
- 'Sangre'	GBin MAvo
- 'September Spires'	NDov
- 'Seven Oaks Village'	GBin SCob
- 'Summer Dance'	CKno EBee ECtt EPPr GQue LPla
- Taurus = 'Blotau'	CElw CHVG CKno CSam ECha ECtt EPPr GBin GBuc GQue IPot LRHS MBri NCGa NLar NSti SMHy WCAu WFar WHil WHoo WPGP WPnP WWEG
- 'White Eastfield' new	SPhx
§ ***bistorta***	CArn GPoy LSun MHer MMuc MWhi NBir NLar SEND SRms SWat WFar WOut

- subsp. ***carnea***	EBee ECha EHoe ELon EPPr EPla GBin LPla LRHS MBNS MMuc NBir NBro WCot WMoo
- 'Hohe Tatra'	EBee EPPr GMaP LRHS NDov WCot WFar
- 'JS Calor'PBR	GBin GQue
- 'Superba' ♀H7	Widely available
campanulata	CElw CRow ECha ECtt EHoe GAbr GMaP IFro LPot MAvo MMuc MRav MSpe MWhi NBro NEgg NOrc SEND SPer WFar WMoo WOut WWtn
- Alba Group	CElw CFis GBin MPie NBro WMoo
- var. ***lichiangense***	GBin
- 'Madame Jigard'	CRow GBin
- 'Rosenrot'	CBre CRow GBin NBir SWat WOld
- 'Southcombe White'	CRow EPla GBin WWEG
§ ***capitata***	CHVG LLWG XLum
- 'Pink Bubbles'	EHoe NBir SWvt
chinensis B&SWJ 11268	WCru
dshawachischwilii	LPla
emodi	GKev
hydropiper 'Fastigiata'	CArn
* - var. ***rubra***	CUse WJek
'Indian Summer' **new**	GCal
'Johanniswolke' **new**	GBin IPot
* ***kahil***	GBin WCot
* ***macrophylla***	EBee
microcephala	CRow EWes MHer MPie
- 'Dragons Eye'PBR **new**	WNPC
- 'Purple Fantasy'	EBee NSoo SCob SMad WMoo WNPC
- 'Red Dragon'PBR	Widely available
milletii	CAby GBuc LRHS NLar WCot WCru
§ ***mollis***	WPGP
nakaii	EBee
neofiliformis	EShb
§ ***nepalensis***	CExl CRow EPPr EShb IMou MSpe MTPN
'October Pink'	CSam
§ ***odorata***	CArn ELau ENfk EOHP GPoy MHer MNHC SHDw SRms WJek
orientalis	CSpe SMrm
polystachya	see *P. wallichii*
'Red Baron'	EPPr
§ ***runcinata***	CRow EBee MMuc NBir WMoo
- Needham's form	CRow CSpe
scoparia	see *Polygonum scoparium*
sphaerostachya Meisn.	see *P. macrophylla*
tenuicaulis	CBre EPla GBin MNFA NLar SBch WCru WMoo
§ ***tinctoria***	CHby EOHP WSFF
§ ***vacciniifolia*** ♀H5	Widely available
§ ***virginiana***	CRow EPPr EPla GCal LEdu LSun WMoo
- 'Alba'	EPPr
- 'Brushstrokes'	MBel
- var. ***filiformis***	CHEx CSam CSpe ELan LBMP LPla MMoz MPie SBrt SRkn SWvt WAul WCot WHil
- - 'Ballet'	WCot
- - 'Batwings'	ESwi LRHS SGSe SPtp
- - 'Compton's Red'	CHEx CRow ECha ECtt EShb EUJe GCal LPla LRHS MMoz SBrt WAul WCot
- - 'Lance Corporal'	CMac CRow EHoe EPPr EShb EUJe GBin LPot MMoz NLar SMrm SPhx
- - 'Moorland Moss'	WMoo
- Variegated Group (v)	CRow ECha EShb EUJe MBNS WCot WMoo
- - 'Painter's Palette' (v)	CBod CHEx CMac CNor CRow CUse ECha ECtt EHoe ELan EPPr EShb EUJe GBuc MHol MRav NBid NSti SGSe SMad SPer SWvt WAul WCot WCru WMoo XLum
vivipara	MMHG
§ ***wallichii***	CSpe MMuc SDix SWat WCot WMoo WPtf WWEG WWtn XLum
§ ***weyrichii***	EPPr GCal NBir NBro NLar WFar WMoo XLum

persimmon see *Diospyros virginiana*

persimmon, Japanese see *Diospyros kaki*

Petalostemon see *Dalea*

Petamenes see *Gladiolus*

Petasites (*Asteraceae*)

albus	GPoy MHer NLar NSti
fragrans	LLWG SWat WHer XLum
§ ***frigidus*** var. ***palmatus***	NLar
- - JLS 86317CLOR	SMad
- - 'Golden Palms'	CHid EUJe LPla WBor
hybridus	EBee LEdu MSKA SWat
- 'Variegatus' (v)	XLum
japonicus	CBcs GPoy
- var. ***giganteus***	CArn CHEx CHid CMac CRow ECha EPfP EUJe LEdu MBel SGSe SWat WCru
§ - - 'Nishiki-buki' (v)	CHEx CMac CRow EBee ECha EPPr EPla EUJe EWld GQue LEdu MBel MHer MSKA NBir NSti SGSe SMad WBor WFar WWEG XLum
- - 'Variegatus'	see *P. japonicus* var. *giganteus* 'Nishiki-buki'
- f. ***purpureus***	EBee EPPr MMoz SGSe
palmatus	see *P. frigidus* var. *palmatus*
paradoxus	CDes CLAP EWld LEdu LPot MBel WCot WFar

Petrea (*Verbenaceae*)

volubilis	CCCN

Petrocallis (*Brassicaceae*)

lagascae	see *P. pyrenaica*
§ ***pyrenaica***	WAbe
- white-flowered	WAbe

Petrocoptis (*Caryophyllaceae*)

pyrenaica	SRms
§ - subsp. ***glaucifolia***	GKev

Petrocosmea (*Gesneriaceae*)

begoniifolia	WAbe
§ ***cryptica***	CTal WDib WThu
formosa 'Crûg's Capricious'	WCru
forrestii	CTal WAbe WDib
grandiflora	WAbe WDib
- 'Crème de Crûg'	CDes WCru
iodioides	WDib
kerrii	WCot
martini **new**	CTal
minor	CPBP WAbe WDib
rosettifolia misapplied	see *P. cryptica*

sericea	WAbe

Petrophytum (*Rosaceae*)

caespitosum	WAbe
§ ***hendersonii***	WAbe WThu

Petrorhagia (*Caryophyllaceae*)

illyrica PAB 4871	LEdu
'Pink Starlets'	EPfP
saxifraga ♀H4	CSpe ECho SRms WMoo XLum

Petroselinum (*Apiaceae*)

§ ***crispum***	CArn ENfk GPoy LPot MNHC SIde SPoG SRms WJek
- 'Bravour' ♀H4	ELau MHer
- 'Champion Moss Curled'	SVic
- 'Darki'	ELau NPri
- French	CArn ELau ENfk MHer MNHC NPri SPoG SRms WJek
- 'Italian'	see *P. crispum* var. *neapolitanum* plain-leaved
- 'Moss Curled' ♀H4	SRms
§ - var. ***neapolitanum*** plain-leaved	ELau ENfk SIde SPoG SRms SVic
§ - var. ***tuberosum***	MHer MNHC SIde SRms SVic
hortense	see *P. crispum*
tuberosum	see *P. crispum* var. *tuberosum*

Petteria (*Papilionaceae*)

ramentacea	EBtc

Petunia (*Solanaceae*)

'Baby Duck Yellow' **new**	NPri
'Back to Black' **new**	LAst
Black Velvet = 'Balpevac'	LAst NPri
Candyfloss = 'Kercan'PBR) (Tumbelina Series) (d	LSou NPri
(Cascadias Series) Cascadias Bicolor Pastel = 'Dancasbipas'	NPri
- Cascadias Rim Violet	LAst NPri
Cherry Ripple = 'Kerripcherry'PBR (Tumbelina Series) (d)	LSou
Conchita Doble Lavender = 'Condost177'PBR (Conchita Doble Series) (d)	LAst
(Corona Series) 'Corona Amethyst'	NPri
- 'Corona Rose Rim'	NPri
Daddy Series	CWCL
(Easy Wave Series) Easy Wave Blue = 'Pas320593' **new**	NPri
- Easy Wave Burgundy Star = 'Pas760702' **new**	NPri
- Easy Wave Coral Reef = 'Pas481972' **new**	NPri
- Easy Wave Neon Rose = 'Pas760700' **new**	NPri
- Easy Wave Pink = 'Pas3189' **new**	NPri
- Easy Wave Plum Vein = 'Pas739163' **new**	NPri
- Easy Wave Red **new**	NPri
- Easy Wave White = 'Pas760712' **new**	NPri
(Fanfare Series) 'Fanfare Crème de Cassis'	NPri
- 'Fanfare Hot Rose'	NPri
- 'Fanfare Yellow'	NPri
'Happy Copper'	LAst
Inga (Tumbelina Series) (d)	LSou
Joanna (Tumbelina Series)	LAst LSou
Katrina = 'Kerkat'PBR (Tumbelina Series) (d)	LAst
Littletunia Bicolour Illusion (Littletunia Series)	LAst
'Marvel Beauty Blueberry' (Marvel Beauty Series) **new**	LAst
Melissa = 'Kermelis'PBR (Tumbelina Series) (d)	LAst LSou
multiflora (Frenzy Series) 'Frenzy Blue Star'	NPri
- - 'Frenzy Mid Blue'	NPri
- - 'Frenzy Rose Vein'	NPri
patagonica	ECho WAbe
Phantom = 'Balpephan'	NPri
'Pink Star' (Designer Series)	LAst
(Potunia Series) Potunia Blackberry Ice	LAst
- 'Potunia Papaya'	LAst
Priscilla = 'Kerpril'PBR (Tumbelina Series) (d)	LAst LSou NPri
'Purple Flash' (Designer Series) **new**	NPri
'Rosy Wave'PBR **new**	NPri
(Sophistica Series) Sophistica Blackberry = 'Pas933539' **new**	NPri
- Sophistica Lime Green = 'Pas933349' **new**	NPri
'Stardust' (Designer Series)	LAst
Supercascade Series	CWCL
Supertunia Pretty Much Picasso = 'Bhtun31501'PBR (Supertunia Series)	NPri
(Surfinia Series) Surfinia Blue = 'Sunblu'	LAst LSou NPri
- Surfinia Blue Picotee	LSou
- Surfinia Blue Vein = 'Sunsolos'PBR	LAst
- Surfinia Burgundy = 'Keiburtel'PBR	LAst
- Surfinia Double Blue Star = 'Sunsurfelevi'PBR (d)	LAst
- Surfinia Double Red = 'Keidoreral'PBR (d)	LAst
- Surfinia Hot Pink 06 = 'Sunrovein'PBR	LAst
- Surfinia Hot Pink = 'Marrose'PBR	LSou
- Surfinia Hot Red = 'Sunhore'PBR	NPri
- Surfinia Impulz Yellow = 'Sunpatiki'PBR	LAst NPri
- Surfinia Lime = 'Keiyeul'PBR	LAst
- Surfinia Pink Ice = 'Hakice'PBR (v)	LAst NPri
- Surfinia Purple = 'Shihi Brilliant'	LAst LSou NPri
- Surfinia Red = 'Keirekul'PBR	LAst

- Surfinia Rose Vein = 'Sunrove'PBR	LAst
- Surfinia Sky Blue = 'Keilavbu'PBR	LAst NPri
- Surfinia Sweet Pink = 'Sunsurfmomo'PBR	LSou
- Surfinia Vanilla = 'Sunvanilla'PBR	LSou
- Surfinia Variegated Mini Purple (v) new	LAst
- Surfinia White = 'Kesupite'	LAst
Susanna (Tumbelina Series)	LAst
Sweetunia Mystery (Sweetunia Series)	LAst
Victoria = 'Kervic'PBR (Tumbelina Series)	LAst LSou

Peucedanum (*Apiaceae*)

* ***aromaticum***	IMou
officinale	CBod CSpe GBin LRHS SPlb SPtp
ostruthium	GPoy LEdu WPtf
- 'Daphnis' (v)	CSpe EBee ETwe LEdu LPla MAvo MMoz MNrw NChi NEoE NLar WCFE WCot WHrl WWFP XLum
verticillare	CArn CSam CSpe EBee GAbr IMou ITim LRHS MBel MNFA SDix SKHP SMrm SPhx WSHC WWEG

Peumus (*Monimiaceae*)

boldus	CBcs

Phacelia (*Boraginaceae*)

tanacetifolia	SPhx

Phaedranassa (*Amaryllidaceae*)

BKBlount 2623	WCot
carmiolii	WCot
cinerea	ECho WCot
dubia	NRog WCot
glauciflora new	NRog
* ***montana***	ECho
tunguraguae	ECho NRog
viridiflora	ECho NRog WCot

Phaenocoma (*Asteraceae*)

prolifera	SPlb

Phaenosperma (*Poaceae*)

globosa	CSam CSpe EBee ECha EHoe EPPr EShb GQue LRHS NLos NWsh SPoG WCot WPGP WPtf XLum

Phaiophleps see *Olsynium*

nigricans	see *Sisyrinchium striatum*

Phalaris (*Poaceae*)

arundinacea	CBAq LPot MBNS MSKA SCob SPlb SVic SWat
- cream-flowered	WWEG
- 'Elegantissima'	see *P. arundinacea* var. *picta* 'Picta'
- var. ***picta***	CBen CHEx CTri MJak MSKA NBir NPer SPoG XLum XSen
- - 'Arctic Sun' (v)	CKno EBee ELon EPPr GBin LLWG SDix SPoG STPC WWEG
- - 'Aureovariegata' (v)	CBcs MRav NPer SWat WMoo XLum
- - 'Feesey' (v) ♀H7	Widely available
- - 'Luteopicta' (v)	EPPr MMuc WWEG XLum
§ - - 'Picta' (v)	ELan EPfP LBMP LRHS MJak MMuc SEND SPer SWat WMoo
- - 'Streamlined' (v)	EPPr EPla LLWG NWsh
- - 'Tricolor' (v)	EHoe EPla

Phanerophlebia (*Dryopteridaceae*)

caryotidea	see *Cyrtomium caryotideum*
falcata	see *Cyrtomium falcatum*
fortunei	see *Cyrtomium fortunei*

Pharbitis see *Ipomoea*

Phaseolus (*Papilionaceae*)

caracalla	see *Vigna caracalla*

Phedimus see *Sedum*

Phegopteris (*Thelypteridaceae*)

§ ***connectilis***	EFer EFtx NHar
decursive-pinnata	CBty CDes CLAP EFtx LPal LRHS SEND WFib WPnP

Phellodendron (*Rutaceae*)

amurense	CBcs CCCN CDul CLnd CMCN EBee ELan EPfP EWTr GBin IDee IVic LEdu MBri SEND WBor WPGP
- B&SWJ 11000	WCru
- var. ***sachalinense***	LEdu
japonicum B&SWJ 11175	WCru

Phenakospermum (*Strelitziaceae*)

guianense	XBlo

Pherosphaera (*Podocarpaceae*)

fitzgeraldii	CKen WThu

Philadelphus ✿ (*Hydrangeaceae*)

SDR 2823	CExl
SDR 4946	CExl GKev
SDR 5111	GKev
'Atlas' (v)	NLar
'Avalanche'	CExl NLar SPer SRms
'Beauclerk' ♀H6	CBod CDoC CDul COtt CTri EBee ECrN EPfP EWTr GGal GQui IVic LRHS MBri MGos MMuc MRav NBro NWea SCob SKHP SLim SPer SRms SWvt WHar WPat
'Belle Etoile' ♀H6	Widely available
'Bialy Karzel' new	NLar
'Bicolore'	WHar
'Boule d'Argent' (d)	WHar
'Bouquet Blanc'	MRav NLar SRms WCFE WPat
brachybotrys	MRav
'Buckley's Quill' (d)	EBee ECrN EPfP EWes LRHS MRav SGol SWvt WGrn
'Burfordensis'	CWSG LAst MRav SEND
calcicola	CFil
§ ***calvescens***	MRav
aff. ***calvescens*** BWJ 8005	WCru
caucasicus	CFil
coronarius	CBcs CBod CDul EPfP LBuc MLHP MRav NWea SEND
- 'Aureus' ♀H6	Widely available
- 'Bowles's Variety'	see *P. coronarius* 'Variegatus'
§ - 'Variegatus' (v) ♀H6	CMHG ELan EPfP EWTr LAst LBMP LRHS MGos MMuc MRav MSwo NBir NLar NSoo SLim SMad SPer

	SPoG SRms WCFE WCot WFar WKif WMoo WPat WSHC
coulteri	WPGP
'Coupe d'Argent'	MRav
'Dainty Lady'	LBuc LRHS SLon
'Dame Blanche' (d)	EPfP EWTr LSou MRav NLar WBor
delavayi	CFil EPfP GBin GGal NLar SKHP WPGP
- var. ***calvescens***	see *P. calvescens*
- f. ***melanocalyx***	EPfP GCra MRav SChF WPGP WPat
- - B&L 12168	CFil WPGP
- 'Nymans' ♀H6	CExl CFil SKHP WKif WPGP
'Enchantement' (d)	MRav SDix
'Erectus'	CSBt EBee ELon EPfP EWTr LRHS MRav NLar SKHP SLim SPer SPoG WPat
'Etoile Rose'	WMoo
'Falconeri'	MRav
'Frosty Morn' (d)	CBcs CBod EPfP EWTr LRHS MBlu MMuc MRav NBro NLar SEND SPer
incanus B&SWJ 8616	WCru
§ 'Innocence' (v) ♀H6	CExl CMac EHoe ELan EPfP LAst LRHS MAsh MGos MMuc MRav MSwo NEoE SEND SGol SKHP SLim SPad SPer SPoG SRms WFar WPat WSHC
'Innocence Variegatus'	see *P.* 'Innocence'
§ ***insignis***	MRav
karwinskianus	CFil
- F&M 152 **new**	WPGP
× ***lemoinei***	CBcs CBod CDul CTri MGos MWat NSoo SCob SGol WGrn WHar
I - 'Lemoinei'	NWea
'Lemon Hill'	NLar
lewisii	CExl
- L 1896	CExl
'Limestone'	MRav
maculatus	CFil WPat
- 'Mexican Jewel'	CExl CFil CHel EBee ELon NLar SKHP WKif WPGP WPat WSHC
- 'Scented Storm'	CMHG CSam
- 'Sweet Clare' ♀H5	LRHS MBri SHil
maculatus × ***mexicanus*** **new**	CFil
madrensis	MRav
- F&M 326	CFil WPGP
'Manteau d'Hermine' (d) ♀H6	Widely available
'Marjorie'	NLar
mexicanus	CFil GCal
- B&SWJ 10253	WCru
- 'Rose Syringa'	CExl CFil SKHP WPGP
mexicanus × ***palmeri***	WPGP
microphyllus	CDul CMCN CTri EBee ELan ELon EPfP EWTr LAst LRHS MAsh MGos MRav MWhi SKHP SLon SPer SPhx SPoG SSpi WFar WKif WPGP WPat WSHC
- var. ***occidentalis***	NLar
'Miniature Snowflake' (d)	MAsh WPat
'Minnesota Snowflake' (d)	CBcs EPfP EWes LRHS LSqu MMuc MRav NEoE NLar SGol WFar
'Mont Blanc'	CBcs GKin MRav NLar
'Mrs E.L. Robinson' (d)	CMac ELon EPfP LAst LLHF LRHS MAsh MBri MGos NEgg SHil WBor WCFE
myrtoides B&SWJ 10436	WCru
'Natchez' (d)	CMac EAEE ELon EWTr LEdu LLHF NLar WHar
'Oeil de Pourpre'	MRav
palmeri	CFil WPGP WPat
pekinensis	CExl NLar
'Perryhill'	MRav
'Polar Star'	ELon GBin NLar WKif
purpurascens	CExl CJun EBee EPfP EWes GBin GQui LLHF MRav NLar SChF SKHP WPGP WPat
- BWJ 7540	WCru
× ***purpureomaculatus***	ELon LLHF MAsh MRav WPat
sargentianus	CFil
satsumi B&SWJ 10811	WCru
- B&SWJ 11004	WCru
schrenkii	CFil NLar
- B&SWJ 8465	WCru
sericanthus **new**	NLar
§ 'Silberregen' ♀H6	CBod CDul CMac CSam EBee ECrN ELon EPfP EWTr LRHS MAsh MGos MMuc MRav NEoE NLar SGol SPoG SRms SWvt WGrn WPat
Silver Showers	see *P.* 'Silberregen'
'Snow Velvet'	EPfP LLHF LRHS
'Snowbelle' (d)	EPfP LBMP LRHS MAsh MBri MWat NBro NLar SKHP SWvt
'Snowflake'	COtt WMoo
'Snowgoose'	LRHS
'Souvenir de Billiard'	see *P. insignis*
'Starbright'	EMil LRHS MAsh
subcanus	CExl
- L 524	CExl CFil WPGP
'Sybille' ♀H6	CDul CMac CWld ECrN EPfP LRHS MAsh MRav MSwo SDix SKHP SPer SRms SSpi WKif WPat WSHC
tomentosus	CExl
- AC 3678	MSnd
- B&SWJ 2707	WCru
- GWJ 9215	WCru
'Virginal' (d)	Widely available
'Voie Lactée'	EWTr MRav NLar
White Icicle = 'Bialy Sopel'	CCCN
White Rock = 'Pekphil' ♀H6	CMac EBee EPfP IVic LLHF LRHS MRav NLar SKHP SLim SPer
'Yellow Hill'	CMac EPfP LRHS NLar SKHP

Philesia (*Philesiaceae*)

buxifolia	see *P. magellanica*
§ ***magellanica***	CExl CFil GGGa IBlr ITim MGil SSpi WAbe WCru WSHC
- 'Rosea'	EPfP IBlr SSpi

Phillyrea (*Oleaceae*)

angustifolia	CBcs CDul CFil CMCN EBee ELan EPfP EUJe IVic LRHS MBri MGos MRav NLar SBig SEND SPer SSpi WPGP WSHC XSen
- f. ***rosmarinifolia***	CCCN CExl ELan EPfP EPla NLar
- - 'French Fries'	WPGP
decora	see *Osmanthus decorus*
§ ***latifolia***	CBcs CDul CFil CTsd EBee ELan EPfP EShb EUJe LRHS NLar SArc SEND SSpi WPGP XSen
media	see *P. latifolia*

Philodendron (*Araceae*)

'Angra dos Reis'	see *P. cordatum*
§ ***angustisectum*** ♀H1b	XBlo
bipinnatifidum ♀H1c	SEND XBlo
corcovadense	XBlo

§	***cordatum***	XBlo
	elegans	see *P. angustisectum*
	erubescens 'Red Emerald'	XBlo
*	***radiatum***	XBlo
	var. ***pseudoradiatum*** 'Simmonds'	
*	***rubrum***	XBlo
	scandens 'Green Emerald'	XBlo
	- 'Mica'	XBlo
	tripartitum	XBlo
	xanadu	LPal XBlo

Phlebodium (*Polypodiaceae*)

§	***aureum*** ♀H1b	CSpe WCot
	- 'Blue Star' **new**	ISha
	- 'Mandaianum'	ISha
	pseudoaureum	ISha WCot

Phleum (*Poaceae*)

	phleoides	EHoe LRHS MMHG
	pratense	EHoe MAvo NMir WSFF

Phlomis (*Lamiaceae*)

	NJM 10.020 **new**	WPGP
*	***anatolica***	LRHS NLar XSen
I	- 'Lloyd's Variety' ♀H5	CAbP CSam ELan LRHS MAsh NLar SPer
	angustifolia	EBee LRHS XSen
	anisodonta white-flowered	XSen
	armeniaca	XSen
	atropurpurea BWJ 7922	WCru
	bourgaei	XSen
	bovei subsp. ***maroccana***	SEND WHal XLum XSen
	breviflora HWJCM 250	WCot WCru
	capitata	XSen
	cashmeriana	CCon ECha EHoe EWTr GCal GJos LAst LRHS LSou SKHP SMad SPhx WCFE WWEG
	chrysophylla ♀H4	CAbP ECha ELan EPfP LRHS MAsh MRav NLar SDix SPer WCFE XSen
	cretica	XSen
	crinita	XSen
	cypria	XSen
	× ***cytherea***	XSen
	'Edward Bowles'	CHel EBee ECha EPfP EWTr LRHS MRav NLar SEND SIgm SKHP SWvt XSen
*	'Elliot's Variety'	CExl
	fruticosa ♀H4	Widely available
	grandiflora	SEND XSen
	- NJM 10.014 **new**	WPGP
	herba-venti	XSen
	italica	Widely available
	- 'Pink Glory'	CMac
	lanata	CAbP CSde ELan EPfP LAst LRHS SBrt SCob SPer WCFE WSHC XSen
	- 'Pygmy'	CHVG XSen
	'Le Sud'	XSen
	leucophracta	SVen
	longifolia	CHel EBee EPfP LRHS MNrw NLar SBrt SEND SKHP SPer WGrn WPGP XSen
	- var. ***bailanica*** ♀H4	CSam EPfP LRHS XLum
	lunariifolia	XSen
	lychnitis	XSen
	lycia	XSen
	- NJM 10.015 **new**	WPGP
	- NJM 10.016 **new**	WPGP
	macrophylla	SPhx
	× ***margaritae***	XSen
	monocephala	XSen
	nissolei	XSen
	platystegia	XSen
	purpurea	CAbP CArn CExl ELan EPfP LRHS MAsh NBir SEND WCot WGrn XSen
I	- 'Alba'	EBee EPfP GMaP LRHS SKHP XSen
	- subsp. ***almeriensis***	CPom XSen
	- subsp. ***caballeroi***	XSen
§	***russeliana*** ♀H7	Widely available
	- 'Dappled Shade' (v)	WCot
	- 'Mosaic' (v)	XSen
	samia Boiss.	see *P. russeliana*
	samia L.	CKno CMac CSpe EWoo LBMP LRHS LSun NBir NGdn NLar NPCo SEND SKHP WOut WPtf XSen
	sieheana	XSen
	taurica	EPfP LSun SEND SPhx
	× ***termessi***	XSen
	tuberosa	CArn CBcs CBod CCon CKno CMac CPou EHoe EPfP EWTr LEdu LRHS MMuc NGdn NLar NPCo SDix SGSe SPhx WCAu WCFE WPtf XLum XSen
	- 'Amazone' ♀H5	CBod CKno CMos ECha EPfP GBin MBel MRav NBid NDov NOrc NPCo NSti SCob SMad SMrm WFar WMnd WSHC XSen
	- 'Bronze Flamingo'	CKno EPfP GJos GMaP LAst LBMP LRHS MNrw MPnt MRav MSCN NOrc SKHP SPoG WMnd WWEG
	viscosa misapplied	see *P. russeliana*

Phlox ✿ (*Polemoniaceae*)

	adsurgens ♀H5	WAbe
	- 'Alba'	WAbe
	- 'Red Buttes'	ECho
	- 'Wagon Wheel'	ECho ECtt EPot EWes GBuc GCrg LBMP LRHS NHar SPlb SRms SRot WAbe WIce
	'Amazone'	CBod
	amplifolia	MSpe XLum
	× ***arendsii*** 'Andrew'	WCot
	- 'Autumn's Pink Explosion'	WCot
	- 'Babyface'	ELon NGdn
	- 'Casablanca'	EBee NDov
	- 'Dylan'	WCot
	- 'Eyecatcher'	NBro
	- 'Gary'	WCot
	- 'Hesperis'	CSam EBee ECha ELon GBin GQue IPot LRHS MAvo MSpe MTis NDov NLar SMrm SPhx WHil
	- 'Luc's Lilac'	ECtt EPPr GBin LLHF LRHS MCot MSpe NBro NDov NEgg NGdn NSti SGbt SMrm SPhx WAul WCAu WCot
§	- 'Miss Jill' (Spring Pearl Series)	EBee ELan EPfP IPot WCot
§	- 'Miss Karen' (Spring Pearl Series)	ELan NBro
§	- 'Miss Margie' (Spring Pearl Series)	LEdu
§	- 'Miss Mary' (Spring Pearl Series)	ECtt ELan EPfP MSpe
§	- 'Miss Wilma' (Spring Pearl Series)	EBee ELan EPfP
	- 'Paul'	WCot
	- 'Ping Pong'	SGbt

	Name	Suppliers
	- 'Pink Attraction'	MNrw NBro
	- 'Sweet William'	MSpe
	- 'Utopia'	CDes CSam EBee ELon IMou IPot LPla NLar SPhx WCot
	'Aureole'PBR (Neon Series)	EBee MSCN
	austromontana	CTal EPot GKev NWad
	bifida	ECho
	- 'Alba'	ECho LLHF MWat
	- blue-flowered	ECho
	- 'Colvin's White'	ECho
	- 'Frohnleiten'	NHar
	- 'Minima Colvin'	ECho EPot
	- 'Ralph Haywood'	CPBP CWCL ECtt EPot WAbe
	- 'Thefi'	MNrw WIce
	borealis	see *P. sibirica* subsp. *borealis*
*	- ***arctica***	EPot
	bryoides	see *P. hoodii* subsp. *muscoides*
	caespitosa	CMea ECho EWes
	- subsp. ***pulvinata***	see *P. pulvinata*
	- 'Zigeunerblut'	CMea CPBP CTal ECho EPot GCrg ITim NHar NWad WAbe WHal
	canadensis	see *P. divaricata*
	carolina 'Bill Baker' ♀H5	CSam ECha ECtt ELon EPPr EPfP GMaP LRHS MAsh MNrw NBir NCGa NGdn NLar NSti SGSe WCFE WKif WPtf WSHC WWEG XLum
	- 'Magnificence'	EBee EWes NLar SMad SPhx WCot WSHC
	- 'Miss Lingard' ♀H5	CBod CSam EAEE ECtt ELon EPla LRHS LSou MCot MRav NBir NGdn NLar NSti SMrm WCot WWEG
	'Charles Ricardo'	CSam WHoo
	'Chattahoochee'	see *P. divaricata* subsp. *laphamii* 'Chattahoochee'
	'Daniel's Cushion'	see *P. subulata* 'McDaniel's Cushion'
	diffusa	EPot
§	***divaricata*** ♀H4	SPlb WCot
	- 'Blue Dreams'	CCon ECtt MNrw WFar
	- 'Blue Perfume'	EBee ECtt NBro NGdn NLar
	- 'Charles'	XLum
	- 'Clouds of Perfume'	CAby CBod CWCL EAEE ECtt EPfP EPla GBuc GEdr GMaP LRHS LSou LSun MAsh MSCN MSpe NDov NEgg NLar SBod SGbt SMrm SPoG SWvt WAul WFar WGwG WWEG
	- 'Dirigo Ice'	ECho LRHS
	- 'Eco Texas Purple'	MSCN NCGa WSHC
	- 'Fuller's White'	CWCL
	- subsp. ***laphamii***	EBee EWes
§	- - 'Chattahoochee' ♀H4	CBcs CBod CSpe CWCL EAEE ECho ECtt ELan ELon EPfP EWes GBin GBuc LBMP LPot LRHS LSun MAsh MCot MNrw NLar SMrm SPoG SRkn SRot SWvt WAbe WCFE WHoo
	- 'May Breeze'	ECho ECtt GCra GMaP LRHS MNrw MSCN SHar WSHC WWEG
	- 'Plum Perfect'	CMos ECtt
	- 'White Perfume'	CWCL EBee EWes LRHS LSou NBro NLar SHar SPoG WFar WWEG XLum
	douglasii	SRms
	- 'Alba'	GJos LSun
	- 'Apollo'	CTri ECho ECtt
	- 'Blue Mist'	EPot
	- 'Boothman's Variety' ♀H5	ECha ECho ECtt ELan EPot GCrg ITim MLHP MWat SRms
	- 'Crackerjack' ♀H5	CMea CTri ECho ECtt EDAr ELan ELon EPot GAbr GCrg GJos GMaP ITim LRHS MAsh MHer MLHP MWat NBir NEgg NHol NSla SPoG WIce
	- 'Eva'	ECho ECtt EDAr ELon EPot GCrg GMaP ITim LRHS MAsh MSCN NBir NLar NPri NSla NWad
	- 'Georg Arends'	ECtt EPot GCrg GJos
	- 'Ice Mountain'	CMea CTal CUse ECho ECtt ELan EPot NEgg NHol NSla NWad SPoG SRot
	- 'Iceberg' ♀H5	ECho GJos
	- 'J.A. Hibberson'	EPot GCrg
	- 'Lilac Cloud'	CTal ECho ECtt EDAr GJos NEoE NRya
	- Lilac Queen	see *P. douglasii* 'Lilakönigin'
	- 'Lilac Wonder'	CPBP
§	- 'Lilakönigin'	CTri
	- 'Napoleon'	ECho ECtt EPot NWad
	- 'Ochsenblut'	ECho EPot GEdr LLHF LRHS MHer MLHP NHar NLar
	- 'Red Admiral' ♀H5	ECho ECtt EPfP EWes GCrg GMaP NLar NWad WCFE
	- 'Rose Cushion'	ECho EDAr EWes GCrg MHer
	- 'Rose Queen'	ECho
	- 'Rosea'	ECho EDAr ELan MMuc
	- 'Silver Rose'	ECho ECtt MWat WRHF
	- 'Sprite'	SRms
	- 'Tycoon'	see *P. subulata* 'Tamaongalei'
	- 'Violet Queen'	ECho EWes
	- 'Waterloo'	CMea ECho ECtt EPot GCrg LRHS
I	- 'White Admiral'	CTri ECho ECtt
	drummondii 'Classic Cassis'	SPoG
	- 'Grammy Pink and White' **new**	NPri
I	- 'Phlox of Sheep'	CWCL
	'Fancy Feelings' (Feelings Series)	NBro NLar
	'Flare'	see *P. paniculata* 'Neon Flare'
	glaberrima 'Morris Berd'	CDes EBee WSHC
	hendersonii	CPBP WAbe
§	***hoodii*** subsp. ***muscoides***	WAbe
	idahoensis	SPhx
	'Jeff's Pink'	MSCN
	'Junior Surprise'PBR	GBin
	'Kelly's Eye' ♀H5	CTal ECho ECtt EPot GCrg LRHS NBir NHar SPoG
	kelseyi	WAbe
	- 'Lemhi Purple'	ECho EPot WAbe
	- 'Rosette'	ECho EPot
	Light Pink Flame = 'Bareleven'PBR	ECtt EPfP NPri SPoG
	Lilac Flame = 'Barten'PBR	EPfP SPoG WHil
	longifolia subsp. ***brevifolia***	WAbe
	maculata	NOrc
	- 'Alba'	WAul
	- 'Alpha' ♀H6	CSam CWCL EBee ECha ECtt EPfP EPla EWoo GBuc GCra GMaP LRHS MSpe MWhi NLar NOrc SGbt SKHP SPer SWvt WFar WSHC XLum
	- Avalanche	see *P. maculata* 'Schneelawine'
	- 'Delta'	EBee EPPr GBuc LRHS NLar SGbt SPer SRkn SWvt WFar
	- 'Natascha'	Widely available
	- 'Omega' ♀H6	CExl CMac EAEE EBee ECtt EPla EWTr EWoo GBuc LRHS MCot MMuc MNrw MSpe NLar SGbt SKHP SPer SWvt WCAu WFar WWEG

	Name	Suppliers
	– 'Princess Sturdza' 🏆H6	SDix WCot
	– 'Reine du Jour'	CSam ELon IVic LPla NDov SPhx WSHC
	– 'Rosalinde'	ECtt ELon GAbr GBin GBuc LRHS MCot MMuc MRav NLar SWvt WSHC WWEG XLum
§	– 'Schneelawine'	LRHS SPlb
	'Matineus'	SPhx
	'Millstream'	see *P.* × *procumbens* 'Millstream'
	'Millstream Blue'	EPfP
	'Millstream Jupiter'	ECho
	'Minnie Pearl'	EWes SKHP WCot
	muscoides	see *P. hoodii* subsp. *muscoides*
	'Mystic Green'	LAst
	nivalis 'Jill Alexander'	SBch
	– 'Nivea'	GJos
	paniculata	GCra NBid NDov SDix SEND WCot
	– 'A.E. Amos'	ELon
	– 'Aida'	EBee
	– var. ***alba***	MAvo SDix WCot
	– 'Alba Grandiflora' 🏆H7	GMaP MAvo MNrw WCot WHrl
	– 'Alexandra'[PBR]	MAsh MSCN
	– 'All in One'	EBee ECtt
	– 'Amethyst' misapplied	see *P. paniculata* 'Lilac Time'
	– 'Amethyst' Foerster	CCon GQue LRHS MRav NBir NCGa NLar NOrc SWat
	– 'Anne'	CSam
	– 'Auslese D. Bach'	CSam
	– 'Balmoral'	CMac EBee ECtt GCra LRHS MLHP NEgg NSti SWat SWvt WWEG
	– 'Barnwell'	SWat
	– 'Becky Towe'[PBR] (v)	CAby ECtt LLHF LRHS MBri MHer MNrw MSpe NEgg NHol NLar
	– 'Blue Boy'	EBee ECtt ELan ELon EPfP GMaP LAst LRHS MJak NBir NBro NEgg NLar SKHP SMrm SRms SWvt WFar WMnd
	– 'Blue Evening'	MCot
	– 'Blue Ice' 🏆H7	NBro
	– 'Blue Paradise'	Widely available
	– 'Blushing Bride'	MSpe SRms
	– 'Border Gem'	CAby CBcs CMac ECtt ELon LAst LRHS MCot MRav MSpe MTis MWat NChi NLar SDix SWat SWvt WBrk WSHC WWEG
	– 'Branklyn'	GCra
	– 'Brigadier' 🏆H7	CTri EBee ECtt ELan ELon GMaP LRHS MCot MSpe MWat NEgg NGdn SMrm SPer SRms WFar
	– 'Bright Eyes' 🏆H7	Widely available
	– 'Burgi'	SDix
	– 'Candy Floss'	ELon LLHF
	– 'Cardinal'	MTis NDov
	– 'Caroline van den Berg'	SRms
	– 'Cecil Hanbury'	NLar WSHC
	– 'Charlotte'	MSpe
	– 'Chintz'	MRav SRms
	– 'Cinderella'	ECtt MTis
§	– 'Cool of the Evening'	WKif
	– 'Cool Water' **new**	LAst MAsh
	– Coral Flame = 'Barsixtytwo'[PBR] (Flame Series)	CBod CMac CMea LRHS LSou LSun MBri NLar NPri SRkn
	– 'Cosmopolitan'[PBR]	MAsh MBri MNrw NLar WFar
	– Count Zeppelin	see *P. paniculata* 'Graf Zeppelin'
	– 'Danielle'	CSBt MSCN SGol
	– 'Darwin's Choice'	see *P. paniculata* 'Norah Leigh'
	– 'David'	Widely available
	– 'David's Lavender'	ELon LRHS
	– 'Delilah'[PBR]	CWGN ECtt MAsh
	– 'Discovery'	EWes MCot MRav MSpe NEgg SHar SWat WCAu WFar
	– 'Doghouse Pink'	SDix
	– 'Dresden China'	MTis SWat
	– 'Duchess of York'	MAvo
§	– 'Düsterlohe'	CSBt CSam EBee ECtt GBin GBuc GQue MRav MTis NBir NLar NSoo SGol SMrm SPer SWat WCot WHil WHoo XLum
	– 'Early Light Pink'	IPot
	– 'Eclaireur' misapplied	see *P. paniculata* 'Düsterlohe'
	– 'Eclaireur' Lemoine	SWat
	– 'Eden's Flash'	CElw ECtt LRHS MSpe
	– 'Eden's Glory'	MAvo
	– 'Eden's Glow'	WHil
	– 'Eden's Smile'	ECtt MSpe
	– 'Elisabeth' (v)	EPfP NWad WHil
	– 'Elizabeth Arden'	ECtt MSpe MTis NLar SWat
	– 'Elizabeth Campbell'	GCal
	– 'Empty Feelings' (Feelings Series)	NBro
	– 'Etoile de Paris'	see *P. paniculata* 'Toits de Paris' Symons-Jeune
	– 'Europa'	EBee ECtt ELan MCot NBir NGdn NLar SPer
	– 'Eva Cullum'	CSam EBee ECtt ELan ELon EPfP EPla GCra GMaP LRHS MArl MBri MCot MSpe NLar SPer SWat WCAu WCot
	– 'Eva Foerster'	XLum
	– 'Eventide' 🏆H7	CMac CSam ECtt EPfP GQue LRHS MArl MCot MNrw MRav MSpe MWat SBod SPer SWat WFar WHrl WPtf
	– 'Ferris Wheel'	EBee ECtt MBri SRot
	– 'Flamingo'	EBee ECtt LRHS NLar SWvt XLum
	– 'Fondant Fancy'[PBR]	MBri NLar SPoG WFar
	– 'Franz Schubert'	CSam ECtt ELan EPfP EWTr EWoo GBin GCra LRHS MAvo MBel MBri MCot MLHP MSpe MWat NBir NChi NGdn NLar NSti SPer SWat SWvt WCot WFar WKif
§	– 'Frau Alfred von Mauthner'	GKev SMrm
	– 'Frosted Elegance' (v)	EBee WWEG
	– 'Fujiyama'	see *P. paniculata* 'Mount Fuji'
	– 'Giltmine' (v)	EBee
	– 'Goldmine'[PBR] (v)	ECtt LRHS MNrw
§	– 'Graf Zeppelin'	ECtt ELan MTis NHol SRms XLum
	– 'Grenadine Dream'[PBR]	EBee LAst LRHS MBri SPoG
	– 'Grey Lady' **new**	MNrw
	– 'Harlequin' (v)	CMac CWGN ECha ECtt ELon GMaP LRHS MAvo MHol NBro NEgg NLar NPCo NSti SGSe SPer SPoG WCot WWEG
	– 'Ice Cream' **new**	MAsh WHlf
	– 'Irene Mast'	CSam
	– 'Iris'	MNrw SRms WCot
	– 'Jade'	CAby EBee ECtt ELon EWoo GBin GQue LBMP LRHS MAvo MBri MCot MHol MNrw NLar NPCo NPri NSti WCot WPtf XLum
	– 'Jeff's Blue' **new**	EBee LAst MAsh
	– 'Judy'	GBin NBro NLar
§	– 'Juliglut'	SWat WCot
	– July Glow	see *P. paniculata* 'Juliglut'
	– 'Junior Bouquet'	NLar

- 'Junior Dance' NSoo
- 'Junior Dream' LRHS NLar SPad
- 'Junior Fountain' NLar
- 'Katarina' CElw ECtt NLar
- 'Katherine' IPot LRHS MSpe NLar
- 'Kirchenfürst' CElw IPot LRHS MSpe MTis NBir SHil SMrm XLum
- 'Kirmesländler' ECtt GBin IPot LPla NLar SWat
- 'Lads Pink' SDix
- 'Lady Clare' SRms
- 'Landhochzeit' EBee
- 'Laura' CBod ECtt ELon EPfP GBin IPot LRHS MAvo MTis NBro NPri SGSe SGol SMrm SRkn SRms SWvt WBor WHoo WMnd WSHC XLum

§ - 'Lavendelwolke' CSam GCal LRHS NBir NLar SWat WCot
- Lavender Cloud see *P. paniculata* 'Lavendelwolke'
- 'Le Mahdi' ♀H7 SRms SWat
- 'Lichtspel' LPla NDov SPhx

§ - 'Lilac Time' CBod CElw EBee ECtt ELon EPfP EWTr GKev LRHS MMuc NLar NSoo SHil SWat SWvt
- 'Little Boy' CElw ECtt ELon MNrw NLar NSoo SGbt WHil
- 'Little Laura' CElw ECtt EWTr LRHS MSpe NLar NOrc NPri NWad SDix SPoG WCot
- 'Little Princess' ELon LLHF NLar SMrm WMnd
- 'Little Sara' NDov
- 'Lizzy'[PBR] NLar
- 'Logan Black' EBee GCal SHar
- 'Magic Blue' SPoG
- 'Manoir d'Hézèques' WCot
- 'Mary Christine' (v) CDes EPla NBid
- 'Maude Stella Dagley' MSpe
- 'Mia Ruys' MArl MLHP
- 'Midnight Feelings' (Feelings Series) NBro
- 'Milly van Hoboken' WKif
- 'Miss Elie' SGSe
- 'Miss Holland' NGdn SGbt WWEG XLum
- 'Miss Jill' see *P.* × *arendsii* 'Miss Jill'
- 'Miss Karen' see *P.* × *arendsii* 'Miss Karen'
- 'Miss Kelly' LRHS MSpe NLar WHoo
- 'Miss Margie' see *P.* × *arendsii* 'Miss Margie'
- 'Miss Mary' see *P.* × *arendsii* 'Miss Mary'
- 'Miss Pepper' CWCL ECtt ELon EWoo LSou MMuc MSpe NGdn NLar SEND SGol SMrm SRkn WBor WHil
- 'Miss Universe' SGSe WWEG
- 'Miss Wilma' see *P.* × *arendsii* 'Miss Wilma'
- 'Monica Lynden-Bell' CAby CDes CWGN ELon EWTr EWoo GBin GMaP LBMP LRHS MBel MHol MMuc MNrw MPie MRav MSpe NChi NLar NSti SGbt SKHP SPoG WAul WCot WHoo WKif WPtf WSHC
- 'Monte Cristallo' MSpe
- 'Mother of Pearl' ♀H7 EPla GQue IPot LRHS MSpe MWat NEgg SPer

§ - 'Mount Fuji' ♀H7 Widely available
- 'Mount Fujiyama' see *P. paniculata* 'Mount Fuji'
- 'Mrs A.E. Jeans' SRms
- 'Mystique Black' EBee ECtt LSou WPtf
- 'Natural Feelings'[PBR] (Feelings Series) NBro NLar

§ - 'Neon Flare' (Neon Series) **new** CWGN ECtt
- 'Newbird' ECtt EPfP IBoy LRHS MSpe SRms
- 'Nicky' see *P. paniculata* 'Düsterlohe'
- 'Nirvana' CSam

§ - 'Norah Leigh' (v) Widely available
- 'Orange Perfection' see *P. paniculata* 'Prince of Orange'
- 'Othello' CAby CSam ECGP ECtt ELon LRHS MSpe NSti WMnd
- 'Otley Choice' CSam EBee ECtt EPla LRHS MRav MWat NLar NSti SDix SWat WHrl
- 'Otley Purple' MHer
- 'P.D. Williams' WCot
- 'Pastorale' WCot
- (Peacock Series) Peacock Cherry Red **new** WCFE
- - Peacock Lilac EPfP LRHS
- - Peacock Neon Purple **new** LRHS
- - Peacock Purple Bicolor **new** LRHS
- - Peacock White **new** LRHS
- 'Peppermint Twist' CWCL CWGN EBee ELon LRHS LSou LSun MAsh MBri MHol MMuc MNrw NEgg NLar SPad SPoG SWvt WCot WFar WHil
- 'Picasso' EBee ECtt
- 'Pina Colada'[PBR] CWGN ECtt LSun MAsh NLar SPoG WFar WHil
- Pink Eye Flame = 'Barthirtyfive'[PBR] EPfP LBMP LSou NPri SCob SHar SKHP SPoG SRkn WHil
- 'Pink Lady'[PBR] EBee ELon LAst MSCN WFar
- 'Pink Posie' (v) WCot
- Pink Red Eye Flame = 'Barthirtyfour'[PBR] EPfP LSou NPri SPoG
- 'Pinky Hill' CElw CSBt EBee
- 'Pleasant Feelings'[PBR] (Feelings Series) NBro
- 'Popeye' LPla WCot
- 'Prime Minister' ELon

§ - 'Prince of Orange' ♀H7 CSam EBee ECtt ELon EPfP EPla EWTr IBoy LAst LRHS MCot MJak MRav MSpe NEgg NHol NLar NWad SGbt SGol SHil SPer SWvt WBor WMnd XLum
- 'Prospero' ♀H7 CSam CSpe MRav NBid SWat
- Purple Eye Flame = 'Barthirtythree'[PBR] LLHF LRHS LSou MBri NLar NPri SHar SKHP SRkn SWvt WFar WHil
- 'Purple Kiss'[PBR] CWGN ECtt LSou WFar WHil
- 'Rainbow' ELon NLar
- 'Red Caribbean' ECtt
- 'Red Feelings' (Feelings Series) NBro
- 'Red Flame' CWGN CWld EBee ECtt EPfP GBin LRHS LSou MHol MNrw NLar SKHP SRkn WFar WHil
- 'Red Riding Hood' ECtt EWTr IBoy LAst LRHS MBri MSCN SRkn WRHF

I - 'Reddish Hesperis' MAvo
- 'Rembrandt' CExl ELon EPfP EWoo LRHS XLum
- 'Rijnstroom' CBcs ECha ECtt ELon LRHS MArl MSpe NLar SCob SMrm SRot WBrk
- 'Robert Poore' ELon
- 'Rosa Goliath' CSam
- 'Rosa Pastell' CAby CEnd CSpe ECGP ECtt ELon EWoo GBin GQue IPot LPla LRHS LSun MAvo MHol MPie MSCN NDov NWad SPer SPoG WAul WCot
- 'Rosanne' IPot
- 'Rowie' NBid
- 'Rubymine' (v) LLHF

- 'Sandringham' CAby LRHS MArl MLHP MRav MSpe NBir NHol SPer SWvt
§ - 'Schneerausch' LPla SPhx
- 'Septemberglut' EBee EPfP LRHS NLar SHil
- 'Shockwave' (v) **new** WCot
- 'Sir Malcolm Campbell' IPot
- 'Skylight' NBro SDix
- Snowdrift see *P. paniculata* 'Schneerausch'
- 'Speed Limit 45' WCot
- 'Spitfire' see *P. paniculata* 'Frau Alfred von Mauthner'
- 'Starburst' NBro
- 'Starfire' ♀H7 Widely available
I - 'Stars and Stripes' **new** MAsh MSCN
- 'Steeple Bumpstead' WCot
I - 'Stellata' **new** LRHS
- 'Sternhimmel' LPla MTis
- 'Strawberry Daiquiri'PBR SPoG WFar
- (Sweet Summer Series) Sweet Summer Candy = 'Ditosdre'PBR MAsh
- - Sweet Summer Festival = 'Ditoros'PBR **new** MAsh
- - Sweet Summer Fragrance = 'Ditomfra'PBR **new** MAsh
- - Sweet Summer Lilac **new** LBuc
- - Sweet Summer Purple White **new** LBuc
- - Sweet Summer Queen = 'Ditoran' **new** MAsh
- - Sweet Summer Rose White **new** LBuc
- - Sweet Summer Surprise = 'Ditomsur'PBR ECtt MAsh
- - Sweet Summer Temptation = 'Ditostem'PBR MAsh
- 'Swizzle' CWGN ECtt LSou LSun MAsh MBri SPoG WBor WFar
- 'Tenor' CCon CMac CTri CWCL ECtt ELon EPfP EPla GBuc IBoy LAst LRHS MCot MSpe NLar SCob SPoG SWvt WSHC WWEG
- 'Tequila Sunrise'PBR MBri
- 'The King' EBee ECtt LRHS MAvo NBro NLar SWat WSHC
- 'Tiara'PBR (d) EBee ECtt ELon IPot LRHS LSou MBri MHol MPie NLar SPer SWvt WCot
- 'Toits de Paris' misapplied see *P. paniculata* 'Cool of the Evening'
§ - 'Toits de Paris' Symons-Jeune WSHC
- 'Twister' EBee LSou MAsh MAvo MNrw MSCN WFar
- 'Uspekh' CAby CSam EBee ECtt EPPr EPla EWes LRHS MCot MRav MSpe MWhi NBro NLar NOrc NSti SPer WCAu WFar WHrl WWEG
- 'Van Gogh' CCse
- 'Velvet Flame' EPfP LBMP LSou MBel NPri SKHP
- 'Vintage Wine' MNrw
- 'Violetta Gloriosa' ELon LPla SMrm
- 'Visions' WHil
- 'Volcano Betty' **new** GBin
- 'Watermelon Punch' ECtt LRHS NLar WFar
- 'Wendy House' EBee ECtt LEdu LLHF MNrw NHol WRHF
- 'Wenn Schon Denn Schon' EBee
- 'White Admiral' ♀H7 Widely available
- White Flame = 'Bartwentynine'PBR CMea CWGN ECtt EPfP GBin IPot LBMP LRHS LSou MBri NPri SCob SKHP SWvt WCot WHil
- 'Wilhelm Kesselring' EBee ECtt ELon LRHS WBor
- 'Windsor' ♀H7 EBee ECtt ELon EPfP LRHS MSpe NDov NEgg NHol SPoG SRms SWvt WWEG
- 'Younique White' MAsh
(Paparazzi Series) 'Paparazzi Angelina' **new** WHlf
- 'Paparazzi Lindsay' **new** WHlf
- 'Paparazzi Miley' **new** WHlf
'Peppermint Candy' **new** WFar
'Petticoat' CMea CPBP ECtt EPot MWat NHar SBch SIgm WIce
Pink Flame = 'Bartwelve'PBR EPfP GBin LLHF LRHS LSou MBri NPri SPoG SRkn
'Pride of Rochester' ECho ECtt GJos LRHS
§ × ***procumbens*** 'Millstream' ♀H5 ECtt
- 'Variegata' (v) EBee ECha ECho ECtt GCrg LSun SRot
§ ***pulvinata*** WAbe
'Purple Elite' **new** WHlf
Purple Flame = 'Barfourteen'PBR EBee EPfP GBin LBMP LRHS LSou NPri SCob SPoG SRkn WFar
'Scented Pillow' SGSe
'Sherbet Cocktail'PBR CWGN EBee NHol NLar WCot WHil WPtf
§ ***sibirica*** subsp. ***borealis*** EDAr
stolonifera MNrw
I - 'Alba' EBee EPfP MBri NSoo
- 'Ariane' ECha EWld IPot LSou MCot SBch
- 'Blue Ridge' ♀H5 CExl EBee ECha ECtt EPfP EWld LRHS LSun MCot MHol MRav NSoo SRms
- 'Fran's Purple' ECtt EWld MNrw NBro WCFE
- 'Home Fires' EBee ECho ECtt EPfP LEdu LRHS MCot NBro SPlb WHil XLum
- 'Montrose Tricolor' (v) CMos NBro
- 'Pink Ridge' SBch
- 'Purpurea' EBee EPfP LEdu LSou SGSe
subulata 'Alexander's Surprise' CMea CTal ECho ECtt EDAr EPfP EPot GCrg LBee LRHS MAsh NBir SIgm SPlb
- 'Amazing Grace' CTal CTri CWCL ECho EDAr EPfP EPot EWes GEdr GJos IPot LAst LRHS NSla NWad SPoG WHoo WIce
- 'Apple Blossom' ECho NHol SPoG SRms
- 'Atropurpurea' ECho EDAr EPfP GKev LRHS SPoG XLum
- 'Bavaria' CMea CPBP ECho EPfP GJos IPot LLHF LRHS WIce
- Beauty of Ronsdorf see *P. subulata* 'Ronsdorfer Schöne'
- 'Blue Eyes' see *P. subulata* 'Oakington Blue Eyes'
- 'Bonita' ECho ECtt GCrg GJos LRHS LSun MAsh NLar WHoo WIce XLum
- 'Bressingham Blue Eyes' see *P. subulata* 'Oakington Blue Eyes'
- 'Candy Stripe' see *P. subulata* 'Tamaongalei'
- 'Cavaldes White' ECtt SPoG
- 'Coral Eye' ECtt

- 'Drumm'	see *P. subulata* 'Tamaongalei'
- 'Emerald Cushion'	CTri CWCL ECho ECtt EDAr ELon GEdr LAst MHol MWat NHol NLar SGbt WCFE WRHF
- 'Emerald Cushion Blue'	CExl CTri ECho ECtt EPfP LAst LRHS LSun MAsh NBir NPri SBch SPlb SPoG WAbe
- 'Fort Hill'	ECtt
- 'G.F.Wilson'	see *P. subulata* 'Lilacina'
- 'Holly'	EPot ITim LLHF NHol NWad
- 'Jupiter'	ECho
- 'Kimono'	see *P. subulata* 'Tamaongalei'
§ - 'Lilacina'	CMea ECha ECho MAsh WIce
§ - 'Maischnee'	CTal CTri ECho ECtt MAsh MWat SPlb
- 'Marjorie'	CTal ECho ECtt GEdr GJos LBee MHer NBir SPoG
- May Snow	see *P. subulata* 'Maischnee'
§ - 'McDaniel's Cushion' ♀H5	CExl CHel CTal ECha ECho ECtt EDAr ELan ELon EPfP EPot GJos LAst LBee LRHS MAsh MHol MLHP MMuc MSCN NHar NLar SEND SPlb SPoG WCFE WHoo WIce
- 'Mikado'	see *P. subulata* 'Tamaongalei'
- 'Millstream Daphne'	ECho
- 'Moonlight'	ECho GJos
- 'Nettleton Variation' (v)	ECho ECtt EDAr ELon EPot EWes GCrg GKev LRHS MMuc NRya SPoG WIce
§ - 'Oakington Blue Eyes'	CTri SRms
- 'Purple Beauty'	CMea CTal CUse ECho ECtt GJos LAst LLHF LRHS MMuc NHar NWad SBch SEND SPoG WCFE WSHC XLum
- 'Red Wings' ♀H5	ECho ECtt EPfP GEdr LRHS SRms
§ - 'Ronsdorfer Schöne'	EPot LBee LLHF NBir
- 'Samson'	ECho EDAr GJos LRHS WOld
- 'Sarah'	LLHF
- 'Scarlet Flame'	CMea ECho ECtt EDAr EPfP EPot GJos MAsh NHol SBch WHil WHoo WIce WRHF
- 'Snow Queen'	see *P. subulata* 'Maischnee'
- 'Snowflake'	GCrg MSCN
§ - 'Tamaongalei'	CMea CTal CTri ECho ECtt EDAr ELon EPot EWes GCrg GJos GKev GMaP LAst LRHS LSun MHol MMuc MSCN NSir NWad SEND SHar WCFE WHoo WIce
- 'Temiskaming'	CTri ECho ECtt EDAr EWes GCrg LRHS MLHP SRms WSHC
- 'Tschernobyl'	EPot
- 'White Delight'	CMea ECho ECtt EPfP GJos LAst LBee LRHS LSun SPoG
- 'Winifred'	NEgg
'Swirly Burly'	GQue
'Tiny Bugles'	CPBP
Violet Flame = 'Barsixtyone'PBR	CMea EPfP LRHS MHol NPCo NPri SPer SPoG WCot
White Eye Flame = 'Barsixty'PBR	CMea CWGN EPfP LRHS SCob
'White Kimono'	ECho LRHS
'Zwergenteppich'	CTal EPfP LLHF LRHS

Phoenix (*Arecaceae*)

canariensis ♀H1c	CBcs CExl EPfP EUJe IVic LPal MBri MMuc NPri NSoo SArc SEND SPlb SPoG STrG
dactylifera (F)	SBig
reclinata	XBlo
roebelenii ♀H1b	CDTJ CDoC LPal MBri SBig
- 'Multistem'	XBlo
theophrasti	CPHo LPal

Phormium ✿ (*Hemerocallidaceae*)

§ 'Alison Blackman'PBR	CBcs CDoC COtt EPfP ESwi GBin IVic LPal LRHS MAsh MBri MGos MJak NPla NSoo SCob SCoo SEND SHil SPoG SRkn SWvt
'Amazing Red'	LPal LRHS SCob
'Apricot Queen' (v)	CAbb CBcs CCCN CDoC CSBt EPfP LPal LRHS MGos NLar SCob SEND SEWo SHil SPer SPoG
Back in Black = 'Seilack'PBR	LRHS NPri NSoo SHil WFar
'Black Rage'	CBcs EPfP LRHS NLos
Black Velvet = 'Seivel'	IBoy LBuc LRHS MSwo NPla NPri NSoo SHil
'Bronze Baby'	CBcs CCCN CDoC CNec CSBt EHoe ELan ELon EPfP LRHS MAsh MGos MSwo MWat NSoo SCob SLim SPer SPoG SWvt
'Buckland Ruby'	CDoC
'Chocolate Fingers'	CBcs
'Chocomint'PBR	CBcs
colensoi	see *P. cookianum*
§ ***cookianum***	CHEx GGal SArc SCob
- 'Alpinum Purpureum'	see *P. tenax* 'Nanum Purpureum'
- 'Black Adder'PBR	CBcs CBod EPfP EUJe IBoy LBuc LPal LRHS MAsh SCob SEND SPoG
- 'Flamingo' (v)	CBcs CCCN CDTJ CNec CSBt ELan ELon EPfP LRHS LSou MBri MGos MHol SBod SEWo SLim SPer SPoG
- subsp. ***hookeri*** 'Cream Delight' (v) ♀H4	CAbb CBcs CCCN CDoC CEnd COtt CSBt EPfP EUJe LPal LRHS MAsh MGos MSwo NPri SCob SCoo SGol SHil SPer SWvt WGrn
- - 'Tricolor' (v) ♀H4	CBcs CDTJ CDoC CDul COtt CSBt EHoe ELan ELon EPfP EUJe GBuc LRHS MGos MMuc MWat NPla SArc SCob SEND SGol SHil SLim SPer SPoG SRms SWvt WGrf WGrn
'Crimson Devil'	CBcs EBee LRHS MBri NPri SHil SLim
Dark Avocado = 'Westado'PBR	EBee MAsh SLim
'Dark Delight'	CBcs CDoC
'Dazzler' (v)	CDoC
'Duet' (v)	CCCN CDoC EBee EHoe EPfP LRHS MMuc SEND SEWo SWvt WGrf
'Dusky Chief'	CSBt EPfP LPal NLar
'Emerald Isle'	CDoC
'Evening Glow' (v)	CBcs CCCN COtt CSBt ELan ELon EPfP EUJe LPal LRHS MBri MGos NLar NPri SCob SEND SEWo SPoG SWvt WGrn
'Firebird'	EUJe LRHS MBri SHil SWvt
'Glowing Embers'	CBcs ELon
'Gold Ray'	CBcs EBee LRHS MBri NPri SCob SCoo SHil SWvt
'Gold Sword' (v)	CCCN CDoC CSBt EPfP LRHS MAsh NEgg SCob
'Golden Alison'PBR	see *P.* 'Alison Blackman'
'Golden Ray' (v)	CBod EUJe LRHS NLos NSoo WGrf
'Green Sword'	CBcs CCCN
'Jack Spratt' (v)	ECou EHoe SWvt
'Jester' (v)	Widely available
'Limelight'	SWvt

§ 'Maori Chief' (v) — CSBt EPfP LRHS SWvt WFar
§ 'Maori Maiden' (v) — CBcs CCCN CDoC CDul COtt CTri ELon EPfP MGos MSwo SWvt
§ 'Maori Queen' (v) — CBcs CBod CCCN CChe CDTJ CDoC COtt CSBt ELon EPfP LPal LRHS MBri MGos MSwo MWat NPri NSoo SCoo SEND SHil SPer SPoG SWvt
§ 'Maori Sunrise' (v) — CBcs CCCN CDoC ELon IArd LPal LRHS MGos NPla SCoo SLim SPer SWvt
'Margaret Jones'PBR — CCCN SLim
'Merlot'PBR — NPri
'Moonraker'PBR — CBcs MHol
'Pink Panther' (v) — CAbb CBcs CBod CCCN CDoC ELan ELon EPfP LRHS MBri MGos MSwo MWat NLar NPla NPri SCob SCoo SHil SPoG WGrf
'Pink Stripe' (v) — CBcs CChe CDoC CNec CSBt LPal LRHS MAsh MBri MGos MJak MWat NPri NSoo SHil SPoG SWvt WCot
'Platt's Black' — CBcs CCCN CDoC COtt EPfP EUJe EWes IBoy LRHS MBri MGos MJak MSwo NBir NPla SCob SHil SLim SPoG SRkn SWvt WFar WGrf WGrn
'Rainbow Chief' — see *P.* 'Maori Chief'
'Rainbow Maiden' — see *P.* 'Maori Maiden'
'Rainbow Queen' — see *P.* 'Maori Queen'
'Rainbow Sunrise' — see *P.* 'Maori Sunrise'
'Red Fingers' — CBcs
'Red Sensation' — ELon LRHS SEWo
I 'Rubrum' — EUJe SEND
'Sundowner' (v) ♀H3 — CBcs CCCN CDoC CDul COtt CSBt CTsd EBee ELan EPfP LPal LRHS MAsh MBri MGos MJak MMuc NBir NEgg NLar SCob SCoo SEND SHil SLim SPer SPoG SWvt WGrf WGrn
'Sunset' (v) — CBcs CCCN CSBt EUJe NPri SWvt
'Surfer' (v) — CBcs WGrn
'Surfer Bronze' — CBcs CCCN CSBt
'Surfer Green' — CCCN
'Sussex Velvet' — SCoo SLim
tenax — Widely available
- 'All Black' — LRHS MBri MGos SCoo SHil
- 'Bronze' — CTsd SWvt
- 'Chocolate Dream' — EPfP
- 'Co-ordination' — CBcs CCCN EPfP
- 'Deep Purple' — CHEx
- dwarf — CSpe
I - 'Giganteum' — CHEx
- 'Glenorchy Green' **new** — EAEE
- In The Red = 'Seied'PBR — MHol
- 'Joker' (v) — CBcs ELon LPal
* - ***lineatum*** — MMuc SEND
§ - 'Nanum Purpureum' — SArc
- Purpureum Group ♀H4 — CDoC CDul CHEx CSBt EBee ELan ELon EPfP LPal LRHS MJak MMuc MSwo MWat NLar NSoo SCob SEND SEWo SGol SHil SLim SLon SPer SPlb WFar
- Sweet Mist = 'Phos2'PBR — LBMP
- 'Tiny Tiger' — EPfP
- 'Variegatum' (v) ♀H5 — CDTJ EBee ELon EPfP EUJe LPal MGos MJak MMuc MWat NPri NSoo SArc SCob SEND SEWo SPer SRms
- 'Veitchianum' (v) — SPer
- 'Yellow Queen' — LPal WFar
'Thumbelina' — CCCN
'Tom Thumb' — CBcs
'Wings of Gold' — EBee
'Yellow Wave' (v) ♀H4 — Widely available

Photinia ✿ (*Rosaceae*)

arbutifolia — see *Heteromeles salicifolia*
beauverdiana — CAco
- var. ***notabilis*** — CJun EPfP NLar
Corallina = 'Bourfrits'PBR — NLar
davidiana — CMac CTri ELan EPfP IDee MGil MRav NLar SCob SRms SVen
- 'Palette' (v) — CBcs CDul CMac EBee EHoe ELan ELon EPfP LRHS MAsh MGos MMuc MSwo NEgg SCob SEND SGol SLim SPer SPoG SRms SWvt WFar WMoo
- var. ***undulata*** 'Fructu Luteo' — CAbP GGal MMuc MRav SEND
- - 'Prostrata' — CMac CTri MRav NLar
I × ***fraseri*** 'Atropurpurea Nana' — EPfP LBMP MGos
- 'Birmingham' — CMac EWes
- 'Canivily' ♀H5 — CEnd EWes IVic LRHS MBri MPkF SGol SHil
- Cracklin' Red = 'Parred' — ELon LBuc LRHS MBri MPkF SCob WMoo
- Dynamo Red = 'Parsur' — MBri SCob
- Fireball Red = 'Parbri' — MBri SCob
- 'Goldstar' **new** — MPkF
* - 'Ilexifolium' — ESwi
- 'Little Red Robin' — Widely available
- Pink Marble = 'Cassini' (v) ♀H5 — CBcs CEnd CNec EBee ELan EPfP EPla EUJe LBMP LBuc LRHS MAsh MBri MGos MJak MPkF NPri NSoo SCob SEND SGol SHil SLim SLon SPer SPoG SRms
- 'Red Robin' ♀H5 — Widely available
- 'Red Select' — NPri WPat
- 'Robusta' — CMac EPfP LRHS SWvt
- 'White Lady' **new** — MPkF
glabra — SArc
§ - 'Parfait' (v) — CAbP CMac EBee ETwe LRHS MAsh SLon
- 'Pink Lady' — see *P. glabra* 'Parfait'
- 'Rubens' — CMac EPfP LRHS MAsh MRav WPat
- 'Variegata' — see *P. glabra* 'Parfait'
integrifolia HWJ 946 — WCru
lasiogyna — CMCN
lucida — WCru
microphylla B&SWJ 11837 — WCru
- HWJ 564 — WCru
niitakayamensis — MSnd
- CWJ 12435 **new** — WCru
'Redstart' — CAbP CMac EBee ELan EPfP LRHS NLar SEND SLon SPer SWvt WFar WMoo
§ ***serratifolia*** — CAbP CBcs CDul CHEx CMCN ELan EPfP NLar SArc SBrt SEND SPer WFar WPGP
- Curly Fantasy = 'Kolcurl'PBR — IVic LRHS MRav NLar NSoo
- 'Jenny' — LRHS NLar WFar
serrulata — see *P. serratifolia*
'Super Hedge'PBR — see *P.* Super Hedge
§ Super Hedge = 'Branpara'PBR — EShb LRHS LSou MSwo SCob WFar
'Super Red' — CSBt NLar SLim
villosa — CAbP CTho MBri MSnd SPoG
- B&SWJ 8665 — WCru
- var. ***coreana*** B&SWJ 8789 — WCru

- var. ***laevis*** CExl EPfP MBri WPGP
- - B&SWJ 8877 WCru
- f. ***maximowicziana*** EPfP MBri NLar
* - var. ***zollingeri*** B&SWJ 8903 WCru

Phragmites (*Poaceae*)

sp. CHab
from Sichuan, China EPPr
§ ***australis*** CAco CBAq CBen CHab CWat MSKA NLar NMir SEND SVic SWat WMAq WPnP XLum
- subsp. ***australis*** var. ***striatopictus*** EPPr
- - 'Variegatus' (v) CBen CKno CWat EBee EPPr EPla EShb LLWG MMuc MPie MWhi NBir NLar NWsh SEND SMad WWEG WWtn XLum
- subsp. ***humilis*** CHab
- subsp. ***pseudodonax*** EBee EPPr MMoz
communis see *P. australis*
karka EPPr
- 'Candy Stripe' (v) CBen EPPr MSKA

Phuopsis (*Rubiaceae*)

§ ***stylosa*** Widely available
- 'Purpurea' ECGP MNrw MRav NChi NDov

Phycella (*Amaryllidaceae*)

cyrtanthoides **new** WCot

Phygelius (*Scrophulariaceae*)

aequalis CTca MRav WMoo
- ***albus*** see *P. aequalis* 'Yellow Trumpet'
- 'Aureus' see *P. aequalis* 'Yellow Trumpet'
- 'Cream Trumpet' see *P. aequalis* 'Yellow Trumpet'
- 'Indian Chief' see *P.* × *rectus* 'African Queen'
- 'Pink Trumpet' SMrm
- 'Sani Pass' CPrp ELon GMaP MHer SCob SPlb SWvt
- 'Trewidden Pink' ♀H5 EBee ELan ELon EPfP EWTr GBin MSCN SGSe SLim SWvt WMnd WMoo WWEG XLum
§ - 'Yellow Trumpet' ♀H5 CSBt CTca EBee ELan ELon EPfP EPla GMaP IBoy MAsh MLHP SEND SGbt SLim SWvt WMnd WMoo WWEG XLum
Candy Drops Cream = 'Kerphycrem'PBR (Candy Drops Series) NGBl SCob
§ ***capensis*** CHll ELan GCra GGal MHer SRms WMnd WOut WRHF
- ***coccineus*** see *P. capensis*
'Golden Gate' see *P. aequalis* 'Yellow Trumpet'
Logan form GBin
'Midas Touch' EBee ELon NLar SPad
New Sensation = 'Blaphy'PBR EPfP MRav SCob SWvt
'Passionate'PBR NLar WHlf
§ × ***rectus*** 'African Queen' ♀H5 EBee ELan EPfP LPot MLHP MRav MSwo NBir NGdn SEND SPlb SWvt WKif WMnd WWEG XLum
- 'Bridgetown Beauty' GCal
- Candy Drops Deep Rose = 'Kerphyros'PBR **new** NGBl
- 'Devil's Tears' ♀H5 CBcs CPrp ELan GKev LPot LRHS NEgg NLar SCob SEND SGSe SLim SPer SWvt WHar WHil WMoo
- 'Ivory Twist' ELon NLar
- 'Jodie Southon' ELon LSou SDys WCot
- 'Moonraker' CAby CBcs CHll CPrp CTri ELan EPfP GBin LRHS MAsh MHer MRav NGdn NLar SCob SEND SGSe SMrm SPer SPlb SRms WHil WKif XLum
- 'Raspberry Swirl' ELon
- 'Salmon Leap' ♀H5 CBcs CTri ELan EPfP GBin GBuc LRHS MBNS MGos MRav NEgg NLar SCob SEND SLim SPlb SWvt WMnd WWEG
- Somerford Funfair Series IBoy
- - Somerford Funfair Apricot = 'Yapapr' SWvt
- - Somerford Funfair Coral = 'Yapcor'PBR EPfP LPot LRHS MAsh MBri NLar SBod SCob SLim SRkn SWvt WFar
- - Somerford Funfair Cream = 'Yapcre'PBR CHel EPfP LBMP LRHS NLar SGSe SLim SWvt WFar WPtf
- - Somerford Funfair Orange = 'Yapor'PBR EPfP LBMP LRHS MAsh MBri NLar NPri SGSe SLim SPoG SWvt WFar
- - Somerford Funfair Wine = 'Yapwin' CAby CChe ELan EPfP EShb LBMP LPot LRHS MAsh MBNS MBri NPri SCob SGSe SLim SMrm SPer SPoG SWvt WPtf
- - Somerford Funfair Yellow = 'Yapyel'PBR EPfP LRHS MAsh MBri SLim SPoG SWvt
§ - 'Winchester Fanfare' CSBt ELan GBin LBMP LRHS MGos MRav SCob SEND SLim SMrm SWvt WKif WWEG
- 'Winton Fanfare' see *P.* × *rectus* 'Winchester Fanfare'
'Rory'PBR SRms
Snow Queen = 'Crosnoque'PBR (Croftway Series) **new** SCob

Phyla (*Verbenaceae*)

lanceolata LLWG
§ ***nodiflora*** ECha MHer SRms WJek XSen
- 'Alba' MMuc SEND
§ - var. ***canescens*** XLum

× *Phylliopsis* (*Ericaceae*)

'Coppelia' ♀H5 NHar WPat
'Crinoline' **new** NHar
hillieri 'Askival' WThu
- 'Pinocchio' GKev NHar WAbe WPat WThu
'Hobgoblin' WAbe
'Mermaid' ITim NHar WAbe WThu
'Sprite' CWSG WPat
'Sugar Plum' CCCN LRHS NHar NLar SWvt WAbe WThu
'Swanhilde' WAbe WThu

Phyllitis see *Asplenium*

scolopendrium see *Asplenium scolopendrium*

Phyllocladus (*Podocarpaceae*)

alpinus CDoC CDul ECou EUJe NWad WThu

Phyllodoce (*Ericaceae*)

aleutica ECho NHar NLar SRms WThu
§ - subsp. ***glanduliflora*** 'Flora Slack' WThu
- - white-flowered see *P. aleutica* subsp. *glanduliflora* 'Flora Slack'
caerulea ♀H5 ECho
- ***japonica*** see *P. nipponica*

- 'Murray Lyon'	NHar WAbe WThu
- 'W.M. Buchanan's Peach Seedling'	NHar
empetriformis	ECho SRms WThu
§ ***nipponica***	NHar WThu
'Peach'	NLar WThu

Phyllostachys ✿ (*Poaceae*)

angusta	ERod MWht SBig
arcana 'Luteosulcata'	CEnt CFil EPla ERod MMoz MMuc MWht NLar
§ ***atrovaginata***	ERod SGol
aurea ♀H5	Widely available
- 'Albovariegata' (v)	EPfP EPla ERod LRHS MWht
- 'Flavescens Inversa'	EPla ERod LPal MMuc MWht
- 'Holochrysa'	CDTJ CFil CJun EPla ERod LPal MMuc MWht
- 'Koi'	CDTJ CEnt EPla ERod MMoz MWht SBig SGol WPGP
aureocaulis	see *P. aureosulcata* f. *aureocaulis*, *P. vivax* f. *aureocaulis*
aureosulcata	EPla ERod MMoz MWht WMoo
- f. ***alata***	see *P. aureosulcata* f. *pekinensis*
- 'Argus'	EPla
§ - f. ***aureocaulis***	CAbb CBcs CBod CDoC CEnt CFil CJun CTsd ELon EPfP EPla EUJe GCal LBMP LPal LRHS MBri MGos MMoz MWhi MWht SArc SCob SGol SPer SPoG SWvt
- 'Harbin'	EPla ERod
- 'Harbin Inversa'	EPla ERod
- 'Lama Tempel'	CDTJ CFil CJun EPla
§ - f. ***pekinensis***	EPla MMoz SBig
- f. ***spectabilis*** ♀H5	Widely available
bambusoides	CDTJ EPla ERod SBig SDix
- 'Albovariegata' (v)	EPla
- 'Allgold'	see *P. bambusoides* 'Holochrysa'
- 'Castilloni Inversa'	EPla ERod EWes LEdu MMoz MWht
- 'Castillonii' ♀H5	CBcs CEnt EPla ERod EUJe EWes LEdu LPal MMoz MMuc MWht NLar SArc SBig SDix SEND WPGP
- 'Castillonis Variegata' (v)	ERod
§ - 'Holochrysa' ♀H5	CDTJ CDoC CEnt EPla ERod LPal MMoz MMuc MWht SEND WPGP
- 'Kawadana' (v)	EPla ERod
- f. ***lacrima-deae***	CAgr CDTJ
- 'Marliacea'	EPla ERod SBig
- 'Subvariegata'	EPla
- 'Sulphurea'	see *P. bambusoides* 'Holochrysa'
- 'Tanakae'	CDTJ MMoz SBig
- 'Violascens'	EPla SBig
bissetii ♀H5	Widely available
congesta misapplied	see *P. atrovaginata*
decora	ERod MMoz MMuc MWht SEND
dulcis	CEnt EPfP EPla ERod LPal MWht SBig
§ ***edulis***	CAco CAgr ELon ERod MMoz SArc SBig SPlb
§ - 'Heterocycla'	XBlo
- f. ***pubescens***	see *P. edulis*
flexuosa	CBcs CEnt LPal LRHS MWht SGol
glauca	EPfP EPla ERod MMoz MWht SBig
- f. ***yunzhu***	ERod MWht
heteroclada	CAgr CEnt EPla
- 'Solid Stem' misapplied	see *P. purpurata* 'Straight Stem'
heterocycla	see *P. edulis* 'Heterocycla'
- f. ***pubescens***	see *P. edulis*
humilis	CEnt ERod EUJe LPal MMoz MMuc MWhi MWht SBig SEND
incarnata	EPla
iridescens ♀H5	EPla ERod SBig
lithophila	ERod
makinoi	ERod
mannii	ERod MWht
nidularia	ERod MMoz SBig
nigra ♀H5	Widely available
- 'Boryana'	CCVT CDoC CEnd CEnt EPfP EPla ERod EUJe MGos MMoz MMuc MWht SBig SEND SWvt WMoo
- 'Hale'	MWht
- f. ***henonis*** ♀H5	EPla ERod MMoz MMuc MWht SBig SEND SGol WPGP
- 'Megurochiku'	ERod MWht
- f. ***nigra***	CFil
- f. ***punctata***	CDoC ERod MAvo MMuc MWht SEND WMoo
- 'Tosaensis'	ERod
nuda	EPla ERod MMoz MWht
- f. ***localis***	ERod MWht
parvifolia	CEnt ERod MWht
platyglossa	ERod
praecox f. ***viridisulcata***	ERod
prominens	ERod
propinqua	CDoC ERod LPal MMoz MWht
§ ***purpurata*** 'Straight Stem'	MWht
rubromarginata	CEnt ERod MMuc MWht
'Shanghai 3'	ERod
stimulosa	ERod MWht
sulphurea 'Houzeau'	ERod MMuc SEND
§ - f. ***sulphurea***	ERod
- 'Sulphurea'	see *P. sulphurea* f. *sulphurea*
§ - f. ***viridis***	ERod SBig
violascens	CEnt EPla ERod EUJe MMoz MWht SBig
viridiglaucescens	CDTJ ERod MBrN MMoz MMuc MWht SBig SEND
viridis	see *P. sulphurea* f. *viridis*
vivax	EPfP EPla ERod EUJe MMoz MMuc MWht NLar SBig
§ - f. ***aureocaulis*** ♀H5	CAbb CAgr CBcs CCVT CDoC CEnd CEnt CHEx CWSG EPPr EPfP EPla ERod EUJe IBoy LEdu LPal LRHS MGos MMoz MMuc MWhi MWht NLar SArc SBig SCob SEND SGol WPGP
- - 'Huanwenzii'	CDTJ EPla ERod EUJe MMoz MWht NPla
- 'Katrin'	LEdu
* - 'Sulphurea'	XBlo

× *Phyllothamnus* (*Ericaceae*)

erectus	WThu

Phymatosorus (*Polypodiaceae*)

§ ***diversifolius***	SGSe WPGP

Phymosia (*Malvaceae*)

§ ***umbellata***	MOWG WPGP

Phyodina see *Callisia*

Physalis (*Solanaceae*)

alkekengi ♀H7	CTri NBir NLar SWvt
- var. ***franchetii***	CArn CBcs CBod CMac CSBt EBee ECha ELan EPfP EPla LAst LRHS MBel MHer NBir NBro NEgg NGdn

	NPri SMad SPer SPoG SRms WFar WMnd WOld
- - dwarf	LRHS NLar
- - 'Gigantea'	ECGP LSun NLar SPlb WFar XLum
- - 'Gnome'	see *P. alkekengi* var. *franchetii* 'Zwerg'
- - 'Variegata' (v)	EPla EWes LEdu SEND
§ - - 'Zwerg'	EBee LRHS LSun
- 'Halloween King'	LRHS NLar NPri SPoG
- 'Halloween Queen'	LRHS NLar WHil
campanula B&SWJ 10409	WCru
edulis	see *P. peruviana*
§ ***peruviana*** (F)	CCCN SHDw SPlb SVic

Physaria (*Brassicaceae*)

alpina	CPBP GKev SPlb
rollinsii	CPBP GKev

Physocarpus (*Rosaceae*)

'Burning Embers'	SRms
'Korona' **new**	WMoo
Little Devil[PBR]	see *P. opulifolius* 'Donna May'
'Midnight' **new**	WMoo
opulifolius	CDul
- 'Angel Gold'	CNec EBee ELan EMil EPfP EPla LRHS MAsh MBri NPri
- Coppertina[PBR]	see *P. opulifolius* Diable D'Or
- 'Dart's Gold' ♀H7	Widely available
§ - Diable D'Or = 'Mindia'[PBR]	COtt EPfP LBuc LRHS MAsh MBlu MBri MGos MPkF NEgg NLar NPla SGbt SGol SHil WMoo
- 'Diabolo'[PBR] ♀H7	Widely available
§ - 'Donna May'[PBR]	EBee EPla LBuc MAsh SCob SLon
§ - Lady in Red = 'Tuilad'[PBR] ♀H7	Widely available
§ - 'Luteus'	LBuc MGos MRav WMoo
- 'Nugget'	LRHS MBri MGos
- 'Red Baron' **new**	MBri
- Ruby Spice[PBR]	see *P. opulifolius* Lady in Red
- Summer Wine = 'Seward'[PBR]	EPfP EWes LRHS MAsh
- 'Tilden Park'	EBee SGol
ribesifolius 'Aureus'	see *P. opulifolius* 'Luteus'

Physoplexis (*Campanulaceae*)

§ ***comosa*** ♀H5	CPBP EPot WAbe

Physostegia (*Lamiaceae*)

angustifolia	GQui NBre
I 'Aquatica'	LLWG
§ ***virginiana***	CBAq CBod CSBt CTri GMaP MBel SPoG SRms SWat WCFE WOld
- 'Alba'	CSBt CTri EBee ELon GAbr GJos GMaP LEdu LSun NChi SMrm SPlb WCAu WHrl XLum
§ - 'Crown of Snow'	CCon EBee EPfP MHer MRav MWat MWhi NPri SPoG SWvt WHar WMoo WWEG
- 'Grandiflora'	CCon
- 'Miss Manners'	CHel CMac ECGP ECtt EPla MBri NBre NCGa NGdn NLar SBod SRGP
- 'Pink Manners'	STPC
- 'Rose Crown'	SPer
- 'Rose Queen'	CTri MWat NBre NChi NPri
- 'Rosea'	EPfP GJos IFoB MMuc MNHC MWhi NGdn SHar SPad SPoG SWvt WHrl WWEG
- Schneekrone	see *P. virginiana* 'Crown of Snow'
- 'Snow Queen'	see *P. virginiana* 'Summer Snow'
§ - var. ***speciosa*** 'Bouquet Rose'	CHel CMac COtt CPrp EBee ECGP ECha EPfP EPla LEdu LRHS MCot MRav NBir NLar SGbt SPer SWvt WBrk WHar WMoo WRHF WWEG XLum
- - Rose Bouquet	see *P. virginiana* var. *speciosa* 'Bouquet Rose'
- - 'Variegata' (v)	CMac CSBt EBee ECtt EHoe ELan ELon EPfP EPla MHer MRav NBir NGdn NHol NLar SPer SRms SWat WCAu WCot WHil WMnd WWEG XLum
§ - 'Summer Snow' ♀H7	CBcs COtt ECha ELan EPfP EWoo LRHS NGBl NLar SPer SRms SWat WCot WMnd
- 'Vivid' ♀H7	CBod CKno CMac ECha ELan ELon EPfP EPla LAst LBMP LRHS MBri MCot MHer MNrw MRav NCGa NEgg NHol NLar SDix SPer SPlb SRms WCot WHil WMnd WWEG WWtn XLum
- 'Wassenhove'	SMrm

Phyteuma (*Campanulaceae*)

balbisii	see *P. cordatum*
comosum	see *Physoplexis comosa*
§ ***cordatum***	GJos
hemisphaericum	ECho GEdr GJos GKev NSla
humile	ITim WThu
nigrum	ECho GEdr LLHF NBid WBor
orbiculare	GEdr GJos
scheuchzeri	CDes CSpe EBee ECho EPfP EWld GBin GEdr SGSe SMad SRms WIce WRHF XLum
spicatum	CDes GEdr GJos NBro
- subsp. ***coeruleum***	GJos

Phytolacca (*Phytolaccaceae*)

acinosa	GPoy SBrt SWat
- HWJ 647	WCru
§ ***americana***	CAby CArn EBee ELan EPfP ESwi EUJe GPoy MBNS MHer MNHC MPie NLar NLos SRms SWat WHea WHil WMnd
- B&SWJ 1000	WCru
- B&SWJ 8817A	WCru
- 'Silberstein' (v)	EBee ESwi MBNS NLar NLos WCot
bogotensis	WCru
clavigera	see *P. polyandra*
decandra	see *P. americana*
dioica	CExl SPlb
esculenta	LEdu SEND
icosandra B&SWJ 8988	WCru
- B&SWJ 9033	WCru
- Purpurascens Group B&SWJ 11251	SRms WCru
japonica B&SWJ 3005	NBid WCru
- B&SWJ 3522	WCru
'Laka Boom'	EUJe
octandra B&SWJ 9514	WCru
- B&SWJ 10151	WCru
§ ***polyandra***	NBid NBro SRms
rivinoides B&SWJ 10264	WCru
rugosa B&SWJ 10263	WCru

Picea (*Pinaceae*)

§ ***abies***	CAco CCVT CDul CLnd CMac CSBt CTho CTri EHul EPfP LBuc MJak

	Name	Suppliers
		MMuc NEgg NWea SCoo SEND SPoG WHar WMou
	- 'Acrocona' ♀H7	MBri MGos NLar NPCo
	- 'Archer'	CKen
	- 'Argenteospica' (v)	NPCo
	- 'Aurea'	ELan NPCo
	- 'Capitata'	CKen NLar
	- 'Clanbrassiliana' ♀H7	CKen ELan NLar NWad
	- Compacta Group	NPCo
I	- 'Congesta'	CKen
	- 'Crippsii'	CKen
I	- 'Cruenta'	CKen SLim
	- 'Cupressina'	CKen
	- 'Decumbens'	NLar
	- 'Diffusa'	CKen NLar
	- 'Dumpy'	CKen NHol NLar
	- 'Ellwangeriana'	NLar
	- 'Excelsa'	see *P. abies*
	- 'Fahndrich'	CKen CMen
	- 'Finedonensis'	NLar
	- 'Formanek'	CDoC CMen
	- 'Four Winds'	CKen
	- 'Frohburg'	CKen MJak NLar NPCo NSoo
	- 'Gold Drift'	NLar
	- 'Gregoryana'	CKen CMac
	- 'Heartland Gem'	CKen
	- 'Horace Wilson'	CKen CMen
	- 'Humilis'	CKen
	- 'Hystrix'	CMen NLar NWad
	- 'Inversa' ♀H7	CDul CKen MBlu SLim
	- 'J.W. Daisy's White'	see *P. glauca* 'J.W. Daisy's White'
	- 'Jana'	CKen
	- 'Kral'	CKen
	- 'Little Gem' ♀H7	CDoC CKen CMen EHul ELan EPla EUJe GEdr LBee MAsh MGos NHol NLar NWad NWea SCoo SLim SPoG WGor
	- 'Marcel'	CKen
	- 'Mini Kalous'	CKen
	- 'Nana Compacta'	CKen CMen MAsh
	- 'Nidiformis' ♀H7	CDoC CKen CMac CMen CSBt CTri EHul EUJe LPot MGos NLar NPCo NWea SGol SRms
	- 'Norrköping'	CKen
	- 'Ohlendorffii'	CKen MGos NLar
	- 'Pachyphylla'	CKen
	- 'Pusch'	CKen CMen NLar SLim
	- 'Pygmaea'	CKen NWad
	- 'Reflexa'	MGos NPCo
	- 'Remontii'	MBri NWea
	- 'Rydal' ♀H7	CBcs CDoC CDul CKen MAsh MBri NLar NPCo NWea SLim
	- 'Saint Mary's Broom'	NPCo
	- 'Spring Fire'	CKen
	- 'Typner'	CKen
	- 'Vermont Gold'	CKen NLar
	- 'Walter Bron'	NLar
	- Will's Dwarf	see *P. abies* 'Wills Zwerg'
§	- 'Wills Zwerg'	SGol
§	***alcoquiana*** var. ***alcoquiana***	NWea SLim
	- var. ***reflexa***	MPkF
	asperata	NWea
	bicolor	see *P. alcoquiana* var. *alcoquiana*
I	- 'Prostrata'	NPCo
	breweriana ♀H6	CAco CDoC CDul CMac CTho EHul EPfP GKin IDee LEdu LRHS MBlu MGos MJak MMuc NEgg NLar NPCo NPri NWea SLim SSta WCFE WMou
	- 'Kohout's Dwarf'	CKen
	chihuahuana	SLim
	engelmannii	NWea
	- 'Compact'	SLim
	- subsp. ***engelmannii***	CKen
	- 'Jasper'	CKen
	- 'Lace'	SLim
	glauca	CDul NWea
	- Alberta Blue = 'Haal'PBR	CKen EUJe LRHS
	- var. ***albertiana*** 'Alberta Globe' ♀H7	CDoC CSBt EHul EPla GEdr GKin LBee LRHS MAsh MBri MGos NEgg NHol NWad SBod SCoo SLim SPoG
	- - 'Conica' ♀H7	CBcs CDoC CMac CMea CSBt EHul EPfP EPla EPot EUJe LBee LRHS MAsh MBri MGos MJak MMuc NEgg NHol NWad NWea SBod SEND SGol SLim SPer SPoG SRms WCFE
	- - 'Gnome'	CKen
	- - 'Laurin' ♀H7	CKen EPla NPCo NWad SLim
	- - 'Tiny'	CKen NWad
	- 'Arneson's Blue Variegated' (v)	CDoC CKen MAsh MBri SLim
	- 'Biesenthaler Frühling'	CKen EPla SLim
	- 'Blue Planet'	CKen IVic NLar
	- 'Coerulea'	NPCo
	- 'Cy's Wonder'	CKen
	- 'Dendroforma Gold' **new**	CKen
	- 'Echiniformis' ♀H7	CKen GKin NLar
	- 'Goldilocks'	CKen
§	- 'J.W. Daisy's White' ♀H7	CBcs CDoC CKen EHul EPfP EPla EUJe GKin LAst MAsh MGos MJak NHol NLar NWad NWea SCoo SLim SPer SPoG
I	- 'Julian Potts Monstrosa'	NLar
	- 'Lilliput'	CKen EHul NLar NWad NWea
§	- 'Nana'	CKen
	- 'Pendula'	CKen SLim
	- 'Piccolo'	CBcs CKen NLar SLim
	- 'Pixie'	CKen
	- 'Pixie Dust' **new**	CKen NLar
	- 'Rainbow's End' (v)	CKen EPla NLar SLim
	- 'Sander's Blue'	CAco CKen EHul EPfP EPla GKin LBee LRHS MBri NLar SLim SPoG
	- 'Sleeping Giant' **new**	NLar
	- 'Spring Surprise'	CKen
	- 'Zuckerhut'	GKin NLar
	glehnii 'Sasanosei'	CKen
	- 'Shimezusei'	CKen
	jezoensis	CKen CMen NLar NWea
	- 'Aurea'	SLim
	- subsp. ***hondoensis***	CMen
	- 'Marianbad'	CKen
	- 'Yatsabusa'	CKen CMen
	koraiensis	CDul NLar NWea
	kosteri 'Glauca'	see *P. pungens* 'Koster'
	koyamae 'Bedgebury Blue'	SLim
	- 'Bedgebury Cascade'	NLar SLim
	likiangensis	CDul CMCN CTho EBtc EPfP NLar NWea
	- var. ***balfouriana***	see *P. likiangensis* var. *rubescens*
§	- var. ***rubescens***	NLar NSoo SLim
	mariana	CDul EPfP NWea
	- 'Austria Broom'	CKen
	- 'Bill Archer'	NWad
	- 'Blue Teardrop'	CKen

	- 'Doumetii'	NLar
	- 'Fastigiata'	CKen NPCo
	- 'Nana' ♀H7	CDoC CKen CMac CMen EHul EPfP EPot GEdr MAsh MGos MMuc NHol NWad NWea SCoo SEND SLim SPoG
I	- 'Pygmaea'	CKen NWad
	meyeri	CTho
	morrisonicola	CKen
	omorika ♀H7	CAco CBcs CCVT CDul CJun CMCN CMac CTho EPfP EWTr MMuc NWea SEND SEWo WCFE WHar
	- 'de Ruyter'	IVic NPCo
	- 'Frohnleiten'	CKen
	- 'Frondenberg'	CKen
	- 'Halone'	CKen
	- 'Karel'	CKen
	- 'Minimax'	CKen
	- 'Nana' ♀H7	LRHS NPCo SLim WCFE
	- 'Pendula' ♀H7	CAco CDoC MBlu SLim SSta
	- 'Pendula Bruns'	CAco MBlu NLar SLim SMad
	- 'Peve Tijn'	NLar
	- 'Pimoko'	CKen MBri NLar NPCo SLim
	- 'Pimpf'	IVic
	- 'Pygmy'	CKen
	- 'Schneverdingen'	CKen
	- 'Tijn'	CKen SLim
	- 'Treblitsch'	CKen NLar SLim
	- 'Tremonia'	NLar
	orientalis ♀H7	CDul IDee NWea WThu
	- 'Aurea' (v) ♀H7	CMac EHul ELan EPla MGos MJak NLar NPri NSoo
	- 'Aureospicata'	CDoC CTho MAsh MBlu NLar NPCo SLim
	- 'Bergman's Gem'	CKen
	- 'Golden Start'	NLar NPCo SLim
	- 'Juwel'	CKen NLar
	- 'Kenwith'	CKen
	- 'Mount Vernon'	CKen NLar
	- Nana Group	GKin
	- 'Professor Langner'	CKen MAsh
	- 'Shadow's Broom'	CMen NPCo
	- 'Skylands' ♀H7	CKen ELan MAsh MBri MGos NLar NPCo SLim
	- 'Tom Thumb'	CKen NLar
	- 'Wittboldt'	CKen MBri
	pungens 'Blaukissen'	CKen SLim
	- 'Blue Diamond' **new**	SPoG
	- 'Blue Pearl'	CKen NLar
	- 'Edith' ♀H7	CKen EPla NLar NPCo SLim SPer
	- 'Erich Frahm'	CAco EPla MAsh MBri NLar
	- 'Fat Albert' ♀H7	NPCo NWea SLim
	- 'Frieda'	NLar SLim
	- Glauca Group	CAco CDul CLnd CMac CUse EPla MMuc NWea SCoo SPoG WMou
	- - 'Glauca Pendula'	CAco EUJe
	- - 'Glauca Procumbens'	NWea
§	- - 'Glauca Prostrata'	CMac EHul SLim
	- 'Glauca Globosa'	see *P. pungens* 'Globosa'
	- 'Globe'	CKen CMen
I	- 'Globosa' ♀H7	CBcs CKen CSBt EHul EPfP EPla LRHS MAsh MBri NHol NPCo NPri NSoo NWea SBod SCoo SLim SPer SPoG WCFE
	- 'Gloria'	CKen SLim
	- 'Hoopsii' ♀H7	CAco CDoC CDul EHul EPfP EPla GKin IVic LAst LRHS MAsh MBri MGos MJak NLar NPCo NPri NWea SEWo SLim SPoG SWvt
	- 'Hoto'	EHul
	- 'Hunnewelliana'	EPfP
	- 'Iseli Fastigiate'	GKin MAsh NLar NPCo SCoo SLim SPoG
	- 'Iseli Foxtail'	LAst
§	- 'Koster'	EHul EPfP LAst MAsh NPri NSoo NWea SPoG WMou
	- 'Lucky Strike'	CKen NLar
	- 'Maigold' (v)	CKen IVic SLim
	- 'Moerheimii'	EHul
	- 'Montgomery'	CKen
	- 'Mrs Cesarini'	CKen NLar SLim
	- 'Niemitz'	SLim
	- 'Nimetz'	CKen
	- 'Oldenburg'	NEgg NLar NPCo NWea SLim
	- 'Procumbens'	CKen
	- 'Prostrata'	see *P. pungens* (Glauca Group) 'Glauca Prostrata'
	- 'Saint Mary's Broom'	CKen NPCo
	- 'Schovenhorst'	EHul
	- 'Snowkiss'	NPCo
	- 'The Blues'	CKen NLar
	- 'Thomsen'	EHul EPla
	- 'Thuem'	EHul EPfP NPCo
	- 'Waldbrunn'	CKen NLar SLim
	- 'Wendy'	CKen
	- 'Yvette'	NLar
	retroflexa	NWea
	rubens	NLar
	schrenkiana	CMCN
	sitchensis	CAco CDul MAsh NWea
	- 'Christine Berkau'	NLar
	- 'Nana'	NLar
	- 'Papoose'	see *P. sitchensis* 'Tenas'
	- 'Pévé Wiesje'	NLar
	- 'Silberzwerg'	CKen NLar SLim
	- 'Strypemonde'	CKen
§	- 'Tenas'	CKen EPla NLar SLim SPoG
	smithiana	CDul CTho EPfP NLar
	- 'Sunray'	SLim
	wilsonii	CKen NLar

Picrasma (*Simaroubaceae*)

	ailanthoides	see *P. quassioides*
§	***quassioides***	CMCN EBee EPfP WPGP

Picris (*Asteraceae*)

echioides	WHer

Picrorhiza (*Plantaginaceae*)

kurrooa	GPoy

Pieris (*Ericaceae*)

'Balls of Fire'	CMac
'Bert Chandler'	CMac GKin
'Firecrest' ♀H5	GKev NLar
'Flaming Silver' (v) ♀H5	Widely available
'Forest Flame' ♀H5	Widely available
formosa B&SWJ 2257	WCru
- var. ***forrestii***	GLin
- - 'Charles Michael'	CExl
- - 'Jermyns'	CMac MRav
- - 'Wakehurst' ♀H5	CAbP CDul CExl CMac COtt CTri EPfP GKin LRHS MAsh MGos MMuc MRav SCob SPer SSpi
Havila = 'Mouwsvila' (v)	CMac MAsh NWad

japonica	CMac GGal
- 'Astrid'	IVic
- 'Bisbee Dwarf'	WThu
- 'Bolero'	NSoo
- 'Bonfire' ♀H5	CCCN ELan IVic LRHS LSou MBri MGos MMuc NLar NSoo SCob SHil SLim SPoG WHar
- 'Carnaval' (v) ♀H5	CCCN CMac COtt CSBt ELan ELon EShb IBoy IVic LBuc LRHS LSou MAsh MBri MGos MRav NLar NPri NSoo SCob SCoo SHil SLim SPer SPoG SWvt WFar
- 'Cavatine' ♀H5	CMHG IVic
§ - 'Christmas Cheer'	CMac WMoo
- 'Compacta'	WAbe
- 'Cupido'	IVic MAsh MGos NLar SLim SPoG WFar
- 'Debutante' ♀H5	CBcs COtt ELan GBin GKin IVic LRHS MAsh MBri MGos NLar NPri NSoo SCob SCoo SSpi SWvt WFar WHar
- 'Don'	see *P. japonica* 'Pygmaea'
- 'Dorothy Wyckoff'	MAsh NLar SSta
- 'Flaming Star'	COtt SWvt
- 'Flamingo'	CMac
I - 'Katsura'PBR	Widely available
- 'Little Heath' (v)	Widely available
- 'Little Heath Green'	CDoC CMac ELon GKin IBoy MAsh MGos MMuc NEgg NPCo SCob SPer SPoG SWvt WFar WMoo
- 'Minor'	GKev NWad WFar WThu
- 'Mountain Fire' ♀H5	Widely available
- 'Passion'PBR	CEnd COtt IVic MPkF NLar NSoo SPer
- 'Pink Delight' ♀H5	CAbP CNec LRHS MRav SRms
- 'Prelude' ♀H5	CSBt LRHS MAsh NLar NSoo WAbe WHar
- 'Purity' ♀H5	CBcs CDoC CHel CMHG CMac CNec LRHS MAsh MGos NEgg NLar SLim SPer SWvt WFar WHar
§ - 'Pygmaea'	GKev NWad SSta WThu
- 'Ralto'PBR	MBri MPkF MRav NSoo
- Red Mill = 'Zebris'	CEnd IVic LSou MAsh NSoo SLim SPer SSpi
- 'Rondo'	IVic
- 'Rosalinda'	MAsh
- 'Sarabande' ♀H5	GKin IVic MAsh MJak MPkF SCob SHil
- 'Scarlett O'Hara'	CSBt NSoo
- 'Select'	NSoo
- Taiwanensis Group	GKin LRHS MMuc NLar SRms WFar
- 'Temple Bells'	CSBt
- 'Valley Rose'	CSBt ELan GKin IVic LLHF MGos NLar SPoG SSpi
- 'Valley Valentine' ♀H5	CBcs CDoC CMac CSBt EPfP EUJe GEdr IVic LRHS MAsh MBri MGos MMuc MPkF NPCo NSoo SCob SCoo SHil SLim SPer SPoG SWvt
- 'Variegata' misapplied	see *P. japonica* 'White Rim'
- 'Variegata' ambig.	NLar SCob
- 'Variegata' (Carrière) Bean (v)	EPfP LRHS MRav NSoo WHar
- 'Wada's Pink'	see *P. japonica* 'Christmas Cheer'
- 'White Pearl'	CMac EPfP IVic MAsh NSoo
§ - 'White Rim' (v)	CDul CMac MAsh SPlb
- 'William Buchanan'	WThu
- var. ***yakushimensis***	NLar
nana	WThu
'Tilford'	CMac

Pilea (*Urticaceae*)

§ ***microphylla***	EBak EShb
muscosa	see *P. microphylla*
peperomioides ♀H1c	CHel

Pileostegia (*Hydrangeaceae*)

viburnoides	CBcs CHEx CMac CRHN CSPN EBee ELan EPfP EPla EUJe EWTr GCal IDee LRHS MGos MMuc MRav NLar SArc SEND SLon SPer SPoG SSpi SSta WCot WPGP WPat WSHC
- B&SWJ 3565	WCru
- B&SWJ 3570 from Taiwan	WCru
- B&SWJ 7132	WCru

Pilosella (*Asteraceae*)

§ ***aurantiaca***	CArn ELan LEdu LPot LRHS MHer MNHC NBid NOrc SIde SPhx WCot WHer WMoo WOut WSFF
§ - subsp. ***carpathicola***	MMuc
§ ***officinarum***	NRya
tardans	CFis

Pilularia (*Marsileaceae*)

globulifera	MSKA

Pimelea (*Thymelaeaceae*)

coarctata	see *P. prostrata*
drupacea	IDee
ferruginea	ECou WAbe WThu
- 'Magenta Mist'	MOWG
oreophila	WThu
§ ***prostrata***	CTri
tomentosa	LRHS

Pimpinella (*Apiaceae*)

anisum	CArn SVic
major	LEdu
- 'Rosea'	Widely available
saxifraga	CHab WSFF
tripartita PAB 6112 **new**	LEdu

pineapple see *Ananas comosus*

pineapple guava see *Acca sellowiana*

Pinellia (*Araceae*)

cordata	CDes ECho GKev LEdu WCot WCru
pedatisecta	CCon CDes GKev MRav WCot
pinnatisecta	see *P. tripartita*
ternata	EBee ECho GEdr GKev NLar SMad WCot
- B&SWJ 3532	WCru
§ ***tripartita***	CExl ECho EPPr GKev WCot
- B&SWJ 1102	WCru
- 'Dragon Tails' (v)	SKHP
- 'Purple Face'	WCru

Pinguicula (*Lentibulariaceae*)

ehlersiae	EFEx
esseriana ♀H1c	EFEx
grandiflora ♀H4	ECho EECP EFEx NLos NRya
longifolia subsp. ***longifolia***	EFEx
moranensis var. ***caudata***	EFEx
- ***moreana***	EFEx

	Plant	Suppliers
	- ***superba***	EFEx
	vulgaris	EFEx WHer

pinkcurrant see *Ribes rubrum* (P)

Pinus ✿ (*Pinaceae*)

	Plant	Suppliers
	albicaulis 'Flinck'	CKen
	- 'Nana'	see *P. albicaulis* 'Noble's Dwarf'
	- 'No 3'	CKen
§	- 'Noble's Dwarf'	CKen
	aristata	CDul CMen EHul WHor
	- 'Bashful'	CKen NLar
	- 'Cecilia'	CKen
	- 'Jeff' **new**	NLar
	- 'Kohout's Mini'	CKen
	- 'Sherwood Compact'	CKen SLim
	- 'Silver Love' **new**	NLar
	- 'So Tight'	CKen
	armandii	CAco CDoC CDul CMCN WPGP
	- 'Gold Tip'	CKen
	austriaca	see *P. nigra* subsp. *nigra*
	ayacahuite	CKen
	- var. ***veitchii***	WPGP
	balfouriana dwarf	CKen
	banksiana	CDul
	- 'Chippewa'	CKen
I	- 'Compacta'	CKen
	- 'H.J. Welch'	CKen
	- 'Neponset'	CKen
	- 'Schneverdingen'	CKen NPCo
	- 'Schoodic'	SLim
	bhutanica	WPGP
	bungeana	EPfP MBlu
	- 'Diamant'	CKen NLar
	- 'June's Broom'	CKen
	cembra	CAgr CDul CLnd MMuc NWea SEND
	- 'Aurea'	see *P. cembra* 'Aureovariegata'
§	- 'Aureovariegata' (v)	NLar NPCo SLim
	- 'Barnhourie'	CKen
	- 'Blue Mound'	CKen
	- 'Compacta Glauca'	NLar
I	- 'David' **new**	NLar
	- Glauca Group	MGos
	- 'Inverleith'	CKen
	- 'Jermyns'	CKen
	- 'King's Dwarf'	CKen
	- 'Ortler'	CKen
	- 'Stricta'	CKen
	- witches' broom	CKen
	cembroides NJM 09.022A	WPGP
	contorta	CBcs CDoC CDul NWea SPlb
	- 'Asher'	CKen
	- 'Chief Joseph' ♀H7	CKen NLar SLim
	- var. ***latifolia***	CDul
	- 'Spaan's Dwarf'	CKen MBri SLim
	- 'Taylor's Sunburst'	CKen NLar
	coulteri	EPfP SKHP WPGP
	densiflora	CAco CDul CMCN EUJe
	- 'Alice Verkade' ♀H7	CDoC CMen EUJe LRHS MBri NLar NPCo
	- 'Golden Ghost'	NLar
	- 'Haybud'	EPla
	- 'Jane Kluis' ♀H7	CMen EPla LAst LRHS MGos NLar SLim
	- 'Jim Cross'	CKen
	- 'Low Glow'	CKen NLar NPCo SLim
	- 'Oculus-draconis' (v)	NLar SLim
	- 'Pendula'	CKen MBlu NEgg SLim
I	- 'Pygmaea'	WHor
	- 'Umbraculifera'	CMen GKin NLar NPCo SSta
	- 'Vibrant' **new**	NLar
	edulis 'Juno'	CKen
	elliottii var. ***densa***	CKen
	fenzeliana	CKen
	flexilis 'Blackfoot'	NLar
	- 'Cheyenne' **new**	NLar
	- 'Extra Blue' **new**	NLar
	- 'Firmament'	NLar NSoo SLim
	- 'Glenmore Dwarf'	CKen
	- 'Nana'	CKen
I	- 'Pygmaea'	NLar
	- 'Red Elk' **new**	NLar
	- 'Ririe'	CKen
	- 'Tarryall'	CKen
	- 'Vanderwolf's Pyramid'	NLar
	- WB No 1	CKen
	- WB No 2	CKen
	greggii	CDul EBtc
	griffithii	see *P. wallichiana*
	halepensis	CDul SEND
§	***heldreichii***	CDoC CDul GKin NWea
	- 'Aureospicata'	NLar
	- 'Compact Gem' ♀H7	CDoC CKen EUJe MBri NPCo SLim
	- 'Dolce Dorme'	CKen
	- 'Groen'	CKen
	- var. ***leucodermis***	see *P. heldreichii*
	- 'Malink'	CKen IVic SLim
	- 'Ottocek'	CKen
	- 'Pygmy'	CKen
	- 'Satellit' ♀H7	CKen EUJe LRHS NLar NPCo SLim
	- 'Schmidtii'	see *P. heldreichii* 'Smidtii'
§	- 'Smidtii' ♀H7	CDoC CKen CMen EUJe LRHS MBri NLar NPCo SLim SPoG
	- 'Zwerg Schneverdingen'	CKen NPCo
	× ***holfordiana***	CDoC WPGP
	jeffreyi	CDul CMCN CTho NWea
	- 'Joppi'	CKen SLim
	koraiensis	GKin LEdu
	- 'Bergman'	CKen
	- 'Blue Ball'	CKen
	- 'Dragon Eye'	CKen SLim
	- 'Jack Corbit'	CKen
	- 'Shibamichi' (v)	CKen
	- 'Silver Lining'	NPCo
	- 'Silveray'	NLar
	- 'Silvergrey'	CKen
	- 'Spring Grove'	CKen
	- 'Winton'	CKen NLar
	leucodermis	see *P. heldreichii*
	monophylla 'Miney' **new**	NLar
	- 'Wrinkle' **new**	NLar
	montezumae Lamb.	SArc
	- NJM 09.016	WPGP
	- 'Sheffield Park'	SLim
	monticola 'Ondulata' **new**	NLar
	- 'Pendula'	CKen
	- 'Pygmy'	see *P. monticola* 'Raraflora'
§	- 'Raraflora'	CKen
	- 'Windsor Dwarf'	CKen
	mugo	CArn CBcs CDul CMac EHul EPfP MAsh MGos MJak NWea SCob WBor
	- 'Allgäu'	CKen
	- 'Benjamin'	CKen EPla LRHS NLar
	- 'Brownie'	CKen

	Name	Suppliers
	- 'Carsten' ♀H7	CKen ELan NPCo SCoo SLim
	- 'Carsten's Wintergold'	CDoC LRHS MAsh MBri NLar SPoG
	- 'Chameleon'	NLar
	- 'Corley's Mat'	CKen LAst MGos
	- 'Devon Gem'	NPCo
	- 'Dezember Gold'	IVic SLim
	- 'Flanders Belle'	SLim
	- 'Gnom'	CDul EHul GKin MAsh MGos NEgg NLar NPCo SCoo
	- 'Gold Star'	CMen EPla LRHS SLim
	- 'Golden Glow'	CKen NLar SCoo SLim
	- 'Hana' **new**	NLar
	- 'Hesse'	SCoo
	- 'Hoersholm'	CKen
	- 'Hulk'	CKen
	- 'Humpy' ♀H7	CKen CMen MAsh MBri NPCo SBod SCoo SLim
	- 'Ironsides'	CKen
	- 'Jacobsen'	CKen NLar
	- 'Janovsky'	CKen
	- 'Kissen' ♀H7	CKen EPfP MBri NHol NLar SLim
	- 'Kobold'	NEgg
	- 'Krauskopf'	CKen
	- 'Laurin'	CKen
	- 'March'	CKen
	- 'Mini Mops'	CKen
	- 'Minikin'	CKen MBri
	- 'Mops' ♀H7	CMac CMen EHul EPfP LAst LRHS MAsh MBlu MGos NPCo NWea SBod SCob SCoo SLim SPoG SSta
	- 'Mops Midget'	CMen MAsh NPCo
	- var. ***mughus***	see *P. mugo* subsp. *mugo*
§	- subsp. ***mugo***	CAco NWea SCob SGol
	- 'Mumpitz'	CKen LRHS
	- 'Northern Lights'	CKen
	- 'Ophir' ♀H7	CBcs CDul CKen CMen EHul EPfP EPla LAst LRHS MAsh MGos MJak NLar NPCo SCob SCoo SLim SSta
	- 'Pal Maleter' (v)	NPCo SCoo SLim
	- 'Paul's Dwarf'	CKen
	- 'Picobello'	LRHS MAsh NHol NLar SLim
	- 'Piggelmee'	CKen IVic NLar
	- 'Pincushion' **new**	NLar
	- Pumilio Group	CAco CDoC CDul CLnd EAEE EHul EPfP GQue LAst MGos MMuc NWea SEND WMoo WRHF
	- var. ***rostrata***	see *P. mugo* subsp. *uncinata*
	- 'Rushmore'	CKen
	- 'Sherwood Compact' **new**	NLar
	- 'Spaan'	CKen
	- 'Sunshine' (v)	CKen NLar
	- 'Suzi'	CKen
	- 'Suzy Hexe' **new**	NWad
	- 'Trompenburg'	NPCo
	- 'Tuffet'	CKen NHol SLim
	- 'Uelzen'	CKen NLar
§	- subsp. ***uncinata***	CDul LPal NWea
	- - 'Grüne Welle'	CKen SLim
	- - 'Paradekissen'	CKen NPCo
	- 'Varella'	CKen LPal NLar SCoo SLim
	- 'White Tip'	CKen
	- 'Winter Gold'	EHul ELan EPfP EPla EUJe LAst LPal LRHS MGos MJak NHol NPCo NWea SSta
	- 'Winter Sun'	EPla MAsh NLar
	- 'Winzig'	CKen
	- 'Yellow Tip' (v)	NHol
	- 'Zundert'	CKen NLar SPoG
	- 'Zwergkugel'	CKen
	muricata	CDoC CDul CLnd EBtc NWea
	nigra	CBcs CDul CLnd CMac CTri EUJe LPal MGos SGol WMou
	- var. ***austriaca***	see *P. nigra* subsp. *nigra*
	- 'Bambino'	CKen
	- 'Black Prince' ♀H7	CKen GQue NPCo SBod SLim
	- 'Bobo'	CKen NPCo
	- var. ***calabrica***	see *P. nigra* subsp. *laricio*
	- var. ***caramanica***	see *P. nigra* subsp. *pallasiana*
	- 'Cebennensis Nana'	CKen
	- var. ***corsicana***	see *P. nigra* subsp. *laricio*
*	- 'Fastigiata'	NPCo
	- 'Frank'	CKen NLar SLim
	- 'Green Tower'	NLar
	- 'Hornibrookiana'	CKen
	- 'Komet'	IVic NLar NPCo SLim
§	- subsp. ***laricio***	CAco CCVT CDoC CDul CMac ECrN IVic MMuc NWea SEND
	- - 'Aurea'	MBlu
	- - 'Bobby McGregor'	CKen
	- - 'Globosa Viridis'	NEgg NPCo
	- - 'Goldfingers'	NLar
	- - 'Moseri'	CKen NPCo
	- - 'Pygmaea'	CKen
	- - 'Wurstle'	CKen
	- subsp. ***maritima***	see *P. nigra* subsp. *laricio*
§	- subsp. ***nigra***	CCVT CDoC CJun CLnd CTho LBuc MMuc NLar NWea SCob SEND SEWo SGol
	- - 'Birte'	CKen
	- - 'Bright Eyes'	NPCo
	- - 'Schovenhorst'	CKen
	- - 'Skyborn'	CKen
	- - 'Strypemonde'	CKen NPCo
	- - 'Yaffle Hill'	CKen
	- 'Obelisk'	CKen NLar
	- 'Oregon Green'	CKen
§	- subsp. ***pallasiana***	CDul
	- - 'Pyramidalis'	CDoC
	- 'Pierrick Bregéon'[PBR]	LRHS
	- 'Richard'	CKen
	oocarpa	EBtc
	palustris	CDoC CDul CLnd IVic SKHP SSpi
	parviflora	NPCo SPlb
	- 'Aaba-jo'	CKen
	- 'Adcock's Dwarf' ♀H7	CDoC CKen NLar NPCo SBod SLim
	- 'Al Fordham'	CKen
	- 'Aoi'	CKen CMen NLar
	- 'Ara-kawa'	CKen CMen
	- 'Atco-goyo'	CKen
	- Azuma-goyo Group	CKen CMen
I	- 'Baasch's Form'	CKen NLar
	- 'Bergman'	CDoC MAsh NLar
	- 'Blauer Engel'	CDoC LRHS MBlu
	- 'Blue Giant'	MBlu
	- 'Blue Lou'	NLar
	- 'Bonnie Bergman' ♀H7	CDoC CKen EPfP NHol NLar
	- 'Chikusa Goten'	IArd
	- 'Dai-ho'	CKen
	- 'Daisetsusan'	CKen
	- 'Dendo' **new**	NLar
	- 'Doctor Landis Gold'	CKen
	- 'Dougal'	CKen
	- 'Floppy Joe' **new**	NLar
	- 'Fukai' (v)	CKen NHol NLar WBor
	- 'Fukiju'	CKen
	- Fukushima-goyo Group	CKen CMen

	- 'Fuku-zu-mi'	CKen IVic
	- 'Fu-shiro'	CKen
	- 'Gimborn's Ideal'	IVic
	- 'Gin-sho-chuba'	CKen
	- Glauca Group	CAco EPla MAsh MBlu MBri NPCo SGol SKHP
I	- 'Glauca Nana'	CKen
	- 'Goldilocks'	CKen MAsh NLar
	- 'Green Wave'	CKen
	- 'Gyok-ke-sen'	CKen
	- 'Gyo-ko-haku'	CKen
	- 'Gyokuei'	CKen
	- 'Gyokusen Sämling'	CKen NLar
	- 'Gyo-ku-sui'	CKen CMen
	- 'H2'	CKen
	- 'Hagaromo Seedling'	CKen CMen
	- 'Hakko'	CKen
	- 'Hatchichi'	CKen
	- 'Hobbit'	NWad
	- 'Ibo-can'	CKen CMen
	- 'Ichi-no-se'	CKen
	- 'Iri-fune'	CKen
	- Ishizuchi-goyo Group	CKen NLar
	- 'Jim's Mini Curls'	CKen
	- 'Ka-ho'	CKen
	- 'Kanrico'	CKen
	- 'Kanzan'	CKen
	- 'Kiyomatsu'	CKen
	- 'Kobe'	CKen NLar
	- 'Kokonoe'	CKen CMen
	- 'Kokuho'	CKen
	- 'Kusu-dama'	CKen
	- 'Masami'	CKen
	- 'Meiko'	CKen CMen
	- 'Michinoku'	CKen
	- 'Momo-yama'	CKen
	- 'Myo-jo'	CKen
	- Nasu-goyo Group	CKen
	- 'Negishi' ♀H7	CDoC CKen CMen LRHS MAsh NPCo SCoo SLim
	- 'Nellie D.'	NLar
	- 'Ogon-goyo'	CKen
	- 'Ogon-janome'	CKen MAsh NPCo SLim
	- 'Ossorio Dwarf'	CKen
	- var. ***pentaphylla***	IVic
	- 'Regenhold'	CKen
	- 'Richard Lee'	CKen
	- 'Ryo-ku-ho'	CKen
	- 'Ryu-ju'	CKen IArd NLar
	- 'Sa-dai-jin'	CKen
	- 'San-bo'	CKen
§	- 'Saphir'	CKen
	- 'Schoon's Bonsai'	CDoC NHol NLar
	- 'Setsugekka'	CKen
	- 'Shika-shima'	CKen
	- 'Shimada'	CKen
	- 'Shin Sen'	NLar
	- Shiobara-goyo Group	CKen
	- 'Shirobana'	NLar
	- 'Shizukagoten'	CKen
	- 'Shu-re'	CKen NLar
	- 'Sieryoden'	CKen
	- 'Smout'	CKen
	- 'Tani-mano-uki'	CKen
	- 'Tempelhof'	CAco MGos NPCo
	- 'Tenysu-kazu'	CKen
	- 'Tokyo Dwarf'	CKen NLar
	- 'Tribune'	NLar
	- 'Tsai's Cushion' **new**	NLar
	- 'Walker's Dwarf'	CKen
	- 'Watnong'	CKen
	- 'Zelkova'	CMen
	- 'Zui-sho'	CKen
	patula ♀H4	CBcs CCCN CDoC CDul CHll CLnd CMCN EBee EPfP EUJe IDee IVic LRHS NSoo SArc SBig SCoo SEND SLim SPlb WPGP
	peuce	CAco CLnd NWea
	- 'Arnold Dwarf'	CKen NLar
	- 'Cesarini'	CKen
	- 'Daniel'	CKen
	- 'Thessaloniki Broom'	CKen
	pinaster	CBcs CDoC CDul CLnd EPfP GQue IVic MMuc SBod SEND
	pinea ♀H5	CAco CAgr CArn CCVT CDoC CDul CLnd CTho CUse EPfP EUJe IDee IVic LPal MGos MMuc SArc SCoo SEND SEWo SGol SLim SPlb
	- 'Queensway'	CKen
	ponderosa	CDul CLnd NLar
	- var. ***scopulorum***	NWea
	pseudostrobus	WPGP
	pumila 'Buchanan'	CKen
	- 'Draijer's Dwarf'	SCoo SLim
	- 'Dwarf Blue'	NHol NLar
	- 'Glauca' ♀H7	CDoC CKen MAsh NLar
	- 'Globe'	EUJe MAsh NLar SLim
	- 'Jeddeloh'	CKen
	- 'Knightshayes'	CKen
	- 'Pinocchio'	CKen
	- 'Säntis'	CKen
	- 'Saphir'	see *P. parviflora* 'Saphir'
	radiata	CAco CBcs CCVT CDoC CDul CLnd CMac CSde CTho CTri ECrN ELan EPfP EUJe MMuc NSoo NWea SArc SCoo SEND
	- Aurea Group	CDoC EBee EPfP MBri NEgg NPCo SBod SCoo SLim SPoG
	- 'Bodnant'	CKen
	- 'Isca'	CKen
	- 'Marshwood' (v)	CKen SLim
	resinosa 'Don Smith'	CKen
	- 'Joel's Broom'	CKen
	- 'Quinobequin'	CKen
	rigida	CDul
	roxburghii	EBtc
	× ***schwerinii***	CDoC CKen
	- 'Wiethorst' ♀H7	CKen LRHS NLar SLim WHar
	sibirica 'Blue Smoke'	CKen
	- 'Mariko'	CKen
	strobiformis 'Coronado'	CKen
	- 'Loma Linda'	CKen SLim
	strobus	CAco CBcs CCVT CDul CLnd CMen EPfP MGos MMuc NWea SEND
§	- 'Alba'	SLim
	- 'Amelia's Dwarf'	CKen
	- 'Angel Falls'	CKen
	- 'Anna Fiele'	CKen MBri NLar
	- 'Bergman's Mini'	CKen
	- 'Bergman's Pendula Broom'	CKen
I	- 'Bergman's Sport of Prostrata'	CKen
	- 'Beth'	CKen
	- 'Bloomer's Dark Globe'	CKen
	- 'Blue Shag' ♀H7	CAco EPla EUJe NLar SCoo SLim SPoG

- 'Brevifolia' CKen
- 'Cesarini' CKen
- 'Compacta' NPCo
- 'Contorta' CDoC
- 'Densa' CKen
- 'E.R.' **new** NLar
- 'Ed's Broom' CKen
- 'Elkins Dwarf' CKen NPCo
- 'Fastigiata' CKen
- 'Golden Candles' **new** NLar
- 'Golden Showers' NLar
- 'Green Curls' CKen
- 'Green Twist' MAsh NLar SLim
- 'Greg' CKen
- 'Hershey' CKen
- 'Hillside Gem' CKen
- 'Himmelblau' EUJe IDee MBlu NLar SLim
- 'Horsford' CDoC CKen NLar SLim
- 'Horsford Sister' CKen
- 'Julian Pott' CKen NLar
- 'Julian's Dwarf' CKen
- 'Krügers Lilliput' NLar SLim
- 'Louie' CKen MAsh NLar
- 'Macopin' EPla
- 'Mary Butler' CKen NLar
- 'Merrimack' CKen
- 'Minima' ♀H7 CDoC CDul CKen EUJe MBlu MBri NLar NPCo NWea SLim
- 'Minuta' CKen NPCo
§ - Nana Group EPla NPri SEWo
- 'Nana' see *P. strobus* Nana Group
- 'Nana Compacta' LRHS NPCo
- 'Nivea' see *P. strobus* 'Alba'
- 'Northway Broom' CKen SLim
- 'Pacific Sunrise' NLar
- 'Pendula' CAco CKen IDee MBlu
I - 'Pendula Broom' CKen
- 'Radiata' CTri
- 'Reinshaus' CKen
- 'Sayville' CKen
- 'Sea Urchin' CKen LRHS MAsh NLar SLim
- 'Secrest' LRHS NLar
- 'Squiggles' **new** NLar
- 'Stowe Pillar' NLar SLim
- 'Tiny Kurls' CKen MAsh NLar SLim
- 'Torulosa' MBlu
- 'Uncatena' CKen
- 'Verkade's Broom' CKen NPCo

sylvestris Widely available
- 'Abergeldie' CKen
- 'Alderly Edge' CMen
- 'Andorra' CKen
§ - 'Argentea' CMen NPCo SLim
§ - Aurea Group CDul CKen CMac CMen EBee EHul EPla EUJe MAsh MBlu MJak NEgg NLar NPCo NPri NWea SCoo SLim SSta
- 'Aurea' see *P. sylvestris* Aurea Group
- 'Avondene' CKen
- 'Bergfield' CMen
- 'Beuvronensis' ♀H7 CMen MGos NEgg NPCo
- 'Buchanan's Gold' CKen
- 'Burghfield' CMen
- 'Chantry Blue' CMen EHul MAsh MBri MGos NEgg NLar NPCo SCoo SLim SPoG
- 'Clumber Blue' CKen
- 'Dereham' CKen
- 'Doone Valley' CKen NEgg NPCo
- 'Edwin Hillier' see *P. sylvestris* 'Argentea'
- Fastigiata Group CDoC CDul CEnd CKen CMac CMen GQue IDee LRHS NPCo SCoo SLim SPoG WCFE
- 'Frensham' ♀H7 CKen LRHS MAsh MBri MGos NPCo
- 'Globosa' NPCo
- 'Gold Coin' ♀H7 CDoC CDul CKen CMen EPfP MAsh NEgg NPCo SPoG WGor
- 'Gold Medal' CKen SLim
- 'Grand Rapids' CKen
- 'Gwydyr Castle' CKen
- 'Hillside Creeper' CKen SLim
- 'Humble Pie' CKen
- 'Inverleith' (v) EHul
- 'Jeremy' CKen NPCo
- 'John Boy' CMen
- 'Kelpie' SLim
- 'Kenwith' CKen
- 'Lakeside Dwarf' CMen
- 'Lodge Hill' CMen MAsh NPCo SLim
- 'Longmoor' CKen
- 'Martham' CKen CMen
- 'Mitsch Weeping' CKen
* - 'Moseri' LRHS MAsh NLar NPCo
- Nana Group **new** NPCo
- 'Nana' misapplied see *P. sylvestris* 'Watereri'
- 'Nana Compacta' CMen NPCo
§ - 'Nisbet's Gem' CKen CMen SLim
- 'Padworth' CMen
- 'Perkeo' NLar
- 'Piskowitz' CKen
- 'Pixie' CKen
I - 'Prostrata' NPCo
- 'Pygmaea' NPCo
- 'Repens' CKen
- 'Saint George' CKen
- 'Saxatilis' CKen CMen
- subsp. ***scotica*** GQue NWea
- 'Scott's Dwarf' see *P. sylvestris* 'Nisbet's Gem'
- 'Sentinel' CKen
- 'Skjak I' CKen
- 'Skjak II' CKen
- 'Spaan's Slow Column' CKen SCoo SLim
- 'Tage' CKen
- 'Tanya' CKen
- 'Tilhead' CKen
- 'Treasure' CKen MBri
- 'Trefrew Quarry' CKen
- 'Troll Guld' NLar
- 'Vargguld' CKen
§ - 'Watereri' CNWT EHul LAst LRHS MJak NLar NPCo NPri SCob SCoo SLim
- 'Westonbirt' CKen CMen MAsh
- 'Wintergold' **new** SPer

tabuliformis CAco

taeda EPfP WPGP

taiwanensis CDoC CDul EPfP

thunbergii CDul CLnd CMCN CMen ELan GQue IDee MMuc NSoo SBod
- 'Akame' CKen CMen
- 'Akame Yatsabusa' CMen
- 'Aocha-matsu' (v) CKen CMen
- 'Arakawa-sho' CKen CMen
- 'Banshosho' CKen CMen
- 'Beni-kujaku' CKen CMen
- 'Compacta' CKen CMen
- var. ***corticosa*** 'Fuji' CMen

- - 'Iihara'	CMen
- 'Dainagon'	CKen CMen
- 'Eechee-nee'	CKen
- 'Hayabusa'	CMen
- 'Iwai'	CMen
- 'Janome'	CMen
- 'Katsuga'	CMen
- 'Kotobuki'	CKen CMen NPCo
- 'Koyosho'	CMen
- 'Kujaku'	CKen CMen
- 'Kyokko'	CKen CMen
- 'Kyushu'	CKen CMen
- 'Mikawa'	CMen MBlu
- 'Miyajuna'	CKen CMen
- 'Nishiki-ne'	CKen CMen
- 'Nishiki-tsusaka'	CMen
- 'Oculus-draconis' (v)	CMen NPCo
- 'Ogi-matsu' **new**	CKen
- 'Ōgon'	CMen NLar SLim
- 'Porky'	CKen CMen
§ - 'Sayonara' ♀H7	CMen MAsh NLar NPCo
- 'Senryu'	CKen CMen
- 'Shinsho'	CKen CMen
- 'Shio-guro'	CKen CMen
- 'Suchiro'	NEgg NPCo
- 'Suchiro Yatabusa'	CKen CMen
- 'Sunsho'	CKen CMen
- 'Taihei'	CKen CMen
I - 'Thunderhead' ♀H7	CDoC CKen CMen NLar NSoo SLim
- 'W.B.'	CKen
- 'Yatsubusa'	see *P. thunbergii* 'Sayonara'
- 'Ye-i-kan'	CKen
- 'Yoshimura'	CMen
- 'Yumaki'	CKen CMen
uncinata	see *P. mugo* subsp. *uncinata*
- 'Etschtal'	CKen
- 'Grünne Welle'	SLim
- 'Jezek'	CKen
- 'Kostelnicek'	CKen
- 'Leuco-like'	CKen
- 'Offenpass'	CKen
- 'Süsse Perle'	CKen
virginiana 'Wate's Golden'	CKen NLar SLim
§ ***wallichiana*** ♀H6	Widely available
- 'Densa'	NLar
- 'Frosty'	CKen
- 'Nana' ♀H6	CKen NLar SCoo SLim
- var. ***wallichiana***	EUJe
- 'Zebrina' (v)	MBlu NHol NLar
yunnanensis	CDoC

Piper (*Piperaceae*)

auritum	GPoy LEdu
excelsum	see *Macropiper excelsum*
heydei B&SWJ 10445 **new**	WCru

Piptanthus (*Papilionaceae*)

forrestii	see *P. nepalensis*
laburnifolius	see *P. nepalensis*
§ ***nepalensis***	CBcs CDul CSpe EBee ELan EPfP LAst LRHS MGil MGos MPie MSCN NBid NLar NSoo SBrt SPer SPhx SPoG SRms WPat
aff. ***nepalensis***	SWvt
tomentosus	CFil

Pistacia (*Anacardiaceae*)

chinensis	CBcs EBtc EPfP WPGP
lentiscus	CArn CBcs EBee ETwe EUJe SEND SVen XSen
terebinthus	XSen
- NJM 11.004 **new**	WPGP

Pistia (*Araceae*)

stratiotes	CBAq MSKA NPer SCoo

Pitavia (*Rutaceae*)

punctata	IDee

Pitcairnia (*Bromeliaceae*)

bergii	CHll
grafii **new**	WCot
heterophylla	WCot
recurvata	WCot
ringens	WCot

Pittosporum ✿ (*Pittosporaceae*)

anomalum	CCCN CDoC ECou MOWG SEle
- (f)	ECou
- (m)	ECou
- 'Falcon'	ECou
'Arundel Green' ♀H4	CDoC EPfP LRHS MAsh MBri SCob SHil SLim SWvt
bicolor	CPne CTsd GQui WPGP
buchananii	SVen
colensoi	ECou
- 'Cobb' (f)	ECou
- 'Wanaka' (m)	ECou
'Collaig Silver'	EPfP LRHS MAsh SLim
crassifolium	CBcs CCCN CHEx CSde CTsd ECou
- 'Havering Dwarf' (f)	ECou
- 'Napier' (f)	ECou
- 'Variegatum' (v)	CBcs CCCN WPat
'Crinkles' (f)	ECou SVen
daphniphylloides	CHEx EBee ELan WPGP
- B&SWJ 6789	WCru
- CWJ 12404 **new**	WCru
- RWJ 9913	WCru
'Dark Delight' (m)	ECou
'Essex' (f/v)	ECou
eugenioides	CHEx CSam CSde ESwi SEND
- 'Platinum' (v)	CBcs CCCN ELan
- 'Variegatum' (v) ♀H4	CBcs CCCN CDoC CDul CHEx CHel CMac CSde EHoe ELan EPfP EUJe EWTr GQui IArd LAst LRHS MBri MGos NLar SCob SEND SHil SKHP SLim SVen
'Garnettii' (v) ♀H4	Widely available
glabratum B&SWJ 11685	WCru
heterophyllum	ECou ECrN ELan EPfP EWes SEND
- variegated (v)	EBtc ECou LRHS SEND WSHC
'Holbrook' (v)	CSam
'Humpty Dumpty'	ECou
illicioides	WCru
var. ***angustifolium*** B&SWJ 6771	
- - RWJ 9846	WCru
- var. ***illicioides*** B&SWJ 6712	WCru
- - PAB 9004 **new**	LEdu
× ***intermedium***	SWvt
- 'Craxten' (f)	CCCN ECou
michiei	ECou
- (f)	ECou
- (m)	ECou
- 'Jack' (m)	ECou

- 'Jill' (f) ECou
'Nanum Variegatum' see *P. tobira* 'Variegatum'
obcordatum ECou
oblongilimbum WCru
DJHV 06137
'Oliver Twist' LRHS SCob SCoo
omeiense EWes SKHP
- VdL 80626 **new** WPGP
pimeleoides ECou
var. ***reflexum*** (m)
ralphii CCCN CTsd ECou
- 'Green Globe' SKHP
- 'Variegatum' (v) CCCN LRHS SKHP WPGP
ralphii* × *tenuifolium ECou
'Saundersii' (v) SCoo
tenuifolium Widely available
- 'Abbotsbury Gold' (f/v) Widely available
- 'Atropurpureum' CBcs ELan
- 'Brockhill Compact' LRHS
- 'Cornish Mist' CTsd
- 'County Park' CCCN EUJe
- 'County Park Dwarf' ECou
§ - 'Eila Keightley' (v) CMHG
- 'Elizabeth' (m/v) CAbP CBcs CDoC CMac CNec ECou EHoe EPfP EShb EUJe EWTr IArd LRHS LSou MAsh MBri MGos MRav NLar SCob SEND SHil SLim SPoG
- 'French Lace' CBcs CCCN CSde ELan NLar SEND WFar
- 'Gold Star' CChe CDoC COtt EAEE ECou EHoe ELan ELon EPfP LAst LBMP LRHS MAsh MBri MGos SCob SCoo SLim SPer SPoG SWvt WMoo WRHF
- 'Golden Cut' NLar
- 'Golden King' CCCN CDoC CMHG CMac CSBt EPfP LRHS MAsh MBri MGos NPla SHil SLim SPoG SRms
- 'Golf Ball'PBR CBcs CDoC EPfP EUJe LRHS MBri MGos SCob SHil
- 'Green Elf' ECou
- 'Green Thumb' CMac ELan
- 'Irene Paterson' (m/v) ♀H4 Widely available
- 'James Stirling' CCCN
- 'John Flanagan' see *P. tenuifolium* 'Margaret Turnbull'
- 'Limelight' (v) CSBt EBtc EPfP LRHS MGos SLim SPoG
- 'Loxhill Gold' CCCN IArd LRHS SGol SHil
§ - 'Margaret Turnbull' (v) CBcs ECou ELan EPfP EWes GKin LRHS MGos SGol SHil
- 'Marjory Channon' (v) ELan EPfP LRHS
- 'Moonlight' (v) CBcs EHoe LRHS MRav SCob
- 'Mountain Green' CMac
- 'Nutty's Leprechaun' CCCN
- 'Pompom' CCCN EBee IVic LRHS
- 'Purpureum' (m) CCCN CMac CSBt CSam CTri EHoe EPfP EUJe EWoo LAst LRHS MAsh MWat NEgg NLar SCob SCoo SEND SHil SLim SPer SPoG SRms WFar WSHC
- 'Silver Magic' (v) CBcs COtt EPfP LRHS NLar SCob SEle
- 'Silver Princess' (f) ECou
- 'Silver Queen' (f/v) ♀H4 Widely available
- 'Silver Sheen' (m) CBcs CJun CMac COtt ECou LRHS
- 'Stevens Island' CBcs CJun
- 'Stirling Gold' (f/v) ECou EPfP EWes
- 'Sunburst' see *P. tenuifolium* 'Eila Keightley'
- 'Tandara Gold' (v) CBcs CCCN COtt CSBt ECou EHoe ELan ELon EPfP EUJe LBMP LRHS MAsh MBri MGos SCob SCoo SLim SPoG WCot
- 'Tiki' (m) CBcs CCCN
- 'Tom Thumb' ♀H4 Widely available
- 'Tresederi' (f/m) CCCN CTsd ECou
- 'Variegatum' (m/v) CBcs CDoC CSBt EAEE ECou EPla LRHS MGos MSwo SArc SCob SGbt SHil SLim SPer SPoG SWvt WHar
- 'Victoria' (v) CBcs CCCN LRHS MGos SHil SLim
- 'Warnham Gold' (m) ♀H3 CBcs CDoC CMac CSde EBee ECou ELan EPfP GKin IVic LRHS MAsh MGos SHil SLim SPer SPoG SSpi SVen WCot
- 'Wendle Channon' (m/v) CBcs CCCN CMHG CMac COtt CSBt ECou EHoe EPfP LBMP LRHS MAsh SGol SLim SPer WSHC
- 'Wrinkled Blue' CBcs EPfP LRHS MAsh MRav SPoG
tobira ♀H3 Widely available
- B&SWJ 12758 **new** WCru
* - 'Cuneatum' CCCN CDoC CExl ELan EPfP LRHS SKHP
* - 'Nanum' CAco CBcs CCCN CDoC CHel CMac EAEE ELan EPfP EUJe LPal LRHS MGos MOWG SArc SCob SLim SPer SPoG
- 'Tall 'n' Tough' **new** WPGP
§ - 'Variegatum' (v) ♀H4 CBcs CCCN CMac CSde ELan EPfP EUJe IVic LRHS MGos NLar SArc SCob SEND SKHP SLim SLon SPer SPoG WSHC
'Trim's Hedger' CTho
undulatum CHEx
viridiflorum EShb

Pityrogramma (*Pteridaceae*)

trifoliata WCot

Plagianthus (*Malvaceae*)

betulinus see *P. regius*
lyallii see *Hoberia lyallii*
§ ***regius*** CBcs

Plagiorhegma see *Jeffersonia*

Plantago (*Plantaginaceae*)

asiatica 'Variegata' (v) NBro
coronopus CAgr CArn
holosteum GKev
lanceolata CArn CHab NMir WHfH WSFF
- 'Freaky' WHer
major CArn GPoy WSFF
- 'Atropurpurea' see *P. major* 'Rubrifolia'
- 'Bowles's Variety' see *P. major* 'Rosularis'
- 'Brenda' CNat
- 'Everywhere I Glow' CNat
§ - 'Rosularis' CArn CBre CFis CSpe EBee LEdu MHer NBro NChi SPav SRms WHer
§ - 'Rubrifolia' CArn CBod CHid CSpe EShb LLWG MHer MMuc NBid NBro NChi NDov SHar WHer WMoo WSFF XLum
maritima WHer
media CHab MHer
nivalis GEdr

	psyllium L.	CArn
	rosea	see *P. major* 'Rosularis'
	triandra 'Wanaka'	IMou

Platanthera (*Orchidaceae*)

	hologlottis	EFEx
	metabifolia	EFEx

Platanus ✿ (*Platanaceae*)

	× ***acerifolia***	see *P.* × *hispanica*
§	× ***hispanica*** ♀H6	CAco CBcs CCVT CDul CLnd CMCN EBee ECrN ELan EPfP LAst LBuc MGos MMuc NWea SCob SEND SEWo SGol SPer WMou
	- 'Bloodgood'	CAco CTho
	orientalis	CAco CCVT CDul CLnd CMCN CTho EPfP SCob
	- PAB 346	LEdu
	- 'Cuneata'	ECrN
§	- f. ***digitata*** ♀H6	CCVT CDul CLnd CMCN CTho EBee EPfP ERod
	- 'Laciniata'	see *P. orientalis* f. *digitata*
	- 'Minaret'	CDul
	- 'Mirkovec'	EPfP IArd MBri

Platycarya (*Juglandaceae*)

	strobilacea	CBcs CMCN LEdu

Platycerium (*Polypodiaceae*)

	alcicorne misapplied	see *P. bifurcatum*
§	***bifurcatum*** ♀H1b	CCCN XBlo
	- 'Netherlands'	NLos
	'Lemoinei'	NLos

Platycladus (*Cupressaceae*)

§	***orientalis*** 'Aurea Nana' ♀H7	CKen CMac CSBt EHul ELan EPfP EPla LBee LRHS MAsh MGos MJak NWad NWea SGol SLim SPoG
	- 'Autumn Glow'	CKen
	- 'Beverleyensis'	NLar
	- 'Caribbean Holiday'	MAsh
	- 'Collen's Gold'	EHul
	- 'Conspicua'	CKen CSBt EHul
	- 'Elegantissima'	EHul LRHS
	- 'Franky Boy' ♀H6	CDoC NLar SLim SPoG
	- 'Golden Pygmy'	CKen MAsh
	- 'Juniperoides'	EHul
	- 'Kenwith'	CKen
	- 'Magnifica'	EHul
	- 'Meldensis'	CDoC CTri EHul
	- 'Minima'	EHul
	- 'Minima Glauca'	CKen
I	- 'Pyramidalis Aurea'	LBee
	- 'Rosedalis'	CKen CSBt EHul EPfP LBee MAsh
	- 'Sanderi'	WCFE
	- 'Shirley Chilcott'	MAsh
	- 'Sieboldii'	EHul
	- 'Southport'	LBee
	- 'Summer Cream'	CKen EHul

Platycodon ✿ (*Campanulaceae*)

	grandiflorus ♀H5	CArn CTri ECha ECho ELau EPfP MHer SRms WHar WHoo
	- 'Albus'	ECho EPfP LRHS SPer SWvt WHar WHoo
	- Apoyama Group ♀H5	WHoo WThu
	- - 'Fairy Snow'	CHel EShb WHoo WSHC
	- Astra Series	EBee
	- - 'Astra Blue'	EPfP SPoG SRot
	- - 'Astra Pink'	SPoG
	- - 'Astra White'	EBee SPoG
	- 'Blue Pearl'	WHoo
	- 'Florist Blue'	SGSe
	- 'Florist Rose'	SGSe
	- 'Florist Snow'	SGSe
	- 'Fuji Blue'	WHoo XLum
	- 'Fuji Pink'	ECho ELan LRHS MRav SWvt WHoo WWEG XLum
	- 'Fuji White'	ELan WHoo WWEG XLum
	- 'Hakone'	MRav
	- 'Hakone Blue'	CHel EPfP NBre SGSe
	- 'Hakone Double Blue' (d)	ELan SRms
	- 'Hakone White'	EPfP LSun MRav SGSe
	- 'Mariesii' ♀H5	CBod CSBt EAEE EPfP EPla IBoy LAst LPla LRHS MHol MMuc MNHC MRav MWat NBir NEgg SEND SPer SPlb SRms SWvt WAul WHoo
	- 'Miss Tilly'	MHol
	- Mother of Pearl	see *P. grandiflorus* 'Perlmutterschale'
§	- 'Perlmutterschale'	EBee EPfP MRav
	- 'Pink Star'	EBee
	- ***pumilus***	WHoo
	- 'Sentimental Blue'	XLum
	- 'Shell Pink'	see *P. grandiflorus* 'Perlmutterschale'
	- 'Willy'	XLum
	- 'Zwerg'	EShb NBre

Platycrater (*Hydrangeaceae*)

	arguta	WCru WPGP
	- B&SWJ 6266	WCru

Plectranthus (*Lamiaceae*)

	sp.	LAst
	from Puerto Rico	CArn
	ambiguus	EOHP
	- 'Manguzuku' ♀H1c	EOHP
	- 'Nico'	EOHP
	- 'Umigoye'	EOHP
	amboinicus	CArn EOHP MNHC WJek
*	- 'Variegatus' (v)	EOHP
	- 'Well Sweep Wedgewood' (v)	EOHP
	argentatus ♀H1c	CBcs CDoC CSpe EOHP EUJe GCal IDee MCot SDix SRkn WHea
	- 'Hill House' (v)	CHII CPne EOHP EShb
	- 'Silver Shield'	EShb MPie
	australis misapplied	see *P. verticillatus*
	barbatus	EOHP
	- 'Vicki'	CPne
	behrii	see *P. fruticosus*
	Blue Angel = 'Edelblau' (Cape Angels Series)	EOHP
	caninus	SPoG
	ciliatus	EOHP EShb EUJe SRkn
	- 'Easy Gold' (v) ♀H1c	EOHP
	- 'Richard' **new**	CPne
	- 'Sasha' (v)	CCCN CDoC CHII ECtt EOHP EShb
	'Cloud Nine'	EOHP
	coleoides 'Marginatus'	see *P. forsteri* 'Marginatus'
	- 'Variegatus'	see *P. madagascariensis* 'Variegated Mintleaf'
	Cuban oregano	EOHP
	ecklonii	EOHP
	- 'Medley Wood'	EOHP

	ernstii	EOHP
	excisus	CDes EBee IMou SBrt WPGP
	forskohlii	EOHP
§	***forsteri*** 'Marginatus'	EOHP WHea
	'Frills'	EOHP
§	***fruticosus***	CPne EOHP EUJe
	- 'James' ♀H1c	EOHP EUJe
	hadiensis	EOHP
	var. ***tomentosus***	
	- - 'Carnegie'	EOHP
	- - green-leaved	EOHP
	- - 'Penge' (v)	EOHP
	- var. ***woodii***	EOHP
	madagascariensis	EOHP
	- gold-leaved	EOHP
	- 'Lothlorien' (v)	EOHP
§	- 'Variegated Mintleaf' (v) ♀H1c	EOHP MNHC SRms
	'Marble Ruffles'	EOHP
	'Menthol Eucalyptus' new	EOHP
	menthol-scented, large-leaved	EOHP
	menthol-scented, small-leaved	EOHP
	Mona Lavender = 'Plepalila'PBR ♀H1c	EOHP
	montanus	EOHP
	mutabilis	EOHP
	neochilus	CSpe
§	***oertendahlii*** ♀H1c	EBak EOHP
	- silver-leaved	EOHP
	ornatus	NPla
	- 'Pee Off'	EOHP
	- variegated (v)	EOHP
	prostratus	EOHP
	pseudomarrubioides new	EOHP
	purpuratus small-leaved	EOHP
	rotundifolius	LEdu
	saccatus	EOHP
	subsp. ***longitubus***	
	- subsp. ***pondoensis***	EOHP
	sinensis	LRHS
	spicatus	EOHP
	- 'Nelspruit'	EOHP
	strigosus	EOHP
	Swedish ivy	see *P. verticillatus*, *P. oertendahlii*
§	***thyrsoideus***	EOHP
	venteri new	EOHP
§	***verticillatus***	EOHP
	- 'Barberton'	EOHP
	- 'Pink Surprise'	EOHP
	Vick's plant	EOHP
	zatarhendii	EOHP
	zuluensis	CArn CDoC CPne EOHP EUJe SDix SRkn WBor
	- dark-leaved	EOHP
	- 'Sky'	EOHP

Pleioblastus (*Poaceae*)

	akebono	see *P. argenteostriatus* 'Akebono'
§	***argenteostriatus*** 'Akebono'	ERod
§	- 'Okinadake' (v)	EPla
§	- f. ***pumilus***	CDoC EHoe EPla ERod MMuc MWht SPlb
	auricomus	see *P. viridistriatus*
	- 'Vagans'	see *Sasaella ramosa*
	chino	see *P. argenteostriatus* 'Okinadake'
	var. ***argenteostriatus***	
	- f. ***aureostriatus*** (v)	MMoz
	- f. ***elegantissimus***	CCon CDoC CEnt EPfP EPla ERod EShb MMoz MMuc NLar SBig SEND WMoo
	- var. ***hisauchii***	ERod MWht
	fortunei	see *P. variegatus* 'Fortunei'
	'Gauntlettii'	see *P. argenteostriatus* f. *pumilus*
	glaber 'Albostriatus'	see *Sasaella masamuneana* 'Albostriata'
	gramineus	EPla
§	***hindsii***	EPla ERod MMoz
§	***humilis***	MWhi SEND
	- var. ***pumilus***	see *P. argenteostriatus* f. *pumilus*
	linearis	ERod LRHS MMoz MWht NLar SBig WMoo
§	***pygmaeus***	CDoC CDul CTri CTsd EHoe ELan EPla GKev MBrN MJak MMuc MWhi NBro NGdn NLar SCob SGol SRms WMoo
§	- 'Distichus'	CEnt EPPr EPla MJak MWht NLar WMoo
§	- 'Mirrezuzume'	CExl
*	- var. ***pygmaeus*** 'Mini'	MMuc SEND WCot
§	***simonii***	LRHS MMuc MWht NLar SEND XBlo
	- 'Variegatus' (v)	LRHS SPer
§	***variegatus*** (v) ♀H4	CBcs CDoC CDul CEnt EHoe ELan ELon EPfP EPla LEdu LPot LRHS MBrN MJak MWht NSoo SArc SCob SDix SLim SPlb SWvt WMoo XBlo
§	- 'Fortunei' (v)	CTsd MMuc SEND SGol
	- 'Tsuboii' (v)	CAbb CDTJ CDoC EPla ERod MBrN MBri MJak MMoz MWhi MWht NLar SGol WMoo
§	***viridistriatus*** ♀H5	CBcs CDoC CDul CEnt CExl ECha EHoe ELon EPfP EPla ERod GMaP LEdu LRHS MBri MJak MMoz MMuc MRav MWht NLar NWsh SCob SDix SEND SGol SPer SRms WMoo XBlo
	- 'Chrysophyllus'	EPla
	- f. ***variegatus*** (v)	CTsd SWvt WMoo

Pleione (*Orchidaceae*)

	sp.	NDav
	Alishan gx 'Merlin'	LYaf
	- 'Mother's Day'	GEdr LYaf
	- 'Mount Fuji'	LYaf
	Anstice Harris gx new	LYaf
	Asama gx 'Red Grouse'	GEdr LYaf
	Askia gx	GEdr
	aurita	GEdr GKev LYaf
	Bandai-san gx 'Sand Grouse'	LYaf
	× ***barbarae***	IFoB LYaf
	Barcena gx	LYaf
	Berapi gx 'Purple Sandpiper'	LEdu LYaf
	Betty Arnold gx	LYaf
	Brigadoon gx 'Stonechat'	LEdu LYaf
	Britannia gx 'Doreen'	EPot LYaf
§	***bulbocodioides***	CExl CFil EPot GEdr GKev LYaf
	- 'New Forest'	GEdr
§	- 'Yunnan'	GEdr IFoB
	Burnsall gx	GEdr
	Captain Hook gx	LYaf
	Caroli gx 'Cape Robin'	LYaf
	chunii	EFEx GEdr LAma LYaf
	Confirmation gx new	LYaf
	Eastfield gx 'Purple Emperor'	LYaf

Eiger gx	LYaf
El Pico gx 'Pheasant'	EPot LYaf
Erebus gx 'Redpoll'	GEdr LYaf
formosana ♀H3	CCon CFil CPne CTsd ECho EFEx EPot GKev LAma LEdu LRHS MHer WFar WPGP
- Alba Group	ECho GKev WFar
- - 'Claire'	IFoB LEdu LYaf
- - 'Snow Bunting'	LEdu LYaf
- 'Blush of Dawn'	GLin
- 'Cairngorm'	GKev IFoB
- 'Greenhill'	LYaf
- 'Hanka' **new**	GKev
- Hyb 8001	IFoB
- 'Iris'	IFoB
- 'Litomysi' **new**	GKev
- 'Pitlochry'	LYaf
- (Pricei Group) 'Oriental Grace'	IFoB LYaf
- - 'Oriental Splendour'	LYaf
- 'Snow Cap'	ECho GKev
- 'Snow White'	CExl CFil LEdu LYaf WPGP
forrestii	ECho EFEx EPot GKev LAma
Fuego gx	GKev IFoB
Gerry Mundey gx	GEdr
- 'Tinney's Firs'	LYaf
Glacier Peak gx new	LYaf
Harlequin gx 'Norman'	LYaf
Hekla gx	IFoB
- 'Locking Stumps'	GEdr
- 'Partridge'	GEdr LYaf
- 'Partridge' × **Zeus Weinstein gx**	GEdr
hookeriana	GKev
humilis	GKev LYaf
Irazu gx	IFoB
- 'Cheryl'	GEdr
Jorullo gx 'Long-tailed Tit'	GEdr LYaf
Keith Rattray gx 'Kelty'	LYaf
Kenya gx 'Bald Eagle'	LYaf
Krakatoa gx 'Wheatear'	LYaf
Lascar gx 'Dipper'	LYaf
- 'Purple Finch'	LYaf
Leda gx	LYaf
Lhasa gx 'Blushes'	LYaf
limprichtii ♀H3	ECho EFEx EPot GKev IFoB LEdu LYaf
Lyn Butterfield gx	LYaf
maculata	EFEx GKev
Mageik gx 'Black Kite' **new**	LYaf
Mandalay gx 'Purple Rain'	LYaf
- 'Strawberry Fields'	LYaf
Marion Johnson gx	LYaf
Mauna Loa gx	LYaf
- 'Glossy Starling'	LYaf
Mawenzi gx	LYaf
Michael Butterfield gx	LYaf
Novarupta gx 'Goshawk'	LYaf
- 'Raven'	LYaf
Orinoco gx 'Gemini'	GEdr
Orizaba gx	GEdr
- 'Fish Eagle'	LYaf
Piton gx	EPot LYaf
§ ***pleionoides***	LYaf
pogonioides misapplied	see *P. pleionoides*
pogonioides (Rolfe) Rolfe	see *P. bulbocodioides*
praecox	GKev
Quizapu gx 'Peregrine'	LYaf
Rakata gx	IFoB
- 'Locking Stumps'	EPot GEdr
- 'Redwing'	LYaf
- 'Shot Silk'	GEdr LYaf
'Rossini' **new**	ECho GKev
Salek gx 'Eagle Owl'	LYaf
Sangay gx	LYaf
Santa Maria gx 'Nightjar' **new**	LYaf
Santorini gx	LYaf
- 'Yellow Wagtail'	LYaf
saxicola	LYaf
scopulorum	EFEx LYaf
Shantung gx	CCon EPot LAma
- 'Ducat'	LYaf
- 'Gerry Mundey'	LYaf
- 'Muriel Harberd' ♀H3	GEdr
- 'Ridgeway'	LYaf
- 'Silver Anniversary'	LYaf
Shasta gx	LYaf
Sirena gx	LYaf
Sorea gx	GEdr
Soufrière gx	GEdr LYaf
speciosa Ames & Schltr.	see *P. pleionoides*
Stromboli gx 'Fireball'	CExl CFil EPot LEdu
Taal gx 'Red-tailed Hawk'	LYaf
× ***taliensis***	LYaf
Tarawera gx	LYaf
Tibesti gx	LYaf
Till Eulenspiegel gx new	GKev
Toff gx	LYaf
Tolima gx 'Moorhen'	LEdu LYaf
Tongariro gx	CPBP ECho EPot GEdr GKev
Ueli Wackernagel gx	GEdr
- 'Pearl' **new**	LYaf
'Verdi' **new**	ECho GKev
Versailles gx	EPot
- 'Bucklebury'	EPot GEdr
- 'Muriel Turner'	GEdr
Vesuvius gx	EPot GKev
- 'Grey Wagtail'	LYaf
- 'Leopard'	GKev LYaf
- 'Phoenix'	EPot GKev LYaf
- 'Tawny Owl'	GEdr LYaf
'Vivaldi' **new**	ECho GKev
Volcanello gx 'Honey Buzzard'	GEdr LYaf
- 'Song Thrush'	LYaf
Whakari gx	LYaf
Wharfedale gx 'Pine Warbler'	LYaf
yunnanensis misapplied	see *P. bulbocodioides* 'Yunnan'
yunnanensis ambig.	GEdr GKev LAma
Zeus Weinstein gx	IFoB LYaf WCot
- 'Desert Sands'	GEdr

Pleomele see *Dracaena*

Pleurospermum (Apiaceae)

sp.	CSpe
from Nepal	WCot
aff. ***album*** KWJ 12281	WCru
aff. ***amabile*** BWJ 7886	WCru
benthamii B&SWJ 2988	WCru
calcareum B&SWJ 8008	WCru
camtschaticum B&SWJ 12627 **new**	WCru
aff. ***stylosum*** CC 5355 **new**	WCot

yunnanense BWJ 7952A	WCru

plum see *Prunus domestica*

Plumbago (*Plumbaginaceae*)

§ ***auriculata*** ♀H2	CBcs CCCN CDoC CHEx CSBt CTri CWCL EBak ELan EPfP EPri EShb EUJe IDee MOWG MRav SEND SMrm SPer SPoG SRms
- f. ***alba*** ♀H2	CBcs CCCN CHEx CRHN EPfP EShb IDee MOWG SEND
- 'Crystal Waters'	CCCN CSam EShb
- dark blue-flowered	CRHN CSpe
- 'Escapade Blue' (Escapade Series)	CWGN SPre
capensis	see *P. auriculata*
larpentiae	see *Ceratostigma plumbaginoides*

Plumeria (*Apocynaceae*)

sp.	WSFF
rubra ♀H1b	XBlo
- 'Golden Glow'	XBlo
- 'Velvet Red'	XBlo

Poa (*Poaceae*)

alpina	SMea XLum
chaixii	EHoe EPPr
cita	IMou
colensoi	EHoe GAbr
× ***jemtlandica***	EHoe EPPr
labillardierei	CKno CWCL EBee ECha EHoe EPPr IMou LRHS MAvo MMuc NWsh SEND SPer WMoo XLum
pratensis	CHab

Podalyria (*Papilionaceae*)

calyptrata	SPlb
sericea	SPlb

Podanthus (*Asteraceae*)

ovatifolius	SVen

Podocarpus ✿ (*Podocarpaceae*)

acutifolius	CBcs CDoC ECou IGor
- (f)	ECou
- (m)	ECou
alpinus R. Br. ex Hook. f.	CDul
andinus	see *Prumnopitys andina*
'Autumn Shades' (m)	NLar
'Blaze' (f)	CBcs CDoC LEdu MBrN NLar SLim SPoG
chilinus	see *P. salignus*
'Chocolate Box' (f)	ECou MAsh NLar
'County Park Fire' PBR (f) ♀H6	CBcs CDoC ECou EHul EPfP EPla ESwi MAsh MBri MGos NHol NLar SCoo SLim SPoG SWvt
'County Park Treasure'	ECou
cunninghamii 'Roro' (m)	CBcs CDoC ECou
cunninghamii* × *nivalis (f)	ECou
dacrydioides	see *Dacrycarpus dacrydioides*
elongatus 'Blue Chip'	CBcs
'Flame'	CDoC EHul MAsh NLar
'Guardsman'	ECou
'Havering' (f)	CDoC ECou
'Jill' (f)	ECou
latifolius	ECou
lawrencei	CBcs EHul
- (f)	ECou
- 'Blue Gem' (f)	CDoC ECou MAsh MGos MMuc SCoo SLim
- 'Kiandra'	ECou
- 'Kosciuszko'	ECou
- 'Pine Lake'	ECou
- 'Red Tip'	CDoC CMen MBri MGos SLim
'Lucky Lad'	ECou
macrophyllus	CDoC SArc
- 'Aureus'	CBcs
'Maori Prince' (m)	CDoC ECou NLar
matudae	CFil
nivalis	CBcs CDul CMac ECou GCal SRms WThu
- 'Arthur' (m)	ECou
- 'Bronze'	CDoC GCal
- 'Christmas Lights' (f)	ECou
- 'Clarence' (m)	ECou
- 'Hikurangi'	CDoC
- 'Kaweka' (m)	ECou
- 'Kilworth Cream' (v) ♀H6	CBcs CDoC CMen ECou EPla ESwi NHol NLar SLim SWvt
- 'Little Lady' (f)	ECou
- 'Moffat' (f)	CDoC ECou
- 'Otari' (m)	CDoC ECou MAsh NLar
- 'Park Cover'	ECou
- 'Princess' (f)	MBrN
- 'Ruapehu' (m)	CDoC ECou EPla
- 'Trompenburg'	NLar
nubigenus	CBcs
'Orangeade' (f)	NLar
'Red Embers' (f)	CDoC ECou EPfP ESwi SCoo
§ ***salignus*** ♀H5	CBcs CDoC CExl CHEx CTsd EPfP EUJe GGal IDee SArc SLim WSHC WThu
- (f)	ECou
- (m)	ECou
'Soldier Boy'	ECou
spicatus	see *Prumnopitys taxifolia*
'Spring Sunshine' (f)	ECou NLar
totara	CBcs CBrP ECou LEdu
- 'Aureus'	CBcs CDoC ECou
- 'Pendulus'	CDoC ECou
'Young Rusty' (f)	CBcs CDoC NLar

Podophyllum (*Berberidaceae*)

aurantiocaule	CExl GEdr GGGa
§ ***delavayi***	CBct CCon CExl ECho GEdr GKev SKHP WCot WCru
difforme	CBct CLAP ECho GEdr GKev LEdu SKHP WCot WCru
emodi	see *Sinopodophyllum hexandrum* var. *emodi*
- var. ***chinense***	see *Sinopodophyllum hexandrum* var. *chinense*
hexandrum	see *Sinopodophyllum hexandrum*
- var. ***chinense***	see *Sinopodophyllum hexandrum* var. *chinense*
'Kaleidoscope' (v)	CBct CLAP CUse ESwi EUJe GEdr MHol WCot
peltatum	CAby CArn CBct CBro CHid CLAP CWCL EBee ECho EWld GBBs GBin GKev GPoy LAma LEdu LSun NLar NMyG NSti SPhx WBor WCot WCru WPGP WPnP
pleianthum	CBct CLAP ECho GCal GEdr WCru
- B&SWJ 282 from Taiwan	WCru
- short	WCru

*	***tsayuensis***	GEdr
	veitchii	see *P. delavayi*
	versipelle	GKev LEdu SKHP WCru
	- 'Spotty Dotty'PBR (v)	CBct CExl CHel CLAP ECtt ESwi EUJe GEdr IBoy IKil ITim LEdu LRHS MAvo MHol MMHG MMoz MNrw NLar NSti SHeu SKHP SMad WCot

Podranea (*Bignoniaceae*)

§	***ricasoliana*** ℽH1c	CRHN EShb MOWG SPoG WBor

Pogonatherum (*Poaceae*)

*	***distichum***	XBlo

Pogonia (*Orchidaceae*)

	sp.	NDav
	japonica new	GKev

Pogostemon (*Lamiaceae*)

	from An Veleniki Herb Farm, Pennsylvania	CArn
§	***cablin***	EOHP GPoy
	patchouly	see *P. cablin*

Polemonium ✿ (*Polemoniaceae*)

	ambervicsii	see *P. pauciflorum* subsp. *hinckleyi*
	'Apricot Beauty'	see *P. carneum* 'Apricot Delight'
	archibaldiae ℽH5	NBir SRms WSHC
	'Blue Pearl'	CBod COtt ELan EPla GJos LRHS MNrw NBro NGdn NLar WPtf
§	***boreale***	NPol SWvt WMoo
	- 'Heavenly Habit'	GJos LRHS NGdn
	brandegeei misapplied	see *P. pauciflorum*
§	***brandegeei*** Greene	GBin
	- subsp. ***mellitum***	see *P. brandegeei* Greene
§	***caeruleum***	Widely available
	- subsp. ***amygdalinum***	see *P. occidentale*
	- 'Bambino Blue'	CBod EWoo LRHS SWvt WHar
	- Brise d'Anjou = 'Blanjou'PBR (v)	CMac CMea CMos COtt ECtt ELan EPfP EPla EWes IBoy LRHS LSun MAsh MBri NBir NGdn NPol SCob SMad SPer SWvt WWEG
	- subsp. ***caeruleum***	GKev
	- - f. ***albiflorum***	CBre CSBt CWCL CWld EBee ECha ELan EPfP EWoo GAbr LRHS MBNS MBel MHer MRav NBro SGbt SPer SPoG SRms WMoo
I	- f. ***dissectum***	NPol
	- 'Filigree Clouds'	NGdn NLar
	- 'Filigree Skies'	NGdn NLar
	- var. ***grandiflorum***	see *P. caeruleum* subsp. *himalayanum*
§	- subsp. ***himalayanum***	CSpe GAbr WMoo
	- 'Humile'	see *P.* 'Northern Lights'
	- 'Idylle'	NPol
	- 'Larch Cottage' (v)	NPol
	- 'Pam' (v)	NPol
	- 'Sky Blue'	MBel WWtn
	- 'Snow and Sapphires' (v)	CWGN EBee ECtt MAsh MPnt NLar NPer NPol SWvt
	- 'Southern Skies'	NPol
	- subsp. ***vulgare***	NPol
	- white-flowered	GJos IBoy MMuc
	carneum	CTri EBee ECha GMaP LRHS MCot NLar NPol WMoo
§	- 'Apricot Delight'	GJos MNHC MNrw NGdn NLar NPol SGbt SHar SPad WHer WPtf WWEG WWtn
	cashmerianum	see *P. caeruleum* subsp. *himalayanum*
	chartaceum	LLHF
	'Churchills'	CAby CBre EBee NPol WSHC
	'Dawn Flight'	NPol
	'Eastbury Purple'	CElw NPol
	'Elworthy Amethyst'	CElw EBee NPol
	eximium	ECho LLHF
	flavum	see *P. foliosissimum* var. *flavum*
	foliosissimum misapplied	see *P. archibaldiae*
	foliosissimum Gray	NPol
	- var. ***albiflorum***	see *P. foliosissimum* var. *alpinum*
§	- var. ***alpinum***	NPol
	- 'Bressingham'	NPol
	- 'Cottage Cream'	CDes NPol WCot
§	- var. ***flavum***	NPol
	- var. ***foliosissimum***	NPol
	- 'Scottish Garden'	NPol
	- 'White Spirit'	NPol
	'Glebe Cottage Lilac'	EBee GCra NBir NPol
	'Glebe Cottage Violet'	NPol
	'Hannah Billcliffe'	CDes CElw ECtt EWes MBrN MTis NPol
	'Heaven Scent'PBR	EBee ECtt MBri NDov NLar
	'Heavenly Blue'	IBoy
§	'Hopleys'	GCal MNrw
	× ***jacobaea***	EBee EWes WCot
	'Katie Daley'	see *P.* 'Hopleys'
	'Lambrook Mauve'	Widely available
	'Mary Mottram'	NPol
	mellitum	see *P. brandegeei* Greene
	'North Tyne'	NChi NPol
§	'Northern Lights'	Widely available
	'Norwell Mauve'	MNrw NPol
§	***occidentale***	NPol
§	***pauciflorum***	ECtt GJos IFro NBir WHea WMoo
§	- subsp. ***hinckleyi***	GKev NPol NSbr
§	- subsp. ***pauciflorum***	NPol
	- silver-leaved	see *P. pauciflorum* subsp. *pauciflorum*
	- 'Sulphur Trumpets'	SPad SWvt
	- subsp. ***typicum***	see *P. pauciflorum* subsp. *pauciflorum*
	'Pink Beauty'	CMos EBee ELan EPfP GBuc NGdn NPol WWtn
	pulchellum Salisb.	see *P. reptans*
	pulchellum Turcz.	see *P. caeruleum*
	pulcherrimum misapplied	see *P. boreale*
	- 'Tricolor'	see *P. boreale*
	pulcherrimum Hook.	ECho NBro
	- subsp. ***pulcherrimum***	LLHF
	'Rainbow Magic'	NLar
§	***reptans***	CArn GPoy MHer NBro NPol WMoo WOut
	- 'Album'	see *P. reptans* 'Virginia White'
	- 'Blue Ice'	NPol
	- 'Firmament'	EBee MAvo
*	- 'Sky Blue'	NBro
	- 'Stairway to Heaven'PBR (v)	Widely available
	- 'Touch of Class'PBR (v)	LSou MAsh NLar SPoG
§	- 'Virginia White'	CBre CElw EWes MAvo MTis NChi NPol SBch
	- 'White Pearl'	MHol NPri
	'Ribby'	NPol
	× ***richardsonii*** misapplied	see *P.* 'Northern Lights'
	× ***richardsonii*** Graham	see *P. boreale*
	'Sapphire'	CBre LRHS

	'Sonia's Bluebell'	CDes CElw CWCL ECGP ECtt EPPr EWes MAvo MNrw MPie MTis NDov NLar NPol NSti SBch WWFP
	'Sunnyside Storm'	NPol
	'Theddingworth'	EBee NPol WFar
	viscosum	LLHF NPol SPlb
	- NNS 08-268 new	GKev
	- f. ***leucanthum***	NPol
	yezoense	NBre NPol
	- var. ***hidakanum***	NPol NWad
	- - Bressingham Purple = 'Polbress'	Widely available
	- - 'Purple Rain'	Widely available

Polianthes (*Agavaceae*)

	elongata	WCot
§	***geminiflora***	WCot
	tuberosa ♀H1c	CBcs CCCN ECho GKev SPer WCot XLum
	- 'The Pearl' (d)	ECho GKev LAma SDeJ WCot XLum

Poliomintha (*Lamiaceae*)

	bustamanta	CAby NBir SPhx WSHC

Poliothyrsis (*Salicaceae*)

	sinensis	CBcs EPfP IArd IDee MBri NLar WPGP

Pollia (*Commelinaceae*)

	japonica	CCon ESwi EWes SBrt SPad WCot

Polygala (*Polygalaceae*)

	calcarea Bulley's form	EPot
	- 'Lillet' ♀H5	ECho EPot EWes GEdr LLHF LRHS SIgm WAbe WThu
	chamaebuxus ♀H5	CBcs GKev LLHF MAsh MGos NLar NSla SRms WThu
I	- ***alba***	LBee NLar SChF WAbe
§	- var. ***grandiflora*** ♀H5	CBcs CCon ECho EPfP EPot GAbr GEdr IVic LBee MAsh MGos MWat NSla SChF SPlb SPoG WAbe WIce
	- 'Loibl'	EPot
	- 'Purpurea'	see *P. chamaebuxus* var. *grandiflora*
	- 'Rhodoptera'	see *P. chamaebuxus* var. *grandiflora*
§	× ***dalmaisiana*** ♀H2	CAbb CCCN CHEx CHel CRHN CSde CSpe CTsd CWGN EBee ECre ELan EPri LRHS SEND WAbe WCFE
	'Dolomite'	GEdr
	myrtifolia ♀H2	CCCN CTre ELan GFai IDee LRHS MGos SAdn SPlb
	- Bibi Pink = 'Polylap'	SAdn
	- 'Grandiflora'	see *P.* × *dalmaisiana*
	'Purple Passion'	WHlf
	virgata	CCCN

Polygonatum ✿ (*Asparagaceae*)

	B&SWJ 8246	WCru
	HWJ 551	WCru
	HWJ 567	WCru
	HWJ 573	WCru
	HWJ 588	WCru
	Og 94047	CDes LEdu
	SBQE 130 new	MAvo
	SBQE 310 new	CDes
	acuminatifolium 'Ogon' new	EBee
	altelobatum B&SWJ 286	WCru
	- B&SWJ 1886	WCru
	arisanense B&SWJ 271	CDes WCru
	- B&SWJ 3839	WCru
§	***biflorum***	Widely available
	- dwarf	LRHS
	canaliculatum	see *P. biflorum*
	cathcartii B&SWJ 2429	WCru
	cirrhifolium	CBro CCon CCse CPom EBee ECho EPot GEdr GKev LEdu MMoz MNrw NWad SKHP WCru WPGP
	- ARGS 320	EPPr
	- red-flowered	NLar
	commutatum	see *P. biflorum*
	'Corsley'	CPou
	cryptanthum	WCru
	curvistylum	CAvo CBct CCon CLAP CPom CTal EPPr EWld GEdr IFoB IGor IMou MNFA NLar NRya SPhx WCru WSHC
	- pink-flowered	SBch
	cyrtonema misapplied	see *Disporopsis pernyi*
	cyrtonema Hua	CDes WCru
	- B&SWJ 271	LEdu MAvo
*	***desoulavyi*** var. ***yezoense*** B&SWJ 764	WCru
	falcatum misapplied	see *P. humile*
	falcatum A. Gray	EBee NRya
	- B&SWJ 1077	WCru
	- B&SWJ 5054 new	WCru
	- 'Shikoku Silver'	SMHy WCru
	- 'Variegatum'	see *P. odoratum* var. *pluriflorum* 'Variegatum'
	'Falcon'	see *P. humile*
	filipes	EPPr WCru
	fuscum	WCru
	geminiflorum	CBct CLAP CPom IGor WCru WFar
	- McB 2448	GEdr
	giganteum	see *P. biflorum*
	glaberrimum	CBct
§	***graminifolium***	CAby CBct CLAP CPBP CPom CTal ECho EPPr WCru WThu
	- G-W&P 803	ECho
§	***hirtum***	CBct CLAP CPom CPrp ECho EPPr EPla IFoB LEdu MMoz NMyG WCru
	- BM 7012	ECho
	- 'Robustum'	ECho WCru
	hookeri	CAby CBct CExl CTal ECho EPPr GBin GEdr GKev ITim LEdu LRHS NBid NCGa NLar NMyG NRya NSla SGSe SPhx WCru WFar WWEG
§	***humile***	CBct CDes CLAP CTal EBee ECho ELan EPPr EPfP GCal GEdr IBal LEdu MAvo MHer NGdn NLar NMyG SCob SGSe SWvt WBor WCru WPGP XLum
I	- 'Variegatum' (v)	CMac
§	× ***hybridum*** ♀H7	Widely available
	- 'Bere' new	LEdu
	- 'Betberg'	CAvo CBct CCon CDes CLAP CPom CRow ECha EPPr IFoB IMou LEdu NBir WCot
	- 'Flore Pleno' (d)	CBct ELon WHer
	- 'Nanum'	CBct CHid MRav WCot
	- 'Purple Katie'	NMyG
§	- 'Striatum' (v)	Widely available
	- 'Variegatum'	see *P.* × *hybridum* 'Striatum'
	- 'Weihenstephan'	GCal GKev IPot

- 'Welsh Gold' (v) CAvo
inflatum ECho WCru
- B&SWJ 922 WCru
involucratum ECho WCru
- B&SWJ 4285 WCru
japonicum see *P. odoratum*
kingianum yellow-flowered CDes
- - B&SWJ 6545 WCru
- - B&SWJ 6562 WCru
'Langthorn's Variegated' (v) ELan
lasianthum CPom ECho SMHy WCru
- B&SWJ 671 NMyG WCru
latifolium see *P. hirtum*
maximowiczii CDes EBee EPPr GCal WCru WPGP
'Multifide' EBee GKev
multiflorum misapplied see *P.* × *hybridum*
multiflorum L. Widely available
- CC 4572 WCot
- 'Flore Pleno' (d) **new** WFar
- ***giganteum*** hort. see *P. biflorum*
- 'Ramosissima' SMHy WCru
* ***nanum*** 'Variegatum' (v) CBcs ECho
nodosum WCru
§ ***odoratum*** CAvo CBct CBro CTal CTsd EBee ECho EPla GMaP NBid NLar NMyG NRya SCob WCru WWEG
- RBG 93-101 **new** EBee
- 'Angel's Wings' MAvo
- 'Byakko' (v) **new** GEdr
§ - dwarf CTal ECho LEdu
- 'Flatmate' **new** WCru
- 'Flore Pleno' (d) CDes CLAP CPom ECho LEdu MHer MMoz NMyG WCot WHoo
- 'Grace Barker' see *P.* × *hybridum* 'Striatum'
- Kew form EPot
- 'Koryu' **new** GEdr
- var. ***pluriflorum*** EBee
§ - - 'Variegatum' (v) Widely available
- 'Red Stem' CPom CTal ECho MAvo WCru
- 'Silver Wings' (v) CBct CLAP ECha NBir NLar
- var. ***thunbergii*** WCru
- 'Ussuriland' EPPr GCal MAvo
- 'Ussuriland Roundleaf' GCal MAvo
officinale see *P. odoratum*
oppositifolium B&SWJ 2537 WCru
§ ***orientale*** CBct CLAP ECho GKev
pluriflorum see *P. graminifolium*
polyanthemum see *P. orientale*
prattii CTal ECho WCru
- CLD 325 LEdu
pubescens CBct ECho LEdu WCru WThu
pumilum see *P. odoratum* dwarf
punctatum CBct GEdr LEdu NBid
- B&SWJ 2395 CBct WCru
racemosum IMou
roseum CLAP EPPr GKev LLHF MMoz SGSe WCru
sewerzowii EPPr EPla
sibiricum CAvo CBct CPom GEdr IGor WCru WFar
- DJHC 600 CDes EBee LEdu WPGP
stenanthum CPom ECho
- B&SWJ 5727 LEdu WCru
stenophyllum CAvo IMou WCru
stewartianum CLAP EBee EPPr NRya
tessellatum PAB 8336 **new** LEdu
aff. ***tessellatum*** B&SWJ 9752 WCru
verticillatum CBct CBro CHel CHid CRow CTal EBee ECha EPPr EPfP GEdr IFoB LEdu LRHS MNFA MNrw MRav SKHP SMad WCru WFar WPGP WWtn
- B&SWJ 2147 **new** WCru
- CLD 1308 EPPr
- PAB 2455 LEdu
- 'Giant One' IMou MAvo
- 'Himalayan Giant' CHid ECho EPPr IPot MAvo SGSe WPnP
- 'Krynica' LEdu
* - 'Roseum' CAvo SGSe
- 'Rubrum' CAby CArn CBct CDes CLAP CRow EBee EPPr EPla GEdr IGor LEdu LRHS MAvo NBid NChi NLar WCot WCru WHoo WWEG
- 'Serbian Dwarf' CBct CHid CTal ECho GEdr IPot LEdu
aff. ***verticillatum*** CSpe IFoB
aff. ***wardii*** B&SWJ 6599 WCru
white-flowered HWJ 861 WCru
zanlanscianense CBct CPom EBee EWld IGor WCru

Polygonum (*Polygonaceae*)

affine see *Persicaria affinis*
amplexicaule see *Persicaria amplexicaulis*
aubertii see *Fallopia baldschuanica*
aviculare CArn
baldschuanicum see *Fallopia baldschuanica*
bistorta see *Persicaria bistorta*
capitatum see *Persicaria capitata*
compactum see *Fallopia japonica* var. *compacta*
equisetiforme misapplied see *P. scoparium*
filiforme see *Persicaria virginiana*
molle see *Persicaria mollis*
multiflorum see *Fallopia multiflora*
odoratum see *Persicaria odorata*
polystachyum see *Persicaria wallichii*
runciforme see *Persicaria runcinata*
§ ***scoparium*** EHoe ESwi EWes SDys SVen WOld XLum
tinctorium see *Persicaria tinctoria*
vacciniifolium see *Persicaria vacciniifolia*
weyrichii see *Persicaria weyrichii*

Polylepis (*Rosaceae*)

australis CSpe ESwi IDee LEdu MPie SEND SMad WCot WHil
- tall WPGP

Polymnia (*Asteraceae*)

uvedalia see *Smallanthus uvedalius*

Polypodium ✿ (*Polypodiaceae*)

sp. MLHP
aureum see *Phlebodium aureum*
- 'Glaucum' CSpe WCot
australe see *P. cambricum*
calirhiza 'Sarah Lyman' CDes
§ ***cambricum*** EFer SGSe WCot WFib
- 'Barrowii' CLAP WAbe WFib
I - 'Cambricum' ♀H7 CLAP GCal WAbe
- 'Conwy' WFib
- 'Cristatum' CLAP WFib
- (Cristatum Group) 'Grandiceps Forster' CLAP

	- - 'Grandiceps Fox' ♀H7	MRav WFib
	- 'Hornet'	WFib
	- 'Macrostachyon'	CLAP GBin NBid WFib
	- 'Oakleyae'	EFtx MMoz SMHy WCot
	- 'Omnilacerum Oxford'	CLAP
	- 'Prestonii'	WCot WFib
	- Pulcherrimum Group	CLAP SDys
	- - 'Pulcherrimum Addison'	CDes LEdu WCot WFib WPGP
	- - 'Pulchritudine'	CLAP GBin LLWG WCot
	- 'Richard Kayse' ♀H7	CDes CLAP EWes MMoz WAbe WCot WFib WPGP
	- Semilacerum Group	EFer
	- - 'Carew Lane'	WFib
	- - 'Falcatum O'Kelly'	WCot
	- - 'Robustum'	WFib
	- 'Whilharris' ♀H7	CLAP SMHy
I	× ***coughlinii*** bifid	WFib
	glycyrrhiza	CLAP GPoy WFib
	- bifid	see *P.* × *coughlinii* bifid
	- 'Longicaudatum' ♀H7	CLAP EFer MWhi NMyG WCot WFib
	- 'Malahatense'	CLAP
	- 'Malahatense' (sterile)	CDes WCot WPGP
	interjectum	CLAP EFer LRHS MMoz MRav
	- 'Cornubiense' ♀H7	CHVG CLAP ECGP GBin MMoz NBid NBir SMHy
	- 'Glomeratum Mullins'	WFib
	× ***mantoniae***	WFib
	- 'Bifidograndiceps'	GBin NBid WFib
	scouleri	CBty CFil CLAP EFer ISha LRHS MRav NBro WCot WPGP
	vulgare	Widely available
	- 'Bifidocristatum'	see *P. vulgare* 'Bifidomultifidum'
	- 'Bifidomulticeps'	WCot
§	- 'Bifidomultifidum'	CBty CLAP CWCL ELon GCal GEdr ISha LLWP MGos MRav NLar SGSe WCot WMoo
*	- 'Congestum Cristatum'	SRms
	- 'Cornubiense Grandiceps'	GCal SRms
*	- 'Cornubiense Multifidum'	EBee WCot
	- 'Elegantissimum'	NBid WFib
	- 'Parsley'	WCot
	- 'Trichomanoides Backhouse'	CDes CLAP GCal WAbe WCot WFib
	'Whitley Giant'	EBee ESwi GBin GEdr ISha ITim LLWG MMuc MPie NMyG SEND WCot

Polypompholyx see *Utricularia*

Polyspora (*Theaceae*)

§	***axillaris***	CCCN CHll EBee
	- CWJ 12363	WCru
	longicarpa DJHV 06041	WCru
	- WWJ 11604	WCru
	speciosa B&SWJ 11750	WCru
	- WWJ 11934	WCru
	- from Vietnam new	GLin

Polystichum ✿ (*Dryopteridaceae*)

	acrostichoides	CBty CDTJ CLAP EBee ERod LEdu LRHS MBri MMuc NLar WPGP XLum
	aculeatum ♀H7	CLAP ECha EFer ELan EPfP ERod EShb GMaP LAst LBMP LEdu LRHS MBri MCot MGos MMuc NBid NEgg NLar NOrc SCob SEND SRms SWvt WFib WMoo XLum
I	- Densum Group	EFer
	- Grandiceps Group	EFer
	- 'Portia'	WFib
	andersonii	CLAP
	bissectum	CExl
	braunii	CBcs CMac CWCL EFtx GBin GMaP IKil LRHS MMoz NBid NLar WFib WPnP WWEG XLum
	caryotideum	see *Cyrtomium caryotideum*
	× ***dycei*** ♀H6	CBty ISha LRHS NLos
	falcatum	see *Cyrtomium falcatum*
	falcinellum	GLin
	fortunei	see *Cyrtomium fortunei*
	imbricans	CLAP SArc
	interjectum	MRav
	makinoi	CBty CCCN CLAP EFtx EPPr GBin ISha LRHS NBid SPlb WFib WMoo
	mayebarae new	ISha
	munitum ♀H7	Widely available
	aff. ***munitum*** new	LPal
	neolobatum	EFtx WFib
	- BWJ 8182	WCru
	polyblepharum ♀H7	Widely available
	- 'Jade'	CMac EBee LRHS
	prescottianum new	GCra
	proliferum misapplied	see *P. setiferum* Acutilobum Group
	proliferum ambig.	CBty
	proliferum (R. Br.) C. Presl	CLAP EFtx GCal SBig WFib WPGP
*	- ***plumosum***	LAst LPal SPad SWvt
	richardii	SBig
	rigens	CBty CLAP EFer ISha LPal LRHS LSou NLar SGSe SRms SRot WCru WFib WGrf WWEG
	setiferum ♀H7	Widely available
§	- Acutilobum Group	CLAP CWCL CWSG ECha GMaP LPal LRHS MWat NLos SCob SDix SGol SRms WBor WMoo WPGP XLum
	- Congestum Group	CKel MMoz NCGa NEgg NHol NLar SMad SPer SRms WFib WPat
	- - 'Congestum'	CBty CLAP CWCL EFtx ELan EPPr EPfP ERod IKil ISha LBMP LRHS MRav MWhi NBir NGdn NHol SPoG SPtp WGrf WMoo XLum
	- - 'Congestum Cristatum'	LAst
	- 'Cristatopinnulum'	CLAP NHar WPGP
	- Cristatum Group	CLAP SRms
	- Cruciatum Group	CLAP
	- (Decompositum Group) 'Proliferum' new	CWCL
	- Divisilobum Group ♀H7	CBcs CLAP EFer ELan MCot MGos MLHP MMoz MWat SPer SRms WFar WFib WHoo WPGP
	- - 'Caernarfon'	CLAP EFtx
	- - 'Dahlem'	CBty CDoC CLAP EBee ECha EFer ELan ELon EPfP GBin GEdr GMaP LRHS MMoz NBid SPer SPoG WFib WGrf WMoo XLum
	- - 'Divisilobum Densum' ♀H7	CLAP EPfP MRav NBir NOrc
	- - 'Divisilobum Iveryanum' ♀H7	CLAP EFer SRms WFib
	- - 'Divisilobum Laxum'	CLAP
§	- - 'Divisilobum Wollaston'	CBty CDTJ CKel CLAP CTal CWCL ELon GEdr ISha LRHS MBel MMoz MRav NBid NLar SHil WCot WMoo
	- - 'Herrenhausen'	Widely available

- - 'Madame Patti' MMoz
- - 'Mrs Goffey' WFib
- Foliosum Group CLAP EFer
- 'Gracile' MRav NBir
- 'Grandiceps' CLAP EFer ELan
- 'Hamlet' WFib
- 'Helena' WFib
- 'Hirondelle' SRms
- Lineare Group WFib
- Multilobum Group CLAP SRms WFib
- 'Othello' WFib
- Perserratum Group NBid WFib
- 'Plumo-Densum' see *P. setiferum* Plumosomultilobum Group
- 'Plumosodensum' see *P. setiferum* Plumosomultilobum Group
- Plumosodivisilobum Group CLAP ECha LPal NBid SGSe SMHy WFib
- - 'Baldwinii' CLAP WFib
- - 'Bland' WFib
§ - Plumosomultilobum Group CBty CLAP CWCL EBee EFtx EPfP GBin GEdr ISha MCot MGos MMoz NBir NCGa NLar NMyG WCot WFib WHoo WMoo WPat WRHF
I - - 'Plumosomultilobum Densum' CHVG CMea LRHS LSun MBel MJak SBod SCob WCot XLum
- Plumosum Group CLAP CMac CSpe CTal EFer EFtx ELon MJak NOrc SArc SRot
- - dwarf CSBt
* - ***plumosum grande*** 'Moly' SRms
- Proliferum Group see *P. setiferum* Acutilobum Group
* - 'Proliferum Wollaston' see *P. setiferum* (Decompositum Group) 'Divisilobum Wollaston'
- 'Pulcherrimum Bevis' ♀H6 Widely available
- (Pulcherrimum Group) 'Pulcherrimum' new ISha
- Rotundatum Group CLAP
- - 'Cristatum' CLAP ISha
- - 'Rotundatum Ramosum' CLAP
- 'Smith's Cruciate' CLAP MRav WFib
- 'Wakeleyanum' EFer SRms
tsussimense ♀H6 Widely available
vestitum EFtx MMoz SBig

Polyxena (*Asparagaceae*)

* ***brevifolia*** ECho
corymbosa ♀H2 CTal ECho NRog
§ ***ensifolia*** CPBP CTal ECho LLHF NRog WCot WHil
longituba CPBP CTal ECho NRog WCot
odorata ECho NRya
paucifolia ECho
pygmaea see *P. ensifolia*

Pomaderris (*Rhamnaceae*)

apetala CExl
elliptica CExl

pomegranate see *Punica granatum*

Ponerorchis (*Orchidaceae*)

graminifolia GKev LAma WCot
- purple-on-white-flowered new ECho GKev
- red point new ECho GKev
- white-flowered new GKev

Pontederia (*Pontederiaceae*)

cordata ♀H5 CBAq CBen CHEx CRow CWat EHon ELan EPfP EWay MSKA MWts NPer SCoo SPlb SWat WMAq XLum
- f. ***albiflora*** CBAq CRow CWat EHon EPfP EWay MWts XLum
- 'Blue Spires' MSKA
§ - var. ***lancifolia*** CBen CRow EWay LLWG MNrw MSKA MWts NPer SWat
- 'Pink Pons' CRow
- pink-flowered LLWG
dilatata see *Monochoria hastata*
lanceolata see *P. cordata* var. *lancifolia*

Populus ✿ (*Salicaceae*)

× ***acuminata*** WMou
alba CAco CBcs CCVT CDul CLnd CMac CSBt CTho CTri LBuc NWea SCob SEWo SGol SPer WMou
- 'Bolleana' see *P. alba* f. *pyramidalis*
- 'Nivea' MMuc SEND
§ - f. ***pyramidalis*** SRms WMou
§ - 'Raket' CCVT CTho ECrN ELan SPer
- 'Richardii' EBtc EGFP WCot WMou
- Rocket see *P. alba* 'Raket'
§ 'Balsam Spire' (f) CDul CLnd CTho NWea WMou
§ ***balsamifera*** CCVT CSBt CTri MGos SPer WCot
- 'Vita Sackville West' MBlu
§ × ***canadensis*** 'Aurea' ♀H6 CDul CLnd CTho ECrN SPer WMou
- 'Columbia' WMou
- 'Eugenei' (m) WMou
- 'Robusta' (m) CCVT CDul CLnd CTri LBuc NWea WMou
- 'Serotina' (m) CDul WMou
× ***canescens*** CLnd NWea
deltoides 'Fuego' SGol
- 'Purple Tower'PBR CDul CEnd ELan EPfP MBlu MMuc SMad SPoG WCot
× ***generosa*** 'Beaupré' WMou
× ***jackii*** 'Aurora' (f/v) CBcs CCVT CDul CLnd CMac CSBt ELan LBuc LPot MGos MMuc NPri NWea SGol SPer WHar WMou
lasiocarpa CBcs CExl CLnd CMCN EPfP EPla IArd IDee MBlu SGol WMou WPGP
nigra CHab CMac CTho CTri CTsd NWea SCob WSFF
- (f) ECrN MMuc SEND
- (m) MMuc SEND
- subsp. ***betulifolia*** CCVT CDul CHab CLnd NWea WMou
- - (f) EBtc WMou
- - (m) EBtc WMou
§ - 'Italica' (m) ♀H6 CCVT CDul CLnd CMac CTho CTri ECrN ELan LBuc MGos MMuc NWea SEND SEWo SPer WMou
- 'Pyramidalis' see *P. nigra* 'Italica'
purdomii new WPGP
'Serotina Aurea' see *P.* × *canadensis* 'Aurea'
simonii 'Fastigiata' WMou
szechuanica WMou
§ - var. ***tibetica*** WMou
tacamahaca see *P. balsamifera*
'Tacatricho 32' see *P.* 'Balsam Spire'
tremula CAco CCVT CDul CHab CLnd CMac CTho CTri ECrN ELan EPla GAbr GQue LBuc MJak MMuc

		NWea SCob SEND SEWo SPer WHar WMou WSFF
§	- 'Erecta' ♀H7	CDul CEnd CTho EBee EPla MBlu MMuc SEND WMou
	- 'Fastigiata'	see *P. tremula* 'Erecta'
	- 'Pendula' (m)	CAco CEnd CTho ECrN IDee WMou
	trichocarpa	CDul SPer
	- 'Fritzi Pauley' (f)	CDul CTho WMou
	violascens	see *P. szechuanica* var. *tibetica*
	× ***wilsocarpa*** 'Beloni'	WPGP
	wilsonii	WPGP
	yunnanensis	WMou

Porophyllum (*Asteraceae*)

ruderale	CArn ELau WJek

Portulaca (*Portulacaceae*)

grandiflora	SVic
oleracea	CArn ENfk MHer MNHC SVic WJek
- var. ***aurea***	MNHC WJek

Potamogeton (*Potamogetonaceae*)

crispus	CBAq CWat EHon MSKA MWts WMAq WSFF
malainus new	LLWG
natans	LLWG MSKA WSFF XLum

Potentilla ✿ (*Rosaceae*)

	alba	CTri ECha ECho ELan GCal LPot MLHP MNFA MRav MWat NChi NSti NWad SPer WSHC
	alchemilloides	CMac
	ambigua	see *P. cuneata*
	andicola	EBee
	anglica	CArn
	anserina	CArn MHer NMir WHer XLum
	- 'Golden Treasure' (v)	EBee WHer
	anserinoides	WMoo
	arbuscula misapplied	see *P. fruticosa* 'Elizabeth'
	- 'Beesii'	see *P. fruticosa* 'Beesii'
	'Arc-en-ciel'	Widely available
	argentea	SPlb WFar XLum
	arguta	EBee
	argyrophylla	see *P. atrosanguinea* var. *argyrophylla*
	atrosanguinea	Widely available
	- CC 7167 new	GKev
§	- var. ***argyrophylla***	CCon CSam CWCL EBee ECha ELan EPfP GCal ITim LRHS MMuc MRav MWat NBir NBro NChi NLar SEND SRms WMoo XLum
	- - CC 6945	GKev
	- - 'Golden Starlit'	IBoy
§	- - 'Scarlet Starlit'	CAby EDAr EPfP EPla IBoy LSun
	- 'Fireball' (d)	EPfP GJos
	- var. ***leucochroa***	see *P. atrosanguinea* var. *argyrophylla*
*	- 'Sundermannii'	LLHF
	aurea	ECho ECtt EPfP GBin LBuc
	- 'Aurantiaca'	NEoE NLar
§	- 'Goldklumpen'	ECtt MRav NEoE
	- 'Plena' (d)	NRya
	'Blazeaway'	CBod ECtt LRHS LSou MArl MAvo MBNS NEoE NGdn WCot
	calabra	ECha EWes SPhx WHer
§	***cinerea***	CTri ECho LLHF
	'Coronation Triumph'	NLar
§	***crantzii***	CMea SRms
	- 'Nana'	see *P. crantzii* 'Pygmaea'
§	- 'Pygmaea'	ECho ECtt NBir
§	***cuneata*** ♀H5	ECho GAbr GKev MMuc SEND
	- CC 6951 new	GKev
	davurica 'Abbotswood'	see *P. fruticosa* 'Abbotswood'
	delavayi	MNrw
	dombeyi	IMou
	'Emilie' (d)	CSpe CWCL ECtt GAbr GBuc GCal IKil MBNS MBel MCot MNrw NEoE NLar SWvt WBor WCot
§	***erecta***	GPoy MNHC WHfH
	eriocarpa	CPBP ECho GCrg NSla WAbe WIce
	- var. ***tsarongensis***	WAbe
	'Esta Ann'	CAby CBod CMac ECtt EPla GBuc IPot LRHS MArl MAvo MBNS MCot MNrw NCGa NEoE NLar SRGP
	'Etna'	CHel CWCL ECtt ELan GBuc LRHS MLHP MNFA MNrw NBir NLar WHrl WMoo WPtf
	'Everest'	see *P. fruticosa* 'Mount Everest'
	'Fireflame'	EBee NLar WMoo
	fissa	MNrw NBir NLar SPhx
	'Flambeau' (d)	CWCL ECtt EShb GBuc GKin IPot LAst LPla LRHS MArl MAvo MNFA MRav MSpe NEoE NGdn NLar NSti WMoo
	'Flamenco'	CSam CTri ECtt LRHS MArl MAvo MBNS MBri MLHP MNrw MRav NBir WFar WMoo
	fragariiformis	see *P. megalantha*
	fruticosa	LBuc NHed NWea
§	- 'Abbotswood' ♀H7	Widely available
	- 'Abbotswood Silver' (v)	WMoo
	- 'Annette'	CMac MBrN NEoE WRHF
	- var. ***arbuscula*** hort.	see *P. fruticosa* 'Elizabeth'
	- 'Argentea Nana'	see *P. fruticosa* 'Beesii'
	- 'Baby Bethan'PBR (d)	LLHF
§	- 'Beesii'	EPfP LRHS MAsh SCob SIgm
	- 'Bewerley Surprise'	LBuc
	- 'Bo-Peep' new	CEnd
	- 'Chelsea Star' ♀H7	CDoC CMac LBuc LRHS MAsh MGos SHil
	- 'Chilo' (v)	WMoo
	- 'Clotted Cream'	SGbt
	- var. ***dahurica*** 'Hersii'	see *P. fruticosa* 'Snowflake'
	- 'Dakota Sunrise'	NSoo
	- Danny Boy = 'Lissdan' new	LRHS SLon SPoG
	- 'Daphne' new	NWad
	- 'Dart's Cream'	MBri
	- 'Dart's Golddigger'	CTri NWad
	- 'Daydawn'	CBcs CDul CMac CTri CWSG ELan EPfP LBMP LRHS MAsh MLHP MMuc MRav MSwo NBir NEgg NLar NWad SGol SLim SPer SWvt WHar WMoo
§	- 'Elizabeth'	CBcs CDul COtt ECrN ELan EPfP LAst LBMP LRHS MGos MJak MMuc MSwo NHol NWea SCob SGol SLim SPer SRms SWvt WCFE WFar WHar WMoo
	- 'Farreri'	see *P. fruticosa* 'Gold Drop'
	- 'Floppy Disc'	ELan
	- 'Glenroy Pinkie'	MRav NLar
§	- 'Gold Drop'	CMac NHol
	- 'Golden Dwarf'	WMoo
	- 'Golden Spreader'	LRHS

	Name	Suppliers
	- 'Goldfinger'	CAco CChe CMac CSBt EBee ELan EPfP IBoy LRHS MAsh MGos MJak MMuc MRav MSwo MWat NEgg NHed NSoo SCob SCoo SEND SLim SPer SPlb SPoG WHar WMoo
	- Goldkugel	see *P. fruticosa* 'Gold Drop'
	- 'Goldstar'	COtt CWSG IArd LBuc LRHS MBri NPri SCob SCoo SEND SLim SLon SRms WFar
	- 'Goldteppich'	LBuc
	- 'Grace Darling'	ECrN ELan EPfP EWes NBir NEgg NLar SRGP SWvt WHar WMoo WRHF
	- 'Groneland' ♀H7	EPfP LRHS MAsh SCoo SPoG
	- 'Hopleys Orange' ♀H7	CDoC CSBt CWSG ELon EPfP EWes LRHS MBri MMuc MWat NHol NPri NSoo SCob SCoo SEND SGbt SGol SHil SRms WFar WMoo
	- 'Hurstbourne'	NEoE
	- 'Jackman's Variety' ♀H7	CDoC EPfP IBoy LRHS MAsh SCob SRms
	- 'Katherine Dykes'	CDul CTri EPfP GKin LAst LBMP LRHS MAsh MGos MWat NEgg NSoo NWea SCob SCoo SGbt SLim SPer SRms WFar WHar WMoo
	- 'King Cup' ♀H7	EPfP LRHS MAsh
§	- 'Klondike'	CBcs CSBt NWea
	- 'Kobold'	CDul LRHS MBri
	- 'Limelight' ♀H7	CDoC CSBt EBee ELan EPfP GKin LRHS MAsh MBri MRav MSwo NEoE NSoo NWad SHil SRms WHar
	- 'Longacre Variety'	CMac CTri IArd MSwo NWea
	- 'Lovely Pink'PBR	see *P. fruticosa* 'Pink Beauty'
§	- 'Maanelys'	CSBt ELan MWat NWea SPer WMoo
	- 'Macpenny's Cream'	CMac
§	- 'Manchu'	CMac MRav MWat SCob SPer WCFE WPat
	- Mango Tango = 'Uman'PBR	CSBt EBee EMil EPfP LRHS MBri MWat NSoo SPoG STPC WFar
§	- Marian Red Robin = 'Marrob'PBR ♀H7	CDoC COtt CSBt ELan EPfP GKin IBoy LAst LRHS MAsh MBri MRav MSwo MWat NPri NWea SCoo SLim SLon SPer SPoG SWvt
	- 'McKay's White'	NLar
	- 'Medicine Wheel Mountain' ♀H7	CDoC ELan EWes IArd LRHS MAsh MBri MGos MPkF MRav NLar NWad SCob SCoo SGol SHil SLim SPer SPoG
	- Moonlight	see *P. fruticosa* 'Maanelys'
§	- 'Mount Everest'	CTri MMuc NWea SEND SLon
	- 'Nana Argentea'	see *P. fruticosa* 'Beesii'
	- 'New Dawn'	COtt GKin MBri
	- 'Orangeade'	EPfP LRHS MAsh MBri NLar SCoo SPoG
*	- 'Peachy Proud'	NEoE
§	- 'Pink Beauty'PBR ♀H7	Widely available
	- Pink Paradise = 'Kupinpa'PBR **new**	NCGa
	- 'Pink Pearl'	WMoo
	- 'Pink Queen'	NLar
	- 'Pink Whisper'	COtt NEoE
	- 'Pretty Polly'	ELan LAst LBMP LRHS MSwo NHol NLar NWad WFar WMoo WRHF
	- 'Primrose Beauty' ♀H7	Widely available
§	- Princess = 'Blink'	CAco CBcs CDul EBee ELan EPfP LBMP LRHS MAsh MJak MRav SCob SCoo SGol SLim SRms WFar WMoo
	- 'Red Ace'	Widely available
	- 'Red Lady'PBR	EPfP EWTr LAst LRHS MBri NHol SCob SHil SPoG STPC WMoo
	- Red RobinPBR	see *P. fruticosa* Marian Red Robin
	- 'Red Surprise'	WFar
	- 'Royal Flush'	NWad
	- 'Setting Sun'	LBuc
	- 'Snowbird'	NEoE SLim WFar
§	- 'Snowflake'	CBcs WMoo
	- 'Sommerflor' ♀H7	CAco CDoC EPfP LRHS MAsh
	- 'Sophie's Blush'	MRav NWea WSHC
	- 'Summer Dawn'	LBuc
	- 'Summer Sorbet'	LRHS
	- 'Sunset'	CBcs CMac ELan GKin MJak NBir NWea SCob SCoo SLim SPer SRms WFar WMoo
	- 'Tangerine'	Widely available
	- 'Tilford Cream'	COtt CSBt CTri ELan EPfP GKin IBoy LRHS MJak MRav MSwo MWat NBir NEgg NHol SCob SGbt SGol SLim SPer SPoG SRms WCFE WFar WHar WMoo
	- 'Tom Conway'	CMac NLar
	- var. ***veitchii***	CSBt
	- 'Vilmoriniana'	CTri ELan EMil EPfP GCal LRHS MAsh MLHP MRav SPer SPoG SWvt WPat
	- 'Whirligig'	CMac
	- 'White Lady'	MPkF SPer
	- 'William Purdom'	WHar
	- 'Yellow Bird' ♀H7	LRHS MAsh
	'Gibson's Scarlet' ♀H7	Widely available
§	***glandulosa*** subsp. ***nevadensis***	CTri ECho EWld MAsh SRms
	'Gloire de Nancy' (d)	EBee GBuc IKil MRav NBir NChi NLar
	'Gold Clogs'	see *P. aurea* 'Goldklumpen'
	'Helen Jane'	GBuc GJos GQue LRHS MAvo MBNS MHer NBir NLar WPtf WWFP
	'Herzblut'	NLar
	× ***hopwoodiana***	CMea CSpe CWCL EAJP EBee ECha ECtt ELan EPPr GCal GJos GMaP IKil LAst MCot MNrw MRav NBir NCGa NChi NDov NLar SPer WCAu WMoo WWEG
	× ***hybrida*** 'Jean Jabber'	EBee GLog MAvo MRav NEoE NLar SRGP
	'Jack Elliot'	NEoE
	kurdica	XLum
	'Lemon Drops' **new**	LAst
	'Light My Fire'	ECtt EPfP LLHF MAvo MBNS
§	'Majland'	EBee NDov
	'Mandshurica'	see *P. fruticosa* 'Manchu'
	'Maynard's'	see *P.* 'Majland'
§	***megalantha***	CBro EAJP ECtt EDAr ELan EPfP EPla EPri GBBs GCal GCra LAst LEdu LRHS MBNS MBel MLHP MNrw MRav NBir NBro SGbt SPer SPhx SRms SRot WMoo WWEG XLum
	- 'Gold Sovereign'	EBee EPfP LRHS LSou MBri NEoE SPoG
	'Melton'	MNrw
*	'Melton Fire'	EPfP GJos GKin GQue LBMP MNHC MNrw NBir WMoo WPnP
	micrantha 'Purple Heart' **new**	LEdu
	'Monarch's Velvet'	see *P. thurberi* 'Monarch's Velvet'

'Monsieur Rouillard' (d)	CMac CSam CWCL ECtt GCra IGor IPot LRHS MArl MCot MNrw MRav MWat NGdn NLar WHoo WHrl WMnd
'Mont d'Or'	EBee MRav NLar
nepalensis	EHoe GKev LRHS MLHP NBro NChi XLum
- 'Helen Jane'	IBoy NHol WFar WOut
- 'Master Floris'	WFar WHal
§ - 'Miss Willmott'	Widely available
- 'Ron McBeath'	CCon CHel CKno COtt CWCL ECtt ELan EPfP GBin GCra ITim LAst LRHS MAvo MRav MSCN NHol NLar NSti SGol SPer SPoG SRGP SWvt WHoo WMoo WPtf WWEG
- 'Roxana'	CCon ELan MRav NBro NLar SRGP WMoo
- 'Shogran'	GJos GQue LAst LBMP LRHS MBNS NHol NLar WPtf
§ ***neumanniana***	MAsh NBir NPri
- 'Goldrausch'	IMou LEdu MRav
§ - 'Nana'	ECho ECtt EPot GCrg MHer MWat NRya NWad SPlb SRms WHoo WIce WMoo XLum
nevadensis	see *P. glandulosa* subsp. *nevadensis*
nitida	EPot MAsh SRms WAbe
- 'Alba'	ECho EPot
- 'Rubra'	CMea CPBP ECho EDAr GEdr MWat NBir NHar NSla SRms WAbe
nivalis	ECho
ovina var. ***ovina***	LLHF
- - NNS 08-374	GKev
palustris	CWat EBee EWay LLWG MWts NLar NMir WMoo XLum
parvifolia 'Klondike'	see *P. fruticosa* 'Klondike'
pedata	LLWP NChi XLum
peduncularis CC 5717	GKev
pensylvanica	LLHF
'Pink Panther'	see *P. fruticosa* Princess
aff. ***polyphylla*** CHP&W 314	GKev
recta	NPri WTou XLum
- 'Alba'	GMaP NEgg WPtf
- 'Citrina'	see *P. recta* var. *sulphurea*
- 'Macrantha'	see *P. recta* 'Warrenii'
§ - var. ***sulphurea***	CAby CMea EPau EWoo GAbr GKev LAst LSun MCot MLHP MMuc MNFA MNrw NBir NLar NSti NWad SBch SBod SPhx WBrk WHal WHea WHoo WHrl WMnd WMoo WPtf XLum
§ - 'Warrenii'	CSBt EPfP EPla GMaP LAst LRHS MRav NBir NEgg SHar SPer SRms WHal WHrl WMoo XLum
reptans	CArn CBAq
'Roxanne' (d)	LRHS MHer
rupestris	CMea ECha EWTr LSun MHer NLar NSti WFar WHal WMoo WOut WPtf
'Scarlet Starlet'	see *P. atrosanguinea* var. *argyrophylla* 'Scarlet Starlit'
speciosa	EWes WMoo
sterilis	CHid LEdu WHer WSFF
* ***sundermanii***	WHrl
tabernaemontani	see *P. neumanniana*
thurberi	CMea LRHS MCot MNFA MNrw NLar SPhx WHrl WMoo XLum
§ - 'Monarch's Velvet'	Widely available
tommasiniana	see *P. cinerea*
× ***tonguei*** ♀H5	Widely available
tormentilla	see *P. erecta*
tridentata	see *Sibbaldiopsis tridentata*
'Twinkling Star'	CHel EBee SPad WPtf
verna misapplied	see *P. neumanniana*
- 'Pygmaea'	see *P. neumanniana* 'Nana'
'Versicolor Plena' (d)	NLar
villosa	see *P. crantzii*
'Volcan'	CAby CWCL EBee ECtt EWes GBuc GQue IKil MAvo MNFA NChi SMHy WHal
'White Queen'	GLog MRav SHar
'William Rollisson' ♀H6	Widely available
willmottiae	see *P. nepalensis* 'Miss Willmott'
'Yellow Queen'	CMac CTri EBee GKin GMaP LPot LRHS MNrw MRav NLar SPer WCAu

Poterium see *Sanguisorba*

sanguisorba	see *Sanguisorba minor*

Prangos (*Apiaceae*)

ferulacea new	WCot

Pratia (*Campanulaceae*)

§ ***angulata*** 'Treadwellii'	ECha ECho GEdr SPlb WHal
montana	see *Lobelia montana*
nummularia new	GLin
§ ***pedunculata***	CTri ECha ECho ECou ECtt EDAr ELan EPfP EWTr GAbr LLWG LSun SIgm SPlb SRms SRot WMoo WPtf
I - 'Alba'	ECho EWes SBod
- 'County Park'	CExl CHel CMea CSpe CTri ECha ECho ECou ECtt EDAr ELan ELon EWTr GAbr LLWG LRHS NDov SPlb SPoG SRms SRot WIce WMoo XLum
- 'Tom Stone'	ECtt
- 'White Stars'	ECho LLWG

Preslia see *Mentha*

Primula ✿ (*Primulaceae*)

sp.	SVic
- (Si)	MAsh
acaulis	see *P. vulgaris*
'Adrian Jones' (Au)	IPen
advena var. ***euprepes***	see *P. euprepes*
agleniana (Cy)	IPen
'Alan Robb' (Pr/Prim/d)	ECtt NGdn
albenensis (Au)	IPen
'Alexina' (*allionii* hybrid) (Au)	MFie NHar
algida (Al)	ECho GKev
§ ***allionii*** (Au)	IPen NSum WAbe
- HNG 12	IPen ITim
- 'Agnes' (Au)	IPen ITim MFie WAbe
- 'Aire Waves'	see *P. × loiseleurii* 'Aire Waves'
- 'Alan Burrow' (Au)	IPen
- var. ***alba*** (Au)	IPen MFie
- 'Allen Queen' (Au)	IPen
- 'Andrew' (Au)	IPen WAbe
- 'Anna Griffith' (Au)	CPBP CTal IPen MFie WAbe WHil
- 'Anne' (Au)	IPen
- 'Aphrodite' (Au)	IPen NHar
- 'Apple Blossom' (Au)	GKev
- 'Archer' (Au)	IPen ITim NWad
- 'Ares' (Au)	NHar
- 'Aries Violet' (Au)	IPen NHar
- 'Austen' (Au)	EPot MFie

- 'Avalanche' (Au) IPen WAbe
- 'Beryl' (Au) IPen
- 'Biddy' (Au) IPen
- 'Bill Martin' (Au) IPen ITim NWad
- 'Blood Flake' (Au) IPen ITim
- 'Broadwell No 4' (Au) CPBP
- Burnley form (Au) NWad
- 'Cherry' (Au) WAbe
- 'Chivalry' (Au) CPBP
- 'Circe's Flute' (Au) NHar
- 'Cissie' (Au) CPBP IPen
- 'Claude Flight' (Au) IPen MFie
- 'Crowsley Variety' (Au) ITim
- 'Crusader' (Au) CTal WAbe
- 'Crystal' (Au) CPBP MFie
- 'Daniel Burrow' (Au) IPen
- 'David Burrow' (Au) IPen
- 'David Philbey' (Au) CPBP IPen
§ - 'Edinburgh' (Au) GKev IPen NWad XBar
- 'Edrom' (Au) IPen NWad
- 'Ekli Weib' (Au) IPen
- 'Elizabeth Baker' (Au) IPen ITim MFie
- 'Elizabeth Burrow' (Au) IPen WAbe
- 'Elizabeth Earle' (Au) IPen ITim
- 'Elliott's Large' see *P. allionii* 'Edinburgh'
- 'Elliott's Variety' see *P. allionii* 'Edinburgh'
- 'Emily Jane' (Au) IPen
- 'Eureka' (Au) CPBP WAbe
- 'Eveline Burrow' (Au) CPBP WAbe
- 'Fanfare' (Au) IPen NHar
- 'Flute' (Au) IPen
- 'Frank Barker' (Au) IPen
- 'Gabriele' (Au) MFie
- 'Gavin Brown' (Au) IPen
- 'Gilderdale Glow' (Au) CPBP IPen MFie
- 'Giuseppi's Form' see *P. allionii* 'Mrs Dyas'
- 'Grace Burrow' (Au) IPen
- 'Grandiflora' (Au) ITim
- 'Hannah' (Au) IPen
- 'Hartside' (Au) NWad
- 'Hartside 6' (Au) IPen ITim NHar
- 'Hartside 12' (Au) IPen
- 'Hazey' (Au) ITim
- 'Herald' (Au) **new** ITim
- 'Hocker Edge' (Au) ITim MFie NWad
- 'Horwood' (Au) ITim
- 'Huntsman' (Au) MFie
- 'Hythe Dorothy' (Au) IPen
- 'Imp' (Au) IPen
- Ingwersen's form (Au) MFie
- 'Io 2' (Au) NHar
- 'Ion's Amethyst' (Au) NHar
- 'Isobel' (Au) IPen
- 'Jacqueline' (Au) IPen
- 'James' (Au) IPen WAbe
- 'Jan' (Au) IPen
- 'Jenny' (Au) IPen
- 'Joe Elliott' (Au) IPen ITim
- 'Joseph Collins' (Au) IPen
- 'Julia' (Au) IPen
- 'Kate Evans' (Au) IPen
§ - 'Kath Dryden' (Au) IPen LLHF WCre
§ - 'Ken's Seedling' (Au) IPen MFie
- KRW see *P. allionii* 'Ken's Seedling'
- 'Laura Louise' (Au) IPen
- 'Lepus' (Au) IPen WAbe
- 'Lindisfarne' (Au) IPen
- 'Lindum Prima' (Au) IPen
- 'Lindum Whisper' (Au) **new** LLHF
- 'Lismore 81/19/2' (Au) EPot MFie
- 'Lismore 87/3/2' (Au) MFie
- 'Little O' (Au) NWad WAbe
- 'Louise' (Au) IPen
- 'Lucy' (Au) IPen NHar
- 'Malcolm' (Au) IPen ITim WAbe
- 'Margaret Earle' (Au) IPen
- 'Marion' (Au) IPen
- 'Marjorie Wooster' (Au) CPBP IPen MFie XBar
- 'Martin' (Au) IPen ITim
- 'Mary Anne' (Au) WAbe
- 'Mary Berry' (Au) IPen MFie NWad
- 'Maurice Dryden' (Au) IPen WAbe
- 'Megan' (Au) IPen
- 'Molly' (Au) IPen
§ - 'Mrs Dyas' (Au) IPen MFie NWad WAbe
- 'Neon' (Au) IPen
- 'Neptune's Wave' (Au) NHar
- 'New Dawn' (Au) ITim MFie NHar
- 'Pale Venus' (Au) IPen NHar
- 'Peace' (Au) MFie
- 'Peggy Wilson' (Au) EWld IPen NWad WThu
- 'Pennine Pink' (Au) CPBP IPen
- 'Perkie' (Au) IPen
- 'Phoebe's Moon' (Au) IPen NHar
- 'Pink Ice' (Au) ITim
- 'Pinkie' (Au) IPen WAbe
- 'Praecox' (Au) EPot IPen
- 'Quip' (Au) IPen
- RAH form MFie
- 'Raymond Wooster' (Au) GKev IPen NWad
- 'Roger Bevan' (Au) IPen
- 'Saint Dalmas' (Au) IPen
- 'Scimitar' (Au) IPen MFie
- 'Serendipity' (Au) IPen
- 'Snowflake' (Au) IPen WAbe
- 'Stanton House' (Au) MFie
- 'Stephen' (Au) IPen MFie
- 'Tranquillity' (Au) CPBP CTal ITim NHar
- 'Travellers' (Au) IPen
- 'Viscountess Byng' (Au) IPen WAbe
- white-flowered, thrum-eyed (Au) IPen
- 'William Earle' (Au) CPBP CTal IPen ITim WAbe

allionii* × *auricula misapplied 'Blairside Yellow' (Au) ECho GAgs IPen NSum WThu
allionii* × *auricula misapplied 'Old Red Dusty Miller' (Au) ECho NWad
allionii* × *clusiana (Au) ECho
allionii* × *hirsuta (Au) NWad
allionii* × *pedemontana see *P.* × *sendtneri*
allionii* × *pubescens (Au) ECho
allionii × 'Lismore Jewel' (Au) ITim
allionii × 'Lismore Treasure' (Au) ITim
allionii × 'Snow Ruffles' (Au) IPen ITim
allionii × 'White Linda Pope' (Au) IPen MFie NHar NWad
alpicola (Si) ♀H5 CAby CLAP CWCL GAbr GKev IPen NBid NBro NCGa NGdn NSum NWad SEND WAbe XBar
- var. ***alba*** (Si) CPla CSta GAbr GBuc GKev IPen NBid

§	- var. ***alpicola*** (Si)	CLAP EBee GBin GBuc GCra GKev IPen MMuc MNrw WAbe
	- hybrids (Si)	CBod WMoo
	- 'Kevock Sky' (Si)	GKev
	- 'La Luna' (Si)	CSta MMuc
	- var. ***luna***	see *P. alpicola* var. *alpicola*
	- mixed (Si)	ECho
	- var. ***violacea*** (Si)	CCon CLAP CPla CSta EBee GAbr GBin GCra GKev IPen MMuc MNrw NBid NCGa WAbe WHil
	- - wine red-flowered (Si) **new**	GKev
	'Altaica'	see *P. elatior* subsp. *meyeri*
	altaica grandiflora	see *P. elatior* subsp. *meyeri*
	amoena	see *P. elatior* subsp. *meyeri*
	'Amy Smith'	GAbr
	anisodora	see *P. wilsonii* var. *anisodora*
	'Annemijne'	WCot
	apoclita (Mu)	GKev WHil
	'April Rose' (Pr/Prim/d)	NBid
	× ***arctotis***	see *P.* × *pubescens*
	'Arduaine' (Pe)	LLHF
	aurantiaca (Pf)	CCon CPla EBee GBin GKev IPen WHil
	aureata (Pe)	IPen
	auricula ambig. (Au)	CBod CTsd NSla
	auricula L. (Au) 🏆H5	EDAr GKev IPen LRHS MFie NBro SPer SPlb SPoG WAbe WRHF
	auricula misapplied (Au)	ECha
	- A74 (Au)	SEND
	- K85 (Au/S)	SPop
I	- '1-2-3' (Au) **new**	EBee
	- '2nd Vic' (Au/S)	SPop XBar
	- 'A.C. Hadfield' (Au)	MFie
	- 'Abdor' (Au/St)	SPop
	- 'Abrigde' (Au/d)	WAln
	- 'Abundance' (Au/A)	EWoo SPop
	- 'Achates' (Au/A)	IPen WAln
	- 'Admiral' (Au/A)	GAgs WAln WCre
	- 'Adrian' (Au/A)	EWoo GAgs IPen MFie NBro NDro SPop WBla WCre WHil XBar
	- 'Adrian's Cross' (Au/A)	EWoo
	- 'Adrienne' (Au/A)	SPop
	- 'Adrienne Ruan' (Au/A)	NDro WAln
	- 'After Glow' (Au/St) **new**	SPop
	- 'Aga Khan' (Au/A)	WAln
	- 'Agamemnon' (Au/A)	EWoo IPen MFie SPop WAln WCre
	- 'Airy Fairy' (Au/S)	SPop
	- 'Alamo' (Au/A)	MFie WCre
	- 'Alan Ball' (Au)	WAln WCre
	- 'Alan Ravenscroft' (Au/A)	MFie SPop
	- 'Albert Bailey' (Au/d)	EWoo GAbr GAgs IPen ITim MFie NDro SPop WCre WHil
	- 'Albury' (Au/d)	IPen WCre
	- 'Alchemist' (Au/S)	IPen SPop WAln WCre
	- 'Alexandra Georgina' (Au/A)	MFie WAln
	- 'Alf' (Au/A)	IPen MFie NDro SPop WHil
	- 'Alfred Charles' (Au/A)	SPop WAln
	- 'Alfred Niblett' (Au/S)	GAgs IPen
	- 'Alice' (Au/d)	IPen
	- 'Alice Haysom' (Au/S)	CWCL ELan EWoo GAbr GAgs IPen ITim MAsh NDro SPop WCre WHil XBar
	- 'Alicia' (Au/A)	EWoo GAbr MAsh MFie NDro SPop WCre XBar
	- 'Alison' (Au/S) **new**	GAgs
	- 'Alison Jane' (Au/A)	CPBP GAgs IPen MFie SPop WCre WHil
	- 'Alison Telford' (Au/A)	WHil
	- 'Allard' (Au/A)	WAln
	- 'Allegro' (Au/A)	WAln
	- 'Allensford' (Au/A)	WCre
	- 'Alloway' (Au/d)	WAln
	- 'Almand' (Au/d)	WAln
	- 'Almondbury' (Au/S)	NDro SPop
	- alpine mixed (Au/A)	EPfP MAsh SRms
	- 'Amazon' (Au/St) **new**	SPop
	- 'Amber Light' (Au/S)	SPop WAln
	- 'Amethyst' (Au/S)	WAln
	- 'Amicable' (Au/A)	EWoo GAgs IPen MFie NDro NSum SPop WCre WHil
	- 'Amore' (Au/St)	SPop WAln
	- 'Ancient Order' (Au/A)	IPen WAln
	- 'Ancient Society' (Au/A)	EWoo GAgs IPen MAsh MFie NDro SPop WCre WHil
	- 'Andrea Julie' (Au/A)	GAgs IPen MFie NDro SPop WCre WHil
	- 'Andrew Hunter' (Au/A)	IPen ITim MFie NDro SPop WCre
	- 'Andy Cole' (Au/A)	EWoo IPen NDro SPop WAln
	- 'Angel Eyes' (Au/St)	GAbr IPen SPop WHil
	- 'Angel Islington' (Au/S)	NDro
	- 'Angela Gould' (Au)	EWoo GAbr MFie WHil
	- 'Angela Short' (Au/St)	IPen SPop WAln
	- 'Angostura' (Au/d)	EWoo IPen SPop WCre WHil
	- 'Ann Brookes' (Au/d)	WAln
	- 'Ann Taylor' (Au/A)	IPen WAln
	- 'Anne Hyatt' (Au/d)	GAbr NDro SPop
	- 'Anne Swithinbank' (Au/d)	IPen WAln
	- 'Annie Tustin' (Au/S)	SPop
	- 'Ansells' (Au/S)	WAln
	- 'Antoc' (Au/S)	EWoo SPop
	- 'Anwar Sadat' (Au/A)	EWoo GAbr MFie NDro WCre WHil
	- 'Apple Blossom' (Au/B)	NDro WHil
	- 'Applecross' (Au/A)	IPen NDro SPop WCre WHil
	- 'Apricot Truffle' (Au/d) **new**	SPop
	- 'April Moon' (Au/S)	MAsh MFie NDro SPop WCre WHil
	- 'April Tiger' (Au/St)	EWoo WAln
	- 'Aquarius' (Au/d)	SPop
	- 'Arab Prince' (Au/A)	WAln
	- 'Arab Queen' (Au/A)	WAln
	- 'Arabian Night' (Au/A)	WAln
	- 'Arapaho' (Au/A)	SPop WAln
	- 'Arctic Fox' (Au)	MFie WAln WHil
	- 'Argentine' (Au/S) **new**	XBar
	- 'Argus' (Au/A)	EWoo GAbr GAgs IPen LSun MAsh MFie NDro SPop WCre WHil XBar
	- 'Arlene' (Au/A)	WAln
	- 'Arthur Delbridge' (Au/A)	MFie NDro SPop WHil
	- 'Arundel Cross' (Au)	IPen
	- 'Arundell' (Au/S/St)	CPBP CWCL EBee GAgs IPen ITim MFie NDro SPop WCre WHil
	- 'Arwen' (Au/A)	IPen MFie SPop
	- 'Ascot Gavotte' (Au/S)	WAln
	- 'Ashcliffe Gem' (Au/A)	IPen NDro WAln
	- 'Astolat' (Au/S)	EBee EWoo GAbr GAgs GKev IPen NDro SPop WCre WHil XBar
	- 'Athene' (Au/S)	IPen NDro SPop WAln
	- 'Atlantic' (Au/S)	NDro NEgg
	- 'Aubergine' (Au/B)	NDro
	- 'Audacity' (Au/d)	IPen WAln WCre
	- 'Audrey' (Au/S)	SPop
	- 'Aurora' (Au/A)	EDAr MFie NSum WAln WCre
	- 'Austin' (Au/A)	IPen NDro SPop WAln
	- 'Autumn Fire' (Au/A)	EWoo GAbr GAgs SPop WCre

- 'Autumn Glow' (Au/d) SPop
- 'Aviemore' (Au/A) WCre
- 'Avon Angel' (Au/d) **new** SPop
- 'Avon Carrier' (Au/d) SPop
- 'Avon Citronella' (Au) EWoo SPop
- 'Avon Eclipse' (Au/d) SPop
- 'Avon Elegance' (Au/d) **new** SPop
- 'Avon Khaki' (Au/d) SPop
- 'Avon Tan' (d) GAbr GAgs WCre
- 'Avon Toro' (Au/d) **new** SPop
- 'Avon Twist' (Au/d) EWoo SPop
- 'Avril' (Au/A) IPen NDro SPop WAln WCre WHil
- 'Avril Hunter' (Au/A) GAgs IPen ITim MAsh MFie MHer NDro NSum WCre WHil XBar
- 'Awesome' (Au/St) SPop
- 'Aztec' (Au/d) WAln
- 'Baby Blue' (AU) **new** WHil
- 'Bacchante' (Au/d) SPop WAln
- 'Bacchus' (Au/A) MFie NDro SPop WHil
- 'Baggage' (Au) EWoo GAbr GAgs IPen SPop WCre WHil
- 'Bailey Boy' (Au/B) **new** NDro
- 'Balbithan' (Au/B) EWoo GAbr GAgs
- 'Ballynahinch' (Au) **new** ITim
- 'Baltic Amber' (Au) EWoo GAgs MAsh MFie SPop WAln WBla WCre WHil
- 'Bank Error' (Au/S) IPen NDro SPop WAln
- 'Barbara Mason' (Au) WAln
- 'Barbara Weinz' (Au/S) WAln
- 'Barbarella' (Au/S) IPen MAsh MFie NDro SPop WCre
- Barnhaven Border hybrids (Au/B) **new** XBar
- Barnhaven doubles (Au/d) GAbr NSum XBar
- 'Barnhaven Gold' (Au) IPen
- 'Barr Beacon' (Au/A) IPen ITim NDro
- 'Basilio' (Au/S) NDro WAln
- 'Basuto' (Au/A) EWoo GAbr IPen ITim MFie NDro SPop WCre WHil
- 'Beatrice' (Au/A) CTri EWoo GAbr GAgs IPen MFie NDro SPop WCre WHil WIce
- 'Beauty of Bath' (Au/S) WAln
- 'Beckminster' (Au/A) WAln
- 'Bedford Lad' (Au/A) WCre
- 'Beechen Green' (Au/S) EWoo GAgs IPen ITim MAsh SPop WCre
- 'Behold' (Au) WAln WCre
- 'Belgravia Gold' (Au/B) NDro WCre
- 'Bella' (Au/d) WAln
- 'Bellamy Pride' (Au/B) GAbr IPen NDro SPop WCre
- 'Belle Zana' (Au/S) EWoo GAgs IPen MFie NDro SPop WCre WHil
- 'Ben Lawers' (Au/S) SPop WBla
- 'Ben Wyves' (Au/S) IPen SPop WBla WCre
- 'Bendigo' (Au/S) EWoo MFie SPop WAln WCre
- 'Bengal Rose' (Au/S) SPop
- 'Benno' (Au/St) EWoo
- 'Benny Green' (Au/S) IPen SPop WCre
- 'Beppi' (Au) WHil
- 'Bessie' (Au/d) **new** XBar
- 'Best Wishes' (Au/F) WAln
- 'Bethan McSparron' (Au/B) NDro
- 'Betty Stewart' (Au/A) WAln
- 'Bewitched' (Au/A) MFie NDro WAln
- 'Bilbao' (Au/A) WAln
- 'Bilbo Baggins' (Au/A) NDro SPop WAln WCre
- 'Bill Bailey' (Au/d) EWoo GAbr GAgs NDro WCre
- 'Bilton' (Au/S) SPop WCre
- 'Bingley Folk' (Au/B) NDro SPop
- 'Bisto' (Au/S) WAln
- 'Bitterne Beauty' (Au/d) IPen SPop
- 'Bitterne Bounty' (Au/d) SPop
- 'Bitterne Buttercup' (Au/d) SPop
- 'Bitterne Primrose' (Au/d) **new** SPop
- 'Bittersweet' (Au/St) **new** SPop
- 'Bizarre' (Au) GAgs WCre
- 'Black Adder' (Au/S) IPen SPop WAln
- 'Black Diamond' (Au/d) MFie SPop WHil
- 'Black Ice' (Au/S) WAln
- 'Black Jack'[PBR] (Au/d) EBee ECtt GBin GKin LBMP LRHS MHol NLar NPri SMrm
- 'Blackcurrant' (Au) GAbr
- 'Blackfield' (Au/S) SPop
- 'Blackhill' (Au/S) ITim MFie SPop
- 'Blackpool Rock' (Au/St) CWCL MFie SPop WAln WCre XBar
- 'Blairside Yellow' (Au/B) ECho LLHF NDro NSla WAbe
- 'Blakeney' (Au/d) MFie NDro
- 'Blossom' (Au/A) GAbr MFie SPop WBla
- 'Blossom Dearie' (Au/St) SPop
- 'Blue Bonnet' (Au/A/d) EWoo GAbr GAgs ITim MFie NDro WAln WCre
- 'Blue Boy' (Au/S) NDro WAln WHil
- 'Blue Chip' (Au/S) EWoo GAgs IPen MAsh MFie NDro SPop WCre WHil
- 'Blue Cliff' (Au/S) IPen SPop WAln
- 'Blue Denim' (Au/S) IPen
- 'Blue Fire' (Au/S) MFie SPop
- 'Blue Frills' (Au) WAln
- 'Blue Heaven' (Au/A) EWoo IPen NDro SPop WCre
- 'Blue Jean' (Au/S) GAbr GAgs IPen MFie NDro SPop
- 'Blue Lace' (Au) WAln
- 'Blue Merle' (Au/B) NDro
- 'Blue Night' (Au/B) ITim
- 'Blue Nile' (Au/S) SPop WCre
- 'Blue Ridge' (Au/A) WAln
- 'Blue Skies' (Au/St) SPop
- 'Blue Steel' (Au/S) WAln
- 'Blue Veil' (Au/S) **new** SPop
- 'Blue Velvet' (Au/B) EWoo GAbr GAgs IPen LLHF MFie NBro NDro SPop WCre WHil
- 'Blue Wave' (Au/d) SPop
- 'Blue Yodeler' (Au/A) GAbr GAgs MFie NDro NSum SPop WBla WCre WHil
- 'Blue Yonder' (Au/S) WAln
- 'Blush Baby' (Au/St) EWoo GAbr GAgs NDro SPop WBla WCre WHil XBar
- 'Blusher' (Au/St) WAln
- 'Blyth Spirit' (Au/A) NDro SPop WAln WCre
- 'Bob Dingley' (Au/A) IPen SPop WCre
- 'Bob Lancashire' (Au/S) GAbr GAgs IPen ITim MFie NDro SPop WBla WCre XBar
- 'Bokay' (Au/d) WAln
- 'Bold Tartan' (Au/St) IPen NDro SPop WAln
- 'Bolero' (Au/A) SPop WAln
- 'Bollin Tiger' (Au/St) WAln
- 'Bonafide' (Au/d) SPop WAln WCre
- 'Bonanza' (Au/S) SPop WAln
- 'Bookham Firefly' (Au/A) GAbr GAgs IPen MFie NDro SPop WBla WCre WHil
- 'Border Bandit' (Au/B) GAgs MFie SPop WAln
- 'Border Beauty' (Au/St) NDro
- 'Border Blue' (Au/B) WAln
- 'Border Patrol' (Au/B) WAln

– 'Border Tawny' (Au/B)	NDro
– 'Boromir' (Au/A)	EWoo MFie SPop WAln
– 'Bournebrook' (Au/A)	WAln
– 'Bowen's Blue' (Au/B)	EWoo NDro SPop
– 'Bradford City' (Au/A)	CFis CWCL LRHS NDro SPop WHil XBar
– 'Bradmore Bluebell' (Au)	NDro
– 'Bramley Rose' (Au/B)	SPop
– 'Bran' (Au/B)	NDro
– 'Brandaris' (Au/A)	WAln
– 'Branno' (Au/S)	WAln
– 'Brass Dog' (Au/S)	WAln
– 'Brasso' (Au)	IPen MAsh MFie NDro SPop WAln WCre
– 'Brazen Hussy' (Au/d)	WAln
– 'Brazil' (Au/S)	CTal EBee GAbr GAgs IPen MFie NDro SPop WCre WHil
– 'Brazos River' (Au/A)	EWoo IPen MFie SPop WAln WCre WHil
– 'Breckland Joy' (Au/A)	NDro WAln
– 'Brenda's Choice' (Au/A)	EWoo IPen MFie NDro SPop WBla WCre
– 'Brentford Bees' (Au/St)	WAln
– 'Bright Eyes' (Au/A)	IPen MFie WCre
– 'Bright Ginger' (Au/S)	EWoo SPop WAln WCre
– 'Brimstone and Treacle' (Au/d)	SPop WAln
– 'Broad Gold' (Au/A)	MFie SPop WBla WCre
– 'Broadwell Gold' (Au/B)	GAbr NDro SPop WCre
– 'Brompton' (Au/S)	SPop
– 'Brookfield' (Au/S)	GAbr GAgs IPen MFie NDro SPop WBla WCre
– 'Broughton' (Au/S)	SPop
– 'Brown Ben' (Au)	EWoo IPen MFie WHil
– 'Brown Bess' (Au/A)	GAbr GAgs IPen MFie WCot WCre WHil
– 'Brown Tan Double' (Au/d)	EWoo GAgs
– 'Brownie' (Au/B)	EWoo GAbr GAgs NBir NDro NSum SPop WCre WHil XBar
– 'Brownie Point' (Au/B)	NDro
– 'Bucks Green' (Au/S)	GAbr NDro SPop
– 'Bunty' (Au/A)	MFie
– 'Buoyance' (Au/A)	WAln
– 'Burnished Gold' (Au/d)	WAln
– 'Bush Baby' (Au/B)	NDro
– 'Buttercup' (Au/d) **new**	SPop
– 'Buttermere' (Au/d)	WAln WCre
– 'Butternut' (Au/S)	WAln
– 'Butterwick' (Au/A)	EWoo GAbr GAgs IPen MFie NDro NEgg SPop WBla WCre XBar
– 'C.G. Haysom' (Au/S)	GAbr GAgs NDro SPop WCre WHil
– 'C.W. Needham' (Au/A)	GAbr IPen ITim MFie NDro SPop WCre
– 'Cadiz Bay' (Au/d)	WAln
– 'Café au Lait' (Au/A) **new**	XBar
– 'Callisto' (Au/d) **new**	SPop
– 'Calypso' (Au/d)	NDro SPop WAln
– 'Cambodunum' (Au/A)	IPen MFie NDro NSum SPop WCre WHil
– 'Camelot' (Au/d)	ELan EWoo GAgs GKev MFie NBro NDro SPop WCre WHil
– 'Cameo' (Au/A)	GAgs WCre
– 'Cameo Beauty' (Au/d)	EWoo NDro SPop WCre
– 'Camilla' (Au/A)	WAln
– 'Candida' (Au/d)	GAgs IPen SPop WBla WCre
– 'Candy Stripe' (Au/St)	GAgs SPop
– 'Cappela' (Au/d)	WAln
– 'Caramel' (Au/A)	GAgs IPen WAln
– 'Cardinal Red' (Au/d)	NDro SPop
– 'Cardington' (Au/A)	WAln
– 'Carioca' (Au/A)	WAln
– 'Carl Andrew' (Au/S)	WAln
– 'Carmel' (Au/d)	EWoo SPop WAln WBla WCre
– 'Carnival' (Au/A)	WAln
– 'Carole' (Au/A)	MFie SPop WBla WCre WHil
– 'Carreras' (Au)	MFie NDro
– 'Carsa Wakes' (Au/d)	MAsh WAln
– 'Carzon' (Au/A)	NDro
– 'Catherine Wheel' (Au/St)	SPop WAln
– 'Catta Ha' (Au/d)	NDro
– 'Celtic One' (Au/St)	SPop
– 'Ceri Nicolle' (Au/B)	NDro
– 'Chadwick End' (Au/S)	WAln
– 'Chaffinch' (Au/S)	EWoo GAbr GAgs IPen NDro SPop
– 'Chamois' (Au/B)	EWoo GAbr IPen MFie NDro WCre WHil
– 'Chanel' (Au/S)	EWoo SPop WAln WCre
– 'Chantilly Cream' (Au/d)	WAln
– 'Charles Bronson' (Au/d)	GAbr MFie NDro WAln
– 'Charles Rennie' (Au/B)	EWoo MFie NDro SPop WAln WHil
– 'Charlie's Aunt' (Au/A)	WAln
– 'Charlotte Brookes' (Au/d)	SPop WAln
– 'Checkmate' (Au)	EWoo GAgs MFie SPop WAln WCre
– 'Cheeky' (Au/d)	SPop
– 'Chelsea Bridge' (Au/A)	EWoo GAgs IPen MFie NDro SPop WBla WCre WHil
– 'Cheops' (Au/A)	IPen MFie NDro NEgg WCre XBar
– 'Cherry' (Au/S)	GAbr GAgs IPen SPop WCre
– 'Cherry Picker' (Au/A)	MFie NDro SPop WCre
– 'Cheyenne' (Au/S)	EWoo GAbr GAgs MFie NDro SPop WCre
– 'Chiffon' (Au/S)	CPBP EWoo IPen NDro NSum SPop WCre
– 'Chiquita' (Au/d)	EWoo MAsh SPop
– 'Chirichua' (Au/S)	WAln
– 'Chloë' (Au/S)	IPen NDro SPop
– 'Chloris' (Au/S)	MFie SPop
– 'Choir Boy' (Au/A)	WAln
– 'Chorister' (Au/S)	CPBP EBee GAbr GAgs IPen ITim MFie NDro NSum SPop WCre WHil
– 'Chyne' (Au)	EWoo
– 'Cicero' (Au/A)	MFie SPop WAln
– 'Cinders' (Au/St)	SPop
– 'Cindy' (Au/A)	NDro
– 'Cinnamon' (Au/d)	EWoo GAgs ITim MFie NDro SPop WBla WCre WHil
– 'Cinnamon' (Au/S)	GAbr
– 'Ciribiribin' (Au/A)	WAln
– 'Citron-Ella' (Au/d)	SPop
– 'Clara' (Au/d)	SPop
– 'Clare' (Au/S)	IPen MFie NDro SPop WCre
– 'Clarish' (Au)	ITim
– 'Classic' (Au/A)	WAln
– 'Clatter-Ha' (Au/d)	NSum SPop WCre WHil
– 'Claud Wilson' (Au/St)	WAln WCre
– 'Claudia Taylor' (Au)	EWoo SPop
– 'Cleft Stick' (Au)	IPen
– 'Clipper' (Au/S)	WAln
– 'Cloth of Gold' (Au/A)	NDro WCre
– 'Clotted Cream' (Au/B)	NDro
– 'Cloud Nine' (Au/S)	WCre
– 'Clouded Yellow' (Au/S)	SPop WBla WHil
– 'Cloudy Bay' (Au)	NDro WCot
– 'Cloverdale' (Au/d)	WAln
– 'Clunie' (Au/S)	IPen MFie NDro WCre XBar

- 'Clunie II' (Au/S) GAgs IPen
- 'Cobden Meadows' (Au/A) WAln
- 'Cockle' (Au/S) SPop
- 'Coffee' (Au/S) IPen ITim MAsh MFie NDro SPop WCre WHil XBar
- 'Colbury' (Au/S) NDro SPop WCre XBar
- 'Colonel Champney' (Au/S) EWoo NDro SPop WCre
- 'Comet' (Au/S) IPen NDro
- 'Confederate' (Au/S) WAln
- 'Connaught Court' (Au/A) EWoo IPen NDro WCre
- 'Conquistador' (Au/A) IPen NDro WAln
- 'Conservative' (Au/S) EWoo IPen
- 'Consett' (Au/S) EWoo GAgs IPen ITim MFie SPop WHil
- 'Cooks Hill' (Au/d) WAln
- 'Cooper's Gold' (Au/B) NDro
- 'Coop's Green' (Au/S) EWoo
- 'Copper King' (Au/B) WAln
- 'Coppi' (Au/A) EWoo IPen NDro SPop WCre
- 'Coral' (Au/S) GAgs SPop
- 'Corn Dolly' (Au/S) **new** SPop
- 'Cornish Cream' (Au/B) IPen NDro
- 'Cornmeal' (Au/S) MFie NDro SPop WAln WCre WHil
- 'Corntime' (Au/S) IPen SPop WAln WCre
- 'Corona' (Au/S) WAln
- 'Corporal Jones' (Au/S) SPop WCre
- 'Corporal Kate' (Au/St) WAln WCre
- 'Corrie Files' (Au/d) MFie SPop WAln
- 'Cortez Silver' (Au/S) SPop WAln
- 'Cortina' (Au/S) CPBP ECho EWoo GAbr GAgs IPen ITim MAsh MFie NDro SPop WCre WHil XBar
- 'Country Maid' (Au/A) WAln
- 'County Park Red' (Au/B) NDro
- 'Coventry Street' (Au/S) MAsh MFie NDro NSum SPop WCre
- 'Crackley Tagetes' (Au/d) ECho
- 'Craig Nordie' (Au/B) NDro
- 'Craig Vaughan' (Au/A) MFie NDro SPop XBar
- 'Cranborne' (Au/A) SPop WAln
- 'Crecy' (Au/A) MFie SPop WAln WHil
- 'Cressida' (Au/d) SPop
- 'Crimple' (Au/S) NDro SPop WAln WCre WHil
- 'Crimson Black' (Au/B) SPop
- 'Crimson Glow' (Au/d) EWoo GAbr GAgs MAsh MFie NDro NSum SPop WBla WCre WHil
- 'Crinoline' (Au/S) NDro SPop
- 'Cuckoo Fair' (Au/S) EWoo GAbr GAgs IPen NDro SPop WCre
- 'Cuddles' (Au/A) EWoo MFie WAln WCre
- 'Curly Wurlie' (Au) GAbr
- 'Curry Blend' (Au/B) GAbr IPen NDro SPop WHil
- 'Custard Cream' (Au) **new** WHil
- 'Cutie Pie' (Au/St) IPen SPop WCre
- 'Cuttlefish' (Au/St) SPop
- 'Daftie Green' (Au/S) EWoo GAbr GAgs IPen NDro WCre
- 'Dakota' (Au/S) EWoo MFie SPop
- 'Dales Red' (Au/B) EWoo GAbr GAgs IGor IPen MFie NDro NSum SPop WCre WHil
- 'Dan Tiger' (Au/St) EWoo MFie NDro SPop WAln WHil
- 'Daniel' (Au/A) EWoo NDro SPop WAln
- 'Daniel T. Taylor' (Au/A) WAln
- 'Daphnis' (Au/S) GAbr SPop WAln
- 'Darent Tiger' (Au/St) **new** XBar
- 'Dark Eyes' (Au/d) EWoo GAbr GAgs MFie NDro NSum SPop WHil
- 'Dark Lady' (Au/A) WAln
- 'Dark Red' (Au/S) IPen
- 'Darth Vader' (Au/d) **new** XBar
- 'David Beckham' (Au/d) SPop WAln
- 'Day by Day' (Au/St) SPop
- 'Decaff' (Au/St) WAln
- 'Deckchair' (Au/St) MFie NDro SPop
- 'Dedham' (Au/d) WAln
- 'Del Boy' (Au/A) SPop WAln
- 'Delicious' (Au/St) **new** SPop
- 'Delilah' (Au/d) GAbr GAgs ITim MFie NDro NSum SPop WHil
- 'Denise' (Au/S) WAln
- 'Denna Snuffer' (Au/d) GAbr
- 'Derrill' (Au/B) NDro SPop
- 'Devon Cream' (Au/d) ECho IPen MFie SPop WCre
- 'Diamond' (Au/d) WAln
- 'Diane' (Au/A) IPen MFie
- 'Dick Rogers' (Au/B) NDro
- 'Digby' (Au/d) NDro WAln
- 'Digit' (Au/d) WAln
- 'Dilemma' (Au/A) SPop
- 'Dill' (Au/A) IPen MFie SPop WAln WHil
- 'Dilly Dilly' (Au/A) MFie NDro SPop WCre
- 'Divint Dunch' (Au/A) IPen MFie NDro SPop WCre WHil
- 'Doctor Duthie' (Au/S) SPop WAln
- 'Doctor Lennon's White' (Au/B) GAbr IPen MFie MHer NDro SPop WCre WHil
- 'Doctor Woolhead' (Au/S) SPop
- 'Dolly Viney' (Au/d) GAbr WAln
- 'Donhead' (Au/A) MFie NDro SPop WCre WHil
- 'Donn' (Au/d) SPop WAln WCre
- 'Donna Clancy' (Au/S) MFie SPop WCre XBar
- 'Dorado' (Au/d) SPop WAln
- 'Doreen Stephens' (Au/A) GAgs
- 'Doris Jean' (Au/A) MFie
- 'Dorothy' (Au/S) WAln
- 'Doublet' (Au/d) ECho GAbr GAgs IPen MFie NDro NSum SPop WCre WHil
- 'Doubloon' (Au/d) ECho XBar
- 'Doublure' (Au/d) EWoo GAbr GAgs NDro SPop WCre WHil
- 'Douglas Bader' (Au/A) MFie NDro SPop WCre WHil
- 'Douglas Black' (Au/S) EWoo GAbr GAgs IPen MFie NDro SPop WCre WHil
- 'Douglas Green' (Au/S) EWoo IPen NDro WCre
- 'Douglas Red' (Au/A) IPen
- 'Douglas White' (Au/S) MFie SPop
- 'Dovedale' (Au/S) NDro SPop WAln
- 'Dowager' (Au/A) MFie
- Downtown Doubles (Au/d) SPop
- 'Doyen' (Au/d) EWoo IPen ITim MFie NDro WAln WHil
- 'Drax' (Au/A) SPop WAln
- 'Dream' (Au/St) SPop
- 'Dubarii' (Au/A) MFie WAln
- 'Duchess of Malfi' (Au/S) SPop WAln
- 'Duchess of York' (Au) LLHF
- 'Duke of Edinburgh' (Au/B) NDro WAln
- 'Dusky Girl' (Au/A) NDro WAln
- 'Dusky Maiden' (Au/A) EWoo GAbr GAgs MFie NDro SPop WBla WCre WHil
- 'Dusky Yellow' (Au/B) ECho NDro
- 'Dusty Miller' (Au/B) EBee ECho LRHS NBir
- 'Eastern Promise' (Au/A) EWoo GAgs MFie NDro NSum SPop WBla WHil
- 'Eaton Dawn' (Au/S) SPop

- 'Ed Spivey' (Au/A) NDro WBla WCre
- 'Eddy Gordon' (Au/A) IPen WAln
- 'Eden Alexander' (Au/B) MFie NDro
- 'Eden Amethyst' (Au/B) **new** NDro
- 'Eden Blue Star' (Au/B) EWoo NDro SPop
- 'Eden Carmine' (Au/B) MFie MHer NDro SPop
- 'Eden Cynthia' (Au/B) IPen MFie
- 'Eden David' (Au/B) MFie NDro SPop WHil
- 'Eden Ensign' (Au/B) SPop
- 'Eden Fanfare' (Au/B) NDro
- 'Eden Goldfinch' (Au/B) GAgs IPen SPop
- 'Eden Greenfinch' (Au/B) EWoo GAbr GAgs MAsh MFie NDro SPop WCre
- 'Eden Moonlight' (Au/B) MFie WAln WCre WHil
- 'Eden Sunrise' (Au/B) NDro
- 'Edinburgh' (Au/A) WAln
- 'Edith Allen' (Au/A) WAln
- 'Edith Major' (Au/d) CPBP MFie SPop WHil
- 'Edith Mather' (Au/S) WAln
- 'Edward Sweeney' (Au/S) WAln
- 'Eggborough' (Au/A) **new** SPop
- 'Eglinton' (Au) WCre
- 'Eileen K' (Au/S) NDro
- 'El Zoco' (Au/S) **new** SPop
- 'Elara' (Au/d) **new** SPop
- 'Elegance' (Au/S) SPop
- 'Elf Star' (Au/A) SPop WAln
- 'Eli Jenkins' (Au) WAln
- 'Elizabeth Ann' (Au/A) GAbr NDro SPop
- 'Ellen Thompson' (Au/A) EWoo GAbr IPen MFie NDro SPop WCre WHil XBar
- 'Elsie' (Au/A) WCre
- 'Elsie May' (Au/A) EWoo IPen ITim MFie NDro SPop WCre WHil
- 'Elsinore' (Au/S) IPen SPop WCre
- 'Emberglow' (Au/d) WAln
- 'Embley' (Au/S) NDro SPop WCre
- 'Emery Down' (Au/S) NDro SPop WBla WCre
- 'Emily' (Au/d) IPen
- 'Emma Louise' (Au) IPen
- 'Emmett Smith' (Au/A) NBro NDro WAln
- 'Enigma' (Au/S) SPop WAln
- 'Enlightened' (Au/A) MFie
- 'Envy' (Au/S) MFie WAln
- 'Erica' (Au/A) GAbr IPen MFie NDro NSum SPop WCre WHil
- 'Erjon' (Au/S) MFie NDro SPop
- 'Error' (Au/S) MFie WAln
- 'Eschman Starflower' (Au/S) WHil
- 'Esso' (Au/S) WAln
- 'Ethel' (Au) NDro WCre
- 'Ethel Wild' (Au/d) SPop
- 'Ethel Wilkes' (Au/d) WAln
- 'Etna' (Au/S) WAln WCre
- 'Ettrick' (Au/S) WAln
- 'Europa' (Au/d) SPop
- 'Eve Guest' (Au/A) EWoo NDro SPop WAln
- 'Eventide' (Au/S) MAsh SPop
- 'Everest Blue' (Au/S) EWoo GAbr GAgs MAsh SPop WCre XBar
- 'Everest Flush' (Au/S) WAln
- 'Excalibur' (Au/d) EWoo GAbr GAgs NDro NSum SPop WCre
- 'Exhibition Blau' (Exhibition Series) (Au/B) WHil
- 'Eye Candy' (Au/St) SPop
- 'Eyeopener' (Au/A) IPen MFie NDro SPop WCre WHil
- 'Fabuloso' (Au/St) EWoo SPop WBla WCre
- 'Fairy' (Au/A) WAln
- 'Fairy Light' (Au/S) SPop WAln
- 'Fairy Moon' (Au/S) IPen WAln
- 'Fairy Queen' (Au/S) WAln
- 'Falcon' (Au/S) SPop WAln
- 'Faliraki Fanciful' (Au) EWoo
- 'Faloonside' (Au) IPen
- 'Falstaff' (Au/d) WAln
- 'Fanciful' (Au/S) EWoo MFie NDro WHil XBar
- 'Fancy Free' (Au) SPop
- 'Fancy Pants' (Au/S) SPop
- 'Fandancer' (Au/A) WAln
- 'Fandango' WBla WCre
- 'Fanfare' (Au/S) EWoo MAsh MFie NDro SPop WBla WHil
- 'Fanny Meerbeck' (Au/S) GAbr GAgs IPen MFie NDro SPop WBla WHil
- 'Fantasia' (Au/d) WAln
- 'Faro' (Au/S) NDro SPop WBla WCre
- 'Favourite' (Au/S) EWoo GAbr GAgs IPen ITim MFie NDro SPop WBla WCre WHil XBar
- 'Fearless' (Au/S) WAln
- 'Fen Tiger' (Au/St) SPop WAln
- 'Fenby' (Au/S) EWoo SPop
- 'Fennay' (Au/S) EWoo NSum WAln
- 'Ferrybridge' (Au/A) IPen WAln
- 'Fiddler's Green' (Au/d) CPBP EWoo GAbr GAgs IPen NDro SPop WCot WCre XBar
- 'Figaro' (Au/S) EWoo MFie NDro SPop WCre
- 'Figurine' (Au/d) WAln
- 'Finchfield' (Au/A) GAbr IPen MFie NDro WAln
- 'Finley' (Au/B) NDro
- 'Firecracker' (Au) IPen WAln
- 'Firenze' (Au/A) MFie SPop
- 'Firsby' (Au/d) EWoo NDro SPop WAln WBla WCre WHil
- 'First Lady' (Au/A) IPen SPop WAln WBla WCre
- 'First Light' (Au/B) NDro SPop
- 'Fishtoft' (Au/d) MFie
- 'Fitzroy' (Au/d) EWoo SPop
- 'Fleecy' (Au/S) **new** SPop
- 'Fleet Street' (Au/S) GAgs MFie NDro SPop WHil
- 'Fleminghouse' (Au/S) GAbr MAsh NDro SPop WCre
- 'Florence Brown' (Au/S) IPen
- 'Fluffy Duckling' (Au/S) **new** SPop
- 'For You' (Au/St) SPop
- 'Foreign Affairs' (Au/S) SPop
- 'Forest Beech' (Au/d) SPop
- 'Forest Bordeaux' (Au/d) **new** SPop
- 'Forest Bracken' (Au/d) SPop
- 'Forest Burgundy' (Au/d) SPop
- 'Forest Burnt Gold' (Au/d) **new** WCre
- 'Forest Cappuccino' (Au/d) EWoo SPop
- 'Forest Duet' (Au/d) EWoo SPop
- 'Forest Fire' (Au/d) EWoo SPop
- 'Forest Glade' (Au/d) **new** SPop
- 'Forest Gorse' (Au/d) **new** WCre
- 'Forest Lemon' (Au/d) EWoo SPop WCre
- 'Forest Lime' (Au/d) SPop
- 'Forest Pines' (Au/S) SPop WAln
- 'Forest Shade' (Au/d) SPop
- 'Forest Sunburst' (Au/d) SPop
- 'Forest Sunlight' (Au/d) SPop

- 'Forest Twilight' (Au/d) EWoo MFie SPop WCre
- 'Foxfire' (Au/A) WAln
- 'Fradley' (Au/A) IPen MFie NDro WAln WCre WHil
- 'Françoise' (Au/d) **new** XBar
- 'Frank Bailey' (Au/d) EWoo MAsh MFie SPop WAln
- 'Frank Crosland' (Au/A) MFie NDro NSum WCre WHil
- 'Frank Faulkner' (Au/A) WAln
- 'Frank Jenning' (Au/A) NDro WAln
- 'Frank Taylor' (Au/S) EWoo
- 'Fred Booley' (Au/d) EWoo GAbr GAgs IPen MAsh MFie NDro NSum SPop WCre WHil XBar
- 'Fred Livesley' (Au/A) NDro WAln
- 'Fresco' (Au/A) SPop WAln
- 'Freya' (Au/S) SPop
- 'Friskney' (Au/d) EWoo SPop WAln
- 'Frittenden Yellow' (Au/B) GAbr SPop
- 'Frosty' (Au/S) EWoo NDro SPop WBla WCre
- 'Fuller's Red' (Au/S) ITim NDro SPop WCre WHil XBar
- 'Funny Valentine' (Au/d) EWoo IPen MFie SPop WBla WCre WHil
- 'Fuzzy' (Au/St) WAln
- 'G.L. Taylor' (Au/A) IPen NDro
- 'Gaia' (Au/d) EWoo SPop WCre WHil
- 'Gail Atkinson' (Au/A) SPop WAln WBla
- 'Galatea' (Au/S) WAln
- 'Galator' (Au/A) WAln
- 'Galen' (Au/A) GAbr WCre
- 'Ganymede' (Au/d) SPop WAln
- 'Gary Pallister' (Au/A) MAsh WAln WBla WCre
- 'Gateshead' (Au/S) **new** WCre
- 'Gavin Ward' (Au/S) WAln
- 'Gay Crusader' (Au/A) GAbr IPen MFie NDro SPop WCre WHil
- 'Gazza' (Au/A) WAln
- 'Gee Cross' (Au/A) GAbr IPen MFie NDro WCre
- 'Geldersome Green' (Au/S) ITim NDro SPop
- 'Gemini' (Au/S) NDro
- 'General Champney' (Au) WCre
- 'Generosity' (Au/A) MFie WCre WHil
- 'Geoffrey Bick' (Au/A) SPop
- 'Geordie' (Au/A) WAln
- 'George Edge' (Au/B) NDro
- 'George Harrison' (Au/B) GAgs NDro SPop
- 'George Jennings' (Au/A) MFie NDro
- 'George Swinford's Leathercoat' (Au/B) GAbr NDro
- 'Geronimo' (Au/S) GAbr IPen MAsh MFie NDro SPop WBla WCre
- 'Ghost Grey' (Au) WCre
- 'Gimli' (Au/A) WAln
- 'Girl Guide' (Au/S) WHil
- 'Gizabroon' (Au/S) CFis CPBP CWCL EWoo GAbr GAgs LRHS MFie NDro NEgg NLar SPop WBla WCre WHil XBar
- 'Glasnost' (Au/S) WAln
- 'Glazebrook' (Au/S) SPop
- 'Gleam' (Au/S) CTal CWCL EBee ECho EDAr GAgs IPen LLHF MFie NDro SPop WBla WCre WHil XBar
- 'Glencoe' (Au/S) EWoo GAgs SPop
- 'Gleneagles' (Au/S) EWoo GAgs IPen NDro SPop WAln WBla WCre
- 'Glenelg' (Au/S) EWoo GAbr ITim MFie NDro NSum SPop WBla WCre WHil
- 'Glenluce' (Au/S) EWoo SPop
- 'Gloire de Dijon' (Au/S) **new** XBar
- 'Gnome' (Au/B) GAbr IPen NDro
- 'Goeblii' (Au/B) MFie NDro SPop WHil
- 'Gold Seal' (Au/d) SPop
- 'Gold Seam' (Au/A) EWoo MFie WAln WHil
- 'Golden Boy' (Au/A) MFie NDro NSum SPop WAln
- 'Golden Chartreuse' (Au/d) EWoo GAbr NDro SPop
- 'Golden Fleece' (Au/S) EWoo MAsh MFie NDro SPop WCre
- 'Golden Girl' (Au/A) WAln
- 'Golden Glory' (Au/A) WAln
- 'Golden Harvest' (Au/A) SPop
- 'Golden Hind' (Au/d) EWoo GAbr MFie NBro NDro SPop WBla WCre WHil
- 'Golden Splendour' (Au/d) EWoo GAgs GKev IPen ITim MAsh MFie NDro NSum SPop WBla WCre WHil
- 'Golden Wedding' (Au/A) IPen MFie SPop WAln WCre WHil
- 'Goldie' (Au/S) NDro
- 'Goldthorn' (Au/A) WCre
- 'Gollum' (Au/A) MAsh MFie NDro SPop WAln WBla
- 'Good Report' (Au/A) GAgs MAsh MFie NDro NSum SPop WBla WHil
- 'Goody Goody' (Au/St) SPop
- 'Googie' (Au/d) SPop
- 'Gordon Files' (Au/S) WAln
- 'Gorey' (Au/A) IPen MFie WCre WHil
- 'Gorgeous George' (Au/St) SPop
- 'Grabley' (Au/S) EWoo SPop
- 'Grace' (Au/S) WAln
- 'Grace Ellen' (Au/S) WAln
- 'Grand Slam' (Au/D) MFie
- 'Grandad's Favourite' (Au/B) EWoo NDro SPop
- 'Green Abundance' (Au/B) EWoo
- 'Green Café' (Au/S) SPop
- 'Green Finger' (Au/S) EWoo MFie SPop WHil
- 'Green Frill' (Au) GAgs NDro
- 'Green Goddess' (Au/St) EWoo WAln
- 'Green Heart' (Au/S) EWoo SPop
- 'Green Isle' (Au/S) EWoo GAbr IPen MFie NDro SPop WCre XBar
- 'Green Jacket' (Au/S) IPen SPop WCre
- 'Green Lane' (Au/S) **new** XBar
- 'Green Meadows' (Au/S) SPop WAln
- 'Green Mouse' (Au/S) WAln
- 'Green Mustard' (Au/S) SPop
- 'Green Parrot' (Au/S) EWoo GAbr NDro SPop WCre WHil
- 'Green Shank' (Au/S) EWoo GAgs IPen NDro SPop WHil
- 'Green Woodpecker' (Au/S) IPen
- 'Greenfield's Fancy' (Au) EBee
- 'Greenfinch' (Au/S) EWoo
- 'Greenfinger' (Au/S) WAln
- 'Greenheart' (Au/S) SPop
- 'Greenpeace' (Au/S) EWoo GAbr GAgs NDro SPop WAln WBla WCre XBar
- 'Greswolde' (Au/d) EWoo SPop WAln
- 'Greta' (Au/S) CWCL ECho EWoo GAbr IPen MFie NDro SPop WCre WHil
- 'Gretna Green' (Au/S) EWoo SPop
- 'Grey Bonnet' (Au/S) SPop WAln
- 'Grey Cloud' (Au/B) NDro WHil
- 'Grey Dawn' (Au/S) WAln
- 'Grey Edge' (Au) ECho
- 'Grey Friar' (Au/S) SPop WAln
- 'Grey Hawk' (Au/S) IPen SPop WAln
- 'Grey Lady' (Au/S) WAln
- 'Grey Lag' (Au/S) SPop WHil XBar

- 'Grey Monarch' (Au/S) GAbr IPen MFie SPop WAln WCre WHil
- 'Grey Owl' (Au/S) SPop WAln
- 'Grey Ridge' (Au/S) WAln
- 'Grey Shrike' (Au/S) SPop WAln
- 'Grizedale' (Au/S) SPop
- 'Groupie' (Au/St) SPop
- 'Grüner Veltliner' (Au/S) NDro SPop WCre
- 'Guinea' (Au/S) CTal EWoo GAbr IPen MFie SPop WCre
- 'Gwai Loh' (Au) NDro
- 'Gwen' (Au/A) MFie NDro SPop WAln WCre XBar
- 'Gwen Baker' (Au/d) IPen MFie NDro WAln WCre
- 'Gwenda' (Au/A) SPop WAln WHil
- 'Gypsy Rose Lee' (Au/A) MFie
- 'H Old Gold' (Au/S) **new** NDro
- 'Habanera' (Au/A) MFie NDro SPop WCre
- 'Haffner' (Au/S) IPen MAsh NDro SPop
- 'Hallmark' (Au/A) EWoo MFie NDro WAln
- 'Handsome Lass' (Au/St) EWoo GAgs IPen MFie SPop WAln WCre
- 'Hannah' (Au/A) WAln
- 'Harlequin' (Au/B) NDro
- 'Harmony' (Au/B) EWoo MFie NBro NDro XBar
- 'Harry Hotspur' (Au/A) IPen MFie NDro NSum SPop WCre WHil
- 'Harry 'O'' (Au/S) MFie NDro SPop WCre
- 'Harthorpeburn' (Au/B) NDro
- 'Harvest Glow' (Au/S) IPen NDro SPop WHil
- 'Harvest Gold' (Au/S) **new** WCre
- 'Havana' (Au/d) SPop WAln
- 'Hawkwood' (Au/S) CPBP CWCL GAbr GAgs GKev IPen MAsh MFie NDro NEgg WBla WHil XBar
- 'Hazel' (Au/B) **new** NDro WCre
- 'Hazel' (Au/A) IPen MFie NDro SPop WHil
- 'Headdress' (Au/S) EWoo GAbr IPen MFie SPop
- 'Heady' (Au/A) CWCL EWoo MFie NDro WCre WHil XBar
- 'Heart of Gold' (Au/A) MFie SPop WAln
- 'Hearts of Oak' (Au/A) **new** WAln
- 'Heaven Scent' (Au) **new** WHil
- 'Hebers' (Au) NDro SPop WAln
- 'Helen' (Au/S) GAbr IPen MFie NDro SPop WCre WHil
- 'Helen Barter' (Au/S) NDro NSum SPop WCre WHil
- 'Helen Ruane' (Au/d) EBee EWoo GAgs GKev SPop WCre
- 'Helena' (Au/S) IPen MFie SPop WAln WCre WHil
- 'Helena Brown' (Au/S) SPop WAln
- 'Helena Dean' (Au/d) SPop WAln
- 'Helluinn' (Au/d) **new** SPop
- 'Henry's Bane' (Au/St) SPop
- 'Her Nibs' (Au/St) WCre
- 'Hermes the Cat' (Au) **new** WHil
- 'Hermia' (Au/A) MFie SPop WHil
- 'Hetty Woolf' (Au/S) GAbr ITim NDro SPop WCre
- 'Hew Dalrymple' (Au/S) NDro SPop WAln
- 'High Hopes' (Au) WAln
- 'Highland Park' (Au/A) NDro SPop
- 'Hillhook' (Au/A) WAln
- 'Hinton Admiral' (Au/S) EWoo GAbr IPen NDro SPop WCre WHil XBar
- 'Hinton Fields' (Au/S) CPBP CUse EBee EShb GAbr GAgs IPen LRHS MAsh MFie NDro NEgg SPop WBla WCre WHil
- 'Hobby Horse' (Au) EWoo GAgs ITim NDro WCre
- 'Holyrood' (Au/S) EWoo GAbr IPen ITim NDro SPop WAln XBar
- 'Honey' (Au/d) GAbr NBro NDro NEgg NSum SPop
- 'Honeydawn' (Au/B) NDro
- 'Hopleys Coffee' (Au/d) EWoo GAbr NDro SPop WAln WBla WCre
- 'Hopton Gem' (Au/B) NDro
- 'Howard Telford' (Au/A) MFie SPop
- 'Hughie' (Au/A) WAln
- 'Humphrey' (Au/S) WAln
- 'Hurstwood Midnight' (Au) MFie WAln XBar
- 'Iago' (Au/S) NDro SPop WAln
- 'Ian Greville' (Au/A) IPen MFie NDro SPop WBla WCre
- 'Ibis' (Au/S) WAln
- 'Ice Cap' (Au/d) SPop
- 'Ice Maiden' (Au/A) EWoo GAbr IPen MFie NDro SPop WBla WCre WHil
- 'Icon' (Au/St) SPop
- 'Ida' (Au/A) IPen
- 'Idmiston' (Au/S) CWCL EWoo GAbr IPen NDro SPop WCre WHil XBar
- 'Ilona' (Au/d) SPop
- 'Imari Stripe' (Au/St) MAsh WHil
- 'Immaculate' (Au/A) MFie SPop WBla WCre WHil
- 'Impassioned' (Au/A) MFie SPop WBla WCre XBar
- 'Impeccable' (Au/A) IPen MFie
- 'Imperturbable' (Au/A) IPen MFie NDro SPop
- 'Indian Love Call' (Au/A) GAbr GAgs IPen ITim MFie NDro SPop WBla WCre WHil
- 'Innsworth' (Au/A) SPop WAln
- 'Iris Scott' (Au/A) ITim NDro
- 'Isabel' (Au/S) WAln
- 'Isabella' (Au/A) NDro WAln
- 'Jac' (Au/S) SPop
- 'Jack Dean' (Au/A) EWoo MFie SPop WCre WHil XBar
- 'Jack Horner' (Au) WAln
- 'Jack Redfern' (Au/A) NDro
- 'Jaffa' (Au/A) EWoo NDro NSum WAln WCre
- 'James Arnot' (Au/S) IPen SPop WAln WHil
- 'James Watham' (Au/S) WAln
- 'Jane' (Au/S) WAln
- 'Jane Myers' (Au/d) WAln WHil
- 'Janet' (Au) ECho
- 'Janet Watts' (Au) GAgs WCre
- 'Janie Hill' (Au/A) GAbr MFie SPop WBla WCre
- 'Jealous Lover' (Au/St) **new** SPop
- 'Jean Fielder' (Au/A) NDro SPop WAln
- 'Jean Jacques' (Au/A) WAln
- 'Jean Walker' (Au/B) SPop
- 'Jeanne' (Au/A) EWoo MFie
- 'Jeannie Telford' (Au/A) MFie NDro SPop WCre WHil
- 'Jeff Scruton' (Au/A) SPop WAln
- 'Jenny' (Au/A) EWoo IPen MFie NDro NRya SPop WCre
- 'Jersey Bounce' (Au/A) EWoo GAbr ITim NDro WAln WCre
- 'Jesmond' (Au/S) WAln
- 'Jessie' (Au/d) EWoo
- 'Jilting Jessie' (Au/St) IPen NDro SPop
- 'Joan Butler' (Au) WAln
- 'Joan Curtis' (Au/d) SPop
- 'Joan Elliott' (Au/A) GAbr
- 'Joanne' (Au/A) EWoo GAbr MFie NDro SPop WCre
- 'Joe Perks' (Au/A) EWoo GAgs IPen ITim MFie NBro NDro SPop WCre WHil
- 'Joel' (Au/S) EWoo GAgs IPen ITim MFie NDro SPop WBla WCre WHil XBar
- 'Johann Bach' (Au/B) EWoo SPop
- 'John Stewart' (Au/A) MFie SPop

- 'John Wayne' (Au/A) EWoo GAbr MFie NDro WBla WCre WHil
- 'John Woolf' (Au/S) NDro
- 'Jonathon' (Au/A) EWoo NDro WAln
- 'Jorvik' (Au/S) NDro SPop
- 'Joy' (Au/A) GAgs IPen LLHF MFie NDro NSum SPop WCre WHil
- 'Joyce' (Au/A) EWoo GAbr GAgs IPen MFie NDro SPop WCre WHil XBar
- 'Judith' (Au/B) NDro
- 'Judith Borman' (Au/d) GAgs NDro
- 'Julia' (Au/S) NDro SPop WAln
- 'Julia Jane' (Au/B) NDro WCre
- 'Julie Nuttall' (Au/B) EWoo GAgs NDro WHil
- 'June' (Au/A) NDro SPop WCre
- 'Jungfrau' (Au/d) NDro SPop WAln
- 'Jupiter' (Au/S) NDro SPop WAln
- 'Jupp' (Au) EBee GAgs
- 'Jura' (Au/A) WAln
- 'Just Steven' (Au/A) SPop WAln
- 'K S' (Au/S) NDro
- 'Karen Cordrey' (Au/S) EBee ECho EWoo GAbr GAgs GKev IPen ITim MAsh MFie NDro SPop WBla WCre WHil
- 'Karen McDonald' (Au/A) MFie SPop
- 'Kate Haywood' (Au/B) NDro WCre WHil
- 'Kath Dryden' see *P. allionii* 'Kath Dryden'
- 'Kelso' (Au/A) MFie
- 'Ken Chilton' (Au/A) EWoo GAgs MFie NDro SPop WCre WHil
- 'Kenco' (Au/d) SPop
- 'Kentucky Blues' (Au/d) IPen MFie SPop WAln
- 'Kercup' (Au/A) EWoo MFie SPop WCre
- 'Kerry' (Au/A) EBee GKev WAln
- 'Kersey' (Au/S) SPop
- 'Kevin' (Au/A) SPop WAln
- 'Kevin Keegan' (Au/A) MFie NDro NSum SPop WHil
- 'Key West' (Au/A) NDro SPop WAln
- 'Khachaturian' (Au/A) MFie NDro WAln
- 'Kilby' (Au/A) SPop WBla
- 'Kim' (Au/A) IPen MFie NDro SPop WCre WHil
- 'Kimberworth Boy' (Au/A) NDro
- 'Kincraig' (Au/S) SPop WAln WBla
- 'King George' (Au/d) WAln WHil
- 'King Kong' (Au) WAln
- 'Kingcup' (Au/A) GAbr MFie SPop WCre
- 'Kingfisher' (Au/A) EWoo GAbr IPen ITim MFie NDro SPop WCre WHil
- 'Kingpin' (Au/St) NDro
- 'Kintail' (Au/A) MFie
- 'Kiowa' (Au/S) SPop WCre
- 'Kirklands' (Au/d) EWoo ITim MFie NDro SPop WCre WHil
- 'Knights' (Au/S) **new** SPop
- 'Kohinoor' (Au) MFie WHil
- 'Königin der Nacht' (Au/St) EWoo GAgs MFie NDro SPop WCre WHil
- 'Lady Daresbury' (Au/A) MFie NDro SPop WCre WHil
- 'Lady Day' (Au/d) SPop WAln
- 'Lady Diana' (Au/S) EWoo IPen NDro
- 'Lady Emma Monson' (Au/S) EWoo NDro SPop
- 'Lady Joyful' (Au/S) WCre
- 'Lady of the Vale' (Au/A) NDro WAln
- 'Lady Penelope' (Au/S) WAln
- 'Lady Zoë' (Au/S) EWoo MAsh MFie NDro SPop WCre
- 'Lambert's Gold' (Au) GAbr SPop
- 'Lambrook Gold' (Au/B) **new** NDro
- 'Lamplugh' (Au/d) IPen SPop WHil
- 'Lancelot' (Au/d) EWoo SPop
- 'Landy' (Au/A) MFie NDro SPop WCre
- 'Langley Park' (Au/A) IPen MAsh MFie NDro SPop WCre WHil
- 'Laphroaigh' (Au/S) WAln
- 'Laptop' (Au/St) SPop WBla WCre
- 'Lara' (Au/A) MFie NDro WCre
- 'Laredo' (Au/A) EWoo WAln
- 'Larry' (Au/A) EWoo GAgs MFie NDro SPop WCre
- 'Late Romantic' (Au) ECtt GAgs GBin NDov NLar WIce
- 'Lavender and Old Lace' (Au/d) **new** SPop
- 'Lavender Lady' (Au/B) IPen NDro NEgg
- 'Lavender Ridge' (Au/B) WAln
- 'Lavenham' (Au/S) WAln
- 'Laverock' (Au/S) NBir NBro NEgg WBla WCre WHil
- 'Laverock Fancy' (Au/S) EWoo GAbr IPen ITim NDro
- 'Lazy River' (Au/A) EWoo NDro WAln WCre
- 'Leather Jacket' (Au) GAbr WCre WHil
- 'Leathercoat' (Au) EWoo SPop
- 'Lechistan' (Au/S) GAgs IPen MAsh MFie NDro SPop WCre WHil
- 'Lee' (Au/A) IPen MFie NDro WAln WCre
- 'Lee Clark' (Au/A) MFie WAln
- 'Lee Paul' (Au/A) EWoo GAbr GAgs IPen MFie NDro SPop WAln WBla WCre WHil
- 'Lee Sharpe' (Au/A) EWoo IPen MFie NDro SPop WAln
- 'Legolas' (Au/A) MAsh SPop WAln
- 'Lemmy Getatem' (Au/d) IPen WHil
- 'Lemon Drizzle' (Au/S) WAln
- 'Lemon Drop' (Au/S) EWoo IPen ITim MFie NBro NDro SPop WCre
- 'Lemon Ice' (Au/S) IPen WAln
- 'Lemon Sherbet' (Au/B) EWoo GAbr GAgs IPen NDro SPop WHil
- 'Lemon Zest' (Au/d) WAln
- 'Lemonade' (Au) GAgs
- 'Lepton Jubilee' (Au/S) EWoo GAbr NDro WAln
- 'Leroy Brown' (Au/A) WAln
- 'Lester' (Au/d) SPop WAln WHil
- 'Leverton' (Au/d) EWoo SPop
- 'Lewis Telford' (Au/A) SPop
- 'Lich' (Au/S) NDro
- 'Lichfield' (Au/A/d) EWoo IPen SPop WCre
- 'Light Fantastic' (Au/S) **new** SPop
- 'Light Hearted' (Au/A) CWCL MFie NDro
- 'Light Music' (Au/d) WAln
- 'Likely Lad' (Au/St) EWoo SPop
- 'Lila' (Au/S) NDro SPop WAln WCre
- 'Lilac Domino' (Au/S) GAbr GAgs IPen MFie NDro NEgg SPop WCre WHil
- 'Lilac Ladywood' (Au/d) MFie SPop
- 'Lillian Hill' (Au/A) EWoo MFie WAln WBla
- 'Lillibet' (Au/A) NDro
- 'Lima' (Au/d) IPen WAln
- 'Limaki' (Au/d) SPop
- 'Lime Ridge' (Au) WAln
- 'Limelight' (Au/A) EWoo IPen NDro SPop
- 'Limelight' (Au/S) IPen SPop
- 'Lincoln Biscuit' (Au/d) **new** SPop
- 'Lincoln Bullion' (Au/d) EWoo NDro SPop WBla XBar
- 'Lincoln Charm' (Au/d) GAbr SPop
- 'Lincoln Chestnut' (Au/d) EWoo NDro SPop WBla XBar

- 'Lincoln Consort' (Au/d) SPop
- 'Lincoln Elf' (Au/d) **new** SPop
- 'Lincoln Fair' (Au) MAsh WBla
- 'Lincoln Gem' (Au/d) SPop
- 'Lincoln Glow' (Au/d) SPop
- 'Lincoln Halo' (Au/d) SPop
- 'Lincoln Imperial' (Au/d) SPop
- 'Lincoln Pride' (Au/d) **new** SPop WBla
- 'Linda' (Au/A) SPop WAln
- 'Lindley' (Au/S) NDro SPop
- 'Lindsey Moreno' (Au/S) WAln
- 'Ling' (Au/A) GAbr MFie NDro SPop WCre
- 'Linnet' (Au/B) NDro
- 'Lintz' (Au/B) MFie NDro SPop WCre WHil
- 'Linze 2' (Au/S) NDro
- 'Lisa' (Au/A) EWoo GAbr GAgs IPen MFie SPop WCre WHil
- 'Lisa Clara' (Au/S) EWoo GAbr GAgs IPen MAsh MFie NDro SPop WCre
- 'Lisa's Smile' (Au/S) EWoo MFie NDro SPop WHil
- 'Little Bo Peep' (Au) WAln
- 'Little Rosetta' (Au/d) GAbr MFie NDro NSum WCre WHil
- 'Lizzie Files' (Au/A) SPop WAln
- 'Lockyer's Gem' (Au/B/St) IPen NDro NEgg
- 'Lolita' (Au/St) EWoo SPop WHil
- 'Lord Saye and Sele' (Au/St) CWCL EWoo GAbr GAgs IPen ITim MFie NCGa NDro NEgg NWad SPop WBla WCre WHil XBar
- 'Lothlorien' (Au/A) WAln
- 'Louis' (Au/d) **new** XBar
- 'Louisa Woolhead' (Au/d) EWoo SPop
- 'Louise Jordan' (Au/A) **new** NDro
- 'Love Nest' (Au/S) **new** SPop
- 'Lovebird' (Au/S) CPBP EWoo GAbr MFie NDro SPop WHil
- 'Lucky Strike' (Au) WAln
- 'Lucy Locket' (Au/B) GAbr IPen LRHS NDro NEgg NSum WCre WHil
- 'Ludlow' (Au/S) GAbr SPop WCre
- 'Lune Tiger' (Au/St) SPop
- 'Lupy Minstrel' (Au/S) IPen NDro SPop WAln WCre
- 'Lusty Lad' (Au/St) SPop
- 'Lyn' (Au/A) WCre
- 'Lynn' (Au/A) WAln
- 'Lynn Cooper' (Au) EWoo SPop WBla
- 'MacWatt's Blue' (Au/B) GAbr IGor IPen NDro SPop WCre WHil
- 'Macy the Cat' (Au) **new** WHil
- 'Madelaine Palmer' (Au/d) SPop
- 'Maggie' (Au/S) EWoo GAbr NDro SPop WCre
- 'Magnolia' (Au/B) WCre WHil
- 'Mandarin' (Au/A) CWCL GAbr GAgs MFie NDro NSum SPop WBla WCre WHil
- 'Mandy' (Au/S) MFie
- 'Manka' (Au/S) SPop
- 'Mardi Gras' (Au/d) WAln
- 'Margaret' (Au/S) EWoo GAbr
- 'Margaret Faulkner' (Au/A) GAbr MFie WBla WCre
- 'Margaret Irene' (Au/A) IPen SPop WCre
- 'Margaret Martin' (Au/S) IPen MFie NDro SPop WCre
- 'Margaret Merril' (Au) GAbr
- 'Margot Fonteyn' (Au/A) EWoo GAbr IPen MFie SPop WAln WBla WHil
- 'Marie Crousse' (Au/d) CFis CMea CPBP GMaP IPen ITim MFie NDro SPop WCot WCre WHil
- 'Marie Pierre' (Au/d) **new** XBar
- 'Marion Howard Spring' (Au/A) MFie WCre
- 'Marion Tiger' (Au/St) NDro SPop WAln WCre
- 'Mark' (Au/A) IPen MFie NBro SPop WCre
- 'Marmion' (Au/S) EWoo GAbr GAgs IPen ITim MFie NDro SPop WBla WCre WHil XBar
- 'Martha Livesley' (Au/A) WAln
- 'Martha's Choice' (Au/A) WAln
- 'Martin Fish' (Au) WCre
- 'Martin Luther King' (Au/S) EWoo NDro SPop WCre WHil XBar
- 'Mary' (Au/d) GAbr NDro SPop WAln
- 'Mary Taylor' (Au/S) WAln
- 'Mary Zach' (Au/S) EWoo MFie NDro SPop WAln WHil
- 'Matthew Yates' (Au/d) EBee GAbr IPen ITim MFie NDro SPop WCot WCre WHil WWFP
- 'Maureen Millward' (Au/A) IPen MFie SPop WCre
- 'May' (Au/A) EWoo NDro WCre
- 'May Booley' (Au/d) **new** SPop
- 'Mazetta Stripe' (Au/S/St) GAbr MFie NBro NDro SPop WBla WCre WHil
- 'Meadow Sweet' (Au/S) WAln
- 'Meadowlark' (Au/A) EWoo ITim MFie SPop WCre WHil
- 'Mease Tiger' (Au/St) GAbr
- 'Megan' (Au/d) SPop WAln
- 'Mehta' (Au/A) IPen MFie NDro SPop WAln
- 'Mellifluous' (Au) MFie WBla WCre WHil
- 'Melody' (Au/S) IPen SPop
- 'Menin' (Au/d) SPop
- 'Mere Green' (Au/S) EWoo WAln
- 'Mere Peppermint' (Au) EWoo WAln
- 'Merlin' (Au/S) IPen MFie
- 'Merlin Stripe' (Au/St) CWCL EBee IPen NDro SPop WCre WHil XBar
- 'Mermaid' (Au/d) GAbr IPen NDro
- 'Merridale' (Au/A) GAbr MFie WCre WHil
- 'Mersey Tiger' (Au/S) EWoo GAbr ITim MAsh MFie NDro SPop WCre WHil
- 'Metis' (Au/d) SPop
- 'Mexicano' (Au/A) WAln
- 'Michael' (Au/S) MFie SPop WAln WHil
- 'Michael Wattam' (Au/S) SPop WAln
- 'Mick' (Au/A) MFie WCre WHil
- 'Midland Marvel' (Au/St) SPop WBla
- 'Midnight' (Au/A) WAln
- 'Mikado' (Au/S) IPen MFie SPop WBla WCre WHil
- 'Milkmaid' (Au/A) MFie WMAq
- 'Millicent' (Au/A) MFie WCre WHil
- 'Millie Redfern' (Au/d) **new** SPop
- 'Minley' (Au/S) CPBP EWoo GAbr MFie NBir NBro NDro NEgg SPop WCre WIce
- 'Minotaur' (Au/A) **new** SPop
- 'Minstead' (Au/S) SPop
- 'Minstrel' (Au/S) MFie NDro SPop WCre
- 'Minty' (Au/St) SPop
- 'Mipsie Miranda' (Au/d) SPop
- 'Mirabella Bay' (Au/A) WAln
- 'Miranda' (Au/d) SPop
- 'Miriam' (Au/A) EWoo SPop WAln
- 'Mish Mish' (Au/d) GAbr NDro WHil
- 'Miss Bluey' (Au/d) EWoo MAsh NDro SPop WAln WCre XBar
- 'Miss Jones' (Au/St) SPop WCre
- 'Miss Muffet' (Au/S) WAln
- 'Miss Newman' (Au/A) NSum SPop
- 'Miss Pinky' (Au) EWoo NDro SPop

- 'Mist' (Au/S) WAln
- 'Mojave' (Au/S) EWoo GAbr GAgs IPen MFie NDro NEgg NSum SPop WCre WHil XBar
- 'Mollie Langford' (Au/A) MFie NDro SPop WCre WHil
- 'Mondeo' (Au/A) WAln
- 'Monet' (Au/S) WAln
- 'Moneymoon' (Au/S) EWoo GAbr IPen NDro SPop WCre WHil
- 'Monica' (Au/A) MFie
- 'Monk' (Au/S) EWoo MFie SPop WAln WBla WHil XBar
- 'Monmouth Star' (Au/St) SPop WCre WHil
- 'Moody Cow' (Au/St) MAsh
- 'Moon Fairy' (Au/S) NDro SPop WAln WCre
- 'Moondance' (Au/d) **new** WAln
- 'Moonglow' (Au/S) EWoo GAbr
- 'Moonlight' (Au/S) WAln
- 'Moonrise' (Au/S) EWoo MFie NDro
- 'Moonriver' (Au/A) EWoo SPop WCre WHil
- 'Moonshadow' (Au/d) WAln
- 'Moonshine' (Au/d) SPop WAln
- 'Moonstone' (Au/d) SPop WAln
- 'Morven' (Au) GAbr
- 'Moscow' (Au/S) SPop
- 'Moselle' (Au/S) MAsh MFie NDro SPop WAln
- 'Mossy Vale' (Au/S) SPop
- 'Mr A' (Au/S) EWoo GAgs NDro WHil
- 'Mr Bojangles' (Au/d) SPop WAln
- 'Mr Greenfingers' (Au) WCre
- 'Mrs Cairn's Blue' (Au/B) NDro
- 'Mrs Dargan' (Au/d) NDro WCre
- 'Mrs J.H. Watson' (Au) WCre
- 'Mrs L. Hearn' (Au/A) EWoo GAbr IPen ITim MFie NDro SPop WCre WHil
- 'Mrs R. Bolton' (Au/A) WCre WHil
- 'Mrs Robinson' (Au/St) SPop WCre
- 'Mrs Wilson' (Au) GAbr GAgs
- 'Muriel James' (Au/A) **new** SPop
- 'Murray Lakes' (Au/A) EWoo NDro SPop WAln
- 'Mustard Sauce' (Au/B) NDro
- 'My Buddy' (Au/St) SPop WCre
- 'My Delight' (Au/d) SPop
- 'My Fair Lady' (Au/A) MFie NDro SPop
- 'My Friend' (Au/B) NDro SPop
- 'Myoleboots' (Au/B) SPop
- 'Myrtle Park' (Au/A) WAln
- 'Mystery' (Au) GAbr
- 'Nancy Dalgetty' (Au/B) NDro SPop
- 'Nantenan' (Au/S) GAbr MFie NDro SPop WBla WCre
- 'Neat and Tidy' (Au/S) CTal EWoo GAbr GAgs MFie NDro SPop WBla WCre
- 'Nefertiti' (Au/A) EWoo IPen MFie NDro SPop WCre WHil
- 'Nessun Dorma' (Au/A) EWoo NDro SPop WAln
- 'Neville Telford' (Au/S) GAbr IPen MFie NDro SPop WCre WHil
- 'Newbottle' (Au/S) SPop WAln
- 'Newsboy' (Au/A) WAln
- 'Newton Harcourt' (Au/A) SPop WHil
- 'Nicholas Loakes' (Au/S) WAln
- 'Nick Drake' (Au/d) SPop
- 'Nickity' (Au/A) EWoo GAbr GAgs IPen ITim MFie NDro NSum SPop WAln WCre WHil XBar
- 'Nicola Jane' (Au/A) EWoo GAgs SPop WAln
- 'Nigel' (Au/d) GAbr MFie NDro
- 'Night and Day' (Au/St) SPop WAln WCre
- 'Night Dance' (Au/S) **new** WCre
- 'Nightwink' (Au/S) WAln
- 'Nil Amber' (Au) GAbr SPop
- 'Nina' (Au/A) NDro SPop WAln
- 'Nita' (Au/d) SPop WAln
- 'No 21' (Au/S) NDro SPop
- 'No Deal' (Au/S) **new** WCre
- 'Nocturne' (Au/S) EWoo IPen NBro NDro NSum SPop WBla WCre
- 'Noelle' (Au/S) EWoo GKev IPen
- 'Nona' (Au/d) EWoo MFie NDro NSum SPop
- 'Nonchalance' (Au/A) MFie NDro SPop WHil
- 'Norma' (Au/A) EWoo MFie NDro SPop
- 'Northern Lights' (Au/S) GAbr WAln
- 'Nureyev' (Au/A) EWoo SPop
- 'Nymph' (Au/d) EWoo GAbr GAgs MFie NDro SPop WBla WCre WHil
- 'Oakie' (Au/S) SPop WAln
- 'Oban' (Au/S) MFie NDro SPop WBla XBar
- 'Odette' (Au) IPen MFie SPop WHil
- 'O'er the Moon' (Au/S) WAln
- 'Oikos' (Au/B) NDro SPop
- 'Ol' Blue Eyes' (Au/St) SPop WAln
- 'Old Black Isle Dusty Miller' (Au/B) NDro WHil
- 'Old Buffer' (Au/St) SPop
- 'Old Clove Red' (Au/B) EWoo GAbr GAgs IPen MFie NDro WCre WHil
- 'Old Cottage Blue' (Au/B) GAbr NDro
- 'Old Dublin Blue' (Au/B) NDro
- 'Old England' (Au/S) EWoo GAbr MFie NDro SPop WBla WCre
- 'Old Gold' (Au/S) GAbr IPen NDro SPop WAln WBla WCre
- 'Old Gold Double' (Au/d) EWoo
- 'Old Gold Dusty Miller' (Au/B) NDro
- 'Old Irish Blue' (Au/B) IPen NDro NEgg WCre
- 'Old Irish Green' (Au/B) EWoo GAbr NDro NSum
- 'Old Irish Scented' (Au/B) CTal EWoo GAbr IPen MFie NBro NDro WHil
- 'Old Irish Yellow' (Au/B) NDro NEgg
- 'Old Mustard' (Au/B) NDov NDro SMHy WCre
- 'Old Pink Dusty Miller' (Au/B) GAbr IPen

§ - 'Old Purple Dusty Miller' (Au/B) GAbr
- 'Old Red' (Au) GAgs
- 'Old Red Dusty Miller' (Au/B) GAbr LLHF NDro SPop WHil
- 'Old Red Elvet' (Au/S) GAbr GAgs SPop WCre
- 'Old Smokey' (Au/A) EWoo MFie NDro SPop WHil
- 'Old Suffolk Bronze' (Au/B) GAbr GAgs NDro WCre WHil
- 'Old Tall Purple Dusty Miller' (Au/B) **new** WCre
- 'Old Timer' (Au/S) SPop
- 'Old Yellow Dusty Miller' (Au/B) CTal EWes EWoo GAbr IGor IPen NBro NDro NRya WCre WHil
- 'Old-Fashioned' (Au/B) NDro
- 'Olivia' (Au/d) SPop
- 'Olton' (Au/A) IPen MFie WCre
- 'Ophir' (Au) **new** WBla
- 'Optimist' (Au/St) EWoo IPen NDro SPop WCre
- 'Opus One' (Au/A) EWoo WAln
- 'Orb' (Au/S) IPen MAsh MFie NDro SPop WBla WCre WHil
- 'Ordvic' (Au/S) NDro WAln
- 'Orlando' (Au/S) MFie NDro SPop WAln

- 'Orwell Tiger' (Au/St) EWoo GAgs IPen MFie NDro SPop WCre
- 'Osbaston Bullseye' (Au/St) SPop
- 'Osborne Green' (Au/B) GAbr GAgs GBin IGor NDov NDro SPop WCre WHil
- 'Osorno' (Au/d) **new** SPop
- 'Ossett Sapphire' (Au/A) NDro SPop
- 'Otto Dix' (Au/A) SPop WAln
- 'Overdale' (Au/A) NDro SPop WAln
- 'Paddlin' Madeleine' (Au/A) EWoo GAgs NDro WAln
- 'Pageboy' (Au/A) WAln
- 'Paleface' (Au/A) EWoo IPen MFie NDro NSum WBla WCre
- 'Pam Tiger' (Au/St) WAln WCre
- 'Panache' (Au/S) WAln
- 'Pang Tiger' (Au/St) EWoo WAln
- 'Papageno' (Au/St) WAln
- 'Paphos' (Au/d) IPen SPop
- 'Paradise Yellow' (Au/B) EWoo GAbr MFie NDro NEgg SPop WCre
- 'Paragon' (Au/A) IPen ITim MFie WAln WCre WHil
- 'Parakeet' (Au/S) WAln
- 'Paris' (Au/S) WAln
- 'Party Animal' (Au/St) **new** SPop
- 'Party Time' (Au/S) IPen SPop WBla WCre
- 'Pass Me By' (Au) IPen
- 'Passchendaele' (Au/d) SPop WCre
- 'Passing Cloud' (Au/d) WAln
- 'Pastiche' (Au/A) MFie WCre
- 'Pastures New' (Au) WAln
- 'Pat' (Au/S) SPop
- 'Pat Barnard' (Au) IPen
- 'Pat Mooney' (Au/d) NDro
- 'Patience' (Au/S) ITim NDro SPop WHil
- 'Patricia Barras' (Au/S) EWoo WAln
- 'Pauline' (Au/A) EWoo MFie
- 'Pavarotti' (Au/A) NDro SPop
- 'Peewit' (Au/S) WAln
- 'Pegasus' (Au/d) EWoo NDro SPop
- 'Peggy' (Au/A) GAbr WHil
- 'People's Choice' (Au/d) **new** SPop
- 'Pequod' (Au/A) MFie NDro WBla
- 'Perdito' (Au/S) WAln
- 'Perito Moreno' (Au/d) SPop
- 'Perseus' (Au/S) WAln
- 'Phantom' (Au/d) EWoo SPop WAln
- 'Pharaoh' (Au/A) CWCL EWoo GAbr GAgs MFie NDro SPop WBla WCre XBar
- 'Phoenix' (Au/A) WAln
- 'Phyllis Douglas' (Au/A) EWoo IPen MFie NDro NEgg SPop WCre WHil
- 'Piccadilly' (Au/S) MAsh MFie SPop
- 'Pierot' (Au/A) IPen MFie NDro SPop WCre WHil XBar
- 'Piers Telford' (Au/A) CPBP CTal CWCL EWoo GAbr GAgs IPen LRHS MFie NDro NEgg NSum SBch SPop WCre WHil XBar
- 'Piglet' (Au/d) GAgs NDro SPop WBla WHil
- 'Pikey' (Au/S) SPop
- 'Pimlico' (Au/S) **new** SPop
- 'Pimroagh' (Au/A) EWoo NDro
- 'Pink Floyd' (Au/A) SPop
- 'Pink Fondant' (Au/d) GAbr NDro
- 'Pink Hint' (Au/B) NDro SPop
- 'Pink Lady' (Au/A) GAbr GAgs MFie NBro NSum SPop WHil
- 'Pink Lilac' (Au/A/S) NDro
- 'Pink Triumph' (Au) **new** NDro
- 'Pinkerton' (Au/d) EWoo SPop WAln
- 'Pinkie' (Au/A) WHil
- 'Pinkie Dawn' (Au/B) IPen NDro WCre
- 'Pinky' (Au/d) **new** WCre
- 'Pinstripe' (Au) EWoo GAbr GAgs IPen NDro NSum SPop WHil
- 'Pioneer Stripe' (Au/S) GAbr GAgs IPen SPop
- 'Pippin' (Au/A) CPBP GAbr GAgs IPen MFie NBro NDro SPop WCre WHil XBar
- 'Pixie' (Au/A) EWoo GAgs IPen MFie SPop WCre WHil
- 'Playboy' (Au/A) NDro SPop WAln
- 'Plum Pudding' (Au/d) SPop WAln
- 'Polestar' (Au/A) MFie NDro SPop WBla WCre WHil
- 'Polly' (Au/B) EBee GAgs GKev NDro WCre
- 'Pop's Blue' (Au/S/d) NEgg SPop
- 'Portree' (Au/S) GAbr SPop
- 'Post Master' (Au/S) WAln
- 'Pot o' Gold' (Au/S) CPBP EBee ECho EWoo GAgs IPen MFie NDro NEgg SPop WBla WCre WHil XBar
- 'Powder and Paint' (Au/A) WAln
- 'Powder Puff' (Au/B) EWoo NDro SPop
- 'Prague' (Au/S) EWoo GAbr IPen MAsh MFie NBir NDro SPop WCre
- 'Pretender' (Au/A) MFie SPop
- 'Pretty Prop' (Au/St) SPop
- 'Pretty Purple' (Au/d) **new** WAln
- 'Pride of Poland' (Au/S) EWoo SPop WCre
- 'Prince Bishops' (Au/S) SPop WAln
- 'Prince Charming' (Au/S) EWoo GAgs IPen ITim MFie SPop WCre
- 'Prince Igor' (Au/A) SPop
- 'Prince John' (Au/A) GKev MAsh MFie NBro NDro SPop WBla WCre WHil
- 'Proctor's Yellow' (Au/B) NDro
- 'Prometheus' (Au/d) EWoo MFie NSum SPop WCre WHil
- 'Prosperine' (Au/S) MAsh SPop WAln WCre
- 'Psyche' (Au/S) SPop WAln
- 'Ptarmigan' (Au) WAln
- 'Pumpkin' (Au) GAbr
- 'Puppy Love' (Au/St) SPop
- 'Purbeck' (Au/B) SPop
- 'Purple Dusty Miller' see *P. auricula* 'Old Purple Dusty Miller'
- 'Purple Emperor' (Au/A) MFie
- 'Purple Frills' (Au) MFie
- 'Purple Glow' (Au/d) WAln
- 'Purple Haze' (Au) SPop
- 'Purple Knight' (Au/S) WAln
- 'Purple Lace' (Au/d) **new** SPop
- 'Purple Lovely' (Au) MFie SPop
- 'Purple Orient' (Au/d) SPop
- 'Purple Patch' (Au/d) SPop
- 'Purple Promise' (Au) GAbr ITim SPop
- 'Purple Prose' (Au/St) EWoo MFie SPop WHil
- 'Purple Rose' (Au/d) **new** WAln
- 'Purple Royale' (Au/B) NDro
- 'Purple Sage' (Au/S) EWoo ITim MFie NDro SPop WCre WHil
- 'Purple Star' (Au/d) SPop
- 'Purple Velvet' (Au/S) CWCL EWoo IPen NDro SPop
- 'Quatro' (Au/d) EWoo SPop
- 'Queen Alexandra' (Au/B) EWoo GAbr NDro WHil
- 'Queen Bee' (Au/S) GAbr MFie NDro SPop WBla
- 'Queen's Bower' (Au/S) SPop WCre

- 'Queenswood' (Au/S) EWoo WCre
- 'Quintessence' (Au/A) EWoo MFie NDro WCre WHil
- 'R.L. Bowes' (Au/A) NDro
- 'Rab C. Nesbitt' (Au/A) SPop WAln
- 'Rabley Heath' (Au/A) EWoo GAbr MFie NDro SPop WCre WHil
- 'Rachel' (Au/A) EWoo WAln WCre
- 'Rachel de Thame' (Au/S) WAln
- 'Rachel Labouchere' (Au/S) WAln
- 'Radiance' (Au/A) SPop
- 'Radiant' (Au/A) IPen
- 'Rag Doll' (Au/S) NDro WAln
- 'Ragnald the Magnificent' (Au/S) WAln
- 'Rajah' (Au/S) ECho EWoo GAbr GAgs IPen ITim LRHS MAsh MFie NDro NEgg SPop WBla WCre WHil XBar
- 'Raleigh Stripe' (Au/St) EWoo GAbr GAgs IPen ITim WAln WBla WCre
- 'Rameses' (Au/A) IPen MFie NDro WCre
- 'Rebecca Baker' (Au/d) SPop WHil
- 'Red Admiral' (Au) EWoo NDro SPop WAln WCre
- 'Red Arrows' (Au) SPop WAln WCre
- 'Red Baron' (Au/S) WAln WCre
- 'Red Beret' (Au/S) SPop
- 'Red Bordeaux' (Au/S) GAgs NDro
- 'Red Carpet' (Au/S) SPop
- 'Red Diamond' (Au/d) WAln
- 'Red Embers' (Au/S) SPop WAln WCre
- 'Red Ensign' (Au/B) NDro
- 'Red Gauntlet' (Au/S) EWoo GAbr GAgs GKev IPen MFie NDro SPop WCre
- 'Red King' (Au/S) WAln
- 'Red Mark' (Au/A) MFie SPop WHil
- 'Red Rum' (Au/S) GAbr MFie SPop WAln
- 'Red Sonata' (Au/S) SPop
- 'Red Spin' (Au/S) **new** SPop
- 'Red Vulcan' (Au) WCre
- 'Red Wire' (Au/St) EWoo NDro SPop WCre
- 'Redcar' (Au/A) GAbr MFie NDro WCre
- 'Reddown Apricot' (Au/B) NDro
- 'Reddown Barley Meal' (Au/B) NDro
- 'Reddown Bat' (Au/d) SPop
- 'Reddown First Swallow' (Au/B) NDro
- 'Reddown Rainman' (Au/B) NDro
- 'Reddown Tickled Pink' (Au/B) NDro
- 'Redstart' (Au/S) EBee EWoo GAgs GKev IPen ITim WCre WHil
- 'Regency' (Au/A) NDro WAln
- 'Regency Dandy' (Au/St) SPop
- 'Regency Denja' (Au) IPen
- 'Regency Emperor' (Au/St) EWoo IPen SPop WCre WHil
- 'Regency Paperchase' (Au/St) **new** SPop
- 'Regency Peppermint Tea' (Au/St) **new** SPop
- 'Regency Saint Clements' (Au/St) SPop WAln WCre
- 'Remus' (Au/S) CPBP ECho ELan EWoo GAbr GAgs IPen LLHF MAsh MFie NDro NEgg SPop WCre WHil XBar
- 'Rene' (Au/A) EWoo GAbr IPen MFie SPop WCre WHil XBar
- 'Renown' (Au/A) IPen NDro WAln
- 'Requiem' (Au/d) WAln
- 'Resi' (Au) WHil
- 'Respectable' (Au/A) WAln
- 'Reverie' (Au/d) SPop WAln
- 'Reynardine' (Au/d) SPop WAln
- 'Riatty' (Au/d) GAbr MFie NDro SPop
- 'Richard Shaw' (Au/A) IPen NDro SPop
- 'Ring of Bells' (Au/S) EWoo SPop WAln
- 'Risdene' (Au) IPen SPop WAln WCre
- 'Rivendell' (Au/A) WAln
- 'Robbo' (Au/B) EWoo NDro
- 'Robert Green' (Au/S) EWoo SPop WAln
- 'Robert Lee' (Au/A) WAln
- 'Roberto' (Au/S) NDro SPop WAln
- 'Robin Hood Stripe' (Au/St) EWoo NDro SPop WBla WCre
- 'Robinette' (Au/d) EWoo GAbr IPen SPop
- 'Rock Sand' (Au/S) EWoo GAbr GAgs MFie NDro SPop WBla WCre WHil
- 'Rockbourne' (Au/A) **new** SPop
- 'Rodeo' (Au/A) EWoo GAbr IPen SPop
- 'Rolts' (Au/S) ECho EWoo GAbr GAgs IPen MAsh NBro NDro SPop WBla WCre WHil XBar
- 'Romsley' (Au/S) WAln
- 'Rondy' (Au/S) ITim MFie SPop WAln WHil
- 'Ronnie Johnson' (Au) WAln
- 'Ronny Simpson' (Au) WCre
- 'Rosalie' (Au) SPop
- 'Rosalie Edwards' (Au/S) EWoo MFie SPop WCre
- 'Rose Conjou' (Au/d) EWoo GAbr GAgs IPen MFie NDro SPop WCre WHil
- 'Rose Kaye' (Au/A) GAbr IPen WCre
- 'Rosebud' (Au/S) GAbr SPop
- 'Rosemarket Rackler' (Au/B) NDro
- 'Rosemary' (Au/S) EWoo MAsh MFie SPop WCre WHil
- 'Rosewood' (Au) SPop WAln WCre
- 'Rosie' (Au/S) NDro
- 'Rothesay Robin' (Au/A) WAln
- 'Rouge Gorge' (Au/B) **new** XBar
- 'Rowena' (Au/A) IPen MFie NBro NSum SPop WCre WHil
- 'Roxborough' (Au/A) EWoo GAgs IPen
- 'Roxburgh' (Au/A) MFie NDro SPop WCre
- 'Roy Keane' (Au/A) IPen MFie SPop WAln WBla
- 'Royal Mail' (Au/S) MAsh MFie NDro SPop WAln WBla WCre
- 'Royal Marine' (Au/S) MFie SPop WAln
- 'Royal Scot' (Au/S) SPop
- 'Royal Velvet' (Au/S) GAbr GAgs IPen NDro WHil
- 'Ruby Hyde' (Au/B) EWoo GAbr NDro WCre
- 'Ruddy Duck' (Au/S) SPop WAln WBla WCre
- 'Rumbled' (Au/St) MAsh
- 'Runwell' (Au/B) NDro
- 'Rusty Dusty' (Au) GAbr GAgs
- 'Rusty Red' (Au/B) NDro
- 'Ryecroft' (Au/A) WAln
- 'Sabrina' (Au/A) WAln
- 'Saginaw' (Au/A) EWoo WAln
- 'Sailor Boy' (Au/S) GAgs MFie NDro SPop WAln WHil
- 'Saint Boswells' (Au/S) GAbr SPop
- 'Saint Elmo' (Au/A) GAgs MFie SPop WCre
- 'Saint Quentin' (Au/S) WAln
- 'Salad' (Au/S) EWoo GAbr GAgs
- 'Sale Green' (Au/S) EWoo MFie SPop
- 'Sally' (Au/A) MFie

- 'Sam Brown' (Au/S) WAln
- 'Sam Gamgee' (Au/A) MAsh NDro WAln WCre
- 'Sam Hunter' (Au/A) NDro SPop
- 'Samantha' (Au/A) EWoo WAln WBla WCre
- 'Samantha' (Au/d) EWoo MFie SPop WAln
- 'San Gabriel' (Au/A) WAln
- 'Sanctuary Wood' (Au/d) SPop
- 'Sandhills' (Au/A) MAsh MFie SPop WCre WHil
- 'Sandmartin' (Au/S) MFie
- 'Sandpiper' (Au/d) **new** WAln
- 'Sandra' (Au/A) ELan GAbr GAgs IPen MFie NDro SPop WBla WCre WHil
- 'Sandra's Lass' (Au/A) EWoo SPop
- 'Sandwood Bay' (Au/A) EWoo GAbr MFie NBro NDro NEgg SPop WCre WHil
- 'Sappho' (Au/S) IPen SPop WAln
- 'Sarah Gisby' (Au/d) MFie NDro SPop WBla WCre
- 'Sarah Grey' (Au/d) WAln
- 'Sarah Humphries' (Au/d) WAln
- 'Sarah Lodge' (Au/d) GAbr IPen NDro SPop WCre WHil
- 'Sarah Suzanne' (Au/B) NDro
- 'Saruman' (Au/A) WAln
- 'Sasha Files' (Au/A) IPen WAln
- 'Satchmo' (Au/S) SPop
- 'Satin Doll' (Au/d) MFie SPop
- 'Satsuma' (Au/d) SPop WAln
- 'Scaraben' (Au) GAbr
- 'Schaumburg' (Au/B) NDro
- 'Scipio' (Au/S) NDro SPop WAln
- 'Scorcher' (Au/S) EWoo IPen MAsh MFie NDro SPop WBla WCre
- 'Sea Lavender' (Au/d) WAln
- 'Sea Mist' (Au/d) WAln
- 'Searchlight' (Au) WCre
- 'Second Victory' (Au) CPBP NDro WCre WHil XBar
- 'Seen-a-Ghost' (Au/S) **new** SPop
- 'Serenity' (Au/S) MFie NDro SPop WBla WCre WHil
- 'Sergeant Wilson' (Au) SPop WAln
- 'Serre' (Au/d) **new** SPop
- 'Shaheen' (Au/S) **new** IPen
- 'Shalford' (Au/d) MFie NDro SPop WCot WCre WHil
- 'Sharmans Cross' (Au/S) MFie WAln
- 'Sharon Louise' (Au/S) IPen SPop WCre
- 'Shaun' (Au/d) ECtt GAbr GAgs MHol NDov NLar NPri WIce
- 'Sheila' (Au/S) GAbr IPen MAsh NDro SPop WCre WHil
- 'Shere' (Au/S) EWoo MFie NDro SPop WCre
- 'Shergold' (Au/A) IPen MFie WCre WHil
- 'Sherwood' (Au/S) EWoo GAbr IPen NDro SPop WHil
- 'Shining Hour' (Au/St) SPop
- 'Shirley' (Au/S) SPop WAln
- 'Shotley' (Au/A) MFie SPop
- 'Show Bandit' (Au/St) SPop
- 'Showtime' (Au/S) NDro SPop WCre
- 'Sibsey' (Au/d) EWoo GAgs MAsh NDro SPop WHil
- 'Sidney' (Au/A) WAln
- 'Silas' (Au/B) NDro
- 'Silmaril' (Au) SPop WAln
- 'Silver City' (Au/S) WAln
- 'Silver Rose' (Au) WCre
- 'Silver Surfer' (Au/St) WAln
- 'Silverway' (Au/S) EWoo SPop WAln WCre WHil
- 'Simply Red' (Au) EWoo IPen MAsh MFie NDro SPop WAln WBla WCre
- 'Sir John' (Au/A) MAsh MFie NDro WCre WHil
- 'Sir John Hall' (Au) MFie
- 'Sir Robert' (Au/d) WAln
- 'Sir Titus Salt' (Au/S) WAln
- 'Sirbol' (Au/A) EWoo GAgs IPen MFie NDro SPop WBla WCre WHil
- 'Sirius' (Au/A) EWoo GAbr GAgs IPen MFie NDro NSum SPop WBla WCre WHil XBar
- 'Skylark' (Au/A) GAbr GAgs IPen NDro SPop WBla WCre WHil XBar
- 'Skyliner' (Au/A) NDro
- 'Slack Top Red' (Au) NSla
- 'Sleeping Beauty' (Au/d) SPop
- 'Slim Whitman' (Au/A) NDro SPop WAln WBla WHil
- 'Slioch' (Au/S) EWoo GAbr GAgs IPen MAsh NSum SPop WCre WHil
- 'Slip Anchor' (Au/A) WAln
- 'Smart Tar' (Au/S) WAln WCre
- 'Smoothy' (Au/St) SPop
- 'Snooty Fox' (Au/A) GAbr IPen MFie SPop WCre
- 'Snooty Fox II' (Au/A) MFie NDro WBla
- 'Snow Maiden' (Au/d) SPop WAln
- 'Snowstorm' (Au/S) IPen SPop
- 'Snowy Owl' (Au/S) GAbr IPen MFie NDro SPop WCre
- 'Solario' (Au/F) WAln
- 'Solero' (Au/St) IPen SPop
- 'Somersby' (Au/d) IPen
- 'Soncy Face' (Au/A) MFie SPop WBla WCre WHil
- 'Song of India' (Au/A) SPop
- 'Sonia Nicolle' (Au/B) NDro
- 'Sonny Boy' (Au/A) MAsh SPop WAln
- 'Sooty' (Au/d) IPen SPop
- 'Sophie' (Au/A) **new** NDro
- 'Sophie' (Au/d) SPop WAln
- 'South Barrow' (Au/d) GAbr SPop WCre WHil
- 'Southease Jane' (Au) WAln
- 'Southport' (Au) EWoo NDro
- 'Sparky' (Au/A) MFie NDro WAln
- 'Spartan' (Au) SPop WAln
- 'Spitfire' (Au/S) MFie
- 'Spokey' (Au) IPen
- 'Spring Meadows' (Au/S) EWoo GAbr GKev MAsh MFie NDro NEgg SPop WCre WHil
- 'Springtime' (Au/A) SPop
- 'Standish' (Au/d) GAbr
- 'Stant's Blue' (Au/S) IPen MFie NBro NDro SPop WCre
- 'Star Spangle' (Au/St) NDro WCre
- 'Star Wars' (Au/S) EWoo GAbr MAsh MFie NDro SPop WAln WCre WHil XBar
- 'Star Wars II' (Au) GAgs
- 'Starlight' (Au/S) **new** SPop
- 'Starling' (Au/B) EWoo GAbr IPen NDro SPop
- 'Starry' (Au/S) NDro
- 'Starsand' (Au/S) WAln WCre
- 'Stella' (Au/S) SPop
- 'Stella Coop' (Au/d) NDro WAln
- 'Stella North' (Au/A) WAln
- 'Stella South' (Au/A) IPen SPop WCre
- 'Stetson' (Au/A) WAln
- 'Stoney Cross' (Au/S) SPop WAln
- 'Stonnal' (Au/A) MFie SPop WHil
- 'Stormin' Norman' (Au/A) EWoo MFie NDro SPop WHil
- 'Stormy Weather' (Au/St) SPop WCre
- 'Strawberry Fields' (Au/S) SPop
- 'Stripe Tease' (Au/St) SPop
- 'Striped Ace' (Au/St) NDro SPop WCre WHil
- 'Stripey' (Au/d) IPen
- 'Stromboli' (Au/d) EWoo MFie NDro SPop WBla WCot WCre
- 'Stuart West' (Au/A) WCre

- 'Stubb's Tartan' (Au/S) MFie WAln
- 'Sue' (Au/A) MFie SPop WCre
- 'Sue Ritchie' (Au/d) EWoo SPop
- 'Suede Shoes' (Au/S) SPop
- 'Sugar Plum Fairy' (Au/S) EWoo GAbr GAgs NDro NSum SPop WCre WHil
- 'Sultan' (Au/A) WAln
- 'Summer Sky' (Au/A) SPop WCre
- 'Summer Wine' (Au/A) EWoo MFie NDro SPop
- 'Sumo' (Au/A) EWoo GAbr GAgs MFie NDro SPop WBla WCre WHil
- 'Sunflower' (Au/A/S) EWoo GAbr GAgs ITim MAsh MFie NDro SPop WCre WHil
- 'Sunlight' (Au/A) WAln
- 'Sunlit Tiger' (Au/S) EWoo WAln
- 'Sunray' (Au/St) SPop
- 'Sunsplash' (Au) WBla WCre
- 'Sunspot' (Au/A) EWoo IPen WAln
- 'Sunstar' (Au/S) NDro NSum WCre
- 'Super Para' (Au/S) EWoo GAbr GKev IPen MFie NDro SPop WBla WCre WHil
- 'Superb' (Au/S) MFie WAln WBla
- 'Surething' (Au/A) WAln
- 'Susan' (Au/A) GAbr GAgs MFie NDro WCre
- 'Susannah' (Au/d) EWoo GAgs GMaP IPen MFie NDro NSum SPop WCre WHil
- 'Sweet Chestnut' (Au/S) WAln
- 'Sweet Georgia Brown' (Au/A) MFie WAln
- 'Sweet Pastures' (Au/S) CPBP GAbr IPen MFie NDro SPop WCre
- 'Swiss Royal Velvet' (Au/B) NDro
- 'Sword' (Au/d) CPBP EWoo GAbr GAgs IPen MFie NDro SPop WCre WHil XBar
- 'Symphony' (Au/A) GAgs ITim MFie NDro SPop WBla WCre WHil XBar
- 'T.A. Hadfield' (Au/A) EWoo GAgs MFie NDro SPop WBla WCre WHil
- 'Taffeta' (Au/S) GAbr LRHS NDro NSum SPop WCre WHil
- 'Tall Purple Dusty Miller' (Au/B) SPop
- 'Tally-ho' (Au/A) SPop WAln
- 'Tamar Gold' (Au/d) SPop WAln WCre
- 'Tamar Mist' (Au) MAsh WAln WHil
- 'Tamino' (Au/S) IPen NDro SPop WAln
- 'Tango' (Au/d) WAln
- 'Tarantella' (Au/A) GAbr MFie NDro SPop WCre
- 'Tawny Owl' (Au/B) GAbr NBro
- 'Tay Tiger' (Au/St) EWoo GAbr GAgs MAsh MFie NDro SPop WHil XBar
- 'Taylor's Grey' (Au/S) SPop
- 'Teawell Pride' (Au/d) EWoo SPop WCre WHil
- 'Ted Gibbs' (Au/A) EWoo MFie NDro SPop WBla WCre WHil
- 'Ted Roberts' (Au/A) EWoo ITim MFie NDro SPop WBla WCre WHil
- 'Teem' (Au/S) GAbr IPen NDro SPop WCre
- 'Telesto' (Au/d) SPop
- 'Telford's Surprise' (Au/A) WAln
- 'Temeraire' (Au/A) MFie WHil
- 'Tenby Grey' (Au/S) SPop WCre
- 'Tender Trap' (Au/A) IPen WAln
- 'Terpo' (Au/A) EWoo MFie WAln WBla WCre WHil
- 'Tess' (Au/A) XBar
- 'The Argylls' (Au/St) SPop
- 'The Baron' (Au/S) GAbr GAgs GKev IPen MFie SPop WBla WCre WHil XBar
- 'The Bishop' (Au/S) GAgs IPen MFie SPop WAln WCre WHil XBar
- 'The Bride' (Au/S) MFie NDro SPop WCre
- 'The Cardinal' (Au/d) EWoo WAln
- 'The Czar' (Au/A) MFie NDro SPop
- 'The Egyptian' (Au/A) IPen MFie NDro SPop WBla WCre WHil
- 'The Few' (Au/St) SPop
- 'The Hobbit' (Au/A) WAln
- 'The Lady Galadriel' (Au/A) NDro
- 'The Maverick' (Au/S) MFie SPop
- 'The President' (Au/d) WAln
- 'The Raven' (Au/S) EWoo GAbr GAgs GKev ITim MFie SPop WAln WBla WCre WHil
- 'The Sneep' (Au/A) EWoo GAgs IPen ITim MFie NDro SPop WBla WCre
- 'The Snods' (Au/S) EWoo IPen MFie NDro SPop WBla WCre
- 'The Wrekin' (Au/S) SPop

I - 'Theodora' (Au/S) **new** XBar
- 'Thetis' (Au/A) EWoo MFie SPop WCre
- 'Thisbe' (Au/A) NDro
- 'Three Way Stripe' (St) EWoo GAbr GAgs NDro WBla WCre WHil
- 'Thutmoses' (Au/A) NDro WAln
- 'Tiger Tim' (Au/St) EWoo WAln
- 'Tim' (Au) GAbr GAgs IPen NDro SPop WCre
- 'Tim's Fancy' (Au/S) NDro WCre
- 'Tinker' (Au/S) WAln
- 'Tinkerbell' (Au/S) EWoo IPen MFie SPop WCre
- 'Tiptoe' (Au/St) SPop WCre
- 'Titania' (Au) SPop
- 'Toddington Green' (Au/S) WAln
- 'Toffee Crisp' (Au/A) EWoo IPen NDro SPop WBla
- 'Toffee Nosed' (Au/St) SPop
- 'Tom Farmer' (Au) SPop
- 'Tomboy' (Au/S) EWoo IPen MFie NDro SPop WBla
- 'Tony Bray' (Au/A) SPop
- 'Toolyn' (Au/S) EWoo GAgs NDro WAln WCre
- 'Top Cat' (Au/d) WAln
- 'Top Style' (Au/d) SPop WAln
- 'Tosca' (Au/S) CWCL GAbr IPen NSum SPop WBla WCre WHil XBar
- 'Trafalgar Square' (Au/S) EWoo GAbr GAgs MFie NDro SPop WBla WCre
- 'Tregor Orange' (Au/d) **new** XBar
- 'Tregor Stripe' (Au/St) **new** XBar
- 'Trident' (Au/d) WAln
- 'Trish' (Au) GAbr
- 'Trojan' (Au/S) GKev IPen WCre
- 'Trouble' (Au/d) EWoo GAbr IPen MFie NDro SPop WCre WHil
- 'Troy Aykman' (Au/A) MFie NDro SPop WAln WHil
- 'Trudy' (Au/S) EWoo GAbr IPen ITim NDro SPop WCre WHil
- 'True Briton' (Au/S) IPen MFie NDro SPop WBla WCre
- 'Trumpet Blue' (Au/S) MFie SPop WAln WHil
- 'Tudor Rose' (Au/S) NDov WAln
- 'Tumbledown' (Au/A) EWoo IPen MFie SPop
- 'Tummel' (Au/A) EWoo GAgs NDro SPop WBla WHil
- 'Tupelo Honey' (Au/d) WAln
- 'Turnberry' (Au/S) SPop
- 'Turnbull' (Au/A) **new** IPen
- 'Tut Tut' (Au/A) SPop
- 'Tweedy' (Au/St) **new** SPop

- 'Twiggy' (Au/S) NDro NSum SPop
- 'Two Steeples' (Au/A) SPop
- 'Typhoon' (Au/A) EWoo IPen MFie SPop WCre WHil
- 'Uncle Arthur' (Au/A) MFie WAln WHil
- 'Unforgettable' (Au/A) MFie
- 'Upper Crust' (Au/St) SPop WBla WCre
- 'Upton Belle' (Au/S) IPen MFie NDro SPop WAln WCre
- 'Ursula' (Au/d) WAln
- 'Ushba' (Au/d) SPop
- 'V2 Green' (Au/S) WCre
- 'Valerie' (Au/A) IPen MFie SPop WCre
- 'Valerie Clare' (Au) MFie SPop WAln WHil
- 'Vee Too' (Au/A) GAbr MFie NDro SPop WCre WHil
- 'Vega' (Au/A) EWoo SPop WAln
- 'Velvet Moon' (Au/A) EWoo MFie WAln
- 'Venetian' (Au/A) EWoo GAgs MFie NDro SPop WAln WBla WHil
- 'Venus' (Au/A) WAln
- 'Vera' (Au/A) SPop WAln
- 'Vera Eden' (Au) WAln
- 'Vera Hill' (Au/A) WAln
- 'Verdi' (Au/A) EWoo SPop WAln
- 'Vesuvius' (Au/d) EWoo IPen NDro SPop
- 'Victoria' (Au/S) SPop WAln
- 'Victoria de Wemyss' (Au/A) IPen MFie NDro WBla WCre WHil
- 'Victoria Jane' (Au/A) WAln
- 'Victoria Park' (Au/A) WAln
- 'Violet Surprise' (Au/St) NDro
- 'Vulcan' (Au/A) MAsh MFie NBro WCre XBar
- 'W. Muller' (Au) NBro
- 'Walhampton' (Au/S) SPop
- 'Walter Lomas' (Au/S) WAln
- 'Walton' (Au/A) CPBP EWoo GAbr IPen MAsh MFie NDro SPop WCre WHil XBar
- 'Walton Heath' (Au/d) EWoo GAbr GAgs IPen MFie NDro SPop WBla WCot WCre WHil
- 'Waltz Time' (Au/A) MFie
- 'Wanda's Moonlight' (Au/d) SPop WAln WCre
- 'Warpaint' (Au/St) NDro NSum
- 'Warwick' (Au/S) MFie NDro SPop
- 'Watchett' (Au/S) SPop
- 'Wayward' (Au/S) WAln WCre
- 'Wedding Day' (Au/S) EWoo ITim MFie SPop WBla WCre
- 'Wentworth' (Au/A) IPen WAln
- 'Wheal' (Au) EWoo SPop
- 'Whistlejacket' (Au/S) MFie NDro SPop WBla
- 'White Ensign' (Au/S) EWoo GAbr GAgs IPen ITim MFie NDro SPop WCre
- 'White Pyne' (Au/B) NDro
- 'White Satin' (Au/S) SPop WAln WCre
- 'White Water' (Au/A) EWoo MFie NDro SPop WCre WHil
- 'White Wings' (Au/S) GAgs IPen ITim MFie NDro NSum SPop WCre
- 'Whitecap' (Au/S) WAln
- 'Whoopee' (Au/A) EWoo WAln
- 'Whorton's Claret' (Au/S) WAln
- 'Wichita Falls' (Au/A) NDro WAln
- 'Wide Awake' (Au/A) EWoo MFie SPop
- 'Wild and Grey' (Au/S) NDro
- 'Wilf Booth' (Au/A) MFie SPop WBla
- 'William Gunn' (Au/d) MAsh MFie SPop WAln WBla WCre
- 'Willow Tree' (Au/S) WAln
- 'Wincha' (Au/S) ITim MFie NDro NEgg SPop WBla WCre XBar
- 'Windways Mystery' (Au/B) GAbr NDro
- 'Windways Pisces' (Au/d) WAln
- 'Windy Goldtop' (Au/A) WAln
- 'Winifrid' (Au/A) EWoo GAbr MFie NDro SPop WCre WHil
- 'Witchcraft' (Au) IPen SPop WCre
- 'Woodlands Lilac' (Au/B) NDro WHil
- 'Woodmill' (Au/A) EWoo GAgs IPen MFie NDro NSum SPop WBla WHil XBar
- 'Wookey Hole' (Au/A) MFie NDro SPop
- 'Wor Jackie' (Au/S) SPop
- 'Wycliffe Harmony' (Au/B) NDro
- 'Wycliffe Midnight' (Au/B) GAbr WAln WHil
- 'Wye Hen' (Au/St) SPop WAln
- 'Wye Lemon' (Au/S) EWoo SPop
- 'X2' (Au) WBla WHil
- 'Xavier' (Au) EBee
- 'Yacoubi' (Au/A) **new** SPop
- 'Yellow Ace' (Au) GAbr
- 'Yellow Border' (Au/B) **new** WCre
- 'Yellow Hammer' (Au/S) WAln
- 'Yellow Isle' (Au/S) WAln
- 'Yellow Muff' (Au/S) WAln
- 'Yellow Ribbon' WAln
- 'Yes Indeed' (Au/St) SPop
- 'Yitzhak Rabin' (Au/A) IPen SPop WHil
- 'Yorkshire Grey' (Au/S) GAbr IPen NBro NDro SPop WAln WCre
- 'Zambia' (Au/d) EWoo GAbr IPen NDro WCre
- 'Ziggy' (Au/St) SPop
- 'Zimmer' (Au/St) EWoo SPop WCre
- 'Zircon' (Au/S) MAsh SPop WAln
- 'Zodiac' (Au/S) WAln
- 'Zoe' (Au/A) SPop WAln
- 'Zoe Ann' (Au/S) WAln
- 'Zorro' (Au/St) WAln

auriculata (Or) GKev SVic
- subsp. ***olgae*** (Or) GKev

'Barbara Midwinter' (Pr) CDes CJun EBee GAbr GEdr LLHF NHar SHar WAbe WCot
Barnhaven Blues Group (Pr/Prim) NCGa NSum XBar
Barnhaven doubles (Pr/Prim/d) XBar
Barnhaven Gold-laced Group see *P.* Gold-laced Group Barnhaven
Barnhaven hybrids NSum
'Beatrice Wooster' (Au) GAbr IPen LRHS MFie SBch
'Beeches' Pink' GAbr NHar NSum
beesiana (Pf) ♀H6 Widely available
(Belarina Series) Belarina Buttermilk = 'Kerbelmilk'PBR (Pr/Prim/d) SMrm WHil
- Belarina Butter Yellow = 'Kerbelbut'PBR (Pr/Prim/d) CExl CWCL EPfP LLHF MBNS MFie MHol NLar NWad SRot WHil
- 'Belarina Cobalt Blue' (Pr/Prim/d) CExl CWCL ELon EWll LLHF MBNS MFie MHol NLar SMrm SRot WHil
- Belarina Cream = 'Kerbelcrem'PBR (Pr/Prim/d) CExl CWCL ELon EWll LLHF MFie SRot WBor WHil
- 'Belarina Pink Ice' (Pr/Prim/d) CWCL ELon EPot EWll MBNS MFie MHol NLar WBor WHil
- 'Belarina Rosette Nectarine' (Pr/Prim/d) CExl CWCL ECtt ELon EPot EWll MBNS MFie MHol SMrm WHil

bellidifolia (Mu)	GKev IPen NGdn WHil
beluensis	see *P.* × *pubescens* 'Freedom'
× ***berninae*** (Au)	WCre
§ – 'Windrush' (Au)	WAbe
'Bewerley White'	see *P.* × *pubescens* 'Bewerley White'
bhutanica	see *P. whitei* 'Sherriff's Variety'
bileckii	see *P.* × *forsteri* 'Bileckii'
'Blindsee' (Au) **new**	CTal NHar
blinii (Y)	EPot GKev LLHF
'Blue Julianas' (Pr)	NCGa NSum XBar
'Blue Riband' (Pr/Prim)	LLHF SIgm
'Blue Ribbon'	IGor
'Blue Sapphire' (Pr/Prim/d)	CBod CDes GAbr GBin NCGa WHil
'Blutenkissen' (Pr/Prim)	GAbr
'Bon Accord Cerise' (Pr/Poly/d)	GAbr
'Bon Accord Purple' (Pr/Poly/d)	WRHF XBar
boothii subsp. ***repens*** (Pe)	MNrw
'Boothman's Ruby'	see *P.* × *pubescens* 'Boothman's Variety'
'Bouquet' (Pr/Prim/d) **new**	XBar
bracteata (Bu)	GKev WAbe
§ – subsp. ***dubernardiana*** (Bu)	GKev WAbe
bracteata × ***bracteata*** subsp. ***dubernardiana*** (Bu) **new**	GKev
§ ***bracteosa*** (Pe)	GKev
brevicula (Cy) SDR 4452	GKev
'Brittany Blue' (Pr/Prim/d) **new**	XBar
'Broadwell Chameleon'	ITim
'Broadwell Milkmaid' ♀H5	CPBP IPen WAbe
'Broadwell Oliver' (Au)	IPen
'Broadwell Pink' (Au)	IPen
'Broadwell Ruby' (Au)	CPBP ITim WAbe
'Broadwell Snowstorm' **new**	CPBP
'Broadwell Violet'	CPBP IPen
'Broxbourne' ♀H5	ITim MFie
'Buckland Wine' (Pr/Prim)	CElw GAbr GEdr
× ***bulleesiana*** (Pf)	CAby CBod CSta EPfP GBin GBuc GKev LBMP LRHS MBri MCot MFie MSCN MWts NBro NChi NEgg NGdn NHol NLar NSum SMrm SWat WFar WHar WHil WMoo WPnP WWEG
– Moerheim hybrids (Pf)	GAbr
bulleyana (Pf) ♀H5	Widely available
– ACE 2484	SWat
'Burgundy Ice' (Pr/Prim/d) **new**	XBar
burmanica (Pf)	CPla GBuc GEdr GKev IPen MMuc SWat WMoo
– SDR 5801	GKev
'Butter's Bronze' (Pr/Prim)	WOut
'Butterscotch' (Pr/Prim)	NCGa NSum XBar
'Caerulea Plena' (Pr/Prim)	NBid
calderiana subsp. ***calderiana*** (Pe)	GKev
– subsp. ***strumosa*** (Pe)	GKev
Candelabra hybrids (Pf)	CBre CBro CHVG ECho GAbr IPen ITim LSou MLHP NBir NGdn SGSe SMrm SWat WOut
Candy Pinks Group (Pr/Prim)	NCGa NSum XBar
capitata (Ca)	CMac ECho EPfP EWld GKev IBoy IPen MLHP SCob SPer
– CC 3843	GKev
– CC 6207 **new**	GKev
– CC 6536B	GKev
– CC 6542	GKev
– subsp. ***mooreana*** (Ca)	CCon ÇExl CHid CLAP CSta CTsd ECho EDAr EPfP GKev IPen LRHS NGdn NSum SMrm SPhx SPlb SRot WAbe XBar XLum
– 'Noverna Deep Blue' (Ca) **new**	SHil WCot
– subsp. ***sphaerocephala*** (Ca) ♀H5	GKev
'Captain Blood' (Pr/Prim/d)	IPot
Carnation Victorians Group (Pr/Poly)	XBar
carniolica (Au)	EPot GKev WCot
cernua (Mu)	GKev IPen NSum WHil XBar
'Charlotte' (Pr/Prim)	IPen
Chartreuse Group (Pr/Poly)	XBar
'Cheshire Life'	CMea
§ ***chionantha*** (Cy) ♀H6	CLAP CSta CWCL ECho EPfP GBin GBuc GCra GEdr GKev NBir NCGa NGdn NLar NSum SPer WAbe WHil
– SDR 4426	GKev
– subsp. ***chionantha*** (Cy)	GBuc GKev IPen
§ – subsp. ***sinoplantaginea*** (Cy)	NLar
§ – subsp. ***sinopurpurea*** (Cy)	CLAP CSta EBee EPfP GBin GBuc GKev IPen NBir NCGa NLar NSum WAbe WHil
– – SDR 2747	GKev
– – SDR 4418	GKev
chungensis (Pf)	CAby CBod CHel CLAP CMea CSta CWCL EBee EPfP GBin GCra GEdr GKev GLog IPen NGdn NHol NMyG NSum SWvt WAbe WHil WMAq WMoo XBar
§ ***chungensis*** × ***pulverulenta*** (Pf)	CHid GKev NLar WWEG
× ***chunglenta***	see *P. chungensis* × *pulverulenta*
'Cisca'	GEdr WCot
'Clarence Elliott' (Au) ♀H5	CPBP IPen MFie MPnt NHar NWad WAbe WThu
clarkei (Or)	GEdr WAbe
clusiana (Au)	GKev WAbe
– 'Murray-Lyon' (Au)	NDro
cockburniana (Pf) ♀H6	GAbr GKev GQui IPen NCGa NGdn SWat WAbe XBar
– SDR 1967	EBee
– SDR 5939	GKev
– hybrids (Pf)	SWat
– 'Kevock Sunshine' (Pf)	GKev IPen
concholoba (Mu)	GKev WHil
'Corporal Baxter' (Pr/Prim/d)	ECtt EPfP LLHF XBar
cortusoides (Co)	CLAP EPfP GCra GKev IPen WBor
'Cottage Cream' **new**	SVic
Cowichan Amethyst Group (Pr/Poly)	CDes CWCL NCGa XBar
Cowichan Blue Group (Pr/Poly)	CDes NCGa NSum XBar
Cowichan Garnet Group (Pr/Poly)	CDes NCGa NSum XBar
Cowichan strain (Pr/Poly)	CElw
Cowichan Venetian Group (Pr/Poly)	NCGa NSum XBar
Cowichan Yellow Group (Pr/Poly)	CDes NCGa NSum XBar

'Coy' (Au)	WAbe
'Craddock White' (Pr/Prim)	CFis
'Craven Gem' (Pr/Poly)	GBuc
Crescendo Series (Pr/Poly)	GAbr
- 'Crescendo Blue Shades' (Pr/Poly) ♀H5	LSou
- 'Crescendo Bright Red' (Pr/Poly) ♀H5	LSou
- 'Crescendo Lemon Yellow' (Pr/Poly)	LSou
- 'Crescendo White' (Pr/Poly)	LSou
'Crimson Velvet' (Au)	GAbr IPen WThu XBar
crispa	see *P. glomerata*
cuneifolia (Cu)	GKev
- subsp. ***heterodonta*** (Cu)	GKev
daonensis (Au)	GAgs GKev
darialica (Al)	GKev LLHF
'Dark Rosaleen' (Pr/Poly)	CExl CHVG CHel CUse CWGN ECtt GAbr GBuc GEdr IGor LLHF LRHS MBNS MBri MFie MHol MMuc MNrw MPie NCGa NDov NWad SEND WCot
'David Green' (Pr/Prim)	CDes
'David Valentine' (Pr)	GAbr GBuc GEdr WCot
davidii (Da)	GKev
'Dawn Ansell' (Pr/Prim/d)	CWCL ECtt EPfP EPot GAbr GBuc IGor MBNS MHol MNrw MRav NBir NCGa NDov NSum SPer WCAu WHer WHil
Daybreak Group (Pr/Poly)	CWCL XBar
deflexa (Mu)	GKev IPen NMyG
denticulata (De) ♀H5	Widely available
- CC 4629	GKev
- var. ***alba*** (De)	CBcs CTri EBee ECha ECho EPfP EPla GAbr GBin GCra GMaP LRHS LSun MBel MFie MWat NGdn NLar NPri SCob SGbt SMrm SPer SPoG WBor WFar WGwG WMoo WWEG WWtn
- blue-flowered (De)	CWCL ECho EPfP GAbr LLWG NLar NPri WBor
- 'Bressingham Beauty' (De)	EBee LRHS
- 'Glenroy Crimson' (De)	CLAP EBee LLHF
- hybrids **new**	SCob WFar XBar
- lilac-flowered (De)	CBod ECho EHon LRHS MWat NHol SCob WWEG
- purple-flowered (De)	ECho WMoo
- red-flowered (De)	ECho EPfP MFie NBir SCob WMoo
- 'Robinson's Red' (De)	GBuc
- 'Ronsdorf' (De)	NLar
- 'Rubin' (De)	CBod CWCL CWat EBee ECho EHon GAbr GBin GMaP LLWG LRHS MBrN MLHP NChi NLar SPer SPoG SRms WWEG XLum
- 'Rubinball' (De)	MSCN NHol WCot
× ***deschmannii***	see *P.* × *vochinensis*
'Desert Sunset' (Pr/Poly)	CWCL NCGa XBar
'Devon Cream' (Pr/Prim)	NDro
dickieana (Am)	GKev
'Don Keefe'[PBR]	CBod CMHG ECtt GAbr GBin LLHF LRHS LSou MBNS MBel MFie MHol MMuc MNrw MPie NGdn NLar NWad WCot WMoo
'Dorothy' (Pr/Poly)	MRav
'Double Lilac'	see *P. vulgaris* 'Lilacina Plena'
'Drumcliffe'	ECtt GAbr GEdr LLHF MBel MHol MPie NCGa NLar NSti WCot
dubernardiana	see *P. bracteata* subsp. *dubernardiana*
'Duchess of York' (Pr/Poly)	GAbr LLHF LLWP NLar WCot
'Duckyls Red' (Pr/Prim)	CDes WHal
'Dusky Lady'	CLAP
'Early Bird' (*allionii* hybrid) (Au)	IPen ITim MFie
'Easter Bonnet' (Pr/Prim)	LRHS MMuc NBid XBar
edgeworthii	see *P. nana*
§ ***elatior*** (Pr) ♀H5	CArn CBod CMac CPla CRow CUse ECho EWTr EWoo GKev GMaP MHer MHol MNHC MNrw MWat NChi NEgg NLar NPri SPer SPoG SWvt WBrk WCot WHil
- hose-in-hose (Pr/d)	NBid
- hybrids (Pr)	EPfP SPlb
- subsp. ***intricata*** (Pr)	WHil
§ - subsp. ***meyeri*** (Pr)	LLHF
- subsp. ***pseudoelatior*** (Pr)	WAbe
'Elizabeth Browning'	GAbr WCot
'Elizabeth Killelay'[PBR] (Pr/Poly/d)	CBct CBod CExl CHel CUse CWCL CWGN ECtt ELan GBin GBuc IBoy LSou MHol MMuc MNrw MPie MSCN NBir NEgg NGdn NSti NSum NWad SPer SPoG WBor WCot
'Ellen Page' (Au)	MFie
elliptica (Or)	GKev
erratica (De) **new**	GKev
'Ethel Barker' (Au)	IPen MFie NWad
'Eugénie' (Pr/Prim/d)	ECtt LLHF MRav NCGa
§ ***euprepes***	GKev
'Fairy Rose' (Au)	IPen ITim NWad
farinosa (Al)	GKev IPen NGdn WAbe
fasciculata (Ar)	GKev
- CLD 345	GEdr WAbe
- SDR 3092	GKev
'Feuerkönig' (Au)	NDro
'Fire Opal'	LRHS
Firefly Group (Pr/Poly)	NCGa WCot
§ ***firmipes*** (Si)	GKev IPen LPot WHil
§ ***flaccida*** (Mu)	ECho GEdr GKev IPen NHar NLar NSum WAbe
Flamingo Group (Pr/Poly)	XBar
florindae (Si) ♀H7	Widely available
- bronze-flowered (Si)	GQui NBir
- 'Dave's Red' (Si) **new**	LEdu
- hybrids (Si)	CMac CWld GAbr GMaP MLHP NCGa WFar WHar WHil WWtn XBar
- Keillour hybrids (Si)	CLAP IBoy NGdn NLar
- 'Muadh' (Si)	MMuc SEND
- orange-flowered (Si)	CSam IPen LLWG MNrw WMoo
- peach-flowered (Si)	CSpe
- 'Ray's Ruby' (Si)	CLAP GEdr MNrw NBir NGdn WCot
- red and copper hybrids (Si) **new**	CAby WHil WHoo
- red-flowered (Si)	CSpe CSta GBin IPen LLWG MMuc NBid NLar NSum SEND WFar
- terracotta-flowered (Si)	NGdn
Footlight Parade Group (Pr/Prim)	XBar
forbesii (Mo)	GKev
- CC 4084	CExl
forrestii (Bu)	GKev IPen WAbe
- SDR 4304	CExl GKev
§ × ***forsteri*** (Au)	NLar

	Name	Suppliers
§	– 'Bileckii' (Au)	ECho GMaP LLHF NBir NHar NSla
	– 'Dianne' (Au)	ECho EDAr GAbr GCrg GKev LLHF NBro NRya WAbe WThu
	– 'Dianne' hybrids (Au)	NHar
	'Francisca' (Pr/Poly)	LBMP LRHS MLHP WHer XLum
	'Fred Salter' **new**	NRya
	frondosa (Al) ♀H5	ECho GCra GKev IPen MFie MHol MLHP MPnt WAbe
	Fuchsia Victorians Group (Pr/Poly)	CWCL XBar
	'Gareth' (Pr/Poly) **new**	GEdr
	'Garnet' (*allionii* hybrid) (Au)	MFie XBar
	'Garryarde Crimson'	GEdr LLHF
	'Garryarde Guinevere'	see *P.* 'Guinevere'
	gemmifera (Ar)	ECho GKev LLHF NLar
	– var. ***monantha*** (Ar)	GKev
	geraniifolia (Co)	CLAP GCra GKev
§	'Gigha' (Pr/Prim)	CLAP CWCL GBin GCal GKev MNrw XBar
	'Gilded Ginger'	NCGa XBar
	'Ginger Spice' (Au)	NDro WHil
§	***glomerata*** (Ca)	GKev IPen
	– SDR 3924	GKev
	'Glowing Embers' (Pf)	GKev LLHF MSCN NBir
	glutinosa All.	see *P. allionii*
	Gold-laced Group (Pr/Poly)	Widely available
§	– Barnhaven (Pr/Poly)	GBuc MFie NBir XBar
	– Beeches strain (Pr/Poly)	CWCL IPen XBar
	– red-flowered (Pr/Poly)	IPen LBMP XEll
	'Gold-laced Jack in the Green' Barnhaven	XBar
	gracilipes (Pe)	CLAP GKev LLHF
	– early-flowering (Pe)	GCra
	– late-flowering (Pe)	CLAP GCra
	– 'Major'	see *P. bracteosa*
	– 'Minor'	see *P. petiolaris* Wall.
	graminifolia	see *P. chionantha*
	Grand Canyon Group (Pr/Poly)	CWCL NCGa XBar
	grandis (Sr)	GKev IPen
	'Green Lace' (Pr/Poly)	ECtt
	'Groenekan's Glorie' (Pr/Prim)	CFis GAbr GBuc GEdr NBir NSum
§	'Guinevere' (Pr/Poly) ♀H6	Widely available
	'Hall Barn Blue' (Pr/Prim)	CSam ECho GEdr GMaP NHar NMyG SBch WCot
§	***halleri*** (Al)	GKev IPen MFie XBar
	– 'Longiflora'	see *P. halleri*
	handeliana (Cy)	CWCL GKev
	Harbinger Group (Pr/Prim)	CWCL XBar
	Harbour Lights mixture (Pr/Poly)	CWCL NCGa XBar
	Harlow Car hybrids (Pf)	EPfP GQui LRHS NCGa NLar NSla WHil WMoo
	Harvest Yellows Group (Pr/Poly)	CWCL XBar
	'Hazel's White'	GKev
	helodoxa	see *P. prolifera*
	'Hemswell Abbey' (Au)	GKev
	'Hemswell Blush' (Au)	CSpe GKev ITim LLHF NHar WCre
	'Hemswell Ember' (Au)	CPBP GAgs NWad
	'Heritage Cream' (Pr/Prim) **new**	EBee
	heucherifolia (Co)	IPen WHil
	– SDR 3224	GKev
	hidakana (R)	GEdr
	'High Point' (Au)	WAbe
	hirsuta (Au)	IPen SEND WAbe
	– 'Lismore Snow' (Au)	NHar NWad WAbe
	– red-flowered (Au)	EBee GAgs MMuc
	– white-flowered	EPot
	× ***pedemontana*** 'Alba' **new**	
	hirsuta × ***minima***	see *P.* × *forsteri*
	hoffmanniana	NHar NSum
	hose-in-hose (Pr/Poly/d)	MNrw
	hose-in-hose, Barnhaven (Pr/Poly)	XBar
	'Hyacinthia' (Au)	IPen MFie
	ianthina	see *P. prolifera*
	'Ilana'	IPen
	incana (Al)	GKev
	Indian Reds Group (Pr/Poly)	CWCL XBar
	'Ingram's Blue' (Pr/Poly)	CDes CDoC EBee EPfP MHol
	'Innisfree'	CMea ECtt EPts GAbr GEdr LLHF MBel MPie NCGa NLar NMyG NSti NWad WCot
	Inshriach hybrids (Pf)	CAby CMHG IBoy
	integrifolia (Au)	GKev
§	'Inverewe' (Pf) ♀H5	CWCL GBin GBuc GCra GKev GQui NBir
	involucrata	see *P. munroi*
	ioessa (Si)	EWes GCra IPen NMyG
	– hybrids (Si)	WAbe
	'Iris Mainwaring' (Pr/Prim)	CFis ECtt GAbr GCra GEdr LLHF MCot
	irregularis (Pe)	WAbe
	'Jackie Richards' (Au)	CTal MFie WAbe
	Jack-in-the-Green Group (Pr/Poly)	CLAP CWCL MMuc MNrw NSla WBor WMoo
	– Barnhaven (Pr/Poly)	XBar
	– red-flowered (Pr/Poly)	WHil
	– white-flowered (Pr/Poly)	IFro
	jaffreyana (Pu)	GKev
	'Janet Aldrich'	CPBP
	japonica (Pf)	CMHG CSam ECha GQui IPen LRHS MSCN NBro NGdn SWat WAbe WMoo
	– 'Alba' (Pf)	CSta CTri ECho EHon EPfP EWoo GBuc GCal GEdr IPen LRHS MFie NGdn NWad WAbe WFar WWEG
	– 'Apple Blossom' (Pf)	Widely available
*	– 'Atropurpurea' (Pf)	IPen
	– 'Carminata' (Pf)	IPen
*	– 'Carminea' (Pf)	CHid GEdr GKev IPen MFie MSCN NBro NCGa NGdn NMyG NWad WFar WHil WPnP WWtn
	– 'Cherry Red' (Pf)	IPen
	– 'Cleo' (Pf) **new**	IPen
	– 'Fuji' (Pf)	NBro
	– 'Holly' (Pf) **new**	IPen
	– hybrids (Pf)	CMac GCra MRav WFar
	– 'Jim Saunders' (Pf)	SLon
	– 'Merve's Red' (Pf)	CDes
	– 'Miller's Crimson' (Pf) ♀H6	Widely available
	– 'Oriental Sunrise' (Pf)	CMil GBuc GKev IPen LLHF MSCN NCGa WHil XBar
	– pale pink-flowered (Pf)	ITim NSum
	– 'Peninsula Pink' (Pf)	IPen
	– 'Pinkie' (Pf)	IPen
	– 'Postford White' (Pf) ♀H6	CBcs CBod CHel CLAP COtt CPla CWCL ELan EPfP GAbr GBuc GCra GKev GMaP IBoy ITim LLWG LRHS

NBir NCGa NLar SHil SPer SPoG SPtp SWat SWvt WMoo WPnP XBar
- 'Purpurascens' (Pf) IPen
- Redfield strain (Pf) IPen
- red-flowered (Pf) IPen WAbe
- 'Splendens' (Pf) IFro IPen
I - 'Striatum' (Pf) **new** GKev
- 'Valley Red' (Pf) GKev IPen ITim LRHS NMyG
jesoana (Co) GKev LLHF
- B&SWJ 618 WCru
'Joan Hughes' (*allionii* hybrid) (Au) WAbe
'Joanna' ECou GBuc MPnt
'Johanna' (Pu) GAbr GCrg GEdr GKev NGdn NHar NSum WAbe
'John Fielding' (Pr) CAby CBro CElw EBee
'Jo-Jo' (Au) CTal MFie WAbe XBar
juliae (Pr) CAby ECho EDAr GCrg LRHS NBid NHar NSum SPlb WAbe
I - 'Millicent' (Pr) WCot
- white-flowered (Pr) NSum
'Juliana's Fireflies' (Pr/Poly) CWCL XBar
'Ken Dearman' (Pr/Prim/d) CBod ECtt MRav NBir NCGa
kewensis (Sp) ♀H2 GKev XBar
kialensis (Y) WAbe
'Kinlough Beauty' (Pr/Poly) CFis ECtt GBuc GMaP LLHF XBar
§ ***kisoana*** (Co) CExl CLAP GEdr GKev IPen LLHF XBar
- var. ***alba*** (Co) GEdr NHar
- 'Lyo-beni' (Co) **new** GEdr NHar
- var. ***shikokiana*** see *P. kisoana*
'Koblenz' (Au) NHar
komarovii (Pr) **new** LEdu
'Kusum Krishna' CHel CUse GBin GEdr MBNS MHol NHar NSti NWad WCot WHil
'Lady Greer' (Pr/Poly) ♀H5 CBod CDes CMac CSam CTal EBee ECtt EPfP GAbr GBuc GEdr GKev GMaP IGor LLWP MCot MHer NChi NGdn NHar NLar NSum WHer
'Lambrook Mauve' (Pr/Poly) CElw CFis GAbr
§ ***latifolia*** (Au) GKev
latisecta (Co) IPen
§ ***laurentiana*** (Al) GKev WAbe
'Lavender Shades' (Primlet Series) (Pr/Prim) **new** LRHS
'Lea Gardens' (*allionii* hybrid) (Au) IPen MFie NWad
'Lee Myers' (*allionii* hybrid) (Au) IPen MFie XBar
'Lemon and Lime' CMea
'Lemon' (Primlet Series) (Pr/Prim) **new** LRHS
leucophylla see *P. elatior*
'Lilac Domino' (Au) IPen
lilacina GKev IPen
- SDR 3088 GKev
- SDR 6832 GKev
limbata (Cy) LLHF
'Lindum Buttermilk' IPen
'Lindum Celebration' (Au) **new** NHar
'Lindum Crepes Suzette' IPen MFie
'Lindum Finale' (Au) IPen
'Lindum First Kiss' IPen
'Lindum Frosty Moon' IPen
'Lindum Lace' IPen
'Lindum Lancelot' (Au) **new** NHar
'Lindum Malcolm's Mate' CPBP IPen
'Lindum Moonlight' IPen LLHF MFie
'Lindum Pixie' IPen
'Lindum Rapture' (Au) IPen
'Lindum Rhapsody' **new** LLHF
'Lindum Serenade' (Au) IPen
'Lindum Smoke' IPen
'Lindum Snowball' (Au) **new** NHar
'Lindum Snowdrift' (Au) IPen
'Lindum Wedgwood' (Au) IPen MFie
'Lingwood Beauty' (Pr/Prim) CAby CElw CFis CSam GAbr LLHF WAbe
'Lipstick' CHid
'Lismore 79/7' (Au) NWad
'Lismore Bay' (Au) GKev
'Lismore Pink Ice' (Au) WThu
'Lismore Sunshine' NHar WThu
'Lismore Treasure' (Au) CPBP MFie
'Lismore Yellow' (Au) CPBP NHar WAbe XBar
Lissadel hybrids (Pf) NLar
'Little Egypt' (Pr/Poly) CWCL NCGa XBar
littoniana see *P. vialii*
'Lizzie Green' (Pr/Prim) **new** GEdr
'Loisach' **new** NHar
× ***loiseleurii*** 'Aire Mist' (Au) ♀H5 IPen ITim NHar NRya NSla NSum NWad WAbe WHil WThu XBar
§ - 'Aire Waves' (Au) CWCL ITim NHar NWad WAbe
- 'Pink Aire Mist' (Au) ITim WHil
- 'White Waves' (Au) IPen
longiflora see *P. halleri*
luteola (Or) ECho GKev LLHF NGdn NSum
macrocalyx see *P. veris*
macrophylla (Cy) GKev
- CC 7206 **new** GKev
'MacWatt's Claret' (Pr/Poly) ECho GAbr GBuc LLWP SBch
'MacWatt's Cream' (Pr/Poly) CFis EBee GAbr GCra GEdr LLHF LRHS NHar NLar WCot
magellanica (Al) WAbe
'Maisie Michael' CDes LLHF WAbe
marginata (Au) ♀H5 CPne CTal ECho EWoo IPen LRHS MFie MMuc NSla NSum SBch SEND WAbe WBla
- from the Dolomites (Au) NWad
- 'Adrian Evans' (Au) GEdr GKev SBch
- 'Alba' (Au) LRHS MFie NBro NRya NWad WThu XBar
- 'Ardfearn' (Au) GAgs GEdr
- 'Baldock's Purple' (Au) IPen
- 'Barbara Clough' (Au) GEdr IPen MFie NRya NWad
- 'Beamish' (Au) ♀H5 GEdr NBro NRya NSla NWad
- 'Beatrice Lascaris' (Au) CTal GAgs GEdr MFie NRya WAbe
- 'Caerulea' (Au) ITim MFie NWad
- 'Clear's Variety' (Au) GKev IPen ITim LLHF
- 'Doctor Jenkins' (Au) IPen NLar NRya NWad
- 'Drake's Form' (Au) ECho IPen NLar NRya
- dwarf (Au) ECho GEdr LRHS MFie NRya
- 'Earl L. Bolton' see *P. marginata* 'El Bolton'
§ - 'El Bolton' (Au) IPen NRya NWad
- 'Elizabeth Fry' (Au) IPen MFie
- 'Grandiflora' (Au) IPen NWad
- 'Highland Twilight' (Au) IPen NSla WAbe
- 'Holden Variety' (Au) GKev IPen ITim MFie NRya NWad
- 'Holly Leaf' (Au) GEdr
- 'Ivy Agee' (Au) IPen NRya
- 'Janet' (Au) ECho GEdr LLHF NWad WBla
- 'Jenkins Variety' (Au) ECho

- 'Johannes Holler' (Au)	ITim NRya
- 'Kesselring's Variety' (Au)	CMea ECho IPen ITim LLHF MFie NWad WAbe
- 'Laciniata' (Au)	ECho IPen LRHS
- 'Lemon Sorbet' (Au)	IPen
- lilac-flowered (Au)	IPen
- 'Linda Pope' (Au) ♀H5	ECho GAgs GEdr IPen NBir NHar NSum WAbe WThu
- maritime form (Au)	IPen
- 'Millard's Variety' (Au)	IPen NWad
- 'Miss Fell' (Au)	IPen
- 'Mrs Carter Walmsley' (Au)	NRya
- 'Nancy Lucy' (Au)	WAbe
- 'Napoleon' (Au)	GEdr IPen ITim MFie MSCN NWad
- 'Prichard's Variety' (Au) ♀H5	ECho GEdr IPen ITim LLHF MFie MSCN NLar NRya WAbe
- 'Rosea' (Au)	IPen
- 'Rubra' (Au)	ITim
- 'Sheila Denby' (Au)	IPen
- 'The President' (Au)	GAgs
- violet-flowered (Au)	ECho
- 'Waithman's Variety' (Au)	IPen NRya
- wild-collected (Au)	MFie
'Maria Talbot' (*allionii* hybrid) (Au)	CTal IPen
'Marianne Davey' (Pr/Prim/d)	WKif
Marine Blues Group (Pr/Poly)	CWCL NSum XBar
'Maris Tabbard' (Au)	IPen MFie NLar WAbe XBar
'Mars' (*allionii* hybrid) (Au)	IPen MFie NWad
'Marven' (Au)	IPen
'Mary Anne'	GAbr
'Mascara Blue' (Pr) **new**	SVic
'Mauve Mist' (Au)	MAsh
Mauve Victorians Group (Pr/Poly)	XBar
maximowiczii (Cy)	CSta ECho EDAr EPot GBin GBuc GEdr IPen LLHF MMHG NGdn NHar NLar NSum
- Red-flowered Group	GBuc GKev IPen
megaseifolia (Pr)	GBuc GKev IPen
melanantha (Cy) **new**	CWCL
'Melenoc'h' (Pr/Prim/d) **new**	XBar
§ × ***meridiana*** 'Miniera' (Au)	IPen MFie
Midnight Group	CWCL NCGa XBar
'Miel' (Pr/Prim/d) **new**	XBar
'Mike Smith'	IPen
'Miniera'	see *P.* × *meridiana* 'Miniera'
minima (Au)	NBro WAbe
- var. ***alba*** (Au)	NHar
minima × ***wulfeniana***	see *P.* × *vochinensis*
'Miss Doris' (Pr/Prim/d) **new**	XBar
'Miss Indigo' (Pr/Prim/d)	CTsd CWCL ECtt ELon EPot EWll GAbr GBin GMaP MBNS MFie MRav NSum SPer WCAu
mistassinica (Al)	GKev
- var. ***macropoda***	see *P. laurentiana*
miyabeana (Pf)	GKev IPen
modesta (Al)	XBar
- var. ***faurieae*** (Al)	GKev IPen
- - f. ***leucantha*** (Al)	GKev
- var. ***samanimontana*** (Al)	GKev

'Moerheimii' **new**	GEdr
monticola	GKev
'Moorland Apricot'	WMoo
moupinensis (Pe) ♀H4	CExl GAbr LLHF
- subsp. ***barkamensis*** (Pe)	GKev
'Mrs Eagland'	GAbr
'Mrs Frank Neave' (Pr/Prim)	GEdr IPen
'Mrs Marjorie Banks' (Pr)	GKev
'Mrs McGillivray' (Pr/Prim)	GAbr
§ ***munroi*** (Ar)	GKev IPen NHar WAbe XBar
- CC 6907	GKev
- CC 6908	GKev
- CC 7163 **new**	GKev
- subsp. ***munroi*** (Ar) **new**	GKev
- white-flowered (Ar)	WAbe
§ - subsp. ***yargongensis*** (Ar)	EBee GEdr GKev IPen
- - SDR 3096	GKev
- - SDR 6121	GKev
muscarioides (Mu)	GKev IPen
Muted Victorians Group (Pr/Poly)	NCGa NSum XBar
'Myline' **new**	WThu
§ ***nana*** (Pe)	IPen
'Netta Dennis' (Pe)	LLHF NHar
New Pinks Group (Pr/Poly)	NCGa NSum XBar
'Nightingale'	ITim
nivalis Pallas	see *P. chionantha*
nivalis ambig.	NSum
nutans Delavay ex Franch.	see *P. flaccida*
obconica (Ob) ♀H1c	GKev
SDR 7606 **new**	
'Oberau'	IPen
obtusifolia (Cy)	GKev
'Old Port' (Pr/Poly)	CAby CSam EBee GEdr NSum
Old Rose Victorians Group (Pr/Poly)	NCGa NSum XBar
optata (Cy) **new**	GKev
orbicularis (Cy)	ECho GEdr LLHF NLar
Osiered Amber Group (Pr/Prim)	NCGa NSum XBar
'Page'	IPen MFie
palinuri (Au)	IPen
palmata (Co)	GKev NHar
'Paris '90' (Pr/Poly)	CWCL NCGa NSum XBar
parryi (Pa)	CSta EBee GKev LLHF
pedemontana 'Alba' (Au)	MFie WThu
'Perle von Bottrop' (Pr/Prim)	ECtt GAbr GEdr NHar WCot
petelotii (Ch)	WAbe
'Peter Klein' (Or)	GBuc GKev LLHF WAbe
petiolaris misapplied	see *P.* 'Redpoll'
§ ***petiolaris*** Wall. (Pe)	GCra NHar NSum
- Sherriff's form	see *P.* 'Redpoll'
'Petticoat'	ECtt WCot
'Pink' (Primlet Series) (Pr/Prim) **new**	LRHS
'Pink Aire' (Au)	MFie XBar
'Pink Cabbage' (Poly)	CDes
'Pink Fairy' (Au)	IPen ITim
'Pink Grapefruit' (Pr/Prim/d) **new**	XBar
'Pink Ice' (*allionii* hybrid) (Au)	GKev MFie NHar NWad
poissonii (Pf)	CSta CTri CWCL EBee ELan EPfP GBin GCra GKev GQui IPen LRHS NGdn NLar NSum WAbe WShi

	Name	Suppliers
	- SDR 4617 **new**	GKev
	- SDR 5959	GKev
	polyanthus (Pr/Poly)	CWCL
	polyneura (Co)	CWCL ECho GEdr GKev IPen MSnd NGdn WBor
	'Port Wine' (Pr)	GAbr GCra GEdr
	'Powdery Pink'	LRHS
	prenantha (Pf)	GKev
	- SDR 3909	GKev
	Primlet Series (Pr/Prim)	SVic
	primulina (Mi)	GKev
§	***prolifera*** (Pf) ♀H4	CMHG CSta EPfP GBuc GCra GKev GMaP GQui IPen LRHS NCGa NGdn SWat WAbe WMoo XBar
§	× ***pubescens*** (Au) ♀H5	IPen LRHS MHer NGdn
	- 'A.E. Matthews' (Au)	NWad
	- 'Apple Blossom' (Au)	GAgs IPen MFie
§	- 'Bewerley White' (Au)	EBee ECho EPfP GAgs IPen NDro
	- 'Blue Wave' (Au)	IPen MFie SPop
§	- 'Boothman's Variety' (Au)	CBod CTri ECho EPfP EWoo GKev ITim MFie NHar NSla WHoo
	- 'Carmen'	see *P.* × *pubescens* 'Boothman's Variety'
	- 'Chamois' (Au)	MFie
	- 'Christine' (Au)	CMea EBee GAgs GKev IPen NBir NSum WCot
	- 'Cream Viscosa' (Au)	SPlb
	- 'Faldonside' (Au)	IPen MFie NSum WHil WThu
§	- 'Freedom' (Au)	CTal CTri ECho EWoo GAgs GKev IPen MFie NBir NHar NLar NSla XBar
	- 'George Harrison' (Au)	MFie
	- 'Harlow Car' (Au)	CMea GQui IPen MFie MPnt NSum
	- 'Hazel's White' (Au)	ITim
	- 'Joan Danger' (Au)	IPen NDro
	- 'Joan Gibbs' (Au)	IPen ITim MFie XBar
	- 'Kath Dryden' (Au)	ITim
	- 'Lilac Fairy' (Au)	IPen ITim NWad WThu
	- 'Moonlight' (Au)	NDro
	- 'Mrs G.F. Wilson' (Au) **new**	ECho
	- 'Mrs J.H. Wilson' (Au)	CTal ECho GCrg MFie NRya XBar
	- 'Pat Barwick' (Au)	IPen MFie NDro NRya NWad
	- 'Peggy Fell' (Au)	NWad WHil
	- 'Rufus' (Au) ♀H5	EWes GAbr GAgs GEdr NDro WThu XBar
	- 'S.E. Matthews' (Au)	GAgs
	- 'Sid Skelton' (Au)	IPen NRya
	- 'Slack Top Violet' (Au) **new**	NSla
	- 'Snowcap' (Au)	CPBP IPen ITim XBar
	- 'Sonya' (Au)	IPen
	- 'The General' (Au)	CTri GEdr IPen MFie
§	- 'Wedgwood' (Au)	GAbr IPen MFie WHil
	- 'Winnifred' (Au)	NDro WHil
	- yellow-flowered (Au)	IPen
	pulchella (Pu)	GKev
	pulverulenta (Pf) ♀H6	Widely available
	- 'Bartley' (Pf)	WWtn
	- Bartley hybrids (Pf) ♀H6	CWCL GAbr GKev MMuc NSum SEND WMoo XBar
	- 'Bartley Pink' (Pf)	CPla GBuc
	purdomii	GKev
	'Purple' (Primlet Series) (Pr/Prim) **new**	LRHS
	'Quaker's Bonnet'	see *P. vulgaris* 'Lilacina Plena'
	'Rachel Kinnen' (Au)	GAbr IPen MFie XBar
	'Ramona' (Pr/Poly)	CWCL NCGa XBar
	'Raspberry Ripple' (Pr/Prim/d) **new**	XBar
	'Ravenglass Vermilion'	see *P.* 'Inverewe'
	'Red' (Primlet Series) (Pr/Prim) **new**	LRHS
	'Red Ruffles' (Pr/Poly/d)	CBod ECtt WHil
§	'Redpoll' (Pe)	GBuc LLHF NHar
	reidii (So)	GEdr GKev
	- CC 4624	GKev
	- CC 7201 **new**	GKev
	- var. ***williamsii*** (So)	GEdr GKev IPen
*	- - ***alba*** (So)	GEdr
	reticulata (Si)	GKev
	'Reverie' (Pr/Poly)	XBar
	'Rheniana' (Au)	IPen MFie NLar NRya
	'Rick Lupp'	IPen
	'Romeo' (Pr/Prim)	CLAP LLHF NWad WCot
	'Rose' (Primlet Series) (Pr/Prim) **new**	LRHS
	'Rose Edge' (Primlet Series) (Pr/Prim) **new**	LRHS
	rosea (Or) ♀H5	CAby CBod CElw CWCL EBee ECho EPfP GKev GLog IPen MFie MMuc NBid NBir NRya WPnP WWFP
	- CC 5260	GKev
	- 'Gigas' (Or)	EDAr GAbr NRya WBor WMAq
	- 'Grandiflora' (Or)	CBod CMac ECho EPfP GCrg GKev LRHS NCGa NLar SPoG SRms SWat XLum
	'Rosemary Cottage'	CDes GAbr
	'Rowallane Rose' (Pf)	IPen
I	'Rowena'	GAbr GCra LLHF WCot
	'Roy Cope' (Pr/Prim/d)	NBir
	'Roydon Ruby'	GEdr WCot
	rubra	see *P. firmipes*
	'Ruby Tuesday' (Au)	NDro
	rusbyi (Pa)	GKev
	- subsp. ***ellisiae*** (Pa)	IPen
	'Sapphire'	XBar
	'Saracen'	IPen MFie
	saxatilis ambig. (Co)	MFie
	scandinavica (Al)	GKev
§	'Schneekissen' (Pr/Prim)	CSam CWCL GAbr GBuc GCra LLHF MHer NBro NChi NEoE SCob WHil
	scotica (Al)	GAbr GKev GPoy NSla WAbe
	secundiflora (Pf)	CCon CLAP CSta CWCL ECho ELan EWTr GBin GBuc GCra GKev LLWG MMuc NBir NSum SPer SPlb SWat WAbe WMoo WWFP XBar
	- SDR 4401	GKev
	- SDR 4435	GKev
§	× ***sendtneri*** (Au)	MFie
	× ***serrata***	see *P.* × *vochinensis*
	serratifolia (Pf)	GKev
	- SDR 5165	GKev
	'Shizuko Hara'	IPen
	sibthorpii	see *P. vulgaris* subsp. *sibthorpii*
	sieboldii (Co) ♀H5	ECho EWld GKev IPen MAsh MLHP MNrw NSla SBch SRms WAbe WBla
	- 'Aaimayama' (Co)	CSta
	- 'Aiaigasa' (Co) **new**	WFar
	- 'Akinoysool' (Co)	WFar
	- 'Andromeda' (Co)	EBee
	- 'Aoba-no-fue' (Co) **new**	CSta
	- 'Asahi' (Co)	WFar
	- 'Asahigata' (Co)	CSta
	- 'Ayanami' (Co)	WFar
	- 'Ayasegawa' (Co) **new**	CSta

- 'Beeches Star' (Co) **new**	EBee
- 'Benjamin' (Co) **new**	CSta
- 'Bide-a-Wee Blue' (Co)	NBid
- 'Bide-a-Wee Lace' (Co) **new**	NBid
- 'Bijyonomai' (Co)	WFar
I - 'Blue Lagoon' (Co)	EBee EPfP LLHF LRHS NLar WFar
- 'Blue Shades' (Co)	IPen
- blue-flowered (Co)	CLAP CSta CWCL
- 'Blush' (Co)	CLAP CSta WWEG
- 'Bureikou' (Co)	WFar
- 'Carefree' (Co)	CLAP CSta IPen LLHF NBro NLar WBla
- 'Cherubim' (Co)	CLAP CSta EBee GCra LLHF LRHS WBla
- 'Clouds Over Blighty' (Co) **new**	EBee
- 'Daikoshi' (Co) **new**	CSta
- 'Daiminnisiki' (Co)	NHar
- 'Dancing Ladies' (Co)	CLAP IPen NBro NCGa NHar WBla WFar XBar
- 'Dart Rapids' (Co)	CDes CSta WSHC
- 'Duane's Choice' (Co)	CAby CDes CLAP CSta MNrw SBch
- 'Edasango' (Co)	WFar
- 'Edomurasaki' (Co)	CSta WFar
- 'Essie' (Co) **new**	CSta
- 'Frilly Blue' (Co)	CSta EBee LRHS WWEG
- 'Fujijishi' (Co) **new**	WFar
- 'Galactic' (Co) **new**	CSta
- 'Galaxy' (Co)	NBro
- 'Geisha Girl' (Co)	CCon CLAP CSpe CSta EBee LRHS MRav NLar WAbe WBla WFar WWEG
- 'Ginhukurin' (Co)	CSta WFar
- 'Gunmia Niizatia' (Co) **new**	CSta
- 'Hakutsuri' (Co) **new**	WFar
- 'Hatagarasi' (Co)	WFar
- 'Hatusugato' (Co)	NHar WFar
- 'Heart's Desire' (Co)	EBee
- 'Higurasi' (Co)	WFar
- 'Hinokoromo' (Co)	WFar
- 'Inikina White' (Co)	WFar
- 'Inokima Minoura' (Co)	WFar
- 'Jessica' (Co) **new**	CSta
- 'Kansenden' (Co)	WFar
- 'Karagoromo' (Co)	WFar
- 'Kashima' (Co) **new**	CSta
- 'Kotonosirabe' (Co)	WFar
- f. ***lactiflora*** (Co)	CLAP CSta IPen LRHS NBro SMHy SRot
- 'Lilac Sunbonnet' (Co)	CLAP EPfP LLHF NHar WFar
- 'Managuruma' (Co)	WFar
- 'Manakoora' (Co)	CLAP EBee IPen NBro NCGa NSum WFar XBar
- 'Mangetu' (Co)	WFar
- 'Martin Nest Blue' (Co) **new**	CSta
- 'Martin Nest Pale Pink' (Co) **new**	CSta
- 'Masasino' (Co)	WFar
- 'Matsu-no-yuki' (Co)	CSta WBla
- 'Mikado' (Co)	CLAP CSta EBee IPen LRHS WWEG
- 'Musashino' (Co) **new**	CSta
- 'Noboruko' (Co)	CSta
- 'Okinanotomo' (Co)	WFar
- 'Oshibori' (Co)	CSta
- 'Pago-Pago' (Co)	CDes CLAP CSta IPen NBro WBla WFar XBar
- 'Pink Laced' (Co)	WFar
- pink-flowered (Co)	CWCL GKev NBir
- 'Saiun' (Co)	CSta
- 'Sekidaiko' (Co)	CSta
- 'Senyuu' (Co)	WFar
- 'Seraphim' (Co)	CLAP EBee LRHS MMHG NLar WFar WWEG
- 'Seto-no-ume' (Co)	CSta
- 'Shiokemuri' (Co)	CSta
- 'Shishifunjin' (Co) **new**	CSta
- 'Sinipukurn' (Co)	WFar
- 'Sinseiu' (Co)	WFar
- 'Siritonbo' (Co)	WFar
- 'Snowdrop' (Co)	CUse LSou MBel MHol MNrw MPie NCGa NMyG WBla WCot WFar WMoo
- 'Snowflake' (Co)	CBod CDes CLAP CSta EBee EPfP GKev LRHS NLar WAbe WBla WFar
- 'Sorcha's Pink' (Co) **new**	CSta
- 'Sousiarai' (Co)	CSta
- 'Spring Blush' (Co)	CSta
- 'Spring Song' (Co)	CSta
- 'Sumizomegenji' (Co)	CSta
- 'Sweetie' (Co)	WFar
- 'Syosin' (Co) **new**	CSta
- 'Tagonoura' (Co)	CSta
- 'Tah-ni' (Co)	NBro NSum
- 'Taoyami' (Co)	CSta
- 'Tatutanoyuube' (Co) **new**	CSta
- 'Tokimeki' (Co) **new**	WFar
- 'Toyonoharu' (Co)	WBla WFar
- 'Tukasamesi' (Co) **new**	CSta
- 'Turunokegoromo' (Co)	CSta
- 'Winter Dreams' (Co)	CAby CLAP CWCL NBid NBro NCGa NHar NSum WFar XBar
- 'Yuuhibeni' (Co)	CSta
sikkimensis (Si) ♀H5	CSta EBee ECho EPot GKev IPen LRHS MMuc MSCN MSnd NGdn NSum SPoG XBar
- CC 5730	GKev
- CC 5986	GKev
- CC 6771	GKev
- SDR 5933	GKev
- SDR 7426 **new**	GKev
- var. ***pseudosikkimensis*** (Si)	GKev IPen
- - SDR 4528	GKev
- var. ***pudibunda*** (Si)	GKev
- - SDR 3099	GKev
- - SDR 4919	GKev
- 'Ruby Shades' (Si)	GEdr
- 'Tilman Number 2' (Si)	GBuc
aff. ***sikkimensis*** (Si)	IPen NGdn
'Silver Lace Charlotte'	WIce
Silver-laced Group (Pr/Poly)	EPfP NLar SPoG SWvt WIce
- black-flowered (Pr/Poly)	XEll
sinolisteri (Ob)	GKev
sinoplantaginea	see *P. chionantha* subsp. *sinoplantaginea*
sinopurpurea	see *P. chionantha* subsp. *sinopurpurea*
'Sir Bedivere' (Pr/Prim)	CDes EBee GAbr GBuc GKev NHar WCot
'Siska' (Pr/Poly) **new**	GAbr
smithiana	see *P. prolifera*
'Snow Carpet'	see *P.* 'Schneekissen'
'Snow White' (Pr/Poly)	GBin GEdr MAsh MRav NDov
Snowcushion	see *P.* 'Schneekissen'

'Snowruffles' ITim
sonchifolia (Pe) CCon CLAP GKev
- subsp. ***emeiensis*** GKev
- subsp. ***sonchifolia*** GKev
sorachiana see *P. yuparensis*
'Sorbet' (Pr/Poly) XBar
spectabilis (Au) CDes GBin GKev
Spice Shades Group (Pr/Poly) CHid NCGa XBar
× ***steinii*** see *P.* × *forsteri*
stenocalyx (Pu) GKev
stenodonta (Pf) new GKev
'Stonewash' LRHS
'Stradbrook Charm' (Au) CPBP CWCL EPot MFie WThu
'Stradbrook Dainty' (Au) MFie
'Stradbrook Dream' (Au) ITim MFie
'Stradbrook Lilac Lustre' (Au) MFie
'Stradbrook Lucy' (Au) IPen ITim NWad
'Stradbrook Mauve Magic' (Au) MFie
Striped Victorians Group (Pr/Poly) NCGa NSum XBar
'Strong Beer' (d) CUse EBee ECtt GEdr MHol MNrw MPie NMyG NSum NWad WCot
'Sue Jervis' (Pr/Prim/d) MRav NBir SPer WCAu
suffrutescens (Su) GKev WAbe
'Sundae' (Pr/Prim/d) new XBar
'Sunrise' (Primlet Series) (Pr/Prim) new LRHS
'Sunshine Susie' (Pr/Prim/d) GMaP XBar
szechuanica (Cy) IPen LLHF
'Tango' (Pr/Prim) NCGa XBar
tangutica (Cy) GKev IPen
tanneri (Pe) GKev
'Tantallon' (Pe) LLHF NHar
Tartan Reds Group (Pr/Prim) CWCL XBar
'Tawny Port' (Pr/Poly) CElw NBro
'Theodora' (Pr) CTal GAbr GEdr
'Tie Dye' (Pr/Prim) CBod CUse GAbr LLHF MHol MNrw MPie NLar NWad WCot
'Tinney's Moonlight' (Pe) NHar
'Tipperary Purple' (Pr/Prim) GAbr
'Tomato Red' (Pr/Prim) CDes CFis EBee LLHF WCot
'Tony' (Au) ♀H5 CPBP IPen MFie XBar
'Top Affair' (Au/d) IPen WAln
'Tortoiseshell' (Pr/d) CHid ECtt
tosaensis (R) GEdr
'Tregor Rose' (Pr/Prim/d) new XBar
tschuktschorum (Cy) GKev
tyrolensis (Au) GKev
'Val Horncastle' (Pr/Prim/d) ECtt EPfP GAbr GMaP MFie
Valentine Victorians Group (Pr/Poly) XBar
× ***venusta*** (Au) GKev
'Vera Maud' (Pr) NCGa NSum XBar
§ ***veris*** (Pr) ♀H5 Widely available
- PAB 3777 LEdu
- subsp. ***columnae*** (Pr) EDAr GKev
I - 'Coronation Cowslips' (Pr) GBuc XBar
- hose-in-hose (Pr/d) new MAvo
- hybrids (Pr) LBMP
- 'Katy McSparron' (Pr/d) CExl CUse ECtt GCra GEdr MAvo MHol MNrw MPie SPer SPoG WCot
- 'Lady Agatha' (Pr) new XBar
- subsp. ***macrocalyx*** (Pr) EPot WCot
- orange-flowered (Pr) WMoo
- red-flowered (Pr) CAby NBid NGdn SPer WMoo
- 'Sunset Shades' (Pr) EAJP ECGP GBuc NGdn NLar XEll
vernalis see *P. vulgaris*
verticillata (Sp) IPen
§ ***vialii*** (So) ♀H5 Widely available
'Vicky' IPen
Violet Victorians Group (Pr/Poly) XBar
viscosa All. see *P. latifolia*
§ × ***vochinensis*** (Au) NHar
§ ***vulgaris*** (Pr/Prim) ♀H7 Widely available
- var. ***alba*** (Pr/Prim) CRow NSla WBrk
- 'Alba Plena' (Pr/Prim/d) GAbr GCal NSum
- Barnhaven Gold XBar
- green-flowered see *P. vulgaris* 'Viridis'
- hybrids (Pr/Prim) LSun WFar
§ - 'Lilacina Plena' (Pr/Prim/d) CCon CWCL EBee GAbr GCal IFro LLHF MRav NCGa NSum SIgm WHer
- var. ***pulchella*** (Pr/Prim) CDes
§ - subsp. ***sibthorpii*** (Pr/Prim) ♀H5 CMHG CSam EBee ECho ELon EPfP GBuc IPen LLWP LRHS MCot MFie MHer MLHP MNrw MRav NBro NCGa NChi SKHP SPtp SRms WHil
- - pale-flowered (Pr/Prim) GBuc
- 'Taigetos' (Pr/Prim) CBro CExl CHid
§ - 'Viridis' (Pr/Prim/d) CCon CDes MNrw
- subsp. ***vulgaris*** (Pr/Prim/d) ♀H5 CWld WMAq
waltonii (Si) CLAP CSta CWCL EPfP GBin GKev IPen MNrw NLar NSum
- hybrids (Si) ELon GEdr
'Wanda' (Pr/Prim) ♀H7 CBcs CDoC CTri ECho EPla GAbr GCra LBMP LRHS MBel MCot MHer MMuc NBid NDov SEND SRms WBrk WCFE WCot WGwG
Wanda Group (Pr/Prim) CHVG ECho LBMP NBro SVic
- 'Wanda Hose-in-hose' (Pr/Prim/d) GCra LLWP NBir WHer
- 'Wanda Jack-in-the-Green' (Pr/Prim) CLAP WCot
wardii see *P. munroi*
warshenewskiana (Or) CLAP EPot EWes GBuc GCrg GKev NHar NRya WAbe WGwG
watsonii (Mu) GKev NHar SWat
- ACE 1402 IPen
'Wedgwood' see *P.* × *pubescens* 'Wedgwood'
'Welsh Blue' CSpe
'Wharfedale Bluebell' (Au) IPen NBir NHar WThu
'Wharfedale Buttercup' (Au) IPen ITim NHar NWad WAbe
'Wharfedale Butterfly' (Au) NWad
'Wharfedale Crusader' (Au) IPen
'Wharfedale Gem' (*allionii* hybrid) (Au) MFie NSla NWad XBar
'Wharfedale Ling' (*allionii* hybrid) (Au) CTal GKev MFie NHar NWad XBar
'Wharfedale Sunshine' (Au) CPBP GKev IPen NWad
'Wharfedale Superb' (*allionii* hybrid) (Au) MFie
'Wharfedale Village' (Au) IPen MPnt NHar WThu
'White Linda Pope' (Au) GAgs NSla NWad WThu
'White Petticoat' (d) new NDov

'White Wanda' (Pr/Prim) GAbr XBar
'White Waves' (*allionii* hybrid) (Au) ITim
§ ***whitei*** 'Sherriff's Variety' (Pe) CLAP
'William Genders' (Pr/Poly) CDes GAbr LLHF
wilsonii (Pf) CSta CTri CTsd CWCL LLWG NGdn SGSe SWat WWtn XBar
§ - var. ***anisodora*** (Pf) CLAP GBin GKev GLog IPen NGdn XBar
- var. ***wilsonii*** (Pf) GKev
'Windrush' see *P.* × *berninae* 'Windrush'
'Winter White' see *P.* 'Gigha'
'Wisley Crimson' see *P.* 'Wisley Red'
§ 'Wisley Red' (Pr/Prim) CElw
'Woodland Walk' (Pr/Prim) EPfP
woodwardii (Cy) GKev
wulfeniana (Au) EBee EPot GKev
yargongensis see *P. munroi* subsp. *yargongensis*
'Yellow' (Primlet Series) (Pr/Prim) **new** LRHS
§ ***yuparensis*** (Al) EBee GBuc GKev IPen
- white-flowered (Al) GKev
zambalensis (Ar) GKev IPen
- SDR 1611 GKev
'Zenobia' WCre

Prinsepia (*Rosaceae*)

sinensis CArn MBlu NLar SLon WSHC

Pritchardia (*Arecaceae*)

affinis XBlo
hillebrandii LPal
pacifica XBlo

Pritzelago (*Brassicaceae*)

alpina NSla

Prosartes (*Liliaceae*)

§ ***hookeri*** CLAP EBee ECho LLHF MNrw SGSe WCru
§ - var. ***oregana*** EBee EPPr IBlr IFoB WCru
§ ***lanuginosa*** EBee EPPr LEdu WCru
§ ***maculata*** CAby CDes CLAP CPom CTal IFoB LEdu MNrw NLar WCru
§ ***smithii*** EBee ECho EPfP GKev GLog LEdu MNrw NBir SGSe WCot WCru WPGP
- 'Rick' (v) CTal

Prostanthera (*Lamiaceae*)

aspalathoides CBcs CCCN CSde CTsd MOWG
'Badja Peak' CTsd EBee EWes LRHS MAsh MOWG SLim
baxteri ECou MOWG
- 'Silver Ghost' SLim
cuneata ♀H4 Widely available
- 'Alpine Gold' (v) CMHG CTsd LRHS MAsh
- 'Blushing Bride' **new** CMac LBuc
- Kew form WPGP
* ***digitiformis*** CTsd
incisa CTsd
lasianthos CBcs CCCN CHll CTsd EWes LRHS MOWG SHDw SLim SPlb SVen
- 'Kallista Pink' CTsd MOWG
- var. ***subcoriacea*** CExl
latifolia CTsd
magnifica MOWG
melissifolia CArn CTsd ECre
§ - var. ***parvifolia*** CBcs CCCN CTsd
'Mint Delight' SLim
'Mint Royale' CCCN EBee LEdu LRHS SLim
'Mint-Ice' SLim
nivea ECou
ovalifolia ♀H3 CCCN ECou MOWG
I - 'Variegata' (v) CBcs CCCN CExl CHGN CHel CMac CTsd LRHS LSou MOWG MSCN WGrn
phylicifolia CTsd MOWG
'Poorinda Ballerina' CDul CTsd EBee LRHS MAsh SLim SPer SPoG SRkn
'Poorinda Petite' CCCN CDoC CTsd LRHS
rotundifolia ♀H3 CAbb CBod CCCN CHEx CHel CSde CSpe CTri CTsd CUse EBee ECho MGil MOWG MSCN SPer SVen WCFE WGrn
- 'Chelsea Girl' see *P. rotundifolia* 'Rosea'
§ - 'Rosea' ♀H3 CCCN CDoC CTsd ECou EPfP LRHS MGos MOWG SEND
sericea LRHS
sieberi misapplied see *P. melissifolia* var. *parvifolia*
sieberi Benth. CTsd MOWG
spinosa CTsd MOWG
walteri CCCN CTsd LRHS MOWG

Protea (*Proteaceae*)

aurea SPlb
burchellii SPlb
coronata CTre SPlb
cynaroides CCCN CHEx CTre IDee SBig SPlb
effusa SPlb
eximia CCCN CTre SPlb
grandiceps CCCN SPlb
lacticolor SPlb
laurifolia SPlb
nana SPlb
neriifolia CCCN CTre SPlb
obtusifolia SPlb
repens CTre SPlb
scolymocephala SPlb
subvestita CTre SPlb
susannae CTre SPlb

Prumnopitys (*Podocarpaceae*)

§ ***andina*** CBcs CDoC IArd SLim
elegans see *P. andina*
§ ***taxifolia*** CDoC ECou

Prunella (*Lamiaceae*)

§ ***grandiflora*** CHby CPrp CWld ECha SRms SWat WOut WWEG
- 'Alba' CBre EBee ECha EPfP GMaP NLar SPer WCAu WOut
- 'Blue Loveliness' GBee SWvt
- 'Carminea' EBee MRav SPer
- 'Freelander' EWll MNHC
- light blue-flowered WBor
- 'Loveliness' CDoC CMac CPrp ECha GMaP MBel MRav NBro NGdn NSti SPer SPlb SRGP WFar
- 'Pagoda' CSpe NLar
- 'Pink Loveliness' CPrp SRms WFar
- 'Rosea' WFar WOut
- 'Rubra' GAbr NLar WOut
- violet-flowered EPfP

- 'White Loveliness' CMac CPrp WWEG
hyssopifolia XSen
'Icing Sugar' EBee
incisa see *P. vulgaris*
Summer Daze = 'Binsumdaz'PBR EBee LSou NSti SPoG STPC
§ ***vulgaris*** CArn CHab ENfk GPoy MHer MNHC NMir WHer WHfH WJek WMoo WOut
- f. ***leucantha*** WHer
- 'Rose Pearl' CBod EWll LRHS
× ***webbiana*** see *P. grandiflora*
- 'Gruss aus Isernhagen' EBee

Prunus ✿ (*Rosaceae*)

'Accolade' (d) ♀H6 Widely available
§ 'Amanogawa' ♀H6 Widely available
americana EUJe
amygdalus see *P. dulcis*
andersonii new SBrt
aprium (F) ERea
armeniaca 'Alfred' (F) CDul ERea GTwe SDea SFam SKee WHar
- 'Blenheim' (F) ERea
- 'Bredase' (F) ERea SDea
- 'De Nancy' see *P. armeniaca* 'Gros Pêche'
- 'Delicot' new SFrt
- 'Early Moorpark' (F) CAgr EPfP GTwe MAsh MBri SDea SEND SLon WHar
- 'Farmingdale' (F) SDea
- Flavorcot = 'Bayoto'PBR (F) CAgr CSut EPfP EPom ERea GTwe MCoo SFrt SKee SPer WHar
- 'Garden Aprigold' (F) EPom SPoG
- 'Goldcot' (F) CAgr CDul CTho ERea LRHS MAsh MBri MCoo SDea SKee SPoG WHar
- 'Golden Glow' (F) CAgr CTho EPfP EPom ERea MAsh MBri MCoo SKee WHar
- 'Goldrich' (F) CAgr
§ - 'Gros Pêche' (F) SVic WHar
- 'Hargrand' (F) CAgr SVic
- 'Harogem' (F) CAgr
- 'Hemskirke' (F) ERea SKee
- 'Hongaarse' (F) SDea
- 'Isabella' (F) CAgr ERea
- 'Moniqui' (F) ERea
- 'Moorpark' (F) ♀H4 CDul CHab CSBt CTri ELan EWTr GTwe LAst LBuc MRav SDea SKee SPer
- 'New Large Early' (F) ERea SDea SEND SKee
- 'Petit Muscat' (F) EPom ERea SFrt SKee
- 'Tomcot' (F) CAgr CTho CTri EPfP EPom GTwe LBuc LEdu LRHS MAsh MBri MCoo MWat NOra SFam SFrt SKee SPoG WHar
- 'Tross Orange' (F) SDea
'Asano' see *P.* 'Geraldinae'
avium Widely available
- 'Amber Heart' (F) SKee
- 'Bigarreau de Schrecken' (F) SKee
- 'Bigarreau Gaucher' (F) SKee WHar
§ - 'Bigarreau Napoléon' (F) ELan EPom GTwe SKee SVic
- 'Birchenhayes' see *P. avium* 'Early Birchenhayes'
- 'Black Heart' (F) ELan MMuc SEND
- 'Bottlers' see *P. avium* 'Preserving'
- 'Bradbourne Black' (F) SKee WHar
- 'Bullion' (F) CEnd CTho
- 'Burcombe' (F) CEnd CTho
- Celeste = 'Sumpaca'PBR (D) CAgr CMac CTri EMil ERea GTwe LRHS MBri MCoo NLar NOra SDea SFam SLim SPoG WHar
- 'Cherokee' see *P. avium* 'Lapins'
- 'Colney' (F) ♀H5 ERea GTwe NLar NOra SFam SKee WHar WJas
- 'Cooper's Black' (F) new SKee
- 'Coroon' (F) SKee
- 'Dun' (F) CHab CTho
§ - 'Early Birchenhayes' (F) CEnd CTho
- 'Early Rivers' (F) CDul CLnd CSBt GTwe IArd NLar NOra SDea SKee SVic WHar
- 'Fastigiata' WHar
- 'Fice' (F) CEnd CTho
- 'Florence' (F) SKee
- 'Früheste der Mark' (D) new SKee
- 'Grandiflora' see *P. avium* 'Plena'
- 'Greenstem Black' (F) CTho
- 'Guigne d'Annonay' (D) new SKee
- 'Hannaford' (D/C) CHab CTho
- 'Hertford' (F) ♀H5 NOra SFam SKee WHar
- 'Inga' (F) SFam SKee
- 'Ironsides' (F) SKee
- 'Karina' (D) new SFrt
- 'Kentish Red' (F) SKee
- 'Kordia' (D) EPom GTwe NOra SFam SFrt SKee WHar
§ - 'Lapins' (F) CAgr CDul CLnd CTho CTri ECrN EPfP EPom GTwe LEdu MAsh MBri MRav NLar NOra SDea SFam SKee WHar WJas
- 'May Duke' see *P.* × *gondouinii* 'May Duke'
- 'Merchant' (F) ♀H5 NOra SFrt SKee
- 'Mermat' (F) SKee
- 'Merton Bigarreau' (F) GTwe WHar
- 'Merton Crane' (F) SKee
- 'Merton Glory' (F) CAgr CDul CSBt CSut EPfP GTwe IArd MAsh NOra SCrf SEND SEWo SFam SKee SLim WHar
- 'Merton Late' (F) SKee
- 'Merton Marvel' (F) SKee
- 'Merton Premier' (F) ELan SKee SVic
- 'Merton Reward' see *P.* × *gondouinii* 'Merton Reward'
- 'Nabella' (F) IArd MAsh WJas
- 'Napoléon' see *P. avium* 'Bigarreau Napoléon'
- 'Noble' (F) SKee
- 'Noir de Guben' (F) SKee WHar
- 'Noir de Meched' (D) SKee
- 'Old Black Heart' (F) SKee
- 'Penny'PBR (F) CAgr EPom GTwe NOra SFrt SKee WHar
- 'Petit Noir' (F) GTwe
§ - 'Plena' (d) ♀H6 Widely available
§ - 'Preserving' (F) CTho
- 'Regina' (F) CSut NLar NOra SFam SFrt SKee WHar
- 'Ronald's Heart' (F) SKee
- 'Roundel Heart' (F) SKee WHar
- 'Sasha' (F) SFrt
- 'Schneiders Späete Knorpel' (D) new SFrt
- 'Small Black' (F) CHab CTho
- 'Starking Hardy Giant' (F) SKee
- 'Stella' (F) ♀H5 Widely available
- 'Stella Compact' (F) ECrN LAst SDea WHar

	Name	Suppliers
	- 'Summer Sun' (D) ♀H5	CAgr CDul CLnd CSut CTho CTri EPfP EPom ERea GTwe LBuc LRHS MAsh MBri MCoo MGos NLar NOra SCoo SDea SFam SFrt SKee SLim SPoG WHar
	- 'Summit' (F)	SKee
	- 'Sunburst' (D)	CAgr CCVT CDul CEnd CLnd CMac CTho CTri ECrN EPom ERea GTwe LBuc LRHS MAsh MBri MGos NOra SCoo SDea SEWo SFam SKee SLim SPer SPoG SVic SWvt WHar WJas
	- 'Sweetheart' (F)	CAgr CDul CLnd EPom GTwe LRHS MAsh MBri NOra SKee SLim SPoG SVic WHar
	- 'Sylvia' (F)	CAgr SFam WHar
	- 'Van' (F)	CSBt IArd NOra SFam WHar
	- 'Vega' (F)	CAgr ERea GTwe SFrt SKee WHar WJas
	- 'Waterloo' (F)	SKee
	- 'White Heart' (F)	CHab ECrN SKee
	'Beni-yutaka' ♀H6	CCVT CTsd LAst MAsh MBri MRav MSwo SCoo SLim WHar
	besseyi	CAgr
	'Blaze'	see *P. cerasifera* 'Nigra'
	× ***blireana*** (d) ♀H6	CAco CDul CEnd CLnd CTri EPfP LAst MAsh MBri MGos MRav MSwo MWat NLar NWea SCoo SEND SPer WHar
	Blushing Bride	see *P.* 'Shōgetsu'
	campanulata 'Felix Jury'	EBee
	Candy Floss	see *P.* 'Matsumae-beni-murasaki'
	cerasifera (F)	CDul CHab CTri ECrN EPfP EPom GAbr LBuc MMuc NWea SDea SKee SPer SVic
	- 'Crimson Dwarf'	MBri SCoo SWvt
	- 'First' (F)	CAgr
	- 'Golden Sphere' (F)	CAgr CDul CLnd CTho CTri EPom LRHS NOra SDea SKee SPer WHar
	- 'Gypsy' (F)	CAgr CDul CLnd CTho LRHS NOra SEWo SKee SPer WHar
	- 'Hessei' (v)	EBee MBri MGos MRav NLar
	- 'Kentish Red' (F)	SEND
§	- Myrobalan Group (F)	ECrN MRav SDea SPre SVic
	- - 'Magda Jensen' (C)	CAgr
§	- 'Nigra' ♀H6	Widely available
	- 'Pendula'	CAco ECrN SWvt
§	- 'Pissardii'	ECrN EPfP NWea SCob SCoo SFam SLon SWvt WJas WMou
	- 'Ruby' (F)	CAgr EPom MBri
	cerasus 'Montmorency' (F)	NOra SKee
	- 'Morello' (C) ♀H6	Widely available
	- 'Nabella' (F)	SKee
	- 'Rhexii' (d)	CDul ECrN MAsh MBri
	- 'Semperflorens'	CLnd
	'Cheal's Weeping'	see *P.* 'Kiku-shidare-zakura'
	Chocolate Ice	see *P.* 'Matsumae-fuki'
§	× ***cistena*** ♀H6	CDul EBee ELan EPfP LAst LRHS MAsh MBri MGos MMuc MSwo NHed SCoo SGol SHil SPoG SWvt
	- 'Crimson Dwarf'	see *P.* × *cistena*
	'Collingwood Ingram' ♀H6	EBee EBtc EPfP LRHS MBlu MBri MWat SLim
	davidiana	SPlb
	'Delma'[PBR] (F)	WHar
	domestica (D/C)	SPre
	- 'Allgroves Superb' (D)	ERea
	- 'Angelina Burdett' (D)	CHab SDea SKee
	- 'Anna Späth' (C/D)	SKee
	- 'Ariel' (C/D)	SDea SKee
	- 'Autumn Compote' (C)	SKee
	- 'Avalon' (D)	CAgr CCAT CCVT CLnd GTwe IArd LBuc NOra SDea SFam SFrt SKee WHar
	- 'Beauty' (D)	CSut
	- 'Belgian Greengage' (F)	CHab SKee
	- 'Belgian Purple' (C)	SKee
	- 'Belle de Louvain' (C)	CDul CHab CLnd CTho CTri GTwe NOra SDea SKee WHar
	- 'Birchenhayes' (F)	CEnd
	- 'Black Diamond'	see *P. salicina* 'Black Diamond'
	- 'Blaisdon Red' (C)	CTho GTwe WHar
	- 'Blue Rock' (C/D) ♀H5	SKee
	- 'Blue Tit' (C/D) ♀H5	CAgr CTho EPom ERea GTwe MAsh MMuc NOra SDea SEND SKee WHar
	- 'Bohemian' (C) **new**	SKee
	- 'Bonne de Bry' (D)	SKee
	- 'Brandy Gage' (C/D)	SKee
	- 'Bryanston Gage' (D)	CTho SKee
	- 'Burbank's Giant'	see *P. domestica* 'Giant Prune'
	- 'Burcombe' (F)	CEnd
	- 'Cambridge Gage' (D) ♀H5	Widely available
	- 'Chrislin' (F)	CAgr CTho
	- 'Coe's Golden Drop' (D)	CAgr CHab CLnd ECrN ERea GTwe IArd LAst LRHS MBri MGos MRav NOra SDea SFam SFrt SKee SPer WHar
	- 'Count Althann's Gage' (D)	CHab ERea GTwe SDea SFam SKee
	- 'Cox's Emperor' (C)	SKee
	- 'Crimson Drop' (D)	SKee
	- 'Cropper'	see *P. domestica* 'Laxton's Cropper'
	- 'Curlew' (C)	SDea SKee
	- 'Czar' (C) ♀H6	Widely available
	- 'Delicious'	see *P. domestica* 'Laxton's Delicious'
	- 'Denbigh Plum' (D)	CHab WGwG
	- 'Denniston's Superb'	see *P. domestica* 'Imperial Gage'
	- 'Diamond' (C)	SKee
	- 'Dittisham Black' (C)	CAgr CTho
	- 'Dittisham Ploughman' (C)	CTho SKee
	- 'Dunster Plum' (F)	CAgr CTho CTri
	- 'Early Laxton' (C/D) ♀H5	CDul CHab LAst SDea SEND SFam SKee
	- 'Early Prolific'	see *P. domestica* 'Early Rivers'
§	- 'Early Rivers' (C)	CAgr CCAT CDul CHab CSBt CTho CTri ELan EPom ERea GTwd GTwe LRHS NOra NWea SCoo SDea SFam SKee WHar
	- 'Early Transparent Gage' (C/D)	CAgr CMac CSBt CTho ECrN ERea GTwe IArd LAst LBuc LRHS MBri MCoo NOra SCoo SDea SFam SFrt SKee WHar
	- 'Early Victoria' (C/D)	SDea
	- 'Edda' (D)	NOra WHar
	- 'Edwards' (C/D) ♀H5	CTri EMil GTwe SDea SKee
	- 'Excalibur' (D)	CAgr EPom GTwe IArd LBuc NOra SDea SFam SKee WHar
§	- German Prune Group (C)	SKee
§	- 'Giant Prune' (C)	CDul ECrN GTwe MMuc SDea SEND SFam SKee WHar
I	- 'Godshill Big Sloe' (F)	SDea
	- 'Godshill Blue' (C)	SDea
	- 'Godshill Minigage' (F)	SDea

	- 'Gold Dust' (F)	SPoG
	- 'Golden Transparent' (D)	LAst MCoo SFam SKee
	- 'Goldfinch' (D)	MCoo MMuc SEND SKee
	- 'Gordon Castle'	GQue GTwd WHar
	- Green Gage Group	see *P. domestica* Reine-Claude Group
	- 'Grey Plum' (F)	CAgr CTho
	- 'Guinevere' (C)	CAgr EPom LRHS MBri MCoo NOra SFrt WHar
	- 'Guthrie's Late Green' (D)	SKee
	- 'Haganta'PBR (F)	CAgr ERea NOra SFrt WHar
	- 'Herman' (D)	CAgr CLnd CMac EPom GTwe LRHS MAsh MBri MCoo NOra SDea SFam SFrt SKee WHar
	- 'Heron' (C)	GTwe NOra SKee WHar
	- 'Impérial Epineuse' (D)	SKee
§	- 'Imperial Gage' (D) ♀H5	CAgr CLnd CMac CSBt CTho CTri EPom GQue GTwe LRHS MAsh MMuc NOra SDea SEND SFam SKee WHar
	- 'Italian Prune' (F)	CLnd
	- 'Jan James' (F)	CEnd
	- 'Jefferson' (D) ♀H5	CAgr CHab CLnd GTwe IArd NOra SDea SFam SKee SVic WHar
*	- 'Jubilaeum' (D)	CAgr CCAT CLnd EPom GTwe LBuc LRHS NOra SCoo SEWo SFam SKee WHar
	- 'Kea' (C)	CAgr CLnd CTho SKee
	- 'Kirke's' (D)	CHab CTho ERea GTwe LAst NOra SDea SFam SKee WHar
	- 'Landkey Yellow' (F)	CAgr CTho
	- 'Langley Gage' (D)	CAgr ERea SDea
	- 'Late Muscatelle' (D)	SKee
	- 'Late Transparent Gage' (D)	SKee
§	- 'Laxton's Cropper' (C)	CHab GTwe LAst SKee WHar
§	- 'Laxton's Delicious' (D)	CHab
	- 'Laxton's Gage' (D)	SDea SKee
	- 'Laxton's Jubilee' (C/D)	CSBt NLar
	- 'Mallard' (D) ♀H6	SKee WHar
	- 'Manaccan' (C)	CAgr CTho
	- 'Marjorie's Seedling' (C) ♀H5	Widely available
	- 'Merton Gage' (D)	SKee
	- 'Merton Gem' (D)	SKee
	- 'Monarch' (C)	SKee
	- Old English gage	ECrN EPom ERea LAst
	- 'Olympia' (C/D)	SKee
	- 'Opal' (D) ♀H6	CAgr CCAT CCVT CDoC CDul CLnd CMac EPom GTwd GTwe LBuc LRHS MBri MGos MMuc MWat NLar NOra NPri NWea SCoo SCrf SDea SEND SFam SFrt SKee SLim SPoG WHar
	- 'Orleans' (C)	SKee
	- 'Oullins Gage' (C/D) ♀H5	Widely available
	- 'Pershore' (C) ♀H6	CAgr CHab ERea GTwe LRHS MBri NOra SDea SFam SKee WHar
	- 'Pond's Seedling' (C)	CSBt SDea SKee
	- 'Pozegaca' (D) **new**	SKee
	- 'President' (C)	CHab MMuc SDea SEND SKee
	- 'Priory Plum' (D)	SDea
	- 'Purple Pershore' (C)	CAgr CHab CTri GTwe IArd LAst NEgg NOra SDea SFam SKee WHar
	- 'Quetsche d'Alsace'	see *P. domestica* German Prune Group
	- 'Reeves' (C) ♀H5	CCAT GTwe IArd NOra SFam SKee WHar
	- 'Reine-Claude Dorée'	see *P. domestica* Reine-Claude Group
§	- Reine-Claude Group (D)	CLnd CSBt ELan GTwe SDea SEND SFam SKee SLim SPer
	- - 'Old Green Gage'	see *P. domestica* (Reine-Claude Group) 'Reine-Claude Vraie'
	- - 'Reine-Claude de Bavais' (D)	CCAT CTri GTwe NOra SDea SFam SKee WHar
	- - 'Reine-Claude de Moissac' (D)	SKee
	- - 'Reine-Claude de Vars' (D)	SVic
	- - 'Reine-Claude Tardive de Chambourcy' (D)	SKee
	- - 'Reine-Claude Violette' (D)	SKee
§	- - 'Reine-Claude Vraie' (C/D)	CAgr CDul CLnd CMac CSBt CTsd EPfP EPom LBuc LRHS MAsh NOra NPri SPoG WJas
§	- - 'Willingham Gage' (C/D)	ERea GTwe LRHS SKee WHar
	- 'Royale de Vilvoorde' (D)	SKee
	- 'Sanctus Hubertus' (D) ♀H5	CTri GTwe SDea SKee WHar
	- 'Seneca' (D)	CSut EPom NOra WHar
	- 'Severn Cross' (D)	GTwe SKee
	- 'Stanley' (C/D)	SVic
	- 'Stella'	CCVT ELan LAst NEgg NPri SLim WHar
	- 'Stella's Star'	LBuc MCoo NOra
	- 'Stint' (C/D)	SKee
	- 'Swan' (C)	GTwe NOra SKee WHar
	- 'Syston White'	MGos
	- 'Thames Cross' (D)	CLnd NOra SKee
	- 'Transparent Gage' (D)	SKee
	- 'Utility' (D)	SKee
	- 'Valor' (D) ♀H5	NOra WHar
	- 'Verity' (C/D)	SKee
	- 'Victoria' (D) ♀H5	Widely available
	- 'Violetta'PBR (D)	CAgr GTwe SFam WHar
	- 'Wangenheimer Frühzwetsche' (F)	SKee
	- 'Warwickshire Drooper' (C)	CAgr CHab CTho GTwe IArd LAst MAsh NOra SDea SFam SKee SLon SPer WHar
	- 'Washington' (D)	SDea SKee
	- 'White Magnum Bonum' (C)	SDea
	- 'Willingham'	see *P. domestica* (Reine-Claude Group) 'Willingham Gage'
	- 'Zimmers Frühzwetsche' (F)	SKee
§	***dulcis***	CAco CDul CHab CLnd CTri ELan EPfP EPom LAst LRHS MGos MWat NWea SCoo SDea SEND SFam SWvt WMou
	- 'Ai' (F)	CAgr
	- 'Ardechoise' (F)	CAgr
	- 'Ferraduel' (F)	CAgr
	- 'Ferragnes' (F)	CAgr
	- 'Lauranne' (F)	CAgr
	- 'Mandaline' (F)	CAgr
*	- 'Phoebe' (F)	CAgr
	- 'Supernova' (F)	CCCN
	- 'Tuono' (F)	CCCN
	Easter Bonnet = 'Comet'PBR	CTri EPfP LRHS
	'Flavour Supreme' (F) **new**	EPom
	Fragrant Cloud	see *P.* 'Shizuka'
	Frilly Frock = 'Fpmspl' (v)	EBee LRHS MBri NLar SPoG
	'Fugenzō'	CSBt EBee

	Name	Suppliers
§	'Geraldinae'	CLnd
	glandulosa 'Alba Plena' (d)	CEnd CMac CSBt LBMP MAsh SGol SPlb SRms SWvt
	- 'Rosea Plena'	see *P. glandulosa* 'Sinensis'
§	- 'Sinensis' (d)	CEnd CExl CSBt SRms
§	× ***gondouinii*** 'May Duke' (F)	SKee WHar
§	- 'Merton Reward' (F)	SKee
	grayana B&SWJ 10903 **new**	WCru
	'Gyoikō'	CEnd CLnd EBee
	'Hally Jolivette'	CEnd ELan GKin MAsh MBlu
	'Hillieri Spire'	see *P.* 'Spire'
	'Hilling's Weeping'	EBee SLon
	himalaica	LRHS
	'Hokusai' 🏆H6	EPfP LRHS SGol
	Hollywood	see *P.* 'Trailblazer'
	'Horinji'	LRHS MBri SCoo
	'Ichiyo' (d) 🏆H6	CDul CLnd EBee ECrN EPfP LAst LRHS MAsh MBri SCoo
	× ***incam*** 'Okamé' 🏆H6	CCVT CDoC CDul CLnd CMac COtt CTho EBee ECrN ELon EPfP EWTr IVic LAst LRHS MAsh MGos MMuc MRav NSoo NWea SCob SCoo SEND SEWo SLim SPer SPoG WFar WMou
	incisa	CTri NEgg
	- 'Beniomi'	MRav
	- 'Cunera'	NSoo
	- 'February Pink'	CJun SGol
	- 'Fujimae' 🏆H6	LAst
	- 'Kojo-no-mai' 🏆H6	Widely available
	- 'Mikinori'	CEnd CJun CMac CSBt EBee EPfP LBMP MAsh MBlu MJak MMuc NLar SCoo SEND
	- 'Oshidori' (d) 🏆H6	CMac CSBt ELon EPfP LRHS MBri MRav NLar SLim SRms
	- 'Paean'	NLar
	- 'Pendula' 🏆H6	SCoo
	- 'Praecox'	CHGN CSBt CTho EPfP LRHS MWat SCoo
§	- f. ***yamadei*** 🏆H6	CJun LBMP NLar
	insititia (F)	NWea
	- 'Black Bullace' (F)	ERea
	- 'Blue Violet Damson' (F)	CAgr ERea GTwe MCoo NOra WHar
§	- 'Bradley's King Damson' (C)	GQue MCoo NOra SKee WHar
	- bullace (C)	ERea LEdu SDea
	- 'Countess' (C)	CTri
	- 'Dittisham Damson' (C)	CTho
	- 'Farleigh Damson' (C) 🏆H6	CAgr CHab CLnd EPfP EPom ERea GTwd GTwe IArd LAst LBuc LEdu MJak MMuc NLar NOra NWea SDea SFam SKee SPer SVic WHar WJas
	- 'Godshill Damson' (C)	SDea
	- 'Golden Bullace'	see *P. insititia* 'White Bullace'
	- 'King of Damsons'	see *P. insititia* 'Bradley's King Damson'
	- 'Langley Bullace' (C)	CAgr CDul ERea GTwe LEdu NOra SKee WHar
	- 'Lisna' (C)	CTri
	- 'Merryweather Damson' (C)	Widely available
	- 'Mirabelle de Nancy' (C)	CAgr CDul CLnd CTho EPom ERea GTwe LAst NOra SDea SEWo SFam SFrt SKee WHar
	- 'Mirabelle de Nancy' red (C)	SDea
	- 'Mirabelle Ruby' (C)	LRHS NOra SFrt
§	- 'Prune Damson' (C) 🏆H6	CAgr CCAT CDoC CDul CHab CLnd CTho CTri EPom ERea GTwe IArd LBuc LRHS MAsh MBri MMuc MWat NLar NOra NPri SDea SEND SFam SKee SPer WHar WJas
	- 'Shepherd's Bullace' (C)	CAgr CTho ERea
	- 'Shropshire Damson'	see *P. insititia* 'Prune Damson'
	- 'Small Bullace' (C)	CAgr
	- 'Westmorland Prune' (C) **new**	CHab
§	- 'White Bullace' (C)	CAgr
	- 'Yellow Apricot' (C)	ERea
	'Jō-nioi'	CDul CEnd CLnd CTho MBri
§	'Kanzan' 🏆H6	Widely available
§	'Kiku-shidare-zakura'	Widely available
	Korean hill cherry	see *P. verecunda*
	'Kuboko-zakura'	EBee
	'Kursar'	CDoC CDul CLnd COtt CSBt CTho CTri EBee EPfP GKin LRHS MAsh MBri NLar NWea SCoo SCrf SEWo SLim SLon SPer SPoG SWvt WMou
	laurocerasus	CBcs CCVT CDul CMac CWSG EBee ECrN ELan EPfP EShb GKin IBoy LAst MGos MMuc MRav NHed NPri NWea SArc SCob SEND SGol SPer WMoo WMou
	- 'Angustifolia'	IBoy
	- 'Aureovariegata'	see *P. laurocerasus* 'Taff's Golden Gleam'
	- 'Camelliifolia'	CMac CTri EPla MBlu
	- 'Castlewellan' (v)	CDoC CDul CTri EBee ELon EPfP EShb IBoy LRHS MGos MRav MSwo NLar NWad SCob SDix SPer SPoG SSta WHar WMoo WRHF
	- 'Caucasica'	CEnd NLar SCob SGol
	- 'Cherry Brandy'	SCob SGol
	- Etna = 'Anbri'PBR 🏆H5	CMac EAEE LBuc LRHS LSou MAsh MBri NHed NPri SCob SWvt WMou
	- 'Gajo'PBR	SPer
	- Genolia = 'Mariblon'PBR	MBri SGol
	- 'Green Marble' (v)	CTri EHoe
	- 'Greentorch'PBR **new**	LRHS
	- 'Herbergii'	MAsh
§	- 'Latifolia'	CHEx EUJe LRHS
	- 'Magnoliifolia'	see *P. laurocerasus* 'Latifolia'
	- 'Marbled White'	see *P. laurocerasus* 'Castlewellan'
	- 'Miky'	CJun
	- 'Mount Vernon'	CTri LBuc MBlu SCob
	- 'Novita'	CAco CWSG EPfP NSoo
	- 'Otto Luyken' 🏆H5	CBcs CCVT CDul CMac CTri EBee EHoe ELan EPfP LAst LBMP LBuc LRHS MAsh MGos MJak MSwo MWhi NBir NEgg NHed NLar NWea SCob SGol SPer SPlb WFar WHar
	- 'Reynvaanii'	CJun MBri
	- 'Rotundifolia' 🏆H5	Widely available
§	- 'Taff's Golden Gleam' (v)	CJun
	- 'Van Nes'	CJun MAsh
	- 'Variegata' misapplied	see *P. laurocerasus* 'Castlewellan'
	- 'Variegata' ambig. (v)	SRms
	- 'Whitespot'	MMuc SEND
	- 'Zabeliana'	CDul CMac CTri MJak MSwo NEgg NWad NWea SBod SCob SPer SRms WHar
	litigiosa	CLnd EBee LRHS SCoo
	'Little Pink Perfection'	MBri SCoo SPoG
	lusitanica 🏆H5	Widely available

Plant	Suppliers
– subsp. ***azorica***	CDoC CExl EBee LRHS WPGP
– 'Myrtifolia' ♀^{H5}	CTri EAEE EPfP EShb LRHS MBri MRav NHed SCob SGol SHil SLon SWvt WCFE WMoo
– 'Variegata' (v)	CMac CTri ELan ELon MGos MLHP MMuc MRav MSwo SCob SDix SEND SGol SPer SPoG SSta SWvt WFar WHar WMoo
maackii	CLnd MMuc
– 'Amber Beauty'	CBcs CDul EBee EPfP GBin GKin MRav SEND SGol SLon
mahaleb	CNWT
'Mahogany Lustre'	MGos
maritima	LEdu
§ 'Matsumae-beni-murasaki'	NLar SCoo WHar
'Matsumae-beni-yutaka' **new**	SCob
§ 'Matsumae-fuki' ♀^{H6}	COtt EBee MBri NLar NWea SLim WHar
§ 'Matsumae-hanagasa' ♀^{H6}	CEnd LRHS MBri NLar WMou
maximowiczii B&SWJ 10967	WCru
'Mount Fuji'	see *P.* 'Shirotae'
mume	CMCN CMen
– 'Beni-chidori' ♀^{H5}	CBcs CDul CEnd CMac EBee ELan EPfP EPla IVic LBMP LRHS MBlu MBri NLar SCob SCoo SLim SPoG WJas
§ – 'Omoi-no-mama' (d)	CDul CEnd CMen
– 'Omoi-no-wac'	see *P. mume* 'Omoi-no-mama'
myrobalana	see *P. cerasifera* Myrobalan Group
nipponica var. ***kurilensis***	CBcs CSBt GBin LRHS MBri NHol
'Brillant'	NLar NSoo
– – 'Ruby'	MBri NEgg NSoo
'Oku-miyako' misapplied	see *P.* 'Shōgetsu'
padus	CAco CCVT CDul CHab CLnd CMac CSBt CTri ECrN EWTr LBuc MGos MJak MMuc MSwo NHed NLar NWea SCob SEND SEWo WMou
– 'Albertii'	CCVT MBri SCoo
– 'Colorata' ♀^{H6}	CDul CEnd CMac CTho EBee ECrN ELan EWTr MAsh MGos MRav NLar SCoo SGol SPer SWvt
– 'Grandiflora'	see *P. padus* 'Watereri'
– 'Purple Queen'	ECrN SCob SGol
§ – 'Watereri' ♀^{H6}	CCVT CDul CEnd CMCN CMac CTho ECrN ELan EPfP EWTr GBin LAst NWea SCoo SEWo SGol SPer SPoG WMou
'Pandora' ♀^{H6}	CCVT CDoC CDul CLnd COtt EAEE EBee EPfP LAst LRHS MAsh MBri MGos MMuc MRav MSwo NWea SCob SCoo SEND SEWo SPer SPoG WFar WMou
pendula	SCrf
– 'Pendula Plena Rosea' (d)	WFar
§ – 'Pendula Rosea'	CDoC CDul CEnd CLnd CTri EPfP MAsh SCob SCrf SPer WJas
§ – 'Pendula Rubra' ♀^{H6}	CCVT CDoC CLnd CMac CSBt EBee EPfP LAst LRHS MBri MJak MSwo SCoo SLim SPer SPoG WMou
§ – 'Stellata' ♀^{H6}	LRHS MBri NLar
persica	CPne SPre
– 'Amsden June' (F)	CLnd EBtc GTwe LEdu MWat NLar NRog SDea SFam SKee WHar
– 'Avalon Pride' (F)	CAgr CSut EPfP EPom ERea LBuc LRHS MCoo NRog SFrt SKee
– 'Barrington' (F)	ERea

Plant	Suppliers
– 'Bellegarde' (F)	ERea NRog SDea SFam
– 'Black' (F)	ERea
– 'Bonanza' (F)	EPom ERea
– 'Champion' (F)	CLnd NRog SDea
– 'Crimson Bonfire' (F) **new**	EPom
– 'Darling' (F)	SVic
– 'Diamond' (F) **new**	EPom
– 'Dixi Red' (F)	CAgr ERea
– 'Doctor Hogg' (F)	ERea SDea
– 'Duke of York' (F) ♀^{H4}	CTri ERea GTwe SDea SFam
– 'Dymond' (F)	ERea
– 'Early Alexander' (F)	ERea
– 'Foliis Rubris' (F)	CDul LRHS
– 'Frost' (F)	ERea NRog
– 'Garden Lady' (F)	EPom GTwe NOra SLim WHar
– 'Hale's Early' (F)	GTwe MRav MWat NRog SFam SKee SLim SPer WHar
– 'Harken' (F)	ERea
– 'Hylands' (F)	SDea
– 'Jalousia' (F)	EPom NRog
– 'Johnny Brack' (F)	ERea NRog
– 'Kestrel' (F)	ERea
– 'Madison' (F)	ERea
– 'Mesembrine'^{PBR} (F)	EPom
– 'Natalia' (F)	SDea
– var. ***nectarina*** Crimson Gold (F)	SDea
– – 'Early Blaze' (F)	LEdu
– – 'Early Gem' (F)	ERea SDea
– – 'Early Rivers' (F) ♀^{H4}	ERea GTwe LAst SDea
– – 'Elruge' (F)	ERea SDea
– – 'Fantasia' (F)	EPfP SDea
– – 'Fire Gold' (F)	ERea SDea
– – 'Flavortop' (F)	EPfP ERea SPer
– – 'Garden Beauty' (F/d)	SPoG
– – 'Honey Kist' (F) **new**	EPom
– – 'Humboldt' (F)	CAgr CDul ERea GTwe LAst SDea SFam SKee SPoG WHar
– – 'John Rivers' (F)	SDea
– – 'Lord Napier' (F) ♀^{H4}	CAgr CDoC CDul CSBt CTri EPfP EPom ERea LAst LBuc MAsh MGos MWat NOra SDea SEND SFam SKee SLim SPer SPoG SVic WHar
– – 'Madame Blanchet' (F) **new**	SDea
– – 'Nectarella' (F)	EPom ERea NOra SLim WHar
– – 'Pineapple' (F)	CAgr CTri ERea GTwe SDea SFam SKee WHar
– – Rubis = 'Necta Zee'^{PBR} **new**	EPom
– – 'Ruby Gold' (F)	SDea
– – 'Sauzee Bel' **new**	EPom
– – 'Sauzee King' (F) **new**	EPom
– – 'Snow Baby' **new**	EPom
– – 'Terrace Ruby' (F)	SPoG
– 'Oriane'^{PBR} (F) **new**	NRog
– 'Pallas' (F)	ERea
– 'Peregrine' (F) ♀^{H4}	CAgr CDul CLnd CSBt CTri EPfP EPom ERea GTwe LAst LBuc LRHS MAsh MBri MGos MWat NLar NOra NRog SDea SEND SFam SKee SLim SPer SPoG WHar WJas
– 'Purpurea'	GKin
– 'Raritan Rose' (F)	ERea
– 'Red Haven' (F)	CAgr ERea GTwe NRog SDea SKee SVic WHar
– 'Red Top' (F)	EPfP
– 'Redwing' (F)	CAgr

Name	Suppliers
- 'Reliance' (F)	SDea
- 'Robin Redbreast' (F)	CAgr SDea
- 'Rochester' (F) ♀H4	CAgr CSBt CTri EPom ERea GTwe LAst LRHS MBri NOra NRog SDea SEND SFam SKee SLim SPer SPoG WHar
- 'Royal George' (F)	NRog SFam
- 'Rubira' (F)	NRog
- 'Sanguine de Savoie' (F)	NRog
- 'Sanguinole' (F) **new**	CSut
- 'Saturne' (F)	CLnd EPom ERea MAsh NOra NRog SKee WHar
- 'Springtime' (F)	SDea
- 'Terrace Amber' (F)	SPoG
- 'Terrace Diamond' (F)	SPoG
- 'Wassenberger' (F) **new**	SDea
× ***persicoides*** 'Ingrid' (F)	CAgr CDul EBtc ECrN LBuc LRHS MBri MCoo NOra SCoo WHar
- 'Pollardii' (F)	NWea WJas
- 'Robijn' (F)	CAgr CDul EPom LBuc LEdu SFrt SVic
- 'Spring Glow' (F)	CCVT CDoC CDul CEnd CLnd EPfP LAst MAsh MBri MSwo NWea SCoo SLim SLon WJas
'Petite Noir'	CLnd LRHS
Pink Parasol	see *P.* 'Matsumae-hanagasa'
'Pink Perfection' ♀H6	CBcs CDul CLnd CSBt EPfP EPla LAst LRHS MBri MGos MSwo MWat NLar NSoo SCob SPer WHar WJas
'Pink Shell'	CLnd EPfP MAsh MBri
pissardii	see *P. cerasifera* 'Pissardii'
'Pissardii Nigra'	see *P. cerasifera* 'Nigra'
pumila var. ***depressa***	MRav
'Royal Burgundy' (d) ♀H6	Widely available
rufa ♀H6	CDul CJun CLnd CTho EBee EBtc GKin SKHP SLon WPat
salicina 'Abundance' (F)	ERea
- 'Beauty'	ERea
§ - 'Black Diamond' (F)	SDea
- 'Howard Miracle' (F)	ERea
- 'Lizzie'	EPom
- 'Mariposa' (F)	ERea
- 'Methley' (D)	CAgr ERea LRHS NOra SFrt SPoG WHar
- 'Ozark Premier' (F)	ERea
- 'Santa Rosa' (F)	ERea
- 'Satsuma' (F)	ERea
- 'Shiro' (D)	ERea SFrt
- 'Sierra' (F)	ERea
sargentii	Widely available
- 'Charles Sargent' ♀H6	EBee GBin MBlu
- 'Columnaris'	GBin MBri
- 'Rancho'	CLnd MAsh SCoo SPer SPoG
× ***schmittii***	CCVT ECrN MMuc SCoo SPer WJas
'Sekiyama'	see *P.* 'Kanzan'
serotina	CDul NLar
§ ***serrula***	Widely available
- 'Branklyn' ♀H6	EBee MGos NLar SCob
- 'Princesse Sturdza'	MBlu
- var. ***tibetica***	see *P. serrula*
serrula × ***serrulata***	CBcs CTho
serrulata 'Erecta'	see *P.* 'Amanogawa'
- 'Grandiflora'	see *P.* 'Ukon'
- 'Longipes'	see *P.* 'Shōgetsu'
- 'Miyako' misapplied	see *P.* 'Shōgetsu'
- var. ***pubescens***	see *P. verecunda*
- 'Rosea'	see *P.* 'Kiku-shidare-zakura'
'Shidare-zakura'	see *P.* 'Kiku-shidare-zakura'
'Shimizu-zakura'	see *P.* 'Shōgetsu'
'Shirofugen' ♀H6	CBcs CCVT CDoC CDul CLnd CMCN CMac COtt CSBt CTho ECrN EPfP EPla EWTr GKin LAst LBuc LRHS MAsh MBri MMuc MRav MWat SCob SEND SGol SPer WHar WJas
§ 'Shirotae' ♀H6	Widely available
§ 'Shizuka' ♀H6	COtt ECrN EWTr LAst LRHS MBri MSwo NLar NSoo NWea SCob SCoo SLim SPer SPoG WHar WMou
§ 'Shōgetsu' ♀H6	CBcs CDul CEnd CLnd CMac CSBt CTho EBee ELan EPfP EWTr LAst LRHS MAsh MBri NEgg NLar SCob SEWo SFam SLim SPer WHar
'Shosar' ♀H6	CEnd ECrN EPla MAsh SCoo SPer
× ***sieboldii*** 'Caespitosa'	see *P.* 'Takasago'
'Snow Goose'	CDoC CMac EBee ELan EPfP LAst LRHS MBlu NEgg SCoo SGol
'Snow Showers'	CCVT CDoC CEnd CMac COtt ELan LRHS MAsh MBri MGos MMuc NSoo NWea SEND SLim SPer SPoG
spinosa	CAco CCVT CDoC CDul CHab CMac CTri ECrN EPfP EPom EShb GAbr LAst LBuc MAsh MBlu MJak NHed NLar NWea SCob SEWo SPer SPoG SVic WHar WMou WSFF
- 'Plena' (d)	CEnd CTho MBlu
- 'Purpurea'	CDul CTho EGFP MBlu MBri WMou
§ 'Spire' ♀H6	Widely available
× ***subhirtella*** 'Autumnalis'	Widely available
- 'Autumnalis Rosea'	Widely available
- 'Falling Stars'	SLon
- 'Fukubana'	CLnd CMac EBee EPfP MAsh MBri NLar
- 'Pendula' misapplied	see *P. pendula* 'Pendula Rosea'
- 'Pendula Rosea'	see *P. pendula* 'Pendula Rosea'
- 'Pendula Rubra'	see *P. pendula* 'Pendula Rubra'
- 'Rosea' ♀H6	CLnd MRav WFar
- 'Stellata'	see *P. pendula* 'Stellata'
'Sunset Boulevard' ♀H6	LRHS MBri MGos
'Tai-haku' ♀H6	Widely available
§ 'Takasago'	EBee MBri SCoo
'Taoyame' ♀H6	CLnd
tenella	CAgr ECha ELan WCot
- 'Fire Hill'	CJun CSBt ELan EPfP LRHS MGos SKHP SPer WCFE WCot WJas
'The Bride' ♀H6	CDul CEnd CJun LRHS MAsh MBri SCoo
tibetica	see *P. serrula*
'Tiltstone Hellfire'	EBee GBin MBri
tomentosa	CAgr SBrt SEND
§ 'Trailblazer' (C/D)	CDul CEnd CLnd CMac CSBt ECrN IVic LAst MRav MSwo SCob SLon WMou
triloba	CBcs ECha LAst MBlu NWea
- 'Multiplex' (d)	SRms WJas
§ 'Ukon' ♀H6	CBcs CDoC CDul CLnd CMCN CMac CTho CTri EBee ECrN EPfP EPla EWTr LRHS MAsh MBri MGos MRav NLar NWea SGol SLim SPer WFar WHar
'Umineko'	CCVT CLnd ECrN MGos MMuc SEND SEWo SPer WHar
§ ***verecunda***	CLnd NWea WJas
- 'Autumn Glory' ♀H6	CTho
virginiana 'Schubert'	CDul ECrN EPla SCoo WMou
'White Cloud'	CDul
'Woodfield Cluster'	IArd

	yamadae	see *P. incisa* f. *yamadae*
	× ***yedoensis***	CCVT CDoC CDul EBee EPla MBri MRav SLon SPer WHar WMou
	- 'Ivensii'	CAco CBcs CDul CSBt NWea SCoo
	- 'Pendula'	see *P.* × *yedoensis* 'Shidare-Yoshino'
	- 'Perpendens'	see *P.* × *yedoensis* 'Shidare-Yoshino'
§	- 'Shidare-Yoshino'	CCVT CDoC CDul CLnd COtt CSBt EBee ECrN LRHS MAsh MBri MGos MRav MSwo MWat NLar NWea SLim SLon SPoG
§	- 'Somei-Yoshino' ♀H6	CCVT CLnd CTho CTri EPfP MBri NWea SLim SPer WHar WJas
	'Yoshino'	see *P.* × *yedoensis* 'Somei-Yoshino'
	'Yoshino Pendula'	see *P.* × *yedoensis* 'Shidare-Yoshino'

Psacalium (*Asteraceae*)

	pinetorum B&SWJ 10269	WCru

Psammisia (*Ericaceae*)

	ulbrichiana new	WPat

Pseuderanthemum (*Acanthaceae*)

	carruthersii var. ***atropurpureum*** 'Rubrum'	LSou

Pseudocydonia (*Rosaceae*)

§	***sinensis***	CAgr CBcs CMen NLar

Pseudofumaria see *Corydalis*

	alba	see *Corydalis ochroleuca*

Pseudogynoxys (*Asteraceae*)

§	***chenopodioides***	CCCN CRHN CSpe SVen

Pseudolarix (*Pinaceae*)

§	***amabilis*** ♀H6	CAco CDoC CMen CTho EPfP GBin MBlu MBri MPkF NPCo NWea SCoo SKHP SLim SPoG
	kaempferi	see *P. amabilis*

Pseudomuscari see *Muscari*

	azureum	see *Muscari azureum*

Pseudopanax (*Araliaceae*)

	(Adiantifolius Group) 'Adiantifolius'	CBcs CDoC CHEx EBee ECou ESwi SVen
	- 'Cyril Watson' ♀H3	CBcs CDoC CHEx ELan ETwe IDee LRHS SBig SVen WCot
	arboreus	see *Neopanax arboreus*
	chathamicus	CDoC CHEx ECou SArc
	County Park hybrid new	ECou
	crassifolius	CAbb CBcs CBct CBrP CCCN CDTJ CHEx ECou ELon ESwi EUJe GBin IDee LRHS NLos SArc SBig SMad SPoG WCot
	- var. ***trifoliolatus***	CHEx
	discolor	ECou IDee LEdu
	ferox	CAbb CBcs CBct CBrP CDTJ CTsd ECou ESwi EUJe GBin LRHS NLos SArc SBig SLim SMad SPoG SVen
	'Forest Gem'	CDoC
	laetus	see *Neopanax laetus*
	lessonii	CBcs CBrP CHEx ECou
	- 'Black Ruby'	ECou
	- 'Gold Splash' (v) ♀H3	CBcs CDoC CHEx EPfP IVic LRHS SBig SEND SLim SVen
	- 'Rangitira'	CBcs CDoC LRHS SBig SLim
	'Linearifolius'	CHEx IDee LEdu
	linearis new	ECou
	'Purpureus' ♀H3	CDoC ESwi IDee SEND SVen
	'Sabre'	CBcs CDoC CHEx ECou EUJe LRHS SLim
	'Trident' ♀H3	CDoC CHEx ECou LRHS SBig SLim SVen

Pseudosasa (*Poaceae*)

	amabilis misapplied	see *Arundinaria gigantea*
§	***amabilis*** (McClure) Keng f.	EPla
§	***japonica*** ♀H5	CAbb CAco CBcs CDoC CEnt CHEx CTsd EPfP EPla LPal LRHS MMoz MMuc MWht NLar SArc SCob SEND SEWo SPer SPoG WCFE WMoo
§	- 'Akebonosuji' (v)	CEnt EPla MWht WPGP
I	- var. ***pleioblastoides***	EPla MWht
	- 'Tsutsumiana'	CHEx ELon EPla ERod EUJe MMoz MWht NLar SBig
	- 'Variegata'	see *P. japonica* 'Akebonosuji'
	usawai	EPla
	viridula	ERod MWht

Pseudotsuga (*Pinaceae*)

§	***menziesii***	CAco CBcs CDul CLnd EPfP MBlu MMuc NWea SEND
	- 'Bhiela Lhota'	CKen
	- 'Blue Wonder'	CKen
	- 'Densa'	CKen
	- 'Fastigiata'	CKen
	- 'Fletcheri'	CKen
	- var. ***glauca***	CAco CDul CTho
	- 'Glauca Pendula'	CKen MBlu
I	- 'Gotelli's Pendula'	CKen
	- 'Graceful Grace'	CKen
	- 'Hillside Pride' new	NLar
	- 'Idaho Gem'	CKen NLar
	- 'Julie'	CKen
	- 'Little Jamie'	CKen
	- 'Lohbrunner'	CKen
	- 'McKenzie'	CKen
	- 'Nana'	CKen
	- Pendula Group	NPCo
	- 'Serpentine' new	MBlu
	- 'Stairii'	CKen
	taxifolia	see *P. menziesii*

Pseudowintera (*Winteraceae*)

§	***colorata***	CBcs CDoC CExl CMac CPla CTsd GAbr GKin IVic MPkF MRav NLar WPat
	- 'Marjorie Congreve'	IVic LRHS
	- 'Moulin Rouge'	CBcs LRHS
	- 'Mount Congreve'	CBcs GKin IArd NLar WPat
	- 'Red Glow'	CBcs
	- 'Red Leopard'	CDoC CMil LRHS NLar NSoo SEle

Psidium (*Myrtaceae*)

	cattleyanum	see *P. littorale* var. *longipes*
	guajava (F)	CCCN SPlb XBlo
	littorale (F)	CPne
§	- var. ***longipes*** (F)	CCCN XBlo

Psilotum (*Psilotaceae*)

	nudum	ECou

Psoralea (*Papilionaceae*)

*	***fleta***	SPlb

glabra	SPlb
glandulosa	SBrt SPlb WSHC
* ***macrothyrsa***	EBee
oligophylla	SPlb
onobrychis	SPhx
pinnata	CExl

Psychotria (*Rubiaceae*)

capensis	CExl

Ptelea (*Rutaceae*)

trifoliata	CArn CBcs CDul CLnd CMac ELan EPfP MBlu SChF SPer SRms WPGP
- 'Aurea' ♀H5	CAbP CBcs CExl CJun CLnd CMac CTho ELan EPfP EPla GBin LRHS MBlu MBri NLar SPer SSpi WBor WPGP
- 'Fastigiata'	EPfP

Pteracanthus see *Strobilanthes*

Pteridium (*Dennstaedtiaceae*)

aquilinum	XLum

Pteridophyllum (*Papaveraceae*)

racemosum	CTal EFEx WCru

Pteris (*Pteridaceae*)

angustipinna B&SWJ 6738	WCru
cretica ♀H1c	CHEx SArc
- var. ***albolineata*** ♀H1c	CBty LPal LRHS WCot XBlo
- 'Mayi' (v)	CBty LRHS
- 'Ouvradii'	CBty
- 'Parkeri'	LPal LRHS
- 'Rowei'	CBty LPal LRHS XBlo
- 'Wimsettii'	CBty LRHS
ensiformis 'Evergemiensis' (v)	CBty
* ***staminea***	XBlo
tricolor	CBty
wallichiana	CBty CFil CHEx EBee EFtx WPGP

Pterocactus (*Cactaceae*)

hickenii F&W 10240	WCot

Pterocarya ✿ (*Juglandaceae*)

fraxinifolia	CBcs CCVT CLnd CMCN CTho ECrN EPfP GQui IArd IDee MBlu MBri MMuc MRav SEND
macroptera var. ***insignis***	CExl CFil WPGP
× ***rehderiana***	CTho MBlu WMou
stenoptera	CBcs CDTJ CLnd CMCN CTho NLar
- 'Fern Leaf' ♀H6	CExl CFil CHid LRHS MBlu WMou WPGP

Pteroceltis (*Cannabaceae*)

tatarinowii	CBcs

Pterocephalus (*Caprifoliaceae*)

parnassi	see *P. perennis*
§ ***perennis***	CMea ECho MHer NBir NRya SRms WAbe WHoo XSen
pinardii	WAbe XSen
spathulatus new	WAbe

Pterodiscus (*Pedaliaceae*)

aurantiacus	LToo
luridus	LToo
ngamicus	LToo

Pterostylis (*Orchidaceae*)

curta ♀H2	CTal ECho

Pterostyrax (*Styracaceae*)

corymbosa	CBcs CJun CMCN NLar SSpi
hispida ♀H5	CAbP CBcs CDoC CDul CHGN CJun CMCN CTsd EPfP ETwe GBin IDee IVic LRHS MBlu MBri MRav NLar SChF SPoG WFar WHar
psilophyllus	WPGP

Ptilostemon (*Asteraceae*)

§ ***diacantha***	EPfP IFoB LRHS WCot
niveus	WCot

Ptilotrichum see *Alyssum*

Ptilotus (*Amaranthaceae*)

exaltatus	SPlb

Pueraria (*Papilionaceae*)

montana var. ***lobata***	CArn

Pulicaria (*Asteraceae*)

§ ***dysenterica***	CArn CHab LLWG NMir WHer WSFF

Pulmonaria (*Boraginaceae*)

sp.	CUse
angustifolia ♀H7	EPfP GKev GMaP MNrw NOrc SHeu SRms
- 'Azurea'	CElw CHVG CTca EAEE ELan EPPr EPfP EWoo GAbr GMaP IGor LRHS MCot MMuc MRav NBro NLar SEND SRms
- 'Blaues Meer'	EBee ECtt GAbr LBMP LRHS SGbt SHeu
- 'Munstead Blue'	CElw CLAP GBuc MCot MRav NRya SRms
'Apple Frost'	LRHS SGol SHeu WWEG
'Barfield Regalia'	NSti WWEG
'Benediction'	CDes MAvo MNrw NSti WCot
'Beth Chatto'	CElw
'Beth's Pink'	GAbr
'Blake's Silver'	CAby CBre CMea ECha ECtt GAbr LPla MBel MHol NCGa NPCo NSti SMrm SPer SPoG WCot WGrn WPGP WRHF
'Blauer Hügel'	LLHF NSti
'Blauhimmel'	GCra
'Blue Buttons'	CCon ECtt EPla WWEG
'Blue Crown'	CElw EWes
'Blue Ensign' ♀H6	Widely available
'Blue Moon'	see *P. officinalis* 'Blue Mist'
'Blue Pearl'	LRHS
'Blueberry Muffin'	CSpe
'Bubble Gum'PBR	MBri SHeu
Cally hybrid	CLAP GCal
'Cedric Morris'	CElw
'Chintz'	MAvo
'Coral Springs'	GBuc LLHF NLar
'Cotton Cool'	CBod CLAP CTca EAEE EBee ECha ECtt EPla EWoo GBin GBuc LRHS MAvo MBNS MBel MCot MRav MSpe NEgg NHol NOrc NSti NWad SGbt SHeu SPer WMoo WSHC WWtn
'Crawshay Chance'	CElw SMHy

	Name	Suppliers
	'Dark Vader'	ECtt GBin MNrw SHeu
	'Darkling Thrush' **new**	CDes
	'Diana Clare' 🏆H6	Widely available
	'Elworthy Rubies'	CDes CElw
	'Excalibur'	ECtt NLar SHeu
	'Fiona'	WWEG
	'Glacier'	CTca EPfP MNrw WCot WWEG
	'Hazel Kaye's Red'	LLWP
	'High Contrast'	ECtt SHeu
	'Highdown'	see *P.* 'Lewis Palmer'
	'Ice Ballet' (Classic Series)	CLAP EBee ECtt EPfP SCob SHeu WCAu
§	'Lewis Palmer' 🏆H7	CBro CSam CTca GCal GMaP LRHS MNrw NBir SRGP SRms WHea WHoo WWEG
	'Little Star'	CElw EBee ECha ECtt GBuc LRHS MAvo SHeu SRGP WFar WWEG
	longifolia	CBod EAEE ECha EHoe ELan EPfP EPla GAbr GBin GKev MWat NBir NLar NOrc NSti
§	- 'Ankum'	CElw CLAP EPla NBir WCot WSHC WWEG
	- 'Bertram Anderson'	CTca EBee ECtt GMaP IBoy LRHS NBir NLar SCob SHeu SPer SRGP SRms SWvt WMnd WWEG
	- subsp. ***cevennensis***	CLAP LRHS NLar NSti SHeu WFar WWEG
	- 'Coen Jansen'	see *P. longifolia* 'Ankum'
	- 'Dordogne'	CLAP EBee NBir NLar
	- 'Howard Eggins'	WWEG
	'Mado'	ECha WWEG
	'Majesté'	CLAP EBee ECha ELan EPfP EWes GBuc GMaP IFro LRHS MBel MBri MRav NBir NLar NOrc NSti SCob SHeu SMad SPer SPoG WCot WMnd WWEG
	'Margery Fish'	CLAP CSam EPfP LRHS SHeu WMnd
	'Mary Mottram'	CElw ECtt NBir NSti SHeu WCot WMnd
	'Mawson's Blue' 🏆H6	CLAP EWes NBir NChi SWvt WMoo WSHC
	'Merlin'	CLAP SKHP
	'Milky Way'	ECtt SHeu
	mollis	GCal IMou MNrw NSti WCAu
	- 'Royal Blue'	MRav
	'Monksilver'	CElw
	'Moonshine'[PBR]	ECtt SHeu
	'Moonstone'	CElw
	'Mrs Kittle'	CCon CElw CSam GQue IMou LRHS MBel MRav NBir NHol NSti SHeu WCAu WMnd WWEG
	'Netta Statham'	EBee NSti
	'Nürnberg'	CElw WWEG
	officinalis	CArn CHby IFoB MLHP NChi SIde WBrk
§	- 'Blue Mist'	CLAP ELan GMaP NBir WCot WHoo WMnd WMoo
	- 'Bowles's Blue'	see *P. officinalis* 'Blue Mist'
	- Cambridge Blue Group	EPfP MRav MWat NBir WCAu WCot WWtn
	- 'Stillingfleet Gran'	LLHF
	- 'White Wings'	CLAP EBee NLar
	'Oliver Wyatt's White'	CLAP SRGP
	Opal = 'Ocupol'	Widely available
	'Pierre's Pure Pink' **new**	SHeu
	'Pink Haze'[PBR]	EBee ECtt GEdr ITim LPla LRHS MHol MPie NLar NSti SCob SPoG SWvt WRHF
	'Raspberry Splash'[PBR]	CLAP CWCL ECtt GBin LRHS MMuc NLar SCob SEND SGol SHeu SIde SMrm SPoG
	'Roy Davidson'	CLAP CSam CTca ECtt EPfP IGor LRHS MCot NBir NHol NSti SRms SWvt WCAu WGwG WWEG
	rubra	CBcs CElw CPom ECha ELan EPPr GAbr LBMP LLWP MLHP MMuc MNrw NBid NOrc NSti SEND SHeu SRms WHea
	- var. ***alba***	see *P. rubra* var. *albocorollata*
§	- var. ***albocorollata***	CBre CElw EBtc GAbr GBin NBid WWEG
	- 'Barfield Pink'	ELan GCal IFro MWat NBir NLar SHeu
	- 'Bowles's Red'	CBod CHel CNec IFoB LRHS MNrw MRav NBir NGdn NLar SPer WCAu WFar WGwG WHoo WMnd WWtn
	- 'David Ward' (v)	CCon CPla ECha ECtt ELan GCra GMaP LRHS MPnt MRav MSCN NBir NLar NSti SHeu SPer WCFE WCot WMnd WSHC WWEG
	- 'Rachel Vernie' (v)	CElw CLAP CPou MAvo WWEG
	- 'Redstart'	CBod CSBt CSam CTca ECtt EWoo GKev IGor LEdu LLWP LRHS LSun MNrw MRav NBir NGdn NLar SGol SHeu SRms SWvt WFar WMnd WMoo WWEG
§	***saccharata***	ECha ELan GMaP IFro MMuc SRms
	- 'Alba'	CElw IFro MMuc SEND SRms
	- Argentea Group 🏆H7	CTri ELan EPfP GMaP LRHS MMuc MRav NGdn SEND WBrk WWEG
	- 'Dora Bielefeld'	CBod CLAP COtt ECha EPPr EPfP GBuc GMaP LLWP LRHS MNrw MRav NBir NChi NGdn NHol NOrc NSoo SHeu SRGP SWvt WCAu WHoo
	- 'Frühlingshimmel'	CElw LRHS MNrw MRav NSti
	- 'Glebe Cottage Blue'	CElw
	- 'Leopard'	CLAP CMea CSam CTca CWCL ECha ECtt GBin GBuc GMaP LRHS MBel NBir NLar NSti SBod SHeu WCAu WCot WHoo WWEG
	- 'Mrs Moon'	CBod CNec COtt CTri ECtt ELon EPfP GMaP IKil LRHS NLar NOrc SGol SHeu SPer SWvt WCAu WMnd WWEG
	- 'Old Rectory Silver'	NBir
	- 'Picta'	see *P. saccharata*
	- 'Pink Dawn'	CMHG
	- 'Reginald Kaye'	ECha EWes
	- 'Silverado'[PBR]	ECtt LRHS MBri NOrc SHeu
	- 'Stanhoe'	EWes
	'Saint Ann's'	EBee LLHF LRHS NSti
	'Samurai'	GBin LRHS MAvo MBri NSti SHeu WFar
	'Silver Bouquet'[PBR]	CElw ECtt GBin LSou SHeu
	'Silver Lance'	SHeu
	'Silver Sabre'	IBlr
	'Silver Shimmers'[PBR]	SHeu
	'Silver Surprise'	WCot
	'Sissinghurst White' 🏆H7	Widely available
	'Smoky Blue'	CLAP ECtt MRav SCob SHeu SWat WWEG
	'Spilled Milk'	NLar SHeu
	'Stillingfleet Meg'	CHel CLAP EAEE ECtt EPfP EPla LRHS MBNS NLar NSti NWad SHeu SRGP WGwG WWtn

	'Trevi Fountain'	CHid CLAP CWCL EBee ECha ECtt EShb GBin GJos LRHS NPri SHar SHeu SIde SPoG WCot WFar
	'Victorian Brooch'[PBR]	CLAP CSam CWCL ECtt GBin GKev IBoy LRHS LSou MNrw NPri SHeu SIde SMrm SPad SPoG WWEG
	'Weetwood Blue'	CBre CLAP CTca EBee MNrw

Pulsatilla (*Ranunculaceae*)

	alba	CBro SBod
	albana	CBro ECho GKev LLHF LRHS
	- 'Lutea'	EBee LLHF
	alpina	ECho NGdn SRms
§	- subsp. ***apiifolia*** ♀H5	EBee IFro
	- subsp. ***sulphurea*** misapplied	see *P. alpina* subsp. *apiifolia*
	ambigua	CPBP EPot GKev LLHF
	'Blue Select' (Pr/Prim) new	IBoy
	campanella	GEdr LLHF
	caucasica	CBro ECho LRHS
	georgica	EPot GEdr
	halleri ♀H5	CHel EBee ECho GKev
	- subsp. ***rhodopaea***	WAbe
	- subsp. ***slavica*** ♀H5	EPot LLHF
	- subsp. ***taurica***	GEdr
	lutea	see *P. alpina* subsp. *apiifolia*
	montana	SPlb
	occidentalis	GEdr
§	***patens***	EDAr LLHF NGdn WIce
	pratensis	GPoy SRms
	- subsp. ***nigricans***	GEdr GKev SBrt
I	- 'Semiplena'	MMoz
	red-flowered	CHel
	rubra	GKev NGdn SPad SRot
*	***serotina***	EBee GKev
	turczaninovii	GKev LPla
*	***turkestanica*** new	GEdr
§	***vernalis*** ♀H5	GEdr NLar NSla WAbe XEll
	violacea	CBcs GKev
§	***vulgaris*** ♀H5	Widely available
	- 'Alba'	Widely available
	- 'Barton's Pink'	CBro ECho EPot LLHF LRHS SRot
	- 'Blaue Glocke'	CAby CBod GEdr LRHS NPri SHar SMrm SWvt XSen
	- 'Eva Constance'	CBro ECho LLHF LRHS WAbe
	- 'Gotlandica'	LLHF
	- subsp. ***grandis***	GEdr LRHS NSla
	- - 'Budapest Seedling'	GEdr
	- - 'Papageno'	CBod CSpe EAEE ECho GCrg LBMP LRHS MAvo MBel MHol NCGa NHol NLar NSla SMrm WGwG WHil WIce
	- Heiler hybrids	CBod CPrp EAEE EPla LLHF MRav NCGa NDov NEgg NGdn NSla SVic
	- 'Perlen Glocke'	EBee EDAr GEdr LRHS MHer
	- pink-flowered	CHel CMea LLHF NSla WFar
	- Red Clock	see *P. vulgaris* 'Röde Klokke'
	- red-flowered	CTsd EBee IBoy SCob SGbt WFar
§	- 'Röde Klokke'	CAby CBod ECtt EPot EWoo GEdr LRHS LSun MCot MNrw MWat MWhi NPri NWad SHar SHil SMrm SWvt WCot WHil XLum XSen
	- Rote Glocke	see *P. vulgaris* 'Röde Klokke'
	- var. ***rubra***	CHel CMea CNec ECho ELan EPPr EPfP GMaP LRHS MBri MHer MNHC MRav NBir NLar SPer SPoG SRms SRot WHoo WIce
	- violet blue-flowered	LRHS MWat SHil
§	- 'Weisse Schwan'	EBee EPfP GEdr GMaP SRot
	- 'White Bells'	GEdr NHol
	- White Swan	see *P. vulgaris* 'Weisse Schwan'

Pultenaea (*Papilionaceae*)

daphnoides	SVen
juniperina	SPlb SVen

pummelo see *Citrus maxima*

Punica (*Lythraceae*)

	granatum	CArn CBcs CBod CHEx CHel CMen CTsd ELan EPfP IDee LPal MOWG SCob SEND SPre SVic SWvt WJek WSHC
	- 'Chico' (d)	CBcs SEND
	- 'Fina Tendral' (F)	CCCN
	- 'Legrelleae' (F/d)	SEND WPat
	- 'Maxima Rubra' (d)	EShb XSen
	- var. ***nana*** ♀H3	CAgr CCCN CMen EBee EBtc EOHP EPfP EShb LEdu LRHS MHer SMrm SRms SVen SVic WPat
	- f. ***plena*** (d)	CBcs LRHS MRav WCFE WPat
	- - 'Flore Pleno Luteo' (d)	LRHS
	- 'Provence' (F)	EPom XSen
*	- 'Striata'	MOWG
	- 'Wonderful' (F)	CAgr

Puschkinia (*Asparagaceae*)

scilloides	ECho NBir
- 'Aragat's Gem'	ECho
- var. ***libanotica*** ♀H5	ECho EPfP EPot ERCP GKev LAma LEdu LRHS MPie SBod SDeJ SEND SPer WShi
- - 'Alba'	ECho EPot GKev LAma SDeJ SPer

Puya (*Bromeliaceae*)

RH 1809	WCot
RH 2910A	WCot
RH 2961C	WCot
RH 3425B new	WCot
alpestris	CCCN CFil EShb SArc SBig SPlb WCot WPGP
assurgens	WCot
berteroana	CAbb CBcs CCCN CDTJ CDoC CHEx EShb EUJe SPlb WCot
boliviensis	WCot
castellanosii	NLos WCot
chilensis	CAbb CBcs CCCN CDTJ CDoC CHEx LRHS NLos SArc SPlb WCot
coerulea	CCCN CCon CDTJ CTsd MGil NLos SEND SPlb
- var. ***monteroana***	WCot
dyckioides	WCot
- red-bracted	WCot
ferruginea	EUJe NLos SPlb WCot
gilmartiniae F&W 8697	WCot
harmsii new	NLos WCot
laxa	EUJe WCot
mirabilis	CDTJ ESwi GBin LAir NLos
raimondii	WCot WPGP
venusta	CCCN CDTJ NLos SPlb WCot
yakespala	WCot

Pycnanthemum (*Lamiaceae*)

incanum new	SPhx
montanum	GBin
muticum	CArn LEdu LPla
pilosum	CArn ELau MHer MNHC XLum

tenuifolium	NLar SBrt
virginianum	GCal SPhx

Pycnostachys (*Lamiaceae*)

urticifolia	EOHP EWes SDys

Pygmea see *Chionohebe*

Pyracantha (*Rosaceae*)

Alexander Pendula = 'Renolex'	MRav MSwo SRms
angustifolia	WCFE
§ ***atalantioides***	SPlb WCFE
'Brilliant'	SCoo
coccinea 'Lalandei'	CMac
- 'Red Column'	Widely available
- 'Red Cushion'	MJak MRav SCob SRms
crenulata	WCFE
Dart's Red = 'Interrada'	COtt CSBt SLim WHar
'Fiery Cascade'	LRHS SHil SPoG
gibbsii	see *P. atalantioides*
'Golden Charmer'	CMac COtt EPfP IBoy LRHS MBri MGos MSwo NEgg NLar NWea SCob SCoo SGol SPer SPoG SRms SWvt WFar
'Golden Glow'	SLim
'Golden Sun'	see *P.* 'Soleil d'Or'
'Harlequin' (v)	SCob SGol WFar
'Knap Hill Lemon'	MBlu
koidzumii 'Victory'	ECrN
'Mohave'	CMac CTri ECrN ELan ELon IBoy LRHS MAsh MWat SCob SCoo SGol SLim SRms SWvt
'Mohave Silver' (v)	CMac CWSG ELan EShb LBMP LRHS MAsh NHol
'Molten Lava' ♀H6	SMad
'Navaho'	SEWo
'Orange Charmer'	CDul CMac CTri ELan LRHS MBri MGos MWat NHol NLar NWea SCob SPer SPlb WFar WHar WMoo
'Orange Glow' ♀H6	Widely available
'Red Charmer'	NHol
rogersiana	CDul MRav
- 'Flava' ♀H6	CDul CSBt EPfP LRHS MAsh NEgg SPoG SWvt
'Rosedale'	LRHS WHar
Saphyr Jaune = 'Cadaune'PBR	CBcs CCVT CDoC CEnd CSBt CWSG EBee ECrN EPfP EPla LRHS MGos MRav NHol NLar NPri SCob SCoo SGol SPer WHar
Saphyr Orange = 'Cadange'PBR ♀H6	CBcs CCVT CDoC CEnd CMac CSBt CWSG EBee EPfP LRHS MBri MGos MRav NEgg NLar NPri SCob SCoo SGol SPer WHar
Saphyr Rouge = 'Cadrou'PBR ♀H6	CBcs CCVT CChe CDoC CEnd CMac CSBt CWSG EBee ELan EPfP EPla LRHS MBri MGos MMuc MRav NLar NPri SCob SCoo SEND SGol SPer SWvt WFar WHar
'Shawnee'	CMac MSwo MWat
§ 'Soleil d'Or'	CBod CTri ECrN ELan EPfP IBoy LAst LBuc LRHS MAsh MBri MJak MMuc MRav NHed NLar SCob SEND SEWo SGol SHil SLim SLon SPer SPlb SWvt WFar WHar WMoo
'Sparkler' (v)	CMac EHoe SCob
'Teton' ♀H6	CMac COtt ELan EPfP LAst LRHS MAsh MBri MJak MSwo NWea SCob SGol SHil SRms WFar
'Ventoux Red'	SCoo
'Watereri'	NWea
'Yellow Sun'	see *P.* 'Soleil d'Or'

Pyrethropsis see *Rhodanthemum*

Pyrethrum see *Tanacetum*

Pyrola (*Ericaceae*)

rotundifolia	LEdu WHer

Pyrostegia (*Bignoniaceae*)

venusta	MOWG

Pyrrocoma (*Asteraceae*)

clementis	EBee

Pyrrosia (*Polypodiaceae*)

caudifrons	WCot
hastata	CMen
linearifolia 'Urakoryu Jishi'	CMen
lingua	CMen WPGP
polydactyla	CMen
sheareri	CBty ISha

Pyrus ✿ (*Rosaceae*)

amygdaliformis	CMCN WCot
- var. ***cuneifolia***	CLnd SCoo
calleryana 'Chanticleer'	Widely available
- 'Chanticleer' variegated (v)	CDul MAsh
- 'Redspire'	CCVT
communis (F)	CAco CCVT CDul CTri ECrN LBuc NWea SPer SPlb WMou
- 'Abbé Fétel' (D)	SKee
- 'Bambinella' (D)	SKee
- 'Barland' (Perry)	CHab
- 'Barnet' (Perry)	CHab
- 'Baronne de Mello' (D)	CTho SFam SKee
- 'Beech Hill' (F)	CDul EBee ECrN EPla SGol SPer
- 'Belle Guérandaise' (D)	SKee
- 'Belle Julie' (D)	SKee
- 'Bellissime d'Hiver' (C)	SKee
- 'Bergamotte d'Automne' (D)	SKee
- 'Bergamotte Esperen' (D)	SKee
- 'Beth' (D) ♀H6	CAgr CDoC CHab CMac CSBt CTri EBee ECrN EPfP EPom GTwe IArd LAst LBuc LRHS MAsh MBri MGos NLar NOra SDea SFam SFrt SKee SLim SPer WHar
- 'Beurré Alexandre Lucas' (D)	SKee
- 'Beurré Bedford' (D)	SKee
- 'Beurré Clairgeau' (C)	SKee
- 'Beurré d'Amanlis' (D)	SKee
- 'Beurré d'Anjou' (F)	SKee
- 'Beurré d'Avalon' (D)	SKee
- 'Beurré de Beugny' (D)	SKee
- 'Beurré de Naghin' (C/D)	SKee
- 'Beurré Diel' (D)	SKee
- 'Beurré Dumont' (D)	CAgr SFam
- 'Beurré Giffard' (D)	CAgr
- 'Beurré Gris d'Hiver' (D)	SKee
- 'Beurré Hardy' (D) ♀H6	Widely available
- 'Beurré Mortillet' (D)	SKee
§ - 'Beurré Precoce Morettini' (D)	SDea
- 'Beurré Six' (D)	SKee

- 'Beurré Superfin' (D) ♀H6 GTwe SFam SKee WHar
- 'Bianchettone' (D) SKee
- 'Bishop's Thumb' (D) SDea SKee
- 'Black Worcester' (C) CDul CHab GTwe LRHS MAsh NOra SDea SFam SKee WHar WJas
- 'Blakeney Red' (Perry) CCAT CHab NOra SDea SKee WHar
- 'Blickling' (D) SKee
- 'Bon Chrétien d'Hiver' (D) SKee
- 'Brandy' (Perry) CAgr CCAT CHab CTho NOra SDea SFrt SKee SVic WHar
- 'Bristol Cross' (D) CAgr CHab SKee
- 'Butt' (Perry) CHab
- 'Calebasse Bosc' (D) NOra SKee
- 'Canal Red' (F) SKee
- 'Cannock' (F) SKee
- 'Catillac' (C) ♀H6 CAgr CHab ECrN GTwe SFam SKee WHar
- 'Chalk' see *P. communis* 'Crawford'
- 'Chaumontel' (D) SKee
- 'Clapp's Favourite' (D) CHab CTho ECrN ELan NOra SKee SVic
- 'Concorde'PBR (D) ♀H6 Widely available
- 'Conference' (D) ♀H6 Widely available
- 'Craig's Favourite' (D) GTwd
- § 'Crawford' (D) GTwd
- 'Deacon's Pear' (D) SDea
- Delbardélice = 'Delété' (F) LRHS
- 'Devoe' (D) SDea
- 'Docteur Jules Guyot' (D) CAgr SDea SKee
- 'Double de Guerre' (C/D) SKee
- 'Doyenné Blanc' (F) SKee
- 'Doyenné Boussoch' (D) SKee
- 'Doyenné d'Été' (D) ERea MCoo SFam SKee
- 'Doyenné du Comice' (D) ♀H6 Widely available
- 'Doyenné Georges Boucher' (D) SKee
- 'Duchesse d'Angoulême' (D) SKee
- 'Durondeau' (D) ERea GTwe NOra SDea SFam SKee
- 'Easter Beurré' (D) SKee
- 'Emile d'Heyst' (D) GQue GTwe MCoo SKee WHar
- 'Fair Maid' (D) GTwd
- 'Fertility' (D) CLnd SFrt
- 'Fertility Improved' see *P. communis* 'Improved Fertility'
- 'Fondante d'Automne' (D) CAgr CTho LRHS SKee WHar
- 'Forelle' (D) ERea SKee
- 'Gin' (Perry) CHab
- 'Glou Morceau' (D) CAgr ECrN ERea GTwe LRHS MCoo MWat SDea SFam SFrt SKee WHar
- 'Glow Red Williams' (D) SFam
- 'Gorham' (D) ♀H6 CAgr CDul CTho GTwe LRHS SFam SKee WHar
- 'Green Horse' (Perry) CCAT CHab SKee
- 'Green Pear of Yair' (D) SKee
- 'Hacon's Imcomparable' (D) SKee
- 'Harley Gum' (F) WHar
- 'Harrow Delight' (D) SDea
- 'Harvest Queen' (D/C) CAgr SDea
- 'Hellen's Early' (Perry) CHab ERea SKee WHar
- 'Hendre Huffcap' (Perry) CAgr CCAT CHab CTho NOra SFrt SKee WHar
- 'Hessle' (D) CAgr CHab GTwe NWea SDea SFam SKee
- 'Highland' (D) SKee
- Humbug = 'Pysanka' (F) EPom GQue LBuc LRHS MBri NOra WHar
- § 'Improved Fertility' (D) CAgr ERea SDea
- Invincible = 'Delwinor' (D/C) CAgr CDul CSut CTho EPom LBuc LRHS MAsh MBri MCoo MNHC NLar NOra SLim WHar
- 'Jargonelle' (D) CAgr CDul CHab CTho GTwe SDea SFam SKee WHar
- 'Jeribasma' (F) SKee
- 'Joséphine de Malines' (D) ♀H6 CAgr ERea GTwe IArd NOra SDea SFam SKee WHar
- 'Judge Amphlett' (Perry) CTho SKee WHar
- 'Kieffer' (C) CAgr
- 'Laxton's Foremost' (D) CAgr SKee
- 'Laxton's Satisfaction' (D) SFam
- 'Légipont' (F) CAgr
- Löffelbirne (F) CSut
- 'Louise Bonne of Jersey' (D) ♀H6 CAgr CMac CTri ECrN EPom ERea GTwe IArd LAst LRHS MGos NOra SDea SFam SKee WHar
- 'Marguérite Marillat' (D) SDea SKee
- 'Marie-Louise' (D) SKee WHar
- 'Merrylegs' (Perry) CHab
- 'Merton Pride' (D) CAgr CLnd CTho GTwe IArd LRHS MCoo MWat NOra SDea SFam SKee WHar
- 'Merton Star' (D) SKee
- 'Moonglow' CAgr ERea LRHS NOra SDea SKee
- 'Moorcroft' (Perry) SKee
- 'Morettini' see *P. communis* 'Beurré Precoce Morettini'
- 'Nouveau Poiteau' (C/D) CAgr ECrN SKee
- 'Nuvar Celebration' (F) SKee
- 'Nye Russet Bartlett' (F) CAgr
- 'Oldfield' (Perry) CHab
- 'Olivier de Serres' (D) SKee
- 'Onward' (D) ♀H6 CAgr CDul CHab CLnd CTho CTri ECrN EPom ERea GTwe IArd LRHS MAsh MBri NLar NOra NWea SDea SFam SKee WHar
- 'Ovid' (D) CAgr
- § 'Packham's Triumph' (D) CAgr CDoC CTri ECrN GTwe LAst SDea SKee SVic WHar
- 'Parsonage' (Perry) CHab
- 'Passe Crassane' (D) SKee
- 'Pear Apple' (D) CHab SDea
- 'Penrhyn' (D) WGwG
- 'Pero Nobile' (D) SKee
- I 'Petite Poire' (F) CSut EPom
- 'Pitmaston Duchess' (C/D) ♀H6 ECrN GTwe MCoo SDea SFam SKee WHar
- 'Précoce de Trévoux' (D) SKee WHar
- 'Président Barabé' (F) SKee
- 'Red Comice' (D/C) GTwe SKee
- 'Red Pear' (Perry) CHab
- 'Red Sensation Bartlett' (D/C) EPom GTwe LBuc LRHS NOra SKee
- 'Robin' (C/D) ERea SDea SKee
- 'Santa Claus' (D) SDea SFam SKee
- 'Seckel' (D) NOra SFam SKee
- 'Shipova' (F) CAgr MAsh WHar
- 'Sierra' (D) CAgr
- 'Snowdon Queen' (D) CHab WGwG
- 'Souvenir du Congrès' (D) CAgr
- 'Swan's Egg' (D) SKee
- 'Terrace Pearl' (D) SPoG
- 'Tettenhall Dick' (C/D) WHar
- 'Thompson's' (D) SFam
- 'Thorn' (Perry) CAgr CCAT CHab SKee WHar
- 'Triomphe de Vienne' (D) SFam
- 'Triumph' see *P. communis* 'Packham's Triumph'

- 'Uvedale's St Germain' (C)	SFam SKee
- 'Verbelu' (F)	SKee
- 'Verdi' (F)	EPom
- 'Vicar of Winkfield' (C)	ECrN GTwe SDea SKee
- 'Williams' Bon Chrétien' (D/C) 🏆H6	Widely available
- 'Williams' Red' (D/C)	GTwe SKee
- 'Williams' Rouge Delbard' (F)	EPom
- 'Winnal's Longdon' (Perry)	WHar
- 'Winter Nelis' (D)	CAgr CHab CTri ECrN GTwe LAst LRHS NOra SDea SFam SKee WHar
cordata	CDul CTho
elaeagnifolia	MAsh
- var. ***kotschyana***	CDul SLim
- 'Silver Sails'	CLnd EBee EMil MBri SCoo SSpi
fauriei	CTho
× ***michauxii*** new	SVen
nivalis	CDul CTho EBee ECrN EPfP EPla LBuc LEdu MBri SCoo SPer
- 'Catalia'	MAsh MBri SCoo
pashia	CMCN EBee LEdu NLar
pyraster	CDul CHab WCot
pyrifolia	MBri
- '20th Century'	see *P. pyrifolia* 'Nijisseiki'
- 'Chojuro' (F)	LEdu
- 'Hosui' (F)	CAgr LEdu SVic
- 'Kosui' (F)	SVic
- 'Kumoi' (F)	EPom ERea LRHS MAsh MCoo SDea SKee WHar
§ - 'Nijisseiki' (F)	CDul SVic
- 'Shinko' (F)	CAgr LEdu
- 'Shinseiki' (F)	CAgr CLnd ERea MAsh SDea SKee WHar
- 'Shinsui' (F)	SDea SKee
* ***salicifolia*** var. ***orientalis***	CAco CTho
- 'Pendula' 🏆H6	Widely available
ussuriensis	CTho

Q

Qiongzhuea see *Chimonobambusa*

Quercus ✿ (*Fagaceae*)

NJM 09.181	WPGP
acerifolia	EPfP
acherdophylla	SBir WPGP
§ ***acuta***	CMCN
acutifolia	SBir
acutifolia × ***mexicana***	SBir
acutissima	CAco CBcs CDul CMCN EPfP NLar SBir SGol
aegilops	see *Q. ithaburensis* subsp. *macrolepis*
affinis 🏆H5	EPfP SBir
agrifolia	CDul CMCN EBtc
alba	CDul CMCN
aliena	CDul CMCN
- PAB 8972 new	LEdu
alnifolia	CDul
arkansana	SBir
× ***atlantica***	SBir
austrina	CMCN SBir
× ***beadlei***	see *Q.* × *saulii*
× ***benderi***	SBir
berberidifolia	CMCN SBir
bicolor	CAco CDul CMCN EPfP MBlu
× ***bimundorum***	SBir
§ - 'Crimschmidt'	CDul CLnd EPfP MBlu MBri SBir SGol
borealis	see *Q. rubra*
breweri	see *Q. garryana* var. *breweri*
buckleyi	CMCN SBir
× ***bushii***	CMCN EPfP MBlu MBri SBir WPat
- 'Seattle Trident'	EPfP MBlu MBri
canariensis 🏆H5	CDul CLnd CMCN CTho EPfP SGol WPGP
candicans	SBir
× ***capesii***	SBir
castanea	WPGP
castaneifolia	CDul CMCN
- 'Green Spire' 🏆H6	CDul CLnd CMCN EBee EPfP IArd MBlu MBri MMuc SEND
cerris	CBcs CCVT CDoC CDul CLnd CMCN EBee ECrN EPfP EPla MGos MMuc NWea SCob SEND SGol SPer
- 'Afyon Lace'	MBlu SBir
§ - 'Argenteovariegata' (v)	CEnd CMCN EBee ELan EPfP EPla IArd MAsh MBlu MBri SBir SEND SMad WPat
- 'Athena'	MBlu
- 'Curly Head'PBR	SMad
- 'Marmor Star'	SEND
- 'Variegata'	see *Q. cerris* 'Argenteovariegata'
- 'Wodan'	MBlu
chenii	CDul CMCN SBir
chrysolepis	CBcs CMCN EPfP SBir
coccifera	CAco CMCN SGol SVen WCot WPGP
coccinea	CAco CBcs CDul CLnd CMCN CTho CTri EPfP MBlu MWht NEgg NPCo NWea SBir SEWo SPer WPat
- 'Splendens' 🏆H6	CDoC CDul CEnd CHll CJun CMCN CTri EBee ELan EPfP IArd MAsh MBlu MBri NLar SGol SMad SPer WPat
conspersa	SBir
crassifolia	WPGP WPat
crassipes	SBir
Crimson Spire	see *Q.* × *bimundorum* 'Crimschmidt'
crispipilis	SBir
dalechampii	CMCN SBir
dentata	CDul CMCN
- 'Carl Ferris Miller'	CBcs CDul CLnd CMCN EPfP LLHF MBlu MBri MMuc SBig SBir WPGP WPat
- 'Pinnatifida'	CMCN EPfP IDee LLHF MBlu MPkF NLar WCot WPat
- 'Sir Harold Hillier'	MBlu MBri
- subsp. ***yunnanensis***	SBir
dolicholepis	CMCN SBir
'Doring's Zweizack'	SBir
douglasii	CMCN SSpi
dumosa	CMCN
- G 315	WPGP
× ***dysophylla***	CFil WPGP
ellipsoidalis	CMCN SBir SGol
- 'Hemelrijk' 🏆H6	CMCN EPfP MBlu MBri SBir WPGP WPat
emoryi	SBir
× ***exacta***	SBir
fabrei	CMCN SBir
faginea	CDul CMCN WPGP
- subsp. ***broteroi***	CMCN

	Name	Suppliers
	falcata	CMCN EBtc SBir
	- var. ***pagodifolia***	see *Q. pagoda*
	× ***fernaldii***	CMCN EPfP MBlu
	frainetto	CAco CDul CMCN CTho EBee ECrN EPfP EPla NWea SGol SPer WMou
	- 'Hungarian Crown' 🏆H6	CMCN EPfP MBlu MMuc SBir
	- 'Tortworth'	SMad WMou
	- 'Trump'	CDul CMCN MBri
	franchetii	SBir
	fruticosa	see *Q. lusitanica* Lam.
	fusiformis new	SBir
	gambelii	CAco CBcs CMCN EBtc MPkF
	garryana	CBcs CMCN EPfP WPGP
§	- var. ***breweri***	CMCN
	- var. ***fruticosa***	see *Q. garryana* var. *breweri*
	georgiana	CDul CMCN EPfP SBir
	germana new	CFil
	gilva	CMCN SBir
	glabra	see *Lithocarpus glaber*
	glabrescens	WPGP
	glandulifera	see *Q. serrata* Thunb.
	glauca	CBcs CDul CMCN EPfP NLar SArc SBir
	graciliformis	SBir
	gravesii	CMCN EPfP SBir
	greggii	WPGP
	× ***hastingsii***	CMCN SBir
	× ***hawkinsiae***	SBir
	× ***haynaldiana***	SBir
	hemisphaerica	CMCN EPfP SBir
	× ***heterophylla***	CLnd CMCN EPfP SBir
	× ***hickelii***	CMCN EPfP SBir
	hirtifolia	WPGP
§	× ***hispanica***	EUJe
	- 'Ambrozyana'	CDul CMCN NLar
	- 'Bloemendaal'	MBri
	- 'Diversifolia'	CDul CMCN EPfP MBlu
	- 'Fulhamensis'	CDul CMCN MBlu MMuc SBir SEND WMou
§	- 'Lucombeana' 🏆H6	CBcs CDul CHGN CMCN CSBt CTho EBee ELan EPfP EPla IDee MBlu MMuc SBir SEND SPer
	- 'Suberosa'	CTho
	- 'Waasland Select'	IArd MBri NLar WMou
	- 'Wageningen'	CDul CMCN MBri SBir
	aff. × ***hispanica*** new	EPla
	hypoleucoides	CMCN EPfP SBir
	ilex	Widely available
	- 'Fordii'	SBir
	ilicifolia	CMCN EPfP SBir WPGP
	imbricaria	CAco CBcs CDul CLnd CMCN EPfP SBir WPat
	incana Roxb.	see *Q. leucotrichophora*
	infectoria	SBir
§	***ithaburensis***	CMCN LEdu SBir
	subsp. ***macrolepis***	
	- - 'Hemelrijk Silver'	EPfP MBlu SBir WPat
	× ***jackiana***	SBir
	john-tuckeri G 271	WPGP
	kelloggii	CBcs CDul CLnd CMCN EPfP WPGP
	× ***kewensis*** 🏆H6	CMCN MMuc SBir WMou
	laevigata	see *Q. acuta*
	laevis	CDul CMCN EPfP SBir
	'Langtry'	SBir
§	***laurifolia***	CDul CLnd CMCN EPfP SBir
	laurina	SBir WPGP
§	***leucotrichophora***	CMCN LEdu SBir WPGP
	liaotungensis	see *Q. wutaishanica*
	× ***libanerris***	SBir
	- 'Rotterdam'	CMCN SBir
	libani	CDul CMCN EPfP
	lobata	CMCN LEdu
	× ***lucombeana***	see *Q.* × *hispanica*
	- 'William Lucombe'	see *Q.* × *hispanica* 'Lucombeana'
	× ***ludoviciana***	CDul EPfP SBir
§	***lusitanica*** Lam.	SBir
	lyrata	CDul CMCN SGol
	- 'Arnold' new	MBlu
	macranthera	CDul CMCN EPfP
	macrocarpa	CAco CDul CMCN EPfP
	macrolepis	see *Q. ithaburensis* subsp. *macrolepis*
	marilandica	CDul CMCN EPfP IDee MBlu MBri SBir
	mexicana	CMCN IArd SBir WPGP
§	***michauxii***	CBcs CDul CMCN EPfP MBlu
	mohriana new	SBir
	mongolica	CBcs MBlu SBig
	- subsp. ***crispula***	CMCN
	muhlenbergii	CAco CMCN MBlu MPkF SBir
	- 'Dallas' new	EPfP
	× ***mutabilis***	SBir
	myrtifolia	SBir
	nigra	CDul CMCN EGFP SBir
	- 'Beethoven'	MBlu SBir
I	- 'Nyewoodii'	SBir
	nuttallii	see *Q. texana*
	obtusa	see *Q. laurifolia*
	oglethorpensis	SBir
	oxyodon	SBir
	pacifica G 301	WPGP
	- G 305	WPGP
	- G 313	WPGP
§	***pagoda***	CAco CMCN EGFP IGor SBir
	palustris 🏆H6	CAco CCVT CDoC CDul CLnd CMCN CTho EBee ELan EPfP EPla EWTr MAsh MBlu MMuc NEgg NLar NWea SBir SCob SEWo SGol SPer WMou
	- 'Flaming Suzy' new	MBlu
	- 'Green Dwarf'	CMCN MBlu NLar SEWo SLim
	- Green Pillar = 'Pringreen'	MBlu MBri NLar SEWo SGol
	- 'Isabel'	EPfP MBri NLar WHor
	- 'Pendula'	CEnd CMCN
	- 'Silhouette'	CJun SBir
	- 'Swamp Pygmy'	CMCN EPfP EUJe MBlu
	- 'Windischleuba'	MBlu
	pannosa	SBir
	parvula var. ***parvula***	SBir
§	× ***pauciloba***	CMCN
	pedunculata	see *Q. robur*
	pedunculiflora	see *Q. robur* subsp. *pedunculiflora*
§	***petraea***	CAco CDoC CDul CHab CLnd CTri ECrN EPfP GAbr MBlu NLar NWea SCob SGol WMou
	- 'Acutiloba'	SBir
	- 'Laciniata'	see *Q. petraea* 'Laciniata Crispa'
§	- 'Laciniata Crispa'	CDul CEnd CMCN EPfP MBlu
	- Mespilifolia Group	CDul
§	- 'Purpurea'	CMCN MBlu NLar
	- 'Rubicunda'	see *Q. petraea* 'Purpurea'
§	***phellos***	CAco CDul CMCN EBee EBtc EPfP EPla MBlu MBri NLar SBir
	phillyreoides	CBcs CDul CMCN EPfP
	polymorpha	CDul CMCN EGFP MPkF SBir
	Pondaim Group	CMCN WMou

	pontica	CDul CMCN EPfP LLHF MBlu WPat
	prinoides	CMCN
	prinus misapplied	see *Q. michauxii*
§	***prinus*** L.	CMCN WPGP
	pubescens	CDul CMCN MMuc SEND
	pumila Michx.	see *Q. prinus* L.
	pumila Walt.	see *Q. phellos*
	pungens	CMCN
	pyrenaica	CAco CDul CLnd CMCN CTho EBtc MMuc SBir SEND
	- 'Pendula' ♀H6	CMCN EPfP
	Regal Prince	see *Q.* × *warei* 'Long'
	rhysophylla	CMCN EPfP MBlu SBir WPGP
	- 'Maya' ♀H5	CDul CJun EBee ELan EPfP EUJe IArd MBri MRav NLar SBir WHor WMou WPGP WPat
	× ***richteri*** 'Mauri'	CDul MBlu MBri SBir
	× ***riparia***	SBir
§	***robur***	Widely available
	- 'Argenteomarginata' (v)	CDul CMCN MBlu WPat
	- 'Atropurpurea'	MPkF NWea
	- 'Blue Gnome' **new**	MBlu
	- 'Compacta'	MBlu
	- 'Concordia'	CEnd CMCN EBtc ELan EPfP EPla MBlu MPkF NLar SKHP
	- 'Dissecta'	CMCN
	- 'Facrist'	CDul SBir
	- Fastigiata Group	CAco CDoC CDul CLnd COtt CTho EBee EPfP IArd IVic MGos NWea SBir SCob SGol SLim SPer
	- - 'Koster' ♀H6	CDul CMCN CMac CNWT CTri EPfP MBlu NWea SCob
	- - 'Zeeland'	SBir
	- 'Filicifolia' misapplied	see *Q. robur* 'Pectinata'
	- 'Filicifolia'	CEnd LLHF WPat
	- var. ***haas***	CDul
	- - 'Cankiri'	SBir
	- 'Irtha'	EPfP MBlu
	- 'Menhir'	LLHF MAsh MBlu WCot WPat
§	- 'Pectinata'	EPfP MBlu WPat
§	- subsp. ***pedunculiflora***	CMCN
	- 'Pendula'	CEnd CMCN MBlu
	- 'Purpurascens'	CDul CEnd CMCN
	- 'Purpurea'	MBlu
	- 'Raba'	CMCN
	- 'Rita's Gold'	WPat
§	- 'Salfast'	CDul MBlu
	- 'Salicifolia Fastigiata'	see *Q. robur* 'Salfast'
	- 'Strypemonde'	CMCN
	- 'Timuki'	IArd MBlu WPat
	- (Variegata Group) 'Fürst Schwarzenburg' (v)	MBlu
	robur × ***macrocarpa*** × ***virginiana***	SBir
	rotundifolia	CAgr CMCN EBee EPfP WPGP
§	***rubra***	Widely available
	- 'Aurea'	CEnd CJun CMCN EBee EPfP MBlu MBri
	- 'Boltes Gold'	CJun MBlu MBri
	- 'Cyrille'	SBir
	- 'Magic Fire' ♀H6	CMCN EPfP MBlu SBir
	- 'Red Queen'	MBlu
*	- 'Sunshine'	CDul CMCN MBlu MBri WPat
	× ***rudkinii***	EPfP
	rugosa	CFil
	× ***runcinata***	SBir
	salicina	WPGP
	× ***sargentii*** 'Thomas'	CDul EPfP MBlu MBri
	sartorii	SBir
§	× ***saulii***	CMCN SBir
	× ***schochiana***	CLnd EPfP MBlu MBri SBir
	× ***schuettei***	SBir
	semecarpifolia	MBlu
§	***serrata*** Thunb.	CDul CMCN EPfP LEdu MBri SBir WPGP
	- 'Herkenrode' **new**	MBlu
	sessiliflora	see *Q. petraea*
	shumardii	CAco CDul CMCN EPfP MBlu NLar SBir SGol
	- 'Del Rio' **new**	MBlu
	sinuata subsp. ***breviloba***	SBir
	stellata	CAco CDul CMCN EPfP SBir
	× ***sternbergii*** **new**	SBir
	suber	CAco CAgr CBcs CDoC CDul CFil CMCN CTho EBee ELan EPfP EPla EUJe IArd LEdu MGos MMuc SArc SEND WPGP
	- 'Sopron'	EPfP MBlu
§	***texana***	CAco CMCN EPfP SBir
	- New Madrid Group	CDul EBee EPfP MBlu MBri SBir
	tomentella	SBir
	trojana	CMCN SBir
	tuberculata	WPGP
	turbinella	CMCN
	× ***turneri***	CAco CDoC CMCN CTho EPfP MBri WMou
	- 'Pseudoturneri' ♀H6	CBcs CDul EBee ELan EPla MBlu MMuc SEND WMou
	undulata Torr.	see *Q.* × *pauciloba*
	vacciniifolia	CMCN
	variabilis	CMCN EPfP MPkF SGol
	velutina	CAco CBcs CDul CJun CMCN CTho EPfP IVic NLar SBir
	- 'Albertsii'	CJun CLnd MBlu
	- 'Habiflax' **new**	SBig
	- 'Oakridge Walker'	MBlu
	- 'Rubrifolia'	CJun CMCN EPfP
	'Vilmoriana'	CMCN IArd IDee
	virginiana	CAco CBcs CDul CMCN SBir
	× ***warburgii***	EPfP
	× ***warei*** 'Chimney Fire'	EPfP MBlu MBri
	- Kindred Spirit	see *Q.* × *warei* 'Nadler'
§	- 'Long'	EBee EPfP EPla IDee LRHS MBlu MBri MPkF NLar
§	- 'Nadler' **new**	MBri
	- 'Windcandle'	MBlu MBri SBir
	wislizeni	CBcs CDul CMCN NLar SBir
§	***wutaishanica***	SBir

Quillaja (*Quillajaceae*)

saponaria	CArn CCCN IDee SPlb

quince see *Cydonia oblonga*

Quisqualis (*Combretaceae*)

indica	CCCN MOWG

R

Racosperma see *Acacia*

× *Ramberlea* (*Gesneriaceae*)

'Inchgarth'	WAbe

Ramonda (*Gesneriaceae*)

§ ***myconi*** ♀H5 — CLAP ECho EPot EWes LLHF NSla SRms WAbe
- var. ***alba*** — CLAP ECho GKev WThu
- 'Jim's Shadow' — WAbe
- 'Rosea' — LLHF

nathaliae ♀H5 — CPBP ECho SIgm WAbe WThu
- 'Alba' — CLAP NSla WAbe

pyrenaica — see *R. myconi*
serbica — WThu

Ranunculus (*Ranunculaceae*)

abnormis — WAbe
aconitifolius — EBee ECha ECho GCra GMaP NLar SHar SWat WFar WHal WMnd WMoo WSHC
- 'Flore Pleno' (d) ♀H7 — Widely available

acris — CHab NBir NMir NPer WSFF
- subsp. ***acris*** 'Stevenii' — EPPr IGor LPla SDix WHal
- 'Citrinus' — CElw LLWG LSun MHol NPCo WCot WFar WHal WHrl WMoo WPtf
- 'Flore Pleno' (d) ♀H7 — Widely available
- 'Hedgehog' — ECho EPPr MMHG
- 'Sulphureus' — CBre WHal

alpestris — ECho GEdr LLHF NRya NSla
amplexicaulis — GKev GMaP NHar NSla
aquatilis — CBAq CWat EHon MSKA MWts SWat WMAq WSFF
× ***arendsii*** 'Moonlight' — CElw LRHS
asiaticus — ERCP GKev
- 'Bloomingdale Pink Shades' (Bloomingdale Series) **new** — SDeJ
- Tolmer's hybrids (d) **new** — GKev

baurii — ECho
§ ***bulbosus*** 'F.M. Burton' — GBuc NRya WCot
- ***farreri*** — see *R. bulbosus* 'F.M. Burton'
- 'Speciosus Plenus' — see *R. constantinopolitanus* 'Plenus'

bullatus — WCot
calandrinioides ♀H4 — ECho EWes IFoB NBir SBrt WAbe WCot WThu
- SF 137 — WCot

§ ***constantinopolitanus*** 'Plenus' (d) — GCal MNrw MRav NBid NBro WCot WMoo
cortusifolius — SBrt SWat
crenatus — ECho GEdr NRya
creticus — ECho
ficaria — CArn CTri ESwi MHer SEND WHer WOut WSFF WShi
- 'Aglow in the Dark' — CDes CHid
- var. ***albus*** — CHid CSam LEdu NRya WOut
- anemone-centred — see *R. ficaria* 'Collarette'
- 'Art Nouveau' — CDes
§ - var. ***aurantiacus*** — ECha ECho GCrg MHer NRya SPhx SRms
- 'Bowles's Double' — see *R. ficaria* 'Double Bronze', 'Picton's Double'
- 'Brambling' — CHid CLAP ECho LEdu NLar SBch
- 'Brazen Child' — SHar
- 'Brazen Daughter' — ECho
- 'Brazen Hussy' — Widely available
- 'Broadleas Black' — ECho
- subsp. ***bulbilifer*** 'Chedglow' — WCot
- 'Chocolate Cream' — ECho
§ - subsp. ***chrysocephalus*** — CDes ECha IFro SBch WCot
§ - 'Collarette' (d) — CHid ECho GBuc IGor LEdu MHer NBir NLar NRya WOut
- 'Coppernob' — CHid ECho SBch WCot
- 'Cupreus' — see *R. ficaria* var. *aurantiacus*
- 'Damerham' (d) — CHid
§ - 'Double Bronze' (d) — CHid ECho GBuc LEdu MHer NBir NLar NRya SHar
§ - 'Double Mud' (d) — CHid CLAP ECho GAbr GBuc IFro LEdu NLar NRya SHar WHal
- double, cream-flowered — see *R. ficaria* 'Double Mud'
- double, green-eyed (d) — CHid LEdu
- double, yellow-flowered — see *R. ficaria* Flore Pleno Group
- 'Dusky Maiden' — ECho NLar NRya SBch
- 'E.A. Bowles' — see *R. ficaria* 'Collarette'
- 'Elan' (d) — CDes MMoz
§ - Flore Pleno Group (d) — CHid CTri ECha ECho ELan EPPr GAbr NRya NSti SBch SRms WCot
- 'Fried Egg' — ECho
- 'Granby Cream' — ECho
- 'Green Mantle' — ECho
- 'Green Petal' — CHid ECho EPPr GBuc LEdu MCot MHer NBir NRya WHal WHer
- 'Holly' — see *R. ficaria* 'Holly Green'
§ - 'Holly Green' — ECho
- 'Hyde Hall' — ECho NLar SBch WCot
- 'Jake Perry' — MNrw
- 'Jane's Dress' — CHid
- 'Ken Aslet Double' (d) — CDes LEdu MHer NLar WHal
- 'Lambrook Black' — WHer
- 'Lambrook Variegated' (v) — CFis EPPr
- 'Lemon Queen' — CHid
- 'Leo' — MNrw
- subsp. ***major*** — see *R. ficaria* subsp. *chrysocephalus*
- 'Mobled Jade' — CHid
- 'Monksilver' — IFro
- 'Newton Abbot' — CBre
- 'Old Master' — WCot
- 'Orange Sorbet' — LEdu MNrw NLar
§ - 'Picton's Double' (d) — MNrw
- 'Primrose' — CHid NRya
- 'Primrose Elf' — EBee
- 'Ragamuffin' (d) — CDes EBee
- 'Randall's White' — EBee EPfP SHar
- 'Richard and Val' — WCot
- 'Salmon's White' — CBre ECho EPPr NBir NLar NRya SHar WHal
- 'Sheldon Silver' — CHid
- 'Silver Collar' — LEdu
- 'Single Cream' — MNrw
- 'Tomas' **new** — ECho
- 'Tortoiseshell' — CHid EPPr
- 'Wisley Double' — see *R. ficaria* 'Double Bronze'
- 'Witchampton' — CDes
- 'Yaffle' — CHid ECho

flammula — CBAq CBen CHab CRow CWat EHon EWay MSKA MWts SWat
- subsp. ***minimus*** — CRow EWay

gouanii — NRya
'Gowrie' **new** — GEdr
gramineus ♀H5 — CCon CSpe EBee ECho GBin LRHS NRya SMrm SRms XEll
- 'Pardal' — WCot

hederaceus — LLWG
illyricus — EPPr NRya WHal
kochii — CTal ECho GEdr MNrw NRya WCot
lanuginosus — EPPr
lingua — SPlb WSFF
- 'Grandiflorus' — CBAq CBen CRow EHon MSKA NPer SWat WHal WMAq WPnP

lyallii — GKev

millefoliatus	CPBP ECho GBuc WAbe
montanus double-flowered (d)	SHar WCot
- 'Molten Gold' ♀H5	EBee ECho GEdr GMaP MMHG MRav
nivicola	WCot
parnassiifolius	GEdr LLHF MNrw WAbe WCot
'Pauline Violet' **new**	IFro MPie
platanifolius	EBee LPla LRHS SBrt SMHy
'Purple Heart' (d)	EPfP SPer
repens 'Buttered Popcorn' (v)	CRow EBee NLar
- 'Cat's Eyes' (v)	EBee
- 'Gloria Spale'	CBre CRow
- var. ***pleniflorus*** (d)	CBre CRow LLWG SRot
- 'Snowdrift' (v)	EBee
- 'Timothy Clark' (d)	CBre
seguieri	ECho LLHF LRHS WAbe
serbicus	WSHC
speciosus 'Flore Pleno'	see *R. constantinopolitanus* 'Plenus'
traunfellneri **new**	EPot

Ranzania (*Berberidaceae*)

japonica	GEdr GKev WCru

Raoulia (*Asteraceae*)

australis misapplied	see *R. hookeri*
australis ambig.	GMaP NSla SMad
australis Hook.f. ex Raoul	EPot GKev ITim MAsh MWat
§ - Lutescens Group	ECha ECho
haastii	ECou
§ ***hookeri***	CMea CTal ECha ECho EPot EWes MAsh SPlb SRms WAbe
- var. ***laxa***	EWes
× ***loganii***	see × *Leucoraoulia loganii*
lutescens	see *R. australis* Lutescens Group
petriensis	WAbe
× ***petrimia*** 'Margaret Pringle'	WAbe
tenuicaulis	ECha SPlb

raspberry see *Rubus idaeus*

Ratibida (*Asteraceae*)

columnifera	CBod EPfP LRHS SMrm
- f. ***pulcherrima***	CSpe EPfP LRHS SGSe XLum
- - 'Red Midget'	CSpe EBee LRHS
pinnata	CSam EPfP MMuc NBir SPhx SPlb WCot XLum

Ravenala (*Strelitziaceae*)

madagascariensis	SPlb XBlo

Ravenea (*Arecaceae*)

rivularis	CCCN XBlo

Rechsteineria see *Sinningia*

redcurrant see *Ribes rubrum* (R)

Reevesia (*Sterculiaceae*)

pubescens **new**	CBcs

Rehderodendron (*Styracaceae*)

indochinense B&SWJ 11841 **new**	WCru
kweichowense WWJ 12019 **new**	WCru
macrocarpum	CBcs WPGP

Rehmannia (*Plantaginaceae*)

angulata misapplied	see *R. elata*
§ ***elata*** ♀H2	CBod CCon CMos CSam CSpe CWCL ELan EPfP EPla IDee LAst LBMP LLWP LRHS LSun MMuc MNHC MWat NOrc SDys SGSe SMrm SRms WFar WHil XLum
glutinosa ♀H2	CSpe EWTr
piasezkii	WPGP

Reineckea (*Asparagaceae*)

§ ***carnea***	CCon CExl CHel CHid CHll ECha ECho ELan EPPr GBin GCal GKev IMou LEdu MMuc MPie NSti SDys SEND SGSe SPlb WCot WCru WPGP XLum
- B&SWJ 4808	ELon WCru
- SDR 330	EPPr GKev
- 'Baoxing Booty'	IMou WCru
- 'Crûg's Broadleaf'	WCru
- 'Variegata' (v)	EShb WCot
aff. ***carnea*** from Sichuan	WCot
- 'Crûg's Linearleaf' **new**	WCru

Reinwardtia (*Linaceae*)

§ ***indica***	CCCN CExl CHll
trigyna	see *R. indica*

Remusatia (*Araceae*)

hookeriana	GBin
- B&SWJ 2529	WCru

Reseda (*Resedaceae*)

alba	MHer
lutea	SIde SRms
luteola	CBod CHab CHby GPoy MHer MNHC WHer WHfH WSFF

Restio (*Restionaceae*)

festuciformis	CTre
paniculatus	CCCN CDTJ CTre
subverticillatus	CHEx CTre
tetraphyllus	CCon CHel CHid CTre CTsd SPlb SPoG

Reynoutria see *Fallopia*

Rhabdothamnus (*Gesneriaceae*)

solandri	GLin

Rhamnus (*Rhamnaceae*)

alaternus	XSen
§ - 'Argenteovariegata' (v) ♀H5	Widely available
- 'Variegata'	see *R. alaternus* 'Argenteovariegata'
cathartica	CCVT CDul CHab CLnd CTri ECrN EPfP EShb LBuc NLar NWea SEWo WMou WSFF
davurica B&SWJ 12609 **new**	WCru
frangula	see *Frangula alnus*
imeretina	EBee WCot WPGP WPat
ludovici-salvatoris **new**	SBrt
pallasii	NLar
taquetii	NLar

Rhaphidophora (Araceae)

decursiva	XBlo

× *Rhaphiobotrya* (Rosaceae)

§ 'Coppertone'	LPal SArc SEND WPGP

Rhaphiolepis (Rosaceae)

sp.	IDee
× **delacourii**	ECrN ELan EPfP LAst SEND SRms
- 'Coates' Crimson'	CBcs CDoC CTsd EBee ELan EPfP IVic LRHS MAsh MGil WPat WSHC
- Enchantress = 'Moness'	CTsd ELan EPfP LRHS MAsh MRav SLon
- 'Pink Cloud'	EPfP LRHS
- 'Spring Song'	SLon
indica	SEND
- B&SWJ 8405	WCru
- 'Coppertone'	see × *Rhaphiobotrya* 'Coppertone'
- Springtime = 'Monme'	CBcs EPfP IVic LRHS
umbellata	CBcs CHEx CTri EBee ELan EPfP LAst LRHS MAsh MGil SEND SEle SHil SLon SVen WPGP WPat WSHC
- f. **ovata** B&SWJ 4706	WCru

Rhaphithamnus (Verbenaceae)

cyanocarpus	see *R. spinosus*
§ **spinosus**	CBcs EBee EPfP ETwe GAbr LEdu LRHS MGil

Rhapidophyllum (Arecaceae)

hystrix	CBrP LPal

Rhapis ✿ (Arecaceae)

§ **excelsa** ♀H1b	CCCN LPal XBlo
humilis new	LPal
multifida	LPal

Rhazya (Apocynaceae)

orientalis	see *Amsonia orientalis*

Rheum ✿ (Polygonaceae)

GWJ 9329 from Sikkim	WCru
Chen Yi new	WCot
§ 'Ace of Hearts' ♀H6	Widely available
'Ace of Spades'	see *R.* 'Ace of Hearts'
acuminatum	CSpe
- HWJCM 252	WCru
- HWJK 2354	WCru
- PAB 2487	LEdu WPGP
alexandrae	CBct ESwi EWes GAbr GBin GCal GEdr GKev LEdu MMHG MMuc MNrw NLar SBHP SDix SPlb WFar
- SDR 2924	EBee
- SDR 6031	GKev
altaicum PAB 1055	LEdu
§ **australe**	CAgr CArn CCon CSpe EBee GCal LEdu LRHS NBro NLar WCot WFar
- 'Pink Marble' (v) new	WCot
'Cally Dwarf'	GCal
'Cally Giant'	EBee EWes GCal
× **cultorum**	see *R.* × *hybridum*
delavayi	GCal NLar
- BWJ 7592	WCru
emodi	see *R. australe*
* **henryi** new	EBee
§ × **hybridum**	SEND
- 'Brandy Carr Scarlet'	MRav
- 'Canada Red'	GTwe
- 'Cawood Delight'	GTwe SMHy
- 'Champagne'	CAgr EPfP EPom GTwe LBuc LRHS NPri SKee SPer
- 'Daw's Champion'	GTwe
- 'Fenton's Special'	CTri GTwe MCoo MRav
- 'Fulton's Strawberry Surprise' ♀H4	GTwe
- 'Glaskin's Perpetual'	CAgr EPfP LBuc LRHS NPri WHar
- 'Goliath'	MCoo
- 'Grandad's Favorite' ♀H4	LRHS
- 'Greengage'	GTwe
- 'Hammond's Early'	GTwe
- 'Harbinger'	GTwe
- 'Hawke's Champagne' ♀H4	GTwe WCot
- 'Holsteiner Blut'	NLar SPoG
- 'Livingstone'PBR	LRHS
- 'Mac Red' ♀H4	GTwe
- 'Pink Champagne'	EPfP GQue
- 'Prince Albert'	GTwe
- 'Raspberry Red' ♀H4	CSut EPfP EPom LBuc LRHS NPri
- 'Red Champagne'	ELan EPfP LBuc
- 'Red Prolific'	GTwe
- 'Reed's Early Superb' ♀H4	GTwe
- 'Stein's Champagne' ♀H4	GTwe
- 'Stockbridge Arrow'	CMac CSut CTri EMil GTwe SFrt
- 'Stockbridge Bingo'	GTwe
- 'Stockbridge Emerald'	GTwe
- 'Stockbridge Guardsman'	GTwe
- 'Strawberry'	GTwe NBir
- 'Sutton's Cherry Red'	GTwe
- 'The Sutton'	EPfP GTwe
- 'Timperley Early' ♀H4	CDoC CMac CSBt CTri ELan EMil EPfP EPom GTwe IBoy LRHS MGos MMuc MRav MWat NEgg NPri SCoo SDea SEND SKee SLim SPer SPoG WHar
- 'Tingley Cherry'	GTwe
- 'Victoria'	CAgr CDoC CMac CSBt CSut CTri ELan ELau EMil EPfP EPom GTwe LBuc LRHS MCoo MGos MHer MMuc MNHC NPri SDea SFrt SLim SPoG SVic WHar
- 'Victoria 2'	LAst
- 'Zwolle Seedling'	GTwe
kialense	CBct EBee LEdu NBid NSti WPGP WWEG
nobile	EPot GEdr
officinale	CArn CBct CCon CHEx EPla GCal MBri SIde SWat
palmatum	CArn CBcs CHel EBee ECha ELan EPfP EPla GCra GEdr LRHS MGos MRav NGdn SCob SHar SWat
- 'Atropurpureum'	see *R. palmatum* 'Atrosanguineum'
- 'Atropurpureum Dissectum'	IBoy
§ - 'Atrosanguineum'	Widely available
- 'Bowles's Crimson' ♀H7	CBct LRHS MBri MGos MRav NBid WCot
- 'Hadspen Crimson' ♀H7	CAby CBct MNrw WCot
- 'Red Herald'	CBct LRHS WCot WWEG
- 'Rubrum'	CBct LRHS NBir
- 'Savill'	LRHS MBri MRav WWEG
- var. **tanguticum**	Widely available
rhaponticum	NLar
ribes	WCot WCru
spiciforme	CFil WPGP
tanguticum new	COtt
tataricum	EBee LEdu

Rhinanthus (*Orobanchaceae*)

minor	CHab

Rhodanthemum (*Asteraceae*)

'African Eyes'	ECho ELan EPfP EWoo LRHS MBrN MBri MGos MHol NPri SPoG SRot SVen
Agadir	LRHS
§ ***atlanticum***	ECho EWes
'Casablanca' (Atlas Series) new	LRHS WHil
§ ***catananche***	CCCN ECho EPot EWes MBNS SRot WAbe
§ - 'Tizi-n-Test'	ECho
- 'Tizi-n-Tichka'	ECho EWes LRHS
§ ***gayanum***	CCCN EWes
- 'Flamingo'	see *R. gayanum*
- 'Pretty in Pink'	LAst
§ ***hosmariense*** ♀H4	CCCN ECha ECho ELan EPfP EPla EPot GCrg GMaP LRHS MCot MHol MWat SCoo SEND SPer SRms SRot WAbe WHoo WIce
Marrakech	see *R.* Moondance
§ Moondance = 'Usrhod0701'	EPfP LRHS NPri WHil
Tangier	EPfP LRHS

Rhodiola (*Crassulaceae*)

SSSE 10 new	NWad
crassipes	see *R. wallichiana*
cretinii HWJK 2283	WCru
§ ***fastigiata***	CTal GCal WCot WThu
- BWJ 7544	SKHP WCru
§ ***heterodonta***	ELan MRav WCot
himalensis misapplied	see *R.* 'Keston'
himalensis (D. Don) Fu	CTri GKev
integrifolia subsp. ***integrifolia***	EDAr
§ ***ishidae***	CTri
§ 'Keston'	CTri
§ ***kirilovii***	LRHS
§ ***pachyclados***	CTal ECho ECtt EUJe GBin GCrg GJos GKev GMaP LBee LRHS MHer MMuc NBir NRya NWad SEND SPlb SRot SWvt WAbe XLum
aff. ***purpureoviridis***	WFar
- BWJ 7544	WCru
rhodantha	NLar WAbe
§ ***rosea***	CArn CBod CElw CTal EAEE EBee ECho EDAr ELan EPfP GCal GJos GPoy LRHS MCot MHer MLHP MNFA MRav NBid NBir NGdn NLar SEND SPer SPoG SRms WCFE WCot WFar
semenovii	NLar
sinuata HWJK 2318	WCru
- HWJK 2326	WCru
§ ***trollii***	ECho EPot LRHS SPlb
§ ***wallichiana***	MLHP NBid
- GWJ 9263	WCru
- HWJK 2352	WCru
§ ***yunnanensis*** BWJ 7941	WCru

Rhodochiton (*Plantaginaceae*)

§ ***atrosanguineus***	CBcs CCCN CSpe CWCL ELan EPfP GBee LBuc MPie NPri SLon SPer SPoG WFar WHea
volubilis	see *R. atrosanguineus*

Rhodocoma (*Restionaceae*)

arida	CCCN
capensis	CAbb CCCN CCon CHel CTre CTsd NLos
gigantea	CCCN CCon CTre SPlb

Rhododendron ✿ (*Ericaceae*)

sp.	GKin SEWo
'A.J. Ivens'	see *R.* 'Arthur J. Ivens'
'Abegail'	SLdr
aberconwayi	LMil
- 'His Lordship'	GGGa LMil MSnd
acrophilum (V)	GGGa
'Addy Wery' (EA)	CDoC ECho GKin MGos SPer
adenogynum	GGGa LMil MSnd
adenopodum	GGGa MSnd
adenosum	GGGa
'Admiral Piet Hein'	SReu SSta
'Adonis' (EA/d) ♀H5	CBcs CMac LMil NLar SLdr
'Adriaan Koster' (hybrid)	SHea
aeruginosum	see *R. campanulatum* subsp. *aeruginosum*
aganniphum	MSnd
- var. ***flavorufum***	MSnd
- 'Rusty'	MSnd
'Aksel Olsen'	CTri GEdr
'Aladdin' (EA)	ECho SLdr
'Aladdin' (*auriculatum* hybrid)	GGGa SSta
Aladdin Group	SReu
'Albatross'	SSta
Albatross Group	SReu
'Albatross Townhill Pink'	LMil
'Albert Schweitzer' ♀H5	CDoC COtt CWri LMil NLar NSoo SLdr SLim
albertsenianum	MSnd
albrechtii (A)	CBcs GGGa IVic LMil
- Whitney form (A)	LMil WMoo
'Alexander' (EA) ♀H4	IVic LMil MAsh NLar
'Alice' (hybrid) ♀H5	CMac LMil SHea SLdr
Alison Johnstone Group	CBcs LMil SLdr SReu
- 'Alison Johnstone'	GGGa GGal SHea WThu
'All Gold'	GGGa
Alpine Gem Group	GQui
'Alpine Gem'	IVic
'Altaclerense'	LMil
'Altair' (K)	SHea
§ ***alutaceum*** var. ***alutaceum*** Globigerum Group	GGGa
§ - var. ***iodes***	MSnd
§ - var. ***russotinctum***	MSnd
- - R 158	SLdr
§ - - Triplonaevium Group	GGGa
amagianum (A)	LMil
'Amber Rain' (A)	SHea
ambiguum	LMil MSnd
I - 'Crosswater'	LMil
- 'Golden Summit'	GGGa
- 'Jane Banks'	LMil
'Ambrosia' (EA)	CSBt
'Ambush'	SHea
'America'	MJak SHea
'Amethyst' (EA)	GGal
'Amity'	CWri ECho LMil MAsh MMuc MSnd SLdr WGwG
Amor Group	SHea SLdr
'Amoretto'	IVic

	Name	Suppliers
	'Anah Kruschke'	MAsh SPoG
	'Analin'	see *R.* 'Anuschka'
	'Anatta Gold' (V)	GGGa
	'Anchorite' (EA)	SLdr
	'Androcles'	LMil
	Angelo Group	CWri LMil SReu
	- 'Angelo'	LMil SLdr SSta
	Anita Group	SHea
	'Anna Baldsiefen'	GKin SLim SPoG
	'Anna Rose Whitney'	CBcs CTri CWri EPfP LRHS MAsh MBri MJak SLim
	'Annabella' (K)	NLar SReu SSta
	annae	GGGa LMil
	'Anne Frank' (EA)	CWSG
	'Anne Teese'	GGGa LMil
	'Annegret Hansmann'	GGGa
	'Anneke' (A)	EPfP LMil MMuc NHol NLar SReu SSta
	anthopogon	LMil
	- 'Betty Graham'	GGGa
	- subsp. ***hypenanthum*** 'Annapurna'	GGGa ITim WAbe
§	***anthosphaerum***	GGGa
	'Antilope' (Vs) ♀H6	CBcs CWri ECho LMil MAsh MGos MLea MMuc NLar SHea SReu SSta
	(Antonio Group) 'Antonio'	LMil
§	'Anuschka'	LMil MAsh MBri
	anwheiense	GGGa SHea
	aperantum	GGGa
	apodectum	see *R. dichroanthum* subsp. *apodectum*
	'Apple Blossom' ambig.	CMac GKin
	'Appleblossom' (EA)	see *R.* 'Ho-o'
	'Apricot Blaze' (A)	SReu SSta
	'Apricot Fantasy'	LMil MAsh
	'Apricot Surprise'	CTri MAsh MBri
	'April Chimes'	WThu
	'April Showers' (A)	LMil
	'Aquamarin'	IVic
	'Arabesk' (EA)	GKin LMil MAsh
	araiophyllum	LMil
	- KR 7483	LMil
	arborescens (A) ♀H6	GGGa LMil MSnd
	- pink-flowered (A)	LMil
	arboreum	CDoC CHEx GGGa IDee LMil LRHS MSnd NLar SLdr SReu
	- B&SWJ 2244	WCru
	- subsp. ***arboreum***	MSnd
	- subsp. ***cinnamomeum*** ♀H4	CDoC GGGa IDee LMil MSnd SLdr
	- - var. ***album***	GGGa MSnd SReu
	- - 'Everest Reunion'	LMil
	- - var. ***roseum***	GGGa
	- - - 'Tony Schilling'	GKin LMil SReu SSta
	- subsp. ***delavayi***	GGGa LMil MSnd SLdr
	- - var. ***delavayi***	GLin
	- - var. ***peramoenum*** AC 5577	GLin
	- 'Heligan'	SReu
§	- subsp. ***nilagiricum***	GLin
§	- subsp. ***zeylanicum***	GGGa
	'Arctic Fox' (EA)	GGGa
	'Arctic Regent' (K)	GQui
	'Arctic Tern' ♀H5	CDoC CSBt CTri ECho GQui LMil MLea NSoo SPer WThu
	'Ardeur'	NSoo
§	***argipeplum***	GGGa MSnd
	(Argosy Group) 'Argosy'	LMil SReu
	argyrophyllum	MSnd SLdr

	Name	Suppliers
	- subsp. ***argyrophyllum***	GGGa SLdr
§	- subsp. ***hypoglaucum***	GGGa MSnd
	- subsp. ***nankingense***	GGGa
	- - 'Chinese Silver' ♀H6	CDoC GGGa IDee LMil LRHS MSnd NLar SLdr SReu
	'Arima' (K) **new**	GGGa
	arizelum	GCal GGGa LMil MSnd
	- subsp. ***arizelum*** Rubicosum Group	GGGa LMil
	'Arkona'	IVic
	armitii (V)	GGGa
	'Arneson Gem' (M) ♀H6	CDoC GGGa LMil MBri MMuc NLar
	'Arneson Ruby' (K)	GGGa
§	(Aronense Group) 'Fumiko' (EA)	CBcs CSBt LRHS MLea MMuc SHil WFar
§	- 'Hanako' (EA)	MLea
§	- 'Kazuko' (EA)	NLar SHil
§	- 'Satschiko' (EA) ♀H5	CBcs CSBt CWSG GGGa LRHS MGos MJak NLar NPri NSoo SHil
	'Arpege' (Vs)	LMil NLar SReu
	'Arthur Bedford'	CSBt SLdr SReu
§	'Arthur J. Ivens'	SLdr
	'Arthur Osborn'	SSpi
	'Arthur Stevens'	MSnd SLdr
	'Asa-gasumi' (Kurume) (EA)	SLdr
	asterochnoum	GGGa MSnd
	'Astrid'	IVic LMil
	'Astronaut' (K)	SHea
	atlanticum (A)	GGGa LMil SSta
	- 'Seaboard' (A)	LMil
	Augfast Group	CHel
	augustinii	CWri GGGa GGal LMil MLea MSnd NLar SLdr SSpi SSta
§	- subsp. ***chasmanthum***	GGGa
	- compact EGM 293	LMil
	- Electra Group	CDoC LMil MLea SLdr
§	- - 'Electra' ♀H3	GGGa
	- Exbury form	GGGa LMil SReu
§	- subsp. ***hardyi***	GGGa
*	- 'Trewithen'	GGGa LMil
I	- 'Werrington'	CExl SLdr SReu
§	***aureum***	GGGa WThu
	auriculatum	GGGa LMil MSnd SLdr SSta
	- Reuthe's form	SReu
	auriculatum* × *hemsleyanum	GGGa
	auritum	SLdr
	'Aurora' (K)	SLdr
	austrinum (A)	LMil NLar
	- yellow-flowered (A)	LMil
	Autumn Magic	see *R.* 'Herbstzauber'
	(Avalanche Group) 'Avalanche'	LMil
	Avocet Group	LMil
	'Award'	LMil
	Azor Group	SHea
	Azrie Group	SLdr
§	'Azuma-kagami' (Kurume) (EA)	LMil LRHS
	'Azurika'	IVic NSoo
	'Azurro'	LMil
	'Babuschka'	LMil NLar
	'Baden-Baden' ♀H5	CMac CTri ECho GEdr GKin LMil MAsh NEgg SLdr
	'Bagshot Ruby'	SHea
	baileyi	MSnd
	'Bakkarat' (K)	SHea
	balangense	GGGa

	balfourianum	GGGa
	'Ballerina' (K)	SHea
	'Balzac' (K)	CDoC ECho GKin LMil MAsh MGos NEgg SHea SPer
	'Bambi'	MJak
	'Bandoola'	SReu
	'Barbara Coats' (EA)	SLdr
	'Barbara Reuthe'	SSta
	'Barbarella'	IVic
	barbatum	CDoC CHEx GGGa LMil MSnd
	- B&SWJ 2160	WCru
	- B&SWJ 2237	WCru
	- B&SWJ 2624	WCru
	'Barbecue' (K)	LMil
	'Bariton'	GGGa
	'Barmstedt'	CWri MAsh WMoo
	'Barnaby Sunset'	GGGa IDee LMil LRHS MAsh MBri
	'Bashful' ♀H5	CBcs CSBt ECho EPfP MJak SLdr
§	***basilicum***	CDoC GGGa LMil SLdr
	- AC 616	MSnd
	- KR 7532	LMil
	- KR 7540	LMil
	'Bastion'	LMil
	× ***bathyphyllum***	GGGa
	bauhiniiflorum	see *R. triflorum* var. *bauhiniiflorum*
	beanianum	GGGa
	- APA 60	GGGa
	- KC 0122	GGGa
	- compact	see *R. piercei*
	'Beatrice Keir'	LMil MSnd SReu SSta
	'Beattie' (EA)	SLdr
	(Beau Brummell Group) 'Beau Brummell'	LMil
	'Beaulieu' (K)	SHea
	'Beaulieu Manor'	GQui
	'Beauty of Littleworth'	CBcs
	'Beaver' (EA)	MMuc
	'Beefeater' × ***yakushimanum***	SLdr
	beesianum	GGGa
	- AC 1528	MSnd
	'Beethoven' (Vuykiana) (EA)	SLdr
	'Belami'	LMil
	'Belkanto'	CDoC GKin MJak MMuc
	'Belle Heller'	SLdr
	'Bellini'	LMil
	'Ben Cruachan' (K)	GGGa
	'Ben Lawers' (K)	GGGa
	'Ben Lomond' (K)	GGGa
	'Ben Morrison' (EA)	LMil
	'Ben Vorlich' (K)	GGGa
	'Ben Vrackie' (K)	GGGa
	'Bengal'	ECho LRHS MAsh MBri NLar SLdr SLim
	'Bengal Fire' (EA)	CMac SLdr
	'Beni-giri' (Kurume) (EA)	CMac
	'Bergensiana'	SReu SSta
	'Bergie Larson' ♀H4	CBcs ECho IVic LMil MLea MMuc SLdr
	'Berg's 10'	MLea
	'Berg's Yellow'	CWri ECho LMil MGos MMuc SLdr
	'Bernard Shaw'	SSta
	'Bernstein'	LMil MAsh MJak
	'Berryrose' (K) ♀H6	CBcs CMac CSBt CTri ECho EPfP GKin LMil LRHS MAsh MBri MJak MSnd NSoo SLdr SPer SReu WFar
	'Beryl Taylor'	GGGa
	'Betty Anne Voss' (EA)	ECho LMil MAsh MBri SCoo SLdr
	'Betty Wormald'	CDul CMac CWri ECho MLea MMuc SHea SLdr SPer
	bhutanense	GGGa
	Bibiani Group	LMil SHea
	'Bijou de Ledeberg' (Indian) (EA/v)	CMac
	'Billy Budd'	SLdr
	'Birthday Girl'	CBcs CSBt ECho ELon LMil MAsh MLea SLdr
	'Biscuit Box'	LMil
	(Biskra Group) 'Biskra'	GGGa LMil
	'Blaauw's Pink' (Kurume) (EA) ♀H4	CDoC CMac CSBt ECho EPfP GKin GQui LMil MBri MMuc NLar NSoo SGol SLdr SPer SPlb SPoG SReu
	'Black Knight' (EA)	SLdr
	'Black Magic'	CDoC GKin LMil
	'Black Sport'	MLea
	'Black Widow' **new**	SSta
	Blaue Donau	see *R.* 'Blue Danube'
	'Blaue Jungs'	GGGa
	'Blazecheck'	SCoo
	'Blewbury' ♀H5	LMil SReu
	'Blue Bell'	SHea
	'Blue Boy'	CDoC LMil
	'Blue Chip'	SLdr
§	'Blue Danube' (EA) ♀H3	Widely available
	Blue Diamond Group	CBcs ECho EPfP SReu
	- 'Blue Diamond'	CMac CSBt ECho LRHS MAsh MBri MGos MJak SLdr WGwG
	'Blue Monday' (EA)	SLdr
	'Blue Peter' ♀H5	CBcs CSBt CWri ECho ELon LMil LRHS MAsh MLea MMuc NHol NLar SLdr SPer SReu SSta
	'Blue Pool'	LMil LRHS
	'Blue Silver'	GGGa IVic LMil MAsh MBri NSoo
	'Blue Steel'	see *R. fastigiatum* 'Blue Steel'
	Blue Tit Group	CBcs CDoC EPfP GGGa LRHS MAsh MBri NLar SLdr SLim SReu SSta
	Bluebird Group	CMac CSBt SLdr
	'Blueshine Girl' **new**	SLdr
	'Bluretta'	CDoC CWri MMuc
	'Blutopia'	LMil
	'Boddaertianum'	SHea
	Bohlken's Juditha	GGGa LMil
	Bohlken's Kronjewel	GGGa
	Bohlken's Laura	GGGa LMil
	Bohlken's Lupinenberg	GGGa LMil
	Bohlken's Snow Fire	GGGa
	'Bonfire'	SHea
	(Bonito Group) 'Bonito' **new**	LMil
	boothii	GGGa
	- HECC 10077	GGGa
	Bo-peep Group	CBcs
	- 'Bo-peep'	GQui LMil SLdr
	'Boskoop Ostara'	LMil
	'Bouquet de Flore' (G) ♀H6	CDoC EPfP LMil
	Bow Bells Group	MLea
	- 'Bow Bells' ♀H4	ECho EPfP GEdr LMil LRHS MAsh MBri NHol NPri SHea SLdr
	'Bow Street'	SHea
	'Bowjingles'	GGGa
	brachyanthum subsp. ***hypolepidotum***	GGGa
	brachycarpum	GLin
	- 'Roseum Dwarf'	GGGa
	'Brambling'	GGGa
	'Brazier' (EA)	SLdr

'Brazil' (K)	SHea
'Bremen'	LMil
'Briane' (EA)	GGGa
Bric-à-brac Group	CBcs
- 'Bric-à-brac'	SLdr
'Bright Forecast' (K)	CWri IVic MGos MLea
'Brigitte'	CWri IVic LMil MAsh MBri
'Brilliant' (EA)	SHil
'Brilliant Blue' (EA)	MAsh
'Britannia'	COtt CSBt CWri EPfP MJak NHol SReu SSta
(Brocade Group) 'Brocade'	SHea SLdr
'Bronze Fire' (A)	NHol SLdr SReu SSta
'Brown Eyes'	ECho GKin MMuc
'Bruce Brechtbill'	CDoC CWri ECho GGGa GKin MAsh MBri MGos MMuc SEND
'Bruce Hancock' (Ad)	CEnd ECho SLdr
§ 'Bruns Gloria'	LMil
'Bruns Schneewitchen'	LMil SReu SSta
'Buccaneer' (Glenn Dale) (EA)	SLdr
bullatum	see *R. edgeworthii*
'Bungo-nishiki' (Wada) (EA/d)	CMac WThu
bureavii ♀^{H5}	GGGa GLin IDee LMil LRHS MSnd SReu SSta
bureavii* × *yakushimanum	SReu
bureavioides	LMil MSnd
'Burletta'	IVic LMil
burmanicum	CBcs CPne GGGa GGal
Bustard Group	LMil
'Busuki'	GGGa LMil
'Butter Brickle'	LMil MLea SLdr
'Butter Yellow'	ECho
'Butterfly'	SHea
'Buttermint'	ECho MMuc
calendulaceum (A)	GGGa LMil
- red-flowered (A)	LMil
- yellow-flowered (A)	LMil
Calfort Group	SLdr
- 'Calfort'	GGGa
callimorphum	GGGa LMil
- var. ***myiagrum***	MSnd
calophytum ♀^{H5}	GGGa LMil LRHS MSnd SLdr
calostrotum	WAbe
- subsp. ***calostrotum*** KR 9983 **new**	MSnd
- 'Gigha' ♀^{H4}	GGGa IDee LMil LRHS MAsh WAbe
§ - subsp. ***keleticum*** ♀^{H4}	CDoC GEdr GGGa GKev ITim LRHS NSla
- - R 58	GGGa LMil
§ - - Radicans Group	GEdr GGGa IVic MLea NSla WAbe WThu
- - - USDAPI 59182/R11188	MLea
- - - mound form	ITim
- subsp. ***riparium***	GLin ITim
§ - - Nitens Group	CDoC GGGa MAsh MMuc WAbe WThu
caloxanthum	see *R. campylocarpum* subsp. *caloxanthum*
'Calsap'	GGGa LMil
Calstocker Group	LMil
camelliiflorum	GGGa
campanulatum	GGGa IDee LMil MSnd SReu WAbe
- HWJCM 195	WCru
§ - subsp. ***aeruginosum***	GGGa LMil MSnd
'Campfire' J.B. Gable (EA)	SLdr
campylocarpum	GGGa LMil MSnd
- KR 8212	LMil
§ - subsp. ***caloxanthum***	GGGa
§ - - Telopeum Group	MSnd
campylogynum	GGGa LMil WAbe
- SBEC 0519	GGGa
- 'Album'	see *R.* 'Leucanthum'
- black-flowered	IVic
- Charopoeum Group	WThu
- - 'Patricia'	ECho EPot GEdr NLar NSla
- (Cremastum Group) 'Bodnant Red'	GGGa WThu
- Myrtilloides Group ♀^{H4}	CDoC ECho GGGa GQui LMil MAsh MSnd WAbe WThu
- plum-flowered	WAbe
- salmon pink-flowered	ECho WAbe
camtschaticum	GGGa LMil WThu
- red-flowered	GGGa
canadense (A)	GGGa
- f. ***albiflorum*** (A)	GGGa LMil
- dark-flowered (A)	LMil
'Candy Striped Pink'	IVic
canescens (A)	LMil
'Cannon's Double' (K/d) ♀^{H6}	CBcs CWri GKin LMil LRHS MAsh MBri MLea MMuc NLar WMoo
'Canzonetta' (EA/d) ♀^{H5}	CEnd ECho EPfP GGGa LMil LRHS MAsh MBri
'Capriccio' **new**	LMil
'Captain Jack'	GGGa
'Caractacus'	MJak
'Carat' (A)	NLar
cardiobasis	see *R. orbiculare* subsp. *cardiobasis*
Carita Group	SHea
- 'Carita Charm'	LMil
- 'Carita Inchmery'	SHea
- 'Golden Dream'	LMil
(Carmen Group) 'Carmen' ♀^{H5}	ECho ELon GEdr GGGa GKev GKin LMil MAsh MLea MMuc SLdr
carneum	GGGa
'Carnival' (EA)	CBcs
'Carolina Spring' (v) **new**	LMil
'Caroline Allbrook'	CWri ECho ELon GGGa MAsh MBri MGos MLea NLar NSoo SLdr
'Caruso'	IVic SPoG
'Cary Ann'	CTri LRHS MAsh MBri SReu
'Casablanca' (EA)	SLdr
'Cassata'	LMil
'Cassley' (Vs)	LMil
catacosmum	GGGa
catawbiense	GKev GLin SLdr
'Catawbiense Album'	CTri MAsh
'Catawbiense Boursault'	SLdr
'Catawbiense Grandiflorum'	MAsh NSoo
'Catharine van Tol'	LMil
caucasicum	GGGa
'Caucasicum Pictum'	LMil SLdr
'Cayenne' (EA)	SLdr
'Cecile' (K) ♀^{H6}	CBcs CDoC CMac CWri ECho GBin GKin LMil MAsh MBri MMuc NLar SEND SLdr SPer SReu
'Celestial' (EA)	CMac
'Centennial Gold'^{PBR} **new**	COtt
cephalanthum	GGGa LMil
- subsp. ***cephalanthum*** SBEC 0751	WThu
- - Nmaiense Group	GGGa
- Crebreflorum Group	GGGa LMil WAbe WThu

	- subsp. ***platyphyllum***	GGGa
	- - AC 1926	MSnd
	cerasinum	LMil MSnd
	- 'Cherry Brandy'	GGGa MSnd
	- 'Coals of Fire'	GGGa MSnd
	'Cetewayo'	CWri GGGa LMil
	chaetomallum	see *R. haematodes* subsp. *chaetomallum*
	chamaethomsonii	GGGa
	- var. ***chamaethomsonii***	MSnd
	- - Rock form	GGGa
	championae	GGGa
	'Chanel' (Vs)	GGGa SReu SSta
	changii	GGGa
	'Chanticleer' (Glenn Dale) (EA)	SLdr
	chapaense	see *R. maddenii* subsp. *crassum*
	'Chariots of Fire' (EA)	LMil
	charitopes	GCal LMil
	- F 25570	GGGa LMil
	- subsp. ***charitopes***	MSnd
§	- subsp. ***tsangpoense***	GGGa GQui
*	'Charlotte de Rothschild' (A)	SLdr
	'Charlotte Megan' (A)	LMil
	'Charme La'	GGGa
	chasmanthum	see *R. augustinii* subsp. *chasmanthum*
	'Cheer'	CWri MAsh MMuc NEgg SEND SLim SPer
	'Chelsea Reach' (K/d)	SHea
	'Chelsea Seventy'	MSnd SLdr
	'Chenille' (K/d)	SHea
	'Cherokee' (EA)	SLdr
	'Cherries and Cream'	LMil
	'Cherry Drops' (EA)	EPfP LRHS MAsh
	Cherry Kiss = 'Hachcher'PBR **new**	GGGa
	'Chetco' (K)	LMil NLar
	'Chevalier Félix de Sauvage'	LMil SHea SReu
	'Chikor'	CBcs ECho GBin GGGa GKin MAsh MBri MGos MMuc NLar WThu
	'Chinchilla' (EA)	GQui NLar
	'Chink'	MSnd SLdr
	'Chionoides'	CMac SLdr
	'Chipmunk' (EA/d)	GGGa LRHS MAsh MBri
	'Chippewa' (Indian) (EA)	CTri IVic LMil
	'Chocolate Ice' (K/d)	SHea SLdr
	(Choremia Group) 'Choremia' ♀H3	LMil SHea
	christi (V)	GGGa
	'Christina' (Vuykiana) (EA/d)	MMuc SLdr
	'Christmas Cheer' (EA/d)	see *R.* 'Ima-shojo'
	'Christmas Cheer' (hybrid) ♀H5	CBcs CDoC CSBt CWri GBin GGGa GGal GKin LMil MAsh MLea NLar SLdr SReu
	chrysanthum	see *R. aureum*
	chrysodoron	LMil MSnd
	(Chrysomanicum Group) 'Chrysomanicum'	CHel
	ciliatum	CBcs GGGa IDee LMil SLdr
	ciliicalyx	CBcs
	Cilpinense Group	CBcs GGGa SPer
	- 'Cilpinense' ♀H3	CMac CSBt CWri ECho EPfP LMil LRHS MAsh MMuc NPri SEND SLdr
	cinnabarinum	LMil MSnd SLdr
	- subsp. ***cinnabarinum*** BL&M 234	LMil
	- - Blandfordiiflorum Group	GGGa MSnd SLdr
	- - 'Nepal'	LMil
	- - Roylei Group	GGGa LMil
	- - - 'Vin Rosé'	LMil
	- Cinzan Group	LMil
§	- (Conroy Group) 'Conroy'	CTsd LMil
§	- subsp. ***tamaense*** KW 21003	MSnd
§	- subsp. ***xanthocodon***	GGGa LMil MSnd
§	- - Concatenans Group	GGGa IDee LMil LRHS MSnd SLdr
	- - - KW 5874	LMil
	- - - 'Amber'	LMil
	- - Purpurellum Group	GGGa MSnd
	'Cinzia' (K) **new**	GGGa
	circinnatum	GGGa
	citriniflorum	LMil
	- R 108	LMil
	- var. ***citriniflorum***	LMil MSnd
	- var. ***horaeum***	GGGa MSnd
	'Clarice' (K)	SHea
	'Claudine'	IVic
	clementinae	GGGa MSnd
	- F 25705	LMil
	- subsp. ***aureodorsale***	GKev
	'Cliff Garland'	GQui LMil
	'Coccineum Speciosum' (G) ♀H6	CDoC CMac CSBt GKin LMil SReu SSta
	coeloneuron	GGGa LMil
	- EGM 334	LMil
	- NN 0926 **new**	MSnd
	collettianum	GGGa
	'Colonel Coen'	CWri ELon GBin GKin LMil MLea MMuc SLdr
	Colonel Rogers Group	SLdr SReu
	'Colyer' (EA)	SLdr
	Comely Group	SLdr
	comisteum C 6541	GGGa
	concatenans	see *R. cinnabarinum* subsp. *xanthocodon* Concatenans Group
	concinnoides	GGGa
	concinnum	GGGa SLdr
	- Pseudoyanthinum Group ♀H5	GGGa GQui MSnd SLdr
	'Connie' (Kaempferi) (EA)	NSoo SReu SSta
	'Conroy'	see *R. cinnabarinum* (Conroy Group) 'Conroy'
	'Contina'	LMil
	'Conversation Piece' (EA)	CEnd SLdr
	'Conyan Apricot'	SLdr
	'Cool Haven'	LMil
	'Coral Sea' (EA)	SReu
	'Coral Seas' (V)	GGGa
	'Corany' (A)	LMil
	coriaceum	GGGa LMil MSnd SLdr
	'Corneille' (G/d)	CSBt LMil SReu
	Cornish Early Red Group	see *R.* Smithii Group
	'Cornish Red'	see *R.* Smithii Group
	'Corona'	SHea
	'Coronation Day'	LMil
	'Coronation Lady' (K)	SHea
	coryanum 'Chelsea Chimes'	MSnd
	'Cosmopolitan'	COtt ELon LMil MMuc SEND SPoG WMoo
	Cote Group (A)	SLdr
	'Cotton Candy'	LMil
	'Countess of Derby'	SHea SLdr

	Name	Suppliers
	'Countess of Haddington'	CBcs LMil LRHS SLdr
	Cowslip Group	CTri LMil MAsh MGos MLea
	- 'Cowslip' ♀H4	LRHS MBri
	coxianum	GGGa
	'Crane' ♀H5	EPfP GGGa GQui IVic LMil LRHS MAsh MBri NLar SLdr
	crassum	see *R. maddenii* subsp. *crassum*
	'Cream Crest'	GKin GQui LMil NLar SLdr SLim WMoo
	'Creamy Chiffon'	CWri ECho MLea WGwG
§	'Creeping Jenny'	ECho GGGa GGal MSnd SLdr
	crenulatum	GGGa
	'Crete'	LMil
	crinigerum	CPne GGGa IDee LMil
	- var. ***crinigerum***	MSnd
	- var. ***euadenium***	MSnd
	'Crinoline' (EA)	SLdr
	Crossbill Group	CBcs SLdr
	'Crosswater Belle'	LMil LRHS NLar
	'Crosswater Red' (A)	LMil
	'Csárdás'	GGGa IVic
	cubittii	see *R. veitchianum* Cubittii Group
	cucullatum	see *R. roxieanum* var. *cucullatum*
	cumberlandense (A)	GGGa LMil LRHS
	- 'Sunlight'	LMil
	cuneatum	MSnd
	'Cunningham's Blush'	SGol
	'Cunningham's White'	CBcs CTri CWri ELan EPfP GBin GGGa LMil LRHS MAsh MGos MMuc NHol NLar NPri NSoo SEND SLdr SLim SPer SPoG SReu SSta
	'Cupcake'	GGGa
	'Curlew' ♀H4	CBcs CMac GEdr GKin LMil MAsh MBri MGos MJak MMuc MSnd NHol SLdr SReu SSpi
	cyanocarpum	GGGa MSnd
	'Cynthia' ♀H5	CBcs CMac CSBt CWri ELon EPfP GGGa LMil MBri MMuc MSnd NEgg SLdr SPer SReu SSta WMoo
	'Dagmar'	IVic
	dalhousiae	GGGa
	- LS&T 6694	MSnd
§	- var. ***rhabdotum***	GGGa
	(Damozel Group) 'Damozel'	LMil SHea
	'Danger' (K)	SHea
	'Danuta'	IVic
	'Daphne Daffarn'	SHea
	'Daphne Millais'	SHea
	'Dartmoor Pixie'	WThu
	dasycladum	see *R. selense* subsp. *dasycladum*
	dauricum 'Album'	see *R. dauricum* 'Hokkaido'
§	- 'Hokkaido'	GGGa
	- 'Mid-winter' ♀H6	GGGa LMil
	'David'	SHea
	davidii	GGGa LMil NEgg
	davidsonianum ♀H3	GGGa GGal LMil MSnd
	- Bodnant form	LMil
	- 'Caerhays Blotched'	GGGa
	- 'Ruth Lyons'	LMil
	'Daviesii' (G) ♀H6	CBcs CDoC CDul CEnd CSBt CTri CWri ECho ELan EPfP GKin GQui LMil LRHS MAsh MBri MLea MMuc MSnd NLar NPri SLdr SPer SPoG SReu SSpi WMoo
	(Day Dream Group) 'Day Dream'	SHea
	'Daybreak' (EA/d)	see *R.* 'Kirin'
	'Daybreak' (K)	GQui SHea
	'Dear Barbara'	LMil
	'Dear Grandad' (EA)	CTri LMil MBri SCoo
	'Dear Grandma'	LMil
	'Dearest' (EA)	LMil LRHS MAsh MBri NPri
	'Debutante'	SHea
	decorum ♀H4	CDoC CPne GGGa IDee LMil MSnd SLdr
	- KR 2496	LMil
	- SDR 5026	GKev
	- SDR 5805	GKev
	- subsp. ***cordatum*** C&H 7132	GGGa
	- 'Cox's Uranium Green'	SReu
§	- subsp. ***diaprepes***	MSnd
	- late-flowering	LMil
	- pink-flowered	GGGa
	decorum × ***yakushimanum***	SLdr SReu
§	***degronianum*** subsp. ***degronianum***	LMil MSnd
	- subsp. ***heptamerum*** 'Ho Emma'	LMil
	- - 'Oki Island'	LMil
	- 'Rae's Delight'	LMil
	dekatanum	GGGa
	deleiense	see *R. tephropeplum*
	'Delicatissimum' (O) ♀H5	CBcs CDoC CTsd CWri ECho GGGa GKin GQui MBri MGos MLea MSnd SHea WGwG
	'Delta'	COtt MBri NLar SLdr SLim
	dendrocharis	LMil
	- Cox 5016	GGGa WAbe
	- Glendoick Gem = 'Gle002'	GGGa
	'Denise'	IVic
*	'Denny's Rose' (A)	LMil
	'Denny's Scarlet'	NHol SReu SSta
	'Denny's White' (A)	LMil NHol SReu SSta
	denudatum	GLin LMil MSnd
	- EGM 294	LMil
	- NN 0908 **new**	MSnd
	desquamatum	see *R. rubiginosum* Desquamatum Group
	'Diabolo' (K)	SHea
	Diamant Group lilac-flowered (EA)	ECho LMil MLea
	- pink-flowered (EA)	ECho MLea
§	- purple-flowered (EA)	ECho MLea
§	- red-flowered (EA)	ECho MLea SLdr
	- rosy red-flowered (EA)	ECho
	- white-flowered (EA)	ECho
	'Diamant Purpur'	see *R.* Diamant Group purple-flowered
	'Diamant Rot'	see *R.* Diamant Group red-flowered
I	'Diana' **new**	SLdr
	diaprepes	see *R. decorum* subsp. *diaprepes*
	dichroanthum	GGGa LMil
§	- subsp. ***apodectum***	GGGa LMil MSnd
	- subsp. ***dichroanthum***	MSnd
	- - AC 1079	MSnd
§	- subsp. ***scyphocalyx***	GGGa LMil MSnd NSoo
	- subsp. ***septentrionale***	GGGa
	didymum	see *R. sanguineum* subsp. *didymum*
	'Diorama' (Vs)	SReu SSta
	discolor	see *R. fortunei* subsp. *discolor*
	diversipilosum 'Milky Way'	GGGa

'Doc'	CBcs CMac EPfP SLdr SReu
'Doctor M. Oosthoek' (M)	CSBt GKin SReu
'Doctor Stocker'	LMil MSnd
'Dominik' **new**	GGGa
'Dopey' ♀H4	CBcs CDul CSBt CWri ECho ELon EPfP GGGa LMil LRHS MAsh MBri MJak MLea MMuc MSnd NHol NLar SLdr SLim SReu SSta
'Dora Amateis' ♀H6	CBcs CDoC ECho GGGa IVic LMil LRHS MAsh MBri MMuc NLar NSoo SLdr SLim SReu WThu
Dormouse Group	CBcs ECho LMil MAsh MMuc NLar SLdr SReu SSta
'Dorothy Corston' (K)	SHea
'Dörte Reich'	GGGa
'Dotella'	GGGa
'Double Beauty' (Vuykiana) (EA/d)	SReu SSta
'Double Damask' (K/d)	SLdr
'Double Date' (d)	SLdr
double yellow-flowered (A/d)	SLdr
'Douglas McEwan'	SLdr
Dragonfly Group	SReu SSta
'Dreamland' ♀H5	CBcs CDoC CSBt CWri ECho EPfP LMil LRHS MAsh MBri MGos MLea MSnd NLar NSoo SLdr SLim SPoG SReu SSta
dryophyllum misapplied	see *R. phaeochrysum* var. *levistratum*
'Dufthecke'PBR	see *R.* White Dufthecke
'Dusky Dawn'	SLdr
'Düsselfeuer'	IVic
'Dusty Miller'	LRHS MAsh MBri MJak MSnd NSoo SLdr
'Earl of Donoughmore'	SReu SSta
'Easter Parade' (EA)	SLdr
eastmanii (A)	GGGa
ebianense NN 904	GGGa
'Ebony Pearl'	CBcs ECho ELon MGos SLdr
eclecteum	GGGa LMil MSnd
§ ***edgeworthii*** ♀H3	GGGa WAbe
'Edith Bosley'	NLar SLdr
'Edna Bee' (EA)	LMil SLdr
'Egret' ♀H4	CDoC ECho EPot GEdr GGGa LMil MBri MGos MLea MSnd NSla SLdr
'Eider'	GGGa MAsh SLdr
'Eileen'	LMil
'Eisenhower' (K)	SHea
'El Camino'	ECho MMuc SLdr
'El Greco'	SLdr
Eldorado Group	GQui
(Eleanore Group) 'Eleanore'	SLdr
'Electra'	see *R. augustinii* (Electra Group) 'Electra'
elegantulum	LMil MSnd
(Elisabeth Hobbie Group) 'Elisabeth Hobbie' ♀H5	LMil NLar SLdr
'Eliska'	IVic
'Elizabeth'	CDul CTri CTsd CWri GBin LRHS MSnd NHol SHea
'Elizabeth' (EA)	CMac CSBt EPfP SLdr
Elizabeth Group	CBcs LMil MAsh SLdr SPer SReu
'Elizabeth Jenny'	see *R.* 'Creeping Jenny'
'Elizabeth Lockhart'	ECho GEdr GQui
'Elizabeth Red Foliage'	CTri GGGa LMil LRHS MAsh MBri SPer
'Else Frye'	GGGa
'Elsie Lee' (EA/d) ♀H5	CEnd CSBt CTrh ECho LMil MAsh MMuc NLar SLdr SReu
'Elsie Pratt' (A)	SHea
'Emasculum'	SLdr
'Emma Williams'	CBcs
'Endsleigh Pink'	CBcs CWri LMil LRHS MMuc
'English Roseum'	LMil
eriogynum	see *R. facetum*
eritimum	see *R. anthosphaerum*
'Ernest Inman'	LMil
erosum	MSnd
'Eruption'	IVic
'Esmeralda'	CMac
'Etna' (EA)	SLdr
'Etta Burrows'	CWri GGGa
'Euan Cox'	GGGa
euchroum	MSnd
eudoxum	MSnd
'Europa'	SReu SSta
eurysiphon	MSnd
'Eva Goude' (K)	SHea
'Evelyn Hyde' (EA)	SLdr
'Evening Fragrance' (A)	LMil
'Everbloom' (EA)	SLdr
'Everestianum'	SHea
Everred = '851C'PBR	GGGa
exasperatum	GGGa
- KW 6855 **new**	LMil
Exburiense Group	MMuc
'Exbury Calstocker'	LMil
'Exbury White' (K)	GQui
excellens	GGGa LMil
eximium	see *R. falconeri* subsp. *eximium*
'Explorer' (EA)	MJak
'Exquisitum' (O) ♀H5	CBcs CDoC CWri ECho EPfP GGGa GKin LMil MBri SLdr
exquisitum	see *R. oreotrephes* Exquisitum Group
'Extraordinaire'	GGGa LMil SReu SSta
faberi	GGGa LMil
Fabia Group	CWri
- 'Fabia' ♀H3	CBcs CMac GGGa GGal GKin LMil LRHS MAsh NLar SHea SLdr
§ - 'Fabia Tangerine'	CMac MLea
'Fabia Waterer'	LMil
§ ***facetum***	GGGa LMil
- KR 7593	LMil
'Faggetter's Favourite' ♀H5	LMil SHea SReu SSta
Fairy Light Group	LMil
faithae CGG 14142	GGGa
falconeri ♀H3	CDoC CHEx GGGa LMil MSnd NPCo SLdr
§ - subsp. ***eximium***	CDoC GGGa GKev LMil MSnd
'Falling Snow'	IVic
'Fanal' (K)	NLar
'Fanny'	see *R.* 'Pucella'
'Fantastica' ♀H6	CDoC CWri ELan ELon EPfP GGGa IDee LMil LRHS MAsh MBri MLea MMuc NLar NPri SLim SPoG
fargesii	see *R. oreodoxa* var. *fargesii*
farinosum NN 0904 **new**	MSnd
'Fashion' (EA)	SLdr
fastigiatum	EPot LMil MSnd NSla SLdr
- SBEC 804/4869	GGGa WThu
§ - 'Blue Steel' ♀H6	CBcs CTri ECho ELon GKin IVic LMil LRHS MAsh MBri SLdr SPlb SReu WAbe

Plant	Suppliers
- 'Indigo Steel'	GGGa
'Fastuosum Flore Pleno' (d) ♀H6	CBcs CDul CMac CSBt CWri EPfP GGGa LMil MLea SHea SLdr SPer SReu SSta
'Fatima'	LMil
faucium	GGGa
'Favor Major' (K)	SHea
'Favorite' ambig. (EA)	SLdr
'Fawley' (K)	SHea SLdr
'Fedora' (Kaempferi) (EA)	CBcs
Feenkissen = 'Hachkissen'PBR (EA)	IVic
ferrugineum	GGGa LMil
'Feuerwerk' (K)	IVic MMuc NLar SHea
fictolacteum	see *R. rex* subsp. *fictolacteum*
Fire Bird Group	CHel SHea SLdr
'Fire Rim'	LRHS MAsh
'Fireball' (K) ♀H6	CBcs CDoC CDul CTri CWri EPfP GBin GGGa GKin LMil LRHS MAsh MBri MGos MLea MMuc NLar SEND SLdr SPer SPoG
'Fireball' (hybrid)	MJak
'Firecracker' (A)	LRHS MAsh MBri
'Fireglow' (EA)	GKin LMil
'Firelight' (hybrid)	GKin LMil NLar SPer
'Firetail'	SHea
'Flaming Gold'	LRHS MAsh MBri NPri
'Flanagan's Daughter'	LMil MAsh MBri
'Flautando'	IVic LMil
Flava Group	see *R.* Volker Group
flavidum	GGGa MMuc
fletcherianum 'Yellow Bunting'	GGGa
floccigerum	LMil MSnd
- AC 1863	MSnd
- bicolored	GGGa
'Floriade' × ***yakushimanum***	SLdr
floribundum	GGGa LMil
'Florida' (EA/d) ♀H4	CMac LMil NSoo SLdr SReu
'Flower Arranger' (EA)	LMil MAsh MBri SCoo
formosanum	GGGa
formosum	CBcs GGGa
§ - var. ***formosum*** Iteaphyllum Group	GGGa
- - 'Khasia'	GGGa
- var. ***inaequale***	GGGa
forrestii KR 6113	LMil
- subsp. ***forrestii***	LMil
- - Repens Group	LMil
- - - 'Seinghku'	GGGa WThu
- Tumescens Group	GGGa WThu
Fortune Group	SLdr
fortunei ♀H6	GGGa LMil SLdr
§ - subsp. ***discolor*** ♀H5	LMil MSnd SLdr
- - (Houlstonii Group) 'John R. Elcock'	IDee LMil LRHS
- - 'Hummeltanz'	IVic
- - var. ***kwangfuense*** AC 5208	LMil
- 'Mrs Butler'	see *R.* 'Sir Charles Butler'
fragariiflorum	GGGa
'Fragrantissimum' ♀H2	CBcs CEnd CMac CSBt CTsd CWri ECre GGGa GGal LMil LRHS MRav NLar SKHP SLdr
'Frank Galsworthy'	LMil SLdr
'Frans van der Bom' (M)	MBri
'Fraseri' (M)	LMil
'Fred Peste' ♀H4	CDoC ECho GKin LMil MAsh MBri MGos MLea MMuc MSnd NLar SLdr SLim
(Fred Wynniatt Group) 'Fred Wynniatt'	LMil MSnd
'Fred Wynniatt Stanway'	see *R.* 'Stanway'
'Freda' (EA)	SLdr
'Freya' (R/d)	LMil
'Fridoline' (EA)	IVic
'Frigate' (EA)	SLdr
'Frills' (K/d)	SHea
'Frilly Lemon' (K/d)	EPfP
'Frome' (K)	SHea
'Frosted Orange' (EA)	LMil MAsh NSoo
'Frosthexe'	WAbe
'Frühlingsbeginn'	IVic
'Frühlingsglühen'	IVic
'Frühlingszauber'	SLdr
'Fulbrook'	LMil
fulgens	GGGa GLin LMil MSnd
- KR 8204	LMil
fulvum ♀H4	CDoC GGGa GKin IDee LMil LRHS MSnd NLar SReu SSta
- KR 7614	LMil
- subsp. ***fulvoides***	MSnd
'Furnivall's Daughter' ♀H5	CMac COtt CSBt CWri ECho EPfP GBin GGGa LMil MBri MGos MMuc MSnd NHol SEND SHea SLdr SReu SSta WMoo
(Fusilier Group) 'Fusilier'	SHea
'Gabrielle Hill' (EA)	MAsh SLdr
'Gaiety' (Glenn Dale) (EA)	LMil SLdr
galactinum	GGGa IDee LMil MSnd
'Galathea' (EA)	MMuc
'Gallipoli' (K)	SHea
'Gandy Dancer'	CWri SLdr
'Garden State Glow' (EA/d)	SLdr
'Garibaldi'	SHea
'Garnet'	SHea
'Gartendirektor Glocker'	CWri ECho GGGa IVic MAsh MSnd SLim
'Gartendirektor Rieger' ♀H5	CWri GGGa IVic LMil NLar SHea SReu
'Gauche' (A)	GQui SLdr
'Gaugin'	GQui
'Geisha' (EA)	SGol
'Geisha Lilac'	see *R.* (Aronense Group) 'Hanako'
'Geisha Orange'	see *R.* (Aronense Group) 'Satschiko'
'Geisha Pink'	see *R.* 'Momoko'
'Geisha Purple'	see *R.* (Aronense Group) 'Fumiko'
'Geisha Red'	see *R.* (Aronense Group) 'Kazuko'
'Gena Mae' (A/d)	GGGa SLdr
'General D. Eisenhower'	SHea
'General Practitioner'	SLdr
'General Wavell' (EA)	CMac GGal SLdr
'Gene's Favourite'	SReu SSta
genestierianum	GGGa MSnd
'Geoffroy Millais'	LMil
'Georg Arends' (Ad)	EPfP LRHS MAsh SLdr
'George Hyde' (EA)	EPfP LRHS MAsh MBri SCoo
'George Johnstone'	SLdr
'George Reynolds' (K)	MLea
'George's Delight'	MSnd
§ × ***geraldii***	SLdr
'Germania'	CBcs COtt LMil LRHS MAsh MBri NLar NPri NSoo SPoG SReu SSta
Gertrud Schäle Group	CDoC CTri SHea
Gibraltar Group	WFar

'Gibraltar' (K) ♀H6	CBcs CDoC CDul CMac CSBt CTri CWri EPfP GGGa GKin LMil LRHS MAsh MBri MJak NHol NLar SLdr SLim SPer SReu SSta WMoo
'Gilbert Mullie' (EA)	LMil NLar NSoo SLim SReu SSta
'Gill's Crimson'	SHea SReu
'Ginger' (K)	CSBt GKin LMil
'Ginny Gee' ♀H5	CBcs CDoC CSBt CWri ECho EPfP EPot GEdr GGGa GKin IVic LMil LRHS MAsh MBri MLea MSnd NEgg NLar NSla NWad SReu SSta
§ 'Girard's Hot Shot' (EA)	ECho LRHS SReu SSta
'Girard's Variegated Hot Shot' (EA/v) ♀H4	CDoC ECho GGGa LMil MAsh MGos NEgg SHil SLdr
'Glacier' (EA)	SLdr
glanduliferum	GGGa
- EGM 347	LMil
glaucophyllum	GGGa LMil MSnd
- B&SWJ 2638	WCru
- Borde Hill form	LMil
- 'Deer Dell' **new**	LMil
- var. ***glaucophyllum***	MSnd
§ - subsp. ***tubiforme***	GGGa
Glendoick Butterscotch = 'Gle003'	GGGa
Glendoick Crimson = 'Gle004' (EA)	GGGa
Glendoick Dream = 'Gle005' (EA)	GGGa
Glendoick Ermine = 'Gle006' (EA)	GGGa
Glendoick Frolic = 'Gle007'	GGGa
Glendoick Garnet = 'Gle008' (EA)	GGGa
Glendoick Glacier = 'Gle009' (EA)	GGGa
Glendoick Goblin = 'Gle010' (EA)	GGGa
Glendoick Gold = 'Gle011'	GGGa
Glendoick Ice Cream = 'Gle013'	GGGa
Glendoick Mystique = 'Gle014'	GGGa
Glendoick Petticoats = 'Gle015'	GGGa
Glendoick Rosebud = 'Gle022' (EA)	GGGa
Glendoick Ruby = 'Gle016'	GGGa
'Glendoick Silver'	GGGa
Glendoick Snowflakes = 'Gle001' (EA)	GGGa
'Glendoick Tanager'	GGGa
Glendoick Vanilla = 'Gle017'	GGGa
Glendoick Velvet = 'Gle018'	GGGa
'Glenna'	GGGa
'Gletschernacht'	IVic
glischrum	GGGa
- subsp. ***glischroides***	GGGa LMil
§ - subsp. ***rude***	GGGa MSnd
globigerum	see *R. alutaceum* var. *alutaceum* Globigerum Group
'Glockenspiel' (K/d)	SHea SLdr
'Gloria'	see *R.* 'Bruns Gloria'
'Gloria Mundi' (G)	SHea
(Gloriana Group) 'Coral Reef'	SLdr
'Glory of Littleworth' (Ad)	LMil
'Glowing Embers' (K)	CDoC CMac CTri CWri ECho GKin MAsh MBri MLea NHol NLar NSoo SHea SLdr SLim SReu SSta
'Goblin'	MSnd SLdr
'Gog' (K)	CSBt SHea
§ 'Goldbukett'	GGGa MBri
'Goldcrest' (A)	SHea
'Golden Belle'	MAsh
Golden Bouquet	see *R.* 'Goldbukett'
'Golden Coach'	CWri ECho MGos MLea MSnd SLdr
'Golden Eagle' (K) ♀H6	CBcs CDoC ECho GKin LMil MAsh MGos MJak MSnd NLar NSoo SHea SLdr SPer SReu SSta WMoo
Golden Everest = 'Hachgold'PBR	GGGa
'Golden Flare' (A)	CBcs CDoC CDul CSBt CWri ECho GBin GKin MAsh MBri MGos MMuc NEgg SLdr
'Golden Gate'	CDoC CSBt ECho MMuc NLar
'Golden Hind' (A)	SHea
'Golden Horn' (K)	GQui SHea
(Golden Horn Group) 'Golden Horn'	SLdr
'Golden Lights' (A)	CWri ECho GKin LMil MBri MGos NEgg NLar
(Golden Oriole Group) 'Talavera'	LMil SSpi
'Golden Princess'	LMil
'Golden Ruby'	ECho SPer
'Golden Splendour'	LMil
'Golden Sunset' (K) ♀H6	CMac ECho EPfP LMil MAsh MBri MGos MLea NLar SHea WFar
'Golden Torch' ♀H4	CBcs CDoC COtt CWri ECho EPfP LMil LRHS MAsh MBri MJak MLea MSnd NLar NSoo SLdr SLim SPoG SReu
'Golden Wedding'	CBcs CSBt CWri ECho ELon LMil LRHS MAsh MBri MJak MMuc MSnd SLdr
'Golden Wit'	MAsh MMHG MMuc NEgg
'Goldfinch' (K)	SHea
'Goldflimmer' (v)	CDoC EPfP GGGa GKin LRHS MAsh MBri MJak MMuc NLar NPri SLim SPoG
(Goldfort Group) 'Goldfort'	SReu
'Goldika'	LMil
'Goldinetta'	GGGa LMil LRHS NLar
'Goldkollier'	IVic
'Goldkrone' ♀H5	CWri ELon EPfP GGGa LMil MAsh MLea SPoG SReu SSta
'Goldpracht' (K)	IVic
Goldschatz = 'Goldprinz'	CBcs IVic LMil SPoG
'Goldshine'	NSoo
'Goldsworth Orange'	CAco CWri ECho LMil SLdr
'Goldsworth Yellow'	CSBt
'Goldtopas' (K)	GGGa GKin LMil
'Gomer Waterer' ♀H6	CBcs CDoC CDul CMac COtt CSBt CWri ECho EPfP GGGa LMil LRHS MAsh MBri MJak MMuc NLar SLdr SPer SPoG SReu SSta
'Goosander'	MMuc
'Gorbella'	NSoo SReu
Gowenianum Group (Ad)	LMil
'Grace Seabrook' ♀H5	CDul CSBt CTri CWri ECho ELon GGGa MBri MMuc SLdr SPer SReu
'Graf Lennart'	GGGa LMil
'Graffito'	GGGa IVic LMil
'Graham Thomas'	LMil
'Grand Slam'	ECho MSnd

	grande	GGGa LMil MSnd SLdr
	- KR 9483 **new**	WPGP
	- pink-flowered	MSnd
	gratum	see *R. basilicum*
	'Graziella'	GGGa LMil NPri SPoG SSta
	'Greensleeves'	LMil MAsh
	'Greenway' (Kurume) (EA)	CBcs SLdr
	(Grenadier Group) 'Grenadier'	LMil SHea
	griersonianum	GGGa LMil
	griersonianum* × *yakushimanum	SLdr
	griffithianum	MSnd SLdr
	- B&SWJ 2425	WCru
	- KR 10075 **new**	MSnd
	'Gristede' ♀H5	ECho LMil LRHS MGos MLea NLar SReu SSta
	groenlandicum	ETwe MLea NLar SPer WSHC
	- 'Compactum'	GKin NLar
	- 'Helma'	IVic NLar
	- 'Lenie'	NLar
	(Grosclaude Group) 'Grosclaude'	SHea
	'Grouse' × ***keiskei*** var. ***ozawae*** 'Yaku Fairy'	ECho
	'Grumpy'	CBcs CSBt CWri ECho EPfP GBin LMil LRHS MAsh MBri SReu
	'Gumpo' (EA)	CMac SLdr
	'Gumpo Pink' (Satsuki) (EA)	SLdr
	'Gumpo White' (EA)	LRHS MAsh MBri SPoG
	'Gundula'	LMil
	'Gunter Dinger'	IVic
	'Gwenda' (EA)	CTri SLdr
	'Gwendoline' (A)	SReu SSta
	habrotrichum	GGGa LMil
	'Hachmann's Anastasia'	LMil
	'Hachmann's Brasilia'	SSta
	'Hachmann's Charmant'	EPfP GGGa SPoG
	'Hachmann's Constanze'	LMil
	'Hachmann's Diadem'	LMil
	'Hachmann's Eskimo'	LMil SLdr
	'Hachmann's Junifeuer'	SReu SSta
	'Hachmann's Kabarett'	LMil NLar SPoG
	'Hachmann's Marlis' ♀H6	LMil SPoG SReu
§	'Hachmann's Metallica' **new**	GGGa LMil SPoG
	Hachmann's Picobello = 'Hachpico'PBR	EPfP GGGa SPoG
§	'Hachmann's Polaris' ♀H7	CDoC COtt LMil MJak NLar NSoo
	'Hachmann's Porzellan' ♀H6	LMil
§	'Hachmann's Rokoko' (EA)	CEnd LMil SReu SSta
	'Hachmann's Sunny Boy'	LRHS MBri
§	'Hachmann's Tanaga' **new**	GGGa
	haematodes	GGGa LMil SLdr
§	- subsp. ***chaetomallum***	GGGa LMil MSnd
	- subsp. ***haematodes***	LMil
	'Halfdan Lem' ♀H4	CBcs CDoC ECho GGGa GKin LMil MAsh MBri MMuc NLar SLdr SLim SPer SReu SSta
	'Hallelujah'	IVic
	'Halopeanum'	GGGa SHea
	'Halton'	LMil
	'Hamlet' (M)	LMil
	'Hammondii'	LMil
	'Hampshire Belle'	LMil SReu SSta
	'Hana-asobi' (Kurume) (EA)	SLdr
	hanceanum 'Canton Consul'	GGGa
	- Nanum Group	CBcs GGGa

	'Hanger's Flame' (A)	LMil
	'Hank Windsor' **new**	CAco
	Hans Hachmann = 'Hachhans' **new**	GGGa LMil
	'Hansel'	CDoC CWri ECho LMil MAsh MMuc SLdr
	Happy Group	ECho
	'Hardijzer Beauty' (Ad)	SLdr
	'Hardy Gardenia' (EA/d)	LMil SReu SSta
	hardyi	see *R. augustinii* subsp. *hardyi*
	'Harkwood Red' (EA)	SLdr
	'Harry Tagg'	SLdr
	Harry White's hybrid (A)	SReu SSta
	'Harvest Moon' (K)	MBri NLar SCoo SHea SLdr SSta
	'Hatsu-giri' (EA)	CMac LMil SLdr SPer SReu SSta
	(Hawk Group) 'Crest' ♀H3	CWri GGGa LMil SSta
	'Heather Macleod' (EA)	SLdr
	heatherae	GGGa LMil
	- KR 6176	LMil
	- KR 6187	LMil
	'Heidi'PBR (EA)	SLdr
	'Helen Close' (Glenn Dale) (EA)	SLdr
	'Helena Evelyn' (A)	LMil
	'Helene Schiffner'	LMil SReu
	heliolepis	GGGa LMil
	- var. ***fumidum***	see *R. heliolepis* var. *heliolepis*
§	- var. ***heliolepis***	GGGa
	hemidartum	see *R. pocophorum* var. *hemidartum*
	hemsleyanum	LMil MSnd SLdr
	'Herbert' (EA)	CMac LMil NSoo SLim
§	'Herbstzauber'	LMil LRHS MAsh NLar
	'Heureuse Surprise' (G)	SLdr
	'High Summer'	LMil LRHS
	'Hilda Margaret'	SReu
	'Hille'	LMil
	'Himmelberg'	GGGa
	'Hinamayo'	see *R.* (Obtusum Group) 'Hinomayo'
	'Hino-crimson' (Kurume) (EA) ♀H4	CBcs CDoC CHel CMac CSBt CTri GKin LMil LRHS MAsh MBri MMuc NHol NLar NSoo SGol SLdr SPoG SReu SSta
	'Hinodegiri' (EA)	CMac CSBt SLdr SReu
	'Hino-scarlet' (EA)	CBcs
	hippophaeoides	GKev LMil MSnd SLdr
	- 'Bei-ma-shan'	see *R. hippophaeoides* 'Haba Shan'
§	- 'Haba Shan' ♀H6	GGGa LMil WThu
	hirsutum	LMil MSnd
	- f. ***albiflorum***	MSnd
	- 'Flore Pleno' (d)	ECho
	hirtipes	GGGa MSnd
	hodgsonii	LMil MSnd SLdr
	- B&SWJ 219A **new**	WCru
*	'Hogi-kasane' (A)	NLar
	'Homebush' (K/d) ♀H6	CBcs CDoC CMac CTri CWri EPfP GBin LMil MAsh MBri MGos MJak NLar NSoo SLdr SPoG SReu SSta WMoo
	'Honey Butter'	LMil SLim
	'Honeysuckle' (K)	NHol SHea SReu SSta
§	'Ho-o' (Kurume) (EA)	CBcs SLdr
	hookeri	LMil
	- Tigh-na-Rudha form	GGGa
	'Hoppy'	CBcs CWri LMil MAsh MBri MGos MLea MMuc MSnd NLar SLdr SLim SPer SPoG

	'Horizon Monarch' 🏆H4	CDoC CWri GGGa GKin IVic LMil LRHS MBri MLea NLar SLdr SLim SReu SSta
	horlickianum	GGGa
	'Hortulanus H. Witte' (M)	CSBt SReu
	'Hot Shot'	see *R.* 'Girard's Hot Shot'
	'Hotei'	CBcs CSBt ECho EPfP GKin LMil LRHS MAsh MBri NEgg NHol SLdr SPer SReu SSta
	(Hotspur Group) 'Hotspur' (K)	CWri ECho GBin MGos SLdr
	- 'Hotspur Red' (K) 🏆H6	CDoC GKin LMil MAsh MBri MMuc NEgg SHea WMoo
	huanum	GGGa LMil
	- EGM 316	LMil
	'Hugh Koster'	SLdr
	aff. ***huidongense***	LMil
	'Hullaballoo'	LMil
	Humming Bird Group	CMHG LMil SLdr
	hunnewellianum	MSnd
	'Hussar'	CWri LMil
	'Hyde and Seek'	GQui
	'Hydon Dawn' 🏆H5	CBcs CDoC CWri LMil MBri MLea MMuc MSnd SHea SLdr SReu SSta
	'Hydon Hunter' 🏆H5	CBcs MSnd SHea SReu SSta
	'Hydon Pink'	SHea
	'Hydon Velvet'	CBcs LMil SLdr SReu WMoo
	hylaeum	MSnd
	Hyperion Group	SReu
	hyperythrum	GGGa LMil MSnd
	hypoglaucum	see *R. argyrophyllum* subsp. *hypoglaucum*
	'Ice Cube'	ECho MLea MMuc NLar SLdr
	'Iceberg'	see *R.* (Lodauric Group) 'Lodauric Iceberg'
	(Idealist Group) 'Idealist'	LMil
	'Ightham Yellow'	SHea SReu
	'Ilam Carmen' (K)	SHea
§	'Ilam Melford Lemon' (A)	LMil
§	'Ilam Ming' (A)	LMil
	'Ilam Violet'	LMil
	'Imago' (K/d)	LMil
§	'Ima-shojo' (Kurume) (EA/d)	CMac LRHS SLdr
	impeditum	CBcs CSBt ECho GBin GEdr GKev GQui MJak MLea MMuc MSnd NSoo SLdr SPer SReu SSta
	- 'Blue Steel'	see *R. fastigiatum* 'Blue Steel'
	- 'Indigo'	GKin SLdr SReu WAbe
	- 'Pygmaeum'	NHar WAbe WThu
	imperator	see *R. uniflorum* var. *imperator*
	(Impi Group) 'Impi'	LMil
§	***indicum*** 'Macranthum' (EA)	SLdr
	'Ingrid Mehlquist'	GGGa
	Inkarho Lilac Dufthecke = 'Rhodunter 149'[PBR]	LMil
	insigne 🏆H6	GGGa GLin LMil MSnd
	- Reuthe's form	SReu
	insigne × ***yakushimanum***	SReu
	Intrifast Group	GGGa
	iodes	see *R. alutaceum* var. *iodes*
	'Irene Koster' (O) 🏆H5	CDoC CSBt CWri EPfP GGGa GKin LMil MBri MLea NLar SLdr SLim SPer
	'Irohayama' (Kurume) (EA) 🏆H3	CBcs CEnd CMac EPfP GQui LMil LRHS MAsh NPri SLdr
	irroratum	LMil
	- subsp. ***irroratum***	MSnd

*	- subsp. ***kontumense*** var. ***ningyuenense***	GLin
	- 'Polka Dot'	GGGa LMil
	- subsp. ***yiliangense*** EGM 339	LMil
	'Isabel'	NPri
	'Isabel' (EA)	LRHS MAsh MBri
	'Isola Bella'	GGGa
	iteaphyllum	see *R. formosum* var. *formosum* Iteaphyllum Group
	'Ivette' (Kaempferi) (EA)	CMac
	'J.C. Williams'	CBcs
	'J.M. de Montague'	see *R.* 'The Honourable Jean Marie de Montague'
	'Jack A. Sand' (K)	GGGa
	'Jacksonii'	LMil
	(Jalisco Group) 'Jalisco Eclipse'	LMil
	- 'Jalisco Elect'	CWri SLdr
	- 'Jalisco Janet'	LMil SHea SLdr
	- 'Jubilant'	LMil SHea
	'James Burchett' 🏆H6	LMil SReu
	'James Gable' (EA)	MAsh SLdr
	Janet Group **new**	LMil
	japonicum (A. Gray) Valcken	see *R. molle* subsp. *japonicum*
	- var. ***pentamerum***	see *R. degronianum* subsp. *degronianum*
	jasminiflorum (V)	GGGa
	'Jason'	LMil
	javanicum (V)	GGGa
	'Jean Marie Montague'	see *R.* 'The Honourable Jean Marie de Montague'
	'Jeff Hill' (EA)	ECho SLdr
	'Jenny'	see *R.* 'Creeping Jenny'
	'Jessica Rose' (A)	LMil
	'Jim Russell' (*ciliicalyx* hybrid)	GGGa
	'Jingle Bells'	GGGa
	'Joan Paton' (A)	SLdr
	'Jock'	SLdr
	Jock Group	CBcs CMHG
	'Jock Brydon' (O)	GGGa LMil SHea
	'Johann Sebastian Bach' (EA)	SLdr
	'Johanna' (EA) 🏆H5	CDoC CEnd CTri EPfP LMil LRHS MAsh MBri NHol NPri SLdr SPer
	'John Cairns' (Kaempferi) (EA)	CMac SLdr
	'John Walter'	SHea
	'John Waterer'	SHea
	johnstoneanum	CBcs GGGa LMil SLdr
	- KW 7732	SLdr
	- 'Double Diamond' (d)	IDee LMil
	'Jolie Madame' (Vs) 🏆H6	CWri ECho EPfP GKin LMil LRHS MAsh MBri MLea MMuc NLar NPri SLdr
	'Joseph Hill' (EA)	CEnd ECho NLar
	'Jubilee'	SLdr
	'Juliette' (EA)	IVic
	'June Fire' (A)	GGGa SReu SSta
	'Juniduft' (A) **new**	GGGa
	kaempferi (EA)	CBcs LMil SLdr
	- 'Damio'	see *R. kaempferi* 'Mikado'
§	- 'Mikado' (EA)	LMil NSoo SReu
	- orange-flowered (EA)	CMac
	'Kali'	GGGa
	'Kalinka'	LMil MAsh MBri MMuc NLar SPoG
	'Karen Triplett'	LMil
	'Karin'	MJak

	'Karl Naue' **new**	SReu
	'Kasane-kagaribi' (EA)	SLdr
	'Kate Waterer' ♀H5	SReu
	'Kathleen' de Rothschild (K)	SHea
	'Kathleen' van Nes (EA)	SLdr
	'Katy Watson'	SReu SSta
	'Keija' (EA)	SLdr
	keiskei compact	ITim
	- Cordifolium Group	WAbe
	- var. ***ozawae*** 'Yaku Fairy' ♀H5	LMil WAbe WThu
	keleticum	see *R. calostrotum* subsp. *keleticum*
	'Kelsay's Double'	MLea
	'Ken Janeck'	GGGa
§	***kendrickii***	GGGa
	'Kermesinum' (EA)	CTri MAsh NWad SHil SLim SReu
I	'Kermesinum Rosé' (EA) ♀H5	CSBt ECho LMil MLea SLdr SLim SReu
	kesangiae	GGGa LMil
	- AC 5343	LMil
	- KR 9444 **new**	GKev
	- var. ***album***	GGGa
	Kewense Group	CWri
	keysii	GGGa LMil
	(Kilimanjaro Group) 'Kilimanjaro'	LMil SReu
	'Kimbeth'	GGGa
	'King George' Loder	see *R.* (Loderi Group) 'Loderi King George'
	kingianum	see *R. arboreum* subsp. *zeylanicum*
	'Kings Ride'	LMil
§	'Kirin' (Kurume) (EA/d)	CBcs LMil NLar SLdr
	'Kirsten Begeer'	IVic
	kiusianum (EA)	LMil SReu
I	- 'Album' (EA)	LMil SReu WAbe
	- 'Hillier's Pink' (EA)	LMil
	'Klondyke' (K) ♀H6	CBcs CSBt CTri EPfP GGGa GKin LMil LRHS MAsh NLar NPri SHea SLdr SPoG SReu
	'Kluis Sensation' ♀H5	CMac CSBt SLdr SReu SSta
	'Kluis Triumph'	SReu
	'Knap Hill Apricot' (K)	LMil SHea
	'Knap Hill Red' (K)	CDoC LMil SHea
	'Knap Hill Yellow' (K)	SHea
	'Kobold' (EA)	SLdr
	'Koichiro Wada'	see *R. yakushimanum* 'Koichiro Wada'
	'Kokardia'	LMil
	'Kokette'	IVic
	kongboense	GGGa WAbe
	'Königstein' (EA)	IVic LMil SHil SReu SSta
§	'Koningin Emma' (M)	GKin LMil NLar
	'Konsonanz'	IVic
	'Koromo-shikibu' (EA)	GGGa
	'Koromo-shikibu White' (EA)	GGGa
	'Koster's Brilliant Red' (M)	CSBt EPfP MBri SReu SSta
	'Kranenfee' (A)	GGGa
§	'Kure-no-yuki' (Kurume) (EA/d)	CEnd LMil
	kyawii	CPne GGGa
	'Lackblatt'	see *R.* (Volker Group) 'Flavum Lackblatt'
	(Lactcombei Group) 'Robert Keir'	SLdr
	lacteum	GGGa LMil
	'Lady Alice Fitzwilliam' ♀H3	CBcs CMHG CMac ECre GGGa GKin IDee LMil LRHS
	(Lady Chamberlain Group) 'Bodnant Yellow'	LMil
§	(Lady Chamberlain Group) 'Salmon Trout'	LMil
	'Lady Clare' (K)	SHea
	'Lady Clementine Mitford' ♀H5	CSBt CWri ECho LMil MAsh MLea MMuc SEND SHea SLdr SPer SReu
	'Lady Eleanor Cathcart'	SHea SLdr
	'Lady Louise' (EA)	SLdr
	'Lady Robin' (EA)	SLdr
	'Lady Romsey'	LMil
	laetum (V)	GGGa
	Lamellen Group	LMil
	lanatoides	GGGa
	lanatum	ECho GGGa LMil
	aff. ***lanatum*** Flinckii Group AC 5441	GLin
	'Langworth'	CWri ECho LMil MLea MMuc SLdr SReu
	lanigerum	LMil SReu
	'Lanzette'	IVic
	lapponicum Parviflorum Group	GGGa
	'Lapwing' (K)	NLar SLdr
	'Laramie'	GGGa
	'Late Love' (EA)	CDoC
*	***laterifolium***	GGGa
§	***latoucheae*** (EA)	LMil
	Laura Aberconway Group	SHea SLdr
	'Lavender Brilliant' (EA)	SLdr
	'Lavender Girl' ♀H5	CMac LMil SLdr SReu SSta
	'Le Progrès'	LMil
	'Lea Rainbow'	MLea
	'Ledifolium'	see *R.* × *mucronatum*
	'Ledifolium Album'	see *R.* × *mucronatum*
	'Lee's Dark Purple'	COtt CWri LMil
	'Lee's Scarlet'	LMil
	'Lemon Dream'	LMil LRHS MAsh MBri NLar NPri SLim
*	'Lemon Drop' (A)	GGGa
	'Lemon Meringue'	LMil
	'Lemonora' (M)	CBcs GKin
	'Lem's 45'	CBcs CWri ECho SLdr
	'Lem's Cameo' ♀H3	GGGa LMil SReu SSta
	'Lem's Monarch' ♀H4	CBcs CDoC COtt CWri ELon GGGa LMil LRHS MBri MLea MMuc SLdr SReu SSta
	'Lem's Tangerine'	CDoC LMil
	'Lemur' (EA)	ECho GGGa LMil LRHS MLea NLar WThu
	'Leni'	LRHS MAsh MBri
	'Leo' (EA)	SLdr
	'Leonardslee Giles'	SLdr
	'Leonardslee Primrose'	SLdr
	'Leonore'	LMil
	lepidostylum	CMac CWri GGGa LMil
	lepidotum	GGGa
	- var. ***album***	GGGa
	- yellow-flowered McB 110	WThu
§	***leptocarpum***	GGGa
§	'Leucanthum'	GGGa WThu
	leucaspis	GGal SLdr
	'Leuchtpolster'	IVic
	'Lewis Monarch'	GQui
	'Libretto'	LMil
	'Lila Pedigo'	CWri ECho MGos MMuc SLdr SPer
	'Lilactina'	SLdr
	'Lily Marleen' (EA)	CTri SCoo

	Name	Suppliers
	'Linda' ♀H5	CBcs CTri CWri ECho EPfP GGGa LMil MAsh MBri MJak MLea MMuc
	'Linda Stuart' (EA)	GGGa
	lindleyi	GGGa
	- 'Dame Edith Sitwell'	LMil
	- 'Geordie Sherriff'	GGGa
	'Linearifolium'	see *R. stenopetalum* 'Linearifolium'
	'Linnet' (K/d)	SHea SLdr
	Lionel's Triumph Group	LMil
	'Lisetta'	WMoo
	'Little Beauty' (EA)	SLdr
	'Little Ben'	ECho
	'Loch Arkaig'	GGGa
	'Loch Awe'	GGGa LMil
	'Loch Earn'	GGGa
	'Loch Faskally'	GGGa
	'Loch Laggan'	GGGa
	'Loch Leven'	GGGa
	'Loch Linnhe'	GGGa
	'Loch Lomond'	GGGa
	'Loch Morar'	GGGa
	lochiae (V)	GGGa
	'Lochinch Spinbur'	GQui
	Lodauric Group	SReu
§	- 'Lodauric Iceberg'	LMil SReu
	'Lodbrit'	SReu
	Loderi Group	SLdr SPer
	- 'Loderi Fairy Queen'	SLdr
	- 'Loderi Game Chick'	LMil SLdr
	- 'Loderi Georgette'	SLdr
	- 'Loderi Helen'	LMil SLdr
§	- 'Loderi King George' ♀H4	CAco CBcs CDoC CWri ECho GGGa GKin IVic LMil MLea SLdr SReu SSta WGwG
	- 'Loderi Patience'	SLdr
	- 'Loderi Pink Diamond' ♀H4	CBcs CDoC CWri LMil SLdr
	- 'Loderi Pink Topaz'	SLdr
	- 'Loderi Venus' ♀H4	CBcs LMil SLdr SReu SSta
	- 'Loderi White Diamond'	SLdr
	'Loderi Helen'	LMil SLdr
	'Loderi Pink Coral'	LMil SLdr
	'Loderi Pretty Polly'	SLdr
	'Loderi Princess Marina'	SLdr
	'Loderi Sir Edmund'	LMil SLdr
	'Loderi Sir Joseph Hooker'	SLdr
	'Loderi Titan'	SLdr SReu SSta
	'Loder's White' ♀H3	CBcs LMil MLea SHea SReu SSta
	longesquamatum	GGGa MSnd
	longipes	GGGa LMil MSnd SLdr
	- EGM 336	LMil
	- var. ***chienianum***	LMil MSnd
	'Lord Roberts' ♀H6	CBcs CDoC CMac CSBt CTri CWri ECho EPfP GBin GGGa LMil LRHS MAsh MJak MLea NHol NLar SHea SLdr SLim SPer SReu SSta WMoo
	'Lori Eichelser'	GEdr
	'Louis Pasteur'	SReu
	'Louisa' (EA)	MAsh NLar
	'Louise Dowdle' (Glenn Dale) (EA)	SLdr
	'Lovely William'	CMac LMil SLdr
	lowndesii	WAbe
	'Lucy Lou'	GGGa
	ludlowii	GGGa WAbe
	'Luisella'	IVic
	'Lullaby' (EA)	SLdr
	'Lunar Queen'	SLdr
	luteiflorum	GGGa

	Name	Suppliers
	- KW 7833	MSnd
	lutescens	CBcs CTsd LMil MSnd SLdr SReu WAbe WThu
	- 'Bagshot Sands' ♀H3	GGGa LMil LRHS SLdr
	- 'Exbury'	CExl
	luteum (A) ♀H5	Widely available
	- 'Golden Comet' (A)	GGGa
	lyi	GGGa
*	'Mac Ovata'	CMac
	macabeanum ♀H3	CBcs CDoC GBin GGGa GKev GKin LMil MLea MMuc MSnd SLdr SPer SReu SSpi SSta
	- NAPE 052	GGGa
	- Reuthe's form	SReu
	macabeanum × wardii	GGGa
	'Macarena'	IVic LMil
	macgregoriae (V)	GGGa
	macranthum	see *R. indicum* 'Macranthum'
	macrosmithii	see *R. argipeplum*
	maculiferum	GGGa
	'Madame Ad. van Hecke' (EA)	CTri GKin IVic LMil MAsh MBri MMuc NLar NSoo SHil SLdr SLim
	'Madame de Bruin'	SLdr
	'Madame Galle'	NSoo
	'Madame Masson' ♀H6	CDoC COtt CTri CWri ECho ELan LMil LRHS MAsh MBri MGos MLea MMuc NLar NPri SPer SReu SSta
	maddenii	CDoC LMil
§	- subsp. ***crassum***	CBcs CExl CPne GGGa GLin IVic MSnd SKHP SLdr
§	- subsp. ***maddenii*** Polyandrum Group	CBcs GGGa GGal GQui
	'Madeleine' (K)	SHea
	'Maggie'	IVic
	'Magic Flute' (EA)	LRHS MAsh MBri
I	'Magic Flute' (V)	LMil SCoo
	'Magnificum' (O)	SHea
	magnificum	GKev
	magniflorum	GGGa
	- NN 0959 **new**	MSnd
	'Maharani'	GGGa
	'Mai-ogi' (EA)	IVic
	'Maischnee' (EA)	GGGa
	'Maja' (G)	SReu SSta
	Major Group **new**	LMil
§	***makinoi*** ♀H5	GGGa LMil SReu SSpi SSta
	- 'Fuju-kaku-no-matsu'	MGos
	'Makiyak'	LMil
	mallotum	GGGa LMil MSnd
	Mandalay Group	SHea
	'Mandarin Lights' (A)	LMil NLar
	'Manderley'	LMil
	maoerense	GGGa
	'Maraschino' (EA)	GGGa IVic
	'Marcel Ménard' ♀H6	CBcs CDoC COtt GGGa LMil LRHS MAsh MBri NLar NPri SLdr SReu SSta
	'Marchioness of Lansdowne'	CWri SHea SLdr
	'Mardi Gras'	CDoC MLea NEgg NLar SLdr
	'Margaret Blain'	SReu
	Margaret Dunn Group	CWri
	'Maria Elena' (EA/d)	LMil
	'Marianka' **new**	LMil
	'Marie Curie'	LMil
	'Marie Fortie' **new**	LMil
	'Marie Hoffman'	LMil
	'Marilee' (EA)	CDoC ECho EPfP IVic LRHS MAsh NLar SLdr

'Marina' (K)	SHea
'Marinja' (EA) **new**	LMil
'Marion Merriman' (K)	SHea
'Marion Street'	LMil
'Markeeta's Prize' 🏆H4	CDoC CWri ECho EPfP GGGa LMil LRHS MAsh MBri MLea MMuc NLar NPri SHea SLim SReu
'Marlies' (A)	NLar
'Marmot' (EA)	ECho MLea MMuc NLar
'Mars'	SLdr
'Marsalla'	LMil
'Martha Isaacson' (Ad)	CWri LMil MGos MLea SLdr SReu
'Martha Wright'	EPfP GGGa LRHS MAsh MBri NPri
martinianum	GGGa
'Maruschka' (EA) 🏆H5	GGGa IVic LMil LRHS MAsh SPoG
'Mary Claire' (K)	SHea
'Mary Desby' (EA) **new**	CEnd
'Mary Forte'	NSoo
'Mary Helen' (Glenn Dale) (EA)	CWSG LMil LRHS MAsh MBri NLar SCoo SLim SPoG
'Mary Poppins' (K)	GKin LMil MAsh MBri MMuc NLar SCoo SLdr SLim WMoo
Matador Group	SReu
- 'Matador'	GGGa LMil SHea SLdr
'Mathie' (A) **new**	SReu SSta
maximum	GGGa
§ 'Maxwellii' (EA)	CMac
May Day Group	CBcs CWri MGos
- 'May Day' 🏆H3	CMac MAsh MMuc SHea SLdr
'Mayor Johnstone'	CTri EPfP MAsh NPri
'Mazurka' (K)	IVic SHea SLdr
meddianum	LMil
var. ***atrokermesinum*** F 2649 **new**	
Medusa Group	SHea SLdr
megacalyx	GGGa
'Megan' (EA)	ECho MAsh SLdr WGwG
megaphyllum	see *R. basilicum*
megeratum	GGGa SLdr
- 'Bodnant'	GGGa ITim WAbe WThu
mekongense	see *R. viridescens* Rubroluteum Group
var. ***mekongense*** Rubroluteum Group	
- - Viridescens Group	see *R. viridescens*
'Melford Lemon'	see *R.* 'Ilam Melford Lemon'
'Melidioso'	LMil
'Melina' (EA/d)	LMil
'Melville'	SSta
'Mendosina'	IVic
mengtszense	MSnd
'Mephistopheles' (K)	SHea
'Merganser' 🏆H4	GEdr GGGa LMil MLea WThu
'Merlin' (Glenn Dale) (EA)	LMil SLdr
Metallica	see *R.* 'Hachmann's Metallica'
metternichii var. ***pentamerum***	see *R. degronianum* subsp. *degronianum*
'Mi Amor'	GGGa LMil
'Miami' (A)	SLdr
'Michael Hall'	LMil
'Michael Hill' (EA)	MAsh
'Michael Waterer'	SLdr
'Michael's Pride'	CBcs GQui LMil
'Michiko' (EA)	IVic
microgynum	GGGa MSnd
- Gymnocarpum Group	MSnd
microleucum	see *R. orthocladum* var. *microleucum*
micromeres	see *R. leptocarpum*

'Midnight Beauty' **new**	EPfP
'Midnight Mystique'	GGGa SReu SSta
'Midori' (EA)	SLdr
'Midsummer'	IVic SHea
'Midsummer Mermaid' (A)	LMil MAsh
'Mikado' (EA)	see *R. kaempferi* 'Mikado'
'Millennium Gold' PBR **new**	LMil
'Milton' (R)	LMil
'Mimi' (Kaempferi) (EA)	CMac
'Mindy's Love'	LMil
'Ming'	see *R.* 'Ilam Ming'
miniatum CER 9927	GGGa
'Minikin' (K)	SHea
minus	CBcs
- var. ***minus*** (Carolinianum Group) 'Epoch'	LMil
'Miss Muffet' (EA)	SLdr
'Moerheim' 🏆H5	CBcs CWri ECho LRHS MAsh MGos MMuc NPri SLdr SLim
§ 'Moerheim's Pink'	LMil SLdr
(Mohamet Group) 'Mohamet' **new**	LMil
'Moidart' (Vs)	LMil NLar
'Moira Salmon' (EA)	SLdr
§ ***molle*** subsp. ***japonicum*** (A)	LMil MGos
- subsp. ***molle*** (A)	LMil
Mollis, orange-flowered (M)	GKin SRms
- pink-flowered (M)	GKin SRms
- red-flowered (M)	GKin
- salmon-flowered (M)	GQui
- yellow-flowered (M)	GKin GQui SRms
'Molly Ann'	ECho GEdr NLar
'Molten Gold' (v)	GGGa LMil LRHS MAsh MBri
§ 'Momoko' (EA)	LRHS WFar
monanthum	GGGa
monosematum	see *R. pachytrichum* var. *monosematum*
montroseanum	GGGa LMil MSnd SLdr
'Moon Maiden' (EA)	CDul ECho GGal GQui MMuc
Moonstone Group	MLea
'Moonstone Pink'	SLdr
'Moonstone Yellow'	MSnd SLdr
§ 'Morgenrot'	MMuc NLar
morii	GGGa
'Morning Cloud'	ECho EPfP LRHS MAsh MBri NHol NLar SLim
Morning Red	see *R.* 'Morgenrot'
'Moser's Maroon'	CBcs CWri ECho GGGa MMuc NLar SLdr
'Motet' (K/d)	SHea
'Mother of Pearl'	SLdr
'Mother's Day' (Kurume) (EA) 🏆H4	CBcs CDoC CDul CMac CSBt CTri ECho EPot GKin GQui LMil LRHS MAsh MBri MGos MJak MMuc NEgg NHol NPri SCob SLdr SLim SPer SPoG SReu SSta WFar
Moulten Gold = 'Blattgold'	LMil
'Mount Everest'	LMil SReu SSta
'Mount Saint Helens' (A)	LMil NLar SLdr SLim
'Mount Seven Star'	see *R. nakaharae* 'Mount Seven Star'
moupinense	GGGa GLin MSnd SLdr
- 'Fulmar'	GGGa
'Mrs A.C. Kenrick'	SHea
'Mrs A.T. de la Mare' 🏆H6	LMil SHea SReu SSta
'Mrs Betty Robertson'	CMac ECho GBin MMuc SLdr
'Mrs Charles E. Pearson' 🏆H6	CSBt LMil SHea SLdr
'Mrs Davies Evans'	SReu SSta

	Name	Suppliers
	'Mrs Emil Hager' (EA)	SLdr
	'Mrs Furnivall' ♀H6	CDoC CWri ECho GGGa MLea SLdr SReu
	'Mrs G.W. Leak'	CSBt CWri GGGa LMil MLea SHea SReu
	'Mrs J.C. Williams' ♀H6	LMil
	'Mrs J.G. Millais'	LMil SHea
	'Mrs James Horlick'	CWri
	'Mrs Kingsmill'	SLdr
	'Mrs Lionel de Rothschild'	CBcs CWri SReu
	'Mrs Marks' **new**	LMil
	'Mrs P.D. Williams'	SReu
	'Mrs R.S. Holford'	SHea
	'Mrs T.H. Lowinsky' ♀H6	CBcs CDoC CMac ECho ELon GGGa GKin LMil MAsh MGos MLea MMuc NLar SEND SHea SLdr SLim SPer SReu
§	× ***mucronatum*** (EA)	MSnd
	'Mucronatum'	see *R.* × *mucronatum*
	mucronulatum	CBcs MSnd
	- B&SWJ 786	WCru
	- B&SWJ 8657 **new**	WCru
	- var. ***chejuense***	see *R. mucronulatum* var. *taquetii*
	- 'Cornell Pink' ♀H5	GGGa
§	- var. ***taquetii***	GGGa
	- - B&SWJ 4486	WCru
	'Mulroy Cream'	LMil
	'Muneira' (EA)	IVic
	'Nabucco' (A)	EPfP GGGa MBri MMuc SEND WMoo
	nakaharae (EA)	MSnd SLdr SReu WAbe
	- 'Mariko' (EA)	WAbe WThu
§	- 'Mount Seven Star' (EA) ♀H5	ECho GGGa LMil MGos NWad SLdr WAbe WPat WThu
§	- orange-flowered (EA)	ECho LMil LRHS MAsh MMuc SLdr SReu
	- pink-flowered (EA)	ECho MMuc SLdr SReu
	- red-flowered (EA)	ECho
	'Nakahari Orange'	see *R. nakaharae* orange-flowered
	nakotiltum	MSnd
	'Nancy Buchanan' (K)	SLdr
	'Nancy Evans' ♀H4	CDoC CSBt ECho EPfP GGGa GGal GKin LMil LRHS MAsh MLea NLar NPri SLdr SLim SReu SSpi SSta
	'Nancy of Robinhill' (EA)	SReu
	'Nancy Waterer' (G) ♀H6	EPfP SReu
	'Nanki Poo' (EA)	SLdr
	'Naomi' (EA)	GQui SLdr
	(Naomi Group) 'Exbury Naomi'	LMil
	- 'Naomi Hope'	LMil
	- 'Naomi Nautilus'	LMil
	- 'Naomi Pink Beauty'	LMil
	- 'Naomi Stella Maris'	LMil
	'Narcissiflorum' (G/d) ♀H6	CSBt EPfP GKin LMil LRHS NLar SReu SSta
	'Naselle'	SReu
	'Ne Plus Ultra' (V)	GGGa
	neoglandulosum SIN 1828	GLin
	neriiflorum	GGGa LMil MSnd
	- CN&W 906 **new**	LMil
	- subsp. ***neriiflorum*** AC 1356	MSnd
§	- - Phoenicodum Group Farrer 877	MSnd
	'Newcomb's Sweetheart'	LMil
	'Niagara' (Glenn Dale) (EA) ♀H5	CMac LMil LRHS SLdr SPer

	Name	Suppliers
	'Nico' (EA)	CMac LRHS MAsh MBri
	'Nicoletta'	LMil
	'Night Sky' ♀H5	CDoC ECho EPfP GGGa LMil LRHS MAsh MBri MSnd NLar
	'Nightingale'	SReu
	nigroglandulosum	GGGa
	nilagiricum	see *R. arboreum* subsp. *nilagiricum*
	'Ninotschka'	IVic
	nipponicum	GGGa
	'Nishiki' (EA)	CMac
	nitens	see *R. calostrotum* subsp. *riparium* Nitens Group
	nitidulum var. ***omeiense***	GGGa WThu
	nivale subsp. ***boreale*** Ramosissimum Group	GGGa
§	- subsp. ***nivale***	GKev ITim
	niveum ♀H4	CBcs GGGa LMil MSnd SReu
	- B&SWJ 2611	WCru
	- B&SWJ 2659	WCru
	- B&SWJ 2675	WCru
	nobleanum	see *R.* Nobleanum Group
§	Nobleanum Group	CBcs GGGa LMil MSnd SLdr SSta
	- 'Nobleanum Coccineum'	LMil SLdr SReu
	- 'Nobleanum Venustum'	CWri LMil SReu SSta
	Nobleanum Album Group	GGGa LMil SReu SSta
	(Norderney Group) 'Oudijk's Sensation'	CBcs CWri ECho GQui MAsh MMuc SEND SHea SLdr
	'Nordlicht' (EA)	SLdr
	'Norfolk Candy'	LMil LRHS
	'Noriko' (EA)	SLdr
	'Norma' (R/d)	SReu
	'Northern Hi-Lights' (A)	GKin LMil MBri NLar SLim
	'Nova Zembla'	CBcs CDoC CTri ECho ELon EPfP GGGa LMil LRHS MAsh MMuc NEgg SLim SPer SReu SSta
	'Nuccio's Blue Moon' (EA)	LMil SLdr
	nudiflorum	see *R. periclymenoides*
	nudipes	MSnd
	nuttallii	GGGa LMil
	nymphaeoides CGG 14027	GGGa
	'Oban'	EPot GEdr ITim NSla WAbe WThu
	Obtusum Group (EA)	SLdr
	- 'Amoenum' (EA/d)	CBcs CDoC CMac CSBt ECho LMil SLdr SPer
	- 'Amoenum Coccineum' (EA/d)	CBcs SLdr SReu SSta
§	- 'Hinomayo' (EA) ♀H5	CMac CTri EPfP GKin GQui LMil SLdr SPer SReu
	occidentale (A)	CDul GGal GKin LMil SHea
	- SIN 1830	GGGa GLin
	ochraceum ♀H5	GGGa LMil
	'Odee Wright'	CTri CWri LRHS MAsh SLdr
	'Odoratum' (Ad)	MLea
	'Oh! Kitty'	ECho LMil MLea SLdr
	'Old Gold' (K)	ECho SHea SLdr
	'Old Port'	CWri LMil
	'Olga' ♀H5	LMil NLar SHea SReu SSta
	'Olga Niblett' (EA)	NSoo SReu SSta
	oligocarpum	GGGa
	'Olive'	SLdr
	'Olympic Sunrise'	LMil
I	'Olympic Torch'	LMil
§	'One Thousand Butterflies'	SLdr
	'Ophelia' (EA)	SLdr
	'Opossum' (EA)	GGGa
	'Orange Beauty' (Kaempferi) (EA)	CBcs CDoC CMac ECho GGGa MAsh MGos SGol SLdr SReu

'Orange King' (EA) ♀H5 LMil SLdr SPoG
'Orangeade' (K) SHea
orbiculare ♀H5 CBcs GGGa LMil MSnd
§ - subsp. ***cardiobasis*** GGGa MSnd
'Orchid Lights' MAsh MBri
'Oregon' (EA) SLdr
Oregonia Group LMil
oreodoxa LMil
§ - var. ***fargesii*** ♀H6 GGGa LMil MSnd
- - AC 4052 MSnd
- var. ***oreodoxa*** GGGa LMil
oreotrephes ♀H4 GKev IDee LMil LRHS MSnd SHea SLdr
- 'Bluecalyptus' GGGa
§ - Exquisitum Group SLdr
- 'Pentland' GGGa IDee LMil LRHS
'Orient' (K) SHea
'Orion' ambig. NLar
§ ***orthocladum*** var. ***microleucum*** GGGa WThu
'Oryx' (O) SHea
'Osaraku Seedling' (EA) EPfP SSta
'Osmar' ♀H5 GGGa
'Ostara' MGos
'Osterschnee' IVic
'Oudijk's Favorite' SLdr
'Oxydol' (K) IVic SHea SLdr
§ ***pachypodum*** GGGa
pachysanthum ♀H6 CDoC GGGa GKin IDee LMil LRHS MSnd SLdr SReu SSpi
- 'Crosswater' LMil MAsh
pachysanthum × ***yakushimanum*** SReu
pachytrichum GGGa
§ - var. ***monosematum*** MSnd
'Palestrina' (Vuykiana) (EA) ♀H4 CBcs CDul CMac CSBt ECho EPfP GBin GKin MAsh MJak MMuc NLar SGol SLdr SPer SReu SSta
paludosum see *R. nivale* subsp. *nivale*
'Pancake' CMac
'Panda' (EA) ♀H5 CSBt CTri ECho EPfP EPot GGGa LMil LRHS MAsh MBri MLea NPri SSta
'Paprika Spiced' ECho MGos MLea
'Parfait' (EA) LMil
'Parkfeuer' (A) GGGa IVic
parmulatum LMil
- KW 5876 LMil
- 'Ocelot' GGGa
parryae AM (*roseatum*) GGGa
(Pastel Group) 'Vanessa Pastel' ♀H3 CMac GGGa LMil SReu
'Patty Bee' ♀H5 CBcs CSBt CTri CWri ECho EPfP EPot GBin GEdr GGGa GKev LMil LRHS MAsh MBri MLea NLar NPri NSla SLdr SLim SReu SSpi SSta
patulum see *R. pemakoense* Patulum Group
'Pavane' (K) SHea
'Pearce's American Beauty' LMil
'Peep-bo' (EA) SLdr
'Peeping Tom' NHol SReu SSta
pemakoense GGGa SLdr WThu
§ - Patulum Group SLdr
'Pemakofairy' WThu
pendulum GGGa
Penelope Group SReu
'Penheale Blue' ♀H5 GKin LMil
'Penjerrick' GGGa
'Penny Tomlin' SReu SSta
pentaphyllum (A) GGGa
'Peppermint Candy' **new** LMil
'Peppina' GGGa LMil
'Percy Wiseman' ♀H5 CBcs CDoC CDul COtt CSBt CWri ECho EPfP GBin GGGa GKin LMil LRHS MAsh MBri MJak MLea MMuc MSnd NEgg NLar SLdr SLim SPer SPoG SReu SSta
§ ***periclymenoides*** (A) GGGa GKev LMil
'Persil' (K) ♀H6 CBcs CMac CSBt CTri CWri ECho EPfP GGGa GKin LMil LRHS MAsh MBri MJak MLea MMuc NEgg NHol NLar SCoo SLdr SPer SReu SSta WFar WMoo
'Peter Chapell' GGGa
'Peter Gable' (EA) SLdr
'Peter Koster' (hybrid) GKin SLdr
'Peter Koster' (M) SHea
petrocharis GGGa
'Petrouchka' (K) SHea
'Pfauenauge' GGGa
phaeochrysum MSnd SLdr
§ - var. ***levistratum*** MSnd SLdr
- var. ***phaeochrysum*** GKev
- - C 12529 GGGa
'Phalarope' GEdr MMuc SReu
phoenicodum see *R. neriiflorum* subsp. *neriiflorum* Phoenicodum Group
'Phyllis Korn' CWri IVic LMil
§ ***piercei*** GGGa LMil MSnd
'Pilgrim' LMil
'Pine Marten' (EA) GGGa
pingianum GGGa
'Pink Bride' SLdr
'Pink Cameo' CWri
'Pink Cherub' ♀H6 ECho ELon LMil MAsh MMuc
'Pink Delight' MAsh
I 'Pink Delight' (K) GKin MGos SHea
'Pink Drift' CSBt ECho GEdr LMil MGos MMuc NSla SLdr SPer WThu
'Pink Gin' LMil LRHS
'Pink Pancake' (EA) ♀H4 ECho EPfP GKin LMil MAsh MBri NPri SLdr
'Pink Pearl' (EA) see *R.* 'Azuma-kagami'
'Pink Pearl' (hybrid) ♀H4 CAco CBcs CMac CSBt CTri CWri ECho EPfP GGGa LMil MAsh MBri MJak MMuc NPri SHea SLdr SPer SPoG SReu SSta
'Pink Pebble' ♀H5 CBcs CExl ELon MAsh MLea SLdr
'Pink Perfection' CMac SHea SLdr
'Pink Polar Bear' GKin LMil
'Pink Ruffles' (K) SHea SLdr
'Pintail' GGGa LMil LRHS MAsh
'Pipit' GGGa
'Pippa' (EA) CMac
'PJM Regal' IVic
platypodum CGG 14005 GGGa
'Pleasant White' (EA) LMil
'Plover' GGGa
pocophorum MSnd
§ - var. ***hemidartum*** MSnd
- var. ***pocophorum*** GGGa
'Point Defiance' CWri ECho MSnd
Polar Bear Group CWri ECho LMil MLea
- 'Polar Bear' CBcs CHll CSBt GGGa GKin IVic LMil SLdr SReu

'Polaris'	see *R.* 'Hachmann's Polaris'
'Polaris' (EA)	LRHS NLar
'Polarnacht'	CDoC GGGa GKin IVic LMil
poluninii	GGGa
- KR 8231	LMil
polyandrum	see *R. maddenii* subsp. *maddenii* Polyandrum Group
§ ***polycladum*** Scintillans Group	GGGa
polylepis	MSnd
- AC 3810	MSnd
'Polyroy'	GGGa
'Pomegranate Splash'	GGGa
ponticum	CDul CMac CTri CWri MGos NHol WFar
- 'Filigran'	IVic
- 'Roseum'	SGol
§ - 'Variegatum' (v)	CBcs CMac EPfP MAsh MBri MGos MLea NPri NSoo SLdr SPer SPoG SRms SSta
populare KC 0126	GGGa
'Praecox' ♀H4	CBcs CHel CSBt ECho EPfP GGGa GKev GKin LMil LRHS MAsh MBri MGos MMuc NLar NPri SLdr SLim SPoG SReu
praestans	GGGa GKin LMil LRHS MSnd SLdr
prattii	GGGa
(Prelude Group) 'Prelude' **new**	SLdr
preptum	GGGa SLdr
'President Roosevelt' (v)	CBcs CSBt EPfP GKin MAsh MGos MJak NPri NSoo SPoG SReu SSta
'Pride of Leonardslee'	SLdr
'Pridenjoy'	LMil
primuliflorum ♀H5	MSnd WAbe
- 'Doker-La'	GGGa LMil WAbe
'Prince Camille de Rohan'	LMil SHea
'Princess Alice'	CBcs SLdr
'Princess Anne' ♀H5	CBcs CMHG ECho ELon EPot LMil MAsh MLea NLar NSoo SHea SLdr SLim SPer SPoG SReu SSta
'Princess Juliana'	ECho MMuc
'Princess Margaret of Windsor' (K)	GQui LMil
principis	GGGa LMil
- 'Lost Horizon'	CDoC LMil SLdr
§ ***prinophyllum*** (A)	GGGa GKin IDee LMil LRHS
'Prins Bernhard' (EA)	MAsh SLdr
'Prinses Juliana' (EA)	MMuc SLdr SReu
'Professor Hugo de Vries'	SHea SLdr
pronum	GGGa
- R.B. Cooke form	GGGa
- Towercourt form	GGGa
proteoides	GGGa
protistum	GGGa
pruniflorum	GGGa
prunifolium (A)	GGGa LMil
przewalskii	GGGa MSnd
pseudochrysanthum ♀H5	GGGa LMil MSnd SReu
- dwarf	GGGa
pseudociliipes	GGGa
'Ptarmigan' ♀H5	ECho GEdr GGGa LMil LRHS MAsh MSnd NPri NSoo SLdr WPat WThu
pubicostatum	GLin
- AC 2051	MSnd
§ 'Pucella' (G)	CWri
pudorosum	GGGa
'Pulchrum Maxwellii'	see *R.* 'Maxwellii'

pumilum	GGGa WAbe WThu
'Pumuckl'	IVic
'Puncta'	SLdr
'Purple Cushion' (EA)	EPfP LRHS MAsh NPri
'Purple Diamond'	see *R.* Diamant Group purple-flowered
purple Glenn Dale (EA)	SLdr
'Purple Passion'PBR	LMil NLar SLdr
'Purple Queen' (EA/d)	MAsh
'Purple Splendor' (Gable) (EA)	CMac MMuc SGol SLdr
'Purple Splendour'	CBcs CSBt CWri ECho ELon LMil MLea MMuc NEgg SPer SReu SSta WMoo
'Purple Triumph' (Vuykiana) (EA) ♀H5	LMil NLar SLdr
'Purpureum Grandiflorum' **new**	LMil
'Purpurtraum' (EA) ♀H5	LMil
'Pyari'	GGGa
qiaojiaense NN 0903	GGGa MSnd
'Quail'	GGGa LMil SLdr
'Queen Alice'	NLar
'Queen Anne's'	GGGa
Queen Emma	see *R.* 'Koningin Emma'
'Queen Louise' (K)	SHea
'Queen Mary'	SReu SSta
(Queen of Hearts Group) 'Queen of Hearts'	SHea
'Queen Souriya'	SReu
'Quentin Metsys' (R)	SLdr SReu
quinquefolium (A)	GGGa LMil
Rabatz = 'Hachraba'	GGGa IVic LMil LRHS NLar SPoG
racemosum ♀H4	LMil MSnd SLdr
- 'Rock Rose' ♀H5	IDee LMil
'Racine' (G)	SReu
'Racoon' (EA)	GGGa
radicans	see *R. calostrotum* subsp. *keleticum* Radicans Group
'Raimunde' (K)	IVic
'Ramapo' ♀H6	CDoC ECho ELon EPfP GGGa LMil LRHS MAsh MBri NLar NSoo SLdr SLim SReu
'Rangoon'	LMil
'Raoul Millais'	LMil
'Raphael de Smet' (G/d)	SReu
'Rasputin'	COtt
'Razorbill' ♀H4	CDoC ECho GGGa GKin LMil LRHS NLar SLim
recurvoides	GGGa LMil MSnd SLdr SReu
- Keillour form	GGGa
'Red and Gold'	GGGa
'Red Dawn'	LRHS
'Red Delicious'	LMil SLdr
'Red Diamond'	see *R.* Diamant Group red-flowered
'Red Fountain' (EA)	ECho SLdr
'Red Jack'	COtt LMil SPoG SReu SSta
'Red Panda' (EA)	GGGa
'Red Pimpernel' (EA)	SLdr
'Red Sunset' (A)	SLdr
'Red Velour'	SLdr
'Red Wood'	GGGa
'Redwing' (EA)	CDoC MAsh SLdr
'Rennie' (A)	ECho GKin MLea MMuc SHea
'Renoir' ♀H5	CSBt LMil SLdr SReu
reticulatum (A)	LMil MSnd SReu
'Reuthe's Purple'	SReu WAbe WThu
'Rêve d'Amour' (Vs)	SReu SSta

	Name	Suppliers
	'Rex' (EA)	MAsh SLdr
	rex ♀H4	CDoC GGGa GKin LMil SLdr
	- EGM 295	LMil
§	- subsp. ***fictolacteum*** ♀H4	CDoC GGGa GKin LMil MSnd SLdr
	- - Miniforme Group	MSnd
	- subsp. ***rex*** ♀H4	MSnd
	- - NN 0904 **new**	MSnd
	rex* × *yakushimanum	SReu
	rhabdotum	see *R. dalhousiae* var. *rhabdotum*
	'Rhododendronpark Graal-Müriz' **new**	SReu SSta
	'Ria Hardijzer' (Ad)	LMil
	rigidum	GGGa GLin MSnd
	- 'Album'	LMil
	'Ring of Fire'	CWri ECho IVic LMil MGos MLea
	'Ripe Corn'	MSnd
	'Ripples' (EA)	CTrh
	ririei	GGGa LMil
	- AC 2036	LMil
	'Robert Croux'	SLdr
	'Robert Seleger'	EPfP GGGa GKin LMil LRHS MAsh MBri NSoo SReu
	'Robin Hill Frosty' (EA)	SLdr
	'Robin Hill Gillie' (EA)	SLdr
	'Robinette'	CBcs CWri ECho MAsh SLdr
	'Rocket'	CDoC CTri ELon LMil MAsh MLea MMuc SHea SLdr SLim SPoG
	'Roehr's Peggy Ann' (EA)	LMil
	'Rokoko'	see *R.* 'Hachmann's Rokoko'
	(Romany Chai Group) 'Romany Chai'	SHea
	(Romany Chal Group) 'Romany Chal'	SHea
	'Rosa' (EA)	LMil NSoo
	Rosalind Group	CMac
	'Rosalind' **new**	WFar
	'Rosalinda' (EA)	SLdr
	'Rosata' (Vs) ♀H5	GGGa GKin SReu SSta
	'Rose Bud'	CSBt CTri
	'Rose Elf'	WThu
	'Rose Glow' (A)	SReu SSta
	'Rose Greely' (Gable) (EA) ♀H5	CDoC ECho NLar SLdr SLim SPer SReu
	'Rose Haze' (Vs)	SReu SSta
	'Rosebud' (EA/d)	CBcs CMac SLdr SReu SSta
	roseum	see *R. prinophyllum*
	'Roseum Elegans'	CDoC LMil MAsh SLim
	'Rosevallon'	MSnd
	Rosinetta = 'Hachrosi' (EA)	GGGa LMil
	'Rosy Dream'	CWri ECho MAsh MMuc
	'Rosy Fire' (A)	LMil SReu
	'Rosy Lea'	MLea
	'Rosy Lights' (A)	LMil SLdr
	'Rotglocke'	IVic
	rothschildii	CDoC GGGa LMil MSnd
	'Rotkäppchen'	IVic
	'Rouge'	SHea
	rousei (V)	GGGa
	roxieanum	GGGa LMil MSnd SLdr
	- AC 1753	MSnd
§	- var. ***cucullatum***	GGGa GKev
	- var. ***oreonastes*** ♀H5	GGGa IVic LMil MSnd SSta
	- - Nymans form	SReu
	- var. ***parvum***	GGGa
	'Royal Command' (K)	CBcs CTri CWri GKin MAsh MBri SHea
	'Royal Lodge' (K)	SHea
	'Royal Mail'	SHea

	Name	Suppliers
	'Royal Ruby' (K)	CWri ECho MGos MMuc SHea
	'Royal Windsor' **new**	LMil
	'Roza Stevenson'	LMil SLdr
	'Rubicon'	CWri ECho GGGa MAsh SLdr
	rubiginosum ♀H4	GGGa LMil MSnd
	- SDR 5142	GKev
§	- Desquamatum Group	CBcs SLdr
	- pink-flowered	LMil
	rubroluteum	see *R. viridescens* Rubroluteum Group
	'Ruby Glow' (EA)	GGal
	'Ruby Hart'	GGGa MMuc
	'Ruddy Duck' (K)	SHea
	rude	see *R. glischrum* subsp. *rude*
	rufum	GGGa
	rugosum Sinclair 240 (V)	GGGa
	'Rumba' (K)	SHea
	rushforthii	GGGa
	russatum ♀H5	CBcs EPfP GGGa IDee LMil LRHS MSnd SLdr SSpi WAbe
	- blue-black-flowered	GKin IDee LMil
*	- 'Collingwood Ingram'	GGGa
	- 'Purple Pillow'	CAco NSoo
	Russautinii Group	SLdr
	Russellianum Group	GGal
	russotinctum	see *R. alutaceum* var. *russotinctum*
	'Ryde Heron' (EA)	SLdr
	'Sabina' (EA)	SLdr
	'Sacko'	CWri GGGa LMil NLar SLim
	'Saffrano'	COtt
	'Saffron Queen'	CBcs CHel SLdr
	'Sahara' (K)	SHea
	'Saint Breward'	GQui MLea
	'Saint Merryn' ♀H5	CBcs CWri ECho MMuc NSla SLdr
	'Saint Minver'	SLdr
	'Saint Tudy'	SLdr
	'Saint Valentine' (V)	GGGa
	'Salmon Sander' (EA)	SLdr
	'Salmon's Leap' (EA/v)	CMac ELan LMil LRHS MAsh MBri SReu SSta
	saluenense	LMil SLdr WThu
	'Sammetglut'	CAco CWri
	'Samuel Taylor Coleridge' (M)	GKin
	sanguineum	LMil MSnd
§	- subsp. ***didymum***	GGGa MSnd
	- subsp. ***sanguineum*** var. ***haemaleum***	GGGa LMil MSnd
	- - var. ***sanguineum*** F 25521	LMil
	'Santa Maria' (EA) ♀H5	CAco ECho LMil MGos NSoo SReu SSta
	santapaui (V)	GGGa
	'Sapphire'	WThu
	'Sappho'	CBcs CMac CWri ECho ELon EPfP GGGa GKin LMil LRHS MLea NEgg NLar SLdr SPer SReu SSta WGwG
	sargentianum	GGGa NHar WAbe WThu
	- 'Whitebait'	ITim
	'Sarled'	GGGa LMil NHar SHea WAbe WThu
	'Saskia' (K)	IVic
	'Satan' (K) ♀H6	LMil LRHS NLar NSoo SHea SReu
	Satsuki (EA)	ECho ITim SLdr
	'Saturnus' (M)	GKin
§	***scabrifolium*** var. ***spiciferum***	MSnd SLdr WAbe
	'Scandinavia'	SHea
	'Scarlet Pimpernel' (K)	SHea

'Scarlet Wonder' ♀H5	CAco CBcs CDoC CMHG CSBt CWri ECho EPfP EPot GGGa GKin LMil LRHS MAsh MBri MJak MMuc NPri NSoo SHea SLdr SReu
'Sceptre' (K)	SHea
schistocalyx F 17637	MSnd
schlippenbachii (A)	CBcs GGGa IDee LMil MSnd
- 'Sid's Royal Pink' (A)	LMil
'Schneekrone' ♀H6	GGGa
Schneeperle = 'Hachschnee' (EA) ♀H5	IVic LMil LRHS SHil
'Schneespiegel'	GGGa
scintillans	see *R. polycladum* Scintillans Group
'Scintillation' ♀H6	CBcs CWri GGGa LMil MAsh MBri MGos MLea MMuc NLar SLdr
scopulorum	GGGa SLdr
'Scotian Bells'	GGGa
scottianum	see *R. pachypodum*
'Scottish Marmalade'	GGGa
'Scout' (EA)	MAsh SLdr
scyphocalyx	see *R. dichroanthum* subsp. *scyphocalyx*
searsiae	MSnd
'Seaview Sunset'	GGGa LMil
'Seb'	SLdr
'Second Honeymoon'	CWri ECho MLea MMuc SLdr
'Seikai' (EA)	SLdr
seinghkuense	GGGa LMil
- CCH&H 8106	LMil
§ ***selense*** subsp. ***dasycladum***	MSnd
- subsp. ***jucundum***	GGGa
semibarbatum	GLin
semnoides	GGGa LMil
'Sennocke'	LMil
'September Song' ♀H4	CWri ECho ELon GGGa LMil MAsh MGos MLea MMuc NHol
'Septembercharm' new	LMil
serotinum	GGGa GLin LMil
serpyllifolium (A)	CBcs SLdr
'Sesterianum'	CMHG SLdr
Seta Group	SReu
- 'Seta'	CAbP SHea SLdr WThu
'Seville'	SHea
'Shamrock' ♀H5	CDoC ELon EPfP GEdr LRHS MAsh MBri MLea NEgg NLar NSla NSoo SLim SPoG WThu
'Shanty' (K/d)	SHea
'Sheila' (EA)	CSBt LRHS MAsh NPri
'Shelley' (EA)	LMil
shepherdii	see *R. kendrickii*
sherriffii	GGGa MSnd
'Shiko' (EA)	MAsh
'Shiko Lavender' (A)	SPoG
Shilsonii Group	LMil
'Shin-sekai' (Kurume) (EA/d)	SLdr
'Shrimp Girl'	GKin MSnd
sichotense	GGGa
sidereum	GGGa
siderophyllum	GGGa GLin MSnd
sikangense	GGGa MSnd
- var. ***exquisitum***	GGGa GLin
'Silbervelours'	IVic
§ 'Silberwolke' ♀H6	IVic LMil LRHS MAsh
'Silkeborg Silence'	GGGa
Silver Cloud	see *R.* 'Silberwolke'
'Silver Edge'	see *R. ponticum* 'Variegatum'
'Silver Glow' (EA)	CMac
'Silver Jubilee' ♀H4	LMil
'Silver Moon' (Glenn Dale) (EA)	SLdr
'Silver Queen' (EA)	ECho NSoo
'Silver Sixpence'	CBcs ECho EPfP MAsh MBri MGos MJak MLea MMuc SLdr
'Silver Skies'	LMil
'Silver Slipper' (K) ♀H6	CBcs GKin LMil MLea NHol NLar SHea SReu SSta WFar
'Silver Sword' (EA/v)	EPfP NSoo
'Silverwood' (A)	LMil
'Silvester' (Kurume) (EA)	CAco CTri LMil LRHS MAsh SLdr SReu
'Simona'	LMil
simsii (EA)	CMac LMil SLdr
'Simson'	LMil
sinofalconeri	GGGa LMil MSnd
- KR 7342	LMil
- SEH 229	LMil
sinogrande ♀H3	CBcs CDoC CHEx CPne ELon GBin GCal GGGa GKev GKin IDee LMil LRHS NPCo SLdr SPer
- APA 106 new	GGGa
- KR 4027	LMil
§ 'Sir Charles Butler'	LMil
'Sir Charles Lemon' ♀H3	CDoC CWri ECho GGGa LMil LRHS MAsh MLea SHea SLdr SPer
'Sir Robert' (EA)	MAsh MBri
'Sleeping Beauty'	WAbe
'Sleepy'	CBcs CSBt ECho MAsh MGos MLea MSnd NHol SLdr
smirnowii	GGGa IDee LMil LRHS MSnd
§ Smithii Group	CBcs
smithii	see *R. argipeplum*
'Sneezy' ♀H5	CBcs COtt CSBt CWri ECho EPfP GGGa LMil LRHS MAsh MJak MMuc MSnd SLdr SLim
'Snipe'	CTri ECho GBin GEdr LMil MAsh MBri MMuc NLar SLdr SLim SReu WThu
'Snow Crown' (*lindleyi* hybrid)	MAsh
'Snow Hill' (EA) ♀H5	CEnd LMil LRHS NLar
'Snow Lady'	CBcs CHel ECho EPfP EPot GEdr GKin GQui MAsh MMuc SLdr SReu
'Snow Pearl'	EPfP MAsh MBri
Snow Queen Group	LMil SReu
- 'Snow Queen'	LMil
'Snowbird' (A)	GGal SLdr
'Snowbird' (EA) new	CDul
'Snowflake' (EA/d)	see *R.* 'Kure-no-yuki'
'Snowstorm'	MMuc
'Soft Lips' (K)	SHea
'Soho' (EA)	GQui
'Soir de Paris' (Vs) ♀H6	CEnd CSBt GGGa GKin IVic LMil MLea NHol SReu SSta WFar WGwG
'Soldier Sam'	SReu
(Solent Group) 'Drury Lane' (K)	GQui LMil
'Solidarity'	ECho MGos MLea SLdr SReu
'Solway' (Vs)	LMil
'Sommerduft' (A)	IVic
'Son de Paris' (A)	GQui
'Sonata'	CWri GBin GGGa GGal SReu
'Sonatine'	LMil
'Songbird'	LMil LRHS MSnd SLdr
sororium (V)	LMil
- KR 3085	LMil

souliei	LMil SSpi
– deep pink-flowered	GGGa
'Souvenir de D.A. Koster'	SLdr
'Souvenir de Doctor S. Endtz'	SHea SReu
'Souvenir of Anthony Waterer'	SHea SReu SSta
'Souvenir of W.C. Slocock'	MMuc
'Spätlese'	IVic
'Spek's Orange' (M)	GKin
sperabile	GGGa LMil
– var. ***weihsiense***	LMil MSnd
sphaeranthum	see *R. trichostomum*
sphaeroblastum	GGGa MSnd
– var. ***wumengense***	GGGa GLin
– – KR 1481	MSnd
spiciferum	see *R. scabrifolium* var. *spiciferum*
'Spicy Lights' (A)	LMil
spilotum	LMil
'Spinner's Glory'	MAsh
spinuliferum	CBcs CPne GGGa
– NN 10945 **new**	MSnd
'Spitfire'	NHol SReu SSta
'Spring Beauty' (EA)	CMac SLdr SReu
'Spring Pearl'	see *R.* 'Moerheim's Pink'
'Spring Rose'	SLdr
'Spring Sunshine'	LMil LRHS
'Springday'	CMac
'Squirrel' (EA) 🏆H5	CDoC ECho GGGa GKin LMil MAsh MLea MMuc SLdr SLim SReu
'Staccato'	IVic
Stadt Essen Group	LMil SLdr
'Stadt Westerstede'	LMil
stamineum	GGGa
§ 'Stanway'	LMil
'Starbright Champagne'	MAsh MBri
'Statuette'	IVic
§ ***stenopetalum*** 'Linearifolium' (EA)	CMac LMil SLdr WAbe
stenophyllum	see *R. makinoi*
stewartianum	GGGa LMil
'Stewartstonian' (EA)	CMac MJak SReu
'Stoat' (EA)	GQui MMuc NLar
'Stopham Girl' (A)	LMil
'Stopham Lad' (A)	LMil
'Stour' (K)	SHea
'Strategist'	SHea SLdr
'Strawberry Cream'	GGGa LRHS MAsh MBri
'Strawberry Ice' (K) 🏆H6	CDoC CDul CSBt CWri ECho ELan EPfP GBin GGGa GKin LMil MAsh MBri MMHG SLdr SPer SReu WMoo
'Strawberry Sundae'	MMuc NEgg SLdr
strigillosum	GGGa GLin MSnd
– Reuthe's form	SReu
subansiriense	GGGa
suberosum	see *R. yunnanense* Suberosum Group
'Suga-no-ito' (Kurume) (EA)	SLdr
sulfureum JN 11062 **new**	MSnd
'Summer Blaze' (A)	SLdr
'Summer Dawn'	LMil
'Summer Flame'	SReu
'Summer Fragrance' (O) 🏆H6	LMil SReu SSta
'Summer Snow'	IVic
'Summer Sorbet'	LMil
'Sun Chariot' (K)	CBcs MAsh MMHG
'Sun Fire'	LMil
'Sun of Austerlitz'	SHea SLdr
Sunkist Group	SLdr
'Sunset Pink' (K)	CDul ELan SLdr
'Sunte Nectarine' (K) 🏆H6	ECho GKin GQui LMil MLea NLar SHea
suoilenhensis NVD 18	GGGa
'Surprise' ambig. (EA)	CDoC CTri SLdr
'Surrey Heath'	CBcs CDoC CWri ECho EPfP LMil MAsh MGos MJak MMuc MSnd NLar NSoo SLdr SLim
'Susan' (EA)	MSnd SSta
'Susan' J.C. Williams	LMil SReu
'Susannah Hill' (EA)	CBcs CDoC SLdr
sutchuenense	GGGa LMil MSnd
– var. ***geraldii***	see *R.* × *geraldii*
'Swamp Beauty'	CWri ECho MAsh MGos MLea MMuc SLdr WGwG
'Swansong' (EA)	CMac SLdr
'Sweet Simplicity'	CWri SHea SLdr
'Sweet Sue'	SLdr
'Swift' 🏆H4	ECho GBin GGGa GQui LMil LRHS MAsh MBri MMuc SLdr
'Sylphides' (K)	CMac
'T.S. Black' (EA)	SLdr
taggianum	GGGa
'Taka-no-tsukasa' (EA)	SLdr
taliense	LMil LRHS
– SBEC 0350	GGGa
– 'Honigduft' **new**	LMil
Tally Ho Group	SHea
tamaense	see *R. cinnabarinum* subsp. *tamaense*
Tanaga	see *R.* 'Hachmann's Tanaga'
Tanager	see *R.* 'Glendoick Tanager'
'Tangerine'	see *R.* (Fabia Group) 'Fabia Tangerine'
'Tangiers' (K)	SHea
tapetiforme	GGGa
'Taurus' 🏆H5	CDoC CWri ECho ELon GKin IVic LMil LRHS MAsh MMuc MSnd SLdr SReu WMoo
taxifolium (v)	GGGa
'Teal'	ECho GEdr
'Ted Millais'	LMil
'Teddy Bear'	CWri LMil MLea SReu SSta
telopeum	see *R. campylocarpum* subsp. *caloxanthum* Telopeum Group
Temple Belle Group	ECho
'Teniers' (R)	SReu SSta
§ ***tephropeplum***	CPne GGGa MSnd WAbe
– Deleiense Group	see *R. tephropeplum*
'Tequila Sunrise'	LMil
I 'Tequila Sunrise' USA **new**	LMil
'Terra-cotta'	LMil
'Terra-cotta Beauty' (EA)	NWad WThu
(Tessa Group) 'Tessa'	CBcs ECho SLdr
– 'Tessa Roza'	GKev
thayerianum	GGGa MSnd
§ 'The Honourable Jean Marie de Montague' 🏆H4	CWri EPfP GGGa GKin LMil MAsh MLea MMuc MSnd NLar SReu SSta
'Thomas David' (A)	LMil
thomsonii	CDoC GCal GGGa GKin IDee LMil LRHS MSnd SReu
– AC 113	MSnd
– B&SWJ 2638	WCru
– TDA 073 **new**	MSnd
– subsp. ***lopsangianum***	GGGa
'Thor'	GGGa SReu

'Thousand Butterflies'	see *R.* 'One Thousand Butterflies'
'Thunderstorm'	SReu
'Tibet'	GQui LMil
'Tidbit' ♀H3	CMac GGGa LMil LRHS MLea NLar SLdr
'Tinkerbird'	GGGa LMil LRHS MAsh MBri NPri
'Tinner's Blush' **new**	CBcs
titapuriense	GGGa
'Titian Beauty'	CBcs CDoC CSBt CWri ECho ELon EPfP GGGa LMil LRHS MAsh MGos MMuc NEgg NPri SLdr SLim SPer SPoG WMoo
'Titness Delight'	SLdr
'Tit-Willow' (EA)	LRHS MAsh MBri SCoo
tomentosum	WThu
'Torchlight' (EA) ♀H5	LMil
'Toreador' (EA)	SLdr
'Torridon' (Vs)	LMil
'Tortoiseshell Champagne'	see *R.* (Tortoiseshell Group) 'Champagne'
§ (Tortoiseshell Group) 'Champagne' ♀H3	CBcs CSBt LMil LRHS MAsh NLar SHea SReu
- 'Tortoiseshell Orange' ♀H3	CBcs CSBt CWri LMil MBri NLar SHea SLim SReu SSta
- 'Tortoiseshell Salome'	SHea
- 'Tortoiseshell Wonder' ♀H3	CWri EPfP LMil LRHS MAsh NPri SHea
'Toucan' (K)	CSBt LMil SHea
'Tower Beauty' (A)	SHea
'Tower Dainty' (A)	GGGa SHea
'Tower Daring' (A)	GGGa SHea
'Tower Dragon' (A)	LMil SHea
traillianum	LMil LRHS MSnd
'Treecreeper'	GGGa GKin LMil SLdr
'Tregedna Red'	SReu
'Trewithen Orange'	SLdr
trichanthum	GGGa
- 'Honey Wood'	LMil SLdr
§ ***trichostomum***	GGGa GKev WAbe
- Ledoides Group	LMil
- - 'Collingwood Ingram' ♀H4	IDee LRHS
triflorum	GGGa LMil
§ - var. ***bauhiniiflorum***	CBcs GGGa SLdr
- var. ***triflorum*** Mahogani Group	GGGa MSnd
- - AC 3386 **new**	MSnd
trilectorum	GGGa
triplonaevium	see *R. alutaceum* var. *russotinctum* Triplonaevium Group
'Tromba'	LMil
'Troupial' (K)	SHea
tsangpoense	see *R. charitopes* subsp. *tsangpoense*
tsariense	GGGa LMil MSnd
- var. ***trimoense***	GGGa LMil
- - KW 8288	LMil
- 'Yum Yum'	GGGa
tubiforme	see *R. glaucophyllum* subsp. *tubiforme*
'Tuffet' (EA)	LMil SLdr
'Tunis' (K)	LRHS MAsh NPri
'Turaço'	GGGa LMil SLdr
'Turnstone'	GGGa
ungernii	GGGa MSnd
§ ***uniflorum*** var. ***imperator***	GGGa
'Unique' (*campylocarpum* hybrid)	MAsh MSnd SHea SLdr SReu
'Unique' (G)	CBcs ECho EPfP GGGa MMuc
'Unique Marmalade'	ECho LMil LRHS MAsh SLdr
'Ursine'	IVic
uvariifolium var. ***griseum***	LMil MSnd
- 'Reginald Childs'	LMil
'Valencia'	IVic
valentinianum	CBcs GGGa MSnd SLdr WAbe
- F 24347	MSnd
- var. ***oblongilobatum***	GGGa
'Van'	LMil LRHS NLar SLim
'Van Houttei Flore Pleno' (G/d)	SReu SSta
'Van Nes Sensation'	LMil
Vanessa Group	GGal LMil
vaseyi (A) ♀H5	CBcs GGGa GLin LMil
- 'White Find'	GGGa
- white-flowered (A)	LMil
'Vayo' (EA)	SLdr
§ ***veitchianum*** Cubittii Group	CBcs GGGa
- KNE Cox 9001	GGGa
venator	GGGa MSnd
'Venetian Chimes'	CSBt ECho MGos MSnd SLdr
vernicosum	GGGa MSnd
- AC 1901	MSnd
- AC 4102	MSnd
'Victoria Hallett'	SLdr
'Vida Brown' (Kurume) (EA/d)	CMac SLdr SReu WThu
'Vincent van Gogh'	LMil
'Vinecourt Dream' (M)	GKin MLea NLar SLdr
'Vinecourt Duke' (R/d)	CWri ECho GKin MAsh MBri MMuc NEgg NLar
'Vineland Dream' (K/d)	CWri ECho GKin
'Vintage Rosé' ♀H5	LMil MLea MMuc
'Violetta' (Glenn Dale) (EA)	SLdr
'Violette Funken'	LMil
Virginia Richards Group	CWri LRHS MAsh
'Virginia Richards'	SLdr
§ ***viridescens***	MSnd
- 'Doshong La'	GGGa LMil
§ - Rubroluteum Group	SLdr
viscidifolium	GGGa
'Viscosepalum' (G)	SHea
viscosum (A) ♀H6	CBcs GGGa GQui LMil MBri MLea MMHG MMuc MSnd NLar SHea SReu
- 'Grey Leaf' (Vs)	LMil
- f. ***rhodanthum*** (A)	LMil
- 'Roseum' (Vs)	LMil SHea
'Viscount Powerscourt'	SLdr
'Viscy' ♀H5	CDul CWri ECho EPfP GKin LMil LRHS MGos MMuc MSnd NLar SLdr
§ Volker Group	CWri EPfP LMil LRHS MAsh MBri NLar SSta
§ - 'Flavum Lackblatt'	MGos MSnd SLdr
'Vollblut'	SReu SSta
'Vulcan' ♀H4	GGGa LMil LRHS MLea
'Vuyk's Rosyred' (Vuykiana) (EA) ♀H4	CBcs CDoC CDul CMac CTri GKin LMil MAsh MGos NHol NWad SGol SLdr SPer SPoG SReu WFar
'Vuyk's Scarlet' (Vuykiana) (EA) ♀H4	CBcs CDoC CMac CSBt CTri GKin LRHS MAsh MBri MMuc NHol NPri NWad SGol SLdr SPer SPlb SReu SSta
'W.E. Gumbleton' (M)	SReu
'W.F.H.' ♀H3	CWri IDee LMil MSnd SLdr
'Wagtail'	GGGa
'Walküre'	LMil LRHS
wallichii	GGGa LMil MSnd SLdr

- KR 8227 LMil
- Heftii Group GGGa GLin
'Wallowa Red' (K) ECho MLea MMuc SEND SLdr
'Wally Miller' ECho MAsh
walongense GGGa
'Wanna Bee' LMil
wardii GGGa GKev IDee LMil MSnd SHea
- L&S 5679 GGGa MSnd
- var. ***puralbum*** GGGa
- var. ***wardii*** AC 3425 MSnd
- - AC 3469 MSnd
'Ward's Ruby' (EA) CTrh
wasonii LMil MSnd
- SIN 1852 GLin
- f. ***rhododactylum*** MSnd
- yellow-flowered GGGa
'Water Baby' (A) LMil
'Water Girl' (A) GGGa LMil
'Waterfall' SLdr
watsonii MSnd
'Waxwing' SHea
'Wee Bee' ♀H5 CBcs CDoC ECho EPfP EPot GEdr GKin LMil LRHS MAsh MLea MMuc NLar SLdr SLim SReu SSta
'Wendy' MAsh
'Western Lights' (A) MBri
'Westminster' (O) LMil
'Weston's Pink Diamond' (d) LMil
'What a Dane' GGGa
'Whidbey Island' LMil
'Whisperingrose' LMil
'White Brocade' SSta
§ White Dufthecke = 'Rhodunter 48'PBR LMil
'White Frills' (EA) ECho NLar
'White Glory' SLdr
'White Gold' GGGa
'White Grandeur' (EA) CTrh
'White Jade' (EA) SLdr
'White Lady' (EA) SLdr
'White Lights' (A) ♀H7 EPfP LMil MBri NLar
'White Perfume' (A) SReu SSta
'White Rosebud' (EA) SReu SSta
'White Swan' (K) GKin SHea
'White Swan' (hybrid) SReu
'Whitethroat' (K/d) ♀H6 CWri ECho EPfP GQui LMil LRHS MAsh MBri MMHG MMuc SEND SLdr SReu SSta
'Whitney's Dwarf Red' WMoo
'Wigeon' LMil
wightii GGGa GLin MSnd
'Wilgen's Ruby' CDoC CSBt LMil NLar SLdr SLim
'Willbrit' CBcs CWri ECho MAsh MMuc SLdr
williamsianum ♀H4 CBcs CMac ECho GBin GGGa LMil MLea MSnd SLdr SReu
- 'Andrea' IVic
- Caerhays form CExl
'Willy' (Kaempferi) (EA) LMil SLdr
wilsoniae see *R. latoucheae*
wiltonii ♀H5 GGGa IDee LMil
'Windsor Hawk' CWri
'Windsor Lad' SReu
'Windsor Sunbeam' (K) CWri
'Wine and Roses'PBR GGGa
Winsome Group CMac CWri GGGa MAsh
- 'Winsome' ♀H3 CBcs GGal GKin MBri MJak NLar NPri SHea SLdr SSta
'Winston Churchill' (M) SReu SSta
'Winter Spice' GGGa
'Winterpurpur' IVic
'Witchery' GGGa
'Wombat' (EA) ♀H5 CTri EPfP GGGa LMil LRHS MAsh MBri NLar NPri SLdr SReu
wongii GGGa GQui MSnd SLdr
'Woodcock' SHea SLdr
'Wren' ♀H5 CAco ECho EPot GBin GEdr GGGa GKev IVic LMil LRHS MAsh MLea NSoo SLdr SReu WThu
'Wryneck' (K) SHea SLdr
xanthocodon see *R. cinnabarinum* subsp. *xanthocodon*
xanthostephanum GGGa
'XXL' SReu SSta
'Yaku Angel' IVic LMil
'Yaku Incense' ECho LMil MAsh MLea MMuc MSnd NLar
'Yaku Prince' ECho MAsh MGos MLea MMuc SLdr
'Yaku Princess' CBcs
yakushimanum ♀H5 CBcs CMHG CWri ECho GKin LMil MAsh MBri MGos MLea MMuc NHol NLar SLdr SPer SReu SSta
- 'Edelweiss' IDee LMil LRHS NLar
- Exbury form CMac SReu
- FCC form see *R. yakushimanum* 'Koichiro Wada'
§ - 'Koichiro Wada' ♀H6 CExl CMac GGGa IDee IVic LMil LRHS NLar SLdr SReu
'Yellow Cloud' (K) ECho
'Yellow Hammer' ♀H4 CMac ECho ELan GGGa GKin LMil MMuc NLar SLdr
Yellow Hammer Group CWri MGos MSnd SPer SReu SSta
'Yellow Petticoats' SReu
'Yoga' (K) SHea
yuefengense GGGa
yunnanense GGGa GGal GKev IDee LMil LRHS MSnd SLdr
- SDR 4217 GKev
- SDR 4957 GKev
- SDR 4960 GKev
- 'Openwood' ♀H3 LMil
- pink-flowered GGGa
- 'Red Throat' SLdr
- red-blotched LMil
§ - Suberosum Group SLdr
- white-flowered GGGa
aff. ***yunnanense*** IDee
zaleucum GGGa LMil
- Flaviflorum Group GGGa
- var. ***zaleucum*** MSnd
zeylanicum see *R. arboreum* subsp. *zeylanicum*
ziyuanense AC 4211 MSnd

Rhodohypoxis ✿ (*Hypoxidaceae*)

'1000 Cranes' CTal IBal
'Andromeda' CTal EWes
'Ann Brazier' NWad
'Annelies' **new** CTal
baurii ♀H4 CAvo CCCN CMea CPne ECho IBal MAsh NBir NSla SPoG WAbe WIce XLum
- 'Abigail' EWes
- 'Alba' CTal ECho IBal NSla
- 'Albrighton' CTri ECho EWes GEdr IBal NBir NHol NWad WAbe WPat
- 'Apple Blossom' CTal CTca ECho EWes GKev IBal LBee LEdu NHol NWad WAbe WFar

- 'Badger'	NWad WAbe
- var. ***baurii***	ECho EWes GKev LRHS
- var. ***baurii*** × ***baurii*** var. ***platypetala***	ECho
- 'Bridal Bouquet' (d)	CTal EWes GEdr IBal NHol WAbe
- 'Coconut Ice'	CTal EWes IBal LEdu
- var. ***confecta***	CTal ECho EWes GKev NHol WFar
- 'Daphne Mary'	EWes
- 'David Scott'	EWes
- 'Dawn'	CTal ECho EPot EWes GEdr GKev IBal LRHS WAbe
- 'Douglas'	CTal ECho EPfP EPot EWes GEdr GKev IBal LEdu NBir NHol
- 'Dulcie'	CTal ECho EWes GEdr GKev IBal WAbe
- 'Emily Peel'	CTal ECho EPot EWes GKev IBal LLHF WAbe
- 'Eva-Kate'	CTal ECho EWes GKev IBal WAbe WPat
- 'Fred Broome'	CTal CTca ECho EPot EWes GEdr GKev IBal LRHS NHol NWad WFar WPat
- 'Goliath'	EWes
- 'Harlequin'	CTal ECho EWes GEdr GKev IBal NHol NWad
§ - 'Helen'	CTal ECho EWes GEdr GKev IBal LEdu NHol WAbe
- 'Jacqueline Potterton'	CTal
- 'Kitty'	CTal EWes
- 'Lily Jean' (d)	CAby CTri ECho EPfP EPot EWes GBin GEdr GKev IBal LRHS NWad WCot
- 'Luna'	EWes
- 'Margaret Rose'	CTal CTca ECho EWes GKev IBal LLHF NHol
- 'Mars'	CTal EWes LEdu NBir NHol
- 'Monique'	EWes
- 'Pearl'	CTal ECho LRHS
- 'Perle'	ECho EWes GEdr IBal LRHS NHol NWad
- 'Pictus' (v)	CTal ECho EPot EWes GKev IBal LRHS NHol NWad WPat
- 'Pink Pearl'	CTal EWes IBal NHol WAbe
- pink-flowered	ECho
- var. ***platypetala***	CTal ECho EPfP EPot EWes GEdr GKev IBal NHol NWad WAbe XLum
- - Burtt 6981	EWes
- var. ***platypetala*** × ***milloides***	IBal LLHF NHol NWad WAbe
- 'Rebecca'	ECho EWes
- 'Red King'	EWes IBal
- red-flowered	ECho SPlb
- 'Ruth'	ECho EWes GEdr GKev IBal NHol SDeJ WAbe
- 'Susan Garnett-Botfield'	CTal ECho EWes GEdr IBal WAbe
- 'Tetra Pink'	ECho EWes GEdr IBal LRHS NHol NWad SMrm
- 'Tetra Red'	CTal ECho EWes GEdr GKev LRHS NHol NWad SDeJ WAbe WFar
- 'The Bride'	EWes GEdr
- white-flowered	CTca ECho EPot LRHS
'Betsy Carmine'	CCCN CTal GEdr IBal NWad WAbe
'Blush'	ECho IBal
'Bright Eyes' (d)	EWes
'Burgundy'	LRHS
'Butterfly Wings'	CTal NWad
'Candy Stripe'	CTal ECho EWes GEdr LRHS NWad
'Carina'	CTal ECho EWes
'Cathy' **new**	CTal
'Cayasan'	ECho WAbe
'Confusion'	EWes LEdu NHol NWad WAbe
'Dainty Dee' (d)	EWes
deflexa	CTal CWCL ECho EPot EWes GCrg GKev IBal ITim LEdu LRHS NHol NSla NWad WFar
'Donald Mann'	CTal ECho EWes GEdr LLHF NHol WAbe
'Dusky'	CTal ECho EPot EWes GEdr GKev IBal
'E.A. Bowles'	CTal ECho EWes IBal NSla WFar
'Ellicks'	CTal IBal
'Flashing Rubies'	CTal IBal
'Forge Robies' **new**	EWes
'Garnett'	ECho EWes IBal WAbe WFar
'Gemma' **new**	EWes
'Goya' (d)	ECho IBal WPat
'Great Scot'	ECho EWes GEdr GKev IBal LRHS
'Heather' **new**	CTal
'Hebron Farm Biscuit'	see *Hypoxis parvula* var. *albiflora* 'Hebron Farm Biscuit'
'Hebron Farm Cerise'	see × *Rhodoxis* 'Hebron Farm Cerise'
'Hebron Farm Pink'	see × *Rhodoxis hybrida* 'Hebron Farm Pink'
'Hinky Pinky'	GEdr
'Holden Rose' (d)	CTal ECho NHol NWad
'Hope'	CTal IBal
hybrids	CWCL ELan
'Jap Double' **new**	CTal
'Jupiter'	GEdr NWad
'Kiwi Joy' (d)	CTal EPot EWes GEdr GKev IBal LLHF NHol NWad SDeJ WAbe
'Knockdolian Red'	GEdr NHol NWad
'Louise'	CTal IBal
'Midori'	CTal ECho EWes GEdr LRHS NWad
milloides	CAby CPla CPne CTal CTca ECho EPot EWes GCrg GEdr GKev IBal ITim LBee LEdu LRHS NHol NWad WFar
- 'Claret'	CAby CSam CTal ECho ELon EWes GBin GEdr GKev ITim LLHF LRHS NHol WFar WPat
- 'Damask'	CTal ECho EPot EWes GKev IBal LRHS
- 'Donaldson'	CTal GKev
- 'Drakensberg Snow'	EWes
- giant	ECho GKev
'Monty'	ECho EWes GEdr LRHS NWad WAbe
'Mystery'	EWes NHol
'Naomi'	ECho EWes
'New Look'	CTal ECho EWes GEdr GKev IBal LLHF NWad
'Ori Zuru'	ECho GEdr
'Origami'	CTal IBal LEdu
'Pat Lacey' **new**	EWes
'Pearl White'	ECho IBal
'Pink Ice'	CTal GEdr IBal NBir NWad
'Pink Star'	LRHS
'Pinkeen'	CTal ECho EWes IBal LLHF LRHS WAbe
'Pinkie'	CTal IBal
'Pintado'	CTal ECho EWes GEdr LEdu NWad
'Pretty in Pink'	CTal
'Raspberry Ice'	CTal ECho NHol NWad
'Roman' **new**	CTal
'Rosie Lee'	CTal EWes
'Shell Pink'	CTal EWes IBal NHol NWad

Slack Top hybrids new	NSla
'Snow'	EWes
'Snow White'	EWes NHol
'Starlett'	CTal EWes IBal LRHS NHol
'Starry Eyes' (d)	ECho EWes
'Stella'	CCCN CTal ECho EPot EWes GEdr GKev IBal NHol NWad
'Sunburst'	GEdr NWad
'Telios'	IBal
'Tetra Rose'	GEdr
'Tetra White'	see *R. baurii* 'Helen'
thodiana	CTal ECho EWes GEdr GKev IBal NHol NWad WAbe WFar
'Twinkle Star Mixed'	ECho LRHS SPoG
'Two Tone'	EWes
'Venetia'	CMea CTal ECho GKev IBal NHol NWad
'Westacre Picotee'	EWes
'White Prince'	CTal
'White Wings' new	CTal
'Wild Cherry Blossom'	CTal ECho EWes IBal

Rhodohypoxis × *Hypoxis* see × *Rhodoxis*

R. baurii* × *H. parvula	see × *Rhodoxis hybrida*

Rhodoleia (*Hamamelidaceae*)

championii WWJ 11858 new	WCru
aff. ***henryi*** B&SWJ 11782	WCru
parvipetala	WCru

Rhodophiala (*Amaryllidaceae*)

§ ***advena***	NRog
araucana new	NRog
§ ***bifida***	NRog WCot
- pink-flowered new	NRog
chilensis	NRog
montana	GKev WCot
phycelloides new	NRog
pratensis	CPne
rhodolirion	SPlb
splendens	GKev

Rhodora see *Rhododendron*

Rhodothamnus (*Ericaceae*)

chamaecistus	WAbe
sessilifolius	WThu

Rhodotypos (*Rosaceae*)

kerrioides	see *R. scandens*
§ ***scandens***	CDul CExl CHel CTri ELan EPfP GKin LEdu LRHS MGil MMHG MMuc MNrw NHol NLar NSoo SLon SPoG SSpi WCru WHar WPat WSHC

× *Rhodoxis* ✿ (*Hypoxidaceae*)

'Anne Crock'	ECho EWes IBal
'Aurora'	ECho EWes
'Betsy' new	CTal
'Bloodstone'	CTal ECho EWes IBal NHol NWad
'Hebron Farm Biscuit'	see *Hypoxis parvula* var. *albiflora* 'Hebron Farm Biscuit'
§ 'Hebron Farm Cerise'	CCCN CTal ECho EWes GEdr GKev LEdu LRHS
'Hebron Farm Rose'	LLHF
§ ***hybrida***	ECho EWes IBal WAbe XLum
- 'Aya San'	ECho EWes GKev
§ - 'Hebron Farm Pink'	CBro ECho EWes GEdr GKev IBal LRHS NHol WAbe
- 'Hebron Farm Red Eye'	CCCN CTal ECho EWes GKev IBal
- 'Pink Stars'	CTal ECho IBal
- 'Ruby Giant'	CTal ECho EWes
- 'White Stars'	ECho EWes
'Irene' new	ECho
'Little Pink Pet'	CTal EWes
'Nippon' new	CTal LRHS
'Pink Tips' new	CTal IBal
'Ria' new	ECho EWes
'Sandra' new	EWes
'Sandy' new	CTal ECho EWes
'Sonja' new	ECho
'Sue' new	EWes

Rhoeo see *Tradescantia*

Rhopalostylis (*Arecaceae*)

sapida	CBrP
- 'East Cape'	SBig

rhubarb see *Rheum* × *hybridum*

Rhus (*Anacardiaceae*)

ambigua	ESwi
- B&SWJ 3656	WCru
- large-leaved, B&SWJ 10884	WCru
aromatica	CArn CDul EBtc LRHS NLar
chinensis	CMCN IDee
copallinum	EBtc WOld
coriaria	CArn NLar
cotinus	see *Cotinus coggygria*
glabra	CArn CBcs CDoC EBtc MGos SPer
- 'Laciniata' misapplied	see *R.* × *pulvinata* Autumn Lace Group
- 'Laciniata' Carrière	NLar
hirta	see *R. typhina*
incisa	SPlb
potaninii	EPfP LRHS NLar
§ × ***pulvinata*** Autumn Lace Group	EPfP
- - 'Red Autumn Lace' ♀H5	LRHS MBlu MBri MRav SPer
punjabensis	EGFP
§ ***radicans***	CArn GPoy WHer
succedanea	CDTJ
- NJM 10.154 new	WPGP
toxicodendron	see *R. radicans*
typhina	CAco CBcs CDoC CDul CHEx CLnd CMac EBee ELan EPfP GKin LBMP LRHS MAsh MGos MMuc MRav NEgg NHol NLar NWea SArc SCob SEND SGol SPer SSta WFar
§ - 'Dissecta' ♀H6	CBcs CDoC CDul CMac ELan EPfP LAst LRHS MBri MGos MJak MRav MWat NEgg NLar NPri SCob SEND SGol SPer WFar
- 'Laciniata' hort.	see *R. typhina* 'Dissecta'
- Radiance = 'Sinrus' ♀H6	LRHS MAsh MBlu SPoG
- Tiger Eyes = 'Bailtiger'PBR ♀H6	EBee ELan EPfP EPla GKin LBuc LRHS MAsh MBri MGos NPri NSoo SCob SCoo SGol SHil SPoG SWvt
§ ***verniciflua***	NLar SSpi

Rhynchospora (*Cyperaceae*)

colorata	LLWG NPer
latifolia	CKno SDix SHDw

Ribes ✿ (*Grossulariaceae*)

	Name	Suppliers
	alpinum	CExl ELan EPfP MRav MWht NWea SPer SRms
	- 'Aureum'	CAbP EHoe NEgg
	americanum	EPla
	- 'Variegatum' (v)	EHoe WPat
	aureum misapplied	see *R. odoratum*
	aureum ambig.	IFro
	aureum Pursh. subsp. ***gracillimum***	SBrt
§	× ***beatonii***	CDoC CDul CExl CJun CSBt CSde CWld EBee ECrN ELon ETwe EWTr LAst LEdu LRHS MAsh MMuc MRav NLar SBod SBrt SEND SGol SLim SLon SPoG WCot WFar WHar
	'Ben Hope'[PBR] (B)	CAgr EPom MAsh MCoo MJak SCoo SWvt WHar
	'Black Velvet' (D)	CAgr MCoo
	bracteosum	NLar
	californicum	SBrt
	cereum	SBrt
§	× ***culverwellii*** (F)	CAgr CCCN EPom GTwe LBuc LEdu NLar SDea SPoG SVic WHar
	divaricatum	CAgr LEdu
	gayanum	LEdu NLar
	glaciale	LEdu NLar
	× ***gordonianum***	see *R.* × *beatonii*
	griffithii GWJ 9331	WCru
	- PAB 4871 **new**	LEdu
	jostaberry	see *R.* × *culverwellii*
	laurifolium	CBcs CDoC CDul CEnd CExl CHGN CMHG CPla CTri ELan EWes LAst MRav NLar SCob SPer WCFE WFar WKif WSHC
	- (f)	CMac EPfP SBrt SRms
	- (m)	EPfP SBrt
	- 'Mrs Amy Doncaster'	CMac LEdu WCot WPGP WPat
	- Rosemoor form	CDoC ELan EPfP LRHS SKHP SPoG
	longeracemosum	GGGa
	menziesii	CHll EWes GBin NSbr WCot
	nigrum PAB 3755	LEdu
	- 'Baldwin' (B)	CTri EPfP MAsh NLar SDea SKee SLim SPer SPoG WHar
	- 'Barchatnaja' (B)	CAgr
	- 'Ben Alder'[PBR] (B)	CAgr LRHS MAsh SCoo SDea
	- 'Ben Connan'[PBR] (B) ♀H6	CAgr CMac CSBt EPfP EPom ERea GTwe LBuc LEdu LRHS MAsh MBri MGos MMuc NLar NWea SCoo SDea SFrt SKee SLim SPer SPoG SRms SWvt WHar
	- 'Ben Gairn'[PBR] (B)	CAgr CSBt MCoo WHar
	- 'Ben Lomond'[PBR] (B)	CAgr CMac CSBt CTri ECrN EPfP GTwe LBuc LRHS MAsh MGos MJak MRav NEgg NLar NPri NWea SDea SEND SKee SPer SRms SVic WHar
	- 'Ben More' (B)	CAgr MBri MJak
	- 'Ben Nevis' (B)	CAgr CTri SDea SKee SPer
	- 'Ben Sarek' (B)	CAgr CDoC CMac CSBt CTri ECrN EMil EPfP EPom ERea GTwe LBuc LRHS MAsh MBri MGos MJak MRav NLar NWea SDea SKee SLim SPer SPoG SRms SWvt WHar
	- 'Ben Tirran'[PBR] (B)	CAgr CDoC CSBt ERea LBuc LRHS MAsh MBri MGos NLar SCoo SPoG SRms SWvt WHar
	- 'Big Ben'[PBR] (B) ♀H6	EPom LBuc LRHS NLar NPri SPer SPoG
	- 'Black Reward' (B)	CAgr
	- 'Boskoop Giant' (B)	CAgr ELan NEgg SLim SPer WHar
*	- 'Byelorussian Sweet' (B)	CAgr
	- 'Consort' (B)	CAgr
	- 'Ebony' (B)	CMac CSut EMil EPom ERea LEdu LRHS NPri SLon SVic
*	- 'Hystawneznaya' (B)	CAgr
	- 'Jet' (B)	CAgr NEgg
	- 'Karaka Black' (B)	ERea
*	- 'Kosmicheskaya' (B)	CAgr
	- 'Loch Ness' (B)	ERea WHar
	- 'Noiroma' (B)	CSut
	- 'Pilot Alexander Mamkin' (B)	CAgr
	- 'Seabrook's' (B)	CAgr
	- 'Titania' (B)	LRHS MBri NLar SPoG
	- 'Wellington XXX' (B)	CAgr EMil GTwe LBuc LEdu NWea SPer
§	***odoratum***	CBcs CDoC CDul CSBt CTho CWld EBee ECrN ELan ELon EPfP ETwe EWTr GBin IDee LRHS MGos MMuc MNHC MNrw MRav NLar NWea SCob SKHP SPer SPoG SRms SSpi WHar
	- 'Crandall'	CAgr LEdu
	'Pink Perfection'	CMCN
	praecox	CBcs MMuc SEND
	rubrum 'Blanka' (W)	CAgr CMac CSut ERea SFrt
	- 'Cascade' (R)	CAgr
	- 'Cherry' (R)	CAgr
	- 'Gloire de Sablons' (P)	EPom
	- 'Hollande Rose' (P)	GTwe
	- 'Jonkheer van Tets' (R) ♀H6	CAgr CSBt EMil EPfP EPom GQue GTwe IArd LRHS MAsh MBri MCoo MMuc NLar NWea SDea SEND SKee SLim SPer SRms WHar
	- 'Junifer' (R)	CAgr EPom ERea GTwe LRHS SFrt SKee
	- 'Laxton's Number One' (R)	CAgr CTri EPfP GTwe LEdu LRHS MBri MNHC NLar NWea SDea SLim SPer SPoG SRms WHar
	- 'Lisette' (R)	CSut
	- 'Red Lake' (R) ♀H6	CAgr CTri ELan EPfP ERea GTwe LBuc LEdu LRHS MGos MJak MNHC NEgg NLar NPri SDea SKee SPer SPoG
	- 'Redstart' (R)	CAgr CSBt CTri GTwe LBuc MAsh MBri NLar SKee SPoG WHar
	- 'Rolan' (R) **new**	CAgr
	- 'Rondom' (R)	CAgr SDea SVic
	- 'Rosetta' (R)	CAgr
	- 'Rovada' (R)	CAgr CMac CSBt CSut EPom ERea GTwe LBuc LRHS MAsh MBri SFrt SKee SVic WHar
	- 'Roxby Red' (R)	LEdu MCoo
	- 'Stanza' (R) ♀H6	CAgr GTwe MMuc SDea SEND
	- 'Transparent' (W)	GTwe
§	- 'Versailles Blanche' (W/C)	CAgr CSBt CTri EPfP EPom GQue GTwe LBuc LRHS MBri MGos MMuc NPri SDea SKee SLim SPer SPoG WHar
	- 'Weisse Langtraubige' (W) **new**	CAgr
	- 'White Grape' (W) ♀H6	LEdu
	- 'White Pearl' (W)	ELan SDea SVic
	- White Versailles	see *R. rubrum* 'Versailles Blanche'
	- 'Wilson's Long Bunch' (R)	GTwe
	sanguineum	CDul CNec NEgg NHed WMoo
	- 'Albescens'	EPfP

- 'Brocklebankii'	CExl CMac EBee LRHS MGos MRav MWat NLar SChF SCob SPer SPoG SRms WCFE WSHC
- 'Carneum'	LRHS
- double-flowered	see *R. sanguineum* 'Plenum'
- 'Elkington's White'	CRos EPfP ESwi EWTr LBuc LRHS MBri MGos NLar NSti SHil SLon WBor
- 'Flore Pleno'	see *R. sanguineum* 'Plenum'
- 'Icecrystal'	ESwi
- 'King Edward VII'	Widely available
- 'Koja' ♀[H6]	CRos ELon EPfP GBin LEdu LRHS MGos MWat NLar SHil SPoG WCot WPat
- 'Lombartsii'	EPfP LRHS MRav
- 'Pink Rain'	MBri
§ - 'Plenum' (d)	EPfP
- 'Poky's Pink'	CMac EWTr LLHF LRHS MRav SPoG
- 'Pulborough Scarlet' ♀[H6]	Widely available
- 'Red Bross'	EPfP LBuc LRHS SWvt
- 'Red Pimpernel'	EPfP LRHS MAsh MBNS MGos MMuc SPoG SWvt WFar
- 'Taff's Kim' (v)	WCot
- 'Tydeman's White'	CExl CSBt ELan EPfP MGos NLar NWea WSHC
- var. ***variegata***	CMac
- White Icicle = 'Ubric' ♀[H6]	CBcs CDoC CDul CTri EBee ECtt EPfP EWTr GBin LAst LBMP LRHS MAsh MBlu MHer MRav MSwo MWat NBir NPri SCob SLim SPer SRms SWvt WFar WPat
speciosum ♀[H4]	Widely available
uva-crispa 'Achilles' (D)	GTwe
- 'Admiral Beattie' (F)	GTwe
- 'Annelii' (F)	CAgr
- 'Aston Red'	see *R. uva-crispa* 'Warrington'
- 'Bedford Red' (C/D)	GTwe
- 'Bedford Yellow' (C/D)	GTwe
- 'Blucher' (D)	GTwe
- 'Bright Venus' (D)	GTwe
- 'Broom Girl' (D)	GTwe
- 'Captivator' (C)	CSBt EPom GTwe LBuc LRHS MAsh MCoo NLar SDea SKee WHar
- 'Careless' (C/D) ♀[H6]	CMac CSBt EMil EPom GTwe MAsh MGos MJak NLar SDea SKee SPer WHar
- 'Cook's Eagle' (C)	GTwe
- 'Cousen's Seedling' (D)	GTwe
- 'Criterion' (D)	GTwe
- 'Crown Bob' (C/D)	GTwe
- 'Dan's Mistake' (D)	GTwe
- 'Early Sulphur' (D)	ELan GTwe LEdu SDea
- Easycrisp Lady Late (F)	CSut
- Easycrisp Lady Sun (F)	CSut
- 'Espera' (D)	CSut
- 'Firbob' (D)	GTwe
- 'Forester' (D)	GTwe
- 'Freedom' (C)	GTwe
- 'Glenton Green' (D)	GTwe
- 'Golden Drop' (D)	GTwe
- 'Green Gem' (C/D)	GTwe
- 'Green Ocean' (D)	GTwe
- 'Greenfinch' (C) ♀[H6]	CAgr
- 'Guido' (F)	GTwe
- 'Gunner' (C/D)	GTwe
- 'Heart of Oak' (F)	GTwe
- 'Hedgehog' (D)	GTwe
- 'Hero of the Nile' (D)	GTwe
- 'High Sheriff' (D)	GTwe
- 'Hinnonmäki' (F)	CAgr LBuc NPri SDea SPer
- 'Hinnonmäki Grön' (F)	CSBt EMil EPfP LRHS MAsh MRav NPri SFrt WHar
- 'Hinnonmäki Gul' (D)	CAgr CSBt CSut CTri CUse EMil EPfP EPom ERea GTwe LBuc LEdu LRHS MAsh MGos NLar SDea SKee SPer SPoG SVic WHar
- 'Hinnonmäki Röd' (C/D)	CAgr CMac CTri CUse EMil EPfP EPom ERea GTwe LBuc LRHS MAsh MBri MCoo MRav NLar SDea SFrt SKee SPer SPoG SVic WHar
- 'Howard's Lancer' (C/D)	GTwe SDea
- 'Invicta' (C/D) ♀[H6]	Widely available
- 'Ironmonger' (D)	GTwe
- 'Jubilee' (C/D)	LBuc
- 'Jubilee Careless' (C/D) **new**	EPom
- 'Keen's Seedling' (D)	GTwe
- 'Keepsake' (C/D)	GTwe SDea
- 'King of Trumps' (F)	GTwe
- 'Lancashire Lad' (C/D)	GTwe
- 'Langley Gage' (D)	GTwe MCoo
- 'Laxton's Amber' (D)	GTwe
- 'Leveller' (D) ♀[H6]	CTri GTwe LAst LBuc MCoo MGos SDea SPer WHar
- 'London' (C/D)	GTwe
- 'Martlet' (F)	CAgr GTwe MCoo SLim
- 'May Duke' (C/D)	SDea
- 'Pax'[PBR] (D)	CAgr CSut EPfP GTwe NLar SDea SFrt SLim
- 'Peru' (D)	GTwe
- 'Pitmaston Green Gage' (D)	GTwe
- 'Plunder' (C)	GTwe
- 'Queen of Trumps' (D)	GTwe
- 'Red Champagne' (D)	GTwe
- 'Rifleman' (D)	GTwe
- 'Rokula'[PBR] (C/D)	ELan LRHS MBri MCoo SLim
- 'Scotch Red Rough' (D)	GTwe
- 'Scottish Chieftan' (D)	GTwe
- 'Snow' (F)	EPfP SCoo
- 'Snowdrop' (D)	GTwe
- 'Spinefree' (C)	GTwe
- 'Surprise' (D)	GTwe
- 'Victoria' (C/D)	GTwe
§ - 'Warrington' (F)	GTwe
- 'Whinham's Industry' (C/D) ♀[H6]	CSBt CTri ELan GTwe LAst LBuc LRHS MGos MMuc NEgg SDea SEND SPer WHar
- 'White Lion' (C/D)	GTwe
- 'White Transparent' (C)	GTwe
- 'Whitesmith' (C/D)	CTri GTwe MCoo SDea
- 'Woodpecker' (D)	GTwe
- 'Xenia' (D)	EPfP EPom GQue LBuc LRHS MWat
- 'Yellow Champagne' (D)	GTwe
valdivianum	WCot
- 'Kathleen'	EPfP LRHS
viburnifolium	ETwe NLar SBrt SEND
'Worcesterberry' (C)	CHab SDea SPer

Ricinus (*Euphorbiaceae*)

communis	CDTJ ELan SPlb
- 'Carmencita' ♀[H1c]	NGBl SDys
- 'Carmencita Bright Red'	CWCL
- 'Carmencita Pink'	CDTJ
- 'Carmencita Red'	CDTJ
- 'Dominican Republic'	CDTJ
- 'Gibsonii'	CDTJ
- 'Impala'	CDTJ

- 'New Zealand Black'	CDTJ CSpe SDys
- 'Zanzibariensis' ♀H1c	CDTJ

Rigidella see *Tigridia*

Riocreuxia (*Apocynaceae*)

torulosa	CCCN SPlb

Robinia (*Papilionaceae*)

× ***ambigua***	EBee SKHP
§ ***hispida***	CDul CEnd ECrN ELan EPfP MBlu NLar SPer
- var. ***kelseyi***	CDul EBee EWes
- 'Macrophylla'	CEnd NLar
- 'Rosea' misapplied	see *R. hispida*
- 'Rosea' ambig.	CBcs EBee EPla
× ***margaretta*** Casque Rouge	see *R.* × *margaretta* 'Pink Cascade'
§ - 'Pink Cascade'	CEnd CLnd CTri EBee EPfP LAst MAsh MGos MMuc SCoo SCrf SEND SEWo SGol SLim SPer
pseudoacacia	CAco CCVT CDul CLnd CNWT ELan LBuc MCoo MMuc SCob SEND SGol SPlb
- 'Bessoniana'	CDul EBee EPfP EPla LAst
- 'Frisia'	Widely available
- 'Inermis' hort.	see *R. pseudoacacia* 'Umbraculifera'
§ - 'Lace Lady' PBR	CSBt CWSG EBee ECrN ELan EPfP EUJe LBuc LRHS MAsh MBri MGos NSoo SCoo SLim SPoG
- 'Rozynskiana'	CDul
- 'Tortuosa'	CEnd EBee EBtc EPla SPer
- 'Twisty Baby' PBR	see *R. pseudoacacia* 'Lace Lady'
§ - 'Umbraculifera'	CDul CLnd MBri MGos SCob SCoo
× ***slavinii*** 'Hillieri' ♀H5	CDul CEnd CLnd EBee ECrN ELan EPfP EPla EUJe EWTr MAsh MBlu MBri NLar SCrf SEND SLon SPer SPoG

Rochea see *Crassula*

Rodgersia (*Saxifragaceae*)

ACE 2303	SDix
CLD 1432	CExl
aesculifolia ♀H7	Widely available
- green bud	IBlr
- var. ***henrici***	CLAP GBin GCal GLin GLog IBoy LRHS MRav NBro NMyG SGbt SWat WHoo WMoo
- - 'Cherry Blush' **new**	GBin
- - hybrid	CHid EWTr ITim IVic NLar WWEG XLum
- pink-flowered	SSpi
- 'Red Dawn'	IBlr
- 'Red Leaf'	EWoo GCal IFoB WPnP
'Badenweiter'	ECha
'Blickfang' ♀H7	IBlr
'Bloody Mary'	ECtt EPPr GBin IMou LLWG MAvo SCob SKHP WFar
'Borodin'	EBee
Cally strain	GCal
'Dark Pokers'	ECtt GBin MBri NLar SPoG WMoo
'Die Anmutige'	CRow IMou
'Die Schöne'	CLAP EBee NLar
'Die Stolze'	GBin IMou LEdu MBrN WFar
'Elfenbeinturm'	IBlr
'Fascination'	IBlr
'Herkules'	EBee ECha ECtt EHoe ELon GBin GCal GMaP IFoB LEdu LSou MBNS MMuc NLar NSbr SKHP SSpi WPnP WWEG
'Irish Bronze' ♀H7	EAEE ECtt ELan EPfP EPla GBin GQue IVic LBMP LEdu LRHS MWts WMoo WPnP WWEG
'Koriata'	IBlr
'Kupfermond'	CDes CRow IBlr NBir
'La Blanche'	CMil EBee ECtt ELon LEdu LRHS MHol NGdn NLar SPer WCot WPnP WWEG
'Maigrün'	IBlr
nepalensis	CLAP EBee LEdu LRHS WPGP
- EMAK 713	IBlr
- HWJK 2140	WCru
'Parasol'	CBro CLAP CMac IBlr NBir NHol SKHP SSpi WPGP WWtn
pinnata	Widely available
- B&SWJ 7741A	CBcs WCru
- L 1670	CExl ELan IBlr SSpi WPGP
- SDR 3301	GKev
- 'Alba'	GCal IBlr
- 'Buckland Beauty' ♀H7	CDes EBee IBlr LRHS SSpi WMoo WPGP
- 'Cally Coffee'	GCal
- 'Cally Coral'	EBee GCal
- 'Cally Salmon'	EWes GBin GCal IBlr IMou WPGP
- 'Chocolate Wing'	Widely available
- 'Crûg Cardinal'	GCal WCru
- 'Elegans'	CCon EBee EHoe ELan EPfP EPla GKev GMaP IBlr LAst LBMP LEdu LPal LRHS MRav NEgg NHol NOrc SGSe SPer SPoG SWvt WHil
- 'Fireworks' PBR	CBod CCon CHid CLAP COtt EBee ECtt ELan EPfP GBin IMou LEdu LSou NLar SPer SRkn WHil
- 'Jade Dragon Mountain'	CDes GCal IBlr SKHP WPGP
- 'Maurice Mason'	CExl CLAP EBee ECtt GKev IBlr NLar SMHy WWEG
- 'Mont Blanc'	IBlr
- Mount Stewart form	IBlr
- 'Panache'	IBlr
- 'Perthshire Bronze'	IBlr
- pink-flowered	WCru
- 'Rosea'	IBlr
- 'Snow Clouds' **new**	LSun
- 'Superba' ♀H7	Widely available
- white-flowered	GAbr SWat WCru
pinnata × ***sambucifolia***	IBlr
podophylla	Widely available
- B&SWJ 10818	WCru
- B&SWJ 10823	WCru
- 'Braunlaub'	CLAP GBuc GQue LSun NBro WMoo WPnP WWEG
- 'Bronceblad'	IBlr
- 'Crûg's Colossus' **new**	WCru
- Donard selection	IBlr MBri
- 'Rotlaub' ♀H7	CAby CLAP CRow EBee IBlr IMou IPot IVic MMoz WBor WMoo
- 'Smaragd'	CLAP CRow EShb GCal IBlr LRHS MRav NBir NLar
purdomii hort.	GCal WCot WPGP
'Reinecke Fuchs'	IBlr
'Rosenlicht'	CRow
'Rosenzipfel'	IBlr
sambucifolia	CBcs CLAP CMac CRow GBee GBin GCal LEdu LRHS MLHP MMuc NBir NEgg NLar NSti SEND SPer SWat WFar WMoo WPnP WWEG XLum

- B&SWJ 7899 WCru
- dwarf, pink-flowered IBlr
- dwarf, white-flowered IBlr
- large, red-stemmed NBir
- 'Mountain Select' EBee GCal
tabularis see *Astilboides tabularis*

Roemeria (*Papaveraceae*)

hybrida CSpe

Rohdea (*Asparagaceae*)

japonica CHEx WCot WFar WPGP
- B&SWJ 4853 WCru
- B&SWJ 5091 WCru
- 'Godaishu' (v) WCot
- 'Gunjaku' (v) WCot
- 'Lance Leaf' LEdu
- long-leaved WCot
- 'Miyakonojo' (v) WCot
- 'Talbot Manor' (v) CDes WCot
- 'Tama-jishi' (v) WCot
- 'Tuneshige Rokujo' (v) WCot
tonkinensis HWJ 562 WCru
watanabei IMou
- B&SWJ 1911 WCru

Romanzoffia (*Boraginaceae*)

§ ***sitchensis*** CTri
suksdorfii Greene see *R. sitchensis*
tracyi CDes GEdr NRya
unalaschcensis EBee SRms

Romneya (*Papaveraceae*)

coulteri ♀H7 Widely available
§ - var. ***trichocalyx*** CCon
§ - 'White Cloud' ♀H5 CExl MRav SChF WPGP
× ***hybrida*** see *R. coulteri* 'White Cloud'
trichocalyx see *R. coulteri* var. *trichocalyx*

Romulea (*Iridaceae*)

amoena 'Nieuwoudtville' ECho
atrandra NRog
austinii 'Komsberg' ECho
§ ***autumnalis*** ECho
barkerae 'Paternoster' ECho
biflora 'Vanrhynsdorp' ECho
bulbocodium CBro ECho
- var. ***clusiana*** ECho
- var. ***crocea*** ECho
- late-flowering **new** CDes
- var. ***leichtliniana*** CDes
citrina from Tweerivier ECho
- 'Kamiesberg' ECho
columnae ECho
- subsp. ***columnae*** ECho
cruciata var. ***cruciata*** 'Riverlands' ECho
- var. ***intermedia*** 'Somerset West' ECho
dichotoma ECho
discifera 'Grasberg' ECho
diversiformis 'Komsberg' ECho
eximia ECho
flava var. ***minor*** 'Dassenberg' ECho
- 'Rawsonville' ECho
hirsuta var. ***cuprea*** 'Rawsonville' ECho
- var. ***hirsuta*** 'Klipheuwel' ECho
- var. ***zeyheri*** 'Malmesbury' ECho
hirta ECho
kamisensis ECho
leipoldtii ECho
linaresii ECho
longipes 'Coega' ECho
longituba see *R. macowanii*
* ***luteoflora*** var. ***sanguinea*** ECho
§ ***macowanii*** ECho
montana ECho
namaquensis ECho
nivalis ECho
obscura var. ***blanda*** ECho
- var. ***obscura*** ECho
- var. ***subtestacea*** ECho
pratensis ECho
ramiflora CExl ECho
rosea ECho
- var. ***rosea*** 'Caledon' ECho
- var. ***speciosa*** see *R. autumnalis*
sanguinalis from Tweerivier ECho
setifolia var. ***aggregata*** 'Rawsonville' ECho
sladenii 'Gifberg' ECho
stellata 'Nardouwsberg' ECho
subfistulosa from Roggeveld ECho
tabularis ECho
tempskyana ECho EPot
tetragona var. ***flavandra*** 'Matjiesfontein' ECho
tortuosa subsp. ***aurea*** 'Komsberg' ECho
- var. ***tortuosa*** 'Botuin' ECho
toximontana 'Gifberg' ECho
triflora 'Riverlands' ECho

Rondeletia (*Rubiaceae*)

amoena MOWG

Rorippa (*Brassicaceae*)

amphibia LLWG MSKA
nasturtium-aquaticum MWts WMAq

Rosa ✿ (*Rosaceae*)

sp. SCob
NJM 11.048 from Guizhou, China **new** WPGP
NJM 11.077 from Guizhou, China **new** WPGP
NJM 11.079 from Guizhou, China **new** WPGP
A Shropshire Lad = 'Ausled'PBR (S) ♀H6 CNec CWSG EPfP LBuc LRHS MAsh MAus MBri NEgg NLar SCob SMrm SPer SSea SWCr
A Whiter Shade of Pale = 'Peafanfare'PBR (HT) ♀H6 ECnt ESty LRHS MAus MJak MRav SPer SWCr
Abbeyfield Rose = 'Cocbrose' (HT) MRav SPer
Abracadabra = 'Korhocsel' (HT) ESty
Abraham Darby = 'Auscot' (S) CTri CWSG ELan EPfP EShb IBoy LRHS MAus MBri MJak MRav MWat NEgg NLar SCob SEND SLon SMrm SPer SWCr

Absent Friends = 'Dicemblem'PBR (F)	ESty IBoy SRGP WBor
Absolutely Fabulous = 'Wekvossutono'PBR (F) ♀H6	COtt CSBt CWSG ECnt EPfP ESty LBrs LBuc LRHS LShp MAsh MBri MJak MRav NPri SCoo SMrm SPer SPoG SWCr
abyssinica	LEdu
'Adam Messerich' (Bb)	SLon
'Adélaïde d'Orléans' (Ra) ♀H6	CRHN LBuc LRHS MAus MBri MMuc MRav NLar SEND SFam SPer
African Sunset = 'Jacpik' **new**	MBri
Agatha Christie = 'Kormeita'PBR (ClF)	LRHS MAsh
'Aglaia' (Ra)	CPou MAus
'Agnes' (Ru)	ELon EPfP EWTr IArd LRHS MAus MCot MRav NLar SPer SRGP
'Aimée Vibert' (N)	MAus MRav NLar SEND SPer SRGP
'Alain Blanchard' (G)	CPou MAus
Alan Titchmarsh = 'Ausjive'PBR (S)	CSBt CWSG LRHS MAus MBri SCoo SPer
§ × ***alba*** 'Alba Maxima' (A) ♀H7	CArn GBin MAus MRav NLar SEND SPer WFar WHer
§ - 'Alba Semiplena' (A) ♀H7	EPfP LRHS MAus NLar SPer SWCr WHer
- Celestial	see *R.* 'Céleste'
- 'Maxima'	see *R.* × *alba* 'Alba Maxima'
Alba Meidiland = 'Meiflopan'PBR (S/GC)	EAEE LBuc
'Albéric Barbier' (Ra) ♀H5	CRHN CSBt CSam CTri ECnt ELan EPfP EWTr LRHS MAus MBri MMuc MRav MSwo MWat NLar NWea SCob SEND SMad SMrm SPer SPoG SSea SWCr WHer
'Albertine' (Ra) ♀H6	Widely available
'Alchymist' (S/Cl)	CPou EPfP ESty LRHS MAus MBri MRav NLar SPer WBor
Alec's Red = 'Cored' (HT)	CBcs CTri CWSG IBoy LRHS MAus MJak MRav MWat SPer SPoG SRGP SWCr
Alexander = 'Harlex' (HT) ♀H6	IBoy MAus MRav SPer SSea SWCr
Alexander's Issie = 'Dicland'PBR (F)	IDic
'Alexandre Girault' (Ra) ♀H6	CRHN LBuc LRHS MAus MBri MMuc SPer SWCr WHer
'Alfred de Dalmas' misapplied	see *R.* 'Mousseline'
Alfred Sisley = 'Delstrijor'PBR (S)	ESty LRHS MRav NLar
'Alfresco'PBR (ClHT)	MSwo
§ 'Alibaba'PBR (Cl) ♀H6	ECnt ESty LBrs MRav SMrm SWCr
'Alida Lovett' (Ra)	LRHS MAus
Alison = 'Coclibee'PBR (F)	SWCr
Alissar, Princess of Phoenicia = 'Harsidon'PBR	CPou ESty NLar
§ 'Alister Stella Gray' (N) ♀H5	EBee MAsh MAus MBri MCot MMuc NEgg NLar SLon SPer SSea
All American Magic = 'Meiroylear'PBR (HT)	ESty
Alleluia = 'Delatur' (HT)	ESty
'Allen Chandler' (ClHT)	MAus
'Allgold' (F)	MJak SCob
Alnwick CastlePBR	see *R.* The Alnwick Rose
'Aloha' (ClHT) ♀H7	CBcs CTri ELon EPfP ESty LRHS MAus MCot MJak MRav NLar SCob SEND SMrm SPer SPoG SSea SWCr
alpina	see *R. pendulina*
'Alpine Sunset' (HT)	CTri ELon ESty LBuc MAsh MRav SCob SPer SPoG SWCr
altaica Willd.	see *R. spinosissima*
Altissimo = 'Delmur' (Cl)	LRHS MAus SEND SPer SSea SWCr
'Amadis' (Bs)	MAus
Amanda = 'Beesian' (F)	ESty
'Amazing Grace' (HT)	LBuc
Amber Abundance = 'Harfizz'PBR (Abundance Series) (S)	ESty
Amber Queen = 'Harroony' (F) ♀H6	CSBt CTri EAEE ELan IArd IBoy LBuc LRHS MAsh MAus MJak MRav SMrm SPer SWCr
Amber SunPBR	see *R.* County of Staffordshire
Amber Sweet Dream = 'Fryritz' (Patio)	ECnt
amblyotis RBS 0262	GBin NLar
Ambridge Rose = 'Auswonder' (S)	MAus
'Amélia'	see *R.* 'Celsiana'
Amelia = 'Poulen011'PBR (Renaissance Series) (S)	ECnt SWCr
'American Pillar' (Ra)	COtt CSBt CTri CWSG EBee ECnt ELan EPfP IBoy LAst LRHS MAsh MAus MBri MJak MMuc MRav MSwo NLar SCob SPer SSea SWCr WBor
'Amy Robsart' (RH)	MAus
'Anaïs Ségalas' (G)	MAus
§ 'Anemone' (Cl)	CPou EWTr MAus
anemoniflora	see *R.* × *beanii*
anemonoides	see *R.* 'Anemone'
Angela Rippon = 'Ocaru' (Min)	CSBt SPer
Anisley Dickson = 'Dickimono' (F)	SPer
Ann = 'Ausfete'PBR (S)	MAus
Anna Ford = 'Harpiccolo' (Min/Patio) ♀H5	SPer
Anna Livia = 'Kormetter'PBR (F)	EBee
Anne Boleyn = 'Ausecret'PBR (S)	EPfP IBoy LBuc LRHS MAus MBri NEgg SCoo
'Anne Dakin' (ClHT)	MAus
Anne Harkness = 'Harkaramel' (F)	MAus SPer
Antique = 'Antike' (F)	CPou
Antique '89 = 'Kordalen'PBR (ClF)	MAsh
Aphrodite = 'Tan00847'PBR (S) ♀H6	ESty MRav SWCr
apothecary's rose	see *R. gallica* var. *officinalis*
'Apple Blossom' (Ra)	SHar SMrm
Apple Blossom = 'Noamel' (GC) **new**	EShb
'Apricot Nectar' (F)	MAus
'Apricot Silk' (HT)	CTri SPer
Apricot Sunblaze = 'Savamark' (Min)	CSBt
'Archiduc Joseph' misapplied	see *R.* 'Général Schablikine'
Art Nouveau = 'Pejamark' (F)	SWCr
'Arthur Bell' (F) ♀H7	CSBt CTri ELon EPfP ESty IArd IBoy LAst LRHS MAsh MAus MBri MJak MRav MSwo MWat NEgg NPri SCob SMrm SPer SPoG SRGP SSea SWCr WBor
'Arthur de Sansal' (DPo)	MAus

	Name	Suppliers
	Artistic Licence = 'Guesmarble' (HT)	SWCr
	arvensis	CAco CCVT CHab LBuc MAus NWea SCob
	'Assemblage des Beautés' (G)	MAus
	'Astra Desmond' (Ra)	MNrw
	'At Peace Rose' (HT) **new**	LBuc
	Audrey Wilcox = 'Frywilrey' (HT)	ESty
	'Auguste Gervais' (Ra)	MAus
	Austrian copper rose	see *R. foetida* 'Bicolor'
	Austrian yellow	see *R. foetida*
	'Autumn Delight' (HM)	NLar
	Autumn Fire	see *R.* 'Herbstfeuer'
	'Autumnalis'	see *R.* 'Princesse de Nassau'
	Avon = 'Poulmulti'PBR (GC)	ELan EPfP MRav SPer
	Awakening = 'Probuzení' (ClHT)	EWTr MSwo NLar SWCr
	'Ayrshire Splendens'	see *R.* 'Splendens'
	'Baby Bio' (F/Patio)	ESty
	'Baby Faurax' (Poly)	MAus
	Baby Love = 'Scrivluv'PBR (Min/Patio)	MAus
	Baby Masquerade = 'Tanba' (Min)	MRav MWat SMrm SPer
	Babyface = 'Rawril'PBR (Min)	ESty
	'Ballerina' (HM/Poly) ♀H6	CDul CSBt CTri ECnt ELan EPfP IBoy LEdu LRHS MAsh MAus MRav MSwo MWat NEgg NLar NPri SCob SMad SMrm SPer SSea SWCr WBor WKif
	'Baltimore Belle' (Ra)	CPou MAus NLar
	banksiae (Ra)	CHel CPou SRms
	- ***alba***	see *R. banksiae* var. *banksiae*
§	- var. ***banksiae*** (Ra/d)	CDul CHel CHll CPou CRHN CSBt CSPN CTri ELan EPfP GQui LRHS MAus MNHC SCob SEND SLon SPer XSen
	- 'Lutea' (Ra/d) ♀H5	Widely available
	- var. ***normalis*** (Ra)	CSBt CSam EPfP MAus SKHP SLon WHer WOut WPGP
I	- 'Rosea'	MWat NLar SPer
	'Bantry Bay' (ClHT)	CSBt ELan LAst SCob SLon SPer SSea SWCr
	Barbara Austin = 'Austop'PBR (S)	MAus
	Barbara Windsor = 'Ganleon'PBR (F)	SWCr
	Barkarole = 'Tanelorak'PBR (HT)	CSBt ESty MJak SWCr
	'Baron Girod de l'Ain' (HP)	EBee ELon LAst LRHS MAus MMuc MRav NEgg NLar SPer SWCr
	'Baroness Rothschild'	see *R.* Baronne Edmond de Rothschild, Climbing Baronne Edmond de Rothschild
§	Baronne Edmond de Rothschild = 'Meigriso' (HT)	MAus
	'Baronne Prévost' (HP)	MAus SFam
	Baroque Floorshow = 'Harbaroque'PBR (S)	MRav
§	× ***beanii*** (Ra)	IFro
	Beatrix Potter = 'Beafolly' (S)	ESty
	'Beau Narcisse' (G) ♀H7	MAus
	Beautiful Britain = 'Dicfire' (F)	MRav SCob SWCr
§	Bella = 'Pouljill'PBR (Renaissance Series) (S)	CPou
	'Belle Amour' (A × D)	CPou MAus
	'Belle de Crécy' (G)	CPou CTri MAsh MAus MBri MMuc MNrw NLar NPri SFam SKHP SMad SPer SWCr
	'Belle des Jardins' misapplied	see *R.* × *centifolia* 'Unique Panachée'
	Belle Epoque = 'Adasilthe'PBR (HT) **new**	SCob
	Belle Epoque = 'Fryyaboo'PBR (HT)	ESty SCob SMad SMrm SWCr
	'Belle Isis' (G)	MAus SPer
	'Belle Poitevine' (Ru)	CPou
	'Belle Portugaise' (ClT)	MAus
	Belmonte = 'Harpearl'PBR (F)	LBuc
§	'Belvedere' (Ra) ♀H6	CPou EBee IBoy MAus NLar SPer WBor
	Benita = 'Dicquarrel' (HT)	IDic
	Benjamin Britten = 'Ausencart'PBR (S)	CSBt EPfP ESty IBoy LBuc LRHS MAsh MAus MBri NEgg
	Berkshire = 'Korpinka'PBR (GC) ♀H6	LRHS SCob SSea SWCr
	Beryl Joyce = 'Tan96145'PBR (HT)	ESty MRav SWCr
	Best Wishes = 'Chessnut'PBR (ClHT/v)	SRGP
	'Bewitched' (HT)	LBrs
§	Bewitched = 'Poulbella'PBR (Castle Series) (F)	LBuc MAsh MBri SWCr
	Bianco = 'Cocblanco' (Patio/Min)	MAus MRav MWat SPoG
	Big Purple = 'Stebigpu'PBR (HT)	ECnt ESty
	Billet Doux = 'Delrosar' (S) **new**	ESty
	Birthday Boy = 'Tan97607'PBR (HT)	ESty MRav SCob SWCr
	Birthday Girl = 'Meilasso'PBR (F)	CSBt ESty LBrs LBuc MAsh MJak MRav MWat NPri SCoo SMrm SRGP SVic SWCr
	Birthday WishesPBR (Patio)	see *R.* Shrimp Hit (Patio)
	Birthday Wishes = 'Guesdelay' (HT)	CTri LRHS MBri SSea
	Black Baccara = 'Meidebenne'PBR (HT)	ESty SWCr
	Black Beauty = 'Korfleur' (HT)	MAus
	'Black Jack' (Ce)	see *R.* 'Tour de Malakoff'
	'Blairii Number Two' (ClBb)	CSam EBee EPfP MAus MMuc MRav NEgg NLar SEND SPer
	'Blanche de Vibert' (DPo)	EBee
	'Blanche Double de Coubert' (Ru) ♀H7	CBcs CDul CSBt CSam CTri EBee ECnt ELan EPfP EWTr GBin LBuc MAus MSwo NEgg NLar SCob SEND SMrm SPer SSea SWCr
	'Blanche Moreau' (CeMo)	MAus SKHP SLon SPer
	'Blanchefleur' (Ce × G)	CPou MAus
	'Blesma Soul' (HT)	CSBt
	'Blessings' (HT)	CBcs CSBt CTri LBuc LRHS MAsh MAus MBri MGos MJak MRav NPri SCob SPer SWCr
	'Bleu Magenta' (Ra) ♀H7	CRHN EBee ELan GBin IArd MAus MCot MRav NLar SEND SMad SWCr WKif
	Bloom of Ruth = 'Harmedley' (HT) **new**	CSBt ECnt

'Bloomfield Abundance' (Poly)	CPou MAus NLar SPer SWCr WHer
'Blossomtime' (Cl)	SMad SPer
Blue for You = 'Pejamblu'PBR (F) ♀H6	ECnt EPfP ESty LBrs LBuc LRHS MAsh MAus SCob SCoo SMad SPoG SWCr
Blue Moon = 'Tannacht' (HT)	CTri ELan EPfP IBoy LBrs MGos MJak MRav SCob SPer SPoG SRGP
Blue Peter = 'Ruiblun' (Min)	ESty IBoy MBri
'Blush Excelsior'	SMrm
'Blush Hip' (A)	MAus
'Blush Noisette'	see *R.* 'Noisette Carnée'
'Blush Rambler' (Ra)	CSBt EBee EPfP EWTr LBuc MAus MMuc SPer
Blushing Bride = 'Harfling' (F)	MBri
'Blushing Lucy' (Ra) ♀H6	CPou MTPN SMrm SPer
Blythe Spirit = 'Auschool'PBR (S)	LRHS MAsh MAus MBri NEgg
'Bobbie James' (Ra) ♀H6	CTri EPfP EWTr LBuc LRHS MAsh MAus MBri MRav MSwo NEgg NLar SCob SPer SPoG SSea SWCr WFar
Bobby Dazzler = 'Smi133-02' (F) **new**	ESty
Bonica = 'Meidomonac' (GC) ♀H6	CDul CSBt CSam CTri EBee ECnt ELan EPfP ESty IBoy LShp MAsh MAus MBri MCot MMuc MRav MWat NEgg NLar SCob SEND SMrm SPer SPoG SSea SWCr WKif
§ Bonita = 'Poulen009'PBR (Renaissance Series) (S)	ECnt
Boogie-Woogie = 'Poulyc006'PBR (Courtyard Series) (ClHT)	ECnt LBuc LRHS MAsh MBri SWCr
Born AgainPBR	see *R.* Renaissance
Boscobel = 'Auscousin' (S) **new**	CRos ESty LBuc LRHS MAsh MAus SCob SSea
'Botzaris' (D)	SFam
'Boule de Neige' (Bb)	CBcs CTri ECnt ELan EPfP IBoy LRHS MAsh MAus MBri MRav MWat NLar SFam SMrm SPer SWCr
'Bouquet d'Or' (N)	MAus NLar
Bow Bells = 'Ausbells' (S)	MAus
Bowled Over = 'Tandolgnil'PBR (F) ♀H6	ESty SWCr
§ ***bracteata*** (S)	CRHN ECre EWes GQui MAus SSea
Brave Heart = 'Horbondsmile' (F)	COtt MAus MRav SPoG
Breath of Life = 'Harquanne'PBR (ClHT)	ELan EPfP LBuc MAus MJak MRav SPer SWCr
Breathtaking = 'Hargalore'PBR (HT)	ESty SWCr
Bredon = 'Ausbred' (S)	MAus
Bride and Groom = 'Smi10-98' (HT)	ESty SCoo
Bride = 'Fryyearn'PBR (HT)	MRav
Bridge of Sighs = 'Harglowing'PBR (Cl)	ECnt ESty LBuc LShp MAsh MBri SPoG SSea SWCr
Bright and Breezy = 'Dicjive' (F)	ECnt IDic
Bright as a Button = 'Chewsumsigns' (S)	COtt CSBt ESty GBin LBrs LShp NLar SLon SPer
Bright Fire = 'Peaxi'PBR (ClHT)	MSwo SPer SSea
Bright Future = 'Kirora'PBR (Cl)	ECnt ESty
Bright Ideas = 'Horcoffdrop' (Cl)	LRHS LShp
Bright Smile = 'Dicdance' (F/Patio)	MAus
Brilliant Pink Iceberg = 'Probril' (F)	SWCr
Brilliant Sweet Dream = 'Frysassy' (Patio) **new**	ECnt
Britannia = 'Frycalm'PBR (HT) ♀H6	ECnt
Broadlands = 'Tanmirsch'PBR (GC)	NLar SLon SWCr
Brother Cadfael = 'Ausglobe'PBR (S)	CNec CRos ELon LRHS MAus MBri MWat NEgg NLar SCob SCoo SLon SMrm SPer SSea SWCr
Brown Velvet = 'Maccultra' (F)	ESty SPer SWCr
Brownie = 'Simstripe' (Cl)	ESty
§ ***brunonii*** (Ra)	CExl EWes MAus
- PAB 3083 **new**	LEdu
- 'Betty Sherriff' (Ra)	CDoC
§ - 'La Mortola' (Ra)	MAus NLar
Brush-strokes = 'Guescolour' (F)	ESty SWCr
'Buff Beauty' (HM) ♀H6	CSBt CSam CTri CWSG EBee ECnt ELan EPfP IBoy MAsh MAus MBri MCot MRav MSwo MWat NEgg NLar SCob SEND SFam SMad SPer SSea SWCr WCFE WFar
'Bullata'	see *R.* × *centifolia* 'Bullata'
§ 'Burgundiaca' (G)	MAus
Burgundian rose	see *R.* 'Burgundiaca'
§ Burgundy Ice = 'Prose'PBR (F)	CSBt CWSG EAEE ECnt EPfP ESty LBuc LShp MAsh MRav SCob SCoo SMad SMrm SPoG SSea SWCr
'Burgundy Iceberg'PBR	see *R.* Burgundy Ice
'Burgundy Rose'	see *R.* 'Burgundiaca'
burnet, double pink	see *R. spinosissima* double, pink-flowered
- double white	see *R. spinosissima* double, white-flowered
Buttercup = 'Ausband'PBR (S)	EPfP LBuc LRHS MAus
Buxom Beauty = 'Korbilant'PBR (HT) ♀H6	EPfP ESty LBrs LRHS MAsh MBri MWat SCoo SWCr
californica (S)	MAus
- 'Plena'	see *R. nutkana* 'Plena'
'Callisto' (HM)	MAus
§ Calypso = 'Poulclimb'PBR (ClHT)	ECnt SWCr
'Camayeux' (G)	CPou ECnt MAus NLar SPer
Cambridgeshire = 'Korhaugen'PBR (GC)	CTri MAus NLar SPer SSea SWCr
Camelot = 'Tan05372' (Cl) **new**	ESty
Camille Pisarro = 'Destricol' (F)	ESty
'Canary Bird'	see *R. xanthina* 'Canary Bird'
canina (S)	CAco CArn CCVT CDul CHab CLnd CTri ECrN EPfP EPom LBuc MAus MJak MRav NHed NLar NWea SCob SEWo SPer WHar WMou WOut
'Cantabrigiensis' (S) ♀H6	MAus NLar SLon SPer SSea
'Capitaine Basroger' (CeMo)	MAus
'Capitaine John Ingram' (CeMo)	MAus MMuc NLar SEND SLon
'Captain Christy'	see *R.* 'Climbing Captain Christy'

	Name	Suppliers
	'Captain Scarlet' (ClMin)	ESty
	'Cardinal de Richelieu' (G)	CBcs CPou CSam CTri EPfP GCra IBoy LRHS LShp MAsh MAus MBri MCot MMuc MRav MSwo MWat NEgg NLar NPri SCob SEND SFam SMad SPer SPoG SWCr
	Cardinal Hume = 'Harregale' (S)	ESty
	Carefree Days = 'Meirivouri' (Patio) ♀H6	EPfP IBoy LBuc LRHS MAsh NPri SMrm SPoG SSea
	Carefree Delight = 'Meipotal'[PBR] (S/GC) **new**	LBuc
	Cariad = 'Auspanier'[PBR] (HM)	LBuc LRHS MAus
	Caribbean Dawn = 'Korfeining'[PBR] (Patio)	MAsh
	'Caroline Testout'	see *R.* 'Madame Caroline Testout'
	Caroline Victoria = 'Harprior'[PBR] (HT)	COtt LBuc SWCr
	Carris = 'Harmanna'[PBR] (HT)	ESty
§	Casino = 'Macca' (ClHT)	CTri LBuc MRav SPer
	'Castle Apricot'[PBR]	see *R.* Lazy Days
	'Castle Cream'	see *R.* Perfect Day
	'Castle Fuchsia Pink'[PBR]	see *R.* Bewitched = 'Poulbella'
	'Castle Peach'[PBR]	see *R.* Imagination = 'Pouldron'
	'Castle Shrimp Pink'[PBR]	see *R.* Fascination = 'Poulmax'
	'Castle Yellow'[PBR]	see *R.* Summer Gold
	'Catherine Mermet' (T)	MAus
§	'Cécile Brünner' (Poly) ♀H6	CTri ELan EWTr LEdu LRHS MAsh MAus MCot MMuc NLar SPer SSea
	Cecily Gibson = 'Evebright' (F)	ESty
	Celebration 2000 = 'Horcoffitup'[PBR] (S)	MAus
	Celebration Time[PBR]	see *R.* Cinco de Mayo
§	'Céleste' (A) ♀H7	EPfP MAus NLar SEND SFam SPer SSea
	'Céline Forestier' (N)	CPou EWTr MAus NLar SEND SPer
§	'Celsiana' (D) ♀H7	CPou CSam MAus NLar SFam SPer
	Centenary = 'Koreledas'[PBR] (F)	MAsh SCoo
§	× ***centifolia*** (Ce)	CArn LRHS MAus SPer
§	- 'Bullata' (Ce)	MAus
§	- 'Cristata' (Ce) ♀H7	ECnt ELon LEdu LRHS MAus MMuc NLar SFam SPer WBor
§	- 'De Meaux' (Ce)	MAus NLar SPer
§	- 'Muscosa' (CeMo)	LEdu LRHS MAus MMuc MWat SFam
	- 'Parvifolia'	see *R.* 'Burgundiaca'
§	- 'Shailer's White Moss' (CeMo)	EWTr MAus SFam
	- 'Spong' (Ce)	MAus
§	- 'Unique' (Ce)	MAus NLar
§	- 'Unique Panachée' (Ce)	CPou MAus
	'Centifolia Variegata'	see *R.* × *centifolia* 'Unique Panachée'
	Centre Stage = 'Chewcreepy'[PBR] (S/GC) ♀H6	MAsh MAus
	'Cerise Bouquet' (S) ♀H7	GGal MAus NLar SPer WKif
§	Champagne Moments = 'Korvanaber'[PBR] (F) ♀H6	CBcs COtt CSBt ECnt ELan EPfP ESty LBrs LRHS MAsh MAus MBri MGos MRav MWat NPri SMad SPer SPoG SRGP SSea SWCr
	'Champneys Pink Cluster' (China hybrid)	LRHS MAus SCob
	Chandos Beauty = 'Harmisty'[PBR] (HT) ♀H6	COtt ECnt ELon EPfP ESty LBrs LRHS MAsh MBri MRav SSea SWCr
	'Chanelle' (F)	SDix
	Chapeau de Napoléon	see *R.* × *centifolia* 'Cristata'
	Charles Austin = 'Ausles' (S)	MAus MRav
	Charles Darwin = 'Auspeet'[PBR] (S)	EPfP LBuc LRHS MAus MBri NEgg SCoo SMrm SPer
	Charles de Gaulle	see *R.* Katherine Mansfield
	'Charles de Mills' (G) ♀H7	CSam CTri ECnt ELan EPfP EWTr GCra LRHS LShp MAus MBri MCot MRav MSwo MWat NLar SFam SKHP SPer SWCr WHer
	Charles Rennie Mackintosh = 'Ausren'[PBR] (S)	CSBt LBuc MAus MBri NEgg
	Charlie's Rose = 'Tanellepa' (HT) ♀H6	ELan ESty SWCr
	Charlotte = 'Auspoly'[PBR] (S) ♀H6	CRos EBee ECnt ELan EPfP ESty LBuc LRHS MAsh MAus MBri MWat NEgg SCoo SEND SMrm SPer SSea SWCr
	Charlotte Vieli = 'Diclooker' (F)	IDic
	Charmant = 'Korpeligo'[PBR] (Min)	MAsh
	Charmian = 'Ausmian' (S)	MAus
	Charming Cover = 'Poulharmu'[PBR] (Towne & Country Series) (GC/S)	MAsh
	Chartered = 'Diclingo' (F) **new**	IDic
	Chartreuse de Parme = 'Delviola' (S)	CPou EBee ESty MRav NLar SLon
	'Château de Clos-Vougeot' (HT)	IArd
	Chatsworth = 'Tanotax'[PBR] (Patio/F) ♀H6	MRav SPer
	Chaucer = 'Auscer' (S)	MAus
	Checkmate = 'Diclanky' (Cl) **new**	IDic
§	Cheek to Cheek = 'Poulslas'[PBR] (Courtyard Series) (ClMin)	LBuc MAsh SWCr
	Cheerful Charlie = 'Cocquimmer'[PBR] (F)	MRav
	Cherie[PBR]	see *R.* Songs of Praise
	Cherry Brandy '85 = 'Tanryrandy'[PBR] (HT)	CSBt
	Cheshire = 'Korkonopi'[PBR] (County Rose Series) (S)	LRHS MAus SWCr
	'Cheshire Life' (HT)	MAus
	'Chevy Chase' (Ra)	MCot
	Chianti = 'Auswine' (S)	EBee MAus NLar
	Chicago Peace = 'Johnago' (HT)	SCob SWCr
	Child of Achievement[PBR]	see *R.* Bella
	Chilterns = 'Kortemma'[PBR] (GC)	SWCr
	'Chinatown' (F/S) ♀H7	CTri IBoy LRHS MAsh MAus MBri MRav SCob SPer SSea
	chinensis misapplied	see *R.* × *odorata*
	- 'Minima' *sensu stricto* hort.	see *R.* 'Pompon de Paris'
	- 'Mutabilis'	see *R.* × *odorata* 'Mutabilis'
	- 'Old Blush'	see *R.* × *odorata* 'Pallida'
	- var. ***spontanea***	WPGP
	Chloe = 'Poulen003'[PBR] (Renaissance Series) (S)	CPou EBee ECnt SLon SWCr

	Name	Suppliers
	Chris Beardshaw = 'Wekmeredoc'[PBR] (HT)	SWCr
	Chris = 'Kirsan'[PBR] (ClHT)	ESty LBrs MAus SWCr
	Christopher = 'Cocopher' (HT)	SWCr
	Christopher Columbus = 'Meinronsse' (HT)	IArd
	Christopher Marlowe = 'Ausjump'[PBR] (S)	MAus MBri SCoo
§	'Chromatella' (N)	MAus
	Cider Cup = 'Dicladida'[PBR] (Min/Patio)	IBoy IDic MAus
§	Cinco de Mayo = 'Wekcobeju'[PBR] (F)	ECnt SMrm
	'Cinderella' (Min)	CSBt EWTr NLar
	Cinderella = 'Korfobalt' (ClS)	CPou MAsh SWCr
	City Lights = 'Poulgan'[PBR] (Patio)	CSBt
	City Livery = 'Harhero 2000' (F)	LRHS MAsh
	City of Carlsbad[PBR]	see *R.* Hanky Panky
	'City of Leeds' (F)	SPer
	City of London = 'Harukfore'[PBR] (F)	CSBt
	City of York = 'Direktör Benschop' (Cl/HT)	MCot
	Clair Matin = 'Meimont' (ClS)	CPou MAus
	Claire Austin = 'Ausprior'[PBR] (S)	CWSG EPfP ESty LBuc LRHS MAus MBri NLar SCob SCoo SSea SWCr
	'Claire Jacquier' (N)	CSam EPfP EWTr MAus SPer SWCr
	Claire Marshall = 'Harunite' (F)	ESty
	Claire Rose = 'Auslight'[PBR] (S)	MAus
	'Clarence House' (Cl)	ELan LRHS MBri
	Claret = 'Frykristal'[PBR] (HT) 🏆H6	ECnt ESty MBri MRav SSea SWCr
	Claude Monet = 'Jacdesa' (HT)	ESty
	'Clementina Carbonieri' (T)	CPou EBee NLar
	Clementine = 'Cheworangemane' (Cl) **new**	ECnt ESty
	Cleopatra = 'Korverpea'[PBR] (HT)	MAsh
	'Cliff Richard' (F)	ESty SWCr
	'Climbing Alec's Red' (ClHT)	ELon SPer
	'Climbing Allgold' (ClF)	SLon
	'Climbing Arthur Bell' (ClF)	COtt CSBt CTri ELon ESty IBoy LAst LBrs MSwo SCob SPer SPoG SSea SWCr
	'Climbing Ballerina' (Ra)	CSBt SWCr
§	Climbing Baronne Edmond de Rothschild = 'Meigrisosar' (ClHT)	CSBt
	'Climbing Blue Moon' (ClHT)	LBuc SWCr
§	'Climbing Captain Christy' (ClHT)	MAus
	'Climbing Cécile Brünner' (ClPoly) 🏆H6	CSBt CTri EBee ECnt EPfP MAus MBri MRav NLar SCob SEND SPer SSea SWCr
	'Climbing Château de Clos-Vougeot' (ClHT)	MAus
	'Climbing Christine' (ClHT)	MAus

	Name	Suppliers
§	'Climbing Columbia' (ClHT)	EShb EWTr SPer
	'Climbing Crimson Glory' (ClHT)	CPou LBuc MAus MBri
§	'Climbing Devoniensis' (ClT)	CPou
	'Climbing Ena Harkness' (ClHT)	CTri EBee MAus MRav SEND SPer SPoG SWCr
	'Climbing Etoile de Hollande' (ClHT) 🏆H6	CSBt CTri CWSG EPfP IBoy LBuc MAus MBri MJak MRav NPri SEND SFam SMad SPer SSea SWCr
	Climbing Fragrant Cloud = 'Colfragrasar' (ClHT)	CBcs ELan
	'Climbing Iceberg' (ClF) 🏆H7	COtt CSBt CTri EBee ELan EPfP ESty IArd LBrs LEdu MAus MBri MCot MJak MMuc MRav MSwo NEgg NLar SCob SMrm SPer SPoG SSea SWCr
	'Climbing Jazz'[PBR]	see *R.* That's Jazz
§	'Climbing Lady Hillingdon' (ClT) 🏆H4	EPfP EShb LAst LBuc LRHS MAus MBri MRav NEgg NLar SEND SPer WBor
	'Climbing Lady Sylvia' (ClHT)	CSBt EPfP LRHS MAus SPer
	'Climbing Little White Pet'	see *R.* 'Félicité Perpétue'
	'Climbing Madame Abel Chatenay' (ClHT)	MAus
	'Climbing Madame Butterfly' (ClHT) 🏆H6	MAus
	'Climbing Madame Caroline Testout' (ClHT)	CPou CTri EPfP MAus MRav SPer
§	'Climbing Madame Edouard Herriot' (ClHT)	MAus
	'Climbing Masquerade' (ClF)	CPou CTri MAus MRav NEgg SCob SPer SSea SWCr
	'Climbing Mrs Herbert Stevens' (ClHT)	LRHS MAus MMuc MRav SEND SMrm SPer
	'Climbing Mrs Sam McGredy' (ClHT)	CSBt MAus NLar
	'Climbing Niphetos' (ClT)	MAus
	'Climbing Ophelia' (ClHT)	MAus SPer
§	'Climbing Paul Lédé' (ClT)	EBee LRHS MAus
	'Climbing Peace' (ClHT)	SPer
§	'Climbing Pompon de Paris' (ClMinCh)	CTri MAus MNrw SEND SMrm SPer
	'Climbing Shot Silk' (ClHT) 🏆H6	CSam SPer
§	'Climbing Souvenir de la Malmaison' (ClBb)	CPou MAus SPer
	'Climbing White Cloud'[PBR]	see *R.* White Cloud = 'Korstacha'
	'Cloth of Gold'	see *R.* 'Chromatella'
	'Coconut Ice' (HT)	SCob
	Colchester Beauty = 'Cansend' (F)	ECnt
§	'Colonel Fabvier' (Ch)	MAus NLar
	colonial white	see *R.* 'Sombreuil'
	'Columbia' (HT)	CPou
	'Columbian'	see *R.* 'Climbing Columbia'
	'Commandant Beaurepaire' (Bb)	CPou MAus SMad
	common moss	see *R.* × *centifolia* 'Muscosa'
	'Compassion' (ClHT) 🏆H6	Widely available
*	'Compassionate' (F)	MRav
	'Complicata' (G)	CPou CSam CTri EPfP EWTr LRHS MAus MBri MCot MRav NLar SEND SKHP SPer SSea SWCr
	'Comte de Chambord' misapplied	see *R.* 'Madame Boll'

	Name	Suppliers
	Comte de Champagne = 'Ausufo'[PBR] (S)	LBuc LRHS MAus MBri SCoo
	'Comtesse Cécile de Chabrillant' (HP)	CPou MAus
	'Comtesse de Lacépède' misapplied	see *R.* 'Du Maître d'Ecole'
§	'Comtesse de Murinais' (DMo)	MAus SFam
§	'Comtesse du Caÿla' (Ch)	MAus
	Concert[PBR]	see *R.* Calypso
	'Conditorum' (G)	LEdu SFam
	Congratulations = 'Korlift' (HT)	CSBt ECnt IArd IBoy MAus MGos MJak MRav NPri SCob SMrm SPer SVic SWCr
	Conservation = 'Cocdimple' (Min/Patio)	MJak SMrm
	'Constance Spry' (ClS) ♀H6	CTri EBee EPfP LRHS MAus MBri MMuc MRav MSwo MWat NEgg NLar SCob SEND SMrm SPer
§	'Cooperi' (Ra)	CAbP CSam EWTr LRHS MAus SPer SSea WPGP
	Cooper's Burmese	see *R.* 'Cooperi'
	'Coral Cluster' (Poly)	MAus
	Coral Palace[PBR]	see *R.* Imagination = 'Pouldron'
	Cordelia = 'Ausbottle'[PBR] (S)	MAus MBri
	'Cornelia' (HM) ♀H6	CBcs CSam CTri EPfP IArd LRHS MAsh MAus MBri MCot MRav MWat NLar SCob SFam SPer SRGP SWCr WBor
	Corvedale = 'Ausnetting'[PBR] (S)	CAbP MAus
	cottage maid	see *R.* × *centifolia* 'Unique Panachée'
	Cottage Maid = 'Poulspan' (S)	MAus
	Cottage Rose = 'Ausglisten'[PBR] (S)	MAus MBri MRav SMrm
	Countess Celeste[PBR]	see *R.* Imagination = 'Pouldron'
§	County of Staffordshire = 'Korsoalgu'[PBR] (GC/S)	LRHS
	County of Yorkshire = 'Korstarnow'[PBR] (GC) ♀H6	ELan ESty LRHS
	'Coupe d'Hébé' (Bb)	MAus
	Courage = 'Poulduf'[PBR] (HT)	ECnt
	Courvoisier = 'Macsee' (F)	CSBt
	'Cramoisi Picotée' (G)	MAus
	'Cramoisi Supérieur' (Ch)	MAus
	Crazy for You = 'Wekroalt'[PBR] (F) ♀H6	ECnt ESty LBrs MAsh MBri SWCr
	Cream Abundance = 'Harflax'[PBR] (Abundance Series) (F)	SSea SWCr
	Crème de la Crème = 'Gancre'[PBR] (ClHT)	CSBt ECnt ELon ESty MAus MRav SPer SPoG SRGP SSea SWCr
	'Crépuscule' (N)	MAus NLar
	Cressida = 'Auscress' (S)	MAus
	crested moss	see *R.* × *centifolia* 'Cristata'
	Cricri = 'Meicri' (Min)	MAus
	Crimson Cascade = 'Fryclimbdown'[PBR] (ClHT) ♀H6	ESty LRHS MAsh MBri MRav MSwo SMad SPer SPoG SSea SWCr
	crimson damask	see *R. gallica* var. *officinalis*
	'Crimson Descant' (ClHT)	ECnt
	'Crimson Glory' (HT)	EBee MAsh
	'Crimson Shower' (Ra)	CSam CTri ELan EWTr LBuc LRHS MAus MBNS MBri MMuc MRav MSwo NEgg NLar SEND SMrm SPer WHer
	'Cristata'	see *R.* × *centifolia* 'Cristata'
	Crocus Rose = 'Ausquest'[PBR] (S) ♀H6	EPfP LAst LRHS MAus MBri MRav MWat NEgg NLar SCob SPer SWCr
	Crown Princess Margareta = 'Auswinter'[PBR] (S)	CRos CWSG ECnt ELan EPfP EShb ESty LBuc LRHS MAsh MAus MBri NEgg NLar SCob SCoo SPer SWCr
	cuisse de nymphe	see *R.* 'Great Maiden's Blush'
	Cumberland = 'Harnext'[PBR] (Cl)	ESty LBuc
	'Cupid' (ClHT)	MAus SPer
I	'Cutie' (Patio)	ESty SWCr
	Dacapo = 'Poulcy012'[PBR] (Courtyard Series) (ClPatio)	ECnt
	'D'Aguesseau' (G)	MAus
	'Daily Mail'	see *R.* 'Climbing Madame Edouard Herriot'
	'Dainty Bess' (HT)	EBee MAus SSea
	'Dale Farm' (F/Patio)	ESty
	× ***damascena*** var. ***bifera***	see *R.* × *damascena* var. *semperflorens*
§	- var. ***semperflorens*** (D) ♀H7	CPou MAus NLar SSea SWCr
	- 'Trigintipetala' misapplied	see *R.* × *damescena* 'Professeur Émile Perrot'
§	- 'Versicolor' (D)	MAus SPer SSea SWCr
	Dame Wendy = 'Canson' (F)	MAus
§	× ***damescena*** 'Professeur Émile Perrot' (D)	LEdu MAus WFar
	'Danaë' (HM)	MAus
	Dancing Queen = 'Fryfeston' (ClHT) ♀H6	ECnt ESty LBuc LRHS LShp MAsh MBri MRav SPoG SWCr
	Danny Boy = 'Dicxcon'[PBR] (Patio)	IDic
	'Danse du Feu' (ClF)	CBcs CSBt CTri EBee ELan IBoy LAst LEdu LRHS MAsh MAus MBri MJak MRav SCob SPer SWCr
	Dapple Dawn = 'Ausapple' (S)	MAsh MAus
	Darcey Bussell = 'Ausdecorum'[PBR] (S) ♀H6	COtt CRos CSBt ECnt ELan EPfP ESty LBuc LRHS MAus MBri SCob SPer SSea SWCr
	Darling Flame = 'Meilucca' (Min)	MJak
	davidii (S)	MAus
	Dawn Chorus = 'Dicquasar'[PBR] (HT) ♀H6	CSBt CWSG EPfP ESty IBoy LRHS MAsh MJak MRav MWat SCob SPer SPoG SSea SWCr
	'Daybreak' (HM)	CTri MAus NLar
	'De Meaux'	see *R.* × *centifolia* 'De Meaux'
	'De Meaux, White'	see *R.* 'White de Meaux'
§	'De Resht' (DPo) ♀H7	CPou CTri ECnt EPfP EWTr LRHS MAsh MAus MBri MCot MRav MWat NLar NPri SMrm SPer SWCr WKif
	'Dear Daughter' (F)	ESty
	'Dearest' (F)	CBcs SCob SPer SWCr
	'Debutante' (Ra) ♀H7	EWTr LRHS MAus
	'Deep Secret' (HT)	CBcs CSBt CTri CWSG ECnt ELan ELon EPfP ESty LBrs LBuc LRHS MAsh MBri MCot MJak MRav SCob SPer SRGP SSea SWCr
	'Delambre' (DPo)	MAus
	Della Balfour = 'Harblend'[PBR] (ClHT)	SWCr

	Name	Suppliers
	Dentelle de Malines = 'Lenfiro' (S)	MAus
	Desert Island = 'Dicfizz'[PBR] (F)	ELon
	'Designer Sunset' (Patio)	LBrs LBuc MAsh MBri
§	'Desprez à Fleur Jaune' (N)	EBee IArd LBuc LRHS MAsh MAus MRav NEgg SEND SFam SPer SWCr
	'Devon Maid' (ClHT)	EBee
	'Devoniensis' (ClT)	see *R.* 'Climbing Devoniensis'
	Diamond = 'Korgazell'[PBR] (Patio) ♀H6	EPfP ESty LRHS MAsh NSoo SPoG
	Diamond Anniversary = 'Morsixty' (Min)	LBuc
	'Diamond Celebration' (HT)	SWCr
	Diamond Days = 'Hartribe' (HT) **new**	ESty
	'Diamond Jubilee' (HT)	CSBt SWCr
	'Diamond Wishes'[PBR]	see *R.* Misty Hit
	Diana, Princess of Wales = 'Jacshaq' (HT)	MJak
	Dizzy Heights = 'Fryblissful'[PBR] (ClHT) ♀H6	MAus MRav SPer
	'Docteur Grill' (T)	MAus
	Doctor Jackson = 'Ausdoctor' (S)	MAus
	Doctor Jo = 'Fryatlanta'[PBR] (F)	SWCr
	'Doctor W. Van Fleet' (Ra/Cl)	MAus
	'Don Charlton' (HT)	NEgg
	'Don Juan' (ClHT)	SWCr
	'Doncasteri'	MAus
	'Doris Tysterman' (HT)	CTri LBuc MAus SPer
	Dorothy = 'Cocrocket'[PBR] (F)	MRav
	'Dorothy Perkins' (Ra)	CTri LBrs LBuc LRHS MAus MBri MRav MWat NPer SCob SPer SRGP WHer
	'Dortmund' (S) ♀H7	MAus NLar SPer SWCr
	Double Delight = 'Andeli' (HT)	ESty IBoy LBuc SPer SSea SWCr
	Dream Lover = 'Peayetti'[PBR] (Patio)	ESty SWCr
	'Dreaming Spires' (Cl)	MSwo SPer SWCr
§	'Du Maître d'Ecole' (G)	LRHS MAus WHer
	Dublin Bay = 'Macdub' (ClF) ♀H6	CSBt CSam CTri CWSG ECnt ELan ELon EPfP IArd IBoy LAst LBrs LRHS MAsh MBri MCot MRav MSwo MWat NLar SEND SMrm SPer SPoG SSea SWCr WBor
	'Duc de Guiche' (G) ♀H7	CSam MAsh MAus MMuc NLar SEND SFam SLon SPer WHer
	Duchess of Cornwall = 'Tan97157' (HT) ♀H6	CSBt ESty MRav SCob SWCr
	'Duchess of Portland'	see *R.* 'Portlandica'
	Duchess of York[PBR]	see *R.* Sunseeker
	'Duchesse d'Angoulême' (Ce × G) ♀H7	MAus SFam
	'Duchesse de Buccleugh' (G)	MAus MRav
§	'Duchesse de Montebello' (G) ♀H7	CPou CSam GBin LRHS MAus NLar SFam SLon SPer
	'Duchesse de Verneuil' (CeMo)	MAus SFam
	'Duke of Edinburgh' (HP)	MAus
	Duke of Edinburgh[PBR] (Patio)	see *R.* The Gold Award Rose
	'Duke of Wellington' (HP)	CPou
	'Duke of Windsor' (HT)	SPer
	'Dundee Rambler' (Ra)	MAus
§	'Duplex' (S)	MAus
	'Dupontii' (S) ♀H6	EWTr MAus MMuc NLar SFam SKHP SPer
	'Dusky Maiden' (F)	EBee EWTr MAus SWCr
	Dusty Springfield = 'Horluvdust' (F)	LBuc
	'Dutch Gold' (HT)	MAus SPer
	'E.H. Morse'	see *R.* 'Ernest H. Morse'
	'Easlea's Golden Rambler' (Ra) ♀H6	EBee LRHS MAus MRav NEgg NLar SLon
	East Park = 'Harjope' (HT)	ECnt ESty
	'Easter Morning' (Min)	SPer
§	Easy Does It = 'Harpageant'[PBR] (F) ♀H6	EBee ECnt ESty LBrs MAsh
	Easy Going = 'Harflow'[PBR] (F) ♀H6	IArd LBuc MAsh MRav SWCr
§	Ebb Tide = 'Weksmopur'[PBR] (F)	EBee ECnt ESty
	ecae (S)	MAus
	'Éclair' (HP)	ELon WBor
	'Eddie's Jewel' (*moyesii* hybrid)	MAus
	Eden Rose '88 = 'Meiviolin'[PBR] (ClHT)	CPou SPer SWCr
	'Edward Hyams' (*persica* hybrid)	MAus
	Edward's Rose = 'Smi73/7/97' (F)	ESty
	eglanteria	see *R. rubiginosa*
	Eglantyne = 'Ausmak'[PBR] (S)	CSBt ELan ELon EPfP LAst LRHS MAus MBri MRav SCob SMrm SPer SPoG SSea SWCr
	Elaine Page = 'Poulht008' (HT) **new**	LBrs
	Eleanor = 'Poulberin'[PBR] (S)	CPou EBee ECnt SLon
§	***elegantula*** 'Persetosa' (S)	MAus NLar SKHP SPer
§	Elina = 'Dicjana' (HT) ♀H6	ECnt MAus MJak MRav SMrm SPer SPoG SWCr
	'Elizabeth Harkness' (HT)	MAus SPer
	Elizabeth of Glamis = 'Macel' (F)	CTri SPer
	Elle = 'Meibderos'[PBR] (HT)	ESty SWCr
	Ellen = 'Auscup' (S)	MAus
	'Ellen Willmott' (HT)	MAus MCot SPer
	'Elmshorn' (S)	CBcs
	Emilia Maria[PBR]	see *R.* La Rose de Molinard
	'Emily Gray' (Ra)	CPou EBee ECnt LRHS MAsh MAus SCob SPer
	'Emma Wright' (HT)	MAus
	'Emmerdale' (F)	LBuc
	'Empereur du Maroc' (HP)	IBoy MAus
	'Ena Harkness' (HT)	CRos CTri ELan LBuc LRHS SRGP
	Enchantress = 'Tan97281'[PBR] (HT) **new**	ESty
	England's Rose = 'Auslounge'[PBR] (S)	ESty MAus
§	England's Rose = 'Ausrace' (S)	LRHS
	English Elegance = 'Ausleaf' (S)	MAus
	English Garden = 'Ausbuff' (S)	CTri EPfP LRHS MAus MJak SMrm SPer

Name	Suppliers
'English Miss' (F)	CPou EBee ECnt ELon ESty IBoy LRHS MAsh MAus MBri MJak MRav SPer SPoG SWCr
'English Princess' (F) **new**	LBuc
English Sonnet[PBR]	see *R.* Samaritan
'Eos' (*moyesii* hybrid)	MAus
Epidor = 'Délépi' (HT) **new**	ESty
'Erfurt' (HM)	MAus SPer
§ 'Ernest H. Morse' (HT)	CSBt CTri IBoy MRav SPer SPoG SWCr
Escapade = 'Harpade' (F) 🏆H6	MAus
Especially for You = 'Fryworthy'[PBR] (HT) 🏆H6	CSBt ESty MJak SCob SCoo SSea SWCr
Essex = 'Poulnoz'[PBR] (GC)	MRav SCob SPer SPoG
'Etain' (Ra)	ECnt
§ 'Étendard' (ClHT)	MRav NLar SPer SPoG SWCr
Eternal Flame = 'Korassenet'[PBR] (F)	LBuc LRHS MAsh
Eternally Yours = 'Macspeego'[PBR] (HT)	ESty
Eternity = 'Ricity' (Min) **new**	MBri
Eternity = 'Twoetern' (HT)	MAsh
'Ethel' (Ra)	CPou EBee
'Étoile de Hollande' (HT)	COtt EBee ELan GBin LRHS MAsh MBNS MBri MCot NEgg NLar SCob SLon
'Eugénie Guinoisseau' (Mo)	CPou
Euphoria = 'Intereup'[PBR] (GC/S)	LBuc SWCr
'Euphrosyne' (Ra)	MAus
'Evangeline' (Ra)	MAus
Evelyn = 'Aussaucer'[PBR] (S)	CSBt EBee EPfP ESty LRHS MAus MBri MRav MWat NEgg NLar SLon SMrm SPer
§ Evelyn Fison = 'Macev' (F)	CSBt CTri ELan IBoy MAus MBri MWat SPer
'Evelyn May' (HT)	LRHS LShp
'Excelsa' (Ra)	CSBt CSam CTri EPfP IArd IBoy MAsh MBri MRav NWea SCob SPoG WBor
Eye Paint = 'Maceye' (F)	MAus
Eyes for You = 'Pejbigeye' (F) 🏆H6	CSBt ESty GBin LRHS SLon SPer SWCr WKif
'F.E. Lester'	see *R.* 'Francis E. Lester'
§ 'F.J. Grootendorst' (Ru)	IBoy NEgg SPer
'Fabvier'	see *R.* 'Colonel Fabvier'
Fair Bianca = 'Ausca' (S)	MAus
Fairy Prince = 'Harnougette' (GC)	ESty
Fairy Queen = 'Sperien' (Poly/GC)	LBuc
'Fairy Rose'	see *R.* 'The Fairy'
Fairy Snow = 'Holfairy' (S)	SWCr
Falstaff = 'Ausverse'[PBR] (S)	CRos CSBt EPfP IBoy LAst LRHS MAsh MAus MBNS MBri MJak MRav MSwo NEgg SCob SMrm SPer SSea SWCr
'Fantin-Latour' (*centifolia* hybrid) 🏆H7	CTri ECnt ELan EWTr GCra IBoy LAst LEdu LRHS MAus MBri MCot MMuc MRav MWat NEgg NLar SEND SFam SMad SPer SWCr
farreri var. ***persetosa***	see *R. elegantula* 'Persetosa'
Fascination = 'Jacoyel' (Castle Series) (HT)	SCoo
§ Fascination = 'Poulmax'[PBR] (F) 🏆H6	IBoy LRHS MAsh MBri MRav SPer SWCr
fedtschenkoana misapplied	MAus SPer
Fée des Neiges	see *R.* Iceberg
'Felicia' (HM) 🏆H6	CSBt CSam CTri EBee ECnt ELan EPfP EWTr LRHS MAsh MAus MBri MCot MMuc MRav MSwo MWat NLar SEND SFam SKHP SPer SWCr WKif
'Félicité Parmentier' (A × D) 🏆H7	EPfP LRHS MAus MBri MMuc MRav MWat NLar SFam SPer SWCr
§ 'Félicité Perpétue' (Ra) 🏆H7	CBcs CTri ELan EPfP IBoy LPot LRHS MAus MBri MMuc MRav MSwo NEgg NLar SEND SFam SMad SPer SSea SWCr
'Fellemberg' (ClCh)	EBee MAus
Fellowship = 'Harwelcome'[PBR] (F) 🏆H6	MAus MRav SCob SCoo SSea SWCr
'Ferdinand Pichard' (Bb) 🏆H7	CPou CRos CSBt CSam CTri EBee ECnt ELon EPfP ESty EWTr LAst LRHS MAus MBri MCot MRav NEgg NLar SEND SKHP SMad SPer SSea SWCr WFar WKif
Ferdy = 'Keitoli'[PBR] (GC)	SEND SPer
ferruginea	see *R. glauca* Pourr.
Festival = 'Kordialo'[PBR] (Patio)	COtt ESty IBoy MJak MRav SPer SPoG SWCr
Festive Jewel = 'Beacost' (S)	LRHS MBri
Fetzer Syrah Rosé = 'Harextra'[PBR] (S)	ESty
Fighting Temeraire = 'Austrava' (S)	CRos EPfP LBuc LRHS MAus SSea
§ ***filipes*** 'Kiftsgate' (Ra) 🏆H6	Widely available
filipes × ***glauca*** **new**	MAus
§ 'Fimbriata' (Ru)	CPou LEdu MAus NLar SPer
Financial Times Centenary = 'Ausfin' (S)	MAus
Fiona = 'Meibeluxen' (S/GC)	MSwo
Firestar[PBR]	see *R.* Easy Does It
First Great Western = 'Oracharpam'[PBR] (HT)	ESty
'Fisher and Holmes' (HP)	EBee EWTr MAus
Fisherman's Friend = 'Auschild'[PBR] (S)	MAus
Flashdance = 'Poulyc004'[PBR] (ClMin)	ECnt
'Flora' (HT)	MAus
'Florence Mary Morse' (S)	SDix
Florence Nightingale = 'Ganflor'[PBR] (F)	SPer
Flower Carpet Amber = 'Noa97400a' (GC) 🏆H6	CSBt ELan IBoy LBuc LRHS MAsh SCoo SPoG SWCr
'Flower Carpet Coral'[PBR] (GC) 🏆H6	CSBt LBuc LRHS MAsh MBri SCoo SWCr
Flower Carpet Gold = 'Noalesa'[PBR] (GC)	COtt ECnt IBoy LBrs LBuc LRHS MAsh MBri NPri SPoG
Flower Carpet Pink[PBR]	see *R.* Pink Flower Carpet
Flower Carpet Red Velvet = 'Noare'[PBR] (GC/S) 🏆H6	EBee ELan EPfP IBoy LBuc LRHS MBri NPri SCoo SPer SPoG SWCr
Flower Carpet Ruby (GC)	COtt LBuc LRHS MAsh MBri SCoo SPoG
Flower Carpet Scarlet = 'Noa83100b'[PBR] (GC) 🏆H6	LBuc LRHS MAsh MBri

	Name	Suppliers
	Flower Carpet Sunset = 'Deseo' (S) **new**	LBrs LRHS MBri SCoo
§	Flower Carpet Sunshine = 'Noason'PBR (GC) ♀H6	EBee LRHS MAsh SCoo SPer
§	Flower Carpet Twilight = 'Noatwi'PBR (GC)	SSea
	Flower Carpet White = 'Noaschnee'PBR (GC) ♀H6	COtt CTri ECnt IBoy LBrs LRHS MAsh MAus MBri NPri SCoo SPer SPoG SWCr
	Flower Power = 'Frycassia'PBR (Patio) ♀H6	COtt CSBt ECnt ELon ESty IBoy LRHS MAsh MAus MBri MRav SPoG SWCr
	Flower Power Gold = 'Fryneon' (Patio)	ECnt ESty LBrs LRHS MBri
§	***foetida*** (S)	CBcs MAus SPer
§	- 'Bicolor' (S)	MAus NLar SPer
§	- 'Persiana' (S)	MAus
	Fond Memories = 'Kirfelix'PBR (Patio)	ESty MBri SWCr
	Forget Me Not = 'Coccharm'PBR (HT)	ESty
	forrestiana (S)	LRHS MAus
	Fortune's double yellow	see *R.* × *odorata* 'Pseudindica'
	'Fountain' (HT)	MAus
	Fragrant Cloud = 'Tanellis' (HT)	CBcs COtt CTri CWSG ELan EPfP ESty IBoy LBrs LRHS MAsh MAus MBri MGos MJak MRav NPri SPer SPoG SSea SWCr
	'Fragrant Delight' (F) ♀H6	CSBt ELan ELon MAus MBri MJak MRav MWat SCob SPer SPoG SSea
	Fragrant Dream = 'Dicodour'PBR (HT)	ESty IBoy MRav SMrm SSea
	Fragrant Memories = 'Korpastato'PBR (HT)	CSBt SCoo SKHP
	'Francesca' (HM)	EWTr LRHS MAus SFam SPer
	Francine Austin = 'Ausram'PBR (S/GC)	LRHS MAus MBri NEgg SPer
§	'Francis E. Lester' (HM/Ra) ♀H6	CRHN CSam EBee ELan EPfP LRHS MAus MBri MCot MMuc NLar SEND SMrm SPer SRGP SSea SWCr WBor
	× ***francofurtana*** misapplied	see *R.* 'Impératrice Joséphine'
	- 'Empress Josephine'	see *R.* 'Impératrice Joséphine'
	'François Juranville' (Ra) ♀H6	CPou CRHN EBee EPfP GGal IBoy LRHS LShp MAus MBri MMuc MRav NLar SEND SLon SPer WFar WHer
§	'Frau Karl Druschki' (HP)	MAus
	'Fred Loads' (F) ♀H7	MAus
	Freddie Mercury = 'Batmercury' (HT)	ESty NEgg
	Free Spirit = 'Fryjeru'PBR (F) ♀H6	ECnt
	Freedom = 'Dicjem' (HT) ♀H6	CTri ECnt MAus MJak MRav SCob SPer SVic
	'Frensham' (F)	CBcs SSea SWCr
	Friend for Life = 'Cocnanne'PBR (F) ♀H6	MRav
	Friends Forever = 'Korapriber' (F) ♀H6	EPfP MAsh NPri
	Friends of Ashwood = 'Guesidea' **new**	MAsh
	'Fritz Nobis' (S) ♀H7	CPou MAus NLar SPer
	Frothy = 'Macfrothy'PBR (Patio)	ECnt ESty
	'Fru Dagmar Hastrup' (Ru) ♀H7	CBcs CDul CSBt CTri EBee ECnt ELan EMil EPfP IBoy LBuc LRHS MAus MSwo NEgg NLar NWea SCob SEND SMad SPer SWCr
	'Frühlingsgold' (SpH) ♀H7	CBcs ELan EWTr LRHS MAus NLar NWea SPer
	'Frühlingsmorgen' (SpH) ♀H7	MAus SLon SMad SPer
§	***gallica*** var. ***officinalis*** (G) ♀H7	CArn CTri EPfP GPoy LEdu LRHS MAsh MAus MBri MHer MNHC MRav NLar SFam SKHP SPer SSea SWCr
§	- 'Versicolor' (G) ♀H7	CArn CSBt CSam CTri ECnt ELan EPfP GCra GPoy IBoy LEdu LRHS LShp MAus MBri MCot MHer MNHC MRav MWat NLar NPri NSti SMad SMrm SPer SSea SWCr WBor WKif
	Galway Bay = 'Macba' (ClHT)	CPou IBoy LRHS MAsh MBri SPer SWCr
	Garden of RosesPBR	see *R.* Joie de Vivre
	'Gardeners Glory'PBR (ClHT) ♀H6	ECnt ESty LAst LBrs LRHS MAsh SMad SPoG
	'Gardenia' (Ra)	EBee EWTr LRHS MAus MMuc MSwo NLar SMrm SPer
	'Gaujard'	see *R.* Rose Gaujard
	'Gelbe Dagmar Hastrup'PBR	see *R.* Yellow Dagmar Hastrup
	'Général Jacqueminot' (HP)	MAus
	'Général Kléber' (CeMo) ♀H7	MAus SFam
§	'Général Schablikine' (T)	EWTr MAus NLar
	Genesis = 'Fryjuicy'PBR (Patio)	ECnt ESty LBrs MRav SWCr
	gentiliana misapplied	see *R.* 'Polyantha Grandiflora'
	Gentle Hermione = 'Ausrumba'PBR (S)	CRos ELan EPfP IBoy LBuc LRHS MAus MBri NLar SCob SPer SWCr
	Gentle Touch = 'Diclulu' (Min/Patio)	COtt CSBt LAst MRav SMad SPer SPoG
	Geoff Hamilton = 'Ausham'PBR (S)	EPfP IBoy LBuc LRHS MAsh MAus MBNS MBri NEgg SCob SCoo SPer SSea
	'Georg Arends' (HP)	MAus
	George Best = 'Dichimanher'PBR (Patio) ♀H6	ESty IDic SWCr
	'George Dickson' (HT)	MAus
	'Georges Vibert' (G)	MAus
	'Geranium' (*moyesii* hybrid) ♀H7	CBcs CDul CSam CTri EBee ELan EPfP IArd IBoy LRHS MAsh MAus MBri MRav NLar SCob SEND SPer SSea SWCr WKif
	Gerbe d'Or	see *R.* Casino
	'Gerbe Rose' (Ra)	MAus
	Gertrude Jekyll = 'Ausbord'PBR (S) ♀H6	Widely available
	'Ghislaine de Féligonde' (Ra/S) ♀H6	CPou CSam EBee EPfP EWTr LBuc LRHS MAus MBri MCot NLar SEND SMrm SPer SWCr
	GhitaPBR	see *R.* Millie
	Giardina = 'Tan97286' (Cl)	ESty SWCr
	gigantea	WPGP
	gigantea × ***longicuspis***	WPGP
	Giggles = 'Frynoodle'PBR (Patio)	ECnt
	Ginger Syllabub = 'Harjolina'PBR (ClHT)	EBee ECnt ELon ESty MRav SPoG SRGP SWCr
	Gingernut = 'Coccrazy'PBR (Patio)	SWCr
	Gipsy Boy	see *R.* 'Zigeunerknabe'
	Glad Tidings = 'Tantide'PBR (F)	IBoy MRav SPer SWCr

Glamis Castle = 'Auslevel'[PBR] (S)	CBcs CTri EBee EPfP IBoy LRHS MAus MBri MWat NEgg SCob SCoo SMrm SPer SWCr
glauca ambig.	GCra MHer MSwo SCob
§ ***glauca*** Pourr. (S) ♀H7	Widely available
'Glenfiddich' (F)	CSBt CTri MAus MJak MRav SPer
'Glenn Dale' (Cl)	CPou
Glenshane = 'Dicvood' (GC/S)	MRav
Global Beauty = 'Tan 94448' (HT)	MRav SWCr
'Gloire de Dijon' (ClT)	CSBt CTri EBee ECnt ELan EPfP IBoy LRHS MAus MBri MCot MRav NEgg NLar NPri SCob SPer SRGP SSea SWCr
'Gloire de Ducher' (HP)	MAus
'Gloire de France' (G) ♀H7	MAus MRav WHer
'Gloire de Guilan' (D)	MAus
'Gloire des Mousseuses' (CeMo)	CPou LRHS MAus SFam
'Gloire du Midi' (Poly)	MAus
'Gloire Lyonnaise' (HP)	EBee SLon
'Gloria Mundi' (Poly)	NEgg SMrm
Gloriana = 'Chewpope'[PBR] (ClMin)	ECnt ESty LRHS MAsh MAus MBri MRav MWat SCoo SKHP SMrm SPer SPoG SSea SWCr
Glorious = 'Interictira'[PBR] (HT)	ESty SWCr
'Glory of Seale' (S)	SSea
Glowing Amber = 'Manglow' (Min)	ESty
Gold Charm = 'Chewalbygold' (Cl)	ECnt ESty LRHS MAsh MBri
Gold Rush = 'Jacrebin'[PBR] (F)	ESty
'Golden Anniversary' (Patio)	IBoy NSoo SPer SSea SWCr
'Golden Anniversary' (HT)	LBuc
Golden Beauty = 'Korberbeni'[PBR] (F) ♀H6	CPou EBee ESty MAsh MBri
Golden Celebration = 'Ausgold'[PBR] (S) ♀H6	CRos CSBt CSam CTri CWSG EBee ECnt EPfP ESty IBoy LAst LRHS MAsh MAus MBri MJak MRav MSwo NLar SCob SLon SMrm SPer SPoG SSea SWCr
'Golden Chersonese' (S)	MAus
Golden Future = 'Horanymoll'[PBR] (ClHT) ♀H6	MAus SWCr
Golden Gate = 'Korgolgat'[PBR] (ClHT) ♀H6	ECnt EPfP ESty MAsh MAus SSea
Golden Gate = 'Korrogilo'[PBR] (HT) **new**	EBee
Golden Jewel = 'Tanledolg'[PBR] (F/Patio)	ESty
Golden Jubilee = 'Cocagold' (HT)	MRav
Golden Memories = 'Korholesea'[PBR] (F) ♀H6	CBcs CSBt ESty LBuc LRHS MAsh MBri MGos MJak MRav SCoo SPer SWCr
Golden Moment = 'Smi-99-2-04' (HT)	ESty MRav
Golden Parfum de Provence = 'Meifazeda' (F) **new**	ESty
'Golden Rambler'	see *R.* 'Alister Stella Gray'
'Golden Showers' (Cl)	CBcs COtt CSBt CTri CWSG EBee ELan EPfP GGal IBoy LAst LBrs LRHS MAsh MAus MBri MJak MRav MWat NEgg NLar NPri SMrm SPer SPoG SSea SWCr WBor
Golden Smiles = 'Frykeyno'[PBR] (F) ♀H6	ECnt ESty
Golden Trust = 'Hardish'[PBR] (Patio)	MWat
Golden Wedding = 'Arokris'[PBR] (F)	CSBt CTri CWSG EBee ECnt ELan EPfP ESty IArd IBoy LBrs LRHS MAsh MAus MBri MGos MJak MRav MWat NEgg NPri NSoo SCob SMrm SPer SPoG SSea SVic SWCr
Golden Wedding Anniversary (F)	COtt
'Golden Wedding Celebration' (F)	ESty SWCr
'Golden Wings' (S)	CPou CTri ELan EPfP IBoy LRHS MAus MRav MSwo NLar SKHP SPer SSea SWCr
'Goldfinch' (Ra)	CRos ELan EPfP LRHS MAus MBri MRav NEgg NLar SEND SPer SPoG WBor WFar
Goldstar = 'Candide' (HT)	ECnt
Good as Gold = 'Chewsunbeam'[PBR] (ClMin)	CSBt ECnt ESty SMrm SPer SWCr
Good Life = 'Cococircus'[PBR] (HT)	SCoo SPer
Gordon Snell = 'Dicwriter' (F)	IDic
Grace = 'Auskeppy'[PBR] (S) ♀H6	CRos CSBt EBee EPfP EShb ESty LBuc LRHS MAus MBri MWat NEgg NLar SMrm SPer SSea SWCr
'Graciously Pink' (Min)	MAsh MBri SPoG
Graham Thomas = 'Ausmas' (S) ♀H6	Widely available
Grande Amore = 'Korcoluma'[PBR] (HT) ♀H6	CSBt LRHS
'Grandpa Dickson' (HT)	CBcs IBoy MAsh MAus MBri MJak SPer
Great Expectations = 'Jacdal' (F)	SPoG
Great Expectations = 'Lanican' (HT)	CBcs
Great Expectations = 'Mackalves'[PBR] (F)	EPfP ESty IArd LRHS MRav SCoo SPer
'Great Maiden's Blush'	see *R.* 'Maiden's Blush'
'Great News' (F)	MAus
Greenall's Glory = 'Kirmac'[PBR] (F/Patio)	MAus MRav
Greetings = 'Jacdreco'[PBR] (F)	LBuc MAsh MBri MJak
Grenadine = 'Poulgrena'[PBR] (HT)	EBee
'Grootendorst'	see *R.* 'F.J. Grootendorst'
Grouse = 'Korimro' (S/GC)	MAus MMuc NLar SEND SLon SPer
Grouse 2000 = 'Korteilhab' (GC) ♀H6	CTri MAus
'Gruss an Aachen' (Poly) ♀H6	EBee EPfP EWTr MAus MJak NLar SPer SWCr
'Gruss an Teplitz' (China hybrid)	MAus NLar SPer
'Guinée' (ClHT)	CSBt ELan EPfP EWTr LAst LRHS MAus MRav MSwo NLar NPri SMrm SPer SRGP SSea WCot

	Name	Suppliers
	'Gustav Grünerwald' (HT)	MAus
	Guy Savoy = 'Delstrimen'PBR (F)	ESty LRHS MRav SLon
	Guy's Gold = 'Harmatch'PBR (HT)	ESty
	Gwent = 'Poulurt'PBR (GC)	CSBt ELan SCob SEND SPer SSea
	Gypsy Boy	see *R.* 'Zigeunerknabe'
	'Hakuun' (F/Patio)	MAus
	Hampshire = 'Korhamp'PBR (GC)	MAus
	Hand in Hand = 'Haraztec'PBR (Patio/Min)	LBrs MWat
	Händel = 'Macha' (ClHT)	CBcs COtt CSBt CTri CWSG ELan EPfP IBoy LBuc LRHS MAsh MBri MRav MWat NEgg NLar SMrm SPer SPlb SPoG SSea SWCr
§	Hanky Panky = 'Wektorcent'PBR (F)	ESty LBrs LRHS MBri MRav SCoo SWCr
	Hannah Gordon = 'Korweiso' (F)	SPer SWCr
	'Hansa' (Ru)	EMil LBuc MAus SPer SWCr
	Happy Anniversary ambig.	SSea
	Happy Anniversary = 'Bedfranc'PBR (F)	MBri SWCr
	Happy Anniversary = 'Delpre' (F)	CTri LBrs LRHS MAsh MRav SPoG
	'Happy Birthday' (Min/Patio)	ESty IBoy SSea SWCr
	Happy Child = 'Auscomp'PBR (S)	LRHS MAus
	Happy Days = 'Harquad'PBR	LBuc
	Happy Retirement = 'Tantoras'PBR (F) ♀H6	COtt ESty LBrs LBuc LRHS MAsh MBri MJak MRav SCoo SPoG SSea SWCr
§	× ***harisonii*** 'Harison's Yellow' (SpH)	MAus
§	- 'Lutea Maxima' (SpH)	MAus
§	- 'Williams Double Yellow' (SpH)	MAus
	Harlow Carr ambig.	LRHS SCob
	Harlow Carr = 'Aushouse'PBR (S)	CRos EPfP IBoy LBuc MAus MRav SCob SCoo SMrm SPer
	Harlow Carr = 'Kirlyl' (F)	MBri
	'Harry Edland' (F)	LBuc SWCr
	'Harry Wheatcroft' (HT)	IBoy LBrs MAus SPer
	Harvest Fayre = 'Dicnorth'PBR (F)	MJak SPer
	Havana Hit = 'Poulpah032'PBR (Patio)	EPfP LRHS MAsh MBri
	'Hazel Le Rougetel' (Ru) **new**	WFar
	'Headleyensis' (S)	MAus SLon
	'Heart of Gold' (Ra) **new**	COtt
	Heart of Gold = 'Coctarlotte'PBR (HT) ♀H6	ECnt ESty MRav
	Heathcliff = 'Ausnipper' (S) **new**	CRos CSBt ESty LBuc MAsh MAus SSea
	Heather Austin = 'Auscook'PBR (S)	MAus
	Heavenly Rosalind = 'Ausmash'PBR (S)	MAus
§	'Hebe's Lip' (D × RH)	MAus
	'Helen Knight' (*ecae* hybrid) (S)	ESty LRHS MAsh MAus MBri SSea
	helenae	CTri GBin MAus NLar SPer WPGP
	hemisphaerica (S)	MAus
§	'Henri Martin' (CeMo) ♀H7	IBoy LEdu LRHS MAus NEgg NLar SKHP SLon SMrm SPer
	Henri Matisse = 'Delstrobla' (HT)	ESty LRHS MRav SPoG
	'Henry Nevard' (HP)	MAus
§	'Herbstfeuer' (RH)	CPou EBee NLar
	Heritage = 'Ausblush' (S)	CTri ELan EPfP MAus MBri MJak MRav MWat NEgg NLar SCob SLon SMrm SPer SSea
	'Hermosa' (Ch)	LEdu LRHS MAus
	Hero = 'Aushero' (S)	MAus
	Hertfordshire = 'Kortenay'PBR (GC) ♀H6	ELan LRHS MAus MMuc MRav SCob SEND SPer SWCr
	× ***hibernica***	MAus
	'Hidcote Gold' (S)	MAus
§	'Hidcote Yellow' (Cl)	LRHS SPer
	High Flier = 'Fryfandango'PBR (ClHT)	MBri MWat
	High Hopes = 'Haryup'PBR (ClHT)	CWSG EPfP IBoy LBuc LRHS MAsh MAus MBri SPer SSea SWCr
	'Highdownensis' (*moyesii* hybrid) (S)	ELan MAus
	Highfield = 'Harcomp' (ClHT)	MAus
	Hilda Murrell = 'Ausmurr' (S)	MAus
	'Hillieri' (*moyesii* hybrid)	MAus
	'Hippolyte' (G)	MAus
	holy rose	see *R.* × *richardii*
	'Homère' (T)	MAus
	Hommage à Barbara = 'Delchifrou'PBR (HT)	EBee ESty MRav SMrm WKif
	Honey Bunch = 'Cocglen'PBR (F)	ELon MRav SPer SRGP
	Honey Dijon = 'Weksproulses'PBR (F)	CSBt ESty SWCr
	Honeybun = 'Tan98264'PBR (Patio)	ESty SWCr
	Honeymoon	see *R.* 'Honigmond'
§	'Honigmond' (F)	CBcs
	'Honorine de Brabant' (Bb) ♀H6	CPou LEdu LRHS MAus MCot NLar SPer
	Hope and Glory = 'Tan01360'PBR (HT) **new**	ESty
	Hot Chocolate = 'Wekpaltez' (F) ♀H6	CSBt EBee ECnt ELan ELon EPfP ESty IBoy LBrs LBuc LRHS LShp MAsh MBri MJak MRav NPri SCoo SMad SMrm SPer SPoG SRGP SSea SWCr WBor
	House Beautiful = 'Harbingo' (Patio)	MRav
	'Hugh Dickson' (HP)	CPou MAus NLar
	hugonis	see *R. xanthina* f. *hugonis*
	- 'Plenissima'	see *R. xanthina* f. *hugonis*
	Humanity = 'Harcross'PBR (F)	MRav SMrm
	Hyde Hall = 'Ausbosky'PBR (S)	CRos LBuc LRHS MAus SCob SCoo
	Ice Cream = 'Korzuri'PBR (HT) ♀H6	CSBt CWSG EBee ECnt ESty IBoy MAus MRav MWat SCob SPoG SWCr
§	Iceberg = 'Korbin' (F) ♀H6	Widely available
	'Illusion' (ClF)	SWCr
§	Imagination = 'Pouldron'PBR (F)	MAsh

	Name	Suppliers
	Impératrice Farah = 'Delivour'	ESty
§	'Impératrice Joséphine' (Gn) ♀H7	EWTr IBoy LRHS MAsh NLar SFam
	Indian Summer = 'Harwigwam' (ClMin)	MBri MJak
	Indian Summer = 'Peaperfume'PBR (HT) ♀H6	CSBt CWSG ELon LBuc MAsh MRav MWat SMrm SPoG SWCr
	'Indigo' (DPo)	CPou EWTr MAus SMrm
	Ingrid Bergman = 'Poulman'PBR (HT) ♀H6	CTri ECnt EPfP IBoy LBrs LRHS MBri MGos MRav SMrm SPer SPoG SWCr
	'Inspiration' (Cl/HT)	COtt LShp
	'Ipsilanté' (G)	MAus WBor
	'Irène Watts' (Ch)	CPou ECre NLar SKHP SWCr
	'Irene's Delight' (HT)	ESty
	Irish Eyes = 'Dicwitness'PBR (F) ♀H6	CBcs ESty IArd IBoy LRHS MAsh MBri MJak MRav MWat SCoo SPer SSea SWCr
	Irish Hope = 'Harexclaim'PBR (F)	SWCr
	Irish Wonder	see *R.* Evelyn Fison
	Isabel Rose = 'Hortickle' (HT)	SMrm
	Isabella = 'Poulisab'PBR (Renaissance Series) (S)	CPou CTri EBee ECnt SLon SWCr
	IsisPBR (HT)	see *R.* Silver Anniversary = 'Poulari'
	Isn't She Lovely = 'Diciluvit'PBR (HT) ♀H6	EBee ECnt ESty IDic SWCr
	'Ispahan' (D) ♀H7	EPfP GCra LRHS MAus MBri MCot NEgg NLar SFam SLon SPer WFar
	Ivor's Rose = 'Beadonald' (S)	LRHS LShp MBri
	Ivory Castle = 'Guesoverlay' (HT)	SWCr
	Ivory Romatica = 'Meisabeyla' (HT) **new**	ESty
§	× ***jacksonii*** 'Max Graf' (GC/Ru)	LRHS MAus NLar
	- Red Max Graf	see *R.* Rote Max Graf
§	- White Max Graf = 'Korgram'PBR (GC/Ru)	EAEE
	Jacobite rose	see *R.* × *alba* 'Alba Maxima'
	Jacqueline du Pré = 'Harwanna'PBR (S) ♀H6	EBee ECnt EPfP ESty MAus MCot MRav MWat NLar SEND SLon SPer SSea SWCr
	Jacquenetta = 'Ausjac' (S)	MAus
	'Jacques Cartier' misapplied	see *R.* 'Marchesa Boccella'
	Jam and Jerusalem = 'Frymojo' (F) **new**	ECnt SMad
	James Galway = 'Auscrystal'PBR (S)	CSBt ESty IBoy LBuc LRHS MAus MBri NEgg SCob SCoo SMrm SSea
	'James Mason' (G)	MAus
	'James Mitchell' (CeMo)	MAus
	'James Veitch' (DPoMo)	MAus
	Janet = 'Auspishus'PBR (S)	MAus MBri SSea SWCr
§	'Japonica' (CeMo)	EBee MAus
§	Jardins de Bagatelle = 'Meimafris' (HT)	MRav SMrm
	Jasmina = 'Korcentex'PBR (ClHT)	CPou EBee EPfP ESty LRHS MAsh NPri
	'Jaune Desprez'	see *R.* 'Desprez à Fleur Jaune'
	Jayne Austin = 'Ausbreak'PBR (S)	CSBt LRHS MAus MJak SPer
	JazzPBR (ClF)	see *R.* That's Jazz
	'Jean Mermoz' (Poly)	MAus
	'Jeanne de Montfort' (CeMo)	MAus
	'Jenny Duval' misapplied	see *R.* 'Président de Sèze'
	Jenny's Rose = 'Cansit' (F)	EBee ECnt SWCr
	Jill's Rose = 'Ganjil'PBR (F)	SWCr
	John Clare = 'Auscent'PBR (S)	MAus
	'John Gwilliam'	MAvo
	'John Hopper' (HP)	EWTr MAus
§	Joie de Vivre = 'Korfloci 01'PBR (Patio/S) ♀H6	COtt CPou CSBt CWSG EBee ECnt ELan EPfP ESty GBin IBoy LBrs LBuc LRHS MAsh MBri MRav MWat NLar NPri SCoo SMrm SPer SPoG SWCr
	'Josephine Bruce' (HT)	CBcs
	'Joseph's Coat' (ClS)	IArd LAst SWCr
	Joy Vieli = 'Dickaramel' (F)	IDic
	'Jubilee Celebration' (F)	EPfP LRHS
	Jubilee Celebration = 'Aushunter'PBR (S)	CRos CSBt LBuc LRHS MAus MBri NLar SPer SSea
	Jude the Obscure = 'Ausjo'PBR (S)	CNec CSBt CWSG EPfP ESty LBuc LRHS MAus MBri NEgg SCob SWCr
	'Julia's Rose' (HT)	MAus SPer SWCr
	Julio Iglesias = 'Meistemon'PBR (F)	ESty
	'Juno' (Ch)	CPou MAus
	'Just Joey' (HT) ♀H6	CBcs COtt CSBt CWSG EBee ECnt ELan ELon EPfP IArd IBoy MAus MBri MJak MRav MWat NEgg SCob SMrm SPer SPoG SRGP SSea SWCr
	'Katharina Zeimet' (Poly)	CTri MAus
§	Katherine Mansfield = 'Meilanein' (HT)	CSBt
	'Kathleen Harrop' (Bb)	LRHS MAus MMuc MSwo NLar SEND SFam SPer SRGP SWCr
	Kathryn Morley = 'Ausclub'PBR (F)	MAus
	'Kazanlik' misapplied	see *R.* × *damescena* 'Professeur Émile Perrot'
	Keep Smiling = 'Fryflorida' (HT) ♀H6	MAsh MBri MRav MWat
	'Keith Maughan' (Cl)	LRHS
§	Kent = 'Poulcov'PBR (Towne & Country Series) (S/GC) ♀H6	CSBt EAEE ECnt ELan EPfP ESty IBoy MMuc MRav MSwo MWat NLar SCob SEND SMrm SPer SPoG SSea SWCr
	Kew Gardens = 'Ausfence'PBR (S) ♀H6	EPfP GGal LBuc LRHS MAsh MAus SSea
	'Kew Rambler' (Ra)	CRHN CSam EBee MAus MMuc NLar SFam SLon SPer
	'Kiftsgate'	see *R. filipes* 'Kiftsgate'
	King's Macc = 'Frydisco'PBR (HT) ♀H6	LRHS MAus MWat SWCr
	'King's Ransom' (HT)	CSBt MJak MRav SPer SPoG
	Knirps = 'Korverlandus'PBR (GC)	LRHS
	Knock Out = 'Dadler' (F)	MAsh
§	'Königin von Dänemark' (A) ♀H7	ECnt EPfP IBoy LRHS MBri MRav MWat NEgg NLar SKHP SPer SSea SWCr
	Korona = 'Kornita' (F)	SPer
	'Korresia' (F) ♀H7	CSBt CTri ECnt EPfP ESty IBoy MAsh MAus MBri MJak MRav MWat SCob SPer SPoG SWCr
	'Kronprinzessin Viktoria von Preussen' (Bb)	MAus

	Name	Suppliers
	L.D. Braithwaite = 'Auscrim'[PBR] (S)	CBcs ELan EPfP IBoy LRHS MAus MBNS MBri MRav NLar SCob SLon SMrm SPer SSea
	'La Belle Sultane'	see *R.* 'Violacea'
	'La France' (HT)	MAus
	'La Mortola'	see *R. brunonii* 'La Mortola'
	La Parisienne = 'Delpartricol' (F)	ESty
	'La Perle' (Ra)	CRHN
	'La Reine Victoria'	see *R.* 'Reine Victoria'
§	La Rose de Molinard = 'Delgrarose'[PBR] (S) ♀H6	CPou EBee ESty MRav NLar
	La Rose de Petit Prince = 'Delgramau' (F)	EBee ESty MRav
	'La Rubanée'	see *R.* × *centifolia* 'Unique Panachée'
	La Sévillana = 'Meigekanu' (F/GC)	MSwo SPer WCot
	'La Ville de Bruxelles' (D) ♀H7	CSam GBin LRHS MAus NLar SLon SPer
	Lady Emma Hamilton = 'Ausbrother'[PBR] (S) ♀H6	CNec CRos EPfP ESty IBoy LBuc LRHS MAus MBri SCoo SPer SWCr
	'Lady Gay' (Ra)	WBor
	'Lady Godiva' (Ra)	MAus
	'Lady Hillingdon' (T)	CRos MAsh MAus
	'Lady Hillingdon' (ClT)	see *R.* 'Climbing Lady Hillingdon'
	'Lady Iliffe' (HT)	SWCr
	Lady Marmalade = 'Hartiger' (F) **new**	ECnt ESty
	Lady Mitchell = 'Haryearn' (HT)	ECnt
	Lady of Megginch = 'Ausvolume'[PBR] (S)	EPfP LRHS MAsh MAus MBri
	Lady of Shalott = 'Ausnyson'[PBR] (S) ♀H6	COtt CRos LBuc LRHS MAus MBri SCob SSea
	Lady Penelope = 'Chewdor'[PBR] (ClHT)	CSBt
§	'Lady Penzance' (RH)	CBcs SPer
	Lady Rose = 'Korlady' (HT)	LBrs MAsh MBri
	Lady Salisbury = 'Auscezed' (S)	CRos EPfP LBuc LRHS MAus SCob SCoo
	'Lady Sylvia' (HT)	CTri MAus NEgg SPer
	Lady Taylor = 'Smitling' (F/Patio)	ESty
	'Lady Waterlow' (ClHT)	EWTr MAus
	laevigata (Ra)	MAus MMuc SSea
	- 'Anemonoides'	see *R.* 'Anemone'
	Laguna = 'Koradigel'[PBR] (Cl)	LBrs MAsh NPri
	Laguna = 'Kormulen' (HT) **new**	LRHS
	L'Aimant = 'Harzola'[PBR] (F) ♀H5	CSBt ESty MAus MRav SWCr
	'Lamarque' (N)	CPou EWTr MAus SSea
	Lancashire = 'Korstesgli'[PBR] (GC) ♀H6	ECnt ELan ESty LRHS MAus MRav MSwo SSea SWCr
	Lancelot = 'Tan03542' (Cl) **new**	ESty
§	'Lanei' (CeMo)	EBee
	Laura Ford = 'Chewarvel'[PBR] (ClMin) ♀H5	COtt CTri IBoy LBrs LRHS MAsh MAus MBri MGos MRav MWat SPer SPoG SSea
	'Laure Davoust' (Ra)	CPou MMuc NLar
	Lavender Ice = 'Tan04249' (F)	ESty SWCr
	'Lavender Jewel' (Min)	MAus
	'Lavender Lassie' (HM)	CPou MAus NLar SPer SSea
	Lavender Symphonie = 'Meiptima' (Patio)	ESty SMrm
	Lavinia	see *R.* Lawinia
§	Lawinia = 'Tanklewi' (ClHT) ♀H6	CSBt EBee EPfP LRHS SPer
	'Lawrence Johnston'	see *R.* 'Hidcote Yellow'
§	Lazy Days = 'Poulkalm'[PBR] (F)	ECnt LBrs MAsh MBri
	'Le Rêve' (Cl)	EWTr
	Le Rouge et le Noir = 'Delcart' (HT)	ESty
	'Le Vésuve' (Ch)	CPou MAus
	Lea = 'Poulren019'[PBR] (ClS)	ECnt
	Leah Tutu = 'Hornavel' (S)	ESty LRHS LShp MBri
	Leander = 'Auslea' (S)	MAus
	Leaping Salmon = 'Peamight'[PBR] (ClHT) ♀H6	CSBt EBee ELon ESty MAus MRav SPer SRGP SWCr
	'Leda' (D)	MAus SFam SPer
	'Lemon Pillar'	see *R.* 'Paul's Lemon Pillar'
	Léonardo de Vinci = 'Meideauri'[PBR] (F)	CSBt
	'Léontine Gervais' (Ra)	CRHN LRHS MAus MBri
	'Leo's Eye' (Ra)	CPou EPfP
	Leslie's Dream = 'Dicjoon' (HT)	IDic
	Let's Celebrate = 'Fryraffles' (F)	ECnt ESty
	'Leverkusen' (ClF) ♀H7	EWTr LRHS MAus MRav NLar SEND SPer SWCr
	Lichfield Angel = 'Ausrelate'[PBR] (S) ♀H6	EPfP LBuc LRHS MAus MBri NLar SCob SCoo
	Lichtkönigin Lucia = 'Korlillub' (S)	SSea
	Light Fantastic = 'Dicgottago' (F) ♀H6	IDic MAsh
	'Lilac Dream' (F)	SWCr
	Lilac Rose = 'Auslilac' (S)	MAus
	Lilian Austin = 'Ausli' (S)	MAus
	Liliana = 'Poulsyng'[PBR] (S)	CPou EBee ECnt SLon SMrm SWCr
	Lilli Marlene = 'Korlima' (F)	CSBt IBoy SPer
	Lincoln Cathedral = 'Glanlin'[PBR] (HT)	MJak SPer
	Lincolnshire Poacher = 'Glareabit' (HT)	NEgg
	'Lincolnshire Yellow Belly' (F)	ESty
	Lion's Fairy Tale[PBR]	see *R.* Champagne Moments
	'Little Buckaroo' (Min)	SPer
	'Little Flirt' (Min)	MAus
	'Little Gem' (DPMo)	MAus
	Little Miss Sunshine = 'Dicgungho' (F)	IDic
	Little Rambler = 'Chewramb'[PBR] (MinRa) ♀H6	CSBt CWSG EBee ECnt ELan ESty MAus MBri MGos MMuc MRav MWat SCoo SMrm SSea SWCr
	'Little White Pet'	see *R.* 'White Pet'
	Lochinvar = 'Ausbilda'[PBR] (S)	LRHS MAus
	'Lolabelle'	CPou EBee
	'Long John Silver' (Cl)	ELan MAus SSea
	longicuspis misapplied	see *R. mulliganii*
	longicuspis Bertol. (Ra)	EWTr
§	- var. ***sinowilsonii*** (Ra)	GCal MAus
	Look Good... Feel Better = 'Poulcas034' (Castle Series) (Poly) **new**	LBrs MAsh

Name	Suppliers
Lord Byron = 'Meitosier' (ClHT)	ESty SWCr
'Lord Penzance' (RH)	NLar SPer
'L'Ouche' misapplied	see *R.* 'Louise Odier'
'Louis Gimard' (CeMo)	MAus SFam
'Louis XIV' (Ch)	MCot
§ 'Louise Odier' (Bb)	CTri EAEE ECnt EPfP EWTr IArd LRHS MAus MBri MRav MWat NLar SFam SPer SRGP SSea SWCr
Love & Peace = 'Baipeace'PBR (HT) 🏆H6	ESty LRHS SWCr
Love Knot = 'Chewglorious'PBR (ClMin) 🏆H6	CSBt ECnt EPfP ESty LBrs LRHS MAsh MRav MWat SCoo SMrm SSea SWCr
§ Lovely Bride = 'Meiratcan'PBR (Patio)	EPfP LRHS MAsh MBri SCoo SPoG
Lovely Fairy = 'Spevu'PBR (Poly/GC)	WMoo
Lovely Lady = 'Dicjubell'PBR (HT) 🏆H6	CSBt ECnt ESty MAus MJak MRav MWat SSea SWCr
Lovely MeidilandPBR	see *R.* Lovely Bride
'Lovers' Meeting' (HT)	MJak MRav SPer SWCr
Loving Memory = 'Korgund81' (HT)	COtt CSBt ECnt ESty IArd LBrs LRHS MAsh MGos MJak MRav NPri SPer SPoG SSea SVic SWCr
Lucetta = 'Ausemi' (S)	MAus
'Lucky' (F)	COtt CWSG EPfP ESty LRHS LShp NPri SPer
Lucky! = 'Frylucy' (F) 🏆H6	CSBt ECnt LBuc MAsh MRav SCoo SPoG SWCr
Ludlow Castle	see *R.* England's Rose = 'Ausrace'
'Lutea Maxima'	see *R.* × *harisonii* 'Lutea Maxima'
'Lykkefund' (Ra)	MAus
'Mabel Morrison' (HP)	MAus
Macartney rose	see *R. bracteata*, *R.* The McCartney Rose
Macmillan Nurse = 'Beamac' (S)	ESty LRHS LShp MBri MCot
'Macrantha' (Gallica hybrid)	MAus
macrophylla (S)	MAus
- B&SWJ 2603	WCru
- CC 6259	GKev
§ - 'Master Hugh'	MAus
'Madame Abel Chatenay' (HT)	MAus
'Madame Alfred Carrière' (N) 🏆H5	Widely available
'Madame Alice Garnier' (Ra)	CPou CRHN MMuc SPer
'Madame Antoine Mari' (T)	CPou
§ 'Madame Boll' (DPo) **new**	COtt ESty LEdu MAsh MRav MSwo NLar
'Madame Bravy' (T)	MAus
'Madame Butterfly' (HT)	LRHS MAus
§ 'Madame Caroline Testout' (HT)	CTri LRHS SPoG SRGP
'Madame de la Roche-Lambert' (DPMo)	CPou MAus
'Madame de Sancy de Parabère' (Bs)	EWTr IArd MAus
'Madame Driout' (ClT)	CPou
'Madame Ernest Calvat' (Bb)	CPou
'Madame Eugène Résal' misapplied	see *R.* 'Comtesse du Caÿla'
§ 'Madame Grégoire Staechelin' (ClHT) 🏆H6	CTri ECnt ELan EPfP EWTr IBoy LRHS MAsh MAus MBri MJak MRav MSwo NEgg NLar SCob SPer SPlb SPoG SWCr
'Madame Hardy' (ClD) 🏆H7	CPou CSBt EAEE ECnt EPfP LRHS MAus MBri MRav MSwo MWat NEgg NLar SCob SFam SMrm SPer SSea SWCr WFar
'Madame Isaac Pereire' (ClBb)	CSBt CTri ECnt EPfP IBoy MAus MBri MCot MRav MSwo MWat NLar NPri SCob SFam SMad SPer SPoG SSea SWCr WBor WFar
'Madame Jules Gravereaux' (ClT)	MAus
'Madame Knorr' misapplied	see *R.* 'Madame Boll'
'Madame Knorr' (DPo) 🏆H7	CPou CSam ECnt ELon EPfP LRHS MCot SPer SSea SWCr
'Madame Laurette Messimy' (Ch)	CPou
'Madame Lauriol de Barny' (Bb)	MAus MRav NLar SFam SLon
'Madame Legras de Saint Germain' (A × N)	CPou EWTr LRHS MAus NLar SFam SPer
'Madame Louis Lévêque' (DPMo)	CPou
'Madame Pierre Oger' (Bb)	CTri ECnt EWTr MAus SKHP SPer
'Madame Plantier' (A × N)	CPou MAus NLar SEND SPer WBor WFar
'Madame Rouge' (HT) **new**	MAsh
'Madame Scipion Cochet' (HP)	CPou
'Madame Zöetmans' (D)	MAus
'Madge' (HM)	SDix
Magic Carpet = 'Jaclover'PBR (S/GC) 🏆H6	ELan IBoy MAus MGos MRav MSwo MWat SMrm SPer SWCr
Maid Marion = 'Austobias'PBR (HM)	EPfP LBuc LRHS MAus
Maid of Honour = 'Jacwhink'PBR (F)	IDic
'Maid of Kent'PBR (Cl)	EBee LBuc MAus NLar SCob SCoo SPer SWCr
§ 'Maiden's Blush' (A) 🏆H7	CArn CTri ELan EWTr LEdu LRHS MAsh MAus MBri MRav NLar SFam SPer SWCr WHer
'Maiden's Blush, Great'	see *R.* 'Maiden's Blush'
'Maigold' (ClPiH) 🏆H7	CBcs CTri ELan ELon EPfP LRHS MAsh MAus MBri MCot MRav MSwo MWat NLar SCob SEND SMad SPer SWCr
Maltese rose	see *R.* 'Cécile Brünner'
Malvern Hills = 'Auscanary'PBR (Ra)	CSBt EPfP LBuc LRHS MAus MBri NLar SPer SWCr
'Maman Cochet' (T)	MAus
Mamma Mia! = 'Fryjolly'PBR (HT) 🏆H6	COtt EBee ECnt ESty LBrs LRHS MAsh MBri MRav NPri SPoG SWCr
Mamy Blue = 'Delblue' (HT) **new**	ESty
'Mandarin' (F)	SSea
Mandarin = 'Korcelin'PBR (Min)	ESty IBoy LBrs MRav
'Manning's Blush' (RH)	MAus
Many Happy Returns = 'Harwanted'PBR (F) 🏆H6	CBcs CSBt ECnt ELan EPfP IBoy LBrs LRHS MAsh MBri MGos MJak MRav MWat NPri SCob SPer SPoG SSea SVic SWCr
'Marbrée' (DPo)	MAus
'Märchenland' (F)	MAus

	Name	Suppliers
§	'Marchesa Boccella' (DPo) ♀H7	CPou CSam CTri EPfP LRHS MAsh MBri MCot NLar NPri SEND SPer SPoG SSea SWCr WBor WHer
	'Maréchal Davoust' (CeMo)	LEdu MAus SFam
	'Maréchal Niel' (N)	MAus SPer SSea
	Margaret Merril = 'Harkuly' (F)	CBcs CSBt CTri CWSG EBee ECnt ELan EPfP ESty IArd IBoy LAst LBrs LRHS MAsh MAus MBri MJak MRav MWat NPri SCob SPer SPoG SRGP SSea SWCr
	'Marguerite Hilling' (S)	CTri MAus MSwo NLar SPer
	'Marie Louise' (D)	MAus SFam
	'Marie Pavič' (Poly)	CPou MAus
	'Marie van Houtte' (T)	MAus
	'Marie-Jeanne' (Poly)	MAus
	Marigold Sweet Dream = 'Fryprospa' (Patio)	ECnt
	Marinette = 'Auscam'[PBR] (S)	MAus
	Marjorie Fair = 'Harhero' (Poly/S) ♀H6	ELan EPfP ESty MAus MRav SWCr
	'Marlena' (F/Patio)	MAus
	Marry Me = 'Dicwonder'[PBR] (Patio) ♀H6	ESty IDic LBuc
	'Martin Frobisher' (Ru)	MAus
	Mary Magdalene = 'Ausjolly'[PBR] (S)	MAus
	Mary Rose = 'Ausmary' (S)	CSBt CTri CWSG ELan ELon EPfP IBoy LRHS MAus MBri MJak MRav MWat NLar NPri SCob SLon SPer SPoG SSea SWCr WKif
	'Mary Wallace' (Cl)	MAus
	Mary Webb = 'Auswebb' (S)	MAus
	'Masquerade' (F)	CTri ELan EPfP MRav SMrm SPer SWCr
	'Master Hugh'	see *R. macrophylla* 'Master Hugh'
	Matawhero Magic[PBR]	see *R.* Simply the Best
	Maurice Utrillo = 'Delstavo' (HT) **new**	ESty
	'Max Graf'	see *R.* × *jacksonii* 'Max Graf'
	'Maxima'	see *R.* × *alba* 'Alba Maxima'
	Maxima Romantica = 'Meikerira' (HT) **new**	ESty
	'May Queen' (Ra)	CPou EBee LRHS MAsh MAus MRav NLar SEND SFam SPer SWCr
	Mayor of Casterbridge = 'Ausbrid'[PBR] (S)	LRHS MAus
	'McCartney Rose'[PBR]	see *R.* The McCartney Rose
	'Meg' (ClHT)	EPfP EWTr LRHS MAus MCot MMuc NLar SPer SRGP
	Melody Maker = 'Dicqueen'[PBR] (F)	IBoy MJak
	'Mermaid' (Cl) ♀H5	CBcs CDul CSBt ELon EPfP LEdu LRHS MAus MBri NLar SCob SEND SMrm SPer SSea SWCr
§	'Mevrouw Nathalie Nypels' (Poly)	CTri MAus MMuc MRav NLar SPer SWCr
	'Michèle Meilland' (HT)	MAus
	× *micrugosa*	MAus
	- 'Alba'	MAus
§	Millie = 'Poulren013'[PBR] (Renaissance Series) (S) ♀H6	COtt ECnt ESty LBrs LRHS MAsh MBri MWat NPri SPoG SWCr
	Millie Rose = 'Wekblunez'[PBR] (HT)	SWCr
	Mind Games = 'Dickylie' (F)	ECnt IDic
	'Minnehaha' (Ra)	MAus SSea
	mirifica stellata	see *R. stellata* var. *mirifica*
	Mischief = 'Macmi' (HT)	SPer
	Miss Alice = 'Ausjake'[PBR] (S)	MAsh MAus MBri SWCr
	'Miss Edith Cavell' (Poly)	EBee MAus
§	'Mister Lincoln' (HT)	MJak SPer
	Mistress Quickly = 'Ausky'[PBR] (S)	MAus
§	Misty Hit = 'Poulhi011'[PBR] (PatioHit Series) (Patio)	ECnt LRHS MAsh MBri SWCr
	Mitsouko = 'Delnat' (HT)	ESty
	Molineux = 'Ausmol'[PBR] (S) ♀H6	CRos EPfP LRHS MAsh MAus MBri SMrm SPer SWCr
	Moment in Time = 'Korcastrav'[PBR] (F) ♀H6	COtt EBee ECnt EPfP ESty LShp MAsh MRav MWat NPri NSoo SCoo SMrm SPer SPoG SWCr
	Monica Bellucci = 'Meimonkeur' (HT) **new**	ESty
	Monsieur Pélisson	see *R.* 'Pélisson'
	Moody Blue = 'Fryniche' (HT)	ECnt ESty IBoy LRHS LShp MAsh MRav SWCr
	Moonbeam = 'Ausbeam' (S)	MAus
	'Moonlight' (HM)	CSam CTri EBee ELan EWTr LRHS MAus MRav MSwo SPer SWCr
	Moonshine = 'Tan97123'[PBR] (HT)	ESty
	'Morletii' (Bs)	MMuc SEND
	'Morning Jewel' (ClF) ♀H7	SPer SWCr
	Morning Mist = 'Ausfire' (S)	LBuc LRHS MAsh MAus SSea
§	'Morsdag' (Poly/F)	ELan SCob SVic
	Mortimer Sackler = 'Ausorts'[PBR] (S) ♀H6	CWSG ELon LBuc LRHS MAus MBri SCoo SSea
	moschata (Ra)	MAus MRav SSea
	- 'Autumnalis'	see *R.* 'Princesse de Nassau'
	- var. ***nepalensis***	see *R. brunonii*
I	'Mother's Day'	MJak SRGP
	Mother's Day	see *R.* 'Morsdag'
	Mountain Snow = 'Aussnow' (Ra)	LBuc LRHS MAus MBri
	Mountbatten = 'Harmantelle' (F) ♀H6	ELan LBuc MAus MJak MRav SPer SPoG SSea SWCr
§	'Mousseline' (DPoMo)	CPou MAus MCot SFam SPer
	'Mousseuse du Japon'	see *R.* 'Japonica'
	moyesii (S)	CTri EBee ELan EWTr EWld GCra GKev LAst MAus NEgg NWea SKHP SPer
	'Mr Bluebird' (MinCh)	MAus
	'Mr Lincoln'	see *R.* 'Mister Lincoln'
	'Mrs Anthony Waterer' (Ru)	MAus SPer
	Mrs Doreen Pike = 'Ausdor'[PBR] (Ru)	LRHS MAus
	'Mrs Honey Dyson' (Ra)	CPou EWTr
	'Mrs John Laing' (HP)	LRHS MAus NLar SFam SLon SPer SWCr
	'Mrs Oakley Fisher' (HT)	EBee EWTr MAus MCot SDix SMad SMrm SPer SWCr WCot
	'Mrs Paul' (Bb)	MAus
	'Mrs Sam McGredy' (HT)	CPou LRHS NEgg
§	***mulliganii*** (Ra)	EPfP GKin MAus SPer
	multibracteata (S)	CBcs MAus
	multiflora (Ra)	LBuc MAus
§	- 'Grevillei' (Ra)	MAus MMuc SPer
	- 'Platyphylla'	see *R. multiflora* 'Grevillei'
	- wild-collected	CAco GCal
	Mum in a Million[PBR]	see *R.* Millie
	Mummy[PBR]	see *R.* Newly Wed
	Mum's Blessing = 'Guesimage' (F)	SWCr
	mundi	see *R. gallica* 'Versicolor'

	Munstead Wood = 'Ausbernard'PBR (S) ♀H6	CNec COtt CRos EPfP EShb ESty LBuc LRHS MAus MBri SCob SSea
	'Muscosa Alba'	see *R.* × *centifolia* 'Shailer's White Moss'
	'Mutabilis'	see *R.* × *odorata* 'Mutabilis'
	My Dad = 'Boselftay'PBR (F)	NPri SWCr
	My Girl = 'Tan00798'PBR (HT)	ESty
	My Mum = 'Webmorrow'PBR (F)	ESty LBrs MBri NPri SCob SWCr
	My Valentine = 'Mormyval' (Min)	MAsh MBri NPri SPoG SWCr
	Mystery Girl = 'Dicdothis'PBR (HT)	ECnt
	Nahéma = 'Deléri' (ClHT)	SWCr
	Nancy = 'Poulninga'PBR (Renaissance Series) (S)	CPou EBee
	'Naomi' (HT)	CPou
	'Narrow Water' (Ra) ♀H6	CPou EBee SWCr
	Natasha Richardson = 'Harpacte' **new**	MRav
	'Nathalie Nypels'	see *R.* 'Mevrouw Nathalie Nypels'
	'National Trust' (HT)	CBcs CTri IArd IBoy LRHS SPer
	'Nestor' (G)	EBee MAus
	'Nevada' (S)	CSBt CTri ECnt ELan EPfP EWTr IArd IBoy LEdu LRHS MAus MRav NLar SPer SSea
	New Beginnings = 'Korprofko'PBR (F)	MAsh
§	'New Dawn' (Cl) ♀H7	Widely available
	New Zealand = 'Macgenev'PBR (HT)	SWCr
§	Newly Wed = 'Dicwhynot'PBR (Patio) ♀H6	SSea
	News = 'Legnews' (F)	MAus
	Newsflash = 'Kendutch' (F) **new**	ESty
	Nice Day = 'Chewsea'PBR (ClMin)	ELon EPfP ESty IBoy LRHS MAsh MRav MWat SPer SPoG SSea SWCr
	Night Light = 'Poullight'PBR (Courtyard Series) (Cl)	ECnt
	Night Owl = 'Wekpurosot' (Cl) **new**	ESty
	Nina = 'Mehnina'PBR (S)	SWCr
	Nina = 'Poulren018'PBR (Renaissance Series) (S)	ECnt
	nitida	MAus NWea SEND SPer WHer
	'Noaley'PBR (Min)	LRHS MAsh
	Noble Antony = 'Ausway'PBR (S)	CWSG EBee EPfP LRHS MAus MBri MWat SCob SSea
§	'Noisette Carnée' (N) ♀H7	CPou CSam EPfP EWTr GCra LEdu LRHS MBNS MBri MCot MRav NLar SPer SSea SWCr
	Norfolk = 'Poulfolk'PBR (GC)	CTri ESty MSwo SCob SMrm SPer
	'Norwich Pink' (S)	MAus
	Nostalgia = 'Savarita' (Min)	COtt LRHS MAsh MAus
	Nostalgie = 'Taneiglat'PBR (HT) ♀H6	CSBt ECnt ELon ESty MBri MRav SPoG SSea SWCr
	'Nozomi' (ClMin/GC)	CAbP CTri ELan EPfP ESty EWTr MAus MRav NLar SMrm SPer
	'Nuits de Young' (CeMo) ♀H7	LRHS MAsh MAus MBri NLar SEND SFam SKHP WHer
	'Nur Mahal' (HM)	MAus
	Nurse Tracey Davies = 'Frykookie'PBR (F) ♀H6	ESty
	nutkana (S)	MAus
§	- 'Plena' (S/D) ♀H7	EWTr MAus MCot NLar SKHP WHer
	'Nymphenburg' (HM)	SPer
	'Nyveldt's White' (Ru)	MAus
	Octavia Hill = 'Harzeal'PBR (F)	MBri MRav NLar SMrm SPer SWCr
§	× ***odorata***	CPou
	- 'Fortune's Double Yellow'	see *R.* × *odorata* 'Pseudindica'
§	- 'Mutabilis' (Ch) ♀H5	CPou CRHN CTri ECre ELan EPfP EWTr GBin GGal LRHS MAus MCot MRav NLar SEND SKHP SPer SPoG SSea SWCr WCFE WCot XSen
§	- 'Ochroleuca' (Ch)	CPou
§	- 'Pallida' (Ch)	CPou EPfP MAus MCot NLar SPer SSea
§	- 'Pseudindica' (ClCh)	MAus
§	- Sanguinea Group (Ch)	SEND XSen
	- - 'Bengal Crimson' (Ch) ♀H5	ECre EPfP EWTr LRHS SKHP SLon SPoG WCot WKif
	- - 'Bob's Beauty' (Ch)	WCot
§	- 'Viridiflora' (Ch)	CPou EBee LRHS MAus SLon SPer SSea WCot WHer
	Odyssey = 'Franski'PBR (F)	ESty SWCr
	'Oeillet Flamand'	see *R.* 'Oeillet Parfait'
§	'Oeillet Parfait' (G)	MAus
	officinalis	see *R. gallica* var. *officinalis*
	'Oklahoma' (HT)	ELon LAst
	old blush China	see *R.* × *odorata* 'Pallida'
	old cabbage	see *R.* × *centifolia*
	Old John = 'Dicwillynilly' (F)	IDic
	old pink moss rose	see *R.* × *centifolia* 'Muscosa'
	Old Port = 'Mackati'PBR (F)	ESty IArd
	old red moss	see *R.* 'Henri Martin', *R.* 'Lanei'
	old velvet moss	see *R.* 'William Lobb'
	'Old Velvet Rose'	see *R.* 'Tuscany'
	old yellow Scotch (SpH)	see *R.* × *harisonii* 'Williams Double Yellow'
	'Olympic Flame' (F)	EPfP LRHS MAsh MBri
	Olympic Spirit = 'Peaprince' (F)	LRHS MAsh
	'Omar Khayyám' (D)	MAus NLar
	omeiensis	see *R. sericea* subsp. *omeiensis*
	Open Arms = 'Chewpixcel'PBR (ClMin) ♀H6	ESty LBuc MAus SMad SMrm SPer SSea SWCr
	'Ophelia' (HT)	LRHS MAus
	'Orange Sensation' (F)	CTri MAus
§	Orange Sunblaze = 'Meijikatar'PBR (Min)	CSBt SMrm SPer
	'Orangeade' (F)	SCob
	Oranges and Lemons = 'Macoranlem'PBR (S/F)	CSBt ESty IBoy LBrs MAus SSea SWCr
	Othello = 'Auslo'PBR (S)	LAst MAus SPer
	'Our Beth' (S)	LRHS MBri
	'Our Dream' (Patio)	LRHS MAsh MBri
	Our Jubilee = 'Coccages' (HT)	ESty SVic
	Our Molly = 'Dicreason' (GC/S)	IDic SPer SWCr
	Oxfordshire = 'Korfullwind'PBR (GC) ♀H6	LRHS MRav MWat SCob SSea
	Painted Moon = 'Dicpaint' (HT)	ESty
	Panache = 'Poultop'PBR (Patio/Min)	ECnt IBoy LBrs LRHS SWCr

	Name	Suppliers
	'Papa Gontier' (T)	CPou MAus
	Papa Meilland = 'Meisar' (HT)	CSBt MAus SPer SSea
	Paper Anniversary (Patio)	LBuc
	Papi Delbard = 'Delaby' (ClHT)	ESty MRav
I	'Parade' (Cl) ♀H6	MAus NLar SWCr
	'Parkdirektor Riggers' (F)	CSam EBee EWTr GBin MAus MBri SCob SPer
	Parks's yellow China	see *R.* × *odorata* 'Ochroleuca'
	Parson's pink China	see *R.* × *odorata* 'Pallida'
	Partridge = 'Korweirim' (GC)	MAus SPer
	parvifolia	see *R.* 'Burgundiaca'
	Pas de Deux = 'Poulhult'PBR (Courtyard Series) (ClF)	LRHS MAsh
	Pascali = 'Lenip' (HT)	CBcs CTri ELon IBoy LBuc MAus MJak MWat SCob SPer
	Pat Austin = 'Ausmum'PBR (S)	CRos CSBt CTri EPfP IBoy LRHS MAus MBNS MBri MRav MWat NEgg NLar SCob SEND SMrm SPer SWCr
	Patricia = 'Korpatri' (F)	SWCr
	Paul Gauguin = 'Delstrichoc' (HT) **new**	ESty
	'Paul Lédé' (ClT)	see *R.* 'Climbing Paul Lédé'
	Paul McCartneyPBR (HT)	see *R.* The McCartney Rose
	'Paul Neyron' (HP)	EWTr MAus SPer
	'Paul Noël' (Ra)	CRos LBuc MAus
	'Paul Ricault' (Ce × HP)	MAus
	Paul Shirville = 'Harqueterwife'PBR (HT)	MAus SPer SWCr
	'Paul Transon' (Ra) ♀H6	CPou CRHN LRHS MBri MMuc NEgg NLar SEND SPer SRGP WHer
§	'Paulii' (Ru/GC)	MAus
	'Paulii Alba'	see *R.* 'Paulii'
	'Paulii Rosea' (Ru/GC)	MAus
	'Paul's Himalayan Musk' (Ra) ♀H6	Widely available
§	'Paul's Lemon Pillar' (ClHT)	LRHS MAus NLar SPer SSea
	'Paul's Scarlet Climber' (Cl/Ra)	COtt ELan IBoy LBuc MAsh MAus MJak MRav MSwo NPri SEND SPer SRGP
	'Paul's Single White Perpetual' (Ra)	CTri EWTr MMuc NLar
	'Pax' (HM)	CPou MAus WKif
	Peace = 'Madame A. Meilland' (HT) ♀H6	CBcs CSBt CTri EBee ECnt ELan EPfP ESty IBoy LBrs LRHS MAsh MAus MBri MJak MRav MWat NEgg NPri SCob SPer SPoG SRGP SSea SWCr
	Peacekeeper = 'Harbella'PBR (F)	CSBt
	Peach Blossom = 'Ausblossom' (S)	MAus
	'Peach Grootendorst' (Ru)	CPou EWTr
	Peachy = 'Macrelea' (HT)	LRHS MAsh MBri SPoG
§	Pearl Abundance = 'Harfrisky'PBR (F)	ESty SWCr
	Pearl Anniversary = 'Whitston'PBR (Min/Patio)	COtt CSBt ESty LBuc MRav SSea SWCr
	Pearl Drift = 'Leggab' (S)	MAus MCot MSwo MWat SMrm SPer SWCr
	Pearl = 'Korterschi'PBR (F) ♀H6	MAsh MRav SWCr
	Peaudouce	see *R.* Elina
	Pegasus = 'Ausmoon'PBR (S)	MAus

	Name	Suppliers
§	'Pélisson' (CeMo)	SFam
§	***pendulina***	CAco MAus WOut
	– 'Nana'	NWad
	'Penelope' (HM) ♀H5	CSBt CSam CTri EBee ECnt ELan EPfP EWTr IBoy LRHS MAsh MAus MBri MCot MRav MWat NLar SCob SEND SFam SMad SPer SRGP SSea SWCr
	Penny Lane = 'Hardwell'PBR (ClHT) ♀H6	COtt CSBt EBee ECnt EPfP IBoy LAst LBuc LRHS MAsh MAus MBri MRav MWat NLar NPri SCoo SPer SPoG SSea SWCr
	Penny Lane = 'Talpen' (Min) **new**	MSwo
	× ***penzanceana***	see *R.* 'Lady Penzance'
	Peppermint SplashPBR	see *R.* Rachel Louise Moran
	Perception = 'Harzippee'PBR (HT)	SWCr
	Perdita = 'Ausperd' (S)	LRHS MAus
	Perennial Blue = 'Mehr9601' (Ra) ♀H6	ESty MRav SCob SSea SWCr
	Perennial Blush = 'Mehbarbie'PBR (Ra) ♀H6	ESty MRav SSea SWCr
§	Perfect Day = 'Poulrem' (F)	ECnt
	Perfect Harmony = 'Tangustedv' (HT)	ESty
	'Perle des Jardins' (T)	MAus
§	'Perle d'Or' (Poly) ♀H6	MAus MMuc NLar SDix SLon SMad SPer
	Perle Noire = 'Delurt' (HT) **new**	ESty
	Perpetually Yours = 'Harfable'PBR (Cl)	LAst LBrs LBuc MRav MWat SCoo
	Persian yellow	see *R. foetida* 'Persiana'
	Peter Pan = 'Chewpan'PBR (Min) ♀H6	MAus MWat SWCr
	Peter Pan = 'Sunpete' (Patio)	LRHS MAsh SPoG
	'Petite de Hollande' (Ce)	MAus NLar SPer
	'Petite Lisette' (Ce × D)	MAus NLar
	'Petito' (F)	SMrm
	Phab Gold = 'Frybountiful'PBR (F)	MAsh
	Pheasant = 'Kordapt' (GC)	MAus SPer
	Phoebe (Ru)	see *R.* 'Fimbriata'
	'Phyllis Bide' (Ra) ♀H6	EBee EPfP IArd LRHS MAsh MAus MBri MCot MSwo NLar SEND SPer SRGP SSea SWCr WKif
	Piccadilly = 'Macar' (HT)	CSBt CTri IBoy SPer SWCr
	Piccolo = 'Tanolokip' (F/Patio)	MJak MRav SWCr
	'Picture' (HT)	MAus SPer
	Pigalle '84 = 'Meicloux' (F)	SWCr
	'Pilgrim'PBR	see *R.* The Pilgrim
	pimpinellifolia	see *R. spinosissima*
	– double yellow-flowered	see *R.* × *harisonii* 'Williams Double Yellow'
	– 'Harisonii'	see *R.* × *harisonii* 'Harison's Yellow'
	– 'Lutea'	see *R.* × *harisonii* 'Lutea Maxima'
	Pink Abundance = 'Harfrothy'PBR (Abundance Series) (F)	MBri
	Pink Bells = 'Poulbells' (GC)	SPer
	'Pink Bouquet' (Ra)	CRHN
	'Pink Favorite' (HT)	SCob SPer

Pink Fizz = 'Poulycool' (ClPatio) ECnt
§ Pink Flower Carpet = 'Noatraum'[PBR] (GC) ♀H6 COtt CSBt CTri ECnt ELan IBoy LRHS MAsh MBri NPri SCoo SEND SPer SPoG SWCr
'Pink Grootendorst' (Ru) LRHS MAus NEgg NLar SPer
§ Pink Hit = 'Poultipe'[PBR] (Min/Patio) ECnt LBrs LRHS MAsh MBri SWCr
Pink Knock Out = 'Radcon' (S) MAsh
'Pink Leda' (D) EBee
pink moss see *R.* × *centifolia* 'Muscosa'
Pink Paradise = 'Delfluoro' (HT) **new** ESty
'Pink Parfait' (F) SPer
Pink Perfection = 'Korpauvio'[PBR] (HT) ECnt ESty SWCr
'Pink Perpétué' (Cl) CBcs CNec COtt CSBt CTri CWSG ECnt ELan ELon EPfP IBoy LAst LBuc LRHS MAsh MAus MRav SMrm SPer SPoG SSea SWCr
'Pink Prosperity' (HM) MAus
'Pink Showers' (ClHT) MSwo
Pirouette = 'Poulyc003'[PBR] (ClS) ECnt LRHS MAsh
Playtime = 'Morplati' (F) MAus
Pleine de Grâce = 'Lengra' (S) GGal LEdu MAus
Poetry in Motion = 'Harelan'[PBR] (HT) MBri
Polar Star = 'Tanlarpost' (HT) CSBt ECnt MRav MWat SPer SWCr
§ 'Polyantha Grandiflora' (Ra) MAus SVic
'Pompon Blanc Parfait' (A) MAus
'Pompon de Bourgogne' see *R.* 'Burgundiaca'
'Pompon de Paris' (ClMinCh) see *R.* 'Climbing Pompon de Paris'
§ 'Pompon de Paris' (MinCh) ITim SCob WAbe
'Pompon Panaché' (G) MAus
Pomponella = 'Korpompan'[PBR] (F) ESty
Port Sunlight = 'Auslofty'[PBR] (HM) ♀H6 ESty IBoy LRHS MAsh MAus MBri NLar
Portland rose see *R.* 'Portlandica'
§ 'Portlandica' (Po) CTri LRHS MAsh SPer
Portmeirion = 'Ausguard'[PBR] (S) MAus SCoo
Pot o' Gold = 'Dicdivine' (HT) SWCr
prairie rose see *R. setigera*
'Precious Amber' (F) LBrs
Precious Memories = 'Dichello'[PBR] (F) ESty IDic LBuc
'Precious Platinum' (HT) MJak SPer
§ 'Président de Sèze' (G) ♀H7 CPou CSam MAus NLar SFam SPer
Pretty in Pink = 'Dicumpteen'[PBR] (GC) ♀H6 ECnt
Pretty Jessica = 'Ausjess' (S) LRHS MAus MRav SMrm SPer
Pretty Lady = 'Scrivo'[PBR] (F) ♀H6 MAus
Pretty Polly = 'Meitonje'[PBR] (Min) ♀H6 EPfP ESty IBoy LBrs LRHS MAsh MBri MJak MRav MWat SMrm SPer SPoG SSea SWCr
Pretty Sunrise = 'Meipelmel'[PBR] (S) LBuc
'Prima Ballerina' (HT) CTri EPfP LBrs LRHS MAsh MBri SPer SSea
primula MAus NLar SPer
primula × ***rugosa*** **new** MJak
'Prince Camille de Rohan' (HP) MAus
'Prince Charles' (Bb) MAus WKif
Prince Jardinier = 'Meitroni'[PBR] (HT) ♀H6 ESty
Princess = 'Korspobux'[PBR] (HT) ECnt
Princess Alexandra = 'Pouldra'[PBR] (Renaissance Series) (S) ♀H6 CTri EBee ECnt NLar SWCr
Princess Alexandra of Kent = 'Ausmerchant'[PBR] (S) EPfP EShb ESty LRHS MAus MBri SPer SSea
Princess Anne = 'Auskitchen'[PBR] (S) ♀H6 ECnt EPfP LBuc LRHS MAus MBri SCob
'Princess of Wales' (HP) EPfP
Princess of Wales = 'Hardinkum'[PBR] (F) ♀H6 EPfP LRHS MJak MRav SPer SWCr
Princess Royal = 'Dicroyal'[PBR] (HT) IDic
§ 'Princesse de Nassau' (Ra) MAus SKHP
'Princesse Louise' (Ra) SFam
'Princesse Marie' misapplied see *R.* 'Belvedere'
'Pristine' (HT) MAus
'Prolifera de Redouté' misapplied see *R.* 'Duchesse de Montebello'
Proper Job = 'Tan02733'[PBR] (HT) ESty SWCr
'Prosperity' (HM) ♀H6 CSam CTri EPfP EWTr LRHS MAus MCot MRav NLar SLon SPer SWCr
Prospero = 'Auspero' (S) MAus
Pure Bliss = 'Dictator'[PBR] (HT) ELon SWCr
Pure Gold = 'Harhappen'[PBR] (F) CSBt
'Purezza' (Ra) NLar
Purple Eden[PBR] see *R.* Ebb Tide
Purple Skyliner = 'Franwekpurp'[PBR] (ClS) MCot SMrm SPer
Purple Splash = 'Wekspitrib' (Cl) ESty
Purple Tiger = 'Jacpurr'[PBR] (F) ESty SSea SWCr
Quaker Star = 'Dicperhaps' (F) IDic
quatre saisons see *R.* × *damascena* var. *semperflorens*
'Quatre Saisons Blanche Mousseuse' (DMo) CPou MAus NLar
Queen Anne = 'Austruck' (S) CSBt EPfP ESty LBuc LRHS MAsh MAus MBri SCoo
Queen Elizabeth see *R.* 'The Queen Elizabeth'
Queen Mother = 'Korquemu'[PBR] (Patio) ♀H6 CSBt ELan EPfP MAus MJak MRav SPer SPoG SWCr
'Queen of Bourbons' (Bb) LEdu NLar
Queen of Denmark see *R.* 'Königin von Dänemark'
Queen of Sweden = 'Austiger'[PBR] (S) CNec CRos ECnt EPfP LBuc LRHS MAus MBri SCob SMrm SPer SWCr
'Rachel' (HT) COtt CPou EBee LBrs MAsh
§ Rachel Louise Moran = 'Jacdrama'[PBR] (HT) ESty

Name	Suppliers
Rachel = 'Tangust'PBR (HT) ♀H6	CSBt ESty MRav SPoG SSea SWCr
Rainbow Magic = 'Dicxplosion'PBR (Patio)	MJak
'Rambling Rector' (Ra) ♀H6	Widely available
Rambling Rosie = 'Horjasper'PBR (Ra) ♀H6	CRos CSBt EBee ECnt EPfP ESty LBuc LRHS MAsh MAus MBri MSwo SMrm SSea SWCr
'Raspberry Royale' (F/Patio) ♀H6	LRHS MAsh MBri NPri
'Raubritter' ('Macrantha' hybrid)	EPfP MAus MMuc SPer SWCr
Raymond Blanc = 'Delnado' (HT)	EBee MRav NLar SLon SMrm
'Raymond Carver' (S)	LRHS
'Raymond Chenault' (S)	SWCr
Rebecca (Patio)	ESty
Rebecca Mary = 'Dicjury'PBR (F)	IDic
Reconciliation = 'Hartillery'PBR (HT)	SWCr
Red AbundancePBR	see *R.* Songs of Praise
Red Blanket = 'Intercell' (S/GC)	LAst MAus
Red Coat = 'Auscoat' (F)	MAsh MAus
Red Devil = 'Dicam' (HT)	ESty IBoy MBri SCoo
Red Drift = 'Meigalpio' (GC)	LBuc MAsh
Red Eden Rose = 'Meidrason'PBR (Cl)	ESty SSea SWCr
'Red Facade' (Cl)	LRHS
Red Finesse = 'Korvillade'PBR (F) ♀H6	EBee ECnt LRHS MAsh MBri
'Red Grootendorst'	see *R.* 'F.J. Grootendorst'
'Red Max Graf'	see *R.* Rote Max Graf
Red Medley = 'Noapu'PBR (Min)	MAsh
Red Meidiland = 'Meineble'PBR (GC)	LBuc
red moss	see *R.* 'Henri Martin'
Red New Dawn	see *R.* 'Étendard'
Red Parfum de Provence = 'Meiafone'PBR (HT) **new**	ESty
Red Perfumella = 'Meikeneza'PBR (HT) **new**	ESty
Red Rascal = 'Jacbed' (S/Patio)	CSBt
red rose of Lancaster	see *R. gallica* var. *officinalis*
'Red Wing' (S)	MAus
Redouté = 'Auspale'PBR (S)	LRHS MAus
Reflections = 'Simref' (F)	SWCr
Regensberg = 'Macyoumis'PBR (F/Patio)	IBoy LEdu MAus SPer SWCr
'Reine des Centfeuilles' (Ce)	SFam
'Reine des Violettes' (HP) ♀H7	CPou EAEE ELon EPfP IArd LAst LRHS MAsh MAus MBri MCot MRav MWat NLar SPer SRGP SWCr
§ 'Reine Victoria' (Bb)	EPfP MAus MBri MRav NLar SPer SWCr
§ Remember = 'Poulht001'PBR (HT) ♀H6	ECnt EPfP LBrs LRHS MAsh SWCr
Remember Me = 'Cocdestin' (HT) ♀H6	COtt CSBt CWSG ECnt EPfP ESty IArd IBoy LRHS MAsh MAus MGos MJak MRav NEgg NPri SCob SPer SPoG SWCr
Remembrance = 'Harxampton'PBR (F)	CTri CWSG ESty LBrs LBuc LRHS MAsh MBri MJak MRav NPri SCob SPer SPoG SSea SWCr
§ Renaissance = 'Harzart'PBR (HT)	CSBt ELon MJak MRav SWCr
'René André' (Ra)	CPou CRHN MAus NLar
'René d'Anjou' (CeMo)	MAus
'Rescht'	see *R.* 'De Resht'
'Rêve d'Or' (N)	MAus MCot SLon SPer
'Réveil Dijonnais' (ClHT)	MAus
Rhapsody in Blue = 'Frantasia'PBR (S) ♀H6	Widely available
§ × *richardii*	MAus NLar
'Rival de Paestum' (T)	MAus
'River Gardens'	NPer
Rob Roy = 'Cocrob' (F)	SPer
Robbie Burns = 'Ausburn' (SpH)	MAus
'Robert le Diable' (Ce × G)	MAus SPer
Rock & Roll = 'Wekgobnez' (HT)	ESty
Rockabye Baby = 'Dicdwarf' (Patio)	ESty SWCr
'Roger Lambelin' (HP)	CPou MAus
Romance = 'Tanezamor'PBR (S)	IBoy MBri
'Rosa Mundi'	see *R. gallica* 'Versicolor'
'Rose à Parfum de l'Haÿ' (Ru)	CBcs CTri
'Rose de Meaux'	see *R.* × *centifolia* 'De Meaux'
'Rose de Meaux White'	see *R.* 'White de Meaux'
'Rose de Rescht'	see *R.* 'De Resht'
Rose des Cisterciens = 'Delarle' (HT)	ESty LRHS MRav
'Rose des Maures' misapplied	see *R.* 'Sissinghurst Castle'
'Rose du Maître d'Ecole'	see *R.* 'Du Maître d'Ecole'
'Rose du Roi' (HP/DPo)	ELon LRHS MAus
'Rose du Roi à Fleurs Pourpres' (HP)	MAus
§ Rose Gaujard = 'Gaumo' (HT)	LRHS MAsh MBri
Rose of Picardy = 'Ausfudge' (S)	LRHS MAus MBri
'Rose-Marie Viaud' (Ra)	CPou MAus MMuc
Rosemary Harkness = 'Harrowbond' (HT)	ESty MJak MRav SPer SRGP
'Rosemary Rose' (F)	SPer
Rosemoor = 'Austough'PBR (S) ♀H6	CRos CSBt LBuc LRHS MAus MBri
'Roseraie de l'Haÿ' (Ru) ♀H7	Widely available
Rosy Cushion = 'Interall' (S/GC)	LBuc LRHS MAsh MAus MCot NLar SLon SPer WKif
Rosy Future = 'Harwaderox' (F/Patio)	SWCr
'Rosy Mantle' (ClHT)	CSBt SWCr
§ Rotary Sunrise = 'Fryglitzy' (HT)	CSBt
§ Rote Max Graf = 'Kormax' (GC/Ru)	CDul
Rouge Royale = 'Meikarouz' (HT)	ESty
roxburghii	CBcs LEdu MAus SKHP

	- 'Plena'	see *R. roxburghii* f. *roxburghii*
§	- f. ***roxburghii*** (d)	MAus
	'Royal Air Force' (HT)	ELan
	Royal Bonica = 'Meimodac' (S) **new**	COtt
	Royal Copenhagen^PBR	see *R.* Remember = 'Poulht001'
	'Royal Gold' (ClHT)	SSea
	Royal Jubilee = 'Auspaddle' (S) **new**	CSBt MAus MBri SSea
	'Royal Occasion' (F)	SPer
	Royal William = 'Korzaun' (HT) ♀H6	CSBt ELan ELon LBrs LRHS MAsh MAus MBri MJak MRav NPri SCob SPer SWCr
§	***rubiginosa***	CArn CCVT CDul EPfP GPoy IFro LBuc MAus MRav NWea SFam SPer WMou
	rubrifolia	see *R. glauca* Pourr.
	'Rubrotincta'	see *R.* 'Hebe's Lip'
	rubus (Ra)	MAus
	Ruby Anniversary = 'Harbonny'^PBR (Patio)	COtt CSBt ELon ESty LBuc LRHS MAsh MBri MRav MWat NSoo SCob SCoo SMrm SPoG SSea SVic SWCr
	Ruby Celebration = 'Peawinner'^PBR (F) ♀H6	COtt ESty MRav SWCr
	Ruby Rambler = 'Chewrubyramb' (Ra)	LBuc
	Ruby Ruby	see *R.* Ruby Slippers
§	Ruby Slippers = 'Weksactrumi' (Min)	LBuc LRHS MAsh SPoG
	'Ruby Wedding' (HT)	CBcs CNec CSBt CTri EBee ECnt ELan EPfP IArd IBoy LBrs LRHS MAus MBri MGos MJak MRav NPri NSoo SCob SMrm SPer SPoG SSea SVic SWCr
	rugosa (Ru)	CDul CLnd CTri CTsd ECrN EPfP EPla EPom LBuc LRHS MAus MBri MHer MRav NHed NWea SCob SGol SPlb SVic SWCr WHar WMou
	- 'Alba' (Ru)	CBcs CCVT CDul CTri EAEE EBee ECnt ELan EPfP EPom GBin LAst LBuc LRHS MAus MRav NHed NLar NWea SCob SGol SMrm SPer SSea SVic SWCr WHar
	- 'Rubra' (Ru)	CBcs CCVT CTri ELan EPfP EPom LAst LBuc SCob SEWo SPer SPoG SSea SVic WHar
	'Rugosa Atropurpurea' (Ru)	EPom
	'Rumba' (F)	ELan
	'Rural England' (Ra)	LRHS MBri
	Rushing Stream = 'Austream' (GC)	MAus
	'Russelliana' (Ra)	MAus MMuc NLar SFam
	Safe Haven = 'Jacreraz'^PBR (F)	LBuc
	Saint Alban = 'Auschesnut'^PBR (S)	MAus
	Saint Boniface = 'Kormatt' (F/Patio)	CSBt
	Saint Cecilia = 'Ausmit'^PBR (S)	MAus
	Saint Edmunds Rose^PBR	see *R.* Bonita
	Saint Ethelburga = 'Beabimbo' (S)	LRHS MBri MCot
	Saint John's rose	see *R.* × *richardii*
	'Saint Nicholas' (D)	MAus
	Saint Swithun = 'Auswith'^PBR (S)	EPfP ESty LBuc LRHS MAus MBri SCob SSea
	'Salet' (DPMo)	CPou MAus WHer
	'Sally Holmes' (S) ♀H7	CPou ECnt LRHS MAus MRav MWat SEND SLon SMad SPer SWCr
	Sally Kane = 'Frygroovy'^PBR (HT)	MRav
	Sally's Rose = 'Canrem' (HT)	EBee ECnt
	Salsa^PBR	see *R.* Cheek to Cheek
	Salvation = 'Harlark'^PBR (F)	ESty
§	Samaritan = 'Harverag'^PBR (HT)	CSBt ESty MRav SWCr
	sambucina	WPGP
	sancta	see *R.* × *richardii*
	'Sander's White Rambler' (Ra) ♀H7	CRHN CSam CTri EBee EPfP EWTr LRHS MAus MBri MRav MSwo SPer SWCr WFar
	Sandra = 'Carsandra'	SLon
	'Sanguinea'	see *R.* × *odorata* Sanguinea Group
	Sarah (HT)	see *R.* Jardins de Bagatelle
	'Sarah van Fleet' (Ru)	CTri EPfP IArd IBoy MAus MBri MMuc MRav MSwo MWat NEgg NLar SMad SPer WBor
	Sarah, Duchess of York^PBR	see *R.* Sunseeker
	Savoy Hotel = 'Harvintage'^PBR (HT)	EPfP MAus MBri MRav SPer
	'Scabrosa' (Ru) ♀H7	EBee ECnt EPfP LRHS MAsh MAus NLar SLon SPer SPoG
	Scarborough Fair = 'Ausoran' (S) ♀H6	LBuc LRHS MAsh MAus
	Scarlet Fire	see *R.* 'Scharlachglut'
	Scarlet Glow	see *R.* 'Scharlachglut'
	Scarlet Hit = 'Poulmo'^PBR (PatioHit Series) (Min/Patio)	ECnt IBoy LBrs LRHS SWCr
	Scarlet Patio = 'Kortingle'^PBR (Patio)	ESty LRHS MAsh MBri MWat
	Scarlet Queen Elizabeth = 'Dicel' (F)	CBcs MJak
	Scented Carpet = 'Chewground'^PBR (GC) ♀H6	ECnt ELan MAsh MAus SWCr
	Scented Garden = 'Chewscentity' (S) **new**	ESty
	Scented Memory = 'Poulht002'^PBR (HT)	ECnt
	Scentimental = 'Wekplapep'^PBR (F)	ESty LBrs MAsh MBri MRav SCoo SSea SWCr
	Scent-sation = 'Fryromeo'^PBR (HT)	ELon MRav SCoo SPoG SWCr
	Scepter'd Isle = 'Ausland'^PBR (S)	CSBt EPfP LBuc LRHS MAus MBri SCob SCoo SPer SWCr
§	'Scharlachglut' (ClS)	CPou EPfP GGal LRHS MAus SPer
	Schloss Bad Homburg^PBR	see *R.* 'Alibaba'
	Schneewittchen	see *R.* Iceberg
§	'Schneezwerg' (Ru) ♀H7	MAus NLar SPer
	'Schoolgirl' (ClHT)	CBcs CTri CWSG ELan ELon EPfP IBoy LBuc LRHS MBri MRav MSwo MWat NEgg SPer SSea SWCr
	'Scintillation' (S/GC)	MAus
	Scotch rose	see *R. spinosissima*
	Scotch yellow (SpH)	see *R.* × *harisonii* 'Williams Double Yellow'
	'Sea Foam' (S)	WMoo
	'Seagull' (Ra) ♀H6	CTri CWSG EBee ECnt EPfP EWTr IBoy LAst LEdu LRHS MBri MRav MWat NLar NWea SCob SLon SMad SMrm SPer SPoG SWCr WHer
	'Seale Pink Diamond' (S)	SSea

'Sealing Wax' (*moyesii* hybrid) NLar
'Semiplena' see *R.* × *alba* 'Alba Semiplena'
sempervirens (Ra) SBrt
sericea (S) MAus
- var. ***morrisonensis*** B&SWJ 7139 WCru
§ - subsp. ***omeiensis*** WPGP
- - BWJ 7550 WCru
- - f. ***pteracantha*** (S) CBcs CDul CSBt ELan EPfP EWTr LRHS MAus MRav NLar NWea SPer SSea
- - - 'Atrosanguinea' (S) CArn
§ ***setigera*** MAus
setipoda MAus
seven sisters rose see *R. multiflora* 'Grevillei'
Seventh Heaven = 'Fryfantasy'PBR (HT) SWCr
Sexy Rexy = 'Macrexy' (F) EPfP IBoy LRHS MAsh MAus MBri MRav SCob SMrm SPer SRGP SWCr
'Shailer's White Moss' see *R.* × *centifolia* 'Shailer's White Moss'
Sharifa Asma = 'Ausreef'PBR (S) CSBt ELan MAus MBri MRav MSwo NEgg NLar SLon SPer SWCr
Sheila's Perfume = 'Harsherry' (F) 🏆H6 EBee ECnt ESty IBoy LRHS MBri MRav SPer SPoG SWCr
Shine On = 'Dictalent'PBR (Patio) 🏆H6 CSBt ECnt IBoy MWat SWCr
Shining Light = 'Cocshimmer'PBR (Patio) SCoo
Shocking Blue = 'Korblue' (F) MJak
Shona = 'Dicdrum' (F) IDic
Showmee Music = 'Chewdaybell' (GC) ECnt
Showmee Sunshine = 'Kenveron' (GC) ECnt ESty
Showtime = 'Baitime' (CIS) LBuc MAsh MBri SPoG
§ Shrimp Hit = 'Poulshrimp'PBR (Patio) ECnt LBrs LBuc MAsh
'Shropshire Lass' (S) MAus SPer
Silver Anniversary = 'Jaclav' (HT) EBee MBri MJak NSoo
§ Silver Anniversary = 'Poulari'PBR (HT) 🏆H6 CSBt CTri CWSG ECnt ELan LBrs LRHS MAsh MAus MGos MRav MWat NPri SCoo SPer SPoG SSea SVic SWCr
Silver Ghost = 'Kormifari'PBR (S) 🏆H7 LRHS
'Silver Jubilee' (HT) EPfP IArd IBoy LRHS MAsh MAus MBri MRav SCob SPer SPoG SVic SWCr
'Silver Lining' (HT) SRGP
'Silver Wedding' (HT) CBcs CNec COtt ELan IArd MAus MJak MRav NEgg SCob SPer SVic SWCr
'Silver Wedding Celebration' (F) CTri ESty
Silver WishesPBR see *R.* Pink Hit
§ Simply the Best = 'Macamster'PBR (HT) 🏆H6 COtt CSBt CWSG ECnt ELan ESty LRHS MAsh MAus MBri MGos MJak MRav MWat NPri SCob SCoo SPer SPoG SWCr
sinowilsonii see *R. longicuspis* var. *sinowilsonii*
'Sir Cedric Morris' (Ra) NLar SSea
Sir Clough = 'Ausclough' (S) MAus
Sir Edward Elgar = 'Ausprima'PBR (S) MAus
I 'Sir Galahad' white-flowered (F) MRav
Sir John Betjeman = 'Ausvivid'PBR (S) EPfP IBoy LBuc LRHS MAus MBri
'Sir Joseph Paxton' (Bb) CPou MAus
Sir Paul Smith = 'Beapaul' (ClHT) LRHS
Sir Walter Raleigh = 'Ausspry' (S) MAus MRav MWat
§ 'Sissinghurst Castle' (G) MAus
Sister Elizabeth = 'Auspalette'PBR (S) LBuc LRHS MAus MBri SCoo
Skylark = 'Ausimple'PBR (S) 🏆H6 LBuc LRHS MAus MBri SCob
'Skyrocket' see *R.* 'Wilhelm'
Smarty = 'Intersmart' (S/GC) MAus SPer
Snow Carpet = 'Maccarpe' (Min/GC) MAus
'Snow Dwarf' see *R.* 'Schneezwerg'
Snow Goose = 'Auspom'PBR (ClS) CSBt EPfP LRHS MAus MBri NLar SSea
Snow Hit = 'Poulsnows'PBR (Min/Patio) ECnt SWCr
'Snow Queen' see *R.* 'Frau Karl Druschki'
Snow Sunblaze = 'Meigovin' (Min) CSBt SPer
Snowcap = 'Harfleet'PBR (Patio) ESty SMrm
'Snowdon' (Ru) LRHS MAus
Soeur Emmanuelle = 'Delamo'PBR (S) EBee MRav SLon
Soft Cover = 'Poultco10' (Min) 🏆H7 LRHS MBri
'Soldier Boy' (Cl) CPou
§ Solo Mio = 'Poulen002'PBR (Renaissance Series) (S) CTri ECnt NLar
§ 'Sombreuil' (ClT) EPfP IArd LBuc LRHS MAus MBri MRav NEgg NLar SPer SWCr
Something Special = 'Macwyo'PBR (HT) ESty SWCr
Song and Dance = 'Frydishy'PBR (HT) SWCr
§ Songs of Praise = 'Harkimono'PBR (Abundance Series) (F) ESty SWCr
'Sophia'PBR see *R.* Solo Mio = 'Poulen002'
'Sophie's Perpetual' (ClCh) CPou CTri EWTr LRHS MAus SLon SPer
Sophy's Rose = 'Auslot'PBR (S) CRos LBuc LRHS MAsh MAus MBNS MBri NEgg SPer SWCr
Sorbet Fruité = 'Meihestries'PBR (Cl) SSea
soulieana (Ra/S) MAus
'Soupert et Notting' (DPoMo) CPou LRHS MAus SPer
'Southampton' (F) 🏆H6 MAus SPer SSea SWCr
'Souvenir de Claudius Denoyel' (ClHT) CPou CSam SPer
'Souvenir de Jeanne Balandreau' (HP) CPou
'Souvenir de la Malmaison' (ClBb) see *R.* 'Climbing Souvenir de la Malmaison'
'Souvenir de la Malmaison' (Bb) EPfP EWTr LRHS MAus MRav MWat NLar SPer

Name	Suppliers
'Souvenir de Madame Léonie Viennot' (ClT)	MAus MRav
'Souvenir de Pierre Vibert' (DPMo)	CPou
'Souvenir de Saint Anne's' (Bb)	EWTr MAus
'Souvenir du Docteur Jamain' (ClHP)	CPou CSBt EBee ELan ELon EPfP ESty GGal LRHS MAsh MAus MCot MRav NLar SFam SMrm SPer SPoG SSea SWCr WFar WKif
'Spanish Beauty'	see *R.* 'Madame Grégoire Staechelin'
Sparkle = 'Frymerlin'^{PBR} (HT)	ECnt ESty MAsh
Sparkler^{PBR}	see *R.* Kent
Sparkling Scarlet = 'Meihati' (ClF)	MAsh
Special Anniversary = 'Whastiluc'^{PBR} (HT) ♀^{H6}	COtt CSBt ECnt EPfP ESty LBrs LRHS LShp MAsh MBri MJak MRav MWat NPri SCoo SMrm SPoG SSea SWCr
Special Child = 'Taniripsa'^{PBR} (F/Patio) ♀^{H6}	MRav SSea SWCr
Special Event = 'Meibrelon' (HT)	ESty
Special Friend = 'Kirspec'^{PBR} (Patio)	ESty MWat SCob SWCr
Special Occasion = 'Fryyoung'^{PBR} (HT)	LRHS MAsh MRav SMrm SWCr
Special Son (F)	ESty
'Spectabilis' (Ra)	CPou EWTr SKHP
Spice of Life = 'Diccheeky'^{PBR} (F/Patio)	IDic
§ ***spinosissima***	CDul CSde LBuc MAus NWea SCob SGol SPer
- 'Andrewsii' ♀^{H7}	MAus MRav
§ - double, pink-flowered	SKHP WBor
§ - - white-flowered ♀^{H7}	ECha IGor MAus
- 'Dunwich Rose'	CSam EPfP LRHS MAus NLar SKHP SPer WCot
- 'Falkland'	ECha GCra MAus
- 'Glory of Edzell'	MAus
- 'Marbled Pink'	MAus
- 'Mary, Queen of Scots'	EWTr MAus SRms
- 'Mrs Colville'	MAus
- 'Ormiston Roy'	MAus
- 'Single Cherry'	MAus SSea
- 'William III'	EWes GCra MAus
Spirit of Freedom = 'Ausbite'^{PBR} (S)	EPfP ESty LBuc LRHS MAsh MAus MBri NEgg SSea
§ 'Splendens' (Ra)	GBin MMuc
St Helena = 'Canlish' (F)	ECnt
'Stanwell Perpetual' (SpH) ♀^{H7}	CSam ELan EPfP EWTr IBoy MAus MRav MWat NLar SEND SFam SPer SSea
Star Dust = 'Morstar' (Min)	ELon
'Star of Waltham' (HP)	EBee
'Star Performer'^{PBR} (ClPatio)	CSBt ECnt EPfP ESty LBuc LRHS MBri SPoG SSea SWCr
Stardust = 'Devstar' (HT)	WBor
Stardust = 'Peavandyke'^{PBR} (Patio/F)	CPou ESty
Starlight Express = 'Trobstar'^{PBR} (Cl)	IBoy LRHS MAsh SCoo SPer
Starry Eyed = 'Horcoexist' (Patio)	SWCr
'Stars 'n' Stripes' (Min)	MAus
stellata	MAus
§ - var. ***mirifica***	MAus
Strawberries and Cream = 'Geestraw' (Min/Patio)	ELan ESty
Strawberry Fayre = 'Arowillip'^{PBR} (Min/Patio)	COtt ESty MRav SPoG
Strawberry Hill = 'Ausrimini'^{PBR} (S) ♀^{H6}	CSBt ECnt ESty LRHS MAus MBri SCoo
Strike It Rich = 'Wekbepmey'^{PBR} (HT) ♀^{H6}	ECnt ESty
§ Sue Hipkin = 'Harzazz'^{PBR} (HT)	ESty MRav SWCr
'Suffolk' (HT) **new**	SCob
Suffolk = 'Kormixal'^{PBR} (S/GC) ♀^{H6}	CSBt ELan LRHS MAus MRav SCob SEND SPer SSea
Sugar and Spice = 'Peaallure'^{PBR} (Patio)	SPoG
Sugar Baby = 'Tanabagus'^{PBR} (Patio)	ESty SWCr
Sugar 'n' Spice = 'Tinspice' (Min)	MRav
Suma = 'Harsuma' (GC)	ESty SMrm
Summer Beauty = 'Kororbe'^{PBR} (F) ♀^{H6}	ESty MAsh
Summer Breeze = 'Korelasting'^{PBR} (ClS)	LBrs MAsh
Summer Fragrance = 'Tanfudermos'^{PBR} (Castle Series) (HT)	ELon
§ Summer Gold = 'Poulreb'^{PBR} (F)	MAsh MBri SWCr
'Summer Holiday' (HT)	LBuc
Summer Love = 'Franluv' (F)	CBcs
Summer Memories = 'Koruteli'^{PBR} (Palace Series) (F)	EBee
Summer Song = 'Austango'^{PBR} (S)	CNec EPfP ESty IBoy LBuc LRHS MAsh MAus MBri SCob SWCr
Summer Wine = 'Korizont'^{PBR} (Cl) ♀^{H6}	CSBt ECnt EPfP LRHS MBri SCoo SPer SPoG SWCr
Summertime = 'Chewlarmoll'^{PBR} (ClPatio) ♀^{H6}	CSBt ECnt ELan EPfP IBoy LRHS MAsh MAus MRav MWat NPri SCoo SMrm SPer SPoG SSea
Sun Hit = 'Poulsun'^{PBR} (PatioHit Series) (Min/Patio)	CSBt ECnt LBrs MRav SPoG
'Sunblaze'^{PBR}	see *R.* Orange Sunblaze
Sunblest = 'Landora' (HT)	LRHS MAsh MJak MRav SCob
Sunfire = 'Jacko' (F)	EBee ECnt
Sunny Day = 'Savasun' (S) **new**	EBee
Sunrise = 'Kormarter'^{PBR} (S)	ESty LBrs MAsh MWat SPoG SWCr
§ Sunseeker = 'Dicracer'^{PBR} (F/Patio) ♀^{H6}	COtt LBuc LRHS MAsh MRav SPoG SWCr
Sunset Boulevard = 'Harbabble'^{PBR} (F)	COtt MAsh MAus MRav SCoo SPer
Sunset Celebration^{PBR}	see *R.* Warm Wishes
Sunset Glow^{PBR}	see *R.* 'Alibaba'
Sunshine Abundance	SWCr
Super Dorothy = 'Heldoro' (Ra) ♀^{H6}	MAus SSea SWCr
Super Elfin = 'Helkleger'^{PBR} (Ra)	COtt CRos LBuc MAus MRav NLar SCob SMrm SPer SSea SWCr

Super Excelsa = 'Helexa' (Ra) ♀H6 — ESty IBoy MAus SCob SSea SWCr
Super Fairy = 'Helsufair'[PBR] (Ra) ♀H6 — COtt EBee ECnt MAus MRav SMad SPer SSea SWCr
Super Sparkle = 'Helfels'[PBR] (Ra) — EBee SCob SSea
§ Super Star = 'Tanorstar' (HT) — MAus MRav MWat SSea SWCr
Super Trouper = 'Fryleyeca'[PBR] (F) ♀H6 — COtt CSBt EBee ECnt ESty IBoy LRHS MAsh MBri MRav SCoo SPer SWCr WBor WCot
'Surpasse Tout' (G) — MAus
Surrey = 'Korlanum'[PBR] (GC) ♀H6 — CSBt CTri ELan ESty MAus MRav MSwo MWat NLar SCob SPer SSea SWCr
Susan = 'Poulsue' (S) — EBee ECnt NLar SLon SWCr
Susan Williams-Ellis = 'Ausquirk'[PBR] (S) — EPfP LBuc LRHS MAus MBri
Sussex = 'Poulave'[PBR] (GC) — CSBt MRav MSwo SCob SPer SSea
Swan = 'Auswhite' (S) — MAus
Swan Lake = 'Macmed' (Cl) — CPou EBee ECnt ELan EPfP IBoy MRav NLar SMrm SPer
Swany = 'Meiburenac' (Min/GC) — EAEE ECrN ESty MAus MSwo SPer SWCr
'Sweet Ballymaloe' (S) — IBoy
Sweet Child of Mine (HT) — ESty
Sweet Cover = 'Poulweeto'[PBR] (Towne & Country Series) (F) — MAsh
Sweet Dream = 'Fryminicot'[PBR] (Patio) ♀H6 — COtt CSBt CTri ECnt ELan EPfP IBoy LAst LRHS MAsh MAus MBri MJak MRav NPri SMad SMrm SPer SPoG SRGP SSea SWCr
Sweet Dream Cream = 'Fryniggle'[PBR] (F) — ECnt SMad
'Sweet Fairy' (Min) — CSBt
Sweet Haze = 'Tan97274'[PBR] (F) ♀H6 — CSBt IBoy LRHS MAsh MBri MRav SCoo SPer SWCr
Sweet Juliet = 'Ausleap'[PBR] (S) — CSBt ECnt ELan IBoy LRHS MAus MSwo SPer SWCr
* 'Sweet Lemon Dream' (Patio) — CTri
Sweet Magic = 'Dicmagic'[PBR] (Min/Patio) ♀H6 — CTri ELon EPfP IBoy MBri MJak MRav
Sweet Memories = 'Whamemo' (Patio) — COtt CTri ECnt ELan ELon EPfP ESty IBoy LBrs LRHS MBri MRav NPri SCoo SMrm SPer SSea SWCr
Sweet Parfum de Provence = 'Meiclusif'[PBR] (HT) ♀H6 — ESty
Sweet Remembrance = 'Kirr' (HT) — SCoo
'Sweet Revelation'[PBR] — see *R.* Sue Hipkin
'Sweet Wonder' (Patio) — EPfP LRHS SPoG
'Sweetie' (Patio) — ESty
sweginzowii — MAus
'Sydonie' (HP) — CPou
'Sympathie' (ClHT) — SPer SSea SWCr
Tall Story = 'Dickooky' (F) ♀H6 — EBee MRav SWCr
Tam O'Shanter = 'Auscerise'[PBR] (S) — EPfP LRHS MAus
Tamora = 'Austamora' (S) — MAus
Tango Showground = 'Chewpattens'[PBR] (GC) — ESty SSea
Tatton = 'Fryentice'[PBR] (F) — COtt ESty MAus MRav SMrm SWCr
Tawny Tiger = 'Frygolly'[PBR] (F) — SWCr
Tea Clipper = 'Ausrover'[PBR] (S) — CSBt LRHS MAus MBri SCoo SMrm
Tear Drop = 'Dicomo'[PBR] (Min/Patio) — SCob SPer SSea SWCr
Teasing Georgia = 'Ausbaker'[PBR] (S) ♀H6 — CRos ECnt EPfP ESty IBoy LBuc LRHS MAus MBri NLar SCob SCoo SSea SWCr
Temptress = 'Korramal' (ClS) ♀H6 — CPou EPfP MAsh SMrm
Tenacious = 'Macblackpo'[PBR] (F) — ESty SWCr
Tequila = 'Meiguni' **new** — LRHS
Tequila Sunrise = 'Dicobey'[PBR] (HT) ♀H6 — CTri ELan EPfP ESty IBoy MAus MBri MJak MRav SPer SSea SWCr
Terracotta = 'Meicobuis' (HT) — ESty
Terracotta = 'Simchoca' (S) **new** — WCot
Tess of the d'Urbervilles = 'Ausmove'[PBR] (S) — CRos EBee ELan EPfP EShb ESty IBoy LRHS MAus MBri NEgg NLar SCob SCoo SPer SSea SWCr
Thank You = 'Chesdeep'[PBR] (Patio) — ESty LBuc MWat SMrm
§ That's Jazz = 'Poulnorm'[PBR] (Courtyard Series) (ClF) — EBee ECnt MWat SWCr
The Alexandra Rose = 'Ausday'[PBR] (S) — EPfP GGal LBuc LRHS MAus SEND SPer SSea
§ The Alnwick Rose = 'Ausgrab'[PBR] (S) — EBee EPfP LBuc LRHS MAus MBri MWat NLar SCob SCoo SMrm SPer SSea
I 'The Anniversary Rose' — EPfP LBrs LBuc MAsh MBri SCoo
The Birthday Rose (F) **new** — LBuc
'The Bishop' (Ce × G) — MAus
The Compass Rose = 'Korwisco'[PBR] (S) — EPfP
The Countryman = 'Ausman' (S) — IBoy LBuc LRHS MAus MWat SSea
The Coventry Cathedral Rose = 'Smi72-02' (F) — ESty
The Dark Lady = 'Ausbloom'[PBR] (S) — MAus MBri NEgg SPer
The Diamond Wedding Rose (HT) — LBrs MAsh
§ 'The Fairy' (Poly) ♀H7 — CAco CSBt CTri EAEE ECnt ELan EWTr IBoy LAst LEdu LRHS MAus MRav MWat NLar SCob SEND SMad SMrm SPer SSea SWCr WBor WMoo
'The Garland' (Ra) ♀H6 — EPfP LBuc LRHS MAsh MAus MBri MMuc NLar SFam SPer SWCr
The Generous Gardener = 'Ausdrawn'[PBR] (S) ♀H6 — COtt CRos CWSG ELan EPfP EShb ESty LBuc LRHS MAus MBri MJak MWat SCob SCoo SPer SSea SWCr
§ The Gold Award Rose = 'Poulac008' (Palace Series) (Patio) — ECnt
'The Havering Rambler' (Ra) **new** — ELon
The Herbalist = 'Aussemi' (S) — LRHS MAus SSea
The Hilda Ogden Rose = 'Korchason' (Patio) — LBuc NPri NSoo
The Ingenious Mr Fairchild = 'Austijus'[PBR] (S) — EPfP LRHS MAsh MAus MBri SCoo

Name	Suppliers
The Jack Duckworth Rose = 'Korlutmag'[PBR] (Patio)	LBuc NPri NSoo
The Jubilee Rose = 'Poulbrido'[PBR] (F)	EBee ECnt SCoo
The Lady's Blush = 'Ausoscar'[PBR] (S)	EPfP LRHS MAus MBri
The Lark Ascending = 'Ausursula' (S) **new**	LBuc LRHS MAsh MAus SCoo SSea
The Maidstone Rose = 'Kordauerpa' (S)	SCoo
'The Margaret Coppola Rose'[PBR]	see *R.* White Gold
The Mayflower = 'Austilly'[PBR] (S) ♀[H6]	CSBt ELon IBoy LBuc LRHS MAus MBri MSwo MWat SCob
§ The McCartney Rose = 'Meizeli'[PBR] (HT)	SPer SWCr
'The New Dawn'	see *R.* 'New Dawn'
The Nun = 'Ausnun' (S)	LRHS MAus
§ The Pilgrim = 'Auswalker'[PBR] (S) ♀[H6]	CRos CSBt EPfP LBuc LRHS MAus MBri MJak NLar SCob SMrm SPer SSea SWCr
The Prince = 'Ausvelvet'[PBR] (S)	LRHS MAus NLar SPer
The Prince's Trust = 'Harholding'[PBR] (Cl)	LBuc MAsh MAus SPoG
'The Prioress' (S)	MAus
§ 'The Queen Elizabeth' (F)	CBcs CSBt CTri ELan IBoy LBrs LRHS MAsh MAus MBri MJak MRav MWat NPri SCob SPer SPoG SRGP SWCr WBor
The Reeve = 'Ausreeve' (S)	MAus
§ The Rita Sullivan Rose = 'Korzweenu'[PBR] (Patio)	LBuc NPri NSoo
The Rotarian	see *R.* Rotary Sunrise
The Sheikh Khalifa Rose = 'Dickoolrid' (Patio)	IDic
The Shepherdess = 'Austwist'[PBR] (S)	ELan IBoy LBuc LRHS MAsh MAus MBri SMrm
The Soham Rose[PBR]	see *R.* Pearl Abundance
The Squire = 'Ausquire' (S)	MAus
The Times Rose = 'Korpeahn' (F) ♀[H6]	ECnt MAus SCob SPer SWCr
The Wedgwood Rose = 'Ausjosiah'[PBR] (ClS)	EPfP LBuc LRHS MAus MBri SCob
'Thelma' (Ra)	MAus
'Thérèse Bugnet' (Ru) ♀[H7]	MAus
Thinking of You = 'Frydandy'[PBR] (HT) ♀[H6]	ESty IBoy LBrs LRHS MAsh MAus MBri NPri SRGP SVic SWCr
'Thisbe' (HM)	CPou EBee MAus SPer
'Thomas Graham' (S) **new**	EWTr
'Threave' (Bb)	CPou
threepenny bit rose	see *R. elegantula* 'Persetosa'
Tickled Pink = 'Fryhunky'[PBR] (F) ♀[H6]	COtt CSBt ESty LRHS MAsh MBri MRav MWat SCoo SPer SPoG SWCr
Times Past = 'Harhilt'[PBR] (ClHT)	ELon ESty MRav SPoG SRGP SSea SWCr
Tintinara = 'Dicuptight'[PBR] (HT) ♀[H6]	ECnt
Tip Top = 'Tanope' (F/Patio)	SPer
'Tipo Ideale'	see *R.* × *odorata* 'Mutabilis'
Titanic = 'Macdako'[PBR] (F)	ESty
Together Forever = 'Dicecho'[PBR] (F)	IDic MAsh
Top Marks = 'Fryministar'[PBR] (Min/Patio)	CSBt EPfP MJak MRav MWat SCoo SPer SWCr
Topaz Jewel[PBR]	see *R.* Yellow Dagmar Hastrup
'Topsi' (F/Patio)	SPer
§ 'Tour de Malakoff' (Ce)	CPou IBoy LRHS MAus NLar SFam SPer
Tradescant = 'Ausdir'[PBR] (S)	MAus
Tradition[PBR]	see *R.* Tradition '95
§ Tradition '95 = 'Korkeltin'[PBR] (ClHT)	MAsh
Tranquility = 'Barout' (HT)	LRHS SCob
Tranquillity = 'Ausnoble' (S) **new**	CRos CSBt ESty LBuc MAus SCoo SSea
'Treasure Trove' (Ra)	CRHN LRHS MAus SWCr
Trevor Griffiths = 'Ausold'[PBR] (S)	MAus
'Tricolore de Flandre' (G)	MAus
'Trier' (Ra)	CPou MAus
'Trigintipetala' misapplied	see *R.* × *damescena* 'Professeur Émile Perrot'
'Triomphe de l'Exposition' (HP)	MAus
'Triomphe du Luxembourg' (T)	MAus
triphylla	see *R.* × *beanii*
Troika = 'Poumidor' (HT)	CSBt IBoy LRHS MAsh MAus MBri MRav SPer SPoG SWCr
Troilus = 'Ausoil' (S)	MAus
'Tropicana'	see *R.* Super Star
Truly Scrumptious = 'Smi35-4-02' (HT)	ESty
Trumpeter = 'Mactru' (F) ♀[H6]	CTri EBee ECnt IArd IBoy LRHS MAus MBri MRav MWat SPer SPoG SWCr
§ 'Tuscany' (G)	MAus SPer
'Tuscany Superb' (G) ♀[H7]	CPou CSBt CSam CTri EAEE ELan EPfP EWTr LEdu LRHS MAus MBri MRav NChi NLar SEND SFam SKHP SPer SSea SWCr WBor WFar WHer WKif
Twice in a Blue Moon = 'Tan96138'[PBR] (HT) ♀[H6]	COtt CSBt ECnt ELon ESty IBoy MRav MWat SCob SCoo SMrm SPoG SSea SWCr
'Twilight'[PBR]	see *R.* Flower Carpet Twilight
Twist = 'Poulstri'[PBR] (Courtyard Series) (ClPatio)	ECnt ESty LBrs
Tynwald = 'Mattwyt' (HT)	SPer
'Ulrich Brünner'	see *R.* 'Ulrich Brünner Fils'
§ 'Ulrich Brünner Fils' (HP)	MAus
'Unique Blanche'	see *R.* × *centifolia* 'Unique'
Valencia = 'Koreklia'[PBR] (HT)	MAus SPer
Valentine Heart = 'Dicogle'[PBR] (F) ♀[H6]	CSBt CWSG ESty IArd LRHS MAsh MAus MRav SPoG SWCr
'Vanity' (HM)	MAus
'Variegata di Bologna' (Bb)	EPfP LRHS MAus MMuc MRav SLon SWCr
'Veilchenblau' (Ra) ♀[H7]	CRHN CRos CSBt CTri EAEE EBee ECnt ELan EPfP LEdu LRHS MAsh MAus MRav NEgg NLar SCob SEND SMad SPer SSea SWCr WBor WFar WKif
Velvet Fragrance = 'Fryperdee' (HT)	CSBt ECnt ELon EPfP ESty MAus MRav SPoG SSea SWCr
'Venusta Pendula' (Ra)	MAus
'Verschuren' (HT/v)	ESty
versicolor	see *R. gallica* 'Versicolor'
'Vick's Caprice' (HP)	MAus NLar

'Vicomtesse Pierre du Fou' (ClHT) MAus
Victoria Joy = 'Diciwill' (F) IDic
Viking Princess[PBR] see *R.* Imagination = 'Pouldron'
'Village Maid' see *R.* × *centifolia* 'Unique Panachée'
villosa subsp. ***villosa*** **new** MAus
§ 'Violacea' (G) MAus
'Violette' (Ra) CPou CRHN EWTr LRHS MAus SPer WFar WHer WKif
virginea **new** SPer
virginiana ♀H7 GCal MAus NWea
'Viridiflora' see *R.* × *odorata* 'Viridiflora'
Waltz = 'Poulkrid'[PBR] (Courtyard Series) (ClPatio) ECnt
wardii var. ***culta*** MAus
Warm Welcome = 'Chewizz'[PBR] (ClMin) ♀H6 CWSG ECnt ELan EPfP ESty IBoy LRHS MAsh MAus MRav SMad SMrm SPer SPoG SSea SWCr
§ Warm Wishes = 'Fryxotic'[PBR] (HT) ♀H6 COtt CSBt ECnt IBoy LBrs LBuc LRHS MAsh MAus MBri MJak MRav SCob SPoG SSea SWCr
'Warrior' (F) SPer
Warwick Castle = 'Auslian' (S) MAus
webbiana MAus SKHP
Wedding Celebration = 'Poulht006'[PBR] (HT) ECnt MAsh
'Wedding Day' (Ra) Widely available
Wee Cracker = 'Cocmarris'[PBR] (Patio) ESty
Wee Jock = 'Cocabest' (F/Patio) IBoy
'Weetwood' (Ra) CRHN
Weisse Wolcke[PBR] see *R.* White Cloud = 'Korstacha'
Well-Being = 'Harjangle'[PBR] (S) CSBt ELon
'Wendy Cussons' (HT) CTri MRav SCob SPer SWCr
Wenlock = 'Auswen' (S) MAus SPer
Westerland = 'Korwest' (S) ♀H6 MRav NLar SWCr
Where the Heart Is = 'Cocoplan'[PBR] (HT) ESty
Whisky Mac = 'Tanky' (HT) CBcs CSBt CTri ELan LBuc MJak MRav NPri SCob SPer SRGP
'White Bath' see *R.* × *centifolia* 'Shailer's White Moss'
'White Cécile Brünner' (Poly) LAst
§ White Cloud = 'Korstacha'[PBR] (S/ClHT) EPfP ESty LBrs MWat SKHP SWCr
'White Cockade' (Cl) CPou ESwi MSwo SPer SWCr
White Cover[PBR] see *R.* Kent
§ 'White de Meaux' (Ce) MAus
White Diamond = 'Interamon'[PBR] (S) EBee ECnt
White Eden = 'Meiviowit'[PBR] (Cl) ESty
§ White Gold = 'Cocquiriam'[PBR] (F) ♀H6 CSBt
White Max Graf[PBR] see *R.* × *jacksonii* White Max Graf
White Meidiland = 'Meicoublan' (S/GC) LRHS MAsh
white moss see *R.* 'Comtesse de Murinais', *R.* × *centifolia* 'Shailer's White Moss'
White Parfum de Provence = 'Meidiaphaz' (HT) CSBt ESty
'White Patio' (Min/Patio) LRHS MAsh MBri
White Perfumella = 'Meicalanq'[PBR] (HT) **new** ESty
§ 'White Pet' (Poly) ♀H7 CSBt CTri EBee ECnt ELan EPfP EWTr LRHS MAus MCot MRav NLar SEND SMrm SPer SSea SWCr WHea WKif
white Provence see *R.* × *centifolia* 'Unique'
'White Queen Elizabeth' (F) SCob
white rose of York see *R.* × *alba* 'Alba Semiplena'
White Star = 'Harquill' (ClHT) EBee ECnt ESty LBuc
'White Wings' (HT) IBoy SPer WKif
wichurana (Ra) CBcs EWTr GCal MAus SKHP
- 'Cally Anemone' (Ra) MAus
* - 'Variegata Nana' (Ra/v) MRav
'Wickwar' (Ra) ♀H6 GCal GGal
Wife of Bath = 'Ausbath' (S) MAus
Wild Edric = 'Aushedge'[PBR] (Ru) ♀H6 LBuc LRHS MAus SCoo
Wild Rover = 'Dichirap'[PBR] (F) ♀H6 ESty IDic LRHS
Wild Thing = 'Jactoose'[PBR] (S) ♀H6 IDic
Wild Thing = 'Ruiz510a'[PBR] **new** MBri
Wildeve = 'Ausbonny'[PBR] (S) ♀H6 LBuc LRHS MAus MBri
Wildfire = 'Fryessex' (Patio) ECnt ESty IBoy LBrs LRHS MAsh MAus MBri MRav MWat SPoG SWCr
§ 'Wilhelm' (HM) CPou MAus SPer
'Will Scarlet' (HM) MAus
'William Allen Richardson' (N) MAus
William and Catherine = 'Ausrapper' (S) CRos CSBt ESty LBuc MAsh MAus SSea
'William Cobbett' (F) SSea
§ 'William Lobb' (CeMo) ♀H7 CPou EPfP EWTr IBoy LRHS MAus MBri MNrw MRav NEgg NLar SPer SWCr WHer WKif
William Morris = 'Auswill'[PBR] (S) CRos CSBt LBuc LRHS MAus MBri NEgg SWCr
William Shakespeare = 'Ausroyal' (S) IBoy MCot SCob SPer
William Shakespeare 2000 = 'Ausromeo'[PBR] (S) CRos CSBt EBee ECnt ELan EPfP EShb ESty IBoy LRHS MAsh MAus MBNS MBri MSwo NEgg NLar SCoo SSea SWCr
'William Tyndale' (Ra) CPou WBor
'Williams' Double Yellow' see *R.* × *harisonii* 'Williams Double Yellow'
willmottiae MAus SSea
Wiltshire = 'Kormuse'[PBR] (S/GC) ♀H6 CSBt CTri ECnt ELan ESty EWTr IBoy LRHS MRav NLar SCob SEND SLon SSea SWCr
Winchester Cathedral = 'Auscat'[PBR] (S) CNec CRos CSBt CTri EBee ECnt ELan EPfP IBoy LRHS MAsh MAus MBri MJak MRav MSwo MWat NEgg NLar SCob SLon SMrm SPer SSea SWCr
Windflower = 'Auscross' (S) LBuc MAsh MAus
Windrush = 'Ausrush' (S) MAus
Wise Portia = 'Ausport' (S) MAus
Wisley = 'Ausintense'[PBR] (S) SCoo
Wisley 2008 = 'Ausbreeze'[PBR] (S) CSBt EPfP IBoy LBuc LRHS MAus MBri SCob

With All My Love = 'Coczodiac'PBR (HT) CSBt
With Love = 'Andwit' (HT) SWCr
With Thanks = 'Fransmoov'PBR (HT) MJak
Wizard (HT) ESty
Wollerton Old Hall = 'Ausblanket' (S) CSBt EPfP EShb ESty LBuc LRHS MAus MBri SCob SCoo SPer SSea
'Wolley-Dod' see *R.* 'Duplex'
Wonderful = 'Poulpmt005'PBR (HT) EBee ECnt SWCr
Wonderful News = 'Jonone'PBR (Patio) ESty MWat
woodsii (S) MAus
Worcestershire = 'Korlalon'PBR (GC) ♀H6 LRHS MAus MRav SPer SWCr
Wymondham Abbey = 'Beadevil' (ClHT) LRHS MBri
§ ***xanthina*** 'Canary Bird' (S) ♀H7 CBcs CSBt CTri EBee ECnt ELan EPfP ESty GKin IBoy LAst LRHS MAsh MAus MBri MRav MWat NEgg NLar NPri SEND SKHP SMrm SPer SPoG SSea SWCr SWvt
§ - f. ***hugonis*** CTri ELan LRHS MAus NLar SKHP SPer
'Yellow Cécile Brünner' see *R.* 'Perle d'Or'
Yellow Charles Austin = 'Ausyel' (S) MAus
§ Yellow Dagmar Hastrup = 'Moryelrug'PBR (Ru) CPou EBee NLar SCob SPer
Yellow Flower CarpetPBR see *R.* Flower Carpet Sunshine
'Yellow Patio' (Min/Patio) LBuc LRHS MAsh MBri NPri SPoG SWCr
yellow Scotch see *R.* × *harisonii* 'Williams Double Yellow'
Yellow Sunblaze = 'Meitrisical' (Min) CSBt
'Yesterday' (Poly/F/S) ♀H6 EWTr MAus NLar
'Yolande d'Aragon' (HP) EWTr
York and Lancaster see *R.* × *damascena* 'Versicolor'
York Minster = 'Harquest' (F) **new** MRav SMrm
Yorkshire = 'Korbarkeit'PBR (GC) ELan MRav
'Yorkshire Lady' (HT) NEgg
Yorkshire Princess = 'Dicmouse' (Patio) **new** IDic
You Are My Sunshine = 'Frykwango'PBR (HT) ♀H6 LRHS MJak
Young Lycidas = 'Ausvibrant'PBR (S) CSBt EPfP ESty IBoy LBuc LRHS MAus MBri SSea
You're Beautiful = 'Fryracy' (F) COtt EBee ECnt ESty LBrs LBuc LRHS LShp MAsh MBri MRav NPri SCoo SPer SPoG SWCr
'Yvonne Rabier' (Poly) ♀H7 EBee MAus MRav NLar SLon SPer
'Zéphirine Drouhin' (Bb) Widely available
§ 'Zigeunerknabe' (S) ECnt MAus NLar SKHP SPer WFar
Zwergenfee 09PBR see *R.* The Rita Sullivan Rose

Roscoea ✿ (*Zingiberaceae*)

alpina CAby CBro CExl CLAP CPBP EBee ECho EPot GBuc GEdr GKev WCru XLum
- CC 1820 IBlr
- 'Leaping Salmon' CCon
- pink-flowered IBlr
- purple-flowered IBlr
- short WCru
alpina* × *cautleyoides IBlr
§ ***auriculata*** ♀H5 CAby CAvo CBct CBro CCon CLAP ECho EPfP EPot GBuc GCal GEdr GKev IBlr IFoB MPie NHar NSoo SChF SDeJ SKHP SPer SPoG WCru WHar WSHC
- B&SWJ 2587 **new** WCru
- B&SWJ 2594 WCru
- GWJ 9230 **new** WCru
- 'Anorexia' IBlr
- brown-stemmed × ***purpurea*** IBlr
- early-flowering IBlr WCru
- 'Floriade' CDes CLAP EBee GBuc GKev IBlr WHil WSHC
- green-stemmed × ***purpurea*** IBlr
- late-flowering WCru
- 'Special' CLAP
- 'White Cap' EBee ECho GKev
auriculata* × *australis IBlr
auriculata* × *capitata IBlr
auriculata* × *purpurea **new** WCru
australis CCon CSam CTal ELon GBuc GEdr MNrw WCru WThu
- pink-flowered KW 22124 IBlr
- purple-flowered KW 22124 IBlr
australis* × *humeana IBlr
'Ballyrogan Lavender' IBlr
'Ballyrogan White' **new** IBlr
× ***beesiana*** ♀H5 CAvo EPla SHar
- 'Ballyrogan Purple' IBlr
- Cream Group CBct CDes CLAP CTal EPfP EPot GBuc GKev IBlr LEdu MMHG NBir SKHP WCru WPGP
- Dark Group IBlr
- Gestreept Group CBro CCon CHEx CLAP CMea CTsd EPot GBuc GEdr GKev IBlr LAma LRHS MPie NHar SKHP WCru WHar WHil
- 'Lemon and Lavender' IBlr
- 'Monique' CDes EBee IBlr NHar WHil WPGP
- 'Moonlight' IBlr
- 'Petite Purple' IBlr
Blackthorn strain IBlr WCru
brandisii misapplied see *R. tumjensis*
cangshanensis BWJ 7848 **new** WCru
capitata CLAP GKev IBlr
cautleyoides CAby CAvo CBro CMea CWCL ECha ECho ELon EPot GBuc GEdr GKev IBlr IFoB LAma LRHS MNrw NBid NGdn NSoo SPer SPoG SRot WCru WHar XEll
- CLD 772 GEdr IBlr
- 'Blush Leaves' **new** WHil
- var. ***cautleyoides*** f. ***atropurpurea*** IBlr
- - - 'Giraffe' IBlr
- - white-flowered WHil
- 'Crûg's Late Lemon' WCru
- 'Doge Purple' IBlr
- 'Early Purple' CDes CLAP ECho GBuc WPGP

- 'Early Yellow' CTal
- 'Jeffrey Thomas' ♀H5 CBct CLAP CSam CTal EBee ECho ELan GBuc GCal GEdr GKev IBlr MLHP SRGP WHil
- late, lavender-flowered IBlr
- - yellow-flowered IBlr NCot
- 'Lemon Giraffe' IBlr
- 'Pennine Purple' IBlr NHar
- plum-flowered IBlr
- var. ***pubescens*** IBlr
- 'Purple Giant' CLAP EBee SKHP
- 'Purple Queen' ♀H5 **new** GKev
- purple-flowered CAby IBlr NHar
- 'Reinier' CLAP CTal ECho GCal IBlr SKHP
- f. ***sinopurpurea*** GKev IBlr
- 'Vanilla' LEdu SKHP
- 'Vien Beauty' WHil
- 'Washfield Purple' IBlr
- 'Wine Red' WHil
- 'Yeti' CDes CTal ECho SKHP WHil

cautleyoides × ***humeana*** CLAP IBlr LRHS WHar

cautleyoides × ***praecox*** IBlr

cautleyoides × ***scillifolia*** f. ***atropurpurea*** IBlr

debilis var. ***debilis*** IBlr

forrestii f. ***forrestii*** IBlr
- - pubescent IBlr
- 'Ice Maiden' IBlr
- f. ***purpurea*** IBlr
- f. ***purpurea*** × ***humeana*** IBlr

'Harvington Evening Star' **new** EBee LLHF LRHS NHar

humeana CAby CBct CBro CLAP ECho EPot GBuc GEdr LAma LRHS WThu
- ACE 2539 IBlr
- f. ***alba*** IBlr
- Forrest's form IBlr
- from Cruickshank Botanic Garden IBlr
- 'Guincho White Stripe' IBlr
- 'Harvington Raw Silk' ♀H5 EBee LLHF LRHS NHar
- 'Harvington Royale' EBee LLHF LRHS NHar
- lavender-flowered IBlr
- 'Long Acre Sunrise' CDes CLAP WPGP
- f. ***lutea*** ♀H5 CLAP IBlr
- pink-flowered IBlr
- 'Purple Streaker' CDes WPGP
- purple-flowered **new** EBee ECho
- 'Rosemoor Plum' CAby CDes CLAP WHil WPGP
- 'Snowy Owl' GEdr
- 'Two Tone' IBlr
- f. ***tyria*** ♀H5 IBlr
- - 'Inkling' GBuc

'Ice Maiden' IBlr

'Kew Beauty' ♀H5 CAby CBod CCon CDes CExl CLAP CMea CTal EPfP EPla EUJe GBuc GCal LRHS MMoz NGdn SKHP SMHy WCot WGwG WPGP

'Lavender Mist' IBlr

nepalensis WHil

'Pallid Sun' IBlr

'Pinky' **new** CMea

praecox GEdr IBlr

procera misapplied see *R. auriculata*

procera Wall. see *R. purpurea*

§ ***purpurea*** CAvo CBod CBro CHEx CTal ECha ELan ELon EPfP EPla EUJe GCal GKev IBal IBlr IFoB LAma LRHS MAsh NBir NGdn SPer WCru WHer WHil
- CC 1757 IBlr
- CC 3628 CExl IBlr
- HWJK 2020 WCru
- HWJK 2169 WCru
- HWJK 2175 WCru
- HWJK 2400 WCru
- HWJK 2407 WCru
- KW 13755 IBlr
- MECC 2 IBlr
- MECC 10 IBlr
- 'Bronzed Albino' IBlr
- bronze-leaved CAby
- 'Brown Peacock' CDes CFil CLAP ECho GBuc GKev IBlr MMoz SKHP WCru WPGP
- 'Cinnamon Stick' CWGN ECtt GEdr NHar
- 'Dalai Lama' ♀H4 ECho GEdr GKev
- var. ***gigantea*** CC 1757 IBlr
- 'Himalayan Delight' IBlr
- 'Late Lavender' IBlr
- 'Nico' ECho ELan IBlr SKHP WCot
- 'Peacock' CLAP EBee ECho EPot GKev IBlr SKHP
- 'Peacock Eye' ECho GEdr GKev IBlr SKHP
- var. ***procera*** see *R. purpurea*
- 'Purple Dwarf' IBlr
- 'Purple Tower' IBlr
- 'Red Foot' GKev
- 'Red Gurkha' see *R. purpurea* f. *rubra*
- Rosemoor form CLAP
- Royal Purple hybrids **new** MAsh

§ - f. ***rubra*** ♀H4 CAby CDes CLAP IBlr LLHF LRHS NHar
- short CLAP IBlr
- 'Slender Wisp' IBlr
- 'Spice Island' **new** CWGN ECtt
- tall CLAP WCru WPGP
- 'Typico' IBlr
- 'Vannin' LEdu WCru
- 'Vincent' CTal EBee GKev MMoz
- 'Wisley Amethyst' CBro CLAP CTal EBee IBlr LLHF LRHS NCot SKHP SPoG

'Red Neck' ♀H4 EBee IBlr SKHP

schneideriana IBlr WThu
- robust form IBlr

scillifolia CBro CCon ECho GBuc GEdr GKev LAma LRHS NBir SDeJ WHar
- f. ***atropurpurea*** CAby EBee GBuc GCal IBal IBlr WCru WPGP WThu
- f. ***scillifolia*** CDes EBee IBlr IFoB WCru WHar WHil WThu

aff. ***scillifolia*** purple-flowered GEdr IBlr

'Summer Deep Purple' ♀H5 LRHS

tibetica CCon EBee GEdr GKev IBlr WCru WThu
- ACE 2538 IBlr WCru
- BWJ 7878 WCru
- f. ***atropurpurea*** BWJ 7640 WCru

aff. ***tibetica*** IBlr
- f. ***albo-purpurea*** IBlr

§ ***tumjensis*** CTal IBlr WPGP

wardii ♀H5 CExl IBlr WHil

rosemary see *Rosmarinus officinalis*

Rosmarinus ✿ (*Lamiaceae*)

corsicus 'Prostratus'	see *R. officinalis* Prostratus Group
lavandulaceus misapplied	see *R. officinalis* Prostratus Group
× ***noeanus***	XSen
officinalis	Widely available
- var. ***albiflorus***	CArn CUse ENfk EPfP GPoy LEdu LRHS MHer MNHC SDow SEND SHDw SLim SPlb SRms WGwG WJek XSen
- - 'Lady in White'	CSBt EAJP ELan EPfP LRHS SDow SLim SPer SPoG SRms WGwG WJek
- 'Alderney'	MHer SDow SRms WGwG
§ - var. ***angustissimus*** 'Benenden Blue' 🏆[H4]	CBod CSBt ELan EPfP GPoy LRHS SDix SDow SEND SPer SPlb SPoG SRms WGwG WJek
- - 'Corsican Blue'	CArn CBod EBee ELan EPfP GPoy MHer MHol MNHC SGol SHDw SPer SRms
- 'Arp'	CArn CBod CUse ENfk EWes
- 'Aureovariegatus'	see *R. officinalis* 'Aureus'
§ - 'Aureus' (v)	CBcs CPla SRms WJek
- 'Baby P.J.'	EOHP
- 'Baie d'Audierne'	WGwG XSen
- 'Barbecue'[PBR]	ELan ELau ENfk LEdu LRHS SRms
- 'Blue Lagoon'	CBod ELau ENfk LRHS MHer MNHC SIde SPer SRms WGwG WHer WJek
- 'Blue Rain'	CBod EPfP MHer MJak MSwo WGwG WHfH WPnn
- 'Capercaillie'	SDow WGwG XSen
- 'Collingwood Ingram'	see *R. officinalis* var. *angustissimus* 'Benenden Blue'
- 'Cottage White'	WGwG WHer
- dwarf, blue-flowered	ELau
- 'Farinole'	CArn ELau MNHC SRms WGwG
- 'Fastigiatus'	see *R. officinalis* 'Miss Jessopp's Upright'
- 'Fota Blue'	CArn CBod CSpe CTsd ELau IArd LRHS MHer MNHC SDow SGol SHDw SIde SRms SVen SWvt WGwG WJek WPnn XSen
- 'Foxtail'	CBod LBuc LRHS SRms WJek
- 'Frimley Blue'	see *R. officinalis* 'Primley Blue'
- 'Genges Gold' (v)	MHer WGwG
- 'Gold Dust' (v) **new**	CBod CWGN ENfk LAst
- 'Golden Rain'	see *R. officinalis* 'Joyce DeBaggio'
- 'Gorizia'	CArn CBod LRHS SCob SDow SRms WPnn XSen
- 'Green Ginger' 🏆[H4]	CArn CBod CJun EBee ELan ELau EPfP GBin LEdu LRHS MAsh MBri MGos MHer MNHC MRav MSCN NPer SCob SDow SHil SPer SPoG SRms SVen WGwG WJek WPnn XSen
- 'Guilded'	see *R. officinalis* 'Aureus'
- 'Haifa'	CBod CSde EBtc ELau ENfk NSbr SRms WJek WPnn
- 'Henfield Blue'	SHDw
- 'Huntington Carpet'	ECtt
- 'Iden Blue Boy'	CSpe
- 'Iden Pillar'	WGwG
§ - 'Joyce DeBaggio' (v)	MHer SDow WGwG WHer XSen
- 'Knightshayes Blue'	LRHS
- 'Lady in Blue'	WGwG
- ***lavandulaceus***	see *R. officinalis* Prostratus Group
- 'Lilies Blue'	GPoy WGwG
- 'Lockwood Variety'	see *R. officinalis* (Prostratus Group) 'Lockwood de Forest'
- 'Logee Blue'	CArn
- 'Majorca Pink'	CBcs CBod COtt CSBt CSpe ELau ENfk LRHS MHer MNHC MSCN NPri SDow SPer WGwG WJek XLum
- 'Marenca'	CHll ELau MNHC SRms
- 'McConnell's Blue' 🏆[H4]	CAbP CArn CDoC CPrp ELan ELau LRHS MAsh MGos MNHC SCob SDow SHDw SHil SRms WGwG WHer WHoo WJek WPGP XSen
§ - 'Miss Jessopp's Upright' 🏆[H4]	Widely available
- 'Pat Vlasto'	WGwG
- 'Pointe du Raz'	CAbP CArn CBod ELan EPfP LRHS MAsh SChF SLim SRms WGwG
§ - 'Primley Blue'	CBcs CBod COtt CTsd CUse ECtt ELau MNHC MRav SGol SIde SRms WJek
§ - Prostratus Group	Widely available
- - 'Capri'	CAbP CBod CDul CSBt ELau EPfP LRHS MHer SCob SPoG SRms WFar WJek
- - 'Gethsemane'	CArn WGwG
§ - - 'Lockwood de Forest'	WGwG WHer
- - 'Rampant Boule'	CArn CBod ELau MHer SDow SRms WJek XLum XSen
- - 'Sea Level'	ELau MHer WGwG
- - 'Sheila Dore'	SPlb SVen
- - white-flowered	GPoy
- f. ***pyramidalis***	see *R. officinalis* 'Miss Jessopp's Upright'
- ***repens***	see *R. officinalis* Prostratus Group
- 'Rex'	ELau WGwG
- 'Roman Beauty'[PBR]	CBcs CSBt CUse EHoe LAst LRHS MAsh MBri MHol SLim SRms SWvt WHer
- 'Roseus'	CArn CHVG CWld EAJP ELan ELau ENfk EPfP GPoy LRHS MAsh MHer MNHC SDow SEND SLim SPoG SRms SVen WGwG WHer WJek WPnn XSen
- 'Salem'	CBod MHer
- 'Severn Sea' 🏆[H4]	CArn CBod COtt CSBt CSde CTri ECtt ELan ELau ENfk EPfP EPla GPoy LRHS MAsh MGos MHer MNHC MRav MSwo SIde SLon SPer SRms SVen WCFE WGwG WHoo WJek
- 'Shimmering Stars'	SDow WGwG XSen
- 'Silver Sparkler'	WGwG WPat
- Silver Spires = 'Wolros'	MNHC
- 'Sissinghurst Blue' 🏆[H4]	CArn CBod CSde CWCL EBee ECha ECrN ELan ELau EPfP LRHS MAsh MHer MLHP MNHC MRav SDow SGol SLim SPer SPlb SPoG SRms SWvt WGwG WJek XSen
- 'Sissinghurst White'	WGwG
- 'Sorcerer's Apprentice'	SDow WGwG
- 'South Downs Blue'	SHDw WGwG
- 'Spanish Snow'	WGwG
- 'Spice Island'	CBod SPad SPer
- 'Sudbury Blue'	CBod COtt ELau ENfk EPfP MHer SDow SGol SHDw SPad SRms WFar WJek XSen
- 'Sunkissed'	CSBt LBuc LRHS SLim SRms
- 'Trusty'	WGwG
- 'Tuscan Blue'	CArn CBcs CBod CDoC CExl COtt CPrp ECha ECrN ECtt ELan ELau

EPfP LRHS MHer MNHC MSwo NEgg NPri SDow SGol SPer SRms WGwG WHfH WJek WPGP WPnn XSen
- 'Variegatus' — see *R. officinalis* 'Aureus'
- 'Vatican Blue' new — WJek
- 'Vicomte de Noailles' — WGwG XSen

repens — see *R. officinalis* Prostratus Group
Salcombe form — CHll
'Sappho' — CHll

Rostrinucula (*Lamiaceae*)

dependens — ECre ELon EPfP ESwi EWes MTPN NLar SBrt WCFE
sinensis — CExl

Rosularia ✿ (*Crassulaceae*)

from Sandras Dag, Turkey — CWil
§ ***aizoon*** — ECho LRHS
alba — see *R. sedoides* var. *alba*
§ ***chrysantha*** — ECho EDAr LRHS SFgr SPlb
crassipes — see *Rhodiola wallichiana*
libanotica RCB RL 20 — WCot
§ ***muratdaghensis*** — SPlb
pallida A. Berger — see *R. chrysantha*
pallida Stapf — see *R. aizoon*
pallida ambig. — EPot
platyphylla misapplied — see *R. muratdaghensis*
sedoides — CWil MMuc
§ - var. ***alba*** — ECho EDAr
sempervivum — CWil ECho EWes
§ - subsp. ***glaucophylla*** — CWil ECho LRHS MSCN WHal WThu
spatulata hort. — see *R. sempervivum* subsp. *glaucophylla*

Rubia (*Rubiaceae*)

peregrina — CArn GPoy
tinctorum — CArn CHab CHby EOHP GPoy MNHC SWat WHfH WSFF

Rubus ✿ (*Rosaceae*)

RCB/Eq C-1 — WCot
SDR 4635 — GKev
alceifolius Poir. — SDys
- B&SWJ 1833 new — WCru
arcticus — EBee ECtt EPPr LEdu NHar SHar SRot WThu XLum
- subsp. ***stellatus*** — NHar
'Benenden' ♀H5 — Widely available
'Betty Ashburner' — CAgr CBcs CDoC CDul EBee EPPr EWTr GLog GQui MGos MRav MWhi SCob SPer WHar WMoo XLum
biflorus ♀H5 — EWes LEdu MBlu MMuc SEND WPGP
'Boatsberry' — SDea
'Boysenberry' (F) — LEdu LRHS
boysenberry, thornless (F) — CMac EMil GTwe LBuc NPri SDea SPer
buergeri B&SWJ 5555 — WCru
caesius — WCot
calophyllus — WPGP
calycinoides Hayata — see *R. rolfei*
calycinoides Kuntze — EBtc GKev SGol
chamaemorus — GPoy
cockburnianus (F) — CArn CBcs CTri EBee ELan EPfP EWTr GCra GKin IFoB LBuc MMuc MRav MSwo NSti NWea SCob SPer SPlb SRms WHar
- 'Goldenvale' ♀H5 — CDoC CDul EBee EHoe ELon EPfP EPla EWTr GQui IFro LRHS MAsh MBlu MGos MMuc MRav MSwo MWhi NBir NEgg NLar NSti SCob SEND SLon SPer SPoG
crataegifolius — MRav WPat
'Emerald Spreader' — WMoo
fockeanus misapplied — see *R. rolfei*
formosensis B&SWJ 1798 — ESwi WCru
fruticosus agg. — NHed NWea WSFF
- 'Adrienne' (F) — CAgr CHab CSBt LEdu MAsh MBri SPoG SRms WHar
- 'Apache' (F) — CHab NPri
- 'Ashton Cross' (F) — GTwe LBuc
- 'Bedford Giant' (F) — CHab CSBt GTwe MAsh MGos MMuc SEND SLim SPoG WHar
- 'Black Butte' (F) — CHab EPom LRHS SDea SLon SVic
- 'Black Satin' (F) — CAgr ECrN LRHS NLar NPri SDea SVic
- 'Čačanska Bestrna' (F) — MCoo
- 'Chester' (F) — EPom ERea LEdu LRHS SFrt SKee SPer
- 'Godshill Goliath' (F) — SDea
- 'Helen' (F) — CAgr CSut MAsh MCoo SDea
- 'Himalayan Giant' (F) — CHab MRav NEgg NLar SDea
- 'Karaka Black'[PBR] (F) — CHab ERea LBuc LRHS SVic
- 'Kotata' (F) — MRav
- 'Loch Maree' (F/d) — CHab CMac EPom LEdu LRHS MCoo SFrt SLon
- 'Loch Ness'[PBR] (F) ♀H6 — CAgr CHab EPom GTwe IArd LBuc LRHS SCoo SDea SFrt SKee SVic WHar
- 'Loch Tay'[PBR] (F) — CHab CMac EPom LRHS
- 'Merton Thornless' (F) — CSBt ECrN LAst LEdu MAsh MBri MGos MJak SPlb SRms WHar
- 'Natchez' (F) — LBuc NPri
- 'Navaho' (F) — CHab LRHS
- 'Navaho Big and Early' (F) — CSut
- 'No Thorn' (F) — SDea
- 'Oregon Thornless' (F) — CAgr CDoC CSBt ECrN EPfP GTwe LRHS MAsh MBri MJak MRav NLar SCoo SDea SKee SLim SPoG SRms SVic WHar
- 'Ouachita' (F) — LRHS NPri SPer
- 'Parsley Leaved' (F) — SDea
- 'Reuben' (F) — CHab EPom GQue LBuc LRHS MCoo SBmr SPer
- 'Thornfree' (F) — CAgr CDoC CTri LRHS MBri NLar SDea SKee SLim
- 'Triple Crown' (F) — CHab CMac MCoo
- 'Variegatus' (v) — CMac MBlu WCot
- 'Waldo' (F) — CAgr CSBt LBuc MAsh MBri MGos NPri SDea SRms WHar
'Glencoe' (F) — CSut MCoo
henryi — CBcs ESwi LRHS MAsh WCot
- var. ***bambusarum*** — EPla ESwi MRav WCru
ichangensis — ESwi LEdu
idaeus — GPoy
- 'All Gold' (F) ♀H6 — CAgr EMil EPom ERea LRHS MAsh MCoo NLar NPri SCoo SFrt SPer SVic WHar
- 'Aureus' (F) — ECha ELan LEdu MRav NBid WCot
- 'Autumn Bliss' (F) ♀H6 — Widely available
- 'Autumn Treasure'[PBR] (F) — CSut EPom ERea GTwe LRHS MCoo NPri SLon SVic
- 'Cascade Delight' (F) — EPom LBuc LRHS MAsh
- 'Erika'[PBR] (F) — LBuc NPri SBmr SPer

Plant	Suppliers
- 'Fallgold' (F)	MMuc SKee SPoG
- 'Glen Ample'PBR (F) 🏆H6	CAgr CMac CSBt CTri CWSG ECrN EMil EPfP EPom ERea GTwe LBuc LRHS MAsh MBri MCoo MWat NPri NWea SCoo SDea SEND SFrt SKee SLim SPer SPoG SVic WHar
- 'Glen Clova' (F)	CAgr CSBt CTri ELan GTwe LRHS MAsh MGos MNHC MRav MWat SKee SLim SPoG WHar
- 'Glen Doll'PBR (F)	CAgr GQue GTwe LBuc LRHS MAsh MCoo SCoo SPoG
- 'Glen Fyne'PBR (F)	GTwe
- 'Glen Lyon'PBR (F)	GKin LBuc MAsh MBri MJak SCoo WHar
- 'Glen Magna'PBR (F) 🏆H6	CAgr CMac CSBt ERea GKin LRHS MAsh MBri SCoo SDea SKee SLim
- 'Glen Moy'PBR (F)	CAgr CSBt CTri ECrN EPfP GTwe LAst LRHS MAsh MGos MJak NWea SCoo SDea SKee SLim SPer WHar
- 'Glen Prosen'PBR (F)	CAgr CSBt EPfP GKin GTwe LRHS MAsh MBri MGos MRav NPri SCoo SDea SKee SLim SPlb WHar
- 'Glen Rosa' (F)	ERea MCoo SDea
- 'Heritage' (F)	ELan MAsh SCoo
- Himbo Top = 'Rafzaqu'PBR (F)	CMac
- 'Joan J'PBR (F) 🏆H6	CSut EPom ERea GTwe LRHS MCoo
- 'Leo'PBR (F) 🏆H6	CSBt CTri GTwe MAsh SCoo SKee SPer WHar
- 'Malling Admiral' (F) 🏆H6	CSBt CTri EPom LAst MAsh NWea SCoo SKee SPer WHar
- 'Malling Delight' (F)	CSBt ELan SCoo SPlb
- 'Malling Jewel' (F) 🏆H6	CAgr CSBt EPfP EPom GTwe LAst LBuc MAsh MJak SDea SKee
- 'Malling Promise' (F)	MJak NLar
- 'Octavia'PBR (F)	CAgr CSBt EMil EPom GQue GTwe LBuc LRHS MAsh MCoo MWat NLar NWea SFrt SLim SPoG WHar
- 'Polka'PBR (F) 🏆H6	EPfP EPom LBuc LRHS MAsh MCoo MRav MWat SCoo SKee SLim WHar
- 'Sanibelle' (F)	CSut
- 'Sugana'PBR (F)	CSut LBuc LRHS MAsh MCoo NLar
- 'Summer Gold' (F)	GTwe
- 'Tadmor'PBR (F)	LRHS SPer
- 'Tulameen' (F) 🏆H6	CAgr CSBt CWSG ELan EMil EPom LRHS MAsh MBri MWat NLar SCoo SFrt SKee SLim SPer SPoG SVic WHar
- Twotimer Sugana Yellow (F)	CSut
- 'Valentina' (F)	SFrt
- 'Zeva Herbsternte' (F)	MAsh
illecebrosus (F)	LEdu XLum
irenaeus	EWTr LEdu LRHS SEND
Japanese wineberry	see *R. phoenicolasius*
'Kenneth Ashburner'	CDoC NLar
lambertianus PAB 8931 **new**	LEdu
lineatus	CDTJ EPfP EWTr EWes GBin LRHS MCot SKHP WCru WPGP
- B&SWJ 11261 from Sumatra	WCru
- HWJ 892 from Vietnam	ESwi WCru
- HWJK 2045 from Nepal	GQui WCru
- from Nepal	GCra
× ***loganobaccus*** 'Brandywine' (F)	SDea
- 'Ly 59' (F) 🏆H5	ECrN EPfP MMuc MRav SDea SKee SRms
- 'Ly 654' (F) 🏆H5	CSBt EPom ERea GTwe LBuc LRHS MBri NEgg NPri SDea SPer WHar
- thornless (F)	CAgr CTri EPfP EPom GTwe LEdu SDea SPoG SVic
ludwigii	SBrt
'Malling Minerva' (F)	CAgr CSut EPom SFrt SVic
'Margaret Gordon'	MRav
microphyllus 'Variegatus' (v)	MRav
§ ***nepalensis***	CAgr GCra GKev LEdu
nutans	see *R. nepalensis*
'Obsidian' (F) **new**	LEdu
odoratus	CExl EBee ELan EPPr EWTr LEdu MBlu MRav NBid SPer
palmatus var. ***coptophyllus***	MMuc
parkeri PAB 6891 **new**	LEdu
parviflorus	CArn IFro
- 'Bill Baker'	LEdu
- double-flowered (d)	EPPr
- 'Sunshine Spreader'	EHoe LEdu WPat
parvus	LEdu
pectinellus var. ***trilobus***	SBrt
- - B&SWJ 1669B	NLar WCru
peltatus	CFil NLar WPGP
pentalobus	see *R. rolfei*
§ ***phoenicolasius***	CAgr CCCN CDul CHGN ELan EPPr EPfP EPla EWTr GTwe LEdu LRHS MBlu MCoo MHer MRav SDea SPer SPoG SVic WHea WPGP
§ ***rolfei***	CTri GEdr
- B&SWJ 3546 from Taiwan	WCru
- B&SWJ 3878 from the Philippines	WCru
- 'Emerald Carpet' 🏆H5	CAgr EAEE NLar
rosifolius NJM 10.142 **new**	WPGP
- 'Coronarius' (d)	CSpe ECrN LSou NEoE NLar WCot
sanctus	CNat
saxatilis	LEdu
- PAB 3912	LEdu
setchuenensis	CMCN EPPr NLar
'Silvan' (F) 🏆H6	MCoo MMuc SEND
spectabilis	CBcs CPom ELan EPPr EPla EWTr LEdu MMuc MRav WSHC
- 'Flore Pleno'	see *R. spectabilis* 'Olympic Double'
§ - 'Olympic Double' (d)	Widely available
splendidissimus B&SWJ 2361	ESwi WCru
squarrosus	ECou SMad
'Sunberry' (F)	CCCN SDea
swinhoei B&SWJ 1735	WCru
taiwanicola	GEdr
- B&SWJ 317	ESwi WCru
- CWJ 12400	WCru
- 'Buckingham' **new**	NPer
Tayberry Group (F) 🏆H5	CSBt CTri GTwe LRHS MGos NLar NPri SPer SRms SVic WHar
- 'Buckingham' (F)	CSut EMil EPom ERea GTwe LBuc LRHS NLar SVic
- 'Medana Tayberry' (F)	CAgr EPfP GQue LEdu LRHS MBri NLar NWea SDea SKee SPoG WHar
§ ***thibetanus*** 🏆H5	Widely available
- 'Silver Fern'	see *R. thibetanus*
treutleri B&SWJ 2139	WCru
tricolor	CAgr CBcs CDul CSBt CTri CUse ECrN GKev GKin MBlu MCoo MMuc MRav MSwo MWhi NLar SCob SDix SGol SPer WMoo

aff. ***tricolor***	WHar
trilobus B&SWJ 9096	WCru
'Tummelberry' (F)	EMil GQue GTwe LRHS SVic
ulmifolius 'Bellidiflorus' (d)	MRav
ursinus	SVic
xanthocarpus	NLar XLum
'Youngberry' (F)	SDea

Rudbeckia ✿ (*Asteraceae*)

Autumn Sun	see *R. laciniata* 'Herbstsonne'
'Berlin'	CWGN ECtt GMaP IPot LRHS LSou LSun MAvo MHol MTis NCGa SCob SMrm SPer SPoG WCot WGrn WHil
californica	LRHS
deamii	see *R. fulgida* var. *deamii*
'Denver Daisy' **new**	LSun
'Dublin'	CWGN ECtt IKil IPot LRHS LSou MAvo MHol MTis NLar SCob SPoG WCot WHil
fulgida	SWvt WFar
- 'City Garden'	CKno ECtt GBin LRHS MBri NLar SRms
§ - var. ***deamii*** ♀H7	Widely available
- 'Early Bird Gold'	CWGN ECtt GBin MTis NDov NLar NPCo WCot
- var. ***fulgida***	CMea EBee EPfP LEdu SMrm SPoG
§ - var. ***speciosa*** ♀H7	CBod CKno CPrp CWCL EBee ECha ECtt ELan EPfP GAbr MMuc SBch SEND SHar SPhx SPlb SPtp SRms SWvt WFar WMoo WOld WOut WPtf WWEG XLum
- var. ***sullivantii*** 'Goldsturm' ♀H7	Widely available
- - 'Pot of Gold'	LSou NLar
- Viette's Little Suzy = 'Blovi'	EBee LSun SRms
gloriosa	see *R. hirta*
'Golden Jubilee'	LRHS
grandiflora 'Sundance'	EBee LPla MMuc SPhx WPtf
§ ***hirta***	NBir SVic
- 'Autumn Colours' (mixed)	CBod CMea SPhx
- 'Cappuccino'	CBod
- 'Cherokee Sunset' (d)	CSpe EPfP LRHS
- 'Cherry Brandy'	LRHS NSoo SGol SLon SPhx
- 'Chim Chiminee'	IKil NGBl
- 'Goldilocks'	SVic
- 'Indian Summer' ♀H3	EPfP LRHS MHol MNHC SPav SPhx
- 'Irish Eyes'	SPav SVic
- 'Marmalade'	CRos EPfP LRHS NGBl SVic
- 'Prairie Sun'	CRos ELon EPfP LRHS MBel NGBl SPhx
- 'Sonora'	NGBl
- 'Tiger Eye'	CRos LRHS SPoG
- 'Toto' ♀H3	SPav SWvt
July Gold	see *R. laciniata* 'Juligold'
laciniata	CElw CHVG CKno CMac CSpe EBee ELan GCal GQue LEdu MSpe NCGa NDov NGBl NLar NOrc NPCo SMHy SPhx WCot WMoo WOld WWEG XLum
- var. ***digitata***	IMou
- 'Golden Glow'	see *R. laciniata* 'Hortensia'
- 'Goldkugel' (d) ♀H7	MSpe
- 'Goldquelle' (d)	CBod EBee ECha ECtt ELan EPfP EPla GMaP IVic LAst LRHS MBri MSpe NGdn NOrc NPCo NPri NSoo SCob SMad SPer SPoG SRms SRot SWvt WCAu WFar WMnd WWEG XLum
§ - 'Herbstsonne' ♀H7	Widely available
§ - 'Hortensia' (d)	EBee GQue MAvo MRav WBrk WCot WHoo WOld WWEG
§ - 'Juligold'	CBod CPrp EBee ECtt LBMP LRHS MAvo MBNS MPie NEgg NGdn SMrm SPoG WWEG WWFP
- 'Starcadia Razzle Dazzle'	EWld MAvo WCot WWEG
'Little Gold Star'	CKno EBee ECtt LRHS MAsh MBri MHol MPie NDov NLar NPCo NPri SCob SHar SHil SLon SPoG WCot
maxima	CAby CKno CSpe EBee ECha ELon EWoo GBin IFoB LEdu LRHS LSun MBel MHol MMuc MSpe NCGa NLar NSti SKHP SMad SMrm SPlb WCot WWEG XLum
missouriensis	EBee LRHS
mollis	EBee LRHS NBre WWEG
newmannii	see *R. fulgida* var. *speciosa*
nitida	IBoy
occidentalis	LRHS NBre NChi WWEG
- 'Black Beauty'PBR	ECtt EPfP
- 'Green Wizard'	CBod CMac EBee ECtt ELan EPfP GBin IBoy LRHS MCot MLHP NLar NSti SGSe SMrm SPav SPer SRms WHar WMnd WWEG
* ***paniculata***	EBee LLHF NBre WCot
'Peking'	CWGN ECtt IKil LRHS NCGa SCob SPoG WCot WGrn WHil
purpurea	see *Echinacea purpurea*
speciosa	see *R. fulgida* var. *speciosa*
subtomentosa	CSam EWes GCal LEdu LPla LRHS MSpe NDov NSti SCob SMHy WCot WOld XLum
- 'Henry Eilers'	Widely available
- 'Loofahsa Wheaten Gold'	SPhx
triloba ♀H7	CDes CNec CSpe ECha ELon EPfP IBoy LRHS MBel MMuc MNrw NCGa NGdn SGSe SPhx WCAu WMoo WPGP
- 'Prairie Glow'	CAby IBoy IPot LSun MNrw NCGa NDov NSoo SGol SMrm SPhx

rue see *Ruta graveolens*

Ruellia (*Acanthaceae*)

amoena	see *R. brevifolia*
§ ***brevifolia***	ECre EShb
humilis	EBee EShb SBrt SPhx WHil
macrantha	CCCN EShb
makoyana ♀H1a	CUse EShb
- white-flowered	EShb
strepens	EBee
tweediana	EShb
- 'Katie'	WHil

Rulingia (*Sterculiaceae*)

hermanniifolia	ECou MOWG

Rumex (*Polygonaceae*)

acetosa	CArn CHab CHby CUse ELau ENfk GPoy MCoo MHer MNHC NBir SEND SIde SRms WHer WJek WSFF
- 'Abundance'	ELau LEdu
- subsp. ***acetosa*** 'Saucy' (v)	LEdu WCot
- 'Hortensis' **new**	MMuc
- 'Profusion'	GPoy MHer

acetosella	CArn CHab NMir WSFF
alpinus	EBee LEdu SPhx WCot
crispus	ELau
flexuosus	CElw CSpe EPPr GCal LPot WJek
hydrolapathum	CArn CBAq CHab MMuc MSKA NLar SEND SPlb WCot WSFF
patientia	CArn CHab ELau
sanguineus	CBAq CTri ENfk EShb LEdu MSKA NLar NSbr SRms XLum
- var. ***sanguineus***	CArn CElw CHby CRow CUse ELan GBin IFoB MHer MNHC NBro NPri SGSe WHer WJek
scutatus	CArn CBod CHby CUse ELau ENfk GPoy MNHC SIde SPlb SRms WHer WHfH WJek
- subsp. ***induratus***	SEND
- 'Silver Shield'	CRow ELau LEdu MHer SRms WJek

Rumohra (*Dryopteridaceae*)

adiantiformis ♀H1c	CCCN ISha LRHS NLos SEND WFib WPGP

Ruschia (*Aizoaceae*)

putterillii	SPlb
spinosa new	SPlb
tumidula	SPlb

Ruscus ✿ (*Asparagaceae*)

aculeatus	CArn CBcs CDul CMac CTsd ELan EPfP GPoy LEdu LPal MGil MGos MRav NLar SArc SPlb SRms SWvt WBor WPGP WRHF
- (f)	SCob
- hermaphrodite	EPfP GCal MMuc SEND SMad WPGP WThu
- var. ***aculeatus*** 'Lanceolatus' (f)	GCal
- var. ***angustifolius*** PAB 254	LEdu
- 'Christmas Berry'	EPfP
- 'John Redmond'PBR ♀H5	ELan ELon EPfP EShb LLHF LRHS LSqu MAsh NHol NLar NWad SCob SCoo SKHP SLon SPer SPoG SSpi SWvt WFar WPGP
* - 'Wheeler's Variety' (f/m)	CJun MRav WPGP
hypoglossum	CMac MMuc SEND WCot WPGP
racemosus	see *Danae racemosa*

Ruspolia (*Acanthaceae*)

hypocrateriformis	CCCN
seticalyx	EShb

Russelia (*Plantaginaceae*)

§ ***equisetiformis*** ♀H1c	CAbb MOWG
- 'Lemon Falls' ♀H1c	MOWG
- 'Tangerine Falls'	MOWG
juncea	see *R. equisetiformis*

Ruta (*Rutaceae*)

chalepensis	CArn XLum XSen
corsica	CArn XLum
graveolens	CArn CBod CHab ENfk GPoy MNHC SIde WJek XLum
- 'Jackman's Blue'	CBcs CTri CUse EHoe ELan EPfP GMaP GPoy MGos MHer MNHC MRav MSwo NLar SRms SWvt XLum
- 'Variegata' (v)	MNHC NPer SRms

Ruttya (*Acanthaceae*)

fruticosa	CCCN

× *Ruttyruspolia* (*Acanthaceae*)

lutea	CCCN
'Phyllis van Heerden'	CCCN

Rytidosperma (*Poaceae*)

* ***arundinaceum***	EShb

S

Sabal (*Arecaceae*)

minor	CHEx CPHo LPal NLos SBig SPlb
palmetto	CDoC LPal
uresana	LPal

Saccharum (*Poaceae*)

arundinaceum	CKno
brevibarbe	WCot
var. ***contortum***	
officinarum	SPlb
ravennae	EBee EPPr SMad SMrm SPlb

Sageretia (*Rhamnaceae*)

§ ***thea***	CMen
theezans	see *S. thea*

Sagina (*Caryophyllaceae*)

subulata	ECho EHoe MAvo SVic XLum
- var. ***glabrata***	MAsh
§ - - 'Aurea'	CMea CTri ECha ECho ECtt EDAr GMaP MHer SPoG

Sagittaria (*Alismataceae*)

australis	EWay
'Bloomin' Babe'	CRow EWay
graminea	LLWG
- 'Crushed Ice' (v)	CRow EWay
japonica	see *S. sagittifolia*
lancifolia	EWay
latifolia	LLWG MWts NPer
- 'Flore Pleno' (d)	MWts
* ***leucopetala*** 'Flore Pleno' (d)	NLar NPer
§ ***sagittifolia***	CBAq CRow CWat EHon LLWG MSKA MWts WMAq XLum
- 'Flore Pleno' (d)	CWat EWay WMAq XLum
- var. ***leucopetala***	WMAq

Saintpaulia ✿ (*Gesneriaceae*)

'Aca's Pink Delight'	WDib
'Aca's Red Ember' (v)	WDib
'Ajohn's Fruit Cocktail' new	WDib
'Allegro Appalachian Trail'	WDib
'Always Pink'	WDib
'Aly's Rosy Baby'	WDib
'Anouk'	WDib
'Anthoflores Edith' new	WDib
'Arctic Frost' (d)	WDib
'Baby Brian'	WDib
'Baby's Breath'	WDib
'Baker's Pink Star'	WDib
'Ballet Snowcone' (d) new	WDib

'Beacon Trail' WDib
'Beatrice Trail' WDib
'Betty Stoehr' WDib
'Black Ace' (d) **new** WDib
'Blackie Bryant' WDib
'Bloomlover's Cat' (d) **new** WDib
'Blue Dragon' (d) WDib
'Blue Tail Fly' WDib
'Blushing Ivory' **new** WDib
'Blushing Trail' WDib
'Bob Serbin' (d) WDib
'Bob's Omega' **new** WDib
brevipilosa WDib
'Buffalo Hunt' (d) WDib
'Calico Beauty' **new** WDib
'Candy Swirls' WDib
'Cathedral' WDib
'Chantamara' **new** WDib
'Chantaspring' WDib
'Cherries 'n' Cream' WDib
'Chiffon Fiesta' WDib
'Chiffon Moonmoth' WDib
'Chiffon Pageant' **new** WDib
'Chiffon Vesper' WDib
'Coral Sparkle Trail' WDib
'Country Romance' (d) **new** WDib
'Crimson Ice' WDib
'Cupid's Jewel' WDib
'Deer Trail' WDib
'Delft' (d) WDib
'Desir' WDib
'Dibleys Kaarina' WDib
'Dibleys Mercedes' WDib
'Electric Dreams' WDib
'Emerald Love' WDib
'Falling Raindrops' WDib
'Favorite Child' WDib
'Festive Holiday' (d) **new** WDib
'Fire Mountain' WDib
'Flashy Angel' (v) WDib
'Flower Drum' WDib
'Fun Trail' WDib
'Genetic Blush' WDib
'Gillian' (d) WDib
'Golden Eye' WDib
'Golden Glow' (d) WDib
'Grandmother's Halo' WDib
'Green Ice' WDib
'Green Lace' (d) WDib
'Halo's Aglitter' WDib
'Happy Cricket' WDib
'Hot Summer Day' **new** WDib
'Indigo Ruffles' WDib
ionantha subsp. ***grotei*** **new** WDib
– subsp. ***ionantha*** **new** WDib
– subsp. ***rupicola*** WDib
– subsp. ***velutina*** **new** WDib
'Irish Flirt' (d) WDib
'Jolly Cutie Pie' WDib
'Jolly Orchid' (d) **new** WDib
'Jolly Texan' (d) **new** WDib
'King's Trail' (d) WDib
'Kostina Fantaziia' **new** WDib
'Lemon Drop' (d) WDib
'Lemon Whip' (d) WDib
'Little Axel' WDib
'Lollipop' WDib
'Looking Glass' WDib
'Louisiana Lagniappe' WDib
'Louisiana Lullaby' (d) WDib
'Love Spots' WDib
'Lucky Lee Ann' (d) WDib
'Luminescence' WDib
'Lyon's Paprika' WDib
'Lyon's Plum Pudding' WDib
'Mac's Black Jack' WDib
'Mac's Blowing Bubbles' **new** WDib
'Mac's Carnival Clown' WDib
'Mac's Cheery Cherry' WDib
'Mac's Circus Clown' WDib
'Mac's Coral Cutie' WDib
'Mac's Exquisite Extravaganza' WDib
'Mac's Just Jeff' (d/v) WDib
'Mac's Nocturne' (d) WDib
'Mac's Southern Springtime' (d) **new** WDib
'Mac's Strawberry Sundae' WDib
'Mair' WDib
'Ma's Ching Dynasty' (d) **new** WDib
'Ma's Corsage' WDib
'Ma's Easter Parade' WDib
'Ma's Lily Pad' WDib
'Masked Man' **new** WDib
'Midget Lilian' (v) WDib
'Midnight Flame' (d) WDib
'Midnight Magic' WDib
'Midnight Rascal' (d) WDib
'Midnight Waltz' (d) WDib
'Milky Way Trail' WDib
'Minnie Mine' WDib
'Minstrel's Mary Ruth' WDib
'Motley Crew' WDib
'Munchkin Kisses' (d) **new** WDib
'Ness' Antique Red' WDib
'Ness' Bangle Blue' WDib
'Ness' Blueberry Puff' WDib
'Ness' Cherry Smoke' WDib
'Ness' Crinkle Blue' (d) WDib
'Ness' Dynomite' WDib
'Ness' Jesse' (d) **new** WDib
'Ness' Midnight Fantasy' WDib
'Ness' Orange Pekoe' **new** WDib
'Ness' Satin Rose' WDib
'Ness' Sheer Peach' WDib
'Ness' Viking Maiden' WDib
'Newtown James Peel' **new** WDib
'Newtown Ohio' WDib
nitida WDib
'Ode to Beauty' WDib
'Okie Easter Bunny' WDib
'Oksana' WDib
'Optimara Chico' **new** WDib
'Optimara Dali' **new** WDib
'Optimara Little Moonstone' **new** WDib
'Optimara Little Seneca' WDib
'Otoe' (d) WDib
'Peppermint Doll' **new** WDib
'Petite Blarney' WDib
'Pink Wink' WDib
'Pirate's Treasure' WDib
'Pixie Blue' WDib
'Pixie Pink' WDib

'Pixie Show-off'	WDib
'Podvenechnaia' (d) **new**	WDib
'Powder Keg' (d)	WDib
'Powwow' (d/v)	WDib
'Purple Passion'	WDib
'Rain Man'	WDib
'Rainbow's Limelight' (d)	WDib
'Rainbow's Quiet Riot'	WDib
'Ramblin' Amethyst'	WDib
'Ramblin' Angel' (d)	WDib
'Ramblin' Dots'	WDib
'Ramblin' Lassie'	WDib
'Ramblin' Magic' (d)	WDib
'Ramblin' Sunshine'	WDib
'Rare Tapestry'	WDib
'Raspberry Crisp'	WDib
'Red Lantern' (d)	WDib
'Red Summit'	WDib
'Reflections of Spring' (d) **new**	WDib
'Rhapsodie Clementine'	WDib
'Rhapsodie Rosalie'	WDib
'Robert Mayer'	WDib
'Rob's Argyle Socks' (d) **new**	WDib
'Rob's Bamboozle' (d)	WDib
'Rob's Blue Cat'	WDib
'Rob's Blue Socks'	WDib
'Rob's Boo Hoo'	WDib
'Rob's Chilly Willy' (d/v)	WDib
'Rob's Cloudy Skies' (d)	WDib
'Rob's Dandy Lion' (d/v)	WDib
'Rob's Denim Demon' (d/v)	WDib
'Rob's Dust Storm' (d)	WDib
'Rob's Fuzzy Navel' **new**	WDib
'Rob's Gundaroo' (d)	WDib
'Rob's Hallucination'	WDib
'Rob's Heebie Jeebie'	WDib
'Rob's Hopscotch' (d)	WDib
'Rob's Hot Tamale'	WDib
'Rob's Ice Ripples' (d)	WDib
'Rob's Jitterbug'	WDib
'Rob's June Bug' (d/v)	WDib
'Rob's Love Bite' (d)	WDib
'Rob's Mad Cat' (d)	WDib
'Rob's Peedletuck'	WDib
'Rob's Pink Buttercups' (v)	WDib
'Rob's Rinky Dink' (d)	WDib
'Rob's Ruff Stuff'	WDib
'Rob's Sarsparilla' (d)	WDib
'Rob's Scarecrow'	WDib
'Rob's Scrumptious'	WDib
'Rob's Seduction' (d/v)	WDib
'Rob's Shadow Magic' (d/v)	WDib
'Rob's Smarty Pants' (d)	WDib
'Rob's Sticky Wicket' (d)	WDib
'Rob's Toorooka' (d)	WDib
'Rob's Twinkle Blue' (d)	WDib
'Rob's Vanilla Trail' (d)	WDib
'Rob's Wooloomooloo' (d)	WDib
'Roll Along Blue' (d)	WDib
'RS-Strast' **new**	WDib
'Santa Anita'	WDib
'Scarlet Ribbons' **new**	WDib
shumensis	WDib
'Silly Girl'	WDib
'Sky Bells' (v)	WDib
'Snow Leopard'	WDib
'Sultan' (d) **new**	WDib
'Sweet Amy Sue' (d)	WDib
'Taffeta Blue' (d)	WDib
'Taffeta Petticoats'	WDib
'Teen Thunder'	WDib
'The Madam'	WDib
'Tina's April Fantasy' **new**	WDib
'Tula'	WDib
'Twist 'n' Shout'	WDib
'Vampire's Kiss' (d) **new**	WDib
'Warm Sunshine'	WDib
'Whirligig Star'	WDib
'Wild Irish Rose' **new**	WDib
'Wisteria' (d)	WDib
'Witch Doctor' (d)	WDib
'Yesterday's Child'	WDib

Salicornia (*Amaranthaceae*)

europaea	SVic

Salix ✿ (*Salicaceae*)

	acutifolia 'Blue Streak' (m) ♀H5	CEnd CWiW EPfP EWes MBlu NBir NLar SMHy SWat WMou
	- 'Pendulifolia' (m)	SGol
	'Aegma Brno' (f)	WMou
	aegyptiaca	EBtc MBlu NWea WMou
	alba	CCVT CDul CHab CLnd CWiW LBuc NHed NWea SEWo SGol WMou
	- f. ***argentea***	see *S. alba* var. *sericea*
	- 'Aurea'	CTho WMou
	- var. ***caerulea***	CDul CLnd NWea WMou
	- - 'Wantage Hall' (f)	CWiW
	- 'Cardinalis' (f)	CWiW SWat
	- 'Chermesina' hort.	see *S. alba* var. *vitellina* 'Britzensis'
	- 'Golden Ness' ♀H6	EBee EPla LRHS MAsh MBlu SPoG WFar
	- 'Hutchinson's Yellow'	CTho ECrN MBri NLar NWea
	- 'Liempde' (m)	NWea
	- 'Raesfeld' (m)	CWiW
§	- var. ***sericea*** ♀H6	CBcs CDul CLnd CTho EPfP MBlu MBri MRav MWat NLar NWea SPer WCot WMou
	- 'Splendens'	see *S. alba* var. *sericea*
	- 'Tristis' misapplied	see *S.* × *sepulcralis* var. *chrysocoma*
§	- 'Tristis' ambig.	CLnd CTri ELan IBoy LAst LRHS MBri MGos MRav MSwo NLar NWea SEWo SWat WHar
	- var. ***vitellina***	CDul CTri EPfP GQue LBuc MBNS MBrN MMuc NLar NWea SEND SGol SLon SWat
§	- - 'Britzensis' (m)	Widely available
	- - 'Nova'	SWat
§	- - 'Yelverton' ♀H6	EPfP GQue LRHS MAsh SPoG SWat WFar
	- 'Vitellina Pendula'	see *S. alba* 'Tristis' ambig.
	- 'Vitellina Tristis'	see *S. alba* 'Tristis' ambig.
§	***alpina***	ECho NHar
	'Americana'	CWiW
	amplexicaulis 'Pescara' (m)	CWiW
	amygdaloides	CWiW
	'Aokautere'	see *S.* × *sepulcralis* 'Aokautere'
§	***arbuscula***	ECho XEll
	arenaria	see *S. repens* var. *argentea*
	aurita	CAco NWea
	babylonica	CDul CEnd COtt LPal WMou
	- 'Annularis'	see *S. babylonica* 'Crispa'
	- 'Bijdorp'	NLar

Name	Suppliers
§ - 'Crispa'	ELan LRHS MTPN SMad SPoG WFar
- 'Pan Chih-kang'	CWiW NLar
- var. ***pekinensis*** 'Pendula'	IArd
§ - - 'Tortuosa'	CAco CDul CLnd CSBt ECrN ELan EPfP IBoy IVic LRHS MGos MMuc MWat NBir NPer NWea SCob SEND SGol SLon SPer SPlb SPoG SRms SWat WFar WHar WPos
* - 'Tortuosa Aurea'	IBoy SGol SWvt
× ***balfourii***	SDix
'Blackskin' (f)	CWiW
bockii	EBtc ELan LLHF LRHS SDys SKHP
§ 'Bowles's Hybrid'	WMou
'Boydii' (f) ♀H7	CMea ECho EPot GAbr GBin GCrg ITim LEdu LRHS MGos NBir NHar NRya NSla WAbe WFar WPat WThu
caprea	CAco CBcs CCVT CDul CHab CLnd CTri EPfP LBuc NHed NWea SCob SEWo SPer WMou WSFF
- 'Black Stem'	CDul
§ - 'Kilmarnock' (m)	Widely available
- 'Mas' (m)	CNWT
- var. ***pendula*** (m)	see *S. caprea* 'Kilmarnock' (m)
capusii	WPGP
cashmiriana	GEdr
* ***caspica rubra nana***	SWat
'Chrysocoma'	see *S.* × *sepulcralis* var. *chrysocoma*
cinerea	CAco CBcs CTri LBuc NWea SEWo WMou
- 'Tricolor' (v)	NEoE
daphnoides	CCVT CDul CLnd CMac EPPr EPfP LRHS MGos MMuc MSwo NWea SEND SGol SPer SRms SWat WMou WSFF
- 'Aglaia' (m) ♀H6	CBcs CDul GQue
- 'Meikle' (f)	CWiW SWat
- 'Netta Statham' (m)	CWiW
- 'Ovaro Udine' (m)	CWiW
- 'Oxford Violet' (m)	NWea
- 'Stewartstown'	CWiW
× ***dasyclados***	WPos
- 'Grandis'	NWea
§ × ***doniana*** 'Kumeti'	CWiW
'E.A. Bowles'	see *S.* 'Bowles's Hybrid'
× ***ehrhartiana***	CNat
§ ***elaeagnos***	CCVT CDul CTho CTri ECrN EPfP MBrN MMuc NWea SEND SLon SPer SWat WMou
§ - subsp. ***angustifolia*** ♀H5	CBcs CDul ELan EPfP MBri MMuc MRav MSwo NLar NWea SCob SEND SRms
'Elegantissima'	see *S.* × *pendulina* var. *elegantissima*
eriocephala 'American Mackay' (m)	CWiW
- 'Kerksii' (m)	CWiW
- 'Mawdesley' (m)	CWiW
- 'Russelliana' (f)	CWiW
exigua ♀H5	CBcs CDul CLnd CTho ELan EPfP EWTr EWes IDee LAst LBuc LEdu MBlu MBrN MGos MLHP MSwo NBir NLar NWea SCob SCoo SMad SPer WMou WPGP
fargesii ♀H6	CAbP CDoC CDul CEnd CExl CFil CMac ELan EPfP EPla EUJe GBin GCal IDee LEdu LRHS MBlu MGos MMuc MRav NBid SBrt SEND SKHP SMad SPer SSpi WCot WCru WPat
fargesii × ***magnifica***	CFil
§ × ***finnmarchica***	WAbe
formosa	see *S. arbuscula*
fragilis	CAco CCVT CDul CHab CLnd NWea WMou
§ - var. ***furcata***	CTri GCrg
× ***fruticosa*** 'McElroy' (f)	CWiW
fruticulosa	see *S. fragilis* var. *furcata*
'Fuiri-koriyanagi'	see *S. integra* 'Hakuro-nishiki'
furcata	see *S. fragilis* var. *furcata*
glauca	CNat
'Golden Curls'	see *S.* × *sepulcralis* 'Erythroflexuosa'
gracilistyla	CTho NWea WMou
§ - 'Melanostachys' (m) ♀H5	CBcs CDul CTho ECrN ELan EPfP EPla EWTr GAbr MAsh MBNS MBlu MBrN MGos MMuc MRav NBir NEgg NLar NSoo NWea SBrt SEND SGol SPer SRms SWat WBor
× ***greyi***	NEoE
hastata (f)	SWat
- 'Wehrhahnii' (m) ♀H6	CBcs CDul CMea EBee ECho ELan EPfP GCra IVic LEdu MBlu MJak MMuc MRav MSwo NBir NLar NWea SEND SPer SWat
helvetica ♀H7	CBcs CDul CMac EBee ECho ELan EPfP GAbr IVic MBlu MRav NBir NEgg NLar NWea SPer WFar
herbacea	ECho WAbe
hibernica	see *S. phylicifolia*
hookeriana	CDul CExl CFil ELan MBlu MBrN MBri NLar WCFE WMou
incana	see *S. elaeagnos*
integra 'Albomaculata'	see *S. integra* 'Hakuro-nishiki'
- 'Flamingo'PBR	ELan SPoG
§ - 'Hakuro-nishiki' (v) ♀H5	Widely available
- 'Pendula' (f)	CEnd MAsh MBri
irrorata ♀H5	CDul CLnd EPfP LRHS MBlu MBri MSwo NLar SCob SWat
'Jacquinii'	see *S. alpina*
§ ***koriyanagi***	CWiW
'Kumeti'	see *S.* × *doniana* 'Kumeti'
'Kuro-me'	see *S. gracilistyla* 'Melanostachys'
lanata ♀H7	CBcs CMac CMea ECho ELan ELon EPfP EWTr GAbr GKev MAsh MGos MJak NBir NEgg NLar NWea SBrt SPer SWat
lapponum	LEdu MMuc NLar NWea SRms
- (m)	WAbe
- compact	GKev
magnifica	CDul CEnd CExl CFil CLnd EBee ELan EPfP EPla EWTr IArd IDee LEdu LRHS MBri MSnd SKHP SWat WFar WHer WHor WMou WPGP
'Mark Postill' (f)	CDoC EBee ELon ETwe LRHS MBNS MMuc NLar SEND WWFP
matsudana 'Tortuosa'	see *S. babylonica* var. *pekinensis* 'Tortuosa'
- 'Tortuosa Aureopendula'	see *S.* × *sepulcralis* 'Erythroflexuosa'
'Melanostachys'	see *S. gracilistyla* 'Melanostachys'
× ***meyeriana*** 'Lumley' (f)	CWiW
× ***mollissima*** var. ***hippophaifolia*** 'Jefferies' (m)	CWiW
- - 'Notts Spaniard' (m)	CWiW
- - 'Trustworthy' (m)	CWiW
- 'Q83'	WPos

	Plant	Suppliers
	– var. ***undulata*** 'Kottenheider Weide' (f)	CWiW
	moupinensis	MBri
	aff. ***moupinensis*** from Vietnam	CFil
§	***myrsinifolia***	ELan LRHS MBlu MMuc NLar SEND WGrn
	– 'Black Knight'	EPfP
	myrsinites var. ***jacquiniana***	see *S. alpina*
	myrtilloides 'Pink Tassels' (m)	ECho GEdr SBrt
	myrtilloides × ***repens***	see *S.* × *finnmarchica*
	nakamurana var. ***yezoalpina***	ELan EPot EWes GEdr GQui IVic LRHS MBlu MMuc MRav NHar NLar SBrt WFar WPat
	nigricans	see *S. myrsinifolia*
	nivalis	see *S. reticulata* subsp. *nivalis*
§	× ***pendulina*** var. ***elegantissima***	SWat
	pentandra	CDul CLnd NWea WMou
	– 'Patent Lumley'	CWiW
§	***phylicifolia***	NWea WMou
	– 'Malham' (m)	CWiW
§	***purpurea***	CCVT CDul NWea SCob WMou
	– 'Brittany Green' (f)	CWiW
	– 'Continental Reeks'	CWiW
	– 'Dark Dicks' (f)	CWiW NLar WSFF
	– 'Dicky Meadows' (m)	CWiW
	– 'Goldstones'	CWiW NLar
	– f. ***gracilis***	see *S. purpurea* 'Gracilis'
§	– 'Gracilis'	MMuc NLar NWea SCob SEND SLon WCot
	– 'Green Dicks'	CWiW
	– 'Helix'	see *S. purpurea*
	– 'Howki' (m)	WMou
	– 'Irette' (m)	CWiW
	– 'Jagiellonka' (f)	CWiW
	– var. ***japonica***	see *S. koriyanagi*
	– subsp. ***lambertiana***	CWiW
	– 'Lancashire Dicks' (m)	CWiW
	– 'Leicestershire Dicks' (m)	CWiW
	– 'Light Dicks'	CWiW
	– 'Lincolnshire Dutch' (f)	CWiW
	– 'Nancy Saunders' (f) 🏆H6	CTho CWiW EHoe GBin MBNS MBlu MBrN MRav NBir NEoE NLar NSti SMHy WCot
	– 'Pendula' 🏆H6	CCVT CEnd ECrN LRHS MAsh MBri MGos MSwo NPri NWea
	– 'Read' (f)	CWiW
	– 'Reeks' (f)	CWiW
	– 'Richartii' (f)	CWiW
	– 'Uralensis' (f)	CWiW
	pyrenaica	EWes
	pyrenaica × ***retusa***	ECho
	repens	NLar NWea SRms SWat
§	– var. ***argentea***	CDul ELan EPot EWes LRHS MMuc MRav NWea SEND SPer
	– 'Voorthuizen' (f)	ECho
	reticulata 🏆H7	CMea ECho EPot GCrg NBir NHar NSla WAbe
§	– subsp. ***nivalis***	EPot
	retusa	CTri NBir NHar
	rosmarinifolia misapplied	see *S. elaeagnos* subsp. *angustifolia*
	rosmarinifolia L.	NLar WWtn
	× ***rubens*** 'Basfordiana' (m)	CDul CLnd CTho CWiW MBNS SWat WMou
	– 'Bouton Aigu'	CWiW
	– 'Farndon'	CWiW
	– 'Flanders Red' (f)	CWiW
	– 'Fransgeel Rood' (m)	CWiW
	– 'Glaucescens' (m)	CWiW
	– 'Golden Willow'	CWiW
	– 'Jaune de Falaise'	CWiW
	– 'Jaune Hâtive'	CWiW
	– 'Laurina'	CWiW
	– 'Natural Red' (f)	CWiW
	– 'Parsons'	CWiW
	– 'Rouge Ardennais'	CWiW
	– 'Rouge Folle'	CWiW
	– 'Russet' (f)	CWiW
	× ***rubra***	CWiW
	– 'Abbey's Harrison' (f)	CWiW
	– 'Continental Osier' (f)	CWiW
	– 'Eugenei' (m)	CDul ECrN GQui MBlu SWat
	– 'Fidkin' (f)	CWiW
	– 'Harrison's' (f)	CWiW
	– 'Harrison's Seedling A' (f)	CWiW
	– 'Mawdesley'	CWiW
	– 'Mawdesley Seedling A' (f)	CWiW
	– 'Pyramidalis'	CWiW
I	'Salix Red' **new**	WJPR
	Scarlet Curls = 'Scarcuzam'	WPat
	schraderiana	NWea
	× ***sepulcralis***	NWea
§	– 'Aokautere'	CWiW
	– 'Caradoc'	CWiW
§	– var. ***chrysocoma*** 🏆H5	Widely available
	– 'Dart's Snake'	ELan EPPr EPfP MAsh MBrN MRav NLar WCot
§	– 'Erythroflexuosa' 🏆H5	CAco CBcs CDoC CDul CEnd EBee ELan EPPr EPfP EPla LAst LBMP MGos MMuc MRav NWea SCob SEND SGol SPer SPoG SWat WCFE WHer
	serpyllifolia	CTri NHar WThu
	– 'Chamonix'	NSla
	serpyllum	see *S. fragilis* var. *furcata*
	'Setsuka'	see *S. udensis* 'Sekka'
	sitchensis	NWea
	× ***smithiana***	NWea
	× ***stipularis*** (f)	NWea
	subopposita	EBtc ELan MMuc WAbe
	triandra	CDul WMou
	– 'Black German' (m)	CWiW
	– 'Black Hollander' (m)	CWiW NLar
	– 'Black Maul'	CWiW GQue WPos
	– 'Grisette de Falaise'	CWiW
	– 'Grisette Droda' (f)	CWiW
	– 'Long Bud'	CWiW
	– 'Noir de Challans'	CWiW
	– 'Noir de Touraine'	CWiW
	– 'Noir de Villaines' (m)	CWiW WJPR
	– 'Rouge d'Orléans'	EBtc
	– 'Sarda d'Anjou'	CWiW
	– 'Whissander'	CWiW
	udensis	NWea
§	– 'Sekka' (m)	ELan MBlu MMuc NBir NWea SEND SWat WMou
	uva-ursi	WAbe
	viminalis	CCVT CLnd CMac EPfP LBuc NWea SEWo SVic WJPR WMou WPos WSFF
	– 'Green Gotz'	CWiW
	vitellina 'Pendula'	see *S. alba* 'Tristis' ambig.
	'Yelverton'	see *S. alba* var. *vitellina* 'Yelverton'

Salsola (*Amaranthaceae*)

	soda	CArn

Salvia ✿ (*Lamiaceae*)

	ACE 2172	SPin
	CD&R 1162	CAby EPyc SPhx
	CD&R 1458	SPin
	CD&R 1495	SPin
	CD&R 3071	SPin
	PC&H 226	SPin
	from Catamarca, Argentina	EPyc SDys
	absconditiflora new	SPin
	acerifolia	SPin
	acetabulosa	see *S. multicaulis*
	adenophora	EPyc SPin
	aerea	CPom
	aethiopis	EWes SPav SPin XSen
I	'African Sky'	SDys SPin WHil
§	***africana***	CSpe SPin
	africana-caerulea	see *S. africana*
	africana-lutea	see *S. aurea*
	agnes	EPyc SPin
	algeriensis	EPyc SBch
	'Allen Chickering'	XSen
	amarissima	SPin
	'Amber'	IMou LPla SBrt SPin XSen
	ambigens	see *S. guaranitica*
	'Amistad'	CAbb CMos CPar IPot LBuc LRHS MAsh MBri MCot MHer NDov NPri SDys SPin WGrn WHil WHlf
	ampelophylla	SDys
	- B&SWJ 10751	SPin
§	***amplexicaulis***	EPyc MMuc NLar SEND SPin SRms WHrl XSen
	amplifrons	EPyc SPin
	angustifolia Cav.	see *S. reptans*
	angustifolia Mich.	see *S. azurea*
	'Anna'	SDys
	'Anthony Parker'	WOut XSen
	'Anthony Waterer'	EWld
	apiana	CArn EOHP EPyc MHer SPin SPlb SRms SVen WHfH XSen
	arenaria	SPin
	argentea	CBcs CSpe ECha ELan EPfP EWTr EWoo GMaP LRHS MSpe MWat NSoo SMrm SPer SPin SRkn SWat WJek WKif XLum XSen
	- 'Artemis'	EBee
	arizonica	CSam EPyc EWld GCal LPla MAsh SDys SPin XSen
	aspera	SPin
	atrocyanea	CAby CSam CSpe ECre EPyc EWes MAsh MAvo SBHP SDys SPin WHal WKif
	aucheri	SPin
§	***aurea***	CHll CSpe ELan SPin SPlb SVen XLum
	- 'Kirstenbosch'	CAby ECtt EPyc EWld SDys SPin WKif
	aurita	EPyc SPin
	- var. ***galpinii***	SPin
	austriaca	SPin XSen
§	***azurea***	EPyc SMrm SPhx SPin XSen
	- var. ***grandiflora***	SPin WCot
	bacheriana	see *S. buchananii*
§	***barrelieri***	ESwi SPin XSen
	'Bee's Bliss'	XSen
	'Belhaven'	GCal SPin WOut
	bertolonii	see *S. pratensis* Bertolonii Group
	bicolor	see *S. barrelieri*
	'Black Knight'	CSpe EPyc SDys SPin WOth WPGP
	blancoana	see *S. lavandulifolia* subsp. *blancoana*
	blepharophylla	CAby CPrp ECtt EPyc EUJe MCot MHer MSCN SPin SRkn WHea XSen
	- 'Diablo'	ECtt
	- 'Painted Lady'	CSpe ECtt MAsh SDys SPin
	'Bleu Armor' new	MBri
	'Blue Chiquita'	SPin
	'Blue Moon' new	SDys
	'Blue Note' new	CMos CWGN NDov SCob
	'Blue Sky'	EWld
§	'Blush Pink' new	SDys
	bracteata	XSen
	brandegeei	SPin
	brevilabra	SPin
	'Bright Eyes' new	CWGN
	broussonetii	SPin
§	***buchananii*** ♀H2	CBod CHel CSam ECtt EPyc EWld MAsh MCot MHer MRav SDys SPin SRkn XSen
	bulleyana misapplied	see *S. flava* var. *megalantha*
	bulleyana Diels	CExl CPom EWes EWld XSen
	- 'Blue Lips'	CBod MBri SCob
	bullulata	SPin
	- pale blue-flowered new	SDys SPin
	cacaliifolia ♀H2	CExl CRHN CWCL ECtt EPyc EWld GCal MAsh MHer MSCN SDys SPin SRkn WOth XSen
	cadmica	SPin
	caerulea misapplied	see *S. guaranitica* 'Black and Blue'
	caerulea L.	see *S. africana*
	caespitosa	SPin XSen
	campanulata	CPom EWld SPin
	- B&SWJ 9232	WCru
	- DJHC C394	SPin
	- GWJ 9294	SPin WCru
	- var. ***hirtella*** GWJ 9397	WCru
	canariensis	IDee SEND SPin
	- f. ***albiflora***	SVen
	- f. ***candidissima***	SPin XSen
	candelabrum ♀H3	CAbP CSpe ECre EWes GCal MHer SBch SPav SPhx SPin SVen WCot WKif WPnn XSen
	candidissima	SPin XSen
	canescens	XSen
	cardinalis	see *S. fulgens*
	cardiophylla	SPin
	carnea	CSam SPin
	- from Valle de Bravo, Mexico	EPyc SDys
	castanea	SPin
	caudata	SPin
	'Cavalieri d'Alto' new	WHil
§	***chamaedryoides***	CFil EPyc MAsh SBrt SPhx SPin WHea WSHC XLum XSen
	- var. ***isochroma***	EPyc MAsh SDys SPin WPGP XSen
	- 'Marine Blue'	MAsh MCot
	- silver-leaved	CAby CSpe SPin WSHC XLum
	aff. ***chamaedryoides*** B&SWJ 9032 from Guatemala	SPin
	chamelaeagnea	EPyc GFai MCot SBrt SDys SHar SPin
	chapalensis	SPin
	'Cherry Queen'	CWGN EPyc MAsh SPin XSen

	Name	Suppliers
	chiapensis	EPyc MAsh MCot SDys SPin
	chinensis	see *S. japonica*
	chionophylla	SPin
	'Christine Yeo'	CElw CNor EBee ECtt ELon EPri EPyc EWoo MAsh SBch SDys SEND SPin WHil WHoo WMnd WPGP WSHC XSen
	'Christopher Fairweather' **new**	LRHS
	cinnabarina	SPin
	cleistogama misapplied	see *S. glutinosa*
	clevelandii	MHer SPav SPin WJek
	- 'Winnifred Gilman'	SDys
	clinopodioides	CDes EBee SDys SPin
	'Clotted Cream'	EWld SPoG
	coahuilensis misapplied	see *S. greggii* × *serpyllifolia*
	coahuilensis ambig.	EPyc LRHS LSou MAsh SKHP SLon SMrm SPin SRkn WSHC XLum
	coccinea	SPin
	- 'Brenthurst'	SPin
	- 'Forest Fire'	EPyc
	- (Nymph Series) 'Coral Nymph'	EPyc SPav SPin
	- - 'Lady in Red'	SPav
	- - 'Snow Nymph'	EPyc
	columbariae	CArn
	concolor misapplied	see *S. guaranitica*
	concolor Lamb. ex Benth.	EPyc EWld GCal GGal MHom SDys SPin WSHC
	confertiflora	CAby CCon CDes CExl CHEx CHel CSam CSpe CWCL EBee ECre ECtt ELan EPyc EShb GCal MAsh MHer MHom MSCN SDys SPin SPlb SRkn SVen WHea WKif WOth WPGP XSen
	corrugata	CCon CDes CElw CHel CPne EBee ECtt EPyc EWld GBin GCal LRHS MAsh MHer SDys SPhx SPin WPGP
	'Crème Caramel'	ECtt EPyc MAsh MHom SDys SPoG WHil
	cruickshanksii	SPin
	cryptantha	XSen
	aff. ***curtiflora*** B&SWJ 10356	WCru
	curviflora	CSam CSpe EPyc MAsh SBch SDys SPin WOth XSen
	cyanescens	CMea CPBP EPot EPyc LRHS SBch SBrt SPin XSen
	cyanicalyx	EPyc SDys SPin
	cyclostegia	CExl
	daghestanica	SPin XSen
	'Dancing Dolls'	CWGN LRHS SHil
I	***dangitalis***	SPin
	- SDR 4332	CExl
	darcyi misapplied	see *S. roemeriana*
	darcyi J. Compton	CAby CExl CHll CSpe EPyc EWes EWld MCot SDys SPin WHil WOth WSHC XLum XSen
	davidsonii	SPin
	deserta **new**	WCot
	desoleana	SPin WHil XSen
	dichlamys	SPin
	'Didi'	NDov
	digitaloides	GBin XSen
	- BWJ 7777	SPin WCru
	discolor	CHel CHll CSpe ECtt ELan EPyc EWld GCal MAsh MBel MCot MHer SCob SDys SEND SPin XSen
*	***- nigra***	CArn CCse

	Name	Suppliers
	disermas	SPlb XSen
	- pink-flowered	SPin
	disjuncta	CElw SPin XSen
	- 'Chimbango'	SPin
	divinorum	CArn EOHP GPoy LEdu
	dolichantha	CCon CTsd EPyc MAvo NBir NLar SPin WHer WMoo WPtf XSen
	dolomitica	SPav SPin
	dombeyi	CAby CPne CSam EPyc SDys SPin
	dominica	CArn SPin XSen
	dorisiana	MAsh SDys SPin SVen
	'Dorset Wonder'	NDov
	durifolia	SPin
	'Dyson's Crimson'	CAby CSde MCot SDys
	'Dyson's Gem' **new**	SDys
	'Dyson's Joy'	MCot SDys WHil
	eigii	SPin XSen
	eizi-matudae	SDys SPin
	elegans	ELau EWes GCal GCra IDee WOth XSen
	- 'Golden Delicious'	CBod ECtt ENfk EWes MHer SPin SRms WOut
	- 'Honey Melon'	CAby ENfk EPyc MAsh SDys
§	- 'Scarlet Pineapple'	CAby CArn CBod CExl CPrp ECtt ELan ELau ENfk EWTr GPoy MCot MHer MNHC SDys SPad SPin SRms SVen WJek XSen
	- 'Sonoran Red'	SDys
	- 'Tangerine'	CArn CBod CPrp ELau ENfk EPyc LSou MHer MNHC NSbr SPin SRms WJek
	'Endless Love'	EBee LSou MBri NDov
	euphratica	XSen
	evansiana	SPin XSen
	'Eveline'	CUse CWGN EBee ECtt EPfP GBin LBMP LRHS MBri NLar SHar SPoG STPC WHlf
	excelsa	SPin
	fallax	see *S. roscida*
	farinacea	EPfP SPin
§	***flava*** var. ***megalantha***	CFis LRHS MSpe SPin WOut XSen
	- - BWJ 7974	WCru
	forreri	EBee EPyc MAsh NDov SBHP SDys SPin WPGP
	- 'Karen Dyson'	SDys
§	***forsskaolii***	Widely available
	- white-flowered	SPin XSen
§	***fruticosa***	CArn ELau EPyc LRHS SLon SPin SRms XSen
§	***fulgens*** ♀H3	EPyc GCal MAsh SBHP SDys SPin SRkn WHea
	gesneriiflora	CCon ECtt EPyc SPin WOth WPGP XSen
	- mountain form	SDys WPGP
	- 'Tequila'	SPin WOut
	gilliesii	SPin
	glabrescens	SPin
	- B&SWJ 11152	WCru
*	- var. ***robusta*** B&SWJ 11147	WCru
	glechomifolia	EPyc SPin
§	***glutinosa***	CArn CMac CSpe EBee EPyc GCal IMou LRHS MNrw NBro NLar SPav SPin SPtp WCAu WCot WHea XLum XSen
	graciliramulosa	SPin
	gracilis	SPin
	grahamii	see *S. microphylla* var. *microphylla*

	Name	Suppliers
	gravida	SPin
	'Great Comp'	NDov SDys
	greggii	ECtt EPfP EPyc EWes LRHS MHer WHil XLum XSen
	- CD&R 1148	MCot SDys
	- 'Alba'	CAby SPin WHil XLum XSen
	- 'Blush Pink'	see *S.* 'Blush Pink'
	- 'Caramba' (v)	ESwi LRHS SEND WHil
	- 'Devon Cream'	see *S. greggii* 'Sungold'
	- 'Diane'	MAsh
	- 'Flame'	CWGN WHil
	- 'Icing Sugar'PBR	CNor CWGN ECtt ELan ENfk EPfP EPla EWoo LRHS MAsh MCot MSpe NDov NPri SBod SDys SPoG SRkn WBor WHil WSHC WWFP
	- 'Keter's Red'	WHil
	- 'Lara'	WHlf
	- 'Lipstick'	CExl ECtt EPla MAsh
	- 'Magenta'	WHil
	- 'Magnet'	SPin
	- (Navajo Series) 'Navajo Bright Red'	EPyc
*	- - 'Navajo Cream'	EPyc
*	- - 'Navajo Dark Purple'	EPyc
*	- - 'Navajo Purple'	EPyc
	- - Navajo Salmon Red = 'Rfds016'	EPyc
*	- - 'Navajo White'	EPyc
	- 'Peach' misapplied	see *S.* × *jamensis* 'Pat Vlasto'
	- 'Peach'	CWGN ELau EPfP EPyc MAsh MHer SDys WHea WPGP XLum XSen
	- 'Pink Preference'	MAsh SDys
	- 'Raspberry Red'	XLum
	- salmon-flowered	WHil
	- 'Sierra San Antonio'	see *S.* × *jamensis* 'Sierra San Antonio'
	- 'Sparkler' (v)	ELan EPfP LRHS MAsh SLon SPoG
	- 'Stormy Pink'	CAby CHll CPrp CSam CSpe EPyc LRHS MAsh MCot NDov WHil WOth WPGP WSHC XSen
	- 'Strawberries and Cream' new	WHil
§	- 'Sungold'	CWGN ECtt EPfP EPyc LRHS MAsh NDov SDys SPin XSen
	- variegated (v)	XSen
	- yellow-flowered	CAby XLum
	greggii* × *lycioides	see *S. greggii* × *serpyllifolia*
§	***greggii* × *serpyllifolia***	CAbP CSpe EPyc MAsh NDov NPri SDys SPin SVen
	grewiifolia	SPin
	guadalujarensis	SPin
§	***guaranitica***	CBcs CHEx ECtt EShb MHer SPin WKif WPGP XLum XSen
	- 'Argentina Skies'	CAby CHGN CSpe EPPr EPyc SDys SMrm SPin XSen
§	- 'Black and Blue'	CCon CExl CHel CRHN CWGN EBee ECre ECtt EPfP EPyc EUJe GCal GGal LRHS MBri SDys SMrm SPin SVen WHea WPGP WSHC XSen
	- 'Blue Enigma' 🏆H4	CAby CArn CBod CExl CSpe CWGN EBee ECha ECtt ELan EPfP EWoo GCal IGor LRHS MAsh MGos MRav SDix SDys SMrm SPin WHea XLum XSen
	- 'Costa Rica Blue'	EPyc SDys
	- 'Indigo Blue'	ECtt EPfP MAsh SPin
	- 'Omaha'	SPin
	- 'Omaha Gold' (v)	EPyc
	- 'Purple Splendor'	MHer
	- purple-flowered	CSam SDys
	haematodes	see *S. pratensis* Haematodes Group
	haenkei	CElw SPin XSen
	- 'Prawn Chorus'	CSpe MAsh WOth
	hayatae	SPin
	heerii	SPin
	heldreichiana	SPin XSen
	henryi	SPin
	hians	CPom EWld EWoo GCal GCra SRms XLum
	- CC 1787	CExl
	hierosolymitana	CHid XSen
	hirtella	SPin
	hispanica misapplied	see *S. lavandulifolia*
	hispanica L.	CSam SPin
	holwayi	EPyc SPin
	horminum	see *S. viridis* var. *comata*
	huberi	XSen
	hydrangea	SPin
	hypargeia	XSen
	'Ice Blue'	MHom
	inconspicua	SPin
	indica	EWld XSen
	'Indigo Spires'	CAby CExl CHll CSam CSpe CWGN ECre ECtt EPfP EPyc EShb IMou MAsh MCot NDov SDys SMrm SPhx SPin WOth WSHC XLum XSen
	interrupta	EWld MCot MHer SPin WHea XSen
	involucrata 🏆H3	CAby CCon EPyc EWld GCra MCot MHom NBro SDys SPin SVen WHil WSHC XSen
	- 'Bethellii' 🏆H3	CArn CBod CCon CHel CMHG ECtt ELan EPfP EPyc EWoo LRHS MAsh MHer SBod SDix SDys SKHP SMrm SPin SRkn WGrn WKif WOth XLum
	- 'Boutin' 🏆H3	EPyc MAsh MHom SDys
§	- 'Hadspen'	CCon CDes CHll CRHN CSam CSpe EPyc EWes GCal SBch SPin WOut XLum
	- 'Mrs Pope'	see *S. involucrata* 'Hadspen'
	- 'Pink Icicles'	SDys
*	- var. ***puberula***	MHom SPin
	involucrata* × *wagneriana new	SDys
	iodantha	SPin
	- 'Louis Saso'	SPin
	iodochroa B&SWJ 10252	SPin WCru
	× ***jamensis***	ELau EWes MAsh SPin
	- 'Blue Amor'	MPkF
	- 'California Sunset'	MAsh SDys
	- 'Dark Dancer'	CAby MAsh SDys SPhx WHil XSen
	- 'Desert Blaze' (v)	CAby CMos CWGN ECtt EPfP EPyc LRHS MCot MHer SDys SMrm SPin WGrn WPGP XLum
	- 'Devantville'	NDov XLum
	- 'Dysons' Orangy Pink'	CSpe NDov SDys
	- 'Flammenn'PBR	LRHS MPkF SHil
§	- 'Hot Lips'	Widely available
	- 'James Compton'	EPyc SIgm SMrm
	- 'Javier'	SDys SPin WHil
	- 'Kentish Pink'	EPyc SDys
	- 'La Luna'	CPrp CSam CSpe ECtt EPyc MAsh MCot MHer MRav NDov SPin WOth WPGP WSHC XLum XSen
	- 'La Siesta'	EPyc MAsh XSen
	- 'La Tarde'	CTri EPyc MAsh MHom XSen
	- 'Los Lirios' 🏆H5	CSpe CTri EPyc GGal SPin WHil WOth

	- 'Maraschino'	EPfP EPyc LRHS MAsh SDys SPin SRms WHil WMnd XLum XSen
	- 'Melen'[PBR]	LRHS MBri SPin
	- 'Moonlight Over Ashwood' (v)	EPyc MAsh SPin WSHC
	- 'Moonlight Serenade'	CAby EPyc MAsh SDys
	- 'Nachtvlinder'	CAby CDes CSpe EPyc ETwe MCot NDov SDys SPhx SPin WHil WSHC
§	- 'Pat Vlasto'	EPyc SPin
	- 'Peter Vidgeon'	CDes CWGN EPfP EPyc LRHS MAsh MCot SDys SPhx SPin SPoG WSHC
	- 'Pleasant Pink'	EPyc MAsh XSen
	- 'Pluenn'[PBR]	LRHS MPkF SHil
	- 'Raspberry Royale' ♀[H5]	CPom CWld ECtt EPfP EPyc LRHS MAsh MHer SDys SMrm SPin WMnd WSHC XLum XSen
	- 'Red Velvet'	CAby EBee ECtt EPyc GGal MAsh MCot MHom SDys SPhx WHil WHrl WSHC XSen
	- 'Señorita Leah'	CWGN EPyc MAsh MCot NDov SDys WHil
§	- 'Sierra San Antonio'	CDes CPom EPPr EPfP EPyc LRHS MAsh MHom NDov SDys SMrm WHil WPGP XLum XSen
	- 'Stormy Sunrise'	EPyc SDys
§	- 'Trebah'	CAby CSpe ECre EPyc EWoo LRHS MAsh MCot MHom SDys SPin SPoG SRot WHea WHil WKif WSHC XSen
	- 'Trenance'	CSpe ECre ELon EPyc LRHS MHer MHom SPin SRot WHil XSen
§	***japonica***	SPin
	- 'Alba'	SPin
	'Jean's Purple Passion'	EPyc SDys SPin
	'Jezebel' **new**	SDys
	'Joan'	CWGN EPyc MAsh SDys SPin WHil WSHC
	judaica	CMac SPin WGrn XSen
	jurisicii	EPfP EPyc LRHS SBrt SEND SPav SPin WHea WJek XLum XSen
	- 'Alba'	XSen
	- pink-flowered	CSpe SPin XSen
	karwinskyi	SDys SPin
	karwinskyi* × *univerticillata **new**	SDys
	keerlii	SPin
	koyamae	MBri SPin
	- B&SWJ 10919	WCru
	kronenburgii	XSen
	'Lady Strybing'	SPin
	'Lalarsha'	CElw EPyc MCot NDov SDys
	lanceolata	CSpe EPyc SPin WHil
	languidula **new**	SPin
	lasiantha	SPin
§	***lavandulifolia***	CArn EAJP EBee ECho ELan EPfP EWes GPoy LRHS MAsh MHer MLHP MNHC MRav SMrm SPer SPin SRms WHoo WJek WKif WOut XLum XSen
§	- subsp. ***blancoana***	ECha ELau EPyc MHer SPin WHea XSen
	- subsp. ***gallica*** **new**	XSen
	- subsp. ***pyrenaeorum***	XSen
	- 'Roquefure' **new**	XSen
	- subsp. ***vellerea***	XSen
	lavanduloides	SPin
	lemmonii	see *S. microphylla* var. *wislizeni*
	'Lemon Pie'	SPin WHlf
	leptophylla	see *S. reptans*
	leucantha ♀[H2]	CArn CSpe ECre ELan EPyc MAsh MCot MHer MOWG MRav MSCN SPin SPlb SRkn SVen WOth XSen
	- Danielle's Dream = 'Ferpink'	SPin
	- 'Eder' (v)	MAsh SDys SPin
	- 'Midnight'	CSam
	- 'Purple Velvet'	CAby ECtt EPyc MAsh MHer MHom SDix SDys SPin WHea
	- 'San Marcos Lavender'	EPyc SPin
	- 'Santa Barbara'	CDes CHll MAsh SDys WPGP
	- 'White Mischief'	SPin
	leucocephala	CPne EPyc SDys SPin
	leucophylla	XSen
	- NNS 01-375	SPin
	limbata	XSen
	littae	SDys SPin
	longispicata	SPin
	longistyla	CFil SDys SPin SVen WPGP
	lycioides misapplied	see *S. greggii* × *serpyllifolia*
	lycioides A. Gray	CAbP CHll EPyc LRHS SDys SEND SPhx SPin
	lyrata	XSen
	- 'Burgundy Bliss'	see *S. lyrata* 'Purple Knockout'
§	- 'Purple Knockout'	EPfP LRHS SPin XSen
	- 'Purple Vulcano'	see *S. lyrata* 'Purple Knockout'
	macellaria misapplied	see *S. microphylla*
	macellaria Epling	CSam
	macrophylla	GCal SDys SPin WPGP
	- Cally selection	SPin
	- purple-leaved **new**	SDys
	- upright	CSpe WHil
	- 'Wendy's Surprise'	CBod SDys
	macrosiphon	SPin
	'Madeline'[PBR]	CBod CMos CWGN EPfP GBin IBoy LBMP LRHS LSou MBri SPer SPin STPC WHlf
	madrensis	EPyc SDys SPin
	- 'Dunham'	GCal WHea
	'Magic Potion'	CWGN
	mellifera	CArn SPin XSen
	mexicana	SPin
	- B&SWJ 10288	WCru
	- 'Limelight'	EPyc
	- var. ***minor***	EPyc EWld SDys SPin
	meyeri	EPyc GGal MHom SPin WHil
	- CDPR 3071	WPGP
I	***miahuatlanensis***	SPin
§	***microphylla***	CArn CBod CMHG CMac CPom CPrp CTri ELau EWes LAst MHer SVen WHea WOut XLum
	- CD&R 1141	SPin
	- 'Belize'	CPrp MAsh SBri WHil
	- 'Cerro Potosi'	CElw CPrp CSpe EPyc LBMP MAsh MCot MHer SDys SPhx SPin WCFE WHil XLum
	- 'Hot Lips'	see *S.* × *jamensis* 'Hot Lips'
	- 'Huntington'	EPyc SPin XSen
	- 'Kew Red' ♀[H4]	CCon CHVG MNrw SPin WHil WHoo WPGP
	- 'La Trinidad'	XSen
I	- 'Lutea'	MAsh SDys
	- 'Maroon'	EPyc SDys
	- 'Mauve'	EPyc NDov
§	- var. ***microphylla***	CRHN CTri ECtt ELan ENfk EPyc EWoo MBri MCot MHer MNHC MRav SEND SPin SRkn WHfH WJek XLum XSen

Name	Suppliers
- - 'La Foux'	EPyc MCot SMrm SPhx XSen
- - 'Newby Hall' ♀H4	CDes CPom ECtt EPyc EShb EWes EWoo SPhx WPGP XSen
- var. ***neurepia***	see *S. microphylla* var. *microphylla*
- 'Orange Door'	EPyc SDys XSen
- orange-red-flowered	MRav
- 'Oregon Peach'	EPfP LRHS
- 'Oxford'	SPin
§ - 'Pink Blush' ♀H4	CAby EABi ECtt ELan EPfP EPyc LRHS MAsh MCot MHer MHom MNHC MSpe SEND SMrm SPin SRkn WHil WHoo WKif WPGP WSHC XSen
- 'Pleasant View' ♀H4	EPyc WHil XSen
- 'Ribambelle'	MAsh XLum
- 'Robin's Pride'	EPyc SDys WHil
- 'Rodbaston Red'	WHil
- 'Rosy Cheeks'	WOut
- 'San Carlos Festival'	EPyc MAsh NCGa NDov SBch SDys SPhx SPin WHil WPGP XSen
- 'Trelawny Rose Pink'	see *S.* 'Trelawney'
- 'Trelissick Creamy Yellow'	see *S.* 'Trelissick'
- 'Trewithen Cerise'	see *S.* 'Trewithen'
- 'Violette'	EPyc
- 'Wild Watermelon'	CWGN EBee EPyc MAsh MCot SDys WGrn WHil XSen
§ - var. ***wislizeni***	CElw EPyc SPhx
- 'Zaragoza'	SPin
microstegia	XSen
miltiorhiza	CArn MMuc SPin WOut XLum XSen
miniata	EPyc SPin
misella	SPin
'Miss Elly' **new**	MTis
mocinoi	SPin
mohavensis	XSen
moorcroftiana	EPyc SPin WHea
moschata	SPin
'Mrs Beard'	XSen
muelleri misapplied	see *S. greggii* × *serpyllifolia*
muelleri ambig.	NDov WWFP
muelleri Epling	EPyc
muirii	SPin
'Mulberry Jam'	CAby CHGN CHll CSam CSpe ECtt EPfP EPyc EWes MAsh MCot MHom SDys SPin SRkn WKif WOth WSHC
§ ***multicaulis*** ♀H3	EPyc MAsh SPin XSen
munzii	SDys SPin
* ***murrayi***	SPin
Mystic Spires Blue = 'Balsalmisp'[PBR]	CSpe CWGN EPfP NDov SCob SPin SPoG
namaensis	SPin WHil
nana B&SWJ 10272	SPin
napifolia	EBee EWTr LPot LRHS MMuc NLar SPav SPin XSen
- 'Baby Blue'	EBee
'Nazareth'	SPin XSen
nemorosa	EPyc SPin SRms XLum XSen
- 'Amethyst' ♀H7	CBod EBee ELon EPfP GQue IKil LPot LRHS MBel MBri MHol MPie MRav MSpe MTis NDov SMHy SMrm SPhx SPin SRms WCAu WCot WHoo WKif WWEG XSen
- Blue Mound	see *S.* × *sylvestris* 'Blauhügel'
- 'Caradonna' ♀H7	Widely available
- East Friesland	see *S. nemorosa* 'Ostfriesland'
- 'Experimental Pink' **new**	LRHS
- 'Experimental Rose Compact' **new**	LRHS
- 'Experimental White' **new**	LRHS
- 'Lubecca' ♀H7	ECtt EPfP EPla LRHS MAsh MCot MSpe MTis NDov NEgg NGdn NLar SPer WFar WMnd WWEG XSen
- Lyrical Silvertone = 'Balyricsil' **new**	CBod
- Marcus = 'Haeumanarc'[PBR]	EBee ECtt ELan EPfP EUJe LAst LRHS MBNS MBri MRav NDov NLar SDys SPoG WFar WHrl WSHC
- 'New Dimension Blue'	EPfP
- 'New Dimension Rose'	EBee
§ - 'Ostfriesland' ♀H7	Widely available
- 'Pink Beauty'	MWat
- 'Pink Friesland'[PBR]	CAby ECtt ELon EPfP GBin GMaP GQue LRHS LSou MGos MSpe NDov NSti SPoG WCAu
- 'Plumosa'	see *S. nemorosa* 'Pusztaflamme'
- 'Porzellan' ♀H7	ECtt
§ - 'Pusztaflamme' ♀H7	EBee ECha ECtt EPfP GQue LRHS LSou MRav MSpe NOrc WWEG XSen
- 'Rose Queen'	CBod ELon GMaP LAst MWat NBir SPhx SWat WCot WFar XLum XSen
- 'Rosenwein'	LRHS NGdn SGbt SMrm SPhx XSen
- 'Royal Distinction'	CBod ECtt
- 'Schneekönig'	LSou
- 'Schwellenburg'	CMea ECGP ECtt GBin GBuc GQue LSou MHol NLar WCot WMnd XSen
I - (Sensation Series) 'Sensation Blue Improved'	LRHS
- - 'Sensation Blue'	MBri
- - 'Sensation Deep Blue'	EBee ELon LRHS SHil STPC
I - - 'Sensation Deep Rose Improved'	IBoy LRHS MBel SPoG
- - 'Sensation Rose'	LAst LBMP LLHF LRHS LSou MBri SHar SHil SMrm
- - 'Sensation Sky Blue'	LRHS
- - 'Sensation White'	CWGN MHol
§ - subsp. ***tesquicola***	CBod EPyc LRHS MWhi NGdn SMrm SPhx WFar
- 'Wesuwe'	ELon NDov XSen
neurepia	see *S. microphylla* var. *microphylla*
* ***nevadensis***	SPin
nilotica	SPin XSen
nipponica	GEdr SBrt
- B&SWJ 5829	SPin WCru
- 'Fuji Snow' (v)	EBee MBri
- var. ***trisecta***	SPin
nubicola	CExl GPoy SPin WHil XSen
- CC 4607	EBee
- CC 4762	NLar
'Nuchi'	SPin
nutans	CHVG SBrt SPin XSen
officinalis	Widely available
- 'Albiflora'	CArn CBod SPin WJek XSen
- 'Aurea' ambig.	ECho GPoy
- 'Berggarten' ♀H4	CArn CBod ECha ELau EPla GBin GCal LEdu MCot MHer MRav SDix SPhx SPin WHer WJek XLum XSen
- 'Bicolor' **new**	SPin
§ - broad-leaved	CUse ELau MHer SWat WJek
- 'Crispa'	SPin XSen
- 'Extrakta'	GCal SPhx
- 'Grete Stolze'	SEND XSen
- 'Grower's Friend'	CTsd LAst LBMP
§ - 'Icterina' (v) ♀H4	Widely available

- ***latifolia***	see *S. officinalis* broad-leaved
- narrow-leaved	see *S. lavandulifolia*
- 'Nazareth'PBR	ELau WJek XSen
- ***prostrata***	see *S. lavandulifolia*
- 'Purpurascens' 🏆H5	Widely available
- 'Robin Hill'	EPla LSou
- 'Rosea'	CArn WJek XSen
- 'Tricolor' (v)	CBcs CBod CTri EBee ECho ELan ENfk EPfP GPoy LAst LBMP MAsh MBri MHer MNHC MRav NPri SGol SPer SPin SPoG SRms WHar WHil WJek XSen
- 'Variegata'	see *S. officinalis* 'Icterina'
- variegated (v)	ECho MHer
- 'Würzburg'	XSen
ombrophila	SPin
omeiana	SBrt
- BWJ 8062	SPin WCru
- 'Crûg Thundercloud'	WCru
oppositiflora misapplied	see *S. tubiflora*
oppositiflora ambig.	EPyc SDys SPin WPGP
orbignaei	SPin
'Out of the Mist'	WOut
oxyphora	EPyc SDys SPin
pachyphylla	LRHS SPhx SPin XSen
'Pakhuis Pass'	SPin
palaestina	XSen
pallida	EPyc SPin
'Pam's Purple'	MAsh
§ ***patens*** 🏆H4	Widely available
- 'Alba' misapplied	see *S. patens* 'White Trophy'
- 'Blue Angel'	CHel EPfP EWes MPie NSoo WGrn
- 'Cambridge Blue' 🏆H3	CBod CExl CPrp CSpe CWGN EBee ECtt ELan EPfP EWoo LRHS MAsh MCot MHer MMuc MPie MRav MSpe NLar NPer SDys SEND SIgm SPer SPhx SPin WOth WSHC
- 'Chilcombe'	EPyc MHer SDys SPin WOut
- 'Dot's Delight'	CBod CExl CHel CSpe ECtt EWes LRHS MAsh MHol NCGa SDys SHar SMrm SPer
- 'Guanajuato'	CBcs CExl CSam ECtt EPyc EWes EWoo MAsh MBel MCot MHer NLar SDys SMad SMrm SPad SPin SRot WHil WOut WSHC
- large	CSpe
- 'Lavender Ice' **new**	WOut
- light blue-flowered	LRHS
- 'Oxford Blue'	see *S. patens*
- (Patio Series) 'Patio Deep Blue'	CHel CWGN EPfP SPoG
- - 'Patio Sky Blue'	CHel
- 'Pink Ice'	EPyc SDys WOut
- pink-flowered	SPin
- 'Royal Blue'	see *S. patens*
§ - 'White Trophy'	CExl ECtt ELan EPyc EWld LRHS SDys SMrm SPer SPin
pauciserrata	SPin
pennellii	SPin
'Penny's Smile'	CAby ELon EPyc LRHS MAsh MBri SDys SPhx SPin SPoG WGrn WHil WHoo
'Peru Blue'	CSpe EPyc SDys
'Peter Vider'	EPfP
'Phyllis' Fancy'	CAby CSam CSde CSpe EPyc MAsh MHer NDov SDys SPlb WSHC XSen
pinguifolia	SPin
'Pink Icing'	SPin
pinnata	SPin
pisidica	SPin XSen
plectranthoides	SPin
pogonochila	XSen
polystachya	SPin XSen
- B&SWJ 8985	WCru
* 'Powis Castle'	MHom
pratensis	CArn ELan EPfP EPyc GJos MHer MNHC SPin WCot WHer WOut XSen
§ - Bertolonii Group	EPyc SPin XSen
- 'Dear Anja'	see *S.* × *sylvestris* 'Dear Anja'
§ - Haematodes Group 🏆H7	ELan EPyc MNrw SPin SRms
- 'Indigo' 🏆H7	CDes CMos ECtt ELon GMaP LRHS LSou MCot MRav NEgg NLar SPhx SPin SPoG WCot WMnd WPGP
- 'Lapis Lazuli'	EBee EPyc EWes
- 'Pink Delight'PBR	CMos EBee ECtt EPfP LRHS NDov NLar SMrm SPoG
- 'Rose Rhapsody' (Ballet Series)	CPom EBee EPPr EPfP EPyc EWTr SPhx XSen
- 'Rosea'	ECha SPin
- 'Swan Lake' (Ballet Series)	EBee EPPr EPyc NLar SPhx SPin SPlb XSen
- 'Sweet Esmeralda' (Ballet Series)	EBee EPyc NGdn NLar SPhx WOut XSen
- 'Twilight Serenade' (Ballet Series)	CBod EBee ECtt EPfP EPyc IPot SPhx XSen
- 'White Swan'	MCot
pratensis* × *transylvanica	GJos
procurrens	EBee EPyc SPin XSen
przewalskii	CCon CExl EBee EPyc LRHS SPin XSen
- ACE 1157	WCru
- BWJ 7920	SPin WCru
pulchella	SPin
'Purple Majesty'	CAby CHll CSam ECtt EPyc SDys SMrm SPin SRkn WKif XLum
'Purple Queen'	CAbP CAby EBee EPyc LRHS LSou MCot SDys SPoG WHil
purpurea	LBMP SPin
quitensis **new**	SPin
radula	EPyc SPin
ranzaniana	SPin XSen
raymondii subsp. ***mairanae***	SPin
recognita	LRHS SPin WSHC XSen
recurva	SPin
'Red Swing' **new**	NSti SPoG
reflexa	SPin
regeliana misapplied	see *S. virgata* Jacq.
regeliana Trautv.	NBir
regla	EPyc MAsh SDys SPin WPGP XSen
- 'Jame'	SPin
- 'Royal'	SPin
repens	EPyc SPin XSen
§ ***reptans***	EPyc SBrt SPin XSen
- from western Texas	MPie SDys WCot
retinervia	SPin
rhinosima	EPyc
ringens	SPin XSen
riparia misapplied	see *S. rypara*
roborowskii	SPin
§ ***roemeriana***	CSpe ELon EPyc IFoB SBrt WHea WPGP
- 'Bordeaux Steel Blue'	LRHS SRms
- 'Hot Trumpets'	LRHS

	'Rolando'	SDys SPin
§	***roscida***	SPin
	'Rose Queen' ambig.	MSCN WMnd
	rosifolia	XSen
	'Royal Bumble'	CAby CMos CSpe ECtt ELon EPfP EPyc EShb EWoo IBoy IPot LRHS MAsh MBri MCot NCGa NDov NPri SDys SPhx SVen WHil WHoo WOut WPGP XLum XSen
	'Royal Crimson Distinction'PBR	EBee ECtt EPPr LSou MBri
	rubescens	SPin
	rubiginosa	SPin
	runcinata	EPyc SPin
	rutilans	see *S. elegans* 'Scarlet Pineapple'
§	***rypara***	CPom SPin
	sagittata	CSpe EPyc GCal SPin WOut
	'Salmon Dance' **new**	CWGN
	sanctae-luciae **new**	SPin
	'Savannah Purple' (Savannah Series)	SRot
	- 'Savannah Red'	EPfP
	- 'Savannah Salmon Rose'	SRot
	scabra	EPyc SPin WOut XSen
	schlechteri	SPin
	sclarea	CArn CBod CHby ECtt ENfk GPoy LRHS MHer MHol MNHC SPin SRms WHfH WJek XLum XSen
	- 'Mojito'	MHol
	- var. ***turkestanica*** hort.	CSpe CUse EAJP ECha ECtt ELan EPfP EWTr EWoo LRHS LSun MCot MRav MSpe NEgg NGdn SEND SPav SPer SPhx SPtp SRkn SWat WBrk WKif WMnd XSen
	- var. ***turkestaniana*** Mottet	SPtp
§	- 'Vatican White'	CNor CSpe EAJP EBee ELan LRHS MNHC MSpe SMrm SPhx SPtp WJek XSen
	- white-bracted	SPin SWvt
	scutellarioides	SPin
	semiatrata misapplied	see *S. chamaedryoides*
	semiatrata ambig.	EPyc
	semiatrata Zucc.	CSpe SPin
	serboana	WPGP
	- B&SWJ 10236	WCru
	'Serenade'	MTis NDov SPhx
	serpyllifolia	SPin XSen
	- white-flowered	SPin
	sessei	SPin
	setulosa	SPin
	'Shame'	NCGa NDov
	'Shell Dancer' **new**	MBri
	'Silas Dyson'	CAby CFil CSam CSpe ECre ECtt EPfP EPyc IPot LRHS MBel MHom NDov SBch SDys SPhx SPin SPoG WHil WPGP
	'Silke's Dream'	CAby CDes CFil CPom CSam ECtt EPfP EPyc LRHS MAsh SDys SPin SPoG WPGP XSen
	sinaloensis	MAsh SPin
	smithii	SPin
	'Smoke' **new**	SDys
	'Snow Cushion' **new**	LRHS
	somalensis	CHVG SPin SVen
	'Southern Belle'	SDys SPin
	spathacea ♀H4	SBrt SPin WOut
	- 'Avis Keedy'	SPin
	splendens	SPin
	- 'Dancing Flame' (v)	EPyc
	- 'Helen Dillon'	CSpe EPyc SPin
	- 'Jimi's Good Red'	CSpe SDys WOth
	- 'Red Indian'	SDys
	- 'São Borja'	SDys
	- 'Vanguard'	LAst NPri
§	- 'Van-Houttei' ♀H3	ECre EPyc EWld SDys SVen
	- 'Vista Purple'	LAst
	sprucei	SPin
	squalens	SPin
	stachydifolia	EPyc SPin WHil WPGP
§	***staminea***	SPin
	stenophylla	SPin XSen
	'Stephanie'	EPyc SDys SPin
	stepposa	SPin
	stolonifera	CAby CSam EPyc MAsh SDys SPin WPGP
	striata	EPyc SPin WHil
	- red-flowered	SPin
	styphelus	SDys SPin
	subpalmatinervis	SPin
	subrotunda	EPyc SDys SPin
	'Sunset Strip' **new**	SDys
	× ***superba***	CSBt EBee ECha ECtt ELan EPfP EPla EPyc LRHS MWat NDov SDix SRms WCAu WGwG WHar WHoo
	- 'Adora Blue'	LRHS
	- 'Adrian'	EBee ECtt EPfP LRHS LSou MSpe MWat SPoG WCAu WCot
	- 'Merleau'	LRHS
	- 'Merleau Pink' **new**	LRHS
	- 'Merleau Rose'	EBee LPot MRav SRms
*	- 'Rosea'	EBee
	- 'Rubin' ♀H7	ECtt MBNS NBre SMrm
I	- 'Superba'	ECtt MRav SMrm SPhx SRkn
	× ***sylvestris***	SPin
§	- 'Blauhügel' ♀H7	CSam ECha ECtt ELan EPfP EPla LRHS LSou MArl MRav MSpe NDov NLar NPri SBod SHil SMrm SPhx WCAu WHoo WMnd WOth WWEG XSen
§	- 'Blaukönigin'	CNor ELon EPfP GBin GMaP LAst LRHS MWat NGBl NLar SPer SPlb SPoG SRms SWvt WCot WWEG XSen
	- Blue Queen	see *S.* × *sylvestris* 'Blaukönigin'
§	- 'Dear Anja'	EBee IPot LPla LSou MAvo MTis NDov NLar SPhx
	- 'Lye End'	MRav MWat WCot
§	- 'Mainacht' ♀H7	Widely available
	- May Night	see *S.* × *sylvestris* 'Mainacht'
	- 'Negrito'	EBee ECtt ELon GQue NGdn NLar SMrm XSen
	- 'Rhapsody in Blue'PBR	CAbP GBin LRHS MBNS MBri MHol MTis NLar
	- 'Rose Queen'	ECha ECtt ELan ELon EPfP EPla LRHS MBel MHol MJak MRav NGBl NOrc SCoo SPer SPhx SPoG SWvt WHar WWEG XSen
	- 'Rügen'	ELon GMaP GQue XSen
	- 'Schneehügel'	CMac CSBt EBee ECha ECtt EHoe ELan ELon EPPr EPfP EPla GMaP LRHS MBNS MRav MSpe MTis NLar NPri NSoo SHil SMrm SPer WCAu WHil WMnd WWEG XSen
	- 'Superba'	GBuc
	- 'Tänzerin' ♀H7	EBee ECtt ELon LPla LRHS MTis NDov NLar XSen

- 'Viola Klose'	CBod EAEE EBee ECha ECtt ELan EPla GBuc LRHS MBri MCot MSpe NCGa NDov NGdn NLar NSti SRms WAul XSen
tachiei hort.	see *S. forsskaolii*
taraxacifolia	SPin XSen
tesquicola	see *S. nemorosa* subsp. *tesquicola*
thymoides	SPin WHil
tianschanica	SPin
tiliifolia	SPav SPin SRms WHea
tingitana	SPin XSen
tomentosa	SPin XSen
tortuosa	COtt SPin
transcaucasica	see *S. staminea*
transsylvanica	GAbr IMou MSpe SMrm SPav SPhx SPin XSen
- 'Baumgartenii'	WHfH
- 'Blue Spire'	CMea MCot MWhi SRkn
'Trebah Lilac White'	see *S. × jamensis* 'Trebah'
§ 'Trelawney'	EPPr EPla EPyc LRHS MHom SRot WOth XSen
§ 'Trelissick'	CBod CMea CWld EPPr EPyc LRHS MAsh MCot MHom SDys SEND SPin SRkn SRot WHea WHil
§ 'Trewithen'	CBod CExl CMea ECre EPyc EWoo LRHS MHom MWat SPin SRot WHil WOut XSen
trijuga	EPyc SPin WOut
triloba	see *S. fruticosa*
tubifera	SPin
§ ***tubiflora*** ♀H2	EPyc MAsh SPin
uliginosa ♀H4	Widely available
- 'African Skies'	CChe IPot LRHS SPin
- 'Ballon Azul'	CSam CSpe MAsh SDys WHil WSHC
'Ultra Violet' new	WHlf
univerticillata	SPin
urica	SPin
- short	SDys
'Valerie'	CAby EPyc SDys
'Van-Houttei'	see *S. splendens* 'Van-Houttei'
variana	SPin
'Vatican City'	see *S. sclarea* 'Vatican White'
verbenaca	CArn EPyc MHer SPin WOut XSen
- pink-flowered	SPhx
verticillata	EPfP EPyc LEdu LRHS NLar SPin XSen
§ - 'Alba'	CAbP EBee ECtt EPfP EPla GJos GQue LRHS MRav MTis NGdn NLar SPer SPin WAul WCAu XSen
- 'Hannay's Blue'	EPPr EPyc MAvo SMrm
- 'Hannay's Purple'	ECtt EPPr
- 'Purple Rain'	Widely available
- 'Smouldering Torches'	EBee LPla MTis NDov SPhx
- 'White Rain'	see *S. verticillata* 'Alba'
villicaulis	see *S. amplexicaulis*
'Violin Music' new	CWGN
§ ***virgata*** Jacq.	EBee SPin XSen
viridis	CBod CHby CUse MNHC SPin
§ - var. ***comata***	MCot WJek
- 'Marble Arch Blue' (Marble Arch Series)	CSpe
- var. ***viridis***	WHrl
viscosa ambig.	EPyc
viscosa Jacq.	SPin WHil XSen
vitifolia	CSpe EPyc SDys
- B&SWJ 10236	SPin
wagneriana	SPin
'Waverly'	EPyc EWld MAsh MCot MHer SDys
'Wendy's Wish'	CAby CMos CSam EBee ECtt EPyc LSou MAsh MCot MHol NLar NPri SDys SPin SPoG SRkn WHil
× ***westerae***	SPin
- 'Petra'	SDys
willeana new	SPin
xalapensis	SPin
yunnanensis	SPin
- BWJ 7874	WCru
aff. ***yunnanensis***	SPin

Salvinia (*Salviniaceae*)

natans	LLWG MSKA

Sambucus ✿ (*Adoxaceae*)

adnata	SDix
caerulea	see *S. nigra* subsp. *caerulea*
callicarpa	NLar WCot
coraensis	see *S. williamsii* subsp. *coreana*
ebulus	EPPr LEdu NSti SMad WCot WWtn
formosana	WCot
gaudichaudiana	ECou
* ***himalayensis***	WCot
mexicana B&SWJ 10349	WCot WCru
miquelii	WCot
nigra	CArn CBcs CCVT CDul ECrN EPom GPoy IBoy LBuc NHed NWea SEWo SPer WMou WSFF
- 'Albomarginata'	see *S. nigra* 'Marginata'
- 'Albovariegata' (v)	CMac WCot WMoo
- 'Ardwall'	CAgr GCal WCot
- 'Aurea'	CBcs CDul CMac CSBt ELan EPom MRav NHed NWea SPer WCot WMoo
- 'Aureomarginata' (v)	ECrN ELan EPPr LPot MRav NLar WCot
- 'Bradet'	CAgr NLar WCot
- 'Cae Rhos Lligwy'	CAgr WCot WHer
§ - subsp. ***caerulea***	WCot
- subsp. ***canadensis***	CDul
- - 'Adams' (F)	WCot
- - 'Aurea'	WCot WHar
- - 'Goldfinch'	MAsh
- - 'John's'	CAgr WCot
- - 'Maxima'	SMad WCot
- - 'Rubra'	WCot
- - 'York' (F)	CAgr WCot
- 'Castledean'	WCot
- 'Dolomite' (v)	WCot
- 'Donau'	CAgr WCot
- 'Frances' (v)	EPPr WCot
- 'Franzi'	CAgr WCot
- 'Fructu Luteo'	NLar WCot
- 'Godshill' (F)	CAgr SDea WCot
- 'Haschberg'	CAgr WCot
- 'Heterophylla'	see *S. nigra* 'Linearis'
- 'Hillier's Dwarf'	WCot
- 'Ina'	CAgr WCot
- 'Körsör' (F)	NLar WCot
- f. ***laciniata*** ♀H6	CBcs CDul EBee ELan EPPr EPfP GCal LPot LRHS MBlu MMuc MRav NLar NWea SDix SLon SPer SPoG WCFE WCot WFar WPGP WPat
§ - 'Linearis'	ELan MGil NLar WCot
- 'Long Tooth'	CDul WCot
- 'Lutea Punctata'	WCot
- 'Madonna' (v)	CMac LEdu MBlu MBri MGos MRav NLar NPol NSbr SMad SPer WCot

§	- 'Marginata' (v)	CDul EHoe MHer MRav SDix SPoG WCot WFar
	- 'Marion Bull' (v)	CDul NLar WCot
I	- 'Marmorata'	NLar WCot
	- 'Mint Julep'	WCot
I	- 'Monstrosa'	WCot
	- 'Nana'	WCot
	- 'Naomi'	WCot
	- 'Norfolk Speckled' (v)	WCot
	- 'Pingo Trail'	WCot
	- 'Plena' (d)	WCot
	- f. ***porphyrophylla*** 'Black Beauty'PBR	see *S. nigra* f. *porphyrophylla* 'Gerda'
	- - 'Black Lace'PBR	see *S. nigra* f. *porphyrophylla* 'Eva'
	- - 'Black Tower'	CHid CSBt CWSG ELon EPfP GBin MAsh MBri MMHG MPkF MWat NSoo SPer SPoG WCot WFar WMoo
§	- - 'Eva'PBR ♀H6	Widely available
§	- - 'Gerda'PBR ♀H6	Widely available
§	- - 'Guincho Purple'	CBcs CDul CMac CTri ELan EPPr EPfP EWTr LRHS MHer MRav NLar NWea SGol SPlb WCot WFar WMoo
	- - 'Purple Pete'	CDul WCot
	- - 'Thundercloud' ♀H6	CDul CMHG ECrN ELon EPPr EWes GBin GCal MAsh MMHG MNrw NChi NEoE NLar SPhx WCot WFar WMoo
	- 'Pulverulenta' (v)	EPPr GCal MRav NLar NSbr WCot
	- 'Purpurea'	see *S. nigra* f. *porphyrophylla* 'Guincho Purple'
	- 'Pyramidalis'	MRav WCot
	- 'Riese aus Vossloch'	WCot
	- 'Robert Piggin' (v)	WCot
	- var. ***rotundifolia***	WCot
	- 'Sambu' (F)	CAgr WCot
	- 'Samdal' (F)	CAgr WCot
	- 'Samidan' (F)	CAgr WCot
	- 'Samnor' (F)	CAgr WCot
	- 'Sampo' (F)	CAgr WCot
	- 'Samyl' (F)	CAgr WCot
	- 'Urban Lace'	CAgr WCot
	- 'Variegata'	see *S. nigra* 'Marginata'
	- f. ***viridis***	CAgr WCot
	- Welsh Gold = 'Walfinb' **new**	LRHS
	palmensis	WCot
	racemosa	EPfP NWea WCot
	- 'Aurea'	EHoe WFar
	- 'Crûg Lace'	WCru
	- 'Goldenlocks'	EWes NLar
	- subsp. ***kamtschatica***	WCot
	- 'Plumosa Aurea'	CBcs CSBt ELan EPfP GCra LRHS MGos MRav MSwo NLar NWea SLim WCot
	- var. ***pubens***	WCot
§	- var. ***sieboldiana***	WCot
	- 'Sutherland Gold' ♀H7	Widely available
	- 'Tenuifolia'	EPfP WCot
	- 'Welsh Gold'	MAsh
	sieboldiana	see *S. racemosa* var. *sieboldiana*
	tigranii	WCot
§	***williamsii*** subsp. ***coreana***	WCot

Samolus (*Primulaceae*)

repens	ECou
valerandi	LLWG

Sandersonia (*Colchicaceae*)

aurantiaca	ECho EPot GKev LAma SDeJ

sage see *Salvia officinalis*

sage, annual clary see *Salvia viridis*

sage, biennial clary see *Salvia sclarea*

sage, pineapple see *Salvia elegans*

Sanguinaria (*Papaveraceae*)

canadensis	CArn CAvo CBct CBro CCon CHel EBee ECho EPfP EPot GKev GPoy LAma LEdu LRHS MMuc NHol NLar NOrc NRya SDeJ SEND SMHy SPer SWat WAbe WCru WPnP WShi
- f. ***multiplex*** (d)	CLAP CTal ECho EPot GEdr IFro LRHS NBir SPhx
- - 'Plena' (d) ♀H5	CBct CBro CHel CSpe CWCL EBee ECho ELon EPfP GBin GBuc GCra GKev GPoy LRHS MAvo MNrw NHar NHol NLar NRya NSla SDeJ SKHP SPer WAbe WCot WHil WKif WPnP

Sanguisorba ✿ (*Rosaceae*)

	from Japan **new**	MAvo
§	***albiflora***	CKno EBee ELan EShb GBuc LBMP LEdu LPla LRHS MAvo MRav NEoE NGdn SEND SMrm SPhx SWat WHil WMoo WOut
	'All Time High'	NDov
	alpina **new**	GLog MMuc SEND
	applanata	MAvo WCot
	armena	CElw EBee EWes IMou MBel MNrw MPie WWtn XEll
	'Autumn Bliss'	EBee
	benthamiana	CHEx
	'Blacksmith's Burgundy'	MAvo
	'Blackthorn'	CKno EBee ECtt GMaP IKil MAvo MTis NDov NLar SMHy SPhx WCot WHoo
	'Burr Blanc'	MAvo SMHy SPhx
	canadensis	CDes CKno CMac CRow EBee ECha ECtt EPPr EPfP GCal GMaP GPoy LPla MAvo MNrw MRav NBir NLar NSti SPer SPhx SWat WCot WMoo WOld WWEG WWtn XEll
	- hybrid	MAvo
	'Cangshan Cranberry'	CDes GBin MAvo MHol MTis NDov SMHy WCot WPtf WWEG WWtn
*	***caucasica***	EWes GBee LEdu LPla SPhx
	'Chocolate Tip'	EBee ECtt IPot NBro
	dodecandra	CDes EBee IMou MAvo WPGP
	'Figaro' **new**	WCot
	hakusanensis	CCon CKno EBee GBBs GCal IFro IPot LEdu LRHS MAvo MNFA MNrw NBir NBro NChi NEoE NLar SMad WCot WFar WSHC WWEG
	- B&SWJ 8709	WCru
	- 'Lilac Squirrel'	ECtt MAvo MTis NDov NLar
	'Ivory Towers' **new**	MAvo
	'John Coke'	NLar
	magnifica	EWes GCal LEdu MAvo WCot
	- ***alba***	see *S. albiflora*
	menziesii	Widely available

- 'Dali Marble' (v)	EBee ECtt NLar SPoG WMoo WWEG
- 'Wake Up'	MAvo
§ ***minor***	CArn CHby CPrp CUse EBee ELau GPoy LEdu MHer MJak MNHC NBro NMir SIde SPhx SPlb SRms WHar WHer WHfH WJek WMoo WOut XLum
- subsp. ***minor***	CHab
obtusa	Widely available
- 'Chatto'	MAvo
- silver-leaved	MNrw
- white-flowered	EBee MAvo MMuc MTis WPGP
officinalis	CArn CHab CKno EHoe GQue MHer MNFA NEoE NMir SPer SPhx SWat WCAu WHea WMoo WOut WWEG
- CDC 262	EPPr LEdu SPhx
- CDC 282	CSpe SPhx
- CDC 292	GQue WCot
- DJHC 535 **new**	LEdu
- from Mongolia	CDes
- 'Arnhem'	CCse CKno EBee ECtt EPPr LEdu LPla LRHS MTis NDov SMHy SMrm SPhx WCot WWEG
- 'Crimson Queen'	EBee GQue MAvo MTis
- dark-flowered	MAvo
- early-flowering	CDes
- 'False Tanna'	WFar
- 'Lemon Splash' (v)	EBee LEdu MAvo WCot WFar WWEG
- 'Martin's Mulberry'	CDes EBee EWes GCal LEdu MAvo NDov WPGP
- 'Morning Select'	EBee ECtt EPPr NLar STPC
- 'Red Buttons' **new**	NDov
- 'Red Thunder'	CDes CSpe ECtt EPPr EWoo GBin IPot LEdu LPla LPot LRHS LSun MAvo MBri MTis NDov NLar NOrc WCAu WPGP WWEG
- 'Shiro-fukurin' (v)	EBee ECtt EWes GKin GMaP IKil LEdu LLWG LSun MAvo MBel MHol MSCN MTis NLar NPCo SMrm WCot WFar WHer WOut WSHC
- 'Tsetseguun'	LEdu MAvo
parviflora	see *S. tenuifolia* var. *parviflora*
pimpinella	see *S. minor*
'Pink Brushes'	ECtt GBin GQue IKil IMou IPot LPla MTis NDov NLar
'Pink September' **new**	MAvo
'Pink Tanna'	Widely available
'Raspberry Mivvi'	SPhx
'Rock and Roll'	ECtt EPPr GQue MTis NLar
sitchensis	see *S. stipulata*
§ ***stipulata***	EBee GCal LEdu LPla LRHS MAvo MHer MNrw WWEG
- var. ***riishirensis***	EBee
'Tanna'	Widely available
'Tanna' seedling	EPPr EShb
tenuifolia	CCon GCal IFro MCot NChi NLar SBHP SPhx
- var. ***alba***	CBod CKno CPrp CWCL EBee ELon EPPr EWes GJos GQue IGor IMou LRHS MAvo MBel MMuc MPie MTis NDov NEoE SEND SMrm SPhx WCot WHoo WMoo WPtf WWEG WWFP XLum
- - CDC	GCal MRav
- - 'Korean Snow'	CCse CMea GMaP LEdu LPla MAvo SMHy SMad SPhx WWEG
- 'Big Pink'	GCal MAvo MNrw
- 'Henk Gerritsen'	MAvo SPhx
§ - var. ***parviflora***	CDes EBee LEdu MAvo MNrw NLar WPGP
- 'Pink Elephant'	CKno EBee ECtt EPPr EWTr GBin GJos GQue LEdu LRHS MAvo MTis NLar SMad WCAu WMoo
- var. ***purpurea***	CDes EBee
- 'Purpurea'	CKno EBee EPPr GQue LEdu MAvo MTis SPhx WCot WPGP
- 'Stand Up Comedian'	EBee GBin IMou LEdu MAvo NDov NLar WWEG
- 'Sturdy Guard'	LEdu WWEG
- 'White Tanna'	EBee EPPr GQue MAvo MTis WWEG

Sanicula (*Apiaceae*)

europaea	CArn GPoy IMou

Santolina (*Asteraceae*)

'Apple Court'	LRHS
benthamiana	XSen
§ ***chamaecyparissus***	Widely available
- var. ***corsica***	see *S. chamaecyparissus* 'Nana'
- subsp. ***insularis***	XSen
- 'Lambrook Silver'	CDoC CFis EBee ECtt ENfk EPfP LRHS MAsh NLar SCoo SLim SPoG
- 'Lemon Queen'	CDoC ENfk EPfP EWTr LRHS MAsh MGos MNHC MSwo MWat NBir NLar SRms SWat XSen
§ - 'Nana' ΥH5	CMHG ECho EPfP LRHS MAsh MHer MNHC MRav MSwo SCob SPoG SRms SWat XSen
- 'Pretty Carroll' ΥH5	CBod EBee ECtt ELan EPfP LRHS MAsh MBri NLar WFar
- 'Small-Ness'	ECho ELan EPfP EWes LRHS MHer NLar SWvt WHer
- 'Weston'	ECho
incana	see *S. chamaecyparissus*
* ***lindavica***	XSen
pectinata	see *S. rosmarinifolia* subsp. *canescens*
pinnata	CArn CTri MHer MLHP
§ - subsp. ***neapolitana*** ΥH5	CArn CSBt EBee ECha ELan ENfk EPfP MBri MMuc MRav SDix SEND WWEG
- - cream-flowered	see *S. pinnata* subsp. *neapolitana* 'Edward Bowles'
§ - - 'Edward Bowles'	Widely available
- - 'Sulphurea'	CArn EPfP LRHS MAsh SPer SPhx WKif XSen
rosmarinifolia	CArn CDoC CDul EWTr GPoy LRHS LSun MRav SCob SEND SLon SPlb SPoG SRms
§ - subsp. ***canescens***	EPfP XSen
- 'Lemon Fizz' ΥH5	CBod COtt EHoe ELan ELon EMil ENfk EPfP GBin LBMP LRHS LSou MAsh MBri MHer NBir NLar NPri SCoo SHil SPer SPoG SRms SWvt WFar WHer WPnn
§ - subsp. ***rosmarinifolia***	ECha ELan ENfk EPfP MHer MRav NSoo SDix SIgm SPer SRms SWvt WFar WHoo XLum XSen
- - 'Primrose Gem' ΥH5	CBcs CBod CDoC CSBt CTri EAJP ECha ELon EPfP LRHS MMuc MNHC MSwo MWat NLar NPri SCob SEND SGbt SPer SRms SWvt WHoo WWEG XSen

- - white-flowered	WHer XSen
Shades of Jade = 'Sant101'	EAEE ECrN WRHF
tomentosa misapplied	see *S. pinnata* subsp. *neapolitana*
virens	see *S. rosmarinifolia* subsp. *rosmarinifolia*
viridis	see *S. rosmarinifolia* subsp. *rosmarinifolia*

Sanvitalia (*Asteraceae*)

Aztekengold = 'Starbini'PBR	LAst
procumbens 'Irish Eyes'	CSpe WHil
'Sunbini'PBR	CCCN CSpe LSou NPri

Saponaria (*Caryophyllaceae*)

× ***boissieri***	ECho EPot
'Bressingham' ♀H5	ECho ECtt GCrg MHol WAbe WIce
Bressingham hybrid	MAsh
caespitosa	ECho EDAr EPot EWes
§ ***intermedia*** new	WCot
× ***lempergii*** 'Fritz Lemperg'	NDov WCot
- 'Max Frei'	CSam EBee ELon EPPr LSou MCot MRav NDov SBch SPhx WCot WOld WSHC XLum
lutea	GKev
ocymoides ♀H5	CMea EBee ECha ECho ECtt EDAr EHon EPfP GAbr LAst MAsh MLHP MMuc MNHC MSpe SEND SPer SPlb SPoG SRms SRot XLum
- 'Alba'	EBee ECha
- 'Snow Tip'	ECho EDAr MSpe NGdn WAbe XLum
officinalis	CArn CBod CBre CPbn CWld ENfk GPoy MHer MLHP MNHC SIde SPlb SRms WHer WHfH WJek WMoo WPtf
- 'Alba Plena' (d)	CBre MMuc NLar SEND WPtf XLum
- 'Betty Arnold' (d)	CAby EBee ECtt EWes MHer WCot
§ - 'Dazzler' (v)	WWEG
- 'Flore Pleno' (d)	EAJP GAbr
- 'Rosea Plena' (d)	CAby CBre CMac ECtt ELan EPfP GCra LEdu LLWP LRHS MHer MLHP MMuc NBid NBir NGdn NOrc SCob SEND SIde SMrm SPer WGwG WHlf WMoo WPtf
- 'Rubra Plena' (d)	CPrp ELan EWes MMuc MSCN MWhi SHar WHer
- 'Variegata'	see *S. officinalis* 'Dazzler'
× ***olivana*** ♀H5	CPBP ECho ECtt EPot GCrg GMaP MAsh NLar XLum
'Rosenteppich'	CPBP
sicula subsp. ***intermedia***	see *S. intermedia*
zawadskii	see *Silene zawadskii*

Saposhnikovia (*Apiaceae*)

divaricata	CArn SPhx

Sarcandra (*Chloranthaceae*)

§ ***glabra*** f. ***flava*** new	SRms

Sarcococca ✿ (*Buxaceae*)

confusa ♀H5	Widely available
hookeriana	ELon GKin IFoB LBMP MBlu MSwo NLar NPri NWad SCob SGbt SWvt WFar WPGP
- B&SWJ 2585	WCru
- HWJK 2393	WCru
- HWJK 2428	WCru
- Sch 1160	CExl
- Sch 2396	CExl
- var. ***digyna***	Widely available
- - 'Purple Stem' ♀H5	CEnd CExl CJun CLAP CNec CTri EPfP EPla EUJe GKin LAst LRHS MGos MNrw NLar SCob SCoo SPer SPoG SWvt WCru
* - - 'Schillingii'	CJun WCru
- var. ***hookeriana***	CJun
- - GWJ 9222 new	WCru
- - GWJ 9344 new	WCru
- - GWJ 9369	WCru
- - HWJK 2102	WCru
- - HWJK 2366 new	WCru
- - HWJK 2393 new	WCru
- var. ***humilis***	Widely available
orientalis	CAbP CExl CHel CJun CLAP CMCN CRos EBee ELan ELon EPfP EPla IDee LEdu LRHS MAsh MGos NLar NWad SPoG WPGP WPat
'Roy Lancaster'	see *S. ruscifolia* var. *chinensis* 'Dragon Gate'
'Rudolph'	EPfP LLHF LRHS
ruscifolia	Widely available
- var. ***chinensis***	CJun CSam EPfP EPla SLon WCru WPGP WPat
§ - - 'Dragon Gate' ♀H5	CDoC CExl CJun CLAP CRos EBee ELan EPfP LLHF LRHS MAsh SLim SLon SPoG SWvt WCru WPGP WPat
saligna	CBcs CJun EBtc ELan EPfP LRHS MRav SLon WCot WCru WPat
- MF P2056	WCru
trinervia B&SWJ 9500	WCru
vagans B&SWJ 7285	WCru
aff. ***vagans*** B&SWJ 7265 from north Thailand new	WCru
- B&SWJ 9766 from Vietnam new	WCru
wallichii	CDoC CExl ELon LEdu MBlu SPoG WPGP WPat
- B&SWJ 2291	CJun WCru
- GWJ 9427	WCru
'Winter Gem'	LRHS MBri NHol SLon STPC
zeylanica B&SWJ 10199 new	WCru
- var. ***brevifolia*** GWJ 9480	WCru

Sarmienta (*Gesneriaceae*)

repens ♀H2	CExl CFil WAbe WPGP

Sarothamnus see *Cytisus*

Sarracenia ✿ (*Sarraceniaceae*)

× ***ahlesii***	CHew NLos
alata	CHew EECP WSSs
- from Desoto National Forest, Mississippi new	NLos
- from Robertson County, Texas new	NLos
- from Stone County, Mississippi new	NLos
- 'Black Tube' ♀H3	WSSs
- heavily veined	WSSs
- var. ***nigropurpurea*** new	WSSs
- var. ***ornata*** new	WSSs
- pubescent	EECP NLos WSSs

- - from Deer Park, Alabama **new**	NLos
- 'Red Lid'	EECP NLos WSSs
- 'Red Lid' × ***flava*** var. ***rubricorpora***	EECP NLos
- var. ***rubrioperculata*** **new**	WSSs
- wavy lid	WSSs
- white-flowered	WSSs
alata × ***flava*** **new**	NLos
alata × ***flava*** var. ***maxima***	NLos WSSs
alata × ***leucophylla*** **new**	NLos
(***alata*** red tube × ***flava*** 'Burgundy') × (***leucophylla*** × ***purpurea***)	NLos
× ***areolata***	CHew NLos WSSs
× ***catesbyi***	CHew NLos WSSs
× ***catesbyi*** × ***leucophylla***	NLos
× ***catesbyi*** × ***oreophila***	NLos
× ***catesbyi*** RV clone × ***oreophila***	NLos
courtii × ***minor*** **new**	NLos
'Dixie Lace' ♀H3	NLos
'Eva'	WSSs
× ***excellens***	WSSs
- 'Judy'	NLos
× ***excellens*** × (***minor*** × ***rubra*** subsp. ***rubra***)	NLos
× ***excellens*** × (× ***rehdeii***)	NLos
× ***exornata***	SPlb
× ***farnhamii***	EECP
flava	WSSs
- from Appalachicola National Forest, Florida **new**	NLos
- from Bay County, Florida **new**	NLos
- from Carteret County, North Carolina **new**	NLos
- from Dorchester County, South Carolina **new**	NLos
- from Jedbury, Dorchester County, Florida **new**	NLos
- from Marston Exotics **new**	NLos
- from McClellenville, South Carolina **new**	NLos
- from Santee Coastal Reserve, South Carolina **new**	NLos
- from Shallotte, North Carolina **new**	NLos
- all green giant	see *S. flava* var. *maxima*
- all red tube **new**	NLos
- var. ***atropurpurea***	EECP WSSs
- - from Blackwater, Florida **new**	NLos
- 'Burgundy'	NLos WSSs
- 'Claret'	WSSs
- var. ***cuprea***	WSSs
- var. ***flava***	CHew EECP WSSs
- - Hurleyville, South Carolina **new**	NLos
- - very tall, from Dahlia Bog, Virginia **new**	NLos
- giant red tube **new**	NLos
§ - var. ***maxima***	CHew EECP NLos WSSs
- - from North Carolina **new**	NLos
- var. ***ornata***	CHew EECP NLos WSSs
- var. ***rubricorpora***	CHew EECP SPlb WSSs
- - from Apalachicola National Forest, Florida **new**	NLos
- var. ***rugelii***	CHew EECP NLos WSSs
- - from Homerville Airport, Ware County, Georgia **new**	NLos
- - from SB Creek Road **new**	NLos
((***flava*** × ***leucophylla***) × ***leucophylla***) × (***flava*** × ***rubra***)	NLos
(***flava*** × ***purpurea***) × (***purpurea*** subsp. ***purpurea***)	NLos
flava var. ***maxima*** × (× ***moorei*** Brook's hybrid)	NLos
'Juthatip Soper' ♀H3	NLos WSSs
leucophylla	CHew NLos SPlb WSSs
- from Bens Bog, Baldwin County, Alabama **new**	NLos
- from Citronelle, Alabama **new**	NLos
- from Ctenium Fields, Perdido, Alabama **new**	NLos
- from Gas Station Site, Perdido, Alabama **new**	NLos
- from Hosford, Liberty County, Florida **new**	NLos
- from Okaloosa Co., Florida	NLos
- from Southern Eglin Reserve, Oskaloosa County, Florida **new**	NLos
- var. ***alba*** **new**	WSSs
- 'Deer Park Alabama'	NLos
- green	WSSs
- green and white	NLos WSSs
- pubescent	WSSs
- - from Perdido, Alabama **new**	NLos
- 'Schnell's Ghost' ♀H3	WSSs
- 'Tarnok'	WSSs
- f. ***viridescens*** **new**	WSSs
leucophylla × ***oreophila***	EECP
leucophylla × (***minor*** × ***rubra*** subsp. ***rubra***)	NLos
leucophylla × (× ***popei***)	EECP
leucophylla × ***rubra*** subsp. ***alabamensis***	NLos
'Lynda Butt' ♀H3	WSSs
× ***miniata***	EECP WSSs
minor	EECP WSSs
- from Berkeley County, South Carolina **new**	NLos
- from Fitzgerald, Ben Hill County, Georgia **new**	NLos
- var. ***minor***	CHew
§ - 'Okee Giant'	NLos WSSs
- 'Okefenokee Giant'	see *S. minor* 'Okee Giant'
- var. ***okefenokeensis***	CHew WSSs
minor × ***rubra*** **new**	NLos
(***minor*** × ***oreophila***) × (***leucophylla*** × ***purpurea***)	NLos
× ***mitchelliana***	NLos WSSs
× ***moorei***	CHew WSSs

- 'Brook's Hybrid' ♀H4	CHew EECP NLos WSSs
- 'Marston Clone' new	NLos
× ***moorei*** × ***purpurea*** subsp. ***venosa***	NLos
oreophila	CHew WSSs
- purple throat new	NLos
oreophila × ***purpurea***	NLos
oreophila × ***rubra*** subsp. ***wherryi*** 'Chatom Giant' new	NLos
× ***popei***	NLos WSSs
'Pseudo-Judy' new	NLos
psittacina	CHew EECP WSSs
purpurea	SPlb
- subsp. ***purpurea***	CHew WSSs
- - f. ***heterophylla*** ♀H6	WSSs
- subsp. ***venosa***	CHew WSSs
- - var. ***burkii***	WSSs
× ***readii***	NLos WSSs
rubra	EECP WSSs
- subsp. ***alabamensis*** ♀H3	CHew WSSs
- subsp. ***gulfensis***	CHew WSSs
* - - f. ***heterophylla***	WSSs
* - - - from Yellow River, North Florida new	NLos
- subsp. ***jonesii***	EECP NLos WSSs
* - - f. ***heterophylla***	WSSs
- subsp. ***rubra***	CHew WSSs
- subsp. ***wherryi***	CHew EECP WSSs
- - 'Chatom Giant' new	NLos
- - from near Perdido, Baldwin County, Alabama new	NLos
- - giant	WSSs
- - yellow-flowered	WSSs
'Vogel' ♀H3	WSSs
× ***wrigleyana***	NLos

Saruma (*Aristolochiaceae*)

henryi	CAby CDes CLAP CPom CTal ESwi EWld GLog LEdu MAvo MMoz SBrt WCot WCru WPGP WSHC

Sasa (*Poaceae*)

disticha 'Mirrezuzume'	see *Pleioblastus pygmaeus* 'Mirrezuzume'
glabra f. ***albostriata***	see *Sasaella masamuneana* 'Albostriata'
kagamiana	NLar
kurilensis	MWhi MWht
§ - 'Shima-shimofuri' (v)	EPPr EPla ERod EShb MMoz MWht
- 'Shimofuri'	see *S. kurilensis* 'Shima-shimofuri'
- short	EPla
nana	see *S. veitchii* f. *minor*
oshidensis	EPla
§ ***palmata***	CDul CHel CWSG EHoe MMuc MWhi SEND WHer
- f. ***nebulosa***	CBcs CCon CDoC CHEx EPla LPal MBrN MMoz MWht NLar SArc WMoo
quelpaertensis	EPla
tessellata	see *Indocalamus tessellatus*
tsuboiana	CBcs CDoC EPla LPal LRHS MJak MMoz MWht NLar SBig SGol WMoo
§ ***veitchii***	CBcs EHoe EPla LPal MJak MMoz MMuc MRav MWht NLar SCob SEND SGol SPer WFar WMoo
§ - f. ***minor***	MMuc WMoo

Sasaella (*Poaceae*)

glabra	see *S. masamuneana*
§ ***masamuneana***	EPla
§ - 'Albostriata' (v)	CDoC CEnt EPla ERod LEdu LRHS MMoz MMuc MWht SBig SEND WMoo
- f. ***aureostriata*** (v)	MMoz
§ ***ramosa***	CHEx EPla MWht

Sassafras (*Lauraceae*)

albidum	CArn CBcs CMCN EBee ELan EPfP EPla LRHS MAsh NLar SChF SKHP SLon SPoG SSpi

satsuma see *Citrus reticulata*

Satureja ✿ (*Lamiaceae*)

coerulea ♀H5	EWes NBir XSen
douglasii	EOHP SHDw WJek
- 'Indian Mint'PBR	CArn ENfk MHer
hortensis	CBod ELau ENfk GPoy MHer MNHC SIde SRms WJek
intricata	XSen
montana	CArn CHby CSam CUse ELau ENfk GKev GPoy LLWP MBri MCot MHer MNHC SDix SEND SIde SRms SVic WHfH WJek XSen
* - ***citriodora***	GPoy MHer MNHC XSen
§ - subsp. ***illyrica***	CPBP SPhx WJek XLum XSen
- 'Purple Mountain'	GPoy MHer
- ***subspicata***	see *S. montana* subsp. *illyrica*
obovata	XSen
repanda	see *S. spicigera*
§ ***spicigera***	CArn CBod ENfk EPot LEdu MHer NBir SPhx SRms WJek XLum
spinosa	XSen
thymbra	CArn SHDw XSen

Saurauia (*Actinidiaceae*)

subspinosa	CHEx

Sauromatum (*Araceae*)

gaoligongense	CDes
guttatum	see *S. venosum*
§ ***venosum***	CArn CCon CExl EBee ECho EShb LAma LEdu LRHS MMoz NLos SBig WCot WCru XLum

Saururus (*Saururaceae*)

cernuus	CArn CBAq CBen CHEx CRow CWat EHon ELan LLWG MSKA MWts SRms SWat WMAq WWtn XLum
chinensis	CRow LLWG

Saussurea (*Asteraceae*)

costus	GPoy
japonica	WCru
nepalensis	CArn
stella	CPBP

savory, summer see *Satureja hortensis*

savory, winter see *Satureja montana*

Saxegothaea (*Podocarpaceae*)

conspicua	CBcs CDoC IArd IDee NLar

Saxifraga ✿ (*Saxifragaceae*)

Name	Suppliers
McB 1377/1 (7)	NWad
McB 1377/2 (7)	NWad
SEP 22	CPBP
acerifolia (5) **new**	GEdr
aizoides (9)	ECho
- var. ***atrorubens*** (9)	ECho GKev
aizoon	see *S. paniculata* subsp. *paniculata*
'Alan Hayhurst' (8)	CPBP WAbe
'Alan Martin' (× *boydilacina*) (7)	ECho EPot EWes
'Alba' ambig.	LRHS
'Alba' (× *apiculata*) (7) 🏆H5	ECho NRya SPlb
'Alba' (*oppositifolia*) (7)	ECho ELan EWes ITim NWad WAbe
'Albert Einstein' (× *apiculata*) (7) 🏆H5	CTal
'Albertii' (*callosa*)	see *S.* 'Albida'
§ 'Albida' (*callosa*) (8)	CTal ECho NWad WAbe
'Albrecht Dürer' (Lasciva Group) (7)	EPot
'Allendale Bamby' (× *lismorensis*) (7)	NHar
'Allendale Beau' (× *lismorensis*) (7)	CTal
'Allendale Beauty' (7)	CPBP WAbe
'Allendale Betty' (× *lismorensis*) (7)	EPot
'Allendale Billows' (7)	NHar
'Allendale Bonny' (7)	EPot NHar WAbe
'Allendale Bravo' (× *lismorensis*) (7)	WAbe
'Allendale Cabal' (7)	CPBP ITim
'Allendale Carol' (7)	WAbe
'Allendale Charm' (Swing Group) (7)	ITim WAbe WHoo
'Allendale Chick' (7)	NHar
'Allendale Desire' (7)	WAbe
'Allendale Elegance' (7)	CPBP WAbe
'Allendale Elf' (7)	EPot WAbe
'Allendale Elite' (7)	WAbe
'Allendale Envoy' (7)	ITim WAbe
'Allendale Epic' (7)	NHar
'Allendale Fairy' (7)	ITim NHar WAbe WHoo
'Allendale Frost' (7)	WAbe
'Allendale Ghost' (7)	WAbe
'Allendale Goblin' (7)	WAbe
'Allendale Grace' (7)	WAbe
'Allendale Harvest' (7)	WAbe
'Allendale Hobbit' (7)	NHar WAbe
'Allendale Host' (7)	WAbe
'Allendale Icon' (× *polulacina*) (7)	WAbe
'Allendale Imp' (7)	WAbe
'Allendale Ina' (7)	NHar WAbe
'Allendale Jinn' (7)	WAbe
'Allendale Jo' (7)	EPot WAbe
'Allendale Ruby' (7)	WAbe
alpigena (7)	WAbe
× ***andrewsii*** (8 × 11)	XLum
angustifolia Haw.	see *S. hypnoides*
'Anne Beddall' (× *goringiana*) (7)	WAbe
'Antonio Vivaldi' (7)	WAbe
× ***apiculata*** (7)	ECho MAsh
× ***apiculata*** *sensu stricto* hort.	see *S.* 'Gregor Mendel'
'Apple Blossom' (Mossy Group) (15)	ECtt EPfP NEoE NRya
'Arabella' (× *edithae*) (7)	ECho
× ***arendsii*** purple-flowered (15)	MMuc SEND SPlb
'Asahi' (*fortunei*) (5)	IVic
aspera L. (10)	EDAr WAbe
'Atropurpurea' (*paniculata* subsp. *cartilaginea*) (8)	GMaP NHar NHol WIce XLum
'Aufheiter von Eri' (*fortunei*) (5)	IVic
'Auguste Renoir' (Decora Group) (7)	WAbe
'Aurea Maculata' (*cuneifolia*)	see *S.* 'Aureopunctata'
'Aurea' (*umbrosa*)	see *S.* 'Aureopunctata'
§ 'Aureopunctata' (× *urbium*) (11/v)	CMac CTri ECha ECho ELan EPfP GKev GMaP LPot LRHS MHer MLHP MRav SPer SPlb SPoG SRms WMoo XLum
'Autumn Tribute' (*fortunei*) (5)	CLAP WAbe
'Ayer's Rock' (7)	WAbe
'Balcana' (*paniculata*) (8)	EPot NSla WAbe
'Baldensis'	see *S. paniculata* var. *minutifolia*
§ 'Beatrix Stanley' (× *angelica*) (7)	ECho LRHS MHer NWad
× ***biasolettoi*** *sensu stricto* hort.	see *S.* 'Phoenix'
× ***bilekii*** (7)	ECho
'Black Beauty' (15)	ECtt GCrg LPot MHer
Black Ruby (*fortunei*) (5)	Widely available
'Blackberry and Apple Pie' (*fortunei*) (5)	CBct CElw CExl EBee ECho ECtt EPfP GEdr IBal LRHS MBrN MHol MLHP MNrw NHar NMyG SBch SWvt WCot WMoo
'Blush' (*fortunei*) (5) **new**	LLHF
'Bob Hawkins' (Mossy Group) (15/v)	NHol NWad
'Bohemia' (7)	ECho EPot NLar
× ***borisii*** *sensu stricto* hort.	see *S.* 'Sofia'
'Boston Spa' (× *elisabethae*) (7)	ECho ECtt EPot GCrg LRHS MAsh MHer NLar SPlb
'Bridget' (× *edithae*) (7)	ECho LRHS
'Brimstone' (7)	WAbe
'Brno' (× *elisabethae*) (7)	EPot
brunoniana	see *S. brunonis*
§ ***brunonis*** (1) CC 5315	GKev
'Bryn Llwyd'	WAbe
bryoides (10)	ECho
* 'Buckland' (*fortunei*) (5)	WCot
'Bürgel' (× *poluanglica*) (7)	GKev
× ***burnatii*** (8)	ECho LRHS NSla
burseriana (7)	ECho WAbe
× ***caesia*** misapplied (× *fritschiana*)	see *S.* 'Krain'
× ***caesia*** L. (8)	SRms WAbe
§ ***callosa*** (8) 🏆H5	ECho EDAr MHer MLHP MMuc SEND WAbe
- subsp. ***callosa*** (8)	ECho
§ - - var. ***australis*** (8)	CTal GJos
- var. ***lantoscana***	see *S. callosa* subsp. *callosa* var. *australis*
- ***lingulata***	see *S. callosa*
callosa × ***cochlearis***	see *S.* Silver Farreri Group
'Camyra' (7)	WAbe
× ***canis-dalmatica***	see *S.* 'Canis-dalmatica'
§ 'Canis-dalmatica' (× *gaudinii*) (8)	ECho ECtt EPot GCrg GJos GKev LRHS NHar NWad SIgm

§ 'Carmen' (× *elisabethae*) (7) WAbe
'Carniolica' (× *engleri*) (8) WAbe
§ 'Carniolica' (*paniculata*) (8) NBro NHol
carolinica see *S.* 'Carniolica' (*paniculata*)
cartilaginea see *S. paniculata* subsp. *cartilaginea*
'Caterhamensis' (*cotyledon*) (8) NHar
caucasica (7) ECho WAbe
cebennensis (15) NRya
- dwarf (15) WAbe
'Cecil Davies' (8) NHar
'Celebration' WAbe
cespitosa (15) WAbe
'Chambers' Pink Pride' see *S.* 'Miss Chambers'
'Charles Chaplin' (7) ECho
'Charles Darwin' (7) CPBP EPot
Cheap Confections (*fortunei*) (4) CBct ECtt GEdr IFoB LLHF NMyG SBch SHar WBor WFar WMoo WOld WPGP WWEG
§ ***cherlerioides*** (10) NRya
Cherry Pie (*fortunei*) (5) CBct GEdr LLHF NBir NHar NMyG
'Chodov' (× *megaseiflora*) (Holenka's Miracle Group) (7) EPot
'Christine' (× *anglica*) (7) ECho
cinerea (7) WAbe
- McB 1376 NWad
'Cio-Cio-San' (Vanessa Group) (7) CPBP WAbe
'Citronella' (7) ECho WAbe
'Claire Felstead' (7) WAbe
* 'Clare' (*paniculata*) (8) **new** NSla
'Clare' (× *anglica*) (7) ECtt NHol
§ 'Clarence Elliott' (London Pride Group) (*umbrosa*) (11) ♀H5 CTri ECho EWes GAbr GBin GCal GJos GKev GMaP MHer MWat NDov NLar NRya WIce WThu WWEG
'Cloth of Gold' (*exarata* subsp. *moschata*) (15) ECha ECho ECtt ELan GCrg GMaP LRHS MAsh MHer NHol NRya NWad SBod SPlb SPoG SRms WAbe WIce
cochlearis (8) CTri LRHS MAsh NBro NSla SBch SIgm WAbe
'Cockscomb' (*paniculata*) (8) ECho EPot NHar NWad WAbe
columnaris (7) WAbe
'Conwy Snow' (*fortunei*) (5) CDes CLAP NHar WAbe WFar WMoo
'Conwy Star' (*fortunei*) (5) CLAP NHar WAbe WFar
'Coolock Gem' (7) EPot WAbe
'Coolock Jean' (7) WAbe
'Coolock Kate' (7) ♀H5 WAbe
'Corennie Claret' see *S.* 'Glowing Ember'
'Correvoniana' misapplied see *S.* 'Lagraveana'
'Correvoniana' Farrer (*paniculata*) (8) EDAr EPot MHer MMuc XLum
cortusifolia (5) CLAP EBee ECho
- B&SWJ 5879 WCru
- var. ***stolonifera*** (5) CBct ECho GCal XLum
Cotton Crochet (*fortunei*) (5/d) CAbP CBct ECtt ESwi GEdr MNrw NHar NMyG SHeu WBor WCot WFar WMoo WOld
cotyledon (8) CTal ECho WAbe WCFE
cotyledon* × *cuneifolia (8 × 11) **new** NSla
§ 'Cranbourne' (× *anglica*) (7) ♀H5 CMea ECho LRHS MAsh
'Cream' (*paniculata*) (8) ECho
'Cream Seedling' (× *elisabethae*) (7) ECho
'Crenata' (*burseriana*) (7) ♀H5 EPot LRHS
'Crimscote-love' (*poluanglica*) (7) EPot
'Crimson Rose' (*paniculata*) see *S.* 'Rosea' (*paniculata*)
§ ***crustata*** (8) CPBP ECho NHar WAbe WThu XLum
- var. ***vochinensis*** see *S. crustata*
Crystal Pink (*fortunei*) (5/v) CAbP CBct CExl CHel EBee ECtt GEdr IFoB LBMP MCot MHol MNrw NHar NMyG SGSe WCot WFar WGrn WOld
'Crystalie' (× *biasolettoi*) (7) LRHS
'Cultrata' (*paniculata*) (8) NBro
'Cumulus' (7) ♀H5 EPot GKev WAbe
§ ***cuneifolia*** (11) ECho IMou LBee MHer MLHP MWat NWad WMoo XLum
- var. ***capillipes*** see *S. cuneifolia* subsp. *cuneifolia*
§ - subsp. ***cuneifolia*** (11) ECtt GJos
* - var. ***subintegra*** (11) ECho
'Cuscutiformis' (*stolonifera*) (5) CAby CElw CExl CHid EWld GBuc GEdr MAvo MBel MRav MSCN SBch SMrm SRms WBor WCru WPGP XLum
cymbalaria (2) WHil
dahurica see *S. cuneifolia*
'Dainty Dame' (× *arco-valleyi*) (7) LRHS WAbe
'Dana' (Prichard's Monument Group) (× *megaseiflora*) (7) EPot
'Dawn Frost' (7) EPot WIce
'Delia' (× *hornibrookii*) (7) EPot
densa see *S. cherlerioides*
'Dentata' (× *geum*) see *S.* 'Dentata' (London Pride Group)(× *polita*)
'Dentata' (× *urbium*) see *S.* 'Dentata' (London Pride Group)(× *polita*)
§ 'Dentata' (London Pride Group) (× *polita*) (11) ECha ECho GCal WMoo WWEG
I 'Diana' (× *lincolnii-fosteri*) (7) **new** WIce
diapensioides (7) WAbe
dinnikii (7) WAbe
'Doctor Clay' (*paniculata*) (8) CTal ECho EPot GCrg GKev LRHS NHar NHol NRya SPlb WAbe
'Doctor Ramsey' (8) ECho EWes LRHS NBro NWad WAbe WPnn
'Don Giovanni' (7) WAbe
'Donald Mann' (15) EWes
'Drakula' (*ferdinandi-coburgi*) (7) ECho LRHS
'Edith' (× *edithae*) (7) CTal ECho LRHS
'Elf' (7) see *S.* 'Beatrix Stanley'
'Elf' (*exarata* subsp. *moschata*) (15) ECtt MAsh SIgm SRms
'Elf Rose' **new** EPfP LRHS
× ***elisabethae*** *sensu stricto* hort. see *S.* 'Carmen'
'Elizabeth Sinclair' (× *elisabethae*) (7) EPot
'Elliott's Variety' see *S.* 'Clarence Elliott'
'Emile Burnat' (× *burnatii*) ♀H5 **new** CTal
× ***engleri*** (8) CTal
epiphylla (5) BWJ 8177 WCru

	Name	Suppliers
	'Esther' (× *burnatii*) (8)	CMea ECho LRHS SRGP WHoo WPnn
§	'Eulenspiegel' (× *geuderi*) (7)	EPot NWad
	'Eva Hanzliková' (× *izari*) (7)	WAbe
	exarata (15)	WAbe
	'Excellent' (Exclusive Group) (7)	CPBP EPot
	fair maids of France	see *S.* 'Flore Pleno'
	'Fairy' (*exarata* subsp. *moschata*) (15)	ECtt NBir
	'Faldonside' (× *boydii*) (7)	MAsh WAbe
	'Falstaff' (*burseriana*) (7)	WAbe
	× ***farreri*** (15)	WIce
	'Favorit' (× *bilekii*) (7)	EPot
§	***federici-augusti*** subsp. ***grisebachii*** (7) ♀H5	ECho EPot GCrg LRHS NSla WAbe
	ferdinandi-coburgi (7)	ECtt NSla WAbe
§	- subsp. ***chrysosplenifolia*** var. ***rhodopea*** (7)	ECho EPot LRHS
	- var. ***pravislavii***	see *S. ferdinandi-coburgi* subsp. *chrysosplenifolia* var. *rhodopea*
	- var. ***radoslavoffii***	see *S. ferdinandi-coburgi* subsp. *chrysosplenifolia* var. *rhodopea*
	'Findling' (Mossy Group) (15)	EPfP GCrg NWad SPoG WAbe
	'Firebrand' (× *kochii*) (7)	WAbe
	Five Color (*fortunei*)	see *S.* 'Go-nishiki'
§	***flagellaris*** (1)	WAbe
	'Flavescens' misapplied	see *S.* 'Lutea' (*paniculata*)
§	'Flore Pleno' (*granulata*) (15/d)	EWes NBir
	'Flowers of Sulphur'	see *S.* 'Schwefelblüte'
	fortunei (5) ♀H4	CHEx CLAP CMac ECho GKev GMaP LEdu NBir SRms WAbe WFar
	- B&SWJ 6346	WCru
	- from John Fielding (5)	WCot
	- f. ***alpina*** from Hokkaido (5)	WCru
	- var. ***koraiensis*** (5) B&SWJ 8688	WCru
	- var. ***obtusocuneata*** (5)	CLAP ECho GEdr LLHF WAbe
	- f. ***partita*** (5)	CLAP WCot WCru
	- var. ***pilosissima*** (5) B&SWJ 8557	WCru
	- pink-flowered (5)	CLAP WAbe
	- var. ***suwoensis*** (5)	CLAP
	'Foster's Gold' (× *elisabethae*) (7)	EPot
	'Four Winds' (Mossy Group) (15)	EWes MBrN SPoG
	'Francis Cade' (8)	GAbr NSla WAbe
	'Franz Liszt' (7)	EPot WAbe
	'Freckles'	GKev
	'Frederik Chopin' (7)	EPot WAbe
	'Friar Tuck' (× *boydii*) (7)	NWad
	'Friesei' (× *salmonica*) (7)	CTal EPot
	'Fumiko' (*fortunei*) (5)	WAbe WCru
	'Gaiety' (15)	ECho LRHS SPoG
	'Ganymede' (*burseriana*) (7)	EPot WAbe
	× ***gaudinii*** (8)	XLum
	'Gelber Findling' (7)	WAbe
	'Gelbes Monster' (*fortunei*) (5)	IVic
	'Gem' (× *irvingii*) (7)	WIce
	'Gemma' new	LRHS

	Name	Suppliers
	'Geoff Wilson' (× *biasolettoi*) (7)	EPot
	georgei	EPot WAbe
	× ***geuderi*** *sensu stricto* hort.	see *S.* 'Eulenspiegel'
§	× ***geum*** (11)	CHid ECho MRav WFar WMoo
	- Dixter form (11)	CElw ECha NDov SMHy WWEG
	'Gleborg' (Mossy Group) (15)	SPoG
	'Gloria' (*burseriana*) (7)	ECho LRHS MAsh WIce
	'Gloriana'	see *S.* 'Godiva'
	× ***gloriana*** *sensu stricto* hort. (7)	see *S.* 'Godiva'
	'Gloriosa' (× *gloriana*) (7)	see *S.* 'Godiva'
§	'Glowing Ember' (Mossy Group) (15)	EWes
	'Glückliches Mädchen' (*fortunei*) (5)	IVic
§	'Godiva' (× *gloriana*) (7)	WAbe
	'Gold Dust' (× *eudoxiana*) (7)	ECho GCrg NRya
	'Golden Falls' (Mossy Group) (15/v)	EWes SPlb SPoG
	Golden Prague (× *pragensis*)	see *S.* 'Zlatá Praha'
§	'Go-nishiki' (*fortunei*) (5)	GEdr LLHF NHar NMyG
	'Gorges du Verdon' (8)	GKev
	'Gothenburg' (7)	WAbe
	'Grace Farwell' (× *anglica*) (7)	ECho NLar
	granulata (15)	ECho EWes GJos NMir NSla WAbe
	'Greensleeves' (*fortunei*) (5) new	LLHF
§	'Gregor Mendel' (× *apiculata*) (7) ♀H5	CMea CTal ECho ECtt EPot LRHS NLar NWad SBch SIgm SRms WAbe WHoo
	'Gregor' (× *poluanglica*) (7)	WAbe
	grisebachii	see *S. federici-augusti* subsp. *grisebachii*
	'Haagii' (× *eudoxiana*) (7)	CTri ECho GKev NLar
	'Harbinger' (7)	WAbe
	'Hare Knoll Beauty' (8)	CPBP ECho EPot LRHS NHar NHol NSla WAbe
	'Harlow Car' (× *anglica*) (7)	EPot
	'Harold Bevington' (*paniculata*) (8)	CTal
	'Harry Marshall' (× *irvingii*) (7)	NWad
	'Harvest Moon' (*stolonifera*) (5)	CHEx WBor WHer
	'Hedwig' (× *malbyana*) (7)	WAbe
	'Heisel Kurenai' (*fortunei*) (5)	IVic
	'Henri Rousseau' (Conspecta Group) (7) new	EPot
	'Hi-Ace' (Mossy Group) (15/v)	MHer SPlb
	'Highlander Red Shades' (Mossy Group) (15) new	WIce
	'Hime' (*stolonifera*) (5)	WCru
	'Hindhead Seedling' (× *boydii*) (7)	ECho LRHS WAbe
	hirculus (1) new	CPBP
	hirsuta (11)	EWTr EWld GEdr LEdu MMuc SEND WCru
	'Hirsuta' (× *geum*)	see *S.* × *geum*
	'Hirtifolia' (*paniculata*) (8)	CTal GJos
	'Hiten' (*fortunei*) (5)	GKev

	Name	Suppliers
	'Hocker Edge' (× *arco-valleyi*) (7)	WAbe
	'Holden Seedling' (Mossy Group) (15)	ECtt
	hostii (8)	ECho EDAr GKev NWad XLum
	- subsp. ***hostii*** (8)	XLum
	- - var. ***altissima*** (8)	XLum
	- subsp. ***rhaetica*** (8)	NBro WThu XLum
	'Hsitou Silver' (*stolonifera*) (5)	EPPr
§	***hypnoides*** (15)	NMir SPoG WAbe
	hypostoma (7)	WAbe
	'Iceland' (*oppositifolia*) (7)	EWes SIgm WAbe
	'Ignaz Dörfler' (× *doerfleri*) (7)	WAbe
	imparilis (5)	GEdr WCru
	'Ingeborg' (Mossy Group) (15)	CElw ECha
	iranica (7)	EPot
	'Iris Prichard' (× *hardingii*) (7)	CTal
	× ***irvingii*** (7)	ECho EPot
	× ***irvingii*** *sensu stricto* hort.	see *S.* 'Walter Irving'
	'James' (7)	NSla
	'Jan Neruda' (× *megaseiflora*) (7)	CPBP EPot
	'Jaromir' (8)	NHar
	'Jenkinsiae' (× *irvingii*) (7)	CMea CTal ECho EPot LRHS MAsh MMuc NRya NWad SEND WAbe WIce
§	'Johann Kellerer' (× *kellereri*) (7)	EPot
	'Johann Wolfgang Goethe' (7)	EPot WAbe
	'John Byam-Grounds' (Honor Group) (7)	WAbe
	'Jorg' (× *biasolettoi*) (7)	EPot
	'Joy'	see *S.* 'Kaspar Maria Sternberg'
	'Judith Shackleton' (× *abingdonensis*) (7)	CPBP WAbe
	'Juliet'	see *S.* 'Riverslea'
§	***juniperifolia*** (7)	ECho GAbr SRms XLum
	'Jupiter' (× *megaseiflora*) (Holenka's Miracle Group) (7)	CPBP EPot SIgm
	'Kanna' (*fortunei*) (5)	IVic
	karadzicensis × ***scardica*** (7) **new**	EPot
	'Karel Čapek' (× *megaseiflora*) (Prichard's Monument Group) (7)	ECho LRHS WAbe
	'Karlštejn' (× *borisii*) (7)	EPot
§	'Kaspar Maria Sternberg' (× *petraschii*) (7) ♀H5	ECho LRHS
	'Kath Dryden' (7)	ECho ECtt MSpe NWad
	'Kathleen Pinsent' (8)	ECho
	'Kathleen' (× *polulacina*) (7)	EPot
	'Kath's Delight' (8)	GKev
	× ***kellereri*** *sensu stricto* hort.	see *S.* 'Johann Kellerer'
	'Kew Gem' (× *petraschii*) (7)	ECho
	'King Lear' (× *bursiculata*) (7)	CTal ECho LRHS
	'Kinki Purple' (*stolonifera*) (5)	CBct EShb EWld WCru WPGP
	'Klondike' (× *boydii*) (7)	EPot
	'Knapton Pink' (Mossy Group) (15)	ECtt EDAr EPfP LSun NEoE SPoG WAbe WIce
	'Knebworth' (8)	ECho
	'Kokaku' (*fortunei*) (5)	LLHF
	kotschyi × ***wendelboi*** (7)	EPot
	'Koukan' (*fortunei*) (5)	IVic
§	'Krain' (× *fritschiana*) (8)	ECho
	'Labe' (× *arco-valleyi*) (7)	CPBP ECho EPot LRHS
	'Lady Beatrix Stanley'	see *S.* 'Beatrix Stanley'
§	'Lagraveana' (*paniculata*) (8) ♀H5	ECho EDAr GCrg LRHS SEND
	'Laka' (7)	WAbe
	× ***landaueri*** *sensu stricto* hort.	see *S.* 'Leonore'
	'Lantoscana Superba' (*callosa* subsp. *callosa* var. *australis*) (8)	GKev
	'Lemon Puff' **new**	WIce
	'Lemon Spires' (7)	EPot
	'Lenka' (× *byam-groundsii*) (7)	EPot WAbe
	'Leo Gordon Godseff' (× *elisabethae*) (7)	ECho LRHS
	'Leonardo da Vinci' (7)	EPot WAbe
§	'Leonore' (× *landaueri*) (7)	ECho LRHS SIgm WAbe
	'Letchworth Gem' (London Pride Group) (× *urbium*) (11)	ECho GAbr GCal
	'Licht des Cerise' (*fortunei*) (5)	IVic
	'Lidice' (7)	EPot WAbe WHoo
	'Lilac Time' (× *youngiana*) (7)	EPot
	lilacina (7)	WAbe WThu
	'Limelight' (*callosa* subsp. *callosa* var. *australis*) (8)	NWad
	'Lincoln Foster' (8)	NHar
	lingulata	see *S. callosa*
	'Lismore Carmine' (× *lismorensis*) (7)	EPot
	'Lismore Gem' (× *lismorensis*) (7)	ECho
	'Lissadell' (*callosa*) (8)	GKev IFoB
*	'Little Piggy' (*epiphylla*) (5)	WCru
	llonakhensis	WAbe
	'Lohmuelleri' (× *biasolettoi*) (7)	GKev
	lolaensis (7)	WAbe
	'Long Acre Pink' (*fortunei*) (5)	CLAP
	longifolia (8)	ECho EPot GKev NSla
	- var. ***aitanica*** (8)	WAbe
	'Louis Armstrong' (Blues Group) (7)	EPot WAbe
	Love Me	see *S.* 'Miluj Mne'
	lowndesii (7)	WAbe
	'Luschtinetz' (Mossy Group) (15)	LRHS LSun
	'Lutea' ambig.	GJos
	'Lutea' (*aizoon*)	see *S.* 'Lutea' (*paniculata*)
§	'Lutea' (*paniculata*) (8)	ECho EDAr EHoe EPot GMaP MMuc NBro NHol NRya NSla NWad
	'Lužníce' (× *poluluteopurpurea*) (7)	CTal
	macedonica	see *S. juniperifolia*
	'Maigrün' (*fortunei*) (5)	NHar
	'Marc Chagall' (Decora Group) (7)	WAbe
	marginata (7) ♀H5	WAbe
	- var. ***balcanica***	see *S. marginata* subsp. *marginata* var. *rocheliana*

	Name	Suppliers
	- subsp. ***marginata*** var. ***boryi*** (7)	EPot LRHS WAbe
	- - var. ***coriophylla*** (7)	WAbe
§	- - var. ***rocheliana*** (7)	ECho LRHS
	'Maria Callas' (× *poluanglica*) (7)	EPot WAbe
	'Maria Luisa' (× *salmonica*) (7)	WAbe
	'Marianna' (× *borisii*) (7)	CMea SIgm
	'Maroon Beauty' (*stolonifera*) (5)	EBee ECtt EPPr LPot MCot NBid NBre WCot WWEG
	'Mary Golds' (Swing Group) (7)	GKev ITim NLar
	× ***megaseiflora*** *sensu stricto* hort. /	see *S.* 'Robin Hood'
	mertensiana (6)	GEdr NBir WCru WSHC
	'Meteor' (7)	NHol NRya
	micranthidifolia (4)	CLAP
	'Mikuláš Koperník' (× *zenittensis*) (7)	WAbe
	'Millstream Cream' (× *elisabethae*) (7)	ECho
§	'Miluj Mne' (× *poluanglica*) (7)	CTal ECho WHoo
	'Minnehaha' (× *elisabethae*) (7)	WAbe
	'Minor' (*cochlearis*) (8) 🏆H5	CTal ECho EPot GKev LRHS NHar NWad
	'Mirko Webr' (Harmonia Group) (7)	WAbe
§	'Miss Chambers' (London Pride Group) (11)	EWes GCal SMHy WCot WMoo WSHC WWEG
	'Mollie Broom' (7) new	WAbe
	'Momo Sekisui' (*fortunei*) (5)	IVic
	'Mona Lisa' (× *borisii*) (7)	NWad SIgm
	'Monarch' (8) 🏆H5	ECho GAbr GCrg GKev NWad WAbe WIce
	'Moonlight' (× *boydii*)	see *S.* 'Sulphurea'
	'Morava' (7)	EPot
*	'Mossy Pink'	MMuc SEND SPoG
	'Mossy Red'	SPoG
	'Mossy Triumph'	see *S.* 'Triumph'
	'Mossy White'	GAbr MMuc
	'Mother of Pearl' (× *irvingii*) (7)	ECho WIce
	'Mount Nachi' (*fortunei*) (5)	CBct CDes ECho EPfP EWes GAbr GEdr GMaP IBal LRHS MLHP NBro NMyG SPlb WAbe WCot WFar WMoo WPGP WWEG
	'Mrs Helen Terry' (× *salmonica*) (7) 🏆H5	EPot LRHS WIce
	'Musgrove Pink' (*fortunei*) (5)	CLAP
	'Myra Cambria' (× *anglica*) (7)	NWad
	'Myra' (× *anglica*) (7)	ECho WHoo
	'Myriad' (7)	WAbe
	'Nancye' (× *goringiana*) (7)	EPot
	'Nicholas' (8)	GKev
	'Nisi' (*fortunei*) (5)	IVic
	'Nottingham Gold' (× *boydii*) (7) 🏆H5	EPot NWad SIgm
§	***obtusa*** (7)	EPot MHer
	'Omar Khayyám' (7)	EPot WAbe
	oppositifolia (7)	GCrg GKev MAsh MWat NHol NSla SPlb SRms WAbe WSHC
I	- 'Holden Variety' (7)	NRya NWad
	- subsp. ***oppositifolia*** var. ***latina*** (7)	ECho GAbr
	- subsp. ***paradoxa*** (7) new	EPot
	'Pablo Picasso' (Conspecta Group) (7)	EPot WAbe
	paniculata (8)	ECho EDAr EHoe GKev GMaP MHer MWat NSla SPlb SRms WAbe WHoo
§	- subsp. ***cartilaginea*** (8)	GCrg GKev
	- subsp. ***kolenatiana***	see *S. paniculata* subsp. *cartilaginea*
§	- var. ***minutifolia*** (8)	CTri ECho LRHS MSCN NBro NHar NRya NSla SIgm SPlb WAbe
§	- subsp. ***paniculata*** (8)	MAsh
	paradoxa (15)	ECho EPot LRHS NHol NWad
	'Parcevalis' (× *finnisiae*) (7 × 9)	EPot WAbe
	'Paul Gaughin' (7)	WAbe
	'Paul Rubens' (7)	WAbe
	'Peach Melba' (7) 🏆H5	CTal EPot NLar WAbe WHoo
	'Peachy Head' (7)	WAbe
	'Pearly Gates' (× *irvingii*) (7)	CTal
	'Pearly King' (Mossy Group) (15)	ECtt GKev GMaP LSun WAbe
	'Pearly King' variegated (15/v)	CBod
	× ***pectinata*** Schott, Nyman & Kotschy	see *S.* 'Krain'
	pedemontana from Mount Kazbek, Georgia (15)	WAbe
	'Penelope' (× *boydilacina*) (7)	CTal ECho EPot LRHS NLar WHoo
	pensylvanica (4)	CAby GCal GCra IMou WCot
	'Peter Burrow' (× *poluanglica*) (7)	ECho EPot ITim WIce
	'Peter Pan' (Mossy Group) (15)	EDAr EPfP GCrg GMaP LRHS MAsh MHer NHol NWad SPoG WSHC
	'Petra' (7)	ECho EPot
§	'Phoenix' (× *biasolettoi*) (7)	ECho LRHS
	'Pink Cloud' (*fortunei*) (5)	CLAP GEdr NHar WAbe
	'Pink Haze' (*fortunei*) (5)	CLAP GEdr NHar WAbe
	'Pink Mist' (*fortunei*) (5)	CLAP GEdr NHar WAbe WFar WMoo
	'Pink Pagoda' (*nipponica*) (5)	CDes CLAP WCot WCru WPGP
	'Pink Pearl' (7)	SBch
	'Pink Ray' (*fortunei*) (5)	LLHF
	'Pink Star' (× *boydilacina*) (7)	NLar
	'Pixie' (15)	CTal CTri ECtt GCrg MAsh NHol NRya NWad SPoG SRms
	'Pixie Alba'	see *S.* 'White Pixie'
	'Plena' (*granulata*)	see *S.* 'Flore Pleno'
	'Polar Drift'	NHar NSla WAbe
	poluniniana (7)	WAbe
	poluniniana × 'Winifred' (× *poluanglica*) (7)	ECho EPot
	'Pompadour' (15)	NEoE
	'Popelka' (subsp. *marginata* var. *rocheliana*) (7)	ECho LRHS
	porophylla var. ***thessalica***	see *S. sempervivum* f. *stenophylla*
	'Portae' (× *fritschiana*) (8)	XLum
	'Precious Piggy' (*epiphylla*) (5)	WCru
	'Primrose Bee' (× *apiculata*) (7)	ITim

Name	Suppliers
'Primrose Dame' (× *elisabethae*) (7)	ECho WIce
'Primulaize' (9 × 11)	GCrg
'Primulaize Salmon' (9 × 11)	NHar WHoo
'Primuloides' (*umbrosa*) (11)	ECho EDAr MMuc SEND SRms SWvt
'Prince Hal' (*burseriana*) (7)	ECho EPot LRHS
'Princess' (*burseriana*) (7)	ECho LRHS
'Probynii' (*cochlearis*) (8)	EPot MWat NWad WAbe
× ***prossenii*** *sensu stricto* hort.	see *S.* 'Regina'
× ***proximae*** 'Květy Coventry' (7)	EPot
'Pseudo-valdensis' (*cochlearis*) (8)	WAbe
'Psycho' (7)	WAbe
pubescens (15)	WAbe
- subsp. ***iratiana*** (15)	EPot
'Punctatissima' (*paniculata*) (8)	NHar
* ***punctissima***	NWad
'Pungens' (× *apiculata*) (7)	EPot
'Purple Piggy' (*epiphylla*) (5)	CLAP WCru
'Purpurea' (*fortunei*)	see *S.* 'Rubrifolia'
'Pyramidalis' (*cotyledon*) (8)	EPfP EWTr XLum
'Pyrenaica' (*oppositifolia*) (7)	ECho
quadrifaria (7)	WAbe
'Radvan Horný' (× *cullinanii*) (7)	WAbe
'Rainsley Seedling' (8)	EPot GKev NBro
'Ray Woodliffe' (× *dinninaris*) (7) **new**	WAbe
'Red Cap' (Mossy Group) (15) **new**	LSun
* 'Regent'	WAbe
§ 'Regina' (× *prossenii*) (7)	EPot MHer
'Rembrandt van Rijn' (7)	WAbe
retusa (7)	WAbe
'Rex' (*paniculata*) (8)	ECho EPot NWad
rhodopetala (7)	ECho
§ 'Riverslea' (× *hornibrookii*) (7)	WAbe
§ 'Robin Hood' (× *megaseiflora*) (7)	EPot WHoo
'Rokujō' (*fortunei*) (5)	CLAP EBee IVic NEoE NLar SHeu
'Rosa Tubbs' (8)	GKev
'Rosalind' (7)	WHoo
'Rosea' (*cortusifolia*) (5)	CLAP MHol NHar
§ 'Rosea' (*paniculata*) (8) ♀H5	GMaP LBMP MAvo MMuc NBro NRya NSla SEND SRms
'Rosemarie' (7)	ECho
'Rosina Sündermann' (× *rosinae*) (7)	ECho LRHS
'Rote Stadt' (*fortunei*) (5)	IVic
rotundifolia (12)	EBee ECha EWTr
'Rubra' (*aizoon*)	see *S.* 'Rosea' (*paniculata*)
§ 'Rubrifolia' (*fortunei*) (5)	CAbP CBod CHel CLAP CMac CSpe ECha ECtt EHoe GAbr GEdr IBal LBMP LRHS LSun MCot NMyG SGSe SMad SWvt WBor WCot WCru WFar WMoo WWEG
* 'Ruby Red'	NEoE
* 'Ruby Wedding' (*cortusifolia*) (5)	CLAP
rufescens (5) BWJ 7510	WCru
- BWJ 7684	GEdr WCru
'Russell V. Prichard' (× *irvingii*) (7)	NWad
'Ruth Draper' (*oppositifolia*) (7) ♀H5	EPot WAbe
'Ruth McConnell' (15)	CMea SBch
'Saint John's' (8)	ECho GKev
'Saint Kilda' (*oppositifolia*) (7)	ITim
× ***salmonica*** *sensu stricto* hort.	see *S.* 'Salomonii'
§ 'Salomonii' (× *salmonica*) (7)	EPot SRms
sancta (7)	ECho LRHS SRms
- subsp. ***pseudosancta***	see *S. juniperifolia*
- - var. ***macedonica***	see *S. juniperifolia*
'Sara Sinclair' (× *arco-valleyi*) (7)	CMea
sarmentosa	see *S. stolonifera*
'Satchmo' (Blues Group) (7)	EPot
'Sázava' (× *poluluteopurpurea*) (7)	CTal
scardica (7)	EPot NBro WAbe
- var. ***dalmatica***	see *S. obtusa*
'Schöne Mädchen' (*fortunei*) (5)	IVic
§ 'Schwefelblüte' (15)	ECho GMaP LRHS
sempervivum (7)	NGdn NSla WAbe
§ - f. ***stenophylla*** (7)	ECho MHer
sendaica (5)	WCru
'Seren y Gwanwyn' (*oppositifolia*) (7) **new**	WAbe
'Sherlock Holmes' (7)	CTal WAbe
'Shimmy'	WAbe
'Shinkunomai' (*fortunei*) (5)	IVic
'Shiragiku' (*fortunei*) (5)	WCot
'Silver Beads' (*paniculata*) (8)	NHar
§ 'Silver Cushion' (15/v)	CMea CTri ECho ELan LRHS LSun MAvo MHol SPlb SPoG WAbe
'Silver Edge' (× *arco-valleyi*) (7)	WAbe
'Silver Hill' (*paniculata*) (8) **new**	NSla SIgm
'Silver Maid' (× *engleri*) (8)	GCrg NSla
'Silver Mound'	see *S.* 'Silver Cushion'
'Silver Velvet' (*fortunei*) (5)	CAbP CBct CHel CLAP CSpe ECtt ESwi GEdr IFoB MHol MSCN NMyG NWad SGSe SHeu WBor WCot
'Sir Douglas Haig' (15)	NWad
'Sissi' (7)	CTal EPot WAbe
'Slack's Ruby Southside' (Southside Seedling Group) (8) ♀H5	NSla NWad WIce
'Slack's Sensation'	NSla
'Slack's Supreme'	NHar NSla WCot
'Slzy Coventry' (× *proximae*) (7)	EPot WAbe
'Snowcap' (*pubescens*) (15)	EPot WAbe
'Snowflake' (Silver Farreri Group) (8) ♀H5	WAbe
§ 'Sofia' (× *borisii*) (7)	EPot
'Southside Red'	EPot
Southside Seedling Group (8)	CMea CTal EAEE ECho EDAr EPfP EPot GAbr GJos GKev GMaP LRHS MAsh MAvo MMuc NBro NHol NWad SEND SMad SPer SPoG SRms WAbe WHoo WIce WOld XLum
- 'Southside Star' (8) ♀H5	WAbe
spathularis (11)	WCot

	Name	Suppliers
	'Splendens' (*oppositifolia*) (7) ♀H5	ECho EPfP GAbr GKev MMuc NHar SIgm SRms WAbe WIce
	'Spotted Dog'	see *S.* 'Canis-dalmatica'
	'Sprite' (15)	SPoG
	spruneri (7)	ECho LRHS
	'Stansfieldii' (*rosacea*) (15)	GCrg SPlb SPoG
	'Star Dust' (7)	EPot
	'Štásek' (*dinnikii*) (7)	EPot
	stellaris (4)	WAbe
	stenophylla subsp. ***stenophylla***	see *S. flagellaris*
	stolitzkae (7)	EPot
§	***stolonifera*** (5) ♀H2	CArn CHEx CSpe ECho EShb EWTr NBro SDix SPer SWvt WCot WMoo WPnn WWtn
	- large-flowered (5)	WCot WGrn
	'Strawberry Melba' (7)	EPot
	stribrnyi (7)	EPot
	'Sturmiana' (*paniculata*) (8)	SRms
	'Sue Drew' (*fortunei*) (5)	LLHF
	'Sue Tubbs' (8)	GKev
	'Suendermannii Major' (× *kellereri*) (7)	ECho LRHS
	'Suendermannii' (× *kellereri*) (7)	ECho LRHS
	'Sugar Plum Fairy' (*fortunei*) (5)	EBee ECtt EShb ESwi IVic MHol WCot
§	'Sulphurea' (× *boydii*) (7)	ECho EPot LRHS MAsh NSla NWad WHoo
	'Symons-Jeunei' (8)	NWad WAbe
	'Tenerife' (Swirly Group) (7)	EPot WAbe
	'Theoden' (*oppositifolia*) (7) ♀H5	CMea ECho EWes NHar WAbe
	'Theresa Cooper' (7)	EPot WAbe
	tolmiei (3)	WAbe
	tombeanensis (7)	EPot
	Touran Deep Red = 'Rockred' (Mossy Group) (15)	LBuc
	Touran Large White = 'Rocklarwhi'PBR (Mossy Group) (15)	LBuc
	'Tricolor' (*stolonifera*) (5) ♀H2	EBak
§	'Triumph' (× *arendsii*) (15)	CBod ECtt EPfP GMaP MAsh MAvo NEgg SPoG
	'Tumbling Waters' (8) ♀H5	ECho EPot LRHS MRav NHol NSla WAbe
§	'Tvoje Píseň' (× *poluanglica*) (7)	CTal GKev WHoo WThu
§	'Tvůj Polibek' (× *poluanglica*) (7)	EPot
§	'Tvůj Úsměv' (× *poluanglica*) (7) ♀H5	NLar
§	'Tvůj Úspěch' (× *poluanglica*) (7)	WAbe
	'Tycho Brahe' (× *doerfleri*) (7)	WAbe
	umbrosa (11)	CMac CTri ECho EDAr EPla LAst LEdu LRHS LSun MMuc MRav SBod SCob SEND SPlb SPoG SRms SWvt WMoo XLum
*	- ***subinteger***	MMuc SEND
	× ***urbium*** (11) ♀H5	CHEx CTri ECho ELan EPfP EWoo GMaP LEdu LPot MBel MCot NPri SPer SRms WBor WCAu WHoo WWEG

	Name	Suppliers
	'Vaccariana' (*oppositifolia*) (7)	ECho EPot SHar
	'Valborg'	see *S.* 'Cranbourne'
	'Valentine'	see *S.* 'Cranbourne'
I	'Variegata' (*cuneifolia*) (11/v)	ECho ECtt EPfP GCrg LRHS NHol NRya NWad SPlb SPoG WMoo
I	'Variegata' (*exarata* subsp. *moschata*) (15/v)	GMaP
	'Variegata' (*umbrosa*)	see *S.* 'Aureopunctata'
I	'Variegata' (× *urbium*) (11/v)	EBee ECho EPfP EPla LRHS MBel MSpe NLar SCob SMad SRms WWEG
	'Večerní Hvězda' (7)	WAbe
	veitchiana (5)	NBro XLum
	'Verona' (× *caroli-langii*) (7)	WAbe
	'Vincent van Gogh' (× *borisii*) (7)	EPot
	'Vladana' (× *megaseiflora*) (7)	CPBP ECho LRHS WAbe
	'Vltava' (7)	EPot
	'Vreny' (8)	GKev
	'Vysoké Mýto' (7)	EPot WAbe
	'Wada' (*fortunei*) (5)	Widely available
	'Walpole's Variety' (8)	NWad
	'Walter Ingwersen' (*umbrosa*) (11)	SRms
§	'Walter Irving' (× *irvingii*) (7) ♀H5	WAbe
	'Warmes Herz' (*fortunei*) (5)	IVic
	'Welsh Dragon' (15)	WAbe
	'Welsh Red' (15)	WAbe
	'Welsh Rose' (15)	WAbe
	wendelboi (7)	CTal EPot WAbe
	'Wendy' (× *wendelacina*) (7)	WAbe
	'Wetterhorn' (*oppositifolia*) (7)	GCrg
	'Wheatley Rose' (7)	ECho LRHS
§	'White Pixie' (15)	ECtt EDAr EPfP EWoo GCrg MAsh MHer NEoE NHol NRya NWad SPlb SPoG SRms WIce
	'White Star' (*fortunei*) (5) **new**	LLHF
	'Whitehill' (8) ♀H5	CMea ECho ELan GEdr GJos GMaP LRHS NBro NRya NSla NWad SBch WHoo
	'William Boyd' (× *boydii*) (7)	WAbe
	'William Shakespeare' (Blues Group) (7)	EPot WAbe
	'Winifred Bevington' (8 × 11)	CPBP CTal ECho EDAr GCrg LRHS MMuc NBro NLar NRya NWad WAbe WHoo WPnn
	'Winifred' (× *anglica*) (7)	CTal ECho EPot WAbe
	'Winston Churchill' (15)	CTri ECho LRHS NHol NWad
I	'Winston Churchill Variegata' (15/v)	NHol NWad
	'Winton' (× *paulinae*) (7)	EPot
	'Yellow Rock' (7)	NRya
	'Youkuy' (*fortunei*) (5)	IVic
	Your Good Fortune	see *S.* 'Tvůj Úspěch'
	Your Kiss	see *S.* 'Tvůj Polibek'
	Your Smile	see *S.* 'Tvůj Úsměv'
	Your Song	see *S.* 'Tvoje Píseň'
	Your Success	see *S.* 'Tvůj Úspěch'
	'Yunagi' (*fortunei*) (5)	IVic WOld
	× ***zimmeteri*** (8 × 11)	ECho
§	'Zlatá Praha' (× *pragensis*) (7)	EPot WAbe

Scabiosa (*Caprifoliaceae*)

africana	EWes SHar
– 'Jocelyn'	EWes SHar
alpina L.	see *Cephalaria alpina*
argentea	EWes LEdu
atropurpurea	SPav
– 'Ace of Spades'	CWCL ELan EPfP MCot MGos SCob SPav SPhx
– 'Beaujolais Bonnets'	CNor EAJP EPfP LRHS SHil SPer WHrl
– 'Black Knight'	CSpe SPav
– 'Blue Beau' new	LRHS
– 'Chat Noir' new	SMrm
§ – 'Chile Black'	CAby CBcs CHel EAJP EHoe ELan EPfP EUJe EWes GCal IBoy LAst LRHS MWat NPri SBod SCob SPav SPer SPhx SRkn SWvt WGwG WHar WMnd
§ – 'Chilli Pepper'	CWCL LRHS
§ – 'Chilli Sauce'	EBee LRHS SPer
– 'Derry's Black'	CSpe SPtp
– 'Fata Morgana'	SPav
– 'Night and Day'	LRHS
– 'Snowmaiden'	SPav
banatica	see *S. columbaria*
'Barocca'	CNor CSpe EBee EPfP LRHS
'Black PomPom' new	GBin
'Blackberry Fool' (Dessert Series) new	WHlf
'Blue Diamonds'	EBee GJos IBoy LRHS MHol WHil
'Blueberry Muffin' (Dessert Series) new	WHlf
'Burgundy Blue' new	MCot
Burgundy Bonnets = 'Scabon'^PBR	EPfP LRHS
§ 'Butterfly Blue'	Widely available
'Cambridge Blue'	EPfP
canescens	MSpe
caucasica	CMac EPfP GKev LAst LEdu LRHS WHoo
– var. ***alba***	CBcs CKno EPfP NGBl WHoo
– 'Blausiegel'	CBod CMac MRav NDov
– 'Clive Greaves' ♀H4	EBee ECha ECtt GBuc GMaP IBoy LRHS MBNS MSpe NDov NPri SCob SGbt SPad SRms SWvt WCAu WCot WFar WHil
– 'Deep Waters'	CSpe LRHS
– 'Fama'	COtt CSpe NBir NGBl NLar SPlb SRms WFar
– 'Fama Deep Blue'	SMrm
– 'Fama White'	SMrm
– 'Goldingensis'	CWCL NGdn NPri WHil
– House's hybrids	CSBt MHol NGdn SRms
– 'Isaac House'	XLum
– 'Kompliment'	SMrm WFar WWEG
– 'Miss Willmott' ♀H4	CBod CMac CSam EBee ECha ECtt EHoe EPfP GBin IBoy LAst LRHS MBri MLHP MRav MSpe NPri SGbt SMrm SPer SPoG SWvt WGwG WMnd
– Perfecta Series	LRHS MMHG NGdn NLar SPoG SWat WHar
– 'Perfecta Alba' (Perfecta Series)	ELan ELon EWoo GMaP LAst LRHS MGos MHer MSpe MWat NLar NOrc NPri NSoo SCob SPad SPer SPoG SWat WWEG XLum
– – 'Perfecta Blue'	ELan ELon EWoo GMaP LSun MGos MHer MSpe NSoo SBod WCot XLum
– – 'Perfecta Lilac Blue'	EPfP SPer WWEG
– 'Stäfa'	EBee ECha GBee GBin LRHS NEgg NLar SHar WMnd
– 'Thorp's Variegated' (v)	WCot
'Cherry Pie' (Dessert Series) new	WHlf
'Chile Black'	see *S. atropurpurea* 'Chile Black'
'Chile Pepper'	see *S. atropurpurea* 'Chilli Pepper'
'Chile Sauce'	see *S. atropurpurea* 'Chilli Sauce'
cinerea	SPhx
§ ***columbaria***	CHab EBee ECGP LRHS MLHP MMuc NEgg NMir SMrm SPhx WHer WJek WSFF
* – ***alpina***	GKev WAbe
– 'Blue Note'^PBR	LRHS SMrm
– blue-flowered	LRHS
– 'Misty Butterflies'	CAby ECtt EPfP GBin LBMP NEgg NGdn NLar SMrm WFar WWEG
– 'Nana'	CCse EBee GBin LRHS NBir NGdn NLar SBch WCFE XLum
§ – subsp. ***ochroleuca***	CKno CSpe ECha GLin LRHS MCot MHer MMuc MSpe NBir NLar SCob SGSe SHar SPhx SPoG SRms WCAu WPGP
– – MESE 344	EBee
– – 'Moon Dance'	CAby CCon CMea EAJP EWll GBin LLHF LRHS MSpe NPri SGbt SMad WHoo
– 'Pincushion Blue'	EDAr MSpe
– 'Pincushion Pink'	EDAr LRHS MSpe NGdn SGSe WWEG
– pink-flowered	LRHS
cretica	XLum XSen
drakensbergensis	CHid ELan EWTr EWes GKev IKil LRHS MTPN SGSe SLon WCot WPtf
gigantea	see *Cephalaria gigantea*
graminifolia	ECho GKev LRHS NBir SBch SRms WWEG XLum
– ***rosea***	EWes
'Helen Dillon'	ECre EWes LSou
'Irish Perpetual Flowering'	see *S.* 'Butterfly Blue'
japonica var. ***acutiloba***	SPhx
– var. ***alpina***	CPrp EBee EPfP GKev MMuc MWat NGdn SPhx WHoo WWFP XLum
– – 'Blue Star'	EBee NBre NCGa SGbt
– 'Blue Note' new	NSir
– 'Ritz Blue'	CMea EPfP MHer NCGa SPad
lachnophylla	EBee GCal SPhx WCot
– 'Blue Horizon'	EBee
'Little Cracker' new	GBin LRHS LSou SCob SPoG
'Little Emily'	ELon LSou
lucida	EAEE ECho ECtt EPfP EPla LRHS MMuc MRav WPGP XLum
Magic = 'Pmoore02' new	LSou
'Midnight'	CMea
'Miss Havisham'	EWes
montana Mill.	see *Knautia arvensis*
ochroleuca	see *S. columbaria* subsp. *ochroleuca*
olgae	EBee
parnassi	see *Pterocephalus perennis*
'Perpetual Flowering'	see *S.* 'Butterfly Blue'
Pink Buttons = 'Walminipink'	CBod CCon EBee EPla SMrm
'Pink Diamonds'	EBee ELan EPfP MHol
'Pink Mist'^PBR	EBee ECtt ELan EPfP EPla GBBs IBoy LRHS MAsh MBri NBir NLar SCob SCoo SMrm SPer SPoG SRms

'Plum Pudding' (Dessert Series) new	WHlf
pterocephala	see *Pterocephalus perennis*
rhodopensis	EBee
'Rhubarb Crumble' (Dessert Series) new	WHlf
'Rosie's Pink'	ECtt
rumelica	see *Knautia macedonica*
'Satchmo'	see *S. atropurpurea* 'Chile Black'
succisa	see *Succisa pratensis*
tatarica	see *Cephalaria gigantea*
'Vivid Violet'	CAbP CAbb CSpe CUse CWGN EBee ECtt IPot LRHS LSou MBNS MHol MNrw NLar SHil WBor WCot

Scadoxus ✿ (*Amaryllidaceae*)

chinensis new	GKev
membranaceus	WCot
multiflorus	CCCN ECho LAma SDeJ
§ - subsp. ***katherinae*** 🏆H1b	CPne WCot
§ - subsp. ***multiflorus***	WCot
natalensis	see *S. puniceus*
§ ***puniceus***	CLak WCot

Scaevola (*Goodeniaceae*)

aemula 'Blue Fan'PBR	see *S. aemula* 'Blue Wonder'
§ - 'Blue Wonder'PBR	NPer SWvt
- 'Purple Fan'	LAst
- 'Sparkling Fan'	LAst
- 'Suntastic'	LAst
- 'Zig Zag'PBR	CCCN
Blauer Facher = 'Saphira'PBR	CCCN
'Brillant'PBR	LAst LSou
crassifolia	SPlb
'Mini Blue'	CCCN
'Topaz Pink'	LSou

Sceletium (*Aizoaceae*)

tortuosum	SPlb

Schefflera (*Araliaceae*)

alpina	CFil IVic
- B&SWJ 8247	WCru
- B&SWJ 11827	WCru
- HWJ 936	WCru
- large-leaved WWJ 11999 new	WCru
arboricola 🏆H1c	SEND XBlo
- 'Gold Capella' 🏆H1c	SEND XBlo
- 'Kalahari'	XBlo
brevipedicellata HWJ 870	WCru
- KWJ 12224	WCru
§ ***chapana*** B&SWJ 11848	WCru
- HWJ 983	WCru
delavayi	CFil CHEx WPGP
enneaphylla B&SWJ 11727	WCru
- HWJ 1018	WCru
fantsipanensis	CFil
- B&SWJ 11666	WCru
- B&SWJ 11671	WCru
- NJM 10.137 new	WPGP
fengii	GLin
gracilis HWJ 622	WCru
- HWJ 878	WCru
gracilis × ***taiwaniana*** new	WCru
hoi B&SWJ 11747	WCru
kornasii B&SWJ 11830	WCru
- HWJ 918	WCru
macrophylla	WCru
B&SWJ 8210 new	
- B&SWJ 9788	WCru
- B&SWJ 11842	WCru
- PAB 2788	LEdu
microphylla B&SWJ 3872	WCru
multinervia B&SWJ 11727	WCru
aff. ***myriocarpa*** B&SWJ 11828	WCru
rhododendrifolia	CExl CFil CHEx CMHG WPGP
- GWJ 9375	WCru
taiwaniana 🏆H4	CFil CHEx IVic
- B&SWJ 3575	WCru
- B&SWJ 7096	WCru
- RWJ 10000	WCru
- RWJ 10016	WCru
vietnamensis	see *S. chapana*

Schima (*Theaceae*)

wallichii	CBcs CExl
- subsp. ***noronhae*** var. ***superba***	CCCN CExl EPfP
- subsp. ***wallichii*** var. ***khasiana***	CBcs
- - - PAB 3447 new	LEdu

Schinus (*Anacardiaceae*)

latifolius	CBcs
lentiscifolius	SPlb
molle	SPlb
polygamus	CBcs SPlb

Schisandra (*Schisandraceae*)

sp.	LAst
arisanensis	MBlu NLar WPGP
- B&SWJ 3050	WCru
aff. ***bicolor***	WPGP
chinensis	CAgr CArn CBcs CUse EShb GPoy LEdu MSwo NLar SBrt
- B&SWJ 4204	WCru
- B&SWJ 4611A new	WCru
- B&SWJ 4611B new	WCru
- 'Bere' new	LEdu
grandiflora 🏆H5	CBcs CDoC CHel CRHN CWCL EBee ELan EPfP ESwi LRHS MBlu SKHP SPer
- B&SWJ 2245	WCru WSHC
- var. ***cathayensis***	see *S. sphaerandra*
- 'Jamu' (m)	WCru
- 'Lahlu' (f/F)	WCru
grandiflora × ***rubriflora***	WCru
henryi	WCru
subsp. ***yunnanensis*** B&SWJ 6546	
incarnata BWJ 7898 new	WCru
incarnata × ***rubriflora***	WCru
lancifolia new	MBlu WPGP
nigra	see *S. repanda*
perulata FMWJ 13100 new	WCru
aff. ***plena*** HWJ 664	WCru
propinqua new	WSHC
- subsp. ***sinensis***	CMac CRHN LEdu NLar WPGP
- - BWJ 8148	WCru
§ ***repanda*** B&SWJ 5897	WCru
- B&SWJ 11455	WCru

rubriflora ♀H5	CBcs CTri EBee EPfP IDee LRHS MBlu MGos NLar SKHP SLon SMDP
- BWJ 7557	WCru
- (f)	WSHC
- 'Bodnant Redberry' (f) **new**	WCru
§ ***sphaerandra*** BWJ 7739	WCru
- BWJ 8082 **new**	WCru
sphenanthera	LRHS NLar WSHC
- BWJ 8151	WCru

Schivereckia (*Brassicaceae*)

doerfleri	MWat

Schizachyrium (*Poaceae*)

§ ***scoparium***	CKno EBee ECGP EHoe EPPr EPfP EPla GQue LRHS SGSe SPhx WCot XLum
- 'Blaze'	EPPr
- 'Blue Heaven'	ELon
- 'Prairie Blues'	EPfP LRHS LSun SMea SMrm SPhx WCot

Schizocarphus (*Asparagaceae*)

nervosus	ECho WCot

Schizocodon see *Shortia*

Schizophragma (*Hydrangeaceae*)

corylifolium	NLar
- BWJ 8150	WPGP
fauriei	see *S. integrifolium* var. *fauriei*
hydrangeoides	CBcs CDoC CDul CHel EBee ELan EPfP EWTr GKin LAst LRHS MBlu MGos SGol SLim SLon SPer SWvt WCFE
- 'Brookside Littleleaf'	see *Hydrangea anomala* subsp. *petiolaris* var. *cordifolia* 'Brookside Littleleaf'
- var. ***concolor*** B&SWJ 5954 **new**	WCru
- - 'Moonlight' ♀H5	Widely available
- var. ***hydrangeoides*** B&SWJ 5489	WCru
- - B&SWJ 5732	WCru
- - 'Iwa Garami'	NLar
- 'Rose Sensation'	EBee EPfP EWTr LRHS LSqu SLon
- 'Roseum' ♀H5	CBcs CDoC CMac CSPN ELan EPfP EWes GBin GKin IArd LRHS MBlu MGil MGos NLar SGol SKHP SLon SPer SPoG SSpi SWvt WCru WPGP
- var. ***taquetii*** B&SWJ 8771 **new**	WCru
- - 'Cheju's Early' **new**	WCru
- var. ***ullungdoense*** B&SWJ 8505 **new**	WCru
- - B&SWJ 8522 **new**	WCru
- var. ***yakushimense*** B&SWJ 6119 **new**	WCru
integrifolium ♀H5	CBcs CDul CHel CRHN EBee ELan EPfP LRHS MBlu MMuc SKHP SPer WKif WPGP WSHC
- BWJ 8150 **new**	WCru
§ - var. ***fauriei***	NLar WSHC
- - B&SWJ 1701	WCru
- - B&SWJ 6831 **new**	WCru
- - B&SWJ 7052	WCru
- - CWJ 12405 **new**	WCru
- - CWJ 12433	WCru
molle HWJ 1011 **new**	WCru
- WWJ 11905 **new**	WCru

Schizostylis see *Hesperantha*

coccinea 'Gigantea'	see *Hesperantha coccinea* 'Major'
- 'Grandiflora'	see *Hesperantha coccinea* 'Major'
- 'Sunset'	see *Hesperantha coccinea* 'Sunrise'
'Pink Princess'	see *Hesperantha coccinea* 'Wilfred H. Bryant'

Schoenoplectus (*Cyperaceae*)

§ ***lacustris***	CBAq CWat MMuc MSKA SEND
§ - subsp. ***tabernaemontani***	CBAq CSpe
- - 'Albescens' (v)	CBAq CBen CWat MMuc MNrw MSKA MWts SWat WHal WWtn XLum
- - 'Zebrinus' (v)	CBAq CBen CWat ELan MNrw MSKA MWts NPla SPlb SWat WMAq XLum

Schoenus (*Cyperaceae*)

pauciflorus	EHoe LLWG NOak WMoo

Sciadopitys (*Sciadopityaceae*)

verticillata ♀H6	CAco CBcs CDoC CDul CKen CMac CSBt CTho EHul EPfP GKin IDee MBlu MBri MGos MJak MMuc NHol NWad NWea SCoo SLim SPoG SSpi SWvt WHar
- 'Big Filip' **new**	NLar
I - 'Compacta'	LRHS
- 'Firework'	CKen NLar
- 'Globe'	CKen
- 'Gold Star'	CKen NLar
- 'Goldammer'	NLar
- 'Golden Rush'	CKen NLar
- 'Goldmahne'	CKen
- 'Grüne Kugel'	CKen NLar
- 'Jeddeloh Compact'	CKen
- 'Koja Maki' **new**	NLar
- 'Kupferschirm'	CKen NLar
- 'Mecki'	CKen
- 'Megaschirm'	CKen
- 'Ossorio Gold'	CKen
- 'Perlenglanz'	CKen
- 'Picola'	CKen NLar
- 'Pygmy'	CKen
- 'Richie's Cream'	CKen
- 'Richie's Cushion'	CKen
- 'Shorty'	CKen
- 'Speerspitze'	CKen
- 'Star Wars'	CKen
- 'Starburst'	CKen NLar
- 'Sternschnuppe'	CKen MAsh NLar
- 'Wintergreen'	CKen

Scilla (*Asparagaceae*)

adlamii	see *Ledebouria cooperi*
× ***allenii***	see × *Chionoscilla allenii*
amethystina	see *S. litardierei*
amoena	ECho WCot
aristidis from Algeria	ECho
autumnalis	CAvo CDes ECho EPot GKev LAma LLHF LRHS NRog WShi WThu
- white-flowered **new**	NRog
bifolia ♀H5	CAvo CBro CPom CTca ECho EPot GKev LAma LLWP SBch SDeJ SPhx WRHF WShi

- RS 156/83	ECho
- 'Alba'	ECho EPot SPhx
- 'Rosea'	ECho EPot GKev LAma LLWP MPie SDeJ
bithynica 𝕐H5	WCot WShi
I - 'Alba'	CAvo
campanulata	see *Hyacinthoides hispanica*
chinensis	see *S. scilloides*
cilicica	ECho SPhx
greilhuberi	ECho EPPr LLHF WCot
hohenackeri	CPom ECho LLHF SPhx WCot WThu
- BSBE 811	CDes WCot
§ ***hughii***	CDes ECho
hyacinthoides	CDes ECho ERCP WCot
ingridiae	ECho
- var. ***taurica***	ECho
italica	see *Hyacinthoides italica*
japonica	see *S. scilloides*
latifolia from Morocco	ECho
liliohyacinthus	CBro CRow ECho IBlr MMHG WSHC WShi
lingulata	ECho LLHF WCot
- S&F 253	CDes
- var. ***ciliolata***	CBro ECho EPot NRog SBch
- var. ***lingulata***	ECho
§ ***litardierei*** 𝕐H5	CPom CTca ECho EPPr EPfP EPot ERCP GKev LAma MMuc SBch SDeJ SEND SPhx WShi
lutea hort.	see *Ledebouria socialis*
madeirensis	CLak WCot
- from Madeira	CHll
melaina	WCot
messeniaca	CPom
- from Greece MS 38	WCot
mischtschenkoana 𝕐H5	CAby CAvo CBro CHid ECho EPot IFro LAma LRHS MBri SBch SDeJ WShi
§ - 'Tubergeniana' 𝕐H5	CMea ECho GKev SPhx WCot
- 'Zwanenburg'	ECho
monophyllos	ECho WCot
natalensis	see *Merwilla plumbea*
non-scripta	see *Hyacinthoides non-scripta*
nutans	see *Hyacinthoides non-scripta*
obtusifolia	ECho
- subsp. ***intermedia***	WCot
persica 𝕐H4	CDes ECho WCot
peruviana	Widely available
- SB&L 20/1	WCot
- 'Alba'	CBro CDes CTal CTca CWCL ECho WCot XLum
- var. ***elegans***	CDes
- 'Hughii'	see *S. hughii*
- 'Paul Voelcker'	CDes
- var. ***venusta***	CDes
- - S&L 311/2	WCot
pratensis	see *S. litardierei*
puschkinioides	ECho
reverchonii	CPom ECho
- from Spain	WCot
rosenii	ECho
§ ***scilloides***	ECho GKev NRog WCot
- B&SWJ 8812	WCru
* - 'Alba'	SDeJ
siberica 𝕐H5	CAby CAvo CBro CTca ECho ELan EPfP EShb GAbr GKev LAma LRHS MMuc MWat SPer SPhx WBor WHea WShi
- 'Alba'	CAvo CTca ECho EPfP EPot GKev LAma LRHS SDeJ WShi
- 'Spring Beauty'	CMea ECho EPot ERCP GKev LAma LRHS MBri SDeJ SPhx SRms
'Tubergeniana'	see *S. mischtschenkoana* 'Tubergeniana'
verna	ECho WShi WThu
vicentina	see *Hyacinthoides vincentina*
violacea	see *Ledebouria socialis*

Scirpoides (*Cyperaceae*)

§ ***holoschoenus***	EBee

Scirpus (*Cyperaceae*)

cernuus	see *Isolepis cernua*
'Green Mist' **new**	WCot
holoschoenus	see *Scirpoides holoschoenus*
lacustris	see *Schoenoplectus lacustris*
- 'Spiralis'	see *Juncus effusus* f. *spiralis*
maritimus	see *Bolboschoenus maritimus*
tabernaemontani	see *Schoenoplectus lacustris* subsp. *tabernaemontani*

Scleranthus (*Caryophyllaceae*)

biflorus	ECho EDAr EUJe EWes GBin LEdu MAsh SPlb XLum
uniflorus	ECho IDee LEdu SMad SPlb XLum

Sclerochiton (*Acanthaceae*)

harveyanus	EShb

Scoliopus (*Liliaceae*)

bigelowii	GEdr
hallii	CTal EBee LEdu WCru

Scolopendrium see *Asplenium*

Scopolia (*Solanaceae*)

carniolica	CArn CAvo CCon CElw EBee ELan EWld GPoy LEdu NChi NLar NSti SPlb WCru WPGP WSHC XLum
- from Poland	LEdu
§ - var. ***brevifolia***	EBee EPPr EPfP EWld LEdu LRHS MNrw SPhx WCot
- 'Zwanenburg'	EPPr EWes LEdu NLar SPhx XLum
hladnikiana	see *S. carniolica* var. *brevifolia*
japonica	IMou
lurida	see *Anisodus luridus*

Scorzonera (*Asteraceae*)

hispanica	SVic

Scrophularia (*Scrophulariaceae*)

aquatica misapplied	see *S. auriculata*
§ ***auriculata***	CHab LLWG MHer NMir NPer WHer
§ - 'Variegata' (v)	CBAq CBcs ECha EHoe ELan EPfP EPla GCal GLog LLWG LRHS MHer NPri NSti SHar SPer SPoG
buergeriana 'Lemon and Lime' misapplied	see *Teucrium viscidum* 'Lemon and Lime'
- 'Lemon and Lime' (v)	EBee NEgg
nodosa	CArn GPoy NMir WHer WHfH
- ***variegata***	see *S. auriculata* 'Variegata'
scopolii	EBee
vernalis	CBgR

Scutellaria ✿ (*Lamiaceae*)

albida	EBee GJos
§ ***alpina***	ECho GJos SPlb SRms SRot
- 'Arcobaleno'	GJos LLHF
- 'Moonbeam'	GJos SMrm
altissima	CFis ECha ELan MMuc MSpe NBro SPlb WHea WOut WPtf WWtn XSen
'Amazing Grace'	EWes
baicalensis	CArn GJos GPoy IMou SMrm WPtf
- 'Oriental Blue' new	GJos
canescens	see *S. incana*
diffusa	GEdr
galericulata	CBod CHab ENfk GPoy MHer WHer
hastata	see *S. hastifolia*
§ ***hastifolia***	CTri ECtt
hypericifolia	XSen
§ ***incana***	ECGP ELan EWoo GMaP LPla LRHS MAvo MHol MPie SPhx WCot WMnd
indica	EWld
- var. ***japonica***	see *S. indica* var. *parvifolia*
§ - var. ***parvifolia***	ECho EWes GJos SRot WAbe
- - 'Alba'	ECho LLHF
lateriflora	CArn GJos GPoy SMrm WJek
- PAB 3921	LEdu
maekawae	EBee WPGP
- B&SWJ 557a	CDes WCru
'Mood Indigo'	EPPr
orientalis	CPBP ECtt SBch WAbe
- subsp. ***bicolor***	ECtt
- subsp. ***pinnatifida***	XSen
pontica	CPBP GEdr MMuc SBch SMrm WIce
scordiifolia	CMea ECha ECho IMou NRya NWad SBHP SRms
- 'Seoul Sapphire'	CDes CSpe GAbr GBin LEdu LRHS SPtp WPtf
sevanensis	MNrw WCot WIce
'Sherbert Lemon'	CMea CPBP SRot WHil
suffrutescens	GJos
- 'Texas Rose'	CFis CMea CSpe ECho LLHF LRHS MCot SBch SRot WAbe WIce WSHC
supina	see *S. alpina*
tournefortii	ECtt LLWP LRHS WOut XSen
* ***zhongdianensis***	WPtf

seakale see *Crambe maritima*

Sebaea (*Gentianaceae*)

rehmanii	SPlb
thomasii	WAbe
- 'Bychan'	WAbe

Securigera (*Papilionaceae*)

§ ***varia***	CArn MMuc NPri SEND SRms XLum

Sedastrum see *Sedum*

× *Sedeveria* (*Crassulaceae*)

'Darley Dale'	CSuc
'Fanfare'	CSuc
'Harry Butterfield' new	WCot
'Letizia'	EUJe

Sedum ✿ (*Crassulaceae*)

sp.	SCob
'Abbey Dore'	CBod CPrp ECtt ELan ELon EPfP GCal LPla LRHS LSou MTis NCGa SPhx WCAu WPGP
acre	CTri ECho EPfP GPoy LEdu LRHS MAsh MNHC NMir SCob SPlb XLum
- 'Aureum'	ECho EDAr EHoe ELan EPfP LAst MAsh NLar NPri NRya SCob SPer SPoG XLum
- 'Elegans'	GCrg
- 'Golden Queen'	ECho LRHS MSCN SPlb SPoG
- 'Helvetica'	WCot
- 'Minus'	ECho
§ - subsp. ***neglectum*** var. ***majus***	CChe EPfP NLar
adolphi	EPfP
aizoon	ECho GCal LAst NBre SPlb WFar XLum
- 'Aurantiacum'	see *S. aizoon* 'Euphorbioides'
§ - 'Euphorbioides'	ECha ECtt ELan LPot MHer MMuc MRav NLar SEND SHar SPer SPlb
§ - subsp. ***maximowiczii*** new	NWad
alatum new	WFar
albescens	see *S. forsterianum* f. *purpureum*
alboroseum	see *S. erythrostictum*
§ ***album***	ECho GJos LRHS MMuc NBro NMir SEND XLum
- 'Coral Carpet'	CTal ECho ECtt EDAr EPPr EPfP EPot GAbr GCrg GJos GKev MAsh MRav MWat NLar NRya SFgr SPoG WCot XLum
- subsp. ***teretifolium*** var. ***micranthum*** 'Chloroticum'	XLum
§ - - var. ***murale***	CTri XLum
alpestre	XLum
altissimum	see *S. sediforme*
* ***altum***	NBre
Amber = 'Florseamb' new	EBee
anacampseros	MHer NWad SEND XLum
'Aquarel'	GBin
athoum	see *S. album*
atlanticum	see *S. dasyphyllum* subsp. *dasyphyllum* var. *mesatlanticum*
'Autumn Charm'	see *S.* (Herbstfreude Group) 'Lajos'
Autumn Joy	see *S.* (Herbstfreude Group) 'Herbstfreude'
beauverdii subsp. ***vietnamense*** HWJ 824	WCru
'Bertram Anderson' ♀H7	Widely available
beyrichianum misapplied	see *S. glaucophyllum*
bithynicum 'Aureum'	see *S. hispanicum* var. *minus* 'Aureum'
Black Beauty = 'Florseblab'	ECtt LRHS MBri MNrw NCGa NLar
'Blade Runner'	LRHS LSou
brevifolium	EWes
§ - var. ***quinquefarium***	WIce
'Carl' ♀H7	Widely available
cauticola ♀H5	CSpe ECho EDAr EPot GBuc GCal MAsh MAvo MBrN MHer MRav SRms SRot WAbe WIce XLum
- from Lida, Belarus	ECho
- 'Coca-Cola'	CBod CHel CMac CWGN EAEE ECtt EHoe EPla GBin GJos GKev LAst LBMP LRHS MAsh MCot NDov NPri SPhx SPoG SWvt WCAu WHoo

	Name	Suppliers
	- 'Lidakense'	CMea CSpe CTal CWCL ECha ECho ECtt EPot GBuc GCrg MAsh MBri MLHP MSCN NHol NLar NSla SBch SPlb SRot WCot XLum
	- 'Purpurine'	ECho
	- 'Robustum'	see *S.* 'Ruby Glow'
	'Chocolate Drop'[PBR]	CMos CWGN ECtt NLar SDys SPoG
	'Chocolate Sauce' **new**	MAvo
	chrysicaulum	EPot
	'Class Act'[PBR]	ECtt LRHS MNrw NLar SPoG
	'Cloud Walker'[PBR]	CAbP ECtt LRHS MNrw NCGa SPoG
	confusum Hemsl.	SEND
	crassipes	see *Rhodiola wallichiana*
	crassularia	see *Crassula setulosa* 'Milfordiae'
	'Crazy Ruffles'	ECtt WCot
	cryptomerioides B&SWJ 054	WCru
	cyaneum 'Sakhalin' **new**	WCot
	'Dark Jack'	ECtt ELon EPfP MAvo MNrw NCGa NGdn SMrm WCot
	dasyphyllum	ECho MWat NRya SPlb SRms
§	- subsp. ***dasyphyllum*** var. ***mesatlanticum***	NBir
	- ***mucronatis***	see *S. dasyphyllum* subsp. *dasyphyllum* var. *mesatlanticum*
	'Diamond Edge' (v)	EBee ECtt IKil
	divergens	XLum
	douglasii	see *S. stenopetalum* 'Douglasii'
	drymarioides	NBre WHil
	'Dudley Field'	MHer
	'Eleanor Fisher'	see *S. telephium* subsp. *ruprechtii*
	ellacombeanum	see *S. kamtschaticum* var. *ellacombeanum*
	'Elworthy Rose'	CElw
§	***erythrostictum***	XLum
	- 'Frosty Morn' (v)	Widely available
§	- 'Mediovariegatum' (v)	CNec EAEE EBee ELan LRHS MHer MNrw MRav NLar SWvt WFar WMnd WMoo WWEG XLum
	ewersii	ECho ECtt EDAr EPot GCrg MAsh MMuc NBro NLar SPhx SPlb XLum
	- CC 5288	GKev ITim
	- var. ***homophyllum*** 'Rosenteppich'	EPPr EPfP LBuc LRHS MAsh MBrN SWvt WMoo
	fabaria	see *S. telephium* subsp. *fabaria*
	fastigiatum	see *Rhodiola fastigiata*
	floriferum	see *S. kamtschaticum* var. *floriferum*
	forsterianum subsp. ***elegans***	SEND SPlb XLum
	- - 'Silver Stone' **new**	GJos MMuc
§	- f. ***purpureum***	NRya
	'Frosted Fire'	EBee LSou MAsh NSti
	furfuraceum	GEdr WAbe
	Garnet Brocade = 'Garbro'[PBR]	ECtt
§	***glaucophyllum***	EDAr XLum
	'Gold Mound'	EUJe LAst WHil
	'Goldie'	CDoC
	'Green Expectations'	ECtt GBin LRHS MNFA MRav MWat NBre WCAu
	hakonense 'Chocolate Ball'	CPBP ECtt GBin WHil
	Herbstfreude Group	EPla EWoo NWsh

	Name	Suppliers
	- 'Autumn Fire'	MAsh
	- 'Beka' (v)	LSou MAsh WHil
	- 'Elsie's Gold' (v)	CBod EBee ECtt MAsh MNrw SPoG WHil
§	- 'Herbstfreude' 🏆H7	Widely available
	- 'Jaws'[PBR]	CAby CKno EBee ECtt IKil NLar SMrm WCot WFar XLum
§	- 'Lajos' (v)	LSou MAsh NEoE
	- 'Mini Joy'	ELon GKev LRHS MNrw SHil WRHF
	heterodontum	see *Rhodiola heterodonta*
	hidakanum	ECtt EHoe EPot GMaP NBro NHol NWad SIgm WHoo
	himalense misapplied	see *Rhodiola* 'Keston'
	hispanicum	ECho NBre SPlb
	- 'Blue Carpet'	EPPr EUJe NPri
	- ***glaucum***	see *S. hispanicum* var. *minus*
§	- var. ***minus***	ECho ECtt MMuc MSCN SEND SPlb WCot WMoo
§	- - 'Aureum'	ECho
§	***hybridum***	XLum
	- 'Czar's Gold'	NGdn
	'Ice Ruffles' (v)	MAsh MAvo SPoG
	'Indian Chief'	see *S.* (Herbstfreude Group) 'Herbstfreude'
	indicum var. ***yunnanense*** **new**	EShb
	ishidae	see *Rhodiola ishidae*
	'José Aubergine'[PBR]	CBod CKno CMos EBee ECtt EWoo IPot LRHS MAsh MAvo MBri MRav MTis NCGa NDov NHol NLar NSoo NSti SCob SGol SPoG WHoo WPGP
	'Joyce Henderson'	ECtt ELan EPfP LRHS MCot MRav MTis MWhi NChi NLar SPer SRGP WBrk WCot WMoo WOld WWEG
	kamtschaticum 🏆H5	ECho EDAr GJos
	- B&SWJ 10870	WCru
§	- var. ***ellacombeanum*** 🏆H5	MMuc SEND WCot XLum
	- - B&SWJ 8853	WCru
§	- var. ***floriferum***	XSen
§	- - 'Weihenstephaner Gold'	CTri ECho ECtt EDAr EPfP GAbr GKev GMaP LPot MHer MMuc MRav MSCN MWat NBir SPlb SPoG SRms XLum
	- var. ***kamtschaticum*** 'Variegatum' (v) 🏆H5	CMea ECho EDAr EHoe EPfP GCrg LBMP LRHS MHer MJak MMuc MWat NPri SPoG SRms SRot SWvt XLum
	kirilovii	see *Rhodiola kirilovii*
	lanceolatum	NBre
	lineare 'Variegatum' (v)	WRHF XLum
	'Little Dove'	SBch
	'Little Missy' (v) **new**	ECtt
§	***lydium***	CTri ECho MHer SFgr SPlb
	- 'Aureum'	see *S. hispanicum* var. *minus* 'Aureum'
	- 'Bronze Queen'	see *S. lydium*
I	'Marchants Best Red' 🏆H7	CDes ELon MRav SMHy SPhx WCot
	'Matrona' 🏆H7	Widely available
	maweanum	see *S. acre* subsp. *neglectum* var. *majus*
	maximowiczii	see *S. aizoon* subsp. *maximowiczii*
	middendorffianum	ECho GCrg MBrN MHer MWat SRms SRot XLum
	- 'Striatum'	EDAr
	moranense	XLum
	morganianum 🏆H2	EBak EShb
	morrisonense B&SWJ 7078	WCru

'Mr Goodbud'[PBR] ♀H7	CPrp CUse ECtt GBin LPla LRHS LSun MAvo MHol MNrw NCGa NDov NLar NPCo SPoG WCot WHlf
'Munstead Red'	CBod CPrp CWCL EBee ECha ECtt EPfP GBin LAst LRHS MRav MTis MWat NLar SMrm SPer SPhx SPoG WKif WMnd WMoo
murale	see *S. album* subsp. *teretifolium* var. *murale*
nevii misapplied	see *S. glaucophyllum*
nevii ambig.	SPlb
nicaeense	see *S. sediforme*
'Novem'[PBR]	MBri
obtusatum misapplied	see *S. oreganum*
§ ***obtusatum*** A. Gray	NBro NSla
obtusifolium var. ***listoniae***	EDAr
ochroleucum	NBre WCot
oppositifolium	see *S. spurium* 'Album'
§ ***oreganum***	ECha ECho EDAr GAbr GCrg GKev GMaP MHer MSCN MWat SMad SPlb SRms SRot XLum
- 'Procumbens'	see *S. oreganum* subsp. *tenue*
§ - subsp. ***tenue***	EPot NHol NRya NWad WAbe
§ ***oregonense***	ECho LRHS MHer
pachyclados	see *Rhodiola pachyclados*
pachyphyllum	EPfP
palmeri	CHEx LSou MRav NBir SChr SEND XLum
pilosum	WThu
'Pink Dove'	SBch
§ ***pluricaule***	ECho GCrg LRHS SPlb SRms
populifolium	ECha GCal GEdr GJos IMou MHer MMuc NLar SPhx XLum
praealtum	SChr SEND
pulchellum	ECtt
'Purple Leaf'	LAst
quinquefarium	see *S. brevifolium* var. *quinquefarium*
'Red Cauli' ♀H7	Widely available
'Red Rum'	GBin LPla SPhx
'Red Setter'	WPGP
reflexum L.	see *S. rupestre* L.
rhodiola	see *Rhodiola rosea*
'Ripe Rhubarb'	SMHy
rosea	see *Rhodiola rosea*
rubroglaucum misapplied	see *S. oregonense*
rubroglaucum Praeger	see *S. obtusatum* A. Gray
× ***rubrotinctum*** ♀H2	CHEx
- 'Aurora' ♀H2	SChr
§ 'Ruby Glow' ♀H5	Widely available
'Ruby Port'	CSpe
§ ***rupestre*** L.	ECho GJos LAst MBNS MMuc MNHC MWat SEND SPlb XLum
- 'Angelina'	CKno CTal ECtt EPPr EWes IMou MGos MHer NBir NDov NEoE NHol NPri NWad SPoG SRGP WCot WGrn XLum
- 'Monstrosum Cristatum'	NBir SMad WCot XLum
ruprechtii	see *S. telephium* subsp. *ruprechtii*
sarcocaule hort.	see *Crassula sarcocaulis*
sarmentosum	ECho XLum
§ ***sediforme***	EDAr EPot GAbr SBch SEND XSen
- B&F MA 25	WCot
- ***nicaeense***	see *S. sediforme*
selskianum	GJos NBre NLar SBch XLum
- 'Goldilocks'	GJos
sempervivoides	ECho
'September Ruby'	LRHS
sexangulare	ECho EPot MHer MMuc NRya SEND SFgr SPlb SRms XLum
sibiricum	see *S. hybridum*
sieboldii	CFis ECho NDov
- 'Dragon'	LRHS
- 'Mediovariegatum' (v) ♀H3	CFis CHEx ECho EHoe LPot MHer MRav NPri NWsh SPlb XLum
'Silvermoon'	NWad
spathulifolium	CTri ECha ECho
- 'Aureum'	ECho ECtt GKev MWat WAbe
- 'Cape Blanco' ♀H5	Widely available
- 'Purpureum' ♀H5	ECho ECtt EDAr EHoe EPfP GAbr GKev GMaP LAst LBee LPot LRHS LSun MBel MHer MMuc MWat NHol NPri NRya NWad SPer SPlb SPoG WAbe WMoo XLum
spectabile ♀H7	CArn CHEx CPrp CTri ELan EPfP GJos GMaP LRHS MCot MHer MRav NGdn SCob SPer SPlb SRms WBor WBrk WCAu WFar WSFF WWEG
- 'Album'	CHEx
- Brilliant Group	LAst LBMP WCAu
- - 'Brilliant' ♀H7	CBcs CBod CHel CKno COtt CRos CSBt CTri EAEE ECha ECtt ELan EPfP LAst LPal LRHS MBri MGos MRav NGdn NLar NOrc SCob SPer SPoG SWvt WMoo WWEG
- - 'Carmen'	XLum
- - 'Hot Stuff'	CAby CNor ECtt ELon EPfP LRHS NPri SPoG SPtp SRot WCot
- - 'Lisa'	GBin MTPN NLar
- - 'Meteor'	CPrp LPla MWat NLar SMrm SPhx WWEG
- - 'Neon'	EBee EPfP LRHS MBel NDov
- - 'Pink Fairy'	MNrw WHil
- - 'Rosenteller'	CKno EBee GBin NBre SMrm
§ - - 'Septemberglut'	NBre XLum
- - 'Steven Ward'	CKno EWes NLar SRGP
- 'Crystal Pink'[PBR]	LRHS MNrw NLar
- 'Humile'	XLum
- 'Iceberg'	CUse EBee ECha ECtt EPfP LAst LRHS MAvo MCot MGos MNFA MRav MWat MWhi NCGa NGdn NLar SCob SPhx SPtp SWvt WFar WHil WMnd WMoo WSFF WWEG XLum
* - 'Mini'	MRav
- 'Nordlicht'	GBin
- 'Pink Chablis'[PBR] (v)	NLar WCot
- September Glow	see *S. spectabile* (Brilliant Group) 'Septemberglut'
- 'Stardust'	CKno CRos CTri EBee EPfP GBin GMaP LAst LRHS LSou MRav MTis NCGa NSoo SGol SMad SPer WFar WWEG XLum
- 'Variegatum'	see *S. erythrostictum* 'Mediovariegatum'
- Walberton's Pizazz	EPfP LRHS SPoG
spinosum	see *Orostachys spinosa*
spurium	CHEx ECho GAbr GJos MMuc SEND SRms XSen
§ - 'Album'	NRya XLum
- 'Atropurpureum'	ECha ECho WMoo XLum
- 'Coccineum'	ECho GJos MMuc MNHC SEND
- Dragon's Blood	see *S. spurium* 'Schorbuser Blut'
- 'Fuldaglut'	CTri ECho EHoe EPfP GCrg GMaP GQue IPot LRHS MNrw NRya SMrm WMoo WPnn WRHF

	- 'Green Mantle'	EBee ECha ECho EPfP LRHS
	- 'John Creech'	ECtt
	- Purple Carpet	see *S. spurium* 'Purpurteppich'
	- 'Purpureum'	SRms
§	- 'Purpurteppich'	ECho ECtt GJos MJak MRav NBro NLar NWad SRms SVen
	- 'Roseum'	SRms
	- 'Ruby Mantle'	EWll GKev MSCN MWat NBro NEoE SBch SPoG SWvt WMoo XLum
§	- 'Schorbuser Blut' 🏆[H5]	CTal ECho ECtt EPau EPfP GJos GKev LRHS MAsh MCot MLHP MWat NBir NRya NSla SPlb SRGP SRms WHoo WIce XLum
I	- 'Splendens Roseum'	XLum
	- 'Summer Glory'	NLar
§	- 'Tricolor' (v)	CTri EBee ECha ECho EHoe EPfP GJos GKev MAsh MHer MLHP MRav NHol NRya NWad SPlb SPoG WMoo XLum
	- 'Variegatum'	see *S. spurium* 'Tricolor'
	- 'Voodoo'	ECtt EPfP EWes LRHS MBel MHer MWat NBro NDov NGdn XLum
	stefco	XLum
	stenopetalum	SPlb
§	- 'Douglasii'	MHer SRms
	'Stewed Rhubarb Mountain'	CHel CKno CPrp EAEE EBee ECha ECtt ELan EPfP LRHS MBNS MCot MNFA MRav NBro NLar NOrc SGbt WMoo WWEG
	stoloniferum	ECho
	stribrnyi	see *S. urvillei* Stribrnyi Group
	'Sunset Cloud'	CHEx CMHG EBee ECtt EWes GCal IPot LPla LPot MRav
	takesimense	XLum
	- B&SWJ 8493 new	WCru
	- B&SWJ 8518	WCru
	telephium	CArn EWTr IFro LSun NBir SRms XLum
§	- Atropurpureum Group	MRav SWvt WWEG
	- - 'African Pearl'	GBin MAvo WCFE WCot WWEG
	- - 'Arthur Branch'	CPrp EBee GBin WWEG
I	- - 'Atropurpureum Nanum'	WWEG
	- - 'Bon Bon'	LAst LRHS MBNS NLar SPoG
	- - 'Bressingham Purple'	EBee EPPr LRHS
	- - 'Chocolate'	EBee ECtt EPPr MAvo NLar
	- - 'Dark Knight'	LRHS
	- - 'El Cid'	EWes
	- - 'Hester'	WWEG
	- - 'Karfunkelstein' 🏆[H7]	CKno EBee ECha ECtt EPPr GBin GLog MAvo MHol MTis NDov SPhx WCot XLum
	- - 'Leonore Zuuntz'	NBre
	- - 'Lynda et Rodney'	EWes
	- - 'Lynda Windsor'	ECtt EPfP NLar SWvt
	- - 'Möhrchen'	GBin GMaP LRHS MHer MRav MTis NGdn NLar NWsh SMrm SPhx WMoo
	- - 'Picolette'	CBod ECtt EPfP LBuc LRHS LSou MNrw NCGa SPoG WCot WMoo
	- - 'Postman's Pride'[PBR]	CHel CKno CWGN ECtt EPfP GBin LPla LRHS LSou MSCN MTis MWat NGdn NSbr WCot
§	- - 'Purple Emperor' 🏆[H7]	Widely available
	- - 'Purple Moon'	SPhx
	- - 'Ringmore Ruby'	MHer MNrw SPer SPhx WCot WPGP WWEG

	- - 'Xenox'[PBR] 🏆[H7]	CWGN EBee ECtt EPfP EWll GBin IPot LRHS MAvo MBNS MBri MCot MNrw MTis NDov NLar SCob SMrm SPoG WCAu WHil WPGP
	- 'Bronco'[PBR]	MBri
	- 'Coral Reef'[PBR]	EBee MBri WMoo
	- Emperor's Waves Group	NGdn
§	- subsp. ***fabaria***	ECtt MRav NWsh SMrm WCot WWEG
	- - var. ***borderei***	CElw LBMP LPla SBch SPhx
	- 'Jennifer'	EBee ECtt LSun MAvo MBel MHol NPCo SBch WCot WHoo
	- subsp. ***maximum*** 'Atropurpureum'	see *S. telephium* Atropurpureum Group
	- - 'Gooseberry Fool'	CFis CMea CPrp EBee ECGP ECtt ELan EPfP GMaP SBch SPhx WWEG
	- 'Moonlight Serenade'[PBR]	EBee ECtt LRHS MBri
	- 'Rainbow Xenox'[PBR]	LSou MBri
	- 'Raspberry Truffle' new	SDys
	- 'Roseum'	WWEG
§	- subsp. ***ruprechtii***	CPrp EAEE ECha ECtt EHoe EPPr EPfP GMaP LRHS LSou MCot MRav NLar NSti SPer SPhx WMoo
	- - 'Citrus Twist'	EBee ECtt LRHS MRav
	- - 'Hab Gray'	CSpe EBee ECtt EWes GBin GQue MAvo MTis NLar SBch SMrm WCot
	- - 'Pink Dome'	ECha
	- 'Strawberries and Cream'	Widely available
	- 'Sunkissed'[PBR]	ECtt MBri NCGa NLar
	- subsp. ***telephium***	GCra
	- 'Twinkling Star'[PBR]	MBri MNrw
	- 'Variegatum' (v)	MAvo
	- 'Yellow Xenox'[PBR]	EBee ECtt LRHS LSou MBri WHil
	ternatum	ECho MHer
	tetractinum 'Coral Reef' new	XLum
	'Thundercloud'[PBR]	LBuc LRHS SHil
	'Thunderhead' new	ECtt
	trollii	see *Rhodiola trollii*
	'Twinkle Stars'	EBee
	urvillei Sartorianum Group	MHer XLum
§	- Stribrnyi Group	XLum
	ussuriense	EPfP GCal NBir
	- 'Chuwangsan'	EWld WCru
	'Veluwse Wakel'	ECtt GBin
	'Vera Jameson' 🏆[H5]	CHEx CMac CPrp CRos EAEE ECha ECtt EHoe EPfP EPla EShb GKev LAst LRHS MBel MBrN MCot MNFA MRav MWat NHol NSti NWsh SBch SMrm SPer SWvt WHoo WMoo WWEG
	viviparum	NLar
	- B&SWJ 8662	WCru
	Walberton's Pink Whisper	EPfP LRHS SPoG
	'Washfield Purple'	see *S. telephium* (Atropurpureum Group) 'Purple Emperor'
	'Weihenstephaner Gold'	see *S. kamtschaticum* var. *floriferum* 'Weihenstephaner Gold'
	weinbergii	see *Graptopetalum paraguayense*
	'Winky'	LSou MAsh
	yezoense	see *S. pluricaule*
	yunnanense	see *Rhodiola yunnanensis*

Seemannia see *Gloxinia*

Selaginella (*Selaginellaceae*)

braunii	CLAP WCot
erythropus var. ***sanguinea***	LRHS
helvetica	IMou XLum
kraussiana ♀H2	CKel CLAP EDAr NWad
- 'Aurea'	CBty CCCN ISha LRHS
- 'Brownii' ♀H2	CBty CCCN ISha LRHS
- 'Gold Tips'	CBty CCCN CKel ISha LRHS
lepidophylla	SVic
martensii ♀H1b	CKel
moellendorfii	CBty ISha LPal LRHS
tamariscina	WAbe
uncinata ♀H1b	CBty CKel CLAP ISha LRHS

Selinum (*Apiaceae*)

CC 6869	EWld MSpe
KWJ 12281 from North Vietnam **new**	WCru
carvifolium	CExl CSpe LEdu LLWG SPtp
- PAB 2676	LEdu
tenuifolium	see *S. wallichianum*
§ ***wallichianum***	CBod CCon CExl CHid CPom CSam CSpe ECha ELan EPri EWoo GBin GBuc GCra LBMP LRHS MAvo MSpe MWat NDov SMHy SPer SPhx SPtp SWvt WCot WHil WPtf WWEG
- EMAK 886	EBee GPoy SDix
- HWJK 2329 **new**	WCru
- HWJK 2347	WCru
- PAB 3579	LEdu

Selliera (*Goodeniaceae*)

radicans	GAbr GBin GEdr

Semele (*Asparagaceae*)

androgyna	CHEx CRHN WCot

Semiaquilegia (*Ranunculaceae*)

adoxoides double-flowered (d) **new**	GKev
§ ***ecalcarata*** ♀H5	CAby CPom CWCL ECho EWld GCal GJos GKev IGor MNrw NCGa NGdn SRms WHal
- Australian	CDes
* - f. ***bicolor***	CPom
- 'Flore Pleno' (d)	WTou
simulatrix	see *S. ecalcarata*
'Sugar Plum Fairy'	EPfP GKev LBuc LRHS SPoG

Semiarundinaria (*Poaceae*)

from Korea	EPla
§ ***fastuosa*** ♀H4	CBcs CBod CDoC CEnt CHEx CJun CTsd EPfP EPla ERod EUJe IMou LPal MJak MMoz MMuc MWht SArc SEND SPlb
- var. ***viridis***	CEnt EPla ERod MWht SBig WCru
kagamiana	CDoC EPfP EPla IMou MMoz MMuc MWht SBig SEND
§ ***lubrica***	MWht
makinoi	MWht
I ***maruyamana*** **new**	MWht
nitida	see *Fargesia nitida*
§ ***okuboi***	CEnt EPla ERod MMoz MWht
villosa	see *S. okuboi*
yamadorii	EPla ERod MMoz MWht
- 'Brimscombe'	EPla
yashadake	CEnt ERod MWht
- 'Gimmei'	EPla
- f. ***kimmei***	CBod CDoC CEnt EPla ERod LPal LRHS MMoz MMuc MWht NLar SBig SEND WMoo WPGP
I - - 'Inversa'	CEnt

Semnanthe see *Erepsia*

Sempervivella see *Rosularia*

Sempervivum ✿ (*Crassulaceae*)

sp.	SCob SVic
from Sierra Nova	ESem
'Aaroundina'	CWil
'Abba'	CMea EDAr WHal
'Adelaar'	CWil
'Adelmoed'	CWil SFgr
'Ageet'	CWil
'Aglow'	ESem MHom
'Aladdin'	CWil ESem GEdr MSCN SRms
'Alchimist'	XLum
'Aldo Moro'	CTal CWil EDAr ESem GAbr LBee MHom SFgr WIce XLum
'Alice'	MSCN
'Alidae'	ESem
allionii	see *Jovibarba allionii*
'Allison'	CWil
'Alluring'	ESem GAbr
'Alpha'	CMea ESem LBee SFgr SRms WHal XLum
altum	CWil ECho ESem LRHS MHom SPlb XLum
'Amanda'	CWil EDAr ESem MBrN SRms WHoo
andreanum	see *S. tectorum* var. *alpinum*
'Andrenor'	ESem
'Anna Marie'	ESem
'Apache' Haberer	ESem
'Apollo'	SFgr XLum
'Apple Blossom'	CMea ESem
arachnoideum ♀H5	Widely available
- 'Ararat'	SDys
- 'Boria'	ESem
- var. ***bryoides***	CWil ECho ESem LLHF LRHS SRms
- 'Cebennense'	ESem
- 'Clärchen'	EPot ESem MSCN NSla WAbe
- cristate	CWil
* - ***densum***	EDAr EPPr WAbe
- subsp. ***doellianum***	see *S. arachnoideum* subsp. *tomentosum* var. *glabrescens*
- form No 1	ECho
- 'Laggeri'	see *S. arachnoideum* subsp. *tomentosum* (C.B. Lehm. & Schnittsp.) Schinz & Thell.
- 'Red Papaver'	SFgr
- 'Red Wings'	XLum
- 'Rubrum'	CHEx ECho ELon EUJe GMaP LRHS SPlb XLum
- 'Sultan'	ESem
- subsp. ***tomentosum*** misapplied	see *S.* × *barbulatum* 'Hookeri'
- subsp. ***tomentosum*** ambig.	ECho EPot
§ - subsp. ***tomentosum*** (C.B. Lehm. & Schnittsp.) Shinz & Thell. ♀H5	CHEx CWil ECho GCrg LRHS MSCN NPer NWad SFgr SPlb SRms WAbe
- - GDJ 92.04	CWil
§ - - var. ***glabrescens***	SDys

§	– – 'Stansfieldii'	ECho EPPr EPot LRHS WHal
§	– 'White Christmas'	CWil MHer
	arachnoideum* × *calcareum	CWil
	arachnoideum* × *montanum	see *S.* × *barbulatum*
	arachnoideum* × *nevadense	SDys
	arachnoideum* × *pittonii	WAbe
	arenarium	see *Jovibarba arenaria*
	'Arlet'	EDAr
	armenum	ESem
	'Arondina'	CWil
	'Aross'	CMea ESem
	'Artist'	CWil ESem SFgr
	'Ashes of Roses'	EPot ESem MHom NHol WAbe XLum
	'Asteroid'	CWil ESem
	'Astrid'	CWil
	'Atlantic'	SRms
	atlanticum	CTal ESem MHom NSla SFgr SRot
	– from Atlas Mountains, Morocco	ESem
	– from Oukaïmeden, Morocco	CWil ESem SRms
	– 'Edward Balls'	ESem SDys SFgr
	'Atropurpureum' ambig.	CHEx CWil EDAr GEdr MBrN
	'Attraction'	CWil
	'Aureum'	see *Greenovia aurea*
	'Averil'	CWil
	'Aymon Correvon'	ESem
	'Baby Skrocki'	CWil
	balcanicum	CTal CWil EDAr SRms XLum
	ballsii	ECho LLHF LRHS SRms
	– from Kambeecho, Greece	MHom
	– from Smólikas, Greece	MHom
	– from Tschumba Petzi, Greece	CWil MHom SDys XLum
	'Banyan'	CTal ECho LRHS
§	**× *barbulatum***	ESem LBee SDys WHoo
§	– 'Hookeri'	CTri CWil EPot ESem SFgr WAbe WHoo XLum
	'Bascour Zilver'	CMea CWil LBee SRms WHal
	'Be Mine'	MSCN
	'Beaute'	ESem
	'Bedivere'	CWil LBee SRms
*	'Bedley Hi'	MHom
	'Bella Donna'	CWil ESem MHom
	'Bella Meade'	CWil EDAr ESem SFgr SRms
	'Belle' **new**	WGor
	'Bellotts Pourpre'	CWil ESem
	'Benny Hill'	CWil
	'Bernstein'	CWil EDAr EPot ESem MHer NWad SFgr WHal XLum
	'Beta'	ESem MHom WAbe XLum
	'Bethany'	CMea CWil NWad WHal
	'Bicolor' ambig.	EPfP
	'Big Slipper'	ESem
	'Bijou'	CWil
	'Binstead'	ESem
	'Black Cap'	ESem
	'Black Knight'	ECho LRHS MHer SPlb SRms WHal
	'Black Mini'	CWil EPot GAbr GCrg GKev NBir SRms
	'Black Mountain'	CHEx CWil ESem GKev LBee
	'Black Prince'	ESem
	'Blood Tip'	CHEx CMea CTal CWil ECho ELon EPfP ESem GAbr GCra GKev LAst LRHS LSun MHer MMuc MSCN NHol NRya NWad SBch SEND SPlb SPoG SRms WHal WHoo
	'Bloodgood'	ECho
	'Bloody Goose'	ESem
	'Blue Boy'	CTal CWil ECho ELon EPPr EPot GAbr LBee LRHS MSCN SFgr SRms
	'Blue Moon'	ESem
	'Blue Time'	EPot GEdr LLHF SFgr WHoo XLum
	'Blush'	EDAr
	'Boissieri'	see *S. tectorum* subsp. *tectorum* 'Boissieri'
	'Bombardier'	EDAr
	'Booth's Red'	CHEx
	'Boreale'	see *Jovibarba hirta* subsp. *borealis*
	borisii	see *S. ciliosum* var. *borisii*
	borissovae	EPot MHom SDys
	'Boromir'	CWil EDAr XLum
	'Boule de Neige'	GCrg GEdr NRya
	'Braune Maus'	ESem SFgr
I	'Braunella'	CWil
	'Britta'	ESem SDys
	'Brock'	ECho LLHF LRHS MHom SRms
	'Bronco' ♀H5	CDes CHEx CTal CWil ECho ELon ESem GAbr GBin LBee LRHS MHom MMuc NHol NRya NWad SEND SRms WCot WHfH WPGP WRHF XLum
	'Bronze Beauty'	EDAr
	'Bronze Pastel'	CWil EDAr MHom MSCN NSla SFgr SRms SRot
	'Brown Owl'	CWil ECho ESem SRms
	'Brownii'	ESem
	'Brunette'	ECho GAbr
	bungeanum hort.	ESem
	'Bunny Girl'	SFgr
	'Burnatii'	see *S. montanum* subsp. *burnatii*
	'Burnished Bronze'	CWil
	'Butterfly'	ESem
	'Café'	CWil MSCN NHol SFgr SRms
*	***calabricum***	NHol
	× *calcaratum*	EDAr EPot
	calcareum	CBod CTal CWil ECho EUJe EWll GKev LBMP LRHS MAsh MMuc NBro NHol SArc SEND SPlb SPoG SRms SRot XLum
	– from the Alps, France	CWil ESem
	– from Calde la Vanoise, France	CWil
	– from Ceüze, France	CWil ESem
	– from Cleizé, France	see *S. calcareum* 'Limelight'
	– from Col Bayard, France	CWil GAbr
	– from Colle St Michel, France	CWil ESem SRms
	– from Gorges supérieures du Cians, France	CWil ESem
	– from Mont Ventoux, France	CWil ESem
	– from Petite Ceüse, France	ESem SRot
	– – GDJ 92.15	CWil
	– – GDJ 92.16	CWil SRms
	– from Queyras, France	CWil ESem
	– from Route d'Annôt, France	CWil
	– from Triora, Italy	CWil
	– 'Benz'	ESem SDys
	– 'Extra' ♀H5	CDes CHEx CTal CWil ESem GAbr GEdr MSCN SFgr SRms SRot
	– 'Greenii'	CWil ECho ESem GKev LRHS SPlb SRms
§	– 'Grigg's Surprise'	SPlb WHil

	Name	Suppliers
	- 'Guillaumes' ♀H5	CTal CWil LBee LRHS SFgr SRms SRot WHoo
§	- 'Limelight'	CMea CWil EDAr LBee LRHS WHal WHoo
	- 'Monstrosum'	see *S. calcareum* 'Grigg's Surprise'
	- 'Mrs Giuseppi'	CTal CWil ECho ESem GAbr GCrg GEdr LBee LSun SFgr SRms WAbe WIce XLum
	- 'Pink Pearl'	CWil MSCN SDys SFgr SPlb XLum
	- 'Sir William Lawrence' ♀H5	CMea CWil ECho EDAr ESem LBee LRHS SFgr SRms WAbe WHal WHoo WThu XLum
	'Cancer'	XLum
	cantabricum	CWil ESem WThu XLum
	- from Navafria, Spain	CWil
	- from Riaño, Spain	CWil GAbr
	- from San Glorio, Spain	CWil GAbr
	- from Ticeros	XLum
	- subsp. ***cantabricum*** from Leitariegos, Spain	CWil GAbr MHom
	- - GDJ 93.13 from Peña de Llesba, Spain	CWil
	- - from Pico del Lobo, Spain	CWil
I	- subsp. ***gredense*** GDJ 95.04	CTal CWil
	- subsp. ***guadarramense***	see *S. vicentei* subsp. *paui*
	- - from Pico del Lobo, Spain, No 1	SRms SRot
	- - from Valvanera, Spain, No 1	CWil
	- subsp. ***urbionense***	CWil GEdr SRms
	- - from El Gatón, Spain	CWil
	- - from Picos de Urbión, Spain	CWil ESem
	cantabricum* × *montanum subsp. ***stiriacum***	ESem
	cantabricum* × *montanum subsp. ***stiriacum*** 'Lloyd Praeger'	CWil
	'Carmen'	CWil GAbr SFgr
	'Carnival'	CWil ESem
	caucasicum	CWil LRHS MHom XLum
	'Cavo Doro'	CWil SFgr
	'Celon'	CWil
	'Centennial'	ESem
	charadzeae	CWil ESem LBee XLum
	'Charolensis'	ESem
	'Chartbury'	EDAr
	'Cherry Frost'	ECho ESem NHol XLum
	'Cherry Glow'	see *Jovibarba heuffelii* 'Cherry Glow'
	'Cherry Tart'	SPlb
	'Chivalry'	ESem
	'Chocolate'	ESem WAbe
	'Christmas Time'	SFgr
	chrysanthum	ESem
	ciliosum ♀H4	CMea CPBP CWil ECho ESem NRya SPlb
	- from Alí Butús, Bulgaria	SDys
	- from Ochrid, Macedonia	CWil
	- from Pestani, Macedonia	ESem
§	- var. ***borisii***	CFis EPPr EPfP ESem GCal GKev NRya WAbe WHal
	- var. ***ciliosum*** × ***ciliosum*** var. ***borisii***	CTri
	- var. ***galicicum*** **new**	CTal
	- - 'Mali Hat'	ESem
	ciliosum* × *grandiflorum	CWil ESem
	'Cindy'	SRms
	'Circlet'	CWil
	'Clare'	MHer
	'Cleveland Morgan'	ESem MHom NBro XLum
	'Climax' ambig.	ECho EPfP ESem MHom
	'Cobweb Capers'	ESem MHom
	'Colchicum' **new**	SRms
	'Collage'	ESem
	'Collecteur Anchisi'	CTal ESem SDys SFgr
	'Commander Hay' ♀H5	CHEx CTal EDAr EPfP EWes GBin GCra MHom MSCN NPer NRya SRGP SRms WHal XLum
	'Concorde'	LBee
	'Congo'	ESem SFgr XLum
	'Cornstone'	ESem
	'Corona'	CWil ESem
	'Corsair'	CTal CWil ELon EPPr ESem GEdr MBrN SFgr
	'Cotopaxi'	CWil
	'Cranberry'	ESem
	'Crimson King'	SFgr
	'Crimson Velvet'	CHEx CMea ESem LBee SFgr XLum
§	'Crispyn' ♀H5	CTal CWil ESem LBee LRHS MHer MHom MMuc MSCN SEND SFgr
	'Crucify'	ESem
	'Cupream'	CWil ESem SRms
	'Dakota'	CWil EDAr SFgr
	'Dallas'	CWil SRms
	'Damask'	CWil LBee SFgr
	'Darjeeling'	CWil ESem
	'Dark Beauty'	CWil ECho ESem LRHS MSCN NHol SFgr WAbe WCot WHal
	'Dark Cloud'	CWil ESem GAbr LBee WHoo XLum
	'Dark Point'	CWil MHom MSCN SFgr
	'Dark Velvet'	CMea
	'Darkie'	CWil ESem SFgr
	'Deep Fire'	CWil ESem SRms
	× ***degenianum***	GAbr SFgr XLum
	'Delta' ♀H5	MHom WHoo
	densum	see *S. tectorum*
	'Devon Glow'	MSCN
	'Diane'	CWil ESem SFgr
	'Director Jacobs'	CWil EDAr ESem SFgr
	dolomiticum	XLum
	dolomiticum* × *montanum	NBro SFgr
	'Donarrose'	ESem SFgr
	'Downland Queen'	CWil ESem
	'Dragoness'	ESem
	'Dream Catcher'	CWil
	'Dusky'	ESem
	'Dyke'	CTri CWil EDAr SFgr WHal
	dzhavachischvilii	CWil XLum
	'Edge of Night'	CWil
	'Eefje'	CWil ESem
	'El Greco'	ESem
	'El Toro'	MHom MSCN
	'Elvis'	CWil GAbr MHom SFgr
	'Emerald Giant'	CWil ESem SFgr
	'Emerson's Giant'	CWil
	'Eminent'	ESem
	'Emmchen'	CWil SFgr
	'Engle's'	CMea CTri ECho GKev LRHS MHer MMuc MSCN SEND SPlb SRms WHal
	'Engle's 13-2'	NBro
	'Engle's Rubrum'	CTal EPot LBee

Name	Suppliers
erythraeum	ECho LLHF LRHS MHom SPlb SRms WAbe WHal
'Excalibur'	ESem
'Exhibita'	CWil EPPr SDys
'Exorna'	CWil EDAr ESem MHom SFgr
'Fair Lady'	CWil MHom
'Fame'	CWil ESem SPlb
'Fat Jack'	CWil
× ***fauconnetii***	CTal CWil EDAr ESem
- 'Thompsonii'	CWil
'Feldmaier'	GAbr
'Fernwood'	CTal
'Festival'	EDAr
'Fiery Furness'	ESem
'Fiesta' ambig.	WHal
fimbriatum	see *S.* × *barbulatum*
'Finerpointe'	ESem
'Fire Glint'	CWil GEdr SRms
'Firebird'	SFgr
'Firgrove Silver'	SFgr
flagelliforme	XLum
'Flaming Heart'	CWil EDAr ESem MBrN
'Flamingo'	ESem
'Flanders Passion'	EWes LBee SRms
'Fluweel'	MSCN
'Forden'	CHEx SFgr
'Ford's Amiability'	SDys
'Ford's Giant'	XLum
'Ford's Shadows'	SDys
'Ford's Spring'	CWil ESem
'Frolic'	ESem
'Fronika'	CWil
'Frosty'	CWil ESem SFgr SRms
'Fuego' ♀H5	CWil LRHS MHom SFgr
× ***funckii***	CHEx CWil EDAr ESem MBrN SFgr XLum
'Furryness'	ESem
'Fuzzy Wuzzy'	EDAr ESem
'Gallivarda' ♀H5	CWil ESem LRHS MSCN SFgr SRms
'Gambol'	NWad
'Gamma'	CHEx CWil ESem LBee
'Garnet'	ECho
'Gay Jester'	CTal CTri CWil SFgr WHoo
'Gazelle'	ESem XLum
'Genevione'	CWil
'Georgette'	CWil ESem XLum
'Gilosum'	EDAr
'Ginnie's Delight'	CWil
giuseppii ♀H5	EAEE ECho ESem LBee LRHS MHer MMuc SRms
- GDJ 93.17 from Coriscao, Spain	CWil
- from Coriscao, Spain	CTal LBee
- from Peña Espigüete, Spain	CWil SDys SRms
- from Peña Prieta, Spain	CWil
'Gizmo'	CWil SFgr
globiferum	XLum
subsp. ***globiferum*** 'Minor'	
- subsp. ***hirtum***	SFgr
'Gloriosum' ambig.	EDAr ESem MSCN SFgr
'Glowing Embers'	CWil ESem MHom SFgr WHal XLum
'Godaert'	MMuc SEND XLum
'Goldie'	ESem SFgr
'Grammens'	ESem
'Granada'	EDAr ESem
'Granat'	ESem LBee MHer SRms XLum
'Granby'	ECho ESem LBee SDys
grandiflorum	CTal CWil ESem WThu XLum
- from Valpine	ESem
- 'Fasciatum'	ESem
'Grape Idol'	CWil
'Grapetone'	ESem MHom SDys WHal
'Graupurpur'	CWil XLum
'Green Apple'	CWil MHom SDys
'Green Disk'	SRms
'Green Dragon'	CTal ECho ESem LRHS MSCN SRms WOut
'Green Gables'	EDAr ESem
'Green Ice'	CWil ESem SFgr
'Greenwich Time'	EDAr
'Grey Dawn'	ECho ESem LRHS MHom SRms XLum
'Grey Ghost'	ESem
'Grey Green'	CWil
'Grey Lady'	CWil
'Grey Owl'	ECho LRHS MSCN SRms
'Grey Velvet'	CWil LBee
'Greyfriars'	CDes CMea CTal ECho EDAr EPot LBee LRHS SFgr
'Greyolla'	CWil ESem
'Grünschnabel'	XLum
'Gulle Dame'	CWil ESem MHom SFgr
'Halemaumau'	CWil ESem
I 'Hall's Hybrid'	CWil GAbr MSCN NBro
'Happy'	CTal CWil ESem SFgr SRms WThu
'Hart'	CWil
'Havana'	CWil ESem
'Hayling'	ECho ESem LRHS SRms XLum
'Heigham Red'	CWil ECho EPPr ESem GKev LBee LRHS SRms WIce
'Heike'	CWil
'Helen'	EDAr GEdr
'Heliotroop'	SDys SRot
helveticum	see *S. montanum*
'Hester'	CHEx CWil ECho ESem MBrN NBro
'Hey-hey'	CTal ECho ELon GBin LBee LRHS MBrN SPlb WCot XLum
'Hidde'	CWil ESem SFgr SPlb
'Hirsutum'	see *Jovibarba allionii*
hirtum	see *Jovibarba hirta*
'Hookeri'	see *S.* × *barbulatum* 'Hookeri'
'Hopi'	CWil
'Hortulanus Smit'	XLum
'Hot Peppermint'	ESem
'Huggable Helen'	GKev
'Hullabaloo'	EDAr ESem SFgr
'Hurricane'	CWil ESem
'Icicle'	CHEx CMea ECho ELon LRHS MSCN NBro NHol SRms WAbe
imbricatum	see *S.* × *barbulatum*
'Imperial'	CWil MHom SPlb
'Infinity'	SFgr
ingwersenii	CTal ESem MHom XLum
ingwersenii × ***pumilum***	SRms
'Iophon'	LBee
'Irazu'	CTal CWil ECho EPot ESem GAbr LRHS MSCN SDys SFgr SRms
'Irene'	ESem SFgr
'Isaac Dyson'	SDys SRot
'Isabelle'	CWil
italicum	MHom XLum
'Iwo'	CHEx SFgr
'Jack Frost'	ESem NBro SFgr XLum
'Jacquette'	CWil ESem
'Jadestern'	CWil

	'Jelly Bean'	CWil SFgr
	'Jet Stream' 🏆H5	CWil ECho ELon ESem LRHS MHom SDys SPlb SRms
	'Jetson' **new**	WGor
	'Jewel Case'	CTal CWil ECho LRHS
I	'John Hobbs seedling No. 2'	ESem
	'John T.'	ESem
	'Jolly Green Giant'	MHom
	'Jubilee'	CMea CWil ECho EDAr ELan ESem GEdr MAsh MHer XLum
	'Jubilee Tricolor'	ESem GCrg GEdr NHol SFgr WAbe
	'Jungle Fires'	CMea CWil ESem SDys SRms WHoo
	'Jungle Shadows'	EDAr ESem XLum
	'Jupiter'	GKev XLum
	'Justine's Choice'	CWil ESem SRms
	'Kalinda'	MHom
	'Kappa'	CTri CWil ESem NBro SDys SRot
	'Katmai'	CWil ESem
	'Kaya'	CWil
	'Kelly Jo'	CWil ECho ESem NBro SFgr
	'Kelut'	ESem
	'Kermit'	MHom
	'Kia'	CWil
	'Kiara'	CWil
	'Kibo'	ESem
	'Kimba'	CWil
	'Kimble'	ESem
	'Kimono'	NWad
	kindingeri	CWil ESem MHom XLum
	'King George'	CTal CTri CWil ESem GKev LBee MMuc SEND SFgr SRms WHal WHoo XLum
	'King Lear'	ESem GBin
	'Kip'	CMea
	'Koko Flanel'	CTal CWil ESem SFgr
	'Korspelsegietje'	CWil GAbr SRms
	kosaninii	ESem SFgr
	- from Koprivnik, Slovenia	MSCN WAbe XLum
	- 'Hepworth'	SPlb
	'Kramer's Spinrad'	CHEx CMea CTal CWil EPPr ESem GAbr GEdr LBee MBel SFgr SPlb SRms WHoo
	'Krater'	CWil
	'Kubi'	ESem
	'Laura Lee'	MMuc SEND
	'Lavender and Old Lace'	CHEx CWil ECho LBee LRHS MSCN SPlb SRms WIce
	'Laysan'	CWil
	'Lemon and Lime'	ESem
	'Lennik's Glory'	see *S.* 'Crispyn'
	'Lentezon'	ESem
	'Les Yielding'	ESem
	leucanthum	XLum
	'Lilac Time' 🏆H5	CMea CTal CWil ECho EPPr ESem LRHS MBrN MHer MSCN SFgr SPlb SRms WHal XLum
	'Lion King'	CTal CWil ESem MSCN
	'Lipari'	WCot XLum
	'Little Coffee Cup'	SFgr
	'Little Flirt'	MSCN
	'Lively Bug'	CWil ECho EDAr EPPr ESem LBee LRHS MSCN SDys SRms
	'Lloyd Praeger'	see *S. montanum* subsp. *stiriacum* 'Lloyd Praeger'
	'Long Shanks'	MSCN SFgr
	'Lonzo'	ESem SRms
	'Lynn's Choice'	CWil GAbr SFgr WHal
	macedonicum	SPlb SRms XLum
	- from Ljuboten, Macedonia/Kosovo	CWil
	'Madeleine'	CWil ESem
	'Magic Spell'	CWil ESem
	'Magical'	CWil
	'Magnificum'	CWil ESem
	'Mahogany'	CHEx CTal CTri CWil ECho EDAr ESem GKev LBee MHer MSCN NHol SFgr SRms WHal XLum
	'Maigret'	CWil
	'Majestic'	CWil ESem LBee
	'Major White'	CHEx
	'Malby's Hybrid'	see *S.* 'Reginald Malby'
	'Marella'	ESem
	'Maria Laach'	CWil ESem
	'Marijntje'	CWil ESem
	'Marjorie Newton'	CWil ESem
	'Marland Ruby' **new**	CWil
	'Marmalade'	CMea
§	***marmoreum***	ECho EPot LBee LRHS SRms WHal
	- from Kanzan Gorge, Bulgaria	ESem XLum
	- 'Brunneifolium'	CTal CWil GAbr LBee XLum
	- subsp. ***marmoreum*** var. ***dinaricum***	MHer
§	- - 'Rubrifolium'	XLum
	'Mate'	ESem
	'Matthew's Day Dream'	GKev
	'Maubi'	CHEx
	'Mauna Kea'	ESem
	'Mauvine'	XLum
	'Mayfair'	EDAr
	'Meisse'	ECho
	'Melanie'	CWil ESem MBrN
	'Memorial Merit'	ESem
	'Mercury'	CWil ECho ESem GAbr GCrg LRHS NBro SRms
	'Merlin'	ESem MSCN
	'Midas'	CTal CWil ECho ESem LRHS SFgr
	'Mini Frost'	ESem
	'Mixed Spice'	CWil
	'Moerkerk's Merit'	CTal CWil GAbr LRHS XLum
	'Mondstein'	CWil ESem
	'Monseigneur Desmet'	ESem
	'Montage'	CWil
§	***montanum***	ESem
	- from Arbizion, France	CWil
	- from Monte Tirone, Italy	LBee
	- from Monte Tonale, Italy	CWil
	- from Windachtal, Germany	CWil
§	- subsp. ***burnatii***	CWil EPot ESem MHom
	- 'Caesar'	MSCN
	- subsp. ***carpaticum***	CWil XLum
	- - 'Cmiral's Yellow'	MSCN SFgr WAbe
*	- Fragell form	SFgr
	- subsp. ***montanum***	CWil
	- 'Rubrum'	see *S.* 'Red Mountain'
	- subsp. ***stiriacum***	CWil ESem SFgr SRms XLum
§	- - 'Lloyd Praeger'	CTal CWil ESem LBee SDys SFgr
	'More Honey'	CWil
	'Morning Glow'	CMea ESem WHal
	'Mount Hood'	ECho ELon ESem LRHS SRms WHal
	'Mulberry Wine'	CWil LBee SRms WHoo
	'Mystic'	CWil ESem MBrN
	'Neon'	CWil
	nevadense	CTal CWil EPot SRms
	- from Puerto de San Francisco	CWil ESem

Name	Suppliers
'Nico'	CWil NWad SRms
'Nigrum'	see *S. tectorum* 'Nigrum'
'Niobe'	CWil SFgr WHal
'Noellie'	CWil
'Noir'	CWil EDAr ESem GKev LAst MSCN NBro WAbe
'Norbert'	CTal CWil EDAr SRms XLum
'Nouveau Pastel'	CFis CMea CWil ESem WHal XLum
'Octet'	CWil
octopodes	NBir XLum
- var. ***apetalum***	CTal CWil EPPr ESem GAbr GKev MSCN SRms WHoo
'Oddity'	CWil GBin MBrN MHer WHal
'Ohio Burgundy'	ECho ESem LRHS SRms WAbe
'Old Copper'	ESem
'Old Rose'	SFgr
'Olivette'	ESem XLum
'Omega'	ESem
'Ornatum'	EPot ESem MHer MHom MWat WHal
ossetiense	CTal CWil EDAr GAbr XLum
'Othello' ♀H5	CDes CHEx CTri CWil EPfP GAbr GCra GKev NBir WCot WPGP XLum
'Pacific Hep'	CWil
'Pacific Opal'	CWil
'Pacific Purple Shadows'	CWil
'Pacific Spring Frost'	SFgr
'Packardian'	CWil ESem GKev NWad SFgr
'Painted Lady'	ESem
'Palissander'	EDAr XLum
'Pam Wain'	MHom
'Passionata'	CWil SFgr
'Pastel'	CWil ESem MHer SFgr
patens	see *Jovibarba heuffelii*
'Patrician'	CWil LBee SRms
'Peggy'	CWil
'Pekinese'	CTal ECho EDAr EPot ESem GEdr LRHS MBrN NBro SFgr SRms XLum
'Peridot'	SFgr
'Peterson's Ornatum'	SDys
'Petsy'	ESem SFgr SRms
'Pilatus'	MSCN SRms XLum
'Pink Astrid'	CWil
'Pink Button'	CWil
'Pink Cloud'	CWil
'Pink Dawn'	ESem
'Pink Delight'	MSCN
'Pink Lemonade'	CWil MHom
'Pink Mist'	SRms
'Pink Puff'	CWil MHom SFgr
'Pippin'	CMea CTal CWil ESem SRms
'Piran'	CWil
pittonii ♀H5	CMea CWil ECho EPot ESem WHal XLum
'Pixie'	CPBP CWil SFgr
'Plum Frosting'	ESem MSCN SFgr
'Plum Mist'	NWad
'Plumb Rose'	CWil ESem
'Pluto'	CWil ESem LBee XLum
'Poke Eat'	ESem
'Polaris'	CWil ESem MHom
'Ponderosa'	CWil
'Pottsii'	CWil ESem
'President Arsac'	XLum
'Procton'	ESem
'Proud Zelda'	CWil EDAr ESem
'Průhonice'	CWil
'Pseudo-ornatum'	LBee SRms
'Pumaros'	SDys
pumilum	CWil ECho GKev LRHS SRms
- from Adyl-Su, Chechnya, No 1	CWil
- from El'brus, Russia, No 1	CWil ESem
- from Techensis, Caucasus Mountains	CWil SRms
- 'Sopa'	CWil MSCN
'Purdy'	MHom WAbe
'Purdy's 50-6'	CWil
'Purple Beauty'	GKev
'Purple King'	CMea MHom SDys
'Purple Passion'	ESem
'Purple Queen'	CWil ECho EDAr ELon EPPr LRHS SFgr SRms
'Pygmalion'	CWil ESem
'Queen Amalia'	see *S. reginae-amaliae*
'Quintessence'	CWil MSCN SRms
'Racey'	ESem
'Ramses'	ESem SDys
'Raspberry Ice'	CFis CMea ESem LBee MSCN NBro
'Rauer Kulm'	CWil
'Rauhreif'	XLum
'Red Ace'	GEdr MBel NBro SFgr
'Red Beam'	CWil LRHS MSCN
'Red Chips'	EDAr MHom
'Red Delta'	CDes NBir SFgr WCot WPGP
'Red Devil'	CMea CWil ECho ELon ESem LLHF LRHS SFgr SPlb SRms WHoo
'Red King'	GBin
'Red Lion'	SFgr
'Red Lynn'	CWil ESem
§ 'Red Mountain'	CWil ESem LBee SRms
'Red Pink'	CWil
'Red Robin'	EDAr
'Red Shadows'	LBee
'Red Spider'	EPPr EPot MHom NBro
'Red Summer'	ESem
'Regal'	ESem
reginae	see *S. reginae-amaliae*
§ ***reginae-amaliae***	CWil EPot GKev LRHS SRms XLum
- from Kambeecho, Greece, No 2	SDys
- from Mavri Petri, Greece	CWil
- from Sarpun, Turkey	CWil SDys
- from Vardusa, Serbia	CWil
§ 'Reginald Malby'	CTri ECho ESem GMaP LRHS SFgr SRms
'Reinhard' ♀H5	CMea CTal CWil ECho EDAr ELon EPot ESem GCrg GEdr GKev LRHS MAsh MBrN MHer MSCN NRya SPlb SRms WHal WHoo
'Remus'	CWil ELan ESem SFgr
'Rhône'	CWil LBee
'Rhubarb Crumble' **new**	SFgr
'Rich 'n' Fruity'	MSCN
'Risque'	LBee
'Rita Jane'	CWil ESem MHom SFgr
'Robin'	LBee NBro NHol SFgr
'Ronny'	CWil ESem
'Roosemaryn'	EDAr ESem
× ***roseum***	ESem
'Rosie'	CMea CWil ECho ELon ESem GAbr GEdr GMaP LBee LRHS MAsh MSCN NHol SRms WHal WHoo WIce
'Rotkopf' ♀H5	CTal CWil ESem LRHS MSCN XLum
'Rotund'	CWil GEdr MSCN

	'Royal Opera'	CWil EDAr ESem
	'Royal Ruby'	LBee
	'Royale'	SFgr
	'Rubellum Mahogany'	SFgr
	'Rubin'	CBod CMea CTal CTri EPfP GBin GKev LBMP MAsh MSCN NBir NEgg SPoG SRms WAbe WHoo WIce XLum
I	'Rubra Ash'	CWil ESem WAbe
I	'Rubra Ray'	CWil EDAr MMuc SEND
	'Rubrifolium'	see *S. marmoreum* subsp. *marmoreum* 'Rubrifolium'
*	'Ruby Glow'	EDAr
	'Ruby Heart'	EDAr
	'Russian River'	WHoo
	'Rusty'	CWil ESem SFgr
	ruthenicum	CTal ECho EPPr LLHF LRHS MHom NRya SRms XLum
	- 'Regis-Fernandii'	ECho XLum
	'Safara'	ESem
	'Saga'	MHom
	'Sarah'	EDAr
	'Sarotte'	CWil
	'Saturn'	ESem GEdr SRms
	schlehanii	see *S. marmoreum*
	schnittspahnii	XLum
	'Sea Breeze'	SFgr
	'Sea Urchin'	SFgr
	'Seminole'	CWil ESem
	'Serendipity'	EDAr
	'Sharon's Pencil'	CWil
	'Sheila'	GAbr
	'Shirley Moore'	CWil EDAr SFgr
	'Shirley's Joy'	ESem XLum
	'Sigma'	ESem
	'Silberkarneol' misapplied	see *S.* 'Silver Jubilee'
	'Silberspitz'	CTal CWil ECho ELon LRHS MHer MHom NBro SPlb SRms
	'Silver Cup'	CWil SFgr
§	'Silver Jubilee'	CMea CWil ECho EDAr ESem GAbr GBin LRHS MMuc NBro NRya SEND SPlb SRms XLum
	'Silver Queen'	CWil ESem
	'Silver Shadow'	MSCN
	'Silver Sixpence' **new**	SFgr
	'Silver Thaw'	CWil EDAr LRHS
	'Silverine'	CWil EDAr
	'Silvertone'	CWil ESem
	'Simonkaianum'	see *Jovibarba hirta*
	'Sioux'	CTal CWil ESem LBee MBrN WHal
	'Skrocki's Bronze'	GAbr LRHS SRms
	'Slabber's Seedling'	CWil
	'Smaragd'	LBee XLum
	'Smokey Jet'	ESem SFgr
	'Snowberger'	CMea CTal CWil EPot ESem MSCN SFgr SRms WHal
	'Soarte'	ESem
	soboliferum	see *Jovibarba sobolifera*
	'Soothsayer'	CWil
	sosnowskyi	CWil XLum
	'Soul Sister'	ESem
	'Sparkler'	CTal
	'Speciosum'	ESem
	'Spherette'	CWil EDAr ESem MBrN MSCN WAbe
	'Spider's Lair' ♀H5	EDAr MHom
	'Spinellii'	WThu
	'Spiver's Velvet'	ESem
	'Springmist'	ECho ESem LRHS SFgr SRms
	'Sprite'	CWil GEdr LRHS MBel SDys SRms
	'Squib'	CTal CWil ESem MSCN
	stansfieldii	see *S. arachnoideum* subsp. *tomentosum* 'Stansfieldii'
	'Starburst'	CWil LRHS
	'Starshine'	ESem SFgr
	'State Fair'	CWil EDAr
*	***stoloniferum***	GAbr
	'Strawberry Fields'	ESem
	'Strawberry Sundae'	ESem
	'Strider'	CWil GAbr
	'Stuffed Olive'	SDys SRms SRot
	'Sugar Plum' **new**	SFgr
	'Sun Waves'	CWil ESem SDys
	'Super Dome'	CWil
	'Superama'	ESem
	'Supernova'	ESem
	'Tamberlane'	EDAr
	'Tarita'	CWil
§	***tectorum*** ♀H5	CArn CBod CHby CTal CTri ECho EDAr ELan EPfP GKev GPoy LBee LPot MHer MNHC SIde SPlb WJek XLum
§	- var. ***alpinum***	ECho LRHS MHom NBro SRms
	- var. ***andreanum***	CWil XLum
	- 'Atropurpureum'	ECho ELan
	- 'Atroviolaceum'	EDAr SPlb XLum
*	- 'Aureum'	SFgr
	- var. ***boutignyanum*** GDJ 94.02 from Sant Joan de Caselles, Andorra	CWil
	- - GDJ 94.03	CWil
	- - GDJ 94.04 from Route de Tuixén, Spain	CWil SRms
	- var. ***calcareum***	ECho ESem
§	- 'Nigrum'	ESem LBee MHer NBro SDys
	- 'Red Flush'	EDAr EPPr MBrN SFgr
	- 'Royanum' ♀H5	ESem GAbr MSCN
*	- subsp. ***sanguineum***	EDAr
	- 'Sunset'	CMea EDAr ESem GAbr GCrg SDys WHal
	- subsp. ***tectorum***	ESem GEdr
§	- - 'Boissieri'	CWil
	- - 'Triste'	CHEx CWil LBee XLum
	- 'Tokajense'	ESem
	- 'Violaceum'	MHom SPlb SRms
	'Terlamen'	CWil
	'Terracotta Baby'	CTal CWil ELon ESem SFgr
	'The Platters'	CWil
	'The Rocket'	CWil
	× ***thompsonianum***	CWil LBee SFgr
	'Thunder'	CWil
	'Tip Top'	CWil GEdr SFgr
	'Titania'	CWil NBro WHal
	'Topaz'	CWil LBee SRms XLum
	'Tordeur's Memory'	CWil ESem MSCN SEND
	'Tracy Sue'	EDAr XLum
	'Trail Walker'	CWil LBee SRms
	transcaucasicum	XLum
	'Tree Beard'	CWil
	'Trine'	CWil
	'Tristesse' ♀H5	CWil EDAr GAbr LBee MBrN SFgr
	'Truva'	CWil ESem SFgr
	'Tumpty'	SFgr
	'Twilight Blues'	CWil ECho ESem LRHS SFgr SRms
	'Twizzler'	MSCN
	'Undine'	CWil ESem SFgr

	'Unicorn'	ESem
	× ***vaccarii***	CWil XLum
	'Van der Steen'	GAbr
	'Vanbaelen'	CWil GAbr SDys
	vicentei	ESem MHom
	- from Gaton, Spain	ESem LBee
§	- subsp. ***paui***	NSla
	'Video'	CWil ESem MHom SFgr
	'Vignola'	CWil
	'Violet Queen'	ESem
	'Virgil'	CWil EDAr ESem MBrN MSCN NWad SDys WAbe WCot WIce
I	'Virginius'	CWil
	'Waldalina'	CWil
	'Warrior'	EDAr
	'Wasti'	CWil
	'Watermelon Rind'	ESem
	webbianum	see *S. arachnoideum* L. subsp. *tomentosum* (C.B. Lehm. & Schnittsp.) Schinz & Thell.
	'Webby Flame'	CWil
	'Webbyola'	ESem
	'Weirdo'	CWil
	'Wendy'	ESem SFgr
	'Westerlin'	CWil ESem
	'White Christmas'	see *S. arachnoideum* 'White Christmas'
	'Whitening'	EDAr GAbr GEdr
	'Whitney'	ESem
I	'Woolcott's Variety'	CWil ECho ESem MSCN NBir
	wulfenii	CWil
*	- ***roseum***	EDAr
	'Xaviera'	CWil
	'Yanisha'	CWil
	'Yarnton'	ESem
	'Yolanda'	CWil
	'Yvette'	CWil
	'Zaza'	CWil
	zeleborii	WHal
	'Zenith'	CWil EDAr ESem GAbr SFgr SRms
	'Zenobia'	MHom
	'Zenocrate'	NHol WHal
	'Zepherin'	CWil MSCN
	'Zilver Moon'	CWil ESem
	'Zilver Suzanna'	CWil
	'Zircon'	EDAr
	'Zone'	CHEx

Senecio (*Asteraceae*)

	aquaticus	LLWG
§	***articulatus***	EShb
	bidwillii	see *Brachyglottis bidwillii*
	candicans misapplied	see *S. cineraria*
	cannabinifolius	GCal
	chrysanthemoides	see *Euryops chrysanthemoides*
§	***cineraria***	CWCL LPot MWat SEND
	- 'Silver Dust' ♀H4	EPfP
	cinerascens	SVen
*	***coccinilifera***	SBch
	compactus	see *Brachyglottis compacta*
	confusus	see *Pseudogynoxys chenopodioides*
	crassissimus	EShb
	cristobalensis	WCot
	doria	EBee EShb WHrl
	elegans	SVen
	ficoides	EShb
	formosoides B&SWJ 10736	WCru
	formosus B&SWJ 10700	WCru
	gerberifolius B&SWJ 10357	WCru
	- B&SWJ 10361	WCru
	grandifolius	see *Telanthophora grandifolia*
	'Gregynog Gold'	see *Ligularia* 'Gregynog Gold'
	greyi misapplied	see *Brachyglottis* (Dunedin Group) 'Sunshine'
	greyi Hook. f.	see *Brachyglottis greyi* (Hook. f.) B. Nord.
	heritieri DC.	see *Pericallis lanata* (L'Hér.) B. Nord.
	integrifolius subsp. ***capitatus***	SPlb
	kleiniiformis	EShb
	laxifolius hort.	see *Brachyglottis* (Dunedin Group) 'Sunshine'
	leucostachys	see *S. viravira*
	macroglossus	CHII EShb
	maritimus	see *S. cineraria*
	monroi	see *Brachyglottis monroi*
	petasitis	CBcs CFil CHEx SDix WCot
	polyodon	CCCN CMea CSpe EAJP ECre EDAr EPPr EWll GAbr GBin GLog MHol MNrw MPie MSpe NDov NLar SPhx WCAu WCFE WMoo WPGP WSHC WWEG
	- S&SH 29	EBee NCGa
	- 'Harmony' **new**	NDov
	- subsp. ***subglaber***	EWes
	przewalskii	see *Ligularia przewalskii*
	pulcher	CDTJ SBch SHar WPGP
	reinoldii	see *Brachyglottis rotundifolia*
	rowleyanus	EBak
	scandens	CCCN CExl IMou WPGP
	seminiveus	EBee
§	***serpens***	CDoC EShb EUJe MSCN SEND
§	***smithii***	ELan GBee NBid WWtn
	squalidus	WHer
	subnivalis	XLum
	subulatus var. ***subulatus*** CC 6516	EBee
	'Sunshine'	see *Brachyglottis* (Dunedin Group) 'Sunshine'
	talinoides subsp. ***cylindricus*** 'Himalaya'	EShb
	tanguticus	see *Sinacalia tangutica*
§	***viravira***	EUJe MCot SDix SMrm WSHC

Senna (*Caesalpiniaceae*)

	alata B&SWJ 9772	WCru
	alexandrina	CCCN EShb LRHS WPGP
§	***corymbosa***	CBcs CCCN CHEx CRHN CTri ECre IDee SEle SMrm
	hebecarpa	SBrt SPhx
§	***marilandica***	CArn EBee ELan GBin MGil
	multiglandulosa	WPGP
	retusa	CHEx
	septemtrionalis	CCCN EBee LRHS SEND

Sequoia (*Cupressaceae*)

	sempervirens ♀H6	CAco CBcs CDoC CDul CLnd CMCN CMen CTho ECrN EHul EPfP EWTr GKin MBlu MMuc NWea SArc SEND SGol WMou
	- 'Adpressa'	CDoC CDul CTho EHul MAsh MBri MGos NWea SCoo
	- 'Cantab'	CDoC

- 'Glauca'	MAsh
- 'Henderson Blue'	SLim
- 'Prostrata'	CDoC SEND SLim
- 'Simpson's Silver'	SLim

Sequoiadendron (*Cupressaceae*)

giganteum ♀H6	CAco CBcs CCVT CDoC CDul CMCN CTho CTri EHul ELan EPfP EWTr LRHS MAsh MBlu MBri MGos MMuc NEgg NSoo NWea SEND SEWo SGol SPlb WMou
- 'Barabits Requiem'	IArd MBlu SLim SMad
- 'Blauer Eichzwerg'	NLar
- 'Bultinck Yellow'	MBlu
- 'Curly Green'	NLar
- 'Glaucum'	CAco CDoC CTho MBlu MBri SLim SPoG
* - 'Glaucum Compactum'	MBlu
- 'Greenpeace'	MBlu NLar
- 'Pendulum'	CCVT CDoC CKen ERod LRHS MBlu SLim SMad
- 'Philip Curtis'	NLar
- 'Pirat'	NLar
- 'Powdered Blue'	NLar SLim WPGP

Serapias (*Orchidaceae*)

lingua	CDes SChF

Seriphidium see *Artemisia*

Serratula (*Asteraceae*)

bulgarica	NDov
coronata subsp. ***insularis*** B&SWJ 8698	WCru
- - f. ***alba***	GAbr
lycopifolia new	WCot
§ ***seoanei***	CKno CMea CPom CSam EBee ELan LPla MCot MHer MLHP MNrw MPie MRav MWat NBid SDix SPhx SRms WCot WPGP
shawii	see *S. seoanei*
'Starry Dreams' new	LRHS
tinctoria	CArn NLar NMir SPhx WHer
- subsp. ***macrocephala***	EBee

Serruria (*Proteaceae*)

florida	SPlb
phylicoides	SPlb

Sesamum (*Pedaliaceae*)

indicum	CArn

Sesbania (*Papilionaceae*)

punicea	CCCN

Seseli (*Apiaceae*)

gummiferum	CHid CSam CSpe EAJP MSpe SBrt SKHP SPhx WHil WPtf WWFP
hippomarathrum	LEdu SPhx WCot WHal WHrl WPGP WWtn
lehmannii RCB UA 13 new	WCot
§ ***libanotis***	CArn CSam GBin LEdu LPla LRHS MAvo MSpe NLar SDix SPhx WCot WPtf
montanum	CSam CSpe EBee IMou LPla MNFA NDov WPGP
varium	CArn

Sesleria (*Poaceae*)

§ ***albicans***	SCob
§ ***argentea***	EHoe EPPr
autumnalis	CKno EBee ELon EShb IMou LEdu LPla NDov SCob SPhx XLum
caerulea	CAby CBod CKno CSam EHoe ELan ELon EPfP GQue IMou LEdu LPal MBrN MWhi SPhx SPoG WPtf XLum
- subsp. ***calcarea***	see *S. albicans*
- 'Malvern Mop'	EBee WHrl WWEG
* ***candida***	EPPr
cylindrica	see *S. argentea*
glauca	EHoe NLar NOak
'Greenlee'	CKno NDov
heufleriana	CWCL EHoe EPPr GEdr IMou MBel NLar SMea SPhx SPlb WCot WWEG
insularis	EPPr EShb
'Morning Dew'	EBee GCal
nitida	CKno EBee EHoe IMou LEdu MBrN MMoz SDix SPhx WCot XLum
rigida	EHoe
sadleriana	EBee EPPr EWes

Setaria (*Poaceae*)

macrostachya	CKno LLWP SPhx
palmifolia ♀H2	CHEx CKno EUJe NLos SGSe SPlb WCot
- BWJ 8132	WCru
viridis	CSpe WCot

Setcreasea see *Tradescantia*

shaddock see *Citrus maxima*

Sharon fruit see *Diospyros kaki*

Shepherdia (*Elaeagnaceae*)

argentea	CBcs NLar

Shibataea (*Poaceae*)

kumasaca ♀H5	CAbb CBcs CDoC CEnt ERod GCal LEdu LRHS MBrN MJak MMoz MWht SBig SGol

Shortia (*Diapensiaceae*)

galacifolia	GKev
soldanelloides	GKev
uniflora	NHar WAbe
- var. ***kantoensis***	GKev

Sibbaldia (*Rosaceae*)

procumbens	GKev

Sibbaldiopsis (*Rosaceae*)

§ ***tridentata***	GJos
- 'Lemon Mac'	NHar
- 'Nuuk'	CCon EPPr

Sibthorpia (*Plantaginaceae*)

europaea	CExl CHEx

Sida (*Malvaceae*)

hermaphrodita	EBee

Sidalcea (*Malvaceae*)

'Brilliant'	CBcs COtt GBin IBoy LAst LRHS MJak MNrw MSCN MWat NBir

	NPri NSoo SHar SPer WCAu WMoo WWEG
campestris from Oregon, USA	EPPr
candida	CBod CSam EBee ECtt ELan EPfP GCra GMaP LAst LRHS MAsh MBNS MMuc MRav MTis NChi NGdn NLar NSoo NSti SCob SMHy SMrm SPer WCAu WCot WPtf
- 'Bianca'	EBee EPfP NLar WFar WHal WMoo WOut WWEG
'Candy Girl'	CBod EBee NLar SCob
'Crimson King'	WFar
'Croftway Red'	CBod CCon EBee ELan GCra LRHS MBel NBro NGdn NHol NWad SWvt WFar
cusickii	CBod
'Elsie Heugh' ♀H7	Widely available
'Little Princess' PBR	COtt EBee EWes LRHS MNrw NDov NGdn NLar NSoo SCob SPad SPoG
'Loveliness'	CBod CMos EBee ECtt ELan EShb MRav NBro NCGa NGdn NWad WFar WGwG
malviflora	SRms
- 'Alba'	NChi
- 'Crimson Beauty'	EBee
- subsp. ***purpurea*** new	LRHS
'Moorland Rose Coronet'	WMoo
'Mr Lindbergh'	EBee MPie NLar
'Mrs Borrodaile'	CCon CMac CPrp MRav NBro NEoE NGdn SMrm WMoo WWEG
'Mrs T. Alderson'	EBee
'My Love'	EBee NDov
'Oberon'	EBee LRHS MRav
oregana	NGdn
- subsp. ***spicata***	WMoo
'Party Girl'	CBod CHel CMac COtt CSBt ELan EPfP GJos IBoy LRHS LSun MNHC MRav NBro NGdn NLar NOrc NPri SMrm SPlb SPoG WFar WMnd WMoo WWEG XLum
'Präriebrand'	SMrm
'Purpetta'	EBee ELan EPfP LSun NEoE NGBl NGdn NLar SPad
reptans	CDes EBee WWFP
'Reverend Page Roberts'	MRav WCot WWEG
'Rosaly'	EAJP EWll IFoB LRHS MPie NLar WPtf
'Rosanna'	EPfP GMaP LAst LRHS MNHC NLar WPtf
'Rose Bud'	CPrp EBee ELan
'Rose Queen'	EBee ECha LRHS MRav NBro NHol SHar SPer SRms WFar
Stark's hybrids	LPot LRHS SRms
'Sussex Beauty'	CPrp CSam EBee LRHS MBel MLHP MRav NEgg NGdn NHol SBod SMrm WMoo
'Wensleydale'	CDes EBee LRHS
'William Smith' ♀H7	CBod CCon CSam EBee ECha ECtt EPfP EWes GBuc LRHS MBel MMuc MRav MWat NBir NGdn NLar NOrc SEND WFar WMnd WPtf WWEG
'Wine Red'	CBod CCon CMHG CMos CPrp EBee EShb LRHS NEgg NGdn SPoG SWvt WGwG WWEG

Sideritis (*Lamiaceae*)

RCB UA 2	WCot
clandestina	XSen
cypria	XSen
hyssopifolia	EBee SIgm
- subsp. ***guillonii***	XSen
perfoliata	XSen
phlomoides	SIgm XSen
phrygia	XSen
romana new	WAbe
scardica	XSen
stachydioides	XSen
syriaca	CArn MHer XSen
taurica	XSen

Sieversia (*Rosaceae*)

§ ***pentapetala***	WAbe
- 'Flore Pleno' (d)	WAbe
reptans	see *Geum reptans*

Silaum (*Apiaceae*)

silaus	NMir SBrt

Silene (*Caryophyllaceae*)

RBS	EPPr
SDR 6174	GKev
from Uzbekistan	GCal
acaulis	ECho EDAr GCrg GJos SRms WAbe
§ - subsp. ***acaulis***	ECho SPlb SRms
- 'Alba'	ECho EWes WAbe
- 'Blush'	ECho NSla WAbe
§ - subsp. ***bryoides***	NLar
- 'Correvoniana'	NLar
- subsp. ***elongata***	see *S. acaulis* subsp. *acaulis*
- subsp. ***exscapa***	see *S. acaulis* subsp. *bryoides*
- 'Frances'	CPBP GCrg ITim NHar NLar NRya NSla WAbe
- 'Francis Copeland'	ECho
- 'Helen's Double' (d)	ECho GJos
- 'Mount Snowdon'	ECho EPot EWes MMuc NLar SPlb SPoG SRms SRot WHoo
- 'Pedunculata'	see *S. acaulis* subsp. *acaulis*
- 'Select'	EPot
alba	see *S. latifolia* subsp. *alba*
§ ***alpestris***	ECho SHar SRms SRot WMoo WThu
- 'Flore Pleno' (d) ♀H5	CMea CPBP ECho EWes NSla SBch WIce WWFP
araratica	ITim WAbe
argaea	WAbe
× ***arkwrightii***	see *Lychnis* × *arkwrightii*
armeria	SDys
- 'Aphrodite'	CSpe
- 'Electra'	CAby CSpe
asterias	GCal GCra MNrw SBrt WWFP
- MESE 429	GBin
atropurpurea	see *Lychnis viscaria* subsp. *atropurpurea*
bolanthoides	WAbe
§ ***compacta***	IMou WCot
'Confetti'	MMuc SPhx
'Country Comet'	NChi
§ ***davidii***	EBee GKev
dinarica	WAbe
§ ***dioica***	CArn CHab CMac CWld GJos LEdu MHer MNHC NLar NMir SPhx SPoG SWat WMoo WOut WSFF WShi
- 'Clifford Moor' (v)	ECtt LSun MHer MSCN NSti SCoo
- 'Compacta'	see *S. dioica* 'Minikin'
- 'Firefly' PBR (d)	CMac CWCL ECtt LBMP LRHS MBel NSti SHar SPoG SRkn SWvt

§	- 'Flore Pleno' (d)	GCra MHer MRav NBid NBro NGdn SMrm WFar WHoo
	- golden-leaved	WFar
§	- 'Graham's Delight' (v)	NWad
	- 'Inane'	CDes EBee ELon WBor WPGP WRHF WSHC WWFP
	- 'Innocence'	NChi
	- f. ***lactea***	MHer
§	- 'Minikin'	MAvo MSCN MTis NGdn
	- 'Purple Prince'	SEND WFar WMoo WPtf
I	- 'Ray's Golden Campion'	NWad SPoG WOut WTou
	- 'Rollie's Favorite'[PBR]	ECtt LBMP LRHS MBri MNrw MSCN NDov NPri NSti SHar SPoG WBor
	- 'Rubra Plena'	see *S. dioica* 'Flore Pleno'
	- 'Stella'	NChi
	- 'Thelma Kay' (d/v)	ECtt MAvo NGdn WMoo WWFP
	- 'Underdine'	EWes
	- 'Valley High' (v)	EBee EWes MHol MMuc WHer WHil
	- 'Variegata'	see *S. dioica* 'Graham's Delight'
	elisabethae	EWld
§	***fimbriata***	CCon CSpe EBee ELan EPPr EPyc EShb LEdu LPla MCot MMHG MMuc MNFA MNrw MRav MWat NChi NLar NSti SMrm SPhx WBor WCot WKif WMoo WPGP WPtf WRHF
	hookeri	GKev
	- Ingramii Group	WAbe
	'Ice Clips'	MWat
	kantzeensis	see *S. davidii*
	keiskei var. ***akaisialpina***	ITim NSla
	- var. ***minor***	ECho EWes LRHS NSla WAbe
	laciniata 'Jack Flash'	MSCN
	latifolia	CArn CHab MNHC NMir WOut
§	- subsp. ***alba***	CWld SEND
	maritima	see *S. uniflora*
	multifida	see *S. fimbriata*
	noctiflora	CHab WSFF
	nutans	CArn SRms WSFF
	orientalis	see *S. compacta*
	pusilla	CPBP ITim NLar
	quadridentata	see *S. alpestris*
	regia	SPhx
	- 'Prairie Fire' new	MBel MHol WCot
	rubra	see *S. dioica*
	schafta 🏆[H5]	CTri ECha ECho EPfP GKev MAsh MMuc MRav NBid SEND SRms WHoo XLum
	- 'Abbotswood'	see *Lychnis* × *walkeri* 'Abbotswood Rose'
	- 'Persian Carpet'	SBch
	- 'Shell Pink'	CPBP ECha ECtt EWes GJos LRHS MMuc NBid SBch SEND WHoo
	sieboldii	see *Lychnis coronata* var. *sieboldii*
§	***uniflora***	CHab CWld ECho EPfP MMuc MSCN MWat NBro SPlb SRms SRot WMoo WOut
	- 'Alba Plena'	see *S. uniflora* 'Robin Whitebreast'
I	- 'Compacta'	ECho SHar WMoo
§	- 'Druett's Variegated' (v)	CTri ECho ECtt ELon EPot EWes GJos LRHS MAsh MHer MHol NBid NPri SPlb SPoG SRms WIce XLum
	- 'Flore Pleno'	see *S. uniflora* 'Robin Whitebreast'
§	- 'Robin Whitebreast' (d)	ECha ECho ECtt EPfP NBid NBro SPhx SRms SRot WMoo WSHC XLum
	- 'Rosea'	ECho GCrg GJos MMuc SEND SPlb SRot
	- 'Variegata'	see *S. uniflora* 'Druett's Variegated'
	- Weisskehlchen	see *S. uniflora* 'Robin Whitebreast'
	- 'White Bells'	CTri WKif WSHC
	viridiflora	SPhx
§	***vulgaris***	CArn CHab LEdu MHer MMuc MNHC NMir SEND WHer WOut
	- subsp. ***maritima***	see *S. uniflora*
	wallichiana	see *S. vulgaris*
	'Wisley Pink'	ECtt
	yunnanensis	SPhx WSHC
§	***zawadskii***	GKev MMuc NWad SBrt SEND

Siler (*Umbelliferae*)

	montanum	see *Laserpitium siler*

Silphium (*Asteraceae*)

	integrifolium	NBre SMad SPhx WCot WOld XLum
	laciniatum	CArn LEdu NBre SBrt SMad SPhx WCot WHal XLum
	perfoliatum 🏆[H7]	CArn CFis EBee GPoy IMou MMuc NBre NDov NLar SMrm SPhx WCot WWEG XLum
	- var. ***connatum***	SPhx
	- from Great Dixter new	IMou
	terebinthinaceum	SPhx WCot XLum
	trifoliatum	WCot

Silybum (*Asteraceae*)

	marianum	CArn ELan GAbr GPoy LRHS MCot MNHC SIde SPav WHfH WOut WTou

Simmondsia (*Simmondsiaceae*)

	chinensis	CArn EOHP

Sinacalia (*Asteraceae*)

§	***tangutica***	CSam EPPr GQue MBel MSCN NBid NBro NLar SDix WCot WOld WWtn

Sinapis (*Brassicaceae*)

	alba new	SVic

Sinarundinaria (*Poaceae*)

	anceps	see *Yushania anceps*
	jaunsarensis	see *Yushania anceps*
	maling	see *Yushania maling*
	murielae	see *Fargesia murielae*
	nitida	see *Fargesia nitida*

Sinningia (*Gesneriaceae*)

	sp.	EABi
*	***caerulea***	WDib
	calcaria	WDib
	canescens 🏆[H1c]	WDib
§	***cardinalis***	EBak WDib
	- 'Innocent'	WDib
	conspicua	WDib
	nivalis	WDib
	speciosa 'Blanche de Méru'	SDeJ
	- 'Hollywood'	SDeJ
	- 'Kaiser Friedrich'	SDeJ
	- 'Kaiser Wilhelm'	SDeJ
	- 'Mont Blanc'	SDeJ
	tubiflora	CSpe WCot WKif XLum

× *Sinocalycalycanthus* (*Calycanthaceae*)

raulstonii new — CAbP
- 'Hartlage Wine' ♀H5 — CBcs CJun EPfP EPla EUJe GBin GKin IArd IDee LLHF MBlu MBri NLar SHil SPoG SSpi
'Venus' — CMCN EPfP LLHF LRHS MBlu NLar SSpi

Sinocalycanthus (*Calycanthaceae*)

chinensis — CArn CBcs CHII CJun CMCN EBee ELan EPfP EUJe GKin LRHS MBlu MPkF NLar

Sinofranchetia (*Lardizabalaceae*)

chinensis — CFil CRHN LEdu WPGP
- DJHS 4117 new — WCru

Sinojackia (*Styracaceae*)

xylocarpa — CBcs CMCN NLar

Sinopodophyllum (*Berberidaceae*)

§ **hexandrum** — CArn CBct CBro CWCL EBee ECho EPot GBBs GBuc GCra GKev GMaP GPoy MNrw MRav NBid NBir NChi NLar SKHP SPlb WCot WPnP WSHC
§ - var. **chinense** — CLAP ECho EWld GCal LEdu WCru
- - BWJ 7908 — WCru
- - SDR 4409 — CExl
- 'Chinese White' — CExl WCot
§ - var. **emodi** — CArn GBuc ITim
- - 'Majus' — CCon CLAP GBin WHal

Sinowilsonia (*Hamamelidaceae*)

henryi — CBcs NLar

Siphocranion (*Lamiaceae*)

§ **macranthum** — CDes EBee EWes WPGP

Sison (*Apiaceae*)

amomum — CBre

Sisyrinchium ✿ (*Iridaceae*)

× **anceps** — see *S. angustifolium*
§ **angustifolium** — CMHG ECha EDAr MCot NBir NChi SChF SPlb SRms WBrk
- f. **album** — MCot NChi NLar
§ **arenarium** — GAbr GEdr
atlanticum — NBro
bellum hort. — see *S. idahoense* var. *bellum*
bermudiana — see *S. angustifolium*
- 'Album' — see *S. graminoides* 'Album'
'Biscutella' — CBod CKno CPrp CTri ECho ECtt EPfP EWoo GMaP LEdu MCot SPlb SRot WHal WHoo WKif
'Blue Ice' — CWCL GEdr ITim LRHS MWat NLar WAbe WMoo
boreale — see *S. californicum*
brachypus — see *S. californicum* Brachypus Group
'Californian Skies' — CAby CBro CElw CExl CKno CTri ECha ECho ECtt EWoo GMaP LRHS MNrw NBir NDov NSla SMrm SWvt WKif WMoo
§ **californicum** — CBAq CBen ECho EDAr EHon GEdr IMou LLWG LRHS NBro WMAq XLum
§ - Brachypus Group — ECho EPfP LPot MAsh MJak MWat NBir NLar SPlb SWvt WMoo
- 'Yellowstone' — EPfP
* **capsicum** — CExl
coeruleum — see *Gelasine coerulea*
convolutum — NDov
- B&SWJ 9117 — WCru
cuspidatum — see *S. arenarium*
depauperatum — MNrw
'Devon Skies' — CElw CPBP CWCL ECho ECtt EWoo LRHS MNrw NLar SBch SWvt WAbe WIce
'Doctor Bailey' — EBee GKev
douglasii — see *Olsynium douglasii*
'Dragon's Eye' — CElw CKno CMea CPBP ECtt EDAr EWes EWoo MBrN MHer SCob WIce
'E.K. Balls' — CAby CBod CPBP CTal ECho ECtt EDAr EHoe ELan EPot EWoo GCrg GMaP LAst LBMP LRHS LSun MAsh NRya NSla SMad SPad SPoG SRms SRot SWvt WAbe WIce WMoo
'Emmeline' — EWoo
filifolium — see *Olsynium filifolium*
graminoides — IFoB NBro
§ - 'Album' — NBro
grandiflorum — see *Olsynium douglasii*
'Hemswell Sky' — EHoe EWoo GAbr NLar NRya
'Iceberg' — CElw ECha EWes MWat
idahoense — ECha ECtt GAbr GKev LSou MHer NDov NRya SPlb SRms
§ - var. **bellum** — CKno EBee ECho EPfP SRms WMoo XLum
- - pale-flowered — CKno SMHy
- - 'Rocky Point' — CElw CKno EBee EPfP EWes LRHS SPoG
- var. **macounii** — GEdr SPlb
§ - - 'Album' ♀H5 — CAby CElw CMea ECho EWes GAbr GCrg GEdr GKev LPot MWat WAbe WIce
iridifolium — see *S. micranthum*
'Janet Denman' (v) — ECho EWes
junceum — see *Olsynium junceum*
littorale — CExl NLar
macrocarpon misapplied — see *S. macrocarpum*
macrocarpon E.P. Bicknell ♀H4 — CPBP EBee MNrw
§ **macrocarpum** — ECho
'Marion' — CMea CPBP ECtt MBrN WHoo
'May Snow' — see *S. idahoense* var. *macounii* 'Album'
'Miami' — EWoo
§ **micranthum** — ECho
montanum × **nudicaule** — ECho GAbr SRot
'Mrs Spivey' — MHer NBir
'North Star' — see *S.* 'Pole Star'
palmifolium — CAby CBod CSpe EBee LEdu MHer MNrw SBch SPad WSHC XLum
patagonicum — CExl CTal EBee
§ 'Pole Star' — EWoo NLar
'Quaint and Queer' — CAvo CExl EAJP ECha ECtt EHoe EWoo LPot MBrN MCot MLHP MNrw NBir NBro NChi WMnd WSHC
'Raspberry' — CMea EDAr EWoo
'Sapphire' — CAby CSpe ECha ECtt EDAr EHoe GCrg GEdr LBMP LPot LRHS MBri MHol NLar NPri SCob SPoG WBor WGrn WMoo

§	***striatum***	Widely available
§	- 'Aunt May' (v)	CBcs CBod CMac CSBt ECha ECho EHoe ELan EPfP EWoo GMaP LAst LRHS MGos MRav NSti SCob SGSe SMrm SPoG SRms SWat SWvt WCot WPGP WWEG
	- 'Variegatum'	see *S. striatum* 'Aunt May'
	aff. ***unispathaceum*** B&SWJ 10683	WCru

Sium (*Apiaceae*)

sisarum	CArn ELau GPoy MHer

Skimmia ✿ (*Rutaceae*)

	anquetilia	CMac
	- (f)	IVic WCru
	- (m)	WCru
	arborescens B&SWJ 11799	WCru
	- subsp. ***nitida*** B&SWJ 8239	WCru
	arisanensis B&SWJ 7114	WCru
	- CWJ 12417	WCru
	black-fruited B&SWJ 8259 from northern Vietnam (f/m)	WCru
	× ***confusa*** 'Kew Green' (m) ♀H5	Widely available
	'Daddy's Dream'	NSoo
	japonica	CDul CMHG CMac MGos NPla NWea SCob SSta WFar
	- (f)	CMac CTri ELan EPfP GGal SRms
	- - B&SWJ 5053	WCru
	- (m)	GGal
	- - B&SWJ 5053	WCru
	- 'Alba'	see *S. japonica* 'Wakehurst White'
	- 'Bowles's Dwarf Female' (f)	CDoC CEnd CMHG ELan MGos MRav MWht SLim SLon
	- 'Bowles's Dwarf Male' (m)	CMHG ELan LRHS NWad SLim
*	- 'Bronze Beauty'	MAsh
	- 'Bronze Knight' (m)	CMac EPla IVic MRav NLar NWad
	- 'Carberry' (f)	CMac IVic
	- 'Chameleon' (f)	NLar
	- compact (f)	GGal
	- 'Dad's Red Dragon' (f)	CMac MAsh NHol
	- 'Emerald King' (m)	MAsh WFar
	- 'Finchy'PBR (m)	MBri
	- 'Foremanii'	see *S. japonica* 'Veitchii'
§	- 'Fragrans' (m) ♀H5	CDoC CMac CRos CSBt CTri EBee EPfP LPal LRHS MAsh MGos MJak MRav NLar NPri NSoo NWea SCob SEWo SHil SLim SPer SPoG SWvt WFar WGwG
	- 'Fragrant Cloud'	see *S. japonica* 'Fragrans'
	- 'Fructu Albo'	see *S. japonica* 'Wakehurst White'
	- 'Godrie's Dwarf' (m)	CRos EPfP LRHS NLar SHil WFar
	- 'Hot Chocolate'	NSoo
	- 'Humpty Dumpty' (f) **new**	WFar
	- var. ***intermedia*** f. ***repens*** B&SWJ 11165	WCru
	- - - B&SWJ 5560	LAst WCru
	- 'Kew White' (f)	CAbP CDoC ELan EPfP IArd LAst LRHS MAsh MGos MRav NHol NWad SLon SPer SSta SWvt WCFE
	- Luwian = 'Wanto' (m)	LRHS SHil WCFE
	- 'Macpenny Dwarf' (m) **new**	CMac
	- 'Magic Marlot'PBR (m/v)	EBee EPfP EPot LRHS MAsh MGos MRav NLar NWad SCob SPoG
	- 'Marlot' (m)	EPfP LRHS NLar NWad SPoG
	- 'Nymans' (f) ♀H5	CDoC CEnd CRos EBee ELan EPfP LRHS MAsh MGos MRav SCob SEND SHil SLim SPer SPoG SRms SSpi SWvt
	- Obsession = 'Obsbolwi'PBR (f/m)	LRHS MAsh MGos NPri SCob SHil
	- 'Olympic Flame' (f)	EPfP IArd LRHS MBlu MJak NPri NSoo SHil SPoG
	- 'Pabella' (f) **new**	MAsh
	- 'Pigmy' (f)	CExl
	- 'Red Princess' (f)	MAsh
	- 'Red Riding Hood' (f)	CHel CRos ELan ELon LRHS MAsh NLar SHil SLon SPer
	- 'Redruth' (f)	CBcs CDoC CMac CSBt CTsd ELon MAsh MGos NLar SEND
§	- subsp. ***reevesiana***	CBcs CDoC CDul CMHG CMac CSBt CTri CWSG ELan EPfP IVic LRHS MBri MGos MRav MSwo NLar NSoo SCob SPoG SSpi SWvt
	- - B&SWJ 3763	MAsh WCru
	- - 'Chilan Choice' (f/m)	WPGP
	- - var. ***reevesiana***	MJak
	- - B&SWJ 3544	WCru
§	- Rogersii Group	CMac CTri
	- - 'George Gardner' (m)	EPfP LRHS
	- - 'Nana Mascula' (m)	CTri
	- - 'Rogersii' (f) **new**	CMac
	- 'Rubella' (m) ♀H5	Widely available
	- 'Rubinetta' (m)	EPfP IArd MAsh SCob
	- 'Ruby Dome' (m)	MAsh NWad
	- 'Ruby King' (m)	CDoC CSBt IArd NLar
	- 'Scarlet Dwarf' (f)	MAsh NHol WHar
	- 'Snow White'PBR (m)	MAsh
	- 'Tansley Gem' (f)	LRHS MAsh MWht SPoG
	- 'Temptation'PBR (f)	ELan EPfP LRHS SCob SHil
	- 'Thereza'PBR (m)	EPfP LBuc NPri
§	- 'Veitchii' (f)	CBcs CDul CMac CSBt CTri ELan EPfP IArd LRHS MGos MJak MMuc MRav NLar SCob SEND SLim SPer SPoG SWvt
§	- 'Wakehurst White' (f)	CBcs CMHG CMac CSBt CTri EPfP IVic LRHS MRav SLim SLon SPoG WFar
	- 'White Bella' (m)	LRHS SHil
	- 'Winifred Crook' (f)	LRHS
	- 'Wisley Female' (f)	CTri
	laureola	CDoC CExl MRav SRms WSHC
	- GWJ 9364	WCru
	- 'Kew Green' **new**	CEnd NWad
	- subsp. ***laureola*** HWJK 2095	WCru
	- subsp. ***multinervia*** GWJ 9374	WCru
	'Red Diamonds' **new**	SHil
	reevesiana	see *S. japonica* subsp. *reevesiana*
	rogersii	see *S. japonica* Rogersii Group

Smallanthus (*Asteraceae*)

	sonchifolius	CAgr LEdu
	- 'Morado' **new**	LEdu
§	***uvedalius***	CArn

Smilacina see *Maianthemum*

Smilax (*Smilacaceae*)

sp.	WBor
B&SWJ 6628 from Thailand	WCru
aspera	CArn CMac EShb LEdu WCru WPGP

china B&SWJ 4427	WCru
discotis	CBcs SEND
glaucophylla B&SWJ 2971	WCru
nipponica B&SWJ 4331	WCru
rotundifolia	LEdu
sieboldii	LEdu MRav
- B&SWJ 744	WCru

Smithiantha (*Gesneriaceae*)

'Anni' **new**	EABi
'Extra Sassy'	EABi
'Heartland's Charm' **new**	EABi
'Little One'	WDib
'Moana' **new**	EABi
'Multiflora'	EABi
'Santa Clara'	EABi
I 'Temple Bells'	EABi

Smithiantha × *Eucodonia* see × *Smithicodonia*

× *Smithicodonia* (*Gesneriaceae*)

'Heartland's Joy' **new**	EABi

Smyrnium (*Apiaceae*)

olusatrum	CArn CHab CSpe CUse MHer MNHC SRms SWat WHer WSFF
perfoliatum	CHid CSpe ELan EWes LEdu NBir SDix SMrm WCot WHal WSHC
rotundifolium	LEdu WCot

Solandra (*Solanaceae*)

grandiflora misapplied	see *S. maxima*
hartwegii	see *S. maxima*
§ ***maxima***	CCCN WCot

Solanum (*Solanaceae*)

atropurpureum	CDTJ CSpe SPlb WCot
betaceum (F)	CCCN SVic
capsicastrum	SPlb
conchifolium hort.	see *S. linearifolium*
crispum	NBir
- 'Autumnale'	see *S. crispum* 'Glasnevin'
- 'Elizabeth Jane Dunn' (v)	WCot
§ - 'Glasnevin' ♀H4	Widely available
dulcamara	CArn GPoy WHfH
- 'Lucia' (v)	CNat
- 'Variegatum' (v)	CMac EHoe MAsh
elaeagnifolium	WCru
incanum	LEdu
jasminoides	see *S. laxum*
- 'Blue Ice' **new**	LSou
laciniatum	CCCN CDTJ CExl CHEx CSpe CUse IDee MPie SBig SEND SPav SPlb WOut
§ ***laxum***	EBee GGal LRHS SPer SRms SWvt WSHC
- 'Album' ♀H4	Widely available
- 'Album Variegatum' (v)	LRHS SCob WSHC
* - 'Aureovariegatum' (v)	CMac EShb LBMP NEgg SLim SPlb
- 'Coldham'	GCal SMad
- 'Creche ar Pape'	ECha LRHS
§ ***linearifolium***	CSpe LBMP SKHP WCot WHea WPGP WSHC
muricatum (F)	CCCN CHll EShb SPlb
pinnatum	SPlb
pseudocapsicum variegated (v)	WCot
pyracanthum	CDTJ SPlb WCot
quitoense (F)	CDTJ SBig SPlb
rantonnetii	see *Lycianthes rantonnetii*
rigescentoides **new**	SPlb
sisymbriifolium	SPlb
aff. ***stenophyllum*** B&SWJ 10744	WCru
wendlandii	CCCN CHll

Solaria (*Alliaceae*)

sp.	GCal

Soldanella (*Primulaceae*)

alpicola	GJos
alpina	CCon CTal EBee ECho GBin GCra GKev LLHF SRms WAbe
- SDR 6332	GKev LEdu
- SDR 6915 **new**	LEdu
I - 'Alba'	ECho WAbe
- subsp. ***alpina*** **new**	NSla
carpatica	CTal ECho GKev LEdu LLHF WAbe
- 'Alba'	CTal ECho GEdr LEdu NHar WAbe
carpatica × ***pusilla***	CPBP ECho MNrw NHar NRya NWad WAbe
carpatica × ***villosa***	ECho LEdu
cyanaster	EBee ECho GBin GEdr GJos GKev LEdu LLHF NRya NSbr WAbe
dimoniei	CTal EBee ECho GKev ITim LEdu WAbe
hungarica	ECho EPot GEdr WAbe
minima	ECho GEdr GJos GKev LEdu NHar NSla WAbe
montana	CFis ECho GBin GJos LEdu LLHF NLar SBch
pindicola	CTal ECho GEdr LEdu WAbe
pusilla	GKev NWad
'Spring Symphony'	CTal ECho GEdr GMaP LEdu LLHF NHar
'Sudden Spring'	CTal ECho GEdr LEdu NWad WAbe
villosa ♀H5	CCon CTal EBee ECho EPot GAbr GBin GEdr GKev LEdu NRya NWad SBch WAbe WMoo WSHC WThu

Soleirolia (*Urticaceae*)

soleirolii	CHEx CHel CTri EUJe MMuc MWhi SBHP SCob SEND SMad SPer SVic SWvt WHer XLum
- 'Argentea'	see *S. soleirolii* 'Variegata'
§ - 'Aurea'	CTri SVic SWvt
- 'Golden Queen'	see *S. soleirolii* 'Aurea'
- 'Silver Queen'	see *S. soleirolii* 'Variegata'
§ - 'Variegata' (v)	SCob SVic WHer

Solenopsis (*Campanulaceae*)

axillaris	see *Isotoma axillaris*

Solenostemon ✿ (*Lamiaceae*)

'Autumn Rainbow'	WDib
'Beauty' (v)	WDib
'Beauty of Lyons'	WDib
'Black Heart'	WDib
'Black Prince'	WDib
'Brilliant' (v)	WDib
'Bronze Pagoda'	WDib
'Buttercup'	WDib
'Chamaeleon' (v)	WDib
'City of Sunderland'	WDib
'Combat' (v) ♀H1c	WDib
'Crimson Ruffles' (v) ♀H1c	WDib

	'Dazzler' (v)	WDib
	'Display'	WDib
	'Durham Gala' ♀H1c	WDib
	'Firelight'	WDib
	'Flamingo'	WDib
	'Freckles' (v)	WDib
	'Gay's Delight'	NPri
	'Gingernut'	EUJe NPri SMrm
	'Illumination'	WDib
	'Inky Fingers' (v)	WDib
	'Juliet Quartermain'	EUJe WDib
	'Jupiter'	WDib
	'Kentish Fire' (v)	WDib
	'Kiwi Fern' (Stained Glassworks Series) (v)	WDib
	'Lemon Chiffon'	WDib
	'Lord Falmouth' (v) ♀H1c	WDib
	'Midnight'	EUJe
	'Mrs Pilkington' (v)	WDib
	'Muriel Pedley' (v)	WDib
	'Paisley Shawl' (v)	WDib
	'Palisandra'	CSpe
	'Peter Wonder' (v)	WDib
	'Picturatus' (v) ♀H1c	WDib
	'Pineapple Beauty' (v) ♀H1c	WDib
	'Pineapplette' ♀H1c	WDib
	'Pink Chaos' ♀H1c	WDib
	'Red Angel'	WDib
	'Red Velvet'	WDib
	Redhead = 'Ufo646'PBR	NPri
	'Rose Blush' (v)	WDib
	'Roy Pedley' ♀H1c	WDib
	'Royal Scot' (v) ♀H1c	WDib
	'Salmon Plumes' (v)	WDib
	'Saturn'	WDib
	scutellarioides Henna = 'Balcenna'PBR	ECtt NPri
	'The Flume'	WDib
	thyrsoideus	see *Plectranthus thyrsoideus*
	'Timotei'	WDib
	Trusty Rusty = 'Uf06419'PBR ♀H1c	NPri
	'Walter Turner' (v) ♀H1c	ECtt WDib
	'Winsome' (v)	WDib
	'Winter Sun' (v)	WDib
	'Wisley Flame'	WDib
	'Wisley Tapestry' (v) ♀H1c	WDib
	'Wizard Merlin' **new**	NPri

Solidago (*Asteraceae*)

	sp.	MJak
	Babygold	see *S.* 'Goldkind'
	brachystachys	see *S. cutleri*
	caesia	EBee EWes LRHS NBir SMHy
	canadensis	CTri ELan SPlb WHer WOld WWtn XLum
	- var. ***salebrosa***	EBee LRHS
	- var. ***scabra***	WOld
	'Citronella'	ECtt EWll GQue
	'Cloth of Gold'	CMac COtt ECtt EPfP LRHS NEoE NHol NSoo SPoG SWvt WGwG WMnd
§	'Crown of Rays'	ECtt ELon EPfP LRHS MRav SCob WFar WWEG
§	***cutleri***	EBee ECho MWat NLar SBch SPlb SRms WFar WThu
I	- ***nana***	ECho
	'Ducky'	SCob
	'Early Bird'	NLar WFar
	'Featherbush'	EBee WWEG
	flabelliformis **new**	WCot
§	***flexicaulis***	GMaP WCot XLum
	- 'Variegata' (v)	EBee ECtt ELan GMaP LRHS NLar WHer WMoo WWEG XLum
	'Gardone' ♀H7	WFar
	gigantea	WFar
	glomerata	MMuc NLar SEND SMrm
	Golden Baby	see *S.* 'Goldkind'
§	'Golden Dwarf'	CWCL WPtf WWEG XLum
	'Golden Fleece'	see *S. sphacelata* 'Golden Fleece'
	'Golden Thumb'	see *S.* 'Queenie'
	'Golden Wings'	CBre MWat
	'Goldenmosa' ♀H7	CSBt EWes GKev GMaP SPer WFar
	'Goldilocks'	NPri SRms
§	'Goldkind'	CAby CSBt CTri EBee ECtt ELan EPfP IBoy LPot LRHS MMuc MWhi NEgg NOrc SEND SWvt WBrk WHar WWEG XLum
	Goldzwerg	see *S.* 'Golden Dwarf'
	'Harvest Gold'	CAby CBre CElw
	'Hiddigeigei' (v) **new**	WCot
	hybrida	see *S.* × *luteus*
	latifolia	see *S. flexicaulis*
	'Laurin'	NLar XLum
	'Ledsham'	ECtt EWll LEdu LRHS NBre SPoG
	'Lena'	SRms
	'Linner Gold'	NBre
	'Little Lemon'PBR	EBee ELan LRHS MBri SCob
§	× ***luteus***	EBee SRms WHil WOut XLum
	- 'Lemore' ♀H7	CBod CMea EAJP EBee ECha ELan EPfP GBuc GMaP GQue LAst LRHS LSou MNFA MSpe MWat NCGa NSti SMrm SPer SPhx SRms WCot WFar WWEG WWtn XLum
	ohioensis	XLum
§	***ptarmicoides***	EBee XEll XLum
§	'Queenie'	ECha MHer MLHP WWEG
	rigida	WCot
	rugosa	ECha MBNS MMuc SPhx WCot
	- 'Fireworks' ♀H7	CAby CBre CHVG CMHG CMac CMea CSam EBee ECtt ELon GQue IBoy LRHS MAvo MNFA MSpe NLar SDys SPhx WBrk WCot WFar WHoo WOld WWEG XLum
	- 'Loydser Crown' **new**	NDov
	sempervirens	EBee IMou LRHS WOld WWEG
	'Septembergold'	CSam
	'Sonnenschein'	NBre
	speciosa	SPhx
	spectabilis var. ***confinis***	EBee
	- - KM 27-01 **new**	EBee
§	***sphacelata*** 'Golden Fleece'	CBcs ELan IMou NBre SRms WMnd WWEG
	spiraeifolia	EBee
	Strahlenkrone	see *S.* 'Crown of Rays'
	'Summer Sunshine'	WWEG
	'Super'	CAby
	Sweety = 'Barseven'PBR	LRHS MBri
	'Tom Thumb'	MRav NBir SRms
	uliginosa	EShb XLum
	ulmifolia	EBee
	virgaurea	CArn GPoy MHer MNHC NLar SRms WHer
	- subsp. ***alpestris*** var. ***minutissima***	GEdr

- var. ***cambrica***	see *S. virgaurea* subsp. *minuta*
§ - subsp. ***minuta***	GBin GCrg
§ - 'Variegata' (v)	CBre EHoe NEoE
vulgaris 'Variegata'	see *S. virgaurea* 'Variegata'
'Yellow Stone'	EBee

× *Solidaster* see *Solidago*

hybridus	see *Solidago* × *luteus*

Sollya (*Pittosporaceae*)

fusiformis	see *S. heterophylla*
§ ***heterophylla*** ♀H3	Widely available
- 'Alba'	CBcs CCCN CFlo CSPN EBee ELan EPfP GCal LRHS SEle SLim SLon SWvt WSHC
- mauve-flowered	ECou
- 'Pink Charmer'	CBcs ELan LRHS SLon SPoG
- pink-flowered	CCCN CHll CSPN LBMP LRHS SLim SWvt

Sonchus (*Asteraceae*)

arboreus	WCot
fruticosus	CHEx
giganteus	CHll
pinnatus	SPlb

Sophora (*Papilionaceae*)

arizonica **new**	SIgm
cassioides NJM 08.008	WPGP
- 'Goldilocks'	WPGP
- 'Goughensis'	WPGP
§ ***davidii***	CBcs CExl CWGN EBee EPfP LRHS MBlu MGos MMuc MOWG SBrt SEND SPoG SSpi WPGP WSHC
- dark blue-flowered **new**	WPGP
flavescens	SBrt
fulvida	ECou EPfP WPGP
howinsula	ECou
japonica	see *Styphnolobium japonicum*
§ 'Little Baby'	CAbP EBee ELan EPfP EUJe LBrs LRHS MGos MNHC SEle SPoG SWvt WGrn
longicarinata	ECou
macrocarpa	SWvt
microphylla	CHEx CTri ECou LEdu MGil SEND WPGP
molloyi	ECou
- 'Dragon's Gold'	CBcs ECou ELan EPfP LRHS MAsh SCob SCoo SPoG SSpi SSta SWvt WPGP
- 'Early Gold'	WPGP
prostrata misapplied	see *S.* 'Little Baby'
prostrata ambig.	CBcs
prostrata Buchanan	CMac ECou
Sun King = 'Hilsop'PBR ♀H4	CBcs CDul CWGN ELan EPfP EPla EWes LRHS MBri MGos NLar SCob SCoo SHil SLim SLon SPoG SWvt
tetraptera	CAbP CBcs CDul CTsd ECou EPfP LRHS SEND SWvt WCFE WPGP
viciifolia	see *S. davidii*

Sorbaria (*Rosaceae*)

aitchisonii	see *S. tomentosa* var. *angustifolia*
arborea	see *S. kirilowii*
aff. ***assurgens*** BWJ 8185	WCru
§ ***kirilowii***	CExl CMac MRav NLar SMad WOut
- AC 3433	MSnd
sorbifolia	CAbP CBcs CMCN ELan GAbr MGil MLHP MMuc SBrt SCob SEND SPer SPlb WFar WWtn
- 'Sem'PBR ♀H5	Widely available
- var. ***stellipila*** B&SWJ 776	WCru
§ ***tomentosa***	CBcs CDul CTri ELan EPfP IDee
var. ***angustifolia*** ♀H5	LRHS MMuc MRav NBid SCob SEND SLon SPer WHer

× *Sorbaronia* (*Rosaceae*)

fallax **new**	NLar
- 'Ivan's Beauty'	ECrN

× *Sorbopyrus* (*Rosaceae*)

auricularis	MCoo
- 'Shipova' (F)	CAgr

Sorbus ✿ (*Rosaceae*)

sp.	CMen
KR 5585 (sect. *Discolores*) **new**	WCru WPGP
NJM 09.203 **new**	WPGP
adamii	CMCN
alnifolia	CJun CLnd CMCN EPfP MBlu MBri
- B&SWJ 8461	WCru
- B&SWJ 10948	WCru
- 'Red Bird'	EPfP MBlu
americana	CLnd NWea
anglica	CDul CTho
'Apricot'	CEnd
'Apricot Queen'	CDul CLnd EBee ECrN EPla LAst MJak MMuc SEND SGol WFar
aria	CAco CCVT CDul CHab CLnd CSBt CTri ECrN IBoy LBuc MGos MMuc NWea SCob SEND SEWo SGol WHar WMou
- 'Aurea'	CLnd SPer
- 'Chrysophylla'	CDul CSBt ECrN NWea
- 'Decaisneana'	see *S. aria* 'Majestica'
- 'Gigantea'	EWTr
- 'Lutescens' ♀H6	Widely available
- 'Magnifica'	ECrN ELan NEgg NLar SCoo SEWo WJas
§ - 'Majestica' ♀H6	CCVT CDoC CDul CLnd CMac EBee ECrN EPla MAsh MRav NWea SCob SCoo SPer WFar WHar WJas
- 'Mitchellii'	see *S. thibetica* 'John Mitchell'
- var. ***salicifolia***	see *S. rupicola*
aria × ***pseudovilmorinii*** **new**	WPGP
arnoldiana 'Golden Wonder'	see *S.* 'Lombarts Golden Wonder'
aronioides misapplied	see *S. caloneura*
arranensis	CDul CLnd WPat
§ ***aucuparia***	Widely available
- 'Aspleniifolia'	CBcs CCVT CDul CLnd CMCN CMac CSBt ECrN GBin IBoy LAst LRHS MGos MJak MRav MWat NLar NPCo NWea SCob SLim SPer WFar WJas WMou
§ - 'Beissneri'	CAgr CDul MRav NWea SCoo SLon
- Cardinal Royal = 'Michred'	CCVT CDoC CDul CLnd ECrN MMuc NEgg SCoo SEND SEWo SLon
- 'Dirkenii'	MAsh SGol WJas
§ - var. ***edulis*** (F)	CBcs CDul CLnd CTho ECrN EWTr LBuc MCoo MGos SCob SPer
- - 'Rossica' misapplied	see *S. aucuparia* var. *edulis* 'Rossica Major'

§	– – 'Rossica Major'	CDul ECrN GQui SEWo
§	– 'Fastigiata'	CEnd CTri ELan EPfP GKin LAst MGos NPCo SCob
	– 'Hilling's Spire'	CBcs CTho
	– subsp. ***maderensis***	WPat
	– 'Pendula'	ELan
	– ***pluripinnata***	see *S. scalaris* Koehne
	– var. ***rossica*** Koehne	see *S. aucuparia* var. *edulis*
	– 'Sheerwater Seedling' ♀H6	CBcs CCVT CDoC CDul CMCN COtt CSBt EBee ECrN ELan EPfP EPla GKin IBoy LAst MGos MMuc MRav MSwo NWea SCob SEND SEWo SGol SPer WFar
	– var. ***xanthocarpa***	ECrN ELan
	Autumn Spire = 'Flanrock' ♀H6	CDoC CEnd CLnd CTsd ELan IBoy LRHS MAsh MBri MGos NLar NWea SCoo SEWo SLim SLon SPoG SWvt WHar
	bissetii	WPat
	– Yu 14299	WCru
	brevipetiolata B&SWJ 11771	WCru
§	***caloneura***	EPfP LEdu MBlu WPGP
	– Guiz 80	WCru
	– NJM 11.004 **new**	WPGP
	carmesina B&L 12545	EPfP WCru
	cashmiriana Hedl. ♀H6	Widely available
	aff. ***cashmiriana***	EPla MAsh MJak NHol WFar
	– B 751	WCru
	'Chinese Lace'	Widely available
§	***commixta***	CBcs CDul CEnd CLnd CMCN CTho EBee ECrN IBoy LAst MBlu MGos MJak MMuc MSwo NLar SCob SEND SGol SLim SPer WJas
	– B&SWJ 10839	WCru
	– B&SWJ 11043	WCru
	– 'Embley' ♀H6	CBcs CCVT CDul CMCN CSBt CTho CTri EBee ECrN ELan EPfP MBlu MGos MMuc MRav NEgg NPCo NWea SCob SEND SGol SPer SPoG
	– Olympic Flame = 'Dodong' ♀H6	CEnd COtt EBee EMil EPfP IArd IDee LBuc MBri NLar NWea SCoo SEWo SLim SPer WHar WMou
	– 'Ravensbill'	EBee EPfP NLar SCoo WHar
	– var. ***rufoferruginea***	GQui
	– – B&SWJ 11486	WCru
	– var. ***sachalinensis*** B&SWJ 8496	WCru
	– – B&SWJ 8515	WCru
	aff. ***commixta***	MSnd
	conradinae misapplied	see *S. pohuashanensis* (Hance) Hedl.
	conradinae Koehne	see *S. esserteauana*
	'Copper Kettle' ♀H6	EBee EPfP MAsh MBri MWat NLar SCoo WHar
	'Coral Beauty'	CLnd
	corymbifera WWJ 11860	WCru
	'Covert Gold'	CEnd
	croceocarpa	CDul
	'Croft Coral'	MAsh WHar
	cuspidata	see *S. vestita*
*	***decora*** 'Grootendorst'	CDul
	– var. ***nana***	see *S. aucuparia* 'Fastigiata'
	devoniensis	CDoC CDul CTho
	– 'Devon Beauty'	CAgr
	discolor misapplied	see *S. commixta*
	discolor (Maxim.) Maxim.	EBee LAst MBlu MJak NWea WJas
	– MF 96172	MAsh
	– MF 97103 **new**	WCru
	domestica	CDul EPfP MMuc SEND WCot
	– 'Maliformis'	see *S. domestica* f. *pomifera*
§	– f. ***pomifera***	CLnd LEdu WThu
§	– f. ***pyrifera***	LEdu
	– 'Pyriformis'	see *S. domestica* f. *pyrifera*
	– 'Rosie'	CAgr
	dunnii **new**	WPGP
	'Eastern Promise' ♀H6	COtt EBee EPfP EPla GBin MAsh MBri MSwo MWat NLar NWea SCob SCoo SLim WHCr WHar WMou
§	***eburnea*** Harry Smith 12799	GQui WPGP
	eminens	CDul CNat
	epidendron WWJ 11930	WCru
§	***esserteauana***	CLnd CTho WPat
	fansipanensis **new**	GLin
	– NJM 09.176 **new**	WPGP
	'Fastigiata'	see *S. aucuparia* 'Fastigiata', *S.* × *thuringiaca* 'Fastigiata'
	folgneri	CJun MBri
	– 'Emiel' ♀H6	EBee EPfP MBlu MBri
	– 'Lemon Drop'	CDul CEnd CJun CLnd EPfP MAsh MBri SCoo SMad WHar
§	***foliolosa***	CLnd
	forrestii ♀H6	CBcs CMCN EBee EPfP GKev MBri NLar
*	***fortunei***	CLnd
*	***fosteri***	EBee
§	***frutescens*** ♀H6	NWea WMou WPGP
	fruticosa Crantz	CPom GKev NSla
	– 'Koehneana'	see *S. koehneana* C.K. Schneid.
	'Ghose'	CEnd EBee MBri SCoo
	glabriuscula	EBee GKev
	'Glendoick Gleam'	GGGa
	'Glendoick Glory'	GGGa
	'Glendoick Ivory'	GGGa
	'Glendoick Pearl'	GGGa
	'Glendoick Ruby'	GGGa
	'Glendoick Spire'	GGGa
	'Glendoick White Baby'	GGGa
	glomerulata	LLHF
	'Golden Wonder'	see *S.* 'Lombarts Golden Wonder'
	gonggashanica	EPfP GKev NLar WPGP WPat
*	***gorrodini***	CLnd
§	***graeca***	WPat
	granulosa HWJ 1041	WCru
	harrowiana	GCal WPGP WPat
	– KR 21009 **new**	WPGP
	hedlundii	CExl EBee EBtc EPfP NLar NWea SKHP WPGP
	– KR 1687	WPGP
	– KR 1810	WPGP
	helenae	WPGP
	hemsleyi	CBcs CDul CExl EPfP WPGP WPat
	– 'John Bond' ♀H6	CDoC EBee LRHS SPoG
	× ***hostii***	CLnd
	hupehensis C.K. Schneid. ♀H6	CBcs CDul CLnd CMCN CMac CTho CTri EBee EPfP EWTr MMuc MRav NWea SEND SGol SPer WHar WJas WMou
	– MF 96170	EPfP
	– 'November Pink'	see *S. hupehensis* 'Pink Pagoda'
§	– var. ***obtusa*** ♀H6	CAco CCVT CDoC CDul CLnd EPfP NPCo
§	– 'Pink Pagoda' ♀H6	CDoC CDul CLnd EBee EPfP EWTr GBin IArd LAst LRHS MAsh MBlu MGos MMuc MRav MWat NLar

	Name	Suppliers
		NPri NWea SCob SCoo SEND SEWo SLim SLon SPer SPoG WHCr WMou
	- 'Rosea'	see *S. hupehensis* var. *obtusa*
	aff. ***hupehensis*** **new**	WFar
	hybrida L.	ECrN
	- 'Gibbsii' ♀H6	CDoC EBee ELan EPfP EWTr MAsh SPoG WHar
	insignis	WPGP WPat
	intermedia	CAco CBcs CCVT CDul CLnd CSBt CTho CTri ECrN ELan EWTr MGos MMuc NWea SEND SGol WHar WMou
	- 'Brouwers'	CDoC CLnd ELan
	japonica	CDul
	- B&SWJ 10813	WCru
	- B&SWJ 11048	WCru
	'Joseph Rock'	Widely available
I	***keenanii*** KR 7746 **new**	WPGP
§	× ***kewensis***	CDul CLnd NWea SPlb
	'Kirsten Pink'	EBee ECrN SPer
	koehneana misapplied	see *S. frutescens*
§	***koehneana*** C.K. Schneid.	CBcs CLnd ELan GKev GQui IDee NWea
	aff. ***koehneana*** C.K. Schneid.	see *S. eburnea*
	aff. ***koehneana*** ambig.	GEdr
	lanata misapplied	see *S. vestita*
	lancastriensis	CNat
	latifolia	CLnd NWea
	- 'Henk Vink'	CCVT
	'Leonard Messel' ♀H6	CDoC EPfP LRHS MAsh MBri NLar SCoo WHCr
	'Leonard Springer'	EPfP
	'Likjornaja'	EPfP MBri
§	'Lombarts Golden Wonder'	CBcs CDul MMuc NWea SEND
	matsumurana misapplied	see *S. commixta*
	matsumurana (Makino) Koehne	WPGP
	megalocarpa	CBcs CDoC CJun SKHP SSpi WPGP
	meliosmifolia B&SWJ 11709	WCru
	microphylla	CMCN
	- GWJ 9252	WCru
	minima	WPat
	monbeigii (Card.) Balakr.	CLnd GKev
	moravica 'Laciniata'	see *S. aucuparia* 'Beissneri'
	needhamii NJM 11.005 **new**	WPGP
	aff. ***ovalis*** H 1948	EBee
	'Pearly King'	CTho MAsh WJas
§	'Pink Pearl'	CDul EPfP
	'Pink-Ness'	MBlu MWat SCoo
	pohuashanensis misapplied	see *S.* × *kewensis*
§	***pohuashanensis*** (Hance) Hedl.	WPat
	porrigentiformis	CDul
	poteriifolia ♀H5	GKev NHar WPat
	prattii Koehne	CTho EBee GKev MBri
	pseudobakyonensis	CBcs
	pseudohupehensis	MSnd
	pseudovilmorinii	CDul CPom LRHS MBri NLar WCru WPGP
	- CLD 1437	GKev
	randaiensis	EBee GKev GQui MBri NLar SPlb
	- B&SWJ 3202	EPfP NWad SSpi WCru
	'Red Robin'	IBoy
	'Red Tip'	CDul
	reducta ♀H5	CBcs GAbr GBin GCal GKev GQui MMuc NHar NHol NLar NSla SBrt SPer WPat
	aff. ***reducta***	MSnd
	reflexipetala misapplied	see *S. commixta*
	rehderiana misapplied	see *S. aucuparia*
	rehderiana Koehne	CDul CLnd GKev
	- AC 3459	MSnd
	rosea	GEdr GKev
	- SEP 492	WCru WPGP
	- 'Rosiness' ♀H6	CLnd EBee EPfP MBri SCoo WHar
	'Rowancroft Coral Pink'	EBee
§	***rupicola***	NWea
	rushforthii KR 3412	GKev
	'Salmon Queen'	CLnd
	sambucifolia	EBee SKHP
	sargentiana ♀H6	CCVT CDul CEnd CLnd CMCN CTho CTri EBee ECrN ELan EPfP EPla GQui LRHS MBlu MBri MGos MRav MSwo NLar NWea SLim SPer SPoG WMou
	- EGM 291 **new**	WCru
	scalaris ambig.	CBcs CMCN CNWT ELan IDee MAsh MSwo NWea WHar WMou
§	***scalaris*** Koehne	CCVT CDul CEnd CLnd CTho CTri EBee EPfP IDee MBlu MGos SPer SPoG WJas
	'Schouten'	ECrN
	scopulina misapplied	see *S. aucuparia* 'Fastigiata'
	setschwanensis BWJ 8053 **new**	WCru
	subulata HWJ 925	WCru
	- KWJ 12272	WCru
	'Sunshine'	CCVT CDoC CDul CLnd MAsh MBri MGos MMuc SEND WJas
	thibetica AGS/ES 347	WPGP
§	- 'John Mitchell' ♀H6	CAgr CDul CEnd CLnd CMCN EBee ECrN EPfP MAsh MBlu MBri MGos NWea SLim WMou
	aff. ***thibetica*** BWJ 7757a	WCru
	thomsonii GWJ 9363	WCru
	- HWJ 984	WCru
	- WWJ 12004	WCru
§	× ***thuringiaca*** 'Fastigiata'	CBcs CCVT CDul CLnd CSBt EBee EPfP NEgg SCoo WJas
	torminalis	CBcs CCVT CDul CHab CLnd CMCN CMac CTho CTri ELan EPfP LEdu MBri MGos MMuc MRav MSnd NLar NWea SCoo SEND SEWo SPer SPoG WHar WMou
	umbellata var. ***cretica***	see *S. graeca*
	ursina	see *S. foliolosa*
§	***vestita***	CLnd CMCN CTho EPfP WCru
	vexans	CDul GBin
	vilmorinii ♀H6	Widely available
	- 'Robusta'	see *S.* 'Pink Pearl'
	aff. ***vilmorinii***	GKin IBoy MJak
	- KR 6453 **new**	WCru
	wardii	CBcs CDul CLnd CTho EPfP MBlu MBri WPat
	'White Swan'	MAsh
	'White Wax'	CDul EPfP LAst MGos NWea SPer SPoG
	wilmottiana	CDul WPat
	wilsoniana	CLnd GGGa GQui
	- NN 0929 **new**	MSnd
	'Wisley Gold' ♀H6	EBee GBin MAsh SCoo SLim SPoG WMou
	yuana	WPGP

Sorghastrum (Poaceae)

avenaceum see *S. nutans*
§ **nutans** CBod SMad
- 'Indian Steel' CBod EBee GQue LSun SDix SGSe XLum

sorrel, common see *Rumex acetosa*

sorrel, French see *Rumex scutatus*

Souliea see *Actaea*

soursop see *Annona muricata*

Sparaxis (Iridaceae)

auriculata 'Vanrhynsdorp' ECho
bulbifera ECho
elegans 'Coccinea' WCot
'Fire King' new GKev NRog
fragrans 'Napier' ECho
grandiflora ECho NRog
subsp. **acutiloba**
- subsp. **fimbriata** ECho
- subsp. **grandiflora** ECho
- subsp. **violacea** 'Botriver' ECho
meterlekampiae ECho
'Piekenierskloof'
- 'Rawsonville' ECho
mixed NRog SDeJ
'Moonlight' new LAma NRog
parviflora ECho
'Red Reflex' ECho NRog
'Sunshine' new LAma NRog
tricolor ECho NRog SDeJ
variegata (v) ECho
villosa ECho NRog

Sparganium (Sparganiaceae)

RCB RA G-1 WCot
§ **erectum** CBAq CRow CWat EHon NMir NPer SWat WMAq WSFF XLum
ramosum see *S. erectum*

Sparrmannia (Malvaceae)

africana ♀H1c CHEx CHll ELan EShb SEND SVen
- 'Flore Pleno' (d) CBcs

Spartina (Poaceae)

pectinata SGol XLum
- 'Aureomarginata' (v) CHEx CWCL EBee EHoe ELan EPPr EPfP EPla GMaP LBMP LRHS MBri MLHP MMoz MMuc MWhi NLar NOak NWsh SEND SMrm SPer WMoo WWEG WWtn

Spartium (Papilionaceae)

junceum ♀H5 CAco CArn CBcs CDoC CDul CEnd COtt CSde CWld EBee ELan ELon EPfP EWTr GCal LAst LRHS MGos MMuc SCob SDix SEND SPer SPoG SRms XSen
- 'Brockhill Compact' CDoC CDul ELan EPfP LRHS

Spartocytisus see *Cytisus*

Spathantheum (Araceae)

orbignyanum WCot

Spathipappus see *Tanacetum*

Spathiphyllum (Araceae)

wallisii NGBI SPre

Spathodea (Bignoniaceae)

campanulata SPlb

spearmint see *Mentha spicata*

Speirantha (Asparagaceae)

§ **convallarioides** CDes CLAP CPom CTal EBee ECho ELon EPPr EPfP LEdu MNrw SGSe WCot WCru WHil WPGP
gardenii see *S. convallarioides*

Sphacele see *Lepechinia*

Sphaeralcea (Malvaceae)

ambigua SPlb XSen
'Childerley' CSpe CWGN ECtt MCot MHol SMrm SPad WCot
coccinea SPlb
fendleri CHll CSam CSde
- subsp. **venusta** XSen
grossulariifolia XSen
'Hopleys Lavender' EWoo LAst LSou SWvt WSHC
'Hyde Hall' MHom
incana CSpe LSou
- 'Sourup' CSpe EBee ECtt ELan MHol WCot
laxa XSen
malviflora CDTJ
miniata CCCN CHll SMrm
munroana CDTJ ECtt ELan SRkn WSHC
- pale pink-flowered CSam ECtt
'Newleaze Coral' CBod CWGN ECtt ELan ETwe EWoo LAst LBMP MAsh MHom MNrw SPoG SRkn SWvt WCot WWFP
'Newleaze Pink' SRkn
remota CExl GEdr SPhx SPlb
rivularis LPla
umbellata see *Phymosia umbellata*

Sphaeromeria (Asteraceae)

§ **capitata** CPBP

Sphenomeris (Dennstaedtiaceae)

chinensis B&SWJ 6108 WCru

Spigelia (Loganiaceae)

marilandica EBee GKev SKHP
- 'Red Feather' NLar
- 'Wisley Jester' SKHP

Spilanthes (Asteraceae)

acmella misapplied see *Acmella oleracea*
oleracea see *Acmella oleracea*

Spiloxene (Hypoxidaceae)

canaliculata 'Kamiesberg' ECho
capensis new NRog
- 'Somerset West' ECho
minuta 'Nay' ECho
serrata 'Saldanha' ECho

Spiraea (Rosaceae)

'Abigail' CDoC

alba var. ***latifolia***	MMuc SEND
albiflora	see *S. japonica* 'Albiflora'
arborea	see *Sorbaria kirilowii*
arcuata	MJak
aff. 'Arguta'	EPla SHil
§ 'Arguta' ♀H6	Widely available
× ***arguta*** 'Bridal Wreath'	see *S.* 'Arguta'
betulifolia	GKin MRav SCob WFar
- var. ***aemiliana***	CAbP ECtt MAsh MMuc SCob
- 'Tor'	EPPr MBri
- 'Tor Gold'PBR	EPPr
× ***billardii*** misapplied	see *S.* × *pseudosalicifolia*
blumei CWJ 12829 new	WCru
× ***bumalda*** 'Wulfenii'	see *S. japonica* 'Walluf'
callosa 'Alba'	see *S. japonica* 'Albiflora'
canescens	CExl GKin
- AC 1354	MSnd
- var. ***glaucophylla*** new	MMuc SEND
× ***cinerea*** 'Grefsheim' ♀H6	CAco CBcs CDoC COtt CSBt ELan LBuc MBri MGos MJak MMuc SCob SEND SGol SLim SPer SPlb
crispifolia	see *S. japonica* 'Bullata'
douglasii	CMac SCob
formosana B&SWJ 1597	CExl WCru
fritschiana	CMac
hayatana RWJ 10014	WCru
hendersonii	see *Petrophytum hendersonii*
§ ***japonica*** 'Albiflora'	CBcs CDoC CDul CMac CNec COtt CSBt CTri ECrN ELan LRHS MAsh MGos MRav MSwo MWat NEgg NSoo NWad SCob SGbt SGol SLim SPad SPer SRms SWvt WMoo
- 'Alpina'	see *S. japonica* 'Nana'
- 'Alpine Gold'	NEoE
- 'Anthony Waterer' (v)	Widely available
- 'Barkby Gold'	MGos
- 'Blenheim'	SRms
§ - 'Bullata'	CMac ECho GCrg NLar SRms WAbe WPat
- 'Candlelight' ♀H6	CDoC CSBt ELan EPfP GKin LAst LRHS LSou MAsh MBri MGos MWat NEgg NLar SCob SCoo SGol SLim SPer SPoG SWvt WMoo
- 'Crispa'	CAco EPfP NEoE NSoo NWad WFar WGrn WMoo
- 'Dart's Red' ♀H6	CDul ELan GKin IVic MBri MWat WMoo
- 'Firelight'	Widely available
§ - var. ***fortunei*** 'Macrophylla'	WPat
§ - 'Genpei'	CMac EBee LBuc MJak MMuc SEND SGol SPer SPoG
- 'Gold Mound'	CExl CMac COtt EHoe ELan EPfP LAst LRHS MAsh MGos MJak MMuc MRav MSwo NLar SCoo SEND SLim SPlb SRms WFar WHar
- Golden Princess = 'Lisp' ♀H6	CDoC CMac COtt CTri ELan EPfP IBoy LBuc LRHS MAsh MGos MJak NEgg NLar NPri SCoo SGol SHil SPer SRms SSta WFar WMoo
- 'Goldflame'	Widely available
- 'Little Princess'	CBcs CDoC CDul CMac COtt EBee ELan EPla EShb LRHS MAsh MRav MSwo MWat NLar NSoo NWea SCob SCoo SGol SHil SLim SPer SRGP SRms SSta SWvt WFar WHar WMoo
- Magic Carpet = 'Walbuma'PBR (v) ♀H6	CDoC COtt EPfP GBin LBuc LRHS MAsh MBri MMuc MWat NLar SCob SCoo SEND SPoG
- 'Magnifica'	see *S. japonica* var. *fortunei* 'Macrophylla'
§ - 'Nana' ♀H6	CMac CSBt ECho GCrg MAsh MRav SRms
- 'Nyewoods'	see *S. japonica* 'Nana'
- 'Shiburi'	see *S. japonica* 'Albiflora'
- 'Shirobana' misapplied	see *S. japonica* 'Genpei'
- 'Shirobana'	see *S. japonica* 'Albiflora'
- 'Sparkling Carpet'PBR new	CSBt
§ - 'Walluf'	CMac CTri
- 'White Gold'PBR	CBod CDoC CMac COtt CSBt ELan EPfP LAst LRHS LSqu MAsh MBri NEoE NHol NWad SCoo SLim SPer SPoG SWvt WHar WMoo
'Margaritae'	SPer SWvt
micrantha	CExl
nipponica	CAco CBcs
- 'Halward's Silver'	MBri MRav NEoE
- 'June Bride'	MBri
§ - 'Snowmound' ♀H6	Widely available
- var. ***tosaensis*** misapplied	see *S. nipponica* 'Snowmound'
palmata 'Elegans'	see *Filipendula purpurea* 'Elegans'
prunifolia (d)	CMac EBee ELan EPfP EPla LRHS MRav SPer WCFE WFar WGrn WPat
× ***pseudosalicifolia*** new	CAco
- 'Triumphans'	MMuc SEND SPer
salicifolia	MMuc
'Sparkling Champagne'	LBuc LRHS NWad SLim SLon WNPC
Sundrop = 'Bailcarol'	LBuc
thunbergii ♀H6	CBcs CDul CMac CTri EPfP MMuc MRav NWea SCob SEND SGol SLim SRms
- 'Golden Times'	LRHS SPoG
- 'Mount Fuji'	CMac EHoe MRav NEoE WFar
ulmaria	see *Filipendula ulmaria*
× ***vanhouttei***	CBcs CBod CDul CTri ELan EPfP MMuc MRav MSwo SEND SLim SPer SRms WFar WMoo
- 'Gold Fountain'	CMac ELan EMil EPfP EShb GBin MMuc NHol SCoo SEND SPer SPoG WFar WMoo
- 'Pink Ice' (v)	CBod CDoC COtt EHoe EPfP LAst LBMP LRHS MAsh MGos MMuc MRav SEND SPer SPlb SPoG SWvt
veitchii	MRav
venusta 'Magnifica'	see *Filipendula rubra* 'Venusta'

Spiranthes (*Orchidaceae*)

cernua	NGdn
- var. ***odorata***	LSou
- - 'Chadd's Ford' ♀H4	CBcs CBro CDes CExl EBee ECho ECtt IKil LAma LRHS MBel MNrw NBir SEND WCot WPtf WWEG
spiralis	WHer

Spirodela (*Araceae*)

§ ***polyrrhiza***	EWay

Spodiopogon (*Poaceae*)

sibiricus	CKno EBee EHoe EPPr NLos SGSe SMad WPtf XLum
- 'West Lake'	IMou

Sporobolus (*Poaceae*)

	airoides	CBod CKno EBee EHoe EPPr EShb LPla SGSe SMHy SMad WCot WHrl
	heterolepis	CKno EBee EHoe GQue LRHS NDov SGSe SMHy SMea SPhx WCot
	- 'Cloud'	GBin
I	- 'Wisconsin Strain'	CAby EBee EPPr IMou LPla SPhx
	heterolepsis 'Blue Dust' **new**	NDov
	wrightii	EPPr SMad SPhx

Sprekelia (*Amaryllidaceae*)

	formosissima	CCon CSpe ECho LAma LEdu SDeJ SPav

Stachys (*Lamiaceae*)

	aethiopica 'Danielle'	see *S. thunbergii* 'Danielle'
§	***affinis***	CArn GPoy LEdu SPlb SVic XLum
	albens	XSen
	alpina	EBee
	balcanica	GKev
	- MESE	EBee WPGP
	betonica	see *S. officinalis*
§	***byzantina***	Widely available
§	- 'Big Ears'	Widely available
§	- 'Cotton Boll'	ECha GCal LRHS SPer WFar WWEG
	- 'Countess Helen von Stein'	see *S. byzantina* 'Big Ears'
	- 'Fuzzy Wuzzy' **new**	CBod
	- gold-leaved	see *S. byzantina* 'Primrose Heron'
	- large-leaved	see *S. byzantina* 'Big Ears'
	- 'Limelight'	WCot WSHC XLum
§	- 'Primrose Heron'	EBee ECha GKev LRHS MRav NBid NLar NOrc SMrm SPer SPoG SWvt XLum
	- 'Sheila McQueen'	see *S. byzantina* 'Cotton Boll'
	- 'Silky Fleece'	CBod ECha ELan EPfP EWTr GKev LRHS MMuc NBre SEND SRms WWEG XSen
	- 'Silver Carpet'	Widely available
	chamissonis var. ***cooleyae***	EBee
	citrina	CMea CPBP GCal XSen
	coccinea	CPla ECtt EWld MNrw SIgm WMoo
	cretica subsp. ***salviifolia***	XSen
	densiflora	see *S. monieri* (Gouan) P.W. Ball
§	***discolor***	CFis CMea EWes GEdr IKil LRHS NLar SPhx WCAu
	germanica	NBre WHfH
	- subsp. ***bithynica***	SMrm
	grandidentata	WPGP
	grandiflora	see *S. macrantha*
	'Hidalgo'	CSpe
	lanata Jacq.	see *S. byzantina*
	lavandulifolia	WAbe XSen
§	***macrantha***	CBod CKno CMac CTri ECha GKev GLog LEdu LRHS MCot MLHP MWat NBir NChi NOrc NSti SPhx SRms SWat WCFE WCot WWEG
*	- 'Alba'	ECha
	- 'Ben' (v) **new**	LEdu
	- 'Hummelo'	see *S. officinalis* 'Hummelo'
	- 'Morning Blush'	GEdr SPhx WFar
*	- 'Nivea'	CSam ELan NBir
	- 'Robusta' ♀H7	ELan ELon GCal LEdu MAvo MMuc NBro NGdn SMrm WCot WWEG
	- 'Rosea'	CElw CMHG ELan GBee GMaP LLWP LRHS MArl MAvo MLHP SCob SPlb SWat
	- 'Superba' ♀H7	CPrp CSpe ECtt EPfP GCra GMaP IBoy LEdu MRav NEgg NLar NSoo SCob SPer SWvt WBor WCAu WCot WFar WMnd WMoo WPtf XLum
	- 'Violacea' ♀H7	CDes EBee GKev MBrN NChi WCot WOut
	mexicana misapplied	see *S. thunbergii*
	monieri misapplied	see *S. officinalis*
	monieri ambig.	CPom CPrp EShb LBMP NLar NSti WOut
§	***monieri*** (Gouan) P.W. Ball	LEdu MSpe
*	- 'Rosea'	EBee LEdu NBre NDov NLar
	nivea	see *S. discolor*
	obliqua	NBre WOut
§	***officinalis***	CArn CHab CPrp CUse EBee GPoy LEdu MHer MMuc MNHC MWhi NMir SEND WCot WHer WHfH WJek WOut
	- 'Alba'	CArn EBee LEdu MMuc NBro SCob SEND
	- dwarf, white-flowered	GCal
§	- 'Hummelo'	CAby CBod CKno CSam ECtt ELon EPPr EPfP GAbr GBin GQue IKil IPot LPla LRHS LSou MBel MRav NLar SCob SMrm SPhx WCAu WFar WHrl WPtf WWEG XLum
	- 'Marchant's Pink'	SMHy
	- 'Pink Cotton Candy'	STPC
	- 'Powder Puff'	EBee
	- 'Rosea'	EAJP GCal GQue NBro SCob WFar WWEG
	- 'Rosea Superba'	ECha NBre WCAu WCot
	- 'Saharan Pink'	CMHG EPfP NLar WOut WWEG
	- 'Wisley White'	CAby GQue LPot LRHS NPri SRms WCot WFar WHfH WOut
	olympica	see *S. byzantina*
	ossetica	CDes CFis EBee
	palustris	CArn CHab LLWG MMuc NLar NMir SEND
	- from Islay, Hebrides	MMuc SEND
	- pale-flowered	WOut
	recta	EBee MMuc
	setifera	NBre XLum
	spicata	see *S. macrantha*
	sylvatica	CArn CHab NMir WHer WOut WSFF
	thirkei	XSen
§	***thunbergii***	CDes LEdu MBrN SBch WHrl WPGP
§	- 'Danielle'	GJos LAst LRHS NLar SDys SPhx SRkn SRms WOut
	tuberifera	see *S. affinis*
	tymphaea	XSen

Stachyurus (*Stachyuraceae*)

	chinensis	CBcs CJun CMCN CTri IArd MGos NLar SMad
	- 'Celina' ♀H4	CJun EPfP ETwe GKin LRHS MGos NLar SHil SPoG
	- 'Goldbeater'	NLar
	- 'Joy Forever' (v) ♀H4	CBcs CDoC CEnd CMac EBee EMil EPfP ETwe IArd IDee IVic LLHF LRHS MBri MGos NLar SHil SKHP SLim SSpi SSta SWvt
	- 'Senna'	NLar
	- 'Wonderful Image'	NLar
	himalaicus	CBcs NLar
	- HWJCM 009	WCru
	- HWJK 2035	WCru

- 'Dolly'	NLar
aff. ***himalaicus*** HWJK 2052	WCru
'Magpie' (v)	CJun EPfP MBri NLar WFar
praecox ♀H5	Widely available
- B&SWJ 8898	WCru
- B&SWJ 10899	WCru
- var. ***leucotrichus***	CJun NLar
- var. ***matsuzakii***	CJun NLar
- - B&SWJ 2817	WCru
- - B&SWJ 11229	WCru
- - 'Issai'	ETwe LRHS SHil SSta
- 'Oriental Sun'	MBri
- 'Petra'	CJun
retusus	CExl
'Rubriflorus'	CJun EPfP LRHS MAsh MBri NLar SChF WPGP
salicifolius	CBcs CExl CFil CJun CTho EPfP MBri SKHP SMad WPGP WPat
sigeyosii	CBcs CExl CFil
- B&SWJ 6915	WCru
- CWJ 12420	WCru
- RWJ 10094	WCru
aff. ***szechuanensis***	CExl
- BWJ 8153	WCru
yunnanensis	CBcs CFil CJun IArd IDee NLar WPGP WPat

Staehelina (*Asteraceae*)

dubia	SBrt

Stangeria (*Stangeriaceae*)

eriopus **new**	LPal

Staphylea ✿ (*Staphyleaceae*)

bolanderi	CBcs NLar
bumalda	CJun LEdu NLar
- B&SWJ 11053	WCru
- B&SWJ 12744 from Korea **new**	WCru
colchica	CBcs CDul CHll CJun CMCN ELan EPfP EWes LEdu LRHS MBri MGos MMHG MRav NLar SPer WKif WSHC
holocarpa	CJun EPfP MBri
- 'Innocence'	NLar
- var. ***rosea***	CJun EPfP SMad SWvt
- 'Rosea'	CBcs CJun MBlu NLar SSpi WPGP
pinnata	CAgr CBcs CJun EBtc EPfP EPla IVic MMuc NLar SEND
trifolia	CBcs CJun

Statice see *Limonium*

Stauntonia (*Lardizabalaceae*)

NJM 09.081	WPGP
FMWJ 13177 from North Vietnam **new**	WCru
aff. ***chinensis*** DJHV 06175	WCru
hexaphylla	CBcs CHEx CHel CHll CTri CWGN EBee EPfP ESwi ETwe EUJe LEdu LPal LRHS MAsh NLar SAdn SKHP SPer SPoG SSpi SSta WSHC
- B&SWJ 4858	WCru
leucantha KWJ 12218	WCru
obovata CWJ 12353 **new**	WCru
obovatifoliola B&SWJ 3685	WCru
purpurea B&SWJ 3690	WCru
yaoshanensis HWJ 1024	WCru WPGP
- B&SWJ 8223	WCru

Stegnogramma (*Thelypteridaceae*)

pozoi	EFer

Stellaria (*Caryophyllaceae*)

graminea	CHab
holostea	CHab MMuc NBir NMir WHer WPtf WShi

Stemmacantha (*Asteraceae*)

carthamoides	CArn
§ ***centaureoides***	CDes ECGP ECha EPPr GCal GQue IBoy IGor IPot LPla MAvo MSpe NBid NSti WCot

Stenanthium (*Melanthiaceae*)

gramineum	CFil EWes WPGP

Stenomesson (*Amaryllidaceae*)

coccineum	NRog
incarnatum apricot-flowered **new**	NRog
§ ***miniatum***	WCot
pearcei	ECho NRog WCot
variegatum	WCot
- orange-flowered **new**	NRog
- red-flowered **new**	NRog
- yellow-flowered	NRog WCot

Stenotaphrum (*Poaceae*)

secundatum 'Variegatum' (v) ♀H1c	EShb LSou XLum

Stephanandra (*Rosaceae*)

chinensis	SLon
incisa	CAco CBcs CExl GKev SCob
§ - 'Crispa'	CDoC CDul CMac CTri ELan EPfP EWTr GKin IDee LAst MBlu MJak MRav NEgg NHol NLar NSoo SCob SPer WHar WMoo
- 'Prostrata'	see *S. incisa* 'Crispa'
tanakae	CBcs CDoC CDul CExl CTri ELan EPfP EWTr LAst MBlu MGil MRav NEgg SLon SPer

Stephania (*Menispermaceae*)

japonica CWJ 12823	WCru
longa KWJ 12163	WCru
sinica BWJ 8094	WCru
aff. ***tetrandra*** WWJ 11896	WCru

Stephanotis (*Asclepiadaceae*)

floribunda ♀H1b	CBcs CCCN CSpe MBri

Sternbergia (*Amaryllidaceae*)

'Autumn Gold'	ECho
candida	CBro NRog
§ ***clusiana***	NRog
colchiciflora	NRog
fischeriana	CBro NRog
greuteriana	ECho EPot NRog
lutea ♀H4	CAvo CBro ECha ECho EPfP EPot ERCP EWes LAma LRHS NRog SBch SDeJ SDix WHoo XLum
- Angustifolia Group	CBro CMea ECho WCot
macrantha	see *S. clusiana*

sicula CBro ECho EPot GKev NRog
- 'Arcadian Sun' ECho GKev NRog
- var. **graeca** ECho NRog
- - from Crete ECho
- 'John Marr' WThu

Stevia (*Asteraceae*)

rebaudiana CArn CBod ENfk EOHP EUJe GPoy SHDw SRms WCot WJek

Stewartia ✿ (*Theaceae*)

gemmata see *S. sinensis*
'Korean Splendor' see *S. pseudocamellia* Koreana Group
koreana see *S. pseudocamellia* Koreana Group
malacodendron ♀H5 LRHS
monadelpha CBcs CJun CMen IArd IDee MPkF NLar
ovata LRHS
pseudocamellia ♀H5 Widely available
- B&SWJ 11044 from North Japan WCru
§ - Koreana Group ♀H5 CDul CEnd CMCN EPfP GKin LRHS MBri NLar SSpi WPGP
pteropetiolata CMHG IVic
- B&SWJ 11726 WCru
- NJM 10.107 **new** WPGP
- WWJ 11939 WCru
rostrata CBcs CJun ELan ETwe GBin MBri MPkF NLar SSpi WCru
serrata CJun CMen GBin MPkF NLar WPGP
§ **sinensis** ♀H5 CBcs CDul CJun EPfP IArd IDee MPkF NLar SSpi WPGP

Stigmaphyllon (*Malpighiaceae*)

ciliatum CCCN
littorale CCCN

Stipa (*Poaceae*)

F&M 248 EBee
arundinacea see *Anemanthele lessoniana*
- 'Sunrise' **new** EAEE
barbata CKno CSpe ECha ELon EPPr EWes NCGa SCob WKif
- 'Silver Feather' WPtf
brachytricha see *Calamagrostis brachytricha*
§ **calamagrostis** Widely available
- 'Allgäu' WCot
- 'Lemperg' IMou LRHS NDov
capillata EBee EPPr GCal LRHS MNrw SDix
- 'Brautschleier' CBod
* - 'Lace Veil' MBel
elegantissima CKno EHoe NLos SHDw
extremiorientalis EPPr EWoo MMuc SEND SMad
gigantea ♀H7 Widely available
- 'Gold Fontaene' CDes CElw CKno EBee EPPr EWes LRHS LSqu MAvo MMoz MNrw NDov SMad WCot WMoo WPGP WWEG
- 'Pixie' SGSe WWEG
grandis EPPr WMoo
ichu CKno CSpe LRHS MAvo NLos SDix SHDw SMHy SMad SPoG
- F&M 32 CFil WPGP
joannis EBee GCal
lasiagrostis see *S. calamagrostis*
leptostachya WCot
lessingiana CExl EBee EHoe EPPr LRHS NLos SEND SPhx WMoo
offneri EPPr
pennata CBod EPPr NDov
§ **poeppigiana** EBee
pseudoichu CAbP CBod CFil CSpe EPPr ESwi LBMP MAvo MBel NPCo WCot
- RCB/Arg Y-1 EBee ELon NCGa
pulcherrima EBee EPPr GCal LRHS
- 'Windfeder' CCon
ramosissima CKno
robusta EPPr SPhx
splendens misapplied see *S. calamagrostis*
splendens Trin. ECha
stenophylla see *S. tirsa*
tenacissima CDul IBoy MAsh
tenuifolia misapplied see *S. tenuissima*
tenuifolia Steud. CMea EBee EPfP LRHS MBri MRav NBir NBro NOak NSti WHal WMoo XLum XSen
§ **tenuissima** Widely available
- 'Wind Whispers' CBod CExl CSpe EUJe GBin LEdu LRHS MBel
§ **tirsa** EPPr
turkestanica NDov SWat
ucrainica EPPr NDov

Stoebe (*Asteraceae*)

alopecuroides SPlb

Stokesia ✿ (*Asteraceae*)

cyanea see *S. laevis*
§ **laevis** CHel ECGP ECha EPfP LRHS MMuc NLar SCob SEND SMrm SPlb WMoo WPGP WWEG XLum
- 'Alba' ECha ELan EPfP EPri LEdu LRHS MRav
- 'Blue Star' CAby CBcs CBod CHel CSam CWGN ELan ELon EPfP EPla EWoo LAst LEdu LRHS MBel MHer MRav NPri SGbt SPad SPer SPhx SWvt WHoo WHrl WMnd WMoo
- 'Color Wheel' LRHS SCob
- 'Klaus Jelitto' EPla IPot LEdu LRHS MAvo MBri WHrl
- 'Mary Gregory' CBod CCon CHel CMac CSam EBee ECtt ELan EPfP IKil LEdu LRHS LSou MBel MBri MNrw MRav NCGa NLar NPri SMrm SPhx SRGP SWvt WHrl WPGP WWEG
- 'Mel's Blue' **new** MBri
- mixed CPou
- 'Omega Skyrocket' CPou LSun
- 'Peach Melba' ECtt NCGa WMoo
- 'Peachie's Pick' ECtt
- 'Purple Parasols' CBod CMac CWGN EAEE ECtt EPfP EPla GBin IKil LRHS LSou MBel MWat NCGa SCob SMrm SPoG STPC SWvt WGwG WHrl WMoo WWEG
- 'Purple Pixie'PBR ECtt LRHS
- 'Silver Moon' CCon CHel CMos EAEE ECtt EPfP EPla GBin LRHS MTPN NBir SPer STPC WGwG WHrl WMoo WWEG
§ - 'Träumerei' CWGN EAEE EBee ECtt EPla LRHS MMuc NLar SEND SMrm WHrl WMnd WMoo WWEG XLum
- 'White Star' see *S. laevis* 'Träumerei'

Stranvaesia see *Photinia*

× *Stranvinia* see *Photinia*

Stratiotes (*Hydrocharitaceae*)

aloides	CBAq CBen CWat EHon EWay MWts NPer SVic SWat WMAq WPnP

strawberry see *Fragaria*

Strelitzia (*Strelitziaceae*)

alba	CCCN
juncea	LPal XBlo
nicolai	CAbb LPal NPer SPlb XBlo
reginae ♀H1c	CAbb CBcs CCCN ELan EShb EUJe LPal NPer NPla SBig SEND SPlb XBlo
- 'Kirstenbosch Gold'	LPal XBlo

Streptocarpella see *Streptocarpus*

Streptocarpus ✿ (*Gesneriaceae*)

'Adele' **new**	WDib
'Albatross' ♀H1c	CTsd WDib
'Alissa'PBR	WDib
'Amanda' Dibley ♀H1c	WDib
'Anne' (d) ♀H1c	CTsd WDib
'Awena'	WDib
baudertii	WDib
'Bethan' ♀H1c	CTsd WDib
'Bianca'	WDib
'Black Gardenia'	CTsd WDib
'Black Panther'	CTsd WDib
'Blue Bird'	SBrm
'Blue Frills' **new**	WDib
'Blue Gem'	WDib
'Blue Leyla'PBR	see *S.* 'Leyla'
'Blue Moon'	WDib
'Blue Nymph'	WDib
'Blushing Bride' (d)	WDib
'Boysenberry Delight'	WDib
'Branwen'	CTsd WDib
'Brimstone'	SBrm
'Bristol's Black Bird'	WDib
'Bristol's Very Best'	WDib
'Burgundy Ice' **new**	SBrm
'Buttons'	SBrm
caeruleus	WDib
'Caitlin' ♀H1c	CTsd WDib
candidus	WDib
'Cappuccino' **new**	WDib
'Carol'	WDib
'Carolyn Ann'	SBrm
'Carys' ♀H1c	CTsd WDib
caulescens	WDib
- var. ***pallescens***	WDib
'Charlotte' ♀H1c	SBrm WDib
'Chloe'	WDib
'Chorus Line' ♀H1c	CTsd WDib
'Christine'	SBrm
'Concord Blue'	WDib
'Constant Nymph' ♀H1c	WDib
'Copper Knob'	SBrm
'Crystal Beauty'	WDib
'Crystal Blush'	WDib
'Crystal Charm'	WDib
'Crystal Dawn'	WDib
'Crystal Ice'PBR ♀H1c	WDib
'Crystal Snow'	WDib
'Crystal Wonder'	WDib
cyaneus	WDib
- subsp. ***polackii***	WDib
'Cynthia' ♀H1c	WDib
'Dainty Lady'	SBrm
'Daphne'	WDib
'Dark Eyes Mary'	SBrm
'Denim'	WDib
denticulatus	WDib
'Diana'	WDib
'Dinas'	WDib
'Double Delight' (d) **new**	SBrm
'Dreamtime'	SBrm
dunnii	WDib
'Elegance'	SBrm
'Elizabeth'	SBrm
'Ella'	SBrm
'Ella Mae'	SBrm
'Ellie'	WDib
'Elsi'	CTsd WDib
'Emily'	WDib
'Eve'	WDib
'Falling Stars' ♀H1c	CTsd WDib
'Festival Wales'	WDib
'Fiona'	WDib
floribundus hort.	WDib
'Frances'	SBrm
'Frances Elizabeth' **new**	SBrm
'Franken Alison'	SBrm
'Franken Jenny'	SBrm
'Franken Kelly'	SBrm
'Franken Misty Blue'	SBrm
'Franken Texas Sunset'	SBrm
'Frosty Diamond' ♀H1c	CTsd WDib
gardenii	WDib
'Gillian'	SBrm
glandulosissimus ♀H1c	WDib
'Gloria' ♀H1c	CSpe CTsd WDib
'Gwen' ♀H1c	WDib
'Hannah'	WDib
'Hannah Ellis'	SBrm
'Harlequin Blue'PBR ♀H1c	WDib
'Harlequin Damsel' **new**	WDib
'Harlequin Dawn' **new**	WDib
'Harlequin Delft' **new**	WDib
'Harlequin Lace'	WDib
'Harlequin Purple'	WDib
'Harriet'	WDib
'Hayley'	WDib
'Heather Ice' **new**	SBrm
'Heidi' ♀H1c	CTsd WDib
'Helen'	CTsd WDib
'Hope'	WDib
'Ida'	SBrm
'Inky Fingers'	SBrm
'Iona'	WDib
'Isabella'	WDib
'Izzy'	SBrm
'Jacquie'	WDib
'Jane Elizabeth'	SBrm
'Jennifer' ♀H1c	WDib
'Jessica'	WDib
'Joanna'	CTsd WDib
johannis	WDib
'Josie'	SBrm
'Joy'	WDib
'Judith'	SBrm

'Karen'	WDib
'Katie'PBR ♀H1c	WDib
kentaniensis	WDib
'Kerry's Gold'	SBrm
'Kim' ♀H1c	CSpe WDib
kirkii	WDib
'Kisie'	SBrm
'Lady Lavender'	SBrm
'Largesse'	SBrm
'Laura' ♀H1c	WDib
§ 'Leyla'PBR	WDib
'Louise'	WDib
'Lucy'	WDib
'Lyndee'	WDib
'Lynne'	WDib
'Maassen's White' ♀H1c	WDib
'Magpie'	SBrm
'Margaret' Gavin Brown	WDib
'Marie'	WDib
'Mary'	SBrm
'Megan'	WDib
'Melanie' Dibley	WDib
meyeri	WDib
'Midnight Flame'	CTsd WDib
'Mini Nymph'	WDib
'Misty Pink'	SBrm
'Modbury Lady'	SBrm
modestus	WDib
'Molly'	SBrm
'Monica's Magic'	SBrm
'Myfanwy' ♀H1c	WDib
'Natalie' **new**	WDib
'Nerys' ♀H1c	CTsd WDib
'Nia'	CTsd WDib
'Nicola'	CTsd WDib
'Olga'	WDib
'Olivia'	WDib
'Padarn'	WDib
'Pale Rider'	SBrm
'Patricia'	SBrm
'Paula'	WDib
'Pearl'	WDib
'Penelope' **new**	SBrm
pentherianus	WDib
'Pink Leyla'PBR	WDib
'Pink Souffle'	WDib
polyanthus	WDib
subsp. ***dracomontanus***	
primulifolius	WDib
- subsp. ***formosus***	WDib
'Princesse' (Marleen Series)	WDib
prolixus	WDib
'Purple Pride' **new**	SBrm
'Raspberry Dream'	SBrm
rexii	WDib
'Rhiannon' ♀H1c	CTsd WDib
'Rose Halo'	WDib
'Rosebud'	WDib
(Roulette Series) 'Roulette Azur'PBR	WDib
- 'Roulette Cherry'	WDib
'Rubina'PBR	WDib
'Ruby' ♀H1c	CTsd WDib
'Ruby Anniversary'	SBrm
'Ruffles'	SBrm
'Ruth' **new**	WDib
'Sally'	WDib
'Sandra'	WDib
'Sarah'	WDib
saxorum	CCCN WDib
- compact ♀H1c	CCCN WDib
'Scarlett'	WDib
'Seren'PBR ♀H1c	WDib
'Shannon'	SBrm
'Sian'	WDib
silvaticus	WDib
'Sioned' ♀H1c	WDib
'Snow White' ♀H1c	CSpe WDib
'Spirit'PBR	WDib
'Stacey'	SBrm
'Stella'PBR ♀H1c	WDib
'Stephanie'	WDib
stomandrus	WDib
'Strawberry Fondant'	SBrm
'Summer Skies' **new**	SBrm
'Susan' ♀H1c	CTsd WDib
'Swaybelle'	SBrm
'Sweet Melys'	WDib
'Targa' (Marleen Series)	WDib
'Tatan Blue'	SBrm
'Teleri'	WDib
'Terracotta'	SBrm
'Texas Hot Chili'	CTsd WDib
'Texas Sunrise'	SBrm
thompsonii	WDib
'Tina' ♀H1c	WDib
'Tracey'	WDib
'Twice as Nice' **new**	SBrm
vandeleurii	WDib
'Vanessa'	SBrm
variabilis	WDib
'Velvet Underground'	SBrm
'Vera'	SBrm
'Watermelon Wine'	WDib
wendlandii	WDib
'Wendy'	WDib
'White Butterfly' ♀H1c	WDib
'White Wings'	SBrm
'Wiesmoor Red'	WDib
'Winifred'	WDib

Streptopus (*Liliaceae*)

amplexifolius	EBee ECho MNrw NMyG WCru
roseus	EBee ECho
streptopoides	EBee EPPr EPfP LEdu LRHS MMHG

Streptosolen (*Solanaceae*)

jamesonii ♀H1c	CHll EBak EShb IDee MOWG SWvt

Strobilanthes (*Acanthaceae*)

sp.	WBor
CC 4071	CExl
CC 4573	CExl
anisophylla	EShb SDys
atropurpurea misapplied	see *S. attenuata*
atropurpurea Nees	see *S. wallichii*
§ ***attenuata***	CCon EBee ECGP ECtt EPfP GCal GCra IVic LRHS MBel MCot MRav NChi NDov NSti SGSe WCru WMoo
- 'Blue Carpet'	NDov
- subsp. ***nepalensis***	CHll XLum
dyeriana ♀H1b	EBak EShb WCot
flexicaulis	WPGP
- B&SWJ 354	WCru
aff. ***inflata*** B&SWJ 7754	WCru
nutans	CPou EBee NSti SBrt XLum

pentstemonoides new	WCot
aff. ***pentstemonoides*** HWJK 2019	WCru
rankanensis	CCon EPPr SDys SMHy XLum
- B&SWJ 1771	WCru
violacea	CHVG CPrp EShb
§ ***wallichii***	CAby CMac CSam EBee EWes EWld IGor LLWP MMuc NSti SEND WCru WMoo WSHC WWEG

Stromanthe (*Marantaceae*)

sanguinea 'Triostar'PBR (v)	XBlo

Strongylodon (*Papilionaceae*)

macrobotrys	MOWG

Strophanthus (*Apocynaceae*)

speciosus	CCCN CHll EShb

Strumaria (*Amaryllidaceae*)

aestivalis	ECho
chaplinii	ECho NRog
discifera subsp. ***bulbifera***	NRog WCot
gemmata new	NRog
karooica new	NRog
- 'Komsberg'	ECho
leipoldtii 'Vanrhynsdorp'	ECho
massoniella 'Reitfontein'	ECho
salteri new	NRog
- 'Nardouwsberg'	ECho
tenella subsp. ***orientalis*** new	NRog
truncata	ECho NRog WCot
- 'Garies'	ECho
watermeyeri subsp. ***watermeyeri*** new	NRog

Stuartia see *Stewartia*

Stylidium (*Stylidiaceae*)

adnatum	ECou
graminifolium	SPlb
- Little Saphire = 'St116'	SRot

Stylophorum (*Papaveraceae*)

diphyllum	CPou EWld IMou LEdu MAvo WBor WCru WPnP WWtn
lasiocarpum	CExl CPom CSpe EWes EWld GEdr MMHG NBid WCot WCru

Stypandra (*Phormiaceae*)

glauca	CLak

Styphelia (*Epacridaceae*)

colensoi	see *Leucopogon colensoi*

Styphnolobium (*Leguminosae*)

§ ***japonicum***	CAbP CAco CBcs CDul CHab CLnd CTho EPfP MGos SCob SPlb

Styrax (*Styracaceae*)

americanus	NLar
confusus	CBcs CExl
dasyanthus new	CBcs CExl
faberi	CExl
formosanus	CExl CFil CJun EPfP WPGP
var. ***formosanus***	
- - B&SWJ 3803	WCru
- - B&SWJ 6786	WCru
- var. ***hayatiana*** B&SWJ 6823	WCru
grandiflorus new	CExl
hemsleyanus ♀H5	CBcs CExl CHel CTho EPfP GBin IDee MBlu MMuc NLar SEND SPer SSpi
hookeri	CExl
japonicus	CAco CBcs CDoC CDul CEnd CExl CLnd CMCN CTho CTri ELan EPfP ETwe GKin LRHS MAsh MBlu MGil MGos MMuc MRav NLar SChF SEND SPer SReu SSpi WPGP WPat
- B&SWJ 4405	WCru
- B&SWJ 8770	WCru
- B&SWJ 11078 new	WCru
- Guiz 216	CExl WPGP
§ - Benibana Group ♀H5	WPGP
- - 'Pink Chimes' ♀H5	CBcs CEnd CExl CJun CMCN CMac ELan EPfP GBin GKin IDee MBlu MPkF NLar SSpi
- 'Carillon'	CJun
- 'Fargesii' ♀H5	CAco CBcs CDoC CDul CExl CJun CTho EPfP GBin IVic SKHP SSpi
- 'Fragrant Fountain'	MBlu NLar
- 'Herkenrode' new	MBri
- 'Hyme'	NLar
- 'Issai'	NLar
- 'Masaku'	SSpi
- 'Pendulus'	EPfP WPGP
- 'Purple Dress' ♀H5	CJun MBlu MBri NLar
- 'Roseus'	see *S. japonicus* Benibana Group
- 'Snowfall'	CJun NLar
- 'Sohuksan' ♀H5	CExl CFil CJun MBlu NLar WPGP
limprichtii	CExl CFil
obassia	CBcs CDul CLnd CMCN CTho EPfP GBin IDee IVic LRHS MBlu MBri NLar SSpi WPGP
- B&SWJ 6023	WCru
- B&SWJ 10890	WCru
odoratissimus	CExl
officinalis	CBcs
platanifolius var. ***mollis***	CFil
serrulatus	CExl
shiraianus	CExl CFil NLar WPGP
suberifolius WWJ 11868	WCru
* ***taiwanensis***	SKHP
wilsonii	CExl
wuyuanensis	CBcs NLar WPGP

Succisa (*Caprifoliaceae*)

§ ***pratensis***	CArn CHab CMac CWld EPri LEdu LLWG MAvo MHer MPie NLar SBch SGSe SMHy SPhx WHer WHoo WPtf WSFF WWFP XLum
- 'Alba'	EWes
- 'Cassop'	NRya
- 'Derby Purple'	CSpe WPtf
- 'Peddar's Pink'	EWes LEdu LLWG SPhx

Succisella (*Caprifoliaceae*)

inflexa	EBee LEdu MSpe SPhx WCot
- 'Frosted Pearls'	CFis CMHG LEdu LLWP MMuc WWFP

Sullivantia (*Saxifragaceae*)

sullivantii dwarf	WThu

sunberry see *Rubus* 'Sunberry'

Sutera (*Scrophulariaceae*)

(Abunda Series) Abunda Blue Improved = 'Balabimblu' LAst
- Abunda Colossal Sky Blue = 'Balabolav' NPri
- Abunda Colossal White = 'Balabowite'PBR NPri
(Copia Series) Copia Dark Pink = 'Dancop19'PBR LAst
- Copia Double White (d) LAst
- Copia Gulliver White = 'Dangul14'PBR LAst
cordata 'Blizzard' LSou
- 'Olympic Gold' (v) SCoo
- Scopia Double Pink Pearl (Scopia Series) LAst
§ - 'Snowflake' LAst NPer SCoo SPoG SWvt
'Lime Delight' LAst
microphylla CPBP
neglecta WPGP
(Scopia Series) Scopia Golden Leaves = 'Dancopgoleav' NPri
- Scopia Great Pink Beauty = 'Dancop35'PBR NPri
- Great Purple = 'Dancop21'PBR LSou
(Secrets Series) 'Secrets Blue Delight' LSou
- 'Secrets Central Pink' LSou
- 'Secrets Silver Sky' LSou

Sutherlandia ✿ (*Papilionaceae*)

frutescens CArn CBod CSpe GDun SPlb WJek
- fine-leaved GDun
montana CSpe SBrt WHea

Swainsona (*Papilionaceae*)

galegifolia CHII
- 'Albiflora' MOWG

sweet cicely see *Myrrhis odorata*

Swertia (*Gentianaceae*)

perennis GEdr

Swietenia (*Meliaceae*)

mahogani SPlb

Syagrus (*Arecaceae*)

botryophora XBlo
§ ***romanzoffiana*** XBlo
weddelliana see *Lytocaryum weddellianum*

× *Sycoparrotia* (*Hamamelidaceae*)

semidecidua CBcs CJun MBlu NLar
- 'Purple Haze' CJun NLar WPGP

Sycopsis (*Hamamelidaceae*)

sinensis CAbP CBcs CExl CHel EBee EPfP LRHS NLar SKHP SPoG SSpi SWvt WPGP WSHC

Symphoricarpos (*Caprifoliaceae*)

albus CAco CDul CMac MSwo NWea SCob
- 'Constance Spry' SRms
§ - var. ***laevigatus*** EPfP LBuc
× ***chenaultii*** new CAco
- 'Brain de Soleil'PBR EBee
- 'Hancock' CDul CMac ECrN ELan EPfP MBri MGos MMuc MRav MSwo SCob SGol SLim SPer WCFE
× ***doorenbosii*** 'Magic Berry' MRav NWea SGol
- 'Mother of Pearl' ELan EPfP MMuc MRav NWea SCob SPer
- 'White Hedge' ELan EPla LBuc MMuc NWea SPer SPlb
guatemalensis B&SWJ 1016 WCru
Magical Candy = 'Kolmcan'PBR ELan EPfP
Magical Galaxy = 'Kolmgala'PBR ELan EPfP
orbiculatus SLon
- 'Albovariegatus' see *S. orbiculatus* 'Taff's Silver Edge'
- 'Argenteovariegatus' see *S. orbiculatus* 'Taff's Silver Edge'
- 'Bowles's Golden Variegated' see *S. orbiculatus* 'Foliis Variegatis'
§ - 'Foliis Variegatis' (v) CMac CTri EHoe ELan EPfP MGos MRav SGol SPer
- 'George Gardiner' CMac
§ - 'Taff's Silver Edge' (v) SGol
- 'Variegatus' see *S. orbiculatus* 'Foliis Variegatis'
rivularis see *S. albus* var. *laevigatus*

Symphyandra see *Campanula*

asiatica see *Hanabusaya asiatica*

Symphyotrichum see *Aster*

Symphytum (*Boraginaceae*)

'Angela Whinfield' CDes CMea
asperum ECha MRav NLar WMoo
* ***azureum*** NChi WMnd
'Belsay' GBuc
'Belsay Gold' NBid NBir SDix WBor
bulbosum Schimp. PAB 4886 LEdu
caucasicum CElw CMHG CSde EBee ECha GPoy GQue IFro LEdu NLar NSti SEND SIde WHer WHil WMoo WOut WWtn XLum
- 'Eminence' WWEG
- 'Norwich Sky' CExl EWld
cordatum EPPr LEdu MNrw SKHP
'Denford Variegated' (v) NBid
§ 'Goldsmith' (v) CBod CMea CSam EBee ECha ELan EPfP EPla EWoo LAst LBMP MBri MCot MSCN NBid NBir NEgg NLar NOrc NPer SPer WJek WMnd WWEG
grandiflorum CArn CMac CTri GKev GPoy LEdu
* - 'Sky-blue-pink' IFro
'Hidcote Blue' CBod CBre CNec CTri ECha ECtt EPPr EPfP EPla LBMP LRHS MMuc NBro NEgg NOrc SCob SEND SPer SPoG WCru WGwG WHea WMoo WOut WWEG WWtn
§ 'Hidcote Pink' CBod CNec CWCL ECha ECtt EPPr EPla LBMP LPot LRHS MMuc MNrw NBir SEND SPer SPoG WFar WGwG WMoo WPnP WWEG WWtn XLum
'Hidcote Variegated' (v) CMac WOut

ibericum	CArn CSam ECha EPla GKev GMaP GPoy LRHS MLHP MMuc NSti SEND SRms WGwG WJek WMoo WOut WWtn
- 'All Gold'	ECha LRHS MHer MNrw WMoo
- 'Blaueglocken'	ECha LPla WMoo
- dwarf	IFro WMoo
- 'Gold in Spring'	NLar WFar
- 'Jubilee'	see *S.* 'Goldsmith'
- 'Lilacinum'	CFis WHer
- 'Variegatum'	see *S.* 'Goldsmith'
- 'Wisley Blue'	CBcs CBod SCob WFar WMoo WWEG
'Lambrook Sunrise'	CMac LEdu NBro WCot WMoo WWEG
'Langthorns Pink'	CPom ELan GCal
'Mereworth'	see *S.* × *uplandicum* 'Mereworth'
officinale	CAgr CArn ENfk GJos GPoy MHer MNHC MNrw NPer NPri SIde SPoG SRms WHea WHer WHfH WJek XLum
* - blue-flowered	SEND
- 'Bohemicum'	ECho
- var. ***ochroleucum***	WHer
orientale	CPom EPPr GCal MBel
peregrinum	see *S.* × *uplandicum*
'Roseum'	see *S.* 'Hidcote Pink'
'Rubrum'	CBod EAEE ELan EPfP EWes GBin GCra LEdu LRHS NBro NLar NOrc SPer WGwG WPGP XLum
'Sera Howys'	WOut
tuberosum	CArn CBre CElw CPom CSam EPPr GPoy LEdu MHer MMuc SEND WBor WCot WHer WOut
§ × ***uplandicum***	CTri ELan GCra GPoy SVic WJek
- 'Axminster Gold' (v)	CMea EWes NChi WCot
- 'Bocking 14'	CAgr CBod CHby CPbn CPrp CUse EOHP EShb GAbr LEdu MHer MNHC SIde WSFF XLum
- 'Droitwich' (v)	WCot
§ - 'Mereworth' (v)	CBct SEND
- 'Moorland Heather'	CDes MHer WMoo WWEG
- purple-flowered	MMuc SEND
- 'Variegatum' (v)	ECha ECtt ELan EPfP EWes GBuc LAst LRHS NBir NGdn NSti WMoo WWtn

Symplocarpus (*Araceae*)

foetidus	CDes

Symplocos (*Symplocaceae*)

sawafutagi	CBcs NLar WPGP

Syncarpha (*Asteraceae*)

vestita	SPlb

Syncolostemon (*Lamiaceae*)

'Candy Kisses' **new**	WCot

Syneilesis (*Asteraceae*)

aconitifolia	GEdr MNrw WCot WHal
- B&SWJ 879	CDes LEdu WCru
palmata	GEdr WCot
- B&SWJ 1003	CDes WCru
- B&SWJ 11226	WCru
- 'Kiko' **new**	GEdr
subglabrata B&SWJ 298	WCru
aff. ***tagawae*** B&SWJ 11191	WCru

Syngonium (*Araceae*)

podophyllum ♀H1b	XBlo

Synnotia see *Sparaxis*

Synsepalum (*Sapotaceae*)

dulcificum **new**	SCit

Synthyris (*Plantaginaceae*)

laciniata	EBee
missurica	CLAP
- subsp. ***missurica***	EBee GBuc
- subsp. ***stellata***	CAby CBod CLAP EAEE EBee ECre EPfP EPla EPri EWes GAbr GBin GBuc GCal IGor LEdu LRHS MMHG NCGa NSti SPoG WGwG WHal WMoo WPGP WPtf WSHC WWEG
reniformis	CLAP GBuc WPGP WWEG

Syringa ✿ (*Oleaceae*)

afghanica misapplied	see *S. protolaciniata*
afghanica C.K. Schneid.	IVic WSHC
× ***chinensis*** 'Alba'	see *S.* 'Correlata'
- 'Saugeana'	MMuc SEND SPer
§ 'Correlata' (graft-chimaera)	EBee
emodi 'Aurea'	NLar
- 'Aureovariegata'	see *S. emodi* 'Variegata'
- 'Elegantissima' (v)	CBcs CDoC CEnd CMac EBtc ELan EPfP GQui LLHF LRHS MAsh NEgg NLar SKHP SPoG SSpi
§ - 'Variegata' (v)	LRHS
× ***hyacinthiflora*** 'Anabel' (d) **new**	NLar
- 'Clarke's Giant'	NLar
- 'Esther Staley' ♀H6	EPfP MRav NLar SKHP
- 'Lavender Lady' **new**	NLar
- 'Pocahontas' ♀H6	GBin LRHS NLar
Josée = 'Morjos 060f'	CDoC ELon EPfP LBMP LSou MAsh SCob SMDP SWvt WFar WPat
× ***josiflexa***	CExl
- 'Agnes Smith'	EBee LRHS MMuc NLar
- 'Bellicent' ♀H6	CEnd CMac ELan EPfP LRHS MAsh MMuc MRav NLar NSti SEND SKHP SMad SPer SPoG SRms SWvt WCFE WFar WPat
- 'Lynette'	NEoE
- 'Redwine'	SKHP
§ - 'Royalty'	NLar SKHP
josikaea	CAco CMCN CSBt EWTr NLar SPer
'Kim'	MRav
komarowii	GGGa WPat
§ - subsp. ***reflexa***	CDul EPfP EWTr IDee LLHF NLar SLon
§ × ***laciniata*** Mill.	CJun EBee ELan EPfP IDee LRHS MGos MMuc MRav NLar SPer SPoG SSpi WCFE WHar WPGP
'Lark Song'	NLar
meyeri	SVen
- 'Inge' **new**	NLar
§ - 'Palibin' ♀H5	Widely available
'Minuet'	CBcs LBuc SKHP
'Miss Canada'	LBuc
oblata	CMCN
palibiniana misapplied	see *S. meyeri* 'Palibin'
patula misapplied	see *S. meyeri* 'Palibin'
patula (Palibin) Nakai	see *S. pubescens* subsp. *patula*
pekinensis	see *S. reticulata* subsp. *pekinensis*

- Beijing Gold	see *S. reticulata* subsp. *pekinensis* 'Zhang Zhiiming'
× ***persica*** ♀H6	CExl CJun CTri EPfP EWTr MGos MRav NLar SLon SPer WFar
- 'Alba' ♀H6	CJun MRav WFar WSHC
- var. ***laciniata***	see *S.* × *laciniata* Mill.
'Pink Perfume'PBR **new**	LRHS
pinnatifolia	CBcs GBin NLar
× ***prestoniae*** 'Desdemona'	CWld EBtc EMil LRHS MMuc SEND SKHP SSta
- 'Elinor' ♀H6	CMHG ELan EPfP MRav NSti SKHP
- 'Nocturne'	WFar
- 'Royalty'	see *S.* × *josiflexa* 'Royalty'
§ ***protolaciniata***	LBMP NLar SKHP SLim
- 'Kabul'	EPfP
pubescens subsp. ***julianae*** 'George Eastman'	MRav
- subsp. ***microphylla*** 'Superba' ♀H6	Widely available
§ - subsp. ***patula***	CMac ECho EPfP LRHS MMuc MRav NWea SEND SVen
- - 'Miss Kim' ♀H6	CDoC CMac CSBt EBee ELan ELon GAbr IArd LAst LRHS MAsh MBri MGos MJak MRav MSwo NEgg NHol NLar SCob SCoo SKHP SLim SPoG SSta WFar WPat
'Red Pixie'	CMac ELon EPfP LRHS MBri MGos MMHG SCoo SHil SKHP
reflexa	see *S. komarowii* subsp. *reflexa*
reticulata	MBlu
- 'Ivory Silk'	EPfP LLHF NLar SKHP
§ - subsp. ***pekinensis***	CMCN GBin
- - China Snow = 'Morton' ♀H6	SKHP
- - 'Yellow Fragrance'	NLar
§ - - 'Zhang Zhiiming'	EBee
× ***swegiflexa***	CDul CExl
- 'Fountain'	EPla
tomentella	LRHS NWea SRms WPGP
- subsp. ***sweginzowii***	GKin MMuc NLar SEND SPer
- subsp. ***yunnanensis***	CExl GGGa LLHF
velutina Kom.	see *S. pubescens* subsp. *patula*
villosa	SPlb
vulgaris	CAco CDul EPfP LBuc NWea
§ - 'Andenken an Ludwig Späth' ♀H6	Widely available
- 'Aurea'	MGos MRav NEoE
- Beauty of Moscow	see *S. vulgaris* 'Krasavitsa Moskvy'
- 'Belle de Nancy' (d)	CCCN CDul CLnd CMac EBee ECrN ELan ELon EPla LAst MAsh MMuc MRav NLar SCob SEND SGol SPoG SWvt
- 'Charles Joly' (d) ♀H6	Widely available
- 'Comtesse d'Harcourt'	SEND
- 'Edward J. Gardner' (d) ♀H6	ELon SEND
- 'Firmament' ♀H6	ELan EPfP MRav SEND
- 'Hugo de Vries'	IArd
- 'Katherine Havemeyer' (d) ♀H6	Widely available
§ - 'Krasavitsa Moskvy' (d) ♀H6	CDoC EPfP EPla EWes GBin LRHS MAsh MBri MMuc NLar SEND
- 'Lee Jewett Walker'	SSta
- 'Lila Wonder'PBR	EBee EPfP
- 'Madame Florent Stepman'	CMac NLar
- 'Madame Lemoine' (d) ♀H6	Widely available
- 'Masséna'	SPer
- 'Michel Buchner' (d)	CBcs CDul EBee ELan MBlu MGos MJak NLar NSoo SCob SCoo SLim SPer
- 'Miss Ellen Willmott' (d)	IArd NLar
- 'Mrs Edward Harding' (d) ♀H6	EBee EPfP LBuc MRav NLar NWea SCoo
- 'Olivier de Serres' (d)	NLar
- 'Paul Deschanel' (d)	NLar
- 'Pavlinka' (d)	IArd
- 'Président Grévy' (d)	CDoC CMac EMil EPfP MAsh SLim SPer
- 'Primrose' ♀H6	CBcs CCCN CMac EBee ELan ELon EPfP EPla GBin IArd LRHS MAsh MGos MJak MMuc MSnd NLar SCoo SEND SHil SKHP SPer
- 'Prince Wolkonsky' (d)	EBee EMil EPfP EPla MMuc SEND SPer WFar
- 'Princesse Sturdza'	EMil
- 'Professor Hoser'	IArd
- Rose de Moscou = 'Minkarl'PBR **new**	EPfP SHil
- 'Sensation' ♀H6	CBcs CDoC CMac CSBt CWCL ECrN ELon EPfP EPla GAbr IArd IBoy LAst LRHS LSou MBri MGos MMuc MRav NLar NWea SCob SCoo SEND SHil SKHP SLim SPer SPoG
- 'Souvenir d'Alice Harding' (d) ♀H5	MBri
- 'Souvenir de Louis Spaeth'	see *S. vulgaris* 'Andenken an Ludwig Späth'
- variegated (v)	EWes
- variegated double (d/v)	WCot
- 'Vesper'	IArd
- 'Viviand-Morel' (d)	CMac LLHF SKHP
wolfii	CArn EBtc

Syringodea (*Iridaceae*)

longituba 'Perdekraal'	ECho

Syzygium (*Myrtaceae*)

paniculatum	CExl IDee

T

Tabebuia (*Bignoniaceae*)

chrysotricha **new**	WHil

Tabernaemontana (*Apocynaceae*)

coronaria	see *T. divaricata*
§ ***divaricata***	CCCN

Tacca (*Taccaceae*)

chantrieri	CCCN GKev
- 'Green Isle'	GKev
integrifolia	GKev LPal

Taccarum (*Araceae*)

weddellianum **new**	WCot

Tacitus see *Graptopetalum*

Tagetes (*Asteraceae*)

'Cinnabar'	SDix

	lemmonii	SDix SHDw WJek
	- 'Martin's Mutant' **new**	WCot
	'Lemon Gem'	WJek
	lucida	CArn ENfk LEdu MHer SRms WJek
	patula Durango Series	NPri
	- - 'Durango Bee'	NPri
	- - 'Durango Flame'	NPri
	- - 'Durango Orange'	NPri
	- - 'Durango Yellow'	NPri
	- - 'Durango Yellow Fire'	NPri
	- 'Harlequin'	see *T. patula* 'Old Scotch Pride'
§	- 'Old Scotch Pride'	SPav

Taiwania (*Cupressaceae*)

	cryptomerioides	IArd IDee

Talinum (*Portulacaceae*)

	'Zoe'	CPBP

tamarillo see *Solanum betaceum*

tamarind see *Tamarindus indica*

Tamarindus (*Caesalpiniaceae*)

	indica (F)	SPlb

Tamarix (*Tamaricaceae*)

	chinensis	CSBt
	gallica	CSBt NWea SArc SEND WSHC
	hampeana	SEND
§	***parviflora*** ♀H5	CDul CMac EPfP IVic LRHS NLar SCob SPoG
	pentandra	see *T. ramosissima*
§	***ramosissima***	CCCN CTri ECrN ELan EPfP MAsh MWhi NLar SCob SEWo SLim SLon SRms WHar
	- 'Hulsdonk White'	EBee SPer
	- 'Pink Cascade' ♀H5	CAco CBcs CCCN CDul CMac CSBt EBee ELon EPfP LRHS MBlu MGos MMuc MRav NEgg NSoo SBod SCob SEND SGbt SGol SPer SPoG SWvt WBor
	- 'Rosea'	CBcs
§	- 'Rubra'	CDoC CWSG EPfP IVic MBri SEND SLon
	- 'Summer Glow'	see *T. ramosissima* 'Rubra'
	tetrandra ♀H5	CBcs CCVT CChe CDul CSBt CSde ELan EPfP EPla LBMP LRHS MBlu MBri MGil MGos MMuc MRav MSwo MWat NPer SEND SGol SHil SPer SPlb SRms SWvt WHar
	- var. ***purpurea***	see *T. parviflora*

Tamus (*Dioscoreaceae*)

	communis	CArn

Tanacetum ✿ (*Asteraceae*)

§	***argenteum***	ECho MRav SIde
	- subsp. ***canum***	ECho LRHS SLon
§	***balsamita***	CArn CBod CHby CPrp EBee ELan ELau ENfk GPoy LEdu MHer MMuc MNHC SEND SRms WHer WHfH WJek XLum XSen
§	- subsp. ***balsamita***	GPoy SIde
§	- subsp. ***balsamitoides***	CBod CHby CPrp MHer WJek
	- var. ***tanacetoides***	see *T. balsamita* subsp. *balsamita*
	- ***tomentosum***	see *T. balsamita* subsp. *balsamitoides*
	capitatum	see *Sphaeromeria capitata*
§	***cinerariifolium***	CArn CBod CPrp GPoy MNHC WJek
§	***coccineum***	SVic WFar
	- 'Bees' Pink Delight'	EPla LRHS MBNS NEgg
	- 'Duro'	LRHS
	- 'Eileen May Robinson'	CBod EPfP MBNS MMHG NGdn
	- 'Garden Treasure'	LBuc
	- 'H.M. Pike'	CBod MMHG
	- 'James Kelway'	EPfP NBir
	- 'Laurin'	LRHS
	- Robinson's crimson-flowered	LRHS MNHC
	- - giant-flowered	CTsd LRHS SRms
	- - pink-flowered	EBee EPfP EWll GMaP MHol SCob SGSe WWEG XLum
	- - red-flowered	CBod CSBt EAJP EPfP EPla GMaP MHol SBod SGSe SPlb SWvt WWEG XLum
	- - rose-flowered	EAJP LPal
	- 'Scarlet Glow'	EWll
	- 'Snow Cloud'	CBod ECtt EPfP EPla LRHS WWEG
	- 'Vanessa'	MNrw
§	***corymbosum***	GCal NLar WCot
	- 'Festtafel'	LPla
	densum	ECho WCFE
	- subsp. ***amani***	ECha ECho GMaP LRHS MWat SEND XSen
	- - 'Beth Chatto'	XSen
	- subsp. ***sivasicum***	XSen
§	***haradjanii***	ECho MCot SBch WKif
	huronense	EBee
	macrophyllum misapplied	see *Achillea grandifolia* Friv.
§	***macrophyllum*** (Waldst. & Kit.) Sch.Bip.	CPrp EBee ECtt EPPr LPla SPhx
	- 'Cream Klenza'	WCot
	niveum	ECha WCot
	- 'Jackpot'	CFis EPfP EWes SWvt
§	***parthenium***	CArn CBod CHab CHby CPbn ELau ENfk GPoy MHer MNHC NPer SIde SRms SVic WHer WJek XLum
	- 'Aureum'	CBod CHid CPbn CPrp ECha ELan ELau ENfk EWes GPoy LEdu LPot MBri MHer MLHP MNHC SPer SPlb SRms SWvt WHer WJek WMoo XLum
	- double white-flowered (d)	NPer SRms
	- 'Golden Ball'	EPfP
	- 'Golden Moss'	XLum
	- 'Plenum' (d)	MNrw
§	- 'Rowallane' (d)	MMuc SEND WCot
	- 'Sissinghurst White'	see *T. parthenium* 'Rowallane'
	- 'Snowball' (d)	EPfP
	poteriifolium	EBee LRHS MAvo
	ptarmiciflorum 'Silver Feather'	SRms SVen WJek
	tatsiense	CPBP
*	***tommansii***	EBee LRHS
	vulgare	CArn CHab CHby CMac CUse ECha ECtt ELau ENfk GPoy MHer MNHC SIde SRms SVic WJek WMoo WSFF XSen
	- 'All Gold'	SMad SRms
	- var. ***crispum***	CPrp EBee ELau ENfk MHer MNHC MRav SIde SMad SRms WJek
	- 'Gold Sticks' **new**	CBod
	- 'Golden Fleece'	EBee ECtt EWes LEdu LRHS LSou NPCo NSti SPer WCot WGrn

- 'Isla Gold' (v) — ECtt EWes GMaP LEdu LPla MHer MMuc MRav SEND SMrm WCot WHil WJek WMoo
- 'Silver Lace' (v) — CBre EBee EWes NBid WHer WJek WMoo

Tanakaea (*Saxifragaceae*)

radicans — GEdr WCru
- B&SWJ 11407 **new** — WCru

tangelo see *Citrus* × *aurantium* Tangelo Group

tangerine see *Citrus reticulata* Tangerine Group

tangor see *Citrus* × *aurantium* Tangor Group

Taraxacum (*Asteraceae*)

faeroense — WCot
officinale agg. — CArn CHab
- 'Nettleton' — CNat
rubrifolium — CBre CSpe EPPr

tarragon see *Artemisia dracunculus*

Tasmannia (*Winteraceae*)

§ ***lanceolata*** — Widely available
- (f) — EUJe SPer WPat
- (m) — CDoC SPer WPat
- 'Mount Wellington' — GCal
- 'Red Spice' — EPfP ESwi
- 'Suzette' (v) — LRHS MBlu SRms

Taxodium ✿ (*Cupressaceae*)

ascendens 'Nutans' — see *T. distichum* var. *imbricarium* 'Nutans'
distichum — Widely available
- 'Cascade Falls'PBR — CAco LRHS MBlu MBri MGos NLar SLim
- 'Falling Waters' — CBcs SGol SKHP
- 'Gee Wiz' — SLim
- 'Hursley Park' — NLar
- var. ***imbricarium*** — CMCN EPfP
§ - - 'Nutans' — CBcs EPfP IArd LRHS MBlu SGol SLim
- 'Little Leaf' — SMad
- 'Minaret' — MBlu
* - 'Pendulum' — IDee
- 'Peve Minaret' — CDoC CMen LRHS MGos NLar SGol SKHP SLim
- 'Peve Yellow' — MBlu SLim
- 'Schloss Herten' — SLim
- 'Secrest' — MBlu SLim
- Shawnee Brave = 'Mickelson' — MBlu
mucronatum — CDoC CExl CFil
- NJM 09.037 — WPGP

Taxus ✿ (*Taxaceae*)

baccata ♀H6 — Widely available
- 'Adpressa Aurea' (v) — GKin
- 'Adpressa Variegata' (m/v) — CDoC
- 'Aldenham Gold' — CKen
- 'Amersfoort' — CDoC GKin
- Aurea Group — CDul ELan EPla SRms
I - 'Aureomarginata' (v) — CBcs MAsh NEgg SWvt
- 'Autumn Shades' — CBcs NLar
- 'Bridget's Gold' — CKen
- 'Corleys Coppertip' — CKen EBtc MBri MRav NLar SEND SLim
- 'Cristata' — CKen NLar
- 'David' — IArd MBri MGos NLar SPoG SWvt
- 'Dovastoniana' (f) — CAco CMac NLar NWea WMou
- 'Dovastonii Aurea' (m/v) — CBcs EPla GKin MBlu MBri NLar NPCo NWea SGol SLim
- 'Elegantissima' (f/v) — CTho EHul EPfP NPCo NWea SCoo SLim
§ - 'Fastigiata' (f) ♀H6 — CAco CBcs CDul CMac CNWT CSBt CTho CTri EHul ELan EPfP EUJe LAst MGos MJak MRav MSwo NEgg NPCo NWea SCob SEWo SGol SPer SPoG SRms SWvt WHar
- Fastigiata Aurea Group — CAco CLnd CMac EPfP EPla IArd LRHS MAsh MGos NLar NSoo SCob SGol SRms WHar
- 'Fastigiata Aureomarginata' (m/v) ♀H6 — CDoC CDul CMac CSBt CTri EHul EPfP LBee LRHS MBri MGos MJak NWea SCoo SLim SLon SPer SPoG SWvt
- 'Fastigiata Robusta' (f) — CDoC CSBt EBtc ELan EPfP EPla LRHS MAsh MBri MJak NLar NPCo SCoo SLim SPoG WGor
- 'Goud Elsje' — NLar
- 'Green Column' — CKen
- 'Green Diamond' — CKen
- 'Green Rocket' — CDul
- 'Hibernica' — see *T. baccata* 'Fastigiata'
- 'Icicle' ♀H6 — CBcs MAsh NHol NLar NWad SLim
- 'Itsy Bitsy' — CKen
- 'Ivory Tower' — CBcs CDoC CKen ELan NHol NLar NPCo NWad SLim
- 'Klitzeklein' — CKen
- 'Lutea' (f) — SLim
- 'Micro' — CKen MAsh
- 'Nana' — EPla
- 'Nutans' — CDoC CKen
- 'Prostrata' — CMac
- 'Pygmaea' — CKen
- 'Repandens' (f) ♀H6 — EHul IArd NLar NWea
I - 'Repens Aurea' (v) ♀H6 — CDoC CDul CKen CMac EHul LAst MBri NLar SCoo
- 'Rushmore' — MBri NLar
- 'Semperaurea' (m) ♀H6 — CBcs CDoC CMac EHul EPla LBuc MAsh MBri NLar NWea SCoo SGol SLim SPoG
- 'Standishii' (f) ♀H6 — CBcs CDoC CDul CKen CMac CSBt EHul ELan EPfP EPla GKin IArd LAst LBee LRHS MAsh MBri MGos MRav NEgg NHol NLar NPCo NWad NWea SEND SLim SPer SPoG SWvt
- 'Stove Pipe' — CKen
- 'Summergold' (v) — EHul ELan EPla LRHS MAsh MGos MRav NBir NLar SCoo SLim
brevifolia — NLar
cuspidata — CMen
- 'Aurescens' (v) — CKen
- 'Minuet' — CKen
- 'Straight Hedge' — SLim
× ***media*** 'Hicksii' (f) — CDul LBuc NLar NWea SGol
- 'Hillii' — LBMP LBuc
- 'Lodi' — LBee
- 'Nixe' — SLim
wallichiana — IDee

tayberry see *Rubus* Tayberry Group

Tecoma (Bignoniaceae)

capensis ♀H1c — CHll CRHN EBee SVen
ricasoliana — see *Podranea ricasoliana*

Tecomanthe (Bignoniaceae)

speciosa — ECou

Tecomaria see Tecoma

Tecophilaea (Tecophilaeaceae)

cyanocrocus ♀H3 — ECho EPot GKev LAma LLHF LRHS NMin
- 'Leichtlinii' ♀H3 — CAvo ECho EPot GKev LAma LLHF LRHS SDeJ
- 'Purpurea' — see *T. cyanocrocus* 'Violacea'
- Storm Cloud Group — ECho EPot GKev LLHF
§ - 'Violacea' — CAvo ECho EPot GKev LLHF LRHS
violiflora — ECho GKev

Telanthophora (Asteraceae)

§ **grandifolia** — CHEx

Telekia (Asteraceae)

§ **speciosa** — CCon CMac CSam CSpe ELan EPPr EPfP GAbr GLog MBel MMuc NBro NChi NLar SDix SPlb WBrk WCFE WHer WHoo WMoo WWEG

Telesonix see Boykinia

Teline see Genista

Tellima (Saxifragaceae)

grandiflora — Widely available
- 'Bob's Choice' — WCot
- 'Delphine' (v) — EPPr WCot XLum
- 'Forest Frost' — CBct CBod CFis CMac EHoe ELan EPPr EShb LAst LRHS MBNS MMoz MPnt NDov NLar NOrc SCob SWvt WCAu WCot WGwG WHoo WMoo WOut WWEG
- Odorata Group — CBre ECha EPla WCot WMoo
- 'Purpurea' — see *T. grandiflora* Rubra Group
- 'Purpurteppich' — CBod ECha EPPr EPla LRHS MPnt MRav NDov WCot WMnd WMoo WPnP WWEG
§ - Rubra Group — Widely available
- 'Silver Select' — EPPr

Telopea (Proteaceae)

'Emperor's Torch' — MPkF
oreades — GGal SPlb
speciosissima — CCCN CTre SPlb
truncata — CCCN GGal SPlb WCru

Templetonia (Papilionaceae)

retusa — ECou

Temu see Blepharocalyx

Ternstroemia (Pentaphylacaceae)

chapaensis WWJ 11918 new — WCru
gymnanthera new — WCru

Tetracentron (Trochodendraceae)

sinense — CBcs EPfP IArd NLar

Tetradenia (Lamiaceae)

riparia — EOHP

Tetradium (Rutaceae)

austrosinense NJM 09.215 — WPGP
§ **daniellii** — CBcs CDul CMCN CTho EBee EPfP ESwi IArd LEdu WHar WPGP
§ - Hupehense Group — CMCN CTho GBin MBri MMuc MSnd NLar WPGP
fraxinifolium — LEdu
PAB 9101 new
aff. **fraxinifolium** WWJ 11615 new — WCru
glabrifolium B&SWJ 6882 — WCru
- CWJ 12364 — WCru
ruticarpum — LEdu WPGP
- B&SWJ 3541 — WCru

Tetragonolobus see Lotus

Tetraneuris (Asteraceae)

§ **grandiflora** — SPlb WIce
scaposa — EPot

Tetrapanax (Araliaceae)

§ **papyrifer** ♀H4 — CBrP CDTJ CHEx CHGN ELan ESwi LPal MBri NLos SArc SBig SEND SVen XBlo
- B&SWJ 7135 — EUJe WCru
- 'Di-Sue-Shan' — WCru
- 'Empress' — WCru
- 'Rex' — Widely available
- 'Steroidal Giant' — CDTJ SBig SKHP

Tetrapathaea see Passiflora

Tetrastigma (Vitaceae)

obtectum — CCCN EBee ECre ESwi ETwe EWes SEND WCFE
voinierianum ♀H1b — WCot

Tetratheca (Elaeocarpaceae)

'Bicentennial Belle' — LBuc LRHS
ciliata var. **alba** — MOWG
thymifolia pink-flowered — MOWG

Teucridium (Lamiaceae)

parvifolium — ECou MPie

Teucrium (Lamiaceae)

* **ackermannii** ♀H5 — CMea ECho MHer SBch SIgm WAbe WHoo XSen
arduinoi — XSen
aroanium — CTal ECho EPot MWat SIgm XSen
asiaticum — XSen
aureum — XSen
botrys — MHer
canadense — XSen
chamaedrys misapplied — see *T.* × *lucidrys*
chamaedrys L. — CPom CUse ELon ENfk GMaP GPoy LAst LRHS MCot MNHC MRav MSwo NWad SCob SEND SLim SPer SPlb SRms SVen SWvt WBrk WHar WHfH WJek WWEG XSen
- 'Nanum' — ECho
aff. **chamaedrys** — EPla
divaricatum — XSen

dunense	XSen
flavum	CArn EDAr EPPr WJek XSen
fruticans	Widely available
- 'Azureum' ♀H3	CBcs CBod CHel CSde CTsd EBee ELan EPfP EWTr LAst LRHS MGos MRav NSoo SBrt SEND SMad SPer SPoG SWvt WCFE WHil WKif XSen
- 'Compactum'	CDoC ELan EWTr LAst MGos SLim SLon SPoG SWvt WCFE WPGP WPnn
- 'Drysdale'	CDoC CSBt EBee ELan LRHS SLim SWvt
hircanicum	CAby CArn CSam CUse ECha ECtt ELan EPfP GAbr IFro LLWP LRHS MMuc MNrw MWhi NBir NLar SEND SMrm SPhx SRkn WCFE WJek WMoo WPtf WWFP XSen
- 'Paradise Delight'	ECtt IKil NLar
- 'Purple Tails'	CBod CSpe CTsd EPfP GQue LSou MCot MNHC MRav NBir WWEG
§ × ***lucidrys***	CArn CChe CMea CUse ECha ECrN ELan ENfk EPfP EWoo LRHS MGos MHer MNHC MPie SPer SPoG SRms SWvt WCFE WHar WHoo WJek WPnn XSen
- 'Lucky Gold' new	SPoG
lucidum	GCal SLon
marum	CArn CTri LEdu SBrt SRms WJek XSen
massiliense misapplied	see *T. × lucidrys*
massiliense L.	XSen
montanum	WJek XSen
musimonum	EPot SIgm
orientale	XSen
polium	ECho MWat WJek WThu XSen
pseudochamaepitys	XSen
pyrenaicum ♀H5	CMea CPBP CPom ECho EPot EWes GEdr SBch SIgm XSen
- subsp. ***guarense***	XSen
scorodonia	CArn CHab GPoy MCot MHer MNHC NLar NMir WHer WJek XSen
- 'Binsted Gold'	EBee MMoz NSti
- 'Crispum'	LEdu LRHS MHer MMuc NBro NLar SBch SPer SRms WGrn WJek WKif WMnd WMoo WOut
- 'Crispum Marginatum' (v)	CFis EBee ECGP ECha EHoe EPPr EPfP IKil LEdu LSou MNrw MRav WWEG
- 'Winterdown' (v)	EBee LRHS SBch
subspinosum	ECho LLHF MWat SIgm WHoo WThu
§ ***viscidum*** 'Lemon and Lime' (v)	EBee LSou
webbianum	ECho XSen

Thalia (*Marantaceae*)

dealbata	CBAq CBen CHEx EUJe EWay LLWG MSKA MWts NLar SBig SDix SLon WMAq XLum

Thalictrum (*Ranunculaceae*)

CC 4576	CExl
CC 6859 new	MMoz
CC 7077 new	MMoz
Cox 6118	ITim
from Afghanistan	see *T. isopyroides*
actaeifolium	CLAP
- B&SWJ 4664	WCru
- B&SWJ 6310	WCru
- var. ***brevistylum*** B&SWJ 8819	CDes WCru
- - 'Twinkling Star'	ECtt
- compact B&SWJ 4946 new	WCru
- 'Perfume Star'	CMos CPar ECtt GBin WCot
adiantifolium	see *T. minus* 'Adiantifolium'
alpinum	CTal EDAr EPPr GJos
angustifolium	see *T. lucidum*
'Anne'PBR	CSpe EBee ECtt IKil IPot MSCN NLar
aquilegiifolium	Widely available
- SDR 5463	GKev
- 'Album'	CSpe EBee ECha ELan EPfP GBin GCra GKin LAst LBMP LRHS MMuc MNFA NBid SEND SKHP SPhx SWvt WBor WCAu WFar WMnd WPtf WSHC WWEG
- 'Constable's Clouds' new	EPPr
* - 'Hybridum'	SGSe WMoo
- var. ***intermedium*** B&SWJ 10965	WCru
- 'Purpureum'	CPom NLar WHoo
- var. ***sibiricum***	IMou
- - B&SWJ 11007	WCru
- 'Small Thundercloud'	GCal
- 'Thundercloud' ♀H5	Widely available
baicalense	CPom
'Black Stockings'	CExl CKno CMac EBee ECtt ELan EPfP EShb EWoo GBin IPot LRHS LSou MBel NCGa NDov NLar NPri SCob SKHP SPad SRkn WHil
calabricum	NLar
chelidonii	MMoz NLar
- HWJK 2216	WCru
clavatum	CLAP CPom WPGP
coreanum	see *T. ichangense*
cultratum	CDes EBee LRHS WPGP
dasycarpum	EPPr GJos NLar WCot WPnP
§ ***delavayi*** ♀H7	Widely available
- BWJ 7800 new	WCru
- BWJ 7903	WCru
- var. ***acuminatum*** BWJ 7535	WCru
- - BWJ 7971	WCru
- 'Album'	Widely available
- 'Ankum'	EBee NLar
- var. ***decorum***	CElw CLAP CPom CWCL ELon EPPr SBrt SHar WCot WCru WPGP WSHC
- - BWJ 7770	WCru
- aff. var. ***decorum***	CExl
- 'Gold Laced'	NLar
- 'Hewitt's Double' (d) ♀H7	Widely available
- 'Hinkley'	IPot NLar
- var. ***mucronatum***	WCru
- - DJHC 473	WCru
- purple-stemmed BWJ 7748	WCru
- 'White Cloud'	GBin
aff. ***delavayi*** new	GKin IBoy
diffusiflorum	EWld IMou WCru WSHC
dipterocarpum misapplied	see *T. delavayi*
dipterocarpum Franch.	CMac EBee LRHS XLum
'Elin'	Widely available
fendleri	GBin
- var. ***polycarpum***	EBee IMou WOut
filamentosum	EPPr IMou

Name	Suppliers
- B&SWJ 777	WCru
- B&SWJ 4145	WCru
- var. ***yakusimense*** B&SWJ 6094	WCru
aff. ***finetii*** DJHC 473	CLAP
flavum	CHab CMac EHon ELan GKin LLWG MSCN NBro NMir SMHy SMrm SPhx SWat WFar WShi
- 'Chollerton'	see *T. isopyroides*
§ - subsp. ***glaucum*** ♀H7	Widely available
- - dwarf	WPGP
- - 'True Blue'	SGbt
- 'Illuminator'	CElw CTri EPfP IBoy LRHS MArl MRav NLar SDix SMad SMrm SPoG WCot WFar
flexuosum	see *T. minus* subsp. *minus*
foetidum	NBre
grandidentatum	WCot
honanense	SKHP
- BWJ 7962	WCru
- 'Marble Leaf'	SKHP
§ ***ichangense***	CHid CPom CSpe EPri GEdr IPot LBMP LRHS MBel MPie MSCN NMyG NWad SPad SPer WCot
- B&SWJ 8203	WCru
- Evening Star strain (v)	CAby CMea CSpe ECtt GBin LAst MHol SCob SPoG WCot
- var. ***minus*** 'Chinese Chintz'	WCru
- 'Purple Marble'	CWGN GEdr LEdu MSCN WCot
§ ***isopyroides***	CCon CPom EAEE EBee EPla GCal GKev GKin LAst LRHS MMuc MNFA MRav NLar NWad SEND SHar SMrm WCot
javanicum	LEdu
- B&SWJ 9506	WCru
- var. ***puberulum*** B&SWJ 6770	WCru
johnstonii B&SWJ 9127	WCru
kiusianum	CAby CDes CPne CTal EBee ECha ECho EHoe ELan EWes GCra GMaP ITim LBMP LRHS LSun MBel MHol MPie NBir NLar NSla SKHP SRot SWvt WAbe WCot WFar XEll
- Kew form	WSHC
koreanum	see *T. ichangense*
§ ***lucidum***	CElw CExl EBee ECtt EHoe ELan EShb GBin GCal GKin IMou LEdu LPla LRHS MHol MMuc MPie MTis NLar NSti SEND SKHP SPhx WCot
minus	CArn GBin LEdu LRHS MBel MMuc SEND
§ - 'Adiantifolium'	EBee GBin GJos IPot MBel MRav NGdn NLar SHar SRms XLum
- var. ***hypoleucum*** B&SWJ 8634	WCru
- subsp. ***kemense***	EBee
§ - subsp. ***minus***	GJos NBre
- var. ***sipellatum*** B&SWJ 5051	WCru
morisonii	EBee LRHS NBid
omeiense	CPom
- BWJ 8049	WCru
- DJHC 762	CDes
orientale	LRHS
osmundifolium	WCru
petaloideum	ECha EPPr GCal
platycarpum B&SWJ 2261	WCru
polygamum	see *T. pubescens* Pursh
przewalskii	WCru
§ ***pubescens*** Pursh	EBee ECha ECtt GBin GJos GMaP LRHS MAvo NDov NLar SHar SPhx WCot
punctatum B&SWJ 1272	WCru
ramosum BWJ 8126	WCru
reniforme	CSpe IGor WCot
- B&SWJ 2610	WCru
- GWJ 9311	WCru
- HWJK 2403	WCru
rochebrunianum	Widely available
rubescens B&SWJ 10006	WCru
* ***rugosum***	LRHS
sachalinense	CCon WOut WPGP
- RBS 0279	EBee EPPr NLar
shensiense	CExl
simplex var. ***brevipes*** B&SWJ 4794	WCru
speciosissimum	see *T. flavum* subsp. *glaucum*
* ***sphaerostachyum***	CElw EBee ECtt LRHS MNrw MWhi SMrm WHal WHil
'Splendide'	CAby CExl CSpe EBee ECGP ECtt ELan ELon EPfP GBin IMou IPot LPla MAvo MBel MBri MHol MNrw MTis NDov NLar STPC WCot WHil
'Splendide White'	CMos CSpe IPot NLar SHar STPC
squarrosum	CDes WPGP
tenuisubulatum BWJ 7929	WCru
tuberosum	CElw CSpe LLHF WCot
- 'Rosie Hardy'	SHar
tubiferum B&SWJ 10999	WCru
'Tukker Princess'	EBee ECtt GBin IKil NLar WCot
uchiyamae	CDes GBin GJos WCot WPGP
urbainii B&SWJ 7085 **new**	WCru
'Yubari Mountains' **new**	GEdr
yunnanense	WCru

Thamnocalamus (*Poaceae*)

Name	Suppliers
crassinodus	SBig
- 'Gosainkund'	CEnt EPla ERod MMoz MWht
- 'Kew Beauty' ♀H3	CAbb CDTJ CDoC CEnt EPfP EPla ERod MBrN MMoz MWht SBig WCot WPGP
- 'Lang Tang'	CEnt ERod MMoz MWht WPGP
- 'Merlyn'	CDoC CEnt EPfP ERod MMoz MWht WPGP
falconeri	see *Himalayacalamus falconeri*
khasianus	see *Drepanostachyum khasianum*
maling	see *Yushania maling*
spathaceus misapplied	see *Fargesia murielae*
§ ***spathiflorus***	CEnt
- subsp. ***nepalensis***	ERod MWht SBig
§ ***tessellatus***	ERod MMuc MWht SEND

Thamnochortus (*Restionaceae*)

Name	Suppliers
insignis ♀H2	MPkF SPlb
lucens	SPlb
rigidus	CCCN

Thapsia (*Apiaceae*)

Name	Suppliers
decipiens	see *Melanoselinum decipiens*
villosa	CArn

Thea see *Camellia*

Thelypteris (*Thelypteridaceae*)

Name	Suppliers
dentata	SGSe

	kunthii	ISha
	limbosperma	see *Oreopteris limbosperma*
	noveboracensis	see *Parathelypteris novae-boracensis*
	ovata var. ***lindheimeri***	ISha
	palustris	CKel EBee EShb MMoz NLar SRms WFib WPnP WShi XLum
	phegopteris	see *Phegopteris connectilis*

Themeda (*Poaceae*)

	japonica	SGSe
	triandra	SMad

Thermopsis (*Papilionaceae*)

	caroliniana	see *T. villosa*
	chinensis	EBee ELon LRHS MHer MMuc SEND WBor
	fabacea	see *T. lupinoides*
	lanceolata	CMea CTri EBee ELon EPfP LRHS MMuc NSti SEND SHar SMrm SPad WCot WFar WHrl WKif
§	***lupinoides***	ECha MHer
	mollis	CExl NBid
	montana	see *T. rhombifolia* var. *montana*
§	***rhombifolia*** var. ***montana***	CBod CWCL EAEE EBee ELan EPfP EPla GAbr GCra GMaP LRHS MMuc MSpe NBir NCGa NLar NOrc NPol NSti NWad SEND SGSe SPer SPoG WBor WWEG
§	***villosa***	CAbP CWCL ELon LRHS MRav NGdn NLar SMHy WCot WFar WHoo WWEG WWFP

Therorhodion see *Rhododendron*

Thladiantha (*Cucurbitaceae*)

	dubia	EBee SDix WCot

Thlaspi (*Brassicaceae*)

	sp.	NGdn
	biebersteinii	see *Pachyphragma macrophyllum*
§	***cepaeifolium*** subsp. ***rotundifolium***	GEdr
	densiflorum **new**	GEdr
	rotundifolium	see *T. cepaeifolium* subsp. *rotundifolium*
	zaffrani	GEdr WAbe

Thryptomene (*Myrtaceae*)

	baeckeacea	CCCN
	saxicola	ECou

Thuja ✿ (*Cupressaceae*)

	'Extra Gold'	see *T. plicata* 'Irish Gold'
§	***koraiensis***	IDee NLar
	occidentalis	NWea SEND
	- 'Amber Glow'	CDoC CKen CSBt EPla MAsh NHol NLar NWad SCoo SLim SPoG WBor WGor
	- 'Anniek'PBR **new**	SLim
	- 'Aureospicata'	EHul
	- 'Bateman Broom'	CKen
	- 'Beaufort' (v)	CKen EHul
	- 'Brabant' ♀H6	CDul MGos MJak NLar NWea SCob SCoo SLim WMou
	- 'Brobecks Tower' ♀H6	CDoC CKen EPla NLar SLim
	- 'Caespitosa'	CKen
	- 'Danica' ♀H6	CMac EHul EPla GKin IBoy MAsh MBri MGos MJak NWea SCob SCoo SLim SPoG SRms WCFE
	- 'Degroot's Spire'	CKen NLar SLim
	- 'Douglasii Aurea' (v)	CKen
	- Emerald	see *T. occidentalis* 'Smaragd'
	- 'Ericoides'	CDoC EHul SRms
	- 'Europa Gold' ♀H6	CDoC NLar SGol
	- 'Filiformis'	CKen EPla
	- 'Globosa'	ELan
I	- 'Globosa Variegata' (v)	CKen
	- 'Gold Drop'	CKen
	- 'Golden Anne' **new**	WGor
	- 'Golden Globe'	CDoC EHul IBoy MGos MJak SCoo SLim
	- 'Golden Minaret'	EHul
	- Golden Smaragd = 'Janed Gold'PBR **new**	SLim
	- 'Golden Tuffet' ♀H6	CDoC CKen EHul ELan EPla GKin LBee MBri MPkF NLar NWad SCob SCoo SLim SPer SPoG
	- 'Hetz Midget' ♀H6	CKen EHul GKin IBoy LAst MBri NLar NWad SCob SCoo SLim SPlb WGor
	- 'Holmstrup' ♀H6	CDoC CMac EHul MAsh MBri MGos MJak SCoo SGol SLim SRms
	- 'Hoveyi'	CTri EHul
	- 'Jantar' **new**	NLar
	- 'Linesville'	CKen
	- 'Little Champion'	EHul IBoy NLar
	- 'Little Gem'	EHul NLar SRms
	- 'Lutea Nana'	EHul
	- 'Malonyana'	NLar
	- 'Malonyana Holub'	SLim
	- 'Marrisen's Sulphur'	CDoC EHul
	- 'Meineke's Zwerg' (v)	CKen
	- 'Mirjam'PBR (v) **new**	WGor
	- 'Mr Bowling Ball'	CDoC NLar
	- 'Ohlendorffii'	CDoC CKen EHul
I	- 'Pygmaea'	CKen
	- 'Pyramidalis Aurea'	CAco ECrN
	- 'Pyramidalis Compacta'	EHul
	- 'Recurva Nana'	EHul NWad
	- 'Rheingold' ♀H6	Widely available
§	- 'Smaragd' ♀H6	CCVT CDoC CDul CSBt EHul ELan EPfP EPla IBoy LAst LBuc LRHS MAsh MBri MGos MJak NLar NWea SCob SCoo SGol SLim SPoG SWvt WCFE WMou
*	- 'Smaragd Variegated' (v)	CKen
	- 'Smokey'	CKen
	- 'Spaethii'	EHul
	- 'Spiralis'	EHul NLar WCFE
§	- 'Stolwijk' (v)	EHul
	- 'Sunkist' ♀H6	CKen CMac COtt EHul EPla LAst MAsh MBri MGos MJak NEgg SCoo SGol
	- 'Teddy'	CDoC EHul EPfP LBee MAsh MBri MGos NHol SCoo SPoG
	- 'Tiny Tim'	CDoC CMac EHul IBoy MBri MGos SGol
	- 'Trompenburg'	CDoC EHul NLar
	- 'Wansdyke Silver' (v)	CMac EHul
	- 'Wareana'	CMac
	- 'Wareana Aurea'	see *T. occidentalis* 'Wareana Lutescens'
§	- 'Wareana Lutescens'	EHul
	- 'Waterfield'	NLar NWad

- 'Yellow Ribbon' CDul CKen CSBt EHul MGos MJak SCob SCoo SGol
orientalis see *Platycladus orientalis*
- 'Miller's Gold' see *Platycladus orientalis* 'Aurea Nana'
plicata CAco CBcs CCVT CDul CMac CTho EHul ELan EPfP NWea SCob WHar WMou
- 'Atrovirens' ♀H6 CDul CTri LBee LBuc LRHS MAsh MBri MGos MJak MMuc NHed SCob SCoo SEND SEWo SGol SRms SWvt WHar WMou
- 'Aurea' ♀H6 EHul MAsh SRms
- 'Can-can' (v) ELan MAsh
I - 'Cole's Variety' CDul MMuc
- 'Collyer's Gold' CDul EHul SRms
- 'Copper Kettle' CKen EHul GKin SLim
- 'Cuprea' CKen EHul
- 'Doone Valley' CKen EHul NWad
- 'Emerald' PBR EUJe
- 'Excelsa' CDul WMou
- 'Fastigiata' CDul
- 'Gelderland' ♀H6 EHul ELan EPfP NEgg SCoo
- Goldy = '4ever' PBR CDoC MBri SPoG
- 'Gracilis Aurea' EHul
- 'Hillieri' CDoC CDul
- 'Holly Turner' **new** SLim
§ - 'Irish Gold' (v) CDul CMac SMad
- 'Martin' CJun NHed SWvt
- 'Rogersii' ♀H6 CDoC CKen CMac EHul MAsh NHol SCoo SPoG SRms WThu
- 'Semperaurescens' (v) CMac
- 'Stolwijk's Gold' see *T. occidentalis* 'Stolwijk'
- 'Stoneham Gold' ♀H6 CDoC CMac EHul GKin MAsh MGos MMuc NPCo SEND SRms
- Verigold = 'Courtapli' CCVT MMuc SEND
- 'Whipcord' ♀H6 CBcs CKen EHul ELan EPfP EUJe LRHS MPkF NHol NLar SCoo SLim SPer SPoG WBor
* - 'Windsor Gold' EHul
- 'Winter Pink' (v) CKen
- 'Zebrina' (v) ♀H6 CBcs CDoC CDul CMac CTri EHul ELan EPfP MAsh MGos MJak MMuc NLar NPri NWea SCob SCoo SEND SLim SMad SPoG SWvt WHar
standishii WThu

Thujopsis (*Cupressaceae*)

dolabrata ♀H6 CBcs CDul EHul GKin MJak MMuc NEgg NLar NWea SEND SWvt
- 'Aurea' (v) CDoC CKen EHul NLar SLim
- var. **hondae** IArd SLim
- 'Laetevirens' see *T. dolabrata* 'Nana'
- 'Melbourne Gold' NLar
§ - 'Nana' CDoC CKen CMac EHul MGos NLar SLim SRms
- 'Variegata' (v) CMac EHul GKin NLar
koraiensis (Nakai) hort. see *Thuja koraiensis*

Thunbergia (*Acanthaceae*)

alata EPfP SPoG
- 'African Sunset' CSpe
- 'Lemon Queen' CHll SWvt
- 'Orange Beauty' LBuc LSou SWvt
- 'Sunny Suzy Red-Orange' **new** LBuc
* **arborea** CCCN
battiscombeii CCCN EShb MOWG
coccinea CCCN
erecta CCCN MOWG
fragrans GWJ 9441 WCru
grandiflora ♀H1a CCCN CHll MOWG
- 'Alba' CCCN CHll
gregorii ♀H1c CCCN CHll EShb MOWG
laurifolia B&SWJ 7166 WCru
'Lemon Star' LBuc
'Moonglow' CCCN
mysorensis ♀H1a SVen
natalensis CCCN EShb
'Orange Wonder' CCCN

Thymbra (*Lamiaceae*)

spicata CArn

thyme, caraway see *Thymus herba-barona*

thyme, garden see *Thymus vulgaris*

thyme, lemon see *Thymus citriodorus*

thyme, wild see *Thymus serpyllum*

Thymelaea (*Thymelaeaceae*)

lanuginosa **new** MMuc

Thymus ✿ (*Lamiaceae*)

from Albania CArn
from Turkey EWes LEdu SHDw
'A Touch of Frost' SHDw
'Albus' CBod ENfk
'Anderson's Gold' see *T. pulegioides* 'Bertram Anderson'
'Aureus' ambig. MJak
azoricus see *T. caespititius*
'Bressingham' CArn CBod CMea CPrp CTri ECtt EDAr GCrg GMaP LEdu LLWP LRHS MHer MMuc MNHC NDov SEND SPlb SRms WIce WJek WWEG
'Caborn Fragrant Cloud' LLWP
'Caborn Grey Lady' LLWP
'Caborn Lilac Gem' LLWP SHDw
'Caborn Pink Carpet' LLWP
'Caborn Royale' LLWP
'Caborn Wine and Roses' ENfk LLWP SRms
§ **caespititius** CArn GCrg GPoy MHer NRya SPlb SRot WHer WJek WWEG
caespitosus CTri LEdu
camphoratus CArn ENfk ESwi EWes GCrg MHer SPhx
capitatus CArn
§ **carnosus** Boiss. MHer XSen
'Carol Ann' (v) ENfk EWes MNHC SRms
ciliatus CBod XSen
cilicicus misapplied see *T. caespititius*
cilicicus ambig. MNHC SRms
cilicicus Boiss. & Bail. WAbe
citriodorus misapplied see *T.* 'Culinary Lemon'
citriodorus ambig. CTal CTsd GKev MMuc NDov SRms WCFE XLum
citriodorus (Pers.) Schreb. LEdu
- Schreb. 'Archer's Gold' see *T. pulegioides* 'Archer's Gold'
- 'Aureus' see *T. pulegioides* 'Aureus'
- 'Bertram Anderson' see *T. pulegioides* 'Bertram Anderson'
- 'Silver Posie' see *T.* 'Silver Posie'
'Coccineus' see *T.* Coccineus Group

§	Coccineus Group ♀H5	Widely available
	– 'Atropurpureus' Schleipfer	see *T.* (Coccineus Group) 'Purple Beauty'
§	– 'Purple Beauty'	EPot GCrg MHer SHDw WWEG
§	– 'Red Elf'	CBod GAbr GCrg MHer WWEG
	'Coccineus Major'	CMea EDAr LRHS MHer MNHC SCob WJek
	comosus misapplied	CBod SHDw WJek
	'Creeping Lemon' misapplied	see *T. pulegioides* 'Kurt'
§	'Culinary Lemon'	CArn CHby EDAr ELau ENfk GPoy LLWP MBrN MHer MNHC NPri WJek XLum XSen
	'Dark Eyes'	SHDw
	'Dartmoor'	CBod SHDw WJek WWEG
	'Desboro'	see *T. serpyllum* 'Desborough'
	'Dillington'	ENfk
	doerfleri	XSen
	'Doone Valley' (v)	Widely available
	drucei	see *T. polytrichus* subsp. *britannicus*
	'E.B. Anderson'	see *T. pulegioides* 'Bertram Anderson'
	'Eastgrove Pink'	SHDw
	erectus	see *T. carnosus*
	'Fragrantissimus'	CArn ELau ENfk GPoy LLWP MHer MNHC MWat NPri SIde SPlb WJek WOut XSen
	'Golden King' (v)	ECha EDAr ELan ENfk MAsh MBri MHer SRms WWEG
	'Golden Lemon' misapplied	see *T. pulegioides* 'Aureus'
	'Golden Lemon' (v)	WJek
	'Golden Queen' (v)	CBod CUse CWld EDAr MHol MWat NPri SRms
	'Gratian'	SHDw
§	'Hartington Silver' (v)	CBod ECha ECho ECtt ENfk EWes GCrg GEdr LAst LBMP LEdu LRHS MAsh MHer NRya SPlb SPoG SRms WHoo WJek WWEG
	herba-barona	CArn CBod CMea CTri EDAr ELau ENfk GPoy LEdu LLWP MHer MNHC MWat SIde SRms WJek
	– ***citrata***	see *T. herba-barona* 'Lemon-scented'
§	– 'Lemon-scented'	CBod ECha GPoy LEdu LLWP MHer SHDw SRms WJek
	'Highdown'	ECtt SHDw
	'Highdown Adur'	SHDw
	'Highdown Lemon'	SHDw
	'Highdown Red'	SHDw
	'Highdown Stretham'	SHDw
	'Highland Cream'	see *T.* 'Hartington Silver'
	hirsutus	XSen
	hyemalis	GPoy
§	'Iden'	CBod WJek WWEG
	'Jekka'	CBod SRms WJek
	'Kurt'	see *T. pulegioides* 'Kurt'
	'Lavender Sea'	EWes
	'Lemon Caraway'	see *T. herba-barona* 'Lemon-scented'
	'Lemon Curd'	CWld ELau ENfk LLWP MNHC NHol SHDw SPlb SPoG SRms WJek WWEG
	'Lemon Sorbet'	SHDw
*	'Lemon Variegated' (v)	EDAr ELau ENfk EPfP MNHC SPer SPoG WWEG
	leucotrichus	XSen
	'Lilac Time'	ECtt ENfk EWes LLWP MHer SHDw SPlb SRms WJek WWEG
	'Lime'	LEdu
	linearis	XSen
	longicaulis	CArn CBod ECha ELau LLWP MHer SRms
	'Magic Carpet'	SPhx
	'Marjorie'	LLWP
	marschallianus	see *T. pannonicus*
§	'Massa'	SHDw
	mastichina	CArn SPhx XSen
	– 'Didi'	MHer
	micans	see *T. caespititius*
	minus	see *Calamintha nepeta*
	'Mountain Select'	LLWP SHDw
	neiceffii	CMea ECha SBch WWEG XSen
§	'Nettleton Pink Carpet'	LLWP
	'Orange'	CBod CUse LEdu SRms
§	Orange Spice = 'Tm95'	LLWP SHDw XSen
	pallasianus	ELau SHDw
§	***pannonicus***	MHer
	'Peter Davis'	CBod ENfk LRHS MHer NBir SIde SPoG SRms WAbe WIce XSen
§	'Pinewood'	CTal LEdu MHer WJek XSen
	'Pink Ripple'	CBod CMea CTal ECtt ELau ENfk EWes LEdu LLWP MHer MNHC SHDw SIgm SRms WHal WHoo WJek WWEG
	polytrichus misapplied	see *T. praecox*
§	***polytrichus*** A. Kern. ex Borbás subsp. ***britannicus***	CArn CBod CTri ECha GJos GMaP GPoy LEdu MBNS MBri MHer MLHP MNHC NBir SEND SHDw SPlb SRms WHoo WJek XLum
	– – 'Minor'	see *T.* 'Nettleton Pink Carpet'
§	– – 'Thomas's White' ♀H5	CTri
	'Porlock'	CBod CMea CSam CTri ELau EPfP GPoy MHer SRms WAbe WHoo WJek WWEG
§	***praecox***	CBod CWld EWoo GJos MHer NMir
	– 'Albiflorus'	EWoo
	– subsp. ***arcticus***	see *T. polytrichus* subsp. *britannicus*
	– – 'Albus'	see *T. polytrichus* subsp. *britannicus* 'Thomas's White'
	prostrate **new**	CBod
	pulegioides	CArn CBod CHby CPrp CUse CWld ELau ENfk GPoy LLWP MBri MHer MNHC MSCN SHDw SIde SPhx SRms WJek
§	– 'Archer's Gold'	CTri ECtt EDAr EHoe ELau ENfk EPfP EPot GAbr GJos LEdu LLWP LPot LRHS MAsh MBri MHer MNHC MRav NBir NHol NWad SCob SRms WJek WWEG
§	– 'Aureus' ♀H5	CBod EAEE ENfk GCrg GMaP LLWP MAsh MBri MMuc SPer SPlb SRms WHoo WJek
§	– 'Bertram Anderson' ♀H5	CBod CMea CTal ECha ECtt ENfk EPfP GCrg GMaP LAst LLWP MAsh MCot MHer MMuc NBir NPri NRya SCob SEND SPer SPoG SRms WAbe WHoo WJek WWEG
	– 'Foxley' (v)	CBod CPrp EHoe ELau ENfk EPfP GAbr GEdr LLWP MHer MMuc MNHC NPri SEND SHDw SIde SPlb SPoG SRms WJek WWEG
§	– 'Kurt'	CBod ENfk LLWP MHer SHDw WJek
	– 'Sir John Lawes'	MHer

- 'Tabor'	CBod CUse ENfk MNHC SHDw SRms
'Rainbow Falls' (v)	EPfP MNHC SHDw WWEG
'Rasta' (v)	MHer
'Redstart'	CBod ECha ECtt ENfk EPot LEdu LLWP MHer SHDw SRms WJek WWEG
richardii subsp. ***nitidus*** 'Compactus Albus'	see *T. vulgaris* 'Snow White'
'Rosa Ceeping'	SHDw
'Rosalicht'	see *T.* 'Rosedrift'
§ 'Rosedrift'	SHDw
rotundifolius misapplied	see *T. vulgaris* 'Elsbeth'
'Ruby Glow'	ECtt EWes GCrg MHer SHDw
serpyllum ambig.	EWoo SCob SVic XLum
serpyllum L.	CArn CUse GJos LBuc MBri MMuc SPlb SRms WJek
- var. ***albus***	CTal ECha GMaP GPoy LAst LLWP LRHS MNHC SPer SRms WAbe WHoo WJek WWEG
- 'Albus Variegatus'	see *T.* 'Hartington Silver'
- 'Annie Hall'	CBod CTal EDAr EPfP EPot LLWP LRHS MAsh MHer MNHC SRms WCFE WJek
- 'Atropurpureus'	see *T.* (Coccineus Group) 'Purple Beauty'
- ***coccineus*** 'Minor' misapplied	see *T.* Coccineus Group
- 'Conwy Rose'	CPBP WAbe
§ - 'Desborough'	MHer WWEG
- 'East Lodge'	LLWP MNHC SRms
- 'Elfin'	ECho EPot EWes EWoo GCrg MBri SPlb WAbe WThu
- 'Goldstream' (v)	CBod CPrp ENfk LEdu LRHS MBri MHer SPlb SRms WJek
- 'Iden'	see *T.* 'Iden'
- 'Minimalist'	see *T. serpyllum* 'Minor'
- 'Minimus'	see *T. serpyllum* 'Minor'
§ - 'Minor'	CArn CMea CTal CTri ECha ECtt ENfk GCrg LLWP LRHS MBri MHer MLHP MMuc MNHC NRya NSla SEND SHDw SPlb SRms SRot WAbe WHoo WJek WWEG
- 'Minus'	see *T. serpyllum* 'Minor'
- 'Pink Chintz' ♀H5	CArn CBod EAEE ECha ECtt EDAr ENfk EPfP GEdr GMaP GPoy LLWP LRHS MBri MHer MNHC SPer SPlb SPoG SRms WHoo WIce WJek WWEG
- 'Posh Pinky'	CPBP
- 'Purple Beauty'	see *T.* (Coccineus Group) 'Purple Beauty'
- 'Red Carpet'	ECtt GCrg NWad
- 'Red Elf'	see *T.* (Coccineus Group) 'Red Elf'
- 'Russetings'	CBod CTsd CUse CWld ECtt ENfk EPfP EPot EWoo MHer MNHC NDov SCob SIde SPoG SRms WJek WWEG
- 'September'	MHer
- 'Snowdrift'	CArn CMea ECtt EPfP GKev LLWP MHer MNHC MWat NWad SIde SPlb SRms WCFE WJek WWEG
- 'Variegatus'	see *T.* 'Hartington Silver'
- 'Vey'	CBod CTal EWes LLWP LRHS MHer SHDw SRms WJek WWEG
sibthorpii	CArn
'Silver King' (v)	ENfk
§ 'Silver Posie'	Widely available
'Silver Queen' (v) ♀H5	CBcs CBod CSam ECha EDAr ELan ENfk EPfP GCrg GKev GMaP LAst LLWP MCot MHer MNHC NHol NPri SCob SPer SPlb SRms WJek WWEG
'Spicy Orange'	see *T.* Orange Spice
striatus new	LEdu
valesiacus	see *T.* 'Massa'
§ ***vulgaris***	Widely available
* - 'Compactus'	EAEE ENfk GPoy LEdu LLWP MHer MNHC MRav SRms WCAu WJek
- 'Deutsche Auslese'	see *T. vulgaris*
- 'Dorcas White'	MHer
§ - 'Elsbeth'	ELau LLWP MHer SHDw
- French	see *T. vulgaris*
- 'Golden Pins'	MHer
- 'Lemon Queen'	ELau
- 'Lucy'	LLWP MHer
- 'Pinewood'	see *T.* 'Pinewood'
§ - 'Snow White'	ELau EWes SHDw WJek
'Widecombe' (v)	LLWP SHDw
zygioides new	SIgm
zygis	SPhx

Tiarella ✿ (*Saxifragaceae*)

'Appalachian Trail'	CBcs CHVG EBee ECtt GBin LBMP LSou MAsh MHol MPnt NSoo NWad SHeu SPoG WCot WNPC
'Black Snowflake'	MPnt SHeu
'Black Velvet'	MBel MPnt SHeu
'Braveheart'	CBod EPfP MPnt SHeu WNPC
'Butter and Sugar'	MPnt
'Butterfly Wings'	MPnt
'Candy Striper'	ECtt MPnt NCGa SHeu
'Cascade Creeper' PBR	ECtt LAst LRHS LSou MPnt NWad SHeu WNPC
collina	see *T. wherryi*
cordifolia ♀H5	Widely available
- 'Glossy'	CCon MPnt
- 'Milk Chocolate'	MMoz MPnt
- 'Oakleaf'	CCon MPnt NBro SHeu
- 'Rosalie'	see × *Heucherella alba* 'Rosalie'
- 'Running Tapestry'	MPnt SHeu
- 'Slick Rock'	EPPr
'Crow Feather' PBR	CNec LSou MAsh MPnt NWad SDys SHeu WNPC
'Cygnet'	CLAP ECtt LRHS MPnt SHeu SRot
'Dunvegan'	MPnt
'Elizabeth Oliver'	MPnt
'Freckles'	MRav
'Happy Trails' PBR	MPnt NWad SHeu WCot WNPC
'Hidden Carpet'	CHid
'Inkblot'	ELan LRHS MPnt NBro SHeu WMoo
'Iron Butterfly' PBR (v)	CAby CLAP CMac CWCL EBee ECha ECtt EHoe EPfP EWll EWoo GBin GMaP LAst LRHS LSun MBel MNrw MPnt MRav NBro SCob SGbt SPer SPoG SRot
'Iron Cross'	SPlb
'Jeepers Creepers' PBR	CHid ECha ECtt LBMP LRHS MHol MPnt NWad SHeu WNPC
'Martha Oliver'	CCon CLAP EBee MPnt SBch
'Mint Chocolate'	CLAP EAEE ECtt EHoe ELan GMaP LPot LRHS MBel MNrw MPnt MRav MWhi NBir NGdn NLar SHeu SWvt
'Moorgrün'	EPPr GCal SHeu
Morning Star = 'Tntia042' PBR	CHel CHid CWCL ECtt MPnt SHeu SMrm SRkn SRot WHoo

'Mystic Mist'[PBR] (v)	CBod CHid CWGN ECtt EPla LBMP LSou MPnt MWhi NLar SHeu SPoG WNPC
'Neon Lights'[PBR]	CHid ELan MAsh MPnt NBir NCGa NSoo NWad SCob SHeu SWvt WNPC
§ 'Ninja'	CHid ECtt ELan EUJe GMaP LRHS MPnt NBir NLar NSti SPer SWvt
'Oregon Trail'	ECtt GBin LBMP MBel MNrw MPnt NSoo NWad SHeu WCot WNPC
'Pacific Crest'	ECtt MPnt NWad SHeu WGor WNPC
'Pink Bouquet'	Widely available
'Pink Brushes'[PBR]	CLAP MPnt SHeu WPnP
'Pink Skyrocket'[PBR]	CAbP CLAP ECtt ELan LBMP LLHF LLWG LRHS LSun MBel MCot MHol MPnt NBir NGdn NHol NWad SHar SHeu SPad SWvt WCot
'Pinwheel'	MPnt
'Pirate's Patch'[PBR]	LLHF MPnt SHeu WNPC
polyphylla	MPnt NLar SHeu WCru
- 'Baoxing Pink'	CFis CLAP MPnt WCru
- 'Filigran'	EPfP IBoy MPnt NHol NLar NWad SHeu WPtf
- pink-flowered	CLAP
'Running Tiger'	MPnt
'Sea Foam'	MPnt SHeu
'Simsalabim'	MPnt
'Skeleton Key'	MPnt
'Skid's Variegated' (v)	CBod CCon ECtt LLWG LRHS MHol MNrw MPie MPnt NSti SHeu SWvt WCot
'Skyrocket'	ECtt MCot NLar
'Spanish Cross'	EBee MPnt SHeu
'Spring Symphony'[PBR]	CCon CLAP CNec CWCL ECtt EShb GBin GBuc LRHS LSou MBel MBri MPnt MWat NCGa NPer NWad SHar SHil
Starburst = 'Tntia041'[PBR]	ECtt MPnt NWad SHeu WNPC
'Sugar and Spice'[PBR]	CWGN EAEE EPla LRHS MBrN MPnt MWhi NCGa NDov NWad SHeu SMad WNPC
'Sunset Ridge'	ECtt MPnt NWad SHeu WNPC
'Tiger Stripe'	EPfP LRHS MPnt NBro SHeu
'Timbuktu'	EBee ECtt MAsh MPnt SHeu WNPC
trifoliata	GKev MPnt MRav
- var. ***unifoliata***	MPnt WPtf WWEG
'Viking Ship'	see × *Heucherella* 'Viking Ship'
§ ***wherryi*** [H5]	CBcs CBod CSpe EBee ELan ELon EPfP GAbr GMaP IBoy LAst LPot LRHS LSun MPnt NBir NBro NOrc NPri NRya SCob SPer SPlb SWvt WHar WPnP XLum
- 'Bronze Beauty'	CLAP GBuc IGor MPnt SBch SHeu
- bronze-leaved **new**	SCob
- 'Green Velvet'	ECha MPnt SHeu
- 'Heronswood Mist' (v)	CAbP CBct ECtt ELan MHol MMoz MNrw MPnt SHeu SWvt

Tibouchina (*Melastomataceae*)

grandifolia	CCCN
granulosa	MOWG
heteromalla	CCCN
'Jules'	MOWG WCot
organensis	CCCN CHll SEle SHeu SWvt
paratropica	CRHN
- RCB/Arg X-4	WCot
semidecandra hort.	see *T. urvilleana*
§ ***urvilleana*** [H1c]	CBcs CCCN CDoC CEnd CHEx CHel CRHN CSBt CTri CTsd EBak ELan EUJe MCot MOWG NLos SPer SRkn SWvt WCot
- 'Compacta'	CCCN
- 'Edwardsii' [H1c]	SAdn SMrm WCot
- 'Nana'	CDoC
- variegated (v)	CCCN LSou SPer SWvt WCot

Tigridia (*Iridaceae*)

catarinensis	SDeJ
§ ***immaculata*** B&SWJ 10393	WCru
lutea	ECho
orthantha 'Red-Hot Tiger'	CDes WCru
pavonia	CAby CBro CExl ECho SDeJ WSHC
- 'Alba'	ECho
- 'Alba Grandiflora'	GKev WHil
- 'Alba Immaculata'	CSpe
- 'Aurea'	ECho GKev WHil
- 'Canariensis'	CTca ECho GKev WHil
- lemon-flowered	CSpe
- 'Lilacea'	ECho GKev SDeJ WHil
- red-flowered	ECho
- 'Speciosa'	CTca GKev SDeJ WHil
- yellow-flowered	ECho

Tilia ✿ (*Malvaceae*)

HRS 2808	WPGP
americana	CLnd CMCN
- 'Dentata'	CDul
- 'Nova'	CDoC
argentea	see *T. tomentosa*
begoniifolia	see *T. dasystyla* subsp. *caucasica*
chenmoui	CMCN EPfP MBlu WPGP
chinensis	CMCN EBee WPGP
- F 30558	WPGP
chingiana	CDul CMCN EBee SLon WPGP
cordata	Widely available
§ - 'Böhlje'	CDul ECrN
- 'Dainty Leaf'	CDul
- 'Erecta'	see *T. cordata* 'Böhlje'
- 'Greenspire' [H6]	CCVT CDoC CDul CLnd ECrN EPfP IBoy MRav SCob SEWo WMou
- 'Len Parvin'	EBee WPGP
- 'Roelvo'	CDul
- 'Swedish Upright'	CDul
- 'Winter Orange' [H6]	CDul CEnd EBee ECrN EPfP GQue LAst MBlu MBri NPCo SBir SCoo SEWo WPat
dasystyla	CMCN EBee
§ - subsp. ***caucasica***	CMCN WPGP
- - A&L 16 **new**	WPGP
endochrysea	WPGP
× ***euchlora***	CCVT CDul CLnd CMCN EBee ECrN EPfP EPla NWea SCob SEWo SPer
§ × ***europaea***	CBcs CDul CLnd ELan EWTr MMuc NWea SCob SEND
- 'Koningslinde'	CDul
- 'Pallida'	CDul CLnd MBlu NLar NWea
- 'Wratislaviensis' [H6]	CDul CLnd EBee MAsh MBlu NLar NWea
§ 'Harold Hillier'	CMCN MBlu
henryana	CAco CBcs CDoC CDul CEnd CLnd CMCN CTho EBee ELan EMil EPfP EPla ERod IArd IDee LRHS MBlu MMuc NWea SBir SCoo WMou WPGP

- 'Arnold Select'	WCot WMou
- large **new**	WPGP
§ ***heterophylla***	CDul CMCN EBee ELan EPfP MBlu MBri WPGP
'Hillieri'	see *T.* 'Harold Hillier'
insularis misapplied	see *T. japonica* 'Ernest Wilson'
intonsa	CMCN
japonica	CDul CMCN EPfP WPGP
§ - 'Ernest Wilson' ♀H6	CMCN MBlu
kiusiana	CDul CMCN EBee MBlu MBri WMou WPGP WPat
mandshurica	CDul CMCN EBee WPGP
maximowicziana	WPGP
mexicana	WPGP
- CD&R 1318	WPGP
miqueliana	CMCN IDee
'Moltkei'	CDul CMCN EBee IArd IDee WPGP
mongolica	CBcs CDul CLnd CMCN EPfP EPla MBlu SCoo WMou WPGP
monticola	see *T. heterophylla*
nobilis KR 226	WPGP
oliveri	CDul CMCN EBee MBlu NWea WMou WPGP
paucicostata	WPGP
'Petiolaris' ♀H6	CAco CBcs CCVT CDoC CDul CEnd CLnd CMCN ECrN ELan EPfP EPla LRHS MBlu MSwo NWea SCob SEND SPer WMou
platyphyllos	CAco CCVT CDul CHab CLnd CMCN CSBt CTho CTri ECrN EPfP LAst LBuc MMuc NWea SCob SCoo SEND SPer WMou
- 'Aurea'	CAco CDul CTho ECrN MBlu
- 'Corallina'	see *T. platyphyllos* 'Rubra'
- 'Erecta'	see *T. platyphyllos* 'Fastigiata'
§ - 'Fastigiata'	CDul
- 'Laciniata'	CAco CDul CMCN CTho MBlu
§ - 'Rubra' ♀H6	CAco CCVT CDoC CDul CLnd CTho IBoy LBuc MGos NWea SEWo
- 'Tortuosa'	MBlu WMou
§ ***tomentosa***	CDul CLnd CMCN MMuc NWea SCob SCoo WMou
- 'Brabant' ♀H6	CDul ELan EPfP
- 'Doornik' **new**	MBri
tuan	CMCN WPGP
× ***vulgaris***	see *T.* × *europaea*

Tilingia (*Apiaceae*)

ajanensis B&SWJ 11202	IMou WCru

Tillaea see *Crassula*

Tillandsia (*Bromeliaceae*)

sp.	XBlo
abdita	LAir
aeranthos	LAir SChr
- 'Major' **new**	LAir
albertiana	LAir
albida	LAir SPlb
araujei **new**	LAir
- 'Bronze' **new**	LAir
baileyi	LAir
balbisiana	LAir
bandensis	LAir
bartramii **new**	LAir
bergeri	LAir SPlb
brachycaulos	LAir
bulbosa	LAir
butzii	LAir
cacticola	SPlb
caliginosa	LAir
capillaris	LAir
capitata red-leaved **new**	LAir
caput-medusae	LAir
'Chantilly' **new**	LAir
chiapensis	LAir
concolor	LAir
- 'Cicatlan' **new**	LAir
cyanea ♀H1a	LAir
diaguitensis large **new**	LAir
- small **new**	LAir
duratii	LAir
dyeriana	LAir
edithae **new**	LAir
ehlersiana **new**	LAir
exserta **new**	LAir
fasciculata	LAir
- from Central America **new**	LAir
- var. ***fasciculata*** **new**	LAir
- 'Tropiflora' **new**	LAir
'Feather Duster' **new**	LAir
festucoides **new**	LAir
flabellata	LAir
× ***floridana*** **new**	LAir
fuchsii	SPlb
- f. ***gracilis*** **new**	LAir
funckiana	LAir
gardneri	LAir
glabrior **new**	LAir
'Heather's Blush' **new**	LAir
heteromorpha	LAir
hondurensis **new**	LAir
'Houston' **new**	LAir
'Humbug' **new**	LAir
intermedia **new**	LAir
ionantha	LAir
- from Honduras **new**	LAir
- from Mexico **new**	LAir
* - 'Fuego' **new**	LAir
- var. ***ionantha*** 'Druid' **new**	LAir
- var. ***maxima*** 'Huamelula'	see *T. ionantha* var. *stricta*
- 'Rubra'	LAir
§ - var. ***stricta***	LAir
- var. ***vanhyningii*** **new**	LAir
ixioides	LAir
'Jackie Loinaz' **new**	LAir
juncea	LAir
'Kashkin' **new**	LAir
kirchhoffiana **new**	LAir
latifolia	LAir
var. ***divaricata*** **new**	
- - soft-leaved **new**	LAir
leiboldiana 'Mora'PBR **new**	LAir
leonamiana **new**	LAir
loliacea **new**	LAir
lorentziana **new**	LAir
magnusiana	LAir
mallemontii **new**	LAir
melanocrater	LAir
tricolor **new**	
myosura **new**	LAir
'Mystic Albert' **new**	LAir
neglecta	LAir
oaxacana	LAir
oerstediana **new**	LAir
'Oeseriana' **new**	LAir

paleacea new	LAir
– 'Canta' new	LAir
'Perfectly Peachy' new	LAir
plagiotropica new	LAir
pruinosa new	LAir SPlb
pseudobaileyi new	LAir
punctulata	LAir
recurvata new	LAir
reichenbachii new	LAir
'Samantha' new	LAir
schiedeana new	LAir
– 'Major' new	LAir XTur
'Sparkler' new	LAir
streptocarpa new	LAir XTur
streptophylla	LAir
stricta	LAir
– var. ***albifolia*** new	LAir
– green-leaved new	LAir
– 'Hard Leaf' new	LAir
sucrei new	LAir
'Sweet Isabel' new	LAir
tectorum	LAir
tenuifolia 'Amethyst' new	LAir
– 'Blue Flower' new	LAir
– 'Rubra' new	LAir
– var. ***saxicola*** new	LAir
tricholepis new	LAir
tricolor new	LAir
– var. ***melanocrater***	LAir
usneoides	LAir
utriculata new	LAir
– subsp. ***pringlei*** new	LAir
variabilis new	LAir
velutina new	LAir
vernicosa new	LAir
'Veronica's Mariposa' new	LAir
'Victoria' new	LAir
'White Star' new	LAir
xerographica	LAir SPlb

Tinantia (*Commelinaceae*)

pringlei	GEdr LEdu MNrw MPie SBrt SDys WPGP
– AIM 77	EBee MAvo WCot
– variegated (v)	WCot

Tinnea (*Lamiaceae*)

barbata	GFai

Titanopsis (*Aizoaceae*)

calcarea ♀H2	CCCN EPfP

Titanotrichum (*Gesneriaceae*)

oldhamii new	GEdr

Tithonia (*Asteraceae*)

rotundifolia	CSpe
– 'Torch'	CSpe SMrm

Tofieldia (*Tofieldiaceae*)

coccinea	CTal GCal GEdr NRya WCru

Tolmiea (*Saxifragaceae*)

menziesii	CBod CMac EWld MCot XLum
– 'Goldsplash'	see *T. menziesii* 'Taff's Gold'
– 'Maculata'	see *T. menziesii* 'Taff's Gold'
§ – 'Taff's Gold' (v)	EHoe GMaP LRHS NBid SHil SPlb WPtf XLum
– 'Variegata'	see *T. menziesii* 'Taff's Gold'

Tolpis (*Asteraceae*)

barbata	IMou

Toona (*Meliaceae*)

§ ***sinensis***	CAco CArn CBcs CDul CTho EBee ELan EPfP LEdu SEND WPGP
– 'Flamingo' (v)	CBcs CTho EBee EPfP EPla ESwi ETwe EUJe GKin IVic LEdu LRHS MAsh MGos NLar SChF SHil SPoG SWvt WCot

Torenia (*Linderniaceae*)

'Lovely White'	LAst
(Moon Series) Blue Moon = 'Dantmoon'	LAst
– Purple Moon = 'Dantopur'PBR	LAst LSou
– Rose Moon = 'Dantoromoon'	LAst
– Yellow Moon = 'Danmoon20'PBR	LAst
Summer Wave Series	CCCN SCoo

Torilis (*Apiaceae*)

japonica	CBre

Townsendia (*Asteraceae*)

§ ***alpigena*** var. ***alpigena***	CPBP
condensata	WAbe
formosa	ECho
glabella	CPBP
hookeri	CPBP
incana	WAbe
leptotes	CPBP
montana	see *T. alpigena* var. *alpigena*
nuttallii	CPBP
spathulata	CPBP

Toxicodendron see *Rhus*

Trachelium (*Campanulaceae*)

§ ***asperuloides***	EPot WAbe
caeruleum 'Black Knight'	CSpe
lanceolatum	WCot

Trachelospermum ✿ (*Apocynaceae*)

from Nanjing, China	EShb
§ ***asiaticum*** ♀H4	Widely available
– B&SWJ 4814	WCru
– 'Golden Memories'	CExl CSPN CWGN EBee ELan ELon EPfP LRHS LSqu NLar SKHP SLon SPoG SSpi SSta SWvt WCot WPat
– 'Goshiki' (v)	EShb WPat
– var. ***intermedium***	WPGP
* – 'Kiejiu Chirimen'	SKHP
– 'Kulu Chirimen'	WCot
– 'Nagaba' (v)	SKHP
– 'Ōgon-nishiki' (v)	LRHS MPkF SKHP SPoG
– 'Pink Showers'	SKHP
– 'Shirofu Chirimen' (v)	SKHP
– 'Summer Sunset'	EPfP LRHS MPkF WCot
– 'Theta'	SKHP WCot WPGP WPat
'Chameleon'	SKHP
jasminoides ♀H4	Widely available
– B&SWJ 5117	WCru

§	- 'Japonicum'	CRHN CSPN LRHS NPri SLon SPer SPoG WBor WSHC
	- 'Major'	CMac CSPN EBee ELan MAsh
*	- 'Oblanceolatum'	GCal
	- 'Star of Toscana'	EPfP LRHS
	- 'Tricolor' (v)	LRHS NSoo SEle SGol SLim SWvt WCot
	- 'Variegatum' (v) ♀H4	Widely available
	- 'Waterwheel'	EBee ELan ELon GCal LRHS NLar SKHP SWvt WPGP WSHC
	- 'Wilsonii'	CDul CExl CMac CSPN ELan ELon EPfP EUJe LRHS MRav NLar SAdn SEND SKHP SLim SPer SPoG SWvt WCot WCru WHar WPGP WPat
	majus misapplied	see *T. jasminoides* 'Japonicum'
	majus Nakai	see *T. asiaticum*

Trachycarpus ✿ (*Arecaceae*)

	from Manipur	CPHo
§	***fortunei*** ♀H5	Widely available
	fortunei × ***wagnerianus***	LPal
	geminisectus **new**	LPal NLos
	latisectus	NLos SBig
	martianus	LPal SBig
	'Naggy' **new**	LPal
	oreophilus	NLos
	princeps	CBrP LPal
	takil Becc.	LPal
	wagnerianus	CBrP CCCN CDTJ CExl CPHo EPfP EUJe LPal NLos NPla SArc SBig SChr WPGP

Trachymene (*Apiaceae*)

coerulea	CSpe

Trachyspermum (*Apiaceae*)

ammi	CArn

Trachystemon (*Boraginaceae*)

orientalis	CBre CExl CHEx CMac CUse ECha ELan EPfP EPla EWTr IKil LEdu MAvo MCot MMuc MRav NBid NLar NWad SBig SEND SKHP WBrk WCot WCru WHer WMoo WOut XLum

Tradescantia (*Commelinaceae*)

	albiflora	see *T. fluminensis*
	× ***andersoniana*** W. Ludwig & Rohw. nom. inval.	see *T.* Andersoniana Group
§	Andersoniana Group	WWtn
	- 'Angelic Charm' (Charm Series)	CWGN ECtt SHeu
	- 'Baby Doll'	XLum
	- 'Bilberry Ice'	CBod CMac CPrp CWCL ECtt EPfP EPla GJos GMaP IKil LBMP LRHS MBel MWat MWhi NBir NBro NGdn NLar SBod SCob SGSe SGbt SMrm SPoG SWvt WMnd WWEG WWtn XLum
	- 'Blanca'	WWEG
	- 'Blue and Gold'	CBcs EBee ECtt ELon EPfP LAst LRHS MHol MRav NSti SGSe WCot WFar WWEG
	- 'Blue Stone'	CCse CMea CSBt ECha ECtt IKil MAvo MRav SPad SRkn SRms WHoo WWEG XLum
	- 'Bridal Veil'	CHll
	- 'Caerulea Plena'	see *T. virginiana* 'Caerulea Plena'
	- Carmine Glow	see *T.* (Andersoniana Group) 'Karminglut'
	- 'Charlotte'	ECha ECtt ELan LRHS NBro NGdn NLar SMrm WMnd WWEG WWtn XLum
	- 'Chedglow'	WWEG
	- 'Concord Grape'	Widely available
	- 'Danielle'	EPfP
	- 'Domaine de Courson'	ECtt IKil XLum
	- 'Good Luck'PBR **new**	MAsh
	- 'In the Navy'	NLar
	- 'Innocence'	CAby CMHG CSBt CTri ECha ECtt ELan EPfP EPla GCra GJos GMaP IBoy LRHS MBel MMuc NBir NCGa NGdn NSti SCob SEND SPer SWvt XLum
	- 'Iris Prichard'	EBee ELan GCra GLog GMaP NCGa NLar
	- 'Isis'	CAby CPrp CTri EBee ECtt ELan EPfP GCra LBMP LRHS MMuc MNFA MRav NBir NCGa NGdn NOrc SBod SEND SPer SWvt WKif WMnd WWtn
	- 'J.C. Weguelin'	EPfP LPot NBir NSoo SRms WCAu WMnd WWEG XLum
§	- 'Karminglut'	EBee ECtt ELan EPfP GLog GMaP IBoy NBir NGdn SGSe WHoo WWEG XLum
	- 'Leonora'	MMuc MWat NLar SCob SEND XLum
	- 'Little Doll'	CWCL ECtt EPfP GLog LAst LRHS NBro NLar WWEG XLum
	- 'Little White Doll'	CPrp ECtt EPfP LAst NLar WWEG
	- 'Mac's Double' (d)	EBee IKil
	- 'Mariella'	EBee
	- 'Melissa'	XLum
	- 'Merlot Clusters' **new**	LSun
	- 'Mrs Loewer'	MAvo
	- 'Osprey'	Widely available
	- 'Pauline'	ECtt ELon EPla LSun MRav NBir NLar WHoo WWEG XLum
	- 'Perinne's Pink'	CWCL ECtt EPfP LRHS NSti SPoG WCAu
	- 'Pink Chablis'	CWCL ECtt EPfP IKil MNFA NBro NLar
	- 'Purewell Giant'	CMac CTri GLog LRHS NBro NLar SPer SWvt WKif WMnd
	- 'Purple Dome'	CMos ECtt EPfP EPla GMaP LAst LRHS MAvo MMuc MRav NBir NBro NGdn SEND SPoG WMnd
	- 'Red Grape'	ECtt EWll LPot LRHS MWhi NEoE NSti SCob WWEG
	- 'Regal Charm' (Charm Series)	SHeu
	- 'Rosi'	EBee
	- 'Rubra'	CPrp NOrc SCob SRms XLum
	- 'Satin Doll'PBR	CBcs ECtt EPfP
	- 'Snowbank'	EBee
	- 'Sunshine Charm'PBR (Charm Series)	CWCL NLar SHeu WHil
	- 'Sweet Kate'	CMac CWCL ECtt LBMP LRHS MBNS NBro NLar SGbt SHil SPoG SRGP XLum
	- 'Sylvana'	EBee
	- 'Valour'	CSBt EBee EPfP LRHS
	- 'Zwanenburg Blue'	ECha ECtt ELan GLog LAst LPal LRHS MLHP NLar SGSe SPlb SPoG WMnd WWEG XLum
	'Angel Eyes'	ECtt

	'Blushing Bride' (v)	MPkF
	canaliculata	see *T. ohiensis*
	crassifolia	CFil
	- F&M 258	WPGP
§	***fluminensis***	SChr
§	- 'Aurea' ♡H1c	SChr
	- 'Maiden's Blush' (v)	CSpe EShb SPlb SRms SVen
	- 'Quicksilver' (v) ♡H1c	EShb
	- 'Variegata'	see *T. fluminensis* 'Aurea'
	'Lucky Charm'	NLar SHeu
§	***ohiensis***	MAvo
	pallida 'Kartuz Giant'	CSpe EShb WCot
	- 'Pale Puma' **new**	EShb
§	- 'Purpurea' ♡H1c	EOHP EShb
	pendula	see *T. zebrina*
	'Purple Sabre'	CBcs EUJe LAst SMrm SPlb
	purpurea	see *T. pallida* 'Purpurea'
	sillamontana ♡H1c	EShb
	spathacea	EShb
	- 'Versicolor' **new**	EShb
	tricolor	see *T. zebrina*
	virginiana	LPot MWhi
	- 'Alba'	CMac GCal
*	- 'Brevicaulis'	EBee ECha ECtt NBro WWEG
§	- 'Caerulea Plena' (d)	ELan EPfP LRHS MRav SPer SRms WWEG
	- 'Rubra'	SPlb
§	***zebrina*** ♡H1c	EShb
	- pendula	see *T. zebrina*
	- 'Purpusii' ♡H1c	SRms

Tragopogon (*Asteraceae*)

crocifolius	CSpe MSCN SPhx
porrifolius	CFis GCal MCot SVic WCot
pratensis	CArn CWld NMir

Trapa (*Lythraceae*)

natans	CBAq

Trautvetteria (*Ranunculaceae*)

carolinensis	IMou WSHC
- var. ***japonica***	CLAP GEdr WCru
- - B&SWJ 10861	WCru
- var. ***occidentalis***	EBee LEdu WCru

Triadica (*Euphorbiaceae*)

sebifera	LEdu WCru
- CWJ 12819 **new**	WCru

Trichodiadema (*Aizoaceae*)

intonsum	SPlb

Trichopetalum (*Asparagaceae*)

§	***plumosum***	CBro

Trichostema (*Lamiaceae*)

'Blue Bonnets' **new**	MMuc SEND
dichotomum RCB RL 15	WCot

Tricuspidaria see *Crinodendron*

Tricyrtis (*Liliaceae*)

	B&SWJ 3229 from Taiwan	WCru
	'Abdane' **new**	SGSe
	'Adbane'	CChe CHel CLAP ELan EPPr EWes GBuc GKev LRHS SMrm WGwG
	affinis B&SWJ 2804	CLAP WCru
	- B&SWJ 5645	WCru
	- B&SWJ 6182	WCru
	- B&SWJ 11169	WCru
	- B&SWJ 11442	WCru
	- 'Early Bird'	WCru
	'Amanagowa'	CLAP
	bakeri	see *T. latifolia*
	'Blue Wonder'	CBod EBee IBal LRHS SPer
	dilatata	see *T. macropoda*
	'Empress'	CBct CExl CHel ECha ELon EPfP EThi EWes GBuc IBal LAst LEdu LRHS LSou NEgg NSoo NWad SGSe SMrm SRkn SRot WHil WWEG
	flava	EBee LRHS WCru
	formosana	CAby CAvo CTri ECha ECho ELan EPfP EWoo GKev GLog GMaP IBoy LEdu LPal LPot LRHS MCot MMuc MNrw SDys SRms SRot WKif
	- B&SWJ 355	WCru
	- B&SWJ 3073	WCru
	- B&SWJ 3616	CExl WCru
	- B&SWJ 3635	CLAP
	- B&SWJ 3712	WCru
	- B&SWJ 6741	WCru
	- B&SWJ 6970	WCru
	- RWJ 10109	WCru
	- 'Autumn Glow' (v)	GEdr
	- 'Dark Beauty'	CDes CExl CLAP CWCL ECtt ELan GBuc MNrw MWat SCob SMrm WCAu WPGP
	- dark-flowered	CHel NCGa
	- 'Daruma' **new**	GEdr
	- 'Emperor' (v)	ESwi
	- 'Gilt Edge' (v)	CBct CBod CExl CWCL ECtt ELan ELon EPfP EPot EThi GBuc IBal LRHS LSou MBNS NBro NEgg NLar NSoo NSti NWad SGSe SMrm SWvt WHil WWEG
	- f. ***glandosa*** B&SWJ 7084	WCru
	- aff. f. ***glandosa*** 'Blu-Shing Toad'	WCru
	- var. ***grandiflora*** 'W-Ho-ping Toad'	WCru
	- 'Kestrel' (v)	WCot
	- pale-flowered	EThi
	- 'Purple Beauty'	GKev IGor LSou MNrw MPie MPkF
	- 'Samurai' (v)	CHel CWCL EWes
	- 'Seiryu'	IGor
	- 'Shelley's'	CLAP NBro WWEG
	- 'Small Wonder'	CLAP MNrw WCru
	- 'Spotted Toad'	LEdu MAvo WCru
§	- Stolonifera Group	CBcs CMac ELan EPfP EPla LEdu LRHS MCot MWat NWad SDix SHar
	- - B&SWJ 7046	WCru
	- 'Taiwan Toad'	CExl
	- 'Taroko Toad'	CLAP WCru
	- 'Tiny Toad'	MAvo WCru
	- 'Variegata' (v)	CHel LEdu NBir WCru
	- 'Velvet Toad'	WCru
	'Golden Leopard'	EBee LSou
	'Harlequin'	LEdu WWEG
	'Hiki-yuri' **new**	EWTr
§	***hirta***	CBcs CHel CHid CMac CPrp CTri CTsd ECho EPla GAbr IBoy ITim LRHS LSun MCot NBro NHol SEND SGSe SGbt SPlb SWvt WWEG
	- B&SWJ 5971	WCru
	- B&SWJ 11182	WCru
	- B&SWJ 11227	WCru

	- 'Alba'	CMac SGSe
	- 'Albomarginata' (v)	CMac CPrp EAEE EPPr GCra LLWG LRHS NEgg NLar NSti SGSe SWvt
	- 'Golden Gleam'	WCot
	- var. ***masamunei***	WCru
	- 'Matsukaze'	CExl CLAP EWes
	- 'Miyazaki'	CCon CLAP CMac ECha ECtt EPfP GBuc IFoB IGor LRHS MHer MNrw MPkF WCAu XLum
	- 'Taiwan Atrianne'	CHel ECtt ELan EPla MNrw NBro NEgg NWad SGbt WCAu
	- 'Variegata' (v)	CTri ELon EWes GCra GKev WCot WWEG
	Hototogisu	CBro CExl CHel CLAP EAEE ECha ECtt ELan LRHS MWat NBir NHol NLar WWEG
	ishiiana	CLAP CTal MMoz WCot WCru WSHC
	- var. ***surugensis***	LEdu WCru
	japonica	see *T. hirta*
	'Kohaku'	CLAP EBee ELan WWEG
	lasiocarpa	LEdu MAvo XLum
	- B&SWJ 3635	CExl WCru
	- B&SWJ 6861	WCru
	- B&SWJ 7013	WCru
	- B&SWJ 7103	WCru
	- 'Royal Toad'	WCru
§	***latifolia***	CHel ELan GLog GMaP LEdu SGSe WCru WWEG
	- 'Saffron'	WCru
	- 'Yellow Sunrise'	ECtt EPPr MCot NSti
	'Lemon Lime' (v)	NEoE SGSe WWEG
	'Lightning Strike' (v)	CHel EBee ECha ECtt EWes LEdu WCot
	'Lilac Towers'	WCru
	macrantha	GAbr GLog WCru WSHC
§	- subsp. ***macranthopsis***	CBct CExl CLAP GBuc WCot WCru
	- - 'Juro' (d)	WCru
	macranthopsis	see *T. macrantha* subsp. *macranthopsis*
*	***macrocarpa***	XLum
	macropoda	ELan GLog LEdu LRHS MAvo SGSe WCAu
	- B&SWJ 1271 from Korea	WCru
	- B&SWJ 5013	WCru
	- B&SWJ 5556	WCru
	- B&SWJ 5847 from Japan	WCru
	- B&SWJ 6209	WCru
	- B&SWJ 8700	WCru
	- B&SWJ 8829 from Korea	WCru
	- from Yungi Temple, China	CLAP EPPr NCGa
	- 'Tricolor'	WCot
	maculata HWJCM 470	WCru
	- HWJK 2010	WCru
	- HWJK 2411	WCru
	- PAB 3188	LEdu
	'Mine-no-yuki'	GEdr
	'Momoyama' **new**	GEdr
	'Moonlight Treasure'[PBR]	CExl CLAP EBee IBoy NHol WCot
	nana	WCru
	- B&SWJ 11399	WCru
	ohsumiensis	CAby CLAP ECha GBuc WCru
	perfoliata	CLAP LEdu WCru
	- 'Spring Shine' (v)	WCru
	pilosa	EBee LEdu
	Pink Freckles = 'Innotripf'[PBR]	CBct CHel CMos ELon ESwi EThi LSou MPnt NPri SPoG SRot SWvt WHil
	'Raspberry Mousse'	CLAP CWCL EPfP IFoB MBNS NSti SMrm
	ravenii B&SWJ 3229	WCru
	- RWJ 10012 **new**	WCru
	setouchiensis	WCru
	'Shimone'	CExl CHid CLAP EBee ECha SGSe
	'Sinonome'	EBee IPot MAvo MPkF
	stolonifera	see *T. formosana* Stolonifera Group
	suzukii RWJ 10111	WCru
	'Taipei Silk'[PBR]	CMos ESwi IFoB LSou LSun NCGa NPri NSti
	'Tojen'	CCon EAEE ECha ECtt ELon EPPr EPfP EThi EWTr EWes IBal IGor LEdu LRHS MNrw NBid NBir SPer WCAu WWEG
	'Variegata' (*affinis* hybrid) (v)	WWEG
	'Washfields'	EBee
	'White Towers'	CBro CCon CExl CHid CLAP CWCL EBee ECha EPPr EWoo GBuc IFoB LRHS MBel MRav NEgg NLar NSti SRms XLum

Trifolium (*Papilionaceae*)

	angustifolium	CArn
	dubium	SPre
	incarnatum	CSpe MHer
	nanum	CPBP LLHF
	ochroleucon	EAJP ECha EPPr GMaP LEdu MAvo MCot MNFA MPie NSti SBch SGSe SHar SMHy SMad SPhx WAul WMoo WWEG
	pannonicum	CMea GCal MNrw WOut WWFP
	pratense	CHab MHer NMir WSFF
	- 'Dolly North'	see *T. pratense* 'Susan Smith'
	- 'Ice Cool'	see *T. repens* 'Green Ice'
§	- 'Susan Smith' (v)	CCCN LEdu WHer
	repens	SVic WSFF
	- 'Debbie' **new**	LEdu
	- 'Dragon's Blood'	CMea LEdu LLWG MHol MMuc MPie NSla SEND SPer WPGP
	- 'Gold Net'	see *T. pratense* 'Susan Smith'
§	- 'Green Ice'	CBod EBee LLWG LRHS NSti SBod WHal
	- 'Harlequin' (v)	MHer WCot WMoo WOut
	- 'Hullavington'	CNat
	- 'Isabella' **new**	LEdu
	- 'Josephine' **new**	LEdu
	- 'Purpurascens'	CArn CBre LLWG LRHS MBNS MHer MPie NSla NSti SPoG
§	- 'Purpurascens Quadrifolium'	CBod CMea ECha EHoe EPau EWes GAbr MCot NMir NPer SPer SPlb WHer WRHF
	- 'Quadrifolium'	WWFP
	- 'Tetraphyllum Purpureum'	see *T. repens* 'Purpurascens Quadrifolium'
	- 'Wheatfen'	CNat NDov NPer
	- 'William'	CBre ECGP LEdu MMuc NDov SEND WCot WOut
	rubens	CAby CArn CBod CMea CWCL EAJP ELan EPPr EShb GCal LEdu LRHS MAvo MBel MHer MHol MMHG MMuc MNFA MNHC MNrw NChi SPer SPhx SPlb WAul WCAu WMoo WSHC
	- 'Drama'	ELon MNrw
	- 'Peach Pink'	CSpe ELon EPPr MBel MMHG SPhx WCot

	- 'Red Feathers'	CWCL ELon EPPr EWes LSun MCot SGSe SMad SMrm WWEG
	'Spring' new	LEdu
	trichocephalum	EPPr

Trigonella (*Papilionaceae*)

	foenum-graecum	CArn

Trillidium see *Trillium*

Trillium ✿ (*Melanthiaceae*)

	albidum ♈H5	ECho GBin GBuc GEdr GKev LAma LLHF LRHS MNrw SKHP SSpi WBor
	angustipetalum	EPot GEdr
	apetalon	GEdr
	camschatcense	CExl GEdr LAma
§	***catesbyi***	CCon CExl CWCL ECho GEdr GKev LAma LLHF MNrw NWad
	cernuum	ECho GCra LAma WSHC
	chloropetalum	CBro GBin GBuc GEdr LRHS NWad SChF SSpi
	- var. ***chloropetalum***	GBuc
	- var. ***chloropetalum*** × ***parviflorum***	SKHP
§	- var. ***giganteum*** ♈H5	CExl GBuc SPhx WCru
	- pink-flowered	GEdr
	- var. ***rubrum***	see *T. chloropetalum* var. *giganteum*
	cuneatum	CArn CBcs CBct CBro CExl CHel CWCL ECho EPot GAbr GBuc GEdr GMaP LAma LEdu LRHS MNrw NBir NHol NWad SDeJ SKHP SSpi WPnP
	- 'Ghost'	SKHP
	- 'Moonshine'	SKHP
	decipiens	GEdr
	decumbens	GEdr SKHP
	discolor	GEdr
	erectum ♈H5	CArn CBcs CBro CExl CHel CWCL EBee ECho EPot GAbr GBBs GBuc GEdr GKev GMaP GPoy LAma LRHS MAvo MMoz MNrw NBid NBir NHol NWad SDeJ SKHP SRot SSpi WCot
	- f. ***albiflorum***	CCon ECha ECho GBuc MMoz MNrw NWad SKHP SSpi
	- 'Beige'	GKev
	- f. ***luteum***	GEdr SKHP
	- red-flowered	ECho GKev
	erectum × ***flexipes***	EBee ECho GBuc MNrw NBir SKHP SSpi
	flexipes	CBct CWCL ECho GAbr GEdr GKev LAma LRHS MNrw NHol NWad SKHP SSpi
I	- 'Harvington Selection'	EBee LRHS SKHP
	foetidissimum	GEdr SKHP
	govanianum	GEdr LAma
	gracile	GEdr
	grandiflorum ♈H5	Widely available
	- 'Beige' new	CBct
	- dwarf	GEdr
	- Gothenburg pink new	GEdr
	- 'Kath's Dwarf'	GEdr
	- f. ***polymerum*** 'Flore Pleno' (d)	CWCL EBee GEdr LLHF SKHP
	- - 'Snowbunting' (d)	CWCL EWes GKev LAma LRHS MMHG NHar WThu
	- 'Quicksilver'	SKHP
	- f. ***roseum***	EBee GEdr
	- white-flowered	MAvo
	kurabayashii	CExl CPne EBee ECho ELan EPot EWld GBin GBuc GEdr GKev LRHS MNrw SKHP SSpi WBor WCru WPGP
	lancifolium	GEdr
	ludovicianum	GEdr
	luteum ♈H5	CBcs CBro CCon CExl EBee ECho EPfP EPot GAbr GBuc GEdr GKev GMaP IGor LAma LRHS MAvo MNrw NBid NHar NHol NWad SDeJ SKHP SSpi WCru WPnP
	maculatum	GEdr
	nivale	CBct GEdr NHar
	ovatum	SSpi
	- f. ***hibbersonii***	GBuc GCra
	- 'Roy Elliott'	CExl MNrw
	parviflorum	GEdr MNrw SKHP
	pusillum	CExl CWCL ECho EPot GEdr GKev LAma LLHF MAvo MNrw NHol
*	- var. ***alabamicum***	SKHP
I	- var. ***georgianum***	SKHP
	recurvatum	CBcs CCon CWCL EBee ECho EPot GEdr GKev LAma LEdu NHol NWad SKHP WPnP
	reliquum	GEdr
	rivale ♈H4	CExl ECho GBuc GEdr GKev
	- Purple Heart Group	GEdr
	rugelii	EBee ECho EWes GEdr LAma MNrw SKHP SSpi
	- Askival hybrids	ECho GBuc MNrw SKHP SSpi
	- 'Orchard Pink'	MNrw
	rugelii × ***vaseyi***	EBee EWes MNrw SKHP SSpi
	sessile	CExl CWCL ECho GBuc GEdr GKev IGor LAma LRHS MAvo NBir NWad SDeJ SKHP SMrm WCot WKif WSHC WShi
	- 'Rubrum'	see *T. chloropetalum* var. *giganteum*
	simile	EBee ECho GEdr LLHF LRHS MNrw SKHP SSpi
	smallii	GEdr
	stamineum	GEdr LAma
	stylosum	see *T. catesbyi*
	sulcatum	CExl CWCL EBee ECho GBuc GEdr GMaP LAma LRHS MNrw SKHP SSpi WCot
	- cream-flowered	GBBs
	taiwanense B&SWJ 3411	WCru
	texanum	SKHP
	tschonoskii	GEdr LAma
	underwoodii	GEdr
	undulatum	GEdr MNrw
	vaseyi	CWCL EBee ECho EWes GEdr GKev LAma LRHS MNrw SKHP SSpi
	- large-flowered new	SKHP
	viride	GBBs
	viridescens	GEdr LAma

Triosteum (*Caprifoliaceae*)

	erythrocarpum	EBee SMad
	himalayanum	GCal GKev WSHC
	- BWJ 7907	CLAP WCru
	pinnatifidum	CLAP CPom EBee GCal IMou WCru

Tripsacum (*Poaceae*)

	dactyloides	EPPr

Tripterospermum (*Gentianaceae*)

fasciculatum B&SWJ 7197 WCru
- B&SWJ 11297 WCru
japonicum GEdr LLHF
- B&SWJ 8920 WCru
- B&SWJ 10876 WCru
lanceolatum B&SWJ 085 WCru
- RWJ 9918 WCru

Tripterygium (*Celastraceae*)

doianum B&SWJ 11467 WCru
aff. ***doianum*** CWJ 12852 new WCru
regelii B&SWJ 5453 WCru
- B&SWJ 10921 WCru
- B&SWJ 8666 from Korea new WCru
wilfordii GCal LEdu
- BWJ 7852 from China WCru
- NJM 11.029 from China new WPGP
- WWJ 12009 WCru

Tristagma (*Alliaceae*)

nivale EBee

Triteleia (*Asparagaceae*)

'4U' CAvo CBro EBee ECho EPfP GKev WCot
bridgesii ECho
californica see *Brodiaea californica*
§ 'Corrina' CAvo CBro EBee ECho EPot GKev
'Crystal Pink' SDeJ
grandiflora ECho WCot
hyacinthina EBee ECho GKev WCot
ixioides ECho
- 'Splendens' CBro ECho
- 'Starlight' CAvo CBro CTri ECho EPfP EPot ERCP GKev SDeJ WHil
§ ***laxa*** ECho
- 'Allure' EBee ECho
- 'Dexter' CAbP
§ - 'Koningin Fabiola' CBro CSpe CTri EBee ECho EPot GKev LAma MLHP MNrw NBir SCob SDeJ SEND WCot WRHF
- Queen Fabiola see *T. laxa* 'Koningin Fabiola'
lilacina ECho
'Ocean Queen' CHid CMea EBee ERCP
§ ***peduncularis*** ECho WCot
'Royal Blue' ERCP
'Rudy' CAvo CBro CHid CMea CWCL EBee ECho ERCP GKev SCob SDeJ WCot
'Silver Queen' CBro CMea EBee ECho ERCP
× ***tubergenii*** ECho
uniflora see *Ipheion uniflorum*
'White Sweep' ECho
'www'PBR ECho

Trithrinax (*Arecaceae*)

brasiliensis LPal SBig
campestris CBrP LPal SBig

Tritoma see *Kniphofia*

Tritonia (*Iridaceae*)

crocata ♀H2 ECho
- 'Baby Doll' EBee LEdu WHil WSHC
- 'Bridal Veil' EBee
- 'Pink Sensation' CDes CSpe EBee ECho WHil
- 'Plymouth Pastel' CDes
- 'Prince of Orange' CDes EBee
- 'Princess Beatrix' CDes
- 'Riversdale' ECho
- 'Serendipity' CDes EBee EPri
- 'Tangerine' CDes EBee
deusta CDes EPri
§ ***disticha*** Widely available
subsp. ***rubrolucens***
- - short, red-pink-flowered CDes
- - tall, clear pink-flowered CDes CTca WPGP
flabellifolia ECho
florentiae 'Tanqua Karoo' ECho
karooica 'Middlepos' ECho
laxifolia CDes CTca ECho EPot GKev LEdu NRog
lineata CDes CTca EBee ECho EPri LEdu WPGP
- 'Parvifolia' EBee GKev
pallida ECho SPlb
rosea see *T. disticha* subsp. *rubrolucens*
securigera CDes ECho LEdu
squalida ECho EPri

Trochocarpa (*Ericaceae*)

clarkei WThu
gunnii WThu
thymifolia WThu
- white-flowered WThu

Trochodendron (*Trochodendraceae*)

aralioides Widely available
- B&SWJ 1651 from Taiwan WCru
- CWJ 12357 from Taiwan WCru
- RWJ 9845 from Taiwan WCru
- B&SWJ 6080 from Japan WCru

Trollius (*Ranunculaceae*)

ACE 1187 CExl
acaulis ECho EWes
altaicus LRHS
buddae CDes CWCL EBee EWes MRav
§ ***chinensis*** CHVG ECha GCal GKev NChi SWat
- 'Golden Queen' ♀H7 Widely available
- 'Imperial Orange' GBin
× ***cultorum*** CAby
- 'Alabaster' Widely available
- 'Baudirektor Linne' ECtt MRav NGdn
- 'Byrne's Giant' ECtt IKil
- 'Canary Bird' ELan GCal MJak NGdn SRms
- 'Cheddar' CWCL ECtt ELon EPPr EPfP GBin GCal GEdr GMaP IGor LRHS LSou MBNS MBel MBri MCot MMHG MRav MWts NBro NEoE NLar NOrc SKHP SPoG SWvt WBor WFar WWEG
- 'Earliest of All' CSam CWCL NGdn NLar SPer WWEG
- 'Etna' GBin SHar WWEG
§ - 'Feuertroll' ECha ECtt MRav NEoE NGdn NLar
- Fireglobe see *T.* × *cultorum* 'Feuertroll'
- 'Golden Cup' NBir NGdn
- 'Goldquelle' ♀H7 EBee GBuc
- 'Goliath' NLar
- 'Helios' CSam GBin GBuc LLHF

	- 'Lemon Queen'	CBod CMac COtt CWCL CWat ECtt EPfP GBin GKev GMaP LRHS MBri MNFA MRav NLar NSoo SCob SGol SMrm SPer SWat WCAu
	- 'New Moon'	CMos EBee EShb GAbr GBin GBuc IKil LRHS LSun MNFA NChi WSHC
	- 'Orange Crest'	EBee ECtt GCal MBri WWEG
	- 'Orange Globe'	GMaP
	- 'Orange Glow'	SMad
	- 'Orange Princess' ♀H7	COtt CWCL CWat EPfP IGor LRHS NBro NLar NSoo SPer SRms
	- 'Orange Queen'	SWvt
	- 'Prichard's Giant'	CDes CMHG ECtt ELan ELon NBro NGdn NSbr WCFE WWEG
§	- 'Superbus' ♀H7	CAby CCon CDes ELan ELon EPfP GMaP LRHS MSCN NGdn SPer WFar
	- 'T. Smith'	ECtt NBro
	- 'Taleggio'	LEdu
	europaeus	CAby CWCL ECha ELan EWoo GCal LAst LBMP LEdu LRHS LSun MLHP MRav MWat NGdn SBrt SPhx SRot SWat WCFE WHoo WWEG
	- SDR 6306	GKev
	- subsp. ***europaeus*** new	WFar
	- 'Lemon Supreme'	GKev LRHS
	- 'Superbus'	see *T.* × *cultorum* 'Superbus'
	hondoensis	LLHF NEoE NLar
	ircuticus	GKev
	laxus	EWes
	- 'Albiflorus'	CExl
	ledebourii misapplied	see *T. chinensis*
	pumilus	ECha ECho ELan EPfP GKev LRHS NLar NSla SGSe SPer WAbe
	- ACE 1818	CExl GCal MHer
	- 'Wargrave'	ECho
	vaginatus	EBee
	yunnanensis ♀H6	EBee GBin GKev LRHS
	- orange-flowered	CExl GKev

Tropaeolum ✿ (*Tropaeolaceae*)

	azureum	CCCN CExl CFil CPla
	beuthii ♀H2	ECho
	brachyceras	CCCN CPne EBee ECho GKev WCot
	ciliatum	CCCN CCon CFil CPla ECho GKev NBid WCot WCru WPGP
	hookerianum	CExl
	- subsp. ***austropurpureum***	CExl CFil
	- subsp. ***hookerianum***	CFil
	incisum	CCCN CWCL EBee ECho WCot
	lepidum	CPla
	majus	ENfk GPoy SVic
	- Alaska Series (v) ♀H3	CWCL ENfk MNHC NPri SIde WJek
	- 'Apricot Twist'	GBee
	- 'Crimson Beauty'	CSpe
§	- 'Darjeeling Double' (d) ♀H3	WCot
	- 'Darjeeling Gold'	see *T. majus* 'Darjeeling Double'
	- 'Empress of India'	MNHC WJek
	- 'Hermine Grashoff' (d)	CSpe GBee GCal NPer
	- Jewel of Africa Group (v)	CWCL
	- Jewel Series	ENfk
	- 'Margaret Long' (d)	CSpe GCal WCot
	- 'Peaches and Cream'	WJek
	- 'Red Wonder'	CCCN CSpe EPfP NPri
	- Tom Thumb mixed	MNHC WJek
	nubigenum* × *polyphyllum	CFil
	pentaphyllum	CExl CFil CPne CSpe EBee ECho GCal
	peregrinum	ECho
	polyphyllum ♀H3	CCCN CSpe CWCL EBee ECho EPot GBuc NBir SMHy WCot WPGP
	sessilifolium	CFil EBee ECho
	smithii	GCal
	speciosum ♀H5	Widely available
	tricolor ♀H2	CAvo CCCN CFil ECho GKev WBor XEll
	tuberosum	CEnd ECho GKev GPoy SDeJ WHer
	- var. ***lineamaculatum***	CBcs CBro CCCN CSpe EBee ECha
	'Ken Aslet' ♀H3	ECho ELan EPfP EPot GCra GKev LAma LEdu LRHS NLar SPer SPoG WCot

Tsuga ✿ (*Pinaceae*)

	canadensis	CAco CDul EPfP NWea
	- 'Abbott's Dwarf'	CDoC CKen MGos NHol
§	- 'Abbott's Pygmy'	CKen
	- 'Aurea' (v)	NLar
	- 'Bacon Cristate'	CKen
	- 'Betty Rose' (v)	CKen
	- 'Birkett's White'	CKen
	- 'Brandley'	CKen
§	- 'Branklyn'	CKen
	- 'Cappy's Choice'	CKen
	- 'Cinnamonea'	CKen
	- 'Coffin'	CKen
	- 'Cole's Prostrate' ♀H7	CKen MAsh NLar
	- 'Creamey' (v)	CKen
	- 'Curley'	CKen
	- 'Curtis Ideal'	CKen
	- 'Dr Hornbeck'	see *T. canadensis* 'Hornbeck'
	- 'Eisburg'	SLim
	- 'Essex'	CKen NWad
*	- 'Everitt's Dense Leaf'	CKen
	- 'Everitt's Golden'	CKen SLim
	- 'Fantana'	MAsh NHol NLar SLim
	- 'Gracilis'	WThu
	- 'Greenwood Lake'	WThu
	- 'Hedgehog'	CDoC NLar
§	- 'Hornbeck'	CKen
	- 'Horsford'	CKen NWad
	- 'Horstmann' No 1	CKen
	- 'Hussii'	CKen NHol
	- 'Jacqueline Verkade'	CKen MAsh NLar
	- 'Jeddeloh' ♀H7	CDoC CMac MAsh MGos NEgg NHol NLar SCob SGol SLim
	- 'Jervis'	CKen NHol NWad
	- 'Julianne'	CKen
	- 'Kingsville Spreader'	CKen
	- 'Little Joe'	CKen
	- 'Livingston' new	SLim
I	- 'Lutea'	CKen
	- 'Many Cones'	CKen
	- 'Minima'	CKen
	- 'Minuta' ♀H7	CDoC CKen MGos NHol NWad
	- 'Moon Frost'	MAsh SLim
	- 'Palomino'	CKen
	- 'Pendula' ♀H7	CAco CKen MAsh MBri SLim
	- 'Pincushion'	CKen
	- 'Prostrata'	see *T. canadensis* 'Branklyn'
	- 'Pygmaea'	see *T. canadensis* 'Abbott's Pygmy'
	- 'Rugg's Washington Dwarf'	CKen

	- 'Snowflake'	CKen
	- 'Stewart's Gem'	CKen
	- 'Verkade Petite'	CKen
	- 'Verkade Recurved'	CKen NLar
	- 'Vermeulen's Wintergold'	NLar
	- 'Von Helms' Dwarf'	CKen
	- 'Warnham'	CKen MAsh
	caroliniana 'La Bar Weeping'	CKen NLar
	- 'Planting Fields Broom'	CKen
	chinensis	CKen
	diversifolia 'Gotelli'	CKen
	dumosa	CKen
	heterophylla ♀H6	CAco CBcs CCVT CDul EPfP LBuc NWea SCob SEWo SGol SMad
	- 'Iron Springs'	CKen
	- 'Laursen's Column'	CKen
	- 'Ray Godfrey' **new**	NLar
	- 'Thorsens Weeping'	CKen
	menziesii	see *Pseudotsuga menziesii*
	mertensiana 'Blue Star'	CKen MAsh NLar
	- 'Elizabeth'	CKen
	- 'Glauca'	CKen
I	- 'Glauca Nana'	CKen
I	- 'Horstmann'	CKen
	- 'Quartz Mountain'	CKen
	sieboldii 'Baldwin'	CKen
	- 'Green Ball'	CKen NLar
	- 'Honeywell Estate'	CKen
	- 'Nana'	CKen

Tuberaria (*Cistaceae*)

lignosa	WAbe

Tulbaghia ✿ (*Alliaceae*)

	acutiloba	CTca EBee GKev LEdu MHom NHoy
	'African Moon'	NHoy
	alliacea	ECho EPri GKev LEdu NHoy WCot
	alliacea × violacea	ECho
*	***allioides***	CBro
	'Bob Brown'	CDes LEdu WPGP
	'Bright Eyes'	NHoy
	capensis	CDes CPou LEdu NBir NHoy
	'Cariad'	LEdu
	cernua CD&R 199	CDes EBee
	- hybrid	EPri NHoy
§	***coddii***	CPne LEdu MHom NHoy
	coddii × violacea	NHoy
	cominsii	CExl ECho EPri LEdu SBch
	- 'Harry Hay's Pink'	NHoy
	cominsii × violacea	CAvo CExl CTca MHom NHoy
	'Cosmic'	CDes CPou EPPr EPri LEdu NHoy WPGP
	'Crystal'	NHoy
	'Dreaming Spires'	NHoy
	dregeana	NHoy
	'Elaine Ann'	NHoy
	'Enigma'	NHoy
	'Fairy Snow'	CDes
	'Fairy Star'	CDes CTca EPri LEdu NHoy WCot
	fragrans	see *T. simmleri*
	- 'Alba'	ECho ELan EPot GKev NLar SDeJ
	galpinii	GKev NHoy
	'Grey Dawn'	NHoy
	'Hazel'	CDes CPou LEdu MHer NHoy WPGP
	'Janet'	NHoy
	'John May's Special'	CDes CKno EShb LEdu MHom NHoy SMrm WCot WHoo WPGP
	leucantha ♀H2	CDes CTca ECho EPri GKev LEdu MHom NHoy NWad
	- H&B 11996	CDes LEdu
	ludwigiana	CPne
	maritima	see *T. violacea* var. *maritima*
	Marwood seedling	ECho LEdu MHer MHom MTPN NHoy
	montana	EBee GKev LEdu MHer MPie NHoy
	'Moshoeshoe' **new**	LEdu
	natalensis ♀H2	CBro CPou CPrp ECho GKev NHoy
	- B&V 421	EPri
	- Burtt 6949 **new**	CPne
	- CD&R 84	NHoy
	- pink-flowered	CTca ECho MHom NHoy
	- - B&V 421	CDes LEdu NHoy
	- white-flowered	CTca
	- - B&V 421	NHoy
	natalensis × violacea	NHoy
	poetica	see *T. coddii*
	'Premier'	NHoy
	'Purple Eye' ♀H2	CBro CDes CHel CKno CPne CSpe EBee EWoo GBin LEdu NHoy NSti WCot
	'Rainbow'	NHoy
§	***simmleri*** ♀H2	CPou EBee ECho EPot EPri EWes GKev LAma LEdu NHoy NLar SDeJ
	- 'Cheryl Renshaw'	WCot
	- pink-flowered	CTca
	- 'Snow Queen'	CPrp
	- white-flowered	CPou CPrp CTca ECho NHoy
	'Snow White' **new**	WCot
	'Snowball'	NHoy
	'Suzanne'	NHoy
	verdoorniae	LEdu NHoy
	violacea ♀H2	CAvo CBcs CBro CKno CMHG CPou CPrp CSpe CTca ECha ECho EPot EPri ERCP EWoo GKev LAma LEdu LRHS MHom MSCN NHoy SEND SMrm SWat WHoo WPGP XLum XSen
	- from RBGE	MHom NHoy
*	- 'Alba'	CKno EBee ECho EPri EWoo GCal GKev MHer NHoy SWat WKif
	- 'Dissect White'	NHoy
I	- 'Fine Form'	CKno NHoy WKif
*	- ***grandiflora***	CAvo
	- 'John Rider'	EPri NHoy
*	- var. ***maritima***	CPne EShb GKev LEdu MHom NHoy SMrm WCot
	- var. ***obtusa***	NHoy
	- 'Pallida'	CAvo CBro CCse CDes CPou CTca ECho LEdu NHoy WPGP
	- 'Pearl'	CPou NHoy
	- 'Peppermint Garlic'	CDes CTca LEdu WPGP
	- var. ***robustior***	CAby CPou CTca ECha EWes NHoy
	- 'Seren'	LEdu
§	- 'Silver Lace' (v) ♀H2	Widely available
	- 'Variegata'	see *T. violacea* 'Silver Lace'
	- var. ***violacea***	NHoy
	- 'White Goddess'	CPou

Tulipa ✿ (*Liliaceae*)

'Abba' (2)	LAma SDeJ
'Abra' (3) **new**	LAma
'Absalon' (9)	GKev LAma
'Abu Hassan' (3)	CAby CAvo ERCP LAma MBri NBri SDeJ

acuminata (15)	CAvo CBro CTca ECho ERCP LAma NMin SDeJ SPhx
'Ad Rem' (4)	MBri SDeJ
'Addis' (14)	LAma
'Agrass White' (3) **new**	NBri
'Air' (10)	ERCP
aitchisonii	see *T. clusiana*
'Akebono' (11) **new**	CAvo LAma
'Akela' (5) **new**	LAma
'Alabaster' (5) **new**	LAma
'Aladdin' (6)	LAma NBri SDeJ
'Aladdin's Record' (6)	CBro LAma SDeJ
'Alba Regalis' (1) **new**	LAma
'Albert Heijn' (13)	SDeJ
albertii (15)	ECho LAma NMin
Albion Star = 'Mieke Telkamp' (13) **new**	SDeJ
'Aleppo' (7)	SDeJ
'Alexander Pushkin'PBR (3) **new**	LAma
'Alfred Cortot' (12) ♀H6	LAma SDeJ
'Ali Baba' (14) ♀H6	LAma NBri
'Alice Leclercq' (2)	LAma
'Allegretto' (11)	LAma MBri
'Alliance' (2) **new**	LAma
altaica (15) ♀H6	ECho LAma
amabilis	see *T. hoogiana*
'American Dream' (4) **new**	LAma
'American Eagle' (7)	LAma SDeJ
'Analita' (13)	LAma
'Ancilla' (12) ♀H6	CBro LAma NBri SBod
'Angélique' (11) ♀H6	CAvo CBro CTca EPfP ERCP GKev LAma MBri NBir NBri SDeJ SPer
'Angels Wish' (5) ♀H6	CAvo SDeJ
'Annie Schilder' (3)	ERCP LAma
'Antarctica'PBR (3) **new**	LAma
'Anthony Eden' (2) **new**	LAma
'Antoinette'PBR (5)	LAma
'Antraciet' (11)	ERCP LAma
'Apeldoorn' (4)	GKev LAma MBri NBri SDeJ SPer
'Apeldoorn's Elite' (4) ♀H6	LAma MBri NBri SDeJ
'Apricot Beauty' (1) ♀H6	CAby CHid CTca ERCP LAma MBri NBir NBri SDeJ
'Apricot Emperor' (13)	MCot SDeJ
'Apricot Impression'PBR (4)	LAma
'Apricot Jewel'	see *T. linifolia* (Batalinii Group) 'Apricot Jewel'
'Apricot Magic' (1) **new**	LAma
'Apricot Parrot' (10) ♀H6	CAvo LAma MBri MCot NBri SDeJ
'Aquilla' (11)	LAma SDeJ
'Arabian Mystery' (3)	ERCP LAma NHol SDeJ
'Aria Card' (7)	LAma SDeJ
'Artist' (8) ♀H6	ERCP IFro LAma SDeJ
'Atlantis' (5)	LAma MBri NBri
'Attila' (3)	CAvo LAma
'Attila Graffiti' (3) **new**	LAma
'Attila's Elite' (3) **new**	LAma
aucheriana (15) ♀H5	CBro ECho EPot LAma LLHF NMin
australis (15)	ECho
'Avignon' (5) **new**	SDeJ
aximensis (15)	ECho LAma NMin
'Bacchus' (7)	LAma
bakeri	see *T. saxatilis* Bakeri Group
'Ballade' (6) ♀H6	CAvo ERCP LAma MCot SDeJ
Ballade Dream = 'Sonnet' (6)	LAma SDeJ
'Ballade Gold' (6) **new**	LAma
'Ballerina' (6) ♀H6	CAby CAvo CBro CTca ECho EPfP ERCP LAma MBri MCot NBri SDeJ SPer
'Banja Luka' (4)	LAma NBri SDeJ
'Barbados' (7)	LAma SDeJ
'Barcelona' (3) ♀H6	ERCP LAma
'Baronesse' (5)	SDeJ
'Bastogne' (3) **new**	LAma
'Bastogne Parrot'PBR (10)	LAma
batalinii	see *T. linifolia* Batalinii Group
'Beau Monde' (3) ♀H6	SDeJ
'Beauty of Apeldoorn' (4)	LAma MBri
'Beauty of Bath' (9) **new**	LAma
'Beauty Queen' (1)	LAma SDeJ
'Bel Air'PBR (2) **new**	LAma
'Belcanto' (3)	LAma
'Belicia' (2)	LAma
'Bellflower' (7)	LAma
'Bellona' (3)	LAma SDeJ
'Berlioz' (12)	LAma SDeJ
'Bessie' (5) **new**	LAma
'Bestseller' (1)	SDeJ
biebersteiniana (15)	ECho NMin
§ ***biflora*** (15)	ECho EPot GKev LAma SDeJ SPhx WShi
bifloriformis (15)	ECho LAma LLHF
I - 'Maxima' (15)	ECho NMin SPhx
- 'Starlight' (15) ♀H6	ECho NMin
'Big Chief' (4) ♀H6	LAma
'Black and White' (9) **new**	LAma
'Black Charm' (3) **new**	CAby
'Black Hero' (11)	CAby CAvo EPfP ERCP LAma MCot SDeJ
'Black Horse' (5)	LAma
'Black Jewel' (7)	ERCP LAma SDeJ
'Black Parrot' (10) ♀H6	CAvo CBro CHid EPfP ERCP LAma MBri NBri SDeJ SPer
'Black Stallion' (11)	LAma
'Black Swan' (5)	SDeJ
'Blackjack' (3) **new**	LAma
'Blenda' (3)	LAma
'Bleu Aimable' (5)	CAvo ERCP LAma MCot SDeJ
'Blue Diamond' (11)	CAvo ERCP LAma NBri SDeJ
'Blue Heron' (7) ♀H6	CAvo ERCP LAma SDeJ
'Blue Parrot' (10)	EPfP ERCP LAma NBri SDeJ SPer
'Blue Ribbon' (3)	CAvo
Blueberry Ripple	see *T.* 'Zurel'
'Blumex Favourite'PBR (10) **new**	LAma
'Blushing Apeldoorn' (4)	LAma
'Blushing Beauty' (5)	LAma SDeJ
'Blushing Bride' (5)	LAma SDeJ
'Blushing Girl' (5) **new**	LAma SDeJ
'Blushing Lady' (5)	LAma MCot
'Border Legend' (13) **new**	LAma
'Boston' (3) **new**	LAma
'Boutade' (14)	NPer
'Bridesmaid' (5)	LAma
'Bright Parrot' (10) **new**	LAma
'Brilliant Star' (1)	LAma
'Brown Sugar' (3)	EPfP ERCP SPer
'Bruine Wimpel' (5) **new**	LAma
'Bulldog' (7) **new**	CAvo SDeJ
'Burgundy' (6)	CTca ERCP LAma SDeJ
'Burgundy Lace' (7)	LAma SDeJ
'Burning Heart' (4) ♀H6	LAma SDeJ
'Burning Love' (1) **new**	LAma
'Buttercup' (14)	SDeJ

'Café Noir' (5)	ERCP LAma NHol
'Calgary' (3) ♀H6	CAvo LAma SDeJ
'Calibra' (7)	CAvo LAma
'Californian Sun' (14) **new**	LAma
'Calypso' (14) ♀H6	LAma LRHS NBri
'Canasta' (7)	LAma SDeJ
'Candela' (13) ♀H6	LAma SDeJ
'Candy Club' (5)	LAma
'Candy Prince'PBR (1)	LAma SDeJ
'Canova' (7)	SDeJ
'Cantata' (13)	LAma
'Cape Cod' (14)	LAma NBri SDeJ
'Cape Town' (1) ♀H6 **new**	CAby
'Cardinal Mindszenty' (2)	ERCP LAma LRHS SDeJ
carinata (15)	ECho NMin
'Carlton' (2)	LAma NBri
'Carnaval de Nice' (11/v) ♀H6	CBro CTca ERCP LAma MBri SDeJ SPer
'Caroia' (3) **new**	LAma
'Carrousel' (7)	SDeJ
'Cartouche' (11)	ERCP LAma SDeJ
'Cassini' (3)	LAma SDeJ
§ ***celsiana*** (15)	ECho LAma
'Chanson d'Amour' (14) **new**	LAma
'Charmeur'PBR (3) **new**	SDeJ
'Cheers' (3) **new**	LAma
'Cherida' (3) **new**	LAma
'China Lady' (14)	ECho SDeJ
'China Pink' (6) ♀H6	CAvo CBro CTca ERCP LAma MBri SDeJ
'China Town' (8) ♀H6	ERCP LAma MBri SDeJ
'Chopin' (12)	LAma NHol
'Christmas Dream' (1)	LAma SDeJ
'Christmas Marvel' (1)	LAma NBri SDeJ
'Christmas Sweet' (1) **new**	LAma
chrysantha Boiss. ex Baker	see *T. montana*
'Cilesta' (2) **new**	LAma
'Cistula' (6)	SDeJ
'City Flower' (14) **new**	LAma
'City of Vancouver' (5)	LAma
'Claudia' (6)	LAma NBri SDeJ
'Clearwater'PBR (5) **new**	LAma SDeJ
'Cloud Nine' (5)	ECho
§ ***clusiana*** (15)	CBro ECho ERCP LAma MBri NMin WHer
- var. ***chrysantha*** (15) ♀H5	CAby CExl ECho LAma WHoo WShi
- - 'Tubergen's Gem' (15)	ECho EPot GKev LAma MBri NMin SPhx
- 'Cynthia' (15) ♀H6	CTca ECGP ECho EPot ERCP GKev LAma MBri NMin SDeJ SPhx
- 'Sheila' (15)	CBro ECho LAma NMin SPhx
§ - var. ***stellata*** (15)	ECho LAma
'Colour Spectacle'PBR (5)	CAby LAma
'Columbine' (5)	ECho LAma
'Come-Back' (4) **new**	LAma
'Comedian' (14) **new**	LAma
'Concerto' (13)	CBro LAma MBri NPer SDeJ
'Continental' (3) **new**	LAma
'Cool Crystal' (7) **new**	LAma
'Coquette' (1)	LAma SDeJ
'Coquette Yellow' (1) **new**	LAma
'Cordell Hull' (5)	LAma
'Corona' (12)	ECho LAma NBri SDeJ
'Corsage' (14) ♀H6	LAma SDeJ
'Cortina' (9)	SDeJ
'Cottage Boy' (1) **new**	LAma
'Couleur Cardinal' (3)	CBro ERCP LAma LRHS NBri SDeJ

'Cracker'PBR (3) **new**	LAma
'Cream Perfection' (3) **new**	LAma
'Creme Upstar' (11)	ERCP LAma MBri SDeJ
cretica (15)	ECho LAma NMin
'Crispion Dark' (7)	ERCP
'Crystal Beauty' (7) ♀H6	LAma
'Cuban Night' (7) **new**	LAma
'Cum Laude' (5)	LAma SDeJ
'Cummins' (7)	CAvo ERCP LAma
'Curly Sue' (7)	CAvo ERCP LAma MCot SPer
'Czaar Peter' (14) ♀H6	CAvo EPfP MBri NBri NPer SDeJ
'Daladier' (11) **new**	LAma
'Dallas' (7) **new**	LAma
'Dance' (13)	LAma SDeJ
'Dancing Queen' (2)	MBri
'Dancing Show' (8)	LAma
dasystemon (15)	ECho EPot LAma LLHF
dasystemonoides (15)	ECho
'Davenport' (7)	ERCP
'David Teniers' (2)	ERCP LAma SDeJ
'Daydream' (4) ♀H6	LAma SDeJ
'Daylight' (12)	LAma
'Daytona' (7)	CAvo LAma
'Deep River' (5) **new**	LAma
'Deirdre' (8)	LAma
'Deshima' (3) **new**	LAma
'Design Impression' (4) **new**	LAma
'Destiny' (10) **new**	LAma
'Diana' (1)	LAma
'Doll's Minuet' (8)	EPfP ERCP LAma NBri
'Dom Pedro' (5) **new**	LAma
'Dominiek' (3) **new**	LAma
'Don Quichotte' (3) ♀H6	LAma MBri SDeJ
'Donald Duck' (14) ♀H6	MBri
'Donauperle' (14)	SDeJ
'Donna Bella' (14)	SDeJ
'Dordogne' (5) ♀H6	LAma SDeJ
'Double Dazzle' (2)	LAma
'Double Price' (2)	ERCP
'Double Princess'PBR (2) **new**	LAma
'Double Red Riding Hood' (14v)	LAma SDeJ
'Double Sugar' (11) **new**	LAma
'Douglas Bader' (5)	LAma
'Dragon King' (3)	SBod SDeJ
'Dream Touch' (11) **new**	LAma
'Dreamboat' (14)	LAma MBri
'Dreaming Maid' (3)	LAma MBri
'Dreamland' (5) ♀H6	LAma MBri SDeJ
'Duc van Tol Aurora'	LAma
'Duc van Tol Max Cramoisie' (1)	LAma
'Duc van Tol Primrose' (1)	LAma
'Duc van Tol Red and Yellow' (1)	GKev LAma WHer
'Duc van Tol Rose' (1)	LAma
'Duc van Tol Salmon' (1)	LAma
'Duc van Tol Scarlet' (1) **new**	LAma
'Duc van Tol Violet' (1)	LAma
'Duc van Tol White' (1)	LAma
'Dutch Gold' (3)	MBri
'Dyanito' (6)	LAma
'Dynasty' (3)	SPer
'Early Glory' (3) **new**	LAma
'Early Harvest' (12) ♀H6	CAvo LAma SDeJ
'Early Star' (14)	LAma

'Easter Parade' (13)	LAma
'Easter Surprise' (14) ♀H6	LAma MBri SDeJ
eichleri	see *T. undulatifolia*
'Electra' (5)	LAma MBri NHol
'Elegans Alba' (6)	LAma
'Elegant Lady' (6)	CAvo LAma SDeJ
'Erna Lindgreen' (10)	LAma
'Escape'[PBR] (3) **new**	LAma
'Esperanto' (8/v) ♀H6	CAby LAma SDeJ
'Estella Rijnveld' (10)	ERCP LAma SDeJ
'Esther' (5)	LAma
'Eternal Flame' (2)	LAma
'Evita'[PBR]	LAma
'Exotic Emperor' (13)	CAvo LAma SDeJ
'Eye Catcher' (8)	LAma
'Fabio' (7) **new**	LAma LRHS
'Fairy Nymph' (5) **new**	LAma
'Fancy Frills' (7) ♀H6	ERCP LAma SDeJ
'Fantasy' (10) ♀H6	LAma
'Fashion' (12)	LAma SDeJ
ferganica (15)	ECho LAma NMin
'Fidelio' (3) ♀H6	SDeJ
'Fire of Love' (14) **new**	LAma
'Fire Queen' (3) ♀H6	ERCP LAma
'First Impression' (14)	LAma
'Flair' (1)	LAma NBri SDeJ
'Flamenco' (7)	SDeJ
'Flaming Club' (5) **new**	LAma
'Flaming Coquette'[PBR] (1) **new**	LAma
'Flaming Evita'[PBR] (2) **new**	SDeJ
'Flaming Jewel' (4) **new**	LAma
'Flaming Parrot' (10)	CAby CAvo ERCP GKev LAma MBri NBri
I 'Flaming Purissima' (13)	CAvo LAma MBri SDeJ
'Flaming Springgreen' (8)	CAvo ERCP LAma SDeJ
'Flashback' (10)	ERCP LAma
'Flig Flag' (3)	ERCP
'Florette'[PBR] (5) **new**	LAma
'Florijn Chic' (6) **new**	LAma
'Florosa' (8)	ERCP SDeJ
'Fontainebleau' (3)	LAma SDeJ
'Formosa' (8) **new**	LAma
'Foxtrot'[PBR] (2)	EPfP ERCP LAma
'Françoise' (3)	LAma SDeJ
'Franz Léhar' (12)	SDeJ
'Freeman' (11)	LAma
'Fringed Elegance' (7) ♀H6	LAma
'Fringed Family' (7)	SDeJ
'Fringed Golden Apeldoorn' (7) **new**	LAma
'Fritz Kreisler' (12)	LAma SDeJ
'Fulgens' (6)	ECho LAma
'Fulton' (5) **new**	LAma
'Für Elise' (14)	NBri SDeJ
'Gabriella' (3)	LAma
'Gaiety' (12)	SDeJ
'Gander's Rhapsody' (3) **new**	LAma
'Garanza' (2) **new**	LAma
'Garden Party' (3)	LAma SDeJ
'Garden Show' (14) **new**	LAma
'Gavota' (3) ♀H6	CAvo CBro LAma NBri NHol SDeJ SPer
'Generaal de Wet' (1)	LAma SDeJ
'Georges Grappe' (5) **new**	LAma
'Georgette' (5)	LAma MBri
'Gerbrand Kieft' (11) ♀H6	ERCP

'Gipsy Love' (7) **new**	SDeJ
'Girlfriend' (15)	ECho
'Giuseppe Verdi' (12)	LAma LRHS MBri
'Glück' (12) ♀H6	ECho EPfP LAma LRHS
'Golden Apeldoorn' (4)	LAma MBri NBri SDeJ
'Golden Artist' (8)	LAma MBri SDeJ
'Golden Day' (14) **new**	LAma
'Golden Emperor' (13)	LAma SDeJ
'Golden Melody' (3)	LAma SDeJ
'Golden Nizza' (11)	LAma
'Golden Oxford' (4)	LAma
'Golden Parade' (4)	LAma
'Goldwest' (14)	SDeJ
'Gordon Cooper' (4)	LAma SDeJ
'Goudstuk' (12)	LAma
'Goya' (2) **new**	LAma
'Grand Perfection'[PBR] (3) ♀H6	EPfP
'Grand Prestige' (14) **new**	LAma
'Grand Style' (5) ♀H6 **new**	LAma
'Granny Award' (11) **new**	LAma
'Green Eyes' (8)	SDeJ
'Green River' (8)	LAma SDeJ
'Green Unique' **new**	LAma
'Green Village' (8) **new**	LAma
'Green Wave' (10)	ERCP LAma SDeJ
'Greenstar' (6)	ERCP LAma
greigii (14)	LAma
grengiolensis (15)	ECho LAma NMin
'Groenland' (8)	CAvo CBro LAma MBri MCot NBri SDeJ
'Gudoshnik' (4)	LAma
hageri (15)	ECho LAma LLHF MBri
- 'Red Cup' (13)	NMin
- 'Splendens' (15)	CAby ECho EPot IFro LAma SDeJ
'Hakuun' (4) **new**	LAma
'Halcro' (5) ♀H6	LAma
'Hamilton' (7)	LAma SDeJ
'Happy Family' (3)	LAma
'Happy Generation' (3)	LAma MBri
'Happy Hour' (7)	ERCP
'Havran' (3)	CAvo CBro ERCP LAma
'Heart's Delight' (12)	CBro ECho LAma MBri NBri SDeJ
'Helmar' (3)	LAma SDeJ
'Hemisphere' (3)	EPfP ERCP LAma SDeJ
'Hermitage' (3)	ERCP LAma
heweri (15)	ECho LAma NMin
hissarica (15)	ECho
'Hocus Pocus' (5)	LAma SDeJ
'Holland Baby' (2)	LAma SDeJ
'Holland Bouquet' (3)	LAma
'Holland Chic' (6)	LAma MCot SDeJ
'Holland Emotions' (4) **new**	LAma
'Holland Happening' (10) **new**	LAma
'Holland Queen'[PBR] (3) **new**	LAma
'Holland Ruby' (11) **new**	LAma
'Holland Sun' (3) **new**	LAma
'Hollandia' (3)	LAma MBri
'Hollands Glorie' (4)	LAma SDeJ
'Hollywood' (8)	LAma
'Hollywood Star' (8) **new**	LAma
'Honeymoon' (7)	LAma
'Honky Tonk' (15) ♀H6	CAvo ECho GKev LAma MBri NMin
§ ***hoogiana*** (15)	ECho
'Hot Chocolate' (3) **new**	LAma

	Name	Suppliers
	'Hotpants' (3)	LAma SPer
	'Huis Ten Bosch' (7) **new**	LAma
§	***humilis*** (15)	CBro ECho EWTr GKev LAma LRHS MBri SDeJ WShi
	- 'China Carol' (15)	ECGP ECho LAma LLHF SDeJ
	- 'Eastern Spice' (15)	ECho LAma NMin
	- 'Eastern Star' (15)	ECho GKev LAma MBri NMin
	- 'Helene' (15)	ECho
§	- 'Lilliput' (15)	CBro ECho EPot GKev LAma LRHS NMin
	- 'Magenta Queen' (15)	ECho LAma
	- 'Odalisque' (15)	ECho EPot ERCP GKev LAma LRHS NMin
	- 'Pegasus' (15)	NMin
	- 'Persian Pearl' (15)	CAby CAvo ECho EPfP EPot ERCP GKev LAma MBri NMin SDeJ SMrm
*	- 'Pink Charm' (15)	ECho
	- var. ***pulchella***	CTca ECho EPot ERCP GKev LLHF
	Albocaerulea Oculata Group (15)	MCot NMin
I	- 'Rosea Coerulea Oculata' (15)	NMin
	- 'Tête-à-tête' (15) **new**	LAma
§	- Violacea Group (15)	CAvo ECho LRHS MBri
	- - black base (15)	CBro ECho EPot ERCP GKev LAma MBri NMin
	- - yellow base (15)	ECho EPot GKev LAma
	- 'Zephyr' (15)	NMin
	'Humming Bird' (8)	LAma
	'Ice Cream' (11)	LAma SDeJ
	'Ice Stick' (12) **new**	SDeJ
	'Ile de France' (5)	ERCP LAma SDeJ
	iliensis (15)	ECho EPot LAma LLHF NMin
	'India' (3)	ERCP LAma
	'Indigos' (3) **new**	ECho
	ingens (15)	ECho LAma NMin
	'Insulinde' (9)	LAma
	'Inzell' (3)	EPfP LAma
	'Ivory Floradale' (4) ♀H6	LAma SDeJ
	'Jaap Groot' (4) **new**	LAma
	'Jackpot' (3)	LAma
	'Jacqueline' (6)	LAma
	'Jan Reus' (3)	CAby CAvo CBro ERCP LAma
	'Jazz' (6)	ERCP
	'Jewel of Spring' (4)	LAma
	'Jimmy' (3)	LAma
	'Jochem' (3) **new**	LAma
	'Joffre' (1)	LAma MBri
	'Johann Strauss' (12)	ECho LAma MBri NBri SPer
	'Juan' (13) ♀H6	LAma MBri
	'Judith Leyster' (3)	LAma
	julia (15)	ECho NMin
	'Juliette' (4) **new**	LAma
	'Karel Doorman' (10)	LAma
	'Karimata' (14) **new**	LAma
	'Kathleen Truxton' (5) **new**	LAma
	kaufmanniana (12)	ECho EPot
§	'Kees Nelis' (3)	MBri NBri
	'Keizerskroon' (1)	LAma SDeJ
	'Kingsblood' (5) ♀H6	LAma SDeJ
	'Kleurenpracht'	see *T.* 'Princess Margaret Rose'
	kolpakowskiana (15) ♀H6	ECho EPot ERCP LAma LLHF MBri NMin WShi
	kurdica (15)	ECho LAma SPhx
	- purple-flowered (15)	ECho
	'La Belle Epoque' (2) **new**	SBod SDeJ
	'La Courtine' (5)	LAma
	'La Douceur' (5) **new**	LAma
	'Lac van Rijn' (1)	GKev LAma
*	'Lady Diana' (14)	MBri
	'Lady Jane' (15) ♀H6	CAvo CBro CMea ECho ERCP LAma MBri NMin SPhx WShi
	lanata (15)	NMin
	'Large Copper' (14)	LAma
	'Lasting Love' (3) **new**	LAma
	'Latvian Gold' (15)	ECho LAma NMin
	'Le Mogol' (5) **new**	LAma
	'Leen van der Mark' (3)	LAma MBri NBri
	'Leo Visser' (3) **new**	LAma
	'Libretto Parrot' (10)	LAma SDeJ
	'Lighting Sun' (4)	LAma
	'Lila Star' **new**	LAma
	'Lilac Perfection' (11)	CTca ERCP LAma MBri SDeJ
	'Lilac Time' (6)	LAma
	'Lilac Wonder'	see *T. saxatilis* (Bakeri Group) 'Lilac Wonder'
	'Lilliput'	see *T. humilis* 'Lilliput'
	'Lilybeauty' (6) **new**	LAma
	'Lilyfire' (6)	LAma SDeJ
	'Lingerie' (7) **new**	LAma
	linifolia (15) ♀H5	CAvo ECho EPot ERCP GKev LAma MBri NMin SDeJ WShi
§	- Batalinii Group (15) ♀H5	ECho MBri
§	- - 'Apricot Jewel' (15)	CBro ECho EPot ERCP GKev LAma
	- - 'Bright Gem' (15) ♀H5	CBro ECho EPot GKev LAma MBri NPer SPhx WHoo
	- - 'Bronze Charm' (15)	CAvo ECGP ECho EPot LAma MBri NMin SDeJ SPhx
	- - 'Red Gem' (15)	ECho GKev SPhx
	- - 'Red Hunter' (15) ♀H6	CBro ECho EPfP ERCP GKev LAma MBri SPer
	- - 'Red Jewel' (15)	ECho LAma
	- - (Batalinii Group) 'Salmon Gem' (15)	ECho
	- - 'Yellow Jewel' (15)	ECho GKev LAma
§	- Maximowiczii Group (15)	ECho EPot LAma
	'Lipgloss' (3)	LAma NHol
	'Little Beauty' (15) ♀H6	CAby CAvo CBro ECho EPfP GKev LAma MBri SDeJ SPhx WHoo
	'Little Diamond' (12) **new**	LRHS
	'Little Princess' (15) ♀H6	CAvo CBro CTca ECho ERCP GKev LAma SDeJ SPhx
	'Little Star' (15) ♀H6	GKev LAma NMin
	'London' (4)	LAma
	'Long Lady' (5) **new**	LAma
	'Louvre' (7) ♀H6 **new**	LAma
	'Love Song' (12)	LAma
	'Lovely Surprise' (14)	SDeJ
	'Lucky Strike' (3)	MBri
§	'Lustige Witwe' (3)	LAma SDeJ
	'Lydia' (3)	LAma
	'Mabel' (9)	LAma
§	'Madame Lefeber' (13)	LAma MBri SDeJ
	'Madonna' (10)	EPfP LAma
	'Magier' (5)	MBri
	'Maja' (7)	LAma MBri
	'Makassar' (3) **new**	LAma
	'March of Time' (14)	LAma MBri
	'Margaret Herbst' (14) **new**	LAma
	'Margarita' (2) **new**	LAma
	'Marie José' (14)	SDeJ
	'Marie Louise' (5) **new**	LAma
	'Mariette' (6)	CBro LAma MBri SDeJ
	'Marilyn' (6)	ERCP LAma SDeJ
	'Marit' (4) ♀H6 **new**	LAma
	'Marjolein' (6)	LAma

Name	Suppliers
marjolletii (15)	CBro ECho LAma NMin
'Maroon' (7)	ERCP
'Mary Ann' (14)	LAma
'Mata Hari' (3) **new**	LAma
'Matchpoint' (7/d)	ERCP LAma SDeJ
'Maureen' (5) 🏆H6	ERCP LAma SDeJ
mauritiana 'Cindy' (15)	ECho LAma NMin
maximowiczii	see *T. linifolia* Maximowiczii Group
'Maytime' (6)	LAma MBri MCot SDeJ
'Maywonder' (11)	MBri
'Melody d'Amour' (5)	LAma
'Melrose' (2) **new**	LAma
'Menton' (5) 🏆H6	ERCP LAma SDeJ
'Menton Exotic' (11)	ERCP
'Merlot' (6) **new**	LAma
'Merry Christmas' (1)	LAma
'Merry Christmas Design' (1) **new**	LAma
Merry Widow	see *T.* 'Lustige Witwe'
'Mickey Mouse' (1)	LAma MBri
'Miranda' (11) **new**	LAma
'Miskodeed' (14)	SDeJ
'Miss Elegance' (3) **new**	LAma
'Miss Holland' (3)	MBri
'Mistress' (3)	LAma
'Modern Style' (5)	LAma
'Mona Lisa' (6)	LAma SDeJ
'Mondial'PBR (2) **new**	LAma
'Moneymaker' (6)	ERCP
'Monsella' (2)	LAma NBri
§ ***montana*** (15)	CTca ECho EPot LAma NMin
- yellow-flowered	ECho GKev LAma NMin
'Monte Carlo' (2) 🏆H6	CBro LAma MBri NBri SDeJ
'Montreux' (2)	ECho LAma
'Moonshine' (6)	LAma
'Moonwalker' (4) **new**	LAma
'Mount Tacoma' (11)	CAvo CBro ERCP LAma MBri SDeJ SPer
'Mr Van der Hoef' (2)	LAma MBri SDeJ
'Mrs John T. Scheepers' (5)	LAma SDeJ
'Muriel' (10)	ERCP
'Negrita' (3)	ERCP LAma MBri NBri SDeJ
neustruevae (15)	ECho EPot LAma NMin
'New Design' (3/v)	LAma MBri
'Nightrider' (8)	CAvo ERCP LAma MCot SDeJ
'Noranda' (7) **new**	LAma
'Ollioules' (4) 🏆H6	LAma SDeJ
'Olympic Flame' (4) 🏆H6	LAma SDeJ
'Orange Angelique' (11) **new**	XEll
'Orange Bouquet' (3) 🏆H6	LAma MBri SDeJ
'Orange Brilliant' (13) **new**	LAma
'Orange Cassini' (3)	LAma NBri
'Orange Elite' (14)	MBri
'Orange Emperor' (13) 🏆H6	CAvo LAma MBri SDeJ
'Orange Favourite' (10)	ERCP LAma
'Orange Lion' (4) **new**	LAma
'Orange Monarch' (3) **new**	LAma
'Orange Princess' (11) 🏆H6	CBro CTca ERCP LAma SDeJ
'Orange Queen' (4) **new**	LAma
'Orange Sun'	see *T.* 'Oranjezon'
'Orange Toronto' (14)	LAma
'Orange Triumph' (11)	MBri
'Oranje Nassau' (2) 🏆H6	MBri
§ 'Oranjezon' (4) 🏆H6	ERCP LAma
'Oratorio' (14) 🏆H6	LAma MBri SDeJ
'Oriental Beauty' (14) 🏆H6	LAma
orithyioides	NMin
orphanidea (15)	ECho LAma NMin
- 'Flava' (15)	ECho EPot LAma
§ - Whittallii Group (15) 🏆H6	CAvo ECho EPot ERCP GKev NMin SDeJ SPhx
'Oscar' (3)	LAma NHol
ostrowskiana (15)	ECho LAma NMin
'Oxford' (4) 🏆H6	LAma
'Oxford's Elite' (4)	LAma
'Page Polka' (3)	LAma MBri SDeJ
'Palestrina' (3)	LAma SPer
'Pandour' (14)	LAma MBri
'Panorama' (5) **new**	LAma
'Papillon' (9)	LAma
'Parade' (4) 🏆H6	LAma MBri
'Parrot King' (10) **new**	SDeJ
'Passionale' (3) 🏆H6	EPfP LAma NBri SDeJ SPer
'Paul Scherer' (3) 🏆H6	CAby CHid ERCP LAma SDeJ
'Pax' (3)	LAma
'Peach Blossom' (2)	ERCP LAma LRHS MBri NBri SDeJ SPer
Peacock Group **new**	SDeJ
'Peppermintstick' (15) 🏆H6	CAvo CBro CTca ECho LAma NMin SDeJ
'Perestroyka' (5)	LAma MBri SDeJ
persica	see *T. celsiana*
'Philippe de Comines' (5)	LAma
'Piccolo' (15)	LAma
'Picture' (5)	ERCP LAma SDeJ
'Pieter de Leur' (6)	LAma MBri
'Pimpernel' (8/v)	LAma SDeJ
'Pink Diamond' (5)	CAvo ERCP NBri NHol SDeJ
'Pink Dwarf' (12)	SDeJ
'Pink Impression' (4) 🏆H6	LAma MBri SDeJ
'Pink Lady' (3) **new**	LAma
'Pink Sensation' (14)	SDeJ
'Pinkeen' (13)	LAma
'Pinocchio' (14)	LAma MBri NBri SDeJ
'Pirand' (13) 🏆H6	ERCP SDeJ
'Plaisir' (14) 🏆H6	LAma MBri
platystigma (15)	ECho LAma NMin
'Poco Loco' (13)	SDeJ
polychroma	see *T. biflora*
praestans (15)	ECho SPer WShi
- 'Fusilier' (15) 🏆H6	CBro CExl ECho EPot LAma MBri NBir NBri SDeJ
- 'Red Sun' (15)	ECho
- 'Shogun' (15)	ECho ERCP SDeJ
- 'Unicum' (15/v)	ECho ERCP LAma MBri NBri NMin SDeJ
- 'Van Tubergen's Variety' (15)	ECho LAma NPer
- 'Yari' (15)	ECho
- 'Zwanenburg Variety' (15)	ECho
'Pretty Woman' (6) **new**	LAma
'Princeps' (13)	LAma MBri SDeJ
§ 'Princess Margaret Rose' (5)	LAma
'Princess Unique'PBR (11)	LAma
'Princesse Charmante' (14) 🏆H6	LAma MBri
'Prins Carnaval' (1) 🏆H6	LAma
'Prinses Irene' (3) 🏆H6	CAvo CBro CMea CTca EPfP ERCP LAma LRHS MBri MCot NBir NBri NHol SDeJ
'Prinses Margriet' (3)	ERCP LAma
'Professor Einstein' (3) **new**	LAma
'Professor Röntgen' (10)	ERCP LAma SDeJ
'Professor Schotel' (15) **new**	LAma
pulchella humilis	see *T. humilis*

§ 'Purissima' (13) ♀H6	CAby CAvo CBro LAma MBri NBri SDeJ
'Purple Bouquet' (3)	LAma SDeJ
'Purple Dream' (6)	LAma SDeJ
'Purple Flag' (3) **new**	LAma
'Purple Prince' (5)	CBro LAma LRHS SDeJ
'Purple Rain' (3) **new**	LAma
'Purple Voice' **new**	LAma
'Quebec' (14)	LAma SDeJ
'Queen of Marvel' (2)	LAma SDeJ
'Queen of Night' (5)	CAvo CBro CMea CTca EPfP ERCP GKev LAma MBri NBri SPer SPhx
'Queen of Sheba' (6)	LAma
'Queensday' (11) **new**	LAma
'Queensland' (7)	ERCP LAma
'Quest' (3)	LAma
'Rai' (10)	ERCP LAma
'Rainbow' **new**	LAma
'Real Time' (7) **new**	LAma
'Recreado' (5)	CAvo ERCP LAma SDeJ
'Red Baby Doll' (2) **new**	LAma
'Red Emperor'	see *T.* 'Madame Lefeber'
'Red Georgette' (5) ♀H6	CAby LAma MBri NBir
'Red Impression'PBR (4) ♀H6	LAma
'Red Mark'PBR (3) **new**	LAma
'Red Present' (3) **new**	LAma
'Red Princess' (11) ♀H6	ERCP LAma
'Red Revival' (1) **new**	LAma
'Red Riding Hood' (14) ♀H6	CAby CAvo CBro EPfP GKev LAma LRHS MBri NBir NBri SDeJ SPer
'Red Shine' (6) ♀H6	CAby CAvo CBro LAma MBri NBri SDeJ
'Red Springgreen' (8)	LAma SDeJ
'Red Wing' (7) ♀H6	LAma SDeJ
'Redwood' (14) **new**	SDeJ
Rembrandt mix (9)	MBri
(Rembrandt Group) 'Saskia' (15) **new**	LAma
'Rems Favourite' (3)	CAvo
'Renown' (5)	LAma SDeJ
'Renown Unique' (11)	LAma
'Rex Rubrorum' (2) **new**	LAma
rhodopea	see *T. urumoffii*
'Ringo'	see *T.* 'Kees Nelis'
'Robert Schuller' (14) **new**	LAma
'Rockery Master' (14)	LAma
'Rococo' (10)	CBro ERCP LAma MBri NBri SDeJ
'Roi du Midi' (5) **new**	LAma SDeJ
'Ronaldo' (3)	ERCP LAma
'Rosalie' (3) **new**	LAma
'Rose des Dames' (5) **new**	LAma
* 'Rose Emperor' (13)	MBri
'Rosy Dream' (13)	LAma SDeJ
'Roulette' (3) **new**	LAma
'Royal Acres' (2) **new**	LAma
'Royal Elegance' (7) **new**	LAma
'Ruby Red' (1)	CAby
'Ruud Lubbers' (14) **new**	LAma
'Sahara Rally' (4) **new**	LAma
'Salmon Impression'PBR (4)	LAma MBri NBri
'Salmon Jewel' (3)	EPot
'Salmon Parrot' (10) **new**	LAma
'Salut' (13)	LAma
'Sanne' (3) **new**	LAma
'Sapporro' (6)	ERCP LAma
saxatilis (15)	CBro ECho EPfP GKev LAma MBri SDeJ WShi
§ - Bakeri Group (15)	ECho SEND
§ - - 'Lilac Wonder' (15) ♀H6	CAby CAvo CBro CExl ECho EPot ERCP GKev LAma MBri NPer SPhx
'Scarlet Baby' (12)	EPfP LAma MBri
'Schoonoord' (2)	LAma MBri
schrenkii (15)	ECho ERCP LAma NMin
'Scotland' (2) **new**	LAma
'Seadov' (3) **new**	LAma
'Sensual Touch' (7) ♀H6	LAma SDeJ
'Sexy Lady' (10) **new**	LAma
'Shakespeare' (12)	CBro LAma NBri SDeJ
'Shirley' (3)	CAvo EPfP ERCP LAma MBri NBri NChi SDeJ SPer
'Shirley Dream' (3)	LAma SDeJ
'Shirley Flame' (3) **new**	LAma
'Showtime' (14)	SDeJ
'Showwinner' (12) ♀H6	CAvo CBro LAma MBri NHol SDeJ
'Sihouette Bouquet' (3) **new**	LAma
'Silver Dollar' (3) **new**	LAma
'Silver Parrot' (10) **new**	LAma
'Silverado' (5) **new**	LAma
'Silverstream' (4)	LAma
'Sinopel' (8) **new**	LAma
'Snow Parrot' (10)	ERCP
'Snowboard' (3) **new**	LAma
'Snowpeak' (5)	LAma
sogdiana (15)	ECho LAma LLHF NMin
'Solar' **new**	LAma
'Sorbet' (5) ♀H6	LAma SDeJ
sprengeri (15) ♀H6	CAvo CBro CDes CExl CLAP CTca ECGP ECha ECho EPot ERCP LAma LLHF SDix WHal WShi
- Trotter's form (15)	WCot
'Spring Green' (8) ♀H6	CAvo CBro EPfP ERCP GKev LAma MBri NBri SDeJ SPer SPhx
'Spring Song' (4)	LAma
'Spryng' (3) ♀H6	SDeJ
'Starfighter' (7)	SDeJ
stellata	see *T. clusiana* var. *stellata*
'Stockholm' (2) ♀H6	LAma
'Stresa' (12) ♀H6	CBro LAma LRHS NBri SDeJ
'Striped Sail' (3) **new**	LAma
'Strong Gold' (3) ♀H6 **new**	LAma SDeJ
'Stunning Apricot' (5) **new**	LAma
subpraestans (15)	LAma
'Sun Dance' (14) **new**	LAma
'Sun Lover' (11) **new**	LAma
'Sunny Prince'PBR (1)	CBro
'Super Parrot' (10)	LAma
'Supertwins' (3) **new**	LAma
'Survivor' (5) **new**	SDeJ
'Swan Wings' (7)	ERCP LAma SDeJ
'Sweet Harmony' (5)	LAma MBri
'Sweet Lady' (14)	LAma SDeJ
'Sweetheart' (13)	LAma MBri NBri SDeJ
'Sweety' (3) **new**	LAma
sylvestris (15)	CAby CAvo CBro CTca ECho EPfP EPot ERCP LAma MBri NBir NMin SDeJ SPer SPhx WCot WHer WOut WShi
'Sylvia Warder' (14) **new**	LAma
'Synaeda King' (6) ♀H6	LAma
'Synaeda Orange' (6) **new**	LAma
systola (15)	ECho LAma NMin
'Taco' (15)	ECho LAma MBri NMin
'Talisman' ambig.	LAma

'Tarafa' (14) **new** LAma
tarda (15) ♀H5 CAvo CBro CExl ECho EPfP ERCP GKev LAma LPot LRHS MBri SDeJ SPhx
'Temple of Beauty' (5) ♀H6 LAma SDeJ
'Temple's Favourite' (5) MBri
'Tennessee' (3) **new** LAma
'Tequila Sun' (3) LAma
tetraphylla (15) ECho LAma NMin
'Texas Fire' (10) **new** LAma
'Texas Flame' (10) LAma MBri SDeJ
'Texas Gold' (10) LAma SDeJ
'The First' (12) LAma
'The Lizard' (9) LAma
'Theeroos' (2) LAma
'Tinka' (15) ♀H6 CMea ECho EPfP LAma LSou NMin
'Tiny Timo' (15) LLHF NMin
'Ton Angustinus' (4) **new** LAma
'Toplips' (11) LAma SDeJ
'Topparrot' (10) LAma SDeJ
'Toronto' (14) ♀H6 CTca LAma MBri SDeJ
'Toronto Double' (2) LAma SDeJ
'Totum' (11) **new** LAma
'Toucan' (3) **new** LAma
'Toulon' (13) MBri
'Toyota' (5) SDeJ
'Très Chic' (6) CAvo CTca EPfP LAma MBri SPer
'Tricolored Beauty' (8) ERCP
'Trinket' (14) ♀H6 LAma
'Tropical Lady' (3) **new** LAma
tschimganica (15) ECho LAma
tubergeniana (15) ECho LAma
turkestanica (15) ♀H5 CAby CBro CExl CHid CSpe CTca ECho EPfP EPot ERCP GKev LAma LPot MBri NPer SDeJ WHoo
'Turkish Delight' (14) CAby NPer
'Twilight Princess' (8) **new** LAma
'Typhoon' (3) LAma
'Uncle Tom' (11) ERCP LAma MBri NBri SDeJ
§ ***undulatifolia*** (15) ECho
- 'Clare Benedict' (15) ECho NMin
- 'Excelsa' (15) ECho NMin
'Union Jack' (5) LAma
'United States' (14) LAma NPer
'Upstar' (11) LAma
urumiensis (15) ♀H5 CHid ECho EPot GKev LAma LPot MBri NMin SDeJ SPhx
§ ***urumoffii*** (15) ECho LAma
'Valentine' (3) LAma SDeJ SPer
'Valery Gergiev' (7) ERCP LAma
'Van der Neer' (1) SDeJ
'Van Eijk'[PBR] (4) **new** LAma NBri
'Velvet Lily' (6) NMin
'Verona' (2) LAma SDeJ
'Véronique Sanson' (3) ERCP SDeJ
'Viking' LAma
'Vincent van Gogh' (7) **new** LAma
violacea see *T. humilis* Violacea Group
'Violet Beauty' (5) LAma SDeJ
'Violet Bird' (8) LAma SDeJ
'Virichic' (8) ERCP IFro LAma MCot
'Vivex' (4) LAma
vvedenskyi (15) ECho EPot GKev
- 'Bernadette' LAma
- 'Tangerine Beauty' (15) ♀H6 ECho GKev LAma MBri
'Wallflower' (5) ERCP LAma
'Wapen van Leiden' (1) **new** LAma
'Warbler' (7) LAma SDeJ
* 'Water Lily' ECho
'Weber's Parrot' (10) ERCP LAma MBri MCot
'Weisse Berliner' (3) CBro LAma
'West Point' (6) CAvo CBro CTca LAma MBri SDeJ
* 'White Bouquet' (5) LAma
'White Dream' (3) CAvo LAma MBri NBri SDeJ
'White Elegance' (6) LAma
'White Emperor' see *T.* 'Purissima'
'White Marvel' (3) **new** LAma LRHS
'White Parrot' (10) CAvo ERCP LAma SDeJ
'White Sea' (13) **new** LAma
'White Triumphator' (6) ♀H6 CAvo CBro CMea ERCP GKev LAma MBri NBir SDeJ SPhx
whittallii see *T. orphanidea* Whittallii Group
'Wildhof' (3) ♀H6 ERCP
'Willem van Oranje' (2) LAma LRHS SBod SDeJ
'Willemsoord' (2) LAma LRHS MBri SDeJ
wilsoniana see *T. montana*
'Winterberg' (3) **new** LAma
'Wirosa' (11) ♀H6 NBri
'Wisley' (5) MBri
'World Expression' (5) ♀H6 LAma SDeJ
'Yellow Crown' (3) LAma
'Yellow Emperor' (5) MBri
'Yellow Flight' (3) LAma SDeJ
'Yellow King' (3) **new** LAma
'Yellow Pompenette'[PBR] (11) ♀H6 SDeJ
'Yellow Present' (3) LAma
I 'Yellow Purissima' (13) ♀H6 LAma
'Yellow Springgreen' (8) CBro ERCP LAma SDeJ
'Yellow Wave' (4) **new** LAma
'Yoko Parrot' (10) **new** SDeJ
'Yokohama' (3) LAma NBri SDeJ
'Yonina' (6) **new** LAma
'Zampa' (14) ♀H6 LAma MBri
zenaidae (15) ECho
'Zombie' (13) LAma
'Zomerschoon' (5) LAma
§ 'Zurel' (3) ERCP LAma MCot

tummelberry see *Rubus* 'Tummelberry'

Tunica see *Petrorhagia*

Tupistra (*Asparagaceae*)

aurantiaca LEdu
- B&SWJ 2267 WCot WCru
- B&SWJ 2401 WCru
chinensis 'Eco China Ruffles' WCot
fimbriata WCot
grandistigma WCot
- B&SWJ 11773 **new** WCru
jinshanensis WCot
urotepala HWJ 562 WCru
wattii B&SWJ 8297 WCru

Turnera (*Passifloraceae*)

ulmifolia CArn

Tussilago (*Asteraceae*)

farfara CArn GPoy MHer NMir WHer WHfH WSFF

Tweedia (*Asclepiadaceae*)

§ ***caerulea*** ♀H1c	CBcs CCCN CDTJ CFlo CSPN CSpe MSCN SChF SPad SWvt

Typha (*Typhaceae*)

angustifolia	CBAq CBen CKno CRow CWat EHon LLWG MMuc MSKA NPer SPlb SWat WMAq WPnP
latifolia	CBen CRow CWat EHon MSKA NBir NPer SVic SWat WHer WMAq WPnP XLum
- 'Variegata' (v)	CRow CWat ELan LLWG MSKA MWts NPla WMAq
§ ***laxmannii***	CBAq CBen CRow EHon LLWG MSKA WMAq WPnP XLum
lugdunensis	MWts
minima	CBAq CBen CRow CWat EHoe EHon ELan EPfP MSKA MWts NPer SWat WMAq WPnP XLum
shuttleworthii	CBen CRow LLWG
stenophylla	see *T. laxmannii*

Typhonium (*Araceae*)

giganteum	CAby SKHP WCot
horsfieldii	LEdu WCot
trilobatum	WCot
venosum	EUJe

Typhonodorum (*Araceae*)

lindleyanum	XBlo

U

Uapaca (*Euphorbiaceae*)

kirkiana (F)	XBlo

ugli see *Citrus* × *aurantium* Tangelo Group 'Ugli'

Ugni ✿ (*Myrtaceae*)

candollei	SVen
§ ***molinae***	Widely available
- PAB 1347	LEdu
- 'Butterball'	CBcs EBee EPfP LRHS LSou SWvt
- 'Flambeau' (v)	CBcs CBod CExl CHel CMac CSde EBee ELan EPfP EShb ETwe IVic LBMP LEdu LRHS MAsh MGil MGos NLar SEle SHil SLon SPoG SRkn SWvt WGrn
- orange-leaved	WJek
- 'Variegata' (v)	LEdu WJek

Ulex (*Papilionaceae*)

europaeus	CArn CBcs CCVT CDoC CDul CHab CMac CTri ECrN ELan EPfP LBuc MCoo MGil MGos NHed NWea SCob SEWo SPer WHar
§ - 'Flore Pleno' (d) ♀H4	CBcs CBod CDoC CDul CMac CSBt CSde CTri ELan ELon EPfP GAbr GCal IArd MBlu MGos MMuc NWea SCob SEND SPer WFar WHer
- 'Irish Double' (d) **new**	NLar
- 'Plenus'	see *U. europaeus* 'Flore Pleno'
gallii	NLar
- 'Mizen Head'	GCal GCrg MWhi NLar SLon

Ullucus (*Basellaceae*)

tuberosus	LEdu

Ulmus ✿ (*Ulmaceae*)

americana 'Princeton'	SEWo SGol
- 'Valley Forge'	SGol
carpinifolia var. ***suberosa***	CDul
'Dodoens'	IArd SCoo
'Frontier'	SGol
§ ***glabra***	CDul EPfP NWea SCob SCoo
- 'Camperdownii'	CMac ECrN ELan EPla LAst WMou
- 'Exoniensis'	CTho IVic
- 'Gittisham'	CTho
- 'Horizontalis'	see *U. glabra* 'Pendula'
- 'Lutescens'	CTho CTri NLar NWea SCoo SEWo
§ - 'Pendula'	CMac
§ × ***hollandica*** 'Dampieri Aurea' ♀H6	CDul CTho EBee ELan EPfP EPla LBuc MAsh MBlu MGos MRav NLar NWea SCob SPer SPoG WPat
- 'Jacqueline Hillier'	CDul CMac CSpe ECho ELan EPla LAst LRHS MMuc MRav NLar SEND SGol WCFE WFar WPat
- 'Wredei'	see *U.* × *hollandica* 'Dampieri Aurea'
laevis	CDul EGFP
'Lobel'	CCVT
Lutèce = 'Nanguen'	CDoC CDul SGol
minor	CDul
- 'Dampieri Aurea'	see *U.* × *hollandica* 'Dampieri Aurea'
montana	see *U. glabra*
parvifolia	CAco CMCN CMen WPGP
- Everclear = 'Bsnupf'	SGol
- 'Frosty' (v)	ECho
- 'Geisha' (v)	ECho ELan EPot MAsh WPat
§ - 'Hokkaido'	CMen ECho EWes LLHF WAbe WFar WPat WThu
- 'Pygmaea'	see *U. parvifolia* 'Hokkaido'
- 'Yatsubusa'	ECho MRav NLar
procera	CDul LBuc MCoo MGos SLon WSFF
pumila 'Beijing Gold'	ELan NLar
rubra	CArn
'Sapporo Autumn Gold'	CCVT EBee EPla LBuc MRav SGol WCFE
uyematsui **new**	WPGP
Vada = 'Wanoux'PBR	SGol

Umbellularia (*Lauraceae*)

californica	CArn EPfP IDee SSpi

Umbilicus (*Crassulaceae*)

rupestris	CArn SChr WHer WShi

Uncinia (*Cyperaceae*)

* ***cyparissias*** from Chile	NBir
divaricata	ECou
egmontiana	CUse EBee ECou EPfP LRHS NWad SHil WGrn WMoo
rubra	Widely available
§ - 'Belinda's Find'PBR	CHid CKno EBee ELan IBoy LBuc LLWG LRHS MAsh MNrw SPoG WCot
- EverflamePBR	see *U. rubra* 'Belinda's Find'
uncinata	CBcs ECha SDix
* - ***rubra***	CCon CKno CTri ELon IFro MAsh SCob SLim SMrm SRms SWvt

Uniola (*Poaceae*)

latifolia	see *Chasmanthium latifolium*

Urceolina (*Amaryllidaceae*)

miniata	see *Stenomesson miniatum*
peruviana	see *Stenomesson miniatum*

Urginea (*Asparagaceae*)

capitata 'Sentinel Peak'	ECho
macrocentra	ECho
maritima	CArn EBee ECho LAma WCot
ollivieri	CTal ECho
undulata	ECho

Urospermum (*Asteraceae*)

dalechampii	CSam

Ursinia (*Asteraceae*)

alpina	WHil

Urtica (*Urticaceae*)

from Casa Meca	CNat
dioica 'Chedglow 2' (v)	CNat
- 'Curly-Wurly' **new**	CNat
- 'Judith'	CNat
- OGG mutant	CNat
- 'Winter Yellow'	CNat

Utricularia (*Lentibulariaceae*)

sp.	EECP
australis	EFEx
biloba	CHew
bisquamata 'Betty's Bay' ♀H2	CHew
dichotoma	CHew EFEx
exoleta R. Brown	see *U. gibba*
§ ***gibba***	EFEx
heterosepala	CHew
intermedia	EFEx
lateriflora	CHew EFEx
livida ♀H2	CHew EFEx
menziesii	EFEx
microcalyx	CHew
monanthos	CHew EFEx
nephrophylla	CHew
novae-zelandiae	CHew
ochroleuca	EFEx
paulineae	CHew
praelonga	CHew
prehensilis	CHew
reniformis	EFEx
I - ***nana***	EFEx
sandersonii ♀H2	CHew
simplex	CHew
subulata	EFEx
tricolor	CHew
uniflora	CHew
vulgaris	CBAq EFEx
warburgii	CHew
welwitschii	CHew

Uvularia (*Colchicaceae*)

§ ***caroliniana***	ECho
disporum	ECho
grandiflora ♀H5	Widely available
- dwarf	ECho
- gold-leaved	CAby
- 'Lynda Windsor'	CDes CTal SKHP
- orange-flowered	SKHP
- var. ***pallida***	CAby CAvo CBct CDes CLAP CPom CTal EBee ECho EPPr EPfP EPot GBin GCal GEdr IBlr LEdu LRHS MNFA MRav NCGa NHar SMHy WCru WPnP
- 'Susie Lewis'	WCru
grandiflora* × *perfoliata	ECho EWTr NBir WWEG
perfoliata	CBct CExl CLAP CTal EBee ECha ECho EPPr EPfP EPla EPot GBuc GKev IBlr IMou LEdu MRav NBir WCru
- tall	EPPr
pudica	see *U. caroliniana*
sessilifolia	CBct CExl ECho EPot GEdr GKev IMou LEdu LRHS MMHG WCru
- 'Cobblewood Gold' (v)	EPPr WCru

V

Vaccinium ✿ (*Ericaceae*)

angustifolium var. ***laevifolium***	GLin
arctostaphylos	SWvt
'Berkeley' (F)	CAgr CCCN CEnd GKin LBuc MAsh MBlu NPla SDea SPoG SPre WHar
'Bluecrop' (F)	Widely available
'Bluejay' (F)	ELan LAst LRHS MAsh SCoo SLon WHar
'Blueray' (F)	GKin
'Brigitta' (F)	CEnd CTrh EMil GTwe LRHS NPla SPoG SPre
chaetothrix	WAbe WThu
'Chandler' (F)	CAgr CEnd CMac CTrh EMil EPom GKin LRHS MCoo NPla SKee SPoG
consanguineum B&SWJ 10486	WCru
corymbosum (F)	CBcs CUse MNHC SCoo SSta
- 'Aurora'PBR (F) **new**	SPer
- 'Blauweiss-Goldtraube' (F)	CAgr CSBt CWSG EPfP ESwi GKin MAsh NLar NPri SDea SPoG SVic WHar
- 'Blue Duke' (F)	SFrt
- 'Blue Pearl' (F) **new**	SFrt
- 'Bluegold' (F)	CTrh EMil LRHS MAsh SFrt
- 'Bluetta' (F)	CAgr CTri ELan GTwe SCoo SPoG
- 'Coville' (F)	NLar
- 'Darrow' (F)	CAgr GTwe NPla
- 'Dixie' (F)	CSBt LEdu NPla
- 'Duke' (F) ♀H6	CMac CTrh ELan EPfP EPom LRHS MGos NPla NWea SDea SPer SPre WHar
- 'Grover' (F)	NLar
- 'Hannah's Choice' (F)	CTrh
- 'Hardyblue' (F)	CAgr CUse
- 'Heerma' (F) **new**	NLar
- 'Ivanhoe' (F)	GKin
- 'Jersey' (F)	CAgr CEnd EPfP LAst LRHS MAsh MGos MMuc NLar NPla SCoo SDea SPer SVic WHar
- 'Nelson' (F)	LRHS NPla SCoo
- 'Nui' (F)	CEnd EPom MRav
- 'Patriot' (F)	CAgr CEnd CSBt CTrh GKin GQue GTwe LBuc LRHS MBri MGos MPkF

	MRav NPla NPri SCoo SDea SHil SPoG SPre
- 'Polaris' (F)	CEnd CTrh
- 'Reka' (F)	CAgr CUse NPer
- 'Spartan' (F) ♀H6	CTrh EPom GTwe LEdu LRHS MAsh MGos NPla SKee
- 'Stanley' (F)	ELan EPfP LRHS MAsh
- 'Toro' (F)	CTrh GTwe LRHS MAsh NPla SFrt SPre
- 'Weymouth' (F)	SDea
crassifolium	LRHS MAsh SPoG
subsp. ***sempervirens*** 'Well's Delight' (F)	
cylindraceum ♀H5	CBcs CEnd NLar WPat
- 'Tinkerbell'	ITim
delavayi	LRHS MAsh NHar WAbe WThu
donianum	see *V. sprengelii*
dunalianum	CBcs
- var. ***caudatifolium*** B&SWJ 1716	WCru
- var. ***megaphyllum*** HWJ 515	WCru
'Earliblue' (F)	CAgr CSBt GKin MBri NPla SDea SFrt
floribundum	CBcs CDoC CMHG LRHS MAsh SSpi WPat
glaucoalbum ♀H5	CAbP CDoC CMac EPfP LRHS MAsh MBlu MRav WPGP WPat
'Goldtraube 71'	MAsh NPla
* ***grandiflorum***	ECho
griffithianum	SSta
'Herbert' (F)	CAgr CMac CTrh EPom LBuc
macrocarpon (F)	CArn ECho ELan GTwe LRHS MAsh MMuc NHar SDea SPre SRms
- 'Centennial' (F)	NHar
- 'CN' (F)	CAgr NLar
- 'Early Black' (F)	ELan EPom GKin LBuc NLar SVic
- 'Franklin' (F)	CAgr
- 'Hamilton'	LLHF WThu
- 'Howes' (F)	NHar
- 'Langlois' (F)	NLar
- 'Olson's Honkers' (F)	CAgr CUse NLar
- 'Pilgrim' (F)	CAgr CMac CUse GKin LEdu LRHS MAsh MBri MCoo NHar WHar
- 'Red Star' (F)	CTrh
- 'Stevens' (F)	CAgr
moupinense	LRHS MAsh WThu
- 'Variegatum' (v)	LLHF
myrtillus	CAgr EPom GPoy NLar SVic
'Northland' (F)	CSBt EPfP GQue GTwe MBri NLar NPla NPri SCoo SDea SPoG
nummularia	ECho LRHS NHar NLar SSpi WAbe WThu
ovatum	CBcs CMHG CMac CTsd GKin WPat WThu
- 'Thundercloud'	CAbP LRHS MAsh
§ ***oxycoccos*** (F)	CAgr GPoy MCoo NHar WThu
'Ozarkblue' (F)	CTrh EPom GTwe MCoo
pallidum	IBlr
palustre	see *V. oxycoccos*
'Pink Lemonade' new	EPom LRHS SBmr
retusum	WThu
'Rubel' (F)	NPri
§ ***sprengelii***	CFil
'Spring Surprise'	WAbe
'Sunrise' (F)	GTwe
'Sunshine Blue' (F)	CAgr CEnd CTrh EPom LBuc LRHS SDea SPoG
'Tophat' (F)	CCCN LEdu MPkF
vitis-idaea	CArn EPfP EWes GPoy NWea SVic
- 'Aalshorst' new	NLar
- 'Autumn Beauty'	NLar
- 'Compactum'	EWes LLHF
- 'Erntetraum' new	NLar
- 'Ida'	LBuc
- Koralle Group ♀H5	CAgr EPfP GKin MBri MCoo NLar NWad
- 'Leucocarpa' new	NLar
- subsp. ***minus***	NLar WAbe WThu
- 'Red Candy'	ELan EPfP NWad
- 'Red Pearl'	CSBt EPom LRHS MAsh NLar

Vagaria (*Amaryllidaceae*)

ollivieri	ECho

Valeriana (*Caprifoliaceae*)

'Alba'	see *Centranthus ruber* 'Albus'
alliariifolia	CSam EBee GCal MSpe NBro WCot
- PAB 3001	LEdu
'Coccinea'	see *Centranthus ruber*
dioica	LLWG
jatamansi	CArn GPoy WJek
- PAB 6846 new	LEdu
montana	NBro NRya SRms SWat
officinalis	Widely available
- subsp. ***sambucifolia***	EPPr GCal MNrw MSpe SHar WHil
phu 'Aurea'	CArn CBod CHby CMac EBee ECha EHoe ELan EPfP GKin LRHS MCot MLHP MRav NBid NBir NBro NEgg NLar NSti NWad SPer SRms WMoo
pyrenaica	EBee ECha EPPr GCal LPla LRHS MMHG MMuc MNrw SDix SEND SHar SPhx WCot WMoo
saxatilis	NLar NRya
supina	CPBP
wallrothii	MAvo WCot

Valerianella (*Caprifoliaceae*)

§ ***locusta***	CBod GPoy SVic
olitoria	see *V. locusta*

Vallea (*Elaeocarpaceae*)

stipularis	CHll CTsd

Vallota see *Cyrtanthus*

Vancouveria (*Berberidaceae*)

sp.	CHel
chrysantha	CCon CExl CFil CMil CPom CTal EBee EPPr GEdr GLog MRav NLar NRya SKHP SMad WMoo WPGP
hexandra	CBct CCon CExl CFil CLAP CMac CTal ECha EPPr EPfP EPla GEdr GKev GLog LEdu NSti SKHP SPhx WCru WMoo WPGP WWEG
planipetala	IMou WCru

Vania see *Thlaspi*

veitchberry see *Rubus* 'Veitchberry'

Veltheimia ✿ (*Asparagaceae*)

§ ***bracteata*** ♀H2	CCse CLak EBak ECho LToo NRog WCot
- 'Lemon Flame'	ECho NRog
- yellow-flowered new	NRog

§ ***capensis*** 🏆H2	NRog
viridifolia misapplied	see *V. capensis*
viridifolia Jacq.	see *V. bracteata*

× *Venidioarctotis* see *Arctotis*

Venidium see *Arctotis*

Veratrum ✿ (*Melanthiaceae*)

album 🏆H7	CBct CCon CPne EBee ECha ECho GKev GPoy MNrw MRav NBid WCru
- PAB 537	LEdu
- var. ***flavum***	LPla MNrw SPhx WCot WCru
- subsp. ***lobelianum***	GCal
- 'Lorna's Green'	GCal MNrw WCot
- var. ***oxysepalum***	WCru
californicum	CHGN EBee ECha GCal MNrw NBid SMad WCot
dolichopetalum B&SWJ 4195	WCru
formosanum	CDes EWld MNrw WSHC
- B&SWJ 1575	WCru
- RWJ 9806	WCru
grandiflorum B&SWJ 4416	WCru
longebracteatum	WCru
maackii	EBee MNrw
- B&SWJ 5875 **new**	WCru
- var. ***japonicum***	MNrw WCru
- var. ***maackii***	MNrw
- - B&SWJ 5831	WCru
nigrum 🏆H7	CBct CCon ECha GCal GEdr GMaP IKil LEdu LPla LRHS MAvo MLHP MNrw MRav NBid NBir NLar SMad SPhx SPlb WCot WCru WPnP
- B&SWJ 4450 from South Korea	WCru
schindleri	MNrw
- B&SWJ 4068	WCru
stamineum	WCru
viride	CBct EBee ECha EWes GCal MNrw NBid WCot

Verbascum (*Scrophulariaceae*)

'Annie May'	NOrc
'Arctic Summer'	see *V. bombyciferum* 'Polarsommer'
'Bill Bishop'	ECho
blattaria	NBir SPav SWat WHer
- f. ***albiflorum***	CSpe EWTr GBBs IFro LLWP NDov SPlb WHer WMoo
- yellow-flowered	SPav SWat
'Blue Lagoon'	CBcs CMos CWGN EPfP GBin LRHS MNrw NPri SHil STPC
'Blushing Bride'PBR	LLHF
§ ***bombyciferum***	CBre CUse ECha ELan GMaP LRHS NGBl SCob
* - 'Arctic Snow'	SPav SPoG
§ - 'Polarsommer'	CSpe EPfP GJos LRHS NBir SPer SWat
- 'Silver Lining'	NPer
'Broussa'	see *V. bombyciferum*
'Buttercup'	ECtt LRHS SHil
'Camelot' **new**	LRHS
'Caribbean Crush'	CBcs ECtt ELan ELon GBin IBoy LRHS MGos NLar SPer WCAu
chaixii	CHel CSam ECha LRHS MMHG NBir WFar WMoo
- 'Album'	Widely available
- 'Sixteen Candles'	GJos LSun MBNS NLar WFar WPtf
- 'Wedding Candles'	CBod ELan NGdn NLar SPtp WFar WHil
'Cherry Helen'PBR	LRHS MBri NLar SCob
'Christo's Yellow Lightning' 🏆H7	WCot
'Clementine'	CBcs CMos EBee ECtt ELan LPla LRHS MAvo MBri SCob SHil SPhx
'Coneyhill Yellow'	EPPr
(Cotswold Group) 'Cotswold Beauty'	CHel CSam CSpe EAEE ECtt EPfP EPla EWoo LRHS MRav MWat NGdn SPer WHoo WMnd
- 'Cotswold Gem'	ECtt
- 'Cotswold Queen'	CHel EAEE ECtt ELan EPPr EPfP EPla GBBs LRHS MRav MWat SGol SPer SWvt
- 'Gainsborough' 🏆H6	CBod COtt CSBt EAEE ECha ECtt ELan EPfP EWoo GMaP LRHS LSun MBri MJak MRav MWat NGdn NLar NPri NSoo NSti SCob SGbt SPer SWat SWvt WCAu WHil
- 'Mont Blanc'	EAEE SWat
- 'Pink Domino' 🏆H6	CBod COtt CSam ECtt ELan EPPr EPfP GMaP LRHS LSun MJak MLHP MRav MWat NSoo SPer SWvt WMnd WWFP
- 'Royal Highland'	CHel ECtt ELan EPfP LRHS NGdn NLar SWvt
- 'White Domino'	ECtt
'Cotswold King'	see *V. creticum*
§ ***creticum***	CSpe IKil WCot
'Dark Eyes'PBR	CWGN ECtt LRHS SCob
§ ***densiflorum***	CArn WWEG
epixanthinum 🏆H5	CPla CSpe GEdr
'Flower of Scotland'	MBNS
'Golden Wings' 🏆H4	CPla WAbe
'Guinevere' **new**	LRHS
'Helen Johnson'	CBod CHel CWCL EAEE ECtt ELan EPfP EPla GMaP LRHS MGos MRav NLar NPri SCob SCoo SHil SPer SRkn SWvt WMnd
× ***hybridum*** 'Banana Custard'	NGBl
- 'Copper Rose'	LRHS
- 'Snow Maiden'	CTri EPfP
- 'Wega'	NLar
'Jackie'	CHel ECtt ELan GBBs LBMP LRHS MBri NPri SCob SCoo SPer SPoG
'Jackie in Pink'	ELan LRHS MBri SHil
'Jackie in Yellow'PBR	LLHF MBri
'Jester'	CBcs CMos ECtt MBNS MHol SCob
'Jolly Eyes'	ECtt GBBs
'June Johnson'	EAEE ECtt EPla LRHS NLar SHar
'Kynaston'	IPot LRHS MBNS
'Letitia' 🏆H4	CPla ECho ECtt ELan EPot EWes GCal ITim LRHS SWvt WAbe
'Linda'	ECtt
longifolium var. ***pannosum***	see *V. olympicum*
lychnitis	CArn GEdr SPhx
'Megan's Mauve'	EAEE
'Merlin'PBR	EAEE ECtt IGor LRHS LSou MBNS WMnd
nigrum	CArn CHab EBee NGdn NLar WHer WMoo
- var. ***album***	NChi NGdn NLar WMoo WOut

§ ***olympicum***	CBod ELan EPfP GJos LPot LRHS MBNS MLHP NGBl NSti SCob SDix SVen WCAu WCot WWEG
'Petra'	LPla LRHS SPhx
phlomoides white-flowered	SPhx
phoeniceum	EBee ELan EPfP GJos GKev NBid NBro SPlb SPoG WFar WMoo
* - 'Album'	CSpe
- 'Antique Rose'	WHrl
- 'Flush of White'	CBod ECtt EPfP GBin GQue MSCN NGBl NGdn NLar SCob WCAu WHar WHil WMoo WWEG WWFP
- hybrids	CTri GMaP NEgg NGdn SRms SWat WFar WWEG
- 'Rosetta'	EPfP MCot NGBl NGdn SPad SPhx
- 'Violetta'	CAby CSpe ECtt EPPr EPfP GBBs LBMP MCot MHol MLHP MNFA MSpe MWat NChi NEgg NGBl NGdn NSti SGbt SPav SPer SPhx WCFE WCot WHrl WMoo
'Phoenix'	CTsd
'Pink Kisses'	LLHF LRHS MBNS
'Pink Petticoats'	COtt LBuc LRHS SPoG
(Pixie Series) 'Pixie Apricot'	ECtt MBri NSir
- 'Pixie Blue'	EBee ECtt MBri
- 'Pixie Pink'	MBri
- 'Pixie White'	ECtt MBri
'Plum Smokey'[PBR]	ECtt IBoy LLHF
'Primrose Path'	ECtt EPfP LRHS NPri
pyramidatum	SPhx
'Queen of Hearts' **new**	LRHS
'Raspberry Ripple'	LLHF LRHS MRav SPer
'Rosie'	SCob
'Sierra Sunset'	LRHS NLar
'Southern Charm'	COtt EPfP GJos GMaP MHer NLar NSbr SPoG WPtf
'Spica'	NLar
'Sugar Plum'[PBR]	ECtt ELon LBuc LLHF MBri MHol SPoG WCAu
'Summer Sorbet'	CBcs ECtt LRHS MNrw NSti SPoG
Sunset shades	GJos WOut
thapsiforme	see *V. densiflorum*
thapsus	CHab ENfk GJos GPoy MHer MNHC NBir NMir WOut
'Tropic Sun' ♀H5	WHoo
undulatum	CArn
'Wessex' **new**	LRHS
xanthophoeniceum **new**	WCot

Verbena (*Verbenaceae*)

(Aztec Series) Aztec Cherry Red = 'Balazcherd'[PBR] (G)	NPri
- Aztec Pearl = 'Balazpearl'[PBR] (G)	SCoo
- Aztec Plum Magic = 'Balazplum'[PBR] (G)	NPri
- Aztec Red = 'Balazred' (G)	SCoo
- Aztec Silver Magic = 'Balazsilma'[PBR] (G)	NPri SCoo
'Bampton'	CAby LEdu MNrw WCot
'Blue Prince' (G)	CSpe
'Blue Sapphire' **new**	LRHS
§ ***bonariensis*** ♀H4	Widely available
- 'Little One' **new**	SPad
- 'Lollipop'[PBR]	CBct CBod CKno CMea CMos CRos CSpe EBee ECha ELan EPfP EWTr GBin IBal LRHS MAsh MAvo MBel MGos NLar NPri NSti SCob SGbt SHil SPer SPoG STPC SWvt WCot
brasiliensis misapplied	see *V. bonariensis*
canadensis 'Perfecta' (G)	CSpe
chamaedrifolia	see *V. peruviana*
§ 'Claret' (G)	CMac CSpe CUse EBee ECtt ELan EPfP LAst LRHS LSou MCot MGos MNrw SCoo SMrm SPhx SPoG WWEG
'Corsage Peach' (Corsage Series) (G/d)	LRHS
corymbosa	CHid CHll CWld EBee ECha EWoo LRHS NLar SMrm SPhx WMoo
- 'Gravetye'	LPot
'Diamond Merci' (G)	WHoo
(Donalena Series) Donalena Twinkle Pink (G)	NPri
- Donalena Twinkle Purple (G)	NPri
'Edith Eddleman' (G)	CMac CWGN EPfP LRHS SPoG
elegans **new**	NDov
'Empress Peach Flair'	LAst
'Hammerstein Pink'	EBee EPfP
hastata	CSpe EBee ECtt EPfP LAst LEdu LRHS MNrw NDov NSti SCob SPhx SPlb SRms SWat SWvt WBor WCAu WFar WMnd WMoo WOld WOut WPnn WSHC XLum
* - 'Alba'	CTsd EBee ELan EPfP GBin NLar SCob WMoo
- 'Blue Spires'	EPfP SCob WWEG
- f. ***rosea***	CElw CMea CPom CSpe EHoe ELan EPfP GKev LRHS MCot MLHP MNrw MRav NBid NDov SPer SPhx SWat WCAu WHea WMoo WSHC WWEG
- - 'Pink Spires'	EBee ECtt ELan EPfP SCob WWEG
- 'White Spires'	CMea EPfP WWEG
'Homestead Purple' (G)	CMac CRos CUse EBee ECtt ELan EPfP LRHS MCot MGos MNrw NDov SCob SMrm SRkn SWvt WHoo WWEG
'Jenny's Wine'	see *V.* 'Claret'
'La France' (G)	CHGN ECha EPfP LRHS SDix SMHy SMrm SPhx SPoG
(Lanai Series) Lanai Blue Denim = 'Bludena'[PBR]	MCot
- Lanai Candy Cane Red = 'Veaz0011' **new**	LAst
- Lanai Lime Green = 'Veaz0013' **new**	LAst
- Lanai Royal Purple with Eye = 'Lan Roypureye'[PBR] **new**	MCot
lasiostachys	EBee
'Little Annie' **new**	ECtt
'Lois' Ruby'	see *V.* 'Claret'
macdougalii	WMoo
- 'Lavender Spires'	LPla NDov SDix SPhx
officinalis	CArn ENfk GPoy MHer MNHC SIde SRms WHer WJek
patagonica	see *V. bonariensis*
§ ***peruviana*** (G)	EBee ECho ELan LBMP LRHS SChF SRms XLum
'Pink Bouquet'	see *V.* 'Silver Anne'
'Pink Parfait' (G)	EPfP
Quartz Series	LAst NPri

- 'Quartz Red Polka Dot'	ELan EPfP
- 'Quartz Waterfall' (mixed)	LAst
§ ***rigida*** ♀H3	Widely available
- f. ***lilacina***	NLar
- - 'Lilac Haze'	CMac EPfP LBMP LRHS NSti SRkn
- - 'Polaris'	CBod CMea CMos CSam EAJP EBee ELan ELon EPfP EPla EShb EWTr GCal LRHS MNrw MRav SCob SDix SHar SMHy SMrm SPer SPoG
'Rococo Peach' **new**	LRHS
'Rococo Pink' **new**	LRHS
'Samira Scarlet' **new**	LRHS
Seabrook's Lavender = 'Sealav'PBR	EBee ELon EPfP ESwi LRHS MNrw SCoo SHar SPer SRkn SWvt
serpyllifolia	see *Junellia micrantha*
§ 'Silver Anne' (G) ♀H3	MCot SDix SMrm
§ 'Sissinghurst' (G) ♀H2	CSam ECtt SRms
'Strawberry Kiss'	EPfP SPoG
stricta	EBee EWes NLar SPhx
Superbena Burgundy = 'Usbenal5'PBR (Superbena Series) (G)	CAby
(Tapien Series) Tapien Compact Red = 'Suntapicore'PBR (G)	LAst LRHS
- Tapien Compact Velvet = 'Suntapikovel' (G)	LSou
- Tapien Pink Parfait = 'Suntapipipa'PBR (G)	LSou
- Tapien Pink = 'Sunver'PBR (G)	LAst MCot
- Tapien Salmon = 'Suntapiro'PBR (G)	LAst LSou
- Tapien Sky Blue = 'Suntapilabu'PBR (G)	LAst
- Tapien Violet = 'Sunvop'PBR (G)	LAst LSou
- Tapien White = 'Suntapipurew'PBR (G)	LAst
(Temari Series) Temari Blue = 'Sunmariribu'PBR (G)	LAst MCot
- Temari Coral Pink = 'Sunmariripi'PBR (G)	LAst LSou
- Temari Neon Red = 'Sunmarineopi'PBR (G)	LAst
- Temari Vanilla = 'Sunmarivani'PBR (G)	LAst LSou
'Tenerife'	see *V.* 'Sissinghurst'
venosa	see *V. rigida*
'Venturi Rose' **new**	LRHS

Verbesina (*Asteraceae*)

alternifolia	CArn
- 'Goldstrahl'	EPPr

Vernicia (*Euphorbiaceae*)

fordii	SPlb

Vernonia (*Asteraceae*)

angustifolia × Vernonia ***missurica***	SPhx WCot
§ ***arkansana***	CHGN CSam EBee ECha ECtt EPPr EWes LEdu MAvo NLar SDix SMad SPhx WWEG
- 'Alba'	ECtt
- 'Betty Blindeman'	EBee LEdu
- 'Mammuth'	CDes EBee ECtt EWes EWoo GQue LEdu LPla LRHS MAvo SPhx
baldwinii	SPhx
crinita	see *V. arkansana*
fasciculata	CSpe EShb EWes LEdu LPla LRHS MAvo MRav NLar SMHy SMrm SPhx WCot
gigantea	ELon EWes MAvo MMuc MNrw NLar SBHP SMad SPhx WHrl
glauca	SPhx WCot
lindheimeri	WCot
missurica	SPhx
noveboracensis	EBee EWTr LEdu MAvo NLar SGSe SMad SMrm SPhx XLum
- 'Albiflora'	EPPr EWes

Veronica (*Plantaginaceae*)

amethystina	see *V. spuria* L.
anagallis-aquatica	LLWG
'Anna'PBR	MTis NDov
armena	ECho EDAr EWes MHer MWat SBch SRot WIce XSen
'Atomic Lilac'	LSou
'Atomic Pink'	LSou MBri
'Atomic Pink Ray'PBR **new**	NSir
'Atomic Red Ray'	MBri SMrm
'Atomic Sky Ray'PBR	LSou
'Atomic Violet'	MBri
'Atomic Violet Ray'PBR	LSou MBri
§ ***austriaca***	EWoo NBre NChi WMoo
- dark blue-flowered	NChi
- var. ***dubia***	see *V. prostrata*
- 'Ionian Skies'	CElw CTri ECha ECho ECtt EPPr EWTr EWes MMuc NWad SEND SHar SIgm SPer WIce WKif WSHC WWEG
§ - subsp. ***teucrium***	CArn CSam CTri EBee ECho SRms WKif
- - 'Blue Fountain'	LRHS
- - 'Crater Lake Blue' ♀H6	CAby CMos EBee ECtt ELan EPfP EPla EWoo LEdu LRHS MAvo MRav NGdn SMrm SPhx SPlb SRms WCot WFar WMnd WSHC
- - 'Kapitän'	ECha ECho GBuc LRHS MNrw NGdn WFar
- - 'Knallblau'	SMrm
- - 'Royal Blue' ♀H6	CPrp EBee EPfP EPla EShb GMaP LRHS MJak MWhi NSti SPer SRms WFar WKif WMnd WMoo XLum XSen
'Baby Doll'PBR	LRHS MBNS MBri NLar
beccabunga	CArn CBAq CBen CHab CWat EHon EWay GPoy MMuc MSKA MWts NMir NPer SEND SWat WHer WMAq WSFF
'Bergen's Blue'	NLar SHar WSHC
Blue Bouquet	see *V. longifolia* 'Blaubündel'
'Blue Indigo'	MNrw NBre NGdn
'Blue Spire'	SWat
bombycina	ITim WAbe
- subsp. ***bolkardaghensis***	WAbe
bonarota	see *Paederota bonarota*
caespitosa	CPBP
- subsp. ***caespitosa***	EPot WAbe
candida	see *V. spicata* subsp. *incana*
× ***cantiana*** 'Kentish Pink'	WAul WCFE WMoo WWEG XLum
caucasica	MSCN XSen
chamaedrys	NMir XLum
- 'Pam' (v)	ECtt
'Charlotte' (v)	EBee ECtt EHoe EPts GBin MTis SCob WCot WHil WRHF

'Christa Bubblegum' **new**	EPfP
Christy = 'Henslerone'[PBR]	EPfP LBuc LRHS MBri
cinerea ♀H5	MLHP SBch SBrt WHoo WSHC XSen
dabneyi	EBee WPGP
'Dark Martje'	EBee IPot WSHC
'Darwin's Blue'[PBR]	NGdn NLar NOrc WHrl
'Ellen Mae'	CElw ECtt EWes WCAu WMnd
'Eveline'[PBR]	ECtt EPfP LRHS MBri MSpe NDov NLar
exaltata (d)	NChi SMHy SMrm
'Fairytale'[PBR]	LRHS LSou MBNS MBri NGdn NSti SMrm WHil
'Fantasy'	NDov
filiformis	XLum
'First Love'	LRHS LSou MAsh MBri MNrw NGdn NPri
formosa	see *Parahebe formosa*
§ ***fruticans***	ECho GJos
fruticulosa	LLHF
gentianoides	Widely available
- 'Alba'	CMea GCal LEdu NBre NChi
- 'Barbara Sherwood' ♀H7	EBee LRHS NGdn WWEG
- 'Blue Streak'	EPfP SGSe XLum
- 'Nana'	EBee
- 'Pallida'	EWoo GAbr GKev MBrN MMuc MRav SCob SEND SPlb WBor WWEG XLum
- 'Robusta'	CAby CBod ECtt GKev LRHS NGdn WFar WHoo WMnd
- 'Tissington White'	Widely available
- 'Variegata' (v)	EBee ECha ECtt ELan GCra GMaP LAst LBMP MHer MRav MSCN MSpe NBir NEgg NWad SPer SWat WFar WRHF WWEG
'Giles van Hees'	ECtt
grandis	EBee GAbr IFro LEdu MMuc MWhi NChi NLar SEND WHrl WMoo WPtf XLum
× ***guthrieana***	SRms
incana	see *V. spicata* subsp. *incana*
* - 'Candidissima'	GCal
'Ink'	MAvo SPhx
'Inspiration'	CCse CMea NBre SMrm
'Inspire Blue'	LPot LRHS LSou MMuc MPnt SEND SHil
'Inspire Pink'	LRHS LSou MPnt SHil
kellereri	see *V. spicata*
kiusiana	CMHG EBee IFro LPla NLar NWad SPhx WHrl
* - var. ***maxima***	CAby WPtf
kotschyana	XSen
'Lavender Plume'	CWGN EPfP WHil
liwanensis Mac&W 5936	EPot
longifolia	CMac CSBt ECha ELan GCra MBel MLHP MNFA MSpe NSti WMoo XLum
- 'Alba'	ELan MMuc SEND WMoo
- 'Antarctica'	EBee
- 'Blaubart'	XLum
§ - 'Blaubündel'	CCse LRHS NGdn
- 'Blauer Sommer'	EBee EPfP EPla NEgg NGdn
§ - 'Blauriesin'	CTri ECtt ELan EPfP GMaP NLar NSti SPer
- Blue Giantess	see *V. longifolia* 'Blauriesin'
- 'Blue John'	CAbP ECtt EPfP GBin LSou MPie NBre NSti WCot WHoo
- blue-flowered	CBod SGSe WHar
- 'Charming Pink'	LRHS MSCN
- 'Christa'[PBR] **new**	EPfP
- 'Fascination'	ECtt EHoe LAst NEoE NGdn
- 'Foerster's Blue'	see *V. longifolia* 'Blauriesin'
- 'Incarnata' **new**	EBee LRHS
- 'Joseph's Coat' (v)	NBre
- 'Lilac Fantasy'	MBri MRav MSCN
- 'Oxford Blue'	WBor WHoo
- 'Pacific Ocean'[PBR]	ECtt
- 'Pink Eveline'[PBR]	ECtt LRHS MBri MSpe NDov STPC
- pink-flowered	CBod EShb
- 'Rose Tone'	GJos WMoo
- 'Schneeriesin'	EBee ECha EPfP GMaP LEdu LRHS MAvo MRav MTis NBir NLar
lyallii	see *Parahebe lyallii*
macrostachya	SKHP
'Martje'	SMrm XLum
montana 'Corinne Tremaine' (v)	NBir SRms WHer
officinalis	CArn GJos XLum XSen
oltensis	CPBP ECho EPot GCrg ITim LLHF MHer
orchidea	SRms
ornata	WOld
'Pacific Ocean'	NLar
pectinata 'Rosea'	ECho ECtt EWes XSen
peduncularis 'Oxford Blue'	see *V. umbrosa* 'Georgia Blue'
perfoliata	see *Parahebe perfoliata*
petraea 'Madame Mercier'	SMrm XLum
'Pink Damask'	CSpe ECtt ELan ELon EPfP GMaP MAvo MCot MLHP MRav MSpe MTis NGdn NLar NSti SDys SMrm SPhx WHoo WMnd WWEG
'Pink Harmony'	CBod MAsh NSti SMrm
pinnata	SBrt
- 'Blue Feathers'	EDAr
piroliformis **new**	WAbe
porphyriana	CBod EBee EDAr MMuc NLar
prenja	see *V. austriaca*
§ ***prostrata*** ♀H5	CBod CMea CSpe CTri ECho ECtt EDAr EPfP GCrg GJos GKev LAst LRHS MAsh MHol MLHP MMuc NEgg NHar NHol NPri SEND SRms WHoo WIce WMoo XLum
- 'Alba'	MLHP MWat
- 'Aztec Gold'[PBR]	CMac NEoE
§ - 'Blauspiegel'	CPBP SIgm
- 'Blue Ice'	SMrm
- Blue Mirror	see *V. prostrata* 'Blauspiegel'
- 'Blue Sheen'	ECho ECtt EPfP LRHS NBir
- 'Goldwell'	EBee ECtt EPPr LBMP SRot
- 'Lavender Mist' **new**	LRHS
- 'Lilac Time'	CBod ECho ECtt EPot GMaP LRHS NBir NHol SRms WHil WIce
- 'Loddon Blue'	SRms
- 'Mrs Holt'	ECho ECtt GCrg LRHS MHer NBir NLar NWad SRms WHoo XLum
- 'Nana'	CPBP ECho ECtt EPot EWes GCrg MWat WAbe
- 'Nestor'	CTri CUse ECtt WPtf XLum
- 'Rosea'	ECho MWat
- 'Spode Blue' ♀H5	CBod CMac CMea EBee ECho ECtt GCrg GMaP LBMP LRHS MHer MMuc SEND SPoG SRms WWEG
- 'Trehane'	ECho ECtt EDAr EPfP GCrg LEdu LRHS MAsh MHer NEgg NRya SPlb SPoG SRms WIce

	'Purpleicious Harmony'PBR	EBee EPfP GBin LRHS LSou MBri NPri SMrm WCAu WHil
	repens	ECho EPfP GJos NEoE SPlb
	- 'Sunshine'	WRHF
	'Rosalinde'	NGdn
	'Royal Pink'	LAst MRav NLar
	rupestris	see *V. prostrata*
	saturejoides	GCrg SRms
	saxatilis	see *V. fruticans*
	selleri	see *V. wormskjoldii*
	'Shirley Blue' ♀H6	CPrp ELan EPfP LPot MCot MHer MMuc MWat SEND SPer SPhx SRms WCAu WCFE WWEG
§	***spicata***	CSam ELan EPfP EWTr GJos LRHS MRav NBid SCob SMrm SRms WBrk WMoo WShi XLum
	- 'Alba'	EBee EPfP GJos LPot LRHS MRav MWat NLar WWEG XLum
§	- 'Blaufuchs'	CSam
	- 'Blue Bouquet'	NLar NPri
	- 'Blue Candles'	GQue MTis
	- Blue Fox	see *V. spicata* 'Blaufuchs'
§	- 'Erika'	CSam ECtt EPfP GBin IBoy MAsh MNrw MWat NBid NBir NGdn NLar WHil
§	- 'Glory'PBR	ECtt ELan ELon LRHS MGos MPie NPri NSoo SCob SMrm SPad SPer SPoG WCot WHil WMnd WRHF
	- 'Heidekind'	CHel EBee ECha ECho ECtt EDAr ELan EPfP EPla EPot GCrg GKev LAst LPot MWat NBir NGdn SRms SRot SWat WHil WHoo WIce XLum
	- 'High Five'PBR	EBee
	- subsp. ***hybrida***	WHer
	- - 'Elaine's Form'	WCot
§	- 'Icicle'	EBee SCob WCAu
§	- subsp. ***incana*** ♀H4	ECho EHoe ELan EPfP GJos MMuc SEND SPlb SRms SWat WMoo XSen
	- - 'Nana'	MLHP NBir SRms
	- - 'Silbersee'	MAvo MLHP
	- - 'Silver Carpet'	CPrp ECtt EWTr LAst MRav SPer WGwG WMnd
	- - 'Wendy'	EWes GCal LPla SPhx WSHC
	- 'Nana Blauteppich'	EDAr LRHS NLar
	- 'Pink Goblin'	EDAr ELan EPfP SMrm
	- 'Pink Panther'PBR	LSou WCot
	- Red Fox	see *V. spicata* 'Rotfuchs'
	- 'Romiley Purple'	EBee SPer
	- 'Rosalind'	NLar
	- ***rosea***	see *V. spicata* 'Erika'
§	- 'Rotfuchs'	CBod ECtt EHoe ELan ELon EPfP LAst LPot LRHS LSou MCot MHer MMuc MRav NBid NBir NGdn NLar NOrc NSoo SCob SPad SPer SPoG SRms WCFE WWEG
	- 'Royal Candles'PBR	see *V. spicata* 'Glory'
	- 'Sightseeing'	GJos NBir SRms
	- subsp. ***spicata*** 'Nana'	XSen
	- 'Total Eclipse'PBR	NSti
	- 'Twilight'PBR	ECtt EPfP LRHS NLar
	- 'Ulster Blue Dwarf'	EBee EPfP IBoy IMou LRHS LSou MAsh MAvo MBri MCot NBid NGdn NPri SHil SMrm WCAu WPtf
§	***spuria*** L.	SEND
	stelleri	see *V. wormskjoldii*
	subsessilis 'Blaue Pyramide'	WPtf
	'Sunny Border Blue'	CBod EPfP LRHS NLar NSoo WCot
	tauricola	XSen
	telephiifolia	EWes
	teucrium	see *V. austriaca* subsp. *teucrium*
	thessalica	EPot WAbe
	thymoides	SIgm
	subsp. ***pseudocinerea***	
§	***umbrosa*** 'Georgia Blue' ♀H5	Widely available
	urticifolia	SBrt
	virginica	see *Veronicastrum virginicum*
	'Waterperry Blue'	ECtt
	'White Icicle'	see *V. spicata* 'Icicle'
	'White Jolanda'	NLar NSti
	whitleyi	MMuc
§	***wormskjoldii***	ECho GBin GCrg MAvo MBrN MMuc NWad SBch SEND SRms
	- 'Alba'	MLHP

Veronicastrum ✿ (*Plantaginaceae*)

	'Adoration'	EBee ECtt LPla MAvo MTis NDov SMHy SPhx STPC WCAu
	axillare	IMou
	brunonianum	GCal WSHC
	japonicum var. ***australe*** B&SWJ 11009	WCru
	latifolium	CDes EBee WCot
	- BWJ 8158	WCru
	sibiricum	CKno EBee ECha EShb GCal GQue LRHS MLHP MMuc SEND SHar WMoo XLum
	- BWJ 6352	NLar WCru WFar
	- 'Kobaltkaars'	SMHy SPhx
	- 'Red Arrows'	Widely available
	- var. ***yezoense***	IMou WHoo
	- - RBS 0290	NEoE
	villosulum	CPom EBee EWes IMou NBid NBro WSHC
§	***virginicum***	CArn CKno EBee ECtt GCra GPoy MLHP MMuc MWhi NBir SRms WFar WMoo WRHF WWEG XLum
	- 'Album'	Widely available
	- 'Apollo'	CBct CBod CBre ECtt EPPr EPfP EWll GAbr GBin GMaP IBoy LEdu LPla LRHS LSou MAvo MBri NBro NLar NOrc NSti SMrm SPhx SWvt WAul WBor WCAu WHrl WWEG
	- 'Cupid'	ECtt GBin MAvo MTis NDov STPC
	- 'Diane'	CAby EBee IPot LPla MAvo NDov SPhx SWvt WCAu WHil
	- 'Erica'	CAby CKno EBee ECha ECtt EPPr EPfP GBin GMaP GQue IKil IPot LPla LRHS LSou MAvo MBri MNrw NDov NSti SMHy SMrm SPhx SPoG SWvt WAul WBor WHil WWEG
	- 'Fascination'	Widely available
	- var. ***incarnatum***	see *V. virginicum* f. *roseum*
	- 'Lavendelturm'	Widely available
	- light blue-flowered	SGSe
	- 'Pointed Finger'	CMea GCal GMaP IPot LEdu NLar SMHy SMrm SPhx
§	- f. ***roseum***	CAby CPrp ECha ELan GMaP LPla LRHS MHol MRav MTis NBro NDov SGbt SPad SPer SPhx SWvt WBor WHrl WKif WMoo XLum
	- - 'Pink Glow'	Widely available
	- 'Spring Dew'	CBre LEdu LPla NBid NBro NEoE NLar SPhx WCAu WFar

- 'Temptation'	EBee GMaP IPot LEdu LPla MRav NBro NEoE NLar SPhx

Verschaffeltia (*Arecaceae*)

splendida	XBlo

Vestia (*Solanaceae*)

§ ***foetida***	CBcs CCCN CExl CTsd EBee ELan EPfP IDee LRHS MGil MNrw MPie SBig SBrt SEND SEle WSHC
lycioides	see *V. foetida*

Viburnum ✿ (*Adoxaceae*)

acerifolium	LLHF NWad WPat
alnifolium	see *V. lantanoides*
atrocyaneum	CExl CJun NWad SKHP WPat
- B&SWJ 7272	EPfP WCru
- HIRD 113	WPGP
§ ***awabuki***	CExl CHEx ELon EPfP ETwe EUJe LEdu LRHS MAsh MBlu MGos NLar SEND SLim WPat
- B&SWJ 8404	WCru
- B&SWJ 11374 from Wabuka, Japan	WCru
- 'Emerald Lustre'	CBcs CHEx EBee
betulifolium	CAbP CBcs CExl CJun ELan EPfP EWes GKin IDee NLar SPer WPGP
- PAB 3877	LEdu
- f. ***aurantiacum***	CJun
- 'Hohuanshan'	WCru
bitchiuense	CJun NLar
× ***bodnantense***	CMac CTri EBee EWTr WFar WHar
- 'Charles Lamont' ♀H6	CRos EBee ECrN ELan EPfP GBin GCal LAst LBMP LRHS LSou MAsh MBri MGos MMuc MRav MSwo NEgg NLar NSoo SCob SCoo SEND SGol SHil SLim SPer WFar WPat
- 'Dawn' ♀H6	Widely available
- 'Deben' ♀H6	EBee EPfP MMHG NLar SPer SPoG WPat
brachyandrum B&SWJ 5784	WCru
bracteatum	NLar
buddlejifolium	CMac EBee EBtc EPfP EWes MMuc SKHP WCru
× ***burkwoodii***	Widely available
- 'Anika'	NLar
- 'Anne Russell'	Widely available
- 'Chenaultii'	MRav
- 'Compact Beauty'	CJun WPat
- 'Conoy'	CJun ELon LEdu MAsh NLar WPat
- 'Fulbrook'	CAbP EPfP LEdu LRHS MAsh NLar WHar WPat
- 'Mohawk' ♀H6	CAbP CDoC CEnd CJun ELan ELon EPfP LEdu LRHS MAsh MBri NLar SCoo SHil SKHP SWvt WPat
- 'Park Farm Hybrid' ♀H6	CAbP CDoC CExl CJun CMac CSam CTri EBee ECrN ELan ELon EPfP EPla EWoo LAst LEdu LRHS MAsh MGos MRav NHol NLar SPer SPoG SRms WKif WPat
calvum	CExl
aff. ***calvum*** WWJ 12012	WCru
× ***carlcephalum*** ♀H6	Widely available
- 'Cayuga' ♀H5	ELon MAsh NLar WPat
- 'Van der Maat'	NLar
* - 'Variegatum' (v)	CJun
carlesii	CBcs CCVT CDul CMac CTri EPfP GKin MBlu MGos MRav MSwo SCob SEWo SGol SLim SPer WFar
- B&SWJ 8838	WCru
- 'Aurora' ♀H6	Widely available
- 'Charis'	CJun CSBt LRHS NLar WKif
- 'Compactum'	CJun MAsh NLar WPat
- 'Diana' ♀H6	CDoC CEnd CJun CMHG CMac CRos EPfP LRHS MAsh MBlu NLar SCob SPer SSta WCFE WPat
- 'Marlou'	CJun NLar WPat
cassinoides	CJun WPGP
- 'Bullatum'	EPfP
- 'Sear Charm'	WPGP
'Chesapeake'	CDul CJun EWes SEND
chingii	CJun SLon WCru WPGP WPat
'Chippewa'	CJun
cinnamomifolium ♀H5	CAbP CExl CHEx CSde ELan EPfP EWTr GBin LRHS MAsh NLar NSoo SArc SBrt SCob SEND SLon SPer SPoG SSpi WSHC
cotinifolium	CExl
- CC 4541	CExl NLar
- CC 6258 **new**	GKev
- CC 6267	GKev
cylindricum	EPfP EWTr LRHS NLar SBrt SKHP WCru WPGP WPat
- B&SWJ 6479 from Thailand	WCru
- B&SWJ 7239	WCru
- B&SWJ 9719 from Vietnam	WCru
- HWJCM 434 from Nepal	WCru
- 'Chino-Crûg'	WCru
dasyanthum	NLar
davidii ♀H5	Widely available
- (m)	CBcs CDoC CMac CSBt ELan EPfP MGos SGbt SPer SPoG SRms WHar WPat
- (f)	CBcs CDoC CMac CSBt ELan EPfP EWTr LAst MAsh MGos SPer SPoG SRms WCFE WHar WPat
- 'Angustifolium'	CJun EBee ETwe WPGP
dentatum	EBtc MAsh
- Autumn Jazz	see *V. dentatum* 'Ralph Senior'
- Blue Muffin = 'Christom'	WPat
- Chicago Lustre	see *V. dentatum* 'Synnestvedt'
§ - 'Ralph Senior'	NLar
§ - 'Synnestvedt'	NLar
- 'White and Blue'	CJun NLar
dilatatum	LEdu
- B&SWJ 5844	WCru
- B&SWJ 8734	WCru
- B&SWJ 10830 **new**	WCru
- PAB 6831 **new**	LEdu
- 'Erie'	NLar
- 'Inneke'	NLar
- 'Sealing Wax'	NLar
'Emerald Triumph'	CJun
erosum B&SWJ 8735 **new**	WCru
- B&SWJ 8893	WCru
- B&SWJ 11083	WCru
erubescens	CAbP CJun EPfP NLar SBrt
- HWJK 2163	WCru
- var. ***gracilipes***	CJun IDee LLHF MAsh WPat
- 'Ward van Teylingen'	NLar
'Eskimo' ♀H5	CAbP CBcs CCVT CJun CMac CSBt EBee ELan EPfP GBin LRHS MAsh MBNS MBlu MGos MRav NLar SCob SCoo SKHP SLim SPoG SSta SWvt

fansipanense B&SWJ 8302	WCru
- KWJ 12239	WCru
§ ***farreri*** 🏆H6	CBcs CBod CDoC CDul COtt CSBt CTri EBee ELan EPfP EWoo GGal LBuc LRHS MBri MGos MRav MSwo NLar NSoo SCob SGol SHil SPer SPoG SWvt WHar
- 'Album'	see *V. farreri* 'Candidissimum'
§ - 'Candidissimum'	CDul CExl CMac EBee ELan EPfP IArd LRHS MAsh MRav NLar SGol SPer
- 'December Dwarf'	CJun NLar
- 'Farrer's Pink'	CAbP CExl CJun
- 'Joni' **new**	NLar
- 'Nanum'	CJun CMac EBtc ELan ELon EPfP LRHS MAsh MBrN MRav MWat SKHP WPat
foetens	see *V. grandiflorum* f. *foetens*
foetidum	NLar
var. ***ceanothoides***	
- var. ***rectangulatum*** B&SWJ 1888	WCru
- - B&SWJ 3451	WCru
formosanum	WCru
CWJ 12460 **new**	
fragrans Bunge	see *V. farreri*
'Fragrant Cloud'	ECrN
furcatum 🏆H6	EPfP GKin MAsh MBri NLar SKHP WPat
- B&SWJ 5939	WCru
× ***globosum*** 'Jermyns Globe'	CAbP CCVT CDoC CJun CMHG CMac EPfP MRav NLar SCob SEND SLon SPoG WFar
grandiflorum	CJun CMac NLar
- 'De Oirsprong'	NLar
§ - f. ***foetens***	CJun LRHS
- - GWJ 9227	WCru
- 'Snow White'	CJun
aff. ***griffithianum*** GWJ 9388	WCru
harryanum	CAbP EBtc EWTr MBNS NLar WCru WRHF WSHC
henryi	CAbP CJun EPfP WPat
× ***hillieri***	CHGN
- 'Winton' 🏆H5	CAbP CDoC CJun CMac EBee EPfP GBin IDee LRHS MBri NLar SHil SKHP SLon SPoG SVen WFar WPGP
hoanglienense B&SWJ 8281	WCru
'Huron'	EPfP NLar
ichangense	CJun NLar
japonicum	CExl EPfP EPla NLar SLon
- B&SWJ 5968	WCru
× ***juddii***	Widely available
kansuense	CExl
- BWJ 7737	WCru
koreanum B&SWJ 4231	WCru
lantana	CBcs CCVT CDul CHab CLnd CNWT CTri EAEE ELan EShb LAst LBuc NWea SCob SEND SEWo SPer SVic WMou
- 'Aureum'	CMHG EHoe EPfP MAsh MBlu NLar
- var. ***discolor***	NLar
- 'Mohican'	NLar
- 'Variefolium' (v)	CJun
- 'Variegatum' (v) **new**	ETwe
- 'Xanthocarpum'	WFar
§ ***lantanoides***	SSpi
aff. ***lautum*** B&SWJ 10290	WCru
'Le Bois Marquis'[PBR]	CDoC EPfP EPla EShb ETwe EUJe LRHS SHil
lentago	CAbP CMac
lobophyllum	NLar
luzonicum	CJun
- B&SWJ 3637 **new**	WCru
- var. ***formosanum*** B&SWJ 3585	WCru
- var. ***oblongum*** B&SWJ 3549	WCru
- var. ***sinuatum*** B&SWJ 4009	WCru
macrocephalum	CJun NLar SLon
mariesii	see *V. plicatum* f. *tomentosum* 'Mariesii'
mullaha B&SWJ 2251A **new**	WCru
- GWJ 9227 **new**	WCru
nervosum HWJK 2241 **new**	WCru
nudum	ECrN IDee NLar
- 'Bulk' **new**	WPGP
- 'Pink Beauty'	CJun EPfP EPla LRHS MBri MMHG NLar SHil WFar WPGP WPat
- 'Winterthur'	CJun NLar
odoratissimum misapplied	see *V. awabuki*
odoratissimum Ker Gawl.	EBee LEdu
- RWJ 10046	WCru
- aff. 'Arboricolum'	WCru
aff. ***odoratissimum*** B&SWJ 3913 from the Philippines	WCru
oliganthum 'Kyo Kanzashi' **new**	WPGP
'Oneida'	CJun
opulus	Widely available
- var. ***americanum*** 'Bailey's Compact'	MAsh
- - 'Hans'	NLar
- - 'Phillips'	CAgr
- - 'Wentworth'	CAgr
- 'Amy's Magic Gold'	NLar
- 'Apricot'	NLar
- 'Aureum'	CHel CMac EHoe ELan EPfP LBMP LRHS MAsh MGos MMuc MRav NEgg NLar SCob SPer WCFE WMoo
- var. ***calvescens*** B&SWJ 10544	WCru
- 'Compactum' 🏆H6	Widely available
- 'Fructu Luteo'	SCob SGol
* - 'Harvest Gold'	SCoo SLim SPoG
- 'Lady Marmalade' **new**	NLar
- 'Nanum'	CAbP CBcs ELan EPfP EShb MRav NLar
- 'Notcutt's Variety' 🏆H6	MAsh WPat
- 'Park Harvest'	CDul EBee EBtc EPfP LRHS MAsh NLar SKHP
§ - 'Roseum' 🏆H6	Widely available
- 'Sterile'	see *V. opulus* 'Roseum'
* - 'Sterile Compactum'	LAst SWvt
- 'Sylvie' **new**	NLar
- 'Xanthocarpum' 🏆H6	CBcs CDoC CDul CExl CMac EBee ELan EPfP GBin GKin LRHS MAsh MBlu MGos MMuc MRav MSwo NLar SCob SEND SKHP SLon SPer SRms SWvt WFar WPat WWtn
parvifolium	ETwe NLar
- B&SWJ 3375 **new**	WCru

- B&SWJ 6768 — WCru
***phlebotrichum* B&SWJ 11058** — WCru
***pichinchense* B&SWJ 10660** — WCru
plicatum — CTri
- 'Janny' — IArd
- 'Nanum' — see *V. plicatum* f. *tomentosum* 'Nanum Semperflorens'
§ - f. ***plicatum*** — EPla NSoo SChF
- - 'Grandiflorum' — CAbP CDoC CNec EPfP LRHS NLar SCob SPer WFar WMoo
- - 'Mary Milton' — CJun EPla GBin NLar
- - Newport = 'Newzam' — NLar
- - 'Pink Sensation' — CJun GBin
- - 'Popcorn' ♀H5 — CAbP CDoC CExl CJun CMac EBee ELon EPfP EPla EShb LEdu LRHS MAsh NHol NLar SKHP SLim SPoG SSta WPat
- - 'Rosace' — EPfP LRHS MBlu NLar SSpi
- - 'Rotundifolium' — CRos IArd LRHS MAsh MBri MRav NLar SHil WPat
- - Triumph = 'Trizam' — NLar
- 'Sterile' — see *V. plicatum* f. *plicatum*
- f. ***tomentosum*** 'Cascade' ♀H5 — CJun EWTr LRHS NLar SKHP SSpi
- - 'Dart's Red Robin' — ECtt LLHF MAsh WPat
- - 'Elizabeth Bullivant' — EPfP LLHF LRHS MAsh
- - Kilimanjaro = 'Jww1' — EPfP GBin IDee LSou MBlu NLar NSoo WMoo
- - 'Lanarth' — CBcs CDoC CDul CExl CMac COtt CRos CSBt CTri EAEE ELan EPfP EShb GBin LEdu LRHS MAsh MBlu MGos MJak NLar NSti SCob SCoo SGol SKHP SLim SPer SWvt
§ - - 'Mariesii' ♀H5 — Widely available
- - 'Mariesii Great Star' **new** — LRHS
- - 'Molly Schroeder' — CJun ETwe NLar
§ - - 'Nanum Semperflorens' — CBcs CDoC CMac ECtt EShb LRHS NLar SPoG WFar WPat WSHC
- - 'Pink Beauty' ♀H5 — Widely available
- - 'Rowallane' — WPat
- - 'Saint Keverne' — GKin
- - 'Shasta' — CDoC CDul CJun CMCN EPfP EWTr LEdu LRHS NLar SKHP WFar
- - 'Shoshoni' — GBin NLar
- - 'Summer Snowflake' ♀H5 — CDoC CEnd COtt CWGN ECrN EPfP EShb LRHS MAsh MSwo NLar SKHP SLim SPoG WFar
- 'Watanabe' — see *V. plicatum* f. *tomentosum* 'Nanum Semperflorens'
'Pragense' ♀H6 — CAbP CBcs CDul CJun CMCN EBee EPfP EPla GBin LRHS MGos NHol NLar SEND SLon SPer
propinquum — CAbP ETwe NLar WPat
- CWJ 12426 — WCru
prunifolium — EBtc SGol WCru
- 'Mrs Henry's Large' — CJun
× ***rhytidophylloides*** — IBoy
- 'Alleghany' — NLar
- Dart's Duke = 'Interduke' — WPat
- 'Holland' — IDee
- 'Willowwood' — ELan LRHS MAsh NLar SPer WPat
rhytidophyllum — CBcs CDoC CDul CHEx CMac CNWT EAEE ECrN EPfP GLog LAst LRHS MGos MJak MMuc MSwo NEgg NWea SCob SEND SGol SPer SRms WCFE WHar WMoo WSFF
- 'Aldenham' — GCal
- 'Roseum' — CExl SWvt
- 'Variegatum' (v) — CJun
- 'Wisley Pink' — LRHS SSpi
'Royal Guard' — CJun LLHF
sambucinum HWJ 838 — WCru
- var. ***tomentosum*** HWJ 733 — WCru
sargentii B&SWJ 8695 — WCru
- f. ***flavum*** — NLar
- 'Onondaga' ♀H6 — Widely available
- 'Susquehanna' — EPfP
semperflorens — see *V. plicatum* f. *tomentosum* 'Nanum Semperflorens'
§ ***setigerum*** — WPat
- 'Aurantiacum' — NLar
sieboldii B&SWJ 2837 — WCru
- CWJ 12808 **new** — WCru
- 'Seneca' — CJun NLar
sphaerocarpum B&SWJ 3052 **new** — WCru
subalpinum — NLar
sympodiale **new** — CFil
taiwanianum B&SWJ 3009 — WCru
theiferum — see *V. setigerum*
tinoides B&SWJ 10612 — WCru
tinus — Widely available
- 'Bewley's Variegated' (v) — EBee SPer
I - 'Compactum' — SWvt
- 'Eve Price' ♀H4 — Widely available
- 'French White' ♀H4 — CDoC CDul CMac EBee ELan EPfP LRHS MGos MRav NLar SCob SCoo SLim SPoG SWvt WFar WHar WRHF
- 'Gwenllian' ♀H4 — Widely available
- 'Israel' — MBNS SPer
- 'Lisarose'PBR **new** — EPfP MBri SPoG
- 'Little Bognor' — NLar
- 'Lucidum' — CBcs CJun CSde EPfP NLar SGol
- 'Lucidum Variegatum' (v) — CJun CMac SLim WFar
* - 'Macrophyllum' — EPfP ETwe LRHS NLar SPoG SWvt
- 'Purpureum' — CBcs CJun CNec CSBt ECrN EHoe ELon EPfP EPla LRHS MAsh MGos MSwo MWat NEgg NLar SCob SCoo SGol SLim SPer SPoG WMoo WPat
- Spirit = 'Anvi'PBR — CAbP COtt CSBt EBee ELan ETwe LRHS LSou MAsh MBri NLar NWad SCoo SPoG
- 'Spring Bouquet' — CJun MAsh NLar
- subsp. ***subcordatum*** B&SWJ 12544 — WCru
- 'Variegatum' (v) — CDul CMac CTri EBee EHoe ELan ELon EPfP LAst LRHS MAsh MGos NEgg NLar NPol SCob SEND SGol SLim SPlb SRms SWvt WPat
triphyllum B&SWJ 5784 — WCru
urceolatum B&SWJ 6988 — WCru
utile — WThu
aff. ***venustum*** B&SWJ 10477 — WCru
wrightii — IArd IDee MRav NLar
- B&SWJ 5871 — WCru
- 'Hessei' — WPat
- var. ***stipellatum*** B&SWJ 5856 — WCru
- - B&SWJ 8780A — WCru

Vicia (*Papilionaceae*)

americana — EBee

	cracca	CHab CWld NMir WSFF
	sativa	CHab
	sepium	CWld

Vigna (*Papilionaceae*)

§	***caracalla***	CCCN

Villaresia see *Citronella*

Vinca (*Apocynaceae*)

	sp.	SCob
	balcanica	IMou XLum
	difformis	CNec CPom CSam CTri ECha EWoo LLWP LRHS MGos SDix WHer XLum
	- 'Alba'	CPom CSam
	- Greystone form	CExl EPPr EPfP MMuc SEND WGwG
	- 'Jenny Pym'	CBod CChe CExl CPom CSam EBee EPPr EPla EWes LRHS MBNS MBri MMuc NLar SEND SPoG WBor WGwG WRHF
	- 'Ruby Baker'	EPPr EWes LRHS NChi
	- 'Snowmound'	EWTr LRHS MRav NLar SPoG SWvt
	herbacea RCB UA 21	WCot
	'Hidcote Purple'	see *V. major* var. *oxyloba*
	major	Widely available
	- 'Alba'	CMac
	- 'Elegantissima'	see *V. major* 'Variegata'
	- 'Expoflora' (v)	NLar
	- var. ***hirsuta*** hort.	see *V. major* var. *oxyloba*
§	- subsp. ***hirsuta*** (Boiss.) Stearn	CMac LPla WCot XLum
§	- 'Maculata' (v)	CBcs CDoC CSBt EHoe EShb LRHS MMuc MRav NPri SCob SEND SGol SLim SPer SPoG SWvt WMoo WOut
§	- var. ***oxyloba***	CExl CFis CMac CTri ECha ELan EPla EPri LPot LRHS MRav NLar SPoG SRms WBor WHer XSen
	- var. ***pubescens***	see *V. major* subsp. *hirsuta* (Boiss.) Stearn
	- 'Surrey Marble'	see *V. major* 'Maculata'
§	- 'Variegata' (v) ♀H6	Widely available
	- 'Wojo's Jem' (v)	CDoC CMac ELan EPfP EWes LRHS MBri MGos NLar NPri SCob SHil SLim SPoG SWvt WBor WCot WMoo
	minor	CArn CBcs CBod CDoC CDul CMac CSBt ELan EPfP EWoo GAbr GKin GPoy LAst LRHS MAsh MGos MJak NPri NSoo NWea SCob SLim SVic WHar XLum
	- f. ***alba***	CBcs CDoC CDul CMac ECha EPPr EPfP EWTr LRHS MAsh NLar NPri SCob SGol SPer WCot WHar WPtf XLum
§	- - 'Alba Variegata' (v)	CExl EHoe NEoE SPer SRms WCot WHoo WOut
	- 'Alba Aureovariegata'	see *V. minor* f. *alba* 'Alba Variegata'
	- f. ***alba*** 'Gertrude Jekyll'	Widely available
§	- 'Argenteovariegata' (v) ♀H6	CBcs CDoC CDul CMac CSBt CSam CTri ECha ELan ELon EPfP EPla LAst LBuc LRHS MBri MGos MJak MMuc NPri NWea SCob SEND SGol SLim SPer SPoG SRms WGwG
§	- 'Atropurpurea' ♀H6	Widely available
I	- 'Aureomarginata' **new**	WMoo
§	- 'Aureovariegata' (v)	CBcs CMac EBee ELan EPPr EPfP GAbr LRHS MGos MRav NPri SGol SHil SLim SPer SPlb WRHF
	- 'Azurea'	CHid
§	- 'Azurea Flore Pleno' (d) ♀H6	CArn CMac ECha EPPr EPfP GAbr GCra IFro LLWP LRHS MAsh MRav NLar NPri SHil SLim SPer SPoG SRms SWvt WGwG WHoo WMoo XLum
*	- 'Blue and Gold'	CBod EAEE ECGP ELon MAvo MWat SCob
	- 'Blue Drift'	EWes MSwo
	- 'Bowles's Blue'	see *V. minor* 'La Grave'
	- 'Bowles's Cunningham' **new**	LAst
	- 'Bowles's Purple'	CBod CTsd GMaP WBor
	- 'Bowles's Variety'	see *V. minor* 'La Grave'
	- 'Burgundy'	SRms
	- 'Caerulea Plena'	see *V. minor* 'Azurea Flore Pleno'
	- 'Dartington Star'	see *V. major* var. *oxyloba*
	- 'Double Burgundy'	see *V. minor* 'Multiplex'
	- 'Flower Power' **new**	EPPr
	- Green Carpet	see *V. minor* 'Grüner Teppich'
§	- 'Grüner Teppich'	CDul SGol
	- 'Halstenbek'	XLum
	- 'Hawaii'	ELon
	- 'Illumination' (v)	Widely available
	- 'Josephine'	MHol
§	- 'La Grave' ♀H6	Widely available
	- 'Marie'	EPPr
	- 'Mrs Betty James' (d)	WCot
§	- 'Multiplex' (d)	EBee EPPr LBuc SGol SLim SRms WOut WPtf
	- 'Purpurea'	see *V. minor* 'Atropurpurea'
	- 'Ralph Shugert' ♀H6	CExl CNec ELon EPPr EPfP EWes EWoo LAst LRHS LSqu MBri MGos NLar NPri SCob SCoo SEle SGol SHil SPoG WMoo
	- 'Rubra'	see *V. minor* 'Atropurpurea'
	- 'Sabinka'	CHid EPPr
	- 'Silver Service' (d/v)	CHid MRav
	- 'Snowdrift'	EPPr
	- 'Variegata'	see *V. minor* 'Argenteovariegata'
	- 'Variegata Aurea'	see *V. minor* 'Aureovariegata'
	- 'White Gold'	NEoE
	- 'White Power' **new**	EPPr
	sardoa	EPPr EWes LRHS

Vincetoxicum (*Apocynaceae*)

	cretaceum PAB 3432	LEdu
	forrestii	CExl
	fuscatum **new**	IMou
	hirundinaria	EBee EPPr GEdr GPoy LEdu
	- CC 6289	EWld
	nigrum	CArn EBee GCal LEdu NChi NMyG WCot WTou

Viola ✿ (*Violaceae*)

	'Admiration' (Va)	WGoo
	adunca var. ***minor***	see *V. labradorica* ambig.
§	***alba***	EWes
	'Alethia' (Va)	SDys WGoo
	'Alice' (Vt)	CLAP
	'Alice Kate'	WGoo
	'Alice Witter' (Vt)	LLHF WPtf
*	'Alison' (Va)	WGoo

	alpina **new**	WAbe
	'Amelia' (Va)	WGoo
	'Annette Ross' (Va)	NDov WGoo
I	'Annie' (Vt)	CLAP LLHF
	arborescens	SBrt
	'Ardross Gem' (Va)	ECho ECtt WGoo WKif
	arenaria	see *V. rupestris*
	'Arkwright's Ruby' (Va)	MLHP
	arvensis	CHab
	'Aspasia' (Va) ♀H5	EWoo MNFA WGoo
	'Avril Lawson' (Va)	GKev SHar WGoo
	'Barbara' (Va)	WGoo
	'Baroness de Rothschild' misapplied	see *V.* 'Baronne Alice de Rothschild'
	'Baroness de Rothschild' ambig. (Vt)	CLAP
§	'Baronne Alice de Rothschild' (Vt)	WCot
	'Beatrice' (Vtta)	WGoo
	'Becky Groves' (Vt)	CLAP
§	'Belmont Blue' (C)	CSam CSpe CTri EBee ECho ELon EWes EWoo GAbr GCal GMaP IFro LRHS MAsh MCot MHer MMuc MNFA MRav MSCN NBir NCGa NDov SCob SPer SPhx WCAu WGoo
§	***bertolonii***	EWld WGoo
	'Beshlie' (Va) ♀H5	MNFA WGoo
	biflora	CMHG CPla EWld MNrw
	'Blackout' **new**	SMrm
	'Blue Butterfly' (C)	EWoo
	'Blue Horns' (C)	ELon
	'Blue Moon' (C)	MAsh MNFA WGoo
	'Blue Moonlight' (C)	CElw MPie
	'Boughton Blue'	see *V.* 'Belmont Blue'
§	'Bowles's Black' (T)	CSpe EPfP EShb LEdu NBro NChi NWad SRms WJek
	brevistipulata var. ***hidakana***	GEdr
	'Bruneau' (dVt)	CBre EBee ECtt EWll LEdu MPie WCot
*	'Bryony' (Vtta)	WGoo
	bubanii	GKev
	'Bullion' (Va)	WGoo
	'Burncoose Yellow'	WGoo
	'Buttercup' (Vtta)	ECtt MHol SDys SPoG WGoo
	'Butterpat' (C)	MAsh NDov WGoo
	'Buxton Blue' (Va)	WGoo
	Can Can Series	CWCL
	canina	NBro NMir
	'Catalina'	CLAP
	chaerophylloides 'Beni-zuru'	GEdr
§	- var. ***sieboldiana***	SBrt
	- - pink-flowered **new**	SBrt
	'Charles William Groves' (Vt)	CLAP ELon
	'Charlotte'	EDAr WGoo WJek
	'Clementina' (Va) ♀H5	MRav WGoo
	'Cleo' (Va)	WGoo
	'Clive Groves' (Vt)	CLAP ELon
	'Coeur d'Alsace' (Vt)	CLAP CPBP EBee ECtt GMaP NCGa NLar SHar WHal XLum
	'Colette' (Va)	WGoo
	'Colombine' (Vt)	CAby MAsh
	'Columbine' (Va)	ECtt EPfP GMaP LRHS MHer MHol NBir NDov SPer SPoG WCot WGoo WJek
§	'Conte di Brazza' (dPVt)	SHar
	'Cordelia' (Vt)	CLAP
	cornuta ♀H5	CElw CMea CPla CSpe ECho GKev LRHS MLHP MMuc MNrw MWat NBir NBro SCob SEND SRms WGoo WHoo WTou
	- Alba Group ♀H5	Widely available
	- 'Alba Minor'	ECho EPfP EWes EWoo MNFA NBro NChi NPri NSla
	- blue-flowered	ECho MHer MLHP WMoo
	- 'Cleopatra' (C)	MNrw MPie
	- 'Clouded Yellow'	EWoo MNrw
	- 'Gypsy Moth' (C)	EWoo
	- 'Icy But Spicy'	MAsh MCot MNFA MRav NDov WCot WGoo
	- Lilacina Group (C)	ECha MRav SWat WMnd WPtf
	- 'Mark's Dainty'	MPie
	- 'Minor'	CPla CSam EWoo LSun MAsh NBro NDov NPri NSla WGoo
	- 'Netta Statham'	EWoo LSun MPie WGoo
	- Purpurea Group	CMea ECha WMnd WSHC
	- 'Rosea'	ECha
	- 'Spider'	MAsh MPie SDys WGoo
	- 'Victoria's Blush' (C)	CElw CSpe ELon GMaP MAsh MCot MPie NBir NDov WGoo
	- 'Violacea'	EWoo
	corsica	CMea CSpe EPPr EWTr MMuc NChi SBch SEND WHea
§	***cucullata*** ♀H5	ECho SRms
§	- 'Alba' (Vt)	CBro ECho LLWP NBir SRms
*	- 'Striata Alba'	NBro
	'Czar'	see *V.* 'The Czar'
	'Daisy Smith' (Va)	WGoo
	'Danielle Molly'	WGoo
	'Dawn' (Vtta)	CAby CBod CMea ECtt EPfP GMaP NLar SPoG WGoo
	'Delicia' (Vtta)	NDov SPhx WGoo
	'Desdemona' (Va)	EWoo NDov WGoo
	'Devon Cream' (Va)	WGoo
	dissecta	WCot
	- var. ***sieboldiana***	see *V. chaerophylloides* var. *sieboldiana*
	'Donau' (Vt)	WCot
	'Duchesse de Parme' (dPVt)	IFro SRms
	'D'Udine' (dPVt)	ECtt MPie SRms WCot WHil
	'Dusk'	WGoo
	'E.A. Bowles'	see *V.* 'Bowles's Black'
	'Eastgrove Blue Scented' (C)	EWoo SDys WGoo WOut
	'Eastgrove Ice Blue' (C)	MCot WGoo WOut
	'Elaine Quin'	ECtt MCot MHol NDov NEgg NLar NPri SPoG WGoo WKif
§	***elatior***	CPla EPPr MNrw SBrt WHil WPtf
	'Elizabeth' (Va)	WGoo
	'Elizabeth Lee'	WCot
	'Elliot Adam' (Va)	WGoo
	'Emperor Blue Vein'	EBee EPfP
	erecta	see *V. elatior*
	'Eris' (Va)	WGoo
	'Etain' (Va)	CAby CBod ECho ECtt ELan EPfP EWoo GBuc GMaP LRHS MAsh MHol NDov NEgg NLar NPri NSir SCob SPoG WGoo WIce
	'Fabiola' (Vtta)	EWoo
	'Famecheck Apricot'	CPom
*	'Fantasy'	WGoo
	'Fiona' (Va)	EWoo MCot WGoo
	'Fiona Lawrenson' (Va)	WGoo
	'Fiona Mark' (Va)	WCot

	'Florence' (Va)	WGoo
	'Foxbrook Cream' (C)	MAsh WGoo
	'Francesca' (Va)	WGoo
	'Freckles'	see *V. sororia* 'Freckles'
	Friolina Creamy Pink (Friolina Series)	LAst
	'Gladys Findlay' (Va)	WGoo
	'Glanmore'	WCot
*	'Glenda'	WGoo
	'Glenholme'	EWoo
	'Governor Herrick' (Vt)	CLAP EBee ECtt LLHF NLar WCot WHer
§	***gracilis***	NBir
	- 'Lutea'	CSam
	- 'Major'	WGoo
	'Green Goddess'[PBR]	EPfP MHol
	'Green Jade' (v)	CPla
	'Grey Owl' (Va)	SPhx WGoo
	'Grovemount Blue' (C)	CElw CMea
	grypoceras var. ***exilis*** 'Sylettas'	LEdu
	'Gustav Wermig' (C)	MAsh WGoo
	'Haslemere'	see *V.* 'Nellie Britton'
	'Heartthrob'	ECtt
*	'Heaselands'	SMHy
§	***hederacea***	CExl ECho GQui IFoB MBNS SRms
	- 'Putty Road' (Vt)	ECho
§	'Helen Mount' (T)	ECho
	'Helena' (Va)	WGoo
	'Hespera' (Va)	WGoo
	heterophylla subsp. ***epirota***	see *V. bertolonii*
*	'Hetty Gatenby'	WGoo
	'Holdgate' **new**	WGoo
	'Hudsons Blue'	CElw MNrw
	'Huntercombe Purple' (Va) ♀H5	ECho LRHS NBir SCob WGoo WHal WKif
	'Iden Gem' (Va)	WGoo
	'Inverurie Beauty' (Va) ♀H5	EWoo GBin GMaP SDys WGoo WKif
	'Irish Elegance'	see *V.* 'Sulfurea'
	'Irish Molly' (Va)	CSpe ECho ECtt ELan EPfP GBuc MAsh MHol NDov NEgg NPri SPer SPoG SRms WGoo WIce
	'Isabel'	NDov SRms WGoo
	'Isabella' (Vt)	CLAP
	'Isobel'	MAsh
	'Ivory Queen' (Va)	EWoo MNFA MRav WGoo
	'Jackanapes' (Va) ♀H5	CHVG EBee ECho ECtt ELan EPfP LBMP LRHS MAsh MHol SPer SPoG SRms WGoo WIce
	'Jane Mott' (Va)	EWoo
	'Janet' (Va)	EBee ECtt MHol NPri SDys SPoG
	'Janette' **new**	WGoo
	japonica	SBrt
	'Jean Jeanie' **new**	WGoo
	'Jeannie Bellew' (Va)	SPhx WGoo
	'Jennifer Andrews' (Va)	WGoo
	'Joanna' (Va)	WGoo
	'Johnny Jump Up'	see *V.* 'Helen Mount'
	'Joker Violet Gold' (Joker Series)	CWCL
	jooi	CPBP ECho EPfP GKev NBir SIgm SPhx WAbe WPtf
	'Josie' (Va)	WGoo
	'Joyce Gray' (Va)	WGoo
	'Judy Goring' (Va)	EWoo
	'Julian' (Va)	EWoo WGoo
	'Juno' (Va)	EWoo
	'Katerina' (Va)	SPhx WGoo
	'Kim'	CLAP
	'Kitten'	EWoo MAsh SDys WGoo
	'Kitty White' (Va)	EWoo SDys
§	'Königin Charlotte' (Vt)	EPfP GBBs GBin GMaP LRHS MHer WCot WMoo
	'Kurenai' **new**	SBrt
	labradorica misapplied	see *V. riviniana* Purpurea Group
	- ***purpurea***	see *V. riviniana* Purpurea Group
§	***labradorica*** ambig.	EWTr GJos GQui NPri SCob SMrm WCAu
	'Lady Saville'	see *V.* 'Sissinghurst'
	'Lees Peachy Pink' (Vt)	CLAP
	'Letitia' (Va)	ECho MAsh MCot MNrw MRav SDys WGoo
	'Lianne' (Vt)	CLAP LLHF WCot
	'Lindsay'	WGoo
	'Lisa Tanner' (Va)	WGoo
	'Little Angel' **new**	ECtt
	'Little David' (Vtta) ♀H5	CSam CTri ECtt MCot MNFA NDov SPhx WGoo
	'Lizzy Wootten' (Va)	EWoo
	'Lord Plunket' (Va)	WGoo
§	'Lord Primrose' **new**	ECtt
	'Lorna Cawthorne' (C)	MAsh SDys WGoo
	'Louisa' (Va)	EWoo WGoo
	'Lucy' (Va)	CElw MAsh
§	***lutea***	WGoo
	- subsp. ***elegans***	see *V. lutea*
	'Lydia Groves' (Vt)	CLAP ECtt ELon LLHF LSou SRms WCot
	'Maggie Mott' (Va) ♀H5	ECha ECho ECtt EWoo MCot MRav WGoo
	'Magic'	NDov WGoo
	mandshurica f. ***albiflora***	EPPr SBrt
	- 'Fuji Dawn' (v)	CPla SGSe
	- f. ***hasegawae***	EPPr
	mandshurica × ***patrinii*** **new**	SBrt
	'Margaret' (Va)	WGoo
	'Marie-Louise' (dPVt)	SHar
	'Mars' (Va)	LEdu SMrm
I	'Mars'	CAbP MSCN
	'Martin' (Va) ♀H5	CAby CBod ECha EPfP EWoo GMaP MAsh MHer MHol MNFA MPie NDov SPer SPoG WGoo
	'Mary Mouse'	WGoo
	'Mauve Haze' (Va)	WGoo
	'Mauve Radiance' (Va)	EWoo MNFA WGoo
	'May Mott' (Va)	WGoo
	'Melinda' (Vtta)	WGoo
	'Mercury' (Va)	CElw MCot NDov WGoo
	'Midnight' (Va)	EWoo
	'Milkmaid' (Va)	ELon EWoo GBin NBir
	(Miracle Series) 'Miracle Bride White' (Vt)	SHar
	- 'Miracle Classy Pink' (Vt)	SHar
	- 'Miracle Ice White' (Vt)	NLar SHar
	- 'Miracle Intense Blue' (Vt)	NCGa NLar
	- 'Miracle Vanilla White' (Vt)	SHar
	'Miss Brookes' (Va)	WGoo
	'Misty Guy' (Vtta)	CElw MAsh WGoo
	'Molly Sanderson' (Va) ♀H5	CAby CSpe ECha ECho ECtt ELan EPfP EPot EWoo GMaP LAst LBMP LRHS MAsh MHer MHol NEgg NPri SCob SPer SPlb SPoG WGoo WIce

	Name	Suppliers
	'Moonlight' (Va) ♀H5	ECho ELan LRHS MHer WGoo
	'Moonraker'	NBir
	'Morwenna' (Va)	ECtt MAsh MCot NDov WGoo WKif
	'Mrs Lancaster' (Va)	CAby EBee ECtt ELan EWoo GMaP MCot MHol NBir NLar NPri SDys SPoG WGoo
	'Mrs Pinehurst' (Vt)	EBee GMaP
	'Mrs R. Barton' (Vt)	CLAP ELon SHar
	'Myfawnny' (Va)	ECho LRHS MCot NDov SDys SRms WGoo
§	'Nellie Britton' (Va) ♀H5	ECho SRms
	'Netta Statham'	see *V.* 'Belmont Blue'
	'Nora'	NDov WGoo
	'Norah Church' (Vt)	CLAP
	'Norah Leigh' (Va)	WGoo
	obliqua	see *V. cucullata*
	odorata (Vt)	CArn CBcs CBod CHab EPfP GPoy MRav NMir NPri SEND SIde SPer SRms SVic WJek WOut
	- 'Alba' (Vt)	CPom EBee ECho ELan EPfP GBin LEdu MHer MMuc NPri SEND SRms WMoo
	- 'Albiflora' (Vt)	CLAP EPfP
	- apricot-flowered	see *V.* 'Sulfurea'
	- 'Bethan Davies' (d/Vt)	WCot
	- var. ***dumetorum***	see *V. alba*
	- 'Elsmeer' (Vt)	ECtt LSou WCot
	- 'Hungarian Beauty' (Vt)	EBee
	- 'Katy' (Vt)	CLAP CPom ELon
	- 'King of Violets' (dVt)	EBee ECtt LSou SHar SPer WCot
	- 'Melanie' (Vt)	WCot
	- 'Mrs R.O. Barlow' (Vt)	WCot WSHC
	- pink-flowered	see *V. odorata* Rosea Group
	- 'Princeana'	CBod
	- ***rosea***	see *V. odorata* Rosea Group
§	- Rosea Group (Vt)	CPom EWll GBin IFoB LSou MMuc MPie MRav SEND SIde SPer SRms WCot WSHC
*	- subsp. ***subcarnea*** (Vt)	MMuc SEND
	- 'Sulphurea'	see *V.* 'Sulfurea'
	- 'Vin d'André Thorp' (Vt)	ECtt LEdu WCot WWEG
I	- 'Violett Charm' (Vt)	WCot
	- 'Weimar' (Vt)	GBin
	- 'Wismar' (Vt)	WCot
	'Olive Edwards'	WGoo
	'Opéra' (Vt)	CLAP LLHF
	'Orchid Pink' (Vt)	CLAP GMaP
	palustris	LLWG WHer WSFF WShi
	'Pamela Zambra' (Vt)	CLAP WSHC
	'Papilio'	CBod MHol
	papilionacea	see *V. sororia*
	'Parme de Toulouse' (dPVt)	XLum
	'Pasha' (Va)	EWoo SDys
	'Pat Creasy' (Va)	NDov WGoo
	'Pat Kavanagh' (C)	MAsh WGoo
	'Patience'	NDov WGoo
	'Pearl Rose'	ELon
	pedata	CBro ECho WAbe
	- f. ***alba***	MHer
	- 'Bicolor'	ECho WAbe
	pedatifida	IFoB
	pensylvanica	see *V. pubescens* var. *eriocarpa*
	'Peppered-palms'	SGSe
	'Perle Rose' (Vt)	CLAP
	'Perry's Pride'	NDov
	'Petra' (Vtta)	EWoo WGoo
	'Phyl Dove' (Vt)	CLAP EBee WCot
	'Pickering Blue' (Va)	WGoo
	pinnata **new**	SBrt
	'Primrose Dame' (Va)	WCot WGoo
	'Primrose Pixie' (Va)	WGoo
	'Prince Henry' (T)	MNHC
	'Prince John' (T)	MNHC
	'Princess Mab' (Vtta)	WGoo
	'Princess of Prussia' (Vt)	WCot
	'Princess of Wales'	see *V.* 'Princesse de Galles'
§	'Princesse de Galles' (Vt)	CTri
§	***pubescens*** var. ***eriocarpa***	SRms
	'Purple Wings' (Va)	WGoo
	Queen Charlotte	see *V.* 'Königin Charlotte'
	'Raven'	WGoo
	'Rebecca' (Vtta)	CAby CBod CPla CSam ECho ECtt ELan EPfP GBuc GMaP LBMP LRHS MAsh MCot MHer MHol NBir NDov NEgg NPri SDys SPer SPoG SRms WGoo WIce
	'Red Giant' (Vt)	CBod EAEE LEdu MBNS MWat
	'Red Queen' (Vt)	CLAP
	reichenbachiana	GJos
	'Reine des Blanches' (dVt)	EBee ECtt EWll GBin LEdu LLWP LPla MBel MMuc MPie NGdn SMrm SPer SRms WCot WHil
	'Reine des Neiges' (Vt)	EBee
	reniforme	see *V. hederacea*
	riviniana	CArn CWld GJos MHer MMuc SEND WHer WOut WSFF WShi
	- dark pink-flowered	MMuc
	- 'Ed's Variegated' (v)	EPPr WCot
§	- Purpurea Group	Widely available
	- 'Rosea'	SEND
	- white-flowered	CWld EWes MMuc SEND
	'Roscastle Black'	CMea EPfP EWoo MAsh MHol NDov WGoo
	rotundifolia	LEdu
	'Rubra' (Vt)	EPfP XLum
§	***rupestris***	CTri
*	- ***rosea***	CPla CPom EWTr IFro LLWP SGSe WHer WPtf
	sagittata	LPot
	'Saint Helena' (Vt)	WCot
	selkirkii Pursh ex Goldie	CPla WThu
	sempervirens	SBrt
	seoulensis	LLHF
	septentrionalis	see *V. sororia*
	'Serena' (Va)	WGoo
	'Sherbet Dip'	WGoo
	'Sidborough Poppet'	EWes
	'Silver Samurai'	WCot
§	'Sissinghurst' (Va)	MHer NBir
	'Smugglers' Moon'	WGoo
	somchetica	WCot
	'Sophie' (Vtta)	WGoo
	'Sorbet Series'	NPri
§	***sororia***	EAEE ECha ECho EPPr EWoo LSun MLHP MNrw NBir NBro SCob SPhx
*	- 'Albiflora' ♀H6	CHid ECho EPPr EPfP EWll EWoo GEdr LEdu LLWG LSun MRav SCob SPhx WCFE WHil WJek XLum
	- 'Dark Freckles'	EBee ECho EWTr NRya SPhx XLum
§	- 'Freckles'	Widely available
	- 'Priceana'	EAEE EAJP ECGP EPri EWTr LEdu MRav NBir SPlb WCot
	- 'Sorority Sisters'	NChi
	- 'Speckles' (v)	WCot
	- 'Sweet Emma'	SPhx
*	'Spencer's Cottage'	WGoo

Starry Night — see V. 'Lord Primrose'
'Steyning' (Va) — WGoo
stojanowii — CSpe ECho GCrg LLHF MMuc SEND
§ 'Sulfurea' (Vt) — CLAP CPBP EAJP LLWP MMHG MRav NRya WCot
'Susie' (Va) — WGoo
'Swanley White' — see V. 'Conte di Brazza'
'Sybil' (SP) — NDov WGoo
§ 'The Czar' (Vt) — CBre CLAP ELon SBch SHar WCot
'Tiger Eyes' (Va) — SPoG
'Tom Tit' (Va) — ECtt WGoo
'Tony Venison' (C/v) — ELon EPfP MHol NEgg NPri SPoG WGoo WHer
tricolor — CArn CHab CWld ECho ENfk EPfP GPoy MHer MNHC NDov SIde SRms WJek
- 'Sawyer's Black' — ENfk
velutina — see *V. gracilis*
verecunda — WSHC
- B&SWJ 604a — WCru
§ - var. ***yakusimana*** — WThu
'Victoria Cawthorne' (C) — ECho EWoo GBuc MAsh MHer WGoo
'Violacea' (C) — EWoo
'Virginia' (Va) — WGoo
'Vita' (Va) — EWoo SRms WGoo
'White Ladies' — see *V. cucullata* 'Alba'
'White Pearl' (Va) — SPhx WGoo
'White Swan' (Va) — MAsh
'Winifred Jones' (Va) — WGoo
'Winona Cawthorne' (C) — EWoo NDov
'Wisley White' — LPla LRHS
× ***wittrockiana*** — NPri
Matrix Series
'Woodlands Cream' (Va) — MHer WGoo
'Woodlands Lilac' (Va) — WGoo
yakusimana — see *V. verecunda* var. *yakusimana*
yezoensis — SBrt
'Zara' (Va) — NDov WGoo
'Zoe' (Vtta) — ECtt EPfP GAbr MAsh MHol NEgg NPri NSir SPoG WGoo

Viscaria (*Caryophyllaceae*)

vulgaris — see *Lychnis viscaria*

Vitaliana (*Primulaceae*)

§ ***primuliflora*** — ECho EDAr GKev NRya NSla
- subsp. ***chionantha*** — WAbe
- subsp. ***cinerea*** — EPot GKev
- subsp. ***praetutiana*** — CPBP GCrg NHar NWad WAbe WThu

Vitex (*Lamiaceae*)

agnus-castus — CArn CBcs CHel CMCN COtt CSde EPri EShb ETwe GPoy LEdu LRHS MRav NLar SEND SLon SPer SPoG WSHC XSen
- 'Alba' — CDul EPfP NLar
- var. ***latifolia*** ♀H5 — CAco EBee ELan EPfP LRHS MGos MHer NLar SDix SPoG WPGP XSen
I - 'Rosea' — NLar XSen
- 'Silver Spire' — EBee ELan EPfP LRHS NLar SPoG SSpi WPGP
chinensis — see *V. negundo* var. *heterophylla*
incisa — see *V. negundo* var. *heterophylla*
negundo — CArn LEdu
§ - var. ***heterophylla*** — EWes XSen

Vitis ✿ (*Vitaceae*)

'Abundante' (F) — WSuV
'Alden' (O/B) — WSuV
'Amandin' (G/W) — WSuV
amurensis — EPfP EWoo
- B&SWJ 4138 — WCru
- B&SWJ 4299 — WCru
- B&SWJ 12568 — WCru
'Atlantis' (O/W) — WSuV
§ 'Aurore' (W) — CAgr WSuV
'Baco Noir' (O/B) — CAgr GTwe SDea WSuV
'Beauty Seedless' (B/S) **new** — SDea
betulifolia — EPfP
'Bianca' (O/W) — WSuV
'Birstaller Muscat' (W) — WSuV
Black Hamburgh — see *V. vinifera* 'Schiava Grossa'
* 'Black Strawberry' (B) — CAgr SDea WSuV
'Blanc Seedless' (W/S) — SDea
§ 'Boskoop Glory' (O/B) ♀H5 — CMac ERea LBuc MCoo NLar SCob SCoo SDea WHar WSuV
'Brant' (O/B) ♀H5 — Widely available
'Brilliant' (B) — WSuV
'Buffalo' (B) — WSuV
californica (F) — NLar
'Canadice' (O/R/S) — SDea WSuV
'Cascade' — see V. Seibel 13053
Castel 19637 (B) — WSuV
'Chambourcin' (B) — WSuV
coignetiae ♀H5 — Widely available
- B&SWJ 4550 from Korea — WCru
- B&SWJ 4744 — WCru
- B&SWJ 8553 from Korea — WCru
- B&SWJ 10882 from Japan — WCru
- B&SWJ 10908 from Japan — WCru
- Claret Cloak = 'Frovit'PBR ♀H5 — ELan EPfP EUJe LRHS MAsh MBlu NLar SCoo SPer SPtp WPGP
- var. ***glabrescens*** B&SWJ 8537 — WCru
- 'Purple Cloak' — SCob
- Sunningdale form — NLar WGrn
'Dalkauer' (W) — WSuV
I 'Diamond' (B) — WSuV
'Dutch Black' (O/B) — WSuV
'Edwards No 1' (O/W) — WSuV
'Eger Csillaga' (O/W) — WSuV
'Einset' (B/S) — WSuV
ficifolia — see *V. thunbergii*
flexuosa B&SWJ 5568 — WCru
- var. ***choii*** B&SWJ 4101 — WCru
'Fragola' (O/R) — CAgr CMac CTri ECha EPfP EPom GTwe MCoo MRav NLar SDea SLim SPer SPoG SRms WSuV
'Gagarin Blue' (O/B) — CAgr EPom GTwe SDea SVen WSuV
'Glenora' (F/B/S) — CAgr WSuV
'Hecker' (O/W) — WSuV
henryana — see *Parthenocissus henryana*
'Himrod' (O/W/S) — CCCN ELan ERea GTwe SDea WSuV
'Horizon' (O/W) — WSuV
inconstans — see *Parthenocissus tricuspidata*
'Interlaken' (O/W/S) — CAgr ERea SDea WSuV
'Johanniter' (W) — SPre WSuV
'Kempsey Black' (O/B) — CAgr WSuV
'Kozmapalme Muscatoly' (O/W) — WSuV
'Kuibishevski' (O/R) — WSuV
Landot 244 (O/B) — WSuV

Landot 3217 (O/B) WSuV
'L'Arcadie Blanche' (W) WSuV
'Léon Millot' (O/G/B) CAgr CSBt SDea WSuV
'Lucy Kuhlman' (B) WSuV
'Maréchal Foch' (O/B) WSuV
'Maréchal Joffre' (O/R) CAgr GTwe WSuV
'Mars' (O/B/S) WSuV
'Merzling' (O/W) WSuV
'Munson R.W.' (O/R) WSuV
'Muscat Bleu' (O/B) CCCN EPom LRHS NLar SKee SLim SPoG WSuV
'Nero'PBR CAgr
'New York Muscat' (O/B) ♀H5 ECrN WSuV
'New York Seedless' (O/W/S) WSuV
'Niagara' (O/W) WSuV
'Niederother Monschrebe' (O/R) WSuV
Oberlin 595 (O/B) WSuV
'Orion' (O/W) LRHS MAsh WSuV
'Paletina' (O/W) WSuV
parsley-leaved see *V. vinifera* 'Ciotat'
parvifolia B&SWJ 1946 WCru
'Perdin' (O/W) WSuV
'Phönix' (O/W) CAgr CCCN EPom GTwe MAsh MBri MGos NLar NPla SKee SLim SPoG SPre SVic WSuV
piasezkii WCru
- var. ***pagnuccii*** new WCru
* 'Pink Strawberry' (O) WSuV
'Pirovano 14' (O/B) GTwe SDea WSuV
§ 'Plantet' (O/B) WSuV
'Poloske Muscat' (W) CCCN EPom WSuV
purpurea 'Spetchley Park' (O/B) CAgr WSuV
quinquefolia see *Parthenocissus quinquefolia*
'Ramdas' (O/W) WSuV
Ravat 51 (O/W) WSuV
'Rayon d'Or' (O/W) WSuV
'Regent'PBR (O/B) CAgr CCCN EPom GTwe LRHS MBri MCoo MGos NLar SKee SLim SPoG SPre SVic WSuV
'Reliance' (O/R/S) CAgr ERea WSuV
'Rembrant' (R) CAgr WSuV
riparia CArn NLar
'Romulus' (O/G/W/S) WSuV
'Rondo' (O/B) CAgr NPla SPre SVic WSuV
'Saturn' (O/R/S) CAgr WSuV
'Schuyler' (O/B) CAgr WSuV
Seibel (F) GTwe SDea
Seibel 5279 see *V.* 'Aurore'
Seibel 5409 (W) WSuV
Seibel 5455 see *V.* 'Plantet'
Seibel 7053 WSuV
Seibel 9549 WSuV
§ Seibel 13053 (O/B) CMac LRHS MAsh SDea SEND WSuV
Seibel 138315 (R) WSuV
'Seneca' (W) WSuV
'Serena' (O/W) WSuV
§ 'Seyval Blanc' (O/W) CAgr GTwe MAsh MMuc SDea SEND SVic WSuV
Seyve Villard 12.375 see *V.* 'Villard Blanc'
Seyve Villard 20.473 (F) NPer
Seyve Villard 5276 see *V.* 'Seyval Blanc'
Seyve Villard ambig. LRHS NPer
'Sirius' (B) WSuV
'Solaris' (O/W) SFrt WSuV
'Stauffer' (O/W) WSuV
'Suffolk Seedless' (B/S) ERea GTwe WSuV
'Tereshkova' (O/B) CAgr SDea WSuV
'Thornton' (O/S) WSuV
§ ***thunbergii*** B&SWJ 4702 WCru
'Triomphe d'Alsace' (O/B) CAgr CSBt MCoo NPer SDea WSuV
'Trollinger' see *V. vinifera* 'Schiava Grossa'
'Vanessa' (O/R/S) SDea WSuV
§ 'Villard Blanc' (O/W) WSuV
vinifera EUJe LPal MGos
- EM 323158B WSuV
- 'Abouriou' (O/B) WSuV
- 'Acolon' (O/B) WSuV
- 'Adelheidtraube' (O/W) WSuV
- 'Albalonga' (W) WSuV
§ - 'Alicante' (G/B) CBcs CMac GTwe SDea WSuV
- 'Apiifolia' see *V. vinifera* 'Ciotat'
- 'Augusta Louise' (O/W) WSuV
- 'Auxerrois' (O/W) WSuV
- 'Bacchus' (O/W) CAgr LRHS MBri NLar SDea SFrt SLim SVic WSuV
- 'Baresana' (G/W) NPla WSuV
- 'Beauty' CAgr
- 'Black Alicante' see *V. vinifera* 'Alicante'
- 'Black Corinth' (G/B/S) ERea
- 'Black Frontignan' (G/O/B) WSuV
- Black Hamburgh see *V. vinifera* 'Schiava Grossa'
- 'Black Monukka' (G/B/S) WSuV
- 'Black Prince' (G/B) CAgr WSuV
- 'Blue Portuguese' see *V. vinifera* 'Portugieser'
§ - 'Bouvier' (W) WSuV
- 'Bouviertraube' see *V. vinifera* 'Bouvier'
- 'Buckland Sweetwater' (G/W) GTwe LRHS SDea SLim WSuV
- 'Cabernet Sauvignon' (O/B) EPfP EUJe LRHS MAsh MGos NPer SDea SVic WSuV
- 'Cardinal' (O/R) LRHS WSuV
- 'Carla' (O/R) WSuV
- 'Centennial' (O/N/S) WSuV
- 'Chardonnay' (O/W) CAgr CCCN LRHS MAsh NPer SDea SPer SPre SVic WSuV
§ - 'Chasselas' (G/O/W) LRHS SDea WSuV
- 'Chasselas de Fontainebleau' (F) SVic
- 'Chasselas d'Or' see *V. vinifera* 'Chasselas'
- 'Chasselas Rosé' (G/R) CAgr WSuV
- 'Chasselas Rosé Royal' (O/R) CCCN SVic
- 'Chasselas Vibert' (G/W) WSuV
- 'Chenin Blanc' (O/W) SVic WSuV
§ - 'Ciotat' (F) ERea EShb IDee MRav SDea WSuV
- 'Cot Précoce de Tours' (O/B) WSuV
- 'Crimson Seedless' (R/S) ERea WSuV
- 'Csabyongye' (O/W) WSuV
- 'Dattier de Beyrouth' (G/W) WSuV
- 'Dattier Saint Vallier' (O/W) SVic WSuV
- 'Dolcetto' (O/B) WSuV
- 'Dornfelder' (O/R) CCCN SLim SPoG SVic WSuV
- 'Dunkelfelder' (O/R) WSuV
- 'Early Van der Laan' (F) CMac
- 'Ehrenfelser' (O/W) WSuV
- 'Elbling' (O/W) WSuV

– 'Exalta' (G/W/S)	CCCN WSuV
– 'Excelsior' (W)	WSuV
– 'Faber' (O/W)	WSuV
– 'Fiesta' (W/S)	WSuV
– 'Findling' (W)	WSuV
– 'Flame'	CAgr NPla SVic WHar
– 'Flame Red' (O/D)	CCCN EPom
– 'Flame Seedless' (G/O/R/S)	CMac EPom GTwe SFrt SPoG WSuV
– 'Forta' (O/W)	WSuV
– 'Foster's Seedling' (G/W)	SDea SVic WSuV
– 'Freisamer' (O/W)	WSuV
– 'Frühburgunder' (O/B)	WSuV
– 'Gamay Hâtif des Vosges'	WSuV
– 'Gamay Noir' (O/B)	SVic WSuV
– Gamay Teinturier Group (O/B)	WSuV
– 'Gewürztraminer' (O/R)	LRHS MAsh SDea SVic WSuV
– 'Glory of Boskoop'	see *V.* 'Boskoop Glory'
– 'Golden Chasselas'	see *V. vinifera* 'Chasselas'
– 'Goldriesling' (O/W)	WSuV
– 'Gros Colmar' (G/B)	WSuV
– 'Grüner Veltliner' (O/W)	WSuV
– 'Gutenborner' (O/W)	WSuV
– 'Helfensteiner' (O/R)	WSuV
– 'Huxelrebe' (O/W)	SVic WSuV
– 'Incana' (O/B)	ELon GCal LRHS MRav SVen WCFE WCot WPGP WSHC
– 'Italia' (O/W)	LRHS NPla
– 'Juliaumsrebe' (O/W)	WSuV
– 'Kanzler' (O/W)	WSuV
– 'Kerner' (O/W)	WSuV
– 'Kernling' (F)	WSuV
– 'King's Ruby' (F/S)	ERea WSuV
– 'Lakemont' (O/W/S)	CAgr CCCN CMac ELan EPfP EPom GTwe LRHS MBri MGos NLar NPla SDea SEWo SFrt SKee SLim SPoG SPre SVic WHar WSuV
– 'Lival' (O/B)	WSuV
– 'Madeleine Angevine' (O/W)	CAgr EPfP GTwe LRHS MAsh NPer SDea SPoG SVen SVic WSuV
– 'Madeleine Celine' (B)	WSuV
– 'Madeleine Royale' (G/W)	WSuV
– 'Madeleine Silvaner' (O/W)	CSBt GTwe LRHS MAsh NPer SDea SPoG WSuV
– 'Madresfield Court' (G/B)	GTwe SLim WSuV
– 'Merlot' (G/B)	EUJe LRHS SDea SVic WSuV
§ – 'Meunier' (B)	SVic WSuV
– 'Mireille' (F)	SDea WSuV
– 'Morio Muscat' (O/W)	WSuV
§ – 'Müller-Thurgau' (O/W)	GTwe LRHS MAsh MGos NPri SDea SVic WSuV
– 'Muscat Blanc à Petits Grains' (O/W)	SWvt WSuV
– 'Muscat Cannon Hall' (G/W)	CHll
– 'Muscat de Lierval' (O/B)	WSuV
– 'Muscat de Saumur' (O/W)	WSuV
– 'Muscat Hamburg' (G/B)	COtt LRHS MAsh MGos NPri SDea SWvt WSuV
– 'Muscat of Alexandria' (G/W)	CBcs CCCN CMac CRHN ERea LRHS MRav SDea SFrt SLim SPer SVic WHar
– 'Muscat Ottonel' (O/W)	WSuV
– 'Muscat Saint Laurent' (W)	WSuV
– 'Nebbiolo' (O/B)	WSuV
– 'No 69' (W)	WSuV
– 'Noblessa' (W)	WSuV
– 'Noir Hâtif de Marseille' (O/B)	WSuV
– 'Olive Blanche' (O/W)	WSuV
– 'Oliver Irsay' (O/W)	WSuV
– 'Optima' (O/W)	WSuV
– 'Ora' (O/W/S)	WSuV
– 'Ortega' (O/W)	CCCN WSuV
– 'Palatina' (O/W) **new**	SFrt
– 'Perle' (O/W)	WSuV
– 'Perle de Czaba' (G/O/W)	WSuV
– 'Perlette' (O/W/S)	CCCN EPom GTwe NPri WSuV
– 'Petit Rouge' (R)	WSuV
– 'Pinot Blanc' (O/W)	CCCN LRHS MAsh SVic WSuV
– 'Pinot Gris' (O/B)	SDea SVic WSuV
– 'Pinot Noir' (O/B)	CCCN SVic WSuV
§ – 'Portugieser' (O/B)	WSuV
– 'Précoce de Bousquet' (O/W)	WSuV
– 'Précoce de Malingre' (O/W)	CAgr SDea
– 'Prima' (O/B)	WSuV
– 'Primavis Frontignan' (G/W)	WSuV
– 'Purpurea' (O/B) ♀H5	Widely available
– 'Queen of Esther' (B)	GTwe MBri SKee SLim WSuV
– 'Regner' (O/W)	WSuV
– 'Reichensteiner' (O/G/W)	CAgr SDea SVic WSuV
– 'Riesling' (O/W)	CCCN MAsh SVic WSuV
– Riesling-Silvaner	see *V. vinifera* 'Müller-Thurgau'
– 'Rotberger' (O/G/B)	WSuV
– 'Royal Muscadine' (G/O/W)	GQue WSuV
– 'Saint Laurent' (G/O/W)	SVic WSuV
– 'Sauvignon Blanc' (O/W)	CCCN LRHS SVic WSuV
– 'Scheurebe' (O/W)	WSuV
§ – 'Schiava Grossa' (G/B/D)	CMac CRHN CTri ELan EPfP EPom EUJe EWTr GQue GTwe LRHS MAsh MBri NPer NPla NPri SCob SDea SLim SPer SPoG SPre SVic SWvt WHar WSuV
– 'Schönburger' (O/W)	SDea SVic WSuV
– 'Schwarzriesling'	see *V. vinifera* 'Meunier'
– 'Sémillon'	LRHS MAsh SVic
– 'Senator' (O/W)	WSuV
– 'Septimer' (O/W)	WSuV
– 'Shiraz' (B)	WSuV
– 'Siegerrebe' (O/W/D)	CAgr GTwe LRHS MAsh NPer SDea SVic WSuV
– 'Silvaner' (O/W)	WSuV
– 'Spetchley Red' (O/B) ♀H5	CRHN GCal LEdu NLar WCot WCru WPGP WPat
– strawberry grape	see *V.* 'Fragola'
– 'Suffolk Red' (G/R/S)	ERea
§ – 'Sultana' (W/S)	CAgr GTwe NPla NPri SDea WSuV
– 'Theresa' (O/W)	MBri SLim WSuV
– 'Thompson Seedless'	see *V. vinifera* 'Sultana'
* – 'Triomphe' (O/B)	SVic
– 'Triomphrebe' (W)	WSuV
– 'Vroege van der Laan' (O/W)	NLar
– 'Wrotham Pinot' (O/B)	SDea WSuV
– 'Würzer' (O/W)	WSuV
– 'Zweigeltrebe' (O/B)	WSuV
* 'White Strawberry' (O/W)	WSuV
'Zalagyöngye' (W)	CAgr WSuV

Vriesea (Bromeliaceae)

'Astrid' new	LAir
corcovadensis new	LAir
espinosae new	LAir
gigantea new	LAir
- 'Nova' new	LAir NLos
hieroglyphica	LAir
'Kallisto' new	LAir
splendens ♀H1a	LAir XBlo

Wachendorfia (Haemodoraceae)

multiflora	CLak SVen
paniculata	CLak CTal
thyrsiflora	CAbb CBcs CCon CDes CExl CHEx CPne EBee EPri LEdu NLos SVen WPGP WSHC

Wahlenbergia (Campanulaceae)

albomarginata	ECho GBin
- 'Blue Mist'	ECho
congesta	ECho
gloriosa	MOWG WAbe
pumilio	see *Edraianthus pumilio*
serpyllifolia	see *Edraianthus serpyllifolius*
undulata 'Melton Bluebird'	GJos

Waldsteinia (Rosaceae)

fragarioides	GKev IMou
geoides	EBee EPPr LAst LRHS MGil MMuc NEoE SPer WMoo WWEG XLum
- 'Goldkäfer' new	IMou
ternata	Widely available
§ - 'Mozaick' (v)	EBee EShb EWes NBir NEoE
- 'Variegata'	see *W. ternata* 'Mozaick'

walnut, black see *Juglans nigra*

walnut, common see *Juglans regia*

Wasabia (Brassicaceae)

wasabi	CArn CExl CFil GPoy LEdu

Washingtonia (Arecaceae)

filifera ♀H1c	CAbb CCCN CDoC CPHo SArc SBig SEND SPlb
robusta	CBcs LPal MHin SHil SPlb

Watsonia (Iridaceae)

aletroides	CDes EBee ECho GCal GKev SDeJ SVen
amatolae	IBlr
angusta	CDes CExl CPne CPrp EBee IBlr SGSe SPlb WPGP
'Apricot Queen'	IDee
ardernei	see *W. borbonica* subsp. *ardernei* (Sander) Goldblatt 'Arderne's White'
beatricis	see *W. pillansii*
§ ***borbonica***	CDes CPrp EBee
- subsp. ***ardernei*** misapplied	see *W. borbonica* subsp. *ardernei* (Sander) Goldblatt 'Arderne's White'
§ - subsp. ***ardernei*** (Sander) Goldblatt 'Arderne's White'	CBre CDes CExl CPrp ECho GCal IBlr LRHS
- subsp. ***borbonica***	IBlr WPGP
- 'Paarl'	ECho
- 'Peach Glow' new	GKev
brevifolia	see *W. laccata*
brick red-flowered	CDes EBee WPGP
coccinea 'Somerset West'	ECho
'Dart Sea Trout'	CDes
densiflora	IBlr
fourcadei	GCal
fulgens	LEdu
galpinii	CCon
- lavender-flowered	IBlr
- pink-flowered	IBlr
galpinii* × *knysnana	IBlr
§ ***humilis***	EBee GCal SKHP
knysnana	CDes EBee IBlr
§ ***laccata***	CCon CPne
- orange-flowered	CDes
- pink-flowered	CDes EBee
latifolia	IBlr
lepida	ECho SPlb
marginata	CPrp EBee ECho
- ***alba***	SKHP
meriania	CHel EBee ERCP GBin GKev IBlr
- var. ***bulbillifera***	CCon CPne CPrp EBee ECho GCal GCra GGal GKev IBlr WSHC
'Peachy Pink Orphan'	CDes EBee WPGP
§ ***pillansii***	CAbb CCon CExl CHEx CHel CPne CPrp EBee EPri IBal IBlr LEdu LRHS NCGa SVen
- 'Cathcart'	ECho
- peach-flowered	CExl
- pink-flowered	CExl CPrp IVic
- red-flowered	CExl IVic
- soft pink-flowered	EPri
pink-flowered	CDes
pyramidata	see *W. borbonica*
roseoalba	see *W. humilis*
'Stanford Scarlet'	CAby CCon CDes CExl CPrp EBee ELon IBlr SChr WPGP
stenosiphon	IBlr
strubeniae	IBlr
tabularis	IMou
transvaalensis	EBee
'Tresco Dwarf Pink'	CCon CDes CExl EBee IBlr LEdu WPGP
Tresco hybrids	CAbb CBcs CExl CTre EPri GGal SRkn
vanderspuyae	CExl CPne CPrp EPri IBlr
wilmaniae	CExl CPrp EBee IBlr WPGP
- JCA 3.955200	SKHP
- 'Ice Angel'	SKHP
wordsworthiana	GCal
zeyheri	EBee

Wattakaka see *Dregea*

Wedelia (Asteraceae)

trilobata	LLWG

Weigela ✿ (Caprifoliaceae)

CC 1231	CExl
'Abel Carrière'	CMac CTri ECtt GKin MGos NWea WCFE

'Avalanche' misapplied	see *W.* 'Candida'
'Avalanche' Lemoine	see *W. praecox* 'Avalanche'
'Avant Garde'	MAsh WPat
Black and White = 'Courtacad1' PBR	CWGN EPla LRHS SCob SGol SPoG
'Boskoop Glory'	GQui SPer
'Bouquet Rose'	LPot
§ Briant Rubidor = 'Olympiade' (v)	CDoC CMac COtt EBee EHoe LRHS MAsh MBri MGos MMuc MRav NEgg NLar SCob SEND SGol SHil SLim SPer SPlb SPoG WHar
'Bristol Ruby'	Widely available
§ 'Candida'	CTri ELan ETwe EWes MRav NLar NSoo SBod SGol SPer WOut
Cappuccino = 'Verweig 2' PBR	MBlu MJak NBro NLar SGol
Carnaval = 'Courtalor' PBR ♀H6	CBcs COtt LSou MRav NLar SCob
'Chameleon'	MPkF
coraeensis ♀H6	CHll MAsh MBlu MMHG MNrw SBrt SPer WPat
- 'Alba'	CHll
decora	GQui
- B&SWJ 10834	WCru
'Eva Rathke'	GKin NBir NLar NWea
'Evita'	GKin IBoy MBlu
floribunda B&SWJ 10831	WCru
florida	CDul CMac EPfP
- B&SWJ 8439	WCru
- f. ***alba***	CBcs
* - 'Albovariegata' (v)	CExl
- 'Bicolor'	CMac ELan
- 'Bristol Snowflake'	CDul CMac EPfP EWTr MBlu MHer MSwo NBir NLar SLon
- 'Foliis Purpureis'	Widely available
- Magical Rainbow = 'Kolmagira' PBR	LRHS MGos MPkF SGol
- 'Milk and Honey'	GKin LRHS
- Minor Black = 'Verweig 3' PBR	COtt EPfP GBin LRHS MBri MPkF NBro NHol NLar SPoG WMoo
- Monet = 'Verweig' PBR (v)	Widely available
- Moulin Rouge = 'Brigela' PBR	CBcs CDoC ELan EPfP LRHS MAsh MBri MGos SLim
- 'Pink Princess'	LRHS MSwo WHar
- Rubigold	see *W.* Briant Rubidor
§ - Sunny Fantasy = 'Kolsunn'	MPkF SPoG
- 'Suzanne' (v)	NEoE
- 'Tango'	CJun LRHS MAsh NEoE
- 'Versicolor'	CExl CMHG CMac GQui SLon SMrm
- Wine and Roses = 'Alexandra' PBR	Widely available
'Florida Variegata' (v) ♀H6	Widely available
'Gold Rush'	NLar
'Golden Candy'	NEoE
'Gustave Malet'	CMCN GQui
hortensis	CExl
'Hulsdonk'	NLar
japonica 'Dart's Colourdream'	EHoe ETwe EWes LAst MMuc SEND SGol SLim
- 'Variegated Dart's Colourdream' (v)	ELon
'Jean's Gold'	ELan MBlu MRav
'Kosteriana Variegata' (v)	CSBt EBee EPfP LRHS MAsh MMuc NEgg SEND SHil SLon
'Little Red Robin'	ELon MPkF NSoo
'Looymansii Aurea'	CExl CMHG CTri ELan EPfP NLar SGol SPer WHar
Lucifer = 'Courtared' PBR	CDoC
maximowiczii	CExl GQui
§ ***middendorffiana***	Widely available
'Minuet'	LRHS MRav MSwo NEoE
'Mont Blanc'	MAsh MMHG
Nain Rouge = 'Courtanin' PBR	CTri NLar
'Nana Variegata' (v)	CExl ECrN ELon EPfP EPla LRHS MJak NHed NSoo SCob
Naomi Campbell = 'Bokrashine' PBR	EShb GBin GKin MMHG NEgg NLar NSoo SEND SGol WHar WMoo
'Newport Red'	GKin MBNS MWat NWea WHar WRHF
Pink Poppet = 'Plangen' PBR	CAbP COtt CSBt CWSG EPfP GKin LBMP LRHS LSou MAsh MBri MPkF NLar SCob SCoo SHil SLim SPoG SRkn SWvt
praecox	ECrN
- B&SWJ 8705	WCru
§ - 'Avalanche'	EPfP
'Praecox Variegata' (v) ♀H6	CMac CTri EPfP LAst LRHS MAsh MRav NBir SDix SPer SPoG SRms WCFE WPat
'Red Prince' ♀H6	CWCL ELan EPPr EPfP LRHS MBri MGos MJak MSwo SCob SGol SHil SPoG
Rubidor	see *W.* Briant Rubidor
Rubigold	see *W.* Briant Rubidor
'Ruby Anniversary'	CBcs EPPr LBuc NSoo SLon
'Ruby Queen' PBR	CMac EPfP
'Rumba'	CMac CWSG MRav
sessilifolia	see *Diervilla sessilifolia*
'Snowflake'	ECrN LPot SRms
'Stelzneri'	MMuc
'Styriaca'	NSoo
subsessilis B&SWJ 1056	WCru
- B&SWJ 4206	WCru
'Victoria'	CDul CMac CWSG ECrN EHoe ELan EPPr EPfP LBMP LRHS MGos MSwo NBir NWad SCob SGol SPer WHar WMoo

Weinmannia (*Cunoniaceae*)

racemosa	CDul IVic
trichosperma	IDee SArc

Weldenia (*Commelinaceae*)

candida	ECho GEdr IBlr LLHF NHar SChF

Westringia (*Lamiaceae*)

angustifolia	MOWG
brevifolia	ECou
§ ***fruticosa*** ♀H1c	CBcs CCCN CHll CSde CTsd SRms SVen WJek
- 'Smokie' (v)	CCCN CTsd MOWG
- 'Variegata' (v)	CCCN SRms SVen WJek
longifolia	CCCN
rosmariniformis	see *W. fruticosa*
'Wynyabbie Gem'	CAbb CCCN LRHS SEND SVen

whitecurrant see *Ribes rubrum* (W)

Whiteheadia (*Asparagaceae*)

bifolia 'Nardouwsberg'	ECho

Wigandia (*Boraginaceae*)

caracasana	CHll

Wikstroemia (*Thymelaeaceae*)

gemmata	LRHS

Wilkesia (*Asteraceae*)

gymnoxiphium new	CBrP

wineberry see *Rubus phoenicolasius*

Wisteria ✿ (*Papilionaceae*)

	'Betty's Dwarf Blue'	NLar
§	***brachybotrys***	SCob SLau
§	- Murasaki-kapitan	CEnd CTri CWGN EBtc EMil EPfP LRHS SEND SKHP
	- 'Okayama' ♀H5	EPfP EPla SKHP
	- 'Pink Chiffon'	CWGN EPfP LRHS SKHP
	- 'Shiro-beni'	CTri
§	- 'Shiro-kapitan' ♀H5	CBcs CEnd CFlo CSPN CTri CWGN EPfP EPla IArd LRHS MAsh MBri MGos MRav NHol NLar SEND SHil SKHP SLau SLim SPer WPGP WPat WSHC
	- 'Showa-beni' ♀H5	CDoC CEnd CFlo CSPN CWGN EPfP MGos SCoo SEND SKHP SLau SLim WPGP
*	- 'White Silk'	CBcs COtt EPfP LRHS MGos NPla SLon
§	'Burford' ♀H5	CEnd CFlo CSPN CWGN EBee EPfP LRHS MAsh MBri MWat NLar SCob SCoo SEND SKHP SLau SLim WHar WPGP
	'Caroline'	CBcs CCCN CDoC CFlo COtt CSPN CWGN EBee EBtc EPfP LRHS MAsh MGos MJak MRav NPCo SCob SHil SLau SPer SPoG SRms SSpi WPGP WSHC
	floribunda	CBcs CRHN ELan EPfP IBoy MMuc SCob SEWo SGol
	- B&SWJ 12748 from South Korea new	WCru
§	- 'Alba' ♀H5	Widely available
	- 'Black Dragon'	see *W. floribunda* 'Yae-kokuryū' (d)
	- 'Burford'	see *W.* 'Burford'
*	- 'Cascade'	CBcs COtt LRHS MBri SHil
§	- 'Domino' ♀H5	CBcs CMac CWGN ELon EPfP EPla IArd LBMP LRHS MAsh MGos MJak MRav MSwo NLar NPla SCoo SEND SGol SKHP SLau SLim SPer SPoG SSta
	- 'Ed's Blue Dragon' (d)	LRHS SHil
	- 'Fragrantissima'	see *W. sinensis* 'Jako'
	- 'Geisha'	CBcs CEnd CFlo CHel EBee EWTr SEND SKHP
	- 'Golden Dragon'	EPfP
	- 'Harlequin'	CBcs CFlo COtt CSPN ELon LRHS MJak NPla SEND SKHP
	- 'Hocker Edge'	SLau
	- 'Hon-beni'	see *W. floribunda* 'Rosea'
	- 'Honey Bee Pink'	see *W. floribunda* 'Rosea'
	- 'Honko'	see *W. floribunda* 'Rosea'
	- 'Issai Perfect'	LRHS NLar SCoo SLon
	- 'Issai-naga'	NLar
	- 'Jakohn-fuji'	see *W. sinensis* 'Jako'
§	- 'Kuchi-beni'	CBcs CEnd COtt CSPN ELan EWTr GBin IBoy LRHS MBri MGos MJak MRav NHol NLar SEND SHil SKHP SLau SPer SPoG SRms
	- 'Lawrence' ♀H5	CBcs CDoC CEnd CFlo CSPN CWGN EBtc EPla LRHS NLar SKHP SLau
	- 'Lipstick'	see *W. floribunda* 'Kuchi-beni'
	- 'Longissima'	see *W. floribunda* 'Multijuga'
	- 'Longissima Alba'	see *W. floribunda* 'Alba'
	- 'Macrobotrys'	see *W. floribunda* 'Multijuga'
	- 'Magenta'	LRHS NPla
§	- 'Multijuga' ♀H5	Widely available
	- 'Nana Richin's Purple'	CEnd LRHS SLau
	- 'New Pink' new	LRHS
	- 'Peaches and Cream'	see *W. floribunda* 'Kuchi-beni'
	- 'Pink Ice'	see *W. floribunda* 'Rosea'
	- Reindeer	see *W. sinensis* 'Jako'
§	- 'Rosea' ♀H5	Widely available
	- 'Royal Purple' ♀H5	CEnd EPfP IArd MBri NLar SGol SPoG
	- 'Russelliana'	CBcs CFlo GBin NLar
	- 'Shiro-naga'	see *W. floribunda* 'Alba'
	- 'Shiro-nagi'	see *W. floribunda* 'Alba'
	- 'Shiro-noda'	see *W. floribunda* 'Alba'
	- 'Snow Showers'	see *W. floribunda* 'Alba'
	- 'Variegata' (v)	CWGN
	- 'Violacea Plena' (d) ♀H5	CBcs CDoC CMac EPfP NLar SKHP SWvt
	- 'Yae-kokuryū' (d)	Widely available
	florida Magical Fantasy = 'Kolsunn'	see *Weigela florida* Sunny Fantasy
	× ***formosa***	CEnd SLau SLim
	- 'Black Dragon'	see *W. floribunda* 'Yae-kokuryū'
	- 'Domino'	see *W. floribunda* 'Domino'
	- 'Issai' Wada *pro parte*	see *W. floribunda* 'Domino'
	- 'Kokuryū'	see *W. floribunda* 'Yae-kokuryū'
	- 'Yae-kokuryū'	see *W. floribunda* 'Yae-kokuryū'
	frutescens	EBee EPfP NLar
	- 'Alba'	see *W. frutescens* 'Nivea'
	- 'Amethyst Falls'PBR	CBcs CEnd CWCL CWGN EShb IArd LRHS MGos SCoo SLon SPer SPoG WMoo
	- 'Longwood Purple'	LRHS
§	- 'Nivea'	LRHS
	Kapitan-fuji	see *W. brachybotrys*
	'Lavender Lace'	CBcs COtt EPfP LRHS MAsh MJak NLar SLau
	macrostachya 'Aunt Dee'	CWGN NLar
	- 'Blue Moon'	MGos WHar
	- 'Clara Mack'	CWGN IArd
	multijuga 'Alba'	see *W. floribunda* 'Alba'
	sinensis	Widely available
	- 'Alba'	CAco CBcs CDoC CDul CMen ELan EPfP EWTr IBoy LAst LRHS MAsh MGos MSwo MWat NPla SCob SLau SPer SPoG
	- 'Amethyst' ♀H5	CAco CBcs CEnd CHel COtt CSPN EPfP LRHS MAsh MBri MGos MRav NPla SHil SKHP SLau SLim SPoG WPat
	- 'Blue Sapphire'	CAco CBcs COtt CSPN CWGN EBee EBtc LRHS NEgg NLar NPCo SLau SRms
	- 'Consequa'	see *W. sinensis* 'Prolific'
	- 'Cooke's Special'	CWGN
§	- 'Jako' ♀H5	CEnd NHol
	- 'Oosthoek's Variety'	see *W. sinensis* 'Prolific'

I - 'Pink Ice' NPCo
- 'Prematura' see *W. floribunda* 'Domino'
- 'Prematura Alba' see *W. brachybotrys* 'Shiro-kapitan'
§ - 'Prolific' 🏆H5 CDul CMac CSam CTri CWGN ELan EPfP IBoy LBuc LRHS MBri MGos MJak MMuc MRav MSwo NHol NLar SCob SCoo SGol SKHP SLim SPer SPoG SWvt WPGP WPat
- 'Rosea' SCob SWvt
- 'Shiro-capital' see *W. brachybotrys* 'Shiro-kapitan'
'Tiverton' CBcs EUJe NPla
venusta see *W. brachybotrys* 'Shiro-kapitan'
- 'Alba' see *W. brachybotrys* 'Shiro-kapitan'
- var. **violacea** misapplied see *W. brachybotrys* Murasaki-kapitan

Withania (*Solanaceae*)

somnifera CArn GPoy

Wittsteinia (*Alseuosmiaceae*)

vacciniacea SBrt WCru

Wodyetia (*Arecaceae*)

bifurcata XBlo

Wollemia (*Araucariaceae*)

nobilis CAco CDTJ CDoC CDul CHel CTho EPfP ESwi EUJe GBin MGos SArc WMou

Woodsia (*Woodsiaceae*)

obtusa CBty CDTJ CKel CLAP CTal CWCL EBee EFer ISha LPal LRHS MBri NBro NLar SGol SPoG SRot WGrf XLum
polystichoides SRms

Woodwardia (*Blechnaceae*)

from Emei Shan, China CLAP
areolata SKHP
fimbriata 🏆H3 CBod CBty CCCN CCon CLAP CTal CWCL EFer ELon EPfP ERod EWTr GCal GEdr LEdu LRHS NBro NHol NLar SBig SBod SEND SGSe SPer WFib WMoo WPGP XLum
orientalis CBty CCon ESwi ISha LEdu LPal LRHS NLos WFib
- var. **formosana** B&SWJ 6865 ESwi WCru
radicans 🏆H3 CHEx CHid CKel CLAP EWes SArc WCot WFib
unigemmata 🏆H4 CHEx CLAP EFer EWes ISha SArc SKHP WAbe WFib WHal
virginica CBty CLAP ISha LRHS

Worcesterberry see *Ribes* 'Worcesterberry'

Wulfenia (*Plantaginaceae*)

amherstiana GEdr LEdu
baldaccii GKev
carinthiaca CTal EBee ECho GAbr GEdr GKev LEdu NBir NLar NWad XLum
- 'Alba' EBee GKev
orientalis new CTal
× **schwarzii** CDes EBee IMou LEdu WPGP WSHC

Wurmbea (*Colchicaceae*)

dioica CLak
pusilla 'Sentinel Peak' ECho
recurva ECho
spicata 'Rawsonville' ECho
stricta WCot

Wyethia (*Asteraceae*)

angustifolia new SBrt

Xanthium (*Asteraceae*)

sibiricum CArn

Xanthoceras (*Sapindaceae*)

sorbifolium 🏆H5 CAgr CBcs CDul CLnd CMCN EBee ELan EPfP MBlu NLar SBrt SSpi WBor WPat

Xanthocyparis (*Cupressaceae*)

§ **nootkatensis** IDee
- 'Glauca' MGos NWea
- 'Green Arrow' CKen LRHS MBri SCoo SLim WHar
- 'Jubilee' LRHS SCoo SLim WCFE WHar
- 'Kanada' NLar
- 'Lutea' MGos NWea
- 'Pendula' 🏆H6 CCVT CDoC CDul CKen ELan EPfP EPla GKin IDee LRHS MAsh MBlu MBri NWea WCFE
- 'Strict Weeper' CKen SLim

Xanthorhiza (*Ranunculaceae*)

simplicissima CArn CBcs CDoC CRow EPfP GCal IVic LEdu MBri MGil NLar SDys SSpi WCot WPGP

Xanthorrhoea (*Xanthorrhoeaceae*)

australis SPlb
fulva SPlb
glauca CCCN
johnsonii SPlb
preisii GBin SPlb

Xerochrysum (*Asteraceae*)

§ **bracteatum** SVen
§ - 'Coco' CMHG CSpe
§ - 'Dargan Hill Monarch' CHll CSpe SRms

Xeronema (*Xeronemataceae*)

callistemon CBcs

Xylotheca (*Flacourtiaceae*)

kraussiana SPlb

Youngberry see *Rubus* 'Youngberry'

Ypsilandra (*Melanthiaceae*)

cavaleriei CExl EBee GEdr WCot

	thibetica	CBct CCon CDes CExl CHel CHid CLAP CPrp EBee ELon EPfP GEdr GKev LEdu LLHF LRHS NLar SChF SMad WCru WPGP WSHC
	- narrow-leaved **new**	WCru

Yucca ✿ (*Asparagaceae*)

	SDR 3701	GKev
	aloifolia	CCCN CDoC CHEx LPal SArc SBig SCob SEND SPlb
§	- f. ***marginata*** (v)	SBig
	- 'Purpurea'	SPlb
	- 'Variegata'	see *Y. aloifolia* f. *marginata*
	angustifolia	see *Y. glauca*
	baccata	CCCN NLos SPlb XSen
	carnerosana	WCot
§	***elata***	CCCN WPGP XSen
§	***elephantipes*** ♀H2	CDTJ SEND
	- 'Jewel' (v)	SEND
	- 'Puck' (v)	SEND
	- variegated (v)	SEND
	faxoniana	SPlb
	filamentosa	CAco CBcs CCCN CDul CMac CTri EBee ELan EPfP EUJe EWTr GKev LAst LEdu LRHS LSun MCri MGos MJak MMuc SCob SEND SGol SLim SPer SPlb SRms XLum
	- 'Antwerp'	GCal
	- 'Bright Edge' (v) ♀H3	CBcs CDoC CDul CMHG CMac CTri ELan ELon EPfP LAst LEdu LPal LRHS MBri MJak MRav MSwo SChr SCob SEND SLim SPer SWvt
	- 'Color Guard' (v) ♀H5	EUJe LAst LRHS MAsh MBri NLar SChr WCot
	- 'Garland's Gold' (v)	CBcs CCCN CDoC MAsh MJak SBig
	- 'Gold Heart' (v) **new**	MBri
	- 'Variegata' (v)	CBcs SCob SRms
	filifera	EUJe LPal SPlb
	flaccida	SCob
	- 'Golden Sword' (v) ♀H3	CBcs CDoC CMac CTsd EBee ELan EPfP GMaP LAst LRHS MAsh MGos MSwo NLar SCob SGol SLim SPer SPoG SWvt WHar
	- 'Ivory' ♀H5	CDoC CEnd CTsd ELan ELon GCal GMaP LRHS MBri MRav NLar SPer SRms
	× ***floribunda***	SArc
§	***glauca***	EPfP LRHS MBri SArc WCot
	gloriosa ♀H5	CDoC CHEx CMac CTri EPla EUJe GKev LPal LRHS NPla SArc SCob SEND SPer SPlb SPoG SWvt WBrk
	- 'Aureovariegata'	see *Y. gloriosa* 'Variegata'
	- Bright Star = 'Walbristar'PBR	LBuc LRHS NSoo SCob SPer SPoG WCot
§	- 'Variegata' (v) ♀H5	Widely available
	guatemalensis	see *Y. elephantipes*
	harrimaniae	SIgm XSen
	linearifolia	WCot
	linearis	see *Y. thompsoniana*
	'Nobilis'	CHEx
	pallida	WPGP
	radiosa	see *Y. elata*
	recurvifolia ♀H5	CHEx EBee EPfP SArc
	- Banana Split = 'Monvil' (v)	EBee EPfP LBuc LRHS MBri SPoG
	- 'Gold Stream' (v)	WCot
	rigida	CDTJ WCot WPGP
	rostrata	CCCN CDTJ EUJe LPal SArc SPlb WCot
	- 'Sapphire Skies'	EUJe MAvo WCot
	rupicola	WCot
	schottii	EShb WCot
§	***thompsoniana***	CDTJ LPal WCot XSen
	torreyi	SIgm
	'Vittorio Emanuele II'	SMad
	whipplei	CBcs CCCN CDoC EBee EPfP LRHS SBig WCot WPGP
	- subsp. ***caespitosa*** NNS 01-412 **new**	WCot
	- subsp. ***intermedia*** NNS 01-413	WCot
	- subsp. ***whipplei*** NJM 11.001 **new**	WPGP

Yushania (*Poaceae*)

	KR 7698	ERod MWht
§	***anceps***	CBcs CDoC CDul CEnt CExl CHEx EPla MMoz MMuc MWht SBig SEND WMoo
	- 'Pitt White'	CEnt CExl EPla MWht
	- 'Pitt White Rejuvenated'	ERod
	brevipaniculata	ERod
	chungii	CDul CEnt CExl ERod MWht
	maculata	CDul CEnt CExl EPla ERod MMoz MWht SBig
§	***maling***	CExl ERod MMoz
	Yunnan 5	CExl MWht

Z

Zaluzianskya (*Scrophulariaceae*)

	JCA 15665	WAbe
	elongata	SPlb
	'Katherine'	SRot
	microsiphon	SPlb
	'Orange Eye'	CPBP CWCL GKev NSla WAbe WIce
	ovata	CElw CPBP CTre CWCL EPfP EPot EWld GKev MHer MSCN NSla SBch SPlb SPoG SPtp WAbe WIce
	pulvinata	SPlb
	'Semonkong'	GCal SWvt

Zamia (*Zamiaceae*)

	furfuracea	LPal
	pumila	SPlb

Zamioculcas (*Araceae*)

	zamiifolia	CCCN

Zantedeschia (*Araceae*)

§	***aethiopica***	Widely available
	- 'Apple Court Babe'	CElw CRow ELon SMrm
	- 'Crowborough' ♀H4	Widely available
	- 'Gigantea'	CHEx
	- 'Glow'	CExl CMac ECtt EWoo
	- 'Green Goddess' ♀H2	Widely available
	- 'Little Gem'	SMad
	- 'Luzon Lovely'	WCru

- 'Marshmallow'	ECtt ELan EPfP
- 'Mr Martin'	CCCN CMac EBee ECtt ELon SBig SMad SWvt WCot
- 'Pershore Fantasia' (v)	CExl EBee WCot WWEG
- 'Snow White'PBR	LRHS
- 'White Gnome'	WCot
- 'White Sail'	ECtt ELan EPla MRav NGdn SWat WGwG
albomaculata	CTca LAma SPlb WWEG
'Anneke'	CCCN
'Apricot Glow'	CHll ECho
'Ascari'PBR	CCCN
'Auckland'PBR	SDeJ
'Black Eyed Beauty'	LAma
'Black Magic'	CCCN CMac EPfP
'Black Pearl'	LAma
'Black Star'	see *Z.* 'Edge of Night'
'Cameo'	CCCN LAma SDeJ
'Cantor'PBR new	NBri
(Captain Series) 'Captain Murano'PBR new	SPoG
- 'Captain Prado'PBR new	NBri
- 'Captain Reno'PBR new	SPoG
- 'Captain Tendens'PBR	SDeJ
'Chianti'	SDeJ
'Crystal Blush'	LAma SDeJ
§ 'Edge of Night'	CBcs CCCN ERCP NBri SDeJ
'Elegant Swan'PBR	LRHS NBri SCob
elliottiana ♀H1c	CBcs CCon CHEx CTri LAma
'Esm Puc'PBR new	ECho
'Flame'	CBcs CCCN SPad
'Flamingo'PBR	WCot
'Flavo Gold'	ECho
'Garnet Glow'	WCot
'Helen O'Connor'	CExl
'Hercules'	ESwi
'Kiwi Blush'	CBro CCCN CCon CExl CHEx CHel CSpe EBee ELan ELon EPfP EWll LLWG MGos SEND SKHP SPer SRkn SWat
'Lime Lady'	ECha EWay
'Mango'	EPri LAma MPie WCot
'Mozart'	CCCN
'Odessa'PBR new	SPoG
'Philomena' new	LRHS
'Picasso'PBR	CBcs CCCN ERCP NBri SDeJ SPad SPoG WCot
'Pink Mist'	LAma LLWG NBri SMad
'Pink Persuasion'	LAma
'Purple Sensation'	MPie
'Red Alert'PBR new	NBri
'Red Sox'PBR	CCCN SDeJ
rehmannii ♀H1c	ECho LAma SDeJ SRms
'Samur'PBR new	NBri
'Siberia'PBR new	NBri
'Sunshine'	WCot
'White Giant'	EWay WPGP
'White Pixie'	EPfP

Zanthorhiza see *Xanthorhiza*

Zanthoxylum (*Rutaceae*)

acanthopodium GWJ 9287	WCru
ailanthoides B&SWJ 11115 from Japan	WCru
- B&SWJ 11394 from Japan	WCru
- f. ***inermis*** RWJ 10048	WCru
americanum	ELan LEdu
armatum	CAgr SBrt
- HWJK 2178	WCru
bungeanum BWJ 8040	WCru
fauriei B&SWJ 11080	WCru
aff. ***fauriei*** B&SWJ 11371	WCru
- B&SWJ 11523	WCru
laetum	CFil
- WWJ 11678	WCru
- WWJ 11914	WCru
myriacanthum B&SWJ 11844	WCru
oxyphyllum	LEdu
- GWJ 9428 new	WCru
- HWJK 2131	WCru
piperitum	CAgr GPoy
- B&SWJ 8543	WCru
- B&SWJ 11377	WCru
- B&SWJ 11433	WCru
- purple-leaved	CExl CFil WPGP WPat
schinifolium	CAgr LEdu
- B&SWJ 8593	WCru
- B&SWJ 11080	WCru
- B&SWJ 11391	WCru
simulans	CAgr CArn CBcs CDul CExl GBin IVic LEdu NLar
stenophyllum	CMCN

Zauschneria (*Onagraceae*)

arizonica	see *Z. californica* subsp. *latifolia*
§ ***californica***	CFis CHll CTri ECho MBrN SLon SWat SWvt WPnn XLum
§ - subsp. ***cana***	ECha SWat
- - 'Sir Cedric Morris'	EPfP LRHS
§ - 'Dublin' ♀H4	Widely available
- 'Ed Carman'	ECha ECtt ESwi LSou SEle XLum
§ - subsp. ***garrettii***	ECho SDys SWat
- 'Glasnevin'	see *Z. californica* 'Dublin'
§ - subsp. ***latifolia***	XLum
§ - subsp. ***mexicana***	SRms
- 'Olbrich Silver'	EBee ECha ECho ECtt EWes LRHS SIgm WHoo WKif XLum
- 'Western Hills' ♀H5	CCon CSpe CTri ECha ECho EPfP LRHS LSou MMuc MRav SEND SPhx SWvt WHoo XLum
cana villosa	see *Z. californica* subsp. *mexicana*
'Merriments Orange' new	SMrm
I 'Pumilio'	EPot
§ ***septentrionalis***	WAbe

Zebrina see *Tradescantia*

Zehneria (*Cucurbitaceae*)

scabra new	SVic

Zelkova ✿ (*Ulmaceae*)

carpinifolia	CDul CLnd CMCN SPlb
'Kiwi Sunset'	EBee EPfP NWea
serrata ♀H6	CAco CBcs CCVT CDul CLnd CMCN CMen CTho EBee ECrN ELan EPfP EShb IDee MBri MGos MMuc NWea SEND SGol WMou
- B&SWJ 8491 from Korea	WCru
- 'Goblin'	CJun MBlu NLar WPat
- 'Green Vase'	MBlu SCob
- 'Musashino'	SGol
- 'Ogon'	SGol
- 'Urban Ruby'	NLar

- 'Variegata' (v) CJun CMac MBlu NLar SGol SMad
sinica CMCN CMen
× **verschaffeltii** EPfP IArd MBlu

Zenobia (*Ericaceae*)

pulverulenta CAbP CBcs CDoC CMac CSBt ELan EPfP IVic LRHS MAsh MBlu MGil MGos NLar SCob SLon SSta WAbe WPat WSHC
- 'Blue Sky' CAbP CBcs CDoC CMCN EBee EPfP GBin GKin IDee LRHS MBlu MBri MGos MPkF NLar SCob SPer SPoG SSpi SSta WPGP
- f. **nitida** CMac NLar
- 'Raspberry Ripple' CBcs GKin LRHS MBri NLar SSta
- 'Viridis' NLar

Zephyranthes (*Amaryllidaceae*)

atamasca SKHP
'Big Dude' SKHP
candida CAby CBro CTal EBee ECho EPot EShb EWld GKev LAma LPot LRHS NRog SChF SDeJ WHil
- 'Lemon Drops' **new** NRog
citrina CExl EBee ECho EPot GKev LAma SDeJ WCot
drummondii ECho NRog
flavissima ECho
grandiflora ♀H2 ECho
'Ivory Crocus' **new** NRog
katherinae **new** NRog
'Krakatau' WCot
La Bufa Rosa Group CExl WCot
lindleyana NRog WHil
mexicana EBee ECho
minima ECho NRog
minuta NRog
'Pink Beauty' ECho
'Prairie Sunset' WHil
primulina ECho NRog
robusta see *Habranthus robustus*
rosea ECho EPot GKev SDeJ
'Snow White' ECho
traubii from San Carlos **new** NRog
versicolor **new** NRog

Zigadenus (*Melanthiaceae*)

elegans EBee ECha EPri LEdu LRHS MAvo MHer SMad WCot WSHC
fremontii WCot
glaberrimus GLin
nuttallii CTal ECho WCot
venenosus NNS 03-605 WCot

Zingiber ✿ (*Zingiberaceae*)

mioga CCon CFil EBee GPoy IMou LEdu SChr SPlb WPGP
- 'Crûg's Zing' LEdu WCru WPGP
- 'Dancing Crane' (v) CFil CMac EUJe LEdu
- 'White Feather' **new** LEdu
officinale CTsd SPre SRms

Zinnia (*Asteraceae*)

elegans SVic
'Envy' (d) CSpe
'Profusion Cherry' CWCL
'Red Spider' CSpe
'Swizzle Scarlet and Yellow' CWCL

Zizia (*Apiaceae*)

aptera SPhx WHil
aurea SDix SPhx WSHC XLum

Ziziphus (*Rhamnaceae*)

§ **jujuba** (F) CAgr CBcs CDul ETwe
- 'Lang' (F) CAgr
- 'Li' (F) CAgr
- var. **spinosa** CArn
sativa see *Z. jujuba*

Bibliography

This is by no means exhaustive but lists some of the more useful works used in the preparation of the *RHS Plant Finder*. The websites of raisers of new plants (not listed here) are also an invaluable source of information.

General

Allan, H.H., et al. 2000. *Flora of New Zealand.* Wellington. http://floraseries.landcareresearch.co.nz

Bean, W.J. 1988. *Trees and Shrubs Hardy in the British Isles.* (8th ed.) Sir George Taylor, D.L. Clarke (eds). Supp. D.L. Clarke (ed.). London: John Murray.

Beckett, K. (ed.). 1994. *Alpine Garden Society Encyclopaedia of Alpines.* Pershore, Worcs.: Alpine Garden Society.

Boufford, D.E., et al. (eds). 2003. *Flora of Taiwan Checklist.* A checklist of the vascular plants of Taiwan. Taipei, Taiwan: NTU. http://tai2.ntu.edu.tw

Bramwell, D. & Bramwell, Z.I. 2001. *Wild Flowers of the Canary Islands.* (2nd ed.). Madrid: Editorial Rueda, S.L.

Brickell, C. (ed.). 2008. *The Royal Horticultural Society A-Z Encyclopedia of Garden Plants.* (3rd ed.) London: Dorling Kindersley.

Brickell, C.D. et al (eds.). 2009. *International Code of Nomenclature for Cultivated Plants* (8th ed.). ISHS.

Brummitt, R.K. (comp.). 1992. *Vascular Plant Families and Genera.* Kew: Royal Botanic Gardens. http://data.kew.org

Castroviejo, S. et al. (eds). *Flora Iberica.* 1987-2007. (Vols 1-8,, 10, 14, 15, 21). Madrid: Real Jardín Botánico, C.S.I.C.

Cave, Y. & Paddison, V. 1999. *The Gardener's Encyclopaedia of New Zealand Native Plants.* Auckland: Godwit.

Cooke, I. 1998. *The Plantfinder's Guide to Tender Perennials.* Newton Abbot, Devon: David & Charles.

Cullen, J. et al. (eds). 2011. *The European Garden Flora* (2nd ed.). Cambridge: Cambridge University Press. (5 vols).

Davis, P.H., Mill, R.R. & Tan, K. (eds). 1965-88. *Flora of Turkey and the East Aegean Island.* (Vols 1-10). Edinburgh University Press.

Goldblatt, P. & Manning, J. 2000. *Cape Plants. A Conspectus of the Cape Flora of South Africa.* South Africa/USA: National Botanical Institute of South Africa/Missouri Botanical Garden.

Greuter, W., Brummitt, R.K., Farr, E., Kilian, N., Kirk, P.M. & Silva, P.C. (comps). 1993. *NCU-3.*

Grierson, A.J.C., Long, D.G. & Noltie, H.J. et al. (eds). 2001. *Flora of Bhutan.* Edinburgh: Royal Botanic Garden.

Grimshaw, J. & Bayton, R. 2009. *New Trees. Recent Introductions to Cultivation.* Kew: Royal Botanic Gardens.

Güner, A., Özhatay, N., Ekîm, T., Baser, K.H.C. & Hedge, I.C. 2000. *Flora of Turkey and the East Aegean Islands.* Supp. 2. Vol. 11. Edinburgh: Edinburgh University Press.

Hickman, J.C. (ed.). 1993. *The Jepson Manual. Higher Plants of California.* Berkeley & Los Angeles: University of California Press. Jan 2010. http://ucjeps.berkeley.edu/interchange.html

Hillier, J. & Coombes, A. (eds). 2002. *The Hillier Manual of Trees & Shrubs.* (7th ed.). Newton Abbot, Devon: David & Charles.

Hoffman, M. (ed.). 2005. List of Woody Plants. International Standard ENA 2005-2010. Netherlands: Applied Plant Research.

Huxley, A., Griffiths, M. & Levy, M. (eds). 1992. *The New RHS Dictionary of Gardening.* London: Macmillan.

Iwatsuki, K., et al. 1995. *Flora of Japan.* Vols I-IIIb. Tokyo, Japan: Kodansha Ltd.

Jelitto, L. & Schacht, W.R., Simon, H. 2002. *Die Freiland-Schmuchstauden.* Germany: Verlag Eugen Ulmer.

Krüssmann, G. & Epp, M.E. (trans.). 1986. *Manual of Cultivated Broad-leaved Trees and Shrubs.* London: Batsford (3 vols).

Leslie, A.C. (trans.). *New Cultivars of Herbaceous Perennial Plants 1985-1990.* Hardy Plant Society.

Mabberley, D.J. 2008. *Mabberley's Plant Book. A Portable Dictionary of Plants, their Classification and Uses.* (3rd ed.). Cambridge: Cambridge University Press.

McNeill, J. et al. (eds). 2006. *International Code of Botanical Nomenclature (Vienna Code).* Ruggell, Liechtenstein: A.R.G. Gantner Verlag. Jan 2010. http://ibot.sav.sk.

Metcalf, L.J. 1987. *The Cultivation of New Zealand Trees and Shrubs.* Auckland: Reed Methuen.

Nelson, E.C. 2000. *A Heritage of Beauty: The Garden Plants of Ireland: An Illustrated Encyclopaedia.* Dublin: Irish Garden Plant Society.

Ohwi, J. 1965. *Flora of Japan.* Washington DC: Smithsonian Institution.

Phillips, R. & Rix, M. 1997. *Conservatory and Indoor Plants.* London: Macmillan. (2 vols).

Press, J.R. & Short, M.J. (eds). 1994. *Flora of Madeira.* London: Natural History Museum/HMSO.

Rehder, A. 1940. *Manual of Cultivated Trees and Shrubs Hardy in North America.* (2nd ed.). New York: Macmillan.

Rice, G. (ed.), 2006. *Encyclopedia of Perennials.* London: Dorling Kindersley.
Stace, C. 2010. *New Flora of the British Isles.* (3rd ed.). Cambridge: Cambridge University Press.
Thomas, G.S. 1990. *Perennial Garden Plants. A Modern Florilegium.* (3rd ed.). London: Dent.
Trehane, P. (comp.). 1989. *Index Hortensis. Vol. 1: Perennials.* Wimborne: Quarterjack
Tutin, T.G., et al. 1964. *Flora Europaea.* Cambridge University Press. Vols 1-5. http://rbg-web2.rbge.org.uk

GENERAL PERIODICALS

Dendroflora
New, Rare and Unusual Plants.
The Hardy Plant Society. *The Hardy Plant.*
The Hardy Plant Society. *The Sport.*
Internationale Stauden-Union. *ISU Yearbook.*
Royal Horticultural Society. *Hanburyana.*
Royal Horticultural Society. *The Garden.*
Royal Horticultural Society. *The Plantsman.*
Royal Horticultural Society. *The New Plantsman.*
Royal Horticultural Society. *The Plantsman* (new series).

GENERAL WEBSITES

Annotated Checklist of the Flowering Plants of Nepal. Jan 2010 www.efloras.org/flora_page-aspx?_id=110
Australian Cultivar Registration Authority. Jan 2010. www.anbg.gov.au/acra
Australian Plant Breeders Rights: Database Search. Jan 2010. http://pbr.ipaustralia.optus.com.au
Australian Plant Names Index. Australian National Botanic Gardens (comp.). Jan 2010. www.anbg.gov.au/apni/index.html
Bolivia Checklist. Jan 2010. www.efloras.org/flora_page.aspx?flora_id=40
Botanical Expedition in Myanmar Checklist. Jan 2010. http://botany.si-edu/myanmar/checklistNames.cfm
Brand, H. UConn Plant Database of Trees Shrubs and Vines. Jan 2010. www.hort.uconn.edu
Canadian Ornamental Plant Foundation. Jan 2010. www.copf.org
Canadian Plant Breeders Rights Office: Canadian Food Inspection Agency. Jan 2010. www.inspection.gc.ca
Catálogo de las Plantas Vasculares de las República Argentina. Jan 2010. www.darwin.edu.ar/Publicaciones/catalogoVaseII/CatalogoVaseII.asp
Catalogue of the Vascular Plants of Madagascar: www.efforas.org/flora_page.aspx?flora_id+12
Darwin Checklist of Moroccan Vascular Plants www.herbarium.rdg.ac.uk/
DEFRA Plant Varieties and Seeds Gazette. Jan 2010. www.defra.gov.uk
Euro+Med PlantBase. The information resource for Euro-Mediteranean plant diversity. www.emplantbase.org/home.html
Flora Himalaya Database. Jan 2010. www.leca.univ-savoie.fr
Flora Mesoamericana Internet Version (W3FM). Jan 2013. Missouri Botanical Garden.
www.tropicos.org/Project/FM
Flora of Australia Online. Jan 2010. Australian Biological Resources Study. www.environment.gov.au/biodiversity/abrs/online-resources/flora/index.html
Flora of Chile. Jan 2010. www.efloras.org/flora_page.aspx?flora_id=60
Flora of China Checklist. Jan 2010. http://flora.huh.harvard.edu/china
Flora of Pakistan. Jan 2010. www.efloras.org/flora_page.aspd?flora_id=5
Flora of North America Website. Jan 2010. Morin, N.R., et al. www.efloras.org-page.aspx/flora_id=1
GRIN (Germplasm Resources Information Network) Taxonomy. Jan 2010. www.ars-grin.gov
Hatch, D. Jan 2010. New Ornamentals Society Database. http://members.tripod.com/~Hatch_L/nos.html
International Plant Names Index. Jan 2010. www.ipni.org
International Plant Names Index: Author Query. Jan 2010. www.ipni.org/ipni
IOPI Provisional Global Plant Checklist. Jan 2010. www.bgbm.fu-berlin.de/iopi/gpl/query.asp
Manaaki Whenua: Landcare Research in New Zealand Plants Database Jan 2010. http://nzflora.landcareresearch.co.nz
Manual de plantas de Costa Rica. Jan 2010. www.mobot.org/manual.plantas
Plant List, The. A working list of all plant species www.theplantlist.org.
Plants Database. USDA, NRCS. Jan 2010. http://plants.usda.gov
Plants of Southern Africa: an Online Checklist. Jan 2010. http://posa.sanbi.org
PLUTO: Plant Variety Database www.upov.int/pluto/en
New Zealand Plant Variety Rights Office www.iponz.govt.nz/cms/pvr
Royal Horticultural Society. www.rhs.org.uk/plants/RHS-Publications/Plant-registers
Synonymized Checklist of the Vascular Flora of the United States, Puerto Rico and the Virgin Isles. BIOTA of North America Program. Jan 2010. www.bonap.org
Tropicos. Jan 2010. www.tropicos.org
US Patent Full-Text Database. US Patent and Trademark Office, (comp.). Jan 2010. www.uspto.gov/patft
World Checklist of Selected Families. 2010. apps.kew.org/wcsp

GENERA AND OTHER PLANT GROUPINGS

Acer

Gregory, P. & Angus, H. 2008. *World Checklist of Maple Cultivar Names.* Forestry Commission National Arboreta.

Harris, J.G.S. 2000. *The Gardener's Guide to Growing Maples.* Newton Abbot, Devon: David & Charles.

Van Gelderen, C.J. & Van Gelderen, D.M. 1999. *Maples for Gardens.* A Color Encyclopedia. Portland, Oregon: Timber Press.

Vertrees, J.D. 2001. *Japanese Maples.* Momiji and Kaede. (3rd ed.). Portland, Oregon: Timber Press.

Actaea

Compton, J.A., Culham, A. & Jury, S.L. 1998. Reclassification of *Actaea* to Include *Cimicifuga* and *Souliea (Ranunculaceae). Taxon* 47:593-634.

Adiantum

Goudey, C.J. 1985. *Maidenhair Ferns in Cultivation.* Melbourne: Lothian.

Agapanthus

Snoeijer, W. 2004. *Agapanthus. A Revision of the Genus.* Portland, Oregon: Timber Press.

Agavaceae

Irish, M. & Irish, G. 2000. *Agaves, Yuccas and Related Plants.* A Gardener's Guide. Portland, Oregon: Timber Press.

Aizoaceae

Burgoyne, P. et al. 1998. *Mesembs of the World. Illustrated Guide to a Remarkable Succulent Group.* South Africa: Briza Publications.

Allium

Davies, D. 1992. *Alliums. The Ornamental Onions.* London: Batsford

Gregory, M., et al. 1998. *Nomenclator Alliorum.* Kew: Royal Botanic Gardens.

Mathew, B. 1996. *A Review of Allium Section Allium.* Kew: Royal Botanic Gardens.

Androsace

Smith, G. & Lowe, D. 1997. *The Genus Androsace.* Pershore, Worcs.: Alpine Garden Society.

Anemone, Japanese

McKendrick, M. 1990. Autumn Flowering Anemones. *The Plantsman* 12(3):140-151.

McKendrick, M. 1998. Japanese Anemones. *The Garden* (RHS) 123(9):628-633.

Anthemis

Leslie, A. 1997. Focus on Plants: *Anthemis tinctoria. The Garden* (RHS) 122(8):552-555.

Apiaceae

Pimenov, M.G. & Leonov, M.V. 1993. *The Genera of the Umbelliferae.* Kew: Royal Botanic Gardens.

Aquilegia

Munz, P.A. 1946. *Aquilegia:* the Cultivated and Wild Columbines. *Gentes Herb.* 7(1):1-150.

Araceae

Govaerts, R. & Frodin, D.G. 2002. *World Checklist and Bibliography of Araceae (and Acoraceae).* Kew:Royal Botanic Gardens

Araliaceae

Govaerts, R. & Frodin, D.G. 2002. *World Checklist and Bibliography of Araliaceae.* Kew:Royal Botanic Gardens

Arecaceae (palms)

Craft, P. & Riffle, R.L. 2003. *Encyclopedia of Cultivated Palms.* Portland, Oregon: Timber Press.

Uhl, N.W. & Dransfield, J. 1987. *Genera Palmarum.* A Classification of Palms Based on the Work of Harold E. Moore Jr. Lawrence, Kansas: Allen Press.

Argyranthemum

Humphries, C.J. 1976. A Revision of the Macaronesian Genus *Argyranthemum. Bull. Brit. Mus. (Nat. Hist.) Bot.* 5(4):145-240.

Arisaema

Gusman, G. & Gusman, L. 2002. The Genus Arisaema: A Monograph for Botanists and Nature Lovers. Ruggell, Leichtenstein: A.R. Gantner Verlag Kommanditgesellschaft.

Pradhan, U.C. 1997. *Himalayan Cobra Lilies* (Arisaema). Their Botany and Culture. (2nd ed.). Kalimpong, West Bengal, India: Primulaceae Books.

Arum

Bown, D. 2000. *Plants of the Arum Family.* (2nd ed.). Portland, Oregon: Timber Press.

Boyce, P. 1993. *The Genus Arum.* London: HMSO.

Asclepiadaceae

Eggli, U. (ed.). 2002. *Illustrated Handbook of Succulent Plants: Asclepiadaceae.* Heidelberg, Germany: Springer-Verlag.

Aster

Picton, P. 1999. *The Gardener's Guide to Growing Asters.* Newton Abbot: David & Charles.

Asteraceae

Bremer, K. et al. 1994. *Asteraceae: Cladistics and Classification.* Portland, Oregon: Timber Press.

Cubey, J. & Grant, M. 2004. *Perennial Yellow Daisies: RHS Bulletin No 6.* Wisley, Surrey: RHS.

Astilbe

Noblett, H. 2001. *Astilbe.* A Guide to the Identification of Cultivars and Common Species. Cumbria: Henry Noblett.

Aubrieta

1975. *International Registration Authority Checklist.* Weihenstephan, Germany: (Unpublished).

Bamboos

Ohrnberger, D. 1999. *The Bamboos of the World.* Amsterdam: Elsevier.

Begonia

American Begonia Society Astro Branch Begonia Data Base. Jan 2010. http://absastro.tripod.com

American Begonia Society Registered Begonias. Jan 2010. http://www.begonias.org

Ingles, J. 1990. *American Begonia Society Listing of Begonia Cultivars.* Revised Edition Buxton Checklist. American Begonia Society.

Tebbitt, M.C. 2005. *Begonias: Cultivation, Identification and Natural History*. Portland, Oregon: Timber Press.

Berberidaceae

Stearn, W.T. & Shaw, J.M.H. 2002. *The Genus Epimedium and Other Herbaceous Berberidaceae including the Genus Podophyllum*. Kew: Royal Botanic Gardens.

Betula

Ashburner, K.B. 1980. *Betula* – a Survey. *The Plantsman* 2(1):31-53.

Hunt, D. (ed.). 1993. *Betula: Proceedings of the IDS Betula Symposium 1992*. Richmond, Surrey: International Dendrology Society.

Boraginaceae

Bennett, M. 2003. *Pulmonarias and the Borage Family*. London: Batsford.

Bougainvillea

Gillis, W.T. 1976. Bougainvilleas of Cultivation *(Nyctaginaceae)*. *Baileya* 20(1):34-41.

Iredell, J. 1990. *The Bougainvillea Grower's Handbook*. Brookvale, Australia: Simon & Schuster.

Iredell, J. 1994. *Growing Bougainvilleas*. London: Cassell.

MacDaniels, L.H. 1981. A Study of Cultivars in *Bougainvillea (Nyctaginaceae)*. *Baileya* 21(2):77-100.

Singh, B., Panwar, R.S., Voleti, S.R., Sharma, V.K. & Thakur, S. 1999. *The New International Bougainvillea Check List*. (2nd ed.). New Delhi: Indian Agricultural Research Institute.

Bromeliaceae

Beadle, D.A. 1991. *A Preliminary Listing of all the Known Cultivar and Grex Names for the Bromeliaceae*. Corpus Christi, Texas: Bromeliad Society.

Bromeliad Cultivar Registry Online Databases. Bromeliad Society International. Jan 2010. www.bsi.org

Brugmansia

Wreggitt, L. et al. (comp.). Jan 2010. *Register of Brugmansia Cultivars and Checklist of Names in Use*. American Brugmansia and Datura Society. www.abads.org

Buddleja

Stuart, D.D. 2006. *Buddlejas: Royal Horticultural Society Collector Guide*. Portland, Oregon: Timber Press.

Bulbs

Leeds, R. 2000. *The Plantfinder's Guide to Early Bulbs*. Newton Abbot, Devon: David & Charles.

KAVB Online registration pages. Jan 2010. http://kavb.back2p.soft-orange.com

Buxus

Batdorf, L.R. 1995. *Boxwood Handbook. A Practical Guide to Knowing and Growing Boxwood*. Boyce, VA, USA: The American Boxwood Society. Jan 2010. www.boxwoodsociety.org

Cactaceae

Hunt, D. et al. 2006. *New Cactus Lexicon*. (2 vols.) Sherborne, Dorset: DH Books.

Camellia

Trujillo, D. J. (ed.). 2002. *Camellia Nomenclature*. (24th revd ed.). Southern California Camellia Society.

Savige, T.J. (comp.). 1993. *The International Camellia Register*. (Vol 1-2). Supps. 1-2. 1997-2011. The International Camellia Society.

Ferrari, D. & Sfondrini, N. Web *Camellia* Register. Camellia-unipv.it/camelliadb2

Campanula

Lewis, P. & Lynch, M. 1998. *Campanulas*. A Gardeners Guide. (2nd ed.). London: Batsford.

Lewis, P 2002. *Campanulas in the Garden*. Pershore, Worcs.: Hardy Plant Society.

Campanulaceae

Lammers, T.G. 2007. *World Checklist and Bibliography of Campanulaceae*. Kew Publishing.

Canna

Cooke, I. 2001. *The Gardener's Guide to Growing Cannas*. Newton Abbot, Devon: David & Charles.

Gray, J. & Grant, M. 2003. Canna: RHS Bulletin No 3. Wisley, Surrey: RHS.

Hayward, K. Jan 2010. www.hartcanna.com

Carnivorous Plants

Schlauer, J. (comp.). Jan 2010. Carnivorous Plant Database. www.omnisterra.com

Ceanothus

Fross, D. & D. Wilken. 2006. *Ceanothus*. Portland, Oregon: Timber Press.

Cercidiphyllum

Dosmann, M.S. 1999. Katsura: a Review of *Cercidiphyllum* in Cultivation and in the Wild. *The New Plantsman* 6(1):52-62.

Dosmann, M., Andrews, S., Del Tredici, P. & Li, J. 2003. Classification and Nomenclature of Weeping Katsuras. *The Plantsman* 2(1):21-27.

Chaenomeles

Weber, C. 1963. Cultivars in the Genus *Chaenomeles*. *Arnoldia (Jamaica Plain)* 23(3):17-75.

Chrysanthemum

Brummitt, D. 1997. *Chrysanthemum* Once Again. *The Garden* (RHS) 122(9):662-663.

Chrysanthemums in Aberdeen. Directory of popular cultivars. www.chrysanthemums.info

Gosling, S.G. (ed.). 1964. *British National Register of Chrysanthemums*. Whetstone, London: National Chrysanthemum Society.

National Chrysanthemum Society. 2000. *British National Register of Names of Chrysanthemums Amalgamated Edition 1964-1999*. Tamworth, Staffordshire: National Chrysanthemum Society. Cultivar database. Jan 2010. www.nationalchrysanthemumsociety.org.uk

Cistus

Page, R.G. Feb 2007. Cistus and Halimium Website. www.cistuspage.org.uk

Citrus

Davies, F.S. & Albrigo, L.G. 1994. *Citrus.* Wallingford, Oxon: Cab International.

Page, M. 2008. *Growing Citrus.* London: Timber Press

Saunt, J. 1990. *Citrus Varieties of the World.* An Illustrated Guide. Norwich: Sinclair

Clematis

Clematis on the Web. Jan 2008. www.clematis.hull.ac.uk

Donald, D., *The International Clematis Register and Checklist,* Supp. 4. 2012

Grey-Wilson, C. 2000. *Clematis: the Genus.* London: Batsford

HelpMeFind Clematis. Nov 2006. www.helpmefind.com/clematis

Johnson, M. 2001. *The Genus Clematis.* Södertälje, Sweden: Magnus Johnsons Plantskola AB & Bengt Sundström.

Matthews, V. (comp.). 2002. *The International Clematis Register and Checklist 2002* & Supps 1-3. 2004-2009. London: RHS.

Toomey, M. & Leeds, E. 2001. *An Illustrated Encyclopedia of Clematis.* Portland, Oregon: Timber Press.

Conifers

Anders, A.G. & Spicer, D.P. 2012 *RHS Encyclopedia of Conifers.* (2 vols). London:RHS

den Ouden, P. & Boom, B.K. 1965. *Manual of Cultivated Conifers.* The Hague: Martinus Nijhof.

Eckenwalder, J.E. 2009. *Conifers of the World.* China:Timber Press

Farjon, A. 1998. *World Checklist and Bibliography of Conifers.* Kew: Royal Botanic Gardens.

Knees, S.G. & Springate, L.S. 2009. *The International Conifer Register, Pt 5.* London: RHS.

Krüssmann, G. & Epp, M.E. (trans.). 1985. *Manual of Cultivated Conifers.* London: Batsford.

Lewis, J. & Leslie, A.C. 1987-1998. *The International Conifer Register. Pts 1-4.* London: RHS.

Welch, H.J. 1979. *Manual of Dwarf Conifers.* New York: Theophrastus.

Welch, H.J. 1991. *The Conifer Manual.* Vol. 1. Dordrecht, Netherlands: Kluwer Academic Publishers.

Welch, H.J. 1993. *The World Checklist of Conifers.* Bromyard, Herefordshire: Landsman's Bookshops Ltd.

Cornus

Cappiello, P. & Shadow, D. 2005. *Dogwoods.* Portland, Oregon: Timber Press.

Howard, R.A. 1961. Registration Lists of Cultivar Names in *Cornus L. Arnoldia (Jamaica Plain)* 21(2):9-18.

Corydalis

Lidén, M. & Zetterlund, H. 1997. *Corydalis. A Gardener's Guide and a Monograph of the Tuberous Species.* Pershore, Worcs.: Alpine Garden Society Publications Ltd.

Corylus

Crawford, M. 1995. *Hazelnuts: Production and Culture.* Dartington, Devon: Agroforestry Research Trust.

Cotoneaster

Fryer, J. & Hylmö, B. 2009. *Cotoneasters. A Comprehensive Guide to Shrubs for Flowers, Fruit and Foliage.* Portland, Oregon: Timber Press.

Crassulaceae

Rowley, G. 2003. *Crassula: A Grower's Guide.* Venegono superiore, Italy: Cactus & Co.

Eggli, U. (ed.) 2003. *Illustrated Handbook of Succulent Plants.* Springer.

Crocosmia

Goldblatt, P., Manning, J.C. & Dunlop, G. 2004. *Crocosmia and Chasmanthe.* Portland, Oregon: Timber Press.

Crocus

Jacobsen, N., van Scheepen, J. & Ørgaard, M. 1997. The *Crocus chrysanthus – biflorus* Cultivars. *The New Plantsman* 4(1):6-38.

Mathew, B. 1982. *The Crocus. A Review of the Genus Crocus (Iridaceae).* London: Batsford.

Mathew, B. 2002. *Crocus* Up-date. *The Plantsman* 1(1):44-56.

Cyclamen

Clennett, C. Jan. 2003. Register of Cultivar Names. www.cyclamen.org

Grey-Wilson, C. 2003. *Cyclamen. A Guide for Gardeners, Horticulturists & Botanists.* London: Batsford.

Cypripedium

Cribb, P. 1997. *The Genus Cypripedium.* Portland, Oregon: Timber Press.

Dahlia

American Dahlia Society website. Jan 2010. www.dahlia.org

Bates, D. Dahlia Plant Finder 2007. Jan 2010. www.dahliaworld.co.uk

McDonald, S., & Hedge, R. (comps). 1969. *Tentative Classified List and International Register of Dahlia Names 1969* & Supps 1-22. 1986-2012. London: RHS.

National Dahlia Society. 2005. *Classified Directory and Judging Rules.* (28th ed.) Aldershot, Hants: National Dahlia Society.

Winchester Growers Ltd English National Dahlia Collection website. Jan 2010. www.national-dahlia-collection.co.uk

Daphne

Brickell, C.D. & Mathew, B. 1976. *Daphne. The Genus in the Wild and in Cultivation.* Woking, Surrey: Alpine Garden Society.

Grey-Wilson, C. (ed.). 2001. *The Smaller Daphnes. The Proceedings of 'Daphne 2000', a Conference held at the Royal Horticultural Society.* Pershore, Worcs.: Alpine Garden Society.

White, R. 2006. *Daphnes: A Practical Guide for Gardeners.* Portland, Oregon: Timber Press.

Delphinium

1949. *A Tentative Check-list of Delphinium Names.* London: RHS.

1970. *A Tentative Check-list of Delphinium Names.* Addendum. London: RHS.

Bassett, D. & Wesley, W. 2004. *Delphinium: RHS Bulletin No 5.* Wisley, Surrey: RHS.

Leslie, A.C. 1996. *The International Delphinium Register Cumulative Supp. 1970-1995.* London: RHS.

Leslie, A.C. 1996-2005. The International Delphinium Register Supp. 1994-99. *The Delphinium Society Year Book 1996-2005.* London: RHS.

Dianthus

Galbally, J. & Galbally, E. 1997. *Carnations and Pinks for Garden and Greenhouse.* Portland, Oregon: Timber Press.

Leslie, A.C. *The International Dianthus Register.* 1983-2002. (2nd ed. & Supps 1-19). Supps 19-29, 2002-12. London: RHS.

Dierama

Hilliard, O.M. & Burtt, B.L. 1991. *Dierama. The Harebells of Africa.* Johannesburg; London: Acorn Books.

Dionysia

Grey-Wilson, C. 1989. *The Genus Dionysia.* Woking, Surrey: Alpine Garden Society.

Douglasia

Mitchell, B. 1999. Celebrating the Bicentenary of David Douglas: a Review of *Douglasia* in Cultivation. *The New Plantsman* 6(2):101-108.

Dracaena

Bos, J.J., Graven, P., Hetterscheid, W.L.A. & van de Wege, J.J. 1992. Wild and cultivated *Dracaena fragrans. Edinburgh J. Bot.* 49(3):311-331.

Echeveria

Schulz, L. & Kapitany, A. *Echeveria Cultivars.* Teesdale, Australia: Schulz Publishing.

Episcia

Dates, J.D. 1993. *The Gesneriad Register 1993.* Check List of Names with Descriptions of Cultivated Plants in the Genera *Episcia* & *Alsobia.* Galesburg, Illinois: American Gloxinia & Gesneriad Society, Inc.

Erica (see also **Heathers)**

Baker, H.A. & Oliver, E.G.H. 1967. *Heathers in Southern Africa.* Cape Town: Purnell.

Schumann, D., Kirsten, G. & Oliver, E.G.H. 1992. *Ericas of South Africa.* Vlaeberg, South Africa: Fernwood Press.

Erodium

Clifton, R. 1994. *Geranium Family Species Checklist. Pt 1 Erodium.* (4th ed.). The Geraniaceae Group.

Toomey, N., Cubey, J. & Culham, A. 2002. *Erodium × variabile. The Plantsman* 1(3): 166-172

Victor, D.X. (comp.). 2000. *Erodium: Register of Cultivar Names.* The Geraniaceae Group.

Erythronium

Mathew, B. 1992. A Taxonomic and Horticultural Review of *Erythronium* L. *(Liliaceae). J. Linn. Soc., Bot.* 109:453-471.

Mathew, B. 1998. The Genus *Erythronium. Bull. Alpine Gard. Soc. Gr. Brit.* 66(3):308-321.

Eupatorium sensu lato

Hind, D.J.N. 2006. Splitting *Eupatorium. The Plantsman* (n.s.) 5(2):185-189.

Euonymus

Brown, N. 1996. Notes on Cultivated Species of *Euonymus. The New Plantsman* 3(4):238-243.

Lancaster, C.R. 1981. An Account of *Euonymus* in Cultivation and its Availability in Commerce. *The Plantsman* 3(3):133-166.

Lancaster, C.R. 1982. *Euonymus* in Cultivation – Addendum. *The Plantsman* 4:61-64, 253-254.

Euphorbia

Govaerts, R., Frodin, D.G. & Radcliffe-Smith, A. 2000. *World Checklist and Bibliography of Euphorbiaceae.* Kew: Royal Botanic Gardens.

Turner, R. 1995. *Euphorbias. A Gardeners Guide.* London: Batsford.

Witton, D. 2000. *Euphorbias.* Pershore, Worcs.: Hardy Plant Society.

Fagales

Gocaerts, R. & Frodin, D.G. 1998. *World Checklist and Bibliography of Fagales.* RBG Kew.

Fagus

Dönig, G. 1994. *Die Park-und Gartenformen der Rotbuche Fagus sylvatica L.* Erlangen, Germany: Verlag Gartenbild Heinz Hansmann.

Wyman, D. 1964. Registration List of Cultivar Names of *Fagus* L. *J. Arnold Arbor.* 24(1):1-8.

Fascicularia

Nelson, E.C., Zizka, G., Horres, R. & Weising, K. 1999. Revision of the Genus *Fascicularia* Mez *(Bromeliaceae). Botanical Journal of the Linnean Society* 129(4):315-332.

Ferns

Checklist of World Ferns. Jan 2010. http://homepages.caverock.net.nz/nbj/fern

Johns, R.J. 1996. *Index Filicum.* Supplementum Sextum pro annis 1976-1990. Kew:Royal Botanic Gardens.

Johns, R.J. 1997. *Index Filicum.* Supplementum Septimum pro annis 1991-1995. Kew:Royal Botanic Gardens.

Jones, D.L. 1987. *Encyclopaedia of Ferns.* Melbourne, Australia: Lothian.

Kaye, R. 1968. *Hardy Ferns.* London: Faber & Faber

Rickard, M.H. 2000. *The Plantfinder's Guide to Garden Ferns.* Newton Abbot, Devon: David & Charles.

Rush, R. 1984. *A Guide to Hardy Ferns.* London: British Pteridological Society.

Forsythia

INRA Forsythia website. Jan 2010. www.angers.inra.fr/forsy

Fritillaria

Clark, T. & Grey-Wilson, C. 2003. Crown Imperials. *The Plantsman* 2(1):33-47.

Mathew, B., et al. 2000. *Fritillaria* Issue. *Bot. Mag.* 17(3):145-185.

Pratt, K. & Jefferson-Brown, M. 1997. *The Gardener's Guide to Growing Fritillaries.* Newton Abbot: David & Charles.

Turrill, W.B. & Sealy, J.R. 1980. *Studies in the Genus Fritillaria (Liliaceae).* Hooker's Icones Plantarum Vol. 39 (1 & 2). Kew: Royal Botanic Gardens.

Fruit

Brogdale Horticultural Trust National Fruit Collection. Jan 2010. www.nationalfruitcollection.org.uk

Bowling, B.L. 2000. *The Berry Grower's Companion.* Portland, Oregon: Timber Press.

Hogg, R. 1884. *The Fruit Manual.* (5th ed.). London: Journal of Horticulture Office.

Fuchsia

American Fuchsia Society Registration Database. Jan 2010. www.americanfuchsiasociety.org

Bartlett, G. 1996. *Fuchsias – A Colour Guide.* Marlborough, Wilts: Crowood Press.

Boullemier, Leo.B. (comp.). 1991. *The Checklist of Species, Hybrids and Cultivars of the Genus Fuchsia.* London, New York, Sydney: Blandford Press.

Boullemier, Leo.B. (comp.). 1995. *Addendum No 1 to the 1991 Checklist of Species, Hybrids and Cultivars of the Genus Fuchsia.* Dyfed, Wales: The British Fuchsia Society.

Goulding, E. 1995. *Fuchsias: The Complete Guide.* London: Batsford.

Johns, E.A. 1997. *Fuchsias of the 19th and Early 20th Century.* An Historical Checklist of Fuchsia Species & Cultivars, pre-1939. Kidderminster, Worcs.: British Fuchsia Society

Jones, L. & Miller, D.M. 2005. *Hardy Fuchsias: RHS Bulletin No 12.* Wisley, Surrey: RHS.

Stevens, R. Jan 2010. Find That Fuchsia. www.findthatfuchsia.info

Galanthus

Bishop, M., Davis, A. & Grimshaw, J. 2001. *Snowdrops. A monograph of cultivated Galanthus.* Maidenhead: Griffin Press.

Davis, A.P., Mathew, B. (ed.) & King, C. (ill.). 1999. *The Genus Galanthus. A Botanical Magazine Monograph.* Oregon: Timber Press.

Gentiana

Bartlett, M. 1975. *Gentians.* Dorset: Blandford Press.

Halda, J.J. 1996. *The Genus Gentiana.* Dobré, Czech Republic: Sen.

Ho T.N. & Liu S. 2001. *Worldwide Monograph of Gentiana.* Beijing: Science Press.

Geranium

Armitage, J. 2005-2007. *Hardy Geraniums – Stages 1-3: RHS Bulletin Nos 10, 14* & *18.* Wisley, Surrey: RHS.

Bath, T. & Jones, J. 1994. *The Gardener's Guide to Growing Hardy Geraniums.* Newton Abbot, Devon: David & Charles.

Bendtsen, B.H. 2005. *Gardening with Hardy Geraniums.* Portland, Oregon: Timber Press.

Clifton, R.T.F. 1995. *Geranium Family Species Check List Pt 2.* Geranium. (4th ed. issue 2). Dover: The Geraniaceae Group.

Jones, J., et al. 2001. *Hardy Geraniums for the Garden.* (3rd ed.). Pershore, Worcs.: Hardy Plant Society.

Victor, D.X. 2004. *Register of Geranium Cultivar Names.* (2nd ed.). The Geraniaceae Group.

Yeo, P.F. 2002. *Hardy Geraniums.* (3rd ed.). Kent: Croom Helm.

Gesneriaceae

The Gesneriad Society. Listing of registered gesneriads. Jan 2010. www.aggs.gesneriadsociety.org

Dates, J.D. 1986-1990. *The Gesneriad Register 1986-1987 & 1990.* Galesburg, Illinois: American Gloxinia & Gesneriad Society, Inc.

Gladiolus

British Gladiolus Society List of Cultivars Classified for Show Purposes 1994. Mayfield, Derbyshire: British Gladiolus Society.

1997-1998. British Gladiolus Society List of European, New Zealand & North American Cultivars Classified for Exhibition Purposes 1997 & 1998. Mayfield, Derbyshire: British Gladiolus Society.

Goldblatt, P. & Manning, J. 1998. *Gladiolus in Southern Africa.* Vlaeberg, South Africa: Fernwood Press.

Goldblatt, P. 1996. *Gladiolus in Tropical Africa.* Systematics Biology and Evolution. Oregon: Timber Press.

Gleditsia

Santamour, F.S. & McArdle, A.J. 1983. Checklist of Cultivars of Honeylocust (*Gleditsia triacanthos* L.). *J. Arboric.* 9:271-276.

Grevillea

Olde, P. & Marriott, N. 1995. *The Grevillea Book.* (3). Kenthurst, NSW: Kangaroo Press.

Haemanthus

Snijman, D. 1984. A Revision of the Genus *Haemanthus. J. S. African Bot.* (Supp. Vol. 12).

Hamamelis

Lane, C. 2005. *Witch Hazels.* Portland, Oregon: Timber Press.

Heathers

Nelson, E.C. Aug 2007. International Cultivar Registration Authority for Heathers. www.heathersociety.org.uk

Nelson, E.C. 2011. *Hardy Heathers from the Northern Hemisphere.* London: Kew Publishing

Hebe

Chalk, D. 1988. *Hebes and Parahebes.* Bromley, Kent: Christopher Helm (Publishers) Ltd.

Hutchins, G. 1997. *Hebes: Here and There.* A Monograph on the Genus *Hebe.* Caversham, Berks: Hutchins & Davies.
Metcalf, L.J. 2001. *International Register of Hebe Cultivars.* Canterbury, New Zealand: Royal New Zealand Institute of Horticulture (Inc.).
Metcalf, L.J. 2006. *Hebes: A Guide to Species, Hybrids and Allied Genera.* Portland, Oregon: Timber Press.

Hedera

Jury, S. et al. 2006. *Hedera algeriensis,* a Fine Species of Ivy. *Sibbaldia* 4: 93-108.
McAllister, H. 1988. Canary and Algerian Ivies. *The Plantsman* 10(1):27-29.
McAllister, H.A. & Rutherford, A. 1990. *Hedera helix and H. hibernica* in the British Isles. *Watsonia* 18:7-15.
Rose, P.Q. 1996. *The Gardener's Guide to Growing Ivies.* Newton Abbot, Devon: David & Charles.
Rutherford, A., McAllister, H. & Mill, R.R. 1993. New Ivies from the Mediterranean Area and Macaronesia. *The Plantsman* 15(2):115-128.

Heliconia

Berry, F. & Kress, W.J. 1991. *Heliconia.* An Identification Guide. Washington: Smithsonian Institution Press.

Helleborus

Burrell, C.C. & Tyler, J.K. 2006. *Hellebores: A Comprehensive Guide.* Portland, Oregon: Timber Press.
Mathew, B. 1989. *Hellebores.* Woking: Alpine Garden Society.
Rice, G. & Strangman, E. 1993. *The Gardener's Guide to Growing Hellebores.* Newton Abbot, Devon: David & Charles.

Hemerocallis

Baxter, G.J. (comp.). American Daylily Society Registry of Daylily Cultivars. Jan 2010. www.daylilies.org

Herbs

Phillips, R. & Foy, N. 1990. *Herbs.* London: Pan Books Ltd.

Heuchera and × ***Heucherella***

Heims, D. & Ware, G. 2005. *Heucheras and Heucherellas: Coral Bells and Foamy Bells.* Portland, Oregon: Timber Press.

Hibiscus

Noble, C. Apr 2007. Australian Hibiscus Society Database Register. www.australianhibiscus.com/

Hosta

Hosta Library. Aug 2006. www.hostalibrary.org
Grenfell, D. & Shadrack, M. 2004. *The Color Encyclopedia of Hostas.* Portland, Oregon: Timber Press.
Schmid, W.G. 1991. *The Genus Hosta.* London: Batsford.
Zilis, M.R. 2009. *The Hostapedia. An Encyclopedia of Hostas.* Q.22 Nursery Inc.

Hyacinthaceae (Asparagaceae pro parte*)*

Dashwood, M. & Mathew, B. 2006. *Hyacinthaceae – little blue bulbs: RHS Bulletin No 11.* Wisley, Surrey: RHS.
Mathew, B. 2005. *Hardy Hyacinthaceae* Pt 1: *Muscari. The Plantsman* 4(1):40-53.
Mathew, B. 2005. *Hardy Hyacinthaceae* Pt 2: *Scilla, Chionodoxa* and × *Chinoscilla. The Plantsman* 4(2):110-121.

Hydrangea

Dirr, M.A. 2004. *Hydrangeas for American Gardens.* Portland, Oregon: Timber Press.
Haworth-Booth, M. 1975. *The Hydrangeas.* London: Garden Book Club.
Van Gelderen, C.J. & Van Gelderen, D.M. 2004. *Encyclopedia of Hydrangeas.* Portland, Oregon: Timber Press.

Hypericum

Lancaster, R. & Robson, N. 1997. Focus on Plants: Bowls of Beauty. *The Garden* (RHS) 122(8):566-571.

Ilex

Bailes, C. 2006. *Hollies for Gardeners.* Portland, Oregon: Timber Press.
Dudley, T.R. & Eisenbeiss, G.K. 1973 & 1992. *International Checklist of Cultivated Ilex, Pts 1 & 2.* Washington DC: United States Dept of Agriculture.
Galle, F.C. 1997. *Hollies: the Genus Ilex.* Portland, Oregon: Timber Press.

Impatiens

Morgan, R.J. 2007. *Impatiens: The Vibrant World of Busy Lizzies, Balsams and Touch-me-nots.* Portland, Oregon: Timber Press.

Iris

Austin, C. 2005. *Irises: A Gardener's Encyclopedia.* Oregon:Timber Press.
Hoog, M.H. 1980. Bulbous Irises. *The Plantsman* 2(3):141-64.
Lowe, A. & Lowe, M. *Iris Check List of Registered Cultivar Names 2000-2009.* Hannibal, New York.
Mathew, B. 1981. *The Iris.* London: Batsford.
Mathew, B. 1993. The Spuria Irises. *The Plantsman* 15(1):14-25.
Service, N. 1990. *Iris unguicularis. The Plantsman* 12(1):1-9.
Stebbings, G. 1997. *The Gardener's Guide to Growing Iris.* Newton Abbot: David & Charles.
The Species Group of the British Iris Society, (ed.). 1997. *A Guide to Species Irises.* Their Identification and Cultivation. Cambridge: Cambridge University Press.

Jovibarba see under ***Sempervivum***

Kalmia

Jaynes, R.A. 1997. *Kalmia. Mountain Laurel and Related Species.* Portland, Oregon: Timber Press.

Kniphofia

Taylor, J. 1985. *Kniphofia* – a Survey. *The Plantsman* 7(3):129-160.

Whitehouse, C.M. 2012. Preliminary checklist of *Kniphofia* epithets. *Hanburyana* 6: 9-82.

Kohleria

Dates, J.D. (ed.) & Batcheller, F.N. (comp.). 1985. *The Gesneriad Register 1985. Check List of Names with Descriptions of Cultivated Plants in the Genus Kohleria.* Lincoln Acres, California: American Gloxinia and Gesneriad Society, Inc.

Lachenalia

Duncan, G.D. 1988. *The Lachenalia Hand Book.* Kirstenbosch, South Africa: National Botanic Gardens.

Duncan, G.D. 2012. *The Genus Lachenalia.* London: Kew Publishing.

Lantana

Howard, R.A. 1969. A Check List of Names Used in the Genus *Lantana. Arnoldia.* 29(11):73-109.

Lathyrus

Norton, S. 1996. *Lathyrus. Cousins of Sweet Pea.* Surrey: NCCPG.

Lavandula

Upson, T. & Andrews, S. 2004. *The Genus Lavandula.* Kew: Royal Botanic Garden.

Legumes

ILDIS. International Legume Database and Information Service. Jan 2010. Version 10.01. www.ildis.org/LegumeWeb

Leptospermum

Check List of *Leptospermum* Cultivars. 1963. *J. Roy. New Zealand Inst. Hort.* 5(5):224-30.

Dawson, M. 1997. A History of *Leptospermum scoparium* in Cultivation – Discoveries from the Wild. *The New Plantsman* 4(1):51-59.

Dawson, M. 1997. A History of *Leptospermum scoparium* in Cultivation – Garden Selections. *The New Plantsman* 4(2):67-78.

Lewisia

Davidson, B.L.R. 2000. *Lewisias.* Portland, Oregon: Timber Press.

Elliott, R. 1978. *Lewisias.* Woking: Alpine Garden Society.

Mathew, B. 1989. *The Genus Lewisia.* Bromley, Kent: Christopher Helm.

Lilium

Donald, D. *The International Lily Register 1982-2002.* (4th ed.). Supp. 3, 2012. London: RHS.

Leslie, A.C. *The International Lily Register 1982-2002.* (4th ed.). Supps 1-2, 2008-2010. London: RHS.

Online Lily Register. Jan 2010. www.lilyregister.com

Lonicera

Blahník, Z. 2006. *Lonicera* Cultivar Names: The First World List. *Acta Pruhoniciana* 81:59-64.

Magnolia

Callaway, D.J. Sep 2001. Magnolia Cultivar Checklist. www.magnoliasociety.org

Frodin, D.G. & Govaerts, R. 1996. *World Checklist and Bibliography of Magnoliaceae.* Kew: Royal Botanic Garden.

Maianthemum

Cubey, J.J. 2005 *The Incorporation of Smilacina within Maianthemum. The Plantsman* N.S.4(4).

Malus

Crawford, M. 1994. *Directory of Apple Cultivars.* Devon: Agroforestry Research Trust.

Fiala, J.L. 1994. *Flowering Crabapples.* The genus *Malus.* Portland, Oregon: Timber Press.

Rouèche, A. Oct 2007. Les Crets Fruits et Pomologie. www.pomologie.com

Spiers, V. 1996. *Burcombes, Queenies and Colloggetts.* St Dominic, Cornwall: West Brendon.

Meconopsis

Grey-Wilson, C. 1992. A Survey of the Genus *Meconopsis* in Cultivation. *The Plantsman* 14(1): 1-33.

Grey-Wilson, C. 2002. The True Identity of *Meconopsis napaulensis. Bot. Mag.* 23(2):176-209.

Meconopsis Group website. Jan 2010. www.meconopsis.org

Stevens, E. & Brickell, C. 2001. Problems with the Big Perennial Poppies. *The New Plantsman* 8(1):48-61.

Stevens, E. 2001. Further Observations on the Big Perennial Blue Poppies. *The New Plantsman* 8(2):105-111.

Miscanthus

Jones, L. 2004. Miscanthus: RHS Bulletin No 7. Wisley, Surrey: RHS.

Moraea

Goldblatt, P. 1986. *The Moraeas of Southern Africa.* Kirstenbosch, South Africa: National Botanic Gardens.

Musa

Banana and Plantain Section of Biodiversity International 2001. http://bananas.bioversity international.org

INIBAP *Musa* Germplasm Information System. Jan 2010. www.crop-diversity.org/banana

Narcissus

Blanchard, J.W. 1990. *Narcissus – A Guide to Wild Daffodils.* Woking, Surrey: Alpine Garden Society.

Kington, S. (comp.). 2008. *The International Daffodil Register and Classified List 2008* (4th ed.)

McDonald, S. (comp.) *The International Daffodil Register and Classified List 2008,* Supps 1-5. 2008-2012. London: RHS.

Nematanthus

Arnold, P. 1978. *The Gesneriad Register 1978.* Check List of *Nematanthus.* American Gloxinia and Gesneriad Society, Inc.

Nerium

Pagen, F.J.J. 1987. *Oleanders. Nerium L. and the Oleander Cultivars.* Wageningen, The Netherlands: Agricultural University Wageningen.

Nymphaea

Knotts, K. & Knotts, B. Victoria Adventure

Website. Checklist of Waterlily Cultivars. Jan 2010. www.victoria-adventure.org

Orchidaceae

Shaw, J.M.H. Jan 2010. The International Orchid Register. http://apps.rhs.org.uk/horticulturaldatabase/orchidregister/orchidregister.asp

Origanum

Paton, A. 1994. Three Membranous-bracted Species of *Origanum. Kew Mag.* 11(3):109-117.

White, S. 1998. *Origanum. The Herb Marjoram and its Relatives.* Surrey: NCCPG.

Paeonia

HelpMeFind Peonies. Jan 2010. www.helpmefind.com/peony/index.php

Jakubowski, R. American Peony Society Peony Checklist. www.americanpeonysociety.org

Jakubowski, R. 2008. *Peonies 1997-2007. Registered Peony Cultivars, with a Checklist of Peony Names, References and Originators.* Missouri: American Peony Society.

Osti, G.L. 1999. *The Book of Tree Peonies.* Turin: Umberto Allemandi.

Wang, L., et al. 1998. *Chinese Tree Peony.* Beijing: China Forestry Publishing House.

Papaver

Grey-Wilson, C. 1998. Oriental Glories. *The Garden* (RHS) 123(5):320-325.

Papaveraceae

Grey-Wilson, C. 2000. *Poppies. The Poppy Family in the Wild and in Cultivation.* London: Batsford.

Tebbitt, M. Liden, M. Zetterlund, H. 2008. *Bleeding Hearts, Corydalis and their Relatives.* Portland, Oregon: Timber Press

Passiflora

King, L.A. Jan 2008. Passiflora online passion flower cultivar register. www.passionflow.co.uk

Pelargonium

Anon. 1978 & 1985. *A Checklist and Register of Pelargonium Cultivar Names.* Pts 1 & 2. Australian Pelargonium Society.

Bagust, H. 1988. *Miniature and Dwarf Geraniums.* London: Christopher Helm.

Clifford, D. 1958. *Pelargoniums.* London: Blandford Press.

Clifton, R. 1999. *Geranium Family Species Checklist, Pt 4: Pelargonium.* The Geraniaceae Group.

Complete Copy of the Spalding Pelargonium Checklist. (Unpublished). USA.

Key, H. 2000. *1001 Pelargoniums.* London: Batsford.

Miller, D. 1996. *Pelargonium.* A Gardener's Guide to the Species and Cultivars and Hybrids. London: Batsford.

Pelargonium Palette: The Geranium and Pelargonium Society of Sydney Incorporated. Varieties – Alphabetical List. July 2010. www.elj.com/geranium

Van der Walt, J.J.A., et al. 1977. *Pelargoniums of South Africa.* (1-3). Kirstenbosch, South Africa: National Botanic Gardens.

Penstemon

Lindgren, D.T. & Davenport, B. 1992. List and description of named cultivars in the genus *Penstemon.* University of Nebraska.

Nold, R. 1999. *Penstemons.* Portland, Oregon: Timber Press.

Way, D. & James, P. 1998. *The Gardener's Guide to Growing Penstemons.* Newton Abbott, Devon: David & Charles.

Way, D. 2006. *Penstemons.* Pershore, Worcs.: Hardy Plant Society.

Phlomis

Mann Taylor, J. 1998. *Phlomis: The Neglected Genus.* Wisley: NCCPG.

Phlox

Harmer, J. & Elliott, J. 2001. *Phlox.* Pershore, Worcs.: Hardy Plant Society.

Stebbings, G. 1999. Simply Charming. *The Garden* (RHS) 124(7):518-521.

Wherry, E.T. 1955. *The Genus Phlox.* Philadelphia, Pennsylvania: Morris Arboretum.

Phormium

Heenan, P.B. 1991. *Checklist of Phormium Cultivars.* Royal New Zealand Institute of Horticulture.

McBride-Whitehead, V. 1998. Phormiums of the Future. *The Garden* (RHS) 123(1):42-45.

Pieris

Bond, J. 1982. *Pieris* – a Survey. *The Plantsman* 4(2):65-75.

Wagenknecht, B.L. 1961. Registration Lists of Cultivar Names in the Genus *Pieris* D. Don. *Arnoldia (Jamaica Plain)* 21(8):47-50.

Pittosporum

Miller, D.M. 2006. RHS Plant Assessments: *Pittosporum tenuifolium* hybrids & cultivars.

Plectranthus

Addink, Wouter. Jan 2010. Coleus Finder. http://coleusfinder.org

Miller, D. & Morgan, N. 2000. Focus on Plants: A New Leaf. *The Garden* (RHS) 125(11):842-845.

Shaw, J.M.H. 1999. Notes on the Identity of Swedish Ivy and Other Cultivated *Plectranthus. The New Plantsman* 6(2):71-74.

Van Jaarsveld, E.J. 2006. *South African Plectranthus.* Vlaeberg, South Africa: Fernwood Press.

Pleione

Cribb, P. & Butterfield, I. 1999. *The Genus Pleione.* (2nd ed.). Kew: Royal Botanic Gardens.

Shaw, J.M.H. (comp.). Oct 2002. Provisional List of *Pleione* Cultivars. RHS.

Poaceae

Clayton, W.D., Harman, K.T. & Williamson, H. Jan 2010. GrassBase : The Online World Grass Flora. www.kew.org/data/grasses-syn

Darke, R. 2007. *Encyclopedia of Grasses for Livable Landscapes.* Portland, Oregon: Timber Press.

Grounds, R. 1998. *The Plantfinder's Guide to Ornamental Grasses.* Newton Abott, Devon: David & Charles.

Wood, T. 2002. *Garden Grasses, Rushes and Sedges.* (3rd ed.). Abingdon, Oxon: John Wood.

Polemonium

Nichol-Brown, D. 2000. *Polemonium.* Wisley: NCCPG.

Potentilla

Davidson, C.G., Enns, R.J. & Gobin, S. 1994. *A Checklist of Potentilla fruticosa: the Shrubby Potentillas.* Morden, Manitoba: Agriculture & Agri-Food Canada Research Centre.

Miller, D.M. 2002. *Shrubby Potentilla: RHS Bulletin No 1.* Wisley, Surrey: RHS.

Primula

Richards, J. 2002 (2nd ed.). *Primula.* London: Batsford.

Primula allionii

Archdale, B. & Richards, D. 1997. *Primula allionii Forms and Hybrids.* National Auricula & Primula Society, Midland & West Section.

Primula auricula

Baker, G. *Double Auriculas.* National Auricula & Primula Society, Midland & West Section.

Baker, G. & Ward, P. 1995. *Auriculas.* London: Batsford.

Guest, A. 2009. *The Auricula History, Cultivation and Varieties.* Woodbridge, Suffolk: Garden Art Press

Hawkes, A. 1995. Striped Auriculas. National Auricula & Primula Society, Midland & West Section.

Nicholle, G. 1996. *Border Auriculas.* National Auricula & Primula Society, Midland & West Section.

Robinson, M.A. 2000. *Auriculas for Everyone.* How to Grow and Show Perfect Plants. Lewes, Sussex: Guild of Master Craftsmen Publications.

Telford, D. 1993. *Alpine Auriculas.* National Auricula & Primula Society, Midland & West Section.

Ward, P. 1991. *Show Auriculas.* National Auricula & Primula Society, Midland & West Section.

Proteaceae

International *Proteaceae* Register. July 2002. (7th ed.).

Rebelo, T. 1995. *Proteas.* A Field Guide to the Proteas of Southern Africa. Vlaeberg: Fernwood Press/National Botanical Institute.

Prunus

Crawford, M. 1996. *Plums.* Dartington, Devon: Agroforestry Research Trust.

Crawford, M. 1997. *Cherries: Production and Culture.* Dartington, Devon: Agroforestry Research Trust.

Jacobsen, A.L. 1992. *Purpleleaf Plums.* Portland, Oregon: Timber Press.

Jefferson, R.M. & Wain, K.K. 1984. *The Nomenclature of Cultivated Flowering Cherries (Prunus).* The Sato-Zakura Group. Washington DC: USDA.

Kuitert, W. 1999. *Japanese Flowering Cherries.* Portland, Oregon: Timber Press.

Pulmonaria

Bennett, M. 2003. *Pulmonarias and the borage family.* London: B.T. Batsford.

Hewitt, J. 1994. *Pulmonarias.* Pershore, Worcs.: Hardy Plant Society.

Hewitt, J. 1999. Well Spotted. *The Garden* (RHS) 124(2):98-103.

Pyracantha

Egolf, D.R. & Andrick, A.O. 1995. *A Checklist of Pyracantha Cultivars.* Washington DC: Agricultural Research Service.

Pyrus

Crawford, M. 1996. *Directory of Pear Cultivars.* Totnes, Devon: Agroforestry Research Institute.

Smith, M.W.G. 1976. *Catalogue of the British Pear.* Faversham, Kent: MAFF.

Quercus

International Oak Society. Oak Name Checklist. www.oaknames.org.

Miller, H.A. & Lamb, S.H. 1985. *Oaks of North America.* Happy Camp, California: Naturegraph Publishers.

Mitchell, A. 1994. The Lucombe Oaks. *The Plantsman* 15(4):216-224.

Rhododendron

Argent, G., Fairweather, C. & Walter, K. 1996. *Accepted Names in* Rhododendron *section Vireya.* Edinburgh: Royal Botanic Garden.

Argent, G., Bond, J., Chamberlain, D., Cox, P. & Hardy, A. 1997. *The Rhododendron Handbook 1998.* Rhododendron Species in Cultivation. London: RHS.

Chamberlain, D.F. & Rae, S.J. 1990. A Revision of *Rhododendron* IV. Subgenus *Tsutsusi. Edinburgh J. Bot.* 47(2).

Chamberlain, D.F. 1982. A Revision of *Rhododendron* II. Subgenus *Hymenanthes. Notes Roy. Bot. Gard. Edinburgh* 39(2).

Chamberlain, D., Hyam, R., Argent, G., Fairweather, G. & Walter, K.S. 1996. *The Genus Rhododendron.* Edinburgh:Royal Botanic Garden.

Cullen, J. 1980. A Revision of *Rhododendron* I. Subgenus *Rhododendron* sections *Rhododendron* and *Pogonanthum. Notes Roy. Bot. Gard. Edinburgh* 39(1).

Davidian, H.H. 1982-1992 *The Rhododendron Species* (Vols 1-4). London: Batsford.

Galle, F.C. 1985. *Azaleas.* Portland, Oregon: Timber Press.

Leslie, A. C. (comp.). 1980. *The Rhododendron Handbook 1980.* London: RHS.

Leslie, A.C. (comp.) 2004. *The International Rhododendron Register and Checklist* (2nd ed.) & Supps 1-6, 2004-2012. London: RHS.
Tamura, T. (ed.). 1989. *Azaleas in Kurume.* Kurume, Japan: International Azalea Festival '89.

Ribes

Crawford, M. 1997. *Currants and Gooseberries: Production and Culture.* Dartington, Devon: Agroforestry Research Trust.

Rosa

Beales, P., Cairns, T., et al. 1998. *Botanica's Rose: The Encyclopedia of Roses.* Hoo, Kent: Grange Books.
Cairns, T. (ed.). 2000. *Modern Roses XI. The World Encyclopedia of Roses.* London: Academic Press.
Dickerson, B.C. 1999. *The Old Rose Advisor.* Portland, Oregon: Timber Press.
Haw, S.G. 1996. Notes on Some Chinese and Himalayan Rose Species of Section *Pimpinellifoliae. The New Plantsman* 3(3):143-146.
HelpMeFind Roses. Jan 2010. www.helpmefind.com
McCann, S. 1985. *Miniature Roses.* Newton Abbot, Devon: David & Charles.
Pawsey, Angela (ed.) 2013. *Find That Rose! 2013-2014.* (31st ed.) Colchester, Essex.
Quest-Ritson, C. 2003. *Climbing Roses of the World.* Portland, Oregon: Timber Press.
Quest-Ritson, C. & B. 2003. *The Royal Horticultural Society Encyclopedia of Roses: The Definitive A-Z Guide.* London: Dorling Kindersley.
Thomas, G.S. 1995. *The Graham Stuart Thomas Rose Book.* London: John Murray.
Verrier, S. 1996. *Rosa Gallica.* Balmain, Australia: Florilegium.

Roscoea

Cowley, J. 2007. *The Genus Roscoea.* Kew Publishing.

Rosularia

Eggli, U. 1988. A Monographic Study of the Genus *Rosularia. Bradleya* (Supp.) 6:1-118.

Saintpaulia

Goodship, G. 1987. *Saintpaulia Variety List* (Supp.). Slough, Bucks: Saintpaulia & Houseplant Society.
Moore, H.E. 1957. *African Violets, Gloxinias and Their Relatives.* A Guide to the Cultivated Gesneriads. New York: Macmillan.

Salix

Newsholme, C. 1992. *Willows.* The Genus *Salix.* London: Batsford.
Stott, K.G. 1971 *Willows for Amenity, Windbreaks and Other Uses.* Checklist of the Long Ashton Collection of Willows, with Notes on their Suitability for Various Purposes. Long Ashton Research Station: University of Bristol.

Salvia

Clebsch, B. 2003. *A Book of Salvias.* (2nd ed.). Portland, Oregon: Timber Press.
Compton, J. 1994. Mexican Salvias in Cultivation. *The Plantsman* 15(4):193-215.
Middleton, R. *Robin's Salvias.* www.robinssalvias.com

Saxifraga

Bland, B. 2000. *Silver Saxifrages.* Pershore, Worcs.: Alpine Garden Society.
Dashwood, M. & Bland, B. 2005. Silver Saxifrages: RHS Bulletin No 9. Wisley, Surrey: RHS.
McGregor, M. Jan 2010. Saxbase. Saxifrage Society. www.saxifraga.org
McGregor, M. 1995. *Saxifrages: The Complete Cultivars & Hybrids: International Register of Saxifrages.* (2nd ed.). Driffield, E. Yorks: Saxifrage Society.
Webb, D.A. & Gornall, R.J. 1989. *Saxifrages of Europe.* Bromley, Kent: Christopher Helm.

Sedges

Govaerts, R. & Simpson, D.A. 2007 *World Checklist of Cyperaceae: Sedges.* Richmond, Surrey: RBG Kew

Sedum

Evans, R.L. 1983. *Handbook of Cultivated Sedums.* Motcombe, Dorset: Ivory Head Press.
Lord, T. 2006. *Sedum* up for assessment. *The Plantsman* 5(4):244-252.
Stephenson, R. 1994. *Sedum.* The Cultivated Stonecrops. Portland, Oregon: Timber Press.

Sempervivum

Diehm, H. Jan 2010. www.semperhorst.de
Miklánek, M. 2002. *The List of Cultivars: Sempervivum and Jovibarba v. 7.01.* Pieštany, Slovakia: M. Miklánek (private distribution).
Miklánek, M. 2000. *List of Cultivars: Sempervivum and Jovibarba* v. 15.1. http://miklanek.tripod.com

Sinningia

Dates, J.D. 1988. *The Gesneriad Register 1988. Check List of Names with Descriptions of Cultivated Plants in the Genus Sinningia.* Galesburg, Illinois: American Gloxinia and Gesneriad Society, Inc.

Solenostemon

Pedley, W.K. & Pedley, R. 1974. *Coleus – A Guide to Cultivation and Identification.* Edinburgh: Bartholemew.

Sorbus

McAllister, H. 2005. *The Genus Sorbus: Mountain Ash and Other Rowans.* Kew: Royal Botanical Gardens.
Snyers d'Attenhoven, C. 1999. *Sorbus* Lombarts hybrids *Belgische Dendrologie*: 76-81. Belgium.
Wright, D. 1981. Sorbus – a Gardener's Evaluation. *The Plantsman* 3(2):65-98.

Spiraea

Miller, D.M. 2003. *Spiraea japonica with coloured leaves: RHS Bulletin No 4.* Wisley, Surrey: RHS

Streptocarpus

Arnold, P. 1979. *The Gesneriad Register 1979: Check List of Streptocarpus.* Binghamton, New York: American Gloxinia & Gesneriad.

Succulents

Eggli, U. (ed.) 2002. *Illustrated Handbook of Succulent Plants.* Heidelberg, Germany: Springer-Verlag.

Eggli, U. & Taylor, N. 1994. *List of Names of Succulent Plants other than Cacti Published 1950-92.* Kew: Royal Botanic Gardens.

Grantham, K. & Klaassen, P. 1999. *The Plantfinder's Guide to Cacti and Other Succulents.* Newton Abbot, Devon: David & Charles.

Jacobsen, H. 1973. *Lexicon of Succulent Plants.* London: Blandford.

Syringa

Vrugtman, F. 2000. *International Register of Cultivar Names in the Genus Syringa L. (Oleaceae).* (Contribution No 91). Hamilton, Canada: Royal Botanic Gardens.

Thymus

Easter, M. 2009. *International* Thymus *Register and Checklist.* UK: Owl Prints.

Tiliaceae (Malvaceae* pro parte*)

Wild, H. 1984. *Flora of Southern Africa 21 (1: Tiliaceae).* Pretoria: Botanical Research Institute, Dept of Agriculture.

Tillandsia

Kiff, L.F. 1991. *A Distributional Checklist of the Genus Tillandsia.* Encino, California: Botanical Diversions.

Trillium

Case, F.W.J. & Case, R.B. 1997. *Trilliums.* Portland, Oregon: Timber Press.

Jacobs, D.L. & Jacobs, R.L. 1997. *American Treasures.* Trilliums in Woodland Garden. Decatur, Georgia: Eco-Gardens.

Tulipa

KAVB Online registration pages. http://kavb.back2p.soft-orange.com

Ulmus

Green, P.S. 1964. Registratration of Cultivar Names in *Ulmus. Arnoldia (Jamaica Plain)* 24:41-80.

Vaccinium

Trehane, J. 2004. *Blueberries, Cranberries and Other Vacciniums.* Portland, Oregon: Timber Press.

Vegetables

Official Journal of the European Communities. Oct 2007. Common catalogue of varieties of agricultural plant species: consolidated version. http://ec.europa.eu/food

Viburnum

Dirr, M.A. 2007. *Viburnums: Flowering Shrubs for Every Season.* Portland, Oregon: Timber Press.

Viola

Coombes, R.E. 2003. *Violets.* (2nd ed.). London: Batsford.

Fuller, R. 1990. *Pansies, Violas & Violettas.* The Complete Guide. Marlborough: The Crowood Press.

Perfect, E.J. 1996. *Armand Millet and his Violets.* High Wycombe: Park Farm Press.

Robinson, P.M. & Snocken, J. 2003. Checklist of the Cultivated Forms of the Genus *Viola* including the Register of Cultivars. American Violet Society. http://americanvioletsociety.org

Zambra, G.L. 1950. *Violets for Garden and Market.* (2nd ed.). London: Collingridge.

Vitis

Robinson, J. 1989. *Vines, Grapes and Wines.* London: Mitchell Beazley.

Watsonia

Goldblatt, P. 1989. *The Genus Watsonia.* A Systematic Monograph. South Africa: National Botanic Gardens.

Weigela

Howard, R.A. 1965. A Checklist of Cultivar Names in *Weigela. Arnoldia (Jamaica Plain)* 25:49-69.

Wisteria

Valder, P. 1995. *Wisterias.* A Comprehensive Guide. Balmain, Australia: Florilegium.

Yucca

Smith, C. 2004. *Yuccas: Giants among the Lilies.* NCCPG.

Zauschneria

Raven, P.H. 1977. Generic and Sectional Delimitation in *Onagraceae,* Tribe *Epilobieae. Ann. Missouri Bot. Gard.* 63(2):326-340.

Robinson, A. 2000. Focus on Plants: Piping Hot (*Zauschneria* Cultivars). *The Garden* (RHS) 125(9):698-699.

Zingiberaceae

Branney, T.M.E. 2005. *Hardy Gingers. Including Hedychium, Roscoea and Zingiber.* Cambridge: Timber Press.

Nurseries

The following nurseries between them stock an unrivalled choice of plants. Before making a visit, please remember to check with the nursery that the plant you seek is currently available.

Nursery Codes and Symbols

The first letter of each nursery code represents the area of the country in which the nursery is situated.

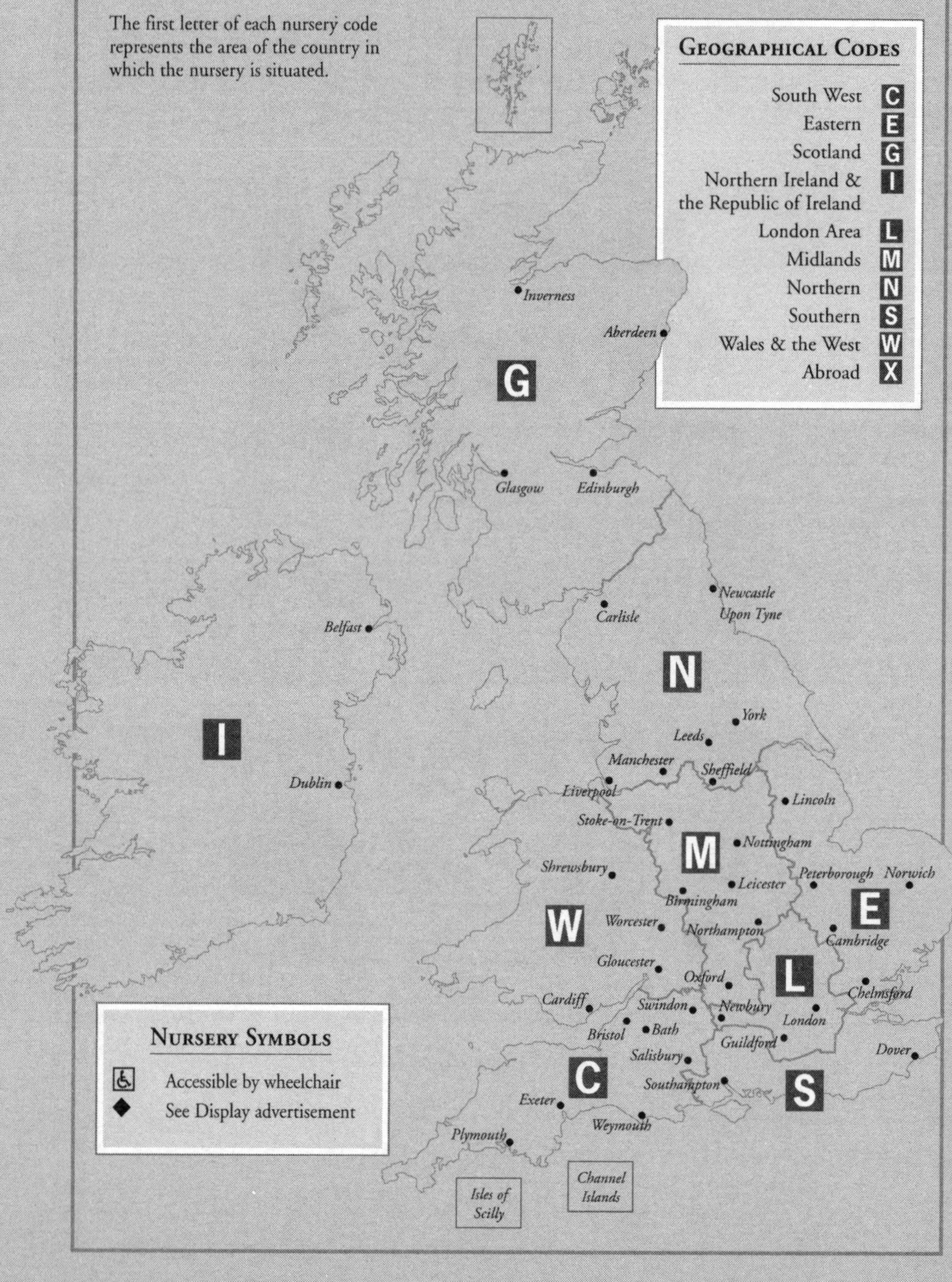

USING THE NURSERY LISTINGS

Your main reference from the Plant Directory is the Nursery Details by Code listing, which includes all relevant information for each nursery in order of nursery code. The Nursery Index by Name is an alphabetical list for those who know a nursery's name but not its code and wish to check its details in the main list.

1 NURSERY DETAILS BY CODE

Once you have found your plant in the Plant Directory, turn to this list to find out the name, address, opening times and other details of the nurseries whose codes accompany the plant.

KEY

♿ Accessible by wheelchair ◆ See Display advertisement

A geographical code is followed by three letters reflecting the nursery's name

SFrt **FRUIT GARDEN PLANTS** ♿ ◆
Woolton Farm, Bekesbourne, Canterbury, Kent CT4 5EA
Ⓣ (01227) 830525
Ⓜ 07710 253690
Ⓕ (01227) 831969
Ⓔ sales@fruitgardenplants.co.uk
Ⓦ www.fruitgardenplants.co.uk
Contact: Mark Mount
Opening Times: 1000-1600 Thu-Sat, 1st Nov-31st Mar. 1000-1700 Thu-Sun, 1st Apr-31st Oct.
Min Mail Order UK: £10.00
Min Mail Order EU: £35.00
Credit Cards: MasterCard, Visa
Specialities: Tree fruits & soft fruits.
Notes: Fruit display garden where visitors can see particular varieties & the methods used for growing them. Small café. Medieval tythe barn. Also sells wholesale. Delivers to shows. Wheelchair accessible.
Map Ref: S, C5 **OS Grid Ref:** TR191568

A brief summary of the plants available

Other information about the nursery

The map letter is followed by the map square in which the nursery is located

The Ordnance Survey national grid reference for use with OS maps

2 NURSERY INDEX BY NAME

If you are looking for a particular nursery, use this alphabetical index to find it, note its code and then turn to the Nursery Details by Code listing for full information.

Forest Edge Nurseries	**CFst**
Frogswell Nursery	IFro
Frosch Exclusive Perennials	XFro
Fruit Garden Plants	**SFrt**
Galloway Plants	GGal
Garden Blooms	NGBl
Garden House Nursery	NGdn
Garden Secrets Nursery	**SGSe**

How to Use the Nursery Listings

The details given for each nursery have been compiled from information supplied to us in answer to a questionnaire. In some cases, because of constraints of space, the entries have been slightly abbreviated.

This year we have removed several of the symbols from the nursery details. We found that more and more nurseries wanted to expand on what they offered and a simple "yes/no" answer was no longer appropriate. Information on mail order, exporting beyond the EU, whether payment in euros is accepted and whether nurseries will deliver to shows is now all given in **Notes**. We hope that this will clarify what services nurseries offer.

We have retained the wheelchair symbol for those nurseries that tell us their site is fully accessible. Please note that this does not necessarily relate to any gardens to which the nursery may be attached. It is important, however, to read the **Notes** section of each nursery's details, as many will offer restricted wheelchair access.

Nurseries are not charged for their entries and inclusion in no way implies a value judgement.

Nursery Details by Code (*page 836*)

Each nursery is allocated a code, for example GPoy. The first letter of each code indicates the main area of the country in which the nursery is situated. In this example, G=Scotland. The remaining three letters reflect the nursery's name, in this case Poyntzfield Herb Nursery.

In this main listing the nurseries are given in alphabetical order of codes for quick reference from the Plant Directory. All of the nurseries' details, such as address, opening times, mail order service etc., will be found here.

Opening Times

Although opening times have been published as submitted and where applicable, **it is always advisable, especially if travelling a long distance, to check with the nursery first**. The initials NGS indicate that the nursery is open under the National Gardens Scheme.

Mail Order

Many nurseries provide a mail order service. **This is, however, often restricted to certain times of the year or to particular genera**. Please check the **Notes** section of each nursery's entry for any restrictions or special conditions.

In some cases, the mail order service extends to all members of the European Union. Where this is offered, the minimum charge to the EU will be noted in the Nursery entry.

Where '**No minimum charge**' (**Nmc**) is shown, please note that to send even one plant may involve the nursery in substantial postage and packing costs. Some nurseries may not be prepared to send tender or bulky plants.

Where a nursery offers a **mail order only** service, this will be noted under **Opening Times** in the nursery entry. Many nurseries also offer an online mail order facility.

Export

Export refers to mail order beyond the European Union. Nurseries that are prepared to consider exporting are indicated. There is usually a substantial minimum charge and, in addition, all the costs of phytosanitary certificates and Customs have to be met by the purchaser.

Catalogue Cost

Some nurseries may not charge for their printed catalogues or may ask for a few stamps to bear the cost of postage, although a large (at least A5) stamped address envelope is always appreciated. Overseas customers should use an equivalent number of International Reply Coupons (IRC) in place of stamps.

If catalogues (or plant lists) are available in an electronic format, some nurseries have indicated that they will email them to enquirers.

An increasing number of nurseries now publish their catalogues only on the internet as this is more cost-effective for them than producing a printed copy and enables them to reflect stock changes throughout the year.

Wheelchair Access ♿

Nurseries are asked to indicate if their premises are suitable for wheelchair users. Where only partial access is indicated, this is noted in the **Notes** field and the nursery is not marked with the symbol.

The assessment of ease-of-access is entirely the responsibility of the individual nursery.

Specialities

Nurseries list here the plants or genera that they supply and any National Collections of plants they may hold. Please note that some nurseries may charge an entry fee to visit a National Collection. Always enquire before visiting. Charges may also be levied to visit a garden attached to the nursery.

Nurseries will also note here if they only have small quantities of individual plants available for sale or if they will propagate to order.

Notes

In this section, you will find notes on any restrictions to mail order or export; on limited wheelchair access; or the nursery site address, if this differs from the office address; together with any other non-horticultural information.

Delivery to Shows

Many nurseries will deliver pre-ordered plants to flower shows for collection by customers. Contact the nursery for details of shows they will be attending.

Payment in Euros

A number of UK nurseries have indicated that they will accept payment in Euros. You should, however, check with the nursery concerned before making such a payment, as some will only accept cash and some only cheques, whilst others will expect the purchaser to pay bank charges.

Maps

If you wish to visit a nursery you can find its approximate location on the relevant map (following p.933), unless the nursery has requested this is not shown. Nurseries are also encouraged to provide their Ordnance Survey national grid reference for use with OS publications such as the Land Ranger series.

Nursery Index by Name

For convenience, an alphabetical index of nurseries is included (*page 927*). This gives the names of all nurseries listed in the book in alphabetical order of nursery name together with their code.

Deleted Nurseries

Every year some nurseries ask to be removed from the book. This may be a temporary measure because, for example, they are relocating or because their plant stocks are low due to adverse growing conditions, or it may be permanent following closure, sale, retirement or a change in the way they trade.

Occasionally, nurseries are unable to meet the closing date and may ask to re-enter the book in the following edition.

Some nurseries simply do not respond at all and, as we have no current information on them, they are not included in the book.

Please, never use an out of date edition

Nursery Details by Code

Please note that all these nurseries are listed in alphabetical order by their code. All nurseries are listed in alphabetical order by their name in the **Nursery Index by Name** on page 927.

South West

CAbb **Abbotsbury Sub-Tropical Gardens** ♿
Abbotsbury, Nr Weymouth, Dorset DT3 4LA
Ⓣ (01305) 871344
Ⓕ (01305) 871344
Ⓔ info@abbotsburygardens.co.uk
Ⓦ www.abbotsburyplantsales.co.uk
Contact: David Sutton
Opening Times: 1000-1800 daily, mid Mar-1st Nov. 1000-1500, Nov-mid Mar.
Min Mail Order UK: Nmc
Credit Cards: Access, Visa, MasterCard, Switch
Specialities: Less common & tender shrubs incl. palms, tree ferns, bamboos & plants from Australia, New Zealand & S. Africa.
Notes: Wheelchair accessible.

CAbP **Abbey Plants** ♿
Chaffeymoor, Bourton, Gillingham, Dorset SP8 5BY
Ⓣ (01747) 840841
Contact: K Potts
Opening Times: 1000-1300 & 1400-1700 Wed-Sat, Mar-Nov. Dec-Feb by appt.
Min Mail Order UK: Nmc
Cat. Cost: 2 × 2nd class.
Credit Cards: None
Specialities: Flowering trees & shrubs.
Notes: Wheelchair accessible.
Map Ref: C, B4 **OS Grid Ref:** ST762304

CAby **The Abbey Nursery** ♿
Forde Abbey, Chard, Somerset TA20 4LU
Ⓣ (01460) 220088
Ⓔ theabbeynursery@hotmail.com
Contact: Paul Bygrave
Opening Times: 1000-1700 7 days, 1st Mar-31st Oct. Please phone first to check opening times in Mar.
Cat. Cost: None issued.
Credit Cards: All major credit/debit cards
Specialities: Hardy herbaceous perennials.
Notes: Delivers to shows. Wheelchair accessible.
Map Ref: C, C4 **OS Grid Ref:** ST359052

CAco **Acorn Trees and Shrubs** ♿
Hilltown Farm, Rackenford, Nr Tiverton, Devon EX16 8DX
Ⓣ (01884) 881633
Ⓜ 07976 807510
Ⓔ goakey101@aol.com
Ⓦ www.acorntreesandshrubs.co.uk
Contact: Grahame Oakey
Opening Times: Most w/ends, excl. B/hols. Also by appt.
Min Mail Order UK: Nmc
Cat. Cost: £8.20
Credit Cards: All major credit/debit cards
Specialities: Trees & shrubs, some climbers, grasses & reeds. Extensive root-trained hedging & native trees. Nearly all stock available for year-round planting. Many species available as seedling, medium & specimen sizes. Also topiary: prancing horses, cloud & pom-pom trees.
Notes: Many species grown on nursery. Most listed items carried in stock but please phone/email to check availability before travelling. Discounts for bulk orders. Also sells wholesale. Wheelchair accessible.
Map Ref: C, B3

CAgr **Agroforestry Research Trust**
46 Hunters Moon, Dartington, Totnes, Devon
TQ9 6JT
Ⓕ (01803) 840776
Ⓔ mail@agroforestry.co.uk
Ⓦ www.agroforestry.co.uk
Contact: Martin Crawford
Opening Times: Not open. Mail order only.
Min Mail Order UK: Nmc
Min Mail Order EU: Nmc
Cat. Cost: 4 × 1st class.
Credit Cards: All major credit/debit cards
Specialities: Top & soft fruit, nut trees

including *Castanea, Corylus, Juglans, Pinus*. Also seeds. Some plants in small quantities only.

CAni ANITA ALLEN
Shapcott Barton Estate, East Knowstone, South Molton, Devon EX36 4EE
Ⓣ (01398) 341664
Ⓕ (01398) 341664
Contact: Anita Allen
Opening Times: By appt. only. Garden open under NGS & Plant Heritage.
Min Mail Order UK: Nmc
Cat. Cost: 5 × 1st class & state which catalogue: Shasta daisies or *Buddleja*.
Credit Cards: None
Specialities: Nat. Collections of *Leucanthemum* × *superbum* & *Buddleja davidii* & hybrids, 70+ cvs. 80+ accurately named Shasta daisies, a few in very short supply. Also many hardy perennials.
Map Ref: C, B3 **OS Grid Ref:** SS846235

CArn ARNE HERBS ♿
Limeburn Nurseries, Limeburn Hill, Chew Magna, Bristol BS40 8QW
Ⓣ (01275) 333399
Ⓔ anthony@arneherbs.co.uk
Ⓦ www.arneherbs.co.uk
Contact: A Lyman-Dixon & Jenny Thomas
Opening Times: 1000-1600 most weekdays, prior telephone call advisable.
Min Mail Order UK: Nmc
Min Mail Order EU: Nmc
Cat. Cost: Detailed illustrated catalogue online or A4 sae for free non-descriptive plantlist. Separate Classical-early Renaissance (c. 1520) list available.
Credit Cards: Maestro, Visa, MasterCard
Specialities: Herbs, some very rare. North American, Mediterranean & UK wild flowers. Also plants for research, conservation projects & historical recreations.
Notes: Also sells wholesale. Euro accepted. Wheelchair accessible.
Map Ref: C, A5 **OS Grid Ref:** ST563638

CAvo AVON BULBS
Burnt House Farm, Mid-Lambrook, South Petherton, Somerset TA13 5HE
Ⓣ (01460) 242177 or 249060
Ⓕ (01460) 249025
Ⓔ info@avonbulbs.co.uk
Ⓦ www.avonbulbs.co.uk
Contact: C Ireland-Jones
Opening Times: Mail order only. Open Thu, Fri, Sat, mid-Sep to end Oct & mid-Feb to end Mar, for collection of pre-booked orders.
Min Mail Order UK: Nmc
Min Mail Order EU: Nmc
Cat. Cost: 4 × 2nd class.
Credit Cards: All major credit/debit cards
Specialities: Some special snowdrops are only available in small quantities.
Notes: Delivers to some shows.
Map Ref: C, B5 **OS Grid Ref:** ST422187

CBAq BOW GARDEN (AQUATICS) CENTRE ♿
Bow, Crediton, Devon EX17 6LA
Ⓣ (01363) 82438
Ⓔ bow@bowaquatics.co.uk
Ⓦ www.bowaquatics.co.uk
Contact: Rachel Setchfield
Opening Times: 0900-1700 Mon-Sat, 1000-1600 Sun.
Credit Cards: All major credit/debit cards
Specialities: Pond plants (inc. water lilies) and plants for damp places. Garden centre with adjoining nursery (not open to public but supplies garden centre). Established 1984.
Notes: Wheelchair accessible.
Map Ref: C, C3 **OS Grid Ref:** SS713018

CBcs BURNCOOSE NURSERIES ♿
Gwennap, Redruth, Cornwall TR16 6BJ
Ⓣ (01209) 860316
Ⓕ (01209) 860011
Ⓔ info@burncoose.co.uk
Ⓦ www.burncoose.co.uk
Contact: C H Williams
Opening Times: 0830-1700 Mon-Sat & 1100-1700 Sun.
Min Mail Order UK: Nmc
Min Mail Order EU: Individual quotations for EU sales.
Cat. Cost: Free
Credit Cards: Visa, MasterCard, Maestro
Specialities: Extensive range of over 3500 ornamental trees & shrubs and herbaceous. Rare & unusual *Magnolia, Rhododendron*. Conservatory plants. 30 acre garden.
Notes: Also sells wholesale. Delivers to shows. Wheelchair accessible.
Map Ref: C, D1 **OS Grid Ref:** SW742395

CBct BARRACOTT PLANTS ♿
Old Orchard, Calstock Road, Gunnislake, Cornwall PL18 9AA
Ⓣ (01822) 832234
Ⓜ 07811 207186
Ⓔ geoffandthelma@barracott.eclipse.co.uk
Ⓦ www.barracottplants.co.uk
Contact: Geoff & Thelma Turner
Opening Times: 0900-1700 Thu & Fri, Mar-end Sep. Other times by appt.
Min Mail Order UK: Nmc
Cat. Cost: 1st class stamp.
Credit Cards: None
Specialities: Herbaceous plants: shade-loving, foliage & form. *Acanthus, Aspidistra, Astrantia, Bergenia, Convallaria, Disporum,*

C

Liriope, Maianthemum, Polygonatum, Roscoea, Trillium & *Uvularia*.
Notes: Also sells wholesale. Delivers to shows. Euro accepted. Wheelchair accessible.
Map Ref: C, C3 **OS Grid Ref:** SX436702

CBen **BENNETTS WATER GARDENS** ♿
Putton Lane, Chickerell, Weymouth, Dorset DT4 0HU
Ⓣ (01305) 785150
Ⓔ info@waterlily.co.uk
Ⓦ www.waterlily.co.uk
Contact: James Bennett
Opening Times: 1000-1700 Apr-Sep, Sun-Fri.
Min Mail Order UK: Nmc
Min Mail Order EU: Nmc
Credit Cards: Visa, MasterCard, JCB, Maestro
Specialities: Nat. Collection of *Nymphaea* (hardy water lilies).
Notes: Loose plants available by mail order. Potted plants available in store. Wheelchair accessible.
Map Ref: C, C5 **OS Grid Ref:** SY650797

CBgR **BEGGAR'S ROOST PLANTS**
Lilstock, Bridgwater, Somerset TA5 1SU
Ⓣ (01278) 741519
Ⓔ ro@lilstock.eclipse.co.uk
Ⓦ www.beggarsroostplants.co.uk
Contact: Lady Rosemary FitzGerald
Opening Times: Not open. Mail order only.
Min Mail Order UK: £10.00
Min Mail Order EU: £15.00
Cat. Cost: 3 × large 2nd class.
Credit Cards: None
Specialities: *Hemerocallis* (incl. heritage) grown in British conditions. *Galanthus* (incl. West Country variants).
Notes: Mail order for specialities *Hemerocallis* & *Galanthus*. Ask for lists. Euro accepted.
Map Ref: C, B4 **OS Grid Ref:** ST168450

CBod **BODMIN NURSERY** ♿
Laveddon Mill, Laninval Hill, Bodmin, Cornwall PL30 5JU
Ⓣ (01208) 72837
Ⓕ (01208) 76491
Ⓔ bodminnursery@aol.com
Ⓦ www.bodminnursery.co.uk
Contact: Mark Lawlor
Opening Times: 0900-1700 Mon-Sat. 1000-1600 Sun.
Credit Cards: All major credit/debit cards
Specialities: Herbs, herbaceous & grasses, hardy geraniums & coastal plants. Interesting shrubs, fruit & ornamental trees.
Notes: Wheelchair accessible.
Map Ref: C, C2 **OS Grid Ref:** SX053659

CBre **BREGOVER PLANTS**
Middlewood, North Hill, Nr Launceston, Cornwall PL15 7NN
Ⓣ (01566) 782661
Ⓔ bregoverplants@gmail.com
Contact: Jennifer Bousfield
Opening Times: 1100-1700 Wed, Mar-mid Oct and by appt.
Min Mail Order UK: Nmc
Min Mail Order EU: Nmc
Cat. Cost: 3 × 1st class. Plant list available as PDF download.
Credit Cards: None
Specialities: Unusual hardy perennials grown in small garden nursery. Available in small quantities only.
Notes: Mail order Oct-Mar only. Delivers to shows.
Map Ref: C, C2 **OS Grid Ref:** SX273752

CBro **BROADLEIGH GARDENS** ♿
Bishops Hull, Taunton, Somerset TA4 1AE
Ⓣ (01823) 286231
Ⓕ (01823) 323646
Ⓔ info@broadleighbulbs.co.uk
Ⓦ www.broadleighbulbs.co.uk
Contact: Lady Skelmersdale
Opening Times: 0900-1600 Mon-Fri for viewing only (charity donation). Orders collected if notice given.
Min Mail Order UK: Nmc
Min Mail Order EU: Nmc
Cat. Cost: 2 × 1st class.
Credit Cards: All major credit/debit cards
Specialities: Jan catalogue: bulbs in growth (*Galanthus, Cyclamen* etc.) & herbaceous woodland plants (trilliums, hellebores etc). Extensive list of *Agapanthus*. June catalogue: dwarf & unusual bulbs, *Iris* (DB & PC). Nat. Collection of Alec Grey hybrid daffodils.
Notes: Delivers to shows. Euro accepted as cash payment only. Wheelchair accessible.
Map Ref: C, B4 **OS Grid Ref:** ST195251

CBrP **BROOKLANDS PLANTS**
25 Treves Road, Dorchester, Dorset DT1 2HE
Ⓣ (01305) 265846
Ⓔ cycads@btinternet.com
Ⓦ botanicalgardenphotography.com
Contact: Ian Watt
Opening Times: By appt. only for collection of plants.
Min Mail Order UK: £25.00 + p&p
Cat. Cost: 2 × 2nd class or by email.
Credit Cards: None
Specialities: Cycad nursery specialising in the more cold-tolerant species of *Encephalartos, Dioon, Macrozamia* & *Cycas*. Also cold-tolerant palms as well as plants from

C

New Zealand. Some species available in small quantities only.
Notes: Euro accepted.
Map Ref: C, C5 **OS Grid Ref:** SY682897

CBth **Barthelmy & Co** ♿
262 Wimborne Road West,
Stapehill, Wimborne, Dorset
BH21 2DZ
Ⓣ (01202) 874283
Ⓕ (01202) 897482
Ⓔ enquiries@barthelemymaples.co.uk
Ⓦ www.barthelemymaples.co.uk
Contact: Wendy Skinner
Opening Times: 0900-1300 & 1400-1700 Mon-Sat, all year round.
Min Mail Order UK: £5.00
Min Mail Order EU: £5.00
Cat. Cost: Sae for free catalogue.
Credit Cards: All major credit/debit cards
Specialities: Japanese Maples, grafted plants & seedlings (150 varieties).
Notes: Also sells wholesale. Exports beyond EU. Wheelchair accessible.

CBty **Bentley Plants** ♿
1 Bentley Wood Cottages, West Tytherley,
Salisbury, Wiltshire SP5 1QB
Ⓣ (01794) 340775
Ⓕ (01794) 340775
Ⓔ john@bentleyplants.fsnet.co.uk
Ⓦ www.bentleyplants.co.uk
Contact: John Wilson
Opening Times: By appt. only.
Min Mail Order UK: Nmc
Cat. Cost: Online only.
Credit Cards: All major credit/debit cards
Specialities: Tree ferns & ground ferns.
Notes: Mail order Oct-Mar. Delivers to shows. Euro accepted. Wheelchair accessible.
Map Ref: C, B6 **OS Grid Ref:** SU258306

CBur **Burnham Nurseries**
Forches Cross, Newton Abbot, Devon
TQ12 6PZ
Ⓣ (01626) 352233
Ⓔ mail@orchids.uk.com
Ⓦ www.orchids.uk.com
Contact: Any member of staff
Opening Times: 1000-1600 Mon-Sun.
Min Mail Order UK: Nmc
Min Mail Order EU: £100.00 + p&p
Cat. Cost: Online.
Credit Cards: Visa, MasterCard, Maestro
Specialities: Many types of tropical orchid species and hybrids.
Notes: Exports beyond EU, please ask for details. Delivers to shows. Euro accepted. Partial wheelchair accessiblity.
Map Ref: C, C4 **OS Grid Ref:** SX841732

CCAT **Cider Apple Trees** ♿
Kerian, Corkscrew Lane, Woolston,
Nr North Cadbury, Somerset BA22 7BP
Ⓣ (01963) 441101
Ⓦ www.ciderappletrees.co.uk
Contact: Mr J Dennis
Opening Times: By appt. only.
Min Mail Order UK: £9.50
Min Mail Order EU: £9.50
Cat. Cost: Free.
Credit Cards: None
Specialities: *Malus* (speciality standard trees).
Notes: Also sells wholesale. Euro accepted. Wheelchair accessible.
Map Ref: C, B5

CCCN **Cross Common Nursery** ◆
The Lizard, Helston, Cornwall TR12 7PD
Ⓣ (01326) 290722/290668
Ⓔ info@crosscommonnursery.co.uk
Ⓦ www.crosscommonnursery.co.uk
Contact: Kevin Bosustow
Opening Times: 1000-1700 7 days, Apr, May & Jun. Reduced hours Jul-Sep, please phone for details.
Min Mail Order UK: Nmc
Cat. Cost: Online only.
Credit Cards: All major credit/debit cards
Specialities: Tropical/sub-tropical, coastal plants & conservatory plants. Wide range of grapevines and citrus trees. Some plants available in small quantities only.
Map Ref: C, D1 **OS Grid Ref:** SW704116

CCha **Chapel Farm House Nursery** ♿
Halwill Junction, Beaworthy, Devon
EX21 5UF
Ⓣ (01409) 221594
Ⓕ (01409) 221594
Contact: Robin or Toshie Hull
Opening Times: 1000-1600 Tue-Sat, 1000-1600 Sun & B/hol Mons.
Cat. Cost: None issued.
Credit Cards: None
Specialities: Plants from Japan. Also herbaceous. Japanese garden design service offered.
Notes: Newly designed & built Japanese garden. Open for NGS, see "Yellow Book" for details. Euro accepted. Wheelchair accessible.
Map Ref: C, C3

CChe **Cherry Tree Nursery (Sheltered Work Opportunities)** ♿
off New Road Roundabout, Northbourne,
Bournemouth, Dorset BH10 7DA
Ⓣ (01202) 593537
Ⓕ (01202) 590626
Ⓔ contactus@cherrytreenursery.org.uk
Ⓦ www.cherrytreenursery.org.uk

C

Contact: Stephen Jailler
Opening Times: 0830-1530 Mon-Fri, 0900-1500 Sat, Apr-Sep & 0900-1300 Sat, Oct-Mar. 1000-1500 Sun, Apr to Jul.
Cat. Cost: A4 sae + £2.20 stamps.
Credit Cards: All, except American Express
Specialities: Hardy shrubs, perennials, climbers, grasses.
Notes: Also sells wholesale. Debit cards accepted. Wheelchair accessible.
Map Ref: C, C6

CCht **CHESTNUT NURSERY (SHELTERED WORK OPPORTUNITIES PROJECT)** ♿
75 Kingland Road, Poole, Dorset BH15 1TN
Ⓣ (01202) 685999
Ⓔ info@chestnutnursery.org.uk
Ⓦ www.chestnutnursery.org.uk
Contact: Laurence Jackson
Opening Times: 0830-1530 Mon-Fri, 1000-1530 Sat.
Specialities: Wide variety of perennials, shrubs, ornamental grasses and seasonal crops.
Notes: A registered charity providing work for adults with severe and enduring mental illness. Wheelchair accessible.
Map Ref: C, C6 **OS Grid Ref:** SZ018909

CCon **CONSTANTINE GARDEN NURSERY (FORMERLY FIR TREE FARM)** ♿
Tresahor, Constantine, Falmouth, Cornwall TR11 5PL
Ⓣ (01326) 340593
Ⓔ plants@cornwallgardens.com
Ⓦ www.cornwallgardens.com
Contact: Sorcha Hitchcox
Opening Times: 1000-1700 Wed-Sat, 1100-1600 Sun, Feb-Sep. By appt. Oct-Jan.
Min Mail Order UK: £15.00 + p&p
Min Mail Order EU: £40.00 + p&p
Cat. Cost: 6 × 1st class.
Credit Cards: Visa, Access, Delta, Switch
Specialities: Over 4000 varieties of cottage garden & rare perennials with many specialities. Also 80 varieties of *Clematis*. Some rare varieties available in small quantities only.
Notes: Display gardens. Dogs welcome. Free planting plans. Expert advice. Garden design. Horticultural courses. Plenty of car parking. Tea, coffee & cake. Delivers to shows. Euro accepted. Wheelchair accessible.
Map Ref: C, D1

CCse **CHASE PLANTS (FORMERLY MEADOWS NURSERY)**
Hookswood Cottage, Farnham, Blandford Forum, Dorset DT11 8DQ
Ⓣ (01725) 516394
Ⓔ sales@chaseplants.co.uk
Contact: Sue Lees & Eddie Wheatley
Opening Times: By appt. only.
Min Mail Order UK: £10.00
Cat. Cost: Large 1st class.
Credit Cards: None
Specialities: Hardy perennials, shrubs & some conservatory plants.
Notes: Delivers to shows.

CCVT **CHEW VALLEY TREES** ♿
Winford Road, Chew Magna, Bristol BS40 8HJ
Ⓣ (01275) 333752
Ⓔ info@chewvalleytrees.co.uk
Ⓦ www.chewvalleytrees.co.uk
Contact: S Scarth
Opening Times: 0800-1700 Mon-Fri all year. 0900-1600 Sat. Closed Sun. Closed B/hols & Sats Jul & Aug.
Min Mail Order UK: Nmc
Cat. Cost: Free.
Credit Cards: All major credit/debit cards
Specialities: Native British & ornamental trees, shrubs, fruit trees & hedging.
Notes: Also sells wholesale. Wheelchair accessible.
Map Ref: C, A5 **OS Grid Ref:** ST558635

CDes **DESIRABLE PLANTS**
(Office) Pentamar, Crosspark, Totnes, Devon TQ9 5BQ
Ⓣ (01803) 864489 evenings
Ⓔ sutton.totnes@lineone.net
Ⓦ www.desirableplants.com
Contact: Dr J J & Mrs S A Sutton
Opening Times: Not open. Mail order only.
Min Mail Order UK: £15.00
Cat. Cost: 4 × 2nd class.
Credit Cards: None
Specialities: Eclectic range of choice & interesting herbaceous perennials & bulbs by mail order.
Notes: Nursery not at this address. Delivers to shows.

CDob **DOBIES OF DEVON**
Long Road, Paignton, Devon TQ4 7SX
Ⓣ 0844 701 7623
Ⓕ 0844 701 7624
Ⓦ www.dobies.co.uk
Contact: Customer Services
Opening Times: Not open. Mail order only. Phone line open 0830-1700 Mon-Fri (office). Also answerphone.
Min Mail Order UK: Nmc
Min Mail Order EU: £5.00
Cat. Cost: Free.
Credit Cards: Visa, MasterCard, Switch, Delta
Specialities: Wide selection of popular flower & vegetable seeds. Also includes young plants,

summer-flowering bulbs & garden sundries.
Notes: Mail order to UK & Rep. of Ireland only.

CDoC **Duchy of Cornwall** ◆
Cott Road, Lostwithiel, Cornwall PL22 0HW
Ⓣ (01208) 872668
Ⓕ (01208) 872835
Ⓔ sales@duchyofcornwallnursery.co.uk
Ⓦ www.duchyofcornwallnursery.co.uk
Contact: Jim Stephens
Opening Times: 0900-1700 Mon-Sat, 1000-1700 Sun & B/hols.
Min Mail Order UK: £10.00
Cat. Cost: None issued.
Credit Cards: All major credit/debit cards
Specialities: *Camellia*, *Fuchsia*, conifers & *Magnolia*. Also a huge range of garden plants incl. trees, shrubs, roses, perennials, fruit & conservatory plants.
Notes: Nursery partially accessible to wheelchair users.
Map Ref: C, C2 **OS Grid Ref:** SX112614

CDoy **Caradoc Doy**
PO Box 28, Exeter, Devon EX3 0WY
Ⓣ (01392) 877225
Ⓕ (01392) 877225
Ⓔ info@caradocdoy.co.uk
Ⓦ www.caradocdoy.co.uk
Contact: Caradoc Doy
Opening Times: Open by appt. only.
Min Mail Order UK: Nmc
Cat. Cost: Online.
Credit Cards: None
Specialities: Olive trees.
Notes: Euro accepted.

CDTJ **Desert to Jungle** ♿
Henlade Garden Nursery, Lower Henlade, Taunton, Somerset TA3 5NB
Ⓣ (01823) 443701
Ⓕ (01458) 250521
Ⓔ plants@deserttojungle.com
Ⓦ www.deserttojungle.com
Contact: Rob Gudge, Dave Root
Opening Times: 1000-1700 Mon, Tues & Thu-Sun (closed Wed), 1st Mar-31st Oct. Thu, Fri & Sat only Nov-Feb. Opening times may vary during RHS shows, so please phone to check.
Min Mail Order UK: Nmc
Credit Cards: All major credit/debit cards
Specialities: Exotic-looking plants giving a desert or jungle effect in the garden. Incl. *Canna*, aroids, succulents, tree ferns & bamboos.
Notes: Nursery shares drive with Mount Somerset Hotel. Also sells wholesale. Delivers to shows. Wheelchair accessible.
Map Ref: C, B4 **OS Grid Ref:** ST273232

CDul **Dulford Nurseries** ♿
Cullompton, Devon EX15 2DG
Ⓣ (01884) 266361
Ⓔ dulford.nurseries@virgin.net
Ⓦ www.dulford-nurseries.co.uk
Contact: Paul Rawlings
Opening Times: 0730-1630 Mon-Fri.
Min Mail Order UK: Nmc
Min Mail Order EU: Nmc
Cat. Cost: Free.
Credit Cards: All major credit/debit cards
Specialities: Native, ornamental & unusual trees, hedging & shrubs incl. oaks, maples, beech, birch, chestnut, ash, lime, *Sorbus* & pines.
Notes: Wheelchair accessible.
Map Ref: C, C4 **OS Grid Ref:** SY062062

CEls **Elsworth Herbs**
Farthingwood, Broadway, Sidmouth, Devon EX10 8HS
Ⓣ (01395) 578689
Ⓔ john.twibell@btinternet.com
Contact: Drs J D & J M Twibell
Opening Times: By appt. only.
Cat. Cost: By email only.
Credit Cards: None
Specialities: Nat. Collection of *Artemisia*. Wide range of *Artemisia*. Stock available in small quantities only. Orders may require propagation from Collection material, for which we are the primary reference source.
Notes: Mail order only on small scale in exceptional situations. Partially accessible for wheelchairs.
Map Ref: C, C4 **OS Grid Ref:** SY119881

CElw **Elworthy Cottage Plants** ♿
Elworthy Cottage. Elworthy, Nr Lydeard St Lawrence, Taunton, Somerset TA4 3PX
Ⓣ (01984) 656427
Ⓔ mike@elworthy-cottage.co.uk
Ⓦ www.elworthy-cottage.co.uk
Contact: Mrs J M Spiller
Opening Times: 1000-1600 Thu, late Mar-end Aug. Also by appt. Feb-Nov.
Cat. Cost: 3 × 2nd class.
Credit Cards: None
Specialities: Unusual herbaceous plants esp. hardy *Geranium*, *Geum*, *Crocosmia*, *Monarda*, *Phlox*, *Pulmonaria*, *Astrantia* & *Viola*. Some varieties only available in small quantities.
Notes: *Galanthus* available by mail order in Feb. Nursery on B3188, 5 miles north of Wiveliscombe, in centre of Elworthy village. Delivers to shows. Wheelchair accessible.
Map Ref: C, B4 **OS Grid Ref:** ST084349

C

CEnd **ENDSLEIGH GARDENS** ♿ ◆
Milton Abbot, Tavistock, Devon PL19 0PG
Ⓣ (01822) 870235
Ⓕ (01822) 870513
Ⓔ info@endsleigh-gardens.com
Ⓦ www.endsleigh-gardens.com
Contact: Michael Taylor
Opening Times: 0800-1700 Mon-Sat. 1000-1700 Sun.
Min Mail Order UK: Nmc
Cat. Cost: 2 × 1st class.
Credit Cards: Visa, Access, Switch, MasterCard
Specialities: Choice & unusual trees & shrubs incl. *Acer* & *Cornus* cvs. Old apples & cherries. *Wisteria*. Grafting service.
Notes: Wheelchair accessible.
Map Ref: C, C3

CEnt **ENTWOOD FARM PLANTS**
Harcombe, Lyme Regis, Dorset DT7 3RN
Ⓣ (01297) 444034
Ⓔ jennyhlyme@hotmail.co.uk
Contact: Jenny & Ivan Harding
Opening Times: By prior arrangement only.
Credit Cards: None
Specialities: Bamboo specialist. Plus selection of shrubs & perennials. Some stock in small quantities.
Notes: Delivers to shows.
Map Ref: C, C4 **OS Grid Ref:** SY335953

CExl **EXCLUSIVE PLANTS NURSERY**
Tretawn, High Cross, Constantine, Falmouth, Cornwall TR11 5RE
Ⓣ (01326) 341496
Ⓜ 07775 811385
Ⓕ (01326) 341496
Ⓔ info@exclusiveplants.com
Ⓦ www.exclusiveplants.com
Contact: Paul Bonavia
Opening Times: Weekends or by appt. only.
Min Mail Order UK: Nmc
Min Mail Order EU: £25.00
Cat. Cost: 2 × 1st class.
Credit Cards: All major credit/debit cards
Specialities: Plantsperson's nursery, offering rare & unusual plants from around the world. Also new introductions & the best form of our better known plants.
Notes: Euro accepted.

CFen **FENTONGOLLAN FARM** ♿
Merther Lane, St Michael Penkivel, Tresillian, Truro, Cornwall TR2 4AQ
Ⓣ (01872) 520209
Ⓕ (01872) 520606
Ⓔ admin@flowerfarm.co.uk
Ⓦ www.flowerfarm.co.uk
Contact: James Hosking
Opening Times: 0900-1700 7 days, Aug-end Nov.
Min Mail Order UK: Nmc
Min Mail Order EU: Nmc
Cat. Cost: Free.
Credit Cards: All major credit/debit cards
Specialities: *Narcissus*.
Notes: Also sells wholesale. Delivers to shows. Euro accepted. Wheelchair accessible.
Map Ref: C, D2

CFil **FILLAN'S PLANTS**
Tuckermarsh Gardens, Yelverton, Devon PL20 7HN
Ⓣ (01822) 841551
Ⓜ 07813 161276
Ⓕ (01822) 841551
Ⓔ fillansplants@yahoo.co.uk
Ⓦ www.fillansplants.co.uk
Contact: Mark Fillan
Opening Times: By appt. only. Please phone or email.
Min Mail Order UK: Nmc
Min Mail Order EU: £50.00
Cat. Cost: 4 × 1st class
Credit Cards: None
Specialities: *Hydrangea* & unusual woody plants. Some plants available in small quanitities only.
Notes: Also sells wholesale.

CFis **MARGERY FISH PLANT NURSERY** ♿
East Lambrook Manor Gardens, East Lambrook, South Petherton, Somerset TA13 5HH
Ⓣ (01460) 240328
Ⓜ 07710 484745
Ⓔ enquiries@eastlambrook.com
Ⓦ www.eastlambrook.com
Contact: Tom Wild
Opening Times: 1000-1700 Feb & May-Jul 7 days. 1000-1700 Tue-Sat & B/hol Mons Mar-Apr & Aug-Oct. Nov-Jan by appt.
Cat. Cost: None issued.
Credit Cards: All major credit/debit cards
Specialities: Hardy geraniums & cottage garden herbaceous plants. Stock available in small quantities only. Major collection of hardy geraniums on site.
Notes: Wheelchair accessible.
Map Ref: C, B5 **OS Grid Ref:** ST431188

CFlo **FLOYDS CLIMBERS AND CLEMATIS**
36 Dowding Drive, Lower Compton, Calne, Wiltshire SN11 8QL
Ⓣ (01249) 823200
Ⓜ 07762 499416
Ⓔ sales@floydsclimbers.co.uk
Ⓦ www.floydsclimbers.co.uk
Contact: Marcel Floyd

Opening Times: Open w/ends twice a year. See website or phone for dates.
Min Mail Order UK: Nmc
Credit Cards: Paypal
Specialities: *Clematis* and climbers.
Notes: Also sells wholesale. Euro accepted. Delivers to shows.
Map Ref: C, A6

CFst **Forest Edge Nurseries**
Verwood Road, Woodlands, Wimborne, Dorset BH21 8LJ
Ⓣ (01202) 829564
Ⓕ (01202) 829564
Ⓔ heathers@forestedgenurseries.co.uk
Ⓦ www.forestedgenurseries.co.uk
Contact: David Edge
Opening Times: 0900-1630 Mon. Collection available by arrangement on other days.
Cat. Cost: £2.00
Credit Cards: Paypal
Specialities: Heathers: *Calluna, Erica, Daboecia.*
Notes: Also sells wholesale. Euro accepted.
Map Ref: C, B6

CFwr **The Flower Bower**
Woodlands, Shurton, Stogursey, Nr Bridgwater, Somerset TA5 1QE
Ⓣ (01278) 732134
Ⓔ theflowerbower@yahoo.co.uk
Ⓦ www.theflowerbower.co.uk
Contact: Sheila Tucker
Opening Times: By appt. only. Visitors welcome during bloom times: Mar-May for *Epiphyllum* & May-Sep for daylilies.
Min Mail Order UK: Nmc
Min Mail Order EU: Nmc
Cat. Cost: Online only.
Credit Cards: None
Specialities: *Hemerocallis*, esp. newer varieties & spiders. Over 700 varieties of *Epiphyllum.* National Collection of *Epiphyllum.*
Notes: Daylilies: newer & rarer varieties mostly available in small quantities. *Epiphyllum*: please send email address to obtain a link to the list.
Map Ref: C, B4 **OS Grid Ref:** ST203442

CHab **Habitat Aid Ltd.**
Hookgate Cottage, South Brewham, Somerset BA10 0LQ
Ⓣ (01749) 812355
Ⓜ 07973 776613
Ⓔ info@habitataid.co.uk
Ⓦ www.habitataid.co.uk
Contact: Nick Mann
Opening Times: Not open. Mail order only.
Min Mail Order UK: £50.00, incl. p&p.
Cat. Cost: None issued.
Credit Cards: All major credit/debit cards
Specialities: British trees, plants and seeds. Local provenance seed mixes in small quantities only. Cottage garden perennials. Non-native trees for bees. Heritage fruit trees. "Family trees".
Notes: Also sells wholesale. Delivers to shows.

CHby **The Herbary**
161 Chapel Street, Horningsham, Warminster, Wiltshire BA12 7LU
Ⓣ (01985) 844442
Ⓔ info@beansandherbs.co.uk
Ⓦ www.beansandherbs.co.uk
Contact: Pippa Rosen
Opening Times: May-Sep strictly by appt. only.
Min Mail Order UK: Nmc
Min Mail Order EU: Nmc
Cat. Cost: 4 × 1st class or online.
Credit Cards: None
Specialities: Culinary, medicinal & aromatic herbs organically grown in small quantities.
Notes: Mail order for seed only and all year for organic vegetable seed & large variety of organic bean & herb seed. Also sells wholesale. Euro accepted.
Map Ref: C, B5 **OS Grid Ref:** ST812414

CHel **Heligan Nursery & Plant Centre**
♿
The Lost Gardens of Heligan, Pentewan, St Austell, Cornwall PL26 6EN
Ⓣ (01726) 845100
Ⓕ (01726) 845101
Ⓔ nursery@heligan.com
Ⓦ www.heligan.com
Contact: Shop staff
Opening Times: 1000-1800 Mon-Sat & 1200-1800 Sun, Apr-Oct. 1000-1700 Mon-Sat & 1100-1700 Sun, Nov-Mar.
Min Mail Order UK: Nmc
Min Mail Order EU: Nmc
Credit Cards: All, except American Express
Specialities: Less common trees, shrubs & perennials. Nat. Collection of Pre-1920 *Rhododendron* & *Camellia*, incl. Tremayne hybrids and rare Heligan camellias. Further information on request.
Notes: Please phone before visiting to ensure required plants in stock, as not always available from plant centre but can be sourced from nursery for collection or mail order. Wheelchair accessible.

CHew **Hewitt-Cooper Carnivorous Plants**
The Homestead, Glastonbury Road, West Pennard, Somerset BA6 8NN
Ⓣ (01458) 832844
Ⓕ (01458) 832712

C

Ⓔ sales@hccarnivorousplants.co.uk
Ⓦ www.hccarnivorousplants.co.uk
Contact: Nigel Hewitt-Cooper
Opening Times: By appt.
Min Mail Order UK: £10.00 + p&p
Min Mail Order EU: £30.00
Cat. Cost: 1 × 1st class/1 × IRC.
Credit Cards: All major credit/debit cards
Specialities: Carnivorous plants.
Notes: Mail order May-Nov. Euro accepted. Delivers to shows.

CHEx **HARDY EXOTICS** ♿
Gilly Lane, Whitecross,
Penzance, Cornwall
TR20 8BZ
Ⓣ (01736) 740660
Ⓕ (01736) 741101
Ⓔ contact@hardyexotics.co.uk
Ⓦ www.hardyexotics.co.uk
Contact: C Shilton/J Smith
Opening Times: 1000-1700 7 days Apr-Oct. 1000-1600 Mon-Sat, Nov-Feb. Please phone first in winter months if travelling a long way.
Min Mail Order UK: £25 carriage.
Credit Cards: All major credit/debit cards
Specialities: Largest selection in the UK of trees, shrubs & herbaceous plants for exotic & desert effects. Hardy & half-hardy plants for gardens, patios & conservatories. Mature plants & plantings to inspire.
Notes: Wheelchair accessible.
Map Ref: C, D1 **OS Grid Ref:** SW524345

CHGN **HIGH GARDEN NURSERIES** ♿
Chiverstone Lane, Kenton, Exeter, Devon
EX6 8NJ
Ⓣ (01626) 899106
Ⓔ highgarden@highgarden.co.uk
Ⓦ highgardenkenton.wordpress.com
Contact: Chris Britton
Opening Times: 0900-1700 Tue-Fri
Cat. Cost: None issued.
Credit Cards: None
Specialities: Quality shrubs, trees & perennials, some unusual & different.
Notes: Wheelchair accessible.
Map Ref: C, C4 **OS Grid Ref:** SX957836

CHid **HIDDEN VALLEY NURSERY**
Umberleigh, Devon EX37 9BU
Ⓣ (01769) 560567
Ⓜ 07899 788789
Ⓔ plalindley@itsosbroadband.co.uk
Contact: Linda & Peter Lindley
Opening Times: Daylight hours, but please phone first.
Cat. Cost: None issued.
Credit Cards: None
Specialities: Hardy perennials esp. shade lovers & Chatham Islands forget-me-nots (*Myosotidium hortensia*).
Notes: Nursery not easy to find using Sat Nav or Google Street Map. Delivers to shows. Euro accepted.
Map Ref: C, B3 **OS Grid Ref:** SS567205

CHII **HILL HOUSE NURSERY LTD** ♿
Landscove, Nr Ashburton, Devon TQ13 7LY
Ⓣ (01803) 762273
Ⓕ 05601 158 218
Ⓔ bluebird@hillhousenursery.com
Ⓦ www.hillhousenursery.com
Contact: Raymond, Sacha & Matthew Hubbard
Opening Times: 1100-1700 7 days, all year. Open all B/hols incl. Easter Sun. Closed Friday before Xmas Eve for two weeks only. Tearoom open 1st Mar-30th Sep.
Min Mail Order UK: Nmc
Cat. Cost: None issued.
Credit Cards: Delta, MasterCard, Switch, Visa, Paypal
Specialities: 3000+ varieties of plants, most propagated on premises, many rare or unusual. The garden, open to the public, was laid out by Edward Hyams. Pioneers of glasshouse pest control by beneficial insects.
Notes: Euro accepted. Wheelchair accessible.
Map Ref: C, C3 **OS Grid Ref:** SX774664

CHVG **HIDDEN VALLEY GARDENS** ♿
Treesmill, Nr Par, Cornwall PL24 2TU
Ⓣ (01208) 873225
Ⓔ hiddenvalleygardens@yahoo.co.uk
Ⓦ www.hiddenvalleygardens.co.uk
Contact: Mrs P Howard
Opening Times: 1000-1800 Thu-Mon (closed Tue & Wed), 20th Mar-15th Oct. Please phone for directions. Garden open as nursery.
Cat. Cost: None issued.
Credit Cards: All major credit/debit cards
Specialities: Cottage garden plants, *Dahlia* & many perennials which can be seen growing in the garden. Some stock available in small quantities. Display garden.
Notes: Award-winning Cornish garden 2010 & 2011. Euro accepted. Wheelchair accessible.
Map Ref: C, D2 **OS Grid Ref:** SX094567

CIri **THE IRIS GARDEN**
Yard House, Pilsdon, Bridport, Dorset DT6 5PA
Ⓣ (01308) 868797
Ⓔ info@theirisgarden.co.uk
Ⓦ www.theirisgarden.co.uk
Contact: Clive Russell
Opening Times: Show garden open by appt. only. Please email or phone for details.
Cat. Cost: None issued.

Credit Cards: American Express, Visa, MasterCard
Specialities: Modern bearded & beardless *Iris* from breeders in UK, USA, France, Italy & Australia. Nat. Collection of Space Age *Iris*. Collection of 6-fall & novelty bearded *Iris* in preparation for ratification in 2013.
Notes: Mail order dept now closed. No sales from website. Ordering in garden only. Plants can be ordered on site with a 25% deposit but customers must be prepared to return & collect at a later date. Euro accepted.
Map Ref: C, C5 **OS Grid Ref:** SY421988

CJas **Jasmine Cottage Gardens**
26 Channel Road, Clevedon, Somerset BS21 7BY
Ⓣ (01275) 871850
Ⓔ margaret@bologrew.net
Ⓦ jasminecottage.bologrew.net/
Contact: Mr & Mrs M Redgrave
Opening Times: May to Aug, daily by appt. Garden open at the same times.
Cat. Cost: None issued.
Credit Cards: None
Specialities: *Rhodochiton, Lophospermum, Maurandya, Dicentra macrocapnos, Salvia, Isotoma*, half-hardy geraniums.
Map Ref: C, A4 **OS Grid Ref:** ST405725

CJun **Junker's Nursery Ltd. (formerly P M A Plant Specialities)**
Higher Cobhay, Milverton, Somerset TA4 1NJ
Ⓣ (01823) 400075
Ⓔ karan@junker.co.uk
Ⓦ www.junker.co.uk
Contact: Karan or Nick Junker
Opening Times: Strictly by appt. only.
Min Mail Order UK: Nmc
Min Mail Order EU: Nmc
Cat. Cost: 6 × 1st class.
Credit Cards: None
Specialities: Choice & unusual shrubs & trees incl. grafted *Acer palmatum, Cornus, Daphne, Magnolia*. Many available in larger, more mature sizes. Small quantities only of some hard to propagate plants, esp. daphnes.
Notes: Extensive planted areas showing how the plants look growing in "real world" conditions. Propagate & grow all own plants with increasing number grown naturally in open ground as well as in pots, incl. larger sizes. Limited wheelchair access.
Map Ref: C, B4

CKel **Kelways** ♿
Picts Hill, Langport, Somerset TA10 9EZ
Ⓣ (01458) 250521
Ⓕ (01458) 253351
Ⓔ sales@kelways.co.uk
Ⓦ www.kelways.co.uk
Contact: Dave Root, Andy Martin
Opening Times: 0900-1700 Mon-Fri, 0900-1700 Sat, 1000-1600 Sun.
Min Mail Order UK: £4.00 + p&p
Min Mail Order EU: £8.00 + p&p
Cat. Cost: Online only.
Credit Cards: All major credit/debit cards
Specialities: *Paeonia, Iris, Hemerocallis* & herbaceous perennials. Nat. Collection of *Paeonia lactiflora*. Wide range of trees, shrubs & herbaceous. Hardy ferns & tree ferns.
Notes: Also sells wholesale. Exports beyond EU. Delivers to shows. Euro accepted. Wheelchair accessible.
Map Ref: C, B5 **OS Grid Ref:** ST434273

CKen **Kenwith Conifer Nursery (Gordon Haddow)** ♿
Blinsham, Nr Torrington, Beaford, Winkleigh, Devon EX19 8NT
Ⓣ (01805) 603274
Ⓕ (01805) 603663
Ⓔ info@kenwithconifernursery.co.uk
Ⓦ www.kenwithconifernursery.co.uk
Contact: Gordon Haddow
Opening Times: 1000-1630 Tue-Sat all year. Closed all B/hols. If travelling a long distance, please phone previous day to ensure nursery will be open.
Min Mail Order UK: £20 + p&p
Min Mail Order EU: £50 + p&p
Cat. Cost: Online only.
Credit Cards: Visa, MasterCard
Specialities: All conifer genera. Grafting a speciality.
Notes: Wheelchair accessible.
Map Ref: C, B3 **OS Grid Ref:** SS518160

CKno **Knoll Gardens** ♿
Hampreston, Wimborne, Dorset BH21 7ND
Ⓣ (01202) 873931
Ⓕ (01202) 870842
Ⓔ enquiries@knollgardens.co.uk
Ⓦ www.knollgardens.co.uk
Contact: N R Lucas
Opening Times: 1000-1700 Tue-Sat, Feb-Dec. Open B/hol Mons. See website for further details.
Min Mail Order UK: Nmc
Min Mail Order EU: Nmc
Cat. Cost: £2.00 + 50p postage.
Credit Cards: Visa, MasterCard
Specialities: Grasses (main specialism). Select perennials. Nat. Collection of *Pennisetum*.
Notes: Also sells wholesale. Wheelchair accessible.
Map Ref: C, C6

C

CLak **Lakka Bulbs**
(Office) 127 Mill Street, Torrington, North Devon EX38 8AW
Ⓣ (01805) 625071
Ⓔ lakkabulbs@talktalk.net
Contact: Jonathan Hutchinson
Opening Times: Not open. Mail order only.
Min Mail Order UK: Nmc
Min Mail Order EU: Nmc
Cat. Cost: None issued.
Credit Cards: None
Specialities: Nat. Collections of *Urginea*, *Veltheimia* & *Scadoxus*. Other South African bulbs of families *Amaryllidaceae* & *Hyacinthaceae*. All available in small quantities only.

CLAP **Long Acre Plants** ♿
South Marsh, Charlton Musgrove, Nr Wincanton, Somerset BA9 8EX
Ⓣ (01963) 32802
Ⓕ (01963) 32802
Ⓔ info@plantsforshade.co.uk
Ⓦ www.plantsforshade.co.uk
Contact: Nigel & Michelle Rowland
Opening Times: 0900-1300 & 1330-1600 Thu & Fri only, Mar-Jun, Sep & Oct.
Min Mail Order UK: £20.00 + p&p
Min Mail Order EU: Nmc
Cat. Cost: 3 × 1st class.
Credit Cards: MasterCard, Visa, Maestro, American Express, JCB
Specialities: Ferns, woodland bulbs & perennials. Marginal/bog plants.
Notes: Some plants available in small numbers and seasonally available. Ship to EU in autumn and winter only. Delivers to shows. Wheelchair accessible.
Map Ref: C, B5

CLnd **Landford Trees**
Landford Lodge, Landford, Salisbury, Wiltshire SP5 2EH
Ⓣ (01794) 390808
Ⓕ (01794) 390037
Ⓔ trees@landfordtrees.co.uk
Ⓦ www.landfordtrees.co.uk
Contact: C D Pilkington
Opening Times: 0800-1700 Mon-Fri.
Cat. Cost: Free.
Credit Cards: All, except American Express
Specialities: Deciduous ornamental trees.
Notes: Also sells wholesale.
Map Ref: C, B6 **OS Grid Ref:** SU247201

CLng **Longcombe Nursery and Garden Centre** ♿
Longcombe, Totnes, Devon TQ9 6PL
Ⓣ (01803) 863098
Ⓔ info@simplyclematis.co.uk
Ⓦ www.simplyclematis.co.uk
Contact: Linda Clarke
Opening Times: 0900-1700 Mon-Sat, 1000-1600 Sun.
Min Mail Order UK: Nmc
Min Mail Order EU: Nmc
Cat. Cost: Online only.
Credit Cards: All major credit/debit cards
Specialities: *Clematis*.
Notes: Also sells wholesale. Delivers to shows. Wheelchair accessible.
Map Ref: C, C3 **OS Grid Ref:** SX834601

CLoc **C S Lockyer (Fuchsias)** ◆
Lansbury, 70 Henfield Road, Coalpit Heath, Bristol BS36 2UZ
Ⓣ (01454) 772219
Ⓕ (01454) 772219
Ⓔ Stuart@lockyerfuchsias.co.uk
Ⓦ lockyerfuchsias.co.uk
Contact: C S Lockyer
Opening Times: 1000-1300, 1430-1700 most days, please ring.
Min Mail Order UK: 6 plants + p&p
Min Mail Order EU: £12.00 + p&p
Cat. Cost: 4 × 1st class or online
Credit Cards: All major credit/debit cards
Specialities: *Fuchsia*.
Notes: Many open days & coach parties. Also sells wholesale. Exports beyond EU. Euro accepted. Partial wheelchair access. Delivers to shows.
Map Ref: C, A5

CMac **Mac Pennys Nurseries**
154 Burley Road, Bransgore, Christchurch, Dorset BH23 8DB
Ⓣ (01425) 672348
Ⓕ (01425) 673917
Ⓔ office@macpennys.co.uk
Ⓦ www.macpennys.co.uk
Contact: T & V Lowndes & S Lowndes
Opening Times: 0900-1700 Mon-Sat, 1000-1700 Sun & B/hols, except closed Xmas-New Year.
Min Mail Order UK: Nmc
Cat. Cost: A4 sae with 4 × 1st class.
Credit Cards: All major credit/debit cards
Specialities: General. Plants available in small quantities only.
Notes: Mail order available Sep-Mar, UK only. Also sells wholesale. Nursery partially accessible for wheelchairs.
Map Ref: C, C6

CMan **Mandy Plants** ♿
(Office) 4 St Mary's Place, Ipplepen, Devon TQ12 5FF
Ⓣ (01803) 813647
Ⓜ 07432 112245

Ⓔ enquiries@mandyplants.com
Contact: Liz Spanton
Opening Times: By appt. only.
Min Mail Order UK: Nmc
Min Mail Order EU: £25.00
Cat. Cost: 2 × 1st class
Credit Cards: Paypal
Specialities: *Mandevilla* & *Dipladenia*.
Notes: Nursery is at Bishopsteignton, Devon. Also sells wholesale. Delivers to shows. Wheelchair accessible.
Map Ref: C, C3 **OS Grid Ref:** SX836667

CMCN MALLET COURT NURSERY ♿
Marshway, Curry Mallet,
Taunton, Somerset
TA3 6SZ
Ⓣ (01823) 481493
Ⓕ (01823) 481493
Ⓔ malletcourtnursery@btinternet.com
Ⓦ www.malletcourt.co.uk
Contact: J G S & P M E Harris F.L.S.
Opening Times: 0930-1700 Mon-Fri summer, 0930-1600 winter. Sat & Sun by appt.
Min Mail Order UK: Nmc
Min Mail Order EU: Nmc
Cat. Cost: £1.50
Credit Cards: All major credit/debit cards
Specialities: Maples, oaks, *Magnolia*, hollies & other rare and unusual plants including those from China & South Korea.
Notes: Mail order Oct-Mar only. Also sells wholesale. Exports beyond EU. Delivers to shows. Euro accepted. Wheelchair accessible.
Map Ref: C, B4

CMea THE MEAD NURSERY ♿
Brokerswood, Nr Westbury, Wiltshire
BA13 4EG
Ⓣ (01373) 859990
Ⓔ info@themeadnursery.co.uk
Ⓦ www.themeadnursery.co.uk
Contact: Steve & Emma Lewis-Dale
Opening Times: 0900-1700 Wed-Sat & B/hol Mons, 1200-1700 Sun, 1st Feb-10th Oct. Closed Easter Sun.
Cat. Cost: 5 × 1st class.
Credit Cards: All major credit/debit cards
Specialities: Perennials, alpines, pot-grown bulbs and grasses.
Notes: Wheelchair accessible.
Map Ref: C, B5 **OS Grid Ref:** ST833517

CMen MENDIP BONSAI STUDIO
Byways, Back Lane, Downside, Shepton Mallet, Somerset BA4 4JR
Ⓣ (01749) 344274
Ⓜ 07711 205806
Ⓔ john@mendipbonsai.co.uk
Ⓦ www.mendipbonsai.co.uk
Contact: John Trott
Opening Times: Private nursery. Visits by appt. only.
Min Mail Order UK: £15.00
Cat. Cost: Large sae for plant & workshop lists
Credit Cards: All major credit/debit cards
Specialities: Bonsai, Potensai, accent plants & garden stock. Acers, conifers, incl. many *Pinus thunbergii* species, *Aciphylla*, *Davallia* & *Pyrrosia*. Many plants available in small numbers only. Young trees for garden or bonsai culture.
Notes: Education classes, lectures, demonstrations & club talks on bonsai. Stockist of most bonsai sundries. Mail orders will normally be despatched late Mar/early Apr-late Sep/Oct. Delivers to shows.
Map Ref: C, B5

CMHG MARWOOD HILL GARDENS ♿
Marwood, Barnstaple, Devon
EX31 4EB
Ⓣ (01271) 342528
Ⓕ (01271) 342528
Ⓔ info@marwoodhillgarden.co.uk
Ⓦ www.marwoodhillgarden.co.uk
Contact: Malcolm Pharoah
Opening Times: 1100-1630, 7 days. Closed Nov-Feb.
Cat. Cost: 3 × 1st class.
Credit Cards: Visa, Delta, MasterCard, Switch, Solo
Specialities: Large range of unusual trees & shrubs. *Eucalyptus*, alpines, *Camellia*, *Astilbe*, bog plants & perennials. Nat. Collections of *Astilbe*, *Tulbaghia* & *Iris ensata*.
Notes: Wheelchair accessible.
Map Ref: C, B3 **OS Grid Ref:** SS545375

CMil MILL COTTAGE PLANTS ♿
Henley Mill, Henley Lane, Wookey, Somerset
BA5 1AW
Ⓣ (01749) 676966
Ⓜ 07851 698759
Ⓔ millcottageplants@gmail.com
Ⓦ www.millcottageplants.co.uk
Contact: Sally Gregson
Opening Times: By appt. only. Phone for directions.
Min Mail Order UK: Nmc
Min Mail Order EU: £25.00 + p&p
Cat. Cost: Online only.
Credit Cards: All major credit/debit cards
Specialities: Rare *Hydrangea serrata* cvs, *H. aspera* cvs, *Epimedium*, shade & damp-loving plants.
Notes: Euro accepted. Wheelchair accessible.
Map Ref: C, B5

C

CMos **IAN & TERESA MOSS**
'Iona', Woolmersdon, Bridgwater, Somerset
TA5 2BP
Ⓣ (01278) 661352
Ⓜ 07903 268718
Ⓔ teresa@hardyandunusualplants.co.uk
Ⓦ www.hardyandunusualplants.co.uk
Contact: Teresa Moss
Opening Times: By appt. only.
Cat. Cost: £1.50
Credit Cards: All, except American Express
Specialities: Hardy & unusual plants. Range of perennials incl. the best of recent introductions as well as more unusual varieties & reliable old favourites.
Notes: Delivers to shows.

CMus **MUSGROVE WILLOWS** ♿
Willowfields, Lakewall, Westonzoyland,
Bridgwater, Somerset TA7 0LP
Ⓣ (01278) 691105
Ⓕ (01278) 699107
Ⓔ info@musgrovewillows.co.uk
Ⓦ www.musgrovewillows.co.uk
Contact: Ellen Musgrove
Opening Times: 0900-1700 Mon-Fri.
Min Mail Order UK: £12.50
Min Mail Order EU: Nmc
Credit Cards: All major credit/debit cards
Specialities: *Salix* (willow). A family nursery since 1928.
Notes: Exports beyond EU. Wheelchair accessible.
Map Ref: C, B4

CNat **NATURAL SELECTION**
1 Station Cottages, Hullavington,
Chippenham, Wiltshire SN14 6ET
Ⓣ (01666) 837369
Ⓜ 07800 583999
Ⓔ martin@worldmutation.demon.co.uk
Ⓦ www.worldmutation.demon.co.uk
Contact: Martin Barber
Opening Times: Please phone first.
Min Mail Order UK: £9.00 + p&p
Cat. Cost: 2 × 2nd class.
Credit Cards: None
Specialities: Unusual British natives & others. Also seed. Only available in small quantities.
Notes: Euro accepted.

CNec **NECTAR PLANTS GARDEN NURSERY**
646 Dorchester Road, Upwey, Weymouth,
Dorset DT3 5LG
Ⓣ (01305) 855988
Ⓔ martinyoung100@btinternet.com
Ⓦ www.nectarplants.co.uk
Contact: Martin Young
Opening Times: 1000-1700 Thu-Sun, mid-March to mid-Oct.
Cat. Cost: A5 sae.
Credit Cards: None
Specialities: Small scale nursery specialising in plants for bees & butterflies; cottage garden favourites & coastal plants. Wide selection of *Buddleja davidii*, *B. weyeriana* & hardy geraniums. Good selection of David Austin roses & many flowering shrubs.
Notes: Nursery is on old Dorchester-Weymouth road. Follow signs to Upwey, large copper beech tree next to green gate.
Map Ref: C, C5 **OS Grid Ref:** SY674838

CNMi **NEWPORT MILLS NURSERY**
Wrantage, Taunton, Somerset
TA3 6DJ
Ⓣ (01823) 490231
Ⓔ john@newportmillsnursery.net
Ⓦ www.newportmillsnursery.net
Contact: John Barrington
Opening Times: Not open. Mail order only.
Min Mail Order UK: Nmc free p&p
Min Mail Order EU: Nmc. EU postal rate per order.
Cat. Cost: Free.
Credit Cards: All major credit/debit cards
Specialities: *Delphinium elatum* hybrids. English scented perpetual flowering carnations. *Dianthus*. Pinks, Exhibition, Modern & Old World.
Notes: Mail order Apr-Sep for young delphiniums in 7cm pots. Dormant plants can be sent out in autumn/winter if requested. Euro accepted.
Map Ref: C, B4 **OS Grid Ref:** ST317234

CNor **NORTHBROOK NURSERY**
47 Northbrook Road, Broadstone, Dorset
BH18 8HD
Ⓣ (01202) 695256
Ⓔ marg@northbrooknursery.co.uk
Ⓦ www.northbrooknursery.co.uk
Contact: Margaret Bailey
Opening Times: By appt. only.
Min Mail Order UK: Nmc
Cat. Cost: None issued.
Credit Cards: Paypal
Specialities: Perennials. Plants available in small quantities only.

CNWT **NEW WOOD TREES**
Oldwood House, Aish Road, Stoke Gabriel,
Totnes, Devon TQ9 6PX
Ⓣ (01803) 782666
Ⓕ (05601) 262999
Ⓔ info@newwoodtrees.co.uk
Ⓦ www.newwoodtrees.co.uk
Contact: Philip Nieuwoudt
Opening Times: 0900-1700 Mon-Fri.
Credit Cards: None

Specialities: Trees. Multi-stem ornamentals, small to medium sized trees and large shrubs.
Notes: Specialises in specimen trees so, when a species is sold out, it takes a while to replenish stocks. Also sells wholesale. Delivers to shows.
Map Ref: C, C3 **OS Grid Ref:** SX847580

CCOtt **OTTER NURSERIES LTD** ♿
Gosford Road, Ottery St Mary, Devon
EX11 1LZ
Ⓣ (01404) 815815
Ⓜ 07875 268429
Ⓕ (01404) 815816
Ⓔ otter@otternurseries.co.uk
Ⓦ www.otternurseries.co.uk
Contact: Garden centre plant information desk
Opening Times: 0800-1730 Mon-Sat, 1030-1630 Sun. Closed Xmas, Boxing Day & Easter Sun.
Cat. Cost: None issued
Credit Cards: All, except American Express
Specialities: Large garden centre & nursery with extensive range of trees, shrubs, conifers, climbers, roses, fruit & hardy perennials.
Notes: Wheelchair accessible.
Map Ref: C, C4

CPar **PARKS PERENNIALS**
242 Wallisdown Road,
Wallisdown, Bournemouth, Dorset
BH10 4HZ
Ⓣ (01202) 524464
Ⓜ 07977 878546
Ⓔ parks.perennials@ntlworld.com
Contact: S. Parks
Opening Times: Apr-Oct most days, please phone first.
Cat. Cost: None issued.
Credit Cards: None
Specialities: Hardy herbaceous perennials.
Notes: Delivers to shows.
Map Ref: C, C6

CPbn **PENBORN GOAT FARM** ♿
Penborn, Bounds Cross, Holsworthy, Devon
EX22 6LH
Ⓣ (01288) 381569
Ⓔ penborngoats@btinternet.com
Ⓦ www.penborngoats.com
Contact: P R Oldfield
Opening Times: By appt. only.
Min Mail Order UK: £20.00
Min Mail Order EU: £24.00
Cat. Cost: Online.
Credit Cards: None
Specialities: *Mentha*, *Melissa*. Available in small quantities only.
Notes: Wheelchair accessible.
Map Ref: C, C2 **OS Grid Ref:** SS290021

CPBP **PARHAM BUNGALOW PLANTS**
Parham Lane, Market Lavington, Devizes, Wiltshire SN10 4QA
Ⓣ (01380) 812605
Ⓔ jjs@pbplants.freeserve.co.uk
Contact: Mrs D E Sample
Opening Times: Please ring first.
Min Mail Order UK: Nmc
Min Mail Order EU: Nmc
Cat. Cost: Sae.
Credit Cards: None
Specialities: Alpines.
Notes: Delivers to shows. Euro accepted.
Map Ref: C, B6

CPen **PENNARD PLANTS**
3 The Gardens, East Pennard, Shepton Mallet, Somerset BA4 6TU
Ⓣ (01749) 860039
Ⓕ 07043 017270
Ⓔ sales@pennardplants.com
Ⓦ www.pennardplants.com
Contact: Chris Smith
Opening Times: By appt. only.
Min Mail Order UK: Nmc
Min Mail Order EU: Nmc
Cat. Cost: 3 × 1st class.
Credit Cards: All major credit/debit cards
Specialities: *Agapanthus*.
Notes: Nursery at The Walled Garden at East Pennard. Exports beyond EU. Delivers to shows. Euro accepted.
Map Ref: C, B5

CPhi **ALAN PHIPPS CACTI**
62 Samuel White Road, Hanham, Bristol
BS15 3LX
Ⓣ (0117) 9607591
Ⓦ www.cactus-mall.com/alan-phipps/index.html
Contact: A Phipps
Opening Times: 1000-1700 but prior phone call essential to ensure a greeting.
Min Mail Order UK: £5.00 + p&p
Min Mail Order EU: £20.00 + p&p
Cat. Cost: Sae or 2 × IRC (EC only).
Credit Cards: None
Specialities: *Mammillaria*, *Astrophytum* & *Ariocarpus*. Species & varieties will change with times. Ample quantities exist in spring. Limited range of *Agave*.
Notes: Specimen-size plants not available by mail order. Euro accepted as cash only.
Map Ref: C, A5 **OS Grid Ref:** ST644717

CPHo **THE PALM HOUSE**
8 North Street, Ottery St Mary, Devon
EX11 1DR
Ⓣ (01404) 815450
Ⓜ 07815 673397
Ⓔ george@thepalmhouse.co.uk

C

Ⓦ www.thepalmhouse.co.uk
Contact: George Gregory
Opening Times: Mail order only. Open by appt. only.
Min Mail Order UK: £15.00
Min Mail Order EU: £10.00
Cat. Cost: 2 × 1st class.
Credit Cards: All major credit/debit cards
Specialities: Palms.
Notes: Also sells wholesale.

CPla **Plant World Botanic Gardens** ♿
St Marychurch Road, Newton Abbot, Devon TQ12 4SE
Ⓣ (01803) 872939
Ⓕ (01803) 875018
Ⓔ raybrown@plant-world-seeds.com
Ⓦ www.plant-world-seeds.com
Contact: Ray Brown
Opening Times: 0930-1700 7 days a week, Apr (Easter if earlier)-Oct.
Min Mail Order UK: Nmc
Min Mail Order EU: Nmc
Cat. Cost: 3 × 1st class or 2 × IRC.
Credit Cards: Visa, Access, EuroCard, MasterCard
Specialities: Alpines & unusual herbaceous plants.
Notes: 4 acre garden correctly planted out as the map of the world (entry charge). Tea room. Mail order for seed only. Also sells wholesale. Exports beyond EU. Euro accepted. Wheelchair accessible.
Map Ref: C, C4

CPne **Pine Cottage Plants** ♿
Pine Cottage, Fourways, Eggesford, Chulmleigh, Devon EX18 7QZ
Ⓣ (01769) 580076
Ⓜ 07718 505053
Ⓔ sales@pcplants.co.uk
Ⓦ www.pcplants.co.uk
Contact: Dick Fulcher
Opening Times: By appt. only. Please phone first.
Min Mail Order UK: £20.00
Min Mail Order EU: £20.00
Cat. Cost: 3 × 1st class.
Credit Cards: Maestro, MasterCard, Visa
Specialities: *Agapanthus* & other unusual plants.
Notes: Mail order *Agapanthus* from Sep-Jun. Exports beyond EU. Wheelchair accessible.
Map Ref: C, B3 **OS Grid Ref:** SS683099

CPom **Pomeroy Plants**
Tower House, Pomeroy Lane, Wingfield, Trowbridge, Wiltshire BA14 9LJ
Ⓣ (01225) 769551
Ⓜ 07895 096564
Ⓔ drsimonyoung@yahoo.co.uk
Contact: Simon Young
Opening Times: Feb-Nov. Please phone first.
Cat. Cost: 2 × 1st class.
Credit Cards: None
Specialities: Hardy, mainly species, herbaceous perennials. Many unusual and often small numbers. Specialities *Allium*, *Salvia* & shade-lovers, esp. *Epimedium*.
Notes: Delivers to shows.
Map Ref: C, B5 **OS Grid Ref:** ST817569

CPou **Pounsley Plants** ♿
Pounsley Combe, Spriddlestone, Brixton, Plymouth, Devon PL9 0DW
Ⓣ (01752) 402873
Ⓜ 07770 758501
Ⓕ (01752) 406682
Ⓔ pou599@aol.com
Ⓦ www.pounsleyplants.com
Contact: Mrs Jane Hollow
Opening Times: Normally 1000-1600 Mon-Sat but please phone first.
Min Mail Order UK: £10.00 + p&p
Min Mail Order EU: €20.00 + p&p
Cat. Cost: 2 × 1st class.
Credit Cards: None
Specialities: Unusual herbaceous perennials & *Clematis*. Comprehensive range of Old Roses & large selection of modern roses.
Notes: Mail order solely bare-root roses, Nov-Mar. Also sells wholesale. Delivers to shows. Euro accepted. Wheelchair accessible.
Map Ref: C, D3 **OS Grid Ref:** SX521538

CPrp **ProperPlants.com**
Penknight, Edgcumbe Road, Lostwithiel, Cornwall PL22 0JD
Ⓣ (01208) 872291
Ⓔ info@ProperPlants.com
Ⓦ www.ProperPlants.com
Contact: Sarah Wilks
Opening Times: 1000-1800 or dusk if earlier, Tue & B/hols mid-Mar to end-Sep & by appt.
Min Mail Order UK: Nmc
Min Mail Order EU: Nmc
Cat. Cost: 3 × 1st class.
Credit Cards: All major credit/debit cards
Specialities: *Agapanthus*, *Crocosmia* & *Hesperantha*.
Notes: Exports beyond EU. Delivers to shows.
Map Ref: C, C2 **OS Grid Ref:** SX093596

CQua **Quality Daffodils**
14 Roscarrack Close, Falmouth, Cornwall TR11 4PJ
Ⓣ (01326) 317959
Ⓜ 07989 243450
Ⓕ (01326) 317959
Ⓔ rascamp@daffodils.uk.com

Ⓦ www.qualitydaffodils.com
Contact: R A Scamp
Opening Times: Not open. Mail order only. Viewing by appt. only.
Min Mail Order UK: Nmc
Min Mail Order EU: Nmc
Cat. Cost: 4 × 1st class.
Credit Cards: All major credit/debit cards
Specialities: *Narcissus* hybrids & species. Some stocks are less than 100 bulbs.
Notes: Also sells wholesale. Exports beyond EU. Euro accepted.
Map Ref: C, D1

CRHN **ROSELAND HOUSE NURSERY**
Chacewater, Truro, Cornwall TR4 8QB
Ⓣ (01872) 560451
Ⓔ clematis@roselandhouse.co.uk
Ⓦ www.roselandhouse.co.uk
Contact: C R Pridham
Opening Times: 1300-1700 Tue & Wed, Apr-Sep. Other times by appt.
Min Mail Order UK: Nmc
Min Mail Order EU: Nmc
Cat. Cost: Online only.
Credit Cards: All major credit/debit cards
Specialities: Climbing & conservatory plants. Nat. Collections of *Clematis viticella* & *Lapageria rosea*. Named *Lapageria* in short supply but occasionally available.
Notes: Garden open to the public. Credit cards accepted from mail order customers only. Delivers to shows.
Map Ref: C, D1 **OS Grid Ref:** SW752445

CRos **RHS GARDEN ROSEMOOR PLANT CENTRE** ♿ ◆
RHS Garden Rosemoor, Torrington, Devon EX38 8PH
Ⓣ (01805) 626842
Ⓕ (01805) 622422
Ⓔ rosemooradmin@rhs.org.uk
Ⓦ www.rhs.org.uk/rosemoor
Contact: Emma Van-Huysse or Sam Smith
Opening Times: 1000-1800 Mon-Sat, 11.30-1730 Sun, Apr-Sep (summer). 1000-1700 Mon-Sat, 1030-1630 Sun, Oct-Mar (winter).
Cat. Cost: None issued
Credit Cards: All major credit/debit cards
Specialities: Wide range of shrubs, herbaceous plants, roses, climbers, alpines & seasonal lines, where possible reflecting the diversity of planting in the garden. Curator's choice selection of plants for sale that are featured in the garden. Highlighted display of AGM plants. National Collections of *Ilex* & *Cornus*.
Notes: Plants subject to seasonal availability but will source plants whenever possible. Wheelchair accessible.
Map Ref: C, B3 **OS Grid Ref:** SS500176

CRow **ROWDEN GARDENS** ♿
Brentor, Nr Tavistock, Devon PL19 0NG
Ⓣ (01822) 810275
Ⓔ rowdengardens1@btinternet.com
Ⓦ www.rowdengardens.com
Contact: John R L Carter
Opening Times: By appt only.
Min Mail Order UK: Nmc
Min Mail Order EU: Nmc
Cat. Cost: 6 × 1st class.
Credit Cards: Paypal
Specialities: Aquatics, damp loving & associated plants incl. rare & unusual varieties. Some stock available in small quantities only. National Collection of Water Iris.
Notes: Exports beyond EU. Wheelchair accessible.
Map Ref: C, C3

CSam **SAMPFORD SHRUBS** ♿
Sampford Peverell, Tiverton, Devon EX16 7EN
Ⓣ (01884) 821164
Ⓔ via website
Ⓦ www.samshrub.co.uk
Contact: M Hughes-Jones & S Proud
Opening Times: 1000-1700 Wed-Fri, 3rd Apr-13th Sep incl.
Min Mail Order UK: £20.00
Cat. Cost: Online only.
Credit Cards: All major credit/debit cards
Specialities: Plants particularly suitable for naturalistic gardening.
Notes: Mail order only via dedicated ecommerce website. Despatched Oct-Mar. Euro accepted. Wheelchair accessible.
Map Ref: C, B4 **OS Grid Ref:** ST043153

CSBt **ST BRIDGET NURSERIES LTD** ♿
Old Rydon Lane, Exeter, Devon EX2 7JY
Ⓣ (01392) 873672
Ⓕ (01392) 876710
Ⓔ sales@stbridgetnurseries.co.uk
Ⓦ www.stbridgetnurseries.co.uk
Contact: Sales Dept
Opening Times: 0900-1700 Mon-Sat, 1030-1630 Sun. Closed Xmas Day, Boxing Day, New Year's Day & Easter Sunday.
Min Mail Order UK: Nmc
Cat. Cost: Free.
Credit Cards: All major credit/debit cards
Specialities: Large general nursery, with two garden centres.
Notes: Mail order available, please contact for prices & carriage charges. Also sells wholesale. Wheelchair accessible.
Map Ref: C, C4 **OS Grid Ref:** SX955905

C

CSde **Seaside Plants**
Marsh Lane Nursery, West Charleton, Kingsbridge, Devon TQ7 2AQ
Ⓜ 07747 661272
Ⓔ info@seasideplants.co.uk
Ⓦ www.seasideplants.co.uk
Contact: Michael Hornby
Opening Times: Not open. View by appt. only.
Min Mail Order UK: Nmc
Min Mail Order EU: Nmc
Cat. Cost: Online only.
Credit Cards: All major credit/debit cards
Specialities: Wide range, esp. coastal plants, *Elaeagnus*, *Euonymus*, *Fuchsia*, grasses, *Griselinia*, *Hydrangea*, *Olearia* & *Pittosporum*.
Notes: Euro accepted.

CSna **Snape Cottage**
Chaffeymoor, Bourton, Dorset SP8 5BZ
Ⓣ (01747) 840330 (evenings only).
Ⓔ ianandangela@snapecottagegarden.co.uk
Ⓦ www.snapestakes.com
Contact: Mrs Angela Whinfield
Opening Times: 1400-1700 last w/end (Sat & Sun) in months Feb-Aug incl.
Min Mail Order UK: Nmc
Cat. Cost: Sae.
Credit Cards: None
Specialities: 'Old' forms of many popular garden plants. Plantsman's garden open same time as nursery. Stock available in small quantities. Snape Stakes plant supports.
Notes: Mail order *Galanthus* only. List issued in Feb. Group visits welcome all year.
Map Ref: C, B5 **OS Grid Ref:** ST762303

CSpe **Special Plants**
Hill Farm Barn, Greenways Lane, Cold Ashton, Chippenham, Wiltshire SN14 8LA
Ⓣ (01225) 891686
Ⓔ derry@specialplants.net
Ⓦ www.specialplants.net
Contact: Derry Watkins
Opening Times: 1000-1700 7 days, Mar-Oct. Other times please ring first to check.
Min Mail Order UK: £10.00 + p&p
Cat. Cost: 2 × 1st class for seed list.
Credit Cards: All major credit/debit cards
Specialities: Tender perennials, *Pelargonium*, *Salvia*, *Streptocarpus*, hardy geraniums, *Anemone*, *Erysimum*, *Papaver*, *Viola* & grasses. Many varieties propagated in small numbers only.
Notes: Mail order Sep-Mar only. Delivers to shows. Euro accepted.
Map Ref: C, A5 **OS Grid Ref:** ST749726

CSPN **Sherston Parva Nursery** ♿
Malmesbury Road, Sherston, Wiltshire SN16 0NX
Ⓣ (01666) 840348
Ⓜ 07887 814843
Ⓔ martdrea@aol.com
Ⓦ www.sherstonparva.com
Contact: Martin Rea
Opening Times: 1000-1700 7 days 1st Feb-31th Dec. Closed Jan.
Min Mail Order UK: Nmc
Min Mail Order EU: Nmc
Cat. Cost: Free.
Credit Cards: MasterCard, Delta, Visa, Switch
Specialities: *Clematis*, wall shrubs & climbers.
Notes: Exports beyond EU. Delivers to shows. Euro accepted. Wheelchair accessible.
Map Ref: C, A5

CSta **Staddon Farm Nurseries** ♿
Staddon Road, Holsworthy, Devon EX22 6NH
Ⓣ 01409 259467
Ⓜ 07547 711189
Ⓔ penny.staddonfarm@yahoo.co.uk
Ⓦ www.pennysprimulas.co.uk
Contact: Penny Jones
Opening Times: By appt. only.
Min Mail Order UK: Nmc
Cat. Cost: Online only.
Credit Cards: All major credit/debit cards
Specialities: *Primula*. National Collection of *Primula sieboldii* applied for.
Notes: Delivers to shows. Wheelchair accessible.

CSto **Stone Lane Gardens**
Stone Farm, Chagford, Devon TQ13 8JU
Ⓣ (01647) 231311
Ⓔ paul.bartlett@stonelanegardens.com
Ⓦ www.stonelanegardens.com
Contact: Paul Bartlett
Opening Times: Open by appt. only. Not open to casual visitors. Website ordering available.
Min Mail Order UK: Nmc
Min Mail Order EU: Nmc
Cat. Cost: 6 × 1st class for colour catalogue with photos or online.
Credit Cards: All major credit/debit cards
Specialities: Comprehensive selection of wild origin *Betula* & *Alnus*, both bare-root & in pots. Choice selection of specially grafted cvs. Nat. Collection of Birch & Alder.
Notes: Arboretum open all year with summer sculpture exhibition (charges apply). Planting service available in West Country, details on request. Also sells wholesale. Credit cards accepted online only.
Map Ref: C, C3 **OS Grid Ref:** SX708908

CSuc **SURREAL SUCCULENTS**
Clowance Wood Nursery, Praze-an-Beeble, Cornwall TR14 0NW
Ⓜ 07707 314823
Ⓔ info@surrealsucculents.co.uk
Ⓦ www.surrealsucculents.co.uk
Contact: Colin Skelly
Opening Times: Mail order only. Open by appt.
Min Mail Order UK: Nmc
Min Mail Order EU: Nmc
Cat. Cost: Online only.
Credit Cards: Paypal
Specialities: Hardy & half-hardy succulents. *Aeonium, Echeveria*. Some in small quantities only. National Collection of *Aeonium* applied for.
Notes: Euro accepted.

CSut **SUTTONS SEEDS**
Woodview Road, Paignton, Devon TQ4 7NG
Ⓣ 0844 922 2899
Ⓕ 0844 922 2265
Ⓦ www.suttons.co.uk
Contact: Customer Services
Opening Times: Office: 0830-1700 Mon-Fri. Also answerphone.
Min Mail Order UK: Nmc
Min Mail Order EU: £5.00
Cat. Cost: Free.
Credit Cards: Visa, MasterCard, Switch, Delta
Specialities: Over 1,000 varieties of flower & vegetable seed, bulbs, plants & sundries.

CTal **TALE VALLEY NURSERY**
Barratt's Cottage, Cullompton, Devon EX15 2NQ
Ⓣ (01884) 277614
Ⓜ 07791 676162
Ⓔ contactus@talevalleynursery.co.uk
Ⓦ www.talevalleynursery.co.uk
Contact: Lorraine & Chris Birchall
Opening Times: Not open.
Min Mail Order UK: £10.00 + p&p
Min Mail Order EU: £25.00 + p&p
Cat. Cost: 4 × 1st class or PDF download from website.
Credit Cards: None
Specialities: Alpines, shade/woodland herbaceous plants & bulbs. Nat. Collections of *Rhodohypoxis* & *x Rhodoxis*. Some specialist plants available in small numbers only.
Notes: Mail order for selection of Nat. Collections, other bulbs & a few select plants. Delivers to shows.

CTca **TRECANNA NURSERY**
The Old Barn, Chilsworthy, Cornwall PL18 9PB
Ⓣ (01822) 834680
Ⓜ 07785 242148
Ⓔ mark@trecanna.com
Ⓦ www.trecanna.com
Contact: Mark Wash
Opening Times: Not currently open to the public.
Min Mail Order UK: £22.00
Min Mail Order EU: £45.00
Cat. Cost: £2.00
Credit Cards: All major credit/debit cards
Specialities: Hardy South African plants. Good collections of *Crocosmia, Eucomis, Kniphofia, Watsonia, Crinum, Albuca*, nerines, *Zantedeschia, Lachenalia* & *Moraea*. Wide range of dry bulbs from around the globe.
Notes: Talks to garden societies. Exports beyond EU. Delivers to shows.
Map Ref: C, B5 **OS Grid Ref:** SX247733

CTho **THORNHAYES NURSERY**
St Andrews Wood, Dulford, Cullompton, Devon EX15 2DF
Ⓣ (01884) 266746
Ⓕ (01884) 266739
Ⓔ trees@thornhayes-nursery.co.uk
Ⓦ www.thornhayes-nursery.co.uk
Contact: K D Croucher
Opening Times: 0800-1600 Mon-Fri. 0930-1400 Sat.
Min Mail Order UK: £30
Min Mail Order EU: £30
Credit Cards: All major credit/debit cards
Specialities: A broad range of forms of ornamental, amenity & fruit trees incl. West Country apple varieties.
Notes: Also sells wholesale. Euro accepted. Limited wheelchair accessible.
Map Ref: C, C4

CTre **TREWIDDEN NURSERY**
Buryas Bridge, Penzance, Cornwall TR20 8TT
Ⓣ (01736) 362087
Ⓕ (01736) 331470
Ⓔ info@trewidden-nursery.com
Ⓦ www.trewidden-online.co.uk
Contact: Jeff Rowe
Opening Times: Not open. Mail order only.
Min Mail Order UK: Nmc
Min Mail Order EU: Nmc
Cat. Cost: Online only.
Credit Cards: None
Specialities: *Protea, Restio*, succulents and other unusual plants.
Notes: Sells at shows around the country and online. Mail order through website only.

CTrh **TREHANE NURSERY** ♿
Stapehill Road, Hampreston, Wimborne, Dorset BH21 7ND
Ⓣ (01202) 873490
Ⓕ (01202) 873490
Ⓔ nursery@trehane.co.uk
Ⓦ www.trehane.co.uk

Contact: Lorraine Keets
Opening Times: 0830-1630 Mon-Fri all year (excl. Xmas & New Year). 1000-1600 Sat-Sun in spring & by special appt.
Min Mail Order UK: Nmc
Min Mail Order EU: Nmc
Cat. Cost: £1.50 cat./book.
Credit Cards: All major credit/debit cards
Specialities: Extensive range of *Camellia* species, cultivars & hybrids. Many new introductions. Evergreen azaleas, *Pieris* & blueberries.
Notes: Also sells wholesale. Delivers to shows. Wheelchair accessible.
Map Ref: C, C6 **OS Grid Ref:** SU059000

CTri **TRISCOMBE NURSERIES** ♿ ◆
West Bagborough, Nr Taunton, Somerset TA4 3HG
Ⓣ (01984) 618267
Ⓔ triscombe.nurseries2000@virgin.net
Ⓦ www.triscombenurseries.co.uk
Contact: S Parkman
Opening Times: 0900-1730 Mon-Sat. 1400-1730 Sun & B/hols.
Min Mail Order UK: Nmc
Cat. Cost: 1 × 1st class.
Credit Cards: None
Specialities: Trees, shrubs, roses, fruit, *Clematis*, herbaceous & rock plants.
Notes: Wheelchair accessible.
Map Ref: C, B4

CTsd **TRESEDERS** ♿
Wallcottage Nursery, Lockengate, St Austell, Cornwall PL26 8RU
Ⓣ (01208) 832234
Ⓔ Treseders@btconnect.com
Ⓦ www.treseders.co.uk
Contact: James Treseder
Opening Times: 0900-1700 Mon-Sat, 1000-1600 Sun. Closed Wed.
Min Mail Order UK: Nmc
Min Mail Order EU: Nmc
Cat. Cost: Plant list available on request.
Credit Cards: All major credit/debit cards
Specialities: A wide range of choice & unusual plants grown in peat-free compost. Establishing collection of *Prostanthera*.
Notes: Plants sometimes only available in small quantities. Also sells wholesale. Wheelchair accessible.
Map Ref: C, C2 **OS Grid Ref:** SX034620

CTyn **TYNINGS CLIMBERS (NATIONAL COLLECTION OF PASSIFLORA & JASMINUM)**
109 Clevedon Road, Tickenham, North Somerset BS21 6RE
Ⓣ (01275) 852439
Ⓜ 07812 134849
Ⓕ (01275) 852439
Ⓔ tynings.climbers@yahoo.co.uk
Ⓦ www.tyningsclimbers.co.uk
Contact: Jane Lindsay or Toni O'Connor
Opening Times: By appt. only.
Min Mail Order UK: £18.00
Min Mail Order EU: £25.00
Cat. Cost: 4 × 1st class.
Specialities: Nat. Collections of *Passiflora* & *Jasminum*. Certain species & cvs only propagated on request, please phone for more information.
Notes: Also sells wholesale. Delivers to shows. Euro accepted.

CUse **USEFUL PLANTS (FORMERLY LOWER SEVERALLS NURSERY)** ♿
Lower Severalls Nursery, Crewkerne, Somerset TA18 7NX
Ⓜ 07786 342958
Ⓔ info@usefulplants.co.uk
Ⓦ www.usefulplants.co.uk
Contact: Dmitry Guskov
Opening Times: 1000-1700 Tue, Wed, Fri, Sat, Mar-end Oct.
Min Mail Order UK: £20.00
Cat. Cost: 4 × 1st class.
Credit Cards: Visa, MasterCard
Specialities: Herbs, herbaceous.
Notes: Also sells wholesale. Wheelchair accessible.
Map Ref: C, B5 **OS Grid Ref:** ST457111

CWat **THE WATER GARDEN** ♿
Hinton Parva, Swindon, Wiltshire SN4 0DH
Ⓣ (01793) 790558
Ⓕ (01793) 791298
Ⓔ mike@thewatergarden.co.uk
Ⓦ www.thewatergarden.co.uk
Contact: Mike & Anne Newman
Opening Times: 1000-1700 Wed-Sun.
Min Mail Order UK: £10.00 + p&p
Cat. Cost: 4 × 1st class.
Credit Cards: Visa, Access, Switch
Specialities: Water lilies, marginal & moisture plants, oxygenators & alpines.
Notes: Also sells wholesale. Wheelchair accessible.
Map Ref: C, A6

CWCL **WESTCOUNTRY NURSERIES** ♿
Donkey Meadow, Woolsery, Devon EX39 5QH
Ⓣ (01237) 431111
Ⓔ info@westcountry-nurseries.co.uk
Ⓦ www.westcountry-nurseries.co.uk
Contact: Sarah Conibear
Opening Times: 1000-1600 Mar-Jul. Closed for lunch 1300-1330.

Min Mail Order UK: Nmc
Cat. Cost: 2 × 1st class + A5 sae for full colour cat.
Credit Cards: All major credit/debit cards
Specialities: *Lupinus, Lewisia, Hellebore, Clematis*, cyclamen, lavender, select perennials, grasses, ferns & climbers. Nat. Collection of Lupins.
Notes: Delivers to shows. Wheelchair accessible.
Map Ref: C, B2 **OS Grid Ref:** SS351219

CWGN **Walled Garden Nursery** ♿
Brinkworth House, Brinkworth,
Nr Malmesbury, Wiltshire
SN15 5DF
Ⓣ (01666) 826637
Ⓜ 07921 436863
Ⓔ f.wescott@btinternet.com
Ⓦ www.clematis-nursery.co.uk
Contact: Fraser Wescott
Opening Times: 1000-1700, 7 days Mar-Oct. 1000-dusk, Mon-Fri Nov & Feb. Closed Dec & Jan.
Min Mail Order UK: Nmc
Credit Cards: All major credit/debit cards
Specialities: *Clematis* & climbers, with a selection of unusual perennials & shrubs.
Notes: Wheelchair accessible.
Map Ref: C, A6 **OS Grid Ref:** SU002849

CWGr **Winchester Growers Ltd** ♿
Varfell Farm, Long Rock,
Penzance, Cornwall
TR20 8AQ
Ⓣ (01736) 335851
Ⓕ (01736) 851033
Ⓔ info@national-dahlia-collection.co.uk
Ⓦ www.national-dahlia-collection.co.uk
Contact: Michael Mann
Opening Times: 1300-1630 mid-Jul to end Aug.
Min Mail Order UK: Nmc
Min Mail Order EU: Nmc
Cat. Cost: Free
Credit Cards: Visa, Delta, MasterCard, Switch
Specialities: Nat. Collection of *Dahlia*. Due to large number of varieties, some stock available in small quantities only.
Notes: Also sells wholesale. Exports beyond EU. Wheelchair accessible.

CWil **Fernwood Nursery**
Peters Marland, Torrington, Devon
EX38 8QG
Ⓣ (01805) 601446
Ⓔ hw@fernwood-nursery.co.uk
Ⓦ www.fernwood-nursery.co.uk
Contact: Howard Wills
Opening Times: Any time by appt. Please phone or email first.
Min Mail Order UK: Nmc
Min Mail Order EU: Nmc
Cat. Cost: Sae for list.
Credit Cards: Paypal
Specialities: Nat. Collection of *Sempervivum, Jovibarba* & *Rosularia*. 5 miles from RHS Rosemoor.
Notes: Mail order for *Sempervivum, Jovibarba* & *Rosularia* only. Exports beyond EU. Euro accepted.
Map Ref: C, C3 **OS Grid Ref:** SS479133

CWiW **Windrush Willow**
Higher Barn, Sidmouth Road,
Aylesbeare, Exeter, Devon
EX5 2JJ
Ⓣ (01395) 233669
Ⓕ (01395) 233669
Ⓔ windrushw@aol.com
Ⓦ www.windrushwillow.com
Contact: Richard Kerwood
Opening Times: Mail order only. Open by appt.
Min Mail Order UK: Nmc
Min Mail Order EU: Nmc
Cat. Cost: 2 × 1st class.
Credit Cards: All major credit/debit cards
Specialities: *Salix*. Unrooted cuttings available Dec-Mar.
Notes: Also sells wholesale. Euro accepted.

CWld **Wild Thyme**
(Office) The Old Orchard, Friggle Street,
Frome, Somerset BA11 5LH
Ⓣ (01373) 464417
Ⓜ 07956 888477
Ⓔ jess@wildthymeplants.co.uk
Ⓦ www.wildthymeplants.co.uk
Contact: Monica Ashman
Opening Times: Not open. Mail order only via online shop.
Min Mail Order UK: £15.00
Credit Cards: Visa, MasterCard, Maestro
Specialities: Wildflowers & fragrant plants.
Notes: Delivers to shows.

CWri **Nigel Wright Rhododendrons** ♿
The Old Glebe, Eggesford, Chulmleigh,
Devon EX18 7QU
Ⓣ (01769) 580632
Ⓔ wrightrhodos@aol.com
Ⓦ www.wrightrhodos.com
Contact: Nigel Wright
Opening Times: By appt. only. 7 days.
Cat. Cost: 2 × 1st class.
Credit Cards: None
Specialities: *Rhododendron* & deciduous azaleas. 200 varieties field grown, root-balled,

some potted. For collection only. Specialist grower. Free advice & planting plans.
Notes: Also sells wholesale. Wheelchair accessible.
Map Ref: C, B3 **OS Grid Ref:** SS684106

E

CWSG **West Somerset Garden Centre** ♿
Mart Road, Minehead, Somerset TA24 5BJ
Ⓣ (01643) 703812
Ⓕ (01643) 706476
Ⓔ wsgc@btconnect.com
Ⓦ www.westsomersetgardencentre.co.uk
Contact: Ms J K Webber
Opening Times: 0800-1700 Mon-Sat, 1000-1600 Sun.
Min Mail Order UK: Nmc
Cat. Cost: None issued.
Credit Cards: Visa, Solo, Maestro, MasterCard
Specialities: Wide general range. *Clematis* & rose varieties change throughout the season.
Notes: Wheelchair accessible.
Map Ref: C, B4

CWVF **White Veil Fuchsias** ♿
Verwood Road, Three Legged Cross, Wimborne Dorset BH21 6RP
Ⓣ (01202) 813998
Contact: A. C. Holloway
Opening Times: 0900-1300 & 1400-1700 Mon-Sat, 1000-1300 & 1400-1600 Sun, Jan-Aug. Closed Sat & Sun, Sep-Dec.
Min Mail Order UK: 8 plants of your choice.
Cat. Cost: 4 × 1st class.
Credit Cards: None
Specialities: Fuchsias. Small plants grown from Jan-Apr. Available in small quantities only.
Notes: Wheelchair accessible.
Map Ref: C, C6

Eastern

EABi **Alison Bilverstone**
22 Kings Street, Swaffham, Norfolk PE37 7BU
Ⓣ (01760) 725026
Ⓔ a.bilverstone@tiscali.co.uk
Contact: Alison Bilverstone
Opening Times: Not open. Mail order only.
Min Mail Order UK: Nmc
Min Mail Order EU: Nmc
Cat. Cost: A5 with large 2nd class.
Credit Cards: None
Specialities: *Achemene*, *Kohleria* & *Smithiantha* rhizomes, available Dec to mid-Apr. Stocked in small quantities.
Notes: Euro accepted.

EACa **Alpine Campanulas (Bellflower Nursery)**
Langham Hall Walled Garden, Langham, Nr Bury St Edmunds, Suffolk IP31 3EE
Ⓜ 07879 644958
Ⓔ campanulas@btinternet.com
Ⓦ www.bellflowernursery.co.uk
Contact: Sue Wooster
Opening Times: 1000-1630 Thu & Fri, 1000-1300 Sat, mid-Mar to end Oct. Other times by appt.
Min Mail Order UK: £10.00
Cat. Cost: 1 × 1st class sae.
Credit Cards: None
Specialities: *Campanula*. Nat. Collection of Alpine Campanulas. Most stock in small numbers only.
Notes: Hardy plant nursery within the Walled Garden, Langham Hall. Groups welcome by appt.
Map Ref: E, C3 **OS Grid Ref:** TL978691

EAEE **AEE – A Lover of Plants** ♿
Snetterton Park, Harling Road (off A11), Snetterton, Norfolk NR16 2JU
Ⓜ 07874 214182
Ⓔ aeesales@fsmail.net
Ⓦ www.aeesupplyingplantlovers.com
Contact: Anne Etheridge
Opening Times: 0900-1700 7 days, Mar-Sep. 0900-1600 Tue, Thu, Fri, Sun, Oct-Feb.
Min Mail Order UK: Nmc
Min Mail Order EU: Nmc
Cat. Cost: 3 × 1st class.
Credit Cards: All major credit/debit cards
Specialities: Perennials & grasses plus a few enticing alpines & shrubs. Alpines available in small quantities only.
Notes: Talks available Mar-Oct. For information on group & trade discounts, please contact nursery. Plants delivered free within 10 miles of Roydon, Diss or Snetterton Park. Wheelchair accessible.
Map Ref: E, C3

EAJP **A & J Plants**
Scenterfields, Chapel Road, Great Tey, Colchester, Essex CO6 1JR
Ⓣ (01206) 212124
Ⓕ (01206) 212124
Ⓔ mail@aandjplants.com
Ⓦ www.aandjplants.com
Contact: Jackie Rhodes
Opening Times: Not open. Mail order only. Orders can be collected from nursery by prior arrangement.
Min Mail Order UK: Nmc
Specialities: Wide variety of choice perennials and ornamental grasses propagated on the nursery, some in small quantities.

Notes: Plant centre at Marks Hall Garden (CO6 1TG) stocked with seasonal selection of perennials & grasses. Also sells wholesale. Delivers to shows.
Map Ref: E, C2

EBak **B & H M Baker** ♿
Bourne Brook Nurseries, Greenstead Green, Halstead, Essex CO9 1RB
Ⓣ (01787) 476369
Contact: Clive Baker
Opening Times: 0800-1600 Mon-Fri, 0900-1200 & 1400-1600 Sat & Sun, Mar-30th Jun.
Cat. Cost: 2 × 1st class + 33p.
Credit Cards: All major credit/debit cards
Specialities: *Fuchsia* & conservatory plants.
Notes: Also sells wholesale. Wheelchair accessible.
Map Ref: E, C2

EBar **Barcham Trees PLC**
Eye Hill Drove, Ely, Cambridgeshire CB7 5XF
Ⓣ (01353) 720748
Ⓜ 07801 917566
Ⓕ (01353) 723060
Ⓔ mike@barchamtrees.co.uk
Ⓦ www.barcham.co.uk
Contact: Mike Glover
Opening Times: 0900-1700 Mon-Fri. Visits to the nursery by appt. only.
Cat. Cost: £10.00
Credit Cards: All major credit/debit cards
Specialities: Large grower of containerised trees. 478 varieties available, from 10-12cm to 40cm girth.
Notes: E-commerce site: www.buythetreeyousee.com. As trees range from 3-8 metres all are despatched on lorries rather than through the mailing service. Also sells wholesale. Exports beyond EU. Euro accepted.

EBee **Beeches Nursery** ♿
Village Centre, Ashdon, Saffron Walden, Essex CB10 2HB
Ⓣ (01799) 584362
Ⓕ (01799) 584421
Ⓔ sales@beechesnursery.co.uk
Ⓦ www.beechesnursery.co.uk
Contact: Alan Bidwell/Kevin Marsh
Opening Times: 0830-1700 Mon-Sat, 1000-1700 Sun & B/hols.
Min Mail Order UK: £15.00
Min Mail Order EU: £20.00
Cat. Cost: Online.
Credit Cards: All major credit/debit cards
Specialities: Herbaceous specialists & extensive range of other garden plants. Rarieties available in limited numbers only.
Notes: Plants dispatched Oct-Feb only. Orders accepted throughout the year. No trees by mail order. Wheelchair accessible.
Map Ref: E, C2 **OS Grid Ref:** TL586420

EBtc **Botanica**
Chantry Farm, Campsea Ashe, Wickham Market, Suffolk IP13 0PZ
Ⓣ (01728) 747113
Ⓜ 07887 423964
Ⓕ (01728) 747725
Ⓔ sales@botanica.org.uk
Ⓦ www.botanica.org.uk
Contact: Daniel Everett
Opening Times: 1000-1700 6 days summer, 1000-1700 5 days August, 1000-1600 7 days winter.
Min Mail Order UK: £15 + p&p
Cat. Cost: Online only.
Credit Cards: All, except American Express
Specialities: Range of rare & unusual hardy plants. All stock is English grown at our nursery and in non-peat based compost.
Notes: Also sells wholesale.
Map Ref: E, C3 **OS Grid Ref:** TM328550

ECGP **Cambridge Garden Plants** ♿
The Lodge, Clayhithe Road, Horningsea, Cambridgeshire CB25 9JD
Ⓣ (01223) 861370
Ⓔ kit@cambridgegardenplants.co.uk
Contact: Kit Buchdahl
Opening Times: 1100-1730 Thu-Sun mid Mar-31st Oct. Other times by appt.
Cat. Cost: 4 × 1st class.
Credit Cards: None
Specialities: Hardy perennials incl. wide range of *Geranium*, *Allium*, *Euphorbia*, *Cyclamen*, *Digitalis*.
Notes: Euro accepted. Wheelchair accessible.
Map Ref: E, C2 **OS Grid Ref:** TL497637

ECha **The Beth Chatto Gardens Ltd** ♿
Clacton Road, Elmstead Market, Colchester, Essex CO7 7DB
Ⓣ (01206) 822007
Ⓕ (01206) 825933
Ⓔ info@bethchatto.fsnet.co.uk
Ⓦ www.bethchatto.co.uk
Contact: Beth Chatto
Opening Times: 0900-1700 Mon-Sat, 1000-1700 Sun, 1st Mar-31st Oct. 0900-1600 Mon-Sat, 1000-1600 Sun, Nov-end Feb.
Min Mail Order UK: £20.00
Min Mail Order EU: Ask for details
Cat. Cost: Free.
Credit Cards: All, except American Express
Specialities: Predominantly herbaceous. Many unusual for special situations.
Notes: Wheelchair accessible.
Map Ref: E, C3 **OS Grid Ref:** TM069238

ECho **CHOICE LANDSCAPES** ♿
Priory Farm, 101 Salts Road,
West Walton, Wisbech, Cambridgeshire
PE14 7EF
Ⓣ (01945) 585051
Ⓔ info@choicelandscapes.org
Ⓦ www.choicelandscapes.org
Contact: Michael Agg & Jillian Agg
Opening Times: By appt.
Min Mail Order UK: £12.00
Min Mail Order EU: £15.00 + p&p
Cat. Cost: 6 × 1st class or 6 IRC
Credit Cards: Visa, MasterCard
Specialities: Alpines, rhododendrons, bulbs, lilies & South African bulbs & seed.
Notes: Exports beyond EU. Delivers to shows. Wheelchair accessible.
Map Ref: E, B1

ECnt **CANTS OF COLCHESTER LTD**
Nayland Road, Mile End,
Colchester, Essex
CO4 5HA
Ⓣ (01206) 844008
Ⓕ (01206) 855371
Ⓔ enquiries@cantsroses.co.uk
Ⓦ www.cantsroses.co.uk
Contact: Angela Pawsey
Opening Times: 0900-1300, 1400-1630 Mon-Fri. Sat varied, please phone first. Sun closed.
Min Mail Order UK: Nmc
Min Mail Order EU: Nmc
Cat. Cost: Free
Credit Cards: Visa, MasterCard, Delta, Maestro
Specialities: Roses. Unstaffed rose field can be viewed dawn-dusk every day from end Jun-end Sep.
Notes: Bare-root mail order end Oct-end Mar, containers Apr-Aug. Exports beyond EU. Partial wheelchair access.
Map Ref: E, C3

ECou **COUNTY PARK NURSERY**
Essex Gardens, Hornchurch, Essex
RM11 3BU
Ⓜ 07935 906866
Ⓔ info@countyparknursery.co.uk
Ⓦ www.countyparknursery.co.uk
Contact: Paul Boosey
Opening Times: By appt. only.
Cat. Cost: Online only.
Credit Cards: None
Specialities: Alpines & rare and unusual plants from New Zealand, Tasmania & the Falklands. Many plants available in small quantities only.
Notes: Euro accepted.
Map Ref: E, D2

ECrc **THE CROCOSMIA GARDENS**
9 North Street, Caistor, Lincolnshire LN7 6QU
Ⓣ (01472) 859269
Ⓜ 07961 470104
Ⓔ mark@thecrocosmiagardens.net
Ⓦ www.thecrocosmiagardens.net
Contact: Mark Fox
Opening Times: 1000-1700 Mon-Sun.
Min Mail Order UK: £5.00
Min Mail Order EU: £5.00
Credit Cards: None
Specialities: *Crocosmia*. Nat. Collection of *Crocosmia*.
Notes: Exports beyond EU. Euro accepted.
Map Ref: E, A1

ECre **CREAKE PLANT CENTRE** ♿
Leicester Road, South Creake, Fakenham,
Norfolk NR21 9PW
Ⓣ (01328) 823018
Ⓜ 07760 762499
Ⓕ (01328) 823018
Ⓔ trevor-harrison@btconnect.com
Ⓦ www.creakeplantcentre.co.uk
Contact: Mr T Harrison
Opening Times: 1000-1300 & 1400-1730 7 days excl. Xmas.
Cat. Cost: None issued
Credit Cards: All major credit/debit cards
Specialities: Unusual shrubs, herbaceous, conservatory plants, old roses. Hellebores.
Notes: Wheelchair accessible.
Map Ref: E, B1 **OS Grid Ref:** TF864353

ECrN **CROWN NURSERY** ♿
High Street, Ufford, Suffolk IP13 6EL
Ⓣ (01394) 460755
Ⓕ (01394) 460142
Ⓔ enquiries@crown-nursery.co.uk
Ⓦ www.crown-nursery.co.uk
Contact: Jill Proctor
Opening Times: 0900-1700 (1600 in winter) Mon-Sat.
Min Mail Order UK: Nmc
Credit Cards: All major credit/debit cards
Specialities: Mature & semi-mature native, ornamental & fruit trees. Heritage fruit varieties.
Notes: Mail order for small/young stock only. Also sells wholesale. Wheelchair accessible.
Map Ref: E, C3 **OS Grid Ref:** TM292528

ECtt **COTTAGE NURSERIES** ♿
Thoresthorpe, Alford, Lincolnshire LN13 0HX
Ⓣ (01507) 466968
Ⓕ (01507) 463409
Ⓔ bill@cottagenurseries.net
Ⓦ www.cottagenurseries.net
Contact: W H Denbigh
Opening Times: 0900-1700 7 days 1st Mar-31st Oct. 1000-1500 w/ends only Nov-Feb.

Min Mail Order UK: £15.00
Cat. Cost: 4 × 1st class.
Credit Cards: Visa, MasterCard, Maestro
Specialities: Hardy perennials. Wide general range.
Notes: Wheelchair accessible.
Map Ref: E, A2 **OS Grid Ref:** TF423716

EDAr **D'Arcy & Everest** ♿
(Office) PO Box 78, St Ives,
Huntingdon, Cambridgeshire
PE27 6ZA
Ⓣ (01480) 497672 answerphone
Ⓜ 07715 374440
Ⓕ (01480) 466042
Ⓔ angela@darcyeverest.co.uk
Ⓦ www.darcyeverest.co.uk
Contact: Angela Whiting, Richard Oliver
Opening Times: Mon-Fri, last week of Mar-Sep, except show dates. Winter by appt. Coach parties welcome by appt.
Min Mail Order UK: £15.00 + p&p
Min Mail Order EU: £30.00 + p&p
Cat. Cost: 6 × 1st class.
Credit Cards: None
Specialities: Alpines & sempervivums.
Notes: Nursery is at Pidley Sheep Lane (B1040), Pidley, Huntingdon, Cambs PE28 3FL. Euro accepted. Delivers to shows. Wheelchair accessible.
Map Ref: E, C2 **OS Grid Ref:** TL338762

EDel **Delfland Nurseries Ltd** ♿
Benwick Road, Doddington, March,
Cambridgeshire PE15 0TU
Ⓣ (01354) 740553
Ⓕ (01354) 741200
Ⓔ info@delfland.co.uk
Ⓦ www.organicplants.co.uk
Contact: Jill Vaughan
Opening Times: 0900-1600 Mon-Fri, 0900-1300 Sat, all year. Additionally, at peak season, 0900-1600 Sat & 1000-1600 Sun.
Min Mail Order UK: £1.90 + p&p
Cat. Cost: Free or online.
Credit Cards: All major credit/debit cards
Specialities: Vegetable, bedding & container plants.
Notes: Mail order and retail organic & peat-free from stock (mainly veg. plants) or to order (for large orders). Retail bedding & container plants not organic or peat-free. Also sells wholesale. Wheelchair accessible.
Map Ref: E, C2 **OS Grid Ref:** TL386908

EECP **Essex Carnivorous Plants**
12 Strangman Avenue, Thundersley, Essex
SS7 1RB
Ⓣ (01702) 551467
Ⓔ Mark@essexcarnivorousplants.com
Ⓦ www.essexcarnivorousplants.com
Contact: Mark Haslett
Opening Times: By appt. only.
Min Mail Order UK: Nmc
Min Mail Order EU: Nmc
Cat. Cost: 2 × 1st class or online.
Credit Cards: None
Specialities: Good range of carnivorous plants. *Sarracenia*, *Dionaea*. Some stock available in small quantities only.
Notes: Also sells wholesale. Delivers to shows.
Map Ref: E, D2 **OS Grid Ref:** TQ797875

EExo **The Exotic Garden Company** ♿
Saxmundham Road, Aldeburgh, Suffolk
IP15 5JD
Ⓣ (01728) 454456
Ⓦ www.theexoticgardencompany.com
Contact: Matthew Couchy
Opening Times: 1000-1700 Mon-Sat, 1000-1600 Sun, Mar-Oct. 1000-dusk Nov-Dec. Closed Jan-Feb.
Cat. Cost: None issued.
Credit Cards: All major credit/debit cards
Specialities: General range of choice & some unusual perennials, shrubs, ferns, tree ferns, olives, palms, bamboos, herbs, box.
Notes: Wheelchair accessible.
Map Ref: E, C3

EFen **Fenbulbs Ltd**
18 The Croft, Christchurch, Wisbech,
Cambridgeshire PE14 9PU
Ⓣ (01354) 638236
Ⓔ info@fenbulbs.net
Ⓦ www.fenbulbs.net
Contact: Mike Saunders
Opening Times: Not open. Mail order only. Orders available for collection by prior arrangement.
Min Mail Order UK: Nmc
Min Mail Order EU: Nmc
Credit Cards: Visa, MasterCard
Specialities: English wild flower bulbs. Snowdrops, bluebells, aconites, anemones, *Fritillaria* & native daffodils. All plants from cultivated UK grown stock.
Notes: Export beyond EU available on request.

EFer **The Fern Nursery** ♿
Grimsby Road, Binbrook, Lincolnshire
LN8 6DH
Ⓣ (01472) 398092
Ⓔ rtimm@fernnursery.co.uk
Ⓦ www.fernnursery.co.uk
Contact: R N Timm
Opening Times: 0900-1700 Fri, Sat & Sun Apr-Oct or by appt.
Min Mail Order UK: Nmc

Min Mail Order EU: Nmc
Cat. Cost: 2 × 1st class.
Credit Cards: None
Specialities: Ferns. Display garden.
Notes: Only plants in the mail order part of the catalogue can be sent mail order. Also sells wholesale. Euro accepted. Wheelchair accessible.
Map Ref: E, A1 **OS Grid Ref:** TF212942

EFEx **FLORA EXOTICA**
Pasadena, South-Green, Fingringhoe, Colchester, Essex CO5 7DR
Ⓜ 07989 456094
Contact: J Beddoes
Opening Times: Not open. Mail order only.
Min Mail Order UK: Nmc
Min Mail Order EU: Nmc
Cat. Cost: 4 × 1st class.
Credit Cards: None
Specialities: Exotica flora incl. orchids.
Notes: Exports beyond EU. Euro accepted.

EFly **THE FLY TRAP PLANTS** ♿
Cooke Road, Berghapton, Norwich, Norfolk NR15 1BA
Ⓣ (01508) 480348
Ⓜ 0776 92556
Ⓔ sales@tftplants.co.uk
Ⓦ www.tftplants.co.uk
Contact: Pauline Steward
Opening Times: By appt. only.
Min Mail Order UK: Nmc
Cat. Cost: 1 × 1st class sae
Credit Cards: None
Specialities: All kinds of carnivorous plants, from *Sarracenia*, *Drosera*, *Pinquicula*, to *Utricularia* aquatic plants.
Notes: Delivers to shows. Euro accepted. Wheelchair accessible.

EFtx **FERNATIX** ♿
Stoke Ash, Suffolk IP23 7EN
Ⓣ (01379) 678197
Ⓕ (01379) 678197
Ⓔ mail@fernatix.co.uk
Ⓦ www.fernatix.co.uk
Contact: Steven Fletcher & Kerry Robinson
Opening Times: By appt. only.
Min Mail Order UK: £15.00
Cat. Cost: None issued.
Credit Cards: All, except American Express
Specialities: Ferns, hardy & greenhouse species & cultivars. Some available in small quantities only. Mainly hardy ferns.
Notes: Delivers to shows, except Chelsea. 10 days notice required. Euro accepted. Wheelchair accessible.
Map Ref: E, C3

EGFP **GRANGE FARM PLANTS** ♿
Grange Farm, 38 Fishergate Road, Sutton St James, Spalding, Lincolnshire PE12 0EZ
Ⓣ (01945) 440240
Ⓜ 07742 138760
Ⓕ (01945) 440355
Ⓔ ellis.family@tinyonline.co.uk
Contact: M C Ellis
Opening Times: Mail order only. Open by appt. only.
Min Mail Order UK: Nmc
Min Mail Order EU: Nmc
Cat. Cost: 1 × 1st class.
Credit Cards: None
Specialities: Rare trees & shrubs, esp. *Juglans*, *Fraxinus*. Some species available in small quantities only.
Notes: Euro accepted. Wheelchair accessible.
Map Ref: E, B2 **OS Grid Ref:** TF382186

EHoe **HOECROFT PLANTS** ♿
Severals Grange, Holt Road, Wood Norton, Dereham, Norfolk NR20 5BL
Ⓣ (01362) 684206
Ⓔ hoecroft@hotmail.co.uk
Ⓦ www.hoecroft.co.uk
Contact: Jane Lister
Opening Times: 1000-1600 Thu-Sun, 1st Apr-31st Oct or by appt.
Min Mail Order UK: Nmc
Min Mail Order EU: Nmc
Cat. Cost: 5 × 2nd class.
Credit Cards: None
Specialities: An extensive range of coloured & variegated-leaved shrubs & herbaceous perennials. 260 ornamental grasses. Free entry to display gardens.
Notes: Nursery 2 miles north of Guist on B1110. Euro accepted. Wheelchair accessible.
Map Ref: E, B3 **OS Grid Ref:** TG008289

EHon **HONEYSOME AQUATIC NURSERY**
The Row, Sutton, Nr Ely, Cambridgeshire CB6 2PB
Ⓣ (01353) 778889
Ⓕ (01353) 777291
Ⓔ info@honeysomeaquaticnursery.co.uk
Ⓦ www.honeysomeaquaticnursery.co.uk
Contact: Mrs L S Bond
Opening Times: At all times by appt. only.
Min Mail Order UK: Nmc
Cat. Cost: 2 × 2nd class.
Credit Cards: Paypal
Specialities: Hardy aquatic, bog & marginal.
Notes: Also sells wholesale.
Map Ref: E, C2

EHul **HULL FARM**
Spring Valley Lane, Ardleigh, Colchester, Essex CO7 7SA

Ⓣ (01206) 230045
Ⓜ 07900 298366
Ⓔ jack.wendyfryer@mail.com
Ⓦ www.fryersfarmshop.co.uk
Contact: Jack Fryer
Opening Times: By appt. only. Please phone for appt.
Min Mail Order UK: £50.00 + p&p
Cat. Cost: 5 × 2nd class.
Credit Cards: MasterCard, Visa
Specialities: Conifers.
Notes: Also sells wholesale.
Map Ref: E, C3 **OS Grid Ref:** GR043274

EIri **IRISESONLINE**
Slade Cottage, Petts Lane, Little Walden, Essex CB10 1XH
Ⓣ (01799) 526294
Ⓔ sales@irisesonline.co.uk
Ⓦ www.irisesonline.co.uk
Contact: Clare Kneen
Opening Times: By appt. only.
Min Mail Order UK: Nmc
Cat. Cost: 3 × 1st class or online.
Credit Cards: None
Specialities: *Iris.* Small family-run nursery. Some varieties available in small quantities only.
Notes: Delivers to shows.
Map Ref: E, C2 **OS Grid Ref:** TL546416

ELad **LADYBIRD NURSERIES** ♿
Gromford Lane, Snape, Saxmundham, Suffolk IP17 1RD
Ⓣ (01728) 688289
Ⓦ www.ladybirdnurseries.co.uk
Contact: Mrs M Booker
Opening Times: 0900-1700, Mon-Sat, 1000-1600 Sun.
Credit Cards: All major credit/debit cards
Notes: Wheelchair accessible.

ELan **LANGTHORNS PLANTERY** ♿
High Cross Lane West, Little Canfield, Dunmow, Essex CM6 1TD
Ⓣ (01371) 872611
Ⓕ 0871 661 4093
Ⓔ info@langthorns.com
Ⓦ www.langthorns.com
Contact: E Cannon
Opening Times: 1000-1700 or dusk (if earlier) 7 days excl. Xmas fortnight.
Min Mail Order UK: £15.00
Cat. Cost: £1.50
Credit Cards: Visa, Access, Switch, MasterCard, Delta
Specialities: Wide general range with many unusual plants.
Notes: Mail order anything under 4ft tall. Mail order not available during spring & summer months. Wheelchair accessible.
Map Ref: E, D2 **OS Grid Ref:** TL592204

ELau **LAUREL FARM HERBS** ♿
Main Road (A12), Kelsale, Saxmundham, Suffolk IP17 2RG
Ⓣ (01728) 668223
Ⓔ laurelfarmherbs@aol.com
Ⓦ www.laurelfarmherbs.co.uk
Contact: Chris Seagon
Opening Times: Please phone or check website for opening hours as times can vary.
Min Mail Order UK: 1 plant + p&p
Min Mail Order EU: 1 plant + p&p
Cat. Cost: Online only.
Credit Cards: Visa, MasterCard, Switch, Delta
Specialities: Herbs esp. rosemary, thyme, mint & sage.
Notes: Nursery will be relocating during 2013 so some plants will be available in small quantities only. Mail orders accepted by email, phone or post. Also sells wholesale. Delivers to shows. Wheelchair accessible.
Map Ref: E, C3

ELon **LONG HOUSE PLANTS** ♿
The Long House, Church Road, Noak Hill, Romford, Essex RM4 1LD
Ⓣ (01708) 371719
Ⓔ tim@longhouse-plants.co.uk
Ⓦ www.longhouse-plants.co.uk
Contact: Tim Carter
Opening Times: 1000-1700 Fri, Sat & B/hols, 1000-1600 Sun, beginning Mar-end Sep, or by appt.
Cat. Cost: None issued.
Credit Cards: All major credit/debit cards
Specialities: Interesting range of choice trees, shrubs, climbers, roses, grasses, herbaceous perennials & ferns. Many unusual varieties. Specialities incl. *Agapanthus*, asters, *Camellia*, *Hemerocallis*, *Iris sibirica*, *Kniphofia*, *Papaver orientale* & *Phlox*. Some plants available in small quantities.
Notes: Wheelchair accessible.
Map Ref: E, D2 **OS Grid Ref:** TQ554194

EMac **FIRECREST TREES & SHRUBS NURSERY** ♿
Hall Road, Little Bealings, Woodbridge, Suffolk IP13 6LG
Ⓣ (01473) 625937
Ⓕ (01473) 625937
Ⓔ mac@firecrest.org.uk
Ⓦ www.firecrest.org.uk
Contact: Mac McGregor
Opening Times: 0830-1630 Mon-Fri, 1230 Sat.
Min Mail Order UK: Nmc
Cat. Cost: 2 × 1st class (bare-root only).
Credit Cards: None

E

Specialities: Trees & shrubs. Japanese maples. Bare-root hedging.
Notes: Also sells wholesale. Euro accepted. Wheelchair accessible.

E

EMal **Marshall's Malmaisons** ♿
Hullwood Barn, Shelley, Ipswich, Suffolk IP7 5RE
Ⓣ (01473) 822400
Ⓜ 07768 454875
Ⓔ jim@malmaisons.plus.com
Ⓦ www.malmaisonsandiris.co.uk
Contact: J M Marshall/Sarah Cook
Opening Times: By appt. only.
Min Mail Order UK: £33.00 incl. p&p
Min Mail Order EU: £36.00 incl. p&p
Cat. Cost: 1st class sae.
Credit Cards: None
Specialities: Nat. Collections of Malmaison Carnations & Cedric Morris Irises. *Iris* stock only available in small quantities.
Notes: Also sells wholesale. Wheelchair accessible.
Map Ref: E, C3 **OS Grid Ref:** TM006394

EMic **Mickfield Hostas** ♿
The Poplars, Mickfield, Stowmarket, Suffolk IP14 5LH
Ⓣ (01449) 711576
Ⓕ (01449) 711576
Ⓔ mickfieldhostas@btconnect.com
Ⓦ www.mickfieldhostas.co.uk
Contact: Mr & Mrs R L C Milton
Opening Times: For specified dates see catalogue or website.
Min Mail Order UK: Nmc
Min Mail Order EU: Nmc
Cat. Cost: 4 × 1st class.
Credit Cards: All, except American Express
Specialities: Holders of Nat. Collection of *Hosta* containing over 2000 varieties. See website for details of cvs held & latest availability. Will split parent plants for customers if practical. Also operates a waiting list for rarities.
Notes: Delivers to shows. Euro accepted. Wheelchair accessible.
Map Ref: E, C3 **OS Grid Ref:** TM136619

EMil **Mill Race Garden Centre** ♿
New Road, Aldham, Colchester, Essex CO6 3QT
Ⓣ (01206) 242521
Ⓔ plantdesk@millracegardencentre.co.uk
Ⓦ www.millracegardencentre.co.uk
Contact: Annette Bayliss
Opening Times: 0900-1730 Mon-Sat, 1000-1630 Sun.
Min Mail Order UK: £9.00
Credit Cards: All major credit/debit cards
Specialities: Stock available in small quantities only.
Notes: Trees & large shrubs not sent by mail order. Wheelchair accessible.
Map Ref: E, C2 **OS Grid Ref:** TL918268

ENfk **Norfolk Herbs** ♿ ◆
Blackberry Farm, Dillington, Dereham, Norfolk NR19 2QD
Ⓣ (01362) 860812
Ⓕ (01362) 860812
Ⓔ info@norfolkherbs.co.uk
Ⓦ www.norfolkherbs.co.uk
Contact: Rosemary or Oliver Clifton-Sprigg
Opening Times: 0900-1700 Mon-Sat, 1000-1600 Sun, Apr-Aug. 1000-1600 Fri & Sat, Feb, Oct & Nov. 1000-1600 Wed-Sat, Mar, Sept & Dec. Closed from Xmas to end Jan. To visit at other times, please contact nursery.
Min Mail Order UK: £5.90
Cat. Cost: 3 × 1st class.
Credit Cards: All major credit/debit cards
Specialities: Naturally raised culinary, medicinal & aromatic herb plants. Bay trees & scented pelagoniums.
Notes: Established 1986. A founding member of Norfolk Nursery Network. Also sells wholesale. Delivers to shows. Wheelchair accessible.
OS Grid Ref: TF967152

EOHP **Old Hall Plants**
1 The Old Hall, Barsham, Beccles, Suffolk NR34 8HB
Ⓣ (01502) 717475
Ⓔ info@oldhallplants.co.uk
Ⓦ www.oldhallplants.co.uk
Contact: Janet Elliott
Opening Times: By appt. only. Please phone first.
Min Mail Order UK: Nmc
Min Mail Order EU: Nmc
Cat. Cost: 4 × 1st class.
Credit Cards: Paypal
Specialities: A variety of rare herbs, house plants, *Plectranthus*. Some plants available in small quantities.
Notes: Partial wheelchair access. Paypal accepted for overseas orders only.
Map Ref: E, C3 **OS Grid Ref:** TM396904

EPau **Paugers Plants Ltd**
Bury Road, Depden, Bury St Edmunds, Suffolk IP29 4BU
Ⓣ (01284) 850527
Ⓜ 07906 618603
Ⓔ geraldine.arnold@btinternet.com
Ⓦ www.paugers-plants.co.uk
Contact: Geraldine Arnold
Opening Times: 0900-1730 Wed-Sat, 1000-

1700 Sun & B/hols, 1st Mar-30th Nov.
Min Mail Order UK: Nmc
Cat. Cost: None issued.
Credit Cards: All major credit/debit cards
Specialities: Hardy shrubs & perennials in large or small quantities.
Notes: Also sells wholesale.
Map Ref: E, C2 **OS Grid Ref:** TL783568

EPfP **The Place for Plants** ♿
East Bergholt Place, East Bergholt, Suffolk CO7 6UP
Ⓣ (01206) 299224
Ⓕ (01206) 299229
Ⓔ sales@placeforplants.co.uk
Ⓦ www.placeforplants.co.uk
Contact: Rupert & Sara Eley
Opening Times: 1000-1700 (or dusk if earlier) 7 days. Closed Easter Sun. Garden open Mar-Oct.
Min Mail Order UK: Nmc
Cat. Cost: 2 × 1st class.
Credit Cards: All major credit/debit cards
Specialities: Wide range of specialist & popular plants. Nat. Collection of Deciduous *Euonymus*. 20 acre mature garden with free access to RHS members during season.
Notes: Mail order from Sep-Feb only. Delivers to shows. Euro accepted. Wheelchair accessible.
Map Ref: E, C3

EPla **P W Plants** ♿
Sunnyside, Heath Road, Kenninghall, Norfolk NR16 2DS
Ⓣ (01953) 888212
Ⓜ 07823 331933
Ⓔ pw@hardybamboo.com
Ⓦ www.hardybamboo.com
Contact: Paul Whittaker
Opening Times: Fri & Sat, Apr-Sep. Fri & last Sat of month, Oct-Mar. Also by appt.
Min Mail Order UK: Nmc
Min Mail Order EU: Nmc
Cat. Cost: Online only.
Credit Cards: All major credit/debit cards
Specialities: Bamboos, ornamental grasses & a wide range of woody plants & perennials.
Notes: Wheelchair accessible.
Map Ref: E, C3 **OS Grid Ref:** TM036846

EPom **Pomona Fruits Ltd**
Pomona House, 12 Third Avenue, Walton-on-the-Naze, Essex CO14 8JU
Ⓣ 0845 676 0607
Ⓕ 0845 676 0608
Ⓔ Info@PomonaFruits.co.uk
Ⓦ www.PomonaFruits.co.uk
Contact: Ming Yang/Claire Higgins
Opening Times: Not open. Mail order only.
Min Mail Order UK: Nmc
Cat. Cost: Free.
Credit Cards: All major credit/debit cards
Specialities: Fruit stock.

EPot **Pottertons Nursery** ♿
Moortown Road, Nettleton, Caistor, Lincolnshire LN7 6HX
Ⓣ (01472) 851714
Ⓕ (01472) 852580
Ⓔ sales@pottertons.co.uk
Ⓦ www.pottertons.co.uk
Contact: Robert Potterton
Opening Times: 1000-1600 Tue-Sun. Closed Mon except B/hols. By appt. only Nov-Feb.
Min Mail Order UK: Nmc
Min Mail Order EU: Nmc
Cat. Cost: £2.00 in stamps
Credit Cards: MasterCard, Visa
Specialities: Alpines, dwarf bulbs & woodland plants. Hardy orchids & *Pleione*.
Notes: External talks nationally & internationally to garden clubs & societies. Group nursery tours by arrangement. Exports beyond EU. Delivers to shows. Euro accepted. Wheelchair accessible.
Map Ref: E, A1 **OS Grid Ref:** TA091001

EPPr **The Plantsman's Preference** ♿
Church Road, South Lopham, Diss, Norfolk IP22 2LW
Ⓣ Office (evenings): (01953) 681439
Ⓜ Nursery (day): 07799 855559
Ⓕ (01953) 688194
Ⓔ tim@plantpref.co.uk
Ⓦ www.plantpref.co.uk
Contact: Tim Fuller
Opening Times: 0930-1700 Fri, Sat & Sun Mar-Oct. Other times by appt.
Min Mail Order UK: Nmc
Min Mail Order EU: Nmc
Cat. Cost: Online only.
Credit Cards: All major credit/debit cards
Specialities: Hardy geraniums & ornamental grasses. Unusual & interesting perennials incl. shade/woodland. Some choice shrubs esp. *Caprifoliaceae*. Nat. Collection of *Molinia*.
Notes: Delivers to shows. Wheelchair accessible.
Map Ref: E, C3 **OS Grid Ref:** TM041819

EPri **Priory Plants** ♿
1 Covey Cottages, Hintlesham, Nr Ipswich, Suffolk IP8 3NY
Ⓣ (01473) 652656
Ⓜ 07798 627618
Ⓕ (01473) 652656
Ⓔ sue.mann3@btinternet.com
Ⓦ www.prioryplants.co.uk
Contact: Sue Mann

E

Opening Times: By appt. only. Please ring first to avoid disappointment.
Min Mail Order UK: £15.00 + p&p
Min Mail Order EU: £25.00
Cat. Cost: Online only.
Credit Cards: None
Specialities: Cottage garden perennials, as well as increasing range of South African plants. *Agapanthus*, *Astrantia*, *Dierama*, *Dietes*, *Geum*, Siberian *Iris*, *Kniphofia*, *Nerine*, *Papaver*, *Tritonia*, *Tulbaghia* & *Watsonia*.
Notes: Sells at plant fairs & agricultural shows. Also sells wholesale. Delivers to shows. Wheelchair accessible.
Map Ref: E, C3 **OS Grid Ref:** TM070448

EPts **POTASH NURSERY** ♿
Cow Green, Bacton, Stowmarket, Suffolk IP14 4HJ
Ⓣ (01449) 781671
Ⓔ enquiries@potashnursery.co.uk
Ⓦ www.potashnursery.co.uk
Contact: M W Clare
Opening Times: Pre-ordered plants can be collected by appt. only.
Min Mail Order UK: £18.00
Cat. Cost: 4 × 1st class.
Credit Cards: Visa, Delta, MasterCard
Specialities: *Fuchsia*.
Notes: Delivers to shows. Wheelchair accessible.
Map Ref: E, C3 **OS Grid Ref:** TM0565NE

EPyc **PENNYCROSS PLANTS**
Earith Road, Colne, Huntingdon, Cambridgeshire PE28 3NL
Ⓣ (01487) 841520
Ⓔ salvias@pennycrossplants.co.uk
Ⓦ www.pennycrossplants.co.uk
Contact: Janet M Buist
Opening Times: 1000-1600 Mon-Fri, 1st Apr-31st Jul. Sep by appt.
Min Mail Order UK: Nmc
Cat. Cost: 1 × 2nd class for *Salvia* list only.
Credit Cards: None
Specialities: Hardy perennials. Salvias. Some plants available in limited quantities only. Will propagate salvias to order.
Notes: Mail order for young *Salvia* plants only. Delivers to shows.
Map Ref: E, C2 **OS Grid Ref:** TL378759

ERCP **ROSE COTTAGE PLANTS**
Bay Tree Farm, Epping Green, Essex CM16 6PU
Ⓣ (01992) 573775
Ⓕ (01992) 561198
Ⓔ anne@rosecottageplants.co.uk
Ⓦ www.rosecottageplants.co.uk
Contact: Anne & Jack Barnard
Opening Times: By appt. & for special events (see website for details).
Min Mail Order UK: Nmc
Min Mail Order EU: £20.00
Cat. Cost: Online only.
Credit Cards: All major credit/debit cards
Specialities: Bulbs.
Notes: Mail order, bulbs only. Delivers to shows.
Map Ref: E, B1 **OS Grid Ref:** TL435053

ERea **READS NURSERY**
Douglas Farm, Bungay, Suffolk NR35 2JG
Ⓣ (01986) 895555
Ⓔ plants@readsnursery.co.uk
Ⓦ www.readsnursery.co.uk
Contact: Stephen Read
Opening Times: Not open. Mail order only.
Min Mail Order UK: Nmc
Min Mail Order EU: Nmc
Cat. Cost: Free.
Credit Cards: All major credit/debit cards
Specialities: Ornamental & unusual fruit trees. Soft fruit. *Magnolia*.

ERod **THE RODINGS PLANTERY** ♿
Anchor Lane, Abbess Roding, Essex CM5 0JW
Ⓣ (01279) 876421
Ⓜ 07790 020940
Ⓔ janeandandy@therodingsplantery.co.uk
Ⓦ www.therodingsplantery.co.uk
Contact: Jane & Andy Mogridge
Opening Times: 1000-1600 Wed & Sat. By appt. only. Occasional open days, please phone for details.
Min Mail Order UK: Nmc
Min Mail Order EU: £500.00 + p&p
Cat. Cost: 3 × 1st class.
Credit Cards: None
Specialities: Bamboos. Rare & unusual trees.
Notes: Delivers to shows. Euro accepted. Wheelchair accessible.
Map Ref: E, D2

ESem **SEMPS BY POST**
28 Mill Road, Newbourne, Woodbridge, Suffolk IP12 4NP
Ⓣ (01473) 736440
Ⓔ Tricia@sempsbypost.co.uk
Ⓦ www.sempsbypost.co.uk
Contact: Tricia Newell
Opening Times: Not open.
Min Mail Order UK: Nmc
Min Mail Order EU: Nmc
Cat. Cost: Online only.
Credit Cards: Paypal
Specialities: *Sempervivum*. Some stock available in small quantities.

ESgl **Seagate Irises** ♿
A17 Long Sutton By-Pass, Long Sutton, Lincolnshire PE12 9RX
Ⓣ (01406) 365138
Ⓜ 07887 856389
Ⓔ sales@irises.co.uk
Ⓦ www.irises.co.uk
Contact: Julian Browse or Wendy Browse
Opening Times: 1000-1700 daily Apr-mid Jul. Please phone for appt. mid-Jul to Mar.
Min Mail Order UK: Nmc
Min Mail Order EU: Nmc. Carriage at cost.
Cat. Cost: £3.50 or € 8.00.
Credit Cards: Maestro, Visa, MasterCard
Specialities: Different types of *Iris*, bearded, beardless & species hybrids with about 1000 varieties in all, both historic & modern. Some only available in small quantities. Many container-grown available to callers.
Notes: Exports beyond EU. Euro accepted. Wheelchair accessible.
Map Ref: E, B1 **OS Grid Ref:** TF437218

EShb **Shrubland Park Nurseries**
Maltings Farm, Whatfield Road, Elmsett, Ipswich, Suffolk IP7 6LZ
Ⓣ (01473) 657012
Ⓜ 07890 527744
Ⓔ gill@shrublandparknurseries.co.uk
Ⓦ www.shrublandparknurseries.co.uk
Contact: Gill & Catherine Stitt
Opening Times: 1000-1500 Fri, Sat & Sun, Jan, Feb, Nov & 1st-24th Dec. 1000-1600 daily, 1st Mar-30th Oct. Closed 27th-31st May for Suffolk Show.
Min Mail Order UK: Nmc
Min Mail Order EU: Nmc
Cat. Cost: 6 × 2nd class or free by email.
Credit Cards: All major credit/debit cards, Paypal
Specialities: Conservatory plants, succulents, hardy perennials, climbers, shrubs, ferns & grasses.
Notes: Delivers to shows.
Map Ref: E, C3 **OS Grid Ref:** TM052466

EStr **Strictly Daylilies** ◆
2 Primes Corner, Histon, Cambridgeshire CB24 9AG
Ⓣ (01223) 236239
Ⓜ 07765 236880
Ⓔ info@strictlydaylilies.com
Ⓦ www.strictlydaylilies.com
Contact: Paula & Chris Dyason
Opening Times: Mail order only. Open by appt.
Min Mail Order UK: Nmc
Cat. Cost: No charge.
Credit Cards: All major credit/debit cards
Specialities: *Hemerocallis*. Some stock available in small quantities only.
Notes: Delivers to shows.
Map Ref: E, C2

ESty **Style Roses** ♿
10 Meridian Walk, Holbeach, Spalding, Lincolnshire PE12 7NR
Ⓣ (01406) 424089
Ⓜ 07760 626750 or 07780 860415
Ⓕ (01406) 490006
Ⓔ mail@styleroses.co.uk
Ⓦ www.styleroses.co.uk
Contact: Margaret Styles
Opening Times: Vary. Nursery address is different from office, so please make an appt. before visiting.
Min Mail Order UK: Nmc
Min Mail Order EU: Nmc
Cat. Cost: Free in UK.
Credit Cards: MasterCard, Visa, Maestro
Specialities: Standard & bush roses.
Notes: Export to EU during bare-root season Nov-Mar. Also sells wholesale. Exports beyond EU. Delivers to shows. Wheelchair accessible.
Map Ref: E, B1

ESwi **Swines Meadow Farm Nursery** ♿ ◆
47 Towngate East, Market Deeping, Peterborough PE6 8LQ
Ⓣ 01778 343340
Ⓜ 07432 627766
Ⓔ ceveandsons@btconnect.com
Ⓦ www.swinesmeadowfarmnursery.co.uk
Contact: Colin Ward
Opening Times: 0900-1700 Mon-Sat, 1000-1600 Sun (summer); 0900-1600 Mon-Sat, 1000-1600 Sun (winter).
Min Mail Order UK: £10.00
Min Mail Order EU: £10.00
Credit Cards: All, except American Express
Specialities: Hardy exotics, tree ferns, bamboos & phormiums. Wollemi pine stockist. Many specialities available in small quantities only.
Notes: Delivers to shows. Euro accepted. Wheelchair accessible.
Map Ref: E, B1 **OS Grid Ref:** TF150113

EThi **Thistlefield Plants and Design**
65 Westgate Street, Shouldham, Kings Lynn, Norfolk PE33 0BL
Ⓣ (01366) 347365
Ⓜ 07899 994071
Ⓕ (01366) 347365
Ⓔ paul@thistlefieldplants.co.uk
Ⓦ www.thistlefieldplants.co.uk
Contact: Paul Welford
Opening Times: Not open. Sells at plant fairs & shows only.

Min Mail Order UK: Nmc
Cat. Cost: Online only.
Credit Cards: None
Specialities: Perennials. *Tricyrtis* available in small quantities only.
Notes: Delivers to shows.

E

ETwe **Twenty Pence Garden Centre** ♿
Twenty Pence Road, Wilburton, Nr Ely, Cambridgeshire CB6 3RN
Ⓣ (01353) 741024
Ⓕ (01353) 749163
Ⓔ sales@twentypence.co.uk
Ⓦ twentypence.co.uk
Contact: John Pierrepont
Opening Times: 0900-1700 Mon-Sat, 1030-1630 Sun.
Credit Cards: All major credit/debit cards
Specialities: Unusual plants.
Notes: Wheelchair accessible.
Map Ref: E, C2 **OS Grid Ref:** TL482744

EUJe **Urban Jungle**
Ringland Lane, Old Costessey, Norwich, Norfolk NR8 5BG
Ⓣ (01603) 744997
Ⓕ (0709) 2366869
Ⓔ lizzy@urbanjungle.uk.com
Ⓦ www.urbanjungle.uk.com
Contact: Elizabeth Browne
Opening Times: 1000-1700 1st Feb-31st Oct 7 days incl B/hols. 1000-1600 Nov-Dec Thu, Fri, Sat, Sun. Closed Jan.
Min Mail Order UK: Nmc
Min Mail Order EU: Nmc
Credit Cards: All major credit/debit cards
Specialities: Wide range of choice plants from exotic bedding to hardy evergreens.
Notes: Display gardens & living walls. Delivers to shows. Limited wheelchair access.
Map Ref: E, B3 **OS Grid Ref:** TG153127

EVic **Victorian Violas**
85 Fulmar Road, Lincoln, Lincolnshire LN6 0RX
Ⓣ (01522) 686343
Ⓔ victorianviolasinfo@fsmail.net
Ⓦ www.victorianviolas.co.uk
Contact: Robert Chapman
Opening Times: Not open.
Min Mail Order UK: Nmc
Specialities: Hardy perennial violas.

EWay **Wayside Aquatics**
Blackmore Road, Doddinghurst, Brentwood, Essex CM15 0HU
Ⓣ (01277) 823603
Ⓔ sales@waysideaquatics.co.uk
Ⓦ www.waysideaquatics.co.uk
Contact: Anna Robinson
Opening Times: 1000-1700 Wed-Sun.
Min Mail Order UK: Nmc
Min Mail Order EU: Nmc
Cat. Cost: Online.
Credit Cards: All major credit/debit cards
Specialities: Range of water garden plants: waterlilies; floating plants; oxygenating plants; marginals; marsh plants. Some stock in small quantities.
Map Ref: E, D2 **OS Grid Ref:** TQ585995

EWes **West Acre Gardens** ♿
Tumbleyhill Road, West Acre, King's Lynn, Norfolk PE32 1UJ
Ⓣ (01760) 755562
Ⓔ info@westacregardens.co.uk
Ⓦ www.westacregardens.co.uk
Contact: J J Tuite
Opening Times: 1000-1700 7 days 1st Feb-30th Nov. Other times by appt.
Cat. Cost: None issued.
Credit Cards: Visa, MasterCard, Delta, Switch
Specialities: Very wide selection of herbaceous & other garden plants incl. *Rhodohypoxis* & *Primula auricula*.
Notes: Delivers to shows. Wheelchair accessible.
Map Ref: E, B1 **OS Grid Ref:** TF792182

EWld **Woodlands**
Peppin Lane, Fotherby, Louth, Lincolnshire LN11 0UW
Ⓣ (01507) 603586
Ⓔ annbobarmstrong@btinternet.com
Ⓦ www.woodlandsplants.co.uk
Contact: Ann Armstrong
Opening Times: Flexible, but please phone or email to avoid disappointment.
Min Mail Order UK: Nmc
Min Mail Order EU: Nmc
Cat. Cost: None issued.
Credit Cards: None
Specialities: Small but interesting range of unusual plants, esp. woodland, *Codonopsis* and *Salvia*, all grown on the nursery in limited quantity.
Notes: Mature garden, art gallery & refreshments.
Map Ref: E, A2 **OS Grid Ref:** TF322918

EWll **The Walled Garden** ♿
Park Road, Benhall, Saxmundham, Suffolk IP17 1JB
Ⓣ (01728) 602510
Ⓕ (01728) 602510
Ⓔ sales@thewalledgarden.co.uk
Ⓦ www.thewalledgarden.co.uk
Contact: Jim Mountain
Opening Times: 0930-1700 Tue-Sun Mar-

Nov, 0930-dusk Tue-Sat Nov-mid Feb.
Specialities: Tender & hardy perennials. For current information see website.
Notes: Wheelchair accessible.
Map Ref: E, C3 **OS Grid Ref:** TM371613

EWoo **Woottens Plants** ♿
Wenhaston, Blackheath, Halesworth, Suffolk
IP19 9HD
Ⓣ (01502) 478258
Ⓕ (01502) 478888
Ⓔ info@woottensplants.co.uk
Ⓦ www.woottensplants.co.uk
Contact: Elizabeth Loftus
Opening Times: 0930-1700 7 days.
Min Mail Order UK: Nmc
Min Mail Order EU: Nmc
Cat. Cost: Online only.
Credit Cards: All, except American Express
Specialities: *Pelargonium, Hemerocallis, Primula auricula, Iris, Chrysanthemum* & *Clivia.*
Notes: Also sells wholesale. Wheelchair accessible.
Map Ref: E, C3 **OS Grid Ref:** TM426749

EWTr **Walnut Tree Garden Nursery**
Flymoor Lane, Rocklands, Attleborough, Norfolk NR17 1BP
Ⓣ (01953) 488163
Ⓔ info@wtgn.co.uk
Ⓦ www.wtgn.co.uk
Contact: Jim Paine & Clare Billington
Opening Times: 0900-1800 Tue-Sun Feb-Nov & B/hols.
Min Mail Order UK: Nmc
Cat. Cost: Online.
Credit Cards: All major credit/debit cards
Map Ref: E, B1 **OS Grid Ref:** TL978973

Scotland

GAbr **Abriachan Nurseries** ♿
Loch Ness Side, Inverness, Inverness-shire
IV3 8LA
Ⓣ (01463) 861232
Ⓔ info@lochnessgarden.com
Ⓦ www.lochnessgarden.com
Contact: Mr & Mrs D Davidson
Opening Times: 0900-1900 daily (dusk if earlier) Feb-Nov.
Min Mail Order UK: Nmc
Cat. Cost: 4 × 1st class.
Credit Cards: All major credit/debit cards
Specialities: Herbaceous perennials, old-fashioned *Primula, Helianthemum*, hardy geraniums, *Sempervivum* & *Primula auricula.*
Notes: Delivers to shows. Wheelchair access to nursery only.
Map Ref: G, B2 **OS Grid Ref:** NH571347

GAgs **Angusplants** ♿
3 Balfour Cottages, Menmuir,
By Brechin, Angus
DD9 7RN
Ⓣ (01356) 660280
Ⓜ 07972 026109
Ⓔ alison@angusplants.co.uk
Ⓦ www.angusplants.co.uk
Contact: Dr Alison S. Goldie & Mark A. Hutson
Opening Times: By appt. only. Please phone first.
Min Mail Order UK: Nmc
Min Mail Order EU: Nmc
Cat. Cost: 2 × 2nd large letter stamps.
Credit Cards: None
Specialities: Predominantly *Primula auricula*, although other *Primula* species are offered. A few available in small quantities only.
Notes: Mail order available all year. Wheelchair accessible.
Map Ref: G, B3 **OS Grid Ref:** NO528643

GBBs **Border Belles** ♿
Old Branxton Cottages,
Innerwick, Nr Dunbar, East Lothian
EH42 1QT
Ⓣ (01368) 840325
Ⓔ mail@borderbelles.com
Ⓦ www.borderbelles.com
Contact: Gillian Moynihan
Opening Times: Open by appt. only.
Min Mail Order UK: Nmc
Cat. Cost: Online only.
Credit Cards: All major credit/debit cards
Specialities: Hardy perennials & woodland plants.
Notes: Also sells wholesale. Wheelchair accessible.
Map Ref: G, C3

GBee **Beeches Cottage Nursery** ♿
High Boreland, Lesmahagow,
South Lanarkshire
ML11 9PY
Ⓣ (01555) 893369
Ⓜ 07930 343131
Ⓔ thebeeches.nursery@talktalk.net
Ⓦ www.beechescottage.co.uk
Contact: Margaret Harrison, Steven Harrison
Opening Times: 1000-1630 7 days incl. Apr-end Jun. 1000-1630 Wed-Sat, Jul-end Sep.
Cat. Cost: None issued.
Credit Cards: None
Specialities: Traditional & unusual hardy cottage garden perennials which can be seen growing in display gardens at 850ft. Some plants available in small quantities only. Hanging basket specialists. Cottage gardens designed and planted.

Notes: Also sells wholesale. Wheelchair access to nursery only.
Map Ref: G, C2 **OS Grid Ref:** NS837403

GBin **Binny Plants** ♿
West Lodge, Binny Estate, Ecclesmachan Road, Nr Broxbourn, West Lothian EH52 6NL
Ⓣ (01506) 858931
Ⓜ 07753 626117
Ⓔ contact@binnyplants.com
Ⓦ www.binnyplants.com
Contact: Billy Carruthers
Opening Times: 1000-1700 7 days. Closed mid-Dec to mid-Jan.
Min Mail Order UK: £25.00
Min Mail Order EU: £25.00
Cat. Cost: £2.50 refundable on ordering.
Credit Cards: Visa, MasterCard, EuroCard, Maestro
Specialities: Perennials incl. *Astilbe, Geranium, Hosta, Paeonia* & *Iris.* Plus large selection of grasses & ferns.
Notes: Mail order Sep-Apr only. Also sells wholesale. Euro accepted. Wheelchair accessible.
Map Ref: G, C3 **OS Grid Ref:** NT050732

GBuc **Buckland Plants** ♿
Whinnieliggate, Kirkcudbright, Kirkcudbrightshire DG6 4XP
Ⓣ (01557) 331323
Ⓕ (01557) 331323
Ⓔ via website
Ⓦ www.bucklandplants.co.uk
Contact: Rob Asbridge
Opening Times: 1000-1700 Thu-Sun 1st Mar-1st Nov & B/hols.
Min Mail Order UK: £20.00 + p&p
Min Mail Order EU: Nmc
Cat. Cost: 3 × 1st class.
Credit Cards: All major credit/debit cards
Specialities: A very wide range of scarce herbaceous, woodland plants & larger alpines incl. *Anemone, Cardamine, Erythronium, Helleborus, Lilium, Meconopsis, Nomocharis, Primula, Tricyrtis* & *Trillium.*
Notes: Euro accepted. Assisted wheelchair accessibility.
Map Ref: G, D2 **OS Grid Ref:** NX719524

GCal **Cally Gardens** ♿
Gatehouse of Fleet, Castle Douglas, Kirkcudbrightshire DG7 2DJ
Ⓣ (01557) 815029 recorded information only.
Ⓔ info@callygardens.co.uk
Ⓦ www.callygardens.co.uk
Contact: Michael Wickenden
Opening Times: 1000-1730 Sat-Sun, 1400-1730 Tue-Fri. Easter Sat-last Sun in Sept.
Min Mail Order UK: £15.00 + p&p
Cat. Cost: 3 × 1st class.
Credit Cards: None
Specialities: Unusual perennials & grasses. Some rare shrubs, climbers & conservatory plants. 3500 varieties growing in an 2.7 acre walled garden built in the 1760s.
Notes: Also sells wholesale. Wheelchair accessible.
Map Ref: G, D2 **OS Grid Ref:** NX604549

GCra **Craigieburn Garden** ♿
Craigieburn House, by Moffat, Dumfriesshire DG10 9LF
Ⓣ (01683) 221250
Ⓜ 07899 055114
Ⓔ ajmw1@aol.com
Ⓦ www.craigieburngarden.com
Contact: Janet & Andrew Wheatcroft
Opening Times: 1030-1800 daily, Easter-31st Oct. Other times by appt.
Specialities: *Meconopsis* plants for damp gardens, herbaceous perennials.
Notes: Wheelchair accessible.
Map Ref: G, D3

GCrg **Craigiehall Nursery**
Carnwath, Lanark, Lanarkshire ML11 8LH
Ⓣ 01555 840027 (answering machine)
Ⓕ 01555 840027
Ⓔ sales@craigiehallnursery.co.uk
Ⓦ www.craigiehallnursery.co.uk
Contact: Innes Hogg
Opening Times: Not open. Mail order only.
Min Mail Order UK: Nmc
Cat. Cost: Online only.
Credit Cards: All major credit/debit cards
Specialities: A very wide range of alpine and rock garden plants; over 500 different varieties on the nursery. Some are quite common, others much less so.

GCro **Croft 16 Daffodils**
16 Midtown of Inverasdale, Poolewe, Achnasheen, Ross-shire IV22 2LW
Ⓣ (01445) 781717
Ⓔ sales@croft16daffodils.co.uk
Ⓦ www.croft16daffodils.co.uk
Contact: Duncan & Kate Donald
Opening Times: Not open. Mail order only.
Min Mail Order UK: Nmc
Min Mail Order EU: Nmc
Cat. Cost: Online. Customers without internet access send 4 × 1st for sales list.
Credit Cards: Paypal
Specialities: Nat. Collection of Daffodils bred pre-1930. Some stocks only available in small quantities. A waiting list for *desiderata* is in operation.
Notes: Please order by Jul if possible as limited availability. Orders unfulfilled in one season

will take priority the following year. Customers outside the EU should contact nursery.
Map Ref: G, A1 **OS Grid Ref:** NG822851

GDun **Dunskey Gardens & Maze** ♿
Portpatrick, Stranraer, Wigtownshire
DG9 8TJ
Ⓣ (01776) 810905
Ⓜ 07899 092070
Ⓕ (01776) 810581
Ⓔ gabygardeners@btinternet.com
Ⓦ www.dunskey.com
Contact: Gabrielle Reynolds
Opening Times: 1000-1600 w/ends only Feb, 1000-1700 daily Easter-Oct. See website for details.
Credit Cards: All major credit/debit cards
Specialities: Broad range, propagated from the gardens, incl. bulbs, tender perennials, herbaceous, trees and shrubs. Available in small quantities only. Provisional Nat. Collections of *Clianthus* & *Sutherlandia*.
Notes: Dunskey Estate Walled Garden & Maze open to the public. Sells at local plant shows. Wheelchair accessible.
Map Ref: G, D2 **OS Grid Ref:** NX004560

GEdr **Edrom Nurseries**
Coldingham, Eyemouth, Berwickshire
TD14 5TZ
Ⓣ (01890) 771386
Ⓕ (01890) 771387
Ⓔ info@edrom-nurseries.co.uk
Ⓦ www.edrom-nurseries.co.uk
Contact: Mr Terry Hunt
Opening Times: 0900-1700 Thu, Fri, Sat & Mon (closed Tue & Wed), 1000-1600 Sun.
Min Mail Order UK: Nmc
Min Mail Order EU: Nmc
Cat. Cost: Free.
Credit Cards: All major credit/debit cards
Specialities: *Cypripedium*, *Epimedium*, *Gentiana*, *Primula*, *Meconopsis*, *Rhodohypoxis*, *Trillium* & Japanese *Hepatica*.
Notes: Delivers to shows.
Map Ref: G, C3 **OS Grid Ref:** NT873663

GFai **Fairholm Plants**
Fairholm, Larkhall, Lanarkshire
ML9 2UQ
Ⓣ (01698) 881671
Ⓕ (01698) 888135
Ⓔ fairholm.plants@stevenson-hamilton.co.uk
Contact: Mrs J M Hamilton
Opening Times: Apr-Oct by appt.
Min Mail Order UK: Nmc
Cat. Cost: 1 × 2nd class for descriptive list.
Credit Cards: None
Specialities: *Abutilon* & unusual half-hardy perennials esp. South African. Nat. Collection of *Abutilon* cvs. Plants & rooted cuttings available in small quantities only.
Notes: Mail order for young/small plants. Euro accepted.
Map Ref: G, C2 **OS Grid Ref:** NS754515

GGal **Galloway Plants** ♿
Claymoddie, Whithorn, Newton Stewart, Dumfries & Galloway DG8 8LX
Ⓣ (01988) 500422
Ⓔ gallowayplants@aol.com
Ⓦ www.gallowayplants.co.uk
Contact: Robin & Mary Nicholson
Opening Times: 1400-1700 Fri, Sat & Sun, Apr-Sep, other times by prior appt.
Min Mail Order UK: £50.00 + p&p
Cat. Cost: 2 × 1st class.
Credit Cards: None
Specialities: Southern hemisphere plants. *Hydrangea*. Available in small quantities only.
Notes: Also sells wholesale. Wheelchair accessible.
Map Ref: G, D2 **OS Grid Ref:** NX450377

GGGa **Glendoick Gardens Ltd** ♿
Glendoick, Perth, Perthshire PH2 7NS
Ⓣ (01738) 860205
Ⓕ (01738) 860630
Ⓔ orders@glendoick.com
Ⓦ www.glendoick.com
Contact: Kenneth Cox
Opening Times: Nursery not open to the public. Garden centre open 0900-1730 (summer), 0900-1700 (winter) 7 days. Gardens open Apr & May, details on website.
Min Mail Order UK: £40.00
Min Mail Order EU: £100.00
Cat. Cost: £1.00.
Credit Cards: All, except American Express
Specialities: Rhododendrons, azaleas and ericaceous, *Primula* & *Meconopsis*. Plants from wild seed. Many catalogue plants available at garden centre. 3 Nat. Collections.
Notes: Exports beyond EU. Wheelchair access to garden centre.
Map Ref: G, C3

GJos **Jo's Garden Enterprise** ♿
Easter Balmungle Farm, Eathie Road, by Rosemarkie, Ross-shire IV10 8SL
Ⓣ (01381) 621006
Ⓔ jos_garden_enterprise@hotmail.co.uk
Contact: Joanna Chance
Opening Times: 1000 to dusk, 7 days.
Cat. Cost: None.
Credit Cards: None
Specialities: Alpines & herbaceous perennials. Selection of native wild flowers.
Notes: Wheelchair accessible.
Map Ref: G, B2 **OS Grid Ref:** NH600742

G

G

GKev **Kevock Garden Plants**
Kevock Road, Lasswade, Midlothian EH18 1HT
Ⓣ 0131 454 0660
Ⓜ 07811 321585
Ⓕ 0131 454 0660
Ⓔ info@kevockgarden.co.uk
Ⓦ www.kevockgarden.co.uk
Contact: Stella Rankin
Opening Times: Not open. Mail order & plant stalls only.
Min Mail Order UK: £25.00
Min Mail Order EU: £25.00
Cat. Cost: 3 × 1st class.
Credit Cards: Visa, MasterCard, Switch
Specialities: Chinese & Himalayan plants. *Androsace, Daphne, Paeonia, Primula, Meconopsis, Iris,* woodland plants, alpines, rock, marginal, bog & bulbs.
Notes: Also sells wholesale. Delivers to shows. Euro accepted.

GKin **Kinlochlaich Garden Plant Centre**
Appin, Argyll PA38 4BB
Ⓣ (01631) 730342
Ⓜ 07881 525754
Ⓔ fiona@kinlochlaich.plus.com
Ⓦ www.kinlochlaichgardencentre.co.uk
Contact: Fiona Hutchison
Opening Times: 0900-1730, 7 days.
Cat. Cost: None issued
Credit Cards: All major credit/debit cards
Specialities: Hardy shrubs, trees, azaleas, perennials. Also Gulf Stream plants such as *Tropaeolum, Embothrium, Eucryphia, Drymis* & more. Good selection of hardy seaside plants.
Notes: Do not offer mail order but will post where possible.
Map Ref: G, C2

GLin **Linn Botanic Gardens** ♿
Cove, Helensburgh, Dunbartonshire G84 0NR
Ⓣ (01436) 842084
Ⓜ 07747 416342
Ⓔ jamie@linnbotanicgardens.org.uk
Ⓦ www.linnbotanicgardens.org.uk
Contact: Jamie Taggart
Opening Times: 1100-1700, 7 days.
Min Mail Order UK: £30.00 + carriage.
Cat. Cost: 4 × 1st class or by email.
Credit Cards: None
Specialities: Small plant sales area offering diverse range of plants grown in connection with Linn Botanic Gardens. Botanic Gardens open (charges apply).
Notes: Euro accepted. Wheelchair accessible for plant sales area but not gardens.
Map Ref: G, C2 **OS Grid Ref:** NS223827

GLog **Logie Steading Plants** ♿
Forres, Moray IV36 2QN
Ⓣ (01309) 611222 or 611278
Ⓕ (01309) 611300
Ⓔ panny@logie.co.uk
Ⓦ www.logie.co.uk
Contact: Mrs Panny Laing
Opening Times: 1030-1700 hours, 7 days, April-end Oct.
Credit Cards: All major credit/debit cards
Specialities: Unusual hardy plants, grown in Scotland for Scottish gardens. Large range of hardy geraniums, bold herbaceous plants, grasses & marginal plants.
Notes: Logie House Garden open every day. Café, farm shop, art gallery, secondhand books, antiques, river walk, heritage centre. Wheelchair accessible.
Map Ref: G, B2 **OS Grid Ref:** NJ006504

GMaP **Macplants** ♿
Berrybank Nursery, 5 Boggs Holdings, Pencaitland, East Lothian EH34 5BA
Ⓣ (01875) 341179
Ⓕ (01875) 340842
Ⓔ sales@macplants.co.uk
Ⓦ www.macplants.co.uk
Contact: Gavin McNaughton
Opening Times: 1030-1700, 7 days, Mar-end Sep.
Min Mail Order UK: Nmc
Cat. Cost: 4 × 2nd class.
Credit Cards: MasterCard, Switch, Visa
Specialities: Herbaceous perennials, alpines, hardy ferns, violas & grasses. *Meconopsis.* National Collection of *Sanguisorba.*
Notes: Also sells wholesale. Delivers to shows. Wheelchair accessible.
Map Ref: G, C3 **OS Grid Ref:** NT447703

GPoy **Poyntzfield Herb Nursery** ♿
Nr Balblair, Black Isle, Dingwall, Ross-shire IV7 8LX
Ⓣ (01381) 610352. Phone between 1200-1300 & 1800-1900 Mon-Sat only.
Ⓕ (01381) 610352
Ⓔ info@poyntzfieldherbs.co.uk
Ⓦ www.poyntzfieldherbs.co.uk
Contact: Duncan Ross
Opening Times: 1300-1700 Mon-Sat 1st Mar-30th Sep, 1300-1700 Sun May-Aug.
Min Mail Order UK: £10.00 + p&p
Min Mail Order EU: £20.00 + p&p
Cat. Cost: 4 × 1st class.
Credit Cards: All major credit/debit cards
Specialities: Over 400 popular, unusual & rare herbs esp. medicinal. Also seeds.
Notes: Mail order operates almost all year round. Exports beyond EU. Wheelchair accessible.
Map Ref: G, B2 **OS Grid Ref:** NH711642

GPPs **POGS PENSTEMONS**
Orchard Villa, The Brae, Crocketford, Dumfriesshire DG2 8QE
Ⓣ (01556) 690504
Ⓜ 07905 825818
Ⓔ pogspenstemons@yahoo.co.uk
Ⓦ www.pogspenstemons.co.uk
Contact: Allison Fitz-Earle
Opening Times: Not open. Mail order only.
Min Mail Order UK: Nmc
Cat. Cost: Free.
Credit Cards: Paypal
Specialities: Penstemons.
Notes: Mail order plants available all year. Also sells wholesale.

GQue **QUERCUS GARDEN PLANTS** ♿
Rankeilour Gardens, Rankeilour Estate, by Springfield, Fife KY15 5RE
Ⓣ (01337) 810444
Ⓔ colin@quercus.uk.net
Ⓦ www.quercus.uk.net
Contact: Colin McBeath, Alyson Sinclair
Opening Times: 1000-1700 Wed-Sun, 1st w/end Apr-mid Oct. 1000-1500 Sat only, mid Oct-end Mar. Closed Xmas fortnight.
Cat. Cost: Free.
Credit Cards: All major credit/debit cards
Specialities: Easy & unusual plants for contemporary Scottish gardens.
Notes: Delivery service available on large orders at nursery's discretion. Wheelchair accessible.
Map Ref: G, C3 **OS Grid Ref:** NO330118

GQui **QUINISH GARDEN NURSERY**
Dervaig, Isle of Mull, Argyll PA75 6QL
Ⓣ (01688) 400344
Ⓕ (01688) 400344
Ⓔ quinishplants@aol.com
Ⓦ www.Q-gardens.org
Contact: Nicholas Reed
Opening Times: By appt. only.
Min Mail Order UK: Nmc
Min Mail Order EU: Nmc
Cat. Cost: 2 × 1st class.
Credit Cards: None
Specialities: Choice garden shrubs & conservatory plants.
Map Ref: G, C1

GSPN **SPRING PARK NURSERY**
Orchard Villa, The Brae, Crocketford, Dumfriesshire DG2 8QE
Ⓣ (01556) 690504
Ⓜ 07905 825818
Ⓔ julianfitzearle@aol.com
Ⓦ www.springparknursery.co.uk
Contact: Julian Fitz-Earle
Opening Times: Not open. Mail order only.
Min Mail Order UK: Nmc
Cat. Cost: Free.
Credit Cards: Paypal
Specialities: Heathers.
Notes: Mail order plants available all year. Also sells wholesale.

GTwd **TWEED VALLEY FRUIT TREES**
Tighnuilt House, Innerleithen, Peeblesshire EH44 6RD
Ⓣ (01896) 831147
Ⓜ 07885 105813
Ⓔ info@tweedvalleyfruittrees.co.uk
Ⓦ www.tweedvalleyfruittrees.co.uk
Contact: Nick Edwardson
Opening Times: Not open. Visits may be possible by prior arrangement only.
Min Mail Order UK: Nmc
Cat. Cost: Online or phone for information.
Specialities: Wide selection of apple, pear and plum trees on a range of different rootstocks, focussing on varieties considered especially suitable for the whole UK and the heritage Scottish varieties in particular.
Notes: Also sells wholesale.

GTwe **J TWEEDIE FRUIT TREES**
Maryfield Road Nursery, Nr Terregles, Dumfriesshire DG2 9TH
Ⓣ (01387) 720880
Contact: John Tweedie
Opening Times: Please ring for times. Collections by appt.
Min Mail Order UK: Nmc
Cat. Cost: Sae
Credit Cards: None
Specialities: Fruit trees & bushes. A wide range of old & new varieties.
Map Ref: G, D2

N. IRELAND & REPUBLIC

IArd **ARDCARNE GARDEN CENTRE** ♿
Ardcarne, Boyle, Co. Roscommon, Republic of Ireland
Ⓣ (353) 7196 67091
Ⓕ (353) 7196 67341
Ⓔ ardcarne@indigo.ie
Ⓦ www.ardcarneplantsplus.ie
Contact: James Wickham, Mary Frances Dwyer, Kirsty Ainge
Opening Times: 0900-1800 Mon-Sat, 1300-1800 Sun & B/hols.
Credit Cards: Access, Visa, American Express
Specialities: Native & unusual trees, perennials, roses, plants for coastal areas, fruit trees & vegetable plants, specimen plants & semi-mature trees. Wide general range.
Notes: Euro accepted. Wheelchair accessible.
Map Ref: I, B1

IBal **BALI-HAI MAIL ORDER NURSERY**
42 Largy Road, Carnlough, Ballymena, Co. Antrim, N. Ireland BT44 0EZ
Ⓣ 028 2888 5289
Ⓜ 07708 257164
Ⓕ 028 2888 5289
Ⓔ balihainursery@btinternet.com
Ⓦ www.mailorderplants4me.com
Contact: Mrs M E Scroggy
Opening Times: Mon-Sat by appt. only.
Min Mail Order UK: Nmc
Min Mail Order EU: Nmc
Cat. Cost: Online only.
Credit Cards: All major credit/debit cards
Specialities: Nat. Collection of *Hosta*, part planted in 1.5 acres, open to the public by appt. *Agapanthus*, *Crocosmia*, *Rhodohypoxis*, tree ferns & other perennials. Hostas grown to order.
Notes: Also sells wholesale. Exports beyond EU restricted to bare-root perennials, no grasses. Euro accepted.
Map Ref: I, A3 **OS Grid Ref:** D287184

IBlr **BALLYROGAN NURSERIES** ♿
The Grange, Ballyrogan, Newtownards, Co. Down, N. Ireland BT23 4SD
Ⓣ 028 9181 0451 (evenings)
Ⓔ gary.dunlop@btinternet.com
Contact: Gary Dunlop
Opening Times: Only open by appt.
Min Mail Order UK: £10.00 + p&p
Min Mail Order EU: £20.00 + p&p
Cat. Cost: 2 × 1st class.
Credit Cards: None
Specialities: Choice herbaceous. *Agapanthus*, *Celmisia*, *Crocosmia*, *Rodgersia*, *Iris*, *Dierama*, *Erythronium* & *Roscoea*.
Notes: Also sells wholesale. Euro accepted. Wheelchair accessible.
Map Ref: I, B3

IBoy **BOYNE GARDEN CENTRE**
Ardcalf, Slane, Co. Meath, Republic of Ireland
Ⓣ 00353 (0)419 824350
Ⓕ 00353 (0)419 824350
Ⓔ boynegardencentre@eircom.net
Ⓦ www.boynegardencentre.com
Contact: Aileen Muldoon Byrne
Opening Times: 0930-1800 Mon-Sat, 1400-1800 Sun, Mar-Sep. 0930-1800 B/hols. W/ends only Oct-Feb.
Credit Cards: All major credit/debit cards
Specialities: Hardy herbaceous perennials. David Austin roses. Trees, shrubs, climbers, grasses, bamboos & ferns.
Notes: Pre-ordered plants delivered to shows. Euro accepted.
Map Ref: I, B3

IDee **DEELISH GARDEN CENTRE**
Skibbereen, Co. Cork, Republic of Ireland
Ⓣ 00 (353) 28 21374
Ⓕ 00 (353) 28 21374
Ⓔ deel@eircom.net
Ⓦ www.deelish.ie
Contact: Bill & Rain Chase
Opening Times: 1000-1800 Mon-Sat, 1400-1800 Sun.
Min Mail Order EU: €50.00 (Ireland only).
Cat. Cost: Sae
Credit Cards: Visa, Access
Specialities: Unusual plants for the mild coastal climate of Ireland. Conservatory plants. Sole Irish agents for Chase Organic Seeds.
Notes: No mail order outside Ireland. Euro accepted.
Map Ref: I, D1

IDic **DICKSON NURSERIES LTD**
Milecross Road, Newtownards, Co. Down, N. Ireland BT23 4SS
Ⓣ 028 9181 2206
Ⓜ 07522 222161
Ⓕ 028 9181 3366
Ⓔ mail@dickson-roses.co.uk
Ⓦ www.dickson-roses.co.uk
Contact: Colin Dickson
Opening Times: 0800-1230 & 1300-1515 Mon-Thu. 0800-1230 Fri.
Min Mail Order UK: Nmc
Min Mail Order EU: £25.00 + p&p
Cat. Cost: Free
Credit Cards: None
Specialities: Roses esp. modern Dickson varieties. Limited selection, check website. Most varieties available in small quantities only.
Notes: Also sells wholesale. Glasshouses accessible for wheelchairs.
Map Ref: I, B3

IFoB **FIELD OF BLOOMS** ♿
Ballymackey, Lisnamoe, Nenagh, Co. Tipperary, Republic of Ireland
Ⓣ (353) 67 29974
Ⓜ (353) 8764 06044
Ⓔ guy2002@eircom.net
Ⓦ www.fieldofblooms.com
Contact: Guy de Schrijver
Opening Times: Strictly by appt.
Min Mail Order UK: Nmc
Min Mail Order EU: Nmc
Cat. Cost: Online only.
Credit Cards: None
Specialities: Hellebores, herbaceous, hardy perennials, ornamental grasses, woodland plants & some alpines.

Notes: Euro accepted. Wheelchair accessible.
Map Ref: I, C2

IFro **Frogswell Nursery**
Clooncoonlan, Straide, Foxford, Co. Mayo, Republic of Ireland
Ⓣ (353) 94 903 1420
Ⓜ (353) 8621 06166
Ⓔ frogswell@gmail.com
Ⓦ www.frogswell.ie
Contact: Celia Graebner
Opening Times: Feb-Oct by appt. Please phone first. Also Garden Open Days & occasional workshops; see website for details.
Cat. Cost: £2.50/€3.00 for plant list.
Credit Cards: None
Specialities: A small garden-based nursery specialising in shade & woodland plants incl. hybrid hellebores & hardy geraniums, plus unusual flowering perennial, bee & food plants for the Irish climate, all raised on site & without chemical inputs. Some in very small quantities.
Notes: Group visits & talks by arrangement. See website for location map. Euro accepted.
Map Ref: I, B1 **OS Grid Ref:** M2497

IGor **Gortkelly Castle Nursery**
Upperchurch, Thurles, Co. Tipperary, Republic of Ireland
Ⓣ (353) 504 54441
Ⓔ clarevbeumer@gmail.com
Contact: Clare Beumer
Opening Times: Mail order only. Not open to the public.
Min Mail Order UK: Nmc
Min Mail Order EU: Nmc
Cat. Cost: 5 × 1st class (UK), 5 × 55c (Rep. of Ireland).
Credit Cards: None
Specialities: Choice perennials. Cultivars of Irish origin. Alpines.
Notes: Euro accepted. Delivers to shows.
Map Ref: I, C2

IKil **Kilmurry Nursery** ♿
Gorey, Co. Wexford, Republic of Ireland
Ⓣ (353) 53 948 0223
Ⓜ (353) 8681 80623
Ⓕ (353) 53 948 0223
Ⓔ kilmurrynursery@eircom.net
Ⓦ www.kilmurrynursery.com
Contact: Paul & Orla Woods
Opening Times: 0900-1700 Mon-Fri, Mar-Sep. Wintertime by appt.
Min Mail Order UK: Nmc
Min Mail Order EU: Nmc
Cat. Cost: Online only.
Credit Cards: None
Specialities: Herbaceous perennials and grasses.
Notes: Tea rooms open during summer. Also sells wholesale. Delivers to shows. Euro accepted. Wheelchair accessible.
Map Ref: I, C3 **OS Grid Ref:** 3C

IMou **Mount Venus Nursery** ♿
The Walled Garden, Mutton Lane, Dublin 16, Republic of Ireland
Ⓣ 00353 (0)1 493 3813
Ⓜ 08632 18789
Ⓔ mountvenusnursery@gmail.com
Ⓦ www.mountvenusnursery.com
Contact: Oliver & Liat Schurmann
Opening Times: 1000-1800 Mon-Sat, Feb-Nov.
Min Mail Order UK: €20
Min Mail Order EU: €35
Credit Cards: All major credit/debit cards
Specialities: Specialist perennials. Grasses & bamboos. Unusual woodland plants.
Notes: Also sells wholesale. Euro accepted. Wheelchair accessible.
Map Ref: I, C3

IPen **Peninsula Primulas**
72 Ballyeasborough Road, Kircubbin, Co. Down, N. Ireland BT22 1AD
Ⓣ 028 4277 2193
Ⓜ 07714 465834
Ⓔ peninsula.primulas@btinternet.com
Ⓦ www.penprimulas.com
Contact: Philip Bankhead
Opening Times: Mail order only. Not open.
Min Mail Order UK: Nmc
Min Mail Order EU: Nmc
Cat. Cost: Free
Credit Cards: Paypal
Specialities: Extensive selection of *Primula* species, plus auriculas. Also *P. allionii* cvs and European hybrid alpines.
Notes: Also sells wholesale. Delivers to shows. Euro accepted.

IPot **The Potting Shed** ♿
Bolinaspick, Camolin, Enniscorthy, Co. Wexford, Republic of Ireland
Ⓣ (353) 5393 83629
Ⓔ susan@camolinpottingshed.com
Ⓦ www.camolinpottingshed.com
Contact: Susan Carrick
Opening Times: 1100-1800, Wed-Sat (incl.), Mar-Sep 2012. Other times by appt.
Min Mail Order UK: Nmc
Min Mail Order EU: Nmc
Cat. Cost: 3 × 1st class.
Credit Cards: MasterCard, Visa
Specialities: We grow a wide range of unusual, hard to find and new introductions of herbaceous perennials, ornamental grasses and *Clematis*,

many of which can be seen growing to their full potential in our many display beds.
Notes: Member of the Irish Specialist Nursery Assoc. (ISNA). Orders outside Ireland can only be delivered by courier, charges at cost. Delivers to shows. Euro accepted. Wheelchair accessible.
Map Ref: I, C3

IRhd **RINGHADDY DAFFODILS**
Ringhaddy Road, Killinchy, Co. Down, N. Ireland BT23 6TU
Ⓣ 028 9754 1007
Ⓜ 07762 337534
Ⓔ info@ringhaddy-daffodils.com
Ⓦ www.ringhaddy-daffodils.com
Contact: Nial Watson
Opening Times: Mail order only. Not open.
Min Mail Order UK: £20.00 + p&p
Min Mail Order EU: £50.00 + p&p
Cat. Cost: £3.00
Credit Cards: Paypal
Specialities: Daffodil bulbs, some varieties only available in small numbers.
Notes: Exports beyond EU. Euro accepted.

ISha **SHADY PLANTS** ♿
Coolbooa, Clashmore, Youghal, Co. Cork, Republic of Ireland
Ⓣ (353) 24 86998
Ⓜ (353) 08605 42171
Ⓔ mike@shadyplants.ie
Ⓦ www.shadyplants.net
Contact: Mike Keep
Opening Times: 1300-1700, Tue-Sat.
Min Mail Order UK: Nmc
Min Mail Order EU: Nmc
Credit Cards: Paypal
Specialities: Specialist fern nursery based near the south coast of Ireland.
Notes: Delivers to shows. Euro accepted. Wheelchair accessible.
Map Ref: I, D2 **OS Grid Ref:** 613,585

ISsi **SEASIDE NURSERY** ♿
Claddaghduff, Co. Galway, Republic of Ireland
Ⓣ (353) 95 44687
Ⓜ (353) 86 3391555
Ⓔ Tom@seasidenursery.biz
Ⓦ www.seasidenursery.biz
Contact: Tom Dyck
Opening Times: 1000-1700 Mon-Sat. Closed Sun.
Min Mail Order UK: Nmc
Min Mail Order EU: Nmc
Cat. Cost: € 3.50
Credit Cards: Visa, MasterCard
Specialities: Plants & hedging suitable for seaside locations. Rare plants originating from Australia & New Zealand esp. *Phormium, Astelia.*
Notes: Also sells wholesale. Euro accepted. Wheelchair accessible.

ITim **TIMPANY NURSERIES & GARDENS** ♿
77 Magheratimpany Road, Ballynahinch, Co. Down, N. Ireland BT24 8PA
Ⓣ 028 9756 2812
Ⓕ 028 9756 2812
Ⓔ s.tindall@btconnect.com
Ⓦ www.timpanynurseries.com
Contact: Susan Tindall
Opening Times: 1000-1730 Tue-Sat, Sun by appt.
Min Mail Order UK: Nmc
Min Mail Order EU: £40.00 + p&p
Cat. Cost: £2.00
Credit Cards: Visa, MasterCard
Specialities: *Celmisia, Androsace, Primula, Saxifraga, Dianthus, Meconopsis, Cassiope, Rhodohypoxis, Cyclamen* & *Primula auricula.*
Notes: Also sells wholesale. Delivers to shows. Wheelchair accessible.
Map Ref: I, B3

IVic **VICTORIA'S NURSERY & GARDEN**
Upper Kells, Kells, Cahirceveen, Co Kerry, Republic of Ireland
Ⓣ (353) 66 947 7605
Ⓜ (353) 879 111465
Ⓔ kellshouse@eircom.net
Contact: Victoria Vogel
Opening Times: 1000-1700 Wed-Sun all year except Xmas. Closed Mon & Tue, except B/hols & by arrangement.
Cat. Cost: None issued.
Credit Cards: None
Specialities: *Rhododendron*, azaleas, *Acer*, tree ferns, seaside & woodland plants, *Saxifraga fortunei* forms.
Notes: Drive along Ring of Kerry, at Kells follow signs to Kells Bay Garden towards Kells Beach, nursery to left after little bridge. Euro accepted.
Map Ref: I, D1

LONDON AREA

LAir **JUST AIRPLANTS**
272a Herndean Road, Caversham, Reading, Berkshire RG4 7QT
Ⓣ 0118 324 3949
Ⓕ 0118 324 3955
Ⓔ info@justairplants.com
Ⓦ www.justairplants.com
Contact: Gill Passman
Opening Times: Not open. Mail order only.
Specialities: Bromeliads. *Neoregelia, Tillandsia, Aechmea, Billbergia, Cryptanthus.*

Notes: Mail order only by phone or online shop. Plants can be ordered for collection at events across UK. Also sells wholesale. Delivers to shows.

LAll **Allwoods** ♿
Cuddington Way, Cheam, Surrey SM2 7JB
Ⓣ 020 8393 7616
Ⓔ info@allwoods.net
Ⓦ www.allwoods.net
Contact: David & Emma James
Opening Times: Office 0900-1630 Mon-Fri. Answer machine all other times. Nursery open to visitors Mar-Jun, check website for detailed opening times.
Min Mail Order UK: Nmc
Min Mail Order EU: Nmc
Cat. Cost: 2 × 1st class.
Credit Cards: Access, Visa, MasterCard, Switch, Maestro
Specialities: *Dianthus* incl. hardy border carnations, pinks, perpetual flowering & spray carnations, Malmaisons & *D. allwoodii*. Unusual & collectors' geraniums & *Pelargoniums*. *Fuchsia*, certain lavender varieties. Penstemons & other garden plants.
Notes: All listed varieties available as plugs but choice varies depending on time of year. Please phone before travelling to avoid disappointment and/or to ensure order is ready for collection. Also sells wholesale. Wheelchair accessible.
Map Ref: L, C3

LAma **Jacques Amand International Ltd** ♿
The Nurseries, 145 Clamp Hill, Stanmore, Middlesex HA7 3JS
Ⓣ (020) 8420 7110
Ⓕ (020) 8954 6784
Ⓔ bulbs@jacquesamand.co.uk
Ⓦ www.jacquesamand.com
Contact: John Amand & Stuart Chapman
Opening Times: 0900-1700 Mon-Fri, 1000-1600 Sat.
Min Mail Order UK: Nmc
Min Mail Order EU: Nmc
Cat. Cost: 1 × 1st class.
Credit Cards: All major credit/debit cards
Specialities: Rare and unusual species bulbs esp. *Arisaema*, *Trillium*, *Fritillaria*, tulips.
Notes: Also sells wholesale. Exports beyond EU. Delivers to shows. Euro accepted. Wheelchair accessible.
Map Ref: L, B3

LAst **Asterby & Chalkcroft Nursery** ♿
The Ridgeway, Blunham, Bedfordshire MK44 3PH
Ⓣ (01767) 640148
Ⓔ sales@asterbyplants.co.uk
Ⓦ www.asterbyplants.co.uk
Contact: Simon & Eva Aldridge
Opening Times: 1000-1700 7 days. Closed Xmas & Jan.
Min Mail Order UK: Nmc
Credit Cards: All major credit/debit cards
Specialities: Hardy shrubs, herbaceous & trees.
Notes: Please ring for mail order information. Wheelchair accessible.
Map Ref: L, A3 **OS Grid Ref:** TL151497

LAyl **Aylett Nurseries Ltd** ♿ ◆
North Orbital Road, St Albans, Hertfordshire AL2 1DH
Ⓣ (01727) 822255
Ⓕ (01727) 823024
Ⓔ info@aylettnurseries.co.uk
Ⓦ www.aylettnurseries.co.uk
Contact: Julie Aylett
Opening Times: 0830-1730 Mon-Fri, 0830-1700 Sat, 1030-1630 Sun.
Cat. Cost: Free.
Credit Cards: All major credit/debit cards
Specialities: *Dahlia*. 2-acre trial ground adjacent to garden centre.
Notes: Wheelchair accessible.
Map Ref: L, B3 **OS Grid Ref:** TL169049

LBee **Beechcroft Nursery** ♿
127 Reigate Road, Ewell, Surrey KT17 3DE
Ⓣ 0208 393 4265
Ⓕ 0208 393 4265
Ⓔ enquiries@beechcroft-nursery.co.uk
Ⓦ www.beechcroft-nursery.co.uk
Contact: C Kimber
Opening Times: 1000-1600 Mon-Sat, 1000-1400 Sun and B/hols. Closed Xmas-New Year week.
Cat. Cost: None issued.
Credit Cards: All major credit/debit cards
Specialities: Conifers.
Notes: Wheelchair accessible.
Map Ref: L, C3

LBMP **Blooming Marvellous Plants**
Korketts Farm, Aylesbury Road, Winslow, Buckinghamshire MK18 3JL
Ⓣ (01296) 714714
Ⓜ 07963 747305
Ⓔ alex@bmplants.co.uk
Ⓦ www.bmplants.co.uk
Contact: Alexia Ballance
Opening Times: 0900-1700 Tue-Sat & 1000-1600 Sun, 9th Feb-27th Oct 2013. Closed Mon (except B/hols). Nov-Jan by appt. only.
Credit Cards: All major credit/debit cards
Specialities: A wide range of unusual and familiar perennials, shrubs, grasses, ferns & bedding plants, most in more generous sizes

than usually found in nurseries. *Heuchera*, *Heucherella*, *Tiarella* & other shade-loving plants. Some more unusual plants available in small quantities only.
Notes: Located on the A413 just outside Winslow (heading in the Aylesbury direction). Delivers to shows. Partial wheelchair access.
Map Ref: L, A2 **OS Grid Ref:** SP777271

LBrs **BURSTOW NURSERIES & GARDEN CENTRE** ♿
Antlands Lane, Horley, Surrey RH6 9SR
Ⓣ (01293) 771942
Ⓕ (01293) 771942
Ⓔ enquiries@burstownurseries.co.uk
Ⓦ www.burstownurseries.co.uk
Contact: Chris Corke
Opening Times: 0900-1700 Mon-Sat, 0930-1600 Sun.
Credit Cards: All major credit/debit cards
Specialities: Roses & shrubs as well as a good range of herbaceous perennials & seasonal bedding plants.
Notes: Please note no mail order. Wheelchair accessible.
Map Ref: L, C4

LBuc **BUCKINGHAM NURSERIES** ♿ ◆
14 Tingewick Road, Buckingham MK18 4AE
Ⓣ (01280) 822133
Ⓕ (01280) 815491
Ⓔ enquiries@buckingham-nurseries.co.uk
Ⓦ www.buckingham-nurseries.co.uk
Contact: R J & P L Brown
Opening Times: 0830-1730 (1800 in summer) Mon-Sat, 1030-1630 Sun.
Min Mail Order UK: Nmc
Min Mail Order EU: Nmc
Cat. Cost: Free.
Credit Cards: Visa, MasterCard, Maestro
Specialities: Bare-rooted and container grown hedging. Fruit trees, soft fruit, trees, shrubs, herbaceous perennials, alpines, grasses & ferns.
Notes: Garden centre with restaurant. Also sells wholesale. Euro accepted. Wheelchair accessible.
Map Ref: L, A2 **OS Grid Ref:** SP675333

LCla **CLAY LANE NURSERY**
3 Clay Lane, South Nutfield, Nr Redhill, Surrey RH1 4EG
Ⓣ (01737) 823307
Ⓔ claylane.nursery@btinternet.com
Ⓦ www.claylane-fuchsias.co.uk
Contact: K W Belton
Opening Times: Variable opening times. Please phone before travelling.
Min Mail Order UK: £10.00
Cat. Cost: 3 × 2nd class.
Credit Cards: None
Specialities: *Fuchsia*. Many varieties in small quantities only.
Notes: Mail order by telephone pre-arangement only. Delivers to shows.
Map Ref: L, C4

LCtg **COTTAGE GARDEN NURSERY** ◆
127 Barnet Road, Arkley, Barnet, Hertfordshire EN5 3JX
Ⓣ (020) 8441 8829
Ⓕ (020) 8531 3178
Ⓔ nurseryinfo@cottagegardennursery-barnet.co.uk
Ⓦ www.cottagegardennursery-barnet.co.uk
Contact: David and Wendy Spicer
Opening Times: 0930-1700 Tue-Sat Mar-Oct, 0930-1600 Tue-Sat Nov-Feb, 1000-1600 Sun & B/hol Mon all year.
Cat. Cost: None issued.
Credit Cards: All major credit/debit cards
Specialities: General range of hardy shrubs, trees, fruit trees & bushes, perennials. Architectural & exotics, *Fuchsia*, seasonal bedding, patio plants.
Map Ref: L, B3 **OS Grid Ref:** TQ226958

LEdu **EDULIS** ♿
(Office) 1 Flowers Piece, Ashampstead, Reading, Berkshire RG8 8SG
Ⓣ (01635) 578113
Ⓜ 07802 812781
Ⓔ edulisnursery@gmail.com
Ⓦ www.edulis.co.uk
Contact: Paul Barney
Opening Times: By appt. only.
Min Mail Order UK: £15.00 + p&p
Min Mail Order EU: £50.00 + p&p
Cat. Cost: 5 × 1st class.
Credit Cards: All, except American Express
Specialities: Unusual edibles, architectural plants, permaculture plants.
Notes: Nursery is at Bere Court Farm, Tidmarsh Lane, Pangbourne, RG8 8HT. Also sells wholesale. Euro accepted. Delivers to shows. Wheelchair accessible.
Map Ref: L, B2 **OS Grid Ref:** SU615747

LHel **HERTS HELLEBORES** ♿
Green Lane Farm, Levens Green, Nr Ware, Hertfordshire SG11 1HD
Ⓣ (01920) 438458
Ⓔ lorna@herts-hellebore.co.uk
Ⓦ www.herts-hellebore.co.uk
Contact: Lorna Jones
Opening Times: 1000-1600 Wed & Sat only, 2nd Feb-30th Mar 2013. Other times Jan-Apr by appt. only. Check with nursery for 2014 opening times.
Min Mail Order UK: £18
Min Mail Order EU: £18

Cat. Cost: Free.
Credit Cards: All major credit/debit cards
Specialities: Hellebore hybrids. Specialising in developments of double & anemone centred hybrids. Seed-raised plants offered by colour. Some available in small quantities only.
Notes: Euro accepted. Wheelchair accessible.
Map Ref: L, A4 **OS Grid Ref:** TL357224

LLHF **LITTLE HEATH FARM (UK)**
Little Heath Lane, Potten End, Berkhamsted, Hertfordshire HP4 2RY
Ⓣ (01442) 864951
Ⓔ lhfnursery@gmail.com
Ⓦ www.littleheathfarmnursery.co.uk
Contact: John Spokes
Opening Times: 1000-1700 or dusk if earlier, 7 days.
Cat. Cost: Online only.
Credit Cards: Visa, MasterCard
Specialities: Large range of alpines, herbaceous, shrubs, many available in small quantities only.
Notes: Delivers to shows.
Map Ref: L, B3

LLoc **W & S LOCKYER**
39 Mitchley Avenue, Riddlesdown, Purley, Surrey CR8 1BZ
Ⓣ 020 8660 1336
Ⓕ 020 8660 1336
Ⓔ williamlockyer@btinternet.com
Contact: William Lockyer
Opening Times: Not open.
Min Mail Order UK: Nmc
Cat. Cost: £2.00: no stamps.
Credit Cards: None
Specialities: Auriculas. Nerines. National Collection of Double Auriculas.
Notes: Also sells wholesale. Delivers to Shows.

LLWG **LILIES WATER GARDENS** ♿
Broad Lane, Newdigate, Surrey RH5 5AT
Ⓣ (01306) 631064
Ⓜ 07801 166244
Ⓔ mail@lilieswatergardens.co.uk
Ⓦ www.lilieswatergardens.co.uk
Contact: Simon Harman
Opening Times: 0900-1700 Wed-Sat, Mar-Aug. By appt. only Sep-Feb.
Min Mail Order UK: Nmc but flat rate £6.50 delivery charge.
Min Mail Order EU: Nmc
Cat. Cost: Online only.
Credit Cards: All major credit/debit cards
Specialities: Waterlilies, moist perennials, bog-garden plants, primulas, marginal plants, ferns, oxygenating plants. Pond, incl. submerged & free-floating, aquatic, water iris, water-garden, floating, stream & deep-water plants. Alpine, rock & creeping plants. Rushes & grasses.
Notes: Wheelchair accessible.

LLWP **LW PLANTS**
23 Wroxham Way, Harpenden, Hertfordshire AL5 4PP
Ⓣ (01582) 768467
Ⓔ lwplants@waitrose.com
Ⓦ www.thymus.co.uk
Contact: Mrs Margaret Easter
Opening Times: 1100-1630 most days, but please phone first.
Min Mail Order UK: Nmc
Cat. Cost: Online only.
Credit Cards: None
Specialities: Plants from a plantsman's garden, esp. *Geranium*, grasses & *Thymus*. Some available in small quantities only. Nat. Collections of *Thymus* (Scientific), *Hyssopus* & *Satureja*. Brickell award 2011. *Thymus* ICRA (provisional).
Map Ref: L, B3 **OS Grid Ref:** TL141153

LMil **MILLAIS NURSERIES** ♿
Crosswater Farm, Crosswater Lane, Churt, Farnham, Surrey GU10 2JN
Ⓣ (01252) 792698
Ⓕ (01252) 792526
Ⓔ sales@rhododendrons.co.uk
Ⓦ www.rhododendrons.co.uk
Contact: David Millais
Opening Times: 1000-1700 Mon-Fri all year. Daily in spring. Please phone or see website for w/end opening in spring.
Min Mail Order UK: Nmc
Min Mail Order EU: Nmc
Cat. Cost: Free list on request. Full catalogue Online.
Credit Cards: All major credit/debit cards
Specialities: Rhododendrons, azaleas, magnolias, camellias & acers. Garden open in spring.
Notes: Mail order all year. Also sells wholesale. Wheelchair accessible.
Map Ref: L, C3 **OS Grid Ref:** SU856397

LPal **THE PALM CENTRE**
Ham Central Nursery, Ham, Richmond, Surrey TW10 7HA
Ⓣ (0208) 255 6191
Ⓕ (02080 255 6192
Ⓔ rbesant@palmcentre.co.uk
Ⓦ www.palmcentre.co.uk
Contact: Toby Shobbrook
Opening Times: 0900-1700, 7 days.
Min Mail Order UK: £10.00 + p&p
Min Mail Order EU: £10.00 + p&p
Cat. Cost: Free.
Credit Cards: All, except American Express
Specialities: Palms, ferns, bamboos. National

Collection of *Trachycarpus*.
Notes: Also sells wholesale. Delivers to shows. Euro accepted.
Map Ref: L, B3

LPla **The Plant Specialist**
7 Whitefield Lane, Great Missenden, Buckinghamshire HP16 0BH
Ⓣ (01494) 866650
Ⓕ (01494) 866650
Ⓔ enquire@theplantspecialist.co.uk
Ⓦ www.theplantspecialist.co.uk
Contact: Sean Walter
Opening Times: 1000-1700 Wed-Sat, 1000-1600 Sun, Apr-Oct.
Cat. Cost: None issued.
Credit Cards: All major credit/debit cards
Specialities: Herbaceous perennials, grasses, half-hardy perennials, bulbs.
Notes: Limited wheelchair access.

LPot **Potash Plants** ♿
Potash Nursery, Drayton Parslow, Buckinghamshire MK17 0JE
Ⓣ (01296) 720578
Ⓔ info@potashplants.co.uk
Ⓦ www.potashplants.co.uk
Contact: Gill Gallon
Opening Times: 0900-1730 Mon-Sat. 1030-1630 Sun.
Cat. Cost: Online.
Credit Cards: All, except American Express
Specialities: Wide range of traditional and unusual hardy perennials, grasses, trees & shrubs. Some available in small quantities only.
Notes: Nursery on B4032 mid-way between Aylesbury and Milton Keynes. Also sells wholesale. Delivers to shows. Wheelchair accessible.
Map Ref: L, A3 **OS Grid Ref:** SP834279

LRHS **Wisley Plant Centre (RHS)** ♿ ◆
RHS Garden, Wisley, Woking, Surrey GU23 6QB
Ⓣ (01483) 211113 or 0845 060 9800
Ⓕ (01483) 212372
Ⓔ wisleyplantcentre@rhs.org.uk
Ⓦ www.rhs.org.uk/wisleyplantcentre
Opening Times: 0900-1700 Mon-Sat, Oct-Feb. 0900-1800 Mon-Sat, Mar-Sep. 1100-1700 Sun all year, browsing from 1030.
Cat. Cost: Online only.
Credit Cards: All major credit/debit cards
Specialities: Over 10,000 plants, many rare or unusual, reflecting the range of the RHS flagship garden at Wisley. Plants subject to seasonal availability. For plants not in stock, we operate a reservation service by phone & in person.
Notes: Programme of free plant events throughout the year. Please ring or check website for details. Wheelchair accessible.
Map Ref: L, C3

LShp **Squire's Garden Centre, Shepperton** ♿
Halliford Road, Upper Halliford, Shepperton, Middlesex TW17 8SG
Ⓣ (01932) 784121
Ⓕ (01932) 785386
Ⓔ shepp.plants@squiresgardencentres.co.uk
Ⓦ www.squiresgardencentres.co.uk
Contact: Plant Area Manager
Opening Times: 0900-1800 Mon-Sat, 1030-1630 Sun.
Cat. Cost: None issued.
Credit Cards: All major credit/debit cards
Specialities: Roses.
Notes: Other garden centres in Middlesex, Surrey, Berkshire and West Sussex. Wheelchair accessible.

LSou **Southon Plants** ♿
Mutton Hill, Dormansland, Lingfield, Surrey RH7 6NP
Ⓣ (01342) 870150
Ⓔ lyn@southon-plants.co.uk
Ⓦ www.southonplants.com
Contact: Mr Southon
Opening Times: 0900-1730 Mar-Oct. Closed Mon from Jul-Dec. For Nov, Dec, Jan & Feb times, please phone first.
Min Mail Order UK: Nmc
Cat. Cost: Online only.
Credit Cards: All major credit/debit cards
Specialities: New & unusual hardy & tender perennials, specialising in *Agapanthus* (over 30 varieties), *Coreopsis*, *Euphorbia* & *Heuchera* (over 40 varieties).
Notes: Mail order Nov-Feb only. Please phone/email for details. Wheelchair accessible.
Map Ref: L, C4

LSqH **Squire's Garden Centre, West Horsley** ♿
Epsom Road, West Horsley, Leatherhead, Surrey KT24 6AR
Ⓣ (01483) 282911
Ⓕ (01483) 281380
Ⓔ hors.plants@squiresgardencentres.co.uk
Ⓦ www.squiresgardencentres.co.uk
Contact: Plant Area Manager
Opening Times: 0900-1800 Mon-Sat, 1030-1630 Sun.
Cat. Cost: None issued.
Credit Cards: All major credit/debit cards
Specialities: Herbaceous.
Notes: Other garden centres in Middlesex, Surrey, Berkshire and West Sussex. Wheelchair accessible.

LSqu **Squire's Garden Centre, Twickenham** ♿
Sixth Cross Road, Twickenham, Middlesex
TW2 5PA
Ⓣ 0208 977 9241
Ⓕ 0208 943 4024
Ⓔ twic.plants@squiresgardencentres.co.uk
Ⓦ www.squiresgardencentres.co.uk
Contact: Plant Area Manager
Opening Times: 0900-1800 Mon-Sat, 1030-1630 Sun.
Credit Cards: All major credit/debit cards
Specialities: *Clematis.*
Notes: Other garden centres in Middlesex, Surrey, Berkshire and West Sussex. Wheelchair accessible.

LSun **The Sunnyside Nursery**
Upper Allotments, New Road,
Northchurch, Hertfordshire
HP4 1NJ
Ⓜ 07743 552154 or 07723 331612
Ⓔ hana@thesunnysidenursery.co.uk
Ⓦ www.thesunnysidenursery.co.uk
Contact: Philip Smith
Opening Times: 0900-1700 Tue-Fri. Mon & w/end collections can be arranged. Also Sat & Sun, Mar-Oct at The Monument, National Trust Ashridge Estate.
Min Mail Order UK: £6.00
Min Mail Order EU: £30.00
Cat. Cost: Online only.
Credit Cards: All major credit/debit cards
Specialities: Hardy perennials.
Notes: Please check website for stock availability & updates. Delivers to shows. Euro accepted.
Map Ref: L, B3

LToo **Toobees Exotics**
20 Inglewood, St Johns, Woking, Surrey
GU21 3HX
Ⓣ (01483) 722600
Ⓜ 07836 334011
Ⓕ (01483) 751995
Ⓔ bbpotter@woking.plus.com
Ⓦ www.toobees-exotics.com
Contact: Bob Potter
Opening Times: Not open. Mail order & online shop only. Visits by appt. only.
Min Mail Order UK: Nmc
Min Mail Order EU: Nmc
Cat. Cost: Sae
Credit Cards: All major credit/debit cards
Specialities: South African & Madagascan succulents, many rare & unusual species, *Euphorbia* & *Pachypodium*. Stock varies constantly.
Notes: Credit cards accepted online only. Exports beyond EU. Euro accepted.

LTop **Topiary Arts**
(Office) 224 Hospital Bridge Road,
Whitton, Twickenham, Middlesex
TW2 6LF
Ⓣ 020 8893 9579
Ⓜ 07775 602704
Ⓔ jcb@topiaryarts.com
Ⓦ www.topiaryarts.com
Contact: James Crebbin-Bailey
Opening Times: By appt. only.
Min Mail Order UK: £30
Cat. Cost: Online only.
Credit Cards: None
Specialities: Topiary. Small quantities of *Buxus, Philyrea, Taxus* & *Ligustrum.*
Notes: Nursery is at Copped Hall Walled Garden, Upshire, Epping, Essex CM16 5HS. Also sells wholesale. Delivers to shows.

LYaf **Yaffles** ♿
Harvest Hill, Bourne End, Buckinghamshire
SL8 5JJ
Ⓣ (01628) 525455
Contact: I Butterfield
Opening Times: 0900-1300 & 1400-1700. Please phone beforehand in case we are attending shows.
Min Mail Order UK: Nmc
Min Mail Order EU: £30.00 + p&p
Cat. Cost: 2 × 2nd class.
Credit Cards: None
Specialities: Nat. Collection of *Pleione.*
Notes: Only *Pleione* by mail order. Delivers to shows. Wheelchair accessible.

Midlands

MArl **Arley Hall Nursery** ♿
Northwich, Cheshire CW9 6NA
Ⓣ (01565) 777479 or 777231
Ⓕ (01565) 777465
Ⓦ www.arleyhallandgardens.com
Contact: Jane Foster, Rosie Jackson
Opening Times: 0930-1730 Mon-Fri, 1100-1730 Sat & Sun, 29th Mar-29th Sep.
Cat. Cost: 4 × 1st class.
Credit Cards: All major credit/debit cards
Specialities: Wide range of herbaceous incl. many unusual varieties, some in small quantities. Wide range of unusual pelargoniums.
Notes: Nursery is beside car park at Arley Hall Gardens. Wheelchair accessible.
Map Ref: M, A1 **OS Grid Ref:** SJ673808

MAsh **Ashwood Nurseries Ltd** ♿ ◆
Ashwood Lower Lane, Ashwood,
Kingswinford, West Midlands DY6 0AE
Ⓣ (01384) 401996
Ⓕ (01384) 401108
Ⓔ mailorder@ashwoodnurseries.com

Ⓦ www.ashwoodnurseries.com
Contact: Karrina Gilbert & Steve Lampitt
Opening Times: 0900-1700 Mon-Sat & 0930-1700 Sun excl. Xmas & Boxing Day.
Min Mail Order UK: Nmc
Min Mail Order EU: Nmc
Cat. Cost: 4 × 1st class.
Credit Cards: All major credit/debit cards
Specialities: Large range of hardy plants, shrubs & dwarf conifers. Roses, alpines & herbaceous plants. Also specialises in *Auricula*, *Cyclamen*, *Galanthus*, hellebores, *Hepatica*, *Hydrangea* & *Salvia*. Nat. Collection of *Lewisia*.
Notes: Tea room overlooking display garden. Ample parking. Regular events. Groups by appt. to visit private garden. Wheelchair accessible.
Map Ref: M, C2 **OS Grid Ref:** SO865879

M

MAus **DAVID AUSTIN ROSES LTD** ♿ ◆
Bowling Green Lane, Albrighton, Wolverhampton, West Midlands WV7 3HB
Ⓣ (01902) 376300
Ⓕ (01902) 375177
Ⓔ retail@davidaustinroses.co.uk
Ⓦ www.davidaustinroses.com
Contact: Customer Services Dept
Opening Times: 0830-1800 Mon-Fri, 0830-1630 Sat, 1000-1400 Sun.
Min Mail Order UK: Nmc
Min Mail Order EU: Nmc
Cat. Cost: Free.
Credit Cards: All major credit/debit cards
Specialities: Roses. Nat. Collection of English Roses.
Notes: Also sells wholesale. Exports beyond EU. Euro accepted. Wheelchair accessible.
Map Ref: M, B2 **OS Grid Ref:** SJ798042

MAvo **AVONDALE NURSERY** ♿
(Office) 3 Avondale Road, Earlsdon, Coventry, Warwickshire CV5 6DZ
Ⓣ (024) 766 73662
Ⓜ 07979 093096
Ⓔ enquiries@avondalenursery.co.uk
Ⓦ www.avondalenursery.co.uk
Contact: Brian Ellis
Opening Times: 1000-1230, 1400-1700 Mon-Sat, 1030-1630 Sun, Mar-Sep. Other times by appt.
Cat. Cost: 4 × 1st class.
Credit Cards: All major credit/debit cards
Specialities: Rare & unusual perennials esp. *Aster*, *Eryngium*, *Leucanthemum*, *Geum*, *Crocosmia*, *Sanguisorba* & grasses. Nat. Collections of *Aster novae-angliae*, *Anemone nemorosa* & *Sanguisorba*. Display garden open. Groups welcome.
Notes: Nursery is at Russell's Nursery, Mill Hill, Baginton, Nr Coventry CV8 3AG. Delivers to shows. Wheelchair accessible.
Map Ref: M, C2 **OS Grid Ref:** SP339751

MBel **BLUEBELL COTTAGE NURSERY (FORMERLY LODGE LANE NURSERY)** ♿
Lodge Lane, Dutton, Cheshire WA4 4HP
Ⓣ (01928) 713718
Ⓔ info@bluebellcottage.co.uk
Ⓦ www.bluebellcottage.co.uk
Contact: Sue Beesley
Opening Times: 1000-1700 Wed-Sun & B/hols, mid Mar-end Sep. By appt. only outside these dates.
Min Mail Order UK: £10.00
Cat. Cost: Online, or by email.
Credit Cards: All major credit/debit cards
Specialities: Hardy perennials incl. *Achillea*, *Astrantia*, *Campanula*, *Digitalis*, *Penstemon*, *Geranium*, *Heuchera*, *Kniphofia*, *Nepeta*, *Papaver*, *Thalictrum* & ornamental grasses. Some items stocked in small quantities.
Notes: Delivers to shows. Wheelchair accessible.
Map Ref: M, A1 **OS Grid Ref:** SJ586779

MBlu **BLUEBELL ARBORETUM & NURSERY** ♿
Annwell Lane, Smisby, Nr Ashby de la Zouch, Derbyshire LE65 2TA
Ⓣ (01530) 413700
Ⓕ (01530) 417600
Ⓔ sales@bluebellnursery.com
Ⓦ www.bluebellnursery.com
Contact: Robert & Suzette Vernon
Opening Times: 0900-1700 Mon-Sat & 1030-1630 Sun Mar-Oct, 0900-1600 Mon-Sat (not Sun) Nov-Feb. Closed 24th Dec-1st Jan incl. & Easter Sun.
Min Mail Order UK: £9.50
Min Mail Order EU: Nmc
Cat. Cost: £1.50 + 3 × 1st class.
Credit Cards: Visa, Access, Switch, MasterCard
Specialities: Uncommon trees & shrubs. Rare *Acer*, *Betula*, *Cornus*, *Fagus*, *Magnolia*, *Liquidambar*, *Quercus* & *Tilia*. Woody climbers.
Notes: Display garden & arboretum. 9-acre woodland garden with unusual trees. Guide dogs only. Working nursery, so wear appropriate clothing & sturdy footwear when visiting. Delivers to shows. Wheelchair accessible.
Map Ref: M, B1 **OS Grid Ref:** SK344187

MBNS **BARNSDALE GARDENS** ♿
Exton Avenue, Exton, Oakham, Rutland LE15 8AH
Ⓣ (01572) 813200
Ⓔ info@barnsdalegardens.co.uk

Ⓦ www.barnsdalegardens.co.uk
Contact: Nick Hamilton
Opening Times: 0900-1700 Mar-May & Sep-Oct, 0900-1900 Jun-Aug, 1000-1600 Nov-Feb, 7 days. Closed 24th & 25th Dec.
Min Mail Order UK: Nmc
Min Mail Order EU: Nmc
Cat. Cost: Online only.
Credit Cards: All major credit/debit cards
Specialities: Wide range of choice & unusual garden plants. Over 160 varieties of *Penstemon*, over 250 varieties of *Hemerocallis*.
Notes: Mail order from website or by telephone ordering only. Delivers to shows. Wheelchair accessible.
Map Ref: M, B3 **OS Grid Ref:** SK912108

MBri BRIDGEMERE NURSERY & GARDEN WORLD ♿
Bridgemere, Nr Nantwich, Cheshire
CW5 7QB
Ⓣ (01270) 521100
Ⓕ (01270) 520215
Ⓔ bridgemere.plantinfo@thegardencentre group.co.uk
Ⓦ www.bridgemere.co.uk
Contact: Ann Foster, Roger Pierce
Opening Times: 0900-1800 7 days. Closed 25th & 26th Dec.
Min Mail Order UK: Nmc
Cat. Cost: None issued.
Credit Cards: Visa, Access, MasterCard, Switch
Specialities: Huge range outdoor & indoor plants, many rare & unusual. Specimen shrubs.
Notes: Mail order restricted to "Click & Collect" & home delivery service available on www.thegardencentregroup.co.uk. Euro accepted. Wheelchair accessible.
Map Ref: M, B1 **OS Grid Ref:** SJ727435

MBrN BRIDGE NURSERY ♿
Tomlow Road, Napton-on-the-Hill,
Nr Rugby, Warwickshire
CV47 8HX
Ⓣ (01926) 812737
Ⓔ pemartino@tiscali.co.uk
Ⓦ www.Bridge-Nursery.co.uk
Contact: Christine Dakin & Philip Martino
Opening Times: 1000-1600 Mon-Sun mid Feb-mid Nov. Other times by appt.
Cat. Cost: Online only.
Credit Cards: All major credit/debit cards
Specialities: Ornamental grasses, sedges & bamboos. Also range of shrubs & perennials. Display garden.
Notes: Also sells wholesale. Euro accepted. Wheelchair accessible.
Map Ref: M, C2 **OS Grid Ref:** SP463625

MCms CHRYSANTHEMUMS DIRECT
Holmes Chapel Road,
Over Peover, Knutsford, Cheshire
WA16 9RA
Ⓣ 0800 046 7443
Ⓜ 07977 312 593
Ⓔ sales@chrysanthemumsdirect.co.uk
Ⓦ www.chrysanthemumsdirect.co.uk
Contact: Martyn Flint
Opening Times: Not open. Mail order only.
Min Mail Order UK: Nmc
Min Mail Order EU: Nmc
Cat. Cost: 4 × 1st class.
Credit Cards: All major credit/debit cards
Specialities: Chrysanthemums. Young plants grown to order. Delivery within 14 days.
Notes: Delivers to shows.

MCoo COOL TEMPERATE
(Office) 45 Stamford Street, Awsworth,
Nottinghamshire NG16 2QL
Ⓣ (0115) 916 2673
Ⓕ (0115) 916 2673
Ⓔ phil.corbett@cooltemperate.co.uk
Ⓦ www.cooltemperate.co.uk
Contact: Phil Corbett
Opening Times: 0900-1700, 7 days. Please ring/write first.
Min Mail Order UK: £30.00
Min Mail Order EU: £50.00
Cat. Cost: 3 × 1st class.
Credit Cards: None
Specialities: Tree fruit, soft fruit, nitrogen-fixers, hedging, own-root fruit trees. Many species available in small quantities only.
Notes: Nursery at Newton's Lane, Cossall, Notts. Also sells wholesale. Exports beyond EU.
Map Ref: M, B2 **OS Grid Ref:** SK481435

MCot COTON MANOR GARDEN
Guilsborough, Northampton,
Northamptonshire
NN6 8RQ
Ⓣ (01604) 740219
Ⓔ nursery@cotonmanor.co.uk
Ⓦ www.cotonmanor.co.uk
Contact: Caroline Tait
Opening Times: 1200-1730 Tue-Sat, 29th Mar-28th Sep. Also Sun Apr, May & B/hol w/ends. Other times in working hours by appt.
Cat. Cost: Online only.
Credit Cards: All major credit/debit cards
Specialities: Wide-range of herbaceous perennials (1200+ varieties), some available in small quantities only. Also many tender perennials & selected shrubs.
Notes: Garden open. Tea rooms. Garden school. Partial wheelchair access.
Map Ref: M, C3 **OS Grid Ref:** SP675715

MCri **CRIN GARDENS**
79 Partons Road, Kings Heath, Birmingham
B14 6TD
Ⓣ 0121 443 3815
Ⓜ 07805 591475
Ⓕ 0121 443 3815
Ⓔ cringardens@tiscali.co.uk
Ⓦ www.cringardens.co.uk
Contact: M Milinkovic
Opening Times: Not open. Mail order only.
Min Mail Order UK: Nmc
Min Mail Order EU: Nmc
Cat. Cost: 2 × 1st class + 1 × 2nd.
Credit Cards: None
Specialities: Lilies. Limited stock available on first come, first served basis.
Notes: Euro accepted.

M

MFie **FIELD HOUSE NURSERY** ♿
Leake Road, Gotham, Nottinghamshire
NG11 0JN
Ⓣ (01159) 830278
Ⓜ 07504 125209
Ⓔ val.woolley@btinternet.com
Contact: Valerie A Woolley & Bob Taylor
Opening Times: By appt. only.
Min Mail Order UK: 4 plants.
Min Mail Order EU: £30.00
Cat. Cost: 4 × 1st class (auriculas/primulas). 2 × 1st class (astrantias).
Credit Cards: Visa, MasterCard, Electron, Maestro, Solo
Specialities: *Primula auricula* & seed, *Astrantia*. Nat. Collections of *Primula auricula* (show & alpine) & *Astrantia*.
Notes: Mail order for *Astrantia*, *Primula* & auricula seeds. Euro accepted. Delivers to shows. Wheelchair accessible.

MGbk **GOSBROOK PELARGONIUMS**
30 Damson Trees, Shrivenham, Oxfordshire
SN6 8BB
Ⓣ (01793) 783329
Ⓜ 07921 089908
Ⓔ sales@gosbrookpelargoniums.com
Ⓦ www.gosbrookpelargoniums.com
Contact: David Taylor
Opening Times: Please ring for appt.
Min Mail Order UK: £20.00
Min Mail Order EU: £20.00
Cat. Cost: 2 × 1st class
Specialities: *Pelargonium*.
Notes: Credit cards accepted online only.
Map Ref: M, D2 **OS Grid Ref:** SU233889

MGil **JOHN GILLIES**
15 Newey Road, Coventry, West Midlands
CV2 5GZ
Ⓜ 07546 064961
Ⓔ enquiries@gilliesrareplants.com
Ⓦ www.gilliesrareplants.com
Contact: John Gillies
Opening Times: Open by appt. only. Contact nursery for plant collection.
Cat. Cost: Online only.
Specialities: A range of choice & rare plants, incl. *Azara*, *Clethra*, *Colquhounia*, *Diostea*, *Embothrium*, *Ercilla*, *Fabiana*, *Mutisia* & *Rhapiolepis*. Most available in small quantities only.
Notes: Sells at plant fairs. See website for list of plant fairs where plants can be collected.

MGos **GOSCOTE NURSERIES LTD** ♿
Syston Road, Cossington, Leicestershire
LE7 4UZ
Ⓣ (01509) 812121
Ⓔ sales@goscote.co.uk
Ⓦ www.goscote.co.uk
Contact: James Toone
Opening Times: 7 days, year round, apart from between Xmas & New Year.
Cat. Cost: Online only.
Credit Cards: Visa, Access, MasterCard, Delta, Switch
Specialities: Japanese maples, rhododendrons & azaleas, *Magnolia*, *Camellia*, *Pieris* & other *Ericaceae*. Ornamental trees & shrubs, conifers, fruit, heathers, alpines, roses, *Clematis* & unusual climbers.
Notes: Design & landscaping service available. Café & show garden. Also sells wholesale. Wheelchair accessible.
Map Ref: M, B3 **OS Grid Ref:** SK602130

MHer **THE HERB NURSERY** ♿
Thistleton, Oakham, Rutland
LE15 7RE
Ⓣ (01572) 767658
Ⓔ herbnursery@southwitham.net
Ⓦ www.herbnursery.co.uk
Contact: Peter Bench
Opening Times: 0900-1800 (or dusk) 7 days excl. Xmas-New Year.
Cat. Cost: Free with A5 sae.
Credit Cards: All major credit/debit cards
Specialities: Herbs, wild flowers, cottage garden plants, scented-leaf pelargoniums. *Thymus*, *Mentha*, *Lavandula*.
Notes: Wheelchair accessible.
Map Ref: M, B3

MHin **HINWICK HALL PLANT CENTRE** ♿
Hinwick Hall College, Hinwick, Wellingborough, Northamptonshire
NN29 7JD
Ⓣ (01933) 350543
Ⓕ (01933) 412470
Ⓔ RHockney@hinwick.livability.org.uk
Contact: Richard Hockney

Opening Times: 0900-1700 Mon-Sat, 1000-1600 Sun, Mar-Nov.
Credit Cards: All major credit/debit cards
Specialities: Range of unusual and common plants, grasses & a selection of sub-tropical.
Notes: Small retail nursery attached to a specialist college working with young adults with learning difficulties and disabilities. Wheelchair accessible.

MHol HOLLIES FARM PLANT CENTRE
Uppertown, Bonsall, Nr Matlock, Derbyshire DE4 2AW
Ⓣ (01629) 822734
Ⓔ rbrt.wells@gmail.com
Ⓦ www.holliesfarmplantcentre.co.uk
Contact: Robert or Linda Wells
Opening Times: 0900-1700 every day except Wed.
Credit Cards: None
Specialities: Range of rare & unusual herbaceous perennials.
Notes: Also sells wholesale.

MHom HOMESTEAD PLANTS
The Homestead, Normanton, Bottesford, Nottingham NG13 0EP
Ⓣ (01949) 842745
Ⓦ www.homesteadplants.com
Contact: Mrs S Palmer
Opening Times: By appt.
Min Mail Order UK: Nmc
Cat. Cost: 2 × 2nd class.
Credit Cards: None
Specialities: Unusual hardy & half-hardy perennials, esp. *Argyranthemum*, *Galanthus*, *Hosta*, *Jovibarba*, *Salvia*, *Sempervivum* & heliotrope. Drought-tolerant asters. Most available only in small quantities. Nat. Collection of *Heliotropium* cultivars.
Notes: Mail order not offered year round. Please check with nursery for details.
Map Ref: M, B3 **OS Grid Ref:** SK812407

MJac JACKSON'S NURSERIES
Clifton Campville, Nr Tamworth, Staffordshire B79 0AP
Ⓣ (01827) 373307
Contact: N Jackson
Opening Times: 0900-1800 Mon & Wed-Sat, 1000-1700 Sun.
Cat. Cost: 2 × 1st class.
Credit Cards: None
Specialities: *Fuchsia*.
Notes: Also sells wholesale.
Map Ref: M, B2

MJak JACKSON'S NURSERIES
Thorney Edge Road, Bagnall, Stoke-on-Trent, Staffordshire ST9 9LE
Ⓣ (01782) 502741
Ⓕ (01782) 504932
Ⓔ sales@jacksonsnurseries.co.uk
Ⓦ www.jacksonsnurseries.co.uk
Contact: Sherrie Davison
Opening Times: 0800-1700 7 days, Mar-Oct. 0800-1630, Nov-Feb.
Credit Cards: MasterCard, Visa
Specialities: Good general range.
Notes: Family-run nursery, established for over 50 years, a short distance from the Peak District. Tea room. Also sells wholesale.

MLea LEA RHODODENDRON GARDENS LTD ♿
Lea, Matlock, Derbyshire DE4 5GH
Ⓣ (01629) 534380/534260
Ⓕ (01629) 534260
Ⓔ lea.gardens@hotmail.co.uk
Ⓦ www.leagarden.co.uk
Contact: Peter Tye
Opening Times: 1000-1730 7 days 20 Mar-30 Jun. Out of season by appt.
Min Mail Order UK: £15.00 + p&p
Min Mail Order EU: £15.00 + p&p
Cat. Cost: 30p + sae.
Credit Cards: All major credit/debit cards
Specialities: Rhododendrons & azaleas.
Notes: Exports beyond EU. Wheelchair accessible.
Map Ref: M, B1 **OS Grid Ref:** SK324571

MLHP LONGSTONE HARDY PLANT NURSERY ♿
Station Road, Great Longstone, Nr Bakewell, Derbyshire DE45 1TS
Ⓣ (01629) 640136
Ⓜ 07762 083674
Ⓔ lucyinlongstone@hotmail.com
Ⓦ www.longstonehardyplants.co.uk
Contact: Lucy Wright
Opening Times: 1000-1700 Wed-Mon (closed Tue), 1st Mar-31st Oct.
Credit Cards: All major credit/debit cards
Specialities: Peat-free nursery displaying all our own hardy perennials, ornamental grasses, herbs & shrubs, incl. many unusual varieties. Some stock available in small quantities only. Can propagate to order.
Notes: Turn across village green between the White Lion Pub & the Cripin Inn. Nursery 100 yds on right. Wheelchair accessible.
Map Ref: M, A2 **OS Grid Ref:** SK198717

MMHG MORTON NURSERIES LTD ♿
Morton Hall, Ranby, Retford, Nottinghamshire DN22 8HW
Ⓣ (01777) 702530
Ⓜ 07940 434398
Ⓔ enquiries@morton-nurseries.com

Ⓦ www.morton-nurseries.co.uk
Contact: Gill McMaster
Opening Times: By appt.only
Min Mail Order UK: £5.00 + p&p
Cat. Cost: 3 × 1st class.
Credit Cards: All major credit/debit cards
Specialities: Shrubs & perennials.
Notes: Delivers to shows. Wheelchair accessible.
Map Ref: M, A3

MMoz **Mozart House Nursery Garden**
84 Central Avenue, Wigston, Leicestershire
LE18 2AA
Ⓣ (0116) 288 9548
Contact: Des Martin
Opening Times: Please phone for appt.
Cat. Cost: Phone for list.
Credit Cards: None
Specialities: Bamboos, ornamental grasses, rushes & sedges, ferns. Shade & woodland plants. Some stock available in small quantities.
Notes: Delivers to shows.
Map Ref: M, C3

MMuc **Mucklestone Nurseries** ♿ ◆
Rock Lane, Mucklestone,
Nr Market Drayton, Shropshire
TF9 4DN
Ⓣ (01630) 674284
Ⓜ 07714 241668
Ⓔ info@botanyplants.co.uk
Ⓦ www.botanyplants.co.uk
Contact: William & Louise Friend
Opening Times: 0900-1700 7 days, winter times may vary, please phone first.
Min Mail Order UK: Nmc
Cat. Cost: Online.
Credit Cards: All major credit/debit cards
Specialities: Trees, shrubs, grasses & perennials for acid & damp soils of the north & west UK. Our nursery in Kent grows complementary range for dry, chalk & coast. See entry under code SEND.
Notes: Any plants on website or listed under nursery code SEND can be collected to order or sent. Also sells wholesale. Wheelchair accessible.
Map Ref: M, B2 **OS Grid Ref:** SJ728373

MNai **Naieus Exotics**
432 Burton Road, Midway, Swadlingcote,
Derbyshire DE11 0DW
Ⓜ 07871 315312
Ⓔ naieus@live.co.uk
Ⓦ www.naieusexotics.co.uk
Contact: Ian
Opening Times: 0900-1800, Mon-Sat. 1000-1630 Sun.
Min Mail Order UK: £15.00
Min Mail Order EU: €15.00
Cat. Cost: £1.00 + 1 × 1st class.
Credit Cards: All major credit/debit cards
Specialities: *Brugmansia*. Available in small quantities only.
Notes: Exports beyond EU. Delivers to shows. Euro accepted.

MNew **Newington Nurseries** ♿ ◆
Newington, Nr Stadhampton, Wallingford,
Oxfordshire OX10 7AW
Ⓣ (01865) 400533
Ⓔ plants@newington-nurseries.co.uk
Ⓦ www.newington-nurseries.co.uk
Contact: Mrs A T Hendry
Opening Times: 0830-1700 Tues-Sun Jan-Dec.
Min Mail Order UK: Nmc
Credit Cards: Access, MasterCard, Visa, Switch
Specialities: Unusual cottage garden plants, hardy exotics, herbs, orchids, grasses, topiary & specimen plants. Nat. Collection of *Alocasia* (*Araceae*).
Notes: Also sells wholesale. Euro accepted. Wheelchair accessible.
Map Ref: M, D3

MNFA **The Nursery Further Afield** ♿
Evenley Road, Mixbury,
Nr Brackley, Northamptonshire
NN13 5YR
Ⓣ (01280) 848808
Ⓔ sinclair@nurseryfurtherafield.co.uk
Ⓦ www.nurseryfurtherafield.co.uk
Contact: Gerald & Mary Sinclair
Opening Times: 1000-1700 Wed-Sat, Apr-mid Sep. Other times by appt.
Min Mail Order UK: £15.00
Cat. Cost: 3 × 1st class.
Credit Cards: None
Specialities: Worthwhile hardy perennials, many unusual. Large selection of *Geranium* & *Hemerocallis*. Nat. Collection of *Hemerocallis*.
Notes: Mail order for *Hemerocallis* only. Wheelchair accessible.
Map Ref: M, C3 **OS Grid Ref:** SP608344

MNHC **The National Herb Centre** ♿
Banbury Road, Warmington, Nr Banbury,
Oxfordshire OX17 1DF
Ⓣ (01295) 690999
Ⓕ (01295) 690034
Ⓔ info@herbcentre.co.uk
Ⓦ www.herbcentre.co.uk
Contact: Plant Centre Staff
Opening Times: 0900-1730 Mon-Sat, 1030-1700 Sun.
Min Mail Order UK: Nmc but carriage charge of £10.00 for orders valued up to £50, more for larger orders.
Credit Cards: All major credit/debit cards

Specialities: Herbs, culinary & medicinal. Extensive selection of rosemary, thyme & lavender, in particular.
Notes: Next day delivery UK mainland only, signature required. Wheelchair accessible.
Map Ref: M, C2 **OS Grid Ref:** SP413471

MNrw **Norwell Nurseries** ♿ ◆
Woodhouse Road, Norwell, Newark, Nottinghamshire NG23 6JX
Ⓣ (01636) 636337
Ⓔ wardha@aol.com
Ⓦ www.norwellnurseries.co.uk
Contact: Dr Andrew Ward
Opening Times: 1000-1700 Mon, Wed-Fri & Sun (Wed-Mon May & Jun). By appt. Aug & 20th Oct-1st Mar.
Min Mail Order UK: £15.00 + p&p
Min Mail Order EU: £40.00
Cat. Cost: 3 × 1st class or online.
Credit Cards: None
Specialities: A large collection of unusual & choice herbaceous perennials esp., hardy geraniums, *Geum*, pond & bog plants, cottage garden plants, *Hemerocallis*, grasses, hardy chrysanthemums & woodland plants. Over 2500 different species & cvs grown. One acre garden open.
Notes: Talks given. Also sells wholesale. Delivers to shows. Wheelchair accessible.
Map Ref: M, B3 **OS Grid Ref:** SK767616

MOld **Old Hall Nursery** ♿
Winkhill, Leek, Staffordshire ST13 7PN
Ⓣ (01538) 308257
Ⓜ 07866 175881
Ⓔ oldhallnursery@hotmail.co.uk
Ⓦ www.oldhallnursery.com
Contact: Sandra Henshall
Opening Times: 1000-1600, 7 days.
Cat. Cost: Not available.
Credit Cards: None
Specialities: Large selection of herbaceous, herbs & alpines. Also shrubs, climbers & fruit trees. All hardy.
Notes: Wheelchair accessible.
Map Ref: M, B2 **OS Grid Ref:** SK051521

MOWG **The Old Walled Garden** ♿
Honeybourne Road, Pebworth, Stratford-upon-Avon, Warwickshire CV37 8XP
Ⓣ (01789) 720788
Ⓕ (01789) 721162
Ⓔ Heather@oldwalledgarden.com
Ⓦ www.oldwalledgarden.com
Contact: Heather Godard-Key
Opening Times: 0900-1700 Mon-Sat, 1st Mar-31st Aug. 0900-1600 Mon-Fri, 1st Sep-28th Feb. 1030-1600 Sat & Sun, 2nd Apr-31st Jul. Closed last 2 weeks of Dec-1st week Jan, Easter Sun & Aug B/hol Mon.
Min Mail Order UK: Nmc
Min Mail Order EU: £30
Cat. Cost: 3 × 1st class
Credit Cards: Switch, MasterCard, Visa, Maestro
Specialities: Many rare & unusual shrubs. Wide range of conservatory plants esp. Australian. *Callistemon* & *Hibiscus*.
Notes: Delivers to shows. Wheelchair accessible.
Map Ref: M, C2 **OS Grid Ref:** SP133458

MPet **Peter Grayson (Sweet Pea Seedsman)**
34 Glenthorne Close, Brampton, Chesterfield, Derbyshire, S40 3AR
Ⓣ (01246) 278503
Ⓕ (01246) 278503
Contact: Peter Grayson
Opening Times: Not open. Mail order only.
Min Mail Order UK: Nmc
Min Mail Order EU: Nmc
Cat. Cost: C5 sae, 1 × 2nd class.
Credit Cards: None
Specialities: *Lathyrus* species & cvs. Large collection of old-fashioned sweet peas & over 100 Spencer sweet peas incl. own cultivars and collection of old-fashioned cottage garden annuals & perennials.
Notes: Mail order for seeds only. Also sells wholesale. Exports beyond EU. Euro accepted.

MPie **Piecemeal Plants** ♿
Whatton House Gardens, Nr Kegworth, Loughborough, Leicestershire LE12 5BG
Ⓣ (01509) 672056
Ⓔ nursery@piecemealplants.co.uk
Ⓦ www.piecemealplants.co.uk
Contact: Mary Thomas
Opening Times: 1300-1600 (1700 in summer) early Mar-late Oct, most Thu, Fri & some Sun. For up to date details, please ring or see website. Also by arrangement.
Cat. Cost: Online only.
Credit Cards: None
Specialities: Interesting range of herbaceous perennials, some half-hardy or tender. Many in small quantities.
Notes: Nursery located at entrance to Whatton Gardens, off A6. Car parking in front of Whatton House at top of drive. Wheelchair accessible.
Map Ref: M, B3 **OS Grid Ref:** SK494242

MPkF **Packhorse Farm Nursery** ♿
Sandyford House, Lant Lane, Tansley, Matlock, Derbyshire DE4 5FW
Ⓣ (01629) 57206
Ⓜ 07974 095752
Ⓕ (01629) 57206

Contact: Hilton W Haynes
Opening Times: 1000-1700 Tues & Wed, 1st Mar-31st Oct. Any other time by appt. only.
Cat. Cost: 2 × 1st class for plant list.
Credit Cards: None
Specialities: *Acer*, rare stock is limited in supply. Other more unusual hardy shrubs, trees & conifers.
Notes: Delivers to shows. Wheelchair accessible.
Map Ref: M, B2 **OS Grid Ref:** SK322617

MPnt **PLANTAGOGO.COM** ♿
Jubilee Cottage Nursery, Snape Lane, Englesea Brook, Crewe, Cheshire CW2 5QN
Ⓣ (01270) 820335
Ⓜ 07713 518271
Ⓔ info@plantagogo.com
Ⓦ www.plantagogo.com
Contact: Vicky & Richard Fox
Opening Times: By appt. only. Also Open Days: 6th & 7th Apr; 6th, 12th & 13th Oct 2013, 1000-1600.
Min Mail Order UK: £8.95 single payment.
Min Mail Order EU: Price on application or see website.
Cat. Cost: 4 × 1st class.
Credit Cards: All major credit/debit cards
Specialities: *Heuchera*, *Heucherella*, *Tiarella*, also large selection of perennials. Nat. Collections of *Heuchera*, *Heucherella* & *Tiarella*. Plants listed in the *RHS Plant Finder* are available in good quantities. Others, not listed here, are available from our collections on request.
Notes: Also sells wholesale. Delivers to shows. Wheelchair accessible.
Map Ref: M, B1 **OS Grid Ref:** SJ750516

MPro **PROCTORS NURSERY**
99 High Lane, Brown Edge, Stoke-on-Trent, Staffordshire ST6 8RT
Ⓣ 07803 940759
Ⓜ 07803 940759
Ⓕ (01782) 505362
Ⓔ proctorsnursery@hotmail.co.uk
Ⓦ www.proctorsnursery.co.uk
Contact: Barry Proctor
Specialities: Azaleas, acers, perennials & shrubs.

MRav **RAVENSTHORPE NURSERY** ♿
6 East Haddon Road, Ravensthorpe, Northamptonshire NN6 8ES
Ⓣ (01604) 770548
Ⓕ (01604) 770548
Ⓔ ravensthorpenursery@hotmail.com
Contact: Jean & Richard Wiseman
Opening Times: 1000-1800 (or dusk if earlier) Tue-Sat. B/hol w/ends in May. Easter Mon.
Min Mail Order UK: Nmc
Min Mail Order EU: Nmc
Cat. Cost: None issued.
Credit Cards: Visa, MasterCard, Delta
Specialities: Over 3000 different trees, shrubs & perennials with many unusual varieties.
Notes: Search & delivery service for large orders, winter months only. Wheelchair accessible.
Map Ref: M, C3 **OS Grid Ref:** SP665699

MSCN **STONYFORD COTTAGE NURSERY** ♿
Stonyford Lane, Cuddington, Northwich, Cheshire CW8 2TF
Ⓣ (01606) 888970/888128 (answerphone)
Ⓜ 07714 205177
Ⓔ stonyfordcottage@yahoo.co.uk
Ⓦ www.stonyfordcottagenursery.co.uk
Contact: Andrew Overland
Opening Times: 1000-1700 Tue-Sun & B/hol Mons 1st Feb-31st Oct.
Min Mail Order UK: Nmc
Min Mail Order EU: Nmc
Cat. Cost: Not available this year
Credit Cards: All major credit/debit cards
Specialities: Wide range of herbaceous perennials, *Iris*, hardy *Geranium*, moisture-loving & bog plants. *Sempervivum*, *Paeonia*, candelabra *Primula*.
Notes: Also sells wholesale. Wheelchair accessible.
Map Ref: M, A1 **OS Grid Ref:** SJ580710

MSKA **SWEET KNOWLE AQUATICS** ♿
Wimpstone-Ilmington Road, Stratford-upon-Avon, Warwickshire CV37 8NR
Ⓣ (01789) 450036
Ⓕ (01789) 450036
Ⓔ sweetknowleaquatics@hotmail.com
Ⓦ www.sweetknowleaquatics.co.uk
Contact: Zoe Harding
Opening Times: 0930-1700 Sun-Fri, closed Sat. Open B/hols.
Min Mail Order UK: Nmc
Min Mail Order EU: Nmc
Cat. Cost: By email only.
Credit Cards: All major credit/debit cards
Specialities: Aquatics. Hardy & tropical water lilies, marginals & oxygenators. 2-acre display garden open to the public (no charge).
Notes: Wheelchair accessible.
Map Ref: M, C2 **OS Grid Ref:** SP207480

MSnd **SOUND GARDEN RHODODENDRONS**
7 Lumber Lane, Burtonwood, Warrington, Cheshire WA5 4AS
Ⓣ (01925) 229100
Ⓜ 07931 340836
Ⓔ timothyatkinson@msn.com
Ⓦ www.sound-garden-designs.co.uk

Contact: Tim Atkinson
Opening Times: By appt. only.
Cat. Cost: 2 × 1st class
Credit Cards: None
Specialities: Species *Rhododendron*. Species *Sorbus*.
Notes: Nursery formerly at Middledale Farm, Dale Road, Marple, Cheshire SK6 6NL. Delivers to shows.
Map Ref: N, B1 **OS Grid Ref:** SJ948901

MSpe SPECIALPERENNIALS.COM
Yew Tree House, Hall Lane,
Hankelow, Crewe, Cheshire
CW3 0JB
Ⓣ (01270) 811443
Ⓜ 07716 990695
Ⓔ plants@specialperennials.com
Ⓦ www.specialperennials.com
Contact: Janet & Martin Blow
Opening Times: Nursery only open when garden open for NGS & Nat. Collection of *Helenium* & *Centaurea* Open Days. See website or phone for details.
Min Mail Order UK: Nmc
Cat. Cost: Online or send A5 large letter sae.
Credit Cards: Paypal
Specialities: Herbaceous perennials. Nat. Collection of *Helenium* cvs (100+ varieties for sale). Nat. Collection of *Centaurea* (50+ varieties). Also *Geum*, border *Phlox*, *Hemerocallis*, *Monada* & *Persciaria*. All plants available in small quantities only.
Notes: All plants grown in garden nursery & some sell out quickly. Garden open for NGS. Talks given. Group visits to garden & nursery welcomed. See website or send sae for details. Delivers to shows.
Map Ref: M, B1 **OS Grid Ref:** SJ699452

MSwo SWALLOWS NURSERY ♿
Mixbury, Brackley, Northamptonshire
NN13 5RR
Ⓣ (01280) 847721
Ⓕ (01280) 848611
Ⓔ enq@swallowsnursery.co.uk
Ⓦ www.swallowsnursery.co.uk
Contact: Chris Swallow
Opening Times: 0900-1300 & 1400-1700 (earlier in winter) Mon-Fri, 0900-1300 Sat.
Min Mail Order UK: £15.00
Cat. Cost: 3 × 1st class (plus phone number).
Credit Cards: All major credit/debit cards
Specialities: Growing a wide range, particularly shrubs, climbers, trees & roses.
Notes: Trees not for mail order unless part of larger order. Nursery transport used where possible, esp. for trees. Also sells wholesale. Wheelchair accessible.
Map Ref: M, C3 **OS Grid Ref:** SP607336

MTis TISSINGTON NURSERY ♿
The Old Kitchen Gardens,
Tissington, Ashbourne, Derbyshire
DE6 1RA
Ⓣ (01335) 390650
Ⓜ 07929 720284
Ⓔ info@tissington-nursery.co.uk
Ⓦ www.tissington-nursery.co.uk
Contact: Mairi Longdon
Opening Times: 1030-1700 daily, end Mar-end Sep.
Min Mail Order UK: Nmc
Cat. Cost: 4 × 1st class or online.
Credit Cards: All major credit/debit cards
Specialities: Choice & unusual perennials esp. *Achillea*, *Geranium*, *Geum*, *Helenium*, *Helianthus*, *Nepeta*, *Salvia*, *Sanguisorba* & *Sedum*.
Notes: Delivers to shows. Wheelchair accessible.
Map Ref: M, B1 **OS Grid Ref:** SK176521

MTPN SMART PLANTS
Sandy Hill Lane, off Overstone Road,
Moulton, Northampton
NN3 7JB
Ⓣ (01604) 454106
Ⓜ 07519 339508
Ⓔ smartplants@hotmail.co.uk
Contact: Stuart Smart
Opening Times: 1000-1500 Thu & Fri, 1000-1700 Sat. Other times by appt.
Min Mail Order UK: Nmc
Cat. Cost: 3 × 1st class
Credit Cards: None
Specialities: Wide range of herbaceous, alpines, shrubs, grasses, hardy *Geranium*. Some plants available in small quantities only.
Notes: Delivers to shows. Limited wheelchair access.

MWat WATERPERRY GARDENS LTD ♿
Waterperry, Nr Wheatley,
Oxfordshire,
OX33 1JZ
Ⓣ (01844) 339226/254
Ⓕ (01844) 339883
Ⓔ pmaxwell@waterperrygardens.co.uk
Ⓦ www.waterperrygardens.co.uk
Contact: Mr R Jacobs
Opening Times: 1000-1730 summer. 1000-1700 winter.
Min Mail Order UK: £30.00
Cat. Cost: Online only.
Credit Cards: All major credit/debit cards
Specialities: General, large range of herbaceous esp. *Aster*, also Nat. Collection of *Saxifraga* (subsect. *Kabschia* & *Engleria*).
Notes: Wheelchair accessible.
Map Ref: M, D3 **OS Grid Ref:** SP630064

MWhi **WHITEHILL FARM NURSERY** ♿
Whitehill Farm, Burford,
Oxfordshire
OX18 4DT
Ⓣ (01993) 823218
Ⓕ (01993) 822894
Ⓔ a.youngson@virgin.net
Ⓦ www.whitehillfarmnursery.co.uk
Contact: P J M Youngson
Opening Times: 0900-1800 (or dusk if earlier) daily except Mon, Mar-Nov. Dec-Feb & Mons by appt.
Min Mail Order UK: £15 + p&p
Min Mail Order EU: £25 + p&p
Cat. Cost: 4 × 1st class. £1.00 of catalogue cost refunded on 1st order.
Credit Cards: All major credit/debit cards
Specialities: Grasses & bamboos, less common shrubs & perennials. Some available in small quantities only.
Notes: Euro accepted. Wheelchair accessible.
Map Ref: M, D2 **OS Grid Ref:** SP268113

MWht **WHITELEA NURSERY** ♿
Whitelea Lane, Tansley, Matlock, Derbyshire
DE4 5FL
Ⓣ (01629) 55010
Ⓔ sales@uk-bamboos.co.uk
Ⓦ www.uk-bamboos.co.uk
Contact: David Wilson
Opening Times: By appt.
Min Mail Order UK: Nmc
Cat. Cost: Online only. Price list available 2 × 1st class.
Credit Cards: None
Specialities: Bamboos. Substantial quantities of 45 cvs & species of bamboo, remainder stocked in small numbers only. Limited stocks of grasses, trees & shrubs.
Notes: Mail order limited by carrier restrictions, please contact nursery or see website for details. Also sells wholesale. Wheelchair accessible.
Map Ref: M, B1 **OS Grid Ref:** SK325603

MWts **WATERSIDE NURSERY**
Sharnford, Leicestershire
Ⓣ (01455) 273730
Ⓜ 07931 557082
Ⓔ watersidenursery@yahoo.co.uk
Ⓦ www.watersidenursery.co.uk
Contact: Linda Smith
Opening Times: By appt. only.
Min Mail Order UK: Nmc
Cat. Cost: Online only.
Credit Cards: All major credit/debit cards
Specialities: Aquatics, marginal pond plants, miniature water lilies, waterlilies, bog garden plants & moisture-loving plants.
Notes: Delivers to shows.

NORTHERN

NAbi **ABI AND TOM'S GARDEN PLANTS** ♿
Halecat Nurseries, Witherslack, Grange Over Sands, Cumbria LA11 6RT
Ⓣ (01539) 552946
Ⓔ info@halecatplants.co.uk
Ⓦ www.halecatplants.co.uk
Contact: Tom & Abi Attwood
Opening Times: 0900-1700 Mon-Sat, 1000-1600 Sun.
Cat. Cost: Online.
Credit Cards: All major credit/debit cards
Specialities: Hardy herbaceous perennials.
Notes: Wheelchair accessible.
Map Ref: N, C1 **OS Grid Ref:** SD433838

NBid **BIDE-A-WEE COTTAGE GARDENS** ♿
Stanton, Netherwitton, Morpeth,
Northumberland NE65 8PR
Ⓣ (01670) 772238
Ⓜ 07976 559416
Ⓕ (01670) 772238
Ⓔ info@bideawee.co.uk
Ⓦ www.bideawee.co.uk
Contact: Mark Robson
Opening Times: 1330-1700 Sat & Wed, 20th Apr-31st Aug 2013. Group visits at other times, except Sun.
Min Mail Order UK: £20.00
Cat. Cost: Online only.
Credit Cards: All major credit/debit cards
Specialities: Unusual herbaceous perennials, *Agapanthus*, *Primula*, ferns, grasses. Nat. Collection of *Centaurea*.
Notes: Wheelchair accessible.
Map Ref: N, B2 **OS Grid Ref:** NZ132900

NBir **BIRKHEADS SECRET GARDENS & NURSERY** ♿
Birkheads Lane, Sunniside,
Gateshead, Tyne & Wear
NE16 5EL
Ⓣ (01207) 232262
Ⓜ 07778 447920
Ⓕ (01207) 232262
Ⓔ birkheadsnursery@gmail.com
Ⓦ www.birkheadssecretgardens.co.uk
Contact: Mrs Christine Liddle
Opening Times: 1000-1700 Wed-Sun (closed Mon & Tues), early Mar to late Sep. Open B/hol Mons. Coach groups by appt.
Cat. Cost: None issued.
Credit Cards: All major credit/debit cards
Specialities: Hardy herbaceous perennials, grasses, bulbs & herbs. *Allium*, *Digitalis*, *Euphorbia*, *Galanthus* & *Geranium*. Max. 30 of any plant propagated each year.
Notes: Wheelchair accessible.
Map Ref: N, B2 **OS Grid Ref:** NZ220569

NBre **Breezy Knees Nurseries** ♿
Common Lane, Warthill, York YO19 5XS
Ⓣ (01904) 488800
Ⓦ www.breezyknees.co.uk
Contact: Any member of staff
Opening Times: 1000-1700 7 days (open 1100 Sun), 1st Apr-30th Sep.
Credit Cards: All major credit/debit cards
Specialities: Very wide range of perennials. All can be viewed in 15-acre gardens (open 24th May-30th Sep).
Notes: Wheelchair accessible.
Map Ref: N, C3 **OS Grid Ref:** SE675565

NBri **Brighter Blooms**
Walton Flats Nursery, Gillibrand Street, Walton-le-Dale, Preston, Lancashire PR5 4AX
Ⓜ 07884 430732
Ⓔ matthew@brighterblooms.co.uk
Ⓦ www.brighterblooms.co.uk
Contact: Matthew Smith
Opening Times: By appt. only.
Credit Cards: All major credit/debit cards
Specialities: *Zantedeschia*, potted & bulbs. Spring & summer bulbs (dry format). Potted bulbs available in small quantities only.
Notes: Also sells wholesale. Delivers to shows.

NBro **Brownthwaite Hardy Plants** ♿
Fell Yeat, Casterton, Kirkby Lonsdale, Lancashire LA6 2JW
Ⓣ (01524) 271340 (after 1800 hours).
Ⓦ www.hardyplantsofcumbria.co.uk
Contact: Chris Benson
Opening Times: 1000-1700, 1st Apr-30th Sep.
Min Mail Order UK: Nmc
Cat. Cost: 4 × 1st class for *Hydrangea* catalogue. Sae for auricula list.
Credit Cards: None
Specialities: Herbaceous perennials incl. *Geranium*, *Hosta*, also *Tiarella*, *Heucherella* & *Primula auricula*. *Hydrangea paniculata* & *H. serrata* varieties.
Notes: Follow brown signs from A65 between Kirkby Lonsdale & Cowan Bridge. Mail order for *Hydrangea* & *P. auricula*. Delivers to shows. Wheelchair accessible.
Map Ref: N, C1 **OS Grid Ref:** SD632794

NCGa **Caths Garden Plants** ♿
The Walled Garden, Heaves Hotel, Heaves, Levens, Cumbria LA8 8EF
Ⓣ (01539) 561126
Ⓕ (01539) 561126
Ⓔ cath@cathsgardenplants.co.uk
Ⓦ www.cathsgardenplants.co.uk
Contact: Bob Sanderson
Opening Times: 1030-1700 7 days, Mar-Oct. 1030-1600 Wed-Fri, Nov-Feb. Closed Xmas & New Year weeks.
Min Mail Order UK: £15.00 + p&p
Min Mail Order EU: £25.00
Cat. Cost: Online only.
Credit Cards: All major credit/debit cards
Specialities: Wide variety of perennials, incl. uncommon varieties & selections of grasses, ferns, shrubs & climbing plants.
Notes: On A590 follow signs for Heaves (not in Levens village). Delivers to shows. Wheelchair accessible.
Map Ref: N, C1 **OS Grid Ref:** SD497867

NChi **Chipchase Castle Nursery** ♿
Chipchase Castle, Wark, Hexham, Northumberland NE48 3NT
Ⓣ (01434) 230083
Ⓜ 07881 630398
Ⓔ info@chipchaseplants.co.uk
Ⓦ www.chipchaseplants.co.uk
Contact: Joyce Hunt & Alison Jones
Opening Times: 1000-1700 Thu-Sun & B/hol Mons Easter (or 1st Apr)-end Aug.
Min Mail Order UK: Nmc
Min Mail Order EU: Nmc
Cat. Cost: A5 sae for list
Credit Cards: All major credit/debit cards
Specialities: Unusual herbaceous esp. *Eryngium*, *Geum* & *Geranium*. Some plants only available in small quantities.
Notes: Delivers to shows. Suitable for accompanied wheelchair users.
Map Ref: N, B2 **OS Grid Ref:** NY880758

NCot **Cottage Garden Plants**
1 Kelton Croft, Kirkland, Cumbria CA26 3YE
Ⓣ (01946) 862664
Ⓔ expressplants@aol.com
Ⓦ http://simplesite.com/hardy_geraniums
Contact: Mrs J Purkiss
Opening Times: Open by appt. only for collecting orders & viewing garden. Consult local press & radio for charity openings.
Min Mail Order UK: £10.00
Min Mail Order EU: £15.00
Cat. Cost: 4 × 1st class sae.
Credit Cards: Paypal
Specialities: Small quantities only of all plants. Own new & exclusive introductions of *Geranium* cvs occasionally available. Plant Heritage Nat. Collection of *Geranium phaeum* Group. Other hardy perennials also sometimes available during the year.
Map Ref: N, C1

NCro **Croston Cactus** ♿
43 Southport Road, Eccleston, Chorley, Lancashire PR7 6ET
Ⓣ (01257) 452555
Ⓕ (01257) 452555
Ⓔ sales@croston-cactus.co.uk

Ⓦ www.croston-cactus.co.uk
Contact: John Henshaw
Opening Times: 0930-1700 by appt. only.
Min Mail Order UK: £5.00 + p&p
Min Mail Order EU: £10.00 + p&p
Cat. Cost: 2 × 1st class or 2 × IRCs.
Credit Cards: All major credit/debit cards
Specialities: Mexican cacti, *Echeveria* hybrids & some bromeliads & *Tillandsia*. Some items held in small quantities only. See catalogue.
Notes: Credit card payment accepted for online orders only. Euro accepted. Wheelchair accessible.
Map Ref: N, D1 **OS Grid Ref:** SD522186

NDav **Dave Parkinson Plants**
4 West Bank, Carlton, Goole, East Yorkshire DN14 9PZ
Ⓣ (01405) 860693
Ⓜ 07773 564945
Ⓕ (01405) 860693
Ⓦ www.daveparkinsonplants.co.uk
Contact: Mary Parkinson
Opening Times: Not open. Mail order only.
Min Mail Order UK: £12 + p&p
Min Mail Order EU: Nmc
Cat. Cost: 1st class stamp.
Credit Cards: None
Specialities: Hardy orchids. Terrestrial South African *Disa* orchids, species & hybrids.
Notes: Delivers to shows.

NDov **Dove Cottage Nursery & Garden** ♿
Shibden Hall Road, Halifax, West Yorkshire HX3 9XA
Ⓣ (01422) 203553
Ⓔ info@dovecottagenursery.co.uk
Ⓦ www.dovecottagenursery.co.uk
Contact: Stephen & Kim Rogers
Opening Times: 1000-1700 Wed-Sat, Mar-Sep. 1000-1700 Sun & B/hols Mar-Jun.
Min Mail Order UK: £20.00
Cat. Cost: 6 × 2nd class.
Credit Cards: All major credit/debit cards
Specialities: Herbaceous perennials & selected grasses, many displayed in adjoining naturalistic garden.
Notes: Wheelchair accessible.
Map Ref: N, D2 **OS Grid Ref:** SE115256

NDro **Drointon Nurseries** ♿
Plaster Pitts, Norton Conyers, Ripon, North Yorkshire HG4 5EF
Ⓣ (01765) 641849
Ⓜ 07909 971529
Ⓔ info@auricula-plants.co.uk
Ⓦ www.auricula-plants.co.uk
Contact: Robin & Annabel Graham
Opening Times: Open days in spring, otherwise by appt. only.
Min Mail Order UK: Nmc
Min Mail Order EU: Nmc
Cat. Cost: 4 × 1st class.
Credit Cards: All major credit/debit cards
Specialities: *Primula auricula.* More than 800 cvs of show, alpine, double & border auriculas. Limited stocks of any one cultivar. Nat. Collection of *Primula auricula* (borders).
Notes: Also sells wholesale. Exports beyond EU. Delivers to shows. Wheelchair accessible.
Map Ref: N, C2 **OS Grid Ref:** SE315753

NEgg **Eggleston Hall Gardens** ♿
Eggleston, Barnard Castle, Co. Durham DL12 0AG
Ⓣ (01833) 650230
Ⓔ mbhock@btinternet.com
Ⓦ www.egglestonhallgardens.co.uk.
Contact: Malcolm Hockham
Opening Times: 1000-1700 7 days. Closed 24th Dec to 6th Jan each year.
Cat. Cost: Online only.
Credit Cards: All major credit/debit cards
Notes: Collection from nursery only. Euro accepted. Wheelchair accessible.

NEoE **East of Eden Nursery** ♿
Ainstable, Carlisle, Cumbria CA4 9QN
Ⓣ (01768) 896604
Ⓜ 07788 142969
Ⓔ roger@east-of-eden-nursery.co.uk
Ⓦ www.east-of-eden-nursery.co.uk
Contact: Roger Proud
Opening Times: By appt. only, Mar-Oct.
Min Mail Order UK: £10.00
Cat. Cost: None issued
Credit Cards: All major credit/debit cards
Specialities: Interesting & unusual shrubs, perennials & alpines, esp. astilbes and geums with over 50 new *Geum* cvs, bred & raised on nursery.
Notes: Mail order available for geums & astilbes only. Delivers to shows. Wheelchair accessible.
Map Ref: N, B1 **OS Grid Ref:** NY467504

NEqu **Equatorial Plant Co.**
The Dovecote, Newgate, Barnard Castle, Co. Durham DL12 8NW
Ⓣ (01833) 908127
Ⓕ (01833) 908127
Ⓔ equatorialplants@teesdaleonline.co.uk
Ⓦ www.equatorialplants.com
Contact: Dr Richard Warren
Opening Times: Mail order only. Open by appt. only.
Min Mail Order UK: Nmc
Min Mail Order EU: Nmc
Cat. Cost: Free.
Credit Cards: Visa, Access, Paypal
Specialities: Laboratory-raised orchids only.

Notes: Also sells wholesale. Exports beyond EU. Delivers to shows. Euro accepted.

NEve **Every Picture Tells a Story** ♿
Lydiate Barn Nursery & Garden Centre, Southport Road, Lydiate, Merseyside, L31 4EE
Ⓣ 0151 286 2033
Ⓜ 07847 939867
Ⓔ don@every-picture.com
Ⓦ www.every-picture.com
Contact: Don Billington
Opening Times: 1000-1700.
Min Mail Order UK: Nmc
Credit Cards: All major credit/debit cards
Specialities: National Collection of Bromeliads (Provisional).
Notes: Delivers to shows. Wheelchair accessible.
Map Ref: N, D1

NFir **Fir Trees Pelargonium Nursery** ♿
Stokesley, Middlesbrough, Cleveland TS9 5LD
Ⓣ (01642) 713066
Ⓕ (01642) 713066
Ⓔ mark@firtreespelargoniums.co.uk
Ⓦ www.firtreespelargoniums.co.uk
Contact: Helen Bainbridge
Opening Times: 1000-1600 7 days 1st Apr-31st Aug, 1000-1600 Mon-Fri 1st Sep-31st Mar.
Min Mail Order UK: £4.00 + p&p
Cat. Cost: 4 × 1st class or £1.00 coin.
Credit Cards: All major credit/debit cards
Specialities: All types of *Pelargonium*, fancy leaf, regal, decorative regal, oriental regal, angel, miniature, zonal, ivy leaf, stellar, scented, dwarf, unique, golden stellar & species.
Notes: Delivers to shows. Wheelchair accessible.
Map Ref: N, C2

NGBl **Garden Blooms**
Fieldgate, Mill Field Road, Fishlake, Doncaster, Yorkshire DN7 5GH
Ⓣ 0845 5440964
Ⓔ info@gardenblooms.co.uk
Ⓦ www.gardenblooms.co.uk
Contact: Liz Webster
Opening Times: Not open, except by appt.
Min Mail Order UK: Nmc
Cat. Cost: Online only.
Credit Cards: None
Specialities: Hardy & tender perennials. Available in small quantities only. Small range of house plants.
Notes: Credit cards accepted online only. Delivers to shows.
Map Ref: N, D2 **OS Grid Ref:** SE659148

NGdn **Garden House Nursery** ♿
The Square, Dalston, Carlisle, Cumbria CA5 7LL
Ⓣ (01228) 710297
Ⓜ 07595 219082
Ⓔ stephickso@hotmail.co.uk
Ⓦ www.gardenhousenursery.co.uk
Contact: Stephen Hickson
Opening Times: 0900-1700 7 days Mar-Oct.
Cat. Cost: Plant list online only.
Credit Cards: None
Specialities: *Geranium, Hosta, Hemerocallis, Iris*, grasses, *Brunnera, Pulmonaria* & *Aconitum*.
Notes: Also sells wholesale. Wheelchair accessible.
Map Ref: N, B1 **OS Grid Ref:** NY369503

NHal **Halls of Heddon**
West Heddon Nurseries, Heddon-on-the-Wall, Northumberland NE15 0JS
Ⓣ (01661) 852445
Ⓕ (01661) 852398
Ⓔ enquiry@hallsofheddon.co.uk
Ⓦ www.hallsofheddon.co.uk
Contact: David Hall
Opening Times: 0900-1700 Mon-Sat 1000-1700 Sun.
Min Mail Order UK: £10.00
Min Mail Order EU: £35.00
Cat. Cost: 3 × 2nd class
Credit Cards: MasterCard, Visa, Switch, Delta
Specialities: *Chrysanthemum* & *Dahlia*.
Notes: Also sells wholesale.
Map Ref: N, B2 **OS Grid Ref:** NZ122679

NHar **Hartside Nursery Garden**
Nr Alston, Cumbria CA9 3BL
Ⓣ (01434) 381372
Ⓕ (01434) 381372
Ⓔ enquiries@plantswithaltitude.co.uk
Ⓦ www.plantswithaltitude.co.uk
Contact: S L & N Huntley
Opening Times: 1130-1630 Mon-Fri, 1230-1600 w/ends & B/hols, Mar-Jun (incl.). 1130-1630 Tue-Fri, 1230-1600 B/hols, w/ends by appt., Jul-Oct (incl.). Winter months by appt. Times may vary during show season, so please phone before travelling.
Min Mail Order UK: Nmc
Min Mail Order EU: £50.00 + p&p
Cat. Cost: 4 × 1st class or 3 × IRC
Credit Cards: All major credit/debit cards
Specialities: Alpines grown at altitude of 1100 feet in Pennines. *Primula*, ferns, *Gentian* & *Meconopsis*.
Notes: Delivers to shows.
Map Ref: N, B1 **OS Grid Ref:** NY708447

NHaw **The Hawthornes Nursery** ♿
Marsh Road, Hesketh Bank, Nr Preston, Lancashire PR4 6XT
Ⓣ (01772) 812379
Ⓔ richardhaw@talktalk.net
Ⓦ www.hawthornes-nursery.co.uk
Contact: Irene & Richard Hodson
Opening Times: 0900-1800 7 days 1st Mar-30th Jun, Thu-Sun July-Oct. Gardens open for NGS. National Collection Open Day 25th July 2013.
Min Mail Order UK: £10.00
Min Mail Order EU: Nmc
Cat. Cost: None issued.
Credit Cards: None
Specialities: *Clematis*. Nat. Collection of *Clematis viticella*.
Notes: Euro accepted. Wheelchair accessible.

N

NHed **Hedges Direct**
Five Acres Nursery, Dawbers Lane, Euxton, Lancashire PR7 6EE
Ⓣ (01257) 263873
Ⓜ 07771 958228
Ⓔ helpdesk@hedgesdirect.co.uk
Ⓦ www.hedgesdirect.co.uk
Contact: Kate James
Opening Times: 0800-1800 Mon-Sat. 1000-1600 Sun.
Min Mail Order UK: Nmc
Notes: Also sells wholesale.

NHer **Herterton House Garden Nursery**
Hartington, Cambo, Morpeth, Northumberland NE61 4BN
Ⓣ (01670) 774278
Contact: Mrs M Lawley & Mr Frank Lawley
Opening Times: 1330-1730 Mon, Wed, Fri-Sun 1st Apr-end Sep. (Earlier or later in the year weather permitting.)
Cat. Cost: None issued.
Credit Cards: None
Specialities: Country garden flowers.
Map Ref: N, B2 **OS Grid Ref:** NZ022880

NHip **Hippopottering Nursery**
Orchard House, East Lound, Nr Doncaster, South Yorkshire DN9 2LR
Ⓜ 07979 764677
Ⓔ hippomaples@hotmail.co.uk
Ⓦ www.hippopottering.com
Contact: Pat Gibbons
Opening Times: By appt. only & Open Days.
Min Mail Order UK: £15.00 + p&p
Min Mail Order EU: £15.00 + p&p
Cat. Cost: Online only.
Credit Cards: Visa, MasterCard
Specialities: Japanese maples. Many available only from us.
Notes: Mail order to UK throughout year; to EU during winter. Delivers to shows. Wheelchair accessible in dry weather only.

NHol **Holden Clough Nursery Ltd.** ♿
Holden, Bolton-by-Bowland, Clitheroe, Lancashire BB7 4PF
Ⓣ (01200) 447615
Ⓔ info@holdencloughnursery.co.uk
Ⓦ www.holdencloughnursery.co.uk
Contact: John Foley
Opening Times: 0900-1700 Mon-Sat, 1000-1600 Sun, incl. b/hols. Closed Xmas Day & Boxing Day.
Min Mail Order UK: Nmc
Min Mail Order EU: Nmc
Cat. Cost: 2 × 1st class.
Credit Cards: All major credit/debit cards
Specialities: Large general list incl. perennials, esp. *Crocosmia*, shrubs, dwarf conifers, alpines, heathers, grasses & ferns.
Notes: Seasonal mail order on some items. Also sells wholesale on some items. Exports beyond EU. Delivers to shows. Wheelchair accessible.
Map Ref: N, C2 **OS Grid Ref:** SD773496

NHoy **Hoyland Plant Centre** ♿
54 Greenside Lane, Hoyland, Barnsley, Yorkshire S74 9PZ
Ⓣ (01226) 744466
Ⓜ 07717 182169
Ⓕ (01226) 744466
Ⓔ stevenhickman@btconnect.com
Ⓦ www.somethingforthegarden.co.uk
Contact: Steven Hickman
Opening Times: All year round by appt. only.
Min Mail Order UK: Nmc
Min Mail Order EU: Nmc
Cat. Cost: 4 × 1st class.
Credit Cards: All major credit/debit cards
Specialities: *Agapanthus* (400+ cvs) & *Tulbaghia* (80+ cvs). Some available in small quantities only. Nat. Collections of *Agapanthus* & *Tulbaghia*.
Notes: Daily practical workshops available, ring for details. Also sells wholesale. Exports beyond EU. Delivers to shows. Euro accepted. Wheelchair accessible.
OS Grid Ref: SE372010

NJRG **JRG Dahlias**
22 Summerville Road, Milnthorpe, Cumbria LA7 7DF
Ⓣ (01539) 562691
Ⓔ jack@jrg-dahlias.co.uk
Ⓦ www.jrg-dahlias.co.uk
Contact: Jack Gott
Opening Times: By appt. only.
Min Mail Order UK: £10.00 + p&p
Min Mail Order EU: Price with order.

Cat. Cost: Sae: 110mm × 220mm, 2nd class.
Credit Cards: None
Specialities: *Dahlia.*
Notes: Delivers to Shows.
Map Ref: N, C1

NLar **LARCH COTTAGE NURSERIES** ♿ ◆
Melkinthorpe, Penrith, Cumbria
CA10 2DR
Ⓣ (01931) 712404
Ⓕ (01931) 712727
Ⓔ plants@larchcottage.co.uk
Ⓦ www.larchcottage.co.uk
Contact: Peter Stott & Joanne McCullock
Opening Times: Daily from 1000-1730 (or dusk in winter), all year round.
Min Mail Order UK: Nmc
Min Mail Order EU: Nmc
Cat. Cost: £7.00
Credit Cards: All major credit/debit cards
Specialities: Comprehensive plant collection in unique garden setting. Rare & unusual plants; particularly shrubs, trees, perennials, dwarf conifers & Japanese maples. *Acer, Hamamelis, Magnolia* & *Cornus kousa* cvs. Old-fashioned roses, bamboo & alpines.
Notes: Terraced restaurant & art gallery. Euro accepted. Wheelchair accessible.
Map Ref: N, C1 **OS Grid Ref:** NY315602

NLos **THE LOST WORLD NURSERY**
The Hawthorns, Hesketh Bank, Nr Preston, Lancashire PR4 6XT
Ⓜ 07810 547629
Ⓔ plants@thelostworldnursery.com
Ⓦ www.thelostworldnursery.com
Contact: Phil Ball
Opening Times: By prior appt. only. Please phone in advance when planning a visit.
Min Mail Order UK: Nmc
Min Mail Order EU: Nmc
Cat. Cost: Online.
Credit Cards: Paypal
Specialities: Carnivorous plants: *Sarracenia, Nepenthes.* Ferns, bromeliads, bananas, palms, grasses, gingers, bamboo. Plants for exotic effect.
Notes: Plants may be pre-ordered for collection either at the nursery or at shows or plant fairs. Delivers to shows. Euro accepted. Wheelchair access in dry weather.
Map Ref: N, D1 **OS Grid Ref:** SD447239

NMin **MINIATURE BULBS & WILDFLOWER BULBS**
3 Ashleigh Gardens, Cleadon, South Tyneside
SR6 7QA
Ⓣ (0191) 536 3599
Ⓜ 07881 560516
Ⓔ facharlton@btinternet.com
Ⓦ www.miniaturebulbs.co.uk
Contact: Frank Charlton
Opening Times: Not open. Mail order only.
Min Mail Order UK: £15.00
Min Mail Order EU: £15.00
Cat. Cost: 1 × 1st class.
Credit Cards: All major credit/debit cards
Specialities: Rare & unusual miniature & wildflower bulbs, incl. *Narcissus, Tulipa, Iris, Crocus, Fritillaria* & others. Spring bulb list sent out in April. Some stock in small quantities.
Notes: Euro accepted. Delivers to shows.

NMir **MIRES BECK NURSERY** ♿
Low Mill Lane, North Cave,
Brough, East Riding, Yorkshire
HU15 2NR
Ⓣ (01430) 421543
Ⓕ (01430) 421543
Ⓔ admin@miresbeck.co.uk
Ⓦ www.miresbeck.co.uk
Contact: Judy Burrow & Martin Rowland
Opening Times: 1000-1600 Mon-Sat 1st Mar-30th Sep. 1000-1500 Mon-Fri 1st Oct-30th Nov & by appt.
Min Mail Order UK: Nmc
Cat. Cost: 3 × 1st class.
Credit Cards: None
Specialities: Wildflower plants of Yorkshire provenance.
Notes: Mail order for wildflower plants & plugs only. Also sells wholesale. Wheelchair accessible.
Map Ref: N, D3 **OS Grid Ref:** SE889316

NMyG **MARY GREEN** ♿
The Walled Garden, Hornby, Lancaster, Lancashire LA2 8LD
Ⓣ (01524) 221989
Ⓜ 07778 910348
Ⓕ (01524) 221989
Ⓔ Marygreenplants@aol.com
Contact: Mary Green
Opening Times: By appt. only.
Cat. Cost: None issued.
Credit Cards: None
Specialities: Hostas, ferns & other shade-loving perennials.
Notes: Delivers to shows. Wheelchair accessible.
Map Ref: N, C1 **OS Grid Ref:** SD588688

NNor **NORCROFT NURSERIES** ♿
Roadends, Intack, Southwaite, Carlisle, Cumbria CA4 0LH
Ⓣ (01697) 473933
Ⓔ stellagbell@btinternet.com
Contact: Keith Bell
Opening Times: Every afternoon excl. Mon (open B/hol), Apr-Jul, or ring for appt.
Min Mail Order UK: Nmc

Cat. Cost: 2 × 2nd class
Credit Cards: None
Specialities: Hardy herbaceous, *Dianthus*, *Aquilegia*, hostas, *Lilium*, *Papaver*.
Notes: Wheelchair accessible.
Map Ref: N, B1 **OS Grid Ref:** NY474433

NOak **OAK TREE NURSERY** ♿
Mill Lane, Barlow, Selby, North Yorkshire YO8 8EY
Ⓣ (01757) 618409
Ⓜ 07706 505688
Ⓔ gill@oaktreenursery.plus.com
Ⓦ www.oaktreenursery.com
Contact: Gill Plowes
Opening Times: By appt. only.
Min Mail Order UK: £10.00 + p&p
Min Mail Order EU: Nmc
Cat. Cost: 4 × 1st class.
Credit Cards: All major credit/debit cards
Specialities: Ornamental grasses & grass-like plants.
Notes: Will export seeds only beyond the EU. Also sells wholesale. Delivers to shows. Wheelchair accessible.

NOra **ORANGE PIPPIN LTD**
(Office) 33 Algarth Rise, Pocklington, York, Yorkshire YO42 2HX
Ⓣ (01759) 392007
Ⓔ trees@orangepippin.com
Ⓦ www.orangepippinshop.com
Contact: Maureen Borrie
Opening Times: Not open. Mail order online only.
Min Mail Order UK: Nmc
Min Mail Order EU: Nmc
Cat. Cost: Online only.
Credit Cards: MasterCard, Visa
Specialities: Wide range of many types of fruit tree, incl. traditional & modern varieties. Wide choice of rootstocks. Fruit tree expert available most days & at w/ends. Website incl. extensive tasting notes & variety comparisons.
Notes: Order online all year round, deliveries from end Aug-end Mar. Exports beyond EU.

NOrc **ORCHARD HOUSE NURSERY** ♿
Orchard House, Wormald Green, Nr Harrogate, North Yorkshire HG3 3NQ
Ⓣ (01765) 677541
Ⓕ (01765) 677541
Contact: Mr B M Corner
Opening Times: 0800-1630 Mon-Fri. Closed B/hols.
Cat. Cost: 4 × 1st class.
Credit Cards: All major credit/debit cards
Specialities: Herbaceous perennials, ferns, grasses, bog plants & unusual cottage garden plants.
Notes: Also sells wholesale. Wheelchair accessible.
Map Ref: N, C2

NPCo **PLANTSMAN'S CORNER**
Sunniside, Barningham, Richmond, Yorkshire DL11 7DW
Ⓜ 07707 694310
Ⓔ plantsmanscorner@btinternet.com
Ⓦ www.plantsmanscorner.co.uk
Contact: Malcolm Hockham
Opening Times: Not yet fully open. Visits by appt. only. Plant orders can be collected by prior arrangement or from Eggleston Hall Gardens (see nursery NEgg for opening hours). Please contact nursery for details.
Credit Cards: All major credit/debit cards
Specialities: *Cornus*, *Ilex*, & Japanese maples. Variable stock levels.

NPer **PERRY'S PLANTS** ♿
The River Garden, Sleights, Whitby, North Yorkshire YO21 1RR
Ⓜ 07879 498623
Ⓔ sharon.perry@virgin.net
Ⓦ www.perrysplants.co.uk
Contact: Sharon & Richard Perry
Opening Times: 1000-1700 mid-March to Oct.
Cat. Cost: None published.
Credit Cards: None
Specialities: *Lavatera*, *Malva*, *Erysimum*, *Euphorbia*, *Anthemis*, *Osteospermum* & *Hebe*. Uncommon hardy & container plants & aquatic plants.
Notes: Euro accepted. Wheelchair accessible.
Map Ref: N, C3 **OS Grid Ref:** NZ869082

NPla **THE PLANT DIRECTORY**
Scawsby Hall Nurseries, Barnsley Road, Scawsby, Doncaster, South Yorkshire DN5 7UB
Ⓣ (01302) 783434
Ⓔ mail@the-plant-directory.co.uk
Ⓦ www.the-plant-directory.co.uk
Contact: David Lawson
Opening Times: Not open. Mail order only.
Min Mail Order UK: Nmc
Cat. Cost: None issued
Credit Cards: Visa, MasterCard, Paypal
Specialities: A wide range of herbaceous perennials, hardy trees, shrubs & indoor plants. Some indoor & aquatic plants in small quantities only.

NPol **POLEMONIUM PLANTERY**
28 Sunnyside, Trimdon Grange, Co. Durham TS29 6HF
Ⓣ (01429) 881529
Ⓔ dandd@polemonium.co.uk

N

Ⓦ www.polemonium.co.uk
Contact: David or Dianne Nichol-Brown
Opening Times: By appt. only.
Min Mail Order UK: £10.00
Cat. Cost: 3 × 1st class
Credit Cards: None
Specialities: Nat. Collections of *Polemonium*, *Collomia*, *Gilia*, *Leptodactylon* (*Polemoniaceae*) & *Hakonechloa*.
Notes: Also sells wholesale. Delivers to shows.
Map Ref: N, B2 **OS Grid Ref:** NZ369353

NPri **PRIMROSE COTTAGE NURSERY** ♿
Ringway Road, Moss Nook, Wythenshawe, Manchester, M22 5WF
Ⓣ (0161) 437 1557
Ⓜ 07798 754457
Ⓔ info@primrosecottagenursery.co.uk
Ⓦ www.primrosecottagenursery.co.uk
Contact: Caroline Dumville
Opening Times: 0830-1730 Mon-Sat, 0930-1730 Sun (summer). 0830-1700 Mon-Sat, 0930-1700 Sun (winter).
Cat. Cost: Plant lists can be sent by email.
Credit Cards: All major credit/debit cards
Specialities: Perennials, herbs, roses, patio & hanging basket plants. Shrubs, ornamental trees, fruit trees, soft fruit bushes & vegetable plants.
Notes: Coffee shop open daily. Wheelchair accessible.
Map Ref: N, D2

NRib **RIBBLESDALE NURSERIES** ♿
Newsham Hall Lane, Woodplumpton, Preston, Lancashire PR4 0AS
Ⓣ (01772) 863081
Ⓕ (01772) 861884
Ⓔ philsd@btinternet.com
Ⓦ www.ribblesdalenurseries.co.uk
Contact: Mr & Mrs Dunnett
Opening Times: 0900-1800 Mon-Sat Apr-Sep, 0900-1700 Mon-Sat Oct-Mar. 1030-1630 Sun.
Credit Cards: Visa, MasterCard, Delta, Switch
Specialities: Trees, shrubs & perennials. Conifers, hedging, alpines, fruit, climbers, herbs, aquatics, ferns & wildflowers. Own grown plants in peat-free compost.
Notes: Wheelchair accessible.

NRob **W ROBINSON & SON (SEEDS & PLANTS) LTD** ♿
Sunny Bank, Forton, Nr Preston, Lancashire PR3 0BN
Ⓣ (01524) 791210
Ⓕ (01524) 791933
Ⓔ info@mammothonion.co.uk
Ⓦ www.mammothonion.co.uk
Contact: Miss Robinson
Opening Times: 1000-1600 7 days Mar-Jun, 0800-1700 Mon-Fri Jul-Feb.
Min Mail Order UK: Nmc
Min Mail Order EU: Nmc
Cat. Cost: Free.
Credit Cards: All major credit/debit cards
Specialities: Mammoth vegetable seed. Onions, leeks, tomatoes & beans. Range of vegetable plants in the spring.
Notes: Also sells wholesale. Exports beyond EU. Delivers to shows. Wheelchair accessible.

NRog **R V ROGER LTD** ♿
The Nurseries, Pickering, North Yorkshire YO18 7JW
Ⓣ (01751) 472226
Ⓕ (01751) 476749
Ⓔ sales@rvrogers.co.uk
Ⓦ www.rvroger.co.uk
Contact: Ian Roger
Opening Times: 0900-1700 Mon-Sat, 1000-1600 Sun.
Min Mail Order UK: Nmc
Min Mail Order EU: Nmc
Cat. Cost: £1.00
Credit Cards: All major credit/debit cards
Specialities: Holders of National Collection of *Erythronium*.
Notes: Also sells wholesale. Wheelchair accessible.
Map Ref: N, C3 **OS Grid Ref:** SE801827

NRya **RYAL NURSERY** ♿
East Farm Cottage, Ryal, Northumberland NE20 0SA
Ⓣ (01661) 886562
Ⓔ alpines@ryal.freeserve.co.uk
Contact: R F Hadden
Opening Times: Mar-Jul by appt., please phone.
Cat. Cost: Sae.
Credit Cards: None
Specialities: Alpine & woodland plants. Mainly available in small quantities only. Nat. Collection of *Primula marginata*.
Notes: Also sells wholesale. Delivers to shows. Wheelchair accessible.
Map Ref: N, B2 **OS Grid Ref:** NZ015744

NSbr **STONEBRIDGE PLANTS (FORMERLY L.B. PLANTS)** ♿
(Office) 20 Grove Road, Brandon, Co. Durham DH7 8AW
Ⓜ 079321 59204 or 07791 203375
Ⓔ stonebridgeplants@hotmail.co.uk
Ⓦ www.stonebridgeplants.co.uk
Contact: Howard Leslie
Opening Times: 1000-1700 (or sunset in winter), 7 days.
Min Mail Order UK: Nmc

Cat. Cost: Online only.
Credit Cards: None
Specialities: Hardy herbaceous & shrubby perennials, incl. small quantities of lesser known and harder to find plants.
Notes: Also sells wholesale. Delivers to shows. Wheelchair accessible.
Map Ref: N, B2

NSir **Sir Plants-Alot Garden Centre & Nursery** ♿
Sandy Lane West, Billingham, Cleveland TS22 5NB
Ⓣ (01740) 644977
Ⓔ info@sirplantsalot.co.uk
Ⓦ www.sirplantsalot.co.uk
Contact: Julie Turner
Opening Times: 0900-1800, 7 days, Mar-Dec. Closed Xmas/New Year period. 1000-1600, Tue-Sun (closed Mon), Jan-Feb.
Notes: Wheelchair accessible.
Map Ref: N, C2 **OS Grid Ref:** NZ436252

NSla **Slack Top Nurseries**
1 Waterloo House, 24 Slack Top, Hebden Bridge, West Yorkshire HX7 7HA
Ⓣ (01422) 845348
Ⓜ 07508 953804
Ⓔ enquiries@slacktopnurseries.co.uk
Ⓦ www.slacktopnurseries.co.uk
Contact: Michael & Allison Mitchell
Opening Times: 1000-1700 Fri-Sun 1st Mar-31st Aug & B/hols. Other times by appt.
Min Mail Order UK: £20.00
Min Mail Order EU: £50.00
Cat. Cost: 2 × 1st class A5 sae or online.
Credit Cards: None
Specialities: Alpine, rockery & woodland plants.
Notes: Talks given to gardening clubs & other groups by appt. Delivers to shows. Euro accepted. Some areas of garden inaccessible for wheelchairs.
Map Ref: N, D2 **OS Grid Ref:** SD977286

NSoo **Sooty's Plants** ♿
113a Southport New Road, Tarleton, Preston, Lancashire PR4 6HX
Ⓣ (01772) 816901
Ⓔ sales@sootysplants.co.uk
Ⓦ www.sootysplants.co.uk
Contact: Amanda Bowers
Opening Times: 0900-1700 Mon-Sat, 1000-1600 Sun. Closed 3rd Dec until 21st Jan 2013.
Cat. Cost: None issued.
Credit Cards: All, except American Express
Specialities: Wide range of common & unusual plants. Some varieties available in small quantities only.
Notes: Wheelchair accessible.

NSti **Stillingfleet Lodge Nurseries** ♿
Stewart Lane, Stillingfleet, North Yorkshire YO19 6HP
Ⓣ (01904) 728506
Ⓔ info@stillingfleetlodgenurseries.co.uk
Ⓦ www.stillingfleetlodgenurseries.co.uk
Contact: Vanessa Cook
Opening Times: 1300-1700 Wed & Fri, 1st Apr-30th Sep. 1300-1700, 1st & 3rd Sat & Sun in each month.
Cat. Cost: Online only.
Credit Cards: None
Specialities: Foliage & unusual perennials. Hardy geraniums, *Pulmonaria*, variegated plants & grasses, interesting climbers.
Notes: Wheelchair accessible.
Map Ref: N, D2

NSue **Sue Proctor Plants**
69 Ings Mill Avenue, Clayton West, Huddersfield, West Yorkshire HD8 9QG
Ⓣ (01484) 866189
Ⓜ 07917 006636
Ⓔ sueproctor@talktalk.net
Ⓦ www.sueproctorplants.co.uk
Contact: Richard Proctor
Opening Times: By appt. only. Please phone first.
Min Mail Order UK: £3.50
Cat. Cost: Large 1st sae.
Credit Cards: All major credit/debit cards
Specialities: *Hosta*, especially miniature hostas.
Notes: Garden & nursery open under the NGS (4th Aug 2013), see NGS Yellow Book for details. Delivers to shows.

NSum **Summerdale Garden Nursery**
Summerdale House, Cow Brow, Lupton, Carnforth, Lancashire LA6 1PE
Ⓣ (01539) 567210
Ⓔ sheals@btinternet.com
Ⓦ www.summerdalegardenplants.co.uk
Contact: Gail Sheals
Opening Times: 0930-1630 Thu, Fri & Sat, 1st Apr-30th Sep. Other times by appt. only.
Min Mail Order UK: £25.00
Cat. Cost: Online only.
Credit Cards: None
Specialities: Wide variety of perennials, large collection of *Primula*. Many moist and shade-loving plants incl. *Meconopsis* & hellebores.
Notes: Mail order for primulas only.
Map Ref: N, C1 **OS Grid Ref:** SD545819

NTay **Taylors Clematis Nursery** ♿
Sutton Road, Sutton, Nr Askern, Doncaster, South Yorkshire DN6 9JZ
Ⓣ (01302) 700716
Ⓕ (01302) 708415

Ⓔ info@taylorsclematis.co.uk
Ⓦ www.taylorsclematis.co.uk
Contact: Chris & Suzy Cocks
Opening Times: Open by appt. only. Please ring for details.
Min Mail Order UK: Nmc
Min Mail Order EU: Nmc
Cat. Cost: 4 × 2nd class.
Credit Cards: All major credit/debit cards
Specialities: *Clematis* (over 350+ varieties).
Notes: Delivers to shows. Wheelchair accessible.
Map Ref: N, D2 **OS Grid Ref:** SE552121

NTPC **Tree Peony Company**
Willow Cottage, Rillington, Malton, North Yorkshire YO17 8JU
Ⓣ (01944) 758280
Ⓔ info@treepeony.co.uk
Ⓦ www.treepeony.co.uk
Contact: Thelma Scruton, Roger Scruton
Min Mail Order UK: Nmc
Min Mail Order EU: Nmc
Cat. Cost: None.
Credit Cards: None
Specialities: Tree peonies. *Paeonia suffruticosa. P.* Gansu Group. *P. rockii.*
Notes: Also sells wholesale.

NTre **Treetyme**
Prospect Hill House, Kirkoswald, Penrith, Cumbria CA10 1ER
Ⓣ (01768) 800238
Ⓕ (01768) 897138
Ⓔ sales@treetyme.co.uk
Ⓦ www.treetyme.co.uk
Contact: Hugh Povey
Opening Times: Not open. Visit by appt. only. Mail order via website only.
Min Mail Order UK: Nmc
Min Mail Order EU: Nmc
Cat. Cost: Online only.
Credit Cards: All major credit/debit cards
Specialities: *Cercis.* Stock available in small quantities only. National Collection of *Cercis* (Provisional).

NWad **Waddow Lodge Garden** ♿
Clitheroe Road, Waddington, Clitheroe, Lancashire BB7 3HQ
Ⓣ (01200) 429145
Ⓔ peterfoleyhcn@hotmail.co.uk
Ⓦ www.gardentalks.co.uk
Contact: Peter Foley
Opening Times: By appt. only all year.
Min Mail Order UK: Nmc
Min Mail Order EU: Nmc
Cat. Cost: Online only.
Credit Cards: None
Specialities: A developing plantsman's garden with a wide-ranging interesting plant collection.
Notes: Open for group visits by appt., incl. evenings. Also open under NGS 26th May & 21st Jul 2013 & 7th Aug for Festival Bowland, with plant sales for Plant Heritage NW Group. Wheelchair accessible.
Map Ref: N, C1 **OS Grid Ref:** SD732434

NWea **Weasdale Nurseries Ltd.**
Newbiggin-on-Lune, Kirkby Stephen, Cumbria CA17 4LX
Ⓣ (01539) 623246
Ⓕ (01539) 623277
Ⓔ sales@weasdale.com
Ⓦ www.weasdale.com
Contact: Andrew Forsyth
Opening Times: 0830-1300 & 1400-1730 Mon-Fri. Closed w/ends, B/hols, Xmas through to the New Year.

Min Mail Order UK: Nmc
Min Mail Order EU: Nmc
Cat. Cost: Free of charge in UK or £2.00 to EU.
Credit Cards: All major credit/debit cards
Specialities: Hardy forest trees, hedging, broadleaved & conifers. Specimen trees & shrubs grown at 850 feet (260 metre) elevation.
Notes: Mail order a speciality. Mail order Nov-Apr only. Also sells wholesale to VAT registered customers.
Map Ref: N, C1 **OS Grid Ref:** NY690039

NWit **D S Witton** ♿
26 Casson Drive, Harthill, Sheffield, Yorkshire S26 7WA
Ⓣ (01909) 771366
Ⓔ donshardyeuphorbias@btopenworld.com
Ⓦ www.euphorbias.co.uk
Contact: Don Witton
Opening Times: By appt. only. Open Day, 1300-1600, Sun 5th May 2013.
Min Mail Order UK: Nmc
Cat. Cost: 1 × 1st class sae.
Credit Cards: None
Specialities: Nat. Collection of Hardy *Euphorbia.* Over 130 varieties.
Notes: Mail order seed only, Oct-June. Wheelchair accessible.
Map Ref: N, D2 **OS Grid Ref:** SK494812

NWsh **Westshores Nurseries**
82 West Street, Winterton, Lincolnshire DN15 9QF
Ⓣ (01724) 733940
Ⓜ 07875 732535
Ⓔ westshnur@aol.com
Ⓦ www.westshores.co.uk
Contact: Gail & John Summerfield
Opening Times: 1st Mar-31st Oct by appt. only.

Min Mail Order UK: £15.00
Credit Cards: All major credit/debit cards
Specialities: Ornamental grasses.
Map Ref: N, D3 **OS Grid Ref:** SE927187

SOUTHERN

SAdn **ASHDOWN FOREST GARDEN CENTRE & NURSERY** ♿
Duddleswell, Ashdown Forest, East Sussex
TN22 3JP
Ⓣ (01825) 712300
Ⓔ victoria@ashdownforestgardencentre.co.uk
Ⓦ www.ashdownforestgardencentre.co.uk
Contact: Victoria Falletti
Opening Times: 0900-1700 winter, 0900-1800 summer.
Min Mail Order UK: Nmc
Cat. Cost: Online only.
Credit Cards: All major credit/debit cards
Specialities: Ornamental grasses, *Lapageria*, *Fuchsia*, conservatory climbers, unusual shrubs.
Notes: Wheelchair accessible.
Map Ref: S, C4 **OS Grid Ref:** TQ468283

S

SAdu **ADUR VALLEY GROWERS (FORMERLY CANNA MAN)**
(Office) 4 Newland Road,
Upper Beeding, Steyning, West Sussex
BN44 3JJ
Ⓣ (01903) 813780
Ⓔ clivethecannaman@gmail.com
Ⓦ www.adurvalleygrowers.co.uk
Contact: Clive Parker
Opening Times: Not open. Mail order only.
Min Mail Order UK: Nmc
Min Mail Order EU: Nmc
Cat. Cost: Online only.
Credit Cards: Paypal
Specialities: A wide range of disease-free *Canna*, many only available in very small numbers. All plants grown in own peat-free compost without the use of chemical pesticides. Will propagate to order.
Notes: Plants only available from May-Oct. Euro accepted.

SArc **ARCHITECTURAL PLANTS** ♿
Nuthurst Street, Nuthurst, Horsham,
West Sussex RH13 6LH
Ⓣ (01403) 891772
Ⓕ (01403) 891056
Ⓔ enquiries@architecturalplants.com
Ⓦ www.architecturalplants.com
Contact: Pen Hopgood
Opening Times: 0900-1700 Mon-Sat & B/hols. Closed Sun.
Min Mail Order UK: Nmc
Min Mail Order EU: £150.00
Cat. Cost: Free
Credit Cards: All, except American Express
Specialities: Architectural plants & hardy exotics esp. rare evergreen broadleaved trees & seaside exotics, spiky plants, yuccas/agaves, climbers & bamboos.
Notes: Mail order subject to pot size & weight. Also sells wholesale. Delivers to shows. Euro accepted. Wheelchair accessible.

SBch **BIRCHWOOD PLANTS**
(Office) 10 Westering, Romsey, Hampshire
SO51 7LY
Ⓣ (01794) 502192 or (02380) 814345
Ⓔ info@birchwoodplants.co.uk
Ⓦ www.birchwoodplants.co.uk
Contact: Lesley Baker
Opening Times: Not open. Plants can be collected by arrangement from nursery or from sales & shows as posted on website.
Min Mail Order UK: £15 + p&p
Cat. Cost: Online only.
Credit Cards: Paypal
Specialities: Plants to attract bees & butterflies. Alpines & drought-tolerant plants. Predominantly growing peat-free. National Collection of *Geranium nodosum*. Most stock only available in very small quantities unless ordered in advance.
Notes: Nursery at Silverwood House, Gardener's Lane, Nr Romsey, SO51 6AD. Mail order mostly for small plants. No mail order sent Dec-Jan. Delivers to shows.
Map Ref: S, D2 **OS Grid Ref:** SU333190

SBHP **BLEAK HILL PLANTS** ♿
Braemoor, Bleak Hill, Harbridge,
Ringwood, Hampshire
BH24 3PX
Ⓣ (01425) 652983
Ⓔ tracy@bleakhillplants.co.uk
Ⓦ www.bleakhillplants.co.uk
Contact: Tracy Netherway
Opening Times: 0900-1730, Mon, Tue, Fri, Sat & 1000-1600 Sun, Mar-Oct. Closed Wed & Thu.
Cat. Cost: 2 × 1st class.
Credit Cards: None
Specialities: Hardy & half-hardy herbaceous perennials. Stock available in small quantities.
Notes: Wheelchair accessible.
Map Ref: S, D1 **OS Grid Ref:** SU132111

SBig **BIG PLANT NURSERY** ♿ ◆
Hole Street, Ashington, West Sussex
RH20 3DE
Ⓣ (01903) 891466
Ⓜ 07957 262845
Ⓕ (01903) 892829
Ⓔ info@bigplantnursery.co.uk

Ⓦ www.bigplantnursery.co.uk
Contact: Bruce Jordan
Opening Times: 0900-1700 Mon-Sat, 1000-1600 Sun & B/hols.
Min Mail Order UK: Please phone for further info.
Cat. Cost: A5 sae with 2 × 1st class.
Credit Cards: All major credit/debit cards
Specialities: Bamboos, hardy exotics & palms, *Ginkgo*, *Betula*.
Notes: Programme of events & propagation tuition, see nursery website for details. Also sells wholesale. Delivers to shows. Wheelchair accessible.
Map Ref: S, D3 **OS Grid Ref:** TQ132153

SBir **Birchfleet Nurseries** ♿ ◆
Greenfields Close, Nyewood,
Petersfield, Hampshire
GU31 5JQ
Ⓣ (01730) 821636
Ⓕ (01730) 821636
Ⓔ gammoak@aol.com
Ⓦ www.birchfleetnurseries.co.uk
Contact: John & Daphne Gammon
Opening Times: By appt. only. Please phone.
Cat. Cost: 2 × 1st class.
Credit Cards: None
Specialities: Oaks. Beech. *Nyssa*. Nat. Collection of *Liquidambar*.
Notes: Also sells wholesale. Nursery accessible for wheelchairs in dry weather.
Map Ref: S, C3

SBmr **Blackmoor Nurseries** ♿
Blackmoor Estate, Blackmoor, Liss,
Hampshire GU33 6BS
Ⓣ (01420) 477978
Ⓕ (01420) 487813
Ⓔ jonmunday@blackmoor.co.uk
Ⓦ www.blackmoor.co.uk
Contact: Jon Munday
Opening Times: 0730-1600.
Min Mail Order UK: Nmc
Min Mail Order EU: Nmc
Cat. Cost: None issued.
Credit Cards: All major credit/debit cards
Specialities: Fruit trees, soft fruit & ornamental trees.
Notes: Also sells wholesale. Wheelchair accessible.

SBod **Bodiam Nursery**
Bodiam, Robertsbridge, East Sussex
TN32 5RA
Ⓣ (01580) 830811
Ⓜ 07971 419302
Ⓔ enquiries@bodiamnursery.co.uk
Ⓦ www.bodiamnursery.co.uk
Contact: Jill Kaye
Opening Times: 1000-1700, 7 days, 1st Mar-31st Oct. Closed Nov-Feb.
Cat. Cost: None issued.
Credit Cards: All major credit/debit cards
Specialities: Wide range of *Acer palmatum*, available in small quantities only. Coastal & Mediterranean plants. Shrubs & perennials.
Notes: Opposite Bodiam Castle, between Great Dixter & Merriments Gardens.

SBri **Brickwall Cottage Nursery** ♿
1 Brickwall Cottages, Frittenden, Cranbrook,
Kent TN17 2DH
Ⓣ (01580) 852425
Ⓜ 07714 529946
Ⓔ sue.martin@talktalk.net
Ⓦ www.geumcollection.co.uk
Contact: Sue Martin
Opening Times: By appt. only.
Min Mail Order UK: Nmc
Min Mail Order EU: Nmc
Credit Cards: None
Specialities: Hardy perennials. Stock available in small quantities only. Nat. Collection of *Geum*.
Notes: Wheelchair accessible.
Map Ref: S, C5 **OS Grid Ref:** TQ815410

SBrm **Brambly Hedge**
Mill Lane, Sway, Hampshire SO41 8LN
Ⓣ (01590) 683570
Contact: Kim Williams
Opening Times: By appt. only in Jul & Aug.
Min Mail Order UK: Nmc
Cat. Cost: Sae for descriptive list.
Credit Cards: None
Specialities: Nat. Collections of *Streptocarpus* & *Begonia rex* cvs. Plants available in small quantities only.
Notes: Mail order Mar-Aug, small quantities only.

SBrt **Brighton Plants** ♿
New Hall Lane, Small Dole, Sussex
BN5 9YJ
Ⓜ 07807 594209
Ⓔ brighton.plants@gmail.com
Ⓦ www.brightonplants.blogspot.com/
Contact: Steve Law
Opening Times: 1000-1700 w/ends, May-Oct. Please email/phone first.
Min Mail Order UK: Nmc
Min Mail Order EU: Nmc
Cat. Cost: 2 × 1st class.
Credit Cards: None
Specialities: Hardy herbaceous and woody plants. Drought-tolerant plants.
Notes: Delivers to shows. Euro accepted. Wheelchair accessible.
Map Ref: S, D3 **OS Grid Ref:** TQ208132

S

SCac **CACTI & SUCCULENTS**
Hammerfield, Crockham Hill, Edenbridge, Kent TN8 6RR
Ⓣ (01732) 866295
Contact: Geoff Southon
Opening Times: Flexible. Please phone first.
Min Mail Order UK: Nmc
Cat. Cost: None issued.
Credit Cards: None
Specialities: *Echeveria* & related genera & hybrids. Haworthias & gasterias. A large range of aeoniums, both species & hybrids. Many available in small quantities only.

SCam **CAMELLIA GROVE NURSERY** ♿
Market Garden, Lower Beeding, West Sussex RH13 6PP
Ⓣ (01403) 891412
Ⓦ www.camellia-grove.com
Contact: Chris Loder
Opening Times: 1000-1600 Mon-Sat, please phone first so we can give you our undivided attention.
Min Mail Order UK: Nmc
Min Mail Order EU: Nmc
Cat. Cost: 2 × 1st class.
Credit Cards: All, except American Express
Specialities: *Camellia japonica*, *C. williamsii*, *C. sasanqua* & *C. reticulata*, from the purest white to richest red flowers.
Notes: Also sells wholesale. Exports beyond EU. Delivers to shows. Euro accepted. Wheelchair accessible.
Map Ref: S, C3 **OS Grid Ref:** TQ221255

SChF **CHARLESHURST FARM NURSERY**
Loxwood Road, Plaistow, Billingshurst, West Sussex RH14 0NY
Ⓣ (01403) 752273
Ⓜ 07736 522788
Ⓔ Charleshurstfarm@aol.com
Ⓦ www.charleshurstplants.co.uk
Contact: Clive Mellor
Opening Times: Normally 0900-1730 Fri, Sat, Sun, Feb-Oct, but please ring first before travelling.
Min Mail Order UK: Nmc
Min Mail Order EU: Nmc
Cat. Cost: 2 × 1st class.
Credit Cards: All major credit/debit cards
Specialities: Shrubs including some more unusual species. Good range of daphnes & Japanese maples.
Notes: Delivers to shows. Euro accepted.
Map Ref: S, C3 **OS Grid Ref:** TQ015308

SChr **JOHN CHURCHER**
47 Grove Avenue, Portchester, Fareham, Hampshire PO16 9EZ
Ⓣ (023) 9232 6740
Ⓜ 07917 350928
Ⓔ johnchurcher47@btinternet.com
Contact: John Churcher
Opening Times: By appt. only. Please phone or email.
Min Mail Order UK: Nmc
Min Mail Order EU: Nmc
Cat. Cost: None issued.
Credit Cards: None
Specialities: Hardy exotics for the Mediterranean-style garden, incl. palms, tree ferns, *Musa*, hedychiums, cycads, *Agave*, *Aloe*, *Opuntia* & echiums. Stock available in small quantities only.
Notes: Exports beyond EU.
Map Ref: S, D2 **OS Grid Ref:** SU614047

SCit **THE CITRUS CENTRE** ♿ ◆
West Mare Lane, Marehill, Pulborough, West Sussex RH20 2EA
Ⓣ (01798) 872786
Ⓔ enquiries@citruscentre.co.uk
Ⓦ www.citruscentre.co.uk
Contact: Amanda & Chris Dennis
Opening Times: 0930-1600 Tue-Sat. Phone for Xmas & B/hol opening times.
Min Mail Order UK: Nmc
Min Mail Order EU: Nmc
Cat. Cost: Online.
Credit Cards: Visa, MasterCard
Specialities: *Citrus* & *Citrus* relatives.
Notes: Wheelchair accessible.
Map Ref: S, D3

SCmr **CROMAR NURSERY** ♿
39 Livesey Street, North Pole, Wateringbury, Maidstone, Kent ME18 5BQ
Ⓣ (01622) 812380
Ⓔ CromarNursery@aol.com
Ⓦ www.cromarnursery.co.uk
Contact: Debra & Martin Cronk
Opening Times: 0930-1700 daily except Wed. Winter opening 0930-1630 Thu, Fri, Sat, Sun. Please check website or phone if travelling far.
Min Mail Order UK: Nmc
Min Mail Order EU: Nmc
Cat. Cost: 2 × 1st class.
Credit Cards: All major credit/debit cards
Specialities: Ornamental & fruit trees.
Notes: Wheelchair accessible.
Map Ref: S, C4 **OS Grid Ref:** TQ697547

SCob **COBLANDS NURSERIES** ♿
Trench Road, Tonbridge, Kent TN11 9NG
Ⓣ (01732) 770999
Ⓔ info@coblands.co.uk
Ⓦ www.coblands.co.uk
Contact: Lewis Normand

Opening Times: 0900-1630 Mon-Sat, all year. Closed for Xmas/New Year.
Min Mail Order UK: Nmc
Min Mail Order EU: Nmc
Cat. Cost: Online & seasonal postings to existing customers.
Credit Cards: All major credit/debit cards
Specialities: Wide range of plants esp. herbaceous perennials of garden-worthiness incl. *Hebe*, *Hydrangea*, *Phormium*, *Brunnera*, *Echinacea*, *Epimedium*, *Heuchera*, *Hosta*, *Rudbeckia* & ferns. Wide range of established specimen plants. New introductions may be in limited supply.
Notes: Direct online ordering service. Bare-rooted fruit trees, ornamental trees & hedging available seasonally. Also sells wholesale. Wheelchair accessible.
Map Ref: S, C4 **OS Grid Ref:** TQ586487

SCog **COGHURST CAMELLIAS** ♿
Ivy House Lane, Nr Three Oaks,
Hastings, East Sussex
TN35 4NP
Ⓣ (01424) 756228
Ⓔ rotherview@btinternet.com
Ⓦ www.rotherview.com
Contact: R Bates & W Bates
Opening Times: 1000-1530 7 days, all year.
Min Mail Order UK: Nmc
Min Mail Order EU: Nmc
Cat. Cost: 6 × 1st class.
Credit Cards: All major credit/debit cards
Specialities: *Camellia.*
Notes: Nursery is on the same site as Rotherview Nursery. Also sells wholesale. Delivers to shows. Euro accepted. Wheelchair accessible.
Map Ref: S, D5

SCoo **COOLING'S NURSERIES LTD** ♿
Rushmore Hill, Knockholt,
Sevenoaks, Kent
TN14 7NN
Ⓣ (01959) 532269
Ⓕ (01959) 534092
Ⓔ Plantfinder@coolings.co.uk
Ⓦ www.coolings.co.uk
Contact: Mark Reeve or Toby Davies
Opening Times: 0900-1700 Mon-Sat & 1000-1630 Sun.
Cat. Cost: None issued
Credit Cards: All, except American Express
Specialities: Large range of perennials, conifers & bedding plants. Many unusual shrubs & trees. Third generation family business.
Notes: Display garden. Coffee shop. Wheelchair accessible.
Map Ref: S, C4 **OS Grid Ref:** TK477610

SCrf **CROFTERS NURSERIES** ♿
Church Hill, Charing Heath, Near Ashford, Kent TN27 0BU
Ⓣ (01233) 712798
Ⓔ croftersnursery@yahoo.co.uk
Contact: John & Sue Webb
Opening Times: 1000-1700. Closed Sun-Tue. Please check first.
Cat. Cost: 3 × 1st class.
Credit Cards: None
Specialities: Fruit, ornamental trees. Old apple varieties. Small number of *Prunus serrula* with grafted ornamental heads.
Notes: Euro accepted. Wheelchair accessible.
Map Ref: S, C5 **OS Grid Ref:** TQ923493

SDay **A LA CARTE DAYLILIES**
Little Hermitage, St Catherine's Down,
Nr Ventnor, Isle of Wight PO38 2PD
Ⓣ (01983) 730512
Ⓔ andy@alacartedaylilies.co.uk
Ⓦ www.alacartedaylilies.co.uk
Contact: Jan & Andy Wyers
Opening Times: Mail order only. Open by appt. only. Difficult to find on an unmade private road.
Min Mail Order UK: Nmc
Min Mail Order EU: Nmc
Cat. Cost: 3 × 1st class.
Credit Cards: None
Specialities: *Hemerocallis*. Nat. Collections of Miniature & Small Flowered *Hemerocallis* & Large Flowered *Hemerocallis* (post-1960 award-winning cultivars).
Notes: Euro accepted.
Map Ref: S, D2 **OS Grid Ref:** SZ499787

SDea **DEACON'S NURSERY** ◆
Moor View, Godshill, Isle of Wight
PO38 3HW
Ⓣ (01983) 840750 (24 hrs) or (01983) 522243
Ⓕ (01983) 523575
Ⓔ info@deaconsnurseryfruits.co.uk
Ⓦ www.deaconsnurseryfruits.co.uk
Contact: G D & B H W Deacon
Opening Times: 0800-1600 Mon-Fri May-Sep, 0800-1700 Mon-Fri 0800-1200 Sat Oct-Apr.
Min Mail Order UK: Nmc
Min Mail Order EU: Nmc
Cat. Cost: Free.
Credit Cards: All major credit/debit cards
Specialities: Over 300 varieties of apple, old & new, apricots, cherries, damsons, gages, nectarines, peaches, pears, plums. Modern soft fruit, grapes, hops, nuts & family trees.
Notes: Also sells wholesale. Exports beyond EU. Euro accepted.
Map Ref: S, D2

SDeJ **P. de Jager & Sons Ltd** ♿ ◆
Church Farm, Ulcombe,
Maidstone, Kent
ME17 1DN
Ⓣ (01622) 840229
Ⓕ (01622) 844073
Ⓔ flowerbulbs@dejager.co.uk
Ⓦ www.dejager.co.uk
Contact: George Clowes
Opening Times: Mail order only. Orders taken from 0900-1700 Mon-Fri
Min Mail Order UK: Nmc
Min Mail Order EU: Nmc
Cat. Cost: Free
Credit Cards: All major credit/debit cards
Specialities: Complete range of all flower bulbs.
Notes: Also sells wholesale. Exports beyond EU. Euro accepted. Wheelchair accessible.

S

SDix **Great Dixter Nurseries**
Northiam, Rye, East Sussex
TN31 6PH
Ⓣ (01797) 254044
Ⓕ (01797) 252879
Ⓔ nursery@greatdixter.co.uk
Ⓦ www.greatdixter.co.uk
Contact: Michael Morphy
Opening Times: 0900-1700 7 days, Apr-Oct. 0900-1630 Mon-Fri, 0900-1230 Sat, closed Sun, Nov-Mar.
Min Mail Order UK: Nmc
Min Mail Order EU: Nmc
Cat. Cost: 5 × 1st class.
Credit Cards: All major credit/debit cards
Specialities: *Clematis*, shrubs and plants. Gardens open.
Notes: Plants dispatched Sep-Mar only. Partially accessible for wheelchairs.

SDow **Downderry Nursery** ♿
Pillar Box Lane, Hadlow, Nr Tonbridge, Kent
TN11 9SW
Ⓣ (01732) 810081
Ⓕ (01732) 811398
Ⓔ info@downderry-nursery.co.uk
Ⓦ www.downderry-nursery.co.uk
Contact: Dr Simon Charlesworth
Opening Times: 1000-1700 Wed-Sun 1st May-30th Sep & B/hols. Other times by appt.
Min Mail Order UK: Nmc
Min Mail Order EU: Nmc
Cat. Cost: Free.
Credit Cards: Delta, MasterCard, Maestro, Visa
Specialities: Nat. Collections of *Lavandula* and *Rosmarinus*.
Notes: Exports beyond EU. Euro accepted. Wheelchair accessible.
Map Ref: S, C4 **OS Grid Ref:** TQ625521

SDys **Dysons Nurseries** ♿
Great Comp Garden, Platt, Sevenoaks, Kent
TN15 8QS
Ⓣ (01732) 885094
Ⓜ 07887 997663
Ⓔ dysonsorders@greatcompgarden.co.uk
Ⓦ www.greatcompgarden.co.uk
Contact: William T Dyson
Opening Times: 1100-1700 7 days 1st Apr-31st Oct. Other times by appt.
Min Mail Order UK: £24.00
Cat. Cost: Online only.
Credit Cards: All major credit/debit cards
Specialities: Salvias & an eclectic range of choice and uncommon plants.
Notes: Delivers to shows. Wheelchair accessible.
Map Ref: S, C4

SEle **Eleplants Nursery**
32 Framfield Road, Uckfield, East Sussex
TN22 5AH
Ⓣ (01825) 769557
Ⓕ (01825) 769557
Ⓔ eleplantsnursery@talk21.com
Ⓦ www.eleplantsnursery.co.uk
Contact: Martin Batchelor
Opening Times: Not open but can be visited by prior appt. only.
Credit Cards: Paypal
Specialities: Shrubs.
Notes: Exports beyond EU. Delivers to shows.

SEND **East Northdown Farm & Gardens** ♿ ◆
George Hill Road (B2052), Margate, Kent
CT9 3TS
Ⓣ (01843) 862060
Ⓜ 07714 241668 or 7
Ⓔ info@botanyplants.co.uk
Ⓦ www.botanyplants.co.uk
Contact: Louise & William Friend
Opening Times: 0900-1700 7 days, all year except Sun in Nov & Jan. Closed Xmas week.
Min Mail Order UK: Nmc
Cat. Cost: Online only.
Credit Cards: Visa, Switch, MasterCard
Specialities: Chalk & coast-loving plants. Specimen shrubs & bamboos available.
Notes: Plants from our other nursery MMuc available to order. Tearoom & gardens. Also sells wholesale. Wheelchair accessible.
Map Ref: S, B6 **OS Grid Ref:** TR383702

SEWo **English Woodlands** ♿
Burrow Nursery, Herrings Lane, Cross-in-Hand, Heathfield, East Sussex TN21 0UG
Ⓣ (01435) 862992
Ⓕ (01435) 867742
Ⓔ sales@englishwoodlands.com

Ⓦ www.englishwoodlands.com
Contact: Joanne Carter
Opening Times: 0800-1700 Mon-Fri. 0800-1630 Sat. Closed Sun & B/hols.
Min Mail Order UK: £25.00
Cat. Cost: Free.
Credit Cards: All, except American Express
Specialities: Trees, shrubs, hedging.
Notes: Also sells wholesale. Wheelchair accessible.
Map Ref: S, C4 **OS Grid Ref:** TQ567222

SFai FAIRWEATHER'S GARDEN CENTRE ♿
High Street, Beaulieu, Hampshire
SO42 7YB
Ⓣ (01590) 612307
Ⓕ (01590) 612519
Ⓔ info@fairweathers.co.uk
Ⓦ www.fairweathers.co.uk
Contact: Sue Greaves
Opening Times: 0900-1700 7 days.
Min Mail Order UK: Nmc
Cat. Cost: None issued.
Credit Cards: Visa, MasterCard
Specialities: *Agapanthus* & *Lavandula*.
Notes: Wheelchair accessible.

SFam FAMILY TREES ♿
Sandy Lane, Shedfield, Hampshire
SO32 2HQ
Ⓣ (01329) 834812
Ⓦ www.familytreesnursery.co.uk
Contact: Philip House
Opening Times: 0930-1230 Tue, Wed, Fri & Sat (closed 20th Dec-10th Jan).
Min Mail Order UK: £10.00
Cat. Cost: Online.
Credit Cards: None
Specialities: Fruit & ornamental trees. Trained fruit tree specialists: standards, espaliers, cordons. Other trees, old-fashioned & climbing roses, evergreens. Trees, except evergreens, sold bare-rooted. Also herbaceous plants & roses.
Notes: Wheelchair accessible.
Map Ref: S, D2

SFgr FIRGROVE PLANTS
24 Wykeham Field, Wickham, Fareham, Hampshire PO17 5AB
Ⓣ (01329) 835206 after 1900 hours.
Ⓔ jenny@firgroveplants.demon.co.uk
Ⓦ www.firgroveplants.demon.co.uk
Contact: Jenny MacKinnon
Opening Times: Not open. Mail order only.
Min Mail Order UK: £9.00
Cat. Cost: Sae.
Credit Cards: None
Specialities: Wide range of houseleeks in small quantities.
Notes: Houseleeks by mail order Apr-mid Oct.

SFrt FRUIT GARDEN PLANTS ♿ ◆
Woolton Farm, Bekesbourne, Canterbury, Kent CT4 5EA
Ⓣ (01227) 830525
Ⓜ 07710 253690
Ⓕ (01227) 831969
Ⓔ sales@fruitgardenplants.co.uk
Ⓦ www.fruitgardenplants.co.uk
Contact: Mark Mount
Opening Times: 1000-1600 Thu-Sat, 1st Nov-31st Mar. 1000-1700 Thu-Sun, 1st Apr-31st Oct.
Min Mail Order UK: £10.00
Min Mail Order EU: £35.00
Credit Cards: MasterCard, Visa
Specialities: Tree fruits & soft fruits.
Notes: Fruit display garden where visitors can see particular varieties & the methods used for growing them. Small café. Medieval tythe barn. Also sells wholesale. Delivers to shows. Wheelchair accessible.
Map Ref: S, C5 **OS Grid Ref:** TR191568

SGbt GILBERT'S NURSERY ♿
Dandy's Ford Lane, Sherfield English, Romsey, Hampshire
SO51 6DT
Ⓣ (01794) 322566
Ⓔ gilbertsnursery@aol.com
Ⓦ www.gilbertsnursery.co.uk
Contact: Nick Gilbert
Opening Times: 0900-1700 Tue-Sat, 10.00-16.30 Sun, all year round. *Dahlia* field open from 2nd week Aug to 2nd week Oct.
Min Mail Order UK: Nmc
Min Mail Order EU: Nmc
Cat. Cost: 2 × 1st class
Credit Cards: All, except American Express
Specialities: *Dahlia*. Proper plant nursery with many unusual plants & staff happy to share their knowledge & help with plant selection.
Notes: *Dahlia* field with over 400 cvs on view (grass pathways). See above for opening times or go to www.gilbertsdahlias.co.uk. Tea room. Delivers to shows. Wheelchair accessible.
Map Ref: S, C2

SGol GOLDEN HILL NURSERIES ♿
Lordsfield, Goudhurst Road, Marden, Kent
TN12 9LT
Ⓣ (01622) 833218
Ⓜ 07826 523655
Ⓕ (01622) 832528
Ⓔ enquiries@goldenhillplants.com
Ⓦ www.goldenhillplants.com
Contact: Roger Butler

S

Opening Times: 0900-1700 Mon-Sat, 1st Mar-31st Oct. 0900-1600 Mon-Sat, 1st Nov-28th Feb. 1100-1600 Sun from 3rd Sun in Feb until Xmas.
Min Mail Order UK: Nmc
Cat. Cost: Online only.
Credit Cards: All major credit/debit cards
Specialities: Specimen plants, shrubs, grasses, bamboos, Japanese maples, conifers & trees.
Notes: Also sells wholesale. Euro accepted. Wheelchair accessible.

SGSe **Garden Secrets Nursery**
Boldre Nurseries, Southampton Road, Sway, Lymington, Hampshire SO41 8ND
Ⓜ 07779 084245
Ⓔ hazelwoodpreschool@hotmail.co.uk
Ⓦ www.gardensecretsnursery.co.uk
Contact: Tim Woodford
Opening Times: 0900-1630 daily except Wed. Please phone before visiting if travelling any distance.
Credit Cards: None
Specialities: Perennials, grasses and ferns.

SHaC **Hart Canna** ♿
25-27 Guildford Road West, Farnborough, Hampshire GU14 6PS
Ⓣ (01252) 514421
Ⓜ 07762 950000
Ⓔ sales@hartcanna.com
Ⓦ www.hartcanna.co.uk
Contact: Keith Hayward
Opening Times: By arrangement.
Min Mail Order UK: Nmc
Min Mail Order EU: Nmc
Cat. Cost: Sae.
Credit Cards: All major credit/debit cards
Specialities: *Canna.* Nat. Collection of *Canna.*
Notes: Also sells wholesale. Euro accepted. Delivers to shows. Wheelchair accessible.
Map Ref: S, C3

SHal **Hall's Court Nursery** ♿
Pluckley Road, Bethersden, Ashford, Kent TN26 3ET
Ⓣ (01233) 820828
Ⓜ 07729 418275
Ⓔ info@hallscourt.co.uk
Ⓦ www.hallscourt.co.uk
Contact: Jeanette Jahnz
Opening Times: 0900-1700 every w/end, end Mar-beginning Oct. Weekdays by appt.
Cat. Cost: Online only.
Credit Cards: None
Specialities: Around 90 varieties of hardy geraniums & around 50 varieties of pelargoniums, incl. some species. Also alpines, herbs, some succulents, perennials & hardy fuchsias. Some plants available in small quantities only.
Notes: Small nursery, situated midway between Ashford and Tenterden in rural Kent. Wheelchair accessible.
Map Ref: S, C5 **OS Grid Ref:** TQ919414

SHar **Hardy's Cottage Garden Plants** ♿
Priory Lane Nursery, Freefolk Priors, Whitchurch, Hampshire
RG28 7NJ
Ⓣ (01256) 896533
Ⓔ info@hardys-plants.co.uk
Ⓦ www.hardys-plants.co.uk
Contact: Rosemary Hardy
Opening Times: 1000-1700 7 days, 1st Mar-30th Sep. 1000-1600 Mon-Fri, 1st Oct-31st Oct, 1000-1500 Mon-Fri, 1st Nov-28th Feb. Closed 23rd Dec-4th Jan.
Min Mail Order UK: Nmc
Cat. Cost: Online only.
Credit Cards: Visa, Access, Electron, Switch, Solo
Specialities: Wide range of herbaceous perennials incl. *Achillea*, *Geum*, *Geranium*, *Hemerocallis*, *Heuchera*, *Lathryus vernus*, *Paeonia*, *Penstemon* & *Salvia*.
Notes: Accepts HTA Gift Tokens. Offers trade discount. Also sells wholesale. Delivers to shows. Wheelchair accessible.
Map Ref: S, C2

SHDw **Highdown Nursery**
New Hall Lane, Small Dole, Nr Henfield, West Sussex BN5 9YH
Ⓣ (01273) 492976
Ⓜ 07900 956456
Ⓕ (01273) 492976
Ⓔ highdown.herbs@btinternet.com
Ⓦ www.highdownnursery.com
Contact: A G & J H Shearing
Opening Times: 0900-1700 7 days.
Min Mail Order UK: £10.00 + p&p
Cat. Cost: 3 × 1st class.
Credit Cards: None
Specialities: Herbs. Grasses.
Notes: Also sells wholesale. Delivers to shows. Euro accepted. Partial wheelchair access.
Map Ref: S, D3 **OS Grid Ref:** TV214134

SHea **Heaselands Garden Nursery**
Isaacs Lane, Haywards Heath, West Sussex RH16 4SA
Ⓣ (01444) 458084
Ⓕ (01444) 458084
Ⓔ headgardener@heaselandsnursery.co.uk
Ⓦ www.heaselandsnursery.co.uk
Contact: Sir Richard Kleinwort
Opening Times: 0800-1700, Mon-Fri by appt. only so please phone first.

Cat. Cost: Online only. Monthly availability lists.
Credit Cards: None
Specialities: *Rhododendron* hybrids and deciduous azaleas, home-produced from cuttings. Some varieties in small quantities. Also *Hydragea*, *Hebe* & *Camellia*.
Notes: Also sells wholesale. Plants for collection only, no mail order. Euro accepted.
Map Ref: S, C4 **OS Grid Ref:** TQ314230

SHeu **Heucheraholics** ♿
(Office) The Paddock, Pilley Street, Pilley, Lymington, Hampshire SO41 5QP
Ⓣ (01590) 670581
Ⓜ 07973 291062
Ⓔ jooles.heucheraholics@googlemail.com
Ⓦ www.heucheraholics.co.uk
Contact: Julie Burton/Sean Atkinson
Opening Times: Visits to nursery by appt. only. Please phone first.
Min Mail Order UK: Nmc
Cat. Cost: No charge.
Credit Cards: All major credit/debit cards
Specialities: *Heuchera*, *Heucherella*, *Pulmonaria* & *Tiarella*. Other foliage plants.
Notes: Nursery is located at Boldre Nurseries, Southampton Road, Boldre, Lymington, Hants. Delivers to shows. Wheelchair accessible.
Map Ref: S, D2 **OS Grid Ref:** SZ310934

SHil **Hillier Garden Centres**
Ampfield House, Ampfield, Romsey, Hampshire SO51 9PA
Ⓣ (01794) 368944
Ⓕ (01794) 367830
Ⓔ info@hillier.co.uk
Ⓦ www.hillieronline.co.uk
Contact: Mark Pitman
Opening Times: Office 0830-1700 Mon-Fri. Garden Centres: 0900-1730 Mon-Sat, 1000-1630 Sun.
Min Mail Order UK: Nmc
Min Mail Order EU: £250
Cat. Cost: None issued.
Notes: Other nursery branches in the south of England.

SHyH **Hydrangea Haven** ♿
Market Garden, Lower Beeding, West Sussex RH13 6PP
Ⓣ (01403) 891412
Ⓦ www.hydrangea-haven.com
Contact: Chris Loder
Opening Times: 1000-1600 Mon-Sat, please phone first, so we can give you our undivided attention.
Min Mail Order UK: Nmc
Min Mail Order EU: Nmc
Cat. Cost: 2 × 1st class.
Credit Cards: All, except American Express
Specialities: *Hydrangea*: mophead, lacecap & panicle. *Agapanthus*.
Notes: Also sells wholesale. Exports beyond EU. Delivers to shows. Euro accepted. Wheelchair accessible.
Map Ref: S, C3 **OS Grid Ref:** TQ221255

SIde **Iden Croft Herbs** ♿
Frittenden Road, Staplehurst, Kent TN12 0DH
Ⓣ (01580) 891432
Ⓔ idencroftherbs@yahoo.co.uk
Ⓦ www.uk-herbs.com
Contact: Tracey Connors-Parry
Opening Times: 0900-1700 Mon-Sat & 1100-1700 Sun & B/hols, Mar-Sep. Closed Oct-Feb.
Min Mail Order UK: £10.00
Min Mail Order EU: £25.00
Cat. Cost: Online only.
Credit Cards: All major credit/debit cards
Specialities: Herbs, aromatic & wildflower plants & plants for bees & butterflies. Nat. Collections of *Mentha*, *Nepeta* & *Origanum*.
Notes: Wheelchairs available at nursery.
Map Ref: S, C5

SIgm **Tim Ingram** ♿
Copton Ash, 105 Ashford Road, Faversham, Kent ME13 8XW
Ⓣ (01795) 535919
Ⓔ coptonash@yahoo.co.uk
Ⓦ coptonash.plus.com
Contact: Dr T J Ingram
Opening Times: 1400-1800 Fri & Sat, Mar-Oct. Other times by appt.
Credit Cards: None
Specialities: Small, specialised nursery, offering mainly alpines and spring plants. Many unusual plants available in small quantities.
Notes: Delivers to shows. Wheelchair accessible.
Map Ref: S, C5 **OS Grid Ref:** TR015598

SIri **Iris of Sissinghurst** ◆
Roughlands Farm, Goudhurst Road, Marden, Kent TN12 9NH
Ⓣ (01622) 831511
Ⓔ orders@irisofsissinghurst.com
Ⓦ www.irisofsissinghurst.com
Contact: Sue Marshall
Opening Times: Contact nursery or see website for opening times.
Min Mail Order UK: Nmc
Min Mail Order EU: Nmc
Cat. Cost: 2 × 1st class.
Credit Cards: None

S

Specialities: *Iris*, short, intermediate & tall bearded, *ensata*, *sibirica* & many species.
Notes: Euro accepted.
Map Ref: S, C4 **OS Grid Ref:** TQ735437

SKee **Keepers Nursery**
Gallants Court, Gallants Lane, East Farleigh, Maidstone, Kent ME15 0LE
Ⓣ (01622) 726465
Ⓕ 0870 705 2145
Ⓔ info@keepers-nursery.co.uk
Ⓦ www.keepers-nursery.co.uk
Contact: Hamid Habibi
Opening Times: Only on a limited number of Open Days & for collection of trees & plants by arrangement.
Min Mail Order UK: Nmc
Cat. Cost: Online only.
Credit Cards: Visa, MasterCard, Switch, Maestro
Specialities: A very large range of fruit trees incl. old & rare as well as modern varieties. Soft fruit plants & nut trees.
Map Ref: S, C4

S

SKHP **Kevin Hughes Plants** ♿
(Office) 89 Ladysmith, East Gomeldon, Salisbury, Wiltshire SP4 6LE
Ⓣ (01722) 782504
Ⓜ 07720 718671
Ⓔ info@kevinsplants.co.uk
Ⓦ www.kevinsplants.co.uk
Contact: Kevin Hughes
Opening Times: 1100-1700 Wed-Sat, 1st Feb-31st Oct. Other times by appt. only.
Min Mail Order UK: £10.00
Min Mail Order EU: £20.00
Cat. Cost: 3 × 1st class
Credit Cards: All, except American Express
Specialities: Less common & new hardy garden plants with a particular emphasis on *Magnolia*, *Trillium*, climbers, *Philadelphus*, *Viburnum* & *Syringa*. We try to select plants that are garden-worthy & attract wildlife. Many plants are slow to propagate & will always be in short supply. None are from wild-dug sources.
Notes: Nursery at Heale Garden, Middle Woodford, Salisbury, SP4 5NT. Exports beyond EU. Euro accepted. Wheelchair accessible.
Map Ref: S, C1 **OS Grid Ref:** SU125363

SKin **Kings Barn Trees**
Kings Barn Farm, Kent Street, Cowfold, West Sussex RH13 8BB
Ⓣ (01403) 865405
Ⓔ sales@kingsbarntrees.co.uk
Ⓦ www.kingsbarntrees.co.uk
Contact: Adrian Rumble
Opening Times: Not open. Mail order via website only.
Min Mail Order UK: £9.95
Min Mail Order EU: £9.95
Cat. Cost: Not available.
Credit Cards: All major credit/debit cards
Specialities: Mainly grow containerised trees, specialising in *Eucalyptus*. Also grow willow for sale as whips & setts during the winter/early spring. *Eucalyptus* available in small quantities only.

SLau **The Laurels Nursery** ♿
Benenden, Cranbrook, Kent TN17 4JU
Ⓣ (01580) 240463
Ⓦ www.thelaurelsnursery.co.uk
Contact: Peter or Sylvia Kellett
Opening Times: 0800-1600 Mon-Fri, 0900-1200 Sat, Sun by appt. only.
Min Mail Order UK: £28.00
Cat. Cost: Free.
Credit Cards: All major credit/debit cards
Specialities: Open ground & container ornamental trees, shrubs & climbers especially birch, beech & *Wisteria*.
Notes: Mail order of small *Wisteria* only. Also sells wholesale. Euro accepted. Wheelchair accessible.
Map Ref: S, C5 **OS Grid Ref:** TQ815313

SLay **Layham Garden Centre & Nursery** ♿
Lower Road, Staple, Nr Canterbury, Kent CT3 1LH
Ⓣ (01304) 813267
Ⓕ (01304) 814007
Ⓔ info@layhamgardencentre.co.uk
Ⓦ www.layhamgardencentre.co.uk
Contact: Ellen Wessel
Opening Times: 0900-1700 7 days.
Min Mail Order UK: Nmc
Min Mail Order EU: £25.00 + p&p
Cat. Cost: Free.
Credit Cards: Visa, MasterCard
Specialities: Roses, herbaceous, shrubs, trees & hedging plants.
Notes: Mail order roses only. Also sells wholesale. Euro accepted. Wheelchair accessible.
Map Ref: S, C6 **OS Grid Ref:** TR276567

SLBF **Little Brook Fuchsias** ♿
Ash Green Lane West, Ash Green, Nr Aldershot, Hampshire GU12 6HL
Ⓣ (01252) 329731
Ⓔ carol.gubler@ntlbusiness.com
Ⓦ www.littlebrookfuchsias.co.uk
Contact: Carol Gubler
Opening Times: 1000-1700 Wed-Sun 1st Jan-3rd Jul.
Cat. Cost: 50p + sae.

Credit Cards: All major credit/debit cards
Specialities: Fuchsias, old & new.
Notes: Nursery located off White Lane in Ash Green. Wheelchair accessible.
Map Ref: S, C3 **OS Grid Ref:** SU901496

SLdr **LODER PLANTS** ♿
Market Garden, Lower Beeding, West Sussex RH13 6PP
Ⓣ (01403) 891412
Ⓔ sales@rhododendrons.com
Ⓦ www.rhododendrons.com
Contact: Chris Loder
Opening Times: 1000-1600 Mon-Sat, please ring first so we can give you our undivided attention.
Min Mail Order UK: Nmc
Min Mail Order EU: Nmc
Cat. Cost: 2 × 1st class.
Credit Cards: All, except American Express
Specialities: Rhododendrons & azaleas in all sizes. Some in very limited quantities only.
Notes: Also sells wholesale. Exports beyond EU. Delivers to shows. Euro accepted. Wheelchair accessible.
Map Ref: S, C3 **OS Grid Ref:** TQ221255

SLim **LIME CROSS NURSERY** ♿
Herstmonceux, Hailsham, East Sussex BN27 4RS
Ⓣ (01323) 833229
Ⓕ (01323) 833944
Ⓔ info@limecross.co.uk
Ⓦ www.limecross.co.uk
Contact: Jonathan Tate, Anita Green
Opening Times: 0830-1700 Mon-Sat & 1000-1600 Sun.
Min Mail Order UK: Nmc
Min Mail Order EU: £50.00
Cat. Cost: Online only.
Credit Cards: All major credit/debit cards
Specialities: Conifers, trees & shrubs, climbers.
Notes: Wheelchair accessible.
Map Ref: S, D4 **OS Grid Ref:** TQ642125

SLon **LONGSTOCK PARK NURSERY** ♿
Longstock, Stockbridge, Hampshire SO20 6EH
Ⓣ (01264) 810894
Ⓕ (01264) 810924
Ⓔ longstocknursery@leckfordestate.co.uk
Ⓦ www.longstocknursery.co.uk
Contact: David Roberts
Opening Times: 0830-1630 Mon-Sat all year excl. Xmas & New Year. 1100-1700 Sun, Mar-Oct, 1100-1600 Sun, Nov-Feb.
Min Mail Order UK: Nmc
Cat. Cost: Lists of *Buddleja*, *Penstemon*, roses, fruit trees & bushes.
Credit Cards: All major credit/debit cards
Specialities: A wide range, over 2000 varieties, of trees, shrubs, perennials, climbers, aquatics & ferns. Extensive collection of *Penstemon*. Nat. Collections of *Buddleja* & *Clematis viticella*.
Notes: Mail order for *Buddleja* only. Wheelchair accessible.
Map Ref: S, C2 **OS Grid Ref:** SO365389

SMad **MADRONA NURSERY** ♿
Pluckley Road, Bethersden, Kent TN26 3DD
Ⓣ (01233) 820100
Ⓕ (01233) 820091
Ⓔ madrona@hotmail.co.uk
Ⓦ www.madrona.co.uk
Contact: Liam MacKenzie
Opening Times: 1000-1700 Sat-Tue 16th Mar-29th Oct. Other times by appt.
Cat. Cost: Free
Credit Cards: All major credit/debit cards
Specialities: Unusual shrubs, conifers & perennials. Eryngiums, *Pseudopanax*.
Notes: Delivers to shows. Euro accepted. Wheelchair accessible.
Map Ref: S, C5 **OS Grid Ref:** TQ918419

SMDP **MARCUS DANCER PLANTS**
Kilcreggan, Alderholt Road, Sandleheath, Fordingbridge, Hampshire SP6 1PT
Ⓣ (01425) 652747
Ⓜ 07709 922730
Ⓔ marcus.dancer@btopenworld.com
Ⓦ www.clematisplants.co.uk
Contact: Marcus Dancer
Opening Times: By appointment only.
Min Mail Order UK: Nmc
Cat. Cost: 4 × 1st class.
Credit Cards: None
Specialities: Wide range of *Clematis*, smaller range of *Daphne*. Some varieties available in small quantities only.
Notes: Mail order available for all plants. Delivers to shows.
Map Ref: S, D1

SMea **MEADOWGATE NURSERY**
Street End Lane, Sidlesham, Chichester, West Sussex PO20 7RG
Ⓣ (01243) 641997
Ⓜ 07736 523262
Ⓔ meadowgatenursery@tiscali.co.uk
Ⓦ www.meadowgatenursery.co.uk
Contact: David Allen
Opening Times: 1000-1700 Sat-Wed.
Min Mail Order UK: Nmc
Credit Cards: All major credit/debit cards
Specialities: Ornamental grasses and complimentary perennials.
Notes: Also sells wholesale. Delivers to shows.

SMHy **Marchants Hardy Plants** ♿
2 Marchants Cottages, Mill Lane, Laughton, East Sussex BN8 6AJ
Ⓣ (01323) 811737
Ⓕ (01323) 811737
Ⓔ graham@marchantsplants.plus.com
Contact: Graham Gough
Opening Times: 0930-1730 Wed-Sat, 16th Mar-22nd Oct 2011.
Cat. Cost: 3 × 2nd class
Credit Cards: Visa, MasterCard
Specialities: Uncommon herbaceous perennials. *Agapanthus*, *Erodium*, *Sedum*, choice grasses, *Miscanthus*, *Molinia*.
Notes: Euro accepted. Wheelchair accessible.
Map Ref: S, D4 **OS Grid Ref:** TQ506119

SMor **Morehavens** ♿
Stocks Lane, Meonstoke, Hampshire SO32 3NQ
Ⓣ (01489) 878501
Ⓔ morehavens@hotmail.co.uk
Ⓦ www.camomilelawns.co.uk
Contact: E. Clements
Opening Times: Mail order only. Open for collection only.
Min Mail Order UK: £18.00
Min Mail Order EU: £18.00 + p&p
Cat. Cost: Free.
Credit Cards: Paypal
Specialities: *Camomile nobile* 'Treneague' and *C. nobile* dwarf.
Notes: Also sells wholesale. Euro accepted for Paypal payments only. Wheelchair accessible.

S

SMrm **Merriments Gardens** ♿
Hawkhurst Road, Hurst Green, East Sussex TN19 7RA
Ⓣ (01580) 860666
Ⓕ (01580) 860324
Ⓔ shop@merriments.co.uk
Ⓦ www.merriments.co.uk
Contact: Taryn Murrells
Opening Times: 0900-1730 Mon-Sat, 1030-1730 Sun (or dusk in winter).
Cat. Cost: Online only.
Credit Cards: Visa, Access, American Express
Specialities: Extensive range of unusual perennials, tender perennials, grasses & annuals. Also large selection of roses & seasonal shrubs. 4-acre show garden.
Notes: Wheelchair accessible.
Map Ref: S, C4

SPad **Paddock Plants**
The Paddock, Upper Toothill Road, Rownhams, Southampton, Hampshire SO16 8AL
Ⓣ (023) 8073 9912
Ⓜ 07763 386717
Ⓔ rob@paddockplants.co.uk
Ⓦ www.paddockplants.co.uk
Contact: Rob & Joanna Courtney
Opening Times: By appt. only. Please telephone in advance.
Min Mail Order UK: £10.00
Cat. Cost: Online only.
Credit Cards: All major credit/debit cards
Specialities: Family-run nursery offering interesting range of perennials, grasses, ferns & shrubs, incl. some unusual varieties, using peat-free growing medium. Some varieties grown in small quantities.
Notes: Local delivery by our own transport. Courier delivery throughout UK. Delivers to shows.
Map Ref: S, D2 **OS Grid Ref:** SU383177

SPav **Pavilion Plants**
18 Pavilion Road, Worthing, West Sussex BN14 7EF
Ⓣ (01903) 821338
Ⓔ rewrew18@hotmail.com
Contact: Andrew Muggeridge
Opening Times: Mail order only. Please phone for details.
Min Mail Order UK: Nmc
Cat. Cost: 4 × 1st class.
Credit Cards: None
Specialities: Perennials and bulbs. *Digitalis*.
Map Ref: S, D3

SPer **Perryhill Nurseries Ltd** ♿
Edenbridge Road, Hartfield, East Sussex TN7 4JP
Ⓣ (01892) 770377
Ⓕ (01892) 770929
Ⓔ sales@perryhillnurseries.co.uk
Ⓦ www.perryhillnurseries.co.uk
Contact: P J Chapman
Opening Times: 0900-1700 7 days 1st Mar-31st Oct. 0900-1630 1st Nov-28th Feb.
Min Mail Order UK: Nmc
Cat. Cost: Online only.
Credit Cards: Maestro, Visa, Access, MasterCard
Specialities: Wide range of trees, shrubs, perennials, roses, fruit trees, soft fruit. Unusual & rare plants may be available in small quantities.
Notes: Mail order despatch depends on size & weight of plants. Wheelchair accessible.
Map Ref: S, C4 **OS Grid Ref:** TQ480375

SPhx **Phoenix Perennial Plants** ♿
Paice Lane, Medstead, Alton, Hampshire GU34 5PR
Ⓣ (01420) 560695
Ⓜ 07909 528191
Ⓕ (01420) 563640
Ⓔ marina@phoenixperennialplants.co.uk
Ⓦ www.phoenixperennialplants.co.uk
Contact: Marina Christopher

Opening Times: Open by appt. only.
Cat. Cost: 4 × 1st class.
Credit Cards: All major credit/debit cards
Specialities: Perennials, many uncommon & hardy, selected for beneficial insects particularly pollinators. *Agastache, Centaurea, Monarda, Sanguisorba, Sedum, Thalictrum, Verbascum,* bulbs, prairie plants, grasses, especially *Molinia* & late-flowering perennials.
Notes: Co-located with Select Seeds SSss. Also sells wholesale. Delivers to shows. Wheelchair accessible.
Map Ref: S, C2 **OS Grid Ref:** SU657362

SPin **John and Lynsey's Plants** ♿
2 Hillside Cottages, Trampers Lane, North Boarhunt, Fareham, Hampshire PO17 6DA
Ⓣ (01329) 832786
Contact: Mrs Lynsey Pink
Opening Times: By appt. only. Open under NGS.
Cat. Cost: None issued.
Credit Cards: None
Specialities: Mainly *Salvia* with a wide range of other unusual perennials. Stock is only available in small quantities but we are happy to try & propagate anything that we have. Nat. Collection of species *Salvia.*
Notes: Wheelchair accessible.
Map Ref: S, D2 **OS Grid Ref:** SU603109

SPlb **Plantbase** ♿
Sleepers Stile Road, Cousley Wood, Wadhurst, East Sussex TN5 6QX
Ⓣ (01892) 785599
Ⓜ 07967 601064
Ⓔ graham@plantbase.freeserve.co.uk
Ⓦ www.plantbase.co.uk
Contact: Graham Blunt
Opening Times: 1000-1700, 7 days all year (appt. advisable).
Min Mail Order UK: Nmc
Min Mail Order EU: Nmc
Cat. Cost: Online only.
Credit Cards: All major credit/debit cards
Specialities: Wide range of alpines, perennials, shrubs, climbers, waterside plants, herbs, Australasian, South African & South American plants in particular. Some available in small quantities only.
Notes: Delivers to shows. Euro accepted. Wheelchair accessible.
Map Ref: S, C5

SPoG **The Potted Garden Nursery** ♿
Ashford Road, Bearsted, Maidstone, Kent ME14 4NH
Ⓣ (01622) 737801
Ⓦ www.thepottedgarden.co.uk
Contact: Any staff member
Opening Times: 0900-1730 (dusk in winter) 7 days. Xmas/New Year period opening times on website or answerphone.
Credit Cards: All major credit/debit cards
Notes: Mail order not available. Wheelchair accessible.
Map Ref: S, C5 **OS Grid Ref:** TQ810550

SPol **Pollie's Perennials and Daylily Nursery** ♿
Lodore, Mount Pleasant Lane, Sway, Lymington, Hampshire SO41 8LS
Ⓣ (01590) 682577
Ⓜ 07415 682288
Ⓕ (01590) 682577
Ⓔ terry@maasz.fsnet.co.uk
Ⓦ www.polliesdaylilies.co.uk
Contact: Pollie Maasz
Opening Times: 1000-1730 w/ends & 1400-1730 Mon-Fri during the daylily season, late-May to mid-Aug. Other times by appt. only.
Min Mail Order UK: Nmc
Min Mail Order EU: £20.00
Cat. Cost: 2 × 1st class.
Credit Cards: None
Specialities: *Hemerocallis,* also less commonly available hardy perennials. Stock available in small quantities only. Nat. Collection of Spider & Unusual Form *Hemerocallis.* 1700+ different cvs can be viewed, mid Jun-mid Sep.
Notes: Mail order, daylilies only. Euro accepted. Wheelchair accessible.
Map Ref: S, D2

SPop **Pops Plants**
Pops Cottage, Barford Lane, Downton, Salisbury, Wiltshire SP5 3PZ
Ⓣ (01725) 511421
Ⓔ mail@popsplants.com
Ⓦ www.popsplants.com
Contact: Lesley Roberts
Opening Times: By appt. only, please.
Min Mail Order UK: 5 plants.
Min Mail Order EU: 5 plants.
Cat. Cost: £2.50
Credit Cards: Paypal
Specialities: *Primula auricula.* Some varieties in limited numbers. Nat. Collection of show, alpine, double & striped auriculas.
Notes: Credit cards accepted online only. Exports beyond EU: min. mail order outside EU 10 plants. Delivers to shows. Euro accepted.

SPre **Plants4Presents** ◆
The Glasshouses, Fletching Common, Newick, Lewes, East Sussex BN8 4JJ
Ⓣ (01825) 721162
Ⓔ plants@4presents.co.uk

Ⓦ www.plants4presents.co.uk
Contact: Emily Rae
Opening Times: Not open. Mail order only.
Min Mail Order UK: Nmc
Min Mail Order EU: Nmc
Cat. Cost: Online only.
Credit Cards: All major credit/debit cards
Specialities: Well-established nursery offering a range of unusual flowering and fruiting plants, incl. citrus trees.

SPtp **Plantstoplant**
Fromefield Nurseries Ltd, Church Lane, Awbridge, Romsey, Hampshire SO51 0HN
Ⓣ (01794) 341123
Ⓕ (01794) 341351
Ⓔ info@plantstoplant.com
Ⓦ www.plantstoplant.com
Contact: David West
Opening Times: Not open. Mail order only.
Min Mail Order UK: £12.00
Cat. Cost: Online only.
Credit Cards: All major credit/debit cards, Paypal
Specialities: Unusual plants.
Notes: Also sells wholesale.

SRea **Really Wild Flowers**
H V Horticulture Ltd, Glenwood, 55 Balcombe Road, Haywards Heath, West Sussex RH16 1PE
Ⓣ (01444) 413376
Ⓕ 0844 443 2503
Ⓔ info@reallywildflowers.co.uk
Ⓦ www.reallywildflowers.co.uk
Contact: Grahame Dixie
Opening Times: Not open. Mail order only.
Min Mail Order UK: £10 + p&p
Cat. Cost: 3 × 1st class.
Credit Cards: All major credit/debit cards
Specialities: Native wild flowers for grasslands, woodlands & wetlands. Seeds & bulbs. Hedge plants & trees. Advisory & soil analysis services.
Notes: Credit card payment accepted for online orders only. Also sells wholesale.

SReu **G Reuthe Ltd**
Crown Point Nursery, Sevenoaks Road, Ightham, Nr Sevenoaks, Kent TN15 0HB
Ⓣ (01732) 865614
Ⓔ reuthe@hotmail.co.uk
Contact: C & P Tomlin
Opening Times: 0900-1600 Thu-Sat. Closed Jan, Feb, Jul & Aug. Please phone before visiting as we are sometimes closed due to circumstances beyond our control. Please ask for details of special spring openings.
Min Mail Order UK: £30.00 + p&p
Credit Cards: Visa, Access
Specialities: Rhododendrons & azaleas, trees, shrubs & climbers. Some plants only available in larger sizes. Large specimen plants available in pots & open ground.
Notes: Landscaping & planting service.
Map Ref: S, C4

SRGP **Rosie's Garden Plants**
Fieldview Cottage, Pratling Street, Aylesford, Kent ME20 7DG
Ⓣ (01622) 715777
Ⓜ 07740 696277
Ⓕ (01622) 715777
Ⓔ jcaviolet@aol.com
Ⓦ www.rosiesgardenplants.biz
Contact: J C Aviolet
Opening Times: Not open. Mail order only.
Min Mail Order UK: Nmc
Min Mail Order EU: Nmc
Cat. Cost: Online only.
Specialities: Hardy *Geranium*, *Buddleja* & *Aster*. Herbaceous & shrubs. Roses. Grows & sells asters, hardy geraniums, roses, plants & shrubs with people's names.
Notes: Exports beyond EU. Delivers to shows. Check web for dates of shows, talks & farmers' markets.

SRiv **River Garden Nurseries**
Troutbeck, Otford, Sevenoaks, Kent TN14 5PH
Ⓣ (01959) 525588
Ⓕ (01959) 525810
Ⓔ box@river-garden.co.uk
Ⓦ www.river-garden.co.uk
Contact: Jenny Alban Davies
Opening Times: By appt. only.
Min Mail Order UK: £10.00 + p&p
Min Mail Order EU: £50.00 + p&p
Cat. Cost: 2 × 1st class.
Credit Cards: None
Specialities: *Buxus* species, cultivars & *Buxus* hedging. *Buxus* topiary.
Notes: Also sells wholesale. Euro accepted.
Map Ref: S, C4 **OS Grid Ref:** TQ523593

SRkn **Rapkyns Nursery** ♿
Street End Lane, Broad Oak, Heathfield, East Sussex TN21 8UB
Ⓣ (01825) 830065
Ⓜ 07771 916933
Ⓕ (01825) 830065
Ⓔ rapkyns@homecall.co.uk
Ⓦ www.rapkynsnursery.co.uk
Contact: Steven Moore
Opening Times: 1000-1700 Tue, Thu & Fri, Mar-Oct incl.
Min Mail Order UK: Nmc
Min Mail Order EU: Nmc
Cat. Cost: 2 × 1st class or online.

Credit Cards: None
Specialities: Unusual shrubs, perennials & climbers. Asters, campanulas, *Ceanothus*, geraniums, lavenders, *Clematis*, penstemons & grasses. New collections of *Crocosmia*, *Anemone*, *Heuchera*, *Heucherella*, *Phlox*, *Coreopsis* & *Helleborus*. Extensive range of salvias.
Notes: Nursery next door to Scotsford Farm, TN21 8UB. Mail order Sep-Apr incl. Also sells wholesale. Delivers to shows. Wheelchair accessible.
Map Ref: S, C4 **OS Grid Ref:** TQ604248

SRms **Rumsey Gardens** ♿
117 Drift Road, Clanfield, Waterlooville, Hampshire PO8 0PD
Ⓣ (023) 9259 3367
Ⓔ info@rumsey-gardens.co.uk
Ⓦ www.rumsey-gardens.co.uk
Contact: Mrs M A Giles
Opening Times: 0900-1700 Mon-Sat & 1000-1600 Sun & B/hols. Closed Sun Nov-Feb.
Min Mail Order UK: £15.00
Cat. Cost: Online only.
Credit Cards: American Express, Visa, MasterCard
Specialities: Wide general range. Herbaceous, alpines, heathers & ferns. Nat. & International Collection of *Cotoneaster*.
Notes: Wheelchair accessible.
Map Ref: S, D2

SRot **Rotherview Nursery** ♿
Ivy House Lane, Three Oaks, Hastings, East Sussex TN35 4NP
Ⓣ (01424) 756228
Ⓔ rotherview@btinternet.com
Ⓦ www.rotherview.com
Contact: Ray & Wendy Bates
Opening Times: 1000-1700 Mar-Oct, 1000-1530 Nov-Feb, 7 days.
Min Mail Order UK: Nmc
Min Mail Order EU: Nmc
Cat. Cost: 6 × 1st class.
Credit Cards: All major credit/debit cards
Specialities: Alpines. Ferns. *Camellia*.
Notes: Nursery is on same site as Coghurst Camellias. Also sells wholesale. Delivers to shows. Euro accepted. Wheelchair accessible.
Map Ref: S, D5

SSea **Seale Nurseries** ♿
Seale Lane, Seale, Farnham, Surrey GU10 1LD
Ⓣ (01252) 782410
Ⓔ catherine@sealenurseries.demon.co.uk
Ⓦ www.sealenurseries.co.uk
Contact: David & Catherine May
Opening Times: 1000-1600 Tue-Sat incl. Other times by appt. Closed 25th Dec-mid Jan.
Cat. Cost: None issued.
Credit Cards: Visa, Access, Delta, MasterCard
Specialities: Roses & *Pelargonium*. Some varieties in short supply, please phone first.
Notes: Wheelchair accessible.
Map Ref: S, C3 **OS Grid Ref:** SU887477

SSpi **Spinners Garden** ♿
School Lane, Boldre, Lymington, Hampshire SO41 5QE
Ⓣ (01590) 675488
Ⓜ 07545 432090
Ⓔ info@spinnersgarden.co.uk
Ⓦ www.spinnersgarden.co.uk
Contact: Andrew Roberts
Opening Times: 1000-1700 Mon-Sat, Mar-Oct. By appt. only Nov, Dec, Jan & Feb.
Min Mail Order UK: £50.00
Cat. Cost: Sae for plant list or available online.
Credit Cards: All major credit/debit cards
Specialities: Less common trees & shrubs esp. *Acer*, *Magnolia*, species & lacecap *Hydrangea*. Bog & woodland plants.
Notes: Limited mail order. Wheelchair accessible.

SSss **Select Seeds** ♿
Paice Lane, Medstead, Nr Alton, Hampshire GU34 5PR
Ⓣ (01420) 560695
Ⓜ 07909 528191
Ⓕ (01420) 563640
Ⓔ marina@phoenixperennialplants.co.uk
Contact: Marina Christopher
Opening Times: Not open. Mail order only.
Min Mail Order UK: £10.00
Cat. Cost: 3 × 1st class.
Credit Cards: All major credit/debit cards
Specialities: Seeds. Unusual hardy perennial seed selection incl. many prairie plants & ornamental umbellifers. Genera incl. *Agastache*, *Angelica*, *Centaurea*, *Seseli*, *Sanguisorba* & *Silphium*.
Notes: Only sells seed by mail order. Credit cards not accepted by phone. Co-located with Phoenix Perennial Plants SPhx. Delivers to shows. Wheelchair accessible.
Map Ref: S, C2 **OS Grid Ref:** SU657362

SSta **Starborough Nursery** ♿
Starborough Road, Marsh Green, Edenbridge, Kent TN8 5RB
Ⓣ (01732) 865614
Ⓔ starborough@hotmail.co.uk
Contact: C & P Tomlin
Opening Times: 0900-1600 Thu, Fri & Sat. Closed Jan, Jul & Aug.
Min Mail Order UK: £30.00 + p&p

Min Mail Order EU: Certain plants only to EU.
Credit Cards: Visa, Access
Specialities: Rare & unusual shrubs esp. *Daphne, Acer, Cercis,* rhododendrons & azaleas, *Magnolia* & *Nyssa.* Some plants only available in larger sizes.
Notes: Mail order only between Oct & Apr. Planting & landscaping services available. Wheelchair accessible.
Map Ref: S, C4

STPC **THE PLANT COMPANY** ♿
Coolham Road, West Chiltington, Pulborough, West Sussex RH20 2LH
Ⓣ (01403) 740100
Ⓔ sales@theplantco.co.uk
Ⓦ www.theplantco.co.uk
Contact: Tim Ricketts
Opening Times: 0900-1730 Mon-Sat.
Min Mail Order UK: £8.95
Min Mail Order EU: Nmc
Credit Cards: Visa, MasterCard
Specialities: A range of herbaceous, shrubs and grasses.
Notes: Also sells wholesale. Delivers to shows. Wheelchair accessible.
Map Ref: S, C3 **OS Grid Ref:** TQ111196

STrG **TERRACE GARDENER**
8 Foxbush, Hildenborough, Kent TN11 9HT
Ⓣ (01732) 832762
Ⓔ johan@terracegardener.com
Ⓦ www.terracegardener.co.uk
Contact: Mr J Hall
Opening Times: Not open. Mail order only, incl. online & by phone. Telephone orders 0930-1500 Mon-Fri.
Min Mail Order UK: Nmc
Cat. Cost: Free
Credit Cards: All major credit/debit cards
Specialities: Patio plants & topiary trees. Container gardening. Architectural & hardy exotics.
Notes: Euro accepted.

SVen **VENTNOR BOTANIC GARDEN** ♿
Undercliff Drive, Ventnor, Isle of Wight PO38 1UL
Ⓣ (01983) 855397
Ⓔ sales@botanic.co.uk
Ⓦ www.botanic.co.uk
Contact: Jason Melia
Opening Times: 1000-1700 7 days, all year.
Min Mail Order UK: Nmc
Min Mail Order EU: Nmc
Cat. Cost: None issued
Credit Cards: All, except American Express
Specialities: Coastal, drought-tolerant, Mediterranean & southern hemisphere plants. Rare & esoteric half-hardy trees, shrubs & perennials.
Notes: Wheelchair accessible.
Map Ref: S, D2 **OS Grid Ref:** SZ548768

SVic **VICTORIANA NURSERY GARDENS** ♿
Challock, Ashford, Kent
TN25 4DG
Ⓣ (01233) 740529
Ⓕ 0203 292 1529
Ⓔ info@victoriananursery.co.uk
Ⓦ www.victoriananursery.co.uk
Contact: Serena Shirley
Opening Times: 0930-1630 (or dusk if sooner) Mon-Fri, 1030-1500 (or dusk if sooner) Sat.
Min Mail Order UK: Nmc
Cat. Cost: Free by post or online.
Credit Cards: All major credit/debit cards
Specialities: Heritage & unusual vegetable plants, seeds, fruit trees & bushes. Also 600+ varieties of *Fuchsia.*
Notes: Also sells wholesale. Wheelchair accessible.
Map Ref: S, C5 **OS Grid Ref:** TR018501

SWat **WATER MEADOW NURSERY** ♿
Cheriton, Nr Alresford, Hampshire
SO24 0QB
Ⓣ (01962) 771895
Ⓔ plantaholic101@btinternet.com
Ⓦ www.plantaholic.co.uk
Contact: Mrs Sandy Worth
Opening Times: 1000-1700 Fri & Sat, 23rd Mar-28th Jul. Other times by prior telephone appt. only.
Min Mail Order UK: £10.00 + p&p
Min Mail Order EU: £50.00 + p&p
Cat. Cost: Full catalogue online only. 2 × 1st class for individual plant lists, please indicate with application.
Credit Cards: All major credit/debit cards
Specialities: Water lilies, extensive water garden plants, unusual herbaceous perennials, aromatic herbs & wildflowers. Nat. Collection of *Papaver orientale* Group. Re-blooming *Papaver* Super Poppy Series.
Notes: Mail order by 24 or 48 hour courier service only. Also sells wholesale. Exports beyond EU. Delivers to shows. Wheelchair accessible.
Map Ref: S, C2

SWCr **WYCH CROSS NURSERIES** ♿
Wych Cross, Forest Row, East Sussex
RH18 5JW
Ⓣ (01342) 822705
Ⓕ (01342) 828246
Ⓔ jp@wychcross.co.uk
Ⓦ www.wychcross.co.uk

Contact: John Paisley
Opening Times: 0900-1730 Mon-Sat.
Min Mail Order UK: Nmc
Cat. Cost: Free
Credit Cards: All major credit/debit cards
Specialities: Roses.
Notes: Wheelchair accessible.
Map Ref: S, C4 **OS Grid Ref:** TQ420320

SWhi **John Hall Plants Ltd** ♿
Whitehall Nursery, Red Lane (Off Churt Road), Headley Down, Hampshire GU35 8SR
Ⓣ (01428) 715505
Ⓜ 07714 344327
Ⓔ info@johnhallplants.com
Ⓦ www.johnhallplants.com
Contact: John Hall
Opening Times: 0900-1630 Mon-Fri, 0900-1300 Sat, by appt. only.
Min Mail Order UK: Nmc
Min Mail Order EU: Nmc
Cat. Cost: By email only.
Credit Cards: None
Specialities: *Erica* and *Calluna*.
Notes: Also sells wholesale. Exports beyond EU. Euro accepted. Wheelchair accessible.

SWvt **Wolverton Plants Ltd** ♿ ◆
Wolverton Common, Tadley, Hampshire RG26 5RU
Ⓣ (01635) 298453
Ⓕ (01635) 299075
Ⓔ Julian@wolvertonplants.co.uk
Ⓦ www.wolvertonplants.co.uk
Contact: Julian Jones
Opening Times: 0900-1800 (or dusk Nov-Feb), 7 days. Closed Xmas/New Year.
Cat. Cost: Online only.
Credit Cards: All major credit/debit cards
Specialities: Wide range of herbaceous perennials & shrubs grown on a commercial scale for the public.
Notes: Horticultural club visits welcome by prior arrangement. Also sells wholesale. Euro accepted. Wheelchair accessible.
Map Ref: S, C2 **OS Grid Ref:** SU555589

Wales and the West

WAbe **Aberconwy Nursery**
Graig, Glan Conwy, Colwyn Bay, Conwy LL28 5TL
Ⓣ (01492) 580875
Contact: Keith & Tim Lever
Opening Times: 1000-1600 Tue-Sun Mar-Sep incl.
Cat. Cost: 2 × 2nd class.
Credit Cards: Visa, MasterCard
Specialities: Alpines, including specialist varieties, esp. gentians, dionysias, dwarf *Dianthus*, *Primula*, *Saxifraga* & dwarf ericaceous plants. Some choice shrubs & woodland plants incl. smaller ferns.
Notes: Delivers to shows.
Map Ref: W, A3 **OS Grid Ref:** SH799744

WAln **L. A. Allen**
Windy Ridge, Llandrindod Wells, Powys LD1 5NY
Ⓔ leslie.allen@mypostoffice.co.uk
Contact: Les Allen
Opening Times: By prior appt.
Min Mail Order UK: Nmc
Min Mail Order EU: Nmc
Cat. Cost: 6 × 1st class.
Credit Cards: None
Specialities: All sections of *Primula auricula*: alpine auricula, show-edged, show-self, doubles, show-stripe. Surplus plants from private collection so available in small quantities, occasionally only 1 or 2 available of some cvs.
Notes: Also sells wholesale.

WAul **Aulden Farm**
Aulden, Leominster, Herefordshire HR6 0JT
Ⓣ (01568) 720129
Ⓔ pf@auldenfarm.co.uk
Ⓦ www.auldenfarm.co.uk
Contact: Alun Whitehead
Opening Times: 0900-1700 Tue & Thu Apr-Aug. Thu only in Sep.
Min Mail Order UK: £25.00
Min Mail Order EU: £25.00
Cat. Cost: Online only.
Credit Cards: Paypal
Specialities: Nat. Collection of Siberian *Iris*.
Notes: If travelling some distance please email to check availability of plants.
Map Ref: W, C4 **OS Grid Ref:** SO462548

WBla **Black Mountain Auriculas**
Whitegrove Nurseries, Fferm Gelliwen, Llanedi, Pontardulais, Swansea, West Glamorgan SA4 0FR
Ⓣ (01269) 832509
Ⓜ 07967 488782
Ⓕ (01269) 832509
Ⓔ whitegrovenurseries@tiscali.co.uk
Contact: Richard Williams
Opening Times: By prior appt. only.
Min Mail Order UK: Nmc
Min Mail Order EU: £50
Cat. Cost: Email for list.
Credit Cards: None
Specialities: *Primula auricula*. Many cultivars available in very small quantities only. Other species of *Primula* available, esp. *P. sieboldii*.

Notes: Also sells wholesale. Delivers to shows. Euro accepted.
Map Ref: W, D3 **OS Grid Ref:** SN573083

WBor **Bordervale Plants** ♿
Nantyderi, Sandy Lane, Ystradowen, Cowbridge, Vale of Glamorgan CF71 7SX
Ⓣ (01446) 774036
Ⓔ lonytwod@gmail.com
Ⓦ www.bordervale.co.uk
Contact: Claire E Jenkins
Opening Times: 1000-1700 Fri-Sun & B/hols Mar-early Oct. Very often open Mon-Thu but please make an appt. on these days if travelling some distance.
Min Mail Order UK: £20.00 + p&p
Cat. Cost: 3 × 1st class.
Credit Cards: None
Specialities: Unusual herbaceous perennials, trees, shrubs & roses, as well as cottage garden plants, many displayed in the 2-acre garden.
Notes: Mail order available for smaller items, subject to season. Garden open May-Sep when nursery open. Also open for NGS. See website for details. Delivers to shows. Nursery wheelchair accessible.
Map Ref: W, D3 **OS Grid Ref:** ST022776

W

WBrk **Brockamin Plants** ♿
Brockamin, Old Hills, Callow End, Worcestershire WR2 4TQ
Ⓣ (01905) 830370
Ⓔ stone.brockamin@btinternet.com
Contact: Margaret Stone
Opening Times: By appt. only.
Cat. Cost: Free.
Credit Cards: None
Specialities: Nat. Collections of *Aster novae-angliae, Erigeron* cvs, *Geranium sanguineum, G. macrorrhizum* & *G.* × *cantabrigiense*. Plants available in small quantities only.
Notes: Wheelchair accessible.
Map Ref: W, C5 **OS Grid Ref:** SO830488

WBuc **Bucknell Nurseries** ♿
Bucknell, Shropshire SY7 0EL
Ⓣ (01547) 530606
Ⓕ (01547) 530699
Ⓔ nickcoull@yahoo.co.uk
Contact: A N Coull
Opening Times: 0800-1700 Mon-Fri & 1000-1300 Sat.
Min Mail Order UK: Nmc
Cat. Cost: Free
Credit Cards: All major credit/debit cards
Specialities: Bare-rooted hedging conifers & forest trees.
Notes: Also sells wholesale. Wheelchair accessible.
Map Ref: W, C4 **OS Grid Ref:** SO356736

WCAu **Claire Austin Hardy Plants**
White Hopton Farm, Wern Lane, Sarn, Newtown, Powys SY16 4EN
Ⓣ (01686) 670342
Ⓔ enquiries@claireaustin-hardyplants.co.uk
Ⓦ www.claireaustin-hardyplants.co.uk
Contact: Claire Austin
Opening Times: Mail order only. Open during Jun when *Iris* field is in flower. See website for details.
Min Mail Order UK: Nmc
Min Mail Order EU: Nmc
Cat. Cost: UK free; Europe €5.00
Credit Cards: MasterCard, Visa, Switch
Specialities: *Paeonia, Iris, Hemerocallis* & hardy plants. Nat. Collections of Bearded *Iris* & Hybrid Herbaceous *Paeonia*.
Notes: Euro accepted.
Map Ref: W, B4

WCFE **Charles F Ellis**
Oak Piece Nurseries, Stanton, Nr Broadway, Worcestershire WR12 7NQ
Ⓣ (01386) 584077
Ⓕ (01386) 584491
Ⓔ ellisplants@cooptel.net
Ⓦ www.ellisplants.co.uk
Contact: Charles Ellis
Opening Times: 1000-1600 7 days 1st Apr-30th Sep. Other times by appt.
Min Mail Order UK: Nmc
Cat. Cost: None issued.
Credit Cards: None
Specialities: Wide range of shrubs, conifers & climbers, some of them unusual. Some available in small quantities only.
Notes: Euro accepted.
Map Ref: W, C5

WChG **Chennels Gate Gardens & Nursery** ♿
Eardisley, Herefordshire HR3 6LT
Ⓣ (01544) 327288
Contact: Mark Dawson
Opening Times: 1000-1700 7 days Mar-Oct.
Cat. Cost: None issued.
Credit Cards: None
Specialities: Interesting & unusual cottage garden plants, grasses & shrubs.
Notes: Wheelchair accessible.

WCot **Cotswold Garden Flowers**
Sands Lane, Badsey, Evesham, Worcestershire WR11 7EZ
Ⓣ nursery: (01386) 833849 or mail order: (01386) 422829
Ⓜ 07812 833849
Ⓕ nursery: (01386) 49844
Ⓔ info@cgf.net
Ⓦ www.cgf.net

Contact: Mandie Potter, Bob Brown
Opening Times: 0900-1730 Mon-Fri, 1000-1730 Sat & Sun, 9th Mar-29th Sep. 0900-1630 Mon-Fri only, Oct-mid Mar. Other times by appt.
Min Mail Order UK: Nmc
Min Mail Order EU: Nmc
Cat. Cost: £1.50 or 6 × 1st class.
Credit Cards: All, except American Express
Specialities: A very wide range of easy & unusual perennials.
Notes: Also sells wholesale. Delivers to shows. Euro accepted. Limited wheelchair access.
Map Ref: W, C5 **OS Grid Ref:** SP077426

WCra **Cranesbill Nursery** ◆
Greenhayes, Upper Westmancote, Tewkesbury, Gloucestershire GL20 7ES
Ⓣ (01684) 773770
Ⓜ 07970 103168
Ⓔ john@cranesbillnursery.com
Ⓦ www.cranesbillnursery.com
Contact: John Dilks
Opening Times: Mail order only. Not always open. Visitors by appt.
Min Mail Order UK: Nmc
Min Mail Order EU: Nmc
Cat. Cost: 4 × 1st class. Current availability list on request.
Credit Cards: MasterCard, Visa, Maestro, Delta
Specialities: Specialist nursery offering a wide range of hardy geraniums. Some of the more unusual cvs available in small quantities.
Map Ref: W, C5 **OS Grid Ref:** SO940378

WCre **Crescent Plants** ♿
Stoney Cross, Marden, Hereford, Herefordshire HR1 3EW
Ⓣ (01432) 880262
Ⓜ 07990 970539
Ⓔ crescent@btinternet.com
Ⓦ www.auriculas.co.uk
Contact: June Poole
Opening Times: Open Days in Apr & May (contact nursery for details). Other times by appt. only. Essential to phone first.
Min Mail Order UK: Nmc
Min Mail Order EU: Nmc
Cat. Cost: Free
Credit Cards: Paypal
Specialities: Named varieties of *Primula auricula* incl. selfs, alpines, double, striped, edges, fancies & border types. Help & advice freely given. Own special recipe auricula compost available for collection only.
Notes: Payment by Paypal via website or send cheque with order. Wheelchair accessible.
Map Ref: W, C4 **OS Grid Ref:** SO525477

WCru **Crûg Farm Plants** ♿
Griffith's Crossing, Caernarfon, Gwynedd LL55 1TU
Ⓣ (01248) 670232
Ⓔ mailorder@crug-farm.co.uk
Ⓦ www.mailorder.crug-farm.co.uk
Contact: B and S Wynn-Jones
Opening Times: 0900-1630 Thu-Sat, last Thu in Mar to 3rd Sat in Sep, incl. Fri B/hol. Or all year Mon-Fri by appt.
Min Mail Order UK: Nmc
Min Mail Order EU: Nmc
Cat. Cost: 5 × 2nd class or online.
Credit Cards: All major credit/debit cards
Specialities: Unusual & rare inc. trees, shrubs, herbaceous & bulbous, mostly self-collected new introductions from the Far East & the Americas. Rare woody & climbers esp. *Acer, Araliaceae, Carpinus, Hydrangeaceae* & *Magnolia* with many other extraordinary introductions. Shade plants esp. *Convallariaceae, Liliaceae, Ranunculaceae* & *Saxifragaceae.* Many supplied bare-rooted. Nat. Collections of *Coriaria, Paris* & *Polygonatum.*
Notes: Delivery by overnight carrier for UK & Ireland. Courier for rest of EU. Delivers to shows. Wheelchair accessible.
Map Ref: W, A2 **OS Grid Ref:** SH509652

WDib **Dibleys Nurseries** ♿ ◆
Llanelidan, Ruthin, Denbighshire LL15 2LG
Ⓣ (01978) 790677
Ⓕ (01978) 790668
Ⓔ sales@dibleys.com
Ⓦ www.dibleys.com
Contact: R Dibley
Opening Times: 1000-1700 7 days, Apr-Aug. 1000-1700 Mon-Fri, Mar, Sep & Oct.
Min Mail Order UK: Nmc
Min Mail Order EU: Nmc
Cat. Cost: Free
Credit Cards: Visa, Access, Switch, Electron, Solo
Specialities: *Streptocarpus, Columnea, Solenostemon, Saintpaulia* & other gesneriads & *Begonia.* Nat. Collections of *Streptocarpus* & *Saintpaulia.*
Notes: Also sells wholesale. Euro accepted. Delivers to shows. Wheelchair accessible.
Map Ref: W, A3

WEuc **Hardy-Eucalyptus**
Grafton Nursery, Worcester Road, Grafton Flyford, Worcester, Worcestershire WR7 4PW
Ⓣ (01905) 888098
Ⓜ 07515 261511
Ⓔ office@hardy-eucalyptus.com
Ⓦ www.hardy-eucalyptus.com
Contact: Hilary Collins
Opening Times: Mail order only. Not open to

W

the public but plants may be collected by appt. Phone or email to arrange a time.
Specialities: Garden-hardy *Eucalyptus*.
Notes: Also sells wholesale. Delivers to shows.

WFar **Farmyard Nurseries** ♿
Dol Llan Road, Llandysul, Carmarthenshire SA44 4RL
Ⓣ (01559) 363389
Ⓜ 01267 220259
Ⓕ (01559) 362200
Ⓔ sales@farmyardnurseries.co.uk
Ⓦ www.farmyardnurseries.co.uk
Contact: Richard Bramley
Opening Times: 0900-1700 7 days, excl. Xmas Day, Boxing Day & New Year's Day.
Min Mail Order UK: Nmc
Min Mail Order EU: Nmc
Cat. Cost: 4 × 1st class.
Credit Cards: Visa, Switch, MasterCard
Specialities: Large range of home grown shrubs & herbaceous perennials, incl. *Geranium*, *Helleborus* & *Primula*. Trees, shrubs, climbers, alpines, conifers & bedding plants.
Notes: Additionally sells from shop/yard in Carmarthen. Also sells wholesale. Euro accepted. Wheelchair accessible.
Map Ref: W, C2 **OS Grid Ref:** SN421406

WFib **Fibrex Nurseries Ltd** ♿
Honeybourne Road, Pebworth, Stratford-on-Avon, Warwickshire CV37 8XP
Ⓣ (01789) 720788
Ⓕ (01789) 721162
Ⓔ sales@fibrex.co.uk
Ⓦ www.fibrex.co.uk
Contact: U Key-Davis & R L Godard-Key
Opening Times: 0900-1700 Mon-Fri, 1st Mar-30th Aug. 0900-1600 Mon-Fri 2nd Sep-28th Feb. 1030-1600 Sat & Sun 30th Mar-28th Jul. Closed last 2 weeks Dec & 1st week Jan. Closed Easter Sun & Aug B/hol Mon.
Min Mail Order UK: £10.00 + p&p
Min Mail Order EU: £20.00 + p&p
Cat. Cost: 3 × 1st class.
Credit Cards: Switch, MasterCard, Visa, Maestro
Specialities: *Hedera*, ferns, *Pelargonium*. Nat. Collections of *Pelargonium* & *Hedera*. Plant collections subject to time of year, please check by phone.
Notes: Also sells wholesale. Delivers to shows. Wheelchair accessible.
Map Ref: W, C5 **OS Grid Ref:** SP133458

WGoo **Wildegoose Nursery home of Bouts Violas**
Lower Farm Cottage, Holdgate, Much Wenlock, Shropshire TF13 6LW
Ⓜ 07717 265212 or 07798 628762
Ⓔ flowers@boutsviolas.co.uk
Ⓦ www.boutsviolas.co.uk
Contact: Laura Crowe
Opening Times: Mail order only. Open strictly by appt. only.
Min Mail Order UK: Nmc
Min Mail Order EU: Nmc
Cat. Cost: 1st class sae.
Credit Cards: None
Specialities: *Viola*.
Notes: Taken over *Viola* stock from Bouts Cottage Nursery. Delivers to shows. Euro accepted.

WGor **Gordon's Nursery** ♿
1 Cefnpennar Cottages, Cefnpennar, Mountain Ash, Mid-Glamorgan CF45 4EE
Ⓣ (01443) 474593
Ⓕ (01443) 475835
Ⓔ sales@gordonsnursery.co.uk
Ⓦ www.gordonsnursery.co.uk
Contact: D A Gordon
Opening Times: 1000-1800 7 days Mar-Jun. 1000-1700 7 days Jul-Oct. 1100-1600 weekends only Nov & Feb. Closed Dec-Jan.
Min Mail Order UK: Nmc
Cat. Cost: 3 × 1st class.
Credit Cards: All major credit/debit cards
Specialities: Shrubs, perennials, alpines & dwarf conifers. Some plants available in small quantities only.
Notes: Mail order only available in some cases, please check for conditions in catalogue. Delivers to shows. Wheelchair accessible.
Map Ref: W, D3 **OS Grid Ref:** SO037012

WGrf **Grafton Nursery**
Worcester Road, Grafton Flyford, Worcester, Worcestershire WR7 4PW
Ⓣ (01905) 888098
Ⓜ 07515 261511
Ⓔ office@grafton-nursery.co.uk
Ⓦ www.grafton-nursery.co.uk
Contact: Hilary Collins
Opening Times: Not open. Mail order only. Plants can be collected by appt. Please phone to arrange a suitable time.
Specialities: Hardy garden ferns.
Notes: Also sells wholesale. Delivers to shows.

WGrn **Green's Leaves** ♿
36 Ford House Road, Newent, Gloucestershire GL18 1LQ
Ⓣ (01531) 820154
Ⓜ 07890 413036
Ⓔ r.paul.green@hotmail.co.uk
Ⓦ www.greensleavesnursery.co.uk
Contact: Paul Green
Opening Times: By appt. only. Please phone to arrange.

Min Mail Order UK: £10.00 + p&p
Cat. Cost: 4 × 2nd class.
Credit Cards: None
Specialities: Range of rare & choice shrubs, also some perennials. Ornamental grasses, sedges & phormiums.
Notes: Also sells wholesale. Delivers to shows. Wheelchair accessible.
Map Ref: W, C4 OS Grid Ref: SO732273

WGwG **Gwynfor Growers**
Gwynfor, Pontgarreg, Llangrannog, Llandysul, Ceredigion SA44 6AU
Ⓣ (01239) 654151
Ⓔ info@gwynfor.co.uk
Ⓦ www.gwynfor.co.uk
Contact: Steve & Angie Hipkin
Opening Times: Usually 1000-1800 or sunset if earlier, Wed, Thu & Sun, all year round.
Min Mail Order UK: Nmc
Cat. Cost: PDF list available by email.
Credit Cards: Paypal
Specialities: National Collection of *Rosmarinus* cvs. Specialist supplier of Welsh fruit trees. Classic & contemporary plants grown organically & peat-free. Some plants available in small quantities only. Rarities propagated to order.
Notes: Plants also available at local farmers' markets, plant fairs & some NGS Open Gardens. Delivers to shows.
Map Ref: W, C2 **OS Grid Ref:** SN331536

WHal **Hall Farm Nursery**
Vicarage Lane, Kinnerley, Nr Oswestry, Shropshire SY10 8DH
Ⓣ (01691) 682135
Ⓔ info@hallfarmnursery.co.uk
Ⓦ www.hallfarmnursery.co.uk
Contact: Christine & Nick Ffoulkes-Jones
Opening Times: 1000-1700 Tue-Sat 1st Mar-5th Oct 2013
Min Mail Order UK: £20.00 +p&p
Cat. Cost: Online only.
Credit Cards: Visa, MasterCard, Electron, Maestro
Specialities: Unusual herbaceous plants, grasses, bog plants, late-flowering perennials, foliage plants, woodland plants, scree alpine plants.
Notes: Euro accepted. Delivers to shows. Partially accessible for wheelchairs.
Map Ref: W, B4 **OS Grid Ref:** SJ333209

WHar **Harley Nursery** ♿
Harley, Shrewsbury, Shropshire SY5 6LN
Ⓣ (01952) 510241
Ⓔ plants@harleynursery.co.uk
Ⓦ www.harleynursery.co.uk
Contact: Nick Murphy & Debbie Plant
Opening Times: 0900-1730 Mon-Sat, 1000-1600 Sun & B/hols. Winter hours 0830-1630 Mon-Sat, 1000-1600 Sun & B/hols.
Min Mail Order UK: £50.00
Cat. Cost: Online only.
Credit Cards: All major credit/debit cards
Specialities: Wide range of trees & shrubs. Large selection of fruit trees & bushes, many old & unusual varieties. Seasonal selection of conifers, climbing & herbaceous plants. Wide range of hedging & forestry plants, many available bare-root.
Notes: Wheelchair accessible.
Map Ref: W, B4 **OS Grid Ref:** SJ598020

WHCr **Hergest Croft Gardens**
Kington, Herefordshire HR5 3EG
Ⓣ (01544) 230160
Ⓜ 07968 435627
Ⓕ (01544) 232031
Ⓔ gardens@hergest.co.uk
Ⓦ www.hergest.co.uk
Contact: Stephen Lloyd
Opening Times: 1200-1730, 7 days, Apr-Oct.
Cat. Cost: None issued
Credit Cards: All major credit/debit cards
Specialities: *Acer*, *Betula* & unusual woody plants.
Notes: Limited wheelchair access.

WHea **Heath Garden**
Heath Hill, Sheriffhales, Shifnal, Shropshire TF11 8RR
Ⓣ (01952) 691341
Ⓔ 1malt@supanet.com
Contact: Gordon Malt
Opening Times: 1000-1800 Tues, Apr-Sep. Other times by appt.
Cat. Cost: None issued.
Credit Cards: None
Specialities: Interesting range of hardy & tender perennials. *Geranium*, *Salvia*, ornamental grasses & silver foliage plants.
Notes: Plants available in small quantities only. Talks & demonstrations to horticultural clubs.
Map Ref: W, B5 **OS Grid Ref:** SJ376313

WHer **The Herb Garden & Historical Plant Nursery**
Ty Capel Pensarn, Pentre Berw, Anglesey, Gwynedd LL60 6LG
Ⓣ (01248) 422208 or (01545) 580893
Ⓜ 07751 583958
Ⓕ (01248) 422208
Ⓔ corinnetremaine@gmail.com
Ⓦ www.HistoricalPlants.co.uk
Contact: Corinne & David Tremaine-Stevenson
Opening Times: By appt. only.

Min Mail Order UK: £15.00 + p&p
Min Mail Order EU: £50.00 + p&p sterling only.
Cat. Cost: Online only.
Credit Cards: None
Specialities: Rarer herbs, rare natives & wild flowers; rare & unusual & historical perennials & old roses.
Map Ref: W, A2

WHfH **Herbs for Healing** ♿
Barnsley Herb Garden, Barnsley,
Nr Cirencester, Gloucestershire GL7 5EE
Ⓣ (01285) 740638
Ⓜ 07773 687493
Ⓔ herbs@herbsforhealing.net
Ⓦ www.herbsforhealing.net
Contact: Davina Wynne-Jones
Opening Times: 1000-1700 Wed.
Min Mail Order UK: Nmc
Credit Cards: Paypal
Specialities: Medicinal & some culinary herbs. Display garden.
Notes: Nursery in Clapton's Lane, Barnsley, behind Barnsley House Hotel. See web for directions. Courses and workshops on use of herbs. Sells at local farmers' markets. Euro accepted. Wheelchair accessible.
Map Ref: W, D5 **OS Grid Ref:** SP048177

WHil **Hillview Hardy Plants** ♿
(off B4176), Worfield, Nr Bridgnorth,
Shropshire WV15 5NT
Ⓣ (01746) 716454
Ⓜ 07974 391608
Ⓕ (01746) 716454
Ⓔ hillview@onetel.net
Ⓦ www.hillviewhardyplants.com
Contact: Ingrid, John & Sarah Millington
Opening Times: 0900-1700 Mon-Sat Mar-mid Oct. At other times, please phone first.
Min Mail Order UK: £10.00 + p&p
Min Mail Order EU: £10.00 + p&p
Cat. Cost: Online only.
Credit Cards: All major credit/debit cards
Specialities: Choice herbaceous perennials incl. *Acanthus* & *Acanthaceae*, *Albuca*, *Aquilegia*, auricula, *Primula*, *Canna*, *Crocosmia*, *Eucomis*, *Ixia*, South African bulbs. Nat. Collections of *Acanthus* & *Albuca*.
Notes: Also sells wholesale. Exports beyond EU. Delivers to shows. Euro accepted. Wheelchair accessible.
Map Ref: W, B4 **OS Grid Ref:** SO772969

WHlf **Hayloft Plants**
Manor Farm, Pensham, Pershore,
Worcestershire WR10 3HB
Ⓣ (01386) 554440 or (01386) 562999
Ⓕ (01386) 553833
Ⓔ info@hayloftplants.co.uk
Ⓦ www.hayloftplants.co.uk
Contact: Yvonne Walker
Opening Times: Not open. Mail order only.
Min Mail Order UK: Nmc
Min Mail Order EU: Nmc
Cat. Cost: Free.
Credit Cards: All major credit/debit cards

WHoo **Hoo House Nursery** ◆
Hoo House, Gloucester Road, Tewkesbury,
Gloucestershire GL20 7DA
Ⓣ (01684) 293389
Ⓕ (01684) 293389
Ⓔ nursery@hoohouse.co.uk
Ⓦ www.hoohouse.co.uk
Contact: Robin & Julie Ritchie
Opening Times: 1000-1700 Mon-Sat, 1100-1700 Sun.
Cat. Cost: 3 × 1st class.
Credit Cards: All major credit/debit cards
Specialities: Wide range of herbaceous & alpines grown peat-free. *Aster*, *Cyclamen*, *Geranium*, *Penstemon* & many later-flowering varieties. Nat. Collections of *Platycodon* & *Gentiana asclepiadea* cvs.
Notes: Also sells wholesale. Euro accepted. Partially wheelchair accessible.
Map Ref: W, C5 **OS Grid Ref:** SO893293

WHor **Horticultural Sales**
Upper Brockington, Berrington Street,
Bodenham, Herefordshire HR1 3HT
Ⓣ (01568) 797747
Ⓜ 07966 635005
Ⓕ (01568) 797013
Ⓔ pdavies@hortsales.fsnet.co.uk
Contact: Peter Davies
Opening Times: By appt. only.
Min Mail Order UK: Nmc
Min Mail Order EU: Nmc
Cat. Cost: Free but available by email only.
Credit Cards: Paypal
Specialities: *Acer*, *Pinus* & grafted conifers, plus wide selection of less commonly grown shrubs, available in small quantities only.
Notes: Offers plant finding service. 37 years experience in trade. Also sells wholesale. Euro accepted. Delivers to shows.

WHrl **Harrells Hardy Plants**
(Office) 15 Coxlea Close, Evesham,
Worcestershire WR11 4JS
Ⓣ (01386) 443077
Ⓜ 07799 577120 or 07733 446606
Ⓔ mail@harrellshardyplants.co.uk
Ⓦ www.harrellshardyplants.co.uk
Contact: Liz Nicklin & Kate Phillips
Opening Times: By appt. only. Please telephone.

Min Mail Order UK: Nmc
Cat. Cost: 4 × 2nd class.
Credit Cards: None
Specialities: Display gardens showcase wide range of hardy perennials, esp. *Hemerocallis* & grasses.
Notes: Nursery located off Rudge Rd, Evesham. Please phone for directions or see catalogue. Partial wheelchair access. Mail order Nov-Mar only.
Map Ref: W, C5 **OS Grid Ref:** SP033443

WIce ICE ALPINES ♿
Lyehead, Bewdley, Worcestershire DY12 2UW
Ⓣ (01299) 269219
Ⓕ (01562) 510003
Ⓔ icealpines@gmail.com
Ⓦ www.Icealpines.co.uk
Contact: Mark Lagomarsino
Opening Times: Mail order. Open by appt. only.
Min Mail Order UK: Nmc
Min Mail Order EU: £18
Credit Cards: Paypal
Specialities: British grown alpine & rockery plants.
Notes: Delivers to shows. Wheelchair accessible.

WJas PAUL JASPER TREES
(Office) The Lighthouse, Bridge Street, Leominster, Herefordshire HR6 8DX
Ⓕ (01568) 616499 for orders.
Ⓔ enquiries@jaspertrees.co.uk
Ⓦ www.jaspertrees.co.uk
Contact: Paul Jasper
Opening Times: Not open. Mail order only.
Min Mail Order UK: £40.00 + p&p
Cat. Cost: Online only.
Credit Cards: All major credit/debit cards
Specialities: Full range of fruit & ornamental trees. Over 100 modern and traditional fruit tree varieties plus 100 ornamental tree varieties, all direct from the grower. Many unusual varieties of *Malus domestica* & *Prunus*.
Notes: Regular catalogue updates & notes on website. Also sells wholesale.
Map Ref: W, C4 **OS Grid Ref:** SO495595

WJek JEKKA'S HERB FARM ♿
Rose Cottage, Shellards Lane, Alveston, Bristol, South Gloucestershire BS35 3SY
Ⓣ (01454) 418878
Ⓕ (01454) 424907
Ⓔ sales@jekkasherbfarm.com
Ⓦ www.jekkasherbfarm.com
Contact: Jekka McVicar
Opening Times: Every Fri throughout season. Please check website for dates.
Min Mail Order UK: £10.00
Min Mail Order EU: Charges per order on application.
Cat. Cost: Online only.
Credit Cards: Visa, MasterCard, Delta, Maestro
Specialities: Culinary, medicinal, aromatic, decorative herbs.
Notes: Only sell seeds via mail order. Plants can be ordered for collection from the farm with 24 hours notice. Delivers to shows. Wheelchair accessible.
Map Ref: W, D4

WJPR JPR ENVIRONMENTAL
The Malt House, Standish, Stonehouse, Gloucestershire GL10 3DL
Ⓣ (01453) 811537
Ⓔ enquiries@jprenvironmental.co.uk
Ⓦ www.jprwillow.co.uk
Contact: John Robinthwaite
Opening Times: Mail order only. 0900-1700.
Min Mail Order UK: £6.00
Credit Cards: All, except American Express
Specialities: *Salix*.
Notes: Also sells wholesale.

WKif KIFTSGATE COURT GARDENS ♿
Kiftsgate Court, Chipping Camden, Gloucestershire GL55 6LN
Ⓣ (01386) 438777
Ⓕ (01386) 438777
Ⓔ anne@kiftsgate.co.uk
Ⓦ www.kiftsgate.co.uk
Contact: Mrs J Chambers
Opening Times: 1200-1800 Sat-Wed, May, Jun & Jul. 1400-1800 Sat-Wed, Aug. 1400-1800 Sun, Mon & Wed, Apr & Sep.
Cat. Cost: None issued
Credit Cards: All, except American Express
Specialities: Small range of unusual plants.
Notes: Wheelchair accessible.
Map Ref: W, C5 **OS Grid Ref:** SP170430

WLav THE LAVENDER GARDEN
Ashcroft Nurseries, Nr Ozleworth, Kingscote, Tetbury, Gloucestershire GL8 8YF
Ⓣ (01453) 860356 or 549286
Ⓜ 07837 582943
Ⓔ Andrew007Bullock@aol.com
Ⓦ www.TheLavenderG.co.uk
Contact: Andrew Bullock
Opening Times: 1100-1700 Sat & Sun. Weekdays variable, please phone. 1st Nov-1st Mar by appt. only.
Min Mail Order UK: £10.00 + p&p
Min Mail Order EU: £20.00 + p&p
Cat. Cost: 2 × 1st class.
Credit Cards: All major credit/debit cards
Specialities: *Lavandula*, *Buddleja*, plants to

attract butterflies. Herbs, wildflowers. Nat. Collection of *Buddleja*.
Notes: Also sells wholesale. Delivers to shows.
Map Ref: W, D5 **OS Grid Ref:** ST798948

WMAq **MEREBROOK WATER PLANTS**
Kingfisher Barn, Merebrook Farm, Hanley Swan, Worcestershire WR8 0DX
Ⓣ (01684) 310950
Ⓜ 07876 777066
Ⓔ enquiries@pondplants.co.uk
Ⓦ www.pondplants.co.uk
Contact: Roger Kings & Biddi Kings
Opening Times: Not open. Mail order only.
Min Mail Order UK: Nmc
Min Mail Order EU: £25.00
Cat. Cost: Online only.
Credit Cards: All major credit/debit cards
Specialities: *Nymphaea*, Louisiana irises & other aquatic plants. International Waterlily & Water Gardening Soc. accredited collection.

W

WMil **ANNE MILNER**
Meadow House, Baunton, Cirencester, Gloucestershire GL7 7BB
Ⓣ (01285) 643731
Ⓔ anne.milner@btinternet.com
Ⓦ www.blissiris.co.uk
Contact: Anne Milner
Opening Times: By appt. only.
Min Mail Order UK: Nmc
Min Mail Order EU: Nmc
Cat. Cost: 50p (UK) £1.00 (EU) to cover postage.
Credit Cards: None
Specialities: Nat. Collection of *Iris* (A.J. Bliss introductions). Available in small quantities only.
Notes: Euro accepted. Delivers to some shows, check with nursery.

WMnd **MYND HARDY PLANTS** ♿
Delbury Hall Estate, Diddlebury, Craven Arms, Shropshire SY7 9DH
Ⓣ (01584) 841222
Ⓔ myndhardyplants@aol.com
Ⓦ www.myndplants.co.uk
Contact: Mark Zenick
Opening Times: 1300-1700 Wed-Fri, 1000-1700 Sat, 16th Mar-14th Sep. 1300-1700 B/Hol Mons. 1300-1700 Sun May-Jul. Other times, phone for appt.
Cat. Cost: 4 × 2nd class.
Credit Cards: All major credit/debit cards
Specialities: Herbaceous plants, specialising in American bred, British grown, *Hemerocallis*. Home to New Hope Garden's *Hemerocallis* plants.
Notes: Also sells wholesale. Wheelchair accessible.
Map Ref: W, B4 **OS Grid Ref:** SO510852

WMoo **MOORLAND COTTAGE PLANTS** ♿
Rhyd-y-Groes, Brynberian, Crymych, Pembrokeshire SA41 3TT
Ⓣ (01239) 891363
Ⓦ www.moorlandcottageplants.co.uk
Contact: Jennifer Matthews
Opening Times: 1030-1730 daily excl. Wed 1st Mar-30th Sep.
Min Mail Order UK: See cat. for details.
Cat. Cost: 4 × 1st class.
Credit Cards: All major credit/debit cards
Specialities: Traditional & unusual hardy perennials. Many garden-worthy rarities. Cottage garden plants, ferns & many shade plants, moisture lovers, ornamental grasses & bamboos, colourful ground cover.
Notes: Display garden open for NGS from mid-May. Wheelchair accessible.
Map Ref: W, C2 **OS Grid Ref:** SN091343

WMou **MOUNT PLEASANT TREES** ♿
Rockhampton, Berkeley, Gloucestershire GL13 9DU
Ⓣ (01454) 260348
Ⓔ info@mountpleasanttrees.com
Ⓦ www.mountpleasanttrees.com
Contact: Tom Locke & Elizabeth Murphy
Opening Times: 0830-1630 Mon-Fri, 0830-1230 Sat, Oct-Apr.
Min Mail Order UK: Nmc but p&p quoted on individual basis.
Cat. Cost: Free.
Credit Cards: All major credit/debit cards
Specialities: Wide range of trees for forestry, hedging, woodlands & gardens esp. *Populus*, *Salix*, *Tilia* & *Quercus*.
Notes: Mail order available for plants under 1m in height, quotes on request. Also sells wholesale. Wheelchair accessible.
Map Ref: W, D4 **OS Grid Ref:** ST654929

WNHG **NEW HOPE GARDENS** ♿
The Old Chapel, Cefn Einion, Nr Bishops Castle, Shropshire SY9 5LF
Ⓣ Office: (01588) 630750 or Nursery: (01584) 841222
Ⓔ Newhopegardensmz@aol.com
Ⓦ www.newhopegardens.com
Contact: Mark Zenick
Opening Times: 1300-1700 Wed-Fri, 1000-1700 Sat, 16th Mar-14th Sep. 1300-1700 B/hol Mons during season. 1300-1700 Sun, May-Jul. Other times phone nursery for appt. Daylily Open W/ends 29th/30th Jun, 6th/7th Jul, 13th/14th Jul, 20th/21st Jul. (NGS Open Days, 1300-1700, 9th & 14th Jul.)
Min Mail Order UK: Nmc
Min Mail Order EU: Nmc
Cat. Cost: Online only. Plant list on request.

Credit Cards: All major credit/debit cards
Specialities: American bred, British grown, *Hemerocallis*. Ships bare-rooted plants.
Notes: Nursery co-located with Mynd Hardy Plants (code WMnd). Wheelchair accessible.
Map Ref: W, B4 **OS Grid Ref:** SO510852

WNPC **Newent Plant Centre** ♿
Ledbury Road, Newent, Gloucestershire GL18 1DL
Ⓣ (01531) 828488
Ⓕ (01531) 828488
Ⓔ markmoir999@btinternet.com
Ⓦ www.newentplantcentre.co.uk
Contact: Mark Moir
Opening Times: 0900-1700 Mon-Sat, 1000-1600 Sun. Closed Jan.
Credit Cards: All major credit/debit cards
Specialities: Extensive range of *Heuchera* & *Euphorbia*. Herbaceous perennials, climbers, shrubs, trees, alpines, herbs, roses & fruit.
Notes: Delivers to shows. Wheelchair accessible.
Map Ref: W, C4 **OS Grid Ref:** SO716282

WOld **Old Court Nurseries**
Colwall, Nr Malvern, Worcestershire WR13 6QE
Ⓣ (01684) 540416
Ⓔ paulpicton@btinternet.com
Ⓦ www.autumnasters.co.uk
Contact: Paul, Meriel or Helen Picton
Opening Times: 1400-1700 Wed-Sat, May-Aug. 1100-1700 Wed-Sun, Aug. 1100-1700 7 days, 1st week Sep-2nd week Oct. Also by appt. May to Oct.
Min Mail Order UK: Nmc
Min Mail Order EU: Nmc
Credit Cards: None
Specialities: Nat. Collection of Michaelmas Daisies. Herbaceous perennials.
Notes: Mail order sent in spring only. Display garden open Aug-Oct.
Map Ref: W, C4 **OS Grid Ref:** SO759430

WOth **Other Fellow Fuchsias**
25 Spring Meadow Road, Lydney, Gloucestershire GL15 5LF
Ⓣ (01594) 844452
Ⓜ 07564 357637
Ⓔ info@otherfellow.co.uk
Ⓦ http://otherfellow.co.uk
Contact: Nick Egginton
Opening Times: Not open. Mail order only.
Min Mail Order UK: Nmc
Min Mail Order EU: £10.50 + p&p
Cat. Cost: Free.
Credit Cards: All major credit/debit cards
Specialities: Expanding collection of *Fuchsia*, esp. unusual, single & exhibition varieties. Small selection of *Salvia* & other tender perennials. Some stock available in small quantities only. Can propagate to order.
Notes: Exports beyond EU. Euro accepted.

WOut **Out of the Common Way**
(Office) Penhyddgan, Boduan, Pwllheli, Gwynedd LL53 8YH
Ⓣ office: (01758) 721577 or nursery: (01407) 720431
Ⓔ ziggymen22@hotmail.co.uk
Contact: Joanna Davidson (nursery) Margaret Mason (office & mail order)
Opening Times: By arrangement.
Min Mail Order UK: Nmc
Min Mail Order EU: Nmc
Cat. Cost: A5 sae large letter rate postage.
Credit Cards: None
Specialities: *Labiates*, esp. *Nepeta* & *Salvia*. *Aster*, *Geranium* & *Crocosmia*. Native plants. Some plants propagated in small quantities only. Will propagate salvias to order.
Notes: Nursery is at Pandy Treban, Bryngwran, Anglesey. Delivers to shows. Euro accepted. Partially accessible for wheelchairs.
Map Ref: W, A2 **OS Grid Ref:** SH370778

WPat **Chris Pattison** ♿
Brookend, Pendock, Gloucestershire GL19 3PL
Ⓣ (01531) 650480
Ⓕ (01531) 650480
Ⓔ cp@chris-pattison.co.uk
Ⓦ www.chris-pattison.co.uk
Contact: Chris Pattison
Opening Times: 0900-1700 Mon-Fri. W/ends by appt. only.
Min Mail Order UK: £10.00 +p&p
Cat. Cost: 3 × 1st class.
Credit Cards: None
Specialities: Choice rare shrubs & trees. Grafted stock esp. Japanese maples & *Liquidambar*. Wide range of *Viburnum* & dwarf/miniature trees & shrubs suitable for bonsai or rockery.
Notes: Mail order Nov-Feb only. Also sells wholesale. Euro accepted. Wheelchair accessible.
Map Ref: W, C5 **OS Grid Ref:** SO781327

WPGP **Pan-Global Plants** ♿
The Walled Garden, Frampton Court, Frampton-on-Severn, Gloucestershire GL2 7EX
Ⓣ (01452) 741641
Ⓜ 07801 275138
Ⓔ info@panglobalplants.com
Ⓦ www.panglobalplants.com
Contact: Nick Macer
Opening Times: 1100-1700 Wed-Sun 1st Feb-31st Oct. Also B/hols. Closed 2nd Sun in Sep.

Winter months by appt., please phone first.
Cat. Cost: 6 × 1st class.
Credit Cards: Maestro, MasterCard, Visa, Solo, Delta
Specialities: A plantsman's nursery offering a very wide selection of correctly named rare & desirable trees, shrubs, herbaceous, bamboos, exotics, climbers, ferns etc. Specialities incl. *Magnolia, Hydrangea, Tilia, Betula, Bamboo* & *Agavaceae.*
Notes: Wheelchair accessible.
Map Ref: W, D5 **OS Grid Ref:** SO750080

WPhe **PHEASANT ACRE PLANTS**
3 Pheasant Walk, Pen-y-Fai, Bridgend, Mid Glamorgan CF31 4DU
Ⓣ (01656) 664086
Ⓜ 07816 236462
Ⓔ sales@pheasantacreplants.co.uk
Ⓦ www.pheasantacreplants.co.uk
Contact: Rob Evans
Opening Times: Nursery visits by appt. only and on Open Days.
Min Mail Order UK: Nmc
Min Mail Order EU: Nmc
Cat. Cost: £1.00
Credit Cards: All major credit/debit cards
Specialities: Bulbous. Ornamental. *Gladiolus.*
Notes: Delivers to shows. Euro accepted.

WPnn **THE PERENNIAL NURSERY**
Rhosygilwen, St Davids, Haverfordwest, Pembrokeshire SA62 6DB
Ⓣ (01437) 721954
Ⓜ 07717 783492
Ⓔ theperennialnursery@tesco.net
Ⓦ www.droughttolerantplants.co.uk
Contact: Mrs Philipa Symons
Opening Times: 1030-1700 Mar-Oct. Closed Tue.
Min Mail Order UK: Nmc
Min Mail Order EU: Nmc
Cat. Cost: Online only.
Credit Cards: Visa, MasterCard
Specialities: *Lampranthus*, wind & drought-tolerant plants.
Notes: Tea room.
Map Ref: W, C1 **OS Grid Ref:** SM775292

WPnP **PENLAN PERENNIALS** ♿
Wern Rhos, Newchapel, Boncath, Pembrokeshire SA37 0EN
Ⓣ (01239) 842260
Ⓜ 07857 675312
Ⓔ info@penlanperennials.co.uk
Ⓦ www.penlanperennials.co.uk
Contact: Richard Cain
Opening Times: Open for collection of orders & by appt.
Min Mail Order UK: Nmc
Min Mail Order EU: Nmc
Cat. Cost: Online PDF, or sae for CD-ROM.
Credit Cards: All major credit/debit cards
Specialities: Aquatic, marginal & bog plants. Shade-loving & woodland perennials, ferns & hardy geraniums, all grown peat-free.
Notes: Mail order all year, next day delivery. Secure online web ordering. Also sells wholesale. Euro accepted. Wheelchair accessible. Delivers to shows.
Map Ref: W, C2 **OS Grid Ref:** SN217392

WPos **POSHPLANTS**
Glanaber, Waunfawr, Caernarfon, Gwynedd LL55 4EZ
Ⓔ na.horticulture@btinternet.com
Ⓦ www.poshplants.biz
Contact: Neil Alcock
Opening Times: Not open. Mail order online only.
Min Mail Order UK: Nmc
Min Mail Order EU: £6.00
Cat. Cost: Online only.
Credit Cards: Paypal
Specialities: Unusual perennials. Range of *Salix.*

WPtf **PANTYFOD GARDEN NURSERY**
Llandewi Brefi, Tregaron, Ceredigion SY25 6PE
Ⓣ 07553 652698 (answering service)
Ⓔ sales@pantyfodgarden.co.uk
Ⓦ www.pantyfodgarden.co.uk
Contact: Susan Rowe
Opening Times: Currently mail order only & not open to visitors but this may change in 2013. Please check website for updates. Garden occasionally open under the National Gardens Scheme when plants are offered for sale. Please check with NGS for Open Days.
Min Mail Order UK: Nmc
Min Mail Order EU: Nmc
Cat. Cost: Online only.
Credit Cards: Paypal
Specialities: Hardy geraniums, unusual hardy perennials, grasses, plants for moist soil, black plants, woodland plants. All plants grown largely peat-free. Many plants available in small quantities.
Notes: Stock changes throughout the year. Some plants ready later in the year. See website for regular updates or phone/email. Emails welcome to enquire about plants not listed on website.
Map Ref: W, C3 **OS Grid Ref:** SN654540

WRHF **RED HOUSE FARM** ♿
Flying Horse Lane, Bradley Green, Nr Redditch, Worcestershire B96 6QT
Ⓣ (01527) 821269
Ⓔ redhousenursery@googlemail.com
Ⓦ www.redhousefarmgardenandnursery.co.uk

Contact: Mrs Maureen Weaver
Opening Times: 0900-1700 Mon-Sat all year. 1000-1700 Sun & B/hols.
Cat. Cost: 2 × 1st class.
Credit Cards: None
Specialities: Cottage garden perennials.
Notes: Wheelchair accessible.
Map Ref: W, C5 **OS Grid Ref:** SO986623

WRou **ROUALEYN NURSERIES**
Trefriw, Conwy LL27 0SX
Ⓣ (01492) 640548
Ⓔ roualeynnursery@btinternet.com
Ⓦ www.roualeynfuchsias.co.uk
Contact: Doug Jones
Opening Times: 1000-1600 Fri, Sat & Sun.
Min Mail Order UK: £15.00
Cat. Cost: 2 × 1st class sae.
Specialities: Fuchsias, incl. species.
Notes: Orders may be collected from any of the flower shows listed in current catalogue.

WSFF **SAITH FFYNNON WILDLIFE PLANTS** ♿
Whitford, Holywell, Flintshire CH8 9EQ
Ⓣ (01352) 711198
Ⓕ (01352) 716777
Ⓔ jan@7wells.org
Ⓦ www.7wells.co.uk
Contact: Jan Miller
Opening Times: By appt. only.
Min Mail Order UK: Nmc
Min Mail Order EU: Nmc
Cat. Cost: 2 × 1st class (list only) or full catalogue online.
Credit Cards: All major credit/debit cards
Specialities: Plants and seeds to attract bees, butterflies and moths. Natural dye plants. Nat. Collection of *Eupatorium.* Stock available in small quantities unless ordered well in advance.
Notes: Percentage of profits go to conservation. Credit cards accepted via website only. Also sells wholesale. Euro accepted. Wheelchair accessible.

WSHC **STONE HOUSE COTTAGE NURSERIES** ♿
Stone, Nr Kidderminster, Worcestershire
DY10 4BG
Ⓣ (01562) 69902
Ⓔ louisa@shcn.co.uk
Ⓦ www.shcn.co.uk
Contact: L N Arbuthnott
Opening Times: 1000-1700 Wed-Sat, late Mar-early Sep only.
Cat. Cost: Sae
Credit Cards: None
Specialities: Small general range esp. wall shrubs, climbers & unusual plants.
Notes: Wheelchair accessible.
Map Ref: W, C5 **OS Grid Ref:** SO863750

WShi **SHIPTON BULBS**
Y Felin, Henllan Amgoed,
Whitland, Carmarthenshire
SA34 0SL
Ⓣ (01994) 240125
Ⓕ (01994) 241180
Ⓔ admin@shiptonbulbs.co.uk
Ⓦ www.shiptonbulbs.co.uk
Contact: John Shipton & Astra Shipton
Opening Times: By appt. only.
Min Mail Order UK: Nmc
Min Mail Order EU: Nmc
Cat. Cost: Sae.
Credit Cards: All major credit/debit cards
Specialities: Native British bulbs. Bulbs & plants for naturalising.
Notes: Delivers to shows. Euro accepted.
Map Ref: W, D2 **OS Grid Ref:** SN188207

WSSs **SHROPSHIRE SARRACENIAS** ♿
5 Field Close, Malinslee, Telford,
Shropshire TF4 2EH
Ⓣ (01952) 501598
Ⓔ mike@carnivorousplants.uk.com
Ⓦ www.carnivorousplants.uk.com
Contact: Mike King
Opening Times: By appt. only.
Min Mail Order UK: Nmc
Min Mail Order EU: Nmc
Cat. Cost: 2 × 1st class.
Credit Cards: Paypal
Specialities: *Sarracenia. Dionaea muscipula* & forms. Some stock available in small quantities only. Nat. Collections of *Sarracenia* & *Dionaea.*
Notes: Exports beyond EU. Delivers to shows. Euro accepted. Wheelchair accessible.
Map Ref: W, B4 **OS Grid Ref:** SJ689085

WSuV **SUNNYBANK VINE NURSERY (NATIONAL VINE COLLECTION)**
Cwm Barn, King Street, Ewyas Harold,
Rowlestone, Herefordshire
HR2 OEE
Ⓣ (01981) 240256
Ⓔ Sarah@sunnybankvines.co.uk
Ⓦ www.sunnybankvines.co.uk
Contact: Sarah Bell
Opening Times: Not open. Mail order only. Open day once a year advertised on both nursery & Plant Heritage websites.
Min Mail Order UK: £12.00 incl. p&p
Min Mail Order EU: £15.00 incl. p&p
Cat. Cost: Online only.
Credit Cards: None
Specialities: Vines. Nat. Collection of *Vitis vinifera* (hardy, incl. dessert & wine). Small quantities of 60-70 varieties available as rooted plants, the entire Collection usually available as bare-wood cuttings for own propagation

depending upon wood ripening this season. **Notes:** EU sales by arrangement. Exports beyond EU.

WTan **Tan-y-Llyn Nurseries**
Meifod, Powys SY22 6YB
Ⓣ (01938) 500370
Ⓔ info@tanyllyn-nursery.co.uk
Ⓦ www.tanyllyn-nursery.co.uk
Contact: Callum Johnston
Opening Times: 1000-1700 Tue-Sat Mar-Jun and at other times by appt.
Min Mail Order UK: Nmc
Cat. Cost: 2 × 1st class or online.
Credit Cards: Paypal
Specialities: Herbs, alpines, perennials.
Map Ref: W, B3 **OS Grid Ref:** SJ167125

WThu **Thuya Alpine Nursery**
Glebelands, Hartpury, Gloucestershire GL19 3BW
Ⓣ (01452) 700548 (after dark)
Contact: S W Bond
Opening Times: 1000-dusk Sat & B/hols. 1100-dusk Sun, weekdays appt. advised.
Min Mail Order UK: £6.00 + p&p
Min Mail Order EU: £12.00 + p&p
Cat. Cost: 4 × 2nd class.
Credit Cards: None
Specialities: Wide and changing range including rarities, available in smallish numbers.
Notes: Will deliver plants to AGS shows only. Partially accessible for wheelchair users.
Map Ref: W, C5

W

WTou **Touchwood Plants**
4 Clyne Valley Cottages, Killay, Swansea, West Glamorgan SA2 7DU
Ⓣ (01792) 522443
Ⓔ Carrie.Thomas@ntlworld.com
Ⓦ www.touchwoodplants.co.uk
Contact: Carrie Thomas
Opening Times: Most reasonable days/times. Please phone first.
Min Mail Order UK: Nmc
Min Mail Order EU: Nmc
Cat. Cost: Online only.
Credit Cards: All major credit/debit cards. Paypal.
Specialities: Seeds & plants. Nat. Collection of *Aquilegia vulgaris* cvs & hybrids. Plant stocks held in small quantities. Main stock is seed. Garden & *Aquilegia* Collection open.
Notes: Plants sent bare-rooted at relevant times of the year. Only seeds (not plants) exported outside UK. Credit cards accepted online only. Exports beyond EU.
Map Ref: W, D3 **OS Grid Ref:** SS600924

WWEG **World's End Garden Nursery** ♿
Moseley Road, Hallow, Worcester, Worcestershire WR2 6NJ
Ⓣ (01905) 640977
Ⓕ (01905) 641373
Ⓔ info@worldsendgarden.co.uk
Ⓦ www.worldsendgarden.co.uk
Contact: Kristina & Robin Pearce
Opening Times: 1000-1700, Mon-Fri, Mar-Oct. Other times by appt. only.
Min Mail Order UK: £20.00
Min Mail Order EU: £20.00
Cat. Cost: Online only.
Credit Cards: All major credit/debit cards
Specialities: Extensive range of herbaceous perennials & ornamental grasses. Especially *Geum, Hosta, Leucantheum, Miscanthus* & *Panicum*.
Notes: Also sells wholesale. Delivers to shows. Wheelchair accessible.
Map Ref: W, C5 **OS Grid Ref:** SO815597

WWFP **Whitehall Farmhouse Plants**
Sevenhampton, Cheltenham, Gloucestershire GL54 5TL
Ⓣ (01242) 820772
Ⓜ 07711 021034
Ⓕ (01242) 821226
Ⓔ info@wfplants.co.uk
Ⓦ www.wfplants.co.uk
Contact: Victoria Logue
Opening Times: By appt. only.
Min Mail Order UK: Nmc
Cat. Cost: 2 × 1st class.
Credit Cards: None
Specialities: A small nursery producing a range of interesting & easy hardy perennials for the garden. Some plants held in small quantities only.
Notes: Delivers to shows.
Map Ref: W, C5 **OS Grid Ref:** SP018229

WWtn **Westonbury Mill Water Garden** ♿
Pembridge, Herefordshire HR6 9HZ
Ⓣ (01544) 388650
Ⓕ (01544) 388650
Ⓔ richardpim@btinternet.com
Ⓦ www.westonburymillwatergardens.com
Contact: Richard Pim
Opening Times: 1100-1700 daily, 1st Apr-30th Sep. By appt. only at other times & to arrange collection.
Specialities: Range of plants, mostly herbaceous, with special emphasis on plants for the water garden. Some plants available in small quantities. Contact nursery to confirm availability.
Notes: Café. Wheelchair accessible.
Map Ref: W, C4

Abroad

XBar **Barnhaven Primroses ◆**
11 rue du Pont Blanc, Plestin-les-grèves
22310, France
Ⓣ 33 (0) 2 9635 6841
Ⓜ 33 (0) 6 6124 7739
Ⓕ 33 (0) 2 9635 6841
Ⓔ info@barnhaven.com
Ⓦ www.barnhaven.com
Contact: Lynne & David Lawson
Opening Times: 1400-1700 Feb-Apr. For visits outside this period, please phone first.
Min Mail Order UK: Nmc
Min Mail Order EU: Nmc
Cat. Cost: €2.00
Credit Cards: Visa, MasterCard
Specialities: Barnhaven strains of polyanthus, incl. gold-laced & anomalous. Also auriculas & alpines. Seeds & plants available worldwide.
Notes: Exports beyond EU. Euro accepted.

XBlo **Table Bay View Nursery**
PO Box 12123, Mill Street, Cape Town 8010, South Africa
Ⓣ (27) 21 683 5108
Ⓕ (27) 21 683 5108
Ⓔ info@tablebayviewnursery.co.za
Contact: Terence Bloch
Opening Times: Mail order only. No personal callers.
Min Mail Order UK: £15.00 + p&p
Min Mail Order EU: £15.00
Cat. Cost: £3.40 (postal order)
Credit Cards: None
Specialities: Tropical & sub-tropical ornamental & fruiting plants. Self-harvested seed, predominently from our own inventory of mother stock plants.
Notes: Due to high local bank charges can no longer accept foreign bank cheques, only undated postal orders. To comply with UK import regulations, prospective buyers must register with DEFRA before placing an order. Exports beyond EU. Euro accepted.

XEll **Ellebore**
La Chamotière, 61360 Saint-Jouin-de-Blavou, France
Ⓣ (33) 2 3383 3772
Ⓜ (33) 6802 28674
Ⓕ (33) 2 3383 3773
Ⓔ pepiniere.ellebore@orange.fr
Ⓦ www.pepiniere-ellebore.fr
Contact: Nadine Albouy & Christian Geoffroy
Opening Times: 1000-1800 Wed-Sat, mid-Feb to late Jun & Sep-Dec. 1500-1800 Thu, Fri & Sat, Jul, Aug & Jan to mid-Feb.
Min Mail Order UK: Nmc
Min Mail Order EU: Nmc
Cat. Cost: Free.
Credit Cards: All major credit/debit cards
Specialities: *Helleborus*. Bulbs. *Clematis*.
Notes: Also sells wholesale. Euro accepted. Delivers to shows.

XFro **Frosch Exclusive Perennials**
Ziegelstadelweg 5, D-83623 Dietramszell-Lochen, Germany
Ⓣ (49) 172 842 2050
Ⓕ (49) 8027 904 9975
Ⓔ info@cypripedium.de
Ⓦ www.cypripedium.de
Contact: Michael Weinert
Opening Times: Not open. Mail order only. Orders taken between 0700-2200 hours.
Min Mail Order UK: £350.00 + p&p
Min Mail Order EU: £350.00 + p&p
Cat. Cost: Online only.
Credit Cards: None
Specialities: *Cypripedium* hybrids. Hardy orchids.
Notes: Also sells wholesale. Exports beyond EU. Euro accepted.

XGra **Graefswinning**
Diestersteenweg 222, 3850, Nieuwerkerken, Belgium
Ⓣ 32 (0) 1188 3611
Ⓕ 32 (0) 1150 1628
Ⓔ info@graefswinning.be
Ⓦ www.graefswinning.be
Contact: Jeaninne Lemmens
Opening Times: Open Apr-Jun to view flower fields. Check website for further information.
Min Mail Order UK: Nmc
Min Mail Order EU: Nmc
Cat. Cost: Online only.
Credit Cards: MasterCard, Visa, Paypal
Specialities: Herbaceous, tree & Itoh peonies. Several acres of peonies in the field. Sell containerised peonies in sturdy 7L pots as well as bare-root plants. Landscape & cut flower varieties.
Notes: Bare-root peonies are shipped in autumn to countries within the EU. Container plants available at nursery & garden shows. Euro accepted.

XLum **Lumen Plantes Vivaces**
Les Coutets, 24100 Creysse-Bergerac, Occitania, France
Ⓣ (33) 5 5357 6215
Ⓕ (33) 5 5358 5488
Ⓔ lumenviva@aol.com
Ⓦ www.lumen.fr
Contact: Michel Lumen
Opening Times: 0900-1200 & 1300-1630 Mon-Thu, 0900-1200 & 1300-1530 Fri.

Closed Sat, Sun & B/hols. 0900-1200 & 1300-1830 Mon-Sat, Mar-Jun.
Min Mail Order UK: Nmc
Min Mail Order EU: Nmc
Cat. Cost: Online only.
Credit Cards: Visa, MasterCard
Specialities: Hardy perennials. French Nat. Collection of *Miscanthus*.
Notes: Also sells wholesale. Exports beyond EU. Delivers to shows. Euro accepted.
Grid Ref: N44 51.789 E0 32.0518

XPou **Koen Van Poucke** ♿
Heistraat 106, Sint-Niklaas, Oost-Vlaanderen, 9100 Belgium
Ⓣ (32) 0377 77642
Ⓕ (32) 0376 61698
Ⓔ kvanpoucke@skynet.be
Ⓦ www.koenvanpoucke.be
Contact: Koen Van Poucke
Opening Times: 0900-1230 & 1300-1800, Tue-Sat. Closed Sun & Mon. Closed Jul. Check website before travelling a long distance.
Min Mail Order UK: €100
Min Mail Order EU: €100
Credit Cards: None
Specialities: *Epimedium*. Also rare Asian shade plants. *Dahlias*.
Notes: Mail order Sep-Apr. Collector's garden open to the public. Delivers to shows. Euro accepted. Wheelchair accessible.

XSen **Les Senteurs Du Quercy** ♿
Mas de Fraysse, Escamps, Lot 46230, France
Ⓣ (33) 5 652 10167
Ⓔ melie.fred@aliceadsl.fr
Ⓦ www.senteursduquercy.com
Contact: Frédéric Prévot
Opening Times: 1400-1800 spring & summer (excl. Aug). Other times, incl. Aug by appt.
Min Mail Order UK: Nmc
Min Mail Order EU: Nmc
Cat. Cost: €5.00
Specialities: *Salvia, Iris, Phlomis, Teucrium, Lavandula* and drought tolerant plants. French Nat. Coll. of *Salvia* species.
Notes: Euro accepted. Wheelchair accessible.

XTur **Etablissements Pierre Turc** ♿ ◆
63 Route de Seiches, 49630 Mazé, France
Ⓣ 02 41 80 64 08
Ⓜ 06 47 56 33 27
Ⓕ 02 41 80 26 96
Ⓔ export@turcieflor.com
Ⓦ www.turcieflor.com
Contact: Mark Hodson
Opening Times: 0800-1215 & 1400-1700 Mon-Fri.
Min Mail Order UK: Nmc + p&p
Min Mail Order EU: Nmc + p&p
Credit Cards: None
Specialities: *Alstroemeria, Agapanthus* & *Canna*. Also *Arum, Begonia, Dahlia, Fuchsia* & *Hippeastrum*.
Notes: Also sells wholesale. Exports beyond EU. Delivers to shows. Euro accepted. Wheelchair accessible.

X

Nursery Index by Name

Nurseries that are included in the *RHS Plant Finder* for the first time this year (or have been reintroduced) are marked in **bold type**. Full details of the nurseries will be found in **Nursery Details by Code** on page 836. For a key to the geographical codes, see the start of **Nurseries**.

Buckingham Nurseries	LBuc
Buckland Plants	GBuc
Bucknell Nurseries	WBuc
Burncoose Nurseries	CBcs
Burnham Nurseries	CBur
Burstow Nurseries & Garden Centre	**LBrs**
Cacti & Succulents	SCac
Cally Gardens	GCal
Cambridge Garden Plants	ECGP
Camellia Grove Nursery	SCam
Cants of Colchester Ltd	ECnt
Caradoc Doy	CDoy
Caths Garden Plants	NCGa
Chapel Farm House Nursery	CCha
Charleshurst Farm Nursery	SChF
Chase Plants (formerly Meadows Nursery)	CCse
Beth Chatto Gardens Ltd, The	**ECha**
Chennels Gate Gardens & Nursery	WChG
Cherry Tree Nursery	**CChe**
Chestnut Nursery (Sheltered Work Opportunities Project)	**CCht**
Chew Valley Trees	CCVT
Chipchase Castle Nursery	NChi
Choice Landscapes	ECho
Chrysanthemums Direct	MCms
John Churcher	SChr
Cider Apple Trees	CCAT
Citrus Centre, The	**SCit**
Clay Lane Nursery	LCla
Coblands Nurseries	**SCob**
Coghurst Camellias	SCog
Constantine Garden Nursery (formerly Fir Tree Farm)	CCon
Cool Temperate	MCoo
Cooling's Nurseries Ltd	SCoo
Coton Manor Garden	MCot
Cotswold Garden Flowers	WCot
Cottage Garden Nursery	LCtg
Cottage Garden Plants	NCot
Cottage Nurseries	ECtt
County Park Nursery	ECou
Craigieburn Garden	GCra
Craigiehall Nursery	**GCrg**
Cranesbill Nursery	WCra
Creake Plant Centre	ECre
Crescent Plants	WCre
Crin Gardens	MCri
Crocosmia Gardens, The	ECrc
Croft 16 Daffodils	GCro
Crofters Nurseries	SCrf
Cromar Nursery	SCmr
Cross Common Nursery	CCCN
Croston Cactus	NCro
Crown Nursery	ECrN
Crûg Farm Plants	WCru
D'Arcy & Everest	EDAr
P. de Jager & Sons Ltd	SDeJ
Deacon's Nursery	SDea
Deelish Garden Centre	IDee
Delfland Nurseries Ltd	EDel
Desert to Jungle	CDTJ
Desirable Plants	CDes
Dibleys Nurseries	WDib
Dickson Nurseries Ltd	IDic
Dobies of Devon	CDob
Dove Cottage Nursery & Garden	NDov
Downderry Nursery	SDow
Drointon Nurseries	NDro
Duchy of Cornwall	CDoC
Dulford Nurseries	CDul
Dunskey Gardens & Maze	**GDun**
Dysons Nurseries	SDys
East Northdown Farm & Gardens	SEND
East of Eden Nursery	NEoE
Edrom Nurseries	**GEdr**
Edulis	LEdu
Eggleston Hall Gardens	NEgg
Eleplants Nursery	**SEle**
Ellebore	XEll
Charles F Ellis	WCFE
Elsworth Herbs	CEls
Elworthy Cottage Plants	CElw
Endsleigh Gardens	CEnd
English Woodlands	SEWo
Entwood Farm Plants	CEnt
Equatorial Plant Co.	NEqu
Essex Carnivorous Plants	EECP
Etablissements Pierre Turc	XTur
Every Picture Tells a Story	**NEve**
Exclusive Plants Nursery	CExl
Exotic Garden Company, The	EExo
Fairholm Plants	GFai
Fairweather's Garden Centre	SFai
Family Trees	SFam
Farmyard Nurseries	**WFar**
Fenbulbs Ltd	**EFen**
Fentongollan Farm	CFen
Fern Nursery, The	EFer
Fernatix	**EFtx**
Fernwood Nursery	CWil
Fibrex Nurseries Ltd	WFib
Field House Nursery	MFie
Field of Blooms	IFoB
Fillan's Plants	CFil
Fir Trees Pelargonium Nursery	NFir
Firecrest Trees & Shrubs Nursery	**EMac**
Firgrove Plants	SFgr
Flora Exotica	EFEx
Flower Bower, The	CFwr
Floyds Climbers and Clematis	CFlo
The Fly Trap Plants	EFly
Forest Edge Nurseries	**CFst**
Frogswell Nursery	IFro
Frosch Exclusive Perennials	XFro

Fruit Garden Plants	**SFrt**
Galloway Plants	GGal
Garden Blooms	NGBl
Garden House Nursery	NGdn
Garden Secrets Nursery	**SGSe**
Gilbert's Nursery	SGbt
John Gillies	**MGil**
Glendoick Gardens Ltd	GGGa
Golden Hill Nurseries	SGol
Gordon's Nursery	WGor
Gortkelly Castle Nursery	IGor
Gosbrook Pelargoniums	**MGbk**
Goscote Nurseries Ltd	MGos
Graefswinning	**XGra**
Grafton Nursery	**WGrf**
Grange Farm Plants	EGFP
Peter Grayson (Sweet Pea Seedsman)	MPet
Great Dixter Nurseries	SDix
Mary Green	NMyG
Green's Leaves	WGrn
Gwynfor Growers	WGwG
Habitat Aid Ltd.	CHab
Hall Farm Nursery	WHal
John Hall Plants Ltd	SWhi
Halls of Heddon	NHal
Hall's Court Nursery	SHal
Hardy-Eucalyptus	**WEuc**
Hardy Exotics	CHEx
Hardy's Cottage Garden Plants	SHar
Harley Nursery	WHar
Harrells Hardy Plants	WHrl
Hart Canna	SHaC
Hartside Nursery Garden	NHar
Hawthornes Nursery, The	NHaw
Hayloft Plants	WHlf
Heaselands Garden Nursery	SHea
Heath Garden	**WHea**
Hedges Direct	**NHed**
Heligan Nursery & Plant Centre	CHel
The Herb Garden & Historical Plant Nursery	WHer
The Herb Nursery	MHer
The Herbary	CHby
Herbs for Healing	WHfH
Hergest Croft Gardens	WHCr
Herterton House Garden Nursery	NHer
Herts Hellebores	LHel
Heucheraholics	SHeu
Hewitt-Cooper Carnivorous Plants	CHew
Hidden Valley Gardens	CHVG
Hidden Valley Nursery	CHid
High Garden Nurseries	CHGN
Highdown Nursery	SHDw
Hill House Nursery Ltd	CHll
Hillier Garden Centres	SHil
Hillview Hardy Plants	WHil
Hinwick Hall Plant Centre	**MHin**
Hippopottering Nursery	**NHip**
Hoecroft Plants	EHoe
Holden Clough Nursery Ltd.	NHol
Hollies Farm Plant Centre	MHol
Homestead Plants	MHom
Honeysome Aquatic Nursery	EHon
Hoo House Nursery	WHoo
Horticultural Sales	WHor
Hoyland Plant Centre	**NHoy**
Kevin Hughes Plants	SKHP
Hull Farm	EHul
Hydrangea Haven	SHyH
Ice Alpines	WIce
Iden Croft Herbs	SIde
Tim Ingram	SIgm
The Iris Garden	CIri
Iris of Sissinghurst	SIri
Irisesonline	EIri
JPR Environmental	WJPR
Jackson's Nurseries	MJak
Jackson's Nurseries	MJac
Jasmine Cottage Gardens	CJas
Paul Jasper Trees	WJas
Jekka's Herb Farm	WJek
Jo's Garden Enterprise	GJos
John and Lynsey's Plants	SPin
JRG Dahlias	**NJRG**
Junker's Nursery Ltd. (formerly P M A Plant Specialities)	CJun
Just Airplants	**LAir**
Keepers Nursery	SKee
Kelways	CKel
Kenwith Conifer Nursery (Gordon Haddow)	CKen
Kevock Garden Plants	GKev
Kiftsgate Court Gardens	WKif
Kilmurry Nursery	IKil
Kings Barn Trees	SKin
Kinlochlaich Garden Plant Centre	GKin
Knoll Gardens	CKno
Ladybird Nurseries	**ELad**
Lakka Bulbs	CLak
Landford Trees	CLnd
Langthorns Plantery	ELan
Larch Cottage Nurseries	NLar
Laurel Farm Herbs	ELau
Laurels Nursery, The	SLau
Lavender Garden, The	WLav
Layham Garden Centre & Nursery	SLay
Lea Rhododendron Gardens Ltd	MLea
Lilies Water Gardens	LLWG
Lime Cross Nursery	SLim
Linn Botanic Gardens	GLin
Little Brook Fuchsias	SLBF
Little Heath Farm (UK)	LLHF
C S Lockyer (Fuchsias)	CLoc
W & S Lockyer	**LLoc**
Loder Plants	SLdr
Logie Steading Plants	GLog

Pounsley Plants	CPou
Poyntzfield Herb Nursery	GPoy
Primrose Cottage Nursery	NPri
Priory Plants	EPri
Sue Proctor Plants	NSue
Proctors Nursery	**MPro**
ProperPlants.com	CPrp
Quality Daffodils	CQua
Quercus Garden Plants	GQue
Quinish Garden Nursery	GQui
Rapkyns Nursery	SRkn
Ravensthorpe Nursery	MRav
Reads Nursery	ERea
Really Wild Flowers	SRea
Red House Farm	WRHF
G Reuthe Ltd	SReu
Ribblesdale Nurseries	NRib
Ringhaddy Daffodils	IRhd
River Garden Nurseries	SRiv
W Robinson & Son (Seeds & Plants) Ltd	NRob
Rodings Plantery, The	ERod
R V Roger Ltd	**NRog**
Rose Cottage Plants	ERCP
Roseland House Nursery	CRHN
Rosemoor, RHS Garden Plant Centre	CRos
Rosie's Garden Plants	SRGP
Rotherview Nursery	SRot
Roualeyn Nurseries	WRou
Rowden Gardens	CRow
Rumsey Gardens	SRms
Ryal Nursery	NRya
St Bridget Nurseries Ltd	CSBt
Saith Ffynnon Wildlife Plants	WSFF
Sampford Shrubs	CSam
Seagate Irises	ESgI
Seale Nurseries	SSea
Seaside Nursery	ISsi
Seaside Plants	**CSde**
Select Seeds	SSss
Semps by Post	ESem
Senteurs Du Quercy, Les	XSen
Shady Plants	ISha
Sherston Parva Nursery	CSPN
Shipton Bulbs	WShi
Shropshire Sarracenias	WSSs
Shrubland Park Nurseries	EShb
Sir Plants-Alot Garden Centre & Nursery	**NSir**
Slack Top Nurseries	NSla
Smart Plants	MTPN
Snape Cottage	CSna
Sooty's Plants	NSoo
Sound Garden Rhododendrons	MSnd
Southon Plants	LSou
Special Plants	CSpe
SpecialPerennials.com	MSpe
Spinners Garden	SSpi
Spring Park Nursery	GSPN
Squire's Garden Centre, Shepperton	LShp
Squire's Garden Centre, Twickenham	LSqu
Squire's Garden Centre, West Horsley	LSqH
Staddon Farm Nurseries	**CSta**
Starborough Nursery	SSta
Stillingfleet Lodge Nurseries	NSti
Stone House Cottage Nurseries	WSHC
Stone Lane Gardens	CSto
Stonebridge Plants (formerly L.B. Plants)	NSbr
Stonyford Cottage Nursery	MSCN
Strictly Daylilies	**EStr**
Style Roses	ESty
Summerdale Garden Nursery	NSum
Sunnybank Vine Nursery (National Vine Collection)	WSuV
Sunnyside Nursery, The	**LSun**
Surreal Succulents	CSuc
Suttons Seeds	CSut
Swallows Nursery	MSwo
Sweet Knowle Aquatics	MSKA
Swines Meadow Farm Nursery	ESwi
Table Bay View Nursery	XBlo
Tale Valley Nursery	**CTal**
Tan-y-Llyn Nurseries	WTan
Taylors Clematis Nursery	NTay
Terrace Gardener	STrG
Thistlefield Plants and Design	EThi
Thornhayes Nursery	CTho
Thuya Alpine Nursery	WThu
Timpany Nurseries & Gardens	ITim
Tissington Nursery	MTis
Toobees Exotics	LToo
Topiary Arts	LTop
Touchwood Plants	WTou
Trecanna Nursery	CTca
Tree Peony Company	NTPC
Treetyme	NTre
Trehane Nursery	CTrh
Treseders	CTsd
Trewidden Nursery	**CTre**
Triscombe Nurseries	CTri
Tweed Valley Fruit Trees	**GTwd**
J Tweedie Fruit Trees	GTwe
Twenty Pence Garden Centre	**ETwe**
Tynings Climbers (National Collection of Passiflora & Jasminum)	**CTyn**
Urban Jungle	EUJe
Useful Plants (formerly Lower Severalls Nursery)	CUse
Ventnor Botanic Garden	SVen
Victorian Violas	**EVic**
Victoriana Nursery Gardens	SVic
Victoria's Nursery & Garden	IVic
Waddow Lodge Garden	NWad
Walled Garden, The	EWll
Walled Garden Nursery	CWGN
Walnut Tree Garden Nursery	EWTr

INDEX MAP

The maps on the following pages show the approximate location of the nurseries whose details are listed in this directory.

KEY

CHEx Details of nurseries with letter codes in boxes are given in the Nursery Details by Code Index starting on page 836.

C
MAP ONE
SOUTH WEST
1
2
3
A
B
C
D
Llanelli
M4
Neath
Swansea
Port Talbot
Ilfracombe
Combe Martin
CMHG
Barnstaple
CAni
Bideford
CHid
CWCL
CRos
CKen
CWri
CPne
A377
Bude
CWil
CBaq
A39
CCha
CPbn
Okehampton
CSto
Launceston
CBre
CRow
CMan
Tavistock
Newton Abbott
Wadebridge
CBod
CBct
CTca
CHll
Bodmin
Liskeard
A38
CLng
CTsd
CDoC
Newquay
CPrp
Plymouth
CNWT
A30
CHVG
CPou
CRHN
St Austell
Truro
St Ives
Redruth
CFen
CHEx
Camborne
CBcS
Penzance
Helston
Falmouth
CCon
CQua
CCCN

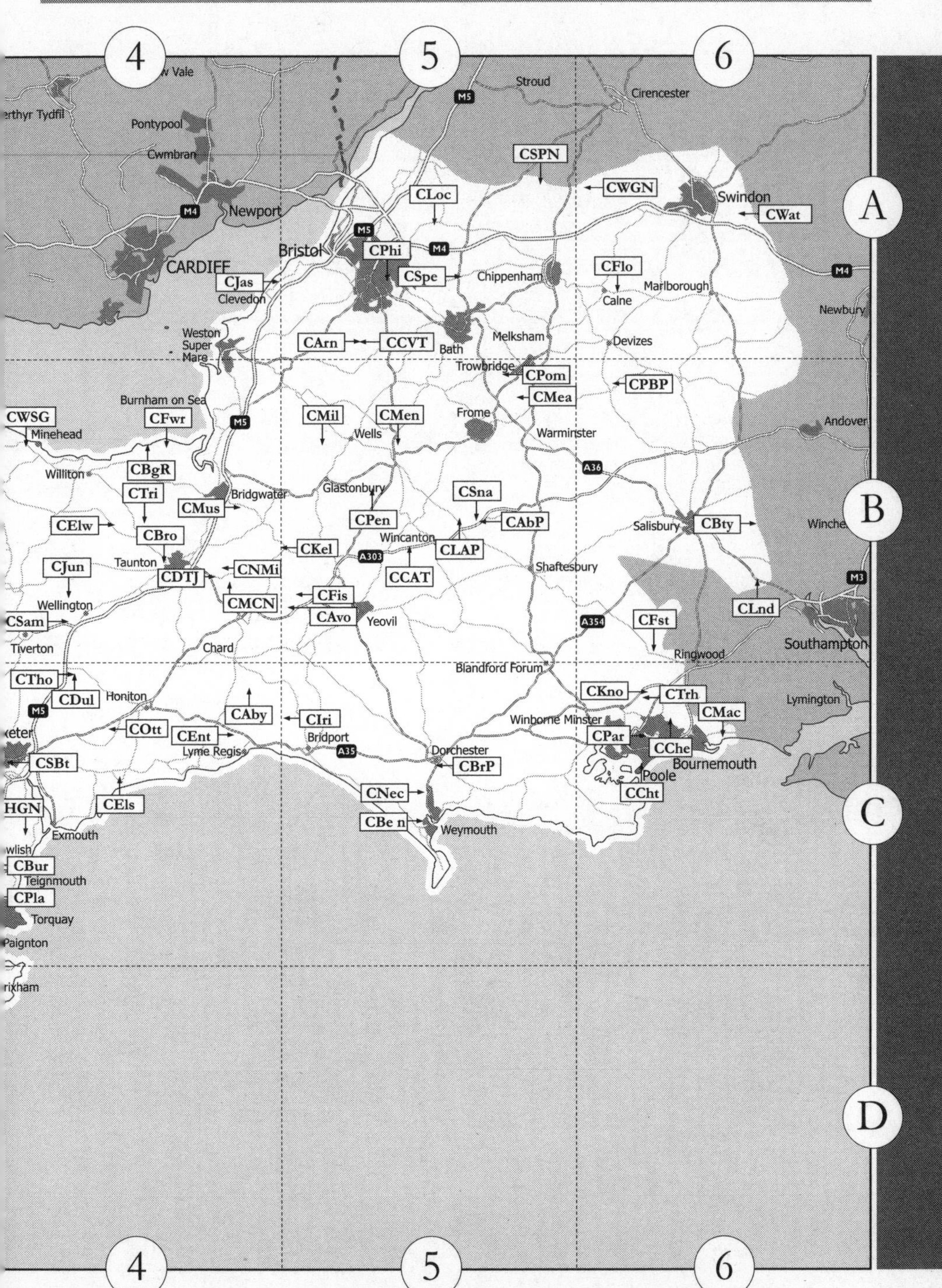

4
5
6
Stroud
Cirencester
M5
Pontypool
Cwmbran
CSPN
CWGN
CLoc
Swindon
CWat
A
M4
Newport
M5
CPhi
M4
Bristol
CARDIFF
CJas
Clevedon
CSpe
Chippenham
CFlo
Calne
Marlborough
M4
Newbury
Weston Super Mare
CArn
CCVT
Bath
Melksham
Devizes
Trowbridge
CPom
CMea
CPBP
Burnham on Sea
CWSG
Minehead
CFwr
M5
CMil
Wells
CMen
Frome
Warminster
Andover
Williton
CBgR
A36
CTri
Bridgwater
Glastonbury
CSna
CMus
CElw
CPen
CAbP
Salisbury
CBty
B
CBro
CKel
Wincanton
CLAP
Taunton
A303
CJun
CDTJ
CNMi
CCAT
Shaftesbury
M3
Wellington
CMCN
CFis
CLnd
CAvo
Yeovil
CSam
A354
CFst
Tiverton
Chard
Southampton
Ringwood
Blandford Forum
CTho
CDul
Honiton
CKno
CTrh
Lymington
M5
CAby
CIri
Winborne Minster
CMac
COtt
CEnt
Bridport
CPar
Lyme Regis
A35
Dorchester
CChe
CSBt
CBrP
Bournemouth
Poole
CNec
CCht
HGN
CEls
C
Exmouth
CBe n
Weymouth
CBur
Teignmouth
CPla
Torquay
Paignton
D
4
5
6

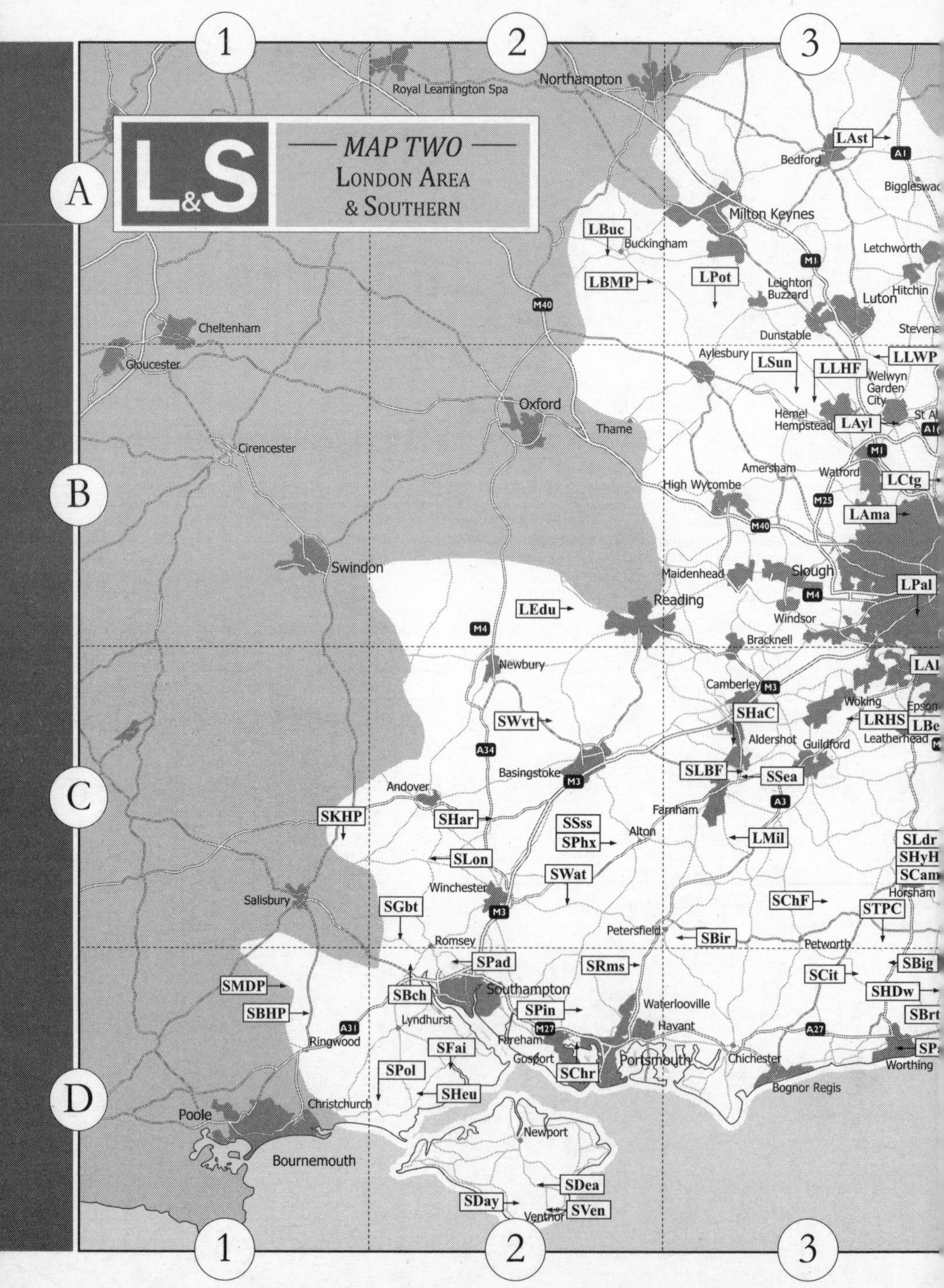
L&S
MAP TWO
London Area
& Southern
1
2
3
A
B
C
D
Royal Leamington Spa
Northampton
LAst
Bedford
Biggleswad
Milton Keynes
LBuc
Buckingham
LBMP
LPot
Leighton Buzzard
Letchworth
Hitchin
Luton
Dunstable
Cheltenham
Gloucester
Aylesbury
LSun
LLHF
LLWP
Welwyn Garden City
Oxford
Thame
Hemel Hempstead
LAyl
St Al
Cirencester
Amersham
Watford
LCtg
High Wycombe
LAma
Swindon
Maidenhead
Slough
Reading
LPal
LEdu
Windsor
Bracknell
Newbury
Camberley
Woking
Epsom
SHaC
LRHS
LBe
SWvt
Aldershot
Guildford
Leatherhead
Basingstoke
SLBF
SSea
Andover
SKHP
SHar
SSss
SPhx
Alton
Farnham
LMil
SLdr
SHyH
SCam
SLon
SWat
Winchester
Horsham
Salisbury
SGbt
SChF
STPC
Petersfield
SBir
Romsey
Petworth
SPad
SRms
SCit
SBig
SMDP
SBch
Southampton
SHDw
SBHP
SPin
Waterlooville
SBrt
Lyndhurst
Havant
Ringwood
SFai
Fareham
Gosport
Portsmouth
Chichester
Worthing
SPol
SChr
Bognor Regis
SHeu
Christchurch
Poole
Newport
Bournemouth
SDea
SDay
Ventnor
SVen
M1
M40
M25
M4
M3
A1
A34
A3
A31
M27
A27

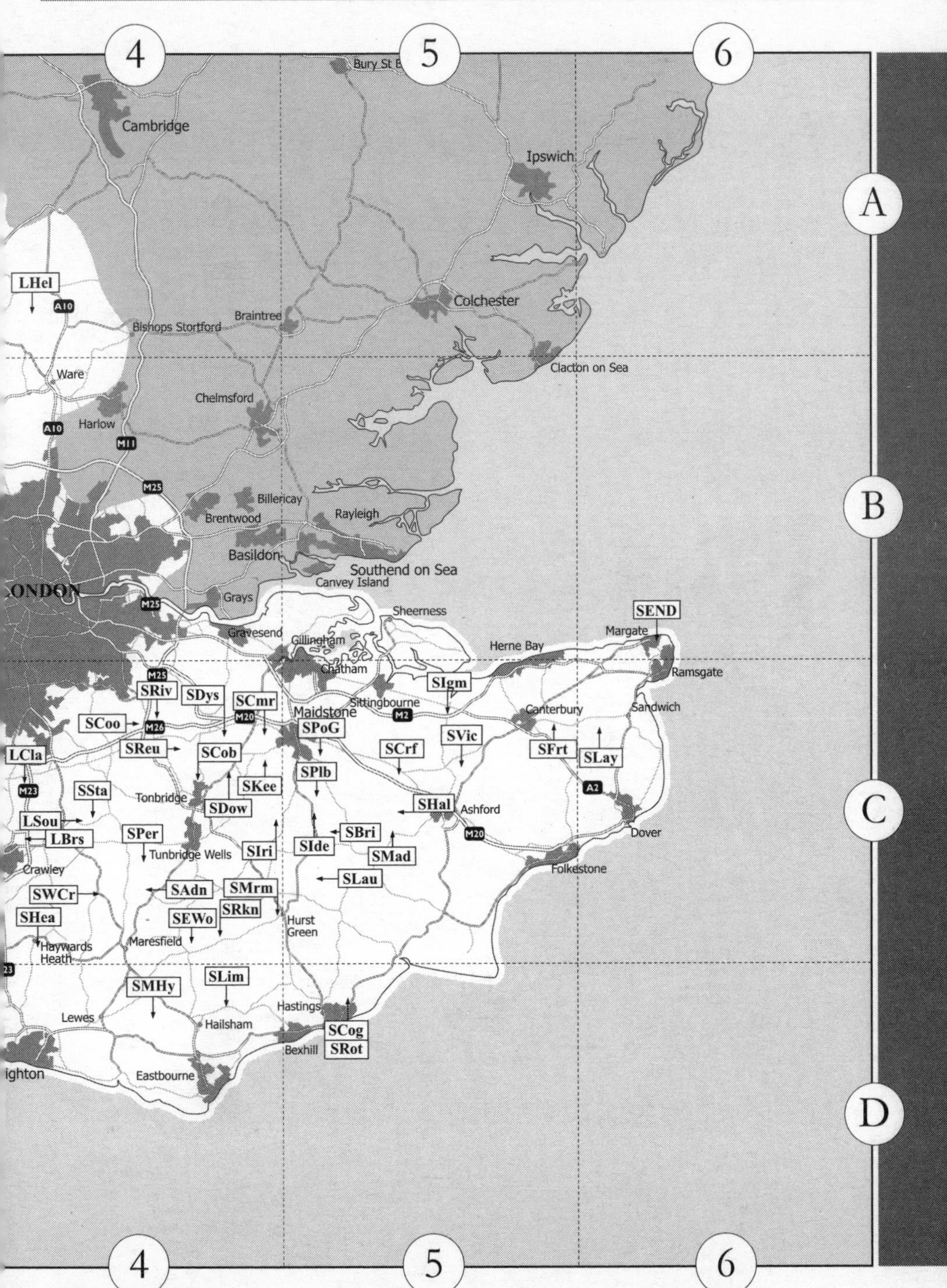
4
5
6
A
B
C
D
Bury St E
Cambridge
Ipswich
LHel
A10
Bishops Stortford
Braintree
Colchester
Ware
Clacton on Sea
Chelmsford
Harlow
A10
M11
M25
Billericay
Brentwood
Rayleigh
Basildon
Southend on Sea
Canvey Island
LONDON
Grays
M25
Sheerness
SEND
Margate
Gravesend
Gillingham
Herne Bay
Chatham
Ramsgate
M25
SRiv
SDys
SCmr
SIgm
Sittingbourne
Maidstone
M2
Canterbury
Sandwich
SCoo
M26
M20
SPoG
SReu
SCob
SCrf
SVic
SFrt
SLay
LCla
SPlb
SKee
M23
SSta
Tonbridge
SDow
SHal
Ashford
A2
LSou
SBri
Dover
LBrs
SPer
M20
Tunbridge Wells
SIri
SIde
SMad
Crawley
Folkestone
SLau
SWCr
SAdn
SMrm
SRkn
SHea
SEWo
Hurst Green
Haywards Heath
Maresfield
SMHy
SLim
Hastings
Lewes
Hailsham
SCog
Bexhill
SRot
Eastbourne
ighton
4
5
6

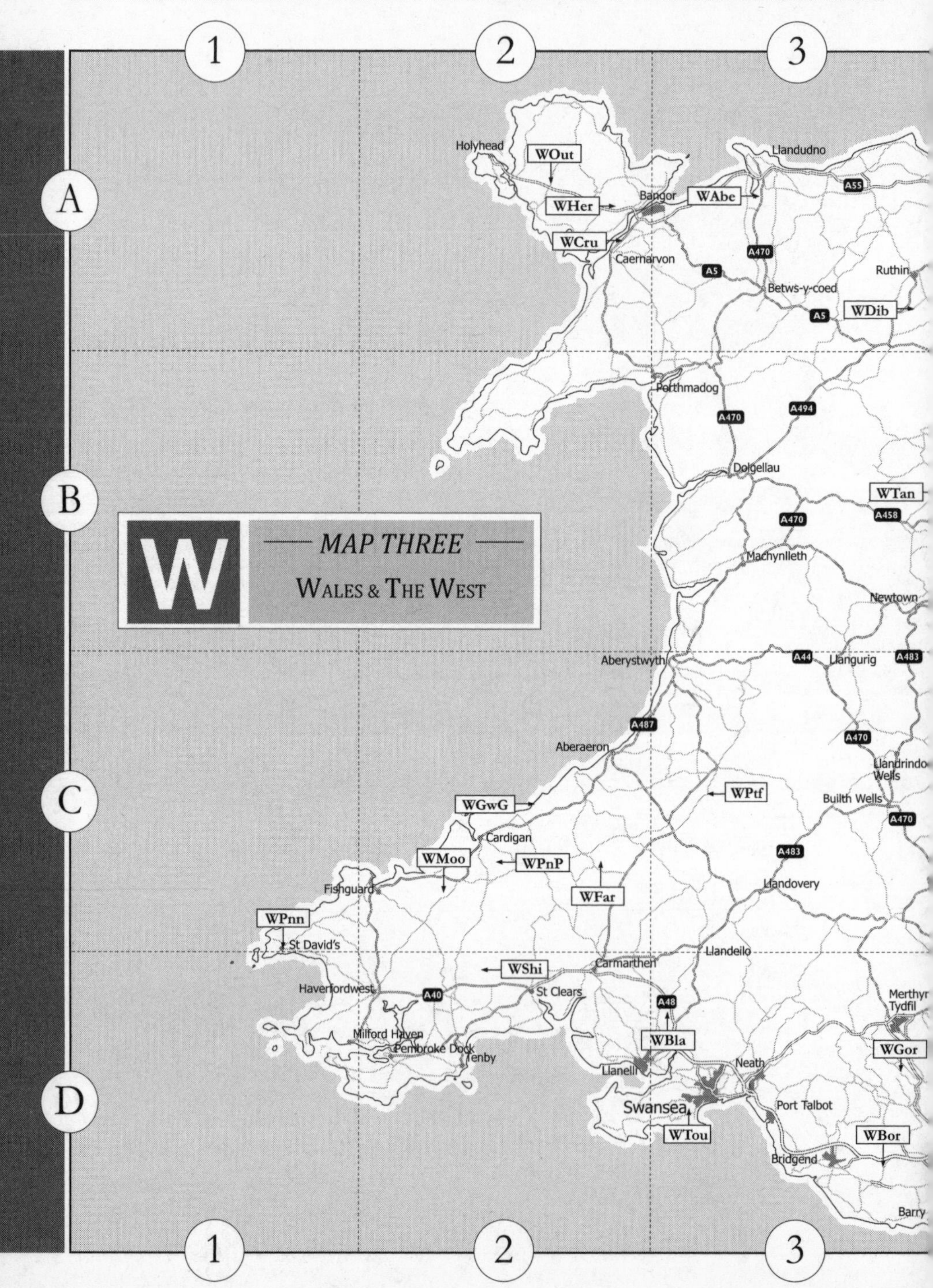
1
2
3
A
B
C
D
W
MAP THREE
Wales & The West
Holyhead
WOut
WHer
WCru
Bangor
WAbe
Llandudno
A55
Caernarvon
A470
A5
Ruthin
Betws-y-coed
WDib
Porthmadog
A494
Dolgellau
WTan
A458
Machynlleth
Newtown
Aberystwyth
A44
Llangurig
A483
A487
Aberaeron
Builth Wells
WPtf
WGwG
Cardigan
WMoo
WPnP
WFar
Fishguard
Llandovery
WPnn
St David's
Llandeilo
Carmarthen
WShi
Haverfordwest
A40
St Clears
A48
Merthyr Tydfil
Milford Haven
Pembroke Dock
Tenby
WBla
WGor
Llanelli
Neath
Swansea
Port Talbot
WTou
WBor
Bridgend
Barry

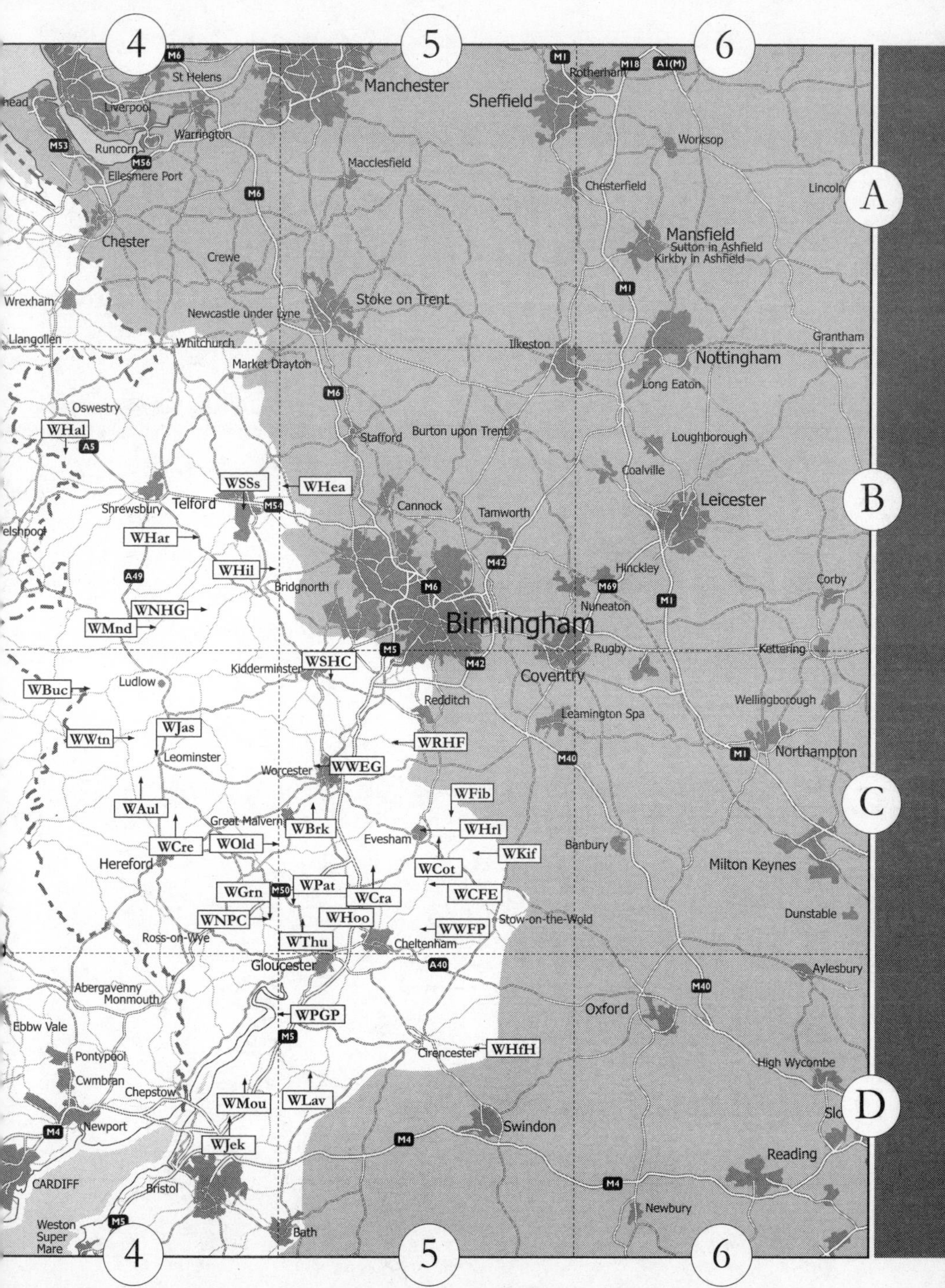

4
5
6
A
B
C
D
Manchester
Sheffield
Liverpool
St Helens
Warrington
Runcorn
Ellesmere Port
Macclesfield
Rotherham
Worksop
Chesterfield
Lincoln
Chester
Crewe
Mansfield
Sutton in Ashfield
Kirkby in Ashfield
Wrexham
Stoke on Trent
Newcastle under Lyne
Llangollen
Whitchurch
Market Drayton
Ilkeston
Nottingham
Grantham
Long Eaton
Oswestry
Stafford
Burton upon Trent
Loughborough
Coalville
Leicester
Shrewsbury
Telford
Cannock
Tamworth
Hinckley
Bridgnorth
Corby
Birmingham
Nuneaton
Rugby
Kettering
Kidderminster
Coventry
Ludlow
Redditch
Wellingborough
Leamington Spa
Leominster
Northampton
Worcester
Great Malvern
Evesham
Banbury
Hereford
Milton Keynes
Stow-on-the-Wold
Dunstable
Ross-on-Wye
Cheltenham
Gloucester
Aylesbury
Abergavenny
Monmouth
Oxford
Ebbw Vale
Pontypool
Cirencester
High Wycombe
Cwmbran
Chepstow
Newport
Swindon
Reading
CARDIFF
Bristol
Newbury
Weston Super Mare
Bath
WHal
WSSs
WHea
WHar
WHil
WNHG
WMnd
WSHC
WBuc
WJas
WWtn
WRHF
WWEG
WFib
WAul
WBrk
WHrl
WCre
WOld
WKif
WCot
WGrn
WPat
WCra
WCFE
WNPC
WHoo
WWFP
WThu
WPGP
WHfH
WMou
WLav
WJek
M6
M1
M18
A1(M)
M53
M56
A5
M54
A49
M42
M69
M5
M40
M50
A40
M4

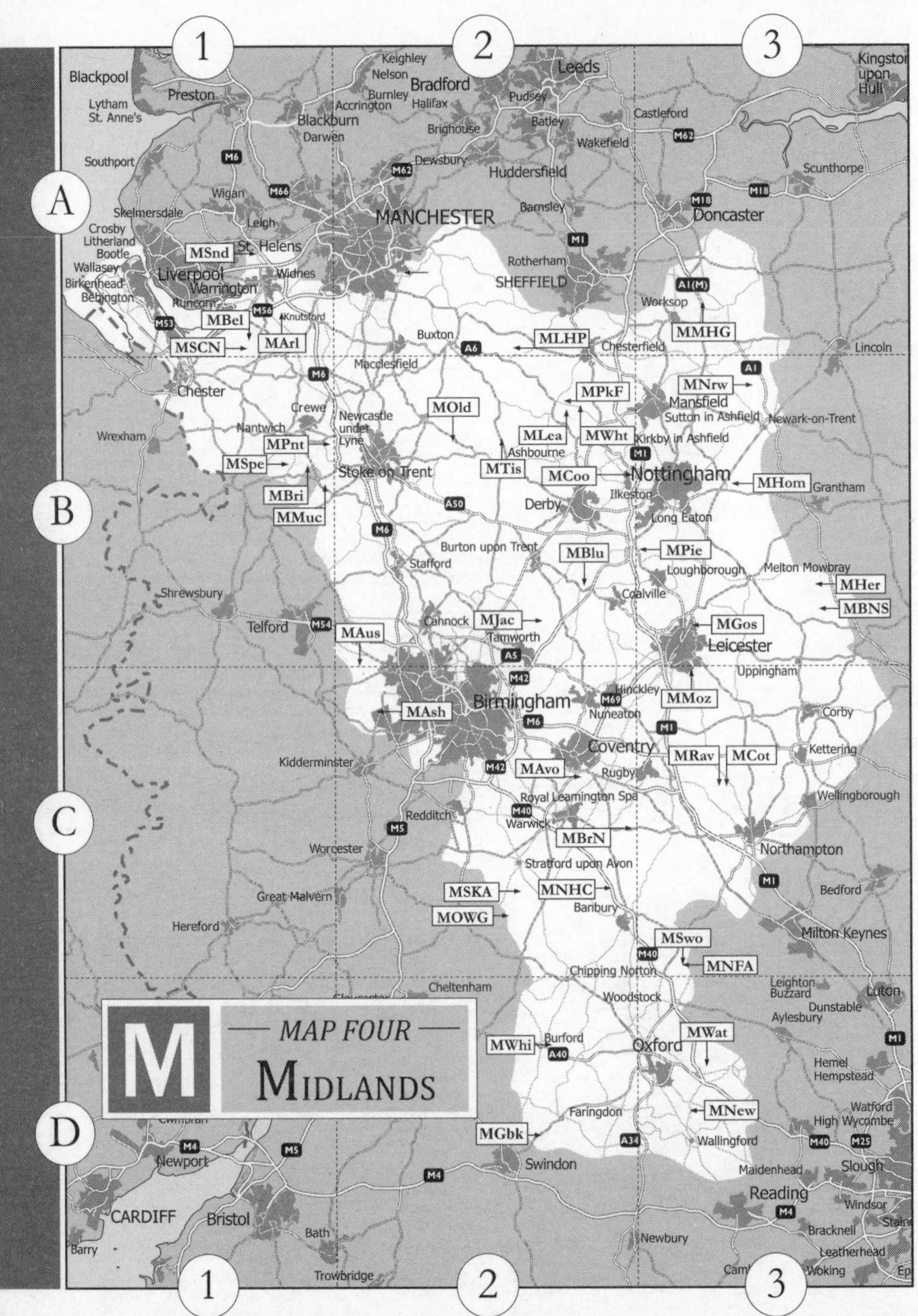

1
2
3
A
B
C
D
Blackpool
Preston
Lytham St. Anne's
Keighley
Nelson
Burnley
Accrington
Blackburn
Darwen
Bradford
Halifax
Brighouse
Leeds
Pudsey
Batley
Wakefield
Castleford
Kingston upon Hull
Southport
Dewsbury
Huddersfield
Scunthorpe
Wigan
Skelmersdale
Crosby
Litherland
Bootle
Wallasey
Birkenhead
Bebington
Liverpool
St. Helens
Widnes
Warrington
Runcorn
Leigh
MANCHESTER
Barnsley
Doncaster
Rotherham
SHEFFIELD
Worksop
Knutsford
Buxton
Macclesfield
Chesterfield
Lincoln
Chester
Crewe
Nantwich
Wrexham
Newcastle under Lyne
Stoke on Trent
Mansfield
Sutton in Ashfield
Kirkby in Ashfield
Newark-on-Trent
Ashbourne
Nottingham
Ilkeston
Derby
Long Eaton
Grantham
Burton upon Trent
Stafford
Loughborough
Melton Mowbray
Coalville
Shrewsbury
Telford
Cannock
Tamworth
Leicester
Uppingham
Birmingham
Hinckley
Nuneaton
Corby
Coventry
Kettering
Kidderminster
Rugby
Royal Leamington Spa
Wellingborough
Redditch
Warwick
Worcester
Northampton
Stratford upon Avon
Great Malvern
Banbury
Bedford
Hereford
Milton Keynes
Chipping Norton
Cheltenham
Woodstock
Leighton Buzzard
Dunstable
Luton
Aylesbury
Burford
Oxford
Hemel Hempstead
Faringdon
Watford
High Wycombe
Wallingford
Newport
Swindon
Maidenhead
Slough
Reading
Windsor
CARDIFF
Bristol
Bath
Barry
Newbury
Bracknell
Leatherhead
Woking
Trowbridge
M6
M66
M62
M1
M18
A1(M)
A1
M56
M53
A6
A50
M54
A5
M42
M69
M40
M5
A40
A34
M4
M25
MSnd
MBel
MSCN
MArl
MLHP
MMHG
MNrw
MPkF
MOld
MLea
MWht
MPnt
MSpe
MTis
MCoo
MHom
MBri
MMuc
MBlu
MPie
MHer
MBNS
MJac
MGos
MAus
MMoz
MAsh
MRav
MCot
MAvo
MBrN
MSKA
MNHC
MOWG
MSwo
MNFA
MWhi
MWat
MNew
MGbk
M
MAP FOUR
MIDLANDS

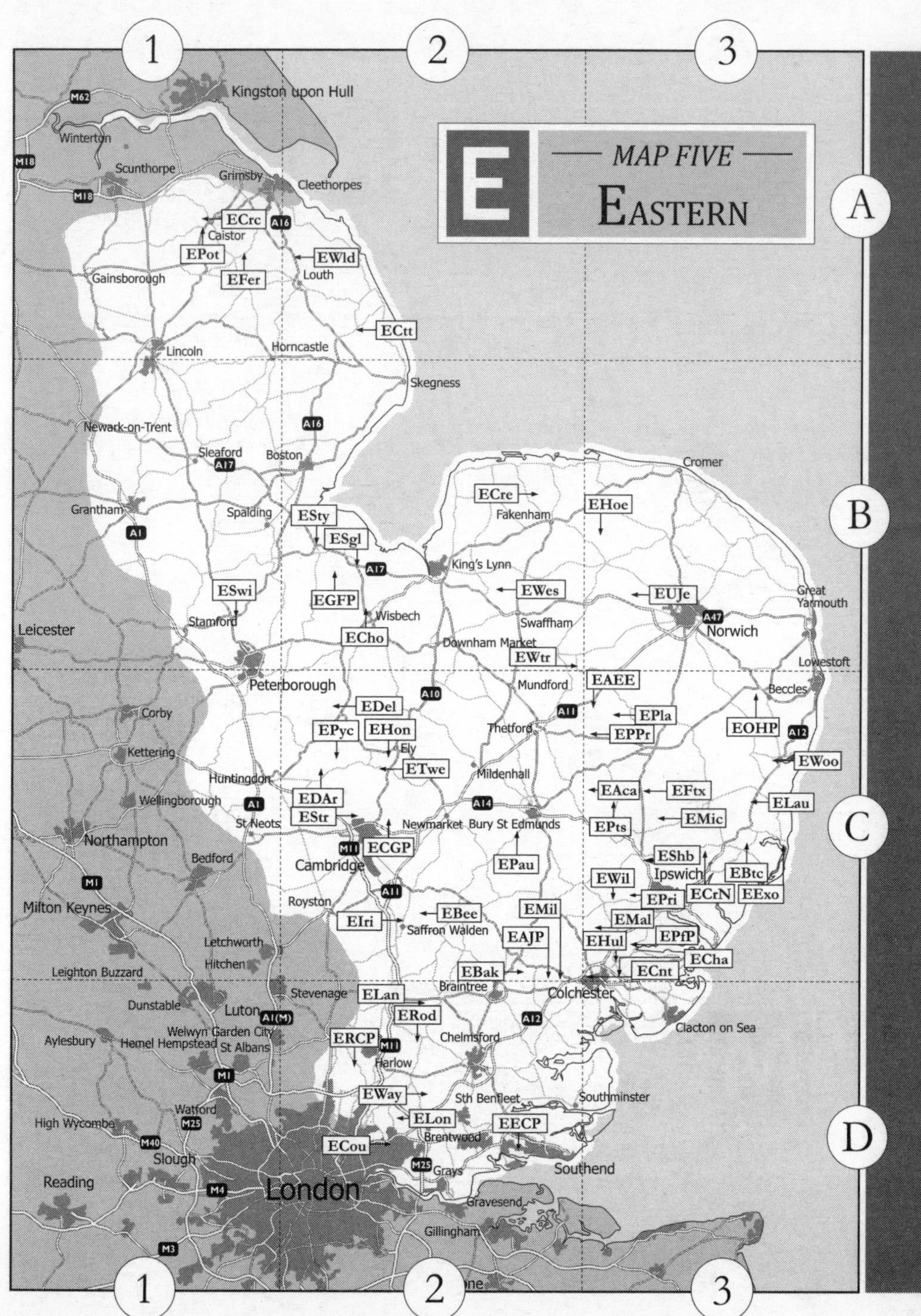

E
MAP FIVE
EASTERN
1
2
3
A
B
C
D
Kingston upon Hull
Winterton
Scunthorpe
Grimsby
Cleethorpes
ECrc
Caistor
EPot
EWld
EFer
Louth
Gainsborough
ECtt
Lincoln
Horncastle
Skegness
Newark-on-Trent
Sleaford
Boston
Grantham
Spalding
ESty
ESgl
Cromer
ECre
Fakenham
EHoe
King's Lynn
ESwi
EGFP
EWes
EUJe
Great Yarmouth
Stamford
Wisbech
Swaffham
Norwich
Leicester
ECho
Downham Market
EWtr
Lowestoft
Peterborough
Mundford
EAEE
Beccles
EDel
EPla
Corby
EPyc
EHon
Thetford
EPPr
EOHP
Kettering
Ely
ETwe
EWoo
Huntingdon
Mildenhall
EAca
EFtx
EDAr
ELau
Wellingborough
EStr
EMic
St Neots
Newmarket
Bury St Edmunds
EPts
Northampton
ECGP
EShb
Bedford
Cambridge
EPau
Ipswich
EBtc
EWil
ECrN
EExo
EPri
Milton Keynes
Royston
EBee
EMil
EIri
Saffron Walden
EMal
EAJP
EHul
EPfP
Letchworth
ECha
Hitchen
Leighton Buzzard
EBak
ECnt
Braintree
Colchester
Stevenage
ELan
Dunstable
Luton
ERod
Clacton on Sea
Welwyn Garden City
Aylesbury
Hemel Hempstead
St Albans
ERCP
Chelmsford
Harlow
EWay
Sth Benfleet
Southminster
Watford
ELon
High Wycombe
EECP
Brentwood
ECou
Slough
Grays
Southend
Reading
London
Gravesend
Gillingham
M62
M18
A16
A17
A1
A47
A10
A11
A12
A14
M11
M1
A1(M)
M25
M40
M4
M3

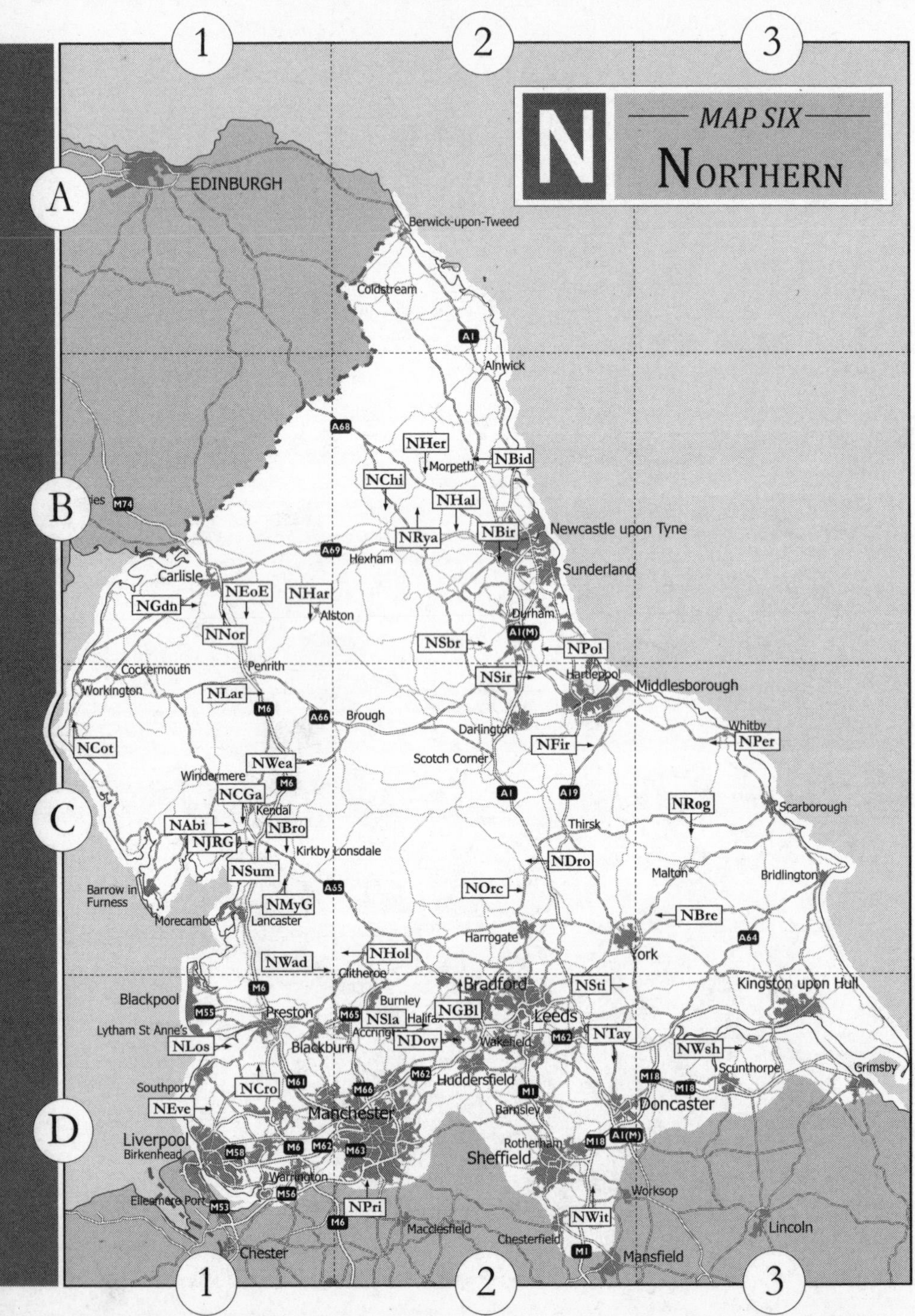
N
MAP SIX
NORTHERN
1
2
3
A
B
C
D
EDINBURGH
Berwick-upon-Tweed
Coldstream
A1
Alnwick
A68
NHer
Morpeth
NBid
NChi
NHal
M74
NRya
NBir
Newcastle upon Tyne
A69
Hexham
Sunderland
Carlisle
NEoE
NHar
NGdn
Alston
Durham
NNor
A1(M)
NSbr
NPol
Cockermouth
Penrith
NSir
Hartlepool
Middlesborough
Workington
NLar
M6
A66
Brough
Darlington
Whitby
NPer
NCot
NFir
NWea
Scotch Corner
Windermere
NCGa
A19
NRog
Scarborough
Kendal
NAbi
NBro
Thirsk
NJRG
Kirkby Lonsdale
NDro
NSum
Malton
Bridlington
Barrow in Furness
NOrc
A65
NMyG
NBre
Morecambe
Lancaster
Harrogate
A64
NHol
York
NWad
Clitheroe
Bradford
NSti
Kingston upon Hull
Blackpool
Burnley
NGBl
M55
Preston
M65
NSla
Halifax
Leeds
Lytham St Anne's
Accrington
NDov
Wakefield
M62
NTay
NWsh
NLos
Blackburn
Scunthorpe
Grimsby
M18
Huddersfield
Southport
M61
M66
M1
NCro
NEve
Manchester
Barnsley
Doncaster
Liverpool
Birkenhead
M58
M63
Rotherham
Sheffield
Warrington
Worksop
M56
Ellesmere Port
M53
NPri
NWit
Macclesfield
Chesterfield
Lincoln
Chester
Mansfield

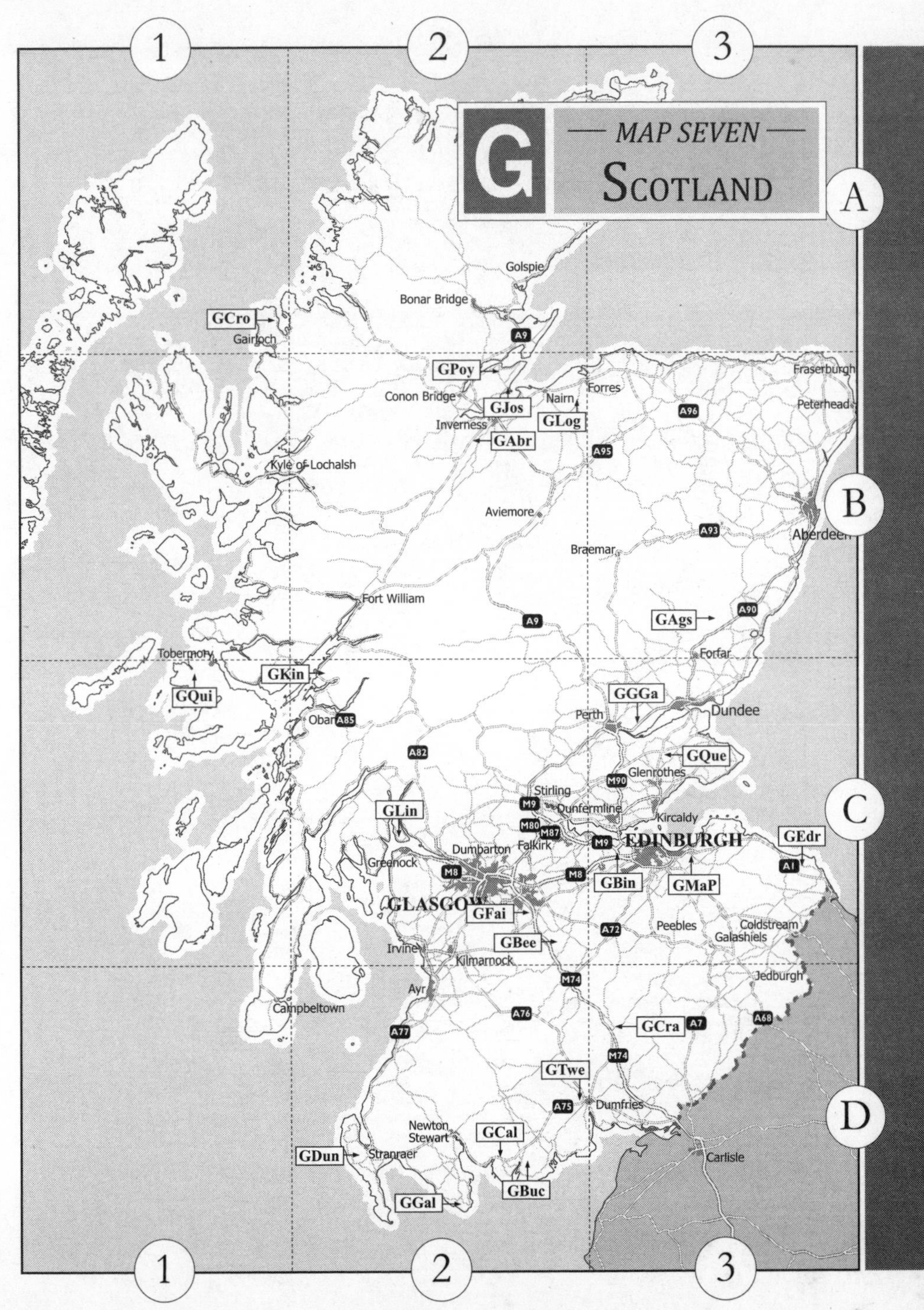
1
2
3
G
— MAP SEVEN —
Scotland
A
B
C
D
Golspie
Bonar Bridge
GCro
Gairloch
A9
GPoy
Conon Bridge
GJos
Nairn
Forres
Inverness
GLog
GAbr
Fraserburgh
Peterhead
A96
A95
Kyle of Lochalsh
Aviemore
Aberdeen
A93
Braemar
Fort William
A9
GAgs
A90
Tobermory
Forfar
GKin
GQui
GGGa
Perth
Dundee
Oban
A85
A82
GQue
Glenrothes
M90
Stirling
M9
Dunfermline
GLin
Kircaldy
M80
M87
Falkirk
M9
EDINBURGH
GEdr
A1
Dumbarton
Greenock
M8
M8
GBin
GMaP
GLASGOW
GFai
Peebles
Coldstream
Galashiels
A72
GBee
Irvine
Kilmarnock
Jedburgh
M74
Ayr
Campbeltown
A76
GCra
A7
A68
A77
M74
GTwe
A75
Dumfries
Newton Stewart
GCal
GDun
Stranraer
Carlisle
GBuc
GGal
1
2
3

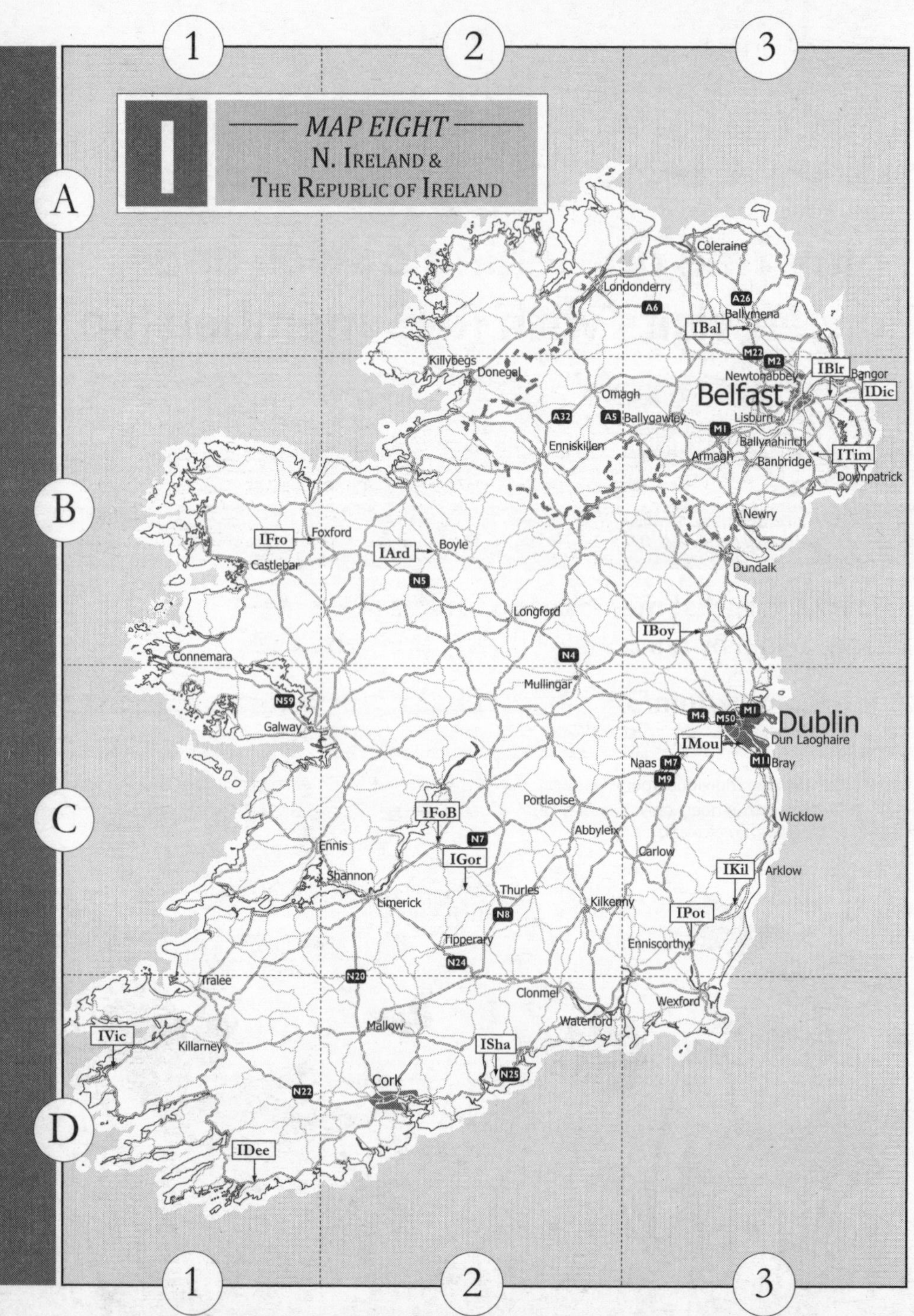
1
2
3
A
B
C
D
I
MAP EIGHT
N. IRELAND &
THE REPUBLIC OF IRELAND
Coleraine
Londonderry
A6
A26
Ballymena
IBal
Killybegs
Donegal
M22
M2
Newtonabbey
IBlr
Bangor
Omagh
Belfast
IDic
A32
A5
Ballygawley
Lisburn
M1
Enniskillen
Ballynahinch
Armagh
Banbridge
ITim
Downpatrick
Newry
IFro
Foxford
IArd
Boyle
Castlebar
N5
Dundalk
Longford
IBoy
Connemara
N4
Mullingar
N59
M4
M50
M1
Dublin
Galway
IMou
Dun Laoghaire
Naas
M7
M11
Bray
M9
Portlaoise
IFoB
Wicklow
N7
Abbyleix
Ennis
IGor
Carlow
IKil
Arklow
Shannon
Thurles
Limerick
N8
Kilkenny
IPot
Tipperary
Enniscorthy
N24
Tralee
N20
Clonmel
Wexford
Mallow
Waterford
IVic
Killarney
ISha
N25
Cork
N22
IDee

INDEX OF ADVERTISERS